the Next EXIT ®

Congratulations...

on your purchase of *the most complete interstate services guide **ever printed!**®*

Developed over many years and updated annually, ***the Next EXIT*®** will save time, money and frustration. This travel tool will help you find services along the USA Interstate Highway System like nothing you have ever used.

PO Box 888
Garden City, UT 84028
theNextEXIT.com

How to use *the Next EXIT*®

MARYLAND

①

Interstate 95

③

②

N

Newark

S

④

Exit #	Services

110mm Maryland/Delaware state line

109b a MD 279, to Elkton, Newark, **E...gas:** Citgo/diesel, Petro/
Iron Skillet/diesel/rest./24hr/@, Shell/diesel, **food:**
Cracker Barrel, KFC/Taco Bell, McDonald's, Waffle
House, **lodging:** Econolodge, Elkton Lodge, Hampton
Inn, Knight's Inn, Motel 6, **other:** HOSPITAL, Blue
Beacon, **W...gas:** TA/Mobil/Subway/diesel/@,
7-11, **other:** to U of DE

100 MD 272, to North East, Rising Sun, **E...gas:** Flying J/
diesel/rest./LP/24hr/@, **food:** McDonald's, Schroeder's
Deli, Wendy's, **lodging:** Crystal Inn, Holiday Inn Express, **other:** Eckerd, museum, st police, to Elk Neck
SP, **W...gas:** Citgo, Mobil, **other:** zoo

**96mm Chesapeake House service area(exits left from both
lanes), Exxon/diesel, Sunoco/diesel, Burger King,
HotDogs, Pizza Hut, Popeye's, Starbucks, TCBY,
gifts**

93 MD 275, to Rising Sun, US 222, to Perryville, **E...gas:**
Exxon/diesel, Pilot/Subway/diesel/24hr/@, **food:**
Denny's, KFC/Taco Bell, **lodging:** Comfort Inn, **other:**
HOSPITAL, Prime Outlets/famous brands, Riverview

Camping, **W...food:** CM Tuggs Diner, Crother's Mkt,
lodging: Douglass Motel, **other:** st police

92mm weigh sta/toll booth

91.5mm Susquehanna River

89 MD 155, to Havre de Grace(last nb exit before toll), **1-3
mi E...food:** McDonald's, MacGregor's Rest., **lodging:** Best Budget Inn, Super 8, Swede Suites, **other:**
HOSPITAL, **W...**to Susquehanna SP

85 MD 22, to Aberdeen, **E...gas:** Amoco/24hr, Citgo/7-11,
Crown/diesel, Enroy, Sunoco/diesel, Shell/diesel/24hr,

① **....state name, state map**

② **....directional arrow**

③ **....interstate hwy #, services at each exit**

④ **....city locator strip**

Exit

In most states exits are numbered by the nearest mile marker(mm). Some states use consecutive
numbers, in which case mile markers are given. Mile markers are the little green vertical signs beside
the interstate at one mile intervals which indicate distance from the southern or western border of a
state. Odd numbered interstates run north/south, even numbered run east/west.

Services

Services are listed alphabetically by category...**gas, food, lodging, other** services(including camping). "HOSPITAL" indicates an exit from which a hospital may be accessed, but it may not be close
to the exit. Services located away from the exit may be referred to by "access to," or "to...," and a
distance may be given. A directional notation is also given, such as "**N...**".

Directional Arrows

*Read services from the page according to your direction of travel; i.e., if traveling
from North to South or East to West, read services DOWN the page. If traveling
S to N or W to E, then read services UP the page.*

N   **E**

S   **W**

*the Next EXIT, inc. makes no warranty regarding the accuracy of the information
contained in this publication. This information is subject to change without notice.*

Table of Contents

Abbreviations used in *the Next EXIT®:*

AFB	Air Force Base	NP	National Park
B&B	Bed&Breakfast	NRA	Nat Rec Area
Bfd	Battlefield	pk	park
bldg	building	pkwy	parkway
Ctr	Center	rest.	restaurant
Coll	College	nb	northbound
$	Dollar	sb	southbound
Mem	Memorial	eb	eastbound
Mkt	Market	wb	westbound
Mtn	Mountain	SP	state park
mm	mile marker	SF	state forest
N...	north side of exit	Sprs	springs
S...	south side of exit	st	street, state
E...	east side of exit	sta	station
W...	west side of exit	TPK	Turnpike
NM	National Monument	USPO	Post Office
NHS	Nat Hist Site	whse	warehouse
NWR	Nat Wildlife Reserve	@	truckstop
NF	National Forest	red print	RV accessible

For Trans Canada Highway(TCH) information and more,
please visit our website at *www.thenextexit.com*

Haystacks
by

Mark Watson
Winter, 2005

Harvest time in America is hard to miss, even from the window of a moving car. Drive down any interstate highway into any region and you will see the fruits of labor being gathered. We can learn a lot by observing the Law of the Harvest. Whether potatoes, wheat, cotton or hay, what we plant is what we pick. It is also true in Life. Once in a while though, Nature swerves, creating the near miss whose value we should never underestimate. So it was in the case of Otis Atkinson's haystacks.

The old barn was many things to many creatures. Within its confines the hens hatched their chicks and we hatched the schemes that would school us in the hard facts of life. Being the youngest in the family meant that my suggestions for adventure were discounted, but that was OK. I was happy to tag along with the older kids. Besides, when it came time to divvy up the blame for plans gone bad, my share was usually small. If my sister and brother and cousin from town thought it was alright to smash a fully loaded wasp nest with a half brick while we all stood there and watched it was fine with me. The fact that the nest was in the loft of the barn and the only way out was down a ladder through a small hole one person at a time only made us all seem more brave.

Handsome Haystacks

How many kittens were born in that hayloft, and how many times did we clean it out to start a club house? Early one afternoon in the clearing dust of its newly swept floor began an event that would leave a lasting impression. Surveying the view from the loft door, we gazed out toward the Big Tree, a giant gum variety that had witnessed the passing of General Sherman's patrols. Underneath its branches stood the tobacco barn, built for flue-curing our main money crop. Across the ditch that ran by them both lay the property of our neighbor, Mr. Atkinson. Since ditches make good neighbors, up until now Daddy had been on pretty good terms with Otis, sharing mules and such when the need arose. As the four of us looked over our prospects that afternoon, into focus beyond the ditch came the handsomest haystacks we had ever seen.

The three older ones were quick to see the possibilities, but it was David who gave them voice. "*Look* at those *haystacks*!" he pointed. Wide-eyed looks were exchanged as the idea glimmered from child to child. We couldn't have scrambled out of that barn any faster if we'd been handed tickets to Disneyland. Down the ladder, across the ditch and into the first stack we jumped, oblivious to the fact that if Otis had wanted his hay on the ground he could have left it there in the first place. Soon enough, the effects of climbing the center pole and diving into the pile of scratchy oat hay took its toll, and we moved on to other stacks, abusing them in the same fashion. After a while and with some practice, we started trying to impress each other by doing flips and diving tricks, scattering hay and flattening stacks, lost in the hilarity of the moment.

It might have continued until we ran out of haystacks, but someone finally sobered enough to realize that we were getting too close to Otis' house, and maybe he wouldn't approve anyhow. So back across the ditch we scampered, to the safety of home territory and other amusing pursuits for the balance of the day. The matter was ended as far as we could see, which wasn't all that far.

My brother and sister, having been born less than a year apart were complicit in many crimes, but when our cousin their age came to visit, it was a lot like throwing gasoline on fire. Her presence also usually meant that I would be relegated farther back in my tag-along status. Such was my condition as evening approached on the Day of the Haystacks. Having more exciting things to do, they had gone elsewhere to do some older children stuff, leaving me in the yard to play alone. That's when I saw Otis drive up.

Daddy saw him too, and quit what he was doing to be neighborly. As the two of them leaned against the back fender of his truck talking, I could hear the polite nature of their conversation change to lower, more somber tones. Playing innocently around the yard, I moved in a little closer, knowing that Mr. Atkinson hardly ever came over just to say hello. I saw the expression on Daddy's face become grave as Otis mumbled something about haystacks and they both turned and looked at me. Lots of things might have been over my head at that age, but I knew when trouble was in the wind, and from the look in Daddy's eye, a breeze was beginning to blow.

Children love bearing bad tidings. Since I had not been detained or questioned by the two men standing in the yard sealing our fate, I skipped nervously away, intent on finding my siblings and *their* cousin. In some strange way I felt honored to be the one to tell them that we were all going to be maimed in a few moments, by a mad man swinging a belt. While the fruits of our day were being served to the ringleaders, I sat quietly in the front room trying my best to look younger than I was. It was like sitting outside the little room where they keep the electric chair knowing your turn is next. Justice would surely be served, but boy you hated being involved at this level.

About that time, the door opened and Daddy stepped in halfway. I tried to concentrate on the black and white images flickering on the big square TV in the corner, but couldn't help cutting my eyes up at him in an attempt to look humble and penitent. He stood there for the longest minute of my short life while I watched his deliberations taking place. Then, wonder of wonders, he slackened a bit and turned to leave. "You *must* have just been following *them*," he said, and paused for another moment to see if he had any second thoughts. He left and I sat there confused, almost disappointed, knowing that the older children would now share in yet another tale in which I had only a lesser part.

It was over after that, all but the retelling. Cousin Scarlett was sent home to a second reckoning with her mother and the gap between me and my brother and sister widened, as their common suffering bonded them closer. What had passed in front of my father that day? What did he see deserving of clemency? Was I the child of his maturity, the son of his hope, the recipient of his many-colored coat? All I knew was that I had narrowly escaped a good thrashing. I truly wish I could report that I never followed the crowd again, but it would take plenty more scrapes and a number of direct hits before I could see that light.

None of us ever feared our father except when we had bought and paid for his discipline, which was swift and sure, but never harsh or unjust. He understood that young people who aren't taught respect for the property rights of others usually learn it harder later, and often at society's expense. As a family we are close, reveling when we can gather as one to recount the events of our youth. Especially during these times, I mentally revisit Otis' yellow field of cut hay, gleaning through the stacks for something I might have missed. Besides a kernel of wisdom I find here and there, I remember it as the place where, just once, what was sown was *not* what was reaped.

In memory of Callis Alma Watson(1912-2004)
on whose farm we learned so much about the Harvest

ii

Interstate 10

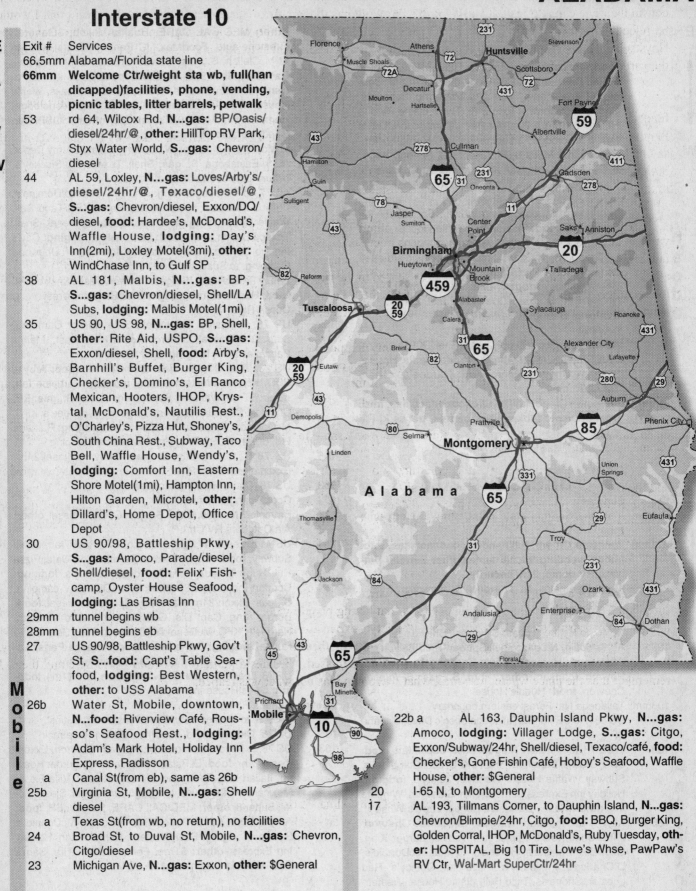

E ↕ **W**

Exit #	Services
66.5mm	Alabama/Florida state line
66mm	**Welcome Ctr/weight sta wb, full(handicapped)facilities, phone, vending, picnic tables, litter barrels, petwalk**
53	rd 64, Wilcox Rd, **N...gas:** BP/Oasis/diesel/24hr/@, **other:** HillTop RV Park, Styx Water World, **S...gas:** Chevron/diesel
44	AL 59, Loxley, **N...gas:** Loves/Arby's/diesel/24hr/@, Texaco/diesel/@, **S...gas:** Chevron/diesel, Exxon/DQ/diesel, **food:** Hardee's, McDonald's, Waffle House, **lodging:** Day's Inn(2mi), Loxley Motel(3mi), **other:** WindChase Inn, to Gulf SP
38	AL 181, Malbis, **N...gas:** BP, **S...gas:** Chevron/diesel, Shell/LA Subs, **lodging:** Malbis Motel(1mi)
35	US 90, US 98, **N...gas:** BP, Shell, **other:** Rite Aid, USPO, **S...gas:** Exxon/diesel, Shell, **food:** Arby's, Barnhill's Buffet, Burger King, Checker's, Domino's, El Ranco Mexican, Hooters, IHOP, Krystal, McDonald's, Nautilis Rest., O'Charley's, Pizza Hut, Shoney's, South China Rest., Subway, Taco Bell, Waffle House, Wendy's, **lodging:** Comfort Inn, Eastern Shore Motel(1mi), Hampton Inn, Hilton Garden, Microtel, **other:** Dillard's, Home Depot, Office Depot
30	US 90/98, Battleship Pkwy, **S...gas:** Amoco, Parade/diesel, Shell/diesel, **food:** Felix' Fishcamp, Oyster House Seafood, **lodging:** Las Brisas Inn
29mm	tunnel begins wb
28mm	tunnel begins eb
27	US 90/98, Battleship Pkwy, Gov't St, **S...food:** Capt's Table Seafood, **lodging:** Best Western, **other:** to USS Alabama
26b	Water St, Mobile, downtown, **N...food:** Riverview Café, Rousso's Seafood Rest., **lodging:** Adam's Mark Hotel, Holiday Inn Express, Radisson
a	Canal St(from eb), same as 26b
25b	Virginia St, Mobile, **N...gas:** Shell/diesel
a	Texas St(from wb, no return), no facilities
24	Broad St, to Duval St, Mobile, **N...gas:** Chevron, Citgo/diesel
23	Michigan Ave, **N...gas:** Exxon, **other:** $General
22b a	AL 163, Dauphin Island Pkwy, **N...gas:** Amoco, **lodging:** Villager Lodge, **S...gas:** Citgo, Exxon/Subway/24hr, Shell/diesel, Texaco/café, **food:** Checker's, Gone Fishin Café, Hoboy's Seafood, Waffle House, **other:** $General
20	I-65 N, to Montgomery
17	AL 193, Tillmans Corner, to Dauphin Island, **N...gas:** Chevron/Blimpie/24hr, Citgo, **food:** BBQ, Burger King, Golden Corral, IHOP, McDonald's, Ruby Tuesday, **other:** HOSPITAL, Big 10 Tire, Lowe's Whse, PawPaw's RV Ctr, Wal-Mart SuperCtr/24hr

Mobile

1

ALABAMA

Interstate 10

15b a — US 90, Tillmans Corner, to Mobile, **N...gas:** BP, Chevron/24hr, Conoco/diesel, RaceTrac, Shell, **food:** Arby's, Azteca Mexican, Burger King, Canton Buffet, Checker's, CiCi's, Godfather's, KFC, McDonald's, Papa John's, Pizza Hut, Pizza Inn, Popeye's, Shoney's, Subway, Taco Bell, Thai Cuisine, Waffle House, **lodging:** Best Western, Comfort Inn, Day's Inn, Econolodge, Guesthouse Inn, Hampton Inn, Holiday Inn, Motel 6, Red Roof Inn, Suite 1, Super 8, Travelodge, **other:** AutoZone, CarQuest, Family$, Firestone/auto, FoodWorld/24hr, Goodyear, K-Mart, O'Reilly Parts, Radio Shack, Rite Aid, Walgreen, Winn-Dixie, **S...gas:** Chevron/24hr, Conoco/diesel, Shell/diesel, **food:** Hardee's, Waffle House, **other:** Johnny's RV Ctr, auto repair, transmissions

13 — to Theodore, **N...gas:** Amoco/McDonald's/diesel/24hr, Conoco, Pilot/Citgo/Wendy's/diesel/24hr/@, Shell/Subway, **food:** Waffle House, **other:** Greyhound Prk, **S...gas:** Chevron/diesel, **other:** I-10 Kamping, Bellingraf Gardens

11 — new exit

4 — AL 188 E, to Grand Bay, **N...gas:** Shell/DQ/Stuckey's, TA/BP/diesel/rest./24hr/@, **food:** Waffle House, **S...gas:** Chevron/24hr, **food:** Hardee's, **other:** Trav-L-Kamp

1mm — **Welcome Ctr eb, full(handicapped)facilities, info, phone, picnic tables, litter barrels, petwalk, RV dump**

0mm — Alabama/Mississippi state line

Interstate 20

Exit #	Services

215mm — Alabama/Georgia state line, Central/Eastern time zone

213mm — **Welcome Ctr wb, full(handicapped)facilities, info, phone, vending, picnic tables, litter barrels, petwalk, RV dump, 24hr security**

210 — AL 49, Abernathy, **N...**fireworks, **S...**fireworks

209mm — Tallapoosa River

208mm — weigh sta wb

205 — AL 46, to Heflin, **N...gas:** BP/diesel, Shell/diesel

199 — AL 9, Heflin, **N...gas:** Shell/Subway/Taco Bell/diesel/24hr, **food:** Hardee's, Pop's Charburgers, **lodging:** Howard Johnson, **other:** Ford, **S...gas:** BP/diesel, Chevron, **food:** Huddle House

198mm — Talladega Nat Forest eastern boundary

191 — US 431, to US 78, **S...**Talladega Scenic Drive, Cheaha SP

188 — to US 78, to Anniston, **N...gas:** Shell, SuperMart, **food:** BBQ, Cracker Barrel, DQ, IHOP, KFC, LoneStar Steaks, Subway, Waffle House, Wendy's, Zaxby's, **lodging:** Holiday Inn Express, Jameson Inn, Sleep Inn, Wingate Inn, **other:** Harley-Davidson, Honda, Lowe's Whse

185 — AL 21, to Anniston, **N...gas:** BP/diesel, Chevron/24hr, Shell, **food:** Applebee's, Arby's, Burger King, Capt D's, Domino's, Hardee's, Krystal, McDonald's, O'Charley's, Piccadilly's, Pizza Hut, Quincy's, Red Lobster, Shoney's, Taco Bell, Waffle House, Western Sizzlin, **lodging:** Best Western, Day's Inn, Holiday Inn, Howard Johnson, Liberty Inn, Red Carpet Inn,

other: MEDICAL CARE, BooksAMillion, $General, Firestone/auto, FoodMax, JC Penney, Sears, mall, to Ft McClellan, **S...gas:** Cowboys/diesel, Express/diesel, RaceTrac, Shell/Subway/diesel, **food:** Chick-fil-A, El Poblano Mexican, Huddle House, Outback Steaks, Waffle House, Wendy's, **lodging:** Comfort Inn, Econolodge, Hampton Inn, Motel 6, Travelodge, **other:** HOSPITAL, Goodyear/auto, Wal-Mart SuperCtr/24hr

179 — to Munford, Coldwater, **N...other:** Anniston Army Depot

173 — AL 5, Eastaboga, **S...gas:** Shell, Texaco/DQ/Stuckey's, **other:** to Speedway/Hall of Fame

168 — AL 77, to Talladega, **N...gas:** Citgo, Conoco/Domino's, Phillips 66/diesel, **food:** Jack's Rest., KFC/Taco Bell, Waffle House, **S...gas:** Chevron/Subway/diesel, Shell, Texaco/Burger King, **food:** McDonald's, **lodging:** Day's Inn, Holiday Inn Express, McCaig Motel, **other:** Dogwood Camping, to Speedway, Hall of Fame

165 — Embry Cross Roads, **S...gas:** Chevron/diesel, Shell/diesel, **food:** Huddle House, **lodging:** McCaig Motel/rest.

164mm — Coosa River

162 — US 78, Riverside, **N...other:** Safe Harbor Camping, **S...gas:** BP/diesel, Chevron, **food:** Hal's Rest., Mary's Pancakes/24hr, **lodging:** Best Western

158 — US 231, Pell City, **N...gas:** Exxon/diesel, **food:** Arby's, BBQ, Krystal, Western Sizzlin, **lodging:** Hampton Inn, **other:** $Tree, Wal-Mart SuperCtr/gas/24hr, **S...gas:** BP, Chevron, Citgo/diesel, **food:** Burger King, Hardee's, KFC, McDonald's, Pizza Hut, Waffle House, **lodging:** Ramada Ltd, **other:** HOSPITAL, Ford, Lakeside Camping

156 — US 78 E, to Pell City, **S...gas:** Chevron/diesel/24hr, Exxon/diesel/24hr, Shell

153 — US 78, Chula Vista, no facilities

152 — Cook Springs, no facilities

147 — Brompton, **N...gas:** Citgo, **S...gas:** Chevron/diesel, **other:** Ala Outdoors RV Ctr/LP

144 — US 411, Leeds, **N...gas:** Amoco, BP, RaceTrac, Shell/Subway, **food:** Arby's, Cracker Barrel, Milo's Café, Pizza Hut, Ruby Tuesday, Waffle House, Wendy's, **lodging:** Comfort Inn, Super 8, **other:** Winn-Dixie, RV camping, **S...gas:** Exxon/24hr, RaceWay, Speedway/diesel, **food:** Burger King, Capt D's, Guadalajara Jalisco Mexican, Hardee's, KFC, McDonald's, Quincy's, Taco Bell, Waffle House, **lodging:** Day's Inn, **other:** Advance Parts, AutoZone, Lowe's Whse, Wal-Mart SuperCtr/24hr

140 — US 78, Leeds, **S...gas:** Chevron, Exxon, Shell(1mi), **lodging:** GuestHouse Inn

139mm — Cahaba River

136 — I-459 S, to Montgomery, Tuscaloosa, no facilities

135 — US 78, Old Leeds Rd, **N...other:** B'ham Racetrack

133 — US 78, to Kilgore Memorial Dr, **N...gas:** Chevron, Exxon/diesel/24hr, **food:** El Palacio Mexican, Hamburger Heaven, Italian Villa Rest., Jack's Rest., Krystal, Villa Fiesta Mexican, Waffle House, **lodging:** Comfort Inn, Siesta Motel, Super 8, **other:** MEDICAL CARE, **S...gas:** BP, **food:** Arby's, BBQ, China Buffet, Gus' Hotdogs, McDonald's, Subway, **lodging:** Best Western, Hampton Inn, Holiday Inn Express, **other:** $Tree, Ford, Graham Tire, Sam's Club, Wal-Mart, same as 132

Interstate 20

E ↕ W

Bessemer

Tuscaloosa

132b a US 78, Crestwood Blvd, **N...gas:** Exxon, **food:** Barnhill's Buffet, Krystal, Waffle House, **other:** Chevrolet, **S...gas:** BP, Crown/24hr, Shell/24hr, **food:** Arby's, Capt D's, China Garden, Denny's, Hooters, IHOP, KFC, Logan's Roadhouse, McDonald's, O'Charley's, Omelet Shop, Olive Garden, Pizza Hut, Red Lobster, Ruby Tuesday, Shoney's, Taco Bell, Wendy's, **lodging:** Delux Inn, USA Lodge, **other:** HOSPITAL, Circuit City, Home Depot, JC Penney, K-Mart, OfficeMax, Sears/auto, Waldenbooks, mall

130b US 11, 1st Ave, **N...gas:** BP, Chevron/24hr, Citgo, **lodging:** Bama Motel, **other:** Advance Parts, AutoZone, Colonial RV Ctr, Food Fair, **S...food:** Capt D's, McDonald's, **lodging:** Interstate Inn, Relax Inn

a I-59 N, to Gadsden

I-59 S and I-20 W run together from B'ham to Meridian, MS

129 Airport Blvd, **N...lodging:** Ramada Inn, **other:** airport, **S...gas:** Conoco, Shell, **food:** Hardee's, **lodging:** Day's Inn, Holiday Inn, **other:** transmissions

128 AL 79, Tallapoosa St, **N...gas:** Cowboys/Blimpie/diesel, Shell

126b 31st St, downtown, to Sloss Furnaces, **N...gas:** Conoco, Shell, **food:** McDonald's

a US 31, US 280, 26th St, Carraway Blvd, downtown, to UAB

125b 22nd St, to downtown, **N...lodging:** Sheraton

a 17th St, to downtown, Civic Ctr

124b a I-65, S to Montgomery, N to Nashville

123 US 78, Arkadelphia Rd, **N...gas:** BP, Chevron/24hr, Pilot/Wendy's/diesel/24hr, **food:** Popeye's, **lodging:** La Quinta, **S...other:** HOSPITAL, to Legion Field

121 Bush Blvd(from wb, no return), Ensley, **N...gas:** BP, Exxon, **food:** Bob's Burger

120 AL 269, 20th St, Ensley Ave, **N...food:** KFC, **other:** GMC/Pontiac, Breeze RV, **S...gas:** BP, Chevrolet, **other:** HOSPITAL, Chrysler/Plymouth/Jeep, Hyundai, Toyota

119b Ave I(from wb), no facilities

a Scrushy Pkwy, Gary Ave, **N...gas:** BP, Chevron/diesel, **food:** Burger King, McDonald's, Seafood Delite, Subway, Taco Bell, **other:** Food Fair, Family$, **S...gas:** Exxon, Mobil, **food:** Omelet Shoppe, **other:** HOSPITAL

118 AL 56, Valley Rd, Fairfield, **S...food:** Papa John's, **lodging:** Fairfield Inn, Villager Lodge, **other:** Home Depot, NTB, Sears, Winn-Dixie

115 Allison-Bonnett Memorial Dr, **N...gas:** Citgo/diesel, Phillips 66, RaceTrac, Shell/diesel, **food:** Church's, Guadalajara Grill, Subway

113 18th Ave, to Hueytown, **S...gas:** Chevron/diesel, **food:** McDonald's

112 18th St, 19th St, Bessemer, **N...gas:** Conoco, RaceTrac, **food:** Church's, Jack's Rest., **other:** OK Tire, **S...gas:** Chevron, **food:** Arby's, Burger King, Krystal, McDonald's, **other:** Lowe's Whse

109 new exit

108 US 11, AL 5 N, Academy Dr, **N...gas:** Exxon, **food:** Applebee's, BBQ, Cracker Barrel, Santa Fe Steaks, Waffle House, **lodging:** Best Western, Comfort Inn, Holiday Inn Express, Jameson Inn, **S...gas:** BP, Citgo/Church's/diesel, **food:** Burger King, Jade Garden, Chinese, McDonald's, Milo's Burgers, Sonic, **lodging:** Day's Inn, Hampton Inn, **other:** HOSPITAL, Big 10 Tire, $Tree, Ford, Radio Shack, **Wal-Mart** SuperCtr/24hr, Winn-Dixie, to civic ctr

106 I-459 N, to Montgomery

104 Rock Mt Lake, **S...gas:** ⚡/Flying J/Conoco/diesel/LP/rest./24hr/@

100 to Abernant, **N...gas:** Citgo, **other:** McCalla Camping, **S...gas:** BP, Exxon, Petro/Chevron/diesel/rest./24hr/@, **other:** Tannehill SP(3mi)

97 US 11 S, AL 5 S, to W Blocton, **S...gas:** BP/KFC/diesel, Exxon/Subway/diesel, Shell/diesel, **food:** Dot's Farmhouse Rest., Jack's Rest.

89 Mercedes Dr, **N...lodging:** Wellesley Inn, **S...other:** Mercedes Auto Plant

86 Vance, to Brookwood, **N...gas:** Shell/diesel/rest./24hr/@

85mm rest area both lanes, full(handicapped)facilities, phone, vending, picnic tables, litter barrels, petwalk, RV dump

79 US 11, University Blvd, Coaling, **S...gas:** Chevron/diesel

77 Cottondale, **N...gas:** Amoco/McDonald's, TA/BP/Subway/Taco Bell/diesel/@, Wilco/Wendy's/diesel/24hr, **food:** Pizza Hut, Ruby Tuesday, **lodging:** Hampton Inn, Microtel, **other:** SpeedCo, USPO, truckwash

76 US 11, E Tuscaloosa, Cottondale, **N...gas:** Citgo, Exxon, Shell/diesel, **food:** Burger King, Cracker Barrel, Waffle House, **lodging:** Comfort Inn, Scottish Inn, **other:** transmissions, **S...gas:** Pilot/Subway/diesel/24hr/@, Shell/diesel, **lodging:** Sleep Inn

ALABAMA

Interstate 20

E / **W** — **Tuscaloosa**

73	US 82, McFarland Blvd, Tuscaloosa, **N...gas:** BP/diesel, Chevron/Subway/diesel, Exxon, Parade, RaceTrac, Shell/diesel, **food:** Arby's, Burger King, Cancun Mexican, Capt D's, Ezell's Buffet, Krystal, LJ Silver, O'Charley's, Red Lobster, Schlotsky's, Waffle House, **lodging:** Best Western, Guest Lodge, Shoney's Inn/rest., **other:** Advance Parts, AllTransmissions, Big 10 Tire, Chrysler/Plymouth/Jeep, Circuit City, Firestone/auto, Goodyear/auto, OfficeMax, Pontiac/Cadillac/GMC, Rite Aid, **S...gas:** Exxon, Shell/diesel, **food:** Chili's, DQ, Guthrie's Café, Hardee's, Huddle House, KFC, Logan's Roadhouse, McDonald's, Papa John's, Pizza Hut, Sonic, Subway, Super China, Taco Bell, Taco Casa, Wendy's, **lodging:** Comfort Inn, Country Inn Suites, Day's Inn, Econolodge, La Quinta, Motel 6, Quality Inn, Ramada Inn, Super 8, **other:** MEDICAL CARE, BooksAMillion, CVS Drug, Dillard's, FoodWorld, Ford, Isuzu, NAPA, Office Depot, Rite Aid, Sam's Club/gas, U-Haul, Wal-Mart SuperCtr/24hr, Winn-Dixie, mall
71b	I-359, Al 69 N, to Tuscaloosa, **N...other:** HOSPITAL, U of AL, to Stillman Coll
a	AL 69 S, to Moundville, **S...gas:** Chevron, Exxon/diesel, Shell/diesel, **food:** Arby's, BBQ, Hooters, IHOP, LoneStar Steaks, OutBack Steaks, Pizza Hut, Ryan's, Waffle House, Wendy's, **lodging:** Courtyard, Fairfield Inn, Jameson Inn, **other:** Advance Parts, K-Mart, Lowe's Whse, Mazda/VW, to Mound SM
68	Northfort-Tuscaloosa Western Bypass, no facilities
64mm	Black Warrior River
62	Fosters, **N...gas:** BP
52	US 11, US 43, Knoxville, **N...gas:** Exxon/diesel, **other:** Knoxville Camping
45	AL 37, Union, **N...food:** Cotton Patch Rest., **S...gas:** BP/diesel/rest./24hr, **food:** Hardee's, Southfork Rest./24hr, **lodging:** Western Inn/rest., **other:** Greene Co Greyhound Park
40	AL 14, Eutaw, **N...other:** to Tom Bevill Lock/Dam, **S...gas:** BP, HOSPITAL
39mm	**rest area wb, full(handicapped)facilities, phone, vending, picnic tables, litter barrels, petwalk, RV dump**
38mm	**rest area eb, full(handicapped)facilities, phone, vending, picnic tables, litter barrels, petwalk, RV dump**
32	Boligee, **N...gas:** BP/diesel/rest./24hr, **S...gas:** Chevron/Subway/24hr
27mm	Tombigbee River, Tenn-Tom Waterway
23	Epes, to Gainesville, no facilities
17	AL 28, Livingston, **S...gas:** BP/diesel/24hr, Chevron/Subway/24hr, Noble/Citgo/Janet's/Waffle King/diesel/24hr/@, Shell/diesel, **food:** Burger King, Pizza Hut, **lodging:** Comfort Inn, Western Inn(1mi)
8	AL 17, York, **S...gas:** BP/diesel/rest., **lodging:** Day's Inn/Briar Patch Rest., **other:** HOSPITAL
1	to US 80 E, Cuba, **N...gas:** Phillips 66/diesel/rest., **S...gas:** Chevron, Dixie

.5mm — Welcome Ctr eb, full(handicapped)facilities, phone, vending, picnic tables, litter barrels, petwalk, RV dump

I-20 E and I-59 N run together from Meridian, MS to B'ham

0mm — Alabama/Mississippi state line

Interstate 59

N / **S** — **Ft Payne** / **Gadsden**

Exit #	Services
241.5mm	Alabama/Georgia state line, Central/Eastern time zone
241mm	**Welcome Ctr sb, full(handicapped)facilities, phone, vending, picnic tables, litter barrels, petwalk, RV dump**
239	to US 11, Sulphur Springs Rd, **E...other:** Sequoyah Caverns Camping(4mi)
231	AL 40, AL 117, Hammondville, Valley Head, **E...other:** Sequoyah Caverns Camping(5mi), **W...gas:** Shell
222	US 11, to Ft Payne, **E...gas:** Shell, **1-2 mi E...food:** Arby's, Bojangles, Jack's Rest., KFC, Krystal, Subway, **lodging:** Ft Payne Inn, **W...gas:** Shell/diesel, **food:** Waffle King
218	AL 35, Ft Payne, **E...gas:** Conoco/diesel, **food:** Capt D's, Durango's Mexican, McDonald's, New China, Papa John's, Pizza Hut, Shoney's, Taco Bell, Wendy's, **lodging:** Mtn View Motel(2mi), **other:** Advance Parts, AutoZone, Buick/Pontiac, Chrysler/Dodge, Goodyear/auto, **W...gas:** Chevron, Cowboys/diesel, Exxon, **food:** Burger King, Cracker Barrel, Hardee's, Ryan's, Ruby Tuesday, Subway, Waffle House, **lodging:** Day's Inn, Econolodge, Holiday Inn Express, **other:** HOSPITAL, Ford/Lincoln/Mercury, Kia, K-Mart, Radio Shack, Wal-Mart SuperCtr/gas/24hr
205	AL 68, Collinsville, **E...gas:** Chevron, **food:** Jack's Rest., **lodging:** Howard Johnson, **other:** to Little River Canyon, Weiss Lake, **W... gas:** Conoco/diesel, Shell, **other:** MEDICAL CARE
188	AL 211, to US 11, Reece City, Gadsden, **E...gas:** Chevron/24hr, **food:** Maw'nPaw's Rest., **W...gas:** BP/diesel
183	US 431, US 278, Gadsden, **E...gas:** BP/diesel, Shell, **food:** Waffle House, Wendy's, **lodging:** Holiday Inn Express, Ramada Ltd, Rodeway Inn, **other:** st police, **W...gas:** Chevron/24hr, Exxon, Texaco, **food:** KFC/Taco Bell, Krystal, McDonald's, Pizza Hut, Quincy's, Subway, **lodging:** Econolodge
182	I-759, to Gadsden, no facilities
181	AL 77, Rainbow City, to Gadsden, **E...gas:** BP/diesel/24hr@, **food:** Austin's Steaks, **lodging:** Day's Inn, **W...gas:** Cowboys/diesel, **food:** Cracker Barrel, DQ, Hardee's, Ruby Tuesday, Subway, Waffle House, **lodging:** Best Western, Comfort Inn
174	to Steele, **E...other:** truck tire service, **W...gas:** Chevron/diesel, JetPep/diesel/@
168mm	**rest area sb, full(handicapped)facilities, phone, vending, picnic tables, litter barrels, petwalk, RV dump**

4

Interstate 59

166 US 231, Whitney, to Ashville, **E...gas:** Chevron, Discount/gas, **W...gas:** Shell/Taco Bell/diesel/24hr, **food:** Jack's Rest., Subway

165mm **rest area nb, full(handicapped)facilities, phone, vending, picnic tables, litter barrels, petwalk, RV dump**

156 to US 11, AL 23, Springville, to St Clair Springs, no facilities

154 AL 174, Springville, to Odenville, **W...gas:** BP/Subway, Chevron, Exxon, Shell/diesel, **food:** Gulf Seafood, Jack's Rest., McDonald's

148 to US 11, Argo, **E...gas:** BP

143 Mt Olive Church Rd, Deerfoot Pkwy, no facilities

141 to Trussville, Pinson, **E...gas:** Amoco/diesel, BP/diesel, Shell/diesel, **food:** Applebee's, Arby's, Cracker Barrel, LoneStar Steaks, McDonald's, Papa Johns, Pizza Hut, Subway, Taco Bell, Waffle House, Wendy's, **lodging:** Comfort Inn, Holiday Inn Express, Jameson Inn, **W...gas:** Chevron/24hr, Exxon, Shell, **food:** Arby's, Chick-fil-A, Bennigan's, Backyard Burger, Burger King, Krystal, Milo's Burgers, Monterrey Mexican, Ruby Tuesday, **other:** CVS Drug, Kohl's, Radio Shack, Sam's Club, Wal-Mart SuperCtr/24hr, Western Foods

137 I-459 S, to Montgomery, Tuscaloosa

134 to AL 75, Roebuck Pkwy, **W...gas:** BP/diesel, Chevron, Mobil, **food:** Barnhill's Buffet, Burger King, Capt D's, Chick-fil-A, ChuckeCheese, Church's, McDonald's, Milo's Burgers, Monterrey Mexican, O'Charley's, Papa John's, Pasquale's Pizza, Rally's, Steak'n Shake, Subway, Taco Bell, Wendy's, **lodging:** Best Inn, **other:** HOSPITAL, Chevrolet, CVS Drug, Dodge, $Tree, Firestone/auto, Food-Giant, Ford, Goodyear/auto, Honda, Hyundai, Jo-Ann Fabrics, Lincoln/Mercury, Mazda/Kia, Mr Transmissions, NTB, Rite Aid, USPO, VW, Wal-Mart SuperCtr/24hr, Winn-Dixie

133 4th St, to US 11(from nb), **W...gas:** Exxon, **food:** Arby's, Catfish Cabin Rest., Checker's, Krystal, Shoney's, Waffle House, **other:** Chrysler/Plymouth, Mazda, mall, accesses same as 134

132 US 11 N, 1st Ave, **W...gas:** Exxon, Chevron/24hr, **food:** Pizza Hut, accesses same as 131

131 77th Ave(from nb), **E...gas:** Chevron, Exxon, **food:** Burger King, Church's, Rally's, Subway, Taco Bell, **other:** CVS Drug, NAPA, U-Haul, accesses same as 132

130 I-20, E to Atlanta, W to Tuscaloosa

I-59 S and I-20 W run together from B'ham to Mississippi. **See Alabama Interstate 20.**

Interstate 65

Exit #   Services

366mm Alabama/Tennessee state line

365 AL 53, to Ardmore, **E...lodging:** Budget Inn

364mm Welcome Ctr sb, full(handicapped)facilities, info, phone, vending, picnic tables, litter barrels, petwalk, RV dump

361 Elkmont, **W...gas:** Citgo/diesel/rest./repair/@, Exxon/diesel, **other:** antiques

354 US 31 S, to Athens, **W...gas:** Chevron/Subway, Conoco, **food:** Dairy Queen, **lodging:** Athens Hotel/rest., Budget Inn, Mark Hotel, **other:** HOSPITAL

351 US 72, to Athens, Huntsville, **E...gas:** BP/diesel, Exxon, RaceTrac, Shell/Subway, **food:** Burger King, Cracker Barrel, McDonald's, Waffle House, Wendy's, **lodging:** Comfort Inn, Country Hearth Inn, Hampton Inn, **other:** R Stover Candy, **W...gas:** Chevron/24hr, Texaco/diesel, **food:** Applebee's, Arby's, Hardee's, Hungry Fisherman, Krystal, Shoney's, Sonic, **lodging:** Best Western, Day's Inn, Sleep Inn, Super 8, **other:** HOSPITAL, Chevrolet, Chrysler/Plymouth/Jeep, $Tree, Big 10 Tire, Ford/Lincoln/Mercury, Goodyear/auto, Staples, Wal-Mart SuperCtr/gas/24hr, to Joe Wheeler SP

340b I-565, to Huntsville, to Ala Space & Rocket Ctr

a AL 20, to Decatur, **W...gas:** Conoco/diesel, RaceTrac, **2 mi W...lodging:** Courtyard, Hampton Inn

337mm Tennessee River

334 AL 67, Priceville, to Decatur, **E...gas:** Amoco/diesel, RaceTrac/diesel/24hr, **lodging:** Day's Inn, Super 8, **W...gas:** BP/diesel, Chevron, Pilot/Subway/diesel/24hr/@, Texaco, **food:** BBQ, DQ, Hardee's, Krystal, McDonald's, Waffle House, **lodging:** Comfort Inn, Hampton Inn, **other:** HOSPITAL

328 AL 36, Hartselle, **W...gas:** BP, Chevron/diesel, Cowboys/diesel, Shell, **food:** BBQ, Huddle House, **lodging:** Express Inn

325 Thompson Rd, to Hartselle, **W...lodging:** Express Inn

322 AL 55, to US 31, to Falkville, Eva, **E...gas:** BP/diesel, rest., **W...gas:** Chevron

318 US 31, to Lacon, **E...gas:** Texaco/DQ/Stuckey's, **lodging:** Lacon Motel

5

ALABAMA

Interstate 65

310 AL 157, Cullman, West Point, **E...gas:** BP, Chevron, Conoco/Subway/diesel, Shell/diesel/24hr, Texaco/Wendy's/diesel, **food:** Arby's, Baxter's Steaks, Burger King, Cracker Barrel, Dairy Queen, Denny's, KFC, McDonald's, Ruby Tuesday, Taco Bell, Waffle House, **lodging:** Best Western, Comfort Inn, Hampton Inn, Holiday Inn Express, Sleep Inn, **other:** HOSPITAL, Ford/Lincoln/Mercury, Pontiac/Buick/GMC, **W...gas:** BP, Exxon/diesel, **lodging:** Super 8, **other:** Cullman Camping(2mi)

308 US 278, Cullman, **E...gas:** Omelet Shoppe/24hr, **lodging:** Day's Inn, **W...gas:** Chevron/24hr

304 AL 69 N, Good Hope, to Cullman, **E...gas:** BP, Exxon/diesel, Shell/diesel/rest/@, Texaco/diesel, **food:** Hardee's, Miguel's Mexican, Waffle House, **lodging:** Econolodge, Ramada Inn, **other:** HOSPITAL, Good Hope Camping, diesel repair, laundry, **W...**JetPep/diesel, to Smith Lake

301mm **E...rest area both lanes, full(handicapped)facilities, phone, vending, picnic tables, litter barrels, pet-walk, RV dump**

299 AL 69 S, to Jasper, **E...gas:** Citgo, **other:** Millican RV Ctr, **W...gas:** BP/diesel, Chevron/diesel, Conoco/diesel, Pure, Texaco/diesel, **food:** Jack's Rest.

291 AL 91, to Arkadelphia, **E...gas:** Chevron/diesel, **other:** Country View RV Park(1mi), **W...gas:** Shell/diesel/@, **food:** GoodDays Rest.

291mm Warrior River

289 to Blount Springs, **W...gas:** Texaco/DQ/Stuckey's, **other:** to Rickwood Caverns SP

287 US 31 N, to Blount Springs, **E...gas:** Chevron/diesel, Citgo/diesel

284 US 31 S, AL 160 E, Hayden, **E...gas:** Conoco/diesel, Phillips 66, Shell/diesel

282 AL 140, Warrior, **E...gas:** Chevron/24hr, Exxon/McDonald's, FuelZ/diesel, **food:** Hardee's, Jack's Rest., Pizza Hut, **W...gas:** BP

281 US 31, to Warrior, **E...other:** Chevrolet

280 to US 31, to Warrior, **E...other:** Chevrolet

279mm Warrior River

275 to US 31, Morris, no facilities

272 Mt Olive Rd, **E...other:** Gardendale Kamp(1mi), **W...gas:** Chevron/24hr, Shell, Texaco/diesel

271 Fieldstown Rd, **E...gas:** BP, Chevron/24hr, Exxon, RaceTrac, Shell, **food:** Arby's, Dairy Queen, Guthrie's Diner, KFC, McDonald's, Milo's Burgers, Pizza Hut, Ruby Tuesday, Shoney's, Subway, Taco Bell, Waffle House, Wendy's, **other:** MEDICAL CARE, AutoZone, Chevrolet, Kia/Subaru, Walgreen, Wal-Mart SuperCtr/gas/24hr, **W...food:** Cracker Barrel, **lodging:** Best Western

267 Walkers Chapel Rd, to Fultondale, **E...gas:** Shell/diesel, **food:** Burger King, O'Charley's, Outback Steaks, Waffle House, **lodging:** Hampton Inn, Holiday Inn Express, **other:** Lowe's Whse, **1 mi E...gas:** BP, **food:** Hardee's, Jack's Rest., Taco Bell, **other:** CVS Drug, $General, Rite Aid, USPO, Winn-Dixie, **W...gas:** Chevron/diesel

266 US 31, Fultondale, **E...gas:** Chevron/24hr, **lodging:** Day's Inn, Super 8

264 41st Ave, **W...gas:** ✈/Flying J/CountryMktdiesel/24hr/@

263 33rd Ave, **E...gas:** Chevron/diesel, **lodging:** Apex Motel, **W...gas:** Crown, Exxon

262b a 16th St, Finley Ave, **E...gas:** Bama/diesel, BP, Texaco/diesel/@, **W...gas:** Chevron/24hr, Citgo/diesel/24hr, Conoco/diesel/@, **food:** Capt D's, McDonald's, Popeye's

261b a I-20/59, E to Gadsden, W to Tuscaloosa, no facilities

260b a 6th Ave, **E...gas:** BP, Shell, **food:** Nicki's Rest., Mrs Winner's, Popeye's, **lodging:** Tourway Inn, **other:** Buick, Nissan, **W...gas:** Chevron, **food:** Church's, **lodging:** Adams Inn, **other:** to Legion Field

259b a University Blvd, 4th Ave, 5th Ave, **E...food:** Waffle House, **lodging:** Best Western, **other:** HOSPITAL, Food Fair, **W...gas:** Chevron, **other:** Goodyear

258 Green Springs Ave, **E...gas:** Chevron, Citgo, **food:** Exotic Wings

256b a Oxmoor Rd, **E...gas:** Exxon/diesel, Mobil, Shell, **food:** Burger King, Cuco's Mexican, KFC, Krystal, Lovoy's Italian, McDonald's, **lodging:** Howard Johnson, **other:** Firestone/auto, Food World, Goodyear/auto, Jo-Ann Fabrics, K-Mart, Office Depot, **W...gas:** BP, Chevron/24hr, **food:** BBQ, Hardee's, Shoney's, **lodging:** Comfort Inn, Fairfield Inn, Guesthouse Inn, Holiday Inn/rest., Microtel, Red Roof Inn, Super 8, **other:** Batteries+

255 Lakeshore Dr, **E...gas:** BP, **other:** HOSPITAL, to Samford U, **W...gas:** Chevron, Citgo, **food:** Arby's, Capt D's, Chili's, Chick-fil-A, Dragon Chinese, Hooters, IHOP, Landry's Seafood, LoneStar Steaks, O'Charley's, Outback Steaks, Schlotsky's, Taco Bell, Tony Roma, Wendy's, **lodging:** Best Suites, La Quinta, Residence Inn, TownePlace Suites, **other:** BooksAMillion, Bruno's Foods, $Tree, Goody's, Lowe's Whse, OfficeMax, Old Navy, Sam's Club, Wal-Mart SuperCtr/24hr, mall

254 Alford Ave, Shades Crest Rd, **E...gas:** Chevron, **W...gas:** BP, Citgo

252 US 31, Montgomery Hwy, **E...gas:** BP, Chevron, Shell, **food:** Arby's, Capt D's, ChuckeCheese, Milo's Burgers, Piccadilly's, Pizza Hut, Taco Bell, Waffle House, **lodging:** Comfort Inn, Hampton Inn, The Motor Lodge/rest., **other:** HOSPITAL, GMC/Saturn/Isuzu, Lincoln/Mercury, Aamco, **W...gas:** BP, Chevron, Exxon, Shell, **food:** BBQ, Burger King, Chick-fil-A, Damon's, Krystal, LoneStar Steaks, McDonald's, Mexicao Lindo, Outback Steaks, Schlotsky's, Subway, Waffle House, **lodging:** Day's Inn, Quality Inn, **other:** BooksAMillion, Bruno's Food, Buick, Chevrolet, Chrysler/Plymouth/Jeep, Circuit City, Eckerd, Goodyear/auto, Hancock Fabrics, Honda, Kia, Nissan, Pontiac, Rite Aid, Toyota, transmissions

250 I-459, US 280, no facilities

247 AL 17, Valleydale Rd, **E...gas:** BP, **food:** BBQ, **W...gas:** Mobil, RaceTrac, Shell, **food:** Arby's, Backyard Burger, IHOP, Milo's Burgers, Papa John's, RagTime Café, Waffle House, **lodging:** Hampton Inn, InTown Motel, La Quinta, Suburban Lodge, **other:** $General, Rite Aid, Walgreen

Interstate 65

N ↑ S

246 AL 119, Cahaba Valley Rd, **E...other:** to Oak Mtn SP, **W...gas:** BP/diesel, Cowboys/Subway, Race-Trac, Shell, **food:** Applebee's, Arby's, BBQ, Blimpie, Buffalo's Café, Capt D's, Chick-fil-A, Cracker Barrel, Dairy Queen, Golden Corral, Hardee's, KFC, Krystal, McDonald's, O'Charley's, Pier Rest., Pizza Hut, Schlotsky's, Shoney's, Sonic, Taco Bell, Two Pesos Mexican, Waffle House, Wendy's, **lodging:** Best Western, Comfort Inn, Hampton Inn, Holiday Inn Express, Ramada Ltd, Sleep Inn, Travelodge, HOSPITAL, CVS Drug, Firestone/auto, Harley-Davidson, Winn-Dixie

242 Pelham, **E...gas:** Chevron/diesel/24hr, Exxon/diesel, Shell, **W...lodging:** Shelby Motel(2mi), **other:** KOA(1mi)

238 US 31, Alabaster, Saginaw, **E...gas:** BP/diesel, **W...gas:** Chevron/diesel, Cannon/gas, Shell, **food:** Waffle House, **2 mi W...food:** Arby's, **lodging:** Shelby Motel, **other:** HOSPITAL

234 Shelby Co Airport, **E...gas:** BP/Subway/diesel, **W...gas:** Chevron/diesel/24hr, Shell/diesel

231 US 31, Saginaw, **E...gas:** BP/diesel, Shell, **food:** BBQ, Capt D's, Golden China, Los Potrillos Mexican, McDonald's, **lodging:** Holiday Inn Express, **other:** Burton RV Ctr, $Tree, Radio Shack, Wal-Mart SuperCtr/gas/24hr, **W...food:** Donna's Café

228 AL 25, to Calera, **E...gas:** Citgo/diesel, Shell/diesel, **lodging:** Best Western, Day's Inn, **W...food:** Hardee's(1mi), **lodging:** Parkside Motel, **other:** to Brierfield Works SP

227mm Buxahatchie Creek

219 Union Grove, Thorsby, **E...gas:** Chevron/diesel/24hr, Exxon/Subway/diesel, **food:** Peach Queen Camping, **W...gas:** Shell, **food:** Smokey Hollow Rest.

213mm rest area both lanes, full(handicapped)facilities, phone, vending, picnic tables, litter barrels, petwalk, RV dump

212 AL 145, Clanton, **E...gas:** Chevron/diesel, **W...gas:** BP/Subway, Headco/diesel, **other:** HOSPITAL, One Big Peach

208 Clanton, to Lake Mitchell, **W...gas:** Exxon/diesel/24hr, **food:** Shoney's, **lodging:** Guesthouse Inn, **other:** Heaton Pecans, Dandy RV Ctr

205 US 31, AL 22, to Clanton, **E...gas:** Amoco, Shell/diesel, **food:** McDonald's, Waffle House, **lodging:** Best Western, Day's Inn, Scottish Inn, **other:** Peach Park, to Confed Mem Park, **W...gas:** BP/diesel/The Store, Chevron/diesel/24hr, **food:** Burger King, Capt D's, Hardee's, Heaton Pecans, KFC, Subway, Taco Bell, **lodging:** Key West Inn, **other:** Durbin Farms Mkt, Wal-Mart SuperCtr/gas/24hr(2mi)

200 to Verbena, **E...gas:** BP/diesel, **W...gas:** Shell/DQ/Stuckey's/diesel, **other:** RV camping

186 US 31, Pine Level, **E...other:** Confederate Mem Park(13mi), **W...gas:** BP/diesel, Chevron/24hr, Citgo/diesel, Conoco/diesel, **food:** Vivian's Café, **lodging:** motel, **other:** HOSPITAL

Clanton

181 AL 14, to Prattville, **E...gas:** Chevron/diesel/24hr, Entec/diesel, **W...gas:** Amoco, Citgo, Conoco/diesel, Exxon, Shell/DQ/diesel, **food:** Cracker Barrel, Ruby Tuesday, Waffle House, **lodging:** Best Western, Comfort Inn, Super 8, **other:** HOSPITAL

179 US 82 W, Millbrook, **E...gas:** Chevron/diesel, **food:** Asian Grill, **other:** K&K RV Park, **W...gas:** Amoco/diesel, BP/diesel, Citgo, Exxon/Subway/24hr, Shell, **food:** Burger King, Hardee's, Longhorn Steaks, McDonald's, O'Charley's, Steak'n Shake, Waffle House, **lodging:** Econolodge, Hampton Inn, Holiday Inn, Jameson Inn, **other:** Lowe's Whse

176 AL 143 N(from nb, no return), Millbrook, Coosada, no facilities

173 AL 152, North Blvd, to US 231, no facilities

172mm Alabama River

172 Clay St, Herron St, downtown, **E...lodging:** Embassy Suites, **W...gas:** Chevron

171 I-85 N, Day St, no facilities

170 Fairview Ave, **E...gas:** Citgo/Subway, **food:** China King, Church's, Krystal, McDonald's, **other:** Advance Parts, AutoZone, CVS Drug, Rite Aid, **W...gas:** Exxon, **food:** Hardee's, **other:** Calhoun Foods, Family$

169 Edgemont Ave(from sb), **E...gas:** Amoco, **other:** carwash

168 US 80 E, US 82, South Blvd, **E...gas:** BP/diesel, Cowboy's, Entec/diesel, TA/Citgo/diesel/rest./24hr/@, **food:** Arby's, Capt D's, KFC, McDonald's, Pizza Hut, Shoney's, Taco Bell, Waffle House, **lodging:** Best Inn, Knight's Inn, Travel Inn, **other:** HOSPITAL, **W...gas:** Amoco, RaceWay, Shell/Subway/diesel, Speedy/diesel, **food:** Dairy Queen, Hardee's, Wendy's, **lodging:** Comfort Inn, Day's Inn, Econolodge, Inn South, Ramada Inn, Valu Inn

167 US 80 W, to Selma, **1 mi W...gas:** Citgo, PaceCar, **food:** Church's, Subway, **other:** CVS Drug

164 US 31, Hope Hull, **E...gas:** Amoco/24hr, Saveway/diesel/24hr, Texaco, **lodging:** Lakeside Motel, **other:** KOA, **W...gas:** BP/Burger King, Chevron/24hr, Liberty/Subway, **food:** Waffle House, **lodging:** Best Western

158 to US 31, **E...gas:** Shell/DQ/Stuckey's

151 AL 97, to Letohatchee, **W...gas:** Amoco/diesel, BP

*(right margin vertical text: Montgomery)*

N

S

Greenville

Atmore

Mobile

142   AL 185, to Ft Deposit, **E...gas:** BP/diesel, Shell/Subway/diesel/24hr, **food:** Priester's Pecans, **W...gas:** Chevron/24hr

133mm rest areas both lanes, full(handicapped)facilities, phone, vending, picnic tables, litter barrels, petwalk, RV dump

130   AL10 E, AL 185, to Greenville, **E...gas:** BP/diesel, Chevron/diesel/24hr, Citgo, Shell/24hr, **food:** Arby's, Beaugez's Steaks, Capt D's, Hardee's, KFC, McDonald's, Pizza Hut, Steak'n Shake, Waffle House, Wendy's, **lodging:** Day's Inn, Econolodge, Thrifty Inn, **other:** Advance Parts, CVS Drug, $General, Goody's, Russell Stover, to Sherling Lake Park, **W...gas:** Exxon, Phillips 66/Subway, Texaco/diesel, Bates Turkey Rest., **food:** Burger King, Cracker Barrel, Krystal, Ruby Tuesday, Shoney's, Taco Bell/TCBY, **lodging:** Best Western, Comfort Inn, Hampton Inn, Jameson Inn, **other:** Chevrolet, Chrysler/Plymouth/Dodge/Jeep, Wal-Mart/auto, Winn-Dixie

128   AL 10, to Greenville, **E...gas:** Shell/Smokehouse/diesel, **other:** HOSPITAL, **W...gas:** Amoco

114   AL 106, to Georgiana, **W...gas:** Amoco, Chevron/24hr, **other:** auto repair

107   AL 8, to Garland, no facilities

101   AL 29, to Owassa, **E...gas:** BP/diesel, **W...gas:** Exxon/diesel

96   AL 83, to Evergreen, **E...gas:** Chevron/24hr, Shell, **food:** Burger King, Hardee's, KFC/Taco Bell, McDonald's, **other:** HOSPITAL, **W...gas:** BP, Citgo/Subway/diesel, **food:** Pizza Hut, Waffle House, **lodging:** Comfort Inn, Day's Inn, Evergreen Inn

93   US 84, to Evergreen, **E...gas:** Exxon, Shell/diesel, **other:** PineCrest RV Park, **W...gas:** BP/diesel

89mm rest area sb, full(handicapped)facilities, phone, vending, picnic tables, litter barrels, petwalk, RV dump

85mm rest area nb, full(handicapped)facilities, phone, vending, picnic tables, litter barrels, petwalk, RV dump

83   AL 6, to Lenox, **E...gas:** Exxon/diesel/LP, Shell, **food:** Louise's Rest., **other:** Sunshine RV Park(4mi)

77   AL 41, to Range, **E...gas:** BP, **W...gas:** Amoco, Shell/Stuckey's/diesel, Texaco/diesel, **food:** Ranch House Rest.

69   AL 113, to Flomaton, **E...gas:** Chevron/Subway, Shell/diesel/24hr, **food:** Angel Ridge Rest., **W...gas:** Conoco/diesel/24hr, **food:** Huddle House

57   AL 21, to Atmore, **E...gas:** Exxon/BBQ/diesel, Shell/diesel, **food:** Creek Family Rest., **lodging:** Best Western, **other:** Indian Bingo, **W...gas:** BP/diesel, **other:** to Kelley SP

54   Escambia Cty Rd 1, **E...gas:** BP/Subway/diesel, Citgo/diesel, **other:** to Creek Indian Res

45   to Perdido, **W...gas:** Amoco/diesel

37   AL 287, to Bay Minette, **E...gas:** BP

34   to AL 59, to Bay Minette, Stockton, **E...HOSPITAL**

31   AL 225, to Stockton, **E...other:** to Blakeley SP, Confederate Mem Bfd, **W...gas:** Conoco/diesel

29mm Tensaw River

28mm Middle River

25mm Mobile River

22   Creola, **E...marine ctr, W...other:** I-65 RV Park(3mi)

19   US 43, to Satsuma, **E...gas:** Chevron/diesel/24hr, Pilot/Arby's/diesel/24hr, **food:** McDonald's, Waffle House, **W...gas:** BP, **other:** I-65 RV Park(5mi)

15   AL 41, **E...gas:** Chevron, **lodging:** Plantation Motel, **W...gas:** Citgo/diesel

13   AL 158, AL 213, to Saraland, **E...gas:** BP/diesel, Shell, Krystal/diesel/24hr, **food:** Ruby Tuesday, Shoney's, Waffle House, **lodging:** Comfort Inn, Day's Inn, Holiday Inn Express, **other:** Plantation Motel(1mi), Wal-Mart SuperCtr/24hr, **W...gas:** Exxon, **food:** Blimpie, Pizza Inn, **lodging:** Hampton Inn

10   W Lee St, **E...gas:** Citgo, Conoco, Shell/Subway, **lodging:** Howard Johnson Express

9   I-165 S, to Mobile, to I-10 E

8b a   US 45, to Prichard, **E...gas:** Chevron/24hr, Shell/diesel, **food:** Church's, Cracker Barrel, My Seafood Café, **lodging:** Star Motel, **other:** Family$, Tiger Foods, **W...gas:** Amoco/24hr, Conoco/diesel, Exxon, Pride Trkstp/diesel, RaceWay, **food:** Burger King, Domino's, Golden Egg Café, McDonald's

5b   US 98, Moffett Rd, **E...gas:** Exxon/diesel, **food:** Burger King, Church's, Sub King, **other:** Advance Parts, Big 10 Tire, **W...gas:** MinuteStop/diesel, **lodging:** Super 8

a   Spring Hill Ave, **E...gas:** Amoco, Chevron, Shell/diesel, **food:** BBQ, Dairy Queen, KFC, McDonald's, **other:** HOSPITAL, AutoZone, Big 10 Tire, CarQuest, Family$, Tiger Foods, **W...gas:** Chevron/diesel/24hr, Exxon, Shell/diesel, **food:** Waffle House, **lodging:** Extended Stay America

4   Dauphin St, **E...gas:** Amoco/diesel, Shell, **food:** Checker's, Chick-fil-A, Cracker Barrel, Godfather's, Hong Kong Island, Krystal, McDonald's, Popeye's, Subway, Taco Bell, TCBY, Waffle House, Wendy's, **lodging:** Comfort Suites, Executive Inn, Red Roof Inn, **other:** Cadillac/Pontiac/GMC, $General, FoodWorld, Hyundai, Lowe's Whse, Mercedes, Mr Transmission, Rite Aid, Subaru, Wal-Mart SuperCtr/24hr, same as 3 & 5a, **W...HOSPITAL**

3   Airport Blvd, to Airport, **E...gas:** BP, **food:** Burger King, Hooters, Piccadilly's, Schlotsky's, Wendy's, **lodging:** Marriott, **other:** HOSPITAL, Acura/Jaguar/Infiniti, Barnes&Noble, Best Buy, BooksAMillion, Daewoo, Dillard's, Firestone/auto, Ford, Goodyear/auto, Harley-Davidson, Mitsubishi, Nissan, Old Navy, Saab, Saturn, Sears/auto, Staples, Target, mall, **W...gas:** Exxon/Subway, Shell, Spur/diesel, **food:** American

Interstate 65

N ↕ S

Mobile

Café, Arby's, Bumpers Grill, Burger King, Carrabba's, Chen Chinese, Chili's, ChuckeCheese, Denny's, El Chico, El Monterey Mexican, Fatzo's Café, IHOP, JR's Smokehouse, LoneStar Steaks, Los Rancheros Mexican, O'Charley's, Olive Garden, Outback Steaks, Pizza Hut, Popeye's, Quizno's, Red Lobster, S China Seafood, Shoney's, Tony Roma, Waffle House, Wanfu Mongolian, **lodging:** Airport Plaza Hotel, Best Inn, Best Value Inn, Best Western, Courtyard, Day's Inn, Drury Inn, Fairfield Inn, Hampton Inn, InTowne Suites, La Quinta, Motel 6, Ramada Inn, Residence Inn, **other:** BooksAMillion, Bruno's Food, Circuit City, $Tree, Home Depot, Jo-Ann Fabrics, Michael's, OfficeMax, Office Depot, PepBoys, Radio Shack, Sam's Club, SteinMart, U-Haul, to USAL

1b a US 90, Government Blvd, **E...gas:** Chevron, **food:** Burger King, McAlister's Deli, Steak'n Shake, **lodging:** Guesthouse Inn, **other:** Aamco, Audi/VW, BMW, Buick/Isuzu/Volvo, Chevrolet, Chrysler/Jeep, Dodge, Family$, Honda, Kia, Lexus, Lincoln/Mercury, Mazda, Toyota, **W...gas:** Shell/diesel, **food:** Waffle House, **lodging:** Rest Inn

0mm I-10, E to Pensacola, W to New Orleans. I-65 begins/ends on I-10, exit 20.

Interstate 85

N ↕ S

Lanett

Exit #	Services
80mm	Alabama/Georgia state line, Chattahoochee River

79 US 29, to Lanett, **E...gas:** Amoco/diesel, Lo-Bucks/24hr, **food:** Arby's, Burger King, BBQ, Capt D's, Hardee's, KFC, Krystal, Magic Wok Chinese, McDonald's, San Marcos Mexican, Subway, Taco Bell, Waffle House/24hr, Wendy's, **other:** Advance Parts, $General, Radio Shack, Wal-Mart SuperCtr/gas/24hr, transmissions, to West Point Lake, **W...gas:** Conoco, Phillips 66/diesel, **food:** Domino's, Shoney's, Sonic, **lodging:** Day's Inn, Econolodge, Super 8, **other:** AutoZone, CVS Drug, Kroger, Parts+

78.5mm **Welcome Ctr sb, full(handicapped)facilities, phone, vending, picnic tables, litter barrels, petwalk**

77 AL 208, to Huguley, **E...gas:** Amoco/diesel/24hr, Chevron/WaffleKing/diesel/24hr, **food:** Waffle House, **lodging:** Holiday Inn Express, **other:** Chevrolet, Chrysler/Dodge, Ford/Lincoln/Mercury

76mm Eastern/Central time zone

70 AL 388, to Cusseta, **E...gas:** Perlis/Subway/diesel/rest./24hr/@

66 to Andrews Rd, no facilities

Opelika
Auburn

64 US 29, to Opelika, **E...gas:** Amoco, **lodging:** IGuesthouse Inn

62 US 280/431, to Opelika, **E...gas:** Amoco, BP/diesel, Chevron, Shell/Church's/diesel/24hr, **food:** Burger King, Denny's, McDonald's, Shoney's, Subway, **lodging:** Budget Inn, Day's Inn, Econolodge, Holiday Inn, Knight's Inn, Motel 6, **other: Lakeside RV Park(4.5mi), W...gas:** Conoco, Shell, **food:** Cracker Barrel, Waffle House, Western Sizzlin, **lodging:** Comfort Inn, Travelodge, **other:** Chevrolet, Chrysler/Plymouth/Dodge, Ford, GNC, Hyundai, Jeep, Toyota, USA Stores/famous brands

60 AL 51, AL 169, to Opelika, **E...gas:** Amoco/diesel, RaceTrac, **food:** Hardee's, **W...gas:** Shell/Krystal/diesel, **food:** Wendy's, **lodging:** Econolodge, **other:** HOSPITAL

58 US 280 W, to Opelika, **E...other:** golf, museum, **W...gas:** BP, Chevron/Subway, **food:** Dairy Queen, Golden Corral, Outback Steaks, Taco Bell, **lodging:** Ramada Ltd, **other:** HOSPITAL, Lowe's Whse

57 Glenn Ave, **W...gas:** Exxon, Conoco/diesel, **lodging:** Hilton Garden, Plaza Motel, Super 8

51 US 29, to Auburn, **E...gas:** Amoco/diesel/24hr, **lodging:** Hampton Inn, **other:** to Chewacla SP, **W...gas:** Exxon/diesel, Raceway, **food:** McDonald's, Philly Connection, Waffle House, **lodging:** Auburn U Hotel/Conf Ctr, Comfort Inn, Econolodge, Heart of Auburn Motel, **other:** Ford/Lincoln/Mercury/Mitsubishi, to Auburn U

44mm **rest area both lanes, full(handicapped)facilities, phone, vending, picnic tables, litter barrels, petwalk, RV dump, 24hr security**

42 US 80, AL 186 E, Wire Rd, **E...other:** to Tuskegee NF, diesel repair/tires, **W...gas:** Amoco/diesel

38 AL 81, to Tuskegee, **E...to** Tuskegee NHS

32 AL 49 N, to Tuskegee, **E...gas:** Amoco/diesel

26 AL 229 N, to Tallassee, **E...gas:** Texaco/diesel, **W...HOSPITAL**

ALABAMA

Interstate 85

N ↕ S

Montgomery

22	US 80, to Shorter, **E...gas:** Amoco/diesel, Chevron/Petro/diesel/rest., Exxon/diesel, **lodging:** Day's Inn, **other:** to Macon Co Greyhound Pk, Windrift RV Park
16	Waugh, to Cecil, **E...gas:** BP/Subway/diesel, **other:** auto repair
11	US 80, to Mt Meigs, **E...gas:** Exxon/Subway/ diesel, Liberty/diesel, **W...gas:** Chevron/24hr
9	AL 271, to AL 110, to Auburn U/Montgomery, **E...food:** Applebee's, Arby's, Atlanta Bread, Subway, **other:** BooksAMillion, **W...gas:** Citgo/diesel, HOSPITAL
6	US 80, US 231, AL 21, East Blvd, **E...gas:** Chevron/24hr, Exxon/diesel/24hr, RaceTrac, **food:** Arby's, Chick-fil-A, Cracker Barrel, Don Pablo, KFC, McAlister's, O'Charley's, Olive Garden, Piccadilly's, Roadhouse Grill, Schlotsky's, Shogun Japanese, Smokey Bones BBQ, Steak-Out, Subway, Taco Bell, Up The Creek Grill, Waffle House, Wendy's, Wings Grill, Zaxby's, **lodging:** Baymont Inn, Best Inn, Comfort Inn, Courtyard, Extended Stay America, Fairfield Inn, Hampton Inn, La Quinta, Quality Inn, Ramada Inn, Residence Inn, SpringHill Suites, Studio+, Wingate Inn, **other:** Home Depot, Lowe's Whse, Pontiac/Cadillac, Radio Shack, USPO, **1 mi E...food:** Copeland's, TGIFriday, Tony Roma, Wal-Mart SuperCtr/24hr, **W...gas:** Amoco, Citgo, Shell, **food:** Burger King, Church's, KFC, LoneStar Steaks, McDonald's, OutBack Steaks, Ruby Tuesday, Waffle House, **lodging:** Best Western, Comfort Suites, Motel 6, Holiday Inn, **other:** BMW, Buick, Chevrolet, Chrysler/Jeep, Ford, Hyundai, Isuzu, Kia, Lexus, Mazda, Mitsubishi, Nissan, Sam's Club/gas, Toyota, VW, to Gunter AFB, **1 mi W...food:** IHOP, **other:** Circuit City, Sears/auto, mall
4	Perry Hill Rd, **E...other:** DENTIST, Bruno's Foods, Rite Aid, **W...gas:** Chevron/24hr
3	Ann St, **E...gas:** BP/diesel, Chevron, **food:** Arby's, BBQ, Capt D's, Domino's, Great Wall Chinese, Hardee's, KFC, Krystal, McDonald's, Pizza Hut, Taco Bell, Waffle House, Wendy's, **lodging:** Day's Inn, **other:** Big 10 Tire, **W...gas:** Amoco, Entec, Exxon, **lodging:** Stay Lodge
2	Forest Ave, **E...other:** CVS Drug, **W...**HOSPITAL
1	Court St, Union St, downtown, **E...gas:** Amoco/ diesel, Exxon, **W...**to Ala St U
0mm	I-85 begins/ends on I-65, exit 171 in Montgomery.

Interstate 459(Birmingham)

N ↕ S

Birmingham

Exit #	Services
33b a	I-59, N to Gadsden, S to Birmingham. I-459 begins/ ends on I-59, exit 137.
32	US 11, Trussville, **E...gas:** Chevron/diesel/24hr, Citgo, RaceTrac/24hr, Shell, Texaco/Wendy's/diesel, **food:** A&W/KFC, Arby's, BBQ, Chili's, Jack's Rest., McDonald's, Waffle House, **lodging:** Hampton Inn, **other:** BooksAMillion, Harley-Davidson, Home Depot, Lowe's Whse, Mazda, Michael's, Pontiac/GMC/Buick, Staples, Target, **W...gas:** BP/24hr, **lodging:** Best Inn(3mi)
31	Derby Parkway, **W...other:** B'ham Race Course
29	I-20, E to Atlanta, W to Birmingham
27	Grants Mill Rd, **S...gas:** Exxon/diesel
23	Liberty Parkway, no facilities
19	US 280, Mt Brook, Childersburg, **N...gas:** Chevron, **other:** Barnes&Noble, **1-2 mi S...gas:** Exxon, **food:** Arby's, Burger King, Chick-fil-A, McDonald's, Piccadilly's, Ruby Tuesday, **lodging:** Courtyard, Drury Inn, Fairfield Inn, Hampton Inn, Hilton, Holiday Inn Express, Homestead Suites, Marriott, Sheraton, Studio Inn
17	Acton Rd, **N...gas:** Shell/diesel/24hr, **food:** BBQ, Krystal, McDonald's
15b a	I-65, N to Birmingham, S to Montgomery
13	US 31, Hoover, Pelham, **N...gas:** Chevron, Shell, **food:** BBQ, Chick-fil-A, DQ, LongHorn Steaks, McDonald's, Quizno's, Schlotsky's, Shoney's, SteakOut, Subway, **lodging:** Comfort Inn, Day's Inn, Hampton Inn, Holiday Inn, RiverChase Inn, **other:** MEDICAL CARE, Acura, BooksAMillion, Bruno's Foods, Buick, Cadillac, Chevrolet, Chrysler/Plymouth/Jeep, Circuit City, Eckerd, Firestone, Goodyear, Honda, Kia, Mitsubishi, Mr Transmissions, Toyota, **S...gas:** Crown Gas, Shell/diesel/24hr, Circle K, **food:** BBQ, Burger King, CiCi's, Grady's Grill, McDonald's, Olive Garden, Omelet Shoppe, Piccadilly's, Sun's Chinese, Taco Bell, Wendy's, **lodging:** AmeriSuites, Courtyard, Winfrey Hotel, **other:** Barnes&Noble, Bruno's Foods, CVS Drug, GNC, Infiniti, JC Penney, K-Mart, Mercedes, Michael's, Wal-Mart(1mi), mall
10	AL 150, Waverly, **N...gas:** Chevron, Shell, **S...gas:** BP/ diesel/24hr, Exxon, **food:** Mei China, AmeriSuites(1mi), GNC, Walgreen, Winn-Dixie
6	AL 52, to Bessemer, **N...gas:** BP, **S...gas:** Crown, Exxon/24hr, Shell, **food:** Arby's, McDonald's, Pizza Hut, Taco Bell, Waffle House, Wendy's, **lodging:** Sleep Inn, **other:** MEDICAL CARE, CVS Drug, Winn-Dixie
1	AL 18, Bessemer, **N...gas:** Shell/diesel, **S...gas:** BP/ diesel, **food:** China King, McDonald's, Subway, **other:** FoodWorld, to Tannehill SP
0mm	I-459 begins/ends on I-20/59, exit 106.

ARIZONA

Interstate 8

E ↑

W ↓

Exit #	Services
178b a	I-10, E to Tucson, W to Phoenix. I-8 begins/ends on I-10, exit 199.
174	Trekell Rd, to Casa Grande, **2-4 mi N...other:** HOSPITAL, gas, food, lodging
172	Thornton Rd, to Casa Grande, **2-4 mi N...food:** Sizzler, **lodging:** Best Western, Holiday Inn, Super 8, **S...other:** Francisco Grande Resort
171mm	Santa Cruz River
169	Bianco Rd, no facilities
167	Montgomery Rd, no facilities
163mm	Santa Rosa Wash
161	Stanfield Rd, no facilities
151	AZ 84 E, Maricopa Rd, to Stanfield, **S...gas:** Gas'n Go, Pullman Motel/rest./diesel, **other:** Saguaro RV Park
150mm	picnic area wb, picnic tables, litter barrels
149mm	picnic area eb, picnic tables, litter barrels
144	Vekol Rd, no facilities
140	Freeman Rd, no facilities
119	Butterfield Trail, to AZ 85, I-10, Gila Bend, **N...gas:** Chevron/Subway/diesel/24hr, Shell/diesel/RV dump, **food:** American/Mexican Café, DQ, Exit West Café, Space Age Rest., **lodging:** Best Western/rest.(3mi), Super 8, Yucca Motel, **other:** RV camping
117mm	Sand Tank Wash
115	AZ 85, to Gila Bend, **1-2 mi N...gas:** Chevron/Subway/diesel, Loves/Taco Bell/diesel, 76/Circle K, Shell/diesel, **food:** A&W, Burger King, DQ, McDonald's, **lodging:** Best Western, El Coronado Motel, Yucca Motel, **other:** HOSPITAL, Big A Parts, Goodyear/auto, NAPA, RV park
111	Citrus Valley Rd, no facilities
106	Paloma Rd, no facilities
102	Painted Rock Rd, no facilities
87	Sentinel, Hyder, **N...gas:** Sentinel Gen Store, **other:** RV camping, towing
85mm	**rest area wb, full(handicapped)facilities, phone, picnic tables, litter barrels, vending, petwalk**
84mm	**rest area eb, full(handicapped)facilities, phone, picnic tables, litter barrels, vending, petwalk**
78	Spot Rd, no facilities
73	Aztec, no facilities
67	Dateland, **S...gas:** Exxon/24hr, **other:** Oasis RV Park/dump
56mm	**rest area both lanes, full(handicapped)facilities, phone, picnic tables, litter barrels, vending, petwalk**
54	Ave 52 E, Mohawk Valley, no facilities
42	Ave 40 E, to Tacna, **N...gas:** Chevron/diesel, **lodging:** Chaparral Motel

Yuma

37	Ave 36 E, to Roll, no facilities
30	Ave 29 E, Wellton, **N...gas:** 76/Circle K, **other:** MEDICAL CARE, Tier Drop RV Park
24mm	Ligurta Wash
23mm	Red Top Wash
22mm	parking area both lanes
21	Dome Valley, **N...food:** Ligurta Sta Café, **other:** RV park, Yuma Proving Ground(16mi)
17mm	insp sta eb
15mm	Fortuna Wash
14	Foothills Blvd, **N...other:** Sundance RV Park, **S...food:** Domino's, FootHills Rest., Mi Fajita Rest., **other:** FootHills RV Park
12	Fortuna Rd, to US 95 N, **N...gas:** Chevron/24hr, Shamrock/Barney's/diesel/24hr, Shell/diesel, **food:** Jack-in-the-Box, Pizza Hut, Tyler's Rest., **lodging:** Courtesy Inn, **S...gas:** 76, Shell/Burger King/diesel, **food:** DQ, Subway, Microtel, **other:** URGENT CARE, Big O Tire, Fry's Foods, Radio Shack

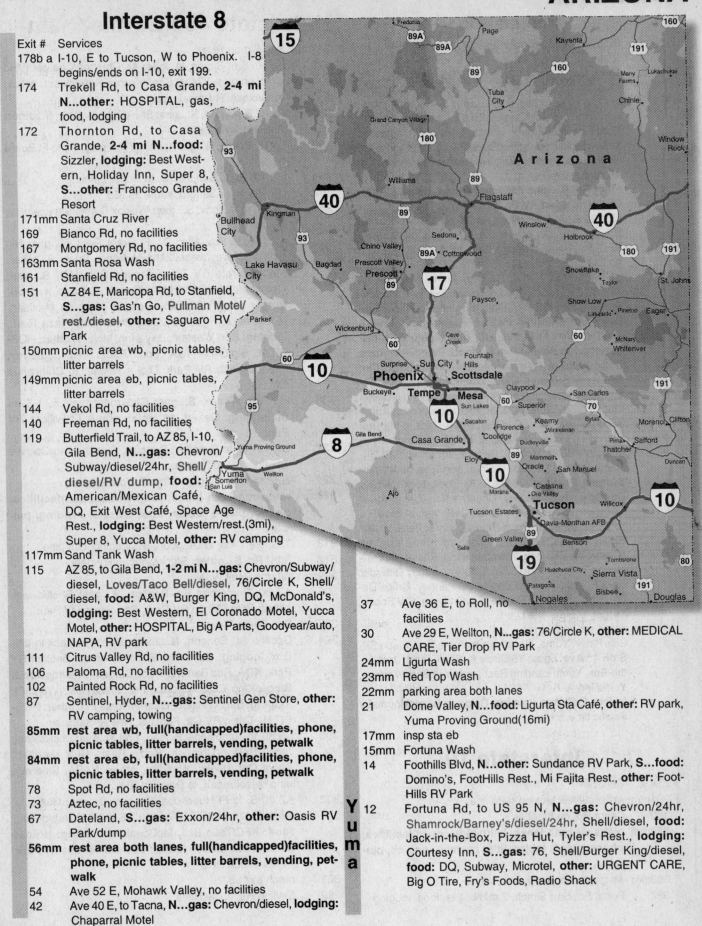

ARIZONA

Interstate 8

E ↕ W

9 32nd St(no EZ wb return), to Yuma, **N...other:** Sun Vista RV Park, **7 mi S...gas:** Chevron, 76/Circle K, **food:** Carl's Jr, Carrow's Rest., DQ, Domino's, KFC, Mandarin Palace, Pizza Hut, Taco Bell, **lodging:** Holiday Inn Express, Ramada Inn, Travelodge, **other:** Albertson's, Buick/Cadillac/GMC, Chevrolet, Dillard's, Ford/Lincoln/Mercury, Honda, Lowe's Whse, Mazda, Mervyn's, Michael's, PepBoys, Plymouth/Jeep/Dodge, Sears/auto, Toyota, Walgreen, **access to services on 4th Ave**

7 Araby Rd, **S...gas:** 76/Circle K/diesel, **other:** La Mesa Ctr, Windhaven RV Park, to AZWU

3 AZ 280 S, Ave 3E, **N...gas:** Yuma 3E/diesel, **food:** Burger King, **S...other:** Big A Parts, **3 mi S...food:** KFC, Pizza Hut, Wendy's(6mi), **other:** to Marine Corp Air Sta

2 US 95, 16th St, Yuma, **N...gas:** Barneys/diesel/café, 76/Circle K, **food:** Cracker Barrel, Denny's, Musick's Rest., Penny's Diner/24hr, **lodging:** Best Western, Day's Inn, Fairfield Inn, La Fuente Inn, Motel 6, OakTree Inn, Shilo Inn/rest., **other:** auto/tire repair, **Services on Pacific Ave S...food:** Peter Piper Pizza, Sonic, Subway, Wienerschnitzel, **other:** Big O Tire, NAPA, Kia, Sam's Club, **Wal-Mart SuperCtr/24hr**, **S...gas:** Arco/diesel/24hr, Chevron/Blimpie/diesel, Mobil/Wendy's/diesel, Shamrock, Shell, **food:** Applebee's, Burger King, Carl's Jr, IHOP, Jack-in-the-Box, Wendy's, Village Inn Pizza, **lodging:** Comfort Inn, Interstate 8 Inn, Motel 6, Super 8, **other:** HOSPITAL, Home Depot, Staples, U-Haul, **services on 4th Ave S...gas:** Chevron, 76/Circle K, Shell, **food:** Arby's, Burger King, China Boy, Church's, Del Taco, Home-Town Buffet, HongKong Buffet, Jack-in-the-Box, JB's, KFC, McDonald's, Papa John's, Rally's, Red Lobster, Rocky's Pizza, Taco Bell, Wienerschnitzel, **lodging:** Holiday Inn Express, Interstate 8 Inn, Radisson, Travelodge, **other:** AutoZone, Checker Parts, Dillard's, Fry's Foods, Hastings Books, JC Penney, Office Depot, Radio Shack, Rite Aid, SavOn Drug, SW Foods, Target, U-Haul, mall

1.5mm weigh sta both lanes

1 Giss Pkwy, Yuma, **N...other:** to Yuma Terr Prison SP, **S on 4th Ave...gas:** 76/Circle K, Shell, **food:** Jack-in-the-Box, Yuma Landing Rest., **lodging:** Best Western, Yuma Inn

0mm Arizona/California state line, Colorado River, Mountain/Pacific time zone

Interstate 10

E ↕ W

Exit #	Services
391mm	Arizona/New Mexico state line
390	Cavot Rd, no facilities
389mm	**rest area both lanes, full(handicapped)facilities, phone, picnic tables, litter barrels, vending, pet-walk**
383mm	weigh sta eb, weigh/insp sta wb
382	Portal Rd, San Simon, **2 mi N...**gas, food, lodging

381mm San Simon River

378 Lp 10, San Simon, **N...gas:** 4K/Chevron/Chester Fried Chicken/diesel/24hr, Shell/Kactus Kafe/diesel, **other:** auto/diesel/RV repair, lodging

366 Lp 10, Bowie Rd, **N... gas:** Shell/Subway/24hr, **S...other:** Alaskan RV park

362 Lp 10, Bowie, **N...**gas, lodging, camping, **S...**to Ft Bowie NHS

355 US 191 N, to Safford, **N...**to Roper Lake SP

352 US 191 N, to Safford, same as 355

344 Lp 10, to Willcox, **S...gas:** Willcox Diesel Service/truck repair

340 AZ 186, to Rex Allen Dr, Ft Grant Field, **N...gas:** Rip Griffin/Subway/diesel/24hr, **lodging:** Super 8, **other:** Magic Circle RV Park, Stout's CiderMill, **S...gas:** Chevron/diesel/24hr, Mobil/diesel, 76/Circle K, **food:** Burger King, KFC/Taco Bell, La Kachina Mexican, McDonald's, Pizza Express, Pizza Hut, Plaza Rest., **lodging:** Best Western, Day's Inn, Motel 6, **other:** HOSPITAL, Big O Tire, IGA Foods, Radio Shack, Safeway, Grande Vista RV Park, Dick's Repair, to Chiricahua NM

336 AZ 186, Willcox, **S...gas:** Chevron/diesel/LP, **1-3 mi S...lodging:** Desert Inn Motel, **other:** Ft Willcox RV Park

331 US 191 S, to Sunsites, Douglas, **S...other:** to Cochise Stronghold, no facilities

322 Johnson Rd, **S...gas:** Citgo/DQ/diesel/gifts

320mm **rest area both lanes, full(handicapped)facilities, phone, picnic tables, litter barrels, vending, pet-walk**

318 Triangle T Rd, to Dragoon, **S...**lodging, camping

312 Sibyl Rd, **S...other:** Stuckey's/gas/RV park

309mm Adams Peak Wash

306 AZ 80, Pomerene Rd, Benson, **S...gas:** Shell/diesel, **other:** Pato Blanco RV Park, San Pedro RV Park

305mm San Pedro River

304 Ocotillo St, Benson, **N...food:** Denny's, Jack-in-the-Box, **lodging:** Day's Inn, Super 8, **other:** Benson RV Park, KOA, Red Barn RV Park, **S...gas:** Chevron, **food:** Burger King, Country Folks Rest., Plaza Rest., Wendy's, **lodging:** Best Western, QuarterHorse Inn, **other:** HOSPITAL, Dillon RV Ctr, Family$, NAPA, Safeway

303 US 80, to Tombstone, Bisbee, **1 mi S...gas:** Shell/diesel, **food:** Beijing Chinese, Reb's Rest., Ruiz Mexican, Shoot Out Steaks, Wendy's, **other:** NAPA, Safeway, auto/diesel/repair, to Douglas NHL

302 AZ 90 S, to Ft Huachuca, Benson, **S...gas:** Gas City/A&W/Pizza Hut/TCBY/diesel, Shell/Subway/diesel, **food:** KFC/Taco Bell, McDonald's, **lodging:** Holiday Inn Express, Motel 6, **other:** Cochise Terrace RV Park, Ft Huachuca NHS

301 ranch exit eb

299 Skyline Rd, no facilities

Willcox

Benson

Interstate 10

E
↕
W

297 Mescal Rd, J-6 Ranch Rd, **N...gas:** QuickPic/diesel/deli/24hr

292 Empirita Rd, no facilities

289 Marsh Station Rd, no facilities

288mm Cienega Creek

281 AZ 83 S, to Patagonia, no facilities

279 Vail/Wentworth Rd, **N...food:** Vail Steakhouse, **other:** to Colossal Caves

275 Houghton Rd, **N...other:** to Saguaro NM, camping, **S...**to fairgrounds

273 Rita Rd, **S...**fairgrounds

270 Kolb Rd, **N...gas:** Chevron/diesel, **S...other:** Voyager RV Resort

269 Wilmot Rd, **N...gas:** Chevron/A&W/diesel, **lodging:** Travel Inn, **other:** RV park, **S...**RV park

268 Craycroft Rd, **N...gas:** Conoco/diesel, TTT/diesel/rest./24hr, 76/Circle K, **S...**diesel repair

267 Valencia Rd, **N...gas:** Arco/Jack-in-the-Box, **other:** Pima Air Museum, **S...**airport

265 Alvernon Way, Davis-Monthan AFB, no facilities

264b a Palo Verde Rd, **N...gas:** Chevron/Wendy's/diesel, **food:** Carl's Jr, Denny's, Waffle House, **lodging:** Crossland Suites, Day's Inn, Fairfield Inn, Holiday Inn, Red Roof Inn, **other:** Hannon RV Ctr, **S...gas:** QuikMart/gas, **food:** Arby's, McDonald's, Motel 6, **lodging:** Ramada Inn, Studio 6 Suites, **other:** Beaudry RV Ctr, Camping World RV Resort, La Mesa RV Ctr, Factory Outlet/famous brands

263b Kino Pkwy N, no facilities

a Kino Pkwy S, **S...gas:** Shamrock, **food:** Fry's Foods, **other:** to Tucson Intn'l Airport

262 Benson Hwy, Park Ave, **S...gas:** Arco/24hr, Chevron, Shell, JB's, **food:** McDonald's, Navaronne Rest., Waffle House, **lodging:** Howard Johnson, Jct Inn, Motel 6, Quality Inn, Rodeway Inn

261 6th/4th Ave, **N...gas:** Chevron, **lodging:** Budget Inn, Econolodge, **S...food:** Burger King, Carrow's Rest., Silver Saddle Steaks, **lodging:** Rodeway Inn, Sandman Inn, Lazy 8 Motel, **other:** Spanish Trail

260 I-19 S, to Nogales

259 22nd St, Starr Pass Blvd, **N...gas:** 76/Circle K/diesel, **S...gas:** 76, Kettle, **food:** Waffle House, Comfort Inn, Holiday Inn Express, Howard Johnson, Knight's Inn, Motel 6, Super 8, Travel Inn

258 Congress St, Broadway St, **N...gas:** Circle K/76, **food:** Garcia's Rest., **lodging:** Holiday Inn, InnSuites Motel, Motel 6, Quality Hotel Suites, Ramada Inn, Travelodge, **S...food:** Bennigan's, Carl's Jr, Whataburger, **lodging:** Days Inn, Pueblo Inn

257a St Mary's Rd, **N...gas:** 76/diesel, **other:** HOSPITAL, **S...gas:** Shell/24hr, **food:** Burger King, Denny's, Furr's Cafeteria, Jack-in-the-Box, **lodging:** La Quinta, **other:** Pim Comm Coll

Tucson

257 Speedway Blvd, **N...gas:** 7-11/24hr, **lodging:** Best Western, **other:** HOSPITAL, Old Town Tucson, museum, U of AZ, **S...gas:** Arco/diesel/24hr

256 Grant Rd, **N...food:** Sonic, diesel/transmission repair, **S...gas:** Exxon, 76/Circle K, Shell, **food:** Del Taco, IHOP, Subway, Waffle House, **lodging:** Baymont Inn, Hampton Inn, Motel 6, Rodeway Inn, Shoney's Inn, **1 mi S...gas:** Circle K, **food:** McDonald's, **other:** Walgreen

255 AZ 77 N, to Miracle Mile

254 Prince Rd, **N...gas:** Circle K, **other:** U-Haul, tires, **S...other:** Prince of Tucson RV Park, golf

252 El Camino del Cerro, Ruthrauff Rd, **N...gas:** Arco/24hr

251 Sunset Rd, **N...other:** auto parts

250 Orange Grove Rd, **N...gas:** Arco/24hr, Circle K, **food:** Wendy's, **other:** Mitsubishi, **N on Thornydale...gas:** Costco/gas, **food:** Casa Molina Mexican, Little Caesar's, **other:** Big O Tire, Home Depot

248 Ina Rd, **N...gas:** Chevron/diesel, Conoco/diesel, Exxon/Circle K, **food:** Arby's, Burger King, Carl's Jr, China House, DQ, Hooters, Jack-in-the-Box, LJ Silver, McDonald's, Perkins, Pizza Hut, Rubio's Grill, Taco Bell, Waffle House, **lodging:** InTown Suites, Motel 6, **other:** CarQuest, Discount Tire, Fry's Foods, Hancock Fabrics, Office Depot, OfficeMax, Osco Drug, PepBoys, Target, **S...gas:** Exxon/Circle K, **food:** Denny's, **lodging:** Comfort Inn, Park Inn, Red Roof Inn

246 Cortaro Rd, **N...gas:** Chevron/Arby's/diesel, **food:** IHOP, Wendy's, **S...gas:** Shell/diesel, **food:** Burger King, Cracker Barrel, KFC, McDonald's, **lodging:** Best Western, Day's Inn, Holiday Inn Express, Ramada Ltd, Super 8, **other:** USPO, Wal-Mart SuperCtr/24hr, access to RV camping

243 Avra Valley Rd, **S...other:** Saguaro NM(13mi), RV camping, airport

240 Tangerine Rd, to Rillito, **S...**USPO

236 Marana, **S...gas:** Chevron/diesel/LP, 76/Circle K, **other:** Sun RV Park, auto repair

232 Pinal Air Park Rd, **S...**Pinal Air Park

228mm wb pulloff, to frontage rd

ARIZONA
Interstate 10

E ↑ ↓ W

226	Red Rock, **S**...USPO
219	Picacho Peak Rd, **N**...**gas:** Citgo/DQ, **S**...**other:** Pichaco Peak RV Park, to Picacho Peak SP
212	Picacho(from wb), **N**...**gas:** Premium Gas, **lodging:** Picacho Motel/RV Park, **other:** USPO
211b	AZ 87 N, AZ 84 W, to Coolidge
a	Picacho(from eb), **S**...**other:** Picacho RV Park, state prison
208	Sunshine Blvd, to Eloy, **S**...**gas:** ♦/Flying J/Conoco/diesel/LP/rest./24hr/@, Pilot/diesel/24hr/@
203	Toltec Rd, to Eloy, **N**...**gas:** Chevron/McDonald's/24hr, Circle K/diesel, **food:** Carl's Jr, El Zarape Rojo Mexican, Waffle House, **lodging:** Super 8, Toltec Inn, **other:** Blue Beacon, Golden Corridor RV Park, diesel/tire repair, **S**...**gas:** Exxon/diesel, TA/A&W/Taco Bell/diesel/24hr/@, **food:** Pizza Hut
200	Sunland Gin Rd, Arizona City, **N**...**gas:** Petro/Mobil/diesel/rest./24hr/@, Pilot/Subway/diesel/24hr, **food:** Burger King, **lodging:** Day's Inn, Sunland Inn/rest., **other:** Blue Beacon, Las Colinas RV Park, **S**...**gas:** Loves/Arby's/Baskin-Robbins/diesel/24hr, **food:** Golden 9 Rest., **lodging:** Motel 6, Quail Run RV Resort
199	I-8 W, to Yuma, San Diego
198	AZ 84, to Eloy, Casa Grande, **N**...**lodging:** Sunland Inn, **S**...**food:** Wendy's, **other:** Tanger Outlet Ctr/famous brands, Buena Tierra RV Pk
194	AZ 287, to Casa Grande, **N**...**other:** Sunscape RV Park(7mi), **S**...**gas:** Arco/diesel/24hr, Chevron/DQ, **food:** Burger King, Cracker Barrel, Del Taco, Denny's, **lodging:** Best Western, Comfort Inn, Holiday Inn, Super 8, **other:** HOSPITAL, Factory Stores/famous brands, Palm Creek RV/golf Resort, **2 mi S**...**gas:** Chevron, 76/Circle K, **food:** Arby's, China King, Church's, Filiberto's Mexican, Golden Corral, Jack-in-the-Box, JB's, Little Caesar's, McDonald's, Peter Piper Pizza, Sizzler, Sonic, Subway, Wendy's, **other:** Albertson's, American CarCare, Basha's Foods, Fry's Foods, Goodyear/auto, GreenBax, JC Penney, OfficeMax, PepBoys, Radio Shack, Walgreen, Wal-Mart SuperCtr/24hr, to Casa Grande Ruins NM
190	McCartney Rd, **N**...**other:** to Central AZ Coll
185	AZ 387, to Casa Grande, Casa Grande Ruins NM, **S**...**other:** hwy patrol, RV camping
183mm	**rest area wb, full(handicapped)facilities, phone, picnic tables, litter barrels, vending, petwalk**
181mm	**rest area eb, full(handicapped)facilities, phone, picnic tables, litter barrels, vending, petwalk**
175	AZ 587 N, Casa Blanca Rd, **S**...**gas:** Shell/diesel, **other:** Casa Blanca RV Camping
173mm	Gila River
167	Riggs Rd, to Sun Lake, **N**...**gas:** Chevron
164	AZ 347 S, Queen Creek Rd, to Maricopa, **N**...**other:** to Chandler Airport
162b a	Maricopa Rd N, **S**...**other:** Firebird Sports Park, Gila River Casino

160	Chandler Blvd, to Chandler, **N**...**gas:** Exxon/Circle K, Mobil, **food:** Burger King, Damon's, Denny's, Marie Callender's, Perkins, Sizzler, Whataburger/24hr, **lodging:** Fairfield Inn, Hampton Inn, Homewood Suites, Red Roof Inn, Southgate Motel, Super 8, Wyndham Garden, **other:** Firestone/auto, to Compadre Stadium, to Williams AFB, **S**...**gas:** Chevron, Citgo/7-11, Phillips 66/diesel, **food:** Cracker Barrel, Del Taco, Hooters, Holiday Inn Express, InTown Suites, La Quinta, **lodging:** Wellesley Inn, **other:** HOSPITAL, Brakes+, Discount Tire
159	Ray Rd, **N**...**gas:** 76/Circle K, Shell/diesel, **food:** Buca Italian, Carrabba's, Charleston's Rest., In-n-Out, Luby's, McDonald's, Outback Steaks, Red Lobster, **lodging:** Courtyard, **other:** Borders Books, CompUSA, Ford, Home Depot, Lowe's Whse, Sam's Club, **S**...**gas:** Exxon/Circle K/diesel, **food:** BBQ, Boston Mkt, IHOP/24hr, Jack-in-the-Box, Macaroni Grill, Mimi's Café, On-the-Border, Peter Piper Pizza, Pizza Hut, Ruby Tuesday, Subway, Sweet Tomato, Wendy's, **lodging:** Extended Stay America, **other:** Albertson's/24hr, Barnes&Noble, Best Buy, FootHills Carwash, Jo-Ann Fabrics, Mervyn's, Michael's, OfficeMax, Old Navy, Osco, Ross, Smith's Food/drug/24hr, SteinMart, SunDevil AutoCare, Target
158	Warner Rd, **N**...**gas:** 76/Circle K, **S**...**gas:** Arco/24hr, 76/Circle K, **food:** Burger King, ChuckeCheese, DQ, Malaya Mexican, McDonald's, Quizno's, Ruffino's Italian, Taco Bell, **other:** Basha's Foods, Big O Tire, Goodyear/auto, Osco Drug, Wild Oats Foods
157	Elliot Rd, **N**...**gas:** Chevron, Circle K, **food:** Applebee's, Arby's, Blackeyed Pea, Burger King, Chili's, Coco's, Country Harvest Buffet, Eastside Mario's, Fuddrucker's, Kyoto Japanese, Mi Amigos Mexican, Olive Garden, Red Robin Rest., Schlotsky's, Sooper Salad, Subway, Taco Bell, Village Inn Rest., Wendy's, **lodging:** Country Suites, **other:** Cadillac/GMC, Circuit City, Costco, Discount Tire, Dodge, Fiddlesticks Funpark, Ford/Lincoln/Mercury, GNC, Honda, Nissan, OfficeMax, PetsMart, Saturn, SportsAuthority, Staples, Toyota, U-Haul, Wal-Mart, **S**...**gas:** Mobil/diesel, 76/Circle K, **food:** Burrito Co, China Star, KFC, McDonald's, Peter Piper Pizza, Pizza Hut, Sub Factory, Taco John's, **lodging:** Best Western, Quality Inn, **other:** MEDICAL CARE, Checker Parts, Radio Shack, Walgreen
155	Baseline Rd, Guadalupe, **N**...**gas:** Mobil, 76/Circle K, Shell/diesel, **food:** Carl's Jr, Jack-in-the-Box, Rusty Pelican Seafood, Shoney's, Waffle House, **lodging:** AmeriSuites, Candlewood Studios, Holiday Inn Express, InnSuites, Ramada Ltd, Residence Inn, **other:** AZ Mills Factory Shops, JC Penney Outlet, Marshall's, Pro Auto Parts, Savco Drugs, **S**...**food:** Aunt Chilada's Mexican, Denny's, **lodging:** Homestead Village, Motel 6, **other:** Fry's Electronics
154	US 60 E, AZ 360, Superstition Frwy, to Mesa, **N**...**other:** to Camping World(off Mesa Dr)

Chandler

Casa Grande

Phoenix

Interstate 10

E

↕

W

Phoenix

153b a AZ 143 N, Broadway Rd E, to Sky Harbor Airport, **N...food:** Denny's, **lodging:** Comfort Suites, Courtyard, Fairfield Inn, Hilton, La Quinta, MainStay Suites, Red Roof Inn, Sheraton, Sleep Inn, **other:** to Diablo Stadium, **S...gas:** Shell/A&W/Taco Bell/24hr, **food:** Del Taco, **lodging:** Hampton Inn

152 40th St, **N...gas:** Cardlock/diesel, Shell/diesel, **other:** U Phoenix, **S...gas:** 76/Circle K, **food:** Burger King

151mm Salt River

151b a 28th St, 32nd St, University Ave, **N...lodging:** Extended Stay America, La Quinta, Radisson, **other:** AZSU, U Phoenix, **S...gas:** 76/Circle K

150b 24th St E(from wb), **N...**Air Nat Guard, **gas:** Exxon, **food:** Durado's Rest., **lodging:** Golden 9 Motel/rest., Knight's Inn, Motel 6, Rodeway Inn, **S...lodging:** Best Western/rest.

a I-17 N, to Flagstaff

149 Buckeye Rd, **N...other:** Sky Harbor Airport

148 Washington St, Jefferson St, **N...gas:** Chevron, Exxon, Tiemco/diesel, **food:** Carl's Jr, McDonald's, Rally's, **lodging:** Motel 6, Rodeway Inn, **other:** to Sky Harbor Airport, **S...gas:** 76/Circle K, **other:** HOSPITAL

147b a AZ 51 N, AZ 202 E, to Squaw Peak Pkwy, no facilities

146 16th St, **N...gas:** 76/Circle K, **food:** KFC, **S...gas:** 76/Circle K, **food:** Church's, Jack-in-the-Box, Ramiro's Mexican, **other:** K-Mart

145 7th St, **N...food:** McDonald's, **other:** Walgreen, **S...gas:** Chevron, 76/Circle K, Shell, **other:** HOSPITAL, to America West Arena

144 7th Ave, Amtrak, central bus dist

143c 19th Ave, US 60, no facilities

b a I-17, N to Flagstaff, S to Phoenix

142 27th Ave(from eb, no return), **N...gas:** Circle K, 7-11, **lodging:** Comfort Inn, **S...gas:** Pacific Pride/diesel

141 35th Ave, **N...gas:** 76/Circle K, **food:** Jack-in-the-Box, Rita's Mexican, **S...gas:** Shell

140 43rd Ave, **N...gas:** Citgo/7-11, Exxon/CircleK/diesel, Mobil, **food:** KFC, Little Caesar's, Mixteca Mexican, Smitty's Foods, Subway, Wendy's, **other:** Big O Tire, Food City, Fry's Foods, Radio Shack, Walgreen

139 51st Ave, **N...gas:** Chevron/diesel, 76/Circle K, Citgo/7-11, **food:** Burger King, Domino's, El Pollo Loco, Little China, McDonald's, Sonic, Waffle House, **lodging:** CrossLand Suites, InTown Suites, Motel 6, Red Roof Inn, Travelodge, **other:** Discount Tire, Goodyear/auto, **S...gas:** DiscountZone/diesel, **food:** Carl's Jr, IHOP, Taco Bell, **lodging:** Fairfield Inn, Hampton Inn, Super 8, Travelers Inn

138 59th Ave, **N...gas:** 76/Circle K, Shamrock, 7-11, **food:** Armando's Mexican/24hr, **other:** AutoZone, Checker Parts, Walgreen, **S...gas:** Pilot/Wendy's/diesel/24hr, **food:** Waffle House, Whataburger/24hr

137 67th Ave, **N...gas:** QT, 76/Circle K, Texaco, **food:** Church's, **S...gas:** ✈/Flying J/Conoco/CountryMkt/diesel/LP/24hr/@

136 75th Ave, **N...gas:** Chevron, 76/Circle K, **food:** Denny's, Taco Bell, Whataburger, **other:** Ford, Home Depot, Lowe's Whse, Staples, Wal-Mart SuperCtr/24hr, **S...gas:** Arco/24hr

135 83rd Ave, **N...gas:** 76/Circle K, **food:** Arby's, Burger King, Jack-in-the-Box, Waffle House, **lodging:** Comfort Suites, Econolodge, **other:** Sam's Club

134 91st Ave, Tolleson, no facilities

133b Lp 101 N, no facilities

a 99th Ave, **S...food:** Pilot/diesel/24hr/@

132 107th Ave(from eb), no facilities

131 115th Ave, to Cashion, **N...gas:** Mobil, **S...other:** to Phoenix International Raceway

129 Dysart Rd, to Avondale, **N...gas:** Chevron, Shell/diesel, **food:** In-n-Out, Jack-in-the-Box/24hr, Palermo's Pizza, **other:** Fry's Foods, OfficeMax, Wal-Mart SuperCtr/24hr, **S...food:** KFC, McDonald's, Subway, Towns Square Café, Waffle House, Whataburger, **lodging:** Comfort Inn, Super 8, **other:** Chevrolet, Chrysler/Plymouth/Dodge/Jeep, Home Depot, Walgreen

128 Litchfield Rd, **N...gas:** Mobil/Blimpie/diesel, **food:** Applebee's, Bennett's BBQ, Chili's, Cracker Barrel, Denny's, Fazoli's, McDonald's, On the Border, Pizza Factory, Taco Cabana, TGIFriday, Wendy's, **lodging:** Hampton Inn, Holiday Inn Express, **other:** Michael's, Target, Wigwam Outlet Stores/famous brands, Wigwam Resort(3mi), to Luke AFB, **S...gas:** Chevron, Mobil/Blimpie, **food:** Arby's, Bamboo Inn Rest., Burger King, JB's, Peter Piper Pizza, Schlotsky's, Taco Bell, **lodging:** Best Western, **other:** MEDICAL CARE, Albertson's, Checker Parts, Goodyear/auto, Pontiac/GMC, Radio Shack

126 PebbleCreek Pkwy, to Estrella Park, no facilities

125mm Roosevelt Canal

124 Cotton Lane, to AZ 303, **N...**st prison, **S...other:** Scenic Destiny RV Park

Phoenix

ARIZONA

Interstate 10

E ↑↓ W

121	Jackrabbit Trail, **N…gas:** Phillips 66/diesel, **S…gas:** 76/Circle K
114	Miller Rd, to Buckeye, **S…gas:** Loves/A&W/Taco Bell/diesel/24hr, **food:** Burger King, **lodging:** Day's Inn, **other:** Leaf Verde RV Park
112	AZ 85, to I-8, Gila Bend, no facilities
109	Sun Valley Pkwy, Palo Verde Rd, no facilities
104mm	Hassayampa River
103	339th Ave, **S…gas:** Rip Griffin/Subway/Pizza Hut/diesel/LP/24hr/@, **other:** truckwash
98	Wintersburg Rd, **S…other:** to Palo Verde Nuclear Sta
97mm	Coyote Wash
95.5mm	Old Camp Wash
94	411th Ave, Tonopah, **S…gas:** Chevron/diesel, Shell/Subway/diesel/LP/24hr, **food:** Joe&Alice's Café/24hr, **lodging:** Mineral Wells Motel, **other:** USPO, tires/repair, Saddle Mtn RV Park
86mm	**rest area both lanes, full(handicapped)facilities, phone, picnic tables, litter barrels, petwalk, vending**
81	Salome Rd, Harquahala Valley Rd, no facilities
69	Ave 75E, no facilities
53	Hovatter Rd, no facilities
52mm	**rest area both lanes, full(handicapped)facilities, phone, vending, picnic tables, litter barrels, petwalk**
45	Vicksburg Rd, **S…gas:** Shamrock/diesel/rest./24hr, Jobski's Diesel Repair/towing
31	US 60 E, to Wickenburg, **12 mi N…other:** food, camping
26	Gold Nugget Rd, no facilities
19	Quartzsite, to US 95, Yuma, **N…gas:** Chevron, Shell/diesel, **food:** Taco Mio, **other:** CarQuest, **other:** Roadrunner Foods, RV camping
18mm	Tyson Wash
17	to US 95, Quartzsite, **N…gas:** Mobil/Burger King/LP, Pilot/Subway/DQ/diesel/24hr, **food:** Best Chinese, McDonald's, Ponderosa Grill, Ted's Bullpen Rest., **other:** RV camping, **S…gas:** Loves/A&W/Taco Bell/diesel/24hr, **lodging:** Best Western, **other:** Desert Gardens RV Park
11	Dome Rock Rd, no facilities
5	Tom Wells Rd, **N…gas:** Beacon/diesel/24hr
4.5mm	**rest area both lanes, full(handicapped)facilities, phone, vending, picnic tables, litter barrels, petwalk**
3.5mm	**eb…**AZ Port of Entry, **wb…**weigh sta
1	Ehrenberg, to Parker, **N…other:** KOA, **S…gas:** ⛽/Flying J/Wendy's/Cookery/diesel/LP/24hr/@, **lodging:** Best Western
0mm	Colorado River, Arizona/California state line, Mountain/Pacific time zone

Interstate 15

Exit #	Services
29.5mm	Arizona/Utah state line
27	Black Rock Rd, no facilities
21mm	turnout sb
18	Cedar Pocket, **S…other:** Virgin River Canyon RA, parking area
16mm	truck parking both lanes
15mm	truck parking nb
14mm	truck parking nb
10mm	truck parking nb
9	Farm Rd, no facilities
8.5mm	Virgin River
8	Littlefield, Beaver Dam, **E…other:** RV park, **1 mi W…**gas/diesel, food, lodging, camping
0mm	Arizona/Nevada state line, Pacific/Mountain time zone

N ↑↓ S

Interstate 17

F l a g s t a f f

Exit #	Services
341	McConnell Dr, I-17 begins/ends. **See Arizona Interstate 40, exit 195b.**
340b a	I-40, E to Gallup, W to Kingman
339	Lake Mary Rd(from nb), Mormon Lake, access to same as 341. **E…gas:** 76/diesel
337	AZ 89A S, Oak Creek Canyon, to Sedona, Ft Tuthill RA
333	Kachina Blvd, Mountainaire Rd, **E…lodging:** Sled Dog B&B, **W…gas:** 76/Subway
331	Kelly Canyon Rd, no facilities
328	Newman Park Rd, no facilities
326	Willard Springs Rd, no facilities
322	Pinewood Rd, to Munds Park, **E…gas:** Chevron/diesel, Woody's/diesel, **food:** Lone Pine Rest., **other:** Motel in the Pines/RV camp, USPO, **W…gas:** Exxon, **other:** Munds RV Park, RV repair
322mm	Munds Canyon
320	Schnebly Hill Rd, no facilities
317	Fox Ranch Rd, no facilities
316mm	Woods Canyon
315	Rocky Park Rd, no facilities
313mm	scenic view sb, litter barrels
306	Stoneman Lake Rd, no facilities
300mm	runaway truck ramp sb
298	AZ 179, to Sedona, Oak Creek Canyon, **7-15 mi W…food:** Burger King, Poco Café, **lodging:** Best Western, Hilton Garden, Holiday Inn Express, Quality Inn, Radisson, Wildflower Inn
297mm	**rest area both lanes, full(handicapped)facilities, phone, picnic tables, litter barrels, vending, petwalk**

N ↑↓ S

ARIZONA

Interstate 17

N ↑ S

293mm Dry Beaver Creek
293 Cornville Rd, McGuireville Rd, to Rimrock, **E...gas:** XpressFuel, **food:** McGuireville Café, **lodging:** Beaver Creek Golf Resort(3mi), **W...gas:** 76/diesel
289 Middle Verde Rd, Camp Verde, **E...gas:** Mobil/diesel, Shell/diesel, **food:** Rockets Café, Sonic, **lodging:** Cliff Castle Lodge/casino, **other:** to Montezuma Castle NM, **W...other:** Distant Drums RV Park
288mm Verde River
287 AZ 260, to AZ 89A, Cottonwood, Payson, **E...gas:** Arco, Chevron, Shell/Subway/diesel/RVdump/LP/24hr, **food:** A&W/KFC, Burger King, DQ, Denny's, McDonald's, Pizza Hut/Taco Bell, **lodging:** Comfort Inn, Day's Inn, Super 8, **other:** Basha's Foods, Trails End RV Park, **W...gas:** Chevron/diesel/24hr, **other:** to Jerome SP, RV camping, **12-14 mi W...food:** Jack-in-the-Box, **lodging:** Best Western, Quality Inn, **other:** HOSPITAL, to DeadHorse SP
285 Camp Verde, Gen Crook Tr, **E...other:** to Ft Verde SP
281mm brake check area nb
278 AZ 169, Cherry Rd, to Prescott, no facilities
268 Dugas Rd, Orme Rd, no facilities
269mm Ash Creek
265.5mm Agua Fria River
262b a AZ 69 N, Cordes Jct Rd, to Prescott, **E...gas:** Chevron/24hr, Shell/Subway/diesel/24hr, **food:** McDonald's, **other:** Lights On Motel/RV Park, **W...food:** Papa's Place Steaks
262mm Big Bug Creek
259 Bloody Basin Rd, to Crown King, Horse Thief Basin RA, no facilities
256 Badger Springs Rd, no facilities
252 **Sunset Point, W...scenic view/rest area both lanes, full(handicapped)facilities, phone, picnic tables, litter barrels, vending**
248 Bumble Bee, **W...other:** HorseThief Basin RA
244 Squaw Valley Rd, Black Canyon City, **E...gas:** Chevron/diesel/24hr, Shell/diesel, **food:** Medicine Horse Café, Smokin Joe's Cantina, Squaw Peak Steaks, **other:** KOA
243.5mm Agua Fria River
242 Rock Springs, Black Canyon City, **E...KOA, W...gas:** Chevron/diesel/24hr, Shell, **food:** Lazy JB Rest., Rock Springs Café, **lodging:** Bradshaw Mtn RV Resort
239.5mm Little Squaw Creek
239mm Moore's Gulch
236 Table Mesa Rd, no facilities
232 New River, no facilities
231.5mm New River

Scottsdale

229 Anthem Way, Desert Hills Rd, **E...gas:** Mobil/diesel, **food:** McDonald's, Subway, **other:** Osco Drug, Safeway, **W...gas:** Chevron/Burger King, Mobil/Blimpie, **lodging:** Comfort Suites, **other:** Prime Outlets/famous brands/food court
227mm Dead Man Wash
225 Pioneer Rd, **W...other:** Pioneer RV Park, museum
223 AZ 74, Carefree Hwy, to Wickenburg, **E...gas:** Chevron, **food:** McDonald's, **other:** Albertson's, **W...other:** Lake Pleasant Park, camping
219mm Skunk Creek
218 Happy Valley Rd, no facilities
217 Pinnacle Peak Rd, no facilities
217b Deer Valley Rd, Rose Garden Ln, **E...gas:** Exxon, Shell/diesel, **food:** Burger King, Jack-in-the-Box, McDonald's, Sonic, Taco Bell, Wendy's, **W...gas:** 76/Circle K, Shell/diesel, **food:** Cracker Barrel, Denny's, Schlotsky's, Waffle House, Wendy's, **lodging:** Budgetel, Day's Inn, Extended Stay America, **other:** N Phoenix RV Park
215 AZ 101 W, **W...lodging:** Country Inn Suites, **other:** HOSPITAL,Target
214b a Yorkshire Dr, Union Hills Dr, **E...gas:** Shamrock, 76/Circle K, **W...gas:** Arco, **food:** ClaimJumper Rest., Jack-in-the-Box, Macaroni Grill, Souper Salad, Subway, Tony Roma, **lodging:** Motel 6, Sleep Inn, Wyndham Garden, **other:** HOSPITAL, Costco/gas, OfficeMax, Radio Shack, Ross, Target
212b a Bell Rd, Scottsdale, to Sun City, **E...gas:** Chevron/diesel, Exxon, Mobil, **food:** Coco's, IHOP/24hr, Jack-in-the-Box, LJ Silver, McDonald's, Quizno's, Sonic, Waffle House, Wendy's, **lodging:** Best Western, Comfort Inn, Fairfield Inn, Motel 6, **other:** Checker Parts, Chevrolet, Dodge, Drug Emporium, Ford/Lexus/Isuzu, Lincoln/Mercury, Nissan/Infiniti, Pontiac/Buick/GMC, Smith's Foods, Toyota, U-Haul, **W...gas:** Mobil, **food:** Applebee's, Denny's, Good Egg Rest., HomeTown Buffet, Hooters, Sizzler, Village Inn Rest., **lodging:** Fairfield Inn, Red Roof Inn, **other:** Fry's Foods, Sam's Club
211 Greenway Rd, **E...gas:** 7-11, **lodging:** Embassy Suites, La Quinta, **other:** MEDICAL CARE

Interstate 17

N ↕ **S**

Phoenix

210 Thunderbird Rd, **E...gas:** Arco, Exxon, 76/Circle K, **food:** Jack-in-the-Box, McDonald's, Pizza Hut/Taco Bell, Schlotsky's, Wendy's, **lodging:** Home Depot, **other:** Osco Drug, Safeway, Walgreen, **W...gas:** QT, **food:** Fazoli's, McDonald's, **lodging:** Hawthorn Suites, **other:** Fry's Electronics, Lowe's Whse

209 Cactus Rd, **W...gas:** Chevron/24hr, Citgo/7-11, **food:** Cousins Subs, Denny's, **lodging:** Red Lion Hotel, **other:** MEDICAL CARE, Basha's Foods, Firestone

208 Peoria Ave, **E...food:** Fajita's, LoneStar Steaks, Pappadeaux, TGIFriday, **lodging:** AmeriSuites, Candlewood Suites, Comfort Suites, Crowne Plaza, Wellesley Inn, **W...gas:** 76/Circle K, **food:** Bennigan's, Black Angus, Burger King, China Gate, Coco's, El Torito, FlashBacks Café, Italian Oven, Mamma Mia's, Olive Garden, Red Lobster, Sizzler, Souper Salad, Wendy's, **lodging:** Premier Inn, Sheraton, **other:** Barnes&Noble, Circuit City, Firestone/auto, Macy's, Michael's, Sears/auto, Staples, mall

208.5mm Arizona Canal

207 Dunlap Ave, **E...gas:** 76, **food:** Blimpie, Fuddrucker's, Outback Steaks, Sweet Tomato, **lodging:** Courtyard, Parkway Inn, Sierra Suites, SpringHill Suites, TownPlace Suites, **other:** Aamco, Firestone, mall, **W...gas:** Exxon/LP, Circle K, **food:** Bobby McGee's, Denny's, Schlotsky's, Subway, **other:** Circuit City, OfficeMax, U-Haul

206 Northern Ave, **E...gas:** Mobil, 76/Circle K, Shell/diesel, **food:** Boston Mkt, Burger King, Denny's/24hr, El Pollo Loco, Marie Callender's, McDonald's, Papa John's, Pizza Hut, South China Buffet, Starbucks, Subway, **lodging:** Hampton Inn, **other:** Albertson's, Checker Parts, USPO, Walgreen, **W...gas:** Arco, **food:** DQ, Furr's Dining, Village Inn Rest., Winchell's, **lodging:** Motel 6, Residence Inn, Super 8, **other:** K-Mart, NAPA AutoCare

205 Glendale Ave, **E...gas:** Circle K/24hr, **food:** BBQ, **other:** VETERINARIAN, **W...gas:** Exxon/diesel, Circle K, **food:** Jack-in-the-Box, **other:** to Luke AFB

204 Bethany Home Rd, **E...gas:** Arco/24hr, 76/Circle K, Shell/Church's, **food:** Isberto's Mexican/24hr, McDonald's, Subway, Teriyaki Grill, Whataburger, **other:** Desert Mkt Foods, **W...gas:** Chevron/diesel, Exxon, **other:** Food City, transmissions/24hr

203 Camelback Rd, **E...gas:** Arco/24hr, Circle K, **food:** Blimpie, Burger King, Church's, Country Boy's Rest./24hr, Denny's/24hr, Pizza Hut, Taco Villa, **other:** Buick, Chrysler/Plymouth/Jeep/Dodge, Volvo, Discount Tire, Firestone/auto, Checker Parts, NAPA, Walgreen, **W...gas:**

Phoenix

Mobil, QT, **food:** DQ, Denny's, Jack-in-the-Box, McDonald's, Taco Bell, Tacos Mexico, Treulich's Rest., **lodging:** Comfort Inn, **other:** AutoZone, Chevrolet, Firestone/auto, to Grand Canyon U

202 Indian School Rd, **E...gas:** Arco/24hr, **food:** Alberto's Mexican, Filiberto's Mexican/24hr, Jimmy's Rest., Pizza Hut, Pizza Mia, Subway, **other:** Albertson's Foods, **W...gas:** Exxon, Circle K, Shell, **food:** Hunter Steaks, JB's, Wendy's, **lodging:** Motel 6, Super 8, **other:** MEDICAL CARE, auto repair

201 Thomas Rd, **E...gas:** Circle K, **food:** Arby's, Denny's, Jack-in-the-Box, McDonald's, Roman's Pizza, Taco Bell/24hr, **lodging:** Day's Inn, EZ Inn, La Quinta, **W...food:** Burger King, **other:** Ford, NAPA

200b McDowell Rd, Van Buren, **E...food:** Wendy's, **other:** Goodyear, **W...lodging:** Travelodge

a I-10, W to LA, E to Phoenix

199b Jefferson St(from sb), Adams St(from nb), Van Buren St(from nb), **E...gas:** Circle K/76/24hr, **food:** Jack-in-the-Box, McDonald's, **lodging:** Sandman Motel, **other:** to st capitol, **W...gas:** Circle K/76, KFC, **food:** La Canasta Mexican, Pete's Fish'n Chips, **other:** Penny Pincher Parts, PepBoys, SW Foods

a Grant St, no facilities

198 Buckeye Rd(from nb), **W...**RV Ctr

197 US 60, 19th Ave, Durango St, to st capitol, **E...food:** Whataburger/24hr

196 7th St, Central Ave, **E...food:** Burger King, **other:** HOSPITAL, Amtrak Sta

195b 7th St, Central Ave, **E...gas:** Exxon/24hr, Circle K, Trailside Gas/diesel/24hr, **food:** McDonald's, Taco Bell, **lodging:** EZ 8 Motel/rest., **other:** HOSPITAL

a 16th St(no EZ return from sb), **E...other:** Checker Parts, Food City, Smitty's Foods, Walgreen, to Sky Harbor Airport

194 I-10 W, to AZ 51, Squaw Peak Pkwy, to Sky Harbor Airport

I-17 begins/ends on I-10, exit 150a.

Interstate 19

N ↕ **S**

Exit # | Services

I-19 uses kilometers (km)

101b a I-10, E to El Paso, W to Phoenix. I-19 begins/ends on I-10, exit 260.

99 AZ 86, Ajo Way, **E...gas:** Conoco, 76/Circle K, **food:** DQ, Hamburger Stand, Peter Piper Pizza, Pizza Hut, Subway, Taco Bell, **other:** Fry's Foods, GNC, Jo-Ann Fabrics, Mervyn's, Osco Drug, Radio Shack, U-Haul, Walgreen, **W...gas:** Chevron/diesel/24hr, Conoco/diesel, 76/Circle K, **food:** Bamboo Chinese, Burger King, **other:** HOSPITAL, IGA Foods, to Old Tucson, museum

Tucson

Interstate 19

N
↑
↓
S

98	Irvington Rd, **E...gas:** Arco/24hr, **other:** Fry's Foods, **W...gas:** Chevron, **food:** China Olive Buffet, McDonald's, **other:** Food4Less, Home Depot, OfficeMax, Target
95b a	Valencia Rd, **E...food:** Church's, Donut Wheel, Eegee's Café, Jack-in-the-Box, KFC, McDonald's, Sonic, Taco Loco, Yokohama RiceBowl, **other:** AutoZone, Checker Parts, IGA Foods, Radio Shack, USPO, **W...gas:** Chevron, 76/Circle K, **food:** Applebee's, Arby's, Burger King, Carl's Jr, Denny's, Golden Corral, IHOP, Papa John's, Pizza Hut, Taco Bell, Wendy's, **other:** MEDICAL CARE, Big O Tire, CarQuest, Osco Drug, Walgreen, Wal-Mart SuperCtr/24hr, repair, transmissions
92	San Xavier Rd, **W...other:** to San Xavier Mission
91.5km	Santa Cruz River
87	Papago Rd, no facilities, emergency phones sb
80	Pima Mine Rd(no sb return), **E...food:** Agave Rest., Diamond Casino
75	Helmut Peak Rd, to Sahuarita, no facilities
69	US 89 N, Green Valley, **E...food:** Denny's, Pizza Hut, Schlotsky's, Subway, **other:** Basha's Food, Radio Shack, Wal-Mart, **W...gas:** 76/diesel, **food:** Burger King, DQ, Rigoberto's Mexican, Taco Bell/TCBY, **lodging:** Holiday Inn Express, **other:** Big O Tire, Ford/Lincoln/Mercury, Green Valley RV Resort, Safeway, Titan Missile Museum
65	Esperanza Blvd, to Green Valley, **E...gas:** Shell/repair, **W...gas:** Exxon/diesel, **food:** AZ Family Rest., La Placita Mexican, Oasis Rest., **lodging:** Baymont Inn, Best Western, **other:** Walgreen
63	Continental Rd, Green Valley, **E...food:** KFC, Quail Valley Rest., **other:** USPO, **2 mi E...other:** San Ignacio Golf Club/rest., **W... gas:** Exxon, **food:** McDonald's, Taco Bell, **other:** MEDICAL CARE, Goodyear/auto, HealthFoods, NAPA, Osco Drug, Safeway, Walgreen, to Madera Cyn RA
56	Canoa Rd, **W...lodging:** San Ignacio Inn
54km	**rest area both lanes, full(handicapped)facilities, phone, picnic tables, litter barrels, vending, petwalk**
48	Arivaca Rd, Amado, **2 mi E...other:** Mtn View RV Park, **W...gas:** Amado Plaza
42	Agua Linda Rd, to Amado, **E...other:** Mtn View RV Park

N o g a l e s

40	Chavez Siding Rd, Tubac, **3-5 mi E...gas:** Tubac Mkt/diesel/deli, **other:** Tubac Golf Resort
34	Tubac, **E...gas:** Tubac Mkt/diesel, **food:** Montura Rest., **other:** Tubac Golf Resort, USPO, to Tubac Presidio SP
29	Carmen, Tumacacori, **E...gas,** food, lodging, **other:** to Tumacacori Nat Hist Park
25	Palo Parado Rd, no facilities
22	Peck Canyon Rd, insp sta nb
17	Rio Rico Dr, Calabasas Rd, **E...food:** Sunset Grill, **W...gas:** Chevron, Gas4Less, **food:** Cayatano Grill, La Placita Mexican, **other:** IGA Foods, Rio Rico Resort, USPO, RV camping
12	AZ 289, to Ruby Rd, **E...gas:** Pilot/Wendy's/diesel/24hr, **other:** to Pena Blanca Lake RA
8	US 89, AZ 82(exits left from sb), Nogales, **1-3 mi E...gas:** 76/Circle K, Shell/diesel, **food:** Denny's, Medici's Rest., **lodging:** Americana Motel, Best Western, Day's Inn, **other:** HOSPITAL, Goodyear/auto, U-Haul, Mi Casa RV Park
4	AZ 189 S, Mariposa Rd, Nogales, **E...gas:** Chevron/DQ, FasTrip, 76, **food:** Arby's, ChinaStar, Denny's, Exquisito Mexican, KFC, McDonald's, Rooster's Grill, Shakey's, Taco Bell, Yokohama Rest., **lodging:** Americana Motel, Best Western, Motel 6, Super 8, **other:** Chevrolet, Ford/Lincoln/Mercury, JC Penney, K-Mart, Pontiac/Buick/GMC, Radio Shack, Safeway, Veterans Foods, Walgreen, Wal-Mart SuperCtr/24hr(N Grand Ave), **W...gas:** Phillips 66/diesel, **food:** Carl's Jr, IHOP, **lodging:** Holiday Inn Express, Chrysler/Plymouth/Dodge/Jeep Western Ave, Nogales, **W...HOSPITAL**
1	I-19 begins/ends in Nogales, Arizona/Mexico Border, **1/2 mi...gas:** 76/Circle K, Shell/repair, **food:** Burger King, Domino's, Jack-in-the-Box, McDonald's, Peter Piper Pizza, **other:** AutoZone, Basha's Mercado, CarQuest, Checker Parts, Family$, NAPA, PepBoys, Walgreen, bank, museum
0km	

E
W

Exit #	Services
359.5mm	Arizona/New Mexico state line
359	Grants Rd, to Lupton, **N...rest area both lanes, full(handicapped)facilities, phone, picnic tables, litter barrels, petwalk, gas:** Speedy's/diesel/rest./24hr, **other:** Tee Pee Trading Post/rest., YellowHorse Indian Gifts, **S...other:** Indian Mkt/gas
357	AZ 12 N, Lupton, to Window Rock, **N...other:** trading post, USPO
354	Hawthorne Rd, no facilities
351	Allentown Rd, **N...other:** Cheese Indian Store, Indian City Gifts
348	St Anselm Rd, Houck, **N...gas:** Chevron, **food:** Pancake House, **other:** Ft Courage Food/gifts
347.5mm	Black Creek
346	Pine Springs Rd, no facilities
345mm	Box Canyon
344mm	Querino Wash
343	Querino Rd, no facilities
341	Ortega Rd, Cedar Point, **N...gas:** Armco/gas/gifts
340.5mm	insp/weigh sta both lanes
339	US 191 S, to St Johns, **S...gas:** Conoco/diesel/24hr, **other:** USPO
333	US 191 N, Chambers, **N...gas:** Chevron/diesel, **other:** to Hubbell Trading Post NHS, RV camping, **S...gas:** Mobil, Best Western/rest., **other:** USPO
330	McCarrell Rd, no facilities
325	Navajo, **S...gas:** Shell/Subway/Navajo Trading Post/diesel/24hr
323mm	Crazy Creek
320	Pinta Rd, no facilities
316mm	Dead River, picnic area both lanes, litter barrels
311	Painted Desert, **N...other:** Petrified Forest NP, Painted Desert
303	Adamana Rd, **N...**Stewarts/gifts, **S...gas:** Painted Desert Indian Ctr/gas
302.5mm	Big Lithodendron Wash
301mm	Little Lithodendron Wash
300	Goodwater, no facilities
299mm	Twin Wash
294	Sun Valley Rd, **N...**RV camping, **S...gas:** AZ StageStop/gifts
292	AZ 77 N, to Keams Canyon, **N...gas:** Conoco/Burger King/diesel/24hr/@, **food:** Red Baron
289	Lp 40, Holbrook, **N...gas:** Chevron/diesel, Hatch's/diesel, **food:** Denny's, Jerry's Rest., Mesa Rest., **lodging:** Best Inn, Best Western, Comfort Inn, Day's Inn, Econolodge, Motel 6, Ramada Ltd, Relax Inn, Sahara Inn, **other:** KOA

Holbrook

Holbrook

Winslow

286	Lp 40, Holbrook, **N...gas:** 76/Circle K, Shamrock/diesel, **food:** KFC, McDonald's, Pizza Hut, Roadrunner Café, Taco Bell, Holiday Inn Express, Super 8, **other:** Checker Parts, KOA, OK RV Park, **S...gas:** Chevron/diesel/repair, MiniMart/gas, 76/repair, Super Fuels, Woody's/diesel, **food:** DQ, **lodging:** Budget Inn, El Rancho Motel, Western Holiday Motel/rest., **other:** HOSPITAL, Ford/Lincoln/Mercury, Plymouth/Jeep/Dodge, museum, rockshops, transmissions
285	US 180 E, AZ 77 S, Holbrook, **1 mi S...gas:** Pacific Pride/diesel, **food:** Butterfield Steaks, Pizza Hut, Wayside Mexican, **lodging:** Best Western, Wigwam Motel, **other:** Safeway, RV repair, to Petrified Forest NP
284mm	Leroux Wash
283	Perkins Valley Rd, Golf Course Rd, **S...gas:** Shell/Country Host Rest./diesel/24hr/@
280	Hunt Rd, Geronimo Rd, **N...other:** Geronimo Trading Post
277	Lp 40, Joseph City, **N...gas:** Love's/A&W/Subway/diesel/24hr/@, **S...other:** to Cholla Lake CP, RV camping
274	Lp 40, Joseph City, **N...**gas, food, lodging, RV camping
269	Jackrabbit Rd, **S...gas:** Jackrabbit Trading Post/gas/diesel
264	Hibbard Rd, no facilities
257	AZ 87 N, to Second Mesa, **N...other:** to Homolovi Ruins SP, camping, **S...other:** SW Indian Ctr
256.5mm	Little Colorado River
255	Lp 40, Winslow, **N...gas:** Shell/rest./RV park, **food:** China Inn Rest., **lodging:** Holiday Inn Express, **S...gas:** ♦/Flying J/CountryMkt/diesel/LP/24hr/@, **food:** Sonic, **lodging:** Best Western(2mi)
253	N Park Dr, Winslow, **N...gas:** Chevron, Pilot/SenorD's/diesel/RV dump/24hr/@, **food:** Arby's, Capt Tony's Pizza, Denny's, Pizza Hut, **other:** Big O Tire, Checker Parts, Wal-Mart, **S...gas:** Gas Depot, **food:** Alfonso's Mexican, KFC, McDonald's, Subway, Taco Bell, **lodging:** Best Western, Econolodge, Motel 6, **other:** HOSPITAL, Basha's Foods, Family$, NAPA, Safeway
252	AZ 87 S, Winslow, **S...gas:** Shell/diesel, **food:** Entre Chinese, **lodging:** Day's Inn, Rest Inn, Super 8, Travelodge, **other:** NAPACare
245	AZ 99, Leupp Corner, no facilities
239	Meteor City Rd, Red Gap Ranch Rd, **S...other:** Meteor City Trading Post, to Meteor Crater
235mm	**rest area both lanes, full(handicapped)facilities, info, phone, picnic tables, litter barrels, petwalk**
233	Meteor Crater Rd, **S...gas:** Mobil/Subway/Meteor Crater RV Park, **other:** to Meteor Crater NL

ARIZONA

Interstate 40

230	Two Guns, no facilities
229.5mm	Canyon Diablo
225	Buffalo Range Rd, no facilities
219	Twin Arrows, no facilities
218.5mm	Padre Canyon
211	Winona, **N...gas:** Shell/diesel/repair, **other:** Winona Trading Post
207	Cosnino Rd, no facilities
204	to Walnut Canyon NM, no facilities
201	US 89, to Flagstaff, **N...gas:** Conoco/diesel, 76/repair, Xpress/diesel, **food:** Arby's, Burger King, Del Taco, Jack-in-the-Box, McDonald's, Pizza Hut, Quizno's, Ruby Tuesday, Sizzler, Taco Bell, Wendy's, Village Inn Rest., **lodging:** Best Western, Day's Inn, Hampton Inn, Howard Johnson, Super 8, Travelodge, **other:** HOSPITAL, Aamco, Checker's Parts, Dillard's, Discount Tire, Flagstaff RV Ctr, Goodyear/auto, JC Penney, KOA, OfficeMax, Safeway, Savers/gas, Sears/auto, Toyota, mall, **S...gas:** Mobil/diesel, **lodging:** Fairfield Resort, Residence Inn
198	Butler Ave, Flagstaff, **N...gas:** Chevron, Conoco/diesel, Shell, **food:** Burger King, Country Host Rest., Cracker Barrel, Denny's, McDonald's, Sonic, Taco Bell, **lodging:** Econolodge, Holiday Inn, Inn Suites, Howard Johnson, Motel 6, Ramada Ltd, Super 8, Travelodge, **other:** NAPA, Sam's Club, **1 mi N on US 89...gas:** 76/diesel, **food:** China House, Denny's, Kachina Mexican, KFC, Yippee-ei-o Steaks, **lodging:** Best Western, Frontier Motel, Red Roof Motel, Relax Inn, Rodeway Inn, Royal Inn, 66 Motel, Travelodge, Timberline Motel, Wonderland Motel, **other:** Albertson's, AutoZone, Big A Parts, Buick/Pontiac/GMC, Firestone, Fry's Foods, High Country Tire/auto, Kia, Nissan/Subaru, Plymouth/Dodge, Smith's Foods, U-Haul, Wienerschnitzel, **S...gas:** Mobil, Sinclair/Little America/diesel/motel/@, **food:** Black Bart's Steaks/RV Park
197.5mm	Rio de Flag
195b	US 89A N, McConnell Dr, Flagstaff, **N...gas:** Chevron, Conoco/diesel, Exxon/Wendy's/diesel, Gasser/diesel, Giant/diesel, Mobil, 76/diesel, Shell/diesel, Circle K, **food:** Arby's, Blimpie, Burger King, Buster's Rest., Carl's Jr, Cilantro's Mexican, Chili's, China Garden, Coco's, DQ, Del Taco, Denny's, Domino's, Fazoli's, IHOP, Jack-in-the-Box, Fuddrucker's, Furr's Café, KFC, McDonald's, Olive Garden, Perkins, Pizza Hut, Quizno's, Red Lobster, Roma Pizza, Sizzler, Souper Salad, Strombolli's, Subway, Taco Bell, TCBY, Village Inn Rest., **lodging:** AZ Motel, AmeriSuites, AutoLodge, Comfort Inn, Crystal

Inn, Day's Inn, Econolodge, Embassy Suites, Fairfield Inn, Hampton Inn, Hilton, La Quinta, Motel 6, Quality Inn, Ramada Ltd, Rodeway Inn, Sleep Inn, **other:** Barnes&Noble, Basha's Foods, CarQuest, Checker Parts, Discount Tire, Hastings Books, Jo-Ann Crafts, K-Mart, Michael's, Osco Drug, Safeway, Staples, Target, Walgreen, Wal-Mart

a	I-17 S, AZ 89A S, to Phoenix
192	Flagstaff Ranch Rd, no facilities
191	Lp 40, Flagstaff, to Grand Canyon, **5 mi N...food:** DQ, **lodging:** Best Western, Budget Host, Comfort Inn, Day's Inn, Econolodge, Embassy Suites, Radisson, Super 8, Travelodge
190	A-1 Mountain Rd, no facilities
189.5mm	Arizona Divide, elevation 7335
185	Transwestern Rd, Bellemont, **N...gas:** Conoco/Subway/diesel/24hr, **lodging:** Microtel, **S...food:** 66 Roadhouse Grill, **other:** Harley-Davidson
183mm	**rest area wb, full(handicapped)facilities, phone, picnic tables, litter barrels, vending, weather info, petwalk**
182mm	**rest area eb, full(handicapped)facilities, phone, picnic tables, litter barrels, vending, weather info, petwalk**
178	Parks Rd, **N...food:** Rack&Bull Café, **other:** Ponderosa Forest RV Park, gas
171	Pittman Valley Rd, Deer Farm Rd, **S...lodging:** Quality Inn/rest.
167	Garland Prairie Rd, Circle Pines Rd, **N...other:** KOA
165	AZ 64, to Williams, to Grand Canyon, **4 mi N...gas:** Shell/diesel, **other:** KOA, Red Lake Camping(9mi), **2-4 mi S...food:** Red's Steaks, **lodging:** Econolodge, Motel 6, Super 8, Travelodge, **other:** RV Ctr
163	Williams, **N...gas:** Chevron/Subway/diesel, **lodging:** Fairfield Inn, **other:** Cyn Gateway RV Park, to Grand Canyon, **S...gas:** Mobil/diesel, Shell/diesel, Circle K, **food:** Buckle's Rest., Jack-in-the-Box, McDonald's, Pizza Hut, **lodging:** Budget Host, Downtowner Motel, Econolodge, Gateway Motel, Holiday Inn, Howard Johnson Express, Rodeway Inn, Rte 66 Inn, Super 8, **other:** USPO, same as 161

21

ARIZONA

Interstate 40

Williams

161 Lp 40, Golf Course Dr, Williams, **N**...RV camping, **1-3 mi S...gas:** Chevron/diesel, Mobil, Shell/diesel, **food:** DQ, Denny's, Old Smoky Rest., Parker House Rest., Red's Steaks, Rosa's Cantina, **lodging:** Best Western, Budget Host, Canyon Country Inn, Comfort Inn, Day's Inn, El Rancho Inn, Highlander Motel, Holiday Inn Express, Motel 6, Norris Motel, Westerner Motel, **other:** HOSPITAL, NAPA, Safeway, Railside RV Ranch

157 Devil Dog Rd, no facilities

155.5mm safety pullout wb, litter barrels

151 Welch Rd, no facilities

149 Monte Carlo Rd, **N...gas:** Monte Carlo Trkstp/diesel/café/repair/24hr

148 County Line Rd, no facilities

146 AZ 89, Ash Fork, to Prescott, **N...gas:** Mobil, **lodging:** Ash Fork Inn/rest., **other:** KOA

144 Ash Fork, **N...lodging:** Ash Fork Inn/rest., **other:** KOA, **S...gas:** Chevron, **other:** Exxon/diesel/RV park

139 Crookton Rd, to Rte 66, no facilities

132mm weigh sta both lanes

123 Lp 40, to Rte 66, Seligman, **N... gas:** Shell/diesel, **other:** to Grand Canyon Caverns, **S...gas:** Chevron/Subway/diesel/24hr

121 Lp 40, to Rte 66, Seligman, **N...gas:** Chevron/A&W

109 Anvil Rock Rd, no facilities

108mm Markham Wash

103 Jolly Rd, no facilities

96 Cross Mountain Rd, no facilities

91 Fort Rock Rd, no facilities

87 Willows Ranch Rd, no facilities

83mm Willow Creek

79 Silver Springs Rd, no facilities

75.5mm Big Sandy Wash

73.5mm Peacock Wash

71 US 93 S, to Wickenburg, Phoenix, no facilities

66 Blake Ranch Rd, **N...gas:** Petro/Mobil/diesel/rest./24hr/@, **food:** Pizza Hut, **other:** Blake Ranch RV Park, Blue Beacon, **S...gas:** Beacon/diesel/café

60mm Frees Wash

59 DW Ranch Rd, **N...gas:** Love's/Subway/diesel/24hr

57mm Rattlesnake Wash

Kingman

53 AZ 66, Andy Devine Ave, to Kingman, **N...gas:** Chevron, ✈/Flying J/Conoco/diesel/LP/24hr/@, Mobil/diesel, Terrible's/diesel, **food:** Arby's, Burger King, Denny's, Jack-in-the-Box, McDonald's, Pizza Hut, Taco Bell, **lodging:** Day's Inn, Motel 6, Silver Queen Motel, Super 8, Travel Inn, Travelodge, **other:** Basha's Foods, Blue beacon, Goodyear/auto, K-Mart, KOA(1mi),

TireWorld, diesel repair, **S...gas:** Exxon/repair, 76/diesel, Shell/repair, **food:** ABC Rest., JB's, Lo's Chinese, Sonic, **lodging:** Best Value Inn, Best Western, Comfort Inn, Day's Inn, High Desert Inn, Lido Motel, Mojave Inn, **other:** MEDICAL CARE, Chrysler/Jeep/Dodge, NAPA, Uptown Drug

51 Stockton Hill Rd, Kingman, **N...gas:** Arco/24hr, Chevron, 76/Circle K, **food:** Cracker Barrel, Del Taco, KFC, Papa John's, Sonic, Taco Bell/24hr, Uncle's Chinese, Whataburger, **other:** HOSPITAL, Albertson's, AutoZone, Checker Parts, Chevrolet/Buick/Pontiac/Cadillac, Ford/Lincoln/Mercury, Honda, Hyundai, Nissan, Smith's Foods, Toyota, Walgreen, Wal-Mart/auto, KOA(2mi), **S...gas:** 76/Circle K, Shell/diesel, **food:** Alfonso's Mexican, A-O Steaks, Pizza Hut, **other:** MEDICAL CARE, CarQuest, Family$, Hastings Books, JC Penney, Radio Shack, Safeway

Kingman

48 US 93 N, Beale St, Kingman, **N...gas:** Chevron, Exxon/diesel, Mobil/diesel/RV dump, Pilot/Subway/diesel/24hr, Shell/diesel/24hr, TA/76/Popeye's/diesel/24hr, Woody's, **food:** Chan Chinese, Wendy's, **lodging:** Budget Inn, Economy Inn, Frontier Motel, **S...gas:** Chevron/diesel/24hr, Circle K, **food:** Calico's Rest., Carl's Jr, **lodging:** AZ Inn, Motel 6, Quality Inn, **other:** CarQuest, Ft Beale RV Park, museum

46.5mm Holy Moses Wash

44 AZ 66, Oatman Hwy, McConnico, to Rte 66, **S...gas:** Crazy Fred's Fuel/diesel/café, **other:** truckwash, Canyon West RV Park(3mi)

40.5mm Griffith Wash

37 Griffith Rd, no facilities

35mm Black Rock Wash

32mm Walnut Creek

28 Old Trails Rd, no facilities

26 Proving Ground Rd, **S...other:** Ford Proving Grounds

25 Alamo Rd, to Yucca, **N...gas:** Micromart/diesel/diner

23mm **rest area both lanes, full(handicapped)facilities, phone, picnic tables, litter barrels, vending, pet-walk**

21mm Flat Top Wash

20 Gem Acres Rd, no facilities

18.5mm Illavar Wash

15mm Buck Mtn Wash

13.5mm Franconia Wash

13 Franconia Rd, no facilities

9 AZ 95 S, to Lake Havasu City, Parker, London Br, **S...gas:** Pilot/Wendy's/diesel/24hr/@

4mm weigh sta both lanes

2 Needle Mtn Rd, no facilities

1 Topock Rd, to Bullhead City, Oatman, Havasu NWR, **N...gas,** food, camping

0mm Arizona/California state line, Colorado River, Mountain/Pacific time zone

Interstate 30

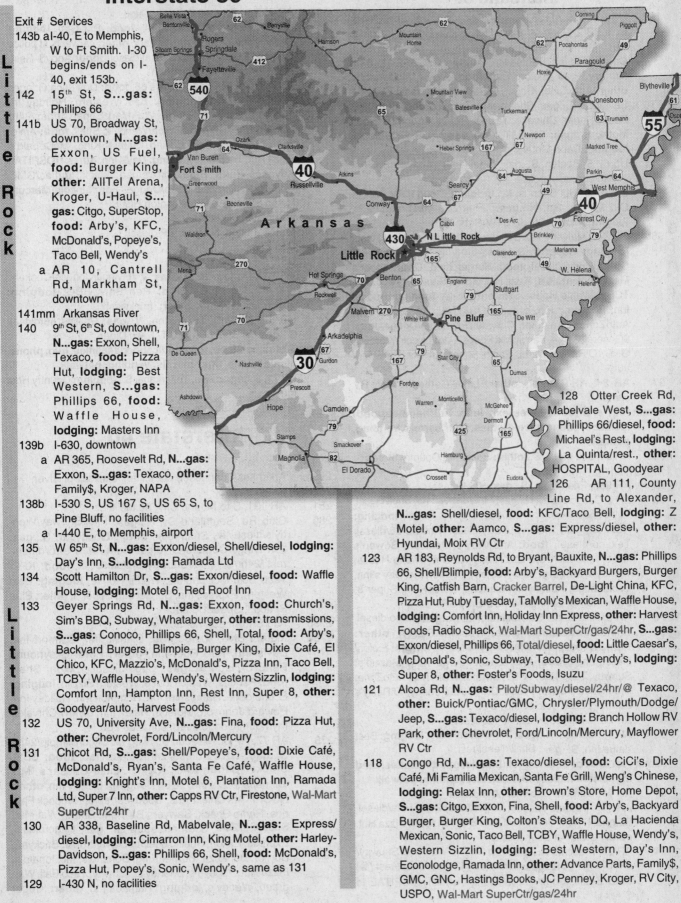

E ↕ W

Little Rock

Exit # Services

143b a I-40, E to Memphis, W to Ft Smith. I-30 begins/ends on I-40, exit 153b.

142 15th St, **S...gas:** Phillips 66

141b US 70, Broadway St, downtown, **N...gas:** Exxon, US Fuel, **food:** Burger King, **other:** AllTel Arena, Kroger, U-Haul, **S... gas:** Citgo, SuperStop, **food:** Arby's, KFC, McDonald's, Popeye's, Taco Bell, Wendy's

a AR 10, Cantrell Rd, Markham St, downtown

141mm Arkansas River

140 9th St, 6th St, downtown, **N...gas:** Exxon, Shell, Texaco, **food:** Pizza Hut, **lodging:** Best Western, **S...gas:** Phillips 66, **food:** Waffle House, **lodging:** Masters Inn

139b I-630, downtown

a AR 365, Roosevelt Rd, **N...gas:** Exxon, **S...gas:** Texaco, **other:** Family$, Kroger, NAPA

138b I-530 S, US 167 S, US 65 S, to Pine Bluff, no facilities

a I-440 E, to Memphis, airport

135 W 65th St, **N...gas:** Exxon/diesel, Shell/diesel, **lodging:** Day's Inn, **S...lodging:** Ramada Ltd

134 Scott Hamilton Dr, **S...gas:** Exxon/diesel, **food:** Waffle House, **lodging:** Motel 6, Red Roof Inn

133 Geyer Springs Rd, **N...gas:** Exxon, **food:** Church's, Sim's BBQ, Subway, Whataburger, **other:** transmissions, **S...gas:** Conoco, Phillips 66, Shell, Total, **food:** Arby's, Backyard Burgers, Blimpie, Burger King, Dixie Café, El Chico, KFC, Mazzio's, McDonald's, Pizza Inn, Taco Bell, TCBY, Waffle House, Wendy's, Western Sizzlin, **lodging:** Comfort Inn, Hampton Inn, Rest Inn, Super 8, **other:** Goodyear/auto, Harvest Foods

132 US 70, University Ave, **N...gas:** Fina, **food:** Pizza Hut, **other:** Chevrolet, Ford/Lincoln/Mercury

131 Chicot Rd, **S...gas:** Shell/Popeye's, **food:** Dixie Café, McDonald's, Ryan's, Santa Fe Café, Waffle House, **lodging:** Knight's Inn, Motel 6, Plantation Inn, Ramada Ltd, Super 7 Inn, **other:** Capps RV Ctr, Firestone, Wal-Mart SuperCtr/24hr

130 AR 338, Baseline Rd, Mabelvale, **N...gas:** Express/diesel, **lodging:** Cimarron Inn, King Motel, **other:** Harley-Davidson, **S...gas:** Phillips 66, Shell, **food:** McDonald's, Pizza Hut, Popey's, Sonic, Wendy's, same as 131

129 I-430 N, no facilities

128 Otter Creek Rd, Mabelvale West, **S...gas:** Phillips 66/diesel, **food:** Michael's Rest., **lodging:** La Quinta/rest., **other:** HOSPITAL, Goodyear

126 AR 111, County Line Rd, to Alexander, **N...gas:** Shell/diesel, **food:** KFC/Taco Bell, **lodging:** Z Motel, **other:** Aamco, **S...gas:** Express/diesel, **other:** Hyundai, Moix RV Ctr

123 AR 183, Reynolds Rd, to Bryant, Bauxite, **N...gas:** Phillips 66, Shell/Blimpie, **food:** Arby's, Backyard Burgers, Burger King, Catfish Barn, Cracker Barrel, De-Light China, KFC, Pizza Hut, Ruby Tuesday, TaMolly's Mexican, Waffle House, **lodging:** Comfort Inn, Holiday Inn Express, **other:** Harvest Foods, Radio Shack, Wal-Mart SuperCtr/gas/24hr, **S...gas:** Exxon/diesel, Phillips 66, Total/diesel, **food:** Little Caesar's, McDonald's, Sonic, Subway, Taco Bell, Wendy's, **lodging:** Super 8, **other:** Foster's Foods, Isuzu

121 Alcoa Rd, **N...gas:** Pilot/Subway/diesel/24hr/@ Texaco, **other:** Buick/Pontiac/GMC, Chrysler/Plymouth/Dodge/Jeep, **S...gas:** Texaco/diesel, **lodging:** Branch Hollow RV Park, **other:** Chevrolet, Ford/Lincoln/Mercury, Mayflower RV Ctr

118 Congo Rd, **N...gas:** Texaco/diesel, **food:** CiCi's, Dixie Café, Mi Familia Mexican, Santa Fe Grill, Weng's Chinese, **lodging:** Relax Inn, **other:** Brown's Store, Home Depot, **S...gas:** Citgo, Exxon, Fina, Shell, **food:** Arby's, Backyard Burger, Burger King, Colton's Steaks, DQ, La Hacienda Mexican, Sonic, Taco Bell, TCBY, Waffle House, Wendy's, Western Sizzlin, **lodging:** Best Western, Day's Inn, Econolodge, Ramada Inn, **other:** Advance Parts, Family$, GMC, GNC, Hastings Books, JC Penney, Kroger, RV City, USPO, Wal-Mart SuperCtr/gas/24hr

ARKANSAS

Interstate 30

E ↑ **W**

Malvern

117   US 64, AR 5, AR 35, **N...gas:** Conoco/diesel, Shell, **food:** Bo's BBQ, Denny's, Pizza Hut, Waffle House, **lodging:** Best Inn, Econolodge, Ramada Inn, Sleep Cheap, Cedarwood Inn, Benton Inn, **S...other:** HOSPITAL, **S on Military...gas:** Exxon, Fina, **food:** Arby's, McDonald's, **other:** AutoZone, Kroger, O'Reilly Parts, Radio Shack

116   Sevier St, **N...gas:** Shell/diesel, Texaco, **food:** Ed&Kay's Rest., Hunan Chinese, Tastee Freeze, **lodging:** Troutt Motel, **S...gas:** Shell, Texaco/diesel, US Fuel/diesel, **lodging:** Capri Motel

114   US 67 S, Benton, **S...gas:** Shell(1mi)

113mm   insp sta eb, st police

111   US 70 W, Hot Springs, **N...lodging:** Cloud 9 RV Park

106   Old Military Rd, **N...gas:** Fina/JJ's Rest./diesel/@, **lodging:** Motel 106, JB'S RV Park

Arkadelphia

98b a   US 270, Malvern, Hot Springs, **N...food:** Fish Nest Rest., **lodging:** Super 8, **S...gas:** Fina/diesel, Phillips 66, Shell/Blimpie/diesel, **food:** Burger King, Chili Pepper's Mexican, Mazzio's, Pizza Hut, Sonic, Subway, Taco Bell, TCBY, Waffle House, Western Sizzlin, **lodging:** Budget Inn, Economy Inn, **other:** HOSPITAL, Advance Parts, AutoZone, Chevrolet, Chrysler/Plymouth/Dodge/Jeep, $General, $Tree, Family Mkt Foods, Ford/Lincoln/Mercury, GNC, O'Reilly's Parts, Radio Shack, USPO, Wal-Mart/auto

97   AR 84, AR 171, **N...other:** Lake Catherine SP, RV camping

93mm   **rest area(both lanes exit left), full(handicapped) facilities, phone, picnic tables, litter barrels, vending, petwalk**

91   AR 84, Social Hill, **S...other:** Social Hill Country Store/RV Park

83   AR 283, Friendship, **S...gas:** Shell/diesel

78   AR 7, Caddo Valley, **N...gas:** Fina/diesel/24hr, Shell/diesel, Total/A&W/diesel/24hr, **food:** Cracker Barrel, **lodging:** KOA, **S...gas:** Exxon/Subway/diesel, Phillips 66/diesel, Texaco/diesel, **food:** Art&Mary's Mexican, Bowen's Rest., McDonald's, Pizza Hut, Taco Bell, Waffle House, Wendy's, **lodging:** Best Western, Comfort Inn, Day's Inn, Econolodge, Holiday Inn Express, Quality Inn, Super 8, **other:** to Hot Springs NP, De Gray SP

73   AR 8, AR 26, AR 51, Arkadelphia, **N...gas:** Citgo/diesel, Shell, **food:** McDonald's, Western Sizzlin, **other:** Plymouth/Jeep, Wal-Mart SuperCtr/24hr, **S...gas:** Exxon/diesel, Shell, **food:** Andy's Rest., Burger King, Mazzio's, Subway, Taco Tico, TCBY, **other:** HOSPITAL, AutoZone, Brookshire Foods, Fred's Drug, JC Penney, O'Reilly's Parts, Pontiac/Buick/GMC, USPO

69   AR 26 E, Gum Springs, no facilities

63   AR 53, Gurdon, **N...gas:** Citgo/diesel/rest., **lodging:** Best Value Inn, **S...gas:** Shell/diesel/rest.

56mm   **rest area both lanes, full(handicapped)facilities,vending, picnic tables, litter barrels, vending, petwalk**

54   AR 51, Gurdon, Okolona, no facilities

46   AR 19, Prescott, **N...gas:** Citgo/diesel/24hr, Fina/diesel, **S...gas:** Love's/Hardee's/diesel/24hr/@, **food:** Pizza Hut, **other:** Crater of Diamonds SP

44   AR 24, Prescott, **N...gas:** Rip Griffin/Phillips 66/Subway/diesel/24hr/@, **S...gas:** Norman's 44 Trkstp/diesel/rest./@, **food:** Sonic, **lodging:** Econolodge, **other:** HOSPITAL, to S Ark U

Hope

36   AR 299, to Emmet, **S...gas:** Citgo

31   AR 29, Hope, **N...gas:** Shell, **food:** Pitt Grill, **lodging:** Econolodge, Village Inn/RV park, **other:** carwash, st police, **S...gas:** Exxon, Texaco, Total/diesel, **food:** Andy's Rest., KFC, **lodging:** Economy Inn

30   AR 4, Hope, **N...gas:** Phillips 66, **food:** Dos Loco Gringos, Western Sizzlin, **lodging:** Best Western, Holiday Inn Express, Super 8, **other:** Wal-Mart SuperCtr/gas/24hr, Millwood SP, **S...gas:** Exxon/Wendy's, Shell, **food:** Amigo Juan Mexican, Burger King, Catfish King, McDonald's, Pizza Hut, Taco Bell, **lodging:** Day's Inn, **other:** HOSPITAL, Advance Parts, Brookshire's/gas, Buick/Pontiac/GMC, Chevrolet, Chrysler/Jeep/Dodge, Ford/Lincoln/Mercury, Radio Shack, Old Washington Hist SP

26mm   weigh sta both lanes

18   rd 355, Fulton, **N...gas:** BP/diesel

17mm   Red River

12   US 67, Fulton, no facilities

7   AR 108, Mandeville, **N...gas:** ✈/FlyingJ/Conoco/Cookery/diesel/LP/24hr/@, **food:** Red Barn BBQ, **lodging:** Texarkana RV Park, **other:** truckwash

2   US 67, AR 245, Texarkana, **N...gas:** Phillips 66/diesel, **S...gas:** BP/diesel, **food:** T-Town Diner

1.5mm   **Welcome Ctr eb, full(handicapped)facilities, info, phone, picnic tables, litter barrels, vending, petwalk**

1   US 71, Jefferson Ave, Texarkana, **S...lodging:** Country Host Inn

0mm   Arkansas/Texas state line

Interstate 40

Exit #	Services

E ↑ **W**

285mm   Arkansas/Tennessee state line, Mississippi River

282mm   weigh sta wb

281   AR 131, S to Mound City, no facilities

280   Club Rd, Southland Dr, **N...gas:** Pilot/Subway/Wendy's/diesel/@, Shamrock, **other:** Goodyear, **S...gas:** ✈/FlyingJ/Conoco/LP/diesel/rest./@, Petro/diesel/rest./24hr/@, Pilot/Subway/DQ/diesel/@, **food:** KFC/Taco Bell, McDonald's, Waffle House, **lodging:** Best Western, Express Inn, Sunset Inn, Super 8, **other:** Blue Beacon, SpeedCo Lube

279b   I-55 S(from eb), no facilities

279a   Ingram Blvd, **N...lodging:** Classic Inn, Comfort Inn, Day's Inn, Red Roof Inn, **other:** Ford, Greyhound Park, U-Haul, **S...gas:** Citgo/diesel, Exxon, Shell, **food:** Perkins, Waffle House, Western Sizzlin, **lodging:** Econolodge, Hampshire Inn, Hampton Inn, Holiday Inn, Howard Johnson, Motel 6, Relax Inn, **other:** Chrysler/Plymouth/Dodge/Jeep, same as 280

278   AR 77, 7th St, Missouri St, **N...gas:** Citgo/Blimpie/24hr, **S...gas:** Love's/diesel/24hr, RaceTrac, **food:** BBQ, Cracker Barrel, KFC, Krystal, Little Caesar's, Mrs Winner's, Pizza Inn, TCBY, **lodging:** Quality Inn, **other:** HOSPITAL, Chief Parts, Goodyear/auto, Hancock Fabrics, Radio Shack, Sawyers RV Park, Sears, Wal-Mart SuperCtr/24hr, **S on Missouri St...gas:** Citgo/diesel, Express, Exxon, Shell/diesel/rest./24hr, **food:** Backyard Burger, Bonanza, Burger King, Domino's, McDonald's, Pizza Hut, Popeye's, Shoney's, Subway, Taco Bell, Walgreen, Wendy's, **lodging:** Ramada Ltd, **other:** Kroger

24

Interstate 40

E ↕ **W**

277   I-55 N, to Jonesboro, no facilities

276   AR 77, Rich Rd, to Missouri St(from eb only), **S...gas:** Exxon, Phillips 66, Shell, **food:** Bonanza, Burger King, McDonald's, **lodging:** Ramada Ltd, **other:** Wal-Mart SuperCtr/24hr, same as 278

275   AR 118, Airport Rd, **S...other:** Hog Pen Funpark

274mm Welcome Ctr wb, full(handicapped)facilities, info, phone, picnic tables, litter barrels, petwalk

273mm   weigh sta both lanes

271   AR 147, to Blue Lake, **S...gas:** Exxon, Phillips 66/PJ's Store/diesel/24hr, Shell, **other:** to Horseshoe Lake, RV camping

265   US 79, AR 218, to Hughes, **S...food:** Bole's Foods

260   AR 149, to Earle, **N...gas:** Citgo/Subway, TA/BP/Burger King/Taco Bell/diesel/24hr/@, Super 8, **lodging:** KOA, **S...gas:** Shell, **other:** diesel repair

256   AR 75, to Parkin, **N...gas:** Express/diesel/rest., **other:** to Parkin SP(12mi)

247   AR 38 E, to Widener, no facilities

245mm   St Francis River

243mm rest area wb, full(handicapped)facilities, phone, vending, picnic tables, litter barrels, petwalk

242   AR 284, Crowley's Ridge Rd, **N...other:** to Village Creek SP, camping, HOSPITAL

241b a   AR 1, Forrest City, **N...gas:** BP/diesel, Phillips 66/Krystal/diesel, **food:** Denny's, HoHo Chinese, Popeye's, Wendy's, **lodging:** Comfort Inn, Day's Inn, Econolodge, Hampton Inn, Holiday Inn, Super 8, **other:** Chevrolet/Pontiac/Buick, Ford/Lincoln/Mercury, Plymouth/Dodge, st police, **S...gas:** Citgo, Exxon, Shell, **food:** Bonanza, Burger King, Dragon China, KFC, McDonald's, Mrs Winners, Old South Pancakes, Pizza Hut, Subway, Taco Bell, Waffle House, **lodging:** Best Western, **other:** Advance Parts, $General, $Tree, Food Giant, SavALot, Wal-Mart SuperCtr/gas/24hr

239   new exit

235mm rest area eb, full(handicapped)facilities, phone, vending, picnic tables, litter barrels, petwalk

234mm   L'Anguille River

233   AR 261, Palestine, **N...gas:** Love's/A&W/Subway/diesel/24hr/@, **lodging:** Rest Inn, **S...gas:** BP/diesel/24hr

221   AR 78, Wheatley, **N...gas:** Exxon, Phillips 66/diesel, **other:** Goodyear/repair, Wheatley RV Park, **S...gas:** Express/Subway/diesel, FuelMart/KFC/diesel/@

216   US 49, AR 17, Brinkley, **N...gas:** Citgo/diesel, Exxon/diesel, Shell/KFC/diesel, **food:** Western Sizzlin, **lodging:** Amerihost, Best Inn, Day's Inn, Super 8/RV/rest., **S...gas:** Express/diesel/24hr, Exxon/diesel, Phillips 66, **food:** BBQ, KFC, Laura's Diner, McDonald's, Pizza Hut, Sonic, Subway, Taco Bell, Waffle House, **lodging:** Best Western, Brinkley Inn(2mi), Heritage Inn/RV Park, **other:** $General, Firestone, Kroger, NAPA, Radio Shack, Wal-Mart

205mm   Cache River

202   AR 33, to Biscoe, no facilities

200mm   White River

199mm rest areas both lanes, full(handicapped)facilities, vending, picnic tables, litter barrels, no phones

193   AR 11, to Hazen, **N...gas:** Exxon, **S...gas:** Citgo/diesel, Shell/diesel/24hr, **food:** Outdoor Café, Subway, **lodging:** Super 8, Travel Inn, **other:** T-rix RV Park

183   AR 13, Carlisle, **S...gas:** Conoco/diesel, Exxon/Subway/diesel, Phillips 66/KFC, Texaco, **food:** Nick's BBQ, Pizza&More, Sonic, **lodging:** Best Western, Carlisle Motel

175   AR 31, Lonoke, **N...gas:** Exxon/diesel, Shamrock, **food:** McDonald's, **lodging:** Day's Inn, Economy Inn/rest., Super 8, **S...gas:** Shell/Subway, **food:** KFC/Taco Bell, Pizza Hut, Sonic, **lodging:** Perry's Motel/rest., **other:** Chevrolet

169.5   insp sta both lanes

169   AR 15, Remington Rd, no facilities

165   Kerr Rd, no facilities

161   AR 391, Galloway, **N...gas:** Love's/A&W/diesel/24hr/@, **S...gas:** Petro/Mobil/diesel/24hr/@, Pilot/Subway/DQ/diesel/24hr/@, TruckOMat/diesel, **lodging:** Galloway Inn, **other:** Blue Beacon, CB Shop

159   I-440 W, to airport, no facilities

157   AR 161, to US 70, **N...gas:** Exxon/diesel, **S...gas:** Citgo/diesel, Phillips 66/diesel, Super S Stop, Shell/diesel, **food:** Burger King, KFC/Taco Bell, McDonald's, Sonic, Subway, Waffle House, **lodging:** Comfort Inn, Day's Inn, Masters Inn, Red Roof Inn, Rest Inn, Super 8

156   Springhill Dr, **N...gas:** Phillips 66, **food:** Cracker Barrel, **lodging:** Fairfield Inn, Holiday Inn Express, Residence Inn

155   US 67 N, US 167, to Jacksonville, Little Rock AFB, **1 mi N on US 167...gas:** Phillips 66, Shell, **food:** Applebee's, Carino's Italian, Chili's, ChuckeCheese, Denny's, Furr's Café, KFC, McDonald's, Outback Steaks, Pizza Hut, Wendy's, **lodging:** Comfort Inn, Hampton Inn, Holiday Inn Express, La Quinta, **other:** Firestone, Best Buy, Chrysler/Plymouth/Dodge, Circuit City, Dillard's, Home Depot, JC Penney, Lowe's Whse, Office Depot, PepBoys, Target, mall

154   to Lakewood(from eb), no facilities

153b   I-30 W, US 65 S, to Little Rock, no facilities

153a   AR 107 N, JFK Blvd, **N...gas:** Exxon, Express, Shell, **food:** Schlotsky's, **lodging:** Travelodge, **S...gas:** Exxon, **food:** Royal Buffet, Waffle House, **lodging:** Country Inn Suites, Hampton Inn, Holiday Inn, Howard Johnson, Motel 6, **other:** HOSPITAL

152   AR 365, AR 176, Camp Pike Rd, Levy, **N...gas:** Shell, US Fuel, **food:** Burger King, EggRoll Express, KFC/Taco Bell, Little Caesar's, McDonald's, Pizza Hut, Rally's, Sim's BBQ, Sonic, Subway, US Pizza, Wendy's, **other:** AutoZone, Fred's Drug, Kroger, Wal-Mart/24hr, **S...gas:** Phillips 66, Shell, **food:** Church's, **other:** HOSPITAL, Chevrolet, Family$, Kroger, Radio Shack, Sav-A-Lot

F o r r e s t   C i t y   **B r i n k l e y**   **L i t t l e   R o c k**

ARKANSAS

Interstate 40

150 AR 176, Burns Park, Camp Robinson, **S...other:** info, camping

148 AR 100, Crystal Hill Rd, **N...gas:** Shell

147 I-430 S, to Texarkana, no facilities

142 AR 365, to Morgan, **N...gas:** Phillips 66, Shamrock/diesel, **lodging:** Day's Inn, Trails End RV Park, **S...gas:** Shell/A&W/Subway/diesel, **food:** I-40 Rest., KFC/Taco Bell, McDonald's, Waffle House, **lodging:** Comfort Suites, Super 8, **other:** antiques

135 AR 365, AR 89, Mayflower, **N...gas:** Hess, **other:** Mayflower RV Ctr(1mi), **S...gas:** Exxon/diesel, Shamrock, **food:** Glory B's Rest., Sonic, **other:** $General

134mm insp sta both lanes

129 US 65B, AR 286, Conway, **S...gas:** Citgo, Express/diesel, Exxon, Shell, **food:** Amazon Grill, Arby's, Subway, **lodging:** Budget Inn, Clements Motel, Continental Motel, **other:** HOSPITAL, Chrysler/Plymouth/Dodge/Jeep, st police

127 US 64, Conway, **N...gas:** BP, Exxon, **food:** Denny's, Waffle House, **lodging:** Best Western, Day's Inn, Economy Inn, Hampton Inn, Ramada Inn, **other:** Belk, Chevrolet, Ford/Mercury, GMC/Buick/Pontiac, Goodyear/auto, Home Depot, Honda, Kohl's, Moix RV Ctr, Nissan, Superior Tire, Target, Toyota, repair/transmissions, to Lester Flatt Park, **S...gas:** RaceWay, Shamrock, Shell/Subway/diesel, Total, **food:** Burger King, Church's, Colton's Steaks, Hardee's, KFC/Taco Bell, LJ Silver, Mazzio's, McDonald's, Pizza Inn, Quizno's, Rally's, TCBY, Wendy's, Western Sizzlin, **lodging:** Kings Inn, **other:** AutoZone, Family$, Hancock Fabrics, Kroger, Radio Shack, Walgreen

125 US 65, Conway, **N...gas:** Conoco/diesel, Exxon, Shell/Subway/diesel/24hr, **food:** Acapulco Mexican, Cracker Barrel, El Chico, Hardee's, MktPlace Grill, McDonald's, Ole South Rest., **lodging:** Comfort Inn, **other:** JC Penney, Office Depot, **S...gas:** Citgo, Exxon/diesel, Fina, **food:** Backyard Burger, Burger King, CiCi's, Evergreen Chinese, Fazoli's, IHOP, McAlister's Deli, Outback Steaks, Ryan's, Shakey's Custard, Sonic, Subway, Village Inn Rest., Waffle House, Wendy's, **lodging:** Holiday Inn Express, Howard Johnson, Motel 6, Stacy Motel, Super 8, **other:** HOSPITAL, $General, $Tree, Hastings Books, Kelly Tire, Lowe's Whse, Wal-Mart SuperCtr/gas/24hr

124 AR 25 N(from eb), to Conway, **S...gas:** Shell, **food:** DQ, Mazzio's, **other:** U-Haul

120mm Cadron River

117 to Menifee, no facilities

112 AR 92, Plumerville, **S...other:** USPO

108 AR 9, Morrilton, **S...gas:** Phillips 66/24hr, Shell/diesel/24hr, **food:** Bonanza, KFC, Mkt Place Café, McDonald's, Pizza Hut, Subway, TCBY, Waffle House, Wendy's, **lodging:** Super 8, **other:** HOSPITAL, Chevrolet/Buick/Pontiac, $General, Ford/Lincoln/Mercury, Goodyear, GMC, Kroger, Radio Shack, Wal-Mart SuperCtr/gas/24hr, to Petit Jean SP(21mi), RV camping

107 AR 95, Morrilton, **N...gas:** Shell/diesel, **food:** Morrilton Rest., **lodging:** Scottish Inn, KOA, **S...gas:** Love's/A&W/Wendy's/diesel/24hr/@, Shell, **lodging:** Day's Inn, **other:** CarQuest

101 Blackwell, **N...other:** Utility Trailer Sales

94 AR 105, Atkins, **N...gas:** BP/McDonald's/diesel, Exxon/Subway/diesel/24hr, **food:** I-40 Grill, KFC/Taco Bell, Sonic, **other:** $General, repair

88 Pottsville, **S...other:** truck repair

84 US 64, AR 331, Russellville, **N...gas:** ♦/FlyingJ/Conoco/Country Mkt/diesel/LP/24hr/@, Shell/diesel, **S...gas:** Phillips 66, Pilot/Subway/Wendy's/diesel/24hr/@, **food:** CiCi's, Hardee's, Hunan Chinese, McDonald's, Ryan's, Sonic, Waffle House, Western Sizzlin, **lodging:** Comfort Inn, Ramada Inn, **other:** AutoZone, Chevrolet, Chrysler/Jeep, Hastings Books, JC Penney, K-Mart, Lowe's Whse, Nissan, PriceCutter Foods/24hr, Staples, USPO, Wal-Mart/auto, **2 mi S...lodging:** Classic Inn, Merrick Motel

81 AR 7, Russellville, **N...gas:** SuperStop/diesel, **lodging:** Econolodge, Knight's Inn, Motel 6, **other:** Outdoor RV Ctr, **S...gas:** Exxon/diesel/24hr, Phillips 66/diesel/24hr, Shell/24hr, **food:** Arby's, Burger King, Colton's Steaks, Cracker Barrel, Dixie Café, New China, Pizza Inn, Ruby Tuesday, Santa Fe Café, Subway, Waffle House, **lodging:** Best Western, Day's Inn, Economy Inn, Fairfield Inn, Hampton Inn, Holiday Inn, Super 8, **other:** antiques, **2 mi S...gas:** Fina, **food:** El Acapulco Mexican, LJ Silver, Mazzio's, McDonald's, Pizza Hut, Taco Bell, Taco John's, Wataburger, Wendy's, **other:** HOSPITAL, Goodyear/auto, to Lake Dardanelle SP, RV camping

80mm Dardanelle Reservoir

78 US 64, Russellville, **S...other:** to Lake Dardanelle SP, RV camping

74 AR 333, London, no facilities

72mm **rest area wb, full(handicapped)facilities, phone, picnic tables, litter barrels, vending, petwalk**

70mm overlook wb lane

68mm **rest area eb, full(handicapped)facilities, phone, picnic tables, litter barrels, vending, petwalk**

67 AR 315, Knoxville, no facilities

64 US 64, Clarksville, Lamar, **S...gas:** Shell/Pizza Pro/diesel/24hr, **lodging:** Dad's Dream RV Park

58 AR 21, AR 103, Clarksville, **N...gas:** Phillips 66/24hr, Shell/diesel, **food:** BBQ, KFC, Mazzio's, McDonald's, Old South Pancakes, Pizza Hut, Pizza Pro, Sonic, Taco Bell, Waffle House, Wendy's, Woodard's Rest., **lodging:** Best Western, Budget Inn, Comfort Inn, Economy Inn, Super 8, **other:** HOSPITAL, Chevrolet, **S...gas:** Shell/diesel/rest./24hr, **food:** Arby's, **other:** Chrysler/Dodge/Jeep, $Tree, Ford/Lincoln/Mercury, Wal-Mart SuperCtr/gas/24hr

57 AR 109, Clarksville, **N...gas:** Citgo, Conoco, **food:** Subway, **S...gas:** Shell/A&W/diesel

55 US 64, AR 109, Clarksville, **N...gas:** Citgo/diesel, **food:** Hardee's, Lotus Chinese, Pizza Hut, Waffle Inn, **lodging:** Day's Inn, Hampton Inn, **other:** st police, **S...gas:** Exxon, **food:** Western Sizzlin

47 AR 164, Coal Hill, no facilities

41 AR 186, Altus, **S...food:** Weinkeller Rest., **other:** Pine Ridge RV Park, winery

37 AR 219, Ozark, **S...gas:** Love's/A&W/Subway/diesel/24hr/@, Shell/McDonald's, **food:** KFC/Taco Bell, **lodging:** Day's Inn, McNutt RV Park, **other:** HOSPITAL

36mm **rest area both lanes, full(handicapped)facilities, phone, picnic tables, litter barrels, petwalk**

Interstate 40

E

W

Ft Smith

35	AR 23, Ozark, **3 mi S...food:** Hardee's, **lodging:** Oxford Inn, **other:** HOSPITAL
24	AR 215, Mulberry, **2 mi S...gas:** Liberty gas, **other:** camping
20	Dyer, **N...gas:** Conoco/diesel, **S...gas:** Shell/diesel, **lodging:** Mill Creek Inn
13	US 71 N, to Fayetteville, **N...gas:** Phillips 66/diesel, Shell, **food:** Burger King, Cracker Barrel, Dairy Queen, KFC, La Fiesta Mexican, Mazzio's, Subway, Taco Bell, **lodging:** Howard Johnson, Meadors Inn, **other:** Crabtree RV Ctr/Park, $General, KOA(2mi), O'Reilly Parts, to U of AR, Lake Ft Smith SP, **S...gas:** Citgo/Piccadilly's/diesel, Shamrock, **food:** Braum's, McDonald's, Sonic, **lodging:** Day's Inn, **other:** Coleman Drug, CV's Foods, NAPA/lube/repair, Wal-Mart
12	I-540 N, to Fayetteville, **N...other:** to Lake Ft Smith SP
9mm	weigh sta both lanes
7	I-540 S, US 71 S, to Ft Smith, Van Buren, **S...**HOSPITAL
5	AR 59, Van Buren, **N...gas:** Citgo, Phillips 66, **food:** Arby's, Burger King, McDonald's, Santa Fe Café, Schlotsky's, **lodging:** Hampton Inn, Holiday Inn Express, **other:** Radio Shack, Wal-Mart SuperCtr/**gas**/24hr, **S...gas:** Citgo, Shell/diesel/24hr, **food:** Braum's, Big Jake's Steaks, Geno's Pizza, Gringo's TexMex, KFC/Taco Bell, Little Caesar's, Mazzio's, Rick's Ribs, Sonic, Subway, Waffle House, Wendy's, **lodging:** Best Western, Motel 6, Super 8, **other:** CV's Foods, $General, Ford, Overland RV Park, Walgreen, diesel repair
3	Lee Creek Rd, **lodging:** Park Ridge Camping
2.5mm	**Welcome Ctr eb, full(handicapped)facilities, info, phone, picnic tables, litter barrels, vending, petwalk**
1	to Ft Smith(from wb), Dora, no facilities
0mm	Arkansas/Oklahoma state line

Interstate 55

N

S

Exit #	Services
72mm	Arkansas/Missouri state line
72	State Line Rd, weigh sta sb
71	AR 150, Yarbro, **W...gas:** Citgo/diesel
68mm	**Welcome Ctr sb, full(handicapped)facilities, phone, picnic tables, litter barrels, petwalk**
67	AR 18, Blytheville, **E...food:** Burger King, Chinese Buffet, Day's Inn, **other:** $Tree, Wal-Mart SuperCtr/24hr, **W...gas:** BP/Blimpie/diesel, Citgo/diesel, Texaco, **food:** Bonanza, Casa Mexican, Grecian Steaks, Hardee's, KFC, Mazzio's, McDonald's, Perkins, Pizza Inn, River Rd Buffet, Sonic, Subway, Taco Bell, Wendy's, **lodging:** Comfort Inn, Drury Inn, Hampton Inn, Holiday Inn, **other:** HOSPITAL, JC Penney
63	US 61, to Blytheville, **E...gas:** BP/diesel, **W...gas:** Citgo/diesel/24hr, Dodge's Store/diesel, Shell/McDonald's/diesel/24hr, Texaco/diesel, **lodging:** Best Western, Delta K Motel, Royal Inn(2mi), **other:** Chevrolet, Nissan, RV Park

Blytheville

W Memphis

57	AR 148, Burdette, **E... other:** Cotton Bowl Tech
53	AR 158, Victoria, Luxora
48	AR 140, to Osceola, **E...gas:** BP/diesel, Shell/diesel, **lodging:** Best Western/rest., Deerfield Inn, Holiday Inn Express, **3 mi E...food:** McDonald's, Pizza Inn, Sonic, Subway, **other:** HOSPITAL
45mm	**rest area nb, full(handicapped)facilities, picnic tables, litter barrels, petwalk**
44	AR 181, Keiser, no facilities
41	AR 14, Marie, **E... other:** to Hampson SP/museum
36	AR 181, to Wilson, Bassett, no facilities
35mm	**rest area sb, full(handicapped)facilities, picnic tables, litter barrels, phones, petwalk**
34	AR 118, Joiner, no facilities
23b a	US 63, AR 77, to Marked Tree, Jonesboro, ASU, **W...gas:** Citgo, **lodging:** Travel Air Motel
21	AR 42, Turrell, **W...gas:** FuelMart/Subway/diesel/24hr/@
17	AR 50, to Jericho, no facilities
14	rd 4, to Jericho, **E...gas:** Citgo/diesel/24hr, **W...gas:** Citgo/Stuckey's, **lodging:** Best Holiday RV Park
10	US 64 W, Marion, **E...gas:** BP, Citgo/Subway, Express/diesel, Shell/McDonald's/diesel, **food:** KFC/Taco Bell, Marion Diner, Sonic, Tops BBQ, **lodging:** Hallmarc Inn, **other:** Family$, Winn-Dixie, **W...gas:** BP, Shell, **lodging:** Best Western, Journey Inn, **other:** to Parkin SP(23mi)
9mm	weigh sta both lanes
8	I-40 W, to Little Rock, no facilities
278	AR 77, 7th St, Missouri St, **E...gas:** Citgo/Blimpie/24hr, **W...gas:** Love's/diesel/24hr, RaceTrac, **food:** BBQ, Cracker Barrel, KFC, Krystal, Little Caesar's, Mrs Winner's, Pizza Inn, TCBY, **lodging:** Quality Inn, **other:** HOSPITAL, Chief Parts, Goodyear/auto, Hancock Fabrics, Radio Shack, Sawyers RV Park, Sears, Wal-Mart SuperCtr/24hr, **S on Missouri St...gas:** Citgo/diesel, Express, Exxon, Shell/diesel/rest./24hr, **food:** Backyard Burger, Bonanza, Burger King, Domino's, McDonald's, Pizza Hut, Popeye's, Shoney's, Subway, Taco Bell, Walgreen, Wendy's, **lodging:** Ramada Ltd, **other:** Kroger
279b	I-40 E, to Memphis
a	Ingram Blvd, **E...lodging:** Classic Inn, Comfort Inn, Day's Inn, Red Roof Inn, **other:** Ford, Greyhound Park, U-Haul, **W...gas:** Citgo/diesel, Exxon, Shell, **food:** Perkins, Waffle House, Western Sizzlin, **lodging:** Econolodge, Hampshire Inn, Hampton Inn, Holiday Inn, Howard Johnson, Motel 6, Relax Inn, **other:** Chrysler/Plymouth/Dodge/Jeep

ARKANSAS

Interstate 55

N ↕ **S** W Memphis

4   King Dr, Southland Dr, **E...gas:** ✈/FlyingJ/Conoco/ diesel/LP/rest./24hr/@, Petro/diesel/rest./24hr/@, Pilot/DQ/Subway/diesel/@, **food:** KFC/Taco Bell, McDonald's, Waffle House, **lodging:** Best Western, Deluxe Inn, Express Inn, Super 8, **other:** Blue Beacon, SpeedCo, **1/2 mi E...gas:** Pilot/Wendy's/ diesel/24hr/@, **other:** Goodyear, **W...food:** Pancho's Mexican, **lodging:** Sunset Inn

3b a   US 70, Broadway Blvd, AR 131, Mound City Rd(exits left from nb), **W...lodging:** Budget Inn

2mm   weigh sta nb

1   Bridgeport Rd, no facilities

0mm   Arkansas/Tennessee state line, Mississippi River

Interstate 430
(Little Rock)

Exit #	Services

N ↕ S Little Rock

13b a   I-40. I-430 begins/ends on I-40, exit 147.

12   AR 100, Maumelle, **W...gas:** Citgo, **other:** NAPA

10mm   Arkansas River

9   AR 10, Cantrell Rd, **W...**Pinnacle Mtn SP

8   Rodney Parham Rd, **E...gas:** Conoco, Shell, **food:** El Chico, McDonald's, Mt Fuji Japanese, **lodging:** Baymont Inn, **other:** Kroger, USA Drug, **W...gas:** Exxon, **food:** Black Angus Steaks, Burger King, ChuckeCheese, CiCi's, Dixie Café, El Acapulco Mexican, Frank's Café, LoneStar Steaks, Olive Garden, Small's Burgers, Wendy's, **lodging:** Best Western, **other:** Cadillac, Firestone, Harvest Foods, K-Mart, Waldenbooks

6   I-630, Kanis Rd, Markham St, to downtown, **E...lodging:** Comfort Inn, Motel 6, SpringHill Suites, **W...gas:** Exxon, Texaco, **food:** Denny's, Rega's Grill, Waffle House, Wendy's, **lodging:** AmeriSuites, Courtyard, Embassy Suites, Extended Stay America, Holiday Inn, La Quinta, Ramada Ltd

5   Shackleford Rd, **W...**HOSPITAL

4   AR 300, Col Glenn Rd, **W...**Nissan

1   AR 5, Stagecoach Rd, no facilities

0mm   I-30. I-430 begins/ends on I-30, exit 129.

Interstate 440
(Little Rock)

Exit #	Services

N ↕ S

11   I-40.

10   US 70, no facilities

8   Faulkner Lake Rd, **W...gas:** BP/mart

7   US 165, to England, **S...**museum

6mm   Arkansas River

5   Fourche Dam Pike, LR Riverport, **N...gas:** Exxon, Shell, **food:** McDonald's, **lodging:** Travelodge, **S...gas:** Fina/diesel/@, Total/diesel

4   Lindsey Rd, no facilities

3   Bankhead Dr, **N...lodging:** Comfort Inn, **other:** LR Airport, **S...gas:** Conoco, **food:** Waffle House, **lodging:** Day's Inn, Holiday Inn, Holiday Inn Express

1   AR 365, Confederate Blvd, no facilities

0mm   I-440 begins/ends on I-30, exit 138.

Interstate 540
(Fayetteville)

Exit #	Services

B Bentonville

93   US 71B, Bentonville, I-540 begins/ends on US 71 N.

88   AR 72, Bentonville, Pea Ridge, **E...gas:** Conoco, **food:** A&W, Dowd's Catfish, River Grille, **lodging:** Courtyard

86   US 62, AR 102, Bentonville, Rogers, **E...gas:** Exxon, **other:** Wal-Mart SuperCtr/diesel/24hr, Pea Ridge NMP, **W...gas:** EZ Mart, Phillips 66/diesel, **food:** Hardee's, McDonald's, Sonic, Subway, **lodging:** Hartland Motel, Quality Inn, **other:** GMC/Pontiac/Buick, Wal-Mart Visitor Ctr

85   US 71B, AR 12, Bentonville, Rogers, **E...gas:** Citgo/diesel, **food:** Applebee's, Atlanta Bread, Carino's Italian, Chili's, CiCi's, Colton's Steaks, Dixie Café, IHOP, KFC, King Buffet, McDonald's, On-the-Border, Quizno's, Small's Rest., Sonic, **lodging:** AmeriSuites, Candlewood Suites, Fairfield Inn, Hampton Inn, Hartland Lodge, Regency Inn, **other:** Barnes&Noble, Belk, Honda, Kohl's, Lowe's Whse, Office Depot, Old Navy, Beaver Lake SP, Prairie Creek SP, **W...gas:** Exxon, **food:** Braum's, Denny's, Waffle House, **lodging:** Comfort Inn, Hilton Garden, Holiday Inn Express, SpringHill Suites, Super 8, **other:** HOSPITAL

F Fayetteville

83   AR 94 E, Pinnacle Hills Pkwy, **E...food:** Hillbilly Smokehouse, Rib House, **other:** Horse Shoe Bend Park, **W...food:** Plaza Rest., **lodging:** Embassy Suites

81   Pleasant Grove Rd, **W...**Green Country RV Park

78   AR 264, Lowell, Cave Sprgs, Rogers, **E...gas:** EZ Mart, Phillips 66, **food:** DQ, McDonald's, Sonic, Subway, Taco Bell, Super 8, **other:** New Hope RV Ctr

76   Wagon Wheel Rd, no facilities

73   Elm Springs Rd, **E...gas:** Total, **food:** AQ Chicken House, **other:** Goodyear

72mm   weigh sta nb

72   US 412, Springdale, Siloam Springs, **E...gas:** Citgo, EZ Mart, Exxon, Phillips 66/Subway, **food:** Armadillo Grill, Braum's, Denny's, McDonald's, Sonic, Taco Bell, Waffle House, Wendy's, **lodging:** Baymont Inn, Best Western, Comfort Inn, Day's Inn, Executive Inn, Extended Stay America, Hampton Inn, Hartland Inn, Holiday Inn, Residence Inn, Springdale Motel, **W...gas:** Pilot/Burger King/diesel/24hr/@, Total, Cracker Barrel, KFC, Santa Fe Café, **other:** Fred's Drug, Hancock Fabrics

69   Johnson, **1-2 mi E...gas:** EZ Mart, **food:** Hooter's, Ryan's, Shogun Japanese, **lodging:** Mill Inn

67   US 71B, Fayetteville, **E...**HOSPITAL

66   AR 112, **E...gas:** Citgo, **lodging:** Day's Inn, **W...**ROTC Grill, Acura/Chevrolet/Honda/Toyota

65   Porter Rd, no facilities

64   AR 16 W, AR 112 E, Wedington Dr, **E...food:** AQ Chicken House, **lodging:** Radisson, **W...gas:** Citgo/McDonald's, Exxon, EZ Mart, Phillips 66, **food:** Sonic, Subway, **lodging:** Country Inn Suites, Holiday Inn Express, Quality Inn

62   US 62, AR 180, Farmington, **E...gas:** Citgo, EZ Mart, Shell, **food:** Arby's, Burger King, Charlie's Chicken, Hardee's, JO China, McDonald's, Mexico Viejo, Sonic, Taco Bell, Taiwan Chinese, Waffle House, Wendy's, **lodging:** Best Western, Red Roof Inn, **other:** USA Drug, **W...gas:** EZ Mart, **food:** Braum's, Denny's, **lodging:** Clarion, Hampton Inn, Regency 7 Motel, Super 8, **other:** Wal-Mart SuperCtr/gas/24hr

60   AR 112, AR 265, Razorback Rd, **E...**to U of AR

58   Greenland, **W...gas:** Phillips 66/diesel, **food:** Lib's Rest.

53   AR 170, West Fork, **E...gas:** EZ Mart, **other:** Winn Creek RV Resort(4mi), **W...**to Devils Den SP

45   AR 74, Winslow, **W...**to Devils Den SP

34   AR 292, to US 71, Chester, **E...**Ozark Mtn Smokehouse

29   AR 282, to US 71, Mountainburg, **E...gas:** Conoco, **food:** Silver Bridge Rest., **other:** to Lake Ft Smith SP

24   AR 282, to US 71, Rudy, **E...**KOA, Boston Mtns Scenic Lp

20   to US 71, **E...food:** KFC, Taco Bell, **lodging:** Day's Inn

I-540 N begins/ends on I-40, exit 12.

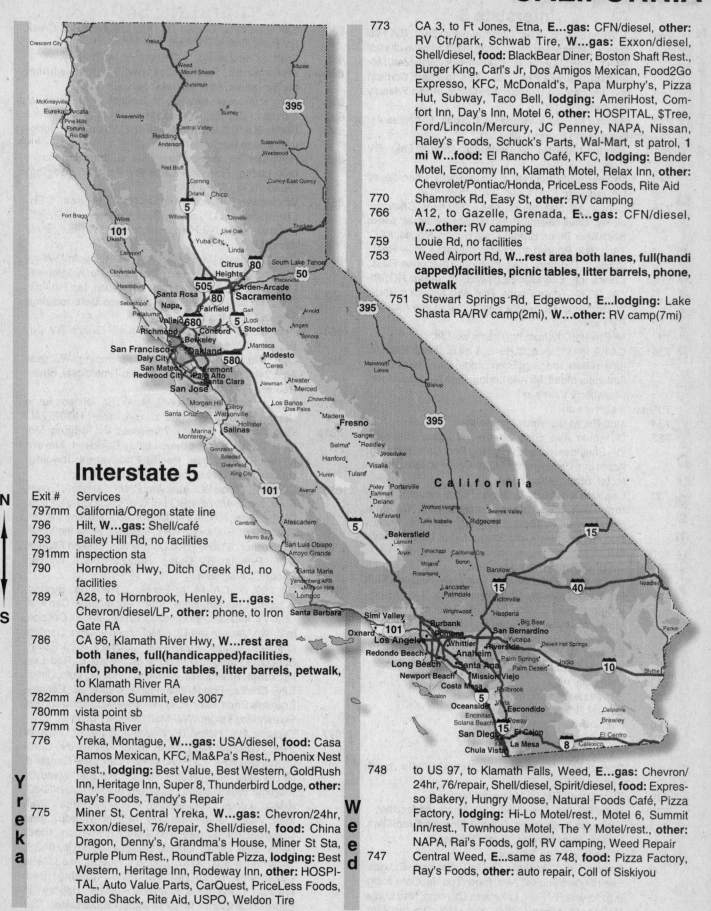

773 CA 3, to Ft Jones, Etna, **E...gas:** CFN/diesel, **other:** RV Ctr/park, Schwab Tire, **W...gas:** Exxon/diesel, Shell/diesel, **food:** BlackBear Diner, Boston Shaft Rest., Burger King, Carl's Jr, Dos Amigos Mexican, Food2Go Expresso, KFC, McDonald's, Papa Murphy's, Pizza Hut, Subway, Taco Bell, **lodging:** AmeriHost, Comfort Inn, Day's Inn, Motel 6, **other:** HOSPITAL, $Tree, Ford/Lincoln/Mercury, JC Penney, NAPA, Nissan, Raley's Foods, Schuck's Parts, Wal-Mart, st patrol, **1 mi W...food:** El Rancho Café, KFC, **lodging:** Bender Motel, Economy Inn, Klamath Motel, Relax Inn, **other:** Chevrolet/Pontiac/Honda, PriceLess Foods, Rite Aid

770 Shamrock Rd, Easy St, **other:** RV camping

766 A12, to Gazelle, Grenada, **E...gas:** CFN/diesel, **W...other:** RV camping

759 Louie Rd, no facilities

753 Weed Airport Rd, **W...rest area both lanes, full(handicapped)facilities, picnic tables, litter barrels, phone, petwalk**

751 Stewart Springs Rd, Edgewood, **E...lodging:** Lake Shasta RA/RV camp(2mi), **W...other:** RV camp(7mi)

Interstate 5

Exit #	Services
797mm California/Oregon state line

796 Hilt, **W...gas:** Shell/café

793 Bailey Hill Rd, no facilities

791mm inspection sta

790 Hornbrook Hwy, Ditch Creek Rd, no facilities

789 A28, to Hornbrook, Henley, **E...gas:** Chevron/diesel/LP, **other:** phone, to Iron Gate RA

786 CA 96, Klamath River Hwy, **W...rest area both lanes, full(handicapped)facilities, info, phone, picnic tables, litter barrels, petwalk,** to Klamath River RA

782mm Anderson Summit, elev 3067

780mm vista point sb

779mm Shasta River

776 Yreka, Montague, **W...gas:** USA/diesel, **food:** Casa Ramos Mexican, KFC, Ma&Pa's Rest., Phoenix Nest Rest., **lodging:** Best Value, Best Western, GoldRush Inn, Heritage Inn, Super 8, Thunderbird Lodge, **other:** Ray's Foods, Tandy's Repair

775 Miner St, Central Yreka, **W...gas:** Chevron/24hr, Exxon/diesel, 76/repair, Shell/diesel, **food:** China Dragon, Denny's, Grandma's House, Miner St Sta, Purple Plum Rest., RoundTable Pizza, **lodging:** Best Western, Heritage Inn, Rodeway Inn, **other:** HOSPITAL, Auto Value Parts, CarQuest, PriceLess Foods, Radio Shack, Rite Aid, USPO, Weldon Tire

748 to US 97, to Klamath Falls, Weed, **E...gas:** Chevron/24hr, 76/repair, Shell/diesel, Spirit/diesel, **food:** Expresso Bakery, Hungry Moose, Natural Foods Café, Pizza Factory, **lodging:** Hi-Lo Motel/rest., Motel 6, Summit Inn/rest., Townhouse Motel, The Y Motel/rest., **other:** NAPA, Rai's Foods, golf, RV camping, Weed Repair

747 Central Weed, **E...same as 748, food:** Pizza Factory, Ray's Foods, **other:** auto repair, Coll of Siskiyou

CALIFORNIA
Interstate 5

N ↕ **S**

Mt Shasta

745 S Weed Blvd, **E...gas:** Chevron/diesel/24hr, 76/CFN/diesel, Shell/diesel/24hr, Travel Plaza/Subway/diesel/24/@, **food:** Burger King, Dos Amigos Mexican, McDonald's, Silva's Rest., Taco Bell, **lodging:** Comfort Inn, Holiday Inn Express, Sis-Q Inn, **other:** Friendly RV camping

743 Summit Dr, Truck Village Dr, **E...gas:** CFN/diesel

742mm Black Butte Summit, elev 3912

741 Abrams Lake Rd, **W...lodging:** Abrams Lake RV Park

740 Mt Shasta City(from sb), **E...gas:** Pacific Pride/diesel/LP, **lodging:** Cold Creek Inn, **other:** KOA

738 Central Mt Shasta, **E...gas:** 76/diesel, Chevron/diesel, Shell/diesel/LP, Spirit/Subway/diesel, **food:** BlackBear Diner, Burger King, Hungry Moose, KFC/Taco Bell, RoundTable Pizza, Shasta Family Rest., Subway, **lodging:** Best Western/Treehouse Rest., Choice Inn, Econolodge, Travel Inn, **other:** HOSPITAL, KOA, Ray's Foods, Rite Aid, Schuck's Parts, **W...lodging:** Mt Shasta Resort/rest., Lake Siskiyou RV Park

737 Mt Shasta City(from nb), same as 738

736 CA 89, to McCloud, to Reno, **1 mi E...food:** Piemont Italian Diner, **lodging:** Econolodge, Evergreen Lodge, Finlandia Motel, Mt Aire Lodge, Pine Needles Motel, Strawberry Valley Inn

735mm weigh sta sb

734 Mott Rd, to Dunsmuir, no facilities

Dunsmuir

732 Dunsmuir Ave, Siskiyou Ave, **W...gas:** 76/diesel/LP, Shell/diesel, **food:** Hitching Post Café, **lodging:** Acorn Inn, Cave Springs Motel, Cedar Lodge, Garden Motel, **other:** Wiley's Mkt

730 Central Dunsmuir, **E...food:** Pizza Factory, **lodging:** Travelodge, **other:** Ford/Mercury, **W...gas:** Shell/diesel/LP, **food:** Hitching Post Café, Micki's Burgers, **lodging:** Cave Springs Motel, **other:** Wiley's Mkt

729 Dunsmuir(from nb), no facilities

728 (727 from nb)Crag View Dr, Dunsmuir, Railroad Park Rd, **E...gas:** Manfreddy's/diesel, **food:** Burger Barn, **lodging:** Best Choice Inn, Oak Tree Inn, Railroad Motel, **W...other:** Railroad Park RV Camp/Resort

726 Soda Creek Rd, to Pacific Crest Trail, no facilities

724 Castella, **W...gas:** Chevron/diesel, **other:** RV camping, Castle Crags SP

723mm vista point nb

723 Sweetbrier Ave, no facilities

721 Conant Rd, no facilities

720 Flume Creek Rd, no facilities

718 Sims Rd, **W...other:** RV camping

714 Gibson Rd, no facilities

712 Pollard Flat, **E...gas:** Exxon/diesel/LP/24hr, **food:** Pollard Flat USA Rest.

710 Slate Creek Rd, La Moine, no facilities

707 Delta Rd, Dog Creek Rd, to Vollmers, no facilities

705mm **rest area both lanes, full(handicapped)facilities, phone, litter barrels, picnic tables**

704 Riverview Dr, no facilities

702 Antlers Rd, Lakeshore Dr, to Lakehead, **E...gas:** Shell/Subway/diesel/24hr, **food:** Top Hat Cafe, **lodging:** Antlers RV Park, Lakehead Camping, Neu Lodge Motel/café, **other:** USPO, auto repair, towing/24hr, **W...gas:** 76/LP, **food:** Basshole Bar/Grill, **lodging:** Shasta Lake Motel/RV, Lakeshore Villa RV Park, **other:** Jack's Foods, RV service/dump

698 Salt Creek Rd, Gilman Rd, **W...lodging:** Salt Creek RV Park, Trail in RV Park

695 Shasta Caverns Rd, to O'Brien, no facilities

694mm **rest area nb, full(handicapped)facilities, phone, picnic tables, litter barrels, petwalk**

693 (from sb)Packers Bay Rd, no facilities

692 Turntable Bay Rd, no facilities

690 Bridge Bay Rd, **W...food:** Tail of a Whale Rest., **lodging:** Bridge Bay Motel

689 Fawndale Rd, Wonderland Blvd, **E...lodging:** Fawndale Lodge, Fawndale Oaks RV Park, **W...lodging:** Wonderland RV Park

687 Wonderland Blvd, Mountain Gate, **E...gas:** CFN, Chevron/diesel/LP, **other:** Bear Mountain RV Resort, Mountain Gate RV Park, Ranger Sta, **W...gas:** Shell/diesel/LP

685 CA 151, Shasta Dam Blvd, Project City, Central Valley, **W...gas:** Chevron/diesel/LP, Shell/Burger King/diesel/LP, **food:** Bakery&Grill, Latino's Mexican, McDonald's, Pizza Factory, StageStop Café, Taco Den, **lodging:** Shasta Dam Motel

684 Pine Grove Ave, **E...other:** Cousin Gary's RV Ctr, **W...gas:** 76/diesel/LP

682 Oasis Rd, **E...other:** CA RV Ctr/camping, **W...gas:** Arco/24hr, LP, Shell/Quizno's/Taco Time/diesel, **other:** Redding RV Ctr, st patrol

681b (from sb, no re-entry)CA 273, Market St, Johnson Rd, to Central Redding, **W...gas:** Exxon, **other:** HOSPITAL

681a Twin View Blvd, **E...gas:** 76/diesel/24hr, **lodging:** Motel 6, Ramada Ltd, **other:** Harley-Davidson, Meyer's Marine/RV, **W...gas:** Pacific Pride/diesel, **lodging:** Holiday Inn Express, **other:** RV camping

680 CA 299E, **1/2 mi W...gas:** Arco/24hr, Chevron, Exxon, Shell, **food:** Arby's, BBQ Pit, Carl's Jr, Figaro's Pizza, Giant Burger, KFC/A&W, McDonald's, Murphy's Pizza, Phil's Pizza, Subway, TCBY, **lodging:** River Inn Motel/rest., **other:** $Tree, Food Connection, Jo-Ann Fabrics, KOA, Premier RV Camp, Raley's Foods, RV Ctr, ShopKO, Walgreen

Redding

678 CA 299 W, CA 44, to Eureka,, Redding, Burney, **E...gas:** Chevron, Shell, **food:** Applebee's, Carl's Jr, Chevy's Mexican, Hometown Buffet, Italian Cottage, In-n-Out, Jack-in-the-Box, McDonald's, Olive Garden, Outback Steaks, Pizza Hut, Quizno's, Red Robin, Starbucks, **lodging:** Holiday Inn, Motel 6, Red Lion Inn, **other:** Albertson's, Barnes&Noble, Big Lots, Circuit City, Costco, Food4Less, Home Depot, JC Penney, Kragen's Parts, Office Depot, OfficeMax, Schwab Tire, Sears/auto, Target, Wal-Mart, WinCo Foods

677 Cypress Ave, Hilltop Dr, Redding, **E...gas:** Chevron/24hr, 76/Burger King, Shell, **food:** Applebee's, Carl's Jr, In n'Out, KFC, La Palomar Mexican, Little Caesar's, McDonald's, RoundTable Pizza, Taco Bell, Wendy's, **lodging:** Park Terrace Inn, **other:** Buick/Pontiac/GMC, K-Mart, Longs Drug, Mervyn's, Rite Aid, Ross, Wal-Mart, Winco foods, mall, **1/4 mi E on Hilltop...gas:** Chevron, Hilltop gas, 76/Circle K/Del Taco, **food:** Black Bear Diner, ChuckeCheese, Denny's, IHOP, Jack-in-the-Box, KFC, Logan's Roadhouse, Marie Callender's, Pizza Hut, Taco Bell, **lodging:** Best Western, Cattlemens Motel, Comfort Inn, Holiday Inn Express, La Quinta, Motel Orleans, Oxford Suites, Red Lion, **W...gas:** 76, Shell, USA/diesel, **food:** BBQ, California Cattle Rest., Denny's, Giant Burger, Lumberjack's

Interstate 5

N ↑ S

Rest., Lyon's Rest., Perko's Rest., Taco Den, **lodging:** Howard Johnson, Motel 6, Vagabond Inn, **other:** Big A Parts, Big O Tire, Chevrolet, FabricLand, Hyundai, Lincoln/Mercury, Mazda/Toyota/Subaru, Nissan, Office Depot, Radio Shack, Raley's Foods, U-Haul, transmissions

675   Bechelli Lane, Churn Creek Rd, **E…gas:** Arco/24hr, Chevron/diesel, **food:** Taco Bell, **lodging:** Super 8, **other:** diesel repair, **W…gas:** Shell/Burger King/diesel, **lodging:** Hilton Garden

673   Knighton Rd, **E…gas:** TA/76/Pizza Hut/Popeye's/diesel/LP/24hr/@, **W…** JGW RV Park(3mi), Sacramento River RV Park

670   Riverside Ave, **ohter:** Gamel RV Ctr

668   Balls Ferry Rd, Anderson, **E…gas:** Beacon, 76/diesel, USA, **food:** Big Taco, Burger King, Denny's, El Mariachi Mexican, McDonald's, Papa Murphy's, Peacock Chinese, Perko's Rest., RoundTable Pizza, Subway, Taco Bell, Walkabout Creek Deli/gifts, **lodging:** Best Western/rest., Valley Inn, **other:** MEDICAL CARE, Ace Hardware, $Tree, NAPA, Rite Aid, Safeway, Schwab Tires, **W…gas:** Beacon/diesel, Chevron, Sarco/diesel, Shell, **food:** City Grill, Giant Burger, Goodtimes Pizza, KFC, Koffee Korner Rest., **other:** Holiday Food/drugs, Kragen Parts, Owen's Drugs, RV Ctr

667   CA 273, Factory Outlet Blvd, **W…gas:** Shell/diesel, TowerMart/diesel, **food:** Arby's, Jack-in-the-Box, LJ Silver, **lodging:** AmeriHost, **other:** GNC, Prime Outlets/famous brands, farmers mkt

665   (from sb) Cottonwood, **E…food:** Branding Iron Rest:, **lodging:** Alamo Motel, Travelers Motel

664   Gas Point Rd, to Balls Ferry, **E…gas:** CFN/diesel, Chevron/MeanGene's/diesel/LP, Gas4Less, Payless/gas/grocery, **lodging:** Travelers Motel, **other:** NAPA, auto repair, **W…gas:** Beacon/diesel/LP, Holiday/diesel, 76/diesel, **other:** Sentry Foods

662   Bowman Rd, to Cottonwood, **E…gas:** Pacific Pride/diesel, Shell/diesel

660mm   weigh sta both lanes

659   Snively Rd, Auction Yard Rd, no facilities

657   Hooker Creek Rd, Auction Yard Rd, **E…other:** Dill's Trailer Works

656mm   **rest area both, full(handicapped)facilities, phone, picnic tables, litter barrels, petwalk**

653   Jellys Ferry Rd, **E…lodging:** Bend RV Park/LP

652   Wilcox Golf Rd, no facilities

651   CA 36W(from sb), Red Bluff, **W…**Exxon/diesel, Ford

650   Adobe Rd, **3/4 mi W…** Exxon, Hwy Patrol

649   CA 33, CA 99, Red Bluff, **E…gas:** Exxon/diesel, Shell/diesel, **food:** Burger King, Perko's Cafe, KFC, McDonald's, RoundTable Pizza, Subway, **lodging:** Best Inn, Comfort Inn, Motel 6, Super 8, **W…gas:** Gas4Less, USA/diesel, **food:** Carl's Jr, Denny's, Egg Roll King, Luigi's Pizza, Marie's Rest., Riverside Dining, RoundTable Pizza, Shari's/24hr, Subway, Wild Bill's Steaks, Winchell's, **lodging:** Best Value, Cinderella Motel, Idle Wheels RV Park, Red Bluff Inn, Travelodge, Value Lodge, **other:** Foodmaxx, Long's Drug

647a b   Diamond Ave, Red Bluff, **E…gas:** 76/diesel, **food:** El Cazador Mexican, **lodging:** Day's Inn, Motel Orleans/rest., **other:** HOSPITAL, **W…gas:** Arco/diesel/24hr, Beacon/diesel, Chevron, **food:** Arby's,

*(side tab: Corning)*
*(side tab: Red Bluff)*

Country Waffles, Crystal Oven Rest., Feedbag Rest., Italian Cottage, Jack-in-the-Box, Pepe's Pizza, Subway, Taco Bell/24hr, Yogurt Alley, **lodging:** Crystal Motel, Flamingo Motel, Sky Terrace Motel, Triangle Motel, **other:** Big O Tire, Chevrolet/Cadillac, $Tree, Ford/Mercury, K-Mart, Kragen Parts, Radio Shack, Raley's Food/drug, Staples, Wal-Mart/auto

642   Flores Ave, to Proberta, Gerber, **2 mi E…other:** Wal-Mart Dist Ctr

636   CA 811, Gyle Rd, to Tehama, **E…other:** RV camping(7mi)

633   Finnell Rd, to Richfield, no facilities

632mm   **rest area both lanes, full(handicapped)facilities, phone, picnic tables, litter barrels, petwalk**

631   A9, Corning Ave, Corning, **E…gas:** Chevron/24hr, Citgo/7-11, Exxon, Shell/diesel/LP, 76/diesel, **food:** Burg e r King, Casa Ramos Mexican, Marcos Pizza, Olive Pit Rest., Papa Murphy's, Rancho Grande Mexican, RoundTable Pizza, Taco Bell, **lodging:** AmeriHost, Best Western, Budget Inn, Economy Inn, Olive City Inn, 7 Inn Motel/RV Park, **other:** Clark Drug, Ford/Mercury/Kia, Heritage RV Park, Holiday Mkt/deli, Kragen Parts, NAPA, Pontiac/Chevrolet/Buick, Rite Aid, Safeway/24hr, Tires+, **W…food:** Giant Burger, **lodging:** Corning RV Park

630   South Ave, Corning, **E…gas:** Petro/Exxon/diesel/rest./@, TA/Arco/Arby's/Subway/diesel/24hr/@, **food:** Iron Skillet, Jack-in-the-Box, McDonald's, **lodging:** Day's Inn, Holiday Inn Express, Shilo Inn/rest./24hr, **other:** Blue Beacon, Goodyear, RV Ctr, RV camping(1-6mi), Woodson Br SRA/RV Park

628   CA 99W, Liberal Ave, **W…**Ramada Ltd/rest./casino

621   CA 7, no facilities

619   CA 32, Orland, **E… gas:** Gas4Less/diesel, Quik Serv, 76, **food:** Burger King, Berry Patch Rest., Subway, **lodging:** Amberlight Motel, Orlanda Inn, **W…gas:** USA/diesel, **food:** Taco Bell, **lodging:** Green Acres RV Park, Old Orchard RV Park

618   CA 16, **E…gas:** Beacon/diesel/24hr, CFN/diesel, USA/diesel, **food:** Pizza Factory, **lodging:** Orland Inn, **other:** Longs Drug, Schwab Tires, laundry

614   CA 27, no facilities

610   Artois, no facilities

608mm   **rest area both lanes, full(handicapped)facilities, phone, picnic tables, litter barrels, petwalk, RV dump**

607   CA 39, Blue Gum Rd, Bayliss, **2-3 mi E…lodging:** Blue Gum Motel/rest.

CALIFORNIA
Interstate 5

Williams

603   CA 162, to Oroville, Willows, **E...gas:** Arco/24hr, Chevron/24hr, Shell/diesel, **food:** BlackBear Diner, Burger King, Casa Ramos Mexican, Denny's/24hr, Java Jim's Café, KFC, McDonald's, RoundTable Pizza, Subway/TCBY, Taco Bell/24hr, **lodging:** Amerihost, Best Value, Best Western/rest., CrossRoads West Inn, Day's Inn, Super 8/RV Park, **other:** HOSPITAL, CHP, **W...food:** Nancy's Café/24hr, **other:** Wal-Mart, RV Park(8mi), airport

601   CA 57, **E...gas:** 76/CFN/diesel

595   Norman Rd, to Princeton, **E...**to Sacramento NWR

591   Delevan Rd, no facilities

588   Maxwell(from sb), access to camping

586   Maxwell Rd, **E...other:** Delavan NWR, **W...gas:** CFN/diesel, Chevron, **lodging:** Maxwell Inn/rest., **other:** Maxwell Parts, NAPA

583   **rest area both lanes, full(handicapped)facilities, phone, picnic tables, litter barrels, petwalk**

578   CA 20 W, Colusa, **W...gas:** Orv's/diesel/rest., **other:** HOSPITAL, hwy patrol

577   CA 20 E, Williams, **E...gas:** Shell/Baskin-Robbins/Togo's/diesel/24hr, **food:** Carl's Jr, Taco Bell, Subway, **lodging:** Holiday Inn Express, **W...gas:** Arco/24hr, CFN/diesel, Chevron/diesel/24hr, 76, Shell/diesel, **food:** A&W, Burger King, Casa Lupe Mexican, Denny's, Granzella's Deli, McDonald's/RV parking, Wendy's, Williams Chinese Rest., **lodging:** Capri Motel, Comfort Inn, El Rancho Motel, Granzella's Inn, Motel 6, StageStop Motel, Travelers Motel, **other:** HOSPITAL, NAPA, U-Haul, USPO, ValuRite Drug, camping, hwy patrol

575   Husted Rd, to Williams, no facilities

569   Hahn Rd, to Grimes, no facilities

567   frontage rd(from nb), to Arbuckle, **E...food:** El Jaliscience Mexican

566   to College City, Arbuckle, **E...gas:** Shell/Pacific Pride/diesel, **other:** Ace Hardware, **W...gas:** J&J/diesel

562   I-505(from sb), to San Francisco, callboxes begin sb

559   Yolo/Colusa County Line Rd, no facilities

557mm   **rest area both lanes, full(handicapped)facilities, phone, picnic tables, litter barrels, petwalk**

556   E4, Dunnigan, **E...gas:** Chevron/diesel/24hr, Valero/diesel/LP, **food:** Bill&Kathy's Rest., Jack-in-the-Box, **lodging:** Best Value Inn, Best Western, **other:** USPO, **W...gas:** 76, **lodging:** Camper's RV Park/golf

554   rd 8, **E...gas:** Pilot/Wendy's/diesel/24hr/@, **other:** Oasis Grill, **lodging:** Budget 8 Motel, HappyTime RV Park, **W...gas:** United/diesel

548   Zamora, **E...gas:** Pacific Pride/diesel, Shell, **other:** Zamora Minimart, camping, **W...other:** USPO

542   Yolo, **1 mi E...**gas

541   CA 16W, Woodland, **3 mi W...other:** HOSPITAL

540   West St, **W...food:** Denny's

538   CA 113 N, E St, Woodland, **W...gas:** Chevron/diesel, **food:** Denny's, **lodging:** Best Western, **other:** Woodland Opera House(1mi)

537   CA 113 S, Main St, to Davis, US/Canada Border, NY state line, I-87 begins/ends, **W...food:** Ruby Tuesday, Taco Bell, Wendy's, **lodging:** Day's Inn, Motel 6, **other:** Food4Less

536   rd 102, **E on Main St...gas:** Arco, Exxon, Shell, **food:** Applebee's, Jack-in-the-Box, McDonalds, Subway, **lodging:** Holiday Inn Express, **other:** Home Depot, Staples, Target, Wal-Mart/gas, museum, **W...gas:** Chevron, **other:** CHP

Sacramento

531   rd 22, W Sacramento, no facilities

530mm   Sacramento River

529mm   **rest area sb, full(handicapped)facilities, phone, picnic tables, litter barrels, petwalk**

528   Airport Rd, **E...gas:** Arco, **other:** airport, food, lodging

525b   CA 99, to CA 70, to Marysville, Yuba City, no facilities

525a   Del Paso Rd, **E...food:** Jack-in-the-box, Arco Arena, no facilities

524   Arena Blvd, **E...other:** Arco Arena

522   I-80, E to Reno, W to San Francisco, no facilities

521b a   Garden Hwy, West El Camino, **W...food:** Baja Fresh, Carl's Jr, Jack-in-the-Box, Jamba Juice, Togo's, **lodging:** Courtyard, Hilton Garden, Homestead Village, Residence Inn

520   Richards Blvd, **E...gas:** Chevron/24hr, **food:** Hungry Hunter Rest., Lyon's Rest./24hr, Memphis BBQ, McDonald's, Monterey Rest., Rusty Duck Rest., **lodging:** Governor's Inn, Hawthorn Suites, Ramamda Inn, Super 8, **W...gas:** Rivermart Gas, Shell, **food:** Coyote Jct Mexican, **lodging:** Best Western/rest., Capitol Inn, Comfort Suites, La Quinta, Motel 6, Super 8

519b   J St, Old Sacramento, **E...food:** Denny's, **lodging:** Holiday Inn, Vagabond Inn, **W...lodging:** Embassy Suites, **other:** Railroad Museum

519a   Q St , downtown, Sacramento, to st capitol, no facilities

518   US 50, CA 99, Broadway, **E...**multiple facilities downtown

516   Sutterville Rd, **E...gas:** Land Park/diesel, **other:** William Land Park, zoo

515   Fruitridge Rd, Seamas Rd, no facilities

514   43rd Ave, Riverside Blvd(from sb), **E...gas:** 76/repair

513   Florin Rd, **E...gas:** Arco/24hr, Chevron/24hr, Shell/repair, **food:** Rosalinda's Mexican, RoundTable Pizza, Subway, **other:** Bel Air Foods, $Tree, Kragen Parts, Longs Drug, **W...food:** Burger King, JimBoy's Tacos, RoundTable Pizza, Shari's, Starbucks, Subway, Wendy's, **other:** Marshall's, Nugget Foods, Radio Shack, Rite Aid

512   CA 160, Pocket Rd, Meadowview Rd, to Freeport, **E...gas:** Shell/24hr, United/diesel, **food:** IHOP, Wendy's, McDonald's, Togo's, **other:** Home Depot, Staples

508   Laguna Blvd, **E...gas:** Chevron, Shell, 76/Circle K/diesel, LP, **lodging:** Extended Stay America, **other:** Big O Tire

506   Elk Grove Blvd, **E...gas:** Arco/diesel, **lodging:** Comfort Suites

504   Hood Franklin Rd, no facilities

498   Twin Cities Rd, to Walnut Grove, no facilities

493   Walnut Grove Rd, Thornton, **E...**76/Subway/diesel

490   Peltier Rd, no facilities

487   Turner Rd, no facilities

485   CA 12, Lodi, **E...gas:** Arco/diesel/24hr, Chevron/Subway/diesel/LP/@, ⚡/Flying J/diesel/24hr/@, NW/Wendy's/diesel, 76/Rocky's Rest./24hr/diesel/@, **food:** Burger King, McDonald's, Taco Bell, **lodging:** Best Western, Microtel, **other:** Blue Beacon, **W...other:** Tower Park Marina Camping(5mi)

481   Eight Mile Rd, **3 mi E...lodging:** **W...**Borders Books, KOA, Kohl's, Target, Mercedes, Volvo

Stockton

478   Hammer Lane, Stockton, **E...gas:** Arco/24hr, 76/Circle K/diesel, **food:** Adalberto's Mexican, Carl's Jr, KFC, Little Caesar's, Shirason Japanese, **other:** Auto Parts Express, S-mart Foods, **W...gas:** Pacific Pride/diesel, QuikStop, **food:** Burger King, Jack-in-the-Box, JimBoy's, Tacos, Subway, Suji Seafood, Taco Bell, **lodging:** InnCal

Interstate 5

N ↕ S

477 Benjamin Holt Dr, Stockton, **E...gas:** Arco, Chevron/24hr, **food:** Pizza Guys, QuikStop, **lodging:** Motel 6, **W...gas:** Shell, **food:** McDonald's, Lyon's/24hr, 7-11, Subway/TCBY, Wong's Chinese, **other:** Ace Hardware

476 March Lane, Stockton, **E...gas:** Citgo/7-11, **food:** Applebee's, Arroyo's Mexican, Black Angus, Carl's Jr, Denny's, El Torito, Jack-in-the-Box, Kowloon Chinese, MacDonald's, Marie Callender, Red Lobster, StrawHat Pizza, Taco Bell, Tony Roma, Wendy's, **lodging:** Comfort Inn, Radisson, **other:** MEDICAL CARE, Longs Drug, Marshall's, OfficeMax, Smart Foods, **W...gas:** 76/diesel/24hr, 7-11, **food:** Carrow's Rest., In-n-Out, Krispy Kreme, Old Spaghetti Factory, Wong's Chinese, **lodging:** La Quinta, Super 8, **other:** Home Depot

475 Alpine Ave, Country Club Blvd, same as 474 b

474b Country Club Blvd(from nb), **W...gas:** Citgo/7-11, USA/Subway/diesel, Safeway/gas, **other:** Big Lots

474a Monte Diablo Ave, **W...other:** Aamco

473 Pershing Ave(from nb), **W...gas:** Arco, **lodging:** BestValue

472 CA 4 E, to CA 99, Fresno Ave, downtown, no facilities

471 CA 4 W, Charter Way, **E...gas:** Chevron/24hr, Shell/24hr, United/diesel, **food:** Burger King, Denny's, McDonald's, **lodging:** Best Western, Motel 6, **other:** Kragen Parts, transmissions, **W...gas:** Beacon/Country MktPlace/TCBY/diesel/@, 76/diesel/rest./24hr, **food:** Taco Bell, **lodging:** Motel 6

470 8th St, Stockton, **W...gas:** Shell/diesel, **food:** Boquita Mexican, **lodging:** Econolodge

469 Downing Ave, **W...food:** China Express, Jalapeños Mexican, Mke's Pizza, Subway, **other:** FoodMaxx/gas

468 French Camp, **E...gas:** 76/Togo's/diesel/@, **W...other:** HOSPITAL, Pan Pacific RV Ctr,

467b Mathews Rd, **E...gas:** CFN/diesel, **other:** RV Ctr, tires/repair, **W...other:** HOSPITAL

467a El Dorado St(from nb), no facilities

465 Roth Rd, Sharpe Depot, **E...other:** Freightliner, Kenworth, truck repair

463 Lathrop Rd, **E...gas:** Chevron/24hr, Joe's Trkstp/Subway/TCBY/diesel/@, TowerMart/diesel, Valero/diesel, **food:** Country Kitchen, **lodging:** Comfort Inn, Day's Inn, **W...other:** Dos Reis CP, RV camping

462 Louise Ave, **E...gas:** Arco/24hr, 76, **food:** A&W/KFC, Carl's Jr, Denny's, Jack-in-the-Box, McDonald's, Taco Bell, **lodging:** Holiday Inn Express, **other:** Mossdale CP

461 CA 120, to Sonora, Manteca, **E...other:** Oakwood Lake Resort Camping, to Yosemite

460 Mossdale Rd, **E...gas:** Exxon/diesel, **W...food:** fruitstand/deli

458b I-205, to Oakland(from sb, no return), no facilities

458a 11th St, to Tracy, Defense Depot, **2 mi W...gas:** gas/diesel/food

457 Kasson Rd, to Tracy, **W...gas:** CFN/diesel

452 CA 33 S, Vernalis, no facilities

449b a CA 132, to Modesto, **W...other:** The Orchard Campground

Tracy

446 I-580(from nb, exits left, no return), no facilities

445mm **Westley Rest Area both lanes, full(handicapped)facilities picnic tables, litter barrels, phone, RV dump, petwalk**

441 Ingram Creek, Howard Rd, Westley, **E...gas:** Beacon/diesel, Bobby Ray's/diesel/rest./24hr/@, Chevron/diesel/24hr, 76/diesel/24hr, **food:** Carl's Jr, McDonald's, **lodging:** Day's Inn, Econolodge, Holiday Inn Express, Super 8, **W...gas:** Shell/diesel/24hr, **food:** Ingram Creek Rest., fruits

434 Sperry Ave, Del Puerto, Patterson, **E...gas:** Arco/24hr, 76/Subway/diesel, **food:** Denny's, Del Lago Steaks, Jack-in-the-Box, Wendy's, **lodging:** Best Western

430mm vista point nb

428 Fink Rd, Crow's Landing, no facilities

423 Stuhr Rd, Newman, **5 mi E...food,** lodging, **other:** HOSPITAL, RV camping

422mm vista point sb

418 CA 140E, Gustine, **E...gas:** 76/diesel, Shell/diesel

409 weigh sta both lanes

407 CA 33, Santa Nella, **E... gas:** Arco, Pilot/Del Taco/diesel/24hr/@, Shell/diesel, TA/76/diesel/rest./24hr/@, **food:** Andersen's Rest., Burger King, Carl's Jr, **lodging:** Best Western, Holiday Inn Express, **W...gas:** Beacon/diesel, Chevron/24hr, Rotten Robbie/diesel, Shell, **food:** Denny's, McDonald's, Taco Bell, **lodging:** Motel 6, Ramada Inn

403b a CA 152, Los Banos, **6 mi E...other:** HOSPITAL, **W...lodging:** Super 8, **other:** San Luis RV Park

391 CA 165N, Mercy Springs Rd, **W...gas:** Shell

386 **rest area both lanes, full(handicapped)facilities, phone, picnic tables, litter barrels, petwalk**

385 Nees Ave, to Firebaugh, **W...gas:** Exxon/CFN/Subway/TCBY/diesel

379 Shields Ave, to Mendota, no facilities

372 Russell Ave, no facilities

368 Panoche Rd, **W...gas:** Chevron, 76, Shell/Foster's Freeze/diesel/burgers/@, **lodging:** Apricot Tree Motel/rest., Shilo Inn, **other:** Palms Mkt

365 Manning Ave, to San Joaquin, no facilities

357 Kamm Ave, no facilities

349 CA 33 N, Derrick Ave, no facilities

337 CA 33 S, CA 145 N, to Coalinga, no facilities

Interstate 5

334	CA 198, to Lemoore, Huron, **E...gas:** Shell/Subway/diesel/24hr/@, **lodging:** Harris Ranch Inn/rest., **W...gas:** Chevron, CFN/diesel, Mobil/diesel, 76/Circle K, **food:** Burger King, Carl's Jr, Cazuela's Mexican, Denny's, McDonald's, Oriental Express Chinese, Red Robin Rest., Taco Bell, Windmill Mkt/deli, **lodging:** Best Western, Big County Inn, Motel 6, Pleasant Valley Inn, **other:** HOSPITAL
325	Jayne Ave, to Coalinga, **W...gas:** Arco/24hr, **lodging:** Almond Tree RV Park, **other:** HOSPITAL
320mm	**rest area both lanes, full(handicapped)facilities, phone, picnic tables, litter barrels, petwalk**
319	CA 269, Lassen Ave, to Avenal, **W...**gas/diesel, food, lodging, st prison
309	CA 41, Kettleman City, **E...gas:** Beacon/diesel, CFN/diesel, Chevron, Exxon/Subway/TCBY/diesel, Mobil/diesel/24hr, 76, Shell, **food:** Carl's Jr, In-n-Out, Jack-in-the-Box, McDonald's, Mike's Roadhouse Café, Pizza Hut/Taco Bell, TCBY, **lodging:** Best Western, Super 8, **other:** Travelers RV Park
305	Utica Ave, no facilities
288	Twisselman Rd, no facilities
278	CA 46, Lost Hills, **E...gas:** Shell/diesel, **other:** to Kern NWR, **W...gas:** Arco/24hr, Beacon/diesel, Chevron/diesel/24hr, Pilot/Wendy's/diesel/24hr/@, 76/24hr, Shell, **food:** Carl's Jr, Denny's, Jack-in-the-Box, **lodging:** Day's Inn, Motel 6, **other:** KOA
268	Lerdo Hwy, to Shafter, **3 mi E...gas:** Minimart/gas
262	7th Standard Rd, Rowlee Rd, to Buttonwillow, no facilities
259mm	**Buttonwillow Rest Area both lanes, full(handicapped)facilities, phone, picnic tables, litter barrels, petwalk**
257	CA 58, to Bakersfield, Buttonwillow, **E...gas:** Arco/24hr, Bruce's/A&W/diesel/@, Chevron/diesel/24hr, Mobil/Subway/TCBY/diesel/@, TA/76/Taco Bell/diesel/24hr/@, Shell/diesel, **food:** Carl's Jr, Denny's, McDonald's, Zippy Freeze, **lodging:** FirstValue Inn, Motel 6, Super 8, Willow Inn, **other:** Roger's Produce/gifts, **W...gas:** Exxon/diesel
253	Stockdale Hwy, **E...gas:** Exxon/IHOP/diesel/24hr, 76/24hr, **food:** Jack-in-the-Box, **lodging:** Best Inn, Best Western, **W...other:** Tule Elk St Reserve
246	CA 43, to Taft, Maricopa, **other:** to Buena Vista RA
244	CA 119, to Pumpkin Center, no facilities
239	CA 223, Bear Mtn Blvd, to Arvin, **W...other:** RV camping
234	Old River Rd, no facilities
228	Copus Rd, no facilities
225	CA 166, to Mettler, **2-3 mi E...**gas/diesel, food
221	I-5 and CA 99(from nb, exits left, no return), no facilities
219b a	Laval Rd, Wheeler Ridge, **E...gas:** Chevron, TA/diesel/rest./@, **food:** Burger King, Pizza Hut, Subway, Taco Bell, TCBY, **other:** Blue Beacon, repair, **W...gas:** Petro/Mobil/diesel/24hr/@, **food:** McDonald's, Starbucks, Wendy's, **lodging:** Best Western
218	truck weigh sta sb
215	Grapevine, **E...gas:** Mobil, **food:** Denny's, Jack-in-the-Box, RanchHouse Rest., **W...gas:** 76/diesel, Shell/Taco Bell/diesel/@, **food:** Farmer's Table Rest., **lodging:** Countryside Inn

Side label: Buttonwillow

210	Ft Tejon Rd, **W...other:** to Ft Tejon Hist SP, towing/repair
209mm	brake check area nb
207	Lebec Rd, **W...other:** USPO, CHP, antiques, towing
206mm	**rest areas both lanes, full(handicapped)facilities, phone, vending, picnic tables litter barrels, petwalk**
205	Frazier Mtn Park Rd, **W...gas:** Arco, Chevron/Subway/diesel/24hr, Flying J/diesel/LP/rest./motel/24hr/@, Shell/Quizno's/diesel, **food:** Jack-in-the-Box, Los Pinos Mexican, **lodging:** BestRest Inn, **other:** Auto Parts+, towing/repair/radiators/transmissions, to Mt Pinos RA
204	Tejon Pass, elev 4144
202	Gorman Rd, to Hungry Valley, **E...gas:** Chevron/diesel/LP, **food:** Carl's Jr, Gorman Plaza Café, Sizzler, **lodging:** Econolodge, **W...gas:** Mobil, **food:** McDonald's, **other:** auto repair
199	CA 138 E(from sb), Lancaster Rd, to Palmdale, no facilities
198b a	Quail Lake Rd, CA 138 E(from nb), no facilities
195	Smokey Bear Rd, Pyramid Lake, **W...other:** Pyramid Lake RV Park
191	Vista del Lago Rd, **W...other:** visitors ctr
186mm	brake inspection area sb, motorist callboxes begin sb
183	Templin Hwy, **W...other:** Ranger Sta, RV camping
176b a	Lake Hughes Rd, Parker Rd, Castaic, **E...gas:** Arco, Citgo/7-11, Castaic Trkstp/diesel/rest./24hr/@, Giant/Chevron/Popeye's/diesel/24hr/@, Shell, **food:** Burger King, Café Mike, Carl's Jr, Del Taco, Domino's, Foster Freeze, McDonald's, Subway, Zorba's Rest., **lodging:** Castaic Inn, Comfort Inn, Day's Inn, **other:** Ralph's Food, Rite Aid, to Castaic Lake, **W...gas:** Mobil, 76/Circle K/Pizza Hut/Taco Bell/repair, **food:** Jack-in-the-Box, **lodging:** Comfort Suites, **other:** auto repair
173	Hasley Canyon Rd, **W...food:** Ameci Pizza/pasta
172	CA 126 W, to Ventura, no facilities
171mm	weigh sta sb
171	Rye Canyon Rd(from sb), **W...gas:** Shell, **food:** Del Taco, Jack-in-the-Box, Tommy's Burgers, **other:** funpark
170	CA 126 E, Magic Mtn Pkwy, Saugus, **E...lodging:** Best Western/rest., **W...gas:** Chevron, **food:** El Torito, Hamburger Hamlet, Marie Callender's, Red Lobster, Wendy's, **lodging:** Hilton Garden, **other:** Six Flags of CA
169	Valencia Blvd, no facilities
168	McBean Pkwy, **E...other:** HOSPITAL, **W...food:** Baskin-Robbins, Chili's, ChuckeCheese, ClaimJumper Rest., Indian Cuisine, JambaJuice, Macaroni Grill, Starbucks, Subway, Wood Ranch BBQ, **other:** Circuit City, Marshall's, Michael's, Old Navy, Staples, Vons Foods, WorldMkt
167	Lyons Ave, Pico Canyon Rd, **E...gas:** Chevron/24hr, 76/Circle K, Shell/diesel, **food:** Burger King, **other:** Chevrolet, **W...gas:** Arco/24hr, Mobil/Blimpie, Shell, **food:** Carl's Jr, Chuy's Chinese, Coco's, Del Taco, Denny's, Foster's Freeze, El Pollo Loco, Fortune Express Chinese, Floridinos Italian, IHOP, In-n-Out, Jack-in-the-Box, McDonald's, Outback Steaks, Taco Bell, Yamato Japanese, **lodging:** Comfort Inn, Extended Stay America, Fairfield Inn, Hampton Inn, Residence Inn, **other:** Camping World RV Service, GNC, Ralph's Foods, SteinMart, Wal-Mart/auto
166	Calgrove Blvd, **E...food:** Carrows Rest.
162	CA 14 N, to Palmdale, no facilities
161b	Balboa Blvd, no facilities
160a	I-210, to San Fernando, Pasadena, no facilities
159	Roxford St, Sylmar, **E...gas:** Chevron/diesel, Mobil/diesel, **food:** Denny's/24hr, McDonald's, **lodging:** Good Nite Inn, Motel 6

Side label: Santa Clarita

Interstate 5

N ↑↓ S

Los Angeles Area

158   I-405 S(from sb, no return), no facilities

157b a   SF Mission Blvd, Brand Blvd, **E...gas:** Mobil, 76/24hr, **food:** Carl's Jr, In-n-Out, Pollo Gordo, Popeye's, **other:** HOSPITAL, AutoZone, Rite Aid

156b   CA 118, no facilities

156a   Paxton St, Brand Ave(from nb), **E...gas:** Arco, Chevron, Shell/24hr, **food:** Carnita's Mexican, Taco Bell, Winchell's

155b   Van Nuys Blvd(no EZ nb return), **E...gas:** Mobil, 76, **food:** Jack-in-the-Box, KFC, McDonald's, Pizza Hut, Popeye's, **other:** AutoZone, **W...food:** Domino's

155a   Terra Bella St(from nb), **E...gas:** Arco, Citgo

154   Osborne St, to Arleta, **E...gas:** Arco/24hr, 76, **food:** Papa's Tacos, Peter Piper Pizza, **other:** Food4Less, Target, **W...gas:** Mobil/Burger King, 7-11, **food:** Mi Taco

153b   CA 170(from sb), to Hollywood, no facilities

152a   Sheldon St, **E...food:** Big Jim's Rest., **other:** HOSPITAL, auto repair

152   Lankershim Blvd, Tuxford, **E...gas:** Shell/diesel, **W...other:** radiators

151   Penrose St, no facilities

150b   Sunland Blvd, Sun Valley, **E...gas:** Mobil, 76, 7-11, **food:** Acapulco Rest., Carl's Jr, El Pollo Loco, Good Fortune Chinese, Town Café, **lodging:** Scottish Inn, **W...gas:** Exxon, Shell, **food:** Dimion's Rest., El Mexicano's, McDonald's

150a   GlenOaks Blvd(from nb), **E...gas:** Arco, **lodging:** Willows Motel

149   Hollywood Way, **E...food:** Carrow's, **W...gas:** Shell/diesel, **other:** U-Haul, airport

148   Buena Vista St, **W...gas:** Exxon/diesel, **food:** Jack-in-the-Box, **lodging:** Buena Vista Motel, Quality Inn, Ramada Inn

147   Scott Rd, to Burbank, **E...gas:** Sevan/diesel, **W... food:** Krispy Kreme, Outback Steaks, Panda Express, Starbucks, Wendy's, **other:** Best Buy, Lowe's Whse, Marshall's, Michael's, Staples, Target

146b   Burbank Blvd, **E...gas:** 76/repair, **food:** CA Pizza, Carl's Jr, Chevy's Mexican, ChuckeCheese, Crabby Bob's, El Pollo Loco, Great Wall Buffet, Harry's Rest., IHOP, In-n-Out, KooRooRoo Kitchen, Marie Callender, McDonald's, Popeye's, Shakey's Pizza, Subway, Taco Bell, Tommy's Burgers, Wienerschnitzel, Yoshinoya, **lodging:** Holiday Inn, **other:** Barnes&Noble, Circuit City, CompUSA, K-Mart, Macy's, Mervyn's, Office Depot, Ralph's Foods, Ross, SavOn Drug, Sears, Von's Foods, **W...gas:** Chevron, **food:** Subway

146a   Olive Ave, Verdugo, **E...food:** Black Angus, Brewhouse Rest., Fuddrucker's, **lodging:** Holiday Inn, **other:** Radio Shack, Sears, **W...other:** HOSPITAL, Chevrolet

145b   Alameda Ave, **E...gas:** Chevron, **food:** Starbucks, **other:** Ralph's Foods, SavOn Drug, **W...gas:** Arco, Mobil/diesel, Shell, **lodging:** Burbank Inn, **other:** U-Haul

145a   Western Ave, **W...other:** Gene Autrey Museum

144b a   CA 134, Ventura Fwy, Glendale, Pasadena, no facilities

142   Colorado St, no facilities

141a   Los Feliz Blvd, **E...other:** HOSPITAL, **W...other:** Griffith Park, zoo

140b   Glendale Blvd, **E...gas:** 76, Shell, **other:** auto repair

---

140a   Fletcher Dr(from sb), **E...other:** U-Haul, **W...gas:** Arco/24hr, Chevron, 76, **food:** Charburger, Rick's Drive-In, **other:** Ralph's Foods

139b a   CA 2, Glendale Fwy, no facilities

138   Stadium Way, Figueroa St, **E...other:** Home Depot, **W...other:** to Dodger Stadium

137b a   CA 2, Glendale Fwy, no facilities

136b   Broadway St(from sb), industrial area

136a   Main St, **E...gas:** Chevron/24hr, 76, **food:** Burgers+, Chinatown Express, McDonald's, Mr Pizza, **other:** HOSPITAL, Parts+

135c   I-10 W(from nb), Mission Rd(from sb), **E...gas:** Chevron, 76, **food:** Jack-in-the-Box, McDonald's, **lodging:** Howard Johnson, **other:** HOSPITAL

135b   Ceasar Chavez Ave, **W...other:** HOSPITAL

135a   4th St, Soto St, no facilities

134b   Ca 60 E(from sb), Soto St(from nb), no facilities

134a   CA 60 W, Santa Monica Fwy, no facilities

133   Euclid Ave(from sb), Grand Vista(from nb), **E...gas:** Arco, USA/diesel, **W...gas:** Mobil, Shell, **other:** HOSPITAL

132   Calzona St, Indiana St, **E...gas:** Arco/diesel

131b   Indiana St(from nb), no facilities

131a   Olympic Blvd, **E...food:** McDonald's, **W...food:** Jack-in-the-Box, King Taco, **other:** HOSPITAL

130c b   I-710, to Long Beach, Eastern Ave, **E...food:** McDonald's

130a   Triggs St(from sb), **E...food:** Winchell's, **other:** outlet mall, **W...gas:** 76/diesel, **food:** Denny's/24hr, **lodging:** Destiny Inn, **other:** Ford

129   Atlantic Blvd N, Eastern Ave(from sb), **E...food:** Carl's Jr, **other:** outlet mall/famous brands, **W...food:** Denny's, Steven's Steaks

128b   Washington Blvd, Commerce, **E...gas:** Chevron/diesel/repair/24hr, **food:** McDonald's, **lodging:** Commerce Hotel, Crowne Plaza Hotel, Wyndham Garden, **other:** Commerce Casino, Firestone, Old Navy, mall

128a   Garfield Blvd, **E...lodging:** Commerce Hotel, **other:** Home Depot, Office Depot, **W...other:** Staples

126b   Slauson Ave, Montebello, **E...gas:** Shell/diesel, **food:** Burger King, Subworks, **lodging:** Best Western, Super 8, **W...gas:** Arco, **food:** Denny's, **lodging:** Guesthouse Suites, Ramada Inn

126a   Paramount Blvd, Downey, **E...gas:** Circle K, Shell/Jack-in-the-Box

125   CA 19 S, Lakewood Blvd, Rosemead Blvd, **E...gas:** Arco, Mobil, Thrifty, **food:** El Pedregal Mexican, Sam's Burgers, Taco Bell, **lodging:** Econolodge, **W...other:** Ford

CALIFORNIA
Interstate 5

124   I-605, no facilities

123   Florence Ave, to Downey, **W...other:** Honda

122   Imperial Hwy, Pioneer Blvd, **E...gas:** Chevron, **food:** IHOP, Jack-in-the-Box, McDonald's, Red Lobster, Subway, Wendy's, **lodging:** Best Western, **other:** Audi/Porsche, BMW, Firestone/auto, Payless Foods, Rite Aid, Target, **W...gas:** Shell, **food:** Denny's, HongKong Express, Pizza Hut, Rally's, Sizzler, Tacos Mexico, **lodging:** Anchor Inn, Comfort Inn, Vistaland Motel, **other:** Ford

121   San Antonio Dr, to Norwalk Blvd, **E...food:** IHOP, McDonald's, Outback Steaks, **lodging:** Marriott, **W...gas:** 76, **other:** Hall's Automotive

120b   Firestone Blvd(exits left from nb), no facilities

120a   Rosecrans Ave, **E...gas:** Arco/24hr, Mobil/diesel, Shell/diesel, **food:** Burger King, Casa Adelita Mexican, Jim's Burgers, KFC, Pizza Hut/Taco Bell, Taco Joe, **other:** HOSPITAL, BigSaver Foods, **W...gas:** Arco/24hr, **food:** El Pollo Loco, **other:** El Monte RV Ctr, Nissan

119   Carmenita Rd, Buena Park, **E...gas:** Arco, 76/diesel, **food:** Burger King, Carrows, Jack-in-the-Box, Pizza Hut/Taco Bell, **lodging:** Motel 6, **other:** Ford Trucks, Lowe's Whse, **W...gas:** Arco/24hr, Mobil, **food:** Carl's Jr, China Express, Galaxy Burger, **lodging:** Best Western, Dynasty Suites, Super 8

118   Valley View Blvd, **E...gas:** Arco/24hr, **food:** Carl's Jr, In-n-Out, Red Robin, **lodging:** Holiday Inn, **other:** Staples, **W...gas:** Chevron, Shell/diesel, **food:** Blimpie, Denny's, El Pollo Loco, Taco Tio, Winchell's, **lodging:** Residence Inn, **other:** Thompson RV Ctr, to Camping World

117   Artesia Blvd, Knott Ave, **E...gas:** 76/24hr, Shell/Subway/diesel/24hr, **lodging:** Extended Stay America, **W...gas:** Cardlock/diesel, **other:** Chevrolet, Chrysler/Plymouth, Knotts Berry Farm, to Camping World RV Service/supplies

116   CA 39, Beach Blvd, **E...gas:** Chevron, **other:** HOSPITAL, Acura, BMW, Buick/Pontiac/GMC, Honda, Hyundai, Nissan, Toyota, VW, **W...gas:** Chevron, Mobil, **food:** Arby's, Black Angus, Denny's, KFC, Pizza Hut, Subway, **lodging:** Hampton Inn, Red Roof Inn, **other:** to Knotts Berry Farm

115   Manchester(from nb), no facilities

114b   CA 91 E, Riverside Fwy, **W...**to airport

114a   Magnolia Ave, Orangethorpe Ave, **E...gas:** Mobil/diesel, **food:** Burger King, Taco Bell, **other:** BMW, Harley-Davidson, Mercedes, Nissan

113c   CA 91 W(from nb), no facilities

113b a   Brookhurst St, LaPalma, **E...gas:** Chevron/24hr, **W...gas:** Arco/24hr, Shell, **food:** La Estrella Mexican, **other:** Staples

112   Euclid St, **E...gas:** Mobil, 7-11, **food:** Chris&Pitt's BBQ, Marie Callender's, McDonald's, Subway, **other:** CompUSA, Mervyn's, Kings Drug, OfficeMax, Old Navy, Wal-Mart, **W...gas:** Arco, 76, **food:** Arby's, Burger King, Denny's, **other:** Chevrolet, SavOn Drug

111   Lincoln Ave, to Anaheim, **E...gas:** Shell/diesel, **food:** El Triunfo Mexican, La Casa Garcia Mexican, **W...other:** Discount Auto Repair, Ford

110b   Ball Rd(from sb), **E...gas:** Arco, Chevron/diesel, Citgo/7-11, Shell, **food:** Burger King, El Pollo Loco, McDonald's, Shakey's Pizza, Subway, **lodging:** Anaheim Motel, Courtesy Lodge, Day's Inn, Traveler's World RV Park, **other:** laundry, **W...gas:** Arco/24hr, Shell/diesel, **food:** Paris Rest., Spaghetti Sta, **lodging:** Best Western, Budget Inn, Day's Inn, Sheraton, **other:** Camping World RV Service/supplies

110a   Harbor Blvd, **E...gas:** Shell, **lodging:** Day's Inn, Holiday Inn, **W...**to Disneyland, **food:** Acapulco Mexican, IHOP, McDonald's, Millie's Rest., Tony Roma, **lodging:** Anaheim Resort, Best Inn, Best Western, Carousel Inn, Castle Inn Suites, Desert Inn, Fairfield Inn, Howard Johnson, ParkVue Inn, Ramada Inn, Saga Inn, Tropicana Inn, same as 111

109   Katella Ave, Disney Way, **E...gas:** Arco, 76/repair, **food:** CA Country Café, Denny's, El Torito, McDonald's, Ming Delight, Mr Stox Dining, **lodging:** Angel Inn, Ramada Inn, Travelodge, **W...gas:** 7-11, **food:** Del Taco, Flakey Jake's, Thai&Thai, **lodging:** Arena Inn, Comfort Inn, Desert Palms Suites, Extended Stay America, Hilton, Holiday Inn Express, Marriott, Peacock Suites, Portofino Inn, Radisson, Red Roof Inn, Residence Inn, Super 8, to Disneyland

107c   St Coll Blvd, City Drive, **E...lodging:** Hilton Suites, **W...lodging:** Doubletree Hotel

107b a   CA 57 N, Chapman Ave, **E...gas:** Mobil, **food:** Burger King, Del Taco, Denny's, **lodging:** Hilton Suites, Motel 6, Ramada Inn, **other:** HOSPITAL, to Edison Field, **W...food:** Krispy Kreme, **lodging:** Country Inn/café, DoubleTree, **other:** HOSPITAL

106   CA 22 W(from nb), Garden Grove Fwy, Bristol St, no facilities

105b   N Broadway, Main St, **E...gas:** 76, **food:** Carl's Jr, Food-Court, Jamba Juice, Polly's Café, Rubio's Grill, Starbucks, **lodging:** Red Roof Inn, **other:** Barnes&Noble, BMW, Macy's, Nordstrom's, OfficeMax, Robinsons-May, SavOn Drug, Bowers Museum, mall, **W...lodging:** Golden West Motel, Travel Inn

105a   17th St, **E...gas:** 76/diesel/24hr, **food:** IHOP, McDonald's, **lodging:** Grand Courtyard Inn, **other:** Chevrolet, **W...gas:** Chevron, 7-11, **food:** Marisco's Seafood, Norm's Rest.

104b   Santa Ana Blvd, Grand Ave, **E on Grand...food:** Chabela's Mexican, Denny's, Marie Callender, Popeye's, RoundTable Pizza, Taco Bell, Wienerschnitzel, **other:** Factory2U, Food4Less, Goodyear, Kragen Parts, SavOn Drug, Target

104a   (103c from nb), 4th St, 1st St, to CA 55 N, **E...gas:** Chevron, Shell, **food:** Del Taco

103b   CA 55 S, to Newport Beach, no facilities

103a   CA 55 N(from nb), to Riverside, no facilities

102   Newport Ave(from sb), **W...gas:** Arco

101b   Red Hill Ave, **E...gas:** Arco/repair, Mobil/diesel, Shell/repair, **food:** Del Taco, Wendy's, **lodging:** Key Inn, **other:** Drug Emporium/24hr, 1$World, U-Haul, **W...gas:** Arco/24hr, Chevron/24hr, 76/Circle K, **food:** R&R Pizza, Taco Bell, **other:** Stater Bros Foods

101a   Tustin Ranch Rd, **E...food:** McDonald's, **other:** Acura, Buick, Cadillac, Chevrolet, Costco, Dodge, Ford/Lincoln/Mercury, Infiniti, K-Mart, Lexus, Mazda, Nissan, Pontiac, Toyota

100   Jamboree Rd, **E...gas:** Shell, **food:** Black Angus, Buca Italian, Burger King, CA Pizza, El Pollo Loco, In-n-Out, KooRooRoo Kitchen, Macaroni Grill, On the Border, Red Robin, **other:** AAA, Barnes&Noble, Circuit City, Costco, Loehmann's, Lowe's Whse, OfficeMax, Old Navy, Ralph's Foods, Rite Aid, Ross, Target

Interstate 5

N

99 Culver Dr, **E...gas:** Shell/24hr, **food:** Bullwinkle's Rest., Denny's, Starbucks

97 Jeffrey Rd, no facilities

96 Sand Canyon Ave, Old Towne, **W...gas:** 76/Circle K, Denny's, **food:** Jack-in-the-Box, Knollwood Burgers, **lodging:** La Quinta, **other:** Traveland USA RV Park, Irvine RV Ctr

95 CA 133, Laguna Fwy, N to Riverside, S Laguna Beach, no facilities

94b Alton Pkwy, **E...gas:** Shell, **food:** Carl's Jr, Taco Bell, **other:** Costco, OfficeMax, **W...food:** Chang's Bistro, Dave&Buster's, **lodging:** DoubleTree

94a I-405 N(from nb), no facilities

92b Bake Pkwy, same as 92a

92a Lake Forest Dr, Laguna Hills, **E...gas:** Chevron/24hr, Shell/diesel, **food:** Aldo's Italian, Black Angus, Burger King, Diedrich Coffee, Del Taco, Hunter Steaks, IHOP, Jack-in-the-Box, JuiceStop, McDonald's, Mimi's Café, Pizza Hut, Subway, Taco Bell, Teriyaki Japanese, **lodging:** Best Western, Irvine Suites, Travelodge, **other:** MEDICAL CARE, Audi/Jeep, Chevrolet, Ford/Lincoln/Mercury, GMC/Kia, Honda, Isuzu, Jaguar, Mazda, Mercedes/Suzuki, PepBoys, Staples, Subaru, Toyota, VW, **W...gas:** Chevron/24hr, Shell, **food:** Café Italia, Carl's Jr, Coco's, Del Taco, McDonald's, Subway, **lodging:** Comfort Inn, Courtyard, Quality Suites, Travelodge, **other:** AZ Leather, BMW, Books Etc, JC Penney

91 El Toro Rd, **E...gas:** Arco/24hr, Chevron/diesel, Mobil, Shell/diesel, USA, **food:** Arby's, Bakers Square, Baskin-Robbins, Denny's, Fuddrucker's, Jack-in-the-Box, KFC, McDonald's, MegaBurger, Red Lobster, Scarantino's Rest., Souper Salad, Wendy's, **other:** House of Fabrics, K-Mart, Office Depot, SavOn Drug, **W...gas:** Chevron/diesel/24hr, Shell/24hr, 76, **food:** Bennigan's, Biersch Brewery Rest., CA Pizza, Carrows, Coco's, El Torito, Island Burgers, Kings FishHouse, KooRooRoo Kitchen, LoneStar Steaks, Monterey Seafood, Onami Seafood Buffet, Pizza Hut, Trader Joe's, **lodging:** Laguna Hills Lodge, **other:** HOSPITAL, Circuit City, Firestone/auto, JC Penney, Just Tires, Longs Drugs, Macy's, Marshall's, Sears/auto, Walgreen, mall

90 Alicia Pkwy, Mission Viejo, **E...gas:** Chevron/24hr, 76/diesel, **food:** Carl's Jr, Del Taco, Denny's, Little Caesar's, Subway, Wendy's, Winchell's, **other:** Albertson's, America's Tire, Buick/Pontiac/Mazda, Firestone, Mervyn's, Kragen Parts, Target, **W...food:** Togo's

89 La Paz Rd, Mission Viejo, **E...gas:** Arco/24hr, Mobil, UltrMar/repair, **food:** Diedrich's Coffee, KFC, Pizza Hut, Taco Bell, **other:** Albertson's, **W...gas:** Chevron, 76, 7-11, **food:** Claim Jumper Rest., Del Taco, Flamingo Mexican, Jack-in-the-Box, McDonald's, Outback Steaks, Quizno's, Spasso's Italian, Wienerschnitzel, **lodging:** Holiday Inn, **other:** Best Buy, Borders Books&Café, CompUSA, Goodyear/auto, Jo-Ann Fabrics, Winston Tire, to Laguna Niguel Pk

87 Oso Pkwy, Pacific Park Dr, **E...gas:** Chevron/repair, Mobil, 76/repair, **food:** Carl's Jr, **lodging:** Fairfield Inn

86 Crown Valley Pkwy, **E...gas:** Arco, Chevron, 76, **food:** Coco's, Mexican Cantina, **other:** HOSPITAL, Macy's, OfficeMax, mall, **W...gas:** Chevron/diesel, **other:** Aamco

85b Avery Pkwy, **E...gas:** Shell/diesel, **food:** Booster's Grill, Carrow's, Del Taco, Jack-in-the-Box, McDonald's, Sheesh Kabob, **other:** Acura/Volvo, America's Tire, Goodyear, Infiniti, Land Rover, Lexus, Parts+, Staples, **W...gas:** Arco, Shell/diesel/24hr, **food:** A's Burgers, Buffy's Rest., In-n-Out, **lodging:** Laguna Inn, **other:** Firestone/auto, GMC/Cadillac, Mercedes

85a CA 73 N toll, no facilities

83 Junipero Serra Rd, to San Juan Capistrano, **W...gas:** Shell, UltraMar/diesel

82 CA 74, Ortego Hwy, **E...gas:** Chevron/diesel, Shell/repair, 76, **food:** Denny's, **lodging:** Best Western, **other:** MEDICAL CARE, **W...gas:** Arco, Chevron/24hr, **food:** Burger King, Carl's Jr, Del Taco, Jack-in-the-Box, McDonald's, Pedro's Tacos, Walnut Grove Rest., **lodging:** Mission Inn

81 Camino Capistrano, **E...other:** Peugeot/VW, **W...gas:** Chevron, **food:** Harry's Rest., KFC, Starbucks, **other:** Goodyear, Pic'n Sav Foods, Rite Aid, Ross, Von's Food

79 CA 1, Pacific Coast Hwy, Capistrano Bch, Capistrano, **1 mi W...gas:** Arco/24hr, 76, Shell, **food:** A's Burgers, Carl's Jr, Del Taco, Denny's, Jack-in-the-Box, McDonald's, Subway, **lodging:** Dana Point Inn, DoubleTree, Hilton, Ramada Inn, **other:** Chevrolet, Chrysler/Jeep, Honda, Nissan, Saturn, Toyota, USPO

78 Camino de Estrella, San Clemente, **E...gas:** 76/diesel/24hr, **food:** Bakers Square, Big City Bagel, Café Expresso, Carl's Jr, China Well, JuiceStop, Rubio's Grill, Subway, Trader Joe's, **other:** HOSPITAL, Ralph's Foods, SavOn Drug/24hr, Stater Bros Foods, **W...gas:** Arco/diesel, **other:** K-Mart, Las Golondrienas, Kragen Parts, Pic'n Sav Foods

76 Ave Pico, **E...gas:** Mobil, **food:** Carrow's, McDonald's, NY Pizza, **other:** Albertson's, GNC, **W...gas:** Chevron, Shell/diesel, **food:** BurgerStop, Del Taco, Denny's/24hr, Pizza Hut, Stuft Pizza, Subway, Waffle Lady, **lodging:** Country Side Inn, **other:** Books Etc, $Less, Ralph's Foods, SavOn Drug, Staples, USPO

75 Ave Palizada, Ave Presidio, **W...gas:** Arco, UltraMar, 7-11, **food:** Antoine's Café, Baskin-Robbins, KFC, Subway, **lodging:** Holiday Inn, **other:** Albertson's, Ford

Mission Viejo *Capistrano* *San Clemente*

N↑↓S

74 El Camino Real, **E...gas:** Chevron/24hr, **food:** Pedro's Tacos, same as 75, **W...gas:** Mobil, 76, 7-11, **food:** China Taste, FatBurger, KFC, LoveBurger, Taco Bell, Tommy's Rest./24hr, **other:** Kragen Parts, Radio Shack, Ralph's Foods

73 Ave Calafia, Ave Magdalena, **E...gas:** 76, Shell, 7-11, **food:** Beef Cutter Rest., Coco's, El Marianchi Rest., Jack-in-the-Box, Pedro's Tacos, **lodging:** C-Vu Inn, El Rancho Motel, LaVista Inn, Quality Suites, San Clemente Motel, Trade Winds Motel, Travelodge, **other:** Amato Tire, **W...lodging:** San Clemente Inn, **other:** to San Clemente SP

72 Cristianitios Ave, **E...lodging:** San Mateo RV Park/dump, **W...other:** to San Clemente SP

71 Basilone Rd, **W...other:** San Onofre St Beach

67mm weigh sta both lanes

66mm viewpoint sb

62 Las Pulgas Rd, no facilities

59 **Aliso Creek rest area both lanes, full(handicapped)facilities, phone, vending, picnic tables, litter barrels, petwalk, RV dump**

54c Oceanside Harbor Dr, **W...gas:** Chevron, Mobil, **food:** Burger King(1mi), Del Taco, Denny's/24hr, **lodging:** Comfort Inn, Sandman Hotel, Travelodge, The Bridge Motel, **other:** to Camp Pendleton

O
54b Hill St(from sb), to Oceanside, **W...gas:** Mobil, **food:** Carrow's Rest., **lodging:** Comfort Inn

c
e
54a Ca 76 E, Coast Hwy, no facilities

a
53 Mission Ave, Oceanside, **E...gas:** Arco/24hr, Mobil/diesel, 76/LP, **food:** Arby's, Armando's Tacos, Burger King, China Dynasty, El Charrito Mexican, Jack-in-the-Box, KFC, McDonald's, Mission Donuts, Pizza Hut, **lodging:** Econolodge, Ramada Ltd, **other:** CarQuest, NAPA, PepBoys, Valu+ Foods, **W...food:** Carrow's, El Pollo Loco, Mandarin Chinese, Wendy's, **lodging:** GuestHouse Inn, **other:** AutoZone, Grocery Outlet, 99c Store, Office Depot, Radio Shack, Rite Aid

n
s
52 Oceanside Blvd, **E...gas:** Arco, **food:** Domino's, IHOP, McDonald's, Papa John's, Pizza Hut, Rosarita's Café, Subway, Taco Bell, **other:** Boney's Foods, Longs Drug, 98c Store, Ralph's Food, SavOn Drug, Von's Food, CHP, **W...gas:** Shell/24hr, **lodging:** Best Western

i
d
51c Cassidy St(from sb), **W...gas:** Citgo/7-11, Mobil, 76, **other:** HOSPITAL

e
51b CA 78, Vista Way, Escondido, **E...gas:** Chevron/24hr, 76, **food:** Applebee's, Golden Taipei, McDonald's, Mimi's Café, Olive Garden, Tony Roma, **other:** Best Buy, Cost+, JC Penney, Macy's, Marshall's, Mervyn's, Michael's, Robinsons-May, Saturn, Sears/auto, Staples, Starbucks, Stater Bros Foods, Target, Wal-Mart, **W...food:** Hunter Steaks

C
51a Las Flores Dr, no facilities

a
r
50 Elm Ave, Carlsbad Village Dr, **E...gas:** Shell/24hr, **food:** Lotus Thai Bistro, **W...gas:** Carlsbad/LP, Chevron/repair/24hr, 76, UltraMar, **food:** Carl's Jr, Denny's/24hr, Jack-in-the-Box, KFC/Taco Bell, Mikko Japanese, **lodging:** Motel 6, **other:** Albertson's

l
s
49 Tamarack Ave, **E...gas:** Chevron/24hr, Exxon/diesel, **food:** Village Kitchen, **lodging:** Carlsbad Lodge, Super 8, Travel Inn, **other:** GNC, Rite Aid, Von's Foods, **W...gas:** 76/repair/24hr, **food:** Koko Palms Rest.

b
a
d

48 Cannon Rd, Car Country Carlsbad, **E...other:** Acura, Buick, Chevrolet/Cadillac, Ford, Honda, Isuzu, Lexus, Lincoln/Mercury, Mazda, Mercedes, Toyota, VW

47 Carlsbad Blvd, Palomar Airport Rd, **E...gas:** Chevron, Mobil/diesel, Citgo/7-11, **food:** Carl's Jr, Denny's, Hadley Orchard's Foods, IslandsBurgers, Pat&Oscar's Rest., Subway, Strauss Brewery Rest., Taco Bell, TGIFriday, **lodging:** Holiday Inn, **other:** Costco, **W...gas:** Shell/diesel, **food:** ClaimJumper Rest., In-n-Out, Marie Callender's, McDonald's, **lodging:** Hilton, **other:** S Carlsbad St Bch

45 Poinsettia Lane, **W...gas:** Chevron, **food:** El Pollo Loco, Jack-in-the-Box, Panda Buffet, Raintree Grill, Subway, **lodging:** Inn of America, Motel 6, Quality Inn, Ramada, **other:** Ralph's Food, Rite Aid, Volvo

44 La Costa Ave, **E...vista point, **W...gas:** Chevron/diesel

43 Leucadia Blvd, **E...lodging:** Holiday Inn Express, **W...gas:** Shell/autocare, Texaco/diesel

E
41b Encinitas Blvd, **E...gas:** Arco/diesel, Chevron, Exxon, **food:** Chin's Chinese, Coco's, Del Taco, Stuft Pizza, **other:** Albertson's, Chevrolet, Nissan, SavOn Drug, to Quail Botanical Gardens, **W...gas:** Shell, **food:** Denny's, Wendy's, **lodging:** Best Western/rest., Day's Inn

n
c
41a Santa Fe Dr, to Encinitas, **E...gas:** Shell, 7-11/24hr, **food:** Carl's Jr, Papa Tonie's Pizza, **W...gas:**76/Burger King, **food:** NY Pizza, **other:** HOSPITAL, Rite Aid, Von's Foods

i
n
40 Birmingham Dr, **E...gas:** Chevron, Shell, **food:** Taco Bell, **lodging:** Country Inn, **W...gas:** Arco/24hr

i
t
39mm viewpoint sb

a
39 Manchester Ave, **E...gas:** 76, **other:** to MiraCosta College

s
37 Lomas Santa Fe Dr, Solana Bch, **E...food:** Pizza Nova, Samurai Rest., **other:** Ross, Von's Foods, We-R-Fabrics, **W...gas:** Mobil, Shell/diesel, **food:** Carl's Jr, Starbucks, Thai Kitchen, **other:** Discount Tire, Henry's Foods, Marshall's, SavOn Drug, Staples

36 Via de La Valle, Del Mar, **E...gas:** Chevron, Mobil, **food:** Burger King, Chevy's Mexican, KooRoo Kitchen, McDonald's, Milton's Deli, Pasta Pronto, Papachino's Italian, Taste of Thai, Tony Roma's, **other:** Albertson's, **W...gas:** Arco/24hr, Shell/diesel, **food:** Denny's, FishMkt Rest., Red Tracton's Rest., **lodging:** Hilton, **other:** racetrack

34 Del Mar Heights Rd, **E...gas:** Shell/diesel, **W...gas:** Citgo/7-11, **food:** Bloomberg's Rest., Jack-in-the-Box, Mexican Grill, **other:** Longs Drug, Von's Foods

33b Carmel Valley Rd, **E...gas:** Arco, Shell/repair, **food:** Taco Bell, Tio Leo's Mexican, **lodging:** DoubleTree Hotel, Hampton Inn, Marriott

33a CA 56 E, no facilities

31 I-805(from sb), no facilities

29 Genesee Ave, **E...other:** HOSPITAL, **1 mi W...gas**, food, lodging

28b La Jolla Village Dr, **E...food:** Italian Bistro, **lodging:** Embassy Suites, Hyatt, Marriott, **other:** HOSPITAL, to LDS Temple, **W...gas:** Mobil/diesel, **food:** BJ's Grill, CA Pizza, Domino's, El Torito, Islands Burgers, Pasta Bravo, RockBottom Café, Rubio's Grill, TGIFriday, Trader Joe's, **lodging:** Radisson, **other:** HOSPITAL, Marshall's, Radio Shack, Ralph's Foods, Ross, SavOn Drug, Whole Foods

28a Nobel Dr(from nb), **E...lodging:** Hyatt, **other:** LDS Temple, **W...same as 28b

27 Gilman Dr, La Jolla Colony Dr, no facilities

Interstate 5

26b	CA 52 E, Ardath Rd(from nb), no facilities
26a	Ardath Rd(from nb), no facilities
23b	CA 274, Balboa Ave, **1 mi E…gas:** Shell, **food:** Del Taco, **other:** Albertson's, **W…gas:** Citgo/7-11, Mobil, 76/repair, **food:** Arby's, In-n-Out, Wienerschnitzel, **lodging:** Comfort Inn, SleepyTime Motel, Super 8, **other:** HOSPITAL, Ford, Nissan, Plymouth, Toyota, Winston Tire, Mission Bay Pk
23a	Grand Ave, Garnet Ave, **W…other:** Cadillac
22	Clairemont Dr, Mission Bay Dr, **E…gas:** 76, Shell, **food:** Carl's Jr, HomeTown Buffet, Jack-in-the-Box, KFC, McDonald's, Subway, **lodging:** Best Western, **other:** Chevrolet/VW, Rite Aid, **W…to** Sea World Dr
21	Sea World Dr, Tecolote Dr, **E…gas:** Arco, Shell, **other:** Circle K, Firestone, **W…lodging:** Hilton, **other:** Old Town SP
20	I-8, W to Nimitz Blvd, E to El Centro, CA 209 S(from sb), to Rosecrans St, no facilities
19	Old Town Ave, **E…gas:** Arco/24hr, Shell, **lodging:** Ramada Inn, Travelodge
18b	Washington St, **E…lodging:** Comfort Inn
18a	Pacific Hwy Viaduct, Kettner St, no facilities
17b	India St, Front St, Sassafras St, **E…gas:** Mobil, 76, **W…gas:** Exxon, **lodging:** Motel 6, Super 8, **other:** airport, civic ctr
17a	Hawthorn St, Front St, **W…gas:** Exxon, **other:** HOSPITAL
16b	6th Ave, downtown, no facilities
16a	CA 163 N, 10th St, **E…other:** AeroSpace Museum, **W…gas:** Shell, **lodging:** Budget Motel, El Cortez Motel, Holiday Inn, Radisson, Marriott, **other:** HOSPITAL
15c b	CA 94 E(from nb), Pershing Dr, B St, civic ctr
15a	CA 94 E, J St, Imperial Ave(from sb),, no facilities
14b	Cesar Chavez Pkwy, no facilities
14a	CA 75, to Coronado, **W…toll rd to Coronado**
13b	National Ave SD, 28th St, **E…other:** AutoZone, **W…gas:** Shell
13a	CA 15 N, to Riverside, no facilities
12	Main St, National City, no facilities
11b	8th St, National City, **E…gas:** Mobil, Shell/24hr, **lodging:** Budget Inn, EZ 8 Motel, Holiday Inn, Howard Johnson, Ramada Inn, Super 8, Value Inn, **W…gas:** Chevron/diesel, **other:** MEDICAL CARE
11a	Harbor Dr, Civic Center Way, no facilities
10	Bay Marina, 24th St, Mile of Cars Way, **1/2 mi E…food:** Denny's, In-n-Out
9	CA 54 E, no facilities
8b	E St, Chula Vista, **E…gas:** Mobil, **lodging:** Motel 6, **W…food:** Anthony's Fish Grotto, **lodging:** GoodNite Inn
8a	H St, **E…gas:** Arco/diesel, Chevron, 7-11, **other:** HOSPITAL, Dodge, Goodyear, motel
7b	J St(from sb), **W…other:** Marina Pkwy
7a	L St, **E…gas:** Citgo/7-11, 76, Shell/diesel, **food:** Golden Pagoda Chinese, **lodging:** Best Western, **other:** AutoZone, NAPA, Grocery Outlet, Office Depot

San Diego Area *(left margin)*

San Diego Area *(right margin)*

6	Palomar St, **E…gas:** Arco, **food:** China King, Del Taco, HomeTown Buffet, Jack-in-the-Box, KFC, McDonald's, **lodging:** Palomar Inn, **other:** Office Depot, Ralph's Foods, **E on Broadway…food:** Yoshinoya, **other:** Costco, Michael's, Ross, Target
5b	Main St, to Imperial Beach, **E…gas:** Arco, **food:** AZ Chinese, Garcia's Mexican
5a	CA 75(from sb), Palm Ave, to Imperial Beach, **E…gas:** Arco, 7-11, **food:** Papa John's, Tasty China, **W…gas:** Arco, Citgo/7-11, Mobil, Shell/repair/24hr, **food:** Boll Weevil Diner, Burger King, Carl's Jr, Carrow's, El Pollo Loco, Lydia's Mexican, McDonald's, Rally's, Red Hawk Steaks, Roberto's Mexican, Subway, Taco Bell, Wienerschnitzel, **lodging:** Super 8, **other:** AutoZone, CarQuest, Goodyear/auto, Home Depot, Kragen Parts, Mervyn's, 99c Store, SavOn Drug, Von's Foods
4	Coronado Ave(from sb), **E…gas:** Chevron/service, Shell/service, 7-11, **food:** Denny's, Taco Bell, **lodging:** EZ 8 Motel, San Diego Inn, **W…gas:** Arco/24hr, Shell/diesel/repair, **lodging:** Day's Inn, **other:** to Border Field SP
3	CA 905, Tocayo Ave, **W…gas:** Citgo/7-11
2	Dairy Mart Rd, **E…gas:** Arco/24hr, Circle K, **food:** Burger King, Carl's Jr, Coco's, McDonald's, Roberto's Mexican, **lodging:** Americana Inn, Ramada Ltd, Super 8, Valli-Hi Motel, **other:** CarQuest, Radio Shack, Pacifica RV Resort
1b	Via de San Ysidro, **E…gas:** Chevron, Exxon, Mobil, 76, **food:** Denny's, Si Senor Mexican, **other:** Max's Foods, NAPA, **W…gas:** Chevron, **food:** Denny's, KFC, **lodging:** Economy Inn, International Inn/RV park, Motel 6
1a	I-805 N(from nb), Camino de la Plaza(from sb), **E…food:** Burger King, El Pollo Loco, Jack-in-the-Box, KFC, McDonald's, Subway, **lodging:** Flamingo Motel, Gateway Inn, Holiday Motel, Travelodge, **W…other:** factory outlet, border parking
0	US/Mexico Border, California state line, customs, I-5 begins/ends

CALIFORNIA
Interstate 8

Exit #	Services
	Yuma
172.5mm	California/Arizona state line, Colorado River, Pacific/Mountain time zone
172	4th Ave, Yuma, **N**...Ft Yuma Casino, **S**...**gas:** Chevron, 76/Circle K, Shell/24hr, **food:** Domino's, Jack-in-the-Box, Little Caesar's, Mi Rancho Mexican, Yuma Landing Rest., **lodging:** Best Western, Interstate 8 Inn, Yuma Inn, **other:** Rivers Edge RV Park, to Yuma SP
170	Winterhaven Dr, **S**...Rivers Edge RV Park
166	CA 186, Algodones Rd, Andrade, **S**...to Mexico
165mm	CA Insp Sta
164	Sidewinder Rd, **N**...st patrol, **S**...**gas:** Shell/LP, **other:** Pilot Knob RV Park
159	CA 34, Ogilby Rd, to Blythe, no facilities
156	Grays Well Rd, **N**...Imperial Dunes RA
155mm	**rest area both lanes(exits left), full(handicapped)facilities, picnic tables, litter barrels, petwalk**
151	Gordons Well, no facilities
146	Brock Research Ctr Rd, no facilities
143	CA 98, Midway Well, to Calexico, no facilities
131	CA 115, VanDerLinden Rd, to Holtville, **5 mi N**...gas, food, lodging, RV camping
128	Bonds Corner Rd, no facilities
125	Orchard Rd, Holtville, **4 mi N**...gas/diesel, food
120	Bowker Rd, no facilities
118b a	CA 111, to Calexico, **1 mi N**...**gas:** Shell/diesel/café, **other:** RV park
116	Dogwood Rd, **N**...**other:** RV camping
115	CA 86, 4th St, El Centro, **N**...**gas:** Arco/24hr, Chevron, Citgo/7-11/diesel, Shell/diesel, USA, **food:** Carl's Jr, Fong Chinese, Foster's Freeze, Jack-in-the-Box, McDonald's, Rally's, **lodging:** Holiday Inn Express, Motel 6, **other:** El Sol Foods, Firestone/auto, Goodyear/auto, Ford/Lincoln/Mercury, U-Haul, radiators, **S**...**gas:** Mobil/A&W/Subway/Pizza Hut/diesel/@, **food:** Taco Bell, **lodging:** Best Western, Casa Real Inn, EZ 8 Motel, **other:** Buick/Cadillac/Pontiac, Chevrolet, Chrysler/Plymouth/Dodge/Jeep, Honda, Max Foods, Desert Trails RV Park
	El Centro
114	Imperial Ave, El Centro, **N**...**gas:** Chevron/service, Citgo/7-11/diesel, Shell, USA/diesel, **food:** Del Taco, Denny's/24hr, Domino's, KFC, McDonald's, Pizza Hut, TasteeFreez Burgers, **lodging:** Ramada Inn, **other:** MEDICAL CARE, Vacation Inn/RV Park, Kragen Parts, st patrol, **1-3 mi N**...**gas:** Arco/24hr, **food:** Burger King, Carl's Jr, Carrow's, Church's, Domino's, 4Seasons Buffet, Golden Corral, Jack-in-the-Box, Papa John's, Sizzler, Taco Bell, Wendy's, **lodging:** Brunners Inn, Day's Inn, Super 8, **other:** Aamco, Albertson's, Costco/gas, Goodyear/auto, K-Mart, Mervyn's, PepBoys, Rite Aid, Sears/auto, Staples, Toyota, Wal-Mart, Winston Tire
111	Forrester Rd, to Westmorland, no facilities
108mm	**Sunbeam Rest Area both lanes, full(handicapped)facilities, phone, picnic tables, litter barrels, petwalk, RV dump**
107	Drew Rd, Seeley, **N**...RV camping, **S**...RV camping

101	Dunaway Rd, Imperial Valley, elev 0 ft, **N**...st prison
89	Imperial Hwy, CA 98, Ocotillo, **N**...**gas:** Shell/diesel, Lazy Lizard Saloon, Ocotillo Motel/RV Park, USPO, **S**...**gas:** 76/diesel/repair, **food:** Desert Kitchen, **other:** RV camping
87	CA 98(from eb), to Calexico, no facilities
81mm	runaway truck ramp, eb
80	Mountain Springs Rd, no facilities
77	In-Ko-Pah Park Rd, **N**...phone, towing
75mm	brake insp area eb, phone
73	Jacumba, **S**...**gas:** Shell/diesel/towing/24hr, **other:** NAPA, RV camping
65	CA 94, Boulevard, to Campo, **S**...**gas:** MtnTop/diesel, **food:** Burning Tree Rest., **lodging:** Buena Vista Motel, to McCain Valley RA
63mm	Tecate Divide, elev 4140 ft
61	Crestwood Rd, Live Oak Springs, **S**...**food:** Country Broiler Rest., **lodging:** Live Oak Sprs Country Inn, **other:** FoodSource/diesel/24hr, Vacation Inn/RV Park, RV camping, info
62mm	Crestwood Summit, elev 4190 ft
54	Kitchen Creek Rd, Cameron Station, **S**...food, RV camping
51	rd 1, Buckman Spgs Rd, to Lake Morena, **S**...gas/diesel/LP, food, lodging, RV camping, Lake Morena CP(7mi), Potrero CP(19mi), **rest area both lanes, full(handicapped)facilities, phone, picnic tables, litter barrels, petwalk, RV dump**
47	rd 1, Sunrise Hwy, Laguna Summit, elev 4055 ft, **N**...to Laguna Mtn RA
45	Pine Valley, Julian, **N**...**food:** Major's Diner, **other:** to Cuyamaca Rancho SP
44mm	Pine Valley Creek
42mm	elev 4000 ft
40	CA 79, Japatul Rd, Descanso, **N**...to Cuyamaca Rancho SP, gas, food
37mm	vista point eb, elev 3000 ft
36	E Willows, **N**...Alpine Sprs RV Park, Viejas Indian Res, casino
33	W Willows Rd, to Alpine, **N**...Alpine Sprs RV Park, Viejas Res, casino, **S**...ranger sta
31mm	elev 2000 ft
30	Tavern Rd, to Alpine, **N**...**gas:** Shell/diesel, UltrMar/diesel, **S**...**gas:** 76/Circle K, Shell, **food:** BBQ, Breadbasket Rest., Carl's Jr, La Carreta Mexican, LJ Silver, Mediterraneo Italian, Panda Machi, **lodging:** Countryside Inn, **other:** MEDICAL CARE, Alpine Mkt Foods, Radio Shack, Rite Aid, city park
27	Dunbar Lane, Harbison Canyon, **N**...**other:** RV camping
25mm	elev 1000 ft
24mm	map stop wb, phone
23	Lake Jennings Pk Rd, Lakeside, **N**...**gas:** Arco/Jack-in-the-Box/diesel/24hr, to Lake Jennings CP, **other:** RV camping, **S**...**gas:** Citgo/7-11, **food:** Burger King, Jilberto's Tacos, Marechiaro's Pizza, **other:** Eitsmoes RV Ctr, Flinn Sprgs CP

Interstate 8

E ↕ W

El Cajon

22	Los Coches Rd, Lakeside, **N...gas:** 76/Circle K, Citgo/7-11, Mobil/service, **food:** Laposta Mexican, Pizza Pro, **other:** PillCo Drug, RV camping, **S...gas:** Shell/diesel, **food:** Denny's, McDonald's, Subway, Taco Bell, **other:** Radio Shack, Von's Foods, Wal-Mart/auto
20b	Greenfield Dr, to Crest, **N...gas:** Chevron/diesel, Exxon/diesel/24hr, Shell, 7-11/YumYum, **food:** Janet's Café, McDonald's, Panchos Taco, **other:** HOSPITAL, AutoZone, Ford, 99c Store, RV camping, auto repair, st patrol, **S...gas:** Mobil/LP
20a	E Main St(from wb, no EZ return), **N...food:** Main St Grill, Pernicano's Italian, **lodging:** Budget Inn, Embasadora Motel, **other:** Ford, Vactioner RV Park, **S...food:** Coco's, **other:** Cadillac
19	2nd St, CA 54, El Cajon, **N...gas:** Arco/24hr, Chevron, Regent/diesel, **food:** Taco Shop, **other:** Parts+, Von's Foods, **S...gas:** 76, Shell/A&W/diesel, **food:** Arby's, Burger King, Carl's Jr, DQ, Golden Corral, IHOP, Jack-in-the-Box, KFC, McDonald's, Pizza Hut, Subway, Taco Bell, **other:** Firestone/auto, Ralph's Foods, Radio Shack, Rite Aid, Walgreen
18	Mollison Ave, El Cajon, **N...gas:** Chevron, **food:** Denny's, **lodging:** Best Western, Plaza Inn, **S...gas:** Arco/24hr, **food:** Taco Bell, **lodging:** Super 8, Valley Motel
17c	Magnolia Ave, CA 67(from wb), to Santee, **N...food:** LJ Silver, **other:** Albertson's, JC Penney, K-Mart, mall, same as 19, **S...gas:** Shell/service, **food:** Mexican Rest., Perry's Café, Wienerschnitzel, **lodging:** MidTown Motel, Motel 6, Travelodge, **other:** Nudo's Drug
17b	CA 67(from eb), **N...other:** JC Penney, Sears/auto, mall, same as 19 & 21
17a	Johnson Ave(from eb), **N...food:** Applebee's, Boston Mkt, Burger King, LJ Silver, Subway, **other:** Albertson's, Chevrolet, Home Depot, Honda, JC Penney, K-Mart, Marshall's, Mervyn's, Rite Aid, Robinson-May, Sears/auto, mall, **S...other:** Aamco, Isuzu, Saturn
16	Main St, **N...gas:** Arco/24hr, 7-11, **food:** Denny's/24hr, Sombrero Mexican, **lodging:** ThriftLodge, **other:** Lexus, **S...gas:** 76, Chevron, **other:** Nissan, brakes/transmissions
15	El Cajon Blvd(from eb), **N...lodging:** Day's Inn, **S...gas:** Mobil/diesel, Shell, **food:** BBQ, **other:** Chrysler/Plymouth
14c	Severin Dr, Fuerte Dr(from wb), **N...gas:** Arco/24hr, Mobil, 7-11, **food:** Anthony's Fish Rest., Charcoal House Rest., **lodging:** Econo Inn, Holiday Inn Express, **S...food:** Brigantine Seafood Rest.
14b a	CA 125, to CA 94, no facilities

San Diego Area

13b	Jackson Dr, Grossmont Blvd, **N...gas:** Arco/24hr, Chevron, Mobil, Shell, 7-11/24hr, **food:** Arby's, Burger King, Chili's, Chuck-eCheese, Fuddrucker's, KFC, Olive Garden, Red Lobster, Taco Bell, **other:** Barnes&Noble, Cost+, Dodge, Kragen Parts, Macy's, Staples, Target, USPO, mall, **S...food:** Chile Bandido, Jack-in-the-Box, **other:** Circuit City, Discount Tire, Firestone/auto, Hyundai, Isuzu, Ralph's Foods, VW
13a	Spring St(from eb), El Cajon Blvd(from wb), **N...other:** Dodge/Kia, Jeep, **S...lodging:** Travelodge
12	Fletcher Pkwy, to La Mesa, **N...gas:** Shell, 7-11, **food:** Bakers Square, Boston Mkt, Chili's, McDonald's, **lodging:** EZ 8 Motel, **other:** MEDICAL CARE, Albertson's, Costco, **S...food:** La Salsa Mexican, **lodging:** Motel 6, **other:** Chevrolet, RV Park
11	70th St, Lake Murray Blvd, **N...gas:** Shell, **food:** Pepper's Mexican, Subway, **other:** MEDICAL CARE, **S...gas:** Mobil, Shell/diesel/repair, 7-11, **food:** Aiken's Deli, Denny's, La Casa Maria Mexican, **other:** HOSPITAL, Marie Callender's, **1/4 mi S...**multiple services on El Cajon Blvd
10	College Ave, **N...gas:** Chevron, **other:** Katz's Mkt, USPO, **S...other:** MEDICAL CARE, to San Diego St U
9	Waring Rd, **N...food:** Nicolosi's Italian, **lodging:** Best Inn, Good Nite Inn, Madrid Suites
8	Fairmont Ave(7 from eb), to Mission Gorge Rd, **N...gas:** Arco/24hr, Citgo/7-11, Mobil/diesel, Shell, UltraMar/diesel, **food:** Arby's, Boll Weevil Diner, Boston Mkt, Burger King, Carl's Jr, Chili's, Coco's, Happy Chef, Jack-in-the-Box, El Pollo Loco, KFC, Krazy Pete's Diner, McDonald's, Rally's, Subway, Taco Bell, Tio Leo's Mexican, **lodging:** Super 8, **other:** HOSPITAL, Discount Tire, Home Depot, Longs Drugs, NAPA, Radio Shack, Rite Aid, Toyota, Von's Foods
7b a	I-15 N, CA 15 S, to 40th St
6b	I-805, N to LA, S to Chula Vista
6a	Texas St, Qualcomm Way, **N...gas:** Chevron, same as 5

CALIFORNIA
Interstate 8

5	Mission Ctr Rd, **N…gas:** Chevron, **food:** Bennigan's, Chevy's Mexican, Dave&Buster's, Hogi Yogi, Hooters, In-n-Out, Mandarin Cuisine, Outback Steaks, Quizno's, Taco Bell, Togo's, **lodging:** Marriott, **other:** Best Buy, Borders Books&Café, Chevrolet, Crown Books, Ford, Lincoln/Mercury, Loehmann's, Macy's, Michael's, Nordstrom Rack, Old Navy, Robinson-May, Sak's Off 5th, Staples, mall, **S…gas:** Arco/24hr, **food:** Benihana, Denny's, Todai Rest., Wendy's, **lodging:** Comfort Inn, Hilton, Radisson, Ramada Ltd, Red Lion Inn, **other:** Chrysler/Plymouth, Dodge, GMC/Pontiac, Mazda, Subaru
4c b	CA 163, Cabrillo Frwy, **S…**to downtown, zoo
4a	Hotel Circle Dr(from eb), CA 163 (from wb)
3a	Hotel Circle, Taylor St, **N…gas:** Chevron, **food:** DW Ranch Rest., Hunter Steaks, **lodging:** Best Western Hanalei, Comfort Suites, Handlery Hotel, Motel 6, Red Lion Hotel, Town&Country Motel, **other:** cinema, golf, **S…gas:** Chevron, **food:** Albie's Rest., Valley Kitchen, **lodging:** Best Western, Econolodge, Extended Stay America, Hawthorn Suties, Holiday Inn, Hotel Circle Inn, Howard Johnson, King's Inn/rest., Quality Resort, Ramada Inn, Regency Plaza, Travelodge, Vagabond Inn
2c	Morena Blvd(from wb)
2b	I-5, N to LA, S to San Diego
2a	Rosecrans St(from wb), CA 209, **S…gas:** Chevron, **food:** Burger King, Del Taco, Denny's, In-n-Out, Jack-in-the-Box, McDonald's, Perry's Café, Rally's, **lodging:** Arena Inn, Best Western, Day's Inn, Holiday Inn, Howard Johnson, Quality Inn, Rio Motel, Super 8, **other:** Chrysler/Jeep, Circuit City, Goodyear/auto, House of Fabrics, Pic'n Save, Staples, SaveOn Drug
1	W Mission Bay Blvd, Sports Arena Blvd(from wb), **N…**to SeaWorld, **S…food:** Arby's, Coco's, Embers Café, McDonald's, **lodging:** EZ 8 Motel, Holiday Inn Express, **other:** Home Depot
0mm	I-8 begins/ends on Sunset Cliffs Blvd, **N…**Mission Bay Park, **1/4 mi W…gas:** Mobil/service, Shell, **food:** Anthony's Rest., Jack-in-the-Box, Kaiserhof Deli

Interstate 10

Exit #	Services
245mm	California/Arizona state line, Colorado River, Pacific/Mountain time zone
244mm	inspection sta wb
243	Riviera Dr, **S…other:** Riviera RV Camp
241	US 95, Intake Blvd, Blythe, **N…gas:** Shell, UltraMar, **food:** Steaks'n Cakes Rest., **lodging:** Best Western, Desert Winds Motel, Travelers Inn Express, **other:** diesel repair/24hr, to Needles, **S…**McIntyre Park
240	7th St, **N…gas:** Chevron/service, EZ, **food:** Blimpie, Foster's Freeze, **lodging:** Astro Motel, Blue Line Motel, Blythe Inn, Budget Inn, Comfort Suites, Dunes Motel, **other:** MEDICAL CARE, Albertson's, AutoZone, Chrysler/Dodge/Jeep, Ford, Rite Aid, RV repair/LP

239	Lovekin Blvd, Blythe, **N…gas:** Mobil/Subway/diesel, Shell, **food:** Carl's Jr, Del Taco, Jack-in-the-Box, La Casita Dos Mexican, McDonald's, Pizza Hut, Popeye's, Sizzler, **lodging:** Best Value Inn, Best Western, Comfort Inn, EZ 8 Motel, Hampton Inn, Legacy Inn, Royal Pacific Inn, **other:** MEDICAL CARE, Goodyear, K-Mart, Radio Shack, **S…gas:** Arco/diesel/24hr, Chevron/diesel/24hr/@, 76/diesel, Shell/DQ, UltraMar, **food:** Burger King, Denny's, KFC, Townes Square Café/24hr, Taco Bell, **lodging:** Holiday Inn Express, Motel 6, Super 8, **other:** Chevrolet/Pontiac/Buick/Cadillac, city park/RV dump
236	CA 78, Neighbours Blvd, to Ripley, **N…gas:** Shell/service, **S…**to Cibola NWR
232	Mesa Dr, **N…gas:** Chevron, 76/diesel/rest./24hr, **S…gas:** Mesa Verde/diesel
231	weigh sta wb
222	Wileys Well Rd, **N…rest area both lanes, full(handicapped)facilities, phone, picnic tables, litter barrels, petwalk, S…**to st prison
217	Ford Dry Lake Rd, no facilities
201	Corn Springs Rd, no facilities
192	CA 177, Rice Rd, Desert Center, to Lake Tamarisk, **N…gas:** Stanco/diesel/repair/24hr, **food:** Family Café, **other:** USPO, camping
189	Eagle Mtn Rd, no facilities
182	Red Cloud Rd, no facilities
177	Hayfield Rd, no facilities
173	Chiriaco Summit, **N…gas:** Chevron/diesel/café/24hr, **other:** Patton Museum, truck/tire repair
168	to Twentynine Palms, to Mecca, Joshua Tree NM, **N…**wildlife viewing
162	frontage rd, no facilities
159mm	**Cactus City Rest Area both lanes, full(handicapped)facilities, picnic tables, litter barrels, petwalk**
156mm	0 ft elevation
146	Dillon Rd, to CA 86, to CA 111 S, Coachella, **N…gas:** Chevron/24hr, Loves/Carl's Jr/diesel/24hr/@, Shell/24hr, **S…gas:** TA/Arco/Taco Bell/TCBY/diesel/24hr/@, Shell/Jack-in-the-Box, **other:** casino
145	(from eb), CA 86 S
144	CA 111 N, CA 86 S, Indio, **N…lodging:** Holiday Inn Express, **other:** Classic RV Park, Fantasy Sprgs Casino, **1 mi S…other:** Audi/VW, Chevrolet, Ford/Lincoln/Mercury, Isuzu, Mazda, Nissan
143	Jackson St, Indio, **S…gas:** Circle K, **other:** Big A Parts, NAPA, auto repair
142	Monroe St, Central Indio, **N…other:** RV camping, **S…gas:** Circle K, 76, Shell/diesel/LP, **food:** Alicia's Mexican, Carrow's, Denny's, In-n-Out(1mi), **lodging:** Best Western, Comfort Inn, Holiday Motel, Motel 6, Quality Inn, Super 8, **other:** HOSPITAL, Target, auto/transmissions
139	Jefferson St, Indio Blvd, **N…other:** RV camping, hwy patrol, **2 mi S…lodging:** Best Western, Motel 6

Interstate 10

E
W

Palm Sprgs

Banning

137	Washington St, Country Club Dr, to Indian Wells, **N...gas:** Arco/24hr, **food:** Burger King, Coco's, Del Taco, **lodging:** Comfort Suites, Motel 6, **other:** Buick/Pontiac/GMC, Ford/Lincoln/Mercury, Honda, Toyota, U-Haul, 10k Trails RV Park, **S...gas:** Mobil/diesel, 76/Circle K, **food:** Carl's Jr, Lili's Chinese, Subway, **other:** MEDICAL CARE, Goodyear/auto
134	Cook St, to Indian Wells, **S...lodging:** Courtyard, Residence Inn, **other:** Emerald Desert RV Resort
131	Monterey Ave, Thousand Palms, **N...gas:** Arco/24hr, **food:** Jack-in-the-Box, **S...food:** IHOP, Taco Bell, **other:** Costco/gas, Home Depot
130	Ramon Rd, Bob Hope Dr, **N...gas:** Chevron/24hr, ⚒/Flying J/diesel/LP/rest./24hr/@, Mobil/diesel, UltraMar, **food:** Carl's Jr, Del Taco, Denny's, In-n-Out, McDonald's, **lodging:** Red Roof Inn, **other:** truckwash, **S...other:** HOSPITAL, Agua Caliente Casino/rest.
126	Date Palm Dr, Rancho Mirage, **S...gas:** Arco/24hr, UltraMar
123	Gene Autry Tr, Palm Dr, to Desert Hot Sprgs, **N...gas:** Arco, **other:** camping, **3 mi S...**to Gene Autry Trail
120	Indian Ave, to N Palm Sprgs, **N...gas:** 76/Circle K, Denny's, **food:** Le Chiquita Tacos, **lodging:** Motel 6, **S...gas:** Chevron, Pilot/DQ/Wendy's/diesel/24hr/@, **food:** Jack-in-the-Box, **other:** HOSPITAL
117	CA 62, to Yucca Valley, Twentynine Palms, to Joshua Tree NM
114	Whitewater, many windmills
113mm	**rest area both lanes, full(handicapped)facilities, phone, picnic tables, litter barrels**
112	CA 111(from eb), to Palm Springs, **S...food:** Outback Steaks(9mi)
111	Verbenia Ave, no facilities
106	Main St, to Cabazon, **N...gas:** Shell/diesel, **food:** Burger King, Denny's, **S...gas:** Arco/diesel/24hr
104	Cabazon, **N...gas:** Shell/A&W/diesel/24hr, **food:** Coco's, **other:** Premium Outlets/famous brands, Hadley Orchard Fruits, Morongo Casino/rest.
103	Fields Rd, **N...gas:** Chevron, **food:** McDonald's, **other:** Premium Outlets/famous brands, Morongo Reservation/casino
102.5mm	Banning weigh sta both lanes
102	Ramsey St(from wb), no facilities
101	Hargrave St, Banning, **N...gas:** Shell/diesel/LP, **other:** Parts+, transmissions
100	CA 243, 8th St, Banning, **N...gas:** Chevron, **food:** Ahloo Chinese, Banning Burger, Carolina Seafood, Wing Chinese Garden, **other:** MEDICAL CARE, My Oriental Mkt, Star Parts, **S...other:** RV camping
99	22nd St, to Ramsey St, **N...gas:** Arco/24hr, Mobil, **food:** Carl's Jr, Carrow's, Chelo's Tacos, Del Taco, KFC, McDonald's, Pizza Hut, Sizzler, Starbucks, Taco Bell, Wendy's, **lodging:** Day's Inn, Hacienda Inn, Super 8, Travelodge, **other:** Banning RV Ctr, Ford, Plymouth/Jeep/Dodge, Winston Tire

Beaumont

98	Sunset Ave, Banning, **N...gas:** Chevron/diesel, UltraMar/24hr, **food:** Domino's/Donut Factory, Gus Jr #7 Burger, Subway, **other:** AutoZone, Chevrolet, Radio Shack, Rite Aid, Save-U Foods
96	Highland Springs Ave, **N...gas:** Arco/24hr, Chevron, UltraMar/diesel, **food:** Burger King, Denny's, Guy's Italian, Jack-in-the-Box, Little Caesar's, Subway, **other:** Food4Less, Kragen Parts, Radio Shack, Stater Bros Foods, Walgreen, **S...gas:** Arco/24hr, **food:** Baskin-Robbins, Carl's Jr, **other:** Albertson's, K-Mart, Rite Aid, hwy patrol
95	Pennsylvania Ave, Beaumont, **N...gas:** Circle K, **food:** ABC Rest., Rusty Lantern Rest., **lodging:** Windsor Motel, **other:** Miller's RV Ctr, Tom's RV Ctr
94	CA 79, Beaumont, **N...gas:** Arco, 76, **food:** Baker's DriveThru, Gus Burgers, McDonald's, El Rancho Steaks, YumYum Donuts/24hr, **lodging:** Best Western, Budget Host, **S...food:** Denny's, **other:** RV camping
93	CA 60 W, to Riverside, no facilities
92	San Timoteo Canyon Rd, Oak Valley Pkwy, **N...golf**, **S...golf**
91mm	**rest area wb, full(handicapped)facilities, phone, picnic tables, litter barrels, petwalk**
90	Cherry Valley Blvd, no facilities
89	Singleton Rd(from wb), to Calimesa, no facilities
88	Calimesa Blvd, **N...gas:** Arco/24hr, Chevron/Burger King/diesel, Shell, **food:** McDonald's, Subway, Taco Bell, **lodging:** Calimesa Inn, **other:** Stater Bros Foods, bank, **S...food:** Big Boy, Jack-in-the-Box
87	County Line Rd, to Yucaipa, **N...gas:** FasTrip/gas, Shell/diesel, **food:** Del Taco, **lodging:** Calimesa Inn, **other:** auto repair/tires
86mm	**Wildwood Rest Area eb, full(handicapped)facilities, phone, picnic tables, litter barrels, petwalk**
85	Live Oak Canyon Rd, Oak Glen, no facilities
83	Yucaipa Blvd, **N...gas:** Arco/24hr, Chevron, **food:** Baker's DriveThru
82	Wabash Ave(from wb), no facilities
81	Redlands Blvd, Ford St, **S...gas:** 76

CALIFORNIA
Interstate 10

E ↑ **W**

80   Cypress Ave, University St, **N...**HOSPITAL, to U of Redlands

79b a   CA 38, 6ᵗʰ St, Orange St, Redlands, **N...gas:** Arco, Chevron, **food:** Redland Rest., Ricky's Mexican, **lodging:** Budget Inn, Stardust Motel, **other:** Goodyear, Stater Bros Foods, Viking Tire, **S...gas:** 76, Shell, **food:** Boston Mkt, **other:** Albertson's, Kragen Parts, Lincoln/Mercury, NAPA, Office Depot, Von's Foods

77c   (77b from wb)Tennessee St, **N...other:** Home Depot, **S...gas:** Shell, **food:** Arby's, Bakers DriveThru, Burger King, Carl's Jr, Coco's, El Pollo Loco, Foster's Donuts, Papa John's, Shakey's Pizza, Subway, Taco Bell, Vince's Spaghetti, **lodging:** Best Western, Dynasty Suites, **other:** Ford, Tri-City Mall, USPO

77b   (77c from wb)CA 30, to Highlands, **S...**to Tri-City Mall

77a   Alabama St, **N...gas:** Chevron, **food:** Denny's, Tom's Chiliburgers, **lodging:** Motel 6, 7 West Motel, Super 8, **other:** Ford, VW, U-Haul, **S...gas:** Chevron, Shell/diesel, **food:** Del Taco, IHOP, McDonald's, Nick's Burgers, Zabella's Mexican, **lodging:** Best Western, GoodNite Inn, **other:** Aamco, Chief Parts, Chevrolet, Goodyear/auto, Hyundai, K-Mart, Longs Drug, Mervyn's, Nissan, PepBoys, Pic'n Sav Foods, Ross, Toyota, Tri-City Mall

76   California St, **N...other:** museum, **S...gas:** Arco/24hr, 76, Shell/LP/24hr, **food:** Applebee's, Jack-in-the-Box, Jose's Mexican, **other:** Food4Less, Wal-Mart/auto, Winston Tire, RV camping

75   Mountain View Ave, Loma Linda, **N...gas:** Mobil/diesel, **S...food:** FarmerBoys Burgers, Lupe's Mexican, Subway

74   Tippecanoe Ave, Anderson St, **N...gas:** Arco, **food:** Denny's, In-n-Out, **other:** Costco/gas, Staples, **S...gas:** 76/diesel, **food:** Baker's DriveThru, Blimpie, Del Taco, HomeTown Buffet, KFC, Kool Kactus Café, Napoli Italian, Taco Bell, Wienerschnitzel, **other:** Audi, Harley-Davidson, Honda, Jaguar, Saab, Saturn, transmissions, to Loma Linda U

73b a   Waterman Ave, **N...gas:** 76, Shell/diesel/24hr, **food:** Black Angus, Bobby McGee's, Beef Bowl Chinese, Chili's, Coco's, El Torito, IHOP/24hr, Lotus Garden Chinese, Mimi's Café, Olive Garden, Outback Steaks, Red Lobster, Sizzler, Souplantation, Starbucks, TGIFriday, Thai Garden, Tony Roma, Yamazato Japanese, **lodging:** Comfort Inn, EZ 8 Motel, Hilton, La Quinta, Super 8, Travelodge, **other:** Best Buy, Circuit City, CompUSA, Home Depot, Office Depot, OfficeMax, Sam's Club, **S...gas:** Arco/24hr, Beacon/diesel/rest., **food:** Burger King, Carl's Jr, Gus Jr Burger #8, McDonald's, Popeye's, Taco Bell, **lodging:** Motel 6, **other:** Staples, Camping World RV Service/supplies

72   I-215, CA 91, no facilities

71   Mt Vernon Ave, Sperry Ave, **N...gas:** Arco/24hr, Colton Trkstp/diesel/LP/rest./@, **food:** Peppersteak Rest., **lodging:** Colony Inn, **other:** brake/muffler, repair

70b   9ᵗʰ St, **N...gas:** Mobil, **food:** Baskin-Robbins, Burger King, Carrow's Rest./24hr, Denny's, Jeremiah's Steaks, KFC, LaVilla Mexican, McDonald's, P&G's Burgers, Piccadilly's, Taco Bell, **lodging:** ThriftLodge, **other:** Parts+, Stater Bros Foods

70a   Rancho Ave, **N...gas:** Arco/diesel, **food:** Antonio's Pizza, Del Taco, Diane's Coffee, Wienerschnitzel

69   Pepper Dr, **N...gas:** Shell, **food:** Baker's DriveThru, **other:** Acacia RV, Ford

68   Riverside Ave, to Rialto, **N...gas:** Arco/24hr, Chevron, 10 Trkstp/diesel, **food:** Burger King, China Palace, Coco's, HomeTown Buffet, Izumi Japanese, Jack-in-the-Box, McDonald's, Taco Joe's, **lodging:** Best Western, Rialto Motel, Ross, **other:** Wal-Mart, diesel repair, **S...gas:** Cardlock Fuels/diesel

66   Cedar Ave, to Bloomington, **N...gas:** Arco/24hr, Chevron, Mobil, **food:** Baker's DriveThru, Burger King, FarmerBoys Burgers, **other:** USPO, **S...gas:** Citgo/7-11

64   Sierra Ave, to Fontana, **N...gas:** Arco/24hr, Mobil, Shell, **food:** Applebee's, Arby's, Burger King, China Cook, ChuckeyCheese, DQ, Denny's, Del Taco, In-n-Out, Jack-in-the-Box, KFC, La Buffa Mexican, McDonald's, Millie's Kitchen, Papa John's, Pizza Hut/Taco Bell, Popeye's, Spires Rest., Subway, Wienerschnitzel, **lodging:** Comfort Inn, Econolodge, Motel 6, **other:** Aamco, **other:** HOSPITAL, Albertson's, Chevrolet, $Tree, Food4Less, Goodyear/auto, Honda/GMC, Kia, KidsRUs, K-Mart, Kragen Parts, Mazda, Nissan, PepBoys, Pic'n Sav Foods, Radio Shack, Rite Aid, SavOn Drug, Stater Bros Foods, Winston Tire, **S...gas:** Circle K, **food:** Burger Basket, China Buffet, Mervyn's, **other:** Ross, Target

63   Citrus Ave, **N...gas:** 76, UltarMar/gas, **food:** Baker's DriveThru, Taqueria Mexican, **other:** Ford

61   Cherry Ave, **N...gas:** Arco/24hr, Chevron/Taco Bell, Mobil/diesel/24hr, **food:** Carl's Jr, Jack-in-the-Box, **lodging:** Circle Inn Motel, **other:** Ford Trucks, **S...gas:** 3 Sisters Trkstp/diesel/@, 76/Circle K, **other:** Peterbilt

59   Etiwanda Ave, Valley Blvd, no facilities

58b a   I-15, N to Barstow, S to San Diego

57   Milliken Ave, **N...gas:** Arco, Chevron, Mobil/Subway/diesel, 76/Del Taco/diesel, Shell/diesel, **food:** Burger King, Carl's Jr, Coco's, CoffeeBean, Cucina Italian, Dave&Buster's, FoodCourt, In-n-Out, McDonald's, NY Grill, RainForest Café, Rubio's Rest., Tokyo Japanese, Wendy's, Wienerschnitzel, Wolfgang Puck Café, **lodging:** AmeriSuites, Country Suites, **other:** America's Tire, JC Penney, Sam's Club, mall, **S...gas:** TA/76/diesel/rest./24hr/@, **other:** RV Ctr

56   Haven Ave, Rancho Cucamonga, **N...gas:** Mobil, Benihana, **food:** Black Angus, Crabby's Seafood, El Torito, Quizno's, Tony Roma, **lodging:** Extended Stay America, Hilton, Holiday Inn, La Quinta, **S...food:** Panda Chinese, TGIFriday, **lodging:** Fairfield Inn

55b a   Holt Blvd, to Archibald Ave, **N...gas:** Circle K, Mobil/diesel, **food:** Burger Town, Joey's Pizza, Subway, **other:** MEDICAL CARE

S a n   B e r n a r d i n o

Interstate 10

E / W

Ontario

54 Vineyard Ave, **N...food:** Del Taco, Popeye's, Rocky's Foods, Sizzler, Taco Bell, **other:** Chief Parts, Rite Aid, Stater Bros Foods, **S...gas:** Arco/24hr, Circle K, Mobil, Shell, **food:** Cuisine of India, Denny's, In-n-Out, Marie Callender, Michael J's Rest., Rosa's Italian, Spires Rest., Yoshinoya Japanese, **lodging:** Best Western, Country Suites, DoubleTree Inn, Express Inn, GoodNite Inn, Ramada Ltd, Red Roof Inn, Residence Inn, Sheraton, Super 8, **other:** Chevrolet/Cadillac

53 San Bernardino Ave, 4th St, to Ontario, **N...gas:** Arco, Chevron, Circle K, Shell, **food:** Baskin-Robbins, Burger King, Carl's Jr, Del Taco, Jack-in-the-Box, Popeye's, Sizzler, Taco Bell/24hr, **lodging:** Motel 6, Quality Inn, **other:** Chief Parts, K-Mart, Radio Shack, Ralph's Foods, Rite Aid, **S...gas:** Arco/24hr, Exxon/A&W/diesel/24hr, 76, **food:** Denny's, Gordo's Mexican, KFC, McDonald's, Pizza Hut, YumYum Donut, **lodging:** CA Inn, Travelodge, West Coast Inn

51 CA 83, Euclid Ave, to Ontario, Upland, **N...food:** Coco's Rest.

50 Mountain Ave, to Mt Baldy, **N...gas:** Arco, Chevron, Mobil, Shell/A&W/diesel, **food:** BBQ, Carrow's, Denny's, El Burrito, El Torito, Green Burrito, Happy Wok Chinese, Mimi's Café, Mi Taco, Subway, Trader Joe's, **lodging:** Super 8, **other:** Home Depot, Longs Drug, Mervyn's of CA, Staples, **S...gas:** 76/diesel, **food:** Baskin-Robbins, Carl's Jr, Tacos Mexico, **other:** Albertson's, Food4Less, Rite Aid, Target, USPO

49 Central Ave, to Montclair, **N...gas:** Chevron, Mobil, Shell/24hr, 7-11, **food:** Acapulco Mexican, Burger King, El Pollo Loco, KFC, McDonald's, Subway, Tom's Burgers, **other:** MEDICAL CARE, Borders Books, Circuit City, Firestone/auto, Goodyear/auto, Hi-Lo Auto Supply, JC Penney, Macy's, Office Depot, Ross, Sears/auto, mall, same as 48, **S...gas:** 76, **food:** Jack-in-the-Box, LJ Silver, Wienerschnitzel, **other:** Acura, Costco/gas, Honda, Infiniti, K-Mart, Nissan

48 Monte Vista, **N...gas:** Shell, **food:** Black Angus, Olive Garden, Red Lobster, Tony Roma, **other:** HOSPITAL, Nordstrom's, Robinson-May, mall, same as 49

47 Indian Hill Blvd, to Claremont, **N...gas:** Mobil, **food:** Bakers Square, Tony Roma, **lodging:** Howard Johnson, Travelodge, **S...gas:** Chevron/McDonald's, 76/diesel, Shell, 7-11, **food:** Burger King, Carl's Jr, Chili's, In-n-Out, RoundTable Pizza, Wienerschnitzel, **lodging:** Ramada Inn, **other:** MEDICAL CARE, Albertson's, America's Tire, AutoZone, Ford, Kia, Pic'n Sav, Radio Shack, Toyota

46 Towne Ave, **N...gas:** 7-11, **food:** Jack-in-the-Box

45b Garey Ave(from eb), to Pomona, **N...gas:** Delta, **other:** SavOn Drug, **S...gas:** Arco/24hr, Chevron, Shell/diesel, **other:** HOSPITAL

45a White Ave, Garey Ave, to Pomona, same as 46a

44 (43 from eb)Dudley St, Fairplex Dr, **N...gas:** Arco, 76, **food:** Coppacabana Rest., Denny's, **lodging:** LemonTree Motel, Sheraton, **S...gas:** Chevron/24hr, Mobil, Texaco/diesel, 7-11, **food:** Jack-in-the-Box, McDonald's

42b CA 71 S(from eb), to Corona

42a I-210 N, CA 57 S, no facilities

41 Kellogg Dr(from eb), **S...to** Cal Poly Inst

40 Via Verde, no facilities

38b Holt Ave, to Covina, **N... food:** Blake's Steaks/seafood, **lodging:** Embassy Suites

38a Grand Ave

37b Barranca St, Grand Ave, **N...gas:** Arco, Shell/repair, **food:** Bailey's Rest., Charley Brown Steaks/lobster, Coco's, El Torito, Magic Recipe Rest., Marie Callender, Mariposa Mexican, Monterrey Rest., **lodging:** Best Western, Hampton Inn, Holiday Inn, **S...food:** In-n-Out, McDonald's, **lodging:** Comfort Inn

Los Angeles Area

37a Citrus Ave, to Covina, **N...gas:** Chevron, Mobil, Shell, **food:** Burger King, Carl's Jr, Chili's, Del Taco, IHOP, Jack-in-the-Box, Mandarin Express, TGIFriday, Winchell's, **other:** Acura, Buick, GMC, Honda, Lincoln/Mercury, Longs Drug, Marshall's, Mazda, Mervyn's, Office Depot, Old Navy, Ralph's Foods, Ross, Target, Volvo/VW, **S...gas:** 76/autocare, **food:** Trader Joe's, **lodging:** Comfort Inn, 5 Star Inn, **other:** HOSPITAL, Cadillac

36 CA 39, Azusa Ave, to Covina, **N...gas:** Arco/24hr, Chevron, 76, **food:** Black Angus, McDonald's, Papa John's, Red Lobster, Steak Corral, Subway, **lodging:** El Dorado Motel, **other:** Chrysler/Plymouth, Circuit City, Jeep, **S...gas:** Mobil, Shell, **food:** Carrow's, **other:** Dodge, Honda, Hummer, Jaguar, Mazda, Mercedes, Mitsubishi, Nissan, Saab, Saturn, Toyota

35 Vincent Ave, Glendora Ave, **N...gas:** Arco/24hr, Chevron/24hr, Mobil, 76, **food:** KFC, Pizza Hut, Wienerschnitzel, **S...gas:** 76, **food:** Applebee's, Chevy's Mexican, Red Robin, **other:** Barnes&Noble, Best Buy, JC Penney, Macy's, Robinson-May, Sears/auto, SportMart, mall

CALIFORNIA
Interstate 10

34 Pacific Ave, **N...other:** CarQuest, **S...gas:** Mobil, **other:** HOSPITAL, K-Mart, Goodyear/auto, JC Penney, Jo-Ann Fabrics, Sears, mall, same as 35

33 La Puente Ave, **N...gas:** Chevron, **food:** China Palace, Denny's, Guadalajara Grill, McDonald's, Quizno's, Starbucks, **lodging:** Motel 6, Radisson, Home Depot, Staples, **S...gas:** Arco, **lodging:** Baldwin Motel, **other:** Harley-Davidson, Saturn, U-Haul

32b Francisquito Ave, to La Puente, **N...food:** In-n-Out, **other:** hwy patrol, **S...gas:** Chevron, **food:** Carl's Jr, In-n-Out, Wienerschnitzel, **lodging:** Grand Park Inn

31c a (31b from wb)Frazier St, Baldwin Pk Blvd, **N...gas:** Arco, Chevron, Shell, 7-11, **food:** Burger King, Jack-in-the-Box, McDonald's, Pizza Hut/Taco Bell, **other:** HOSPITAL, Food4Less, OfficeMax, Target, **S...food:** In-n-Out, **other:** Altman's RV Ctr

31b a (31a from wb)I-605 S, to Long Beach

29b Valley Blvd, Peck Rd, **N...gas:** Chevron, **food:** Denny's, **lodging:** Motel 6, **other:** Ford, Dodge, Goodyear, Honda, K-Mart, Nissan, Toyota/Lexus, **S...gas:** Mobil, Shell, **food:** Del Taco, McDonald's, Teriyaki Bowl, **other:** MEDICAL CARE, PepBoys, Pontiac/GMC

29a S Peck Rd(from eb), no facilities

28 Santa Anita Ave, to El Monte, **N...gas:** Shell/diesel, **other:** Chevrolet, Hyundai, **S...gas:** 76, 7-11

27 Baldwin Ave(from eb), **S...gas:** Arco/24hr, **food:** Denny's, Edward's Steaks, same as 27b a

26b CA 19, Rosemead Blvd, Pasadena, **N...food:** Denny's, IHOP, **lodging:** Ramada Inn, **other:** MEDICAL CARE, Goodyear/auto, Target

26a Walnut Grove Ave, no facilities

25b San Gabriel Blvd, **N...gas:** Arco, Mobil, Shell/autocare, **food:** Carl's Jr, Popeye's, Taco Bell, Teriyaki Bowl, Wienerschnitzel, **lodging:** Budget Motel, **other:** MEDICAL CARE, AutoZone, San Gabriel Foods, **S...gas:** Arco, **food:** Burger King, **other:** SavOn Drug

25a Del Mar Ave, to San Gabriel, **N...gas:** 76, **other:** auto repair, **S...gas:** Arco, Chevron

24 New Ave, to Monterey Park, **N...gas:** Mobil, to Mission San Gabriel

23b Garfield Ave, to Alhambra, **N...HOSPITAL, S...gas:** Shell, Texaco

23a Atlantic Blvd, Monterey Park, **N...gas:** Mobil, 76, **food:** Del Taco, Pizza Hut, Popeye's, **other:** HOSPITAL, **S...other:** Firestone/auto

22 Fremont Ave, **N...HOSPITAL,** tuneup, **S...gas:** 7-11

21 I-710, Long Beach Fwy, Eastern Ave(from wb)

20b a Eastern Ave(from eb), City Terrace Dr, **S...gas:** Chevron/service, **food:** McDonald's

19c Soto St(from wb), **N...gas:** Shell, **other:** HOSPITAL, **S...gas:** Mobil, Shell, **food:** Burger King

19b I-5(from wb), US 101 S, N to Burbank, S to San Diego

19a State St, **N...HOSPITAL**

17 I-5 N

16b I-5 S(from eb)

16a Santa Fe Ave, San Mateo St, **S...gas:** Shell, **other:** Hertz Trucks, industrial area

15b Alameda St, **N...downtown, S...industrial area**

15a Central Ave, **N...gas:** Shell/repair

14b San Pedro Blvd, **S...industrial**

14a LA Blvd, **N...conv ctr, S...other:** Kragen Parts, Radio Shack, Rite Aid

13 I-110, Harbor Fwy, no facilities

12 Hoover St, Vermont Ave, **N...gas:** Mobil, Texaco, **food:** Burger King, King Donuts, **other:** PepBoys, Thrifty Drug, Toyota, **S...gas:** Chevron, Shell, **food:** Jack-in-the-Box, **other:** Office Depot, Staples

11 Western Ave, Normandie Ave, **N...gas:** Chevron, Mobil, **food:** McDonald's, Winchell's, **other:** AutoZone, Food4Less, Radio Shack, SavOn Drug, **S...**Chevron, Texaco, Goodyear

10 Arlington Ave, **N...gas:** Chevron, Mobil

9 Crenshaw Blvd, **S...gas:** Chevron, Thrifty, **other:** U-Haul

8 La Brea Ave, **N...gas:** Chevron, Shell/diesel/repair, **other:** Walgreen, transmissions, **S...gas:** Chevron, AutoZone, Ralph's Foods

7b Washington Blvd, Fairfax Ave, **S...gas:** Mobil, same as 8

7a La Cienega Blvd, Venice Ave(from wb), **N...gas:** Chevron/24h, **other:** Firestone/auto, **S...gas:** Arco/24hr, Mobil, **food:** Carl's Jr, McDonald's, Pizza Hut, Subway, **other:** Staples

6 Robertson Blvd, Culver City, **N...gas:** Arco, Chevron, Mobil, **other:** museum, **S...food:** Del Taco, Albertson's, **other:** OfficeMax, SavOn Drug, Ross

5 National Blvd, **N...gas:** 76, 7-11, **other:** Rite Aid, Von's Foods

4 Overland Ave, **S...gas:** Arco/24hr, Mobil, 76, Shell, **food:** Winchell's

3b a I-405, N to Sacramento, S to Long Beach, no facilities

2c b Bundy Dr, **N...gas:** 76, **food:** Eddy's Café, Taco Bell

2a Centinela Ave, to Santa Monica, **N...food:** Don Antonio's Mexican, Taco Bell, **S...food:** McDonald's, Trader Joe's, **lodging:** Santa Monica Hotel

1c 20th St(from wb), Cloverfield Blvd, 26th St(from wb), **N...gas:** Arco, Shell/repair, **other:** HOSPITAL

1b Lincoln Blvd, CA 1 S, **N...food:** Denny's, **lodging:** Holiday Inn, **other:** Jo-Ann Fabrics, Macy's, Sears, auto repair, mall, **S...gas:** Chevron/24hr, **food:** Jack-in-the-Box, **other:** Firestone/auto, U-Haul

1a 4th, 5th,(from wb) **N...other:** Macy's, Sears

0 Santa Monica Blvd, to beaches, I-10 begins/ends on CA 1.

Interstate 15

N
↑
↓
S

Exit #	Services
298	California/Nevada state line, facilities located at state line, Nevada side.
291	Yates Well Rd, **W**...golf
286	Nipton Rd, **E**...E Mojave Nat Scenic Area, to Searchlight
281	Bailey Rd, no facilities
276mm	brake check area for trucks, nb
272	Cima Rd, no facilities
270mm	**Valley Wells Rest Area both lanes, full(handicapped)facilities, phone, picnic tables, litter barrels, petwalk**
265	Halloran Summit Rd, **E...gas:** Hilltop Gas/diesel, **other:** towing/tires/repair
259	Halloran Springs Rd, **E...gas:** Lo Gas/diesel/café
248	to Baker(from sb), access to same as 239
246	CA 127, Kel-Baker Rd, Baker, to Death Valley, **W...gas:** Arco/24hr, Chevron/Taco Bell/24hr, Mobil/Denny's/diesel, 76/diesel, Shell/Jack-in-the-Box/diesel, Texaco/A&W/Pizza Hut/TCBY, UltraMar/DQ/diesel/@, **food:** Arby's, BunBoy Rest., Burger King, Del Taco, Mad Greek Café, **lodging:** Royal Hawaiian Motel, **other:** Arnold's Mkt/repair, Baker Auto Parts, Baker Mkt Foods, Gen Store/NAPA, World's Largest Thermometer, repair
245	to Baker(from nb), access to same as 239
239	Zzyzx Rd, no facilities
233	Rasor Rd, **E...gas:** Rasor Rest Sta/diesel/24hr
230	Basin Rd, no facilities
221	Afton Rd, to Dunn, no facilities
217mm	**rest area both lanes, full(handicapped)facilities, phone, picnic tables, litter barrels, petwalk**
213	Field Rd, no facilities
206	Harvard Rd, to Newberry Springs, **W...other:** Lake Dolores Resort/WaterPark(1mi), Twin Lakes RV Park
198	Minneola Rd, **W...gas:** Mobil/diesel, **other:** to Lake Dolores Resort(5mi)
197mm	agricultural insp sta sb
196	to Yermo, no facilities
194	Calico Rd, **E...gas:** International Café/gas, **other:** repair
191	Ghost Town Rd, **E...gas:** Arco/24hr, Vegas/diesel/rest./24hr/@, **food:** Jack-in-the-Box, Peggy Sue's 50s Diner, **lodging:** OakTree Inn, **W...gas:** Clink's #2/diesel/@, Texaco, **lodging:** Jenny Rose' Rest., **other:** Calico GhostTown(3mi), KOA, to USMC Logistics
189	Ft Irwin Rd, **W...gas:** 76/diesel, RV camping
186	CA 58 W, to Bakersfield, **W...other:** RV camping
184	E Main, Barstow, to I-40, **E...gas:** Chevron, Mobil/diesel, Shell/repair, **food:** Burger King, Krissy's Café, McDonald's, Straw Hat Pizza, Tom's Burgers, **lodging:** Best Western, **other:** Pic'n Sav, mall, **S of I-40...gas:** Arco/24hr, **other:** Wal-Mart/auto, **W...gas:**

Baker / Barstow

Barstow

Baker

Barstow

Arco/24hr, Chevron, 76/Circle K/Subway/TCBY, Shell, **food:** Arby's, Burger King, Carl's Jr, Carrow's Rest., China Gourmet, Coco's, Del Taco, Denny's, Firehouse Italian, Golden Dragon, IHOP, Jack-in-the-Box, KFC, LJ Silver, Sizzler, Taco Bell, **lodging:** AstroBudget Motel, Best Motel, Budget Inn, Comfort Inn, Day's Inn, Desert Inn, Econolodge, Economy Inn, Executive Inn, Quality Inn, Ramada Inn, Super 8, **other:** AutoZone, Goodyear, Kragen Parts, Radio Shack, U-Haul/LP, Von's Foods

184a	I-40 E(from nb), I-40 begins/ends
183	CA 247, Barstow Rd, **E...gas:** 76/Circle K, UltraMar/Pizza Hut/gas, **other:** Rite Aid, Stater Bros Foods, **W...gas:** Chevron/24hr, **other:** HOSPITAL, Food4Less, Mojave River Valley Museum, st patrol,
181	L St, W Main, Barstow, **W...gas:** Arco/24hr, Chevron, TA/diesel/rest./@, **food:** BunBoy Rest., Pizza Palace, **lodging:** Holiday Inn Express, **other:** tires/towing
179	CA 58, to Bakersfield
178	Lenwood, to Barstow, **E...gas:** Chevron/diesel, ⊘/CountryMkt/diesel/24hr/@, Mobil/Blimpie, Shell/24hr, 76/Wendy's/diesel, **food:** Arby's, Burger King, Carl's Jr, Del Taco, Denny's, El Pollo Loco, FoodCourt, In-n-Out, Jack-in-the-Box, KFC, Panda Express, Starbucks, Subway, Taco Bell, Tommy's Burgers, **other:** Tanger Outlet/famous brands, **W...gas:** Arco/24hr, Pilot/DQ/diesel/24hr/@, Rip Griffin/Subway/diesel/24hr/@, **food:** McDonald's, **lodging:** GoodNite Inn, **other:** truck repair
175	Outlet Ctr Dr, Sidewinder Rd, **4 mi E...other:** factory outlets
169	Hodge Rd, no facilities
165	Wild Wash Rd, no facilities
161	Dale Evans Pkwy, to Apple Valley, **W...**airport
154	Stoddard Wells Rd, to Bell Mtn, **E...food:** Peggy Sue's 50s Diner, **other:** KOA, **W...gas:** Mobil, 76, Shell, **food:** Denny's, **lodging:** Howard Johnson, Motel 6, Queens Motel

N ↑↓ S

Victorville

153.5mm Mojave River

153b E St, no facilities

153a CA 18 E, D St, to Apple Valley, **E...gas:** 76, **other:** HOSPITAL, **W...gas:** Arco/24hr

151b Mojave Dr, Victorville, **E...gas:** 76/diesel/24hr, **lodging:** Budget Inn, **W...gas:** UltraMar, **lodging:** Economy Inn, Sunset Inn, **other:** transmissions

151a La Paz Dr, Roy Rogers Dr, **E...gas:** Chevron, Texaco/A&W/TCBY, USA, **food:** Carl's Jr, China Palace, Dairy Queen, HomeTown Buffet, IHOP, Jack-in-the-Box, **lodging:** New Corral Motel, **other:** Asian Mkt, Costco/gas, Daewoo, Food4Less/24hr, Goodyear/auto, Harley-Davidson, Honda, Jo-Ann Fabrics, Pic'n Sav Foods, Rite Aid, Toyota, Winston Tire, same as 144, **W...gas:** Arco/24hr

150 CA 18 W, Palmdale Rd, Victorville, **E... gas:** Arco/24hr, Chevron, Shell, Texaco/diesel/24hr, **food:** Baker's Drive-Thru, Burger King, Carl's Jr, Denny's, Don's Rest., Jack-in-the-Box, KFC, Richie's Diner, YumYum Donuts, **lodging:** Best Western, **other:** Cadillac/GMC, Dodge/Plymouth, PepBoys, **W...gas:** Arco/24hr, Chevron, Mobil, Shell, Thrifty, **food:** Andrew's Rest., Coco's, Del Taco, Los Domingos Mexican, LJ Silver, McDonald's, Pina's Mexican, Pizza Hut, Subway, Taco Bell, Tom's #21 Rest., **lodging:** Budget Inn, EZ 8 Motel, Ramada Inn, **other:** HOSPITAL, Aamco, AutoZone, Buick/Pontiac, Chevrolet/Hyundai, Chrysler/Jeep, Ford/Lincoln/Mercury, Honda/Toyota, Kamper's Korner RV, Kia, Nissan, Ralph's Foods, Target, Town&Country Tire, mall

147 Bear Valley Rd, to Lucerne Valley, **E...gas:** Arco/24hr, Chevron, Citgo/7-11, Mobil, 76/Circle K, Shell, **food:** A&W, Arby's, Baker's Drive-Thru, Burger King, Carl's Jr, Del Taco, Dragon Express, Hogi Yogi, John's Pizza, KFC, LJ Silver, Los Toritos Mexican, Marie Callender, McDonald's, Panda Express, Red Robin, Pizza Palace, Shakey's Pizza, Stein'n Steer, Straw Hat Pizza, TNT Café, Wienerschnitzel, Winchell's, **lodging:** American Inn, Day's Inn, Econolodge, Red Roof Inn, Super 8, **other:** America's Tire, AutoZone, Circuit City, Firestone/auto, Home Depot, Kragen Parts, Michael's, Range RV, Staples, Wal-Mart/auto, funpark, **W...gas:** Chevron/Church's, UtraMar, **food:** Applebee's, Archibald's Drive-Thru, Baja Fresh Grill, ChuckeCheese, El Pollo Loco, El Tio Pepe Mexican, Greenhouse Café, Jack-in-the-Box, Olive Garden, Outback Steaks, Red Lobster, RoadHouse Grill, Starbucks, Subway, Tony Roma, **other:** Barnes&Noble, Best Buy, JC Penney, Lowe's Whse, Mervyn's, OfficeMax, Sears/auto, mall

143 Main St, to Hesperia, Phelan, **E...gas:** Shell, Texaco/A&W/Popeyes/diesel, UltraMar/DQ/pizza, **food:** Burger King, Denny's, In-n-Out, Jack-in-the-Box, **W...gas:** Arco/24hr, **food:** Baker's Drive-thru, **lodging:** Holiday Inn Express, RV camping

Ontario

141 US 395, to Adelanto, **W...gas:** Pilot/Wendy's/diesel/24hr/@, **food:** Newt's Outpost Café, **other:** repair

138 Oak Hill Rd, **E...gas:** Arco/24hr, **food:** Summit Inn/café, **W...other:** RV camping, LP

132 Cajon Summit, elevation 4260, brake check sb

131 CA 138, to Palmdale, Silverwood Lake, **E...gas:** Chevron/McDonald's/24hr, **other:** repair, **W...gas:** 76/Del Taco/Circle K/LP, Shell/diesel, **lodging:** Best Western

131mm weigh sta both lanes, elevation 3000

129 Cleghorn Rd, no facilities

124 Kenwood Ave, no facilities

123 I-215 S, to San Bernardino, **E...gas:** Arco/24hr, to Glen Helen Park

122 Glen Helen Parkway, no facilities

119 Sierra Ave, **W...gas:** Arco/Jack-in-the-Box/diesel/24hr, Shell/Del Taco/diesel/@, to Lytle Creek RA

116 Summit Ave, no facilities

115b a CA 210, Highland Ave, **E...** to Lake Arrowhead

113 Base Line Rd, **E...gas:** USA, **food:** Denny's, Jack-in-the-Box, Starbucks, **lodging:** AmeriHost, **W...gas:** Speedway

112 CA 66, Foothill Blvd, **E...gas:** Chevron, **food:** Arby's, ClaimJumper Rest., Coco's, Golden Spoon, In-n-Out, Subway, Taco Bell, Wienerschnitzel, **other:** Circuit City, Costco, Food4Less, Mervyn's, Michael's, Office Depot, OfficeMax, Radio Shack, Target, Wal-Mart/auto, **1-2 mi W...gas:** Arco, Mobil, **food:** Blimpie, BrewPub, Carl's Jr, China Hut, Denny's, FarmerBoys, Jack-in-the-Box, Old Spaghetti Factory, **lodging:** Best Western, **other:** MEDICAL CARE, AutoZone, Barnes&Noble, Best Buy, Discount Tire, Home Depot, Lowe's Whse, SteinMart, stadium

110 4th St, **W...gas:** Arco/24hr, Mobil/Subway, Texaco/Burger King/diesel, **food:** Dave&Buster's, Carl's Jr, Chevy's Mexican, Coco's, CucinaCucina, Del Taco, FoodCourt, Jack-in-the-Box, KFC, Krispy Kreme, McDonald's, Mi Casa Mexican, NY Grill, Pat Oscar's Rest., Quizno's, Rubio's, Starbucks, Tokyo-Tokyo, Wienerschnitzel, **lodging:** AmeriSuites, **other:** America's Tire, Costco/gas, JC Penney, Ontario Mills Mall, Sam's Club

109b a I-10, E to San Bernardino, W to LA

108 Jurupa St, **E...other:** Affordable RV, BMW, Buick, Chrysler/Jeep/Dodge, GMC/Pontiac, Honda, Lexus, Mitsubishi, Nissan, Saturn, Toyota, Volvo, **W...gas:** Arco/24hr, Carl's Jr, Ford, Lincoln/Mercury, funpark

106 CA 60, E to Riverside, W to LA

103 Limonite Ave, no facilities

100 6th St, Norco Dr, **E...gas:** Arco/24hr, Chevron/24hr, **food:** Jack-in-the-Box, McDonald's, Old Town Norco, **W...gas:** Arco/24hr, UltraMar/diesel, **food:** Country Jct Rest.

Interstate 15

N
S

98   2nd St, **W...gas:** Shell/diesel, Texaco, 7-11, **food:** Burger King, Del Taco, Denny's, Domino's, Fazoli's, In-n-Out, KFC, Little Caesar's, Marie Callender, Miguel's Jr, Wienerschnitzel, **lodging:** Howard Johnson Express, **other:** MEDICAL CARE, America's Tire, AutoZone, Big O Tire, Chrysler/Plymouth, Dodge, Ford, Jeep, Mitsubishi, Pontiac, Norco RV, Staples, Target

97   Yuma Dr, Hidden Valley Pkwy, **W...gas:** Chevron, 76, Shell/diesel, **food:** Alberto's Arby's, Mexican, Carl's Jr, Gus Jr, Dairy Queen, McDonald's, Papa John's, Quizno's, Rubio's, Starbucks, Wendy's, **other:** Albertson's, Kragen Parts, SavOn Drug, Staples, Winston Tire

96b a   CA 91, to Riverside, beaches, no facilities

95   Magnolia Ave, **E...gas:** Chevron/diesel, **W...gas:** Mobil, Shell, **food:** Burger King, Carl's Jr, Coco's, Donut Star, Little Caesar's, Lotus Garden, McDonald's, Pizza Palace, Sizzler, Subway, Zendejas Mexican, **other:** Kragen Parts, Ralph's Foods, Rite Aid, Sav-On Drug, Stater Bros Foods

93   Ontario Ave, to El Cerrito, **W...gas:** Arco/24hr, Chevron/24hr, **food:** Jack-in-the-Box, McDonald's, Porky's Pizza, Quizno's, Wienerschnitzel, **other:** Albertson's, Home Depot, Sam's Club, USPO, Wal-Mart/auto

92   El Cerrito Rd, **E...gas:** 76/Circle K

91   Cajalco Rd, no facilities

90   Weirick Rd, **E...other:** 7 Oaks Gen Store

88   Temescal Cyn Rd, Glen Ivy, **W...gas:** Arco/diesel/24hr, **food:** Carl's Jr, Tom's Farms, **other:** RV camping

85   Indian Truck Trail, no facilities

81   Lake St, no facilities

78   Nichols Rd, **W...gas:** Arco/24hr, **other:** VF Outlet/famous brands, auto repair

77   CA 74, Central Ave, Lake Elsinore, **E...gas:** Arco/24hr, Chevron, Mobil, **food:** Burger King, Douglas Burgers, Italian Deli, **W...other:** craft mall

75   Main St, Lake Elsinore, **W...gas:** 76, Circle K, UltraMar/diesel, **lodging:** Elsinore Motel

73   Railroad Cyn Rd, to Lake Elsinore, **E...gas:** 76/Circle K, **food:** Denny's, El Pollo Loco, In-n-Out, KFC, Papa John's, Wienerschnitzel, **other:** GNC, Kragen Parts, Von's Foods, Wal-Mart/auto, **W...gas:** Arco, Chevron, Mobil/diesel, 7-11, **food:** Carl's Jr, Coco's, Del Taco, Don Jose's Mexican, Green Burrito, McDonald's, Pizza Hut, Sizzler, Subway, Taco Bell, **lodging:** Lake Elsinore Hotel/casino, Lake View Inn, Travel Inn, **other:** MEDICAL CARE, Albertson's, AutoZone, Big O Tire, Chevrolet, Firestone, Ford, Goodyear/auto, NAPA, Radio Shack, SavOn Drug, Stater Bros Foods

71   Bundy Cyn Rd, **W...gas:** Arco/24hr, **food:** Jack-in-the-Box

Lake Elsinore

69   Baxter Rd, no facilities

68   Clinton Keith Rd, **E...HOSPITAL**

65   California Oaks Rd, Kalmia St, **E...gas:** Chevron, Mobil/diesel, 76/Circle K, Shell/Burger King/diesel, Texaco/diesel, **food:** Carl's Jr, DQ, KFC, McDonald's, Papa John's, Stew's Rest., **other:** Albertson's, Goodyear/auto, Kragen Parts, Rite Aid, SavOn Drug, Target, **W...gas:** Arco/24hr, **food:** Carrow's, Jack-in-the-Box, **other:** funpark

64   Murrieta Hot Springs Rd, to I-215, **E... food:** Sizzler, **other:** Ralph's Foods, Rite Aid, Ross, **W...gas:** Shell/Popeyes/diesel, **food:** Arby's, IHOP, McDonald's, Tom's Burgers, Wienerschnitzel, **other:** Best Buy, Home Depot, 99c Store, Pic'n Sav Foods, Staples, Wal-Mart/auto

63   I-215 N(from nb), to Riverside

61   CA 79 N, Winchester Rd, **E... gas:** Chevron, **food:** Carl's Jr, Coco's, 5&Diner, Godfather's, McDonald's, Mimi's Café, On the Border, Roadhouse Grill, Souplantation, Taco Bell, TGIFriday, **other:** MEDICAL CARE, Aamco, America Tire, Big O Tire, Costco/gas, Food 4Less, Goodyear, Dodge, Ford, Honda/Acura, K-Mart, Kragen Parts, Mervyn's, PepBoys, Ralph's Food, Robinsons-May, Toyota, VW, **W...gas:** Arco/24hr, Chevron/diesel, Mobil, UltraMar, **food:** Arby's, Banzai Japanese, Billy B's Burgers, ChungKing Chinese, DQ, Del Taco, El Pollo Loco, Filippi's Café, Golden Corral, Guadalajara Mexican, Hungry Hunter, In-n-Out, Jack-in-the-Box, Richie's Diner, Sizzler, Tecate Grill, Tony Roma's, Wendy's, **lodging:** Best Western, Comfort Inn, Temecula Valley Inn, **other:** MEDICAL CARE, Big A Parts, NAPA, Rancho Richardson's RV, Stater Bros Foods, Winston Tire, st patrol

Temecula

N ↑ ↓ **S**

Escondido

59 Rancho California Rd, **E...gas:** Mobil, 76, Shell/ A&W/diesel, **food:** Black Angus, Buddie's Pizza, Chili's, ClaimJumper, Great Grains Bread, Marie Callender's, Oscar's Rest., RoundTable Pizza, Starbucks, **lodging:** Embassy Suites, **other:** MEDICAL CARE, Albertson's, Michael's, SavOn Drug, Target, Von's Foods, **W...gas:** Chevron/repair, 76/Circle K/ diesel, **food:** Denny's, Domino's, KFC, McDonald's, OldTown Donuts, Penfold's Mexican, Rick's Burgers, Rosa's Café, SW Grill, Taco Bell, Taco Grill, Togo's, **lodging:** Motel 6, **other:** USPO

58 CA 79 S, Temecula, to Indio, **E...gas:** Mobil, 7-11, **food:** Carl's Jr, Temecula Pizza, **lodging:** Rancho Motor Inn, **W...gas:** Shell/diesel/24hr, **food:** Alberto's Drive-Thru Mexican, Hungry Howie's, Wienerschnitzel, **lodging:** Butterfield Inn, Ramada Inn, **other:** Firestone, Goodyear/auto, RV service

55mm check sta nb

54 Rainbow Valley Blvd, **2 mi E...**gas, food, **W...**CA Insp Sta

51 Mission Rd, to Fallbrook, **2 mi E...food:** Rainbow Oaks Rest., **W...**HOSPITAL

46 CA 76, Pala, to Oceanside, **W...gas:** Mobil, **lodging:** La Estancia Inn, Pala Mesa Resort, **other:** RV camp

44mm San Luis Rey River

43 Old Hwy 395, no facilities

41 Gopher Canyon Rd, Old Castle Rd, **1 mi E...gas:** Texaco/diesel, Welk Resort, **other:** RV camping

37 Deer Springs Rd, Mountain Meadow Rd, **W...gas:** Arco/24hr

34 Centre City Pkwy(from sb)

33 El Norte Pkwy, **E...gas:** Arco/24hr, Shell/diesel, Texaco, **food:** Arby's, DQ, IHOP, Taco Bell, **lodging:** Best Western, **other:** Goodyear, SavOn Drug, Von's Foods, **W...gas:** 76, Circle K, **food:** Jack-in-the-Box, Wendy's, **other:** Von's Foods

32 CA 78, to Oceanside, **1 mi E on Mission...gas:** Mobil, **food:** Carl's Jr, ChuckeCheese, Denny's, Jack-in-the-Box, LJ Silver, Wienerschnitzel, **lodging:** Motel 6, Mt Vernon Inn, PalmTree Lodge, Super 8, **other:** AutoZone, PepBoys, K-Mart, U-Haul

31 Valley Pkwy, **E...gas:** Arco/24hr, **food:** Chili's, Coco's, McDonald's, Olive Garden, Togo's, Yoshinoya, **other:** HOSPITAL, Albertson's, Circuit City, Infiniti, mall, **W...gas:** 7-11, **food:** Burger King, Carl's Jr, Coco's, Del Taco, La Salsa, **lodging:** Comfort Inn, Holiday Inn Express, **other:** Mervyn's, Staples, Target

30 9th Ave, Auto Parkway, **W...gas:** Shell, **food:** Applebee's, Starbucks, Subway, Taco Bell, **other:** Home Depot, WorldMkt, same as 25

29 Felicita Rd, no facilities

28 Centre City Pkwy(from nb, no return), **E...food:** Center City Café, **lodging:** Palms Inn

27 Via Rancho Pkwy, to Escondido, **E...gas:** Chevron/ 24hr, Shell, **food:** FoodCourt, Red Lobster, Red Robin, **other:** JC Penney, Macy's, Nordstrom's, Robinsons-May, Sears/auto, Animal Zoo, mall, **W...gas:** Shell/Subway/diesel, **food:** CA Coffee, McDonald's, Olive House Café, Tony's Steer

26 W Bernardo Dr, to Highland Valley Rd, Palmerado Rd, no facilities

24 Rancho Bernardo Rd, to Lake Poway, **E...gas:** Arco/24hr, Mobil, **other:** Baron's Foods, Von's Foods, **W...gas:** 76/Circle K, Shell/repair, Texaco/ diesel/repair, **food:** Elephant Bar Rest., **lodging:** Holiday Inn, Travelodge

23 Bernardo Ctr Dr, **E...gas:** Chevron, 7-11, **food:** Burger King, Carl's Jr, Coco's, Denny's, Hunan Chinese, Jack-in-the-Box, Quizno's, Rubio's Grill, Taco Bell, **other:** Firestone/auto, Goodyear/auto, SavOn Drug

22 Camino del Norte, **E...**HOSPITAL, same as 17, **W...food:** Bernardo Pizza, Togo Eatery

21 Carmel Mtn Rd, **E...gas:** Chevron, Shell, Texaco, **food:** Baskin-Robbins, Boston Mkt, CA Pizza, Carl's Jr, Chevy's Mexican, ClaimJumper, El Pollo Loco, In-n-Out, Islands Burgers, JambaJuice, Marie Callender, McDonald's, Olive Garden, Oscar's Rest., Rubio's Grill, Schlotsky's, Subway, Taco Bell, TGIFriday, Wendy's, **lodging:** Residence Inn, **other:** Barnes&Noble, Borders Books, Circuit City, Home Depot, K-Mart, Marshall's, Mervyn's, Michael's, Ralph's Foods, Rite Aid, Ross, Staples, Trader Joes, USPO, **W... gas:** Chevron, 7-11, **food:** Jack-in-the-Box, Roberto's Mexican, **other:** Albertson's, Office Depot

19 CA 56 W, Ted Williams Pkwy, **E...food:** Tony's Pizza

18 Rancho Penasquitos Blvd, Poway Rd, **E... gas:** Arco/24hr, **food:** Manhattan Deli, **W...gas:** Exxon, Mobil, 76, 7-11, **food:** Burger King, IHOP, Little Caesar's, McDonald's, Subway, Taco Bell, **lodging:** La Quinta

17 Mercy Rd, Scripps Poway Pkwy, no facilities

16 Mira Mesa Blvd, to Lake Miramar, **E... food:** ChuckeCheese, Denny's, Filippi's Pizza, Golden Crown Chinese, **lodging:** Quality Suites, **other:** Medco Drug, USPO, **W...gas:** Arco/24hr, Mobil, 76, Shell, **food:** Applebee's, Arby's, Burger King, Café China, In-n-Out, Islands Burgers, Jack-in-the-Box, Jamba Juice, Little Caesar's, McDonald's, Mimi's Café, On the Border, Rubio's Grill, Starbucks, Subway, Wendy's, **other:** MEDICAL CARE, Albertson's, Barnes&Noble, Home Depot, Longs Drug, Old Navy, Pic'n Sav Foods, Ralph's Foods, Rite Aid, Ross, SavOn Drug, USPO

Interstate 15

N ↕ S

San Diego Area

15	Carroll Canyon Rd, to Miramar College, **E...food:** Carl's Jr
14	Pomerado Rd, Miramar Rd, **W...gas:** Arco/diesel, Chevron, Mobil, Shell/24hr, Texaco/diesel, **food:** Acapulco Mexican, Amber's Rest., Carl's Jr, Keith's Rest., Marie Callender's, Pizza Hut, Subway, **lodging:** Best Western, Budget Inn, Holiday Inn, **other:** Aamco, Audi/Porsche/VW, Kragen Parts, Land Rover, NAPA
13	Miramar Way, US Naval Air Station
12	CA 163 S(from sb), to San Diego, no facilities
11	to CA 52, no facilities
10	Clairemont Mesa Blvd, **W...food:** Carl's Jr, Giovanni's Pizza, McDonald's, Mr Chick Rest., Subway, Sunny Donuts, Taco Bell, Wendy's
9	CA 274, Balboa Ave, no facilities
8	Aero Dr, **W...gas:** Arco/24hr, Shell, **food:** Baja Fresh, D'Amato's Pizza, Fong Chinese, Jack-in-the-Box, McDonald's, Roberto's Café, Sizzler, Starbucks, Stix Chinese, Submarina, Taco Bell, **lodging:** Best Western, Holiday Inn, **other:** Fry's Electronics, Radio Shack, Von's Foods, Wal-Mart/auto
7b	Friars Rd W, **W...**San Diego Stadium
7a	Friars Rd E, no facilities
6b	I-8, E to El Centro, W to beaches
6a	Adams Ave, downtown
5b	El Cajon Blvd, downtown
5a	University Ave, downtown
3	I-805, N to I-5, S to San Ysidro
2b	(2c from nb)CA 94 W, downtown
2a	Market St, downtown
1c	National Ave, Ocean View Blvd
1b	(from sb)I-5 S, to Chula Vista
1a	(from sb)I-5 N. I-15 begins/ends on I-5

Interstate 40

E ↕ W

Exit #	Services
155	Colorado River, California/Arizona state line, Pacific/Mountain time zone
153	Park Moabi Rd, to Rte 66, **N...**boating, camping
149mm	weigh sta eb, insp wb
148	5 Mile Rd, to Topock, Rte 66, no facilities
144	US 95 S, E Broadway, Needles, **N...gas:** Arco/24hr, Chevron/diesel, Shell/diesel, **food:** Burger King, Vito's Pizza, **other:** MEDICAL CARE, Basha's Foods, Rite Aid, U-Haul, **S...lodging:** Super 8
142	J St, Needles, **N...gas:** 76/24hr, **food:** Jack-in-the-Box, McDonald's, **lodging:** Travelers Inn, **other:** NAPA, **S...food:** Denny's, **lodging:** Day's Inn, Motel 6, **other:** st patrol

Needles

141	W Broadway, River Rd, Needles, **N...gas:** Chevron/diesel/24hr, **food:** Denny's, KFC, **lodging:** Best Motel, Econolodge, River Valley Motel, Stardust Motel, Travelodge, **other:** Goodyear/auto, diesel repair, **S...gas:** Arco/24hr, Chevron/diesel/24hr, Mobil/diesel, Shell/DQ/24hr, **food:** Carl's Jr, Hui's Rest., Taco Bell, **lodging:** Best Chalet Inn, Best Western, Budget Inn, Relax Inn, **other:** Chevrolet/Cadillac/Buick/GMC, RV/tire/repair
139	River Rd Cutoff(from eb), **N...**rec area, Hist Rte 66, **other:** KOA, Desert View RV Park
133	US 95 N, to Searchlight, Las Vegas, to Rte 66, no facilities
120	Water Rd, no facilities
115	Mountain Springs Rd, High Springs Summit, elev 2770
107	Goffs Rd, **N...**gas/diesel/food, Hist Rte 66
106mm	**rest area both lanes, full(handicapped)facilities, phone, picnic tables, litter barrels, petwalk**
100	Essex Rd, Essex, **N...**to Providence Mtn SP, Mitchell Caverns
78	Kelbaker Rd, to Amboy, Kelso, to E Mojave Nat Preserve, **S...**Hist Rte 66, **other:** RV camping
50	Ludlow, **N...gas:** 76/DQ/24hr, **S...gas:** Chevron/24hr, **lodging:** Ludlow Motel
33	Hector Rd, to Hist Rte 66, no facilities
28mm	**rest area both lanes, full(handicapped)facilities, phone, picnic tables, litter barrels, petwalk**
23	Ft Cady Rd, **N...gas:** Wesco/diesel/24hr, **S...lodging:** Newberry Mtn Motel/RV Park
18	Newberry Springs, **N...other:** UltraMar/diesel, **S...gas:** Shell/Taco Bell/LP, **other:** RV camp
12	Barstow-Daggett Airport, **N...**airport
7	Daggett, **N...gas:** Daggett Trkstp/diesel, **other:** RV camping(2mi), to Calico Ghost Town
5	Nebo St, to Hist Rte 66, no facilities
2	USMC Logistics Base, no facilities

CALIFORNIA

Interstate 40

E → **W**

Barstow

1 Montara Rd, Barstow, **N...gas:** Chevron, Mobil/diesel, Shell/repair, **food:** Burger King, Krissy's Café, McDonald's, Straw Hat Pizza, Tom's Burgers, **lodging:** Best Western, **other:** Pic'n Sav Foods, **1 mi N...gas:** Arco/24hr, Chevron, 76/Circle K/Subway/TCBY, Shell, **food:** Arby's, Burger King, Carl's Jr, Carrow's Rest., China Gourmet, Coco's, Del Taco, Denny's, FireHouse Italian, Golden Dragon, IHOP, Jack-in-the-Box, KFC, LJ Silver, Sizzler, Taco Bell, **lodging:** AstroBudget Motel, Best Motel, Budget Inn, Comfort Inn, Day's Inn, Desert Inn, Econolodge, Economy Inn, Executive Inn, Quality Inn, Ramada Inn, Super 8, **other:** AutoZone, Kragen Parts, Radio Shack, U-Haul/LP, Von's Foods, **S...gas:** Arco/24hr, **other:** Wal-Mart/auto

0mm I-40 begins/ends on I-15 in Barstow.

Interstate 80

E → **W**

Truckee

Exit #	Services
208	California/Nevada state line
201	Farad, no facilities
199	Floristan, no facilities
194	Hirschdale Rd, **N...**to Boca Dam, Stampede Dam, **S...gas:** United Trails Gen Store, **other:** RV camping, boating, camping
191	weigh sta wb
190	Prosser Village Rd, no facilities
188	CA 89 N, CA 267, to N Shore Lake Tahoe, **N...other:** Coachland RV Park, USFS, **S...gas:** 76, **food:** El Toro Bravo Mexican, Ponderosa Deli, Taco Sta, WagonTrain Café, **lodging:** Best Western, Truckee Hotel, **other:** info, same as 184
186	Central Truckee(no eb return), **S...gas:** 76, **food:** El Toro Bravo Mexican, Ponderosa Café, Wagontrain Café, **lodging:** Star Hotel, Swedish House B&B
185	CA 89 S, to N Lake Tahoe, **N...gas:** Sierra Superstop, 7-11, **food:** Burger King, DQ, La Bamba Mexican, Little Caesar's, Panda Express, Pizza Jct, Pizza Shack, Port of Subs, Sizzler, **other:** MEDICAL CARE, Allied Parts, Book Shelf, CarQuest, Gateway Pets, GNC, NAPA, New Moon Natural Foods, Rite Aid, Safeway, **S...gas:** Shell, **food:** Burger King, KFC, McDonald's, Pizzaria, Subway, **lodging:** Super 8, Truckee Inn, **other:** Albertson's, Longs Drugs, auto repair, to Squaw Valley, RV camping
184	Donner Pass Rd, Truckee, **N...gas:** Shell/diesel, **lodging:** Sunset Inn, **other:** factory outlet/famous brands, **S...gas:** Chevron/diesel/24hr, 76, **food:** Beginning Rest., Donner House Rest., Donner Lake Pizza, **lodging:** Alpine Country Lodge, Holiday Inn Express, **other:** chain service, to Donner SP, RV camp/dump
181mm	vista point both lanes
180	Donner Lake(from wb), **S...lodging:** Donner Lake Village Resort
177mm	**Donner Summit, elev 7239, rest area both lanes, full(handicapped)facilities, view area, phone, picnic tables, litter barrels, petwalk**

Colfax

176	Castle Park, Boreal Ridge Rd, **S...lodging:** Boreal Inn/rest., **other:** Pacific Crest Trailhead, skiing
174	Soda Springs, Norden, **S...gas:** 76/LP/diesel, **food:** Summit Rest., **lodging:** Donner Summit Lodge, **other:** chain services
171	Kingvale, **S...gas:** Shell
168	Rainbow Rd, to Big Bend, **S...lodging:** Rainbow Lodge/rest., **other:** RV camping
166	Big Bend(from eb), ranger sta, RV camping, same as 168
165	Cisco Grove, **N...other:** RV camp/dump, skiing, snowmobiling, **S...gas:** Mobil/24hr, **other:** chain serv
164	Eagle Lakes Rd, **N...other:** RV camping
161	CA 20 W, to Nevada City, Grass Valley, no facilities
160	Yuba Gap, **S...other:** snowpark, phone, picnic tables, boating, camping, skiing
158	Laing Rd, **S...lodging:** Rancho Sierra Inn/café
157mm	vista point wb
158a	Emigrant Gap(from eb), **S...gas:** Shell/Burger King/diesel/24hr, **lodging:** Rancho Sierra Inn/café, phone
156	Nyack Rd, Emigrant Gap, **S...gas:** Shell/Burger King/diesel, **food:** Nyack Café
155	Blue Canyon, no facilities
150	Drum Forebay, no facilities
148b	Baxter, **N...other:** RV camping, chainup services, food, phone
148a	Crystal Springs, no facilities
146	Alta, no facilities
145	Dutch Flat, **N...food:** Monte Vista Rest., **other:** RV camping, **S...gas:** Tesoro/diesel, **other:** CHP, chainup services
143	Gold Run(from wb), **N...gas/diesel,** food, phone, chainup
143mm	**rest area both lanes, full(handicapped)facilities, phone, picnic tables, litter barrels, petwalk**
142	Gold Run, **N...**chainup services
140	Magra Rd, Rollins Lake Rd, Secret Town Rd, no facilities
139	Rollins Lake Road(from wb), RV camping
135	CA 174, to Grass Valley, Colfax, **N...gas:** Chevron, 76/diesel, **food:** McDonald's, Pizza Factory, Rosy's Café, Starbucks, Taco Bell, Togo's, **lodging:** Colfax Motel, **other:** Sierra Mkt Foods, NAPA, **S...gas:** Chevron/diesel, Tesoro/diesel, **food:** BBQ, Dave's Tacos, Shang Garden Chinese, Subway, Sierra RV Ctr
133	Canyon Way, to Colfax, **S...other:** Chevrolet, Sierra NV Tire/repair
131	Cross Rd, to Weimar, park&ride, RV camping
130	W Paoli Lane, to Weimar, **S...gas:** Weimar Store/diesel
129	Heather Glen, elev 2000 ft, no facilities
128	Applegate, **N...gas:** Applegate Gas/diesel, **other:** chainup services
125	Clipper Gap, Meadow Vista, **S...other:** park&ride
124	Dry Creek Rd, **N...other:** CA Conservation Corps, **S...other:** park&ride

Interstate 80

E ↕ W

Auburn

123 Bell Rd, **N...other**: HOSPITAL, KOA(3mi), **S...food**: HQ House Rest.

122 Foresthill Rd, Ravine Rd, Bowman, **N...other**: RV camping/dump, **S...gas**: 76, **food**: Burger King, Ikeba's Burgers, Jack-in-the-Box, Sizzler, Starbucks, **lodging**: Best Western, Country Squire Inn/rest., same as 117

121 (from eb)Lincolnway, Auburn, **N...gas**: Flyers Gas, Sierra, Thrifty, **food**: Arby's, Denny's, JimBoy's Tacos, Pizza Hut/Taco Bell/24hr, Wienerschnitzel, Wimpy's Burgers, **lodging**: Best Inn, Comfort Inn, Foothills Motel, Motel 6, Sleep Inn, Super 8, **S...gas**: Arco/diesel/24hr, Chevron/diesel/24hr, 76, Shell/diesel, Sierra, **food**: Bakers Square, Baskin-Robbins, Burger King, Burrito Shop, Carl's Jr, Country Waffle, DQ, Ikea's Burgers, Izzy's BurgerStop, Jack-in-the-Box, KFC, LaBonte's Rest., Lyon's Rest., McDonald's, Sizzler, Thai Cuisine, **lodging**: Best Western, Country Squire Inn, Travelodge, **other**: Raley's Foods

120 Russell Ave(from wb), **S...gas**: Shell/diesel, **other**: Ryder Trucks, U-Haul, same as 117

119c Elm Ave, Auburn, **N...gas**: 76, Shell, **food**: Blimpie, Foster's Freeze, Taco Bell, **lodging**: Holiday Inn, **other**: Albertson's, Grocery Outlet, Longs Drug, Staples, Thrifty Foods, U-Haul, **S...gas**: Sierra

119b CA 49, to Grass Valley, Auburn, **N...gas**: Shell, **food**: In-n-Out, Marie Callender's, **lodging**: Holiday Inn, **other**: MEDICAL CARE, Staples, Thrifty Foods, **S...food**: Chevy's FreshMex(2mi)

119a Maple St, Nevada St, Old Town Auburn, **S...gas**: Budget, **food**: Tiopete Mexican

118 Ophir Rd, **N...food**: Pizza Lunch, Pop's Place Foods

116 CA 193, to Lincoln, **S...other**: Gamel RV Ctr

115 Newcastle, **N...other**: transmissions, **S...gas**: Arco, Flyers/diesel, **food**: Denny's, CHP

112 Penryn, **N...gas**: Gasco, 76/diesel/LP, **food**: CattleBaron's Café, Old Ground Cow Rest.

110 Horseshoe Bar Rd, to Loomis, **N...food**: Burger King, Taco Bell, Raley's Foods, RoundTable Pizza

109 Sierra College Blvd, **N...gas**: Chevron/McDonald's/diesel, Citgo/7-11, 76/diesel, **food**: Carl's Jr, **lodging**: Day's Inn, **other**: Camping World RV Service/supplies, Kia, KOA

108 Rocklin Rd, **N...gas**: Beacon, Exxon, **food**: Arby's, Baskin-Robbins, Blimpie, Burger King, Carl's Jr, China Gourmet, Denny's, Jack-in-the-Box, Jasper's Giant Burgers, KFC, Outback Steaks, Papa Murphy's, Red Pepper Café, RoundTable Pizza, Starbucks, Subway, Swank's Dinner Theatre, Taco Bell, **lodging**: Howard Johnson, Ramada Ltd, **other**: MEDICAL CARE, Camping World RV Service, CarQuest, Fabric Shop, Gamel RV Ctr, GNC, Harley-Davidson, Kragen Parts, Land Rover, Longs Drug, Radio Shack, Safeway, **S...gas**: Arco/24hr, **food**: Susanne Rest./bakery, **lodging**: Rocklin Park Hotel

106 CA 65, to Lincoln, Marysville, **1 mi N on Stanford Ranch Rd...gas**: 76, Shell, **food**: Applebee's, Carl's Jr, Jack-in-the-Box, **lodging**: Comfort Suites, **other**: Barnes&Noble, FoodSource, Costco, JC Penney, Macy's, Marshall's, Nordstrom's, Old Navy, Wal-Mart

105b Taylor Rd, to Rocklin(from eb), **N...food**: Cattlemen's Rest., **other**: Albertson's(1mi), Complete RV Ctr, **S...gas**: 76/Burger King, **lodging**: Courtyard, Fairfield Inn, Hilton Garden, Larkspur Landing Hotel, Residence Inn, **other**: HOSPITAL

105a Atlantic St, Eureka Rd, **S...gas**: Pacific Pride/diesel, 76, Shell, USA, **food**: Brookfield's Rest., Black Angus, Carver's Steaks, In-n-Out, Taco Bell, Wendy's, **lodging**: Marriott, **other**: America'sTire, Buick/GMC, Chevrolet, Ford, CompUSA, Home Depot, Nissan, OfficeMax, Sam's Club, mall

103b a Douglas Blvd, **N...gas**: Arco/24hr, Beacon, Exxon, 76, **food**: BBQ, Burger King, ClaimJumper, Delicia's Mexican, Jack-in-the-Box, KFC, McDonald's, Mtn Mike's Pizza, Taco Bell, Taquiera Mexican, **lodging**: Best Western, Extended Stay America, Heritage Inn, **other**: HOSPITAL, Ace Hardware, Big O Tire, Chevrolet, $Tree, Firestone/auto, Goodyear, Kragen Parts, Michael's, Old Navy, Radio Shack, Ross, Trader Joe, **S...gas**: Arco/24hr, Chevron/24hr, Shell, Carrow's/24hr, **food**: Carl's Jr, Del Taco, Denny's, Outback Steaks, Quality Inn, Oxford Suites, **other**: Albertson's, Lincoln/Mercury, Mervyn's, Office Depot, Rite Aid

102 Riverside Ave, Auburn Blvd, to Roseville, **N...gas**: Arco/24hr, **other**: MEDICAL CARE, **S...gas**: Flyers/diesel, Shell, UltraMar, **food**: California Burgers, Jack-in-the-Box, JimBoy's Tacos, **other**: AutoZone, BMW Motorcycles, Just Tires, K-Mart, Las Cazuelas Mexican, Riebes Parts, Schwab Tire, Village RV Ctr, Winston Tire

100 Antelope Rd, to Citrus Heights, **N...gas**: 76, **food**: Burger King, Carl's Jr, Del Taco, Giant Pizza, KFC, Little Caesar's, LJ Silver, McDonald's, RoundTable Pizza, 7-11, Subway, Taco Bell, Wendy's, **other**: Albertson's, $Tree, Raley's Foods, Rite Aid, USPO

100mm weigh sta both lanes

Citrus Hts

CALIFORNIA
Interstate 80

98 Greenback Lane, Elkhorn Blvd, Orangevale, Citrus Heights, **N...gas:** 76/service, Circle K, **food:** Carl's Jr, McDonald's, Pizza Hut, Subway, Taco Bell, **other:** Longs Drug, Radio Shack, Safeway

96 Madison Ave, **N...gas:** Beacon/24hr, Shell, **food:** Brookfield's Rest., Denny's, **lodging:** Madison Inn, Motel 6, **other:** Scandia Funpark, to McClellan AFB, **S...gas:** Arco/24hr, 76, Shell/repair, 7-11, **food:** A&W, Boston Mkt, Burger King, Carl's Jr, El Pollo Loco, Eppie's Rest., IHOP, Jack-in-the-Box, LJ Silver, McDonald's, Subway, Taco Bell, **lodging:** Holiday Inn, La Quinta, **other:** Acura/Porsche, America's Tire, Chevrolet, Ford/Isuzu, Goodyear, Office Depot, Pep-Boys, Schwab Tire, Target, U-Haul

94b Auburn Blvd, **S...food:** Burger King, **lodging:** Travelodge, to same as 94

94a Watt Ave, **N...lodging:** Day's Inn, **other:** McClellan AFB, **S...gas:** Arco/24hr, 76/diesel, Shell, 7-11, **food:** Carl's Jr, Carrow's Rest., Church's, DQ, Denny's, Golden Egg Café, KFC, Pizza Hut, Taco Bell, Wendy's, **lodging:** Best Inn, Motel 6, Travelodge, **other:** Firestone

93 Longview Dr, no facilities

92 Winters St, no facilities

91 Raley Blvd, Marysville Blvd, to Rio Linda, **N...gas:** Arco/24hr, Chevron/diesel/24hr, **S...other:** Mkt Basket Foods, tires

90 Norwood Ave, **N...gas:** Arco/Jack-in-the-Box/24hr, Beacon, **food:** Hong Kong Chinese, McDonald's, Subway, **other:** Rite Aid

89 Northgate Blvd, Sacramento, **N...other:** Fry's Electronics, **S...gas:** Circle K, Shell, Texaco/diesel, Valero/diesel, **food:** Burger King, Carl's Jr, IHOP, KFC, Lamp Post Pizza, LJ Silver, McDonald's, Taco Bell, **lodging:** Extended Stay America, Red Roof Inn, **other:** Goodyear/auto, K-Mart, PepBoys, transmissions

88 Truxel Rd, **N...gas:** Shell/diesel, **food:** Applebee's, Del Taco, In-n-Out, Jamba Juice, On the Border, Quizno's, Starbucks, Steve's Place Pizza, **other:** Arco Arena, Home Depot, Michael's, Raley's Depot, Ross, Staples, Wal-Mart, mall

86 I-5, N to Redding, S to Sacramento, to CA 99 N, no facilities

85 W El Camino, **N...gas:** Chevron/Subway/diesel/24hr, 49er Trkstp/Shell/diesel/24hr/@, **food:** Burger King, Subway, **lodging:** Super 8

83 Reed Ave, **N...gas:** 76, **food:** Jack-in-the-Box, Quizno's, Panda Express, Starbuck's, Subway, TCBY, **lodging:** Extended Stay America, **other:** Ford Trucks, diesel repair, **S...gas:** Arco/24hr, Shell/McDonald's/diesel

82 US 50 E, W Sacramento, no facilities

81 Enterprise Blvd, W Sacramento, **N...gas:** Chevron/diesel/24hr/@, **food:** Eppie's Rest/24hr, **lodging:** Granada Inn, **S...gas:** 76/diesel, **food:** Denny's, KOA, Subway

78 Chiles Rd, no facilities

75 Mace Blvd, **S...gas:** Chevron/24hr, 76, Shell, Valero/diesel, **food:** Burger King, Cindy's Rest., Denny's, McDonald's, Subway, Taco Bell/24hr, Wendy's, **lodging:** Howard Johnson, Motel 6, **other:** Chevrolet/Toyota, Chrysler/Jeep, Ford/Mercury/Nissan, Honda, La Mesa RV Ctr, Mazda/VW, Nugget Mkt Foods, Pontiac/Buick/GMC, to Mace Ranch

73 Olive Dr(from wb, no EZ return), **other:** Fair Deal RV Ctr

72b a Richards Blvd, Davis, **N...gas:** Shell/24hr, **food:** Caffe Italia, In-n-Out, **lodging:** Davis Motel/Café Italia, University Park Inn, **other:** NAPA, **S...gas:** Chevron, **food:** Applebee's, Del Taco, IHOP, KFC, RoundTable Pizza, Wendy's, **lodging:** Comfort Suites, Holiday Inn Express, **other:** Kragen Parts

71 to UC Davis, no facilities

70 CA 113 N, to Woodland, **N...HOSPITAL**

69 Kidwell Rd, no facilities

67 Pedrick Rd, **N...gas:** 76/LP

66b Milk Farm Rd(from wb), no facilities

66a CA 113 S, Currey Rd, to Dixon, **S...gas:** Arco, CFN/diesel, 76/Popeye's, Shell/diesel, **food:** Cattlemen's Rest., Jack-in-the-Box, **other:** Wal-Mart/auto

64 Pitt School Rd, to Dixon, **S...gas:** Chevron/24hr, Valero, **food:** Arby's, Burger King, Chevy's Mexican, Denny's, Domino's, IHOP/24hr, Mary's Pizza, McDonald's, Pizza Guy's, Pizza Hut, Solano Bakery, Starbucks, Subway, Taco Bell, **lodging:** Best Western, Microtel, **other:** MEDICAL CARE, Ford, Kragen Parts, Radio Shack, Safeway/gas

63 Dixon Rd, Midway Rd, **N...gas:** Chevron/RV Dump/diesel, **S...gas:** Arco/24hr, Shell/tune, **food:** Carl's Jr, KFC/A&W, Los Altos Mexican, **lodging:** Super 8, **other:** Dixon Fruit Mkt, Food Market

60 Midway Rd, Lewis Rd, Elmyra, **N...RV** camping

59 Meridian Rd, Weber Rd, no facilities

57 Leisure Town Rd, **S...gas:** Beacon/gas, **food:** Black Oak Rest., Jack-in-the-Box, SplitFire Rest., Vaca Joe's, **lodging:** Best Value, Extended Stay America, Fairfield Inn, Holiday Inn Express, Motel 6, Residence Inn, Vaca Valley Inn, **other:** Chevrolet, Chrysler/Plymouth/Dodge/Jeep, Harley-Davidson, Home Depot, Honda, Kohl's, Mazda, Nissan, Toyota, VW

56 I-505 N, to Winters,, no facilities

55 Monte Vista Ave, **N...gas:** Citgo/7-11, Nuttree Gas, 76/Circle K, Shell, **food:** Arby's, Burger King, City Sports Grill, Denny's, Hisui Japanese, IHOP, McDonald's, Murillo's Mexican, Nations Burger, Pelayo's Mexican, RoundTable Pizza, Taco Bell, Wendy's, **lodging:** Best Western, Royal Motel, Super 8, **other:** HOSPITAL, America Tire, Firestone/auto, Goodyear/auto, Nugget Foods, U-Haul, Winston Tire, transmissions, **S...gas:** Arco/24hr, Chevron/24hr, **food:** Applebee's, Baja Fresh Mexican, Carl's Jr, Chevy's FreshMex, Chili's, Chubby's Diner, HomeTown Buffet, In-n-Out, Italian Café, Jack-in-the-Box, KFC, Mel's Cafe, Quizno's, Starbucks, Tahoe Joe's Rest., Togo's, **lodging:** Fairfield Inn, Courtyard, **other:** CompUSA, Goodyear, Mervyn's, Michael's, Old Navy, Ross, Safeway, Sam's Club, Staples, Target, Vacaville Stores/famous brands, Wal-Mart/auto

Interstate 80

E ↕ **W**

54b Mason St, Peabody Rd, **N...gas:** Beacon/Taco Time/diesel, Petro, **lodging:** Hampton Inn, Hawthorn Suites, **other:** AutoZone, NAPA, Schwab Tire, **S...gas:** Shell/repair, **food:** Carl's Jr, Solano's Bakery, Wok'n Roll Chinese, **other:** Aegean Tires, Costco, Ford/Mercury, Goodyear/auto, PepBoys

54a Davis St, **N...gas:** Chevron/McDonald's, **food:** Outback Steaks, **lodging:** Hampton Inn **S...gas:** QuikStop, **other:** Cecil's Repair, Winco Foods

53 Merchant St, Alamo Dr, **N...gas:** Chevron, Shell/diesel, **food:** Baldo's Mexican, Bakers Square, Lyon's/24hr, RoundTable pizza, **lodging:** Alamo Inn, **S...gas:** 76, **food:** Jack-in-the-Box, KFC, McDonald's, Pizza Hut, Port Subs, Starbucks, **other:** Radio Shack

52 Cherry Glen Rd(from wb), no facilities

51b Pena Adobe Rd, **S...lodging:** Ranch Hotel

51a Lagoon Valley Rd, Cherry Glen, no facilities

48 N Texas St, Fairfield, **S...gas:** Arco/24hr, Chevron, Shell, **food:** Burger King, RoundTable Pizza, **lodging:** EZ 8 Motel, **other:** Raley's Foods

47 Waterman Blvd, **N...food:** Dynasty Chinese, Hungry Hunter Rest., RoundTable Pizza, Strings Italian, **other:** Buick/Pontiac/GMC, Chevrolet/Cadillac, Safeway, Village RV Ctr, to Austin's Place, **S...**to Travis AFB, museum

45 Travis Blvd, Fairfield, **N...gas:** Arco/24hr, Chevron/24hr, Shell/diesel, **food:** Burger King, ChuckeCheese, Denny's, In-n-Out, McDonald's, Subway, Taco Bell, **lodging:** Extended Stay America, Holiday Inn, Motel 6, **other:** Raley's Foods, Harley-Davidson, Ford, Hyundai/Daewoo, Nissan, CHP, **S...gas:** Shell, **food:** Applebee's, Baja Fresh Mexican, Blue Frog Brewery/rest., Carino's Italian, Chevy's Mexican, FreshChoice Rest., Gordito's Mexican, Great Wall Chinese, Jamba Juice, Marie Callender's, Mimi's Café, Panda Express, Red Lobster, Red Robin, Subway, **lodging:** Hilton Garden, **other:** HOSPITAL, Barnes&Noble, Best Buy, Circuit City, Firestone/auto, JC Penney, Macy's, Mazda, Mervyn's, Michael's, OfficeMax, Old Navy, Ross, Sears/auto, Trader Joe's, mall

44 W Texas St, same as 46, Fairfield, **N...gas:** Shell/diesel, **food:** ChuckeCheese, Gordito's Mexican, **lodging:** Sleepy Hollow Motel, **other:** Mazda/Subaru, Suzuki, Target, **S...gas:** Exxon, **food:** DQ, Jack-in-the-Box, Johanne's Diner, McDonald's, Nations Burgers, Pelayo's Mexican, **lodging:** Travelodge, **other:** Acura/Honda, Home Depot, Isuzu, Nissan, PepBoys, PostMasters, SavMax Foods, Target, Toyota, Walgreen

43 CA 12 E, Abernathy Rd, Suisun City, **S...other:** Wal-Mart, Budweiser Plant

42mm weigh sta both lanes, phone

41 Suisan Valley Rd, **S...gas:** Arco/24hr, Chevron, Flyers/diesel, 76/Circle K/diesel/24hr, Shell/diesel, **food:** Arby's, Bravo's Pizza, Burger King, Carl's Jr, Denny's, Green Bamboo Chinese, Jack-in-the-

Fairfield

Box, McDonald's, Old SF Expresso, Starbucks, Subway, Taco Bell, Wendy's, **lodging:** Best Western, Comfort Suites, Hampton Inn, Holiday Inn Express, Inns of America, Overnighter Lodge, **other:** Camping World RV Service, Ray's RV Ctr, Scandia FunCtr

40 I-680(from wb), no facilities

39b Green Valley Rd, **N...food:** Happy Garden Chinese, RoundTable Pizza, Subway, **other:** Costco, Longs Drug, Radio Shack, Safeway, TJ Max, **S...** Saturn

39a Red Top Rd, **N...gas:** 76/Circle K/24hr, **food:** Jack-in-the-Box

36 American Canyon Rd, no facilities

34mm **rest area wb, full(handicapped)facilities, info, phone, picnic tables, litter barrels, petwalk, vista parking**

33b a CA 37, to San Rafael, Columbus Pkwy, **N...gas:** Chevron, **food:** Carls Jr., **lodging:** Holiday Inn

32 Redwood St, to Vallejo, **N...gas:** 76, **food:** Denny's, Panda Garden, **lodging:** Day's Inn, Holiday Inn, Motel 6, **other:** HOSPITAL, **S...gas:** Arco, Shell, **food:** Applebee's, Black Angus, Cham Thai Rest., Chevy's Mexican, IHOP, Little Caesar's, Lyon's Rest., McDonald's, Mtn Mike's Pizza, Olive Garden, Red Lobster, Subway, Susie's Café, Taco Bell, Wendy's, **lodging:** Comfort Inn, Ramada Inn, **other:** AutoZone, Buick/GMC, Hancock Fabrics, Home Depot, Honda, Longs Drug, OfficeMax, PepBoys, Radio Shack, Ross, Safeway, SaveMart Foods, Target, Toyota

31b Tennessee St, to Vallejo, **S...gas:** 76, Valero, **food:** Jack-in-the-Box, Pacifica Pizza, **lodging:** Great Western Inn, Quality Inn, **other:** USPO

31a Solano Ave, Springs Rd, **N...gas:** Chevron/diesel/24hr, **food:** Burger King, Church's, Nitti Gritti Rest., Schezuan Chinese, Taco Bell, **lodging:** Best Value Inn, Deluxe Inn, **other:** Ford, Albertson's, Rite Aid, U-Haul, **S...gas:** Beacon, Chemco, Chevron, QuikStop, **food:** Bud's Burgers, DQ, McDonald's, Panino Italian, Pizza Hut, RoundTable Pizza, SmorgaBob's, Subway, **lodging:** Islander Motel, **other:** Kragen Parts, Walgreen

30c Georgia St, Central Vallejo, **N...gas:** Safeway, **other:** Ford, **S...gas:** Shell/Starbucks/diesel, **food:** Mandarin Chinese, **lodging:** California Motel

Vallejo

CALIFORNIA
Interstate 80

E ↑ **W**

30b Benicia Rd(from wb), **S...gas:** Shell/diesel

30a I-780, to Martinez, no facilities

29b Magazine St, Vallejo, **N...gas:** Shell, **food:** Rod's Hickory Pit/24hr, **lodging:** Economy Inn, El Curtola Motel, 7 Motel, **other:** TradeWinds RV Park, **S...gas:** 7-11, **food:** McDonald's, **lodging:** Knight's Inn, Travel Inn

29a CA 29, Maritime Academy Dr, Vallejo, **N...gas:** Chevron/24hr, **food:** Subway, **lodging:** Motel 6, Vallejo Inn

28mm toll plaza, pay toll from eb

27 Crockett Rd, to Rodeo, Crockett, **N...food:** seafood rest

26 Cummings Skyway, to CA 4(from wb), to Martinez, no facilities

24 Willow Ave, to Rodeo, **N...gas:** 76/diesel, **food:** Straw Hat Pizza, **other:** MEDICAL CARE, NAPA, Safeway/24hr, Rodeo Drugs, USPO, **S...gas:** 76/Circle K/diesel, **food:** Burger King, Jamalo's Pizza

23 CA 4, to Stockton, Hercules, **N...gas:** Shell, **food:** Jack-in-the-Box, Starbucks, **other:** Radio Shack, **S on Sycamore...food:** Burgerama, McDonald's, RoundTable Pizza, Subway, Taco Bell, **S...lodging:** Best Western, **other:** MEDICAL CARE, Albertson's, Home Depot, Rite Aid, USPO

22 Pinole Valley Rd, **S...gas:** Arco/24hr, Chevron/diesel, Shell, 76, 7-11, **food:** Jack-in-the-Box, Pizza Plenty, Red Onion Rest., Rico's Mexican, Ristorante Italiano, Subway, Waffle Shop, Zip's Rest., **other:** Albertson's

21 Appian Way, **N...gas:** Beacon, **food:** McDonald's, **other:** MEDICAL CARE, Kragen Parts, Longs Drug, Safeway, **S...gas:** Valero/diesel, **food:** Burger King, Carl's Jr, HomeTown Buffet, HotDog Sta, KFC, Krispy Kreme, In n' Out, LJ Silver, Panda Express, RoundTable Pizza, Sizzler, Starbucks, Subway, Taco Bell, Wendy's, **lodging:** Day's Inn, Motel 6, **other:** Albertson's, Autozone, Best Buy, Goodyear/auto, K-Mart, Radio Shack

20 Richmond Pkwy, to I-580 W, **N...gas:** Chevron, **food:** McDonald's, IHOP, Subway, **other:** Barnes&Noble, Chrysler/Plymouth/Jeep, Circuit City, Ford, OfficeMax, Ross, **S...gas:** Chevron, Shell/diesel, **food:** Applebee's, Chuck Steak, In-n-Out, Krispy Kreme, Outback Steaks, RoundTable Pizza, **other:** FoodMaxx, GoodGuys, Kragen Parts, Old Navy, Mervyn's, Michael's, Staples, Target

19b Hilltop Dr, to Richmond, **N...gas:** Chevron, **food:** Chevy's Mexican, Olive Garden, Red Lobster, Subway, Tokyo Rest., **lodging:** Courtyard, Extended Stay America, **other:** Albertson's, Buick/Pontiac, Chevrolet, Firestone, JC Penney, Jo-Ann Fabrics, Macy's, Nissan, Sears/auto, mall, **S...gas:** Hilltop Fuel/Bobby's BBQ/diesel

19a El Portal Dr, to San Pablo, **N...gas:** Shell, **S...food:** McDonalds, KFC, **other:** Raley's Foods

---

18 San Pablo Dam Rd, **N...gas:** 76, 7-11, **food:** Burger King, Denny's, Jack-in-the-Box, KFC, McDonald's, Nations Burgers, Quizno's, Taco Bell, **lodging:** Holiday Inn Express, **other:** HOSPITAL, Albertson's, K-Mart, Longs Drug, **S...other:** CamperLand RV Ctr

17 Macdonald Ave(from eb), McBryde Ave(from wb), Richmond, **N...gas:** Arco/24hr, Citgo/7-11, **food:** Burger King, Church's, KFC, Taco Bell, **S...gas:** Chevron/24hr, **food:** Bakers Square, Wendy's, **other:** Albertson's, Safeway, auto repair

16 San Pablo Ave, to Richmond, San Pablo, **S...gas:** Chevron, 76, **food:** Subway, Wendy's, **other:** Safeway

15 Cutting Blvd, Potrero St, to I-580 Br(from wb), to El Cerrito, **N...gas:** Arco, **S...gas:** Chevron, 76/diesel, **food:** Carrow's Rest., Church's, Denny's, IHOP, Jack-in-the-Box, McDonald's, **lodging:** Super 8, **other:** FoodsCo Foods, Home Depot, Honda, PepBoys, Staples, Target, Walgreen

14b Carlson Blvd, El Cerrito, **N...gas:** 76, **lodging:** 40 Flags Motel, **S...lodging:** Best Value

14a Central Ave, El Cerrito, **S...gas:** Shell/24hr, 76, Valero, **food:** Burger King, KFC, Nations Burgers, **other:** Branch Mkt Foods, mall

13 to I-580(from eb), Albany, no facilities

12 Gilman St, to Berkeley, **N...**Golden Gate Fields Racetrack

11 University Ave, to Berkeley, **S...gas:** 76, Beacon, **other:** to UC Berkeley

10 CA 13, to Ashby Ave, no facilities

9 Powell St, Emeryville, **N...gas:** Shell, **food:** Chevy's Mexican, **lodging:** Holiday Inn, **S...gas:** Beacon, **food:** Burger King, Denny's, Jamba Juice, Lyon's Rest., Starbucks, Trader Joe's, **lodging:** Courtyard, Day's Inn, Sheraton, Wyndham Suites, **other:** Borders Books, Circuit City, Emery Bay Mkt, Good Guys, Jo-Ann Fabrics, Old Navy, Ross

8c b Oakland, to I-880, I-580, no facilities

8a W Grand Ave, Maritime St, no facilities

7mm toll plaza wb

5mm SF Bay

4 Treasure Island(exits left)

2c b Fremont St, Harrison St, Embarcadero(exits left), no facilities

1 55th St, 7th St, downtown SF

0 I-80 begins/ends at 7th St in San Francisco.

Interstate 110(LA)

Exit #	Services	
21	I-110 begins/ends on I-10.	**E** ↑
20c	Adams Blvd, **E...other:** Nissan	
20b	37th St, Exposition Blvd, **E...repair**, **W...gas:** Chevron/McDonald's, **lodging:** Radisson	
20a	MLK Blvd, Expo Park	
19b	Vernon Ave, **E...gas:** Mobil, Shell, **W...gas:** 76/24hr, Shell, **food:** Jack-in-the-Box, **other:** Ralph's Foods, Rite Aid	
18b	Slauson Ave, **E...gas:** Mobil, Shell, **W...gas:** 76	
18a	Gage Blvd, **E...gas:** Arco, **food:** Church's	↓ **W**

Interstate 110

E ⬍ **W** | **Los Angeles Area**

17 Florence Ave, **E...gas:** Mobil, **food:** Jack-in-the-Box, **W...gas:** Arco, Chevron, Shell/24hr, **food:** Burger King, Pizza Hut

16 Manchester Ave, **E...gas:** Arco, **food:** McDonald's, **W...gas:** 76/Circle K, **food:** Church's, Jack-in-the-Box, Pam's Burgers, Popeye's

15 Century Blvd, **E...gas:** Shell/Subway, **food:** Burger King, **W...gas:** 76

14b Imperial Hwy, **W...gas:** Shell, **food:** McDonald's

14a I-105

13 El Segundo Blvd, **E...gas:** Shell/diesel/24hr, **W...gas:** Arco/24hr, Shell

12 Rosecrans Ave, **E...gas:** Arco/24hr, Cardlock Fuel, Chevron, **W...gas:** Chevron/McDonald's, Mobil, 7-11, **food:** Jack-in-the-Box, KFC, Subway, **other:** Chief Parts

11 Redondo Beach Blvd, **E...food:** McDonald's, Peter Pan Pizza, **W...gas:** Mobil, **other:** HOSPITAL

10b a CA 91, **W...food:** Carl's Jr, Jack-in-the-Box, Krispy Kreme, McDonald's, Taco Bell/Pizza Hut, **other:** Albertson's, Food4Less, Sam's Club

9 I-405, San Diego Fwy

8 Torrance Blvd, Del Amo, **E...food:** Burger King, **other:** K-mart, **W...gas:** Mobil, Shell/diesel

7b Carson St, **E...food:** KFC, **lodging:** Cali Inn, **W...gas:** Mobil, Shell, **food:** Bakers Square, Hong Kong Garden, In-n-Out, Jack-in-the-Box, **other:** HOSPITAL, Harbor Drug, Kragen Parts, Radio Shack

5 Sepulveda Blvd, **E...other:** Target, **W...gas:** Arco/24hr, Chevron, Mobil, Shell, **food:** Carl's Jr, Golden Ox Burger, McDonald's, Popeye's, Taco Bell, **lodging:** Motel 6, **other:** Food4Less, K-Mart, Rite Aid, Von's Foods

4 CA 1, Pacific Coast Hwy, **E...gas:** Shell, **food:** Jack-in-the-Box, **W...gas:** Chevron, Mobil/diesel, **food:** Denny's, El Pollo Loco, EZ TakeOut Burger, **lodging:** Best Western, **other:** HOSPITAL, Discount Parts, Honda, PepBoys

3b Anaheim St, **E...gas:** Shell

3a C St, **E...gas:** Shell/diesel, **other:** radiators, **W...gas:** 76 Refinery

1b Channel St, no facilities

1a CA 47, Gaffey Ave, no facilities

0mm I-110 begins/ends

Interstate 205(Tracy)

E ⬍ **W** | **Tracy**

Exit # Services

12 I-205 begins wb, ends eb, accesses I-5 nb.

9 MacArthur Dr, Tracy, **S...gas** Chevron, **other:** Prime Outlet Ctr/famous brands

8 Tracy Blvd, Tracy, **N...gas:** Chevron, Shell/diesel, Tracy's Trkstp/Mean Gene's Burger/diesel/24hr/@, **food:** Denny's/24hr, **lodging:** Holiday Inn Express, Motel 6, **S...gas:** Arco/24hr, **food:** Arby's, Burger King, In-n-Out, LJ Silver, Lyon's Rest., McDonald's, Nations Burgers, Subway, Wendy's, **lodging:** Best Western, Phoenix Lodge, **other:** HOSPITAL, Albertson's, Food-Maxx, Jo-Ann Fabrics, Kragen Parts, Longs Drugs, Walgreen, CHP

7 Corral Hollow, **N...**same as 6

6 Grant Line Rd, Antioch, **N...gas:** Chevron, **food:** Applebee's, Burger King, IHOP, Olive Garden, Chevy's

Mexican, Panda Express, Quizno's, Sonic, Starbucks, Taco Bell, Wienerschnitzel/TasteeFreeze, **lodging:** Extended Stay America, Fairfield Inn, Hampton Inn, **other:** Chevrolet, Costco/gas, Home Depot, JC Penney, Michael's, Ross, Sears/auto, Staples, Target, Toyota, Wal-Mart/McDonald's/auto, World Mkt, mall, **S...gas:** Arco/24hr, Citgo/7-11, Shell/diesel, Valero, **food:** Carl's Jr, KFC/A&W, Orchard Rest., **other:** Cadillac/Pontiac/GMC, Tracy Marine

4 11TH St(from eb), to Tracy, Defense Depot, no facilities

3 Mtn House Rd, to I-580 E, no facilities

2 Patterson Pass Rd (from wb), no facilities

.0mm I-205 begins eb/ends wb, accesses I-580 wb.

Interstate 210(Pasadena)

E ⬍ **W** | **San Dimas**

Exit # Services

49 I-10, San Bernardino Fwy. CA 57, Orange Fwy. I-210 begins/ends on I-10.

48 CA 71, Corona Fwy, no facilities

47 Raging Waters Dr, Via Verde, **S...other:** Bonelli Park, gas/LP

46 Covina Blvd, no facilities

45 Arrow Hwy, San Dimas, **N...gas:** 76, Shell, **food:** Del Taco, Denny's, McDonald's, Red Robin, Sizzler, Zendeja's Mexican, **lodging:** Comfort Suites, Red Roof Inn, **other:** Home Depot, Lowe's Whse, **S...gas:** Mobil, **food:** IHOP, Trader Joe's, **other:** DressBarn, OfficeMax, PetCo, Ralph's Foods, Rite Aid, Ross, Target

44 CA 30 E(exits left from eb), Lone Hill Ave, **S...food:** Baja Fresh, Blimpie, Coco's, Wendy's, **other:** Chevrolet, Dodge, Ford, Home Depot, Sam's Club, Toyota, Wal-Mart/auto

43 Sunflower Ave, no facilities

42 Grand Ave, to Glendora, **N...gas:** Mobil, **food:** Denny's, **other:** HOSPITAL

41 Citrus Ave, to Covina, no facilities

40 CA 39, Azusa Ave, **N...gas:** Arco/24hr, Chevron, Texaco/Subway/Del Taco, **lodging:** Super 8, **lodging:** Western Inn, **S...gas:** 76, **food:** In-n-Out, **lodging:** Azuza Inn

39 Vernon Ave, **N...food:** Carl's Jr, Taco Bell, **other:** Costco

38 Irwindale, **N...gas:** Arco, **food:** Carl's Jr, Denny's, Don Ramon's Grill, McDonald's, Taco Bell, **other:** MEDICAL CARE, Costco, Health Valley Foods

36b Mt Olive Dr, no facilities

36a I-605 S, no facilities

35b a Mountain Ave, **N...food:** Old Spaghetti Factory, **other:**

CALIFORNIA

Interstate 210

E ↕ **W**

Pasadena

	BMW, Buick, Chevrolet, Ford/Lincoln/Mercury, Honda, Infiniti, Isuzu, Mazda, Mitsubishi, Nissan, Saturn, Staples, Subaru, Target, **S...other:** Home Depot, Ross, Wal-Mart
34	Myrtle Ave, **S...gas:** Chevron, 76, **food:** Jack-in-the-Box
33	Huntington Dr, Monrovia, **N...gas:** Shell, **food:** Acapulco Rest., Applebee's, Black Angus, Burger King, Chili's, ChuckeCheese, Lee Roy's Rest., McDonald's, Mimi's, Orange Julius, Panda Express, Quizno's, Trader Joe's, Winchell's, **lodging:** Sheraton, **other:** CompUSA, GNC, Marshall's, Office Depot, Rite Aid, **S...food:** Baja Fresh, BJ's Grill, Capistrano's, ClaimJumper, KookooRoo, Macaroni Grill, Olive Garden, Red Lobster, Souplantation, Starbucks, Subway, Tokyo Woko, Tony Roma, **lodging:** Embassy Suites, Extended Stay America, Hampton Inn, Holiday Inn, Homestead Suites, OakTree Inn, Residence Inn
32	Santa Anita Ave, Arcadia, **S...gas:** Chevron, **food:** In-n-Out, **other:** carwash
31	Baldwin Ave, to Sierra Madre, no facilities
30b a	Rosemead Blvd, **N...**Shell, **S...gas:** 76
29b a	San Gabriel Blvd, Madre St, **N...gas:** Arco, 76, **lodging:** Panda Inn, Ralph's Foods, Ross, **S...gas:** Arco, 76, **food:** Jack–in-the-Box, **lodging:** Best Western, Ramada Inn, **other:** Buick/Chevrolet/Pontiac/GMC, Cadillac, Circuit City, Staples, Target, Toyota
28	Altadena Dr, Sierra Madre, no facilities
27	Hill Ave, no facilities
26	Lake Ave, **N...gas:** Mobil
25b	CA 134, to Ventura
25a	Del Mar Blvd, CA Blvd, CO Blvd, no facilities
24	Mountain St, no facilities
23	Lincoln Ave, **S...lodging:** Lincoln Motel
22b	Arroyo Blvd, **N...food:** Jack-in-the-Box, **other:** repair, **S...**to Rose Bowl
22a	Berkshire Ave, Oak Grove Dr, no facilities
21	Gould Ave, **S...gas:** Arco, **food:** McDonald's, RoundTable Pizza, Trader Joes, **other:** Firestone, Just Tires, Ralph's Foods
20	Angeles Crest Hwy, no facilities
19	CA 2, Glendale Fwy, **S...other:** HOSPITAL
18	Ocean View Blvd, to Montrose
17b a	Pennsylvania Ave, La Crescenta, **N...gas:** Mobil, Shell, **food:** Wienerschnitzel, **other:** Nissan, Office Depot, Toyota, Von's Foods, **S...other:** Gardenia Mkt/deli
16	Lowell Ave, no facilities
14	La Tuna Cyn Rd, no facilities
11	Sunland Blvd, Tujunga, **N...food:** Sizzler, **other:** Ralph's Foods, Rite Aid
9	Wheatland Ave, **N...other:** food mkt
8	Osborne St, Lakeview Terrace, **N...gas:** 7-11
6a	Paxton St, no facilities
6b	CA 118, no facilities
5	Maclay St, to San Fernando, **S...gas:** Chevron, 76, **food:** El Pollo Loco, McDonald's, Taco Bell, **other:** Home Depot, **other:** Office Depot, Radio Shack, Sam's Club
4	Hubbard St, **N...gas:** Chevron, **other:** Radio Shack, Rite Aid, **S...gas:** Mobil/diesel, Shell, **food:** El Caporal Mexican, Jack-in-the-Box, Shakey's Pizza, Subway
3	Polk St, **S...gas:** Arco, Chevron/24hr, 7-11
2	Roxford St, **N...**HOSPITAL, **S...lodging:** Super 8
1c	Yarnell St, no facilities
1 b a	I-210 begins/ends on I-5, exit 160.

San Fernando

Interstate 215(Riverside)

N ↕ **S**

San Bernardino / **Riverside**

Exit#	Services
55	I-215 begins/ends on I-15.
54	Devore, **E...gas:** Arco/24hr, Devore Minimart, **other:** KOA, **W...food:** Joe's Country Corner
50	Palm Ave, Kendall Dr, **E...gas:** Citgo/7-11, Mobil/diesel, **food:** Burger King, DQ, Popeye's, **W...gas:** Arco/24hr, **food:** Denny's
48	University Pkwy, **E...gas:** Chevron, 76/Subway/Circle K, **food:** Carl's Jr, Del Taco, IHOP, KFC, McDonald's, **other:** Ralph's Foods, **W...gas:** Arco/24hr, Shell/diesel, **food:** Jack-in-the-Box, Pizza Hut, Taco Bell, **lodging:** Motel 6, Quality Inn
46c b	27th St, **E...**golf, **W...**golf
46a	CA 30 W, Highland Ave, no facilities
45b	Muscuplabe Dr, **E...gas:** Shell, **other:** Chevrolet, Home Depot, SavOn Foods, Stater Bros
45a	CA 30 E, Highlands, no facilities
44b	Baseline Rd no facilities
44a	CA 66 W, 5th St, **E...lodging:** Econolodge
43	2nd St, Civic Ctr, **E...gas:** Arco, Chevron, **food:** China Hut, Del Taco, Denny's, In-n-Out, LJ Silver, Pizza Hut/Taco Bell, **lodging:** Radisson, **other:** Ford, Food4Less, JC Penney, Kelly Tire, Marshall's, mall
42b	Mill St, SBD Airport, **E...food:** McDonald's, **other:** Suzuki/Honda, **W...gas:** Shell
42a	Inland Ctr Dr, **E...food:** Carl's Jr, Del Taco, Jack-in-the-Box, Macy's, Robinsons-May, Sears/auto, mall
41	Orange Show Rd, **E...gas:** Chevron, Shell, **food:** Denny's, **lodging:** Budget Inn, Knight's Inn, **other:** Chevrolet, Dodge, Firestone, Macy's, Mazda, 99c Store, Target, **W...lodging:** Villager Lodge, **other:** Cadillac, Daewoo, Giant RV, Isuzu, Jeep, Kia, Mitsubishi, Nissan, Toyota, Volvo
40b a	I-10, E to Palm Springs, W to LA
39	Washington St, Mt Vernon Ave, **E...gas:** Arco/24hr, Chevron/diesel, **food:** Arby's, Bluff's Rest., Siquios Mexican, Taco Joe's, **other:** Asiana Mkt, Goodyear, Rite Aid, **W...gas:** Mobil, **food:** Burger King, Carl's Jr, Del Taco, Denny's, Jack-in-the-Box, McDonald's, Ravi's Indian Cuisine, Sassy Steer, Spike's Teriyaki, Subway, Taco Bell, Yoshinoya, Zendejas Mexican, **lodging:** Red Tile Inn, **other:** Giant RV, 99c Store, Radio Shack, RV Expo, Wal-Mart
38	Barton Rd, **E...gas:** Arco/24hr, Shell, **other:** AutoZone, **W...food:** Dorothy's Burgers
37	La Cadena Dr, **E...gas:** Shell/diesel/24hr, **food:** YumYum Rest., **lodging:** Day's Inn
36	Center St, to Highgrove, **W...gas:** 76/diesel/LP
35	Columbia Ave, **E...gas:** Arco, **W...gas:** Circle K
34b a	CA 91, CA 60, Riverside, to beach cities
33	Blaine St, 3rd St, **E...gas:** 76, Shell, Texaco/repair, UltraMar, **other:** K-Mart, **W...gas:** Arco/24hr
32	University Ave, Riverside, **W...gas:** Arco, Mobil, Shell, **food:** Baker's Drive-Thru, Baskin-Robbins, Carl's Jr, Chan's Oriental, Coco's, Del Taco, Denny's, Domino's, Green Burrito, Gus Jr #11, IHOP, Jilberto's Tacos, Papa John's, Quizno's, Starbucks, Taco Bell, Tempo Del Sol Mexican, Wienerschnitzel, Winchell's, **lodging:** Comfort Inn, Courtyard, Dynasty Suites, Hampton Inn, Motel 6, Super 8, **other:** MEDICAL CARE, Kragen Parts, Rite Aid

Interstate 215

N
↑
S

31	MLK Blvd, El Cerrito, no facilities
30b	Central Ave, Watkins Dr, no facilities
30a	Fair Isle Dr, Box Springs, **E...gas:** Shell, **other:** Margon's RV, **W...gas:** 76/Taco Bell, **other:** Ford
29	CA 60 E, to Indio, **E on Day St...gas:** Arco/24hr, Shell/Del Taco/diesel, **food:** Café Chinese, Carl's Jr, HomeTown Buffet, McDonald's, Red Robin, **other:** MEDICAL CARE, Costco/gas, Home Depot, JC Penney, Mervyn's, Ralph's Foods, Robinsons-May, Sam's Club, Sears/auto, Staples, Wal-Mart, mall
28	Eucalyptus Ave, Eastridge Ave, **E on Day St...other:** Sam's Club, Wal-Mart, same as 29
27b	Alessandro Blvd, **E...gas:** Arco/24hr, Mobil/diesel, **food:** Jack-in-the-Box, Dragon House Chinese, **other:** Big O Tire, auto repair, **W...gas:** Chevron
27a	Cactus Air Blvd, **E...gas:** Chevron, Shell/DelTaco/diesel, **food:** Burger King, Carl's Jr
25	Van Buren Blvd, **E...other:** March Field Museum, **W...other:** Riverside Nat Cen.
23	Oleander Ave, no facilities
22	Ramona Expswy, **1 mi E on Perris Blvd...gas:** Arco/24hr, Mobil, Shell/Subway/diesel, **food:** Jack-in-the-Box, Taco Bell, **other:** Albertson's, Wal-Mart/auto
19	Nuevo Rd, **E...gas:** Arco/24hr, Mobil, 76, **food:** Burger King, Carl's Jr, China Buffet, Del Taco, El Pollo Loco, IHOP, Jenny's Rest., McDonald's, Sizzler, **other:** AutoZone, Food4Less, Rite Aid, Stater Bros Foods
Perris 17	CA 74 W, 4th St, to Perris, Lake Elsinore, **E...gas:** Shell/24hr, **W...gas:** Chevron, **food:** Denny's, Jack-in-the-Box, La Mexicana Taquiera, Popeye's, **lodging:** Best Western, Perris Inn, **other:** Chrysler/Dodge/Plymouth/Jeep, USPO
15	CA 74 E, Hemet, **E...other:** motel, Ford/Lincoln/Mercury
14	Ethanac Rd, **E...food:** KFC/Taco Bell, **other:** Richardson's RV/Marine, **W...gas:** Exxon/diesel
12	McCall Blvd, Sun City, **E...gas:** 76, UltraMar/diesel, **food:** Wendy's, **lodging:** Sun City Motel, Travelodge, **other:** HOSPITAL, **W...gas:** Chevron/diesel, Mobil, 76, Shell, **food:** Burger King, Coco's, McDonald's, **other:** MEDICAL CARE, Rite Aid, Stater Bros Foods, Von's Foods
10	Newport Rd, Quail Valley, **E...gas:** Shell/DelTaco/diesel, **food:** Cathay Chinese, Jack-in-the-Box, Subway, Taco Bell, **other:** AutoZone, GNC, Ralph's Foods, Target, **W...gas:** Arco/24hr
7	Scott Rd, no facilities
4	Clinton Keith Rd, no facilities
2	Los Alamos, **E...gas:** Shell, **food:** CA Grill, Peony Chinese, Taco Bell, Wendy's, **W...gas:** Mobil/McDonald's, **food:** ChuckeCheese, City Deli/bakery, Green Burrito, Jack-in-the-Box, Mongolian BBQ, Subway, **other:** Radio Shack, SavOn Drug, Stater Bros Foods
1	Murrieta Hot Springs, **E...food:** Carl's Jr, Del Taco, Domino's, Sizzler, **other:** Ralph's Foods, Rite Aid, Ross, USPO, Weston's Mkt
0mm	I-215 begins/ends on I-15.

Interstate 280(Bay Area)

Exit #	Services
58	4th St, I-280 begins/ends, downtown
57	6th St, to I-80, downtown
56	Mariposa St, downtown
55	Army St, Port of SF
54	US 101 S, Alemany Blvd, Mission St, **E...gas:** Shell
52	San Jose Ave, Bosworth St(from nb, no return), no facilities
51	Geneva Ave, no facilities
50	CA 1, 19th Ave, **W...gas:** Chevron, **other:** to Bay Bridge, SFSU
49	Daly City, **E...gas:** 76/diesel/LP
48	Serramonte Blvd, Daly City(from sb), **E...other:** Chevrolet, **W...gas:** Olympian, 76, **food:** McDonald's, **other:** Macy's, Mervyn's, Circuit City, Office Depot, Ross, Target
47b	CA 1, Mission St, Pacifica, **E...gas:** Chevron, Silver/gas, **food:** RoundTable Pizza, Sizzler, **other:** HOSPITAL, Dodge, Drug Barn, Ford, Fresh Choice Foods, Home Depot, Isuzu, Jo-Ann Fabrics, Mitsubishi, Nissan, Nordstrom's, mall
46	Hickey Blvd, Colma, **E...gas:** Chevron/diesel/24hr, Shell, **W...gas:** Shell/diesel/24hr, 7-11, **food:** El Torito's, Peppermill Rest., RoundTable Pizza, Sizzler, **other:** Pak'nSave Foods/24hr
45	Avalon Dr, Westborough, **W...gas:** Arco/24hr, Valero/diesel, **food:** Denny's, McDonald's, **other:** Pak n' Sav Foods, Walgreen/24hr, Skyline Coll
43b	I-380 E, to US 101, no facilities
43a	San Bruno Ave, Sneath Lane, **E...food:** Baskin-Robbins, Petrini's Rest., **other:** Longs Drugs, **W...gas:** Chevron, 76, Gas and Shop, 7-11, **food:** Bakers Square
42	Crystal Springs, county park
41	CA 35 N, Skyline Blvd(from wb, no EZ return), to Pacifica, **1 mi W...gas:** Chevron
40	Millbrae Ave, Millbrae, **E...gas:** Beacon, Chevron
39	Trousdale Dr, to Burlingame, **E...HOSPITAL**
36	Black Mtn Rd, Hayne Rd, **W...golf, vista point**
36	**Crystal Springs rest area wb, full(handicapped)facilities, phone, picnic table, litter barrels, petwalk**
35	CA 35, CA 92W(from eb), to Half Moon Bay, no facilities
34	Bunker Hill Dr, no facilities

San Francisco

CALIFORNIA

Interstate 280

E ↕ W

San Jose

33	CA 92, to Half Moon Bay, San Mateo, no facilities
32mm	vista point both lanes
29	Edgewood Rd, Canada Rd, to San Carlos, **E...other:** HOSPITAL
27	Farm Hill Blvd, **E...other:** Cañada Coll, phone
25	CA 84, Woodside Rd, Redwood City, **1 mi W...gas:** Chevron/diesel, **other:** MEDICAL CARE, USPO
24	Sand Hill Rd, Menlo Park, **1 mi E...gas:** Shell, **other:** Longs Drug, Safeway
22	Alpine Rd, Portola Valley, **E...other:** HOSPITAL, **W...gas:** Chevron, Shell/autocare, **food:** RoundTable Pizza
20	Page Mill Rd, to Palo Alto, **E...**HOSPITAL
16	El Monte Rd, Moody Rd, no facilities
15	Magdalena Ave, no facilities
13	Foothill Expswy, Grant Rd, **E...gas:** Chevron/24hr, **food:** Trader Joe's, **other:** Rite Aid, **W...other:** to Rancho San Antonio CP
12b a	CA 85, N to Mtn View, S to Gilroy, no facilities
11	Saratoga-Sunnyvale Rd, Cupertino, Sunnyvale, **E... gas:** Chevron, **food:** Carl's Jr, **lodging:** Cupertino Inn, **other:** Goodyear, Rite Aid, repair, **W...gas:** Chevron, Shell/diesel, USA, **food:** BJ's Rest, Outback Steaks, **other:** Apple Computer Hdqrts, Target
10	Wolfe Rd, **E...gas:** Arco/24hr, **food:** Starbucks, **lodging:** Courtyard, Hilton Garden, **other:** Ranch Mkt, **W...gas:** 76, **food:** Alexander Steaks, McDonald's, TGIFriday, **other:** JC Penney, Sears/auto, Vallco Fashion Park, RV Ctr
9	Lawrence Expswy, Stevens Creek Blvd(from eb), **N...food:** McDonalds, Panda Express, Quizno's, Starbucks, **other:** Land Rover, Rite Aid, Safeway, Marshall's, **S...gas:** Rotten Robbie gas, 76, 7-11, **food:** IHOP, Subway, **lodging:** Howard Johnson, Wellsley Inn, Woodcrest Hotel
7	Saratoga Ave, **N...gas:** Arco/24hr, Chevron/24hr, 7-11, **food:** Black Angus, Burger King, Garden City Rest., Happi House, McDonald's, **lodging:** Towne Place Suites, **other:** Albertson's, **S...gas:** 76, Exxon, Shell, Valero, **food:** Applebee's, Denny's, RoundTable Pizza, Tony Roma's, **lodging:** Moor Park Hotel
5c	Winchester Blvd, Campbell Ave(from eb), **S...gas:** Hansra Gas
5b	CA 17 S, to Santa Cruz, I-880 N, to San Jose, no facilities
5a	Leigh Ave, Bascom Ave, no facilities
4	Meridian St(from eb), **N...other:** Big O Tire, Foodmaxx, **S...gas:** Chevron/Fastpay, 76, **food:** KFC, Mr. Chau's Cafe, Taco Bell, Wienerschnitzel
3b	Bird Ave, Race St, no facilities
3a	CA 87, **N...lodging:** Hilton, Holiday Inn, Hotel Sainte Claire, Mariott
2	7th St, to CA 82, **N...**conv ctr
1	10th St, 11th St, **N...gas:** 7-11, **other:** to San Jose St U
0mm	I-280 begins/ends on US 101.

Interstate 405(LA)

Exit # Services

Los Angeles Area — N ↕ S

73	I-5, N to Sacramento
72	Rinaldi St, Sepulveda, **E...gas:** Arco, 76, **food:** Arby's, Presidente Mexican, Subway, **other:** HOSPITAL, Toyota, **W...gas:** Shell, **lodging:** Granada Motel
71	CA 118 W, Simi Valley, no facilities
70	Devonshire St, Granada Hills, **E...gas:** Mobil, 76, Shell/diesel, **food:** Holiday Burger, Millie's Rest., Starbucks, **other:** Discount Tire, Nissan, Ralph's Foods, Rite Aid, Von's Foods
69	Nordhoff St, **E...gas:** Mobil/diesel, 7-11/24hr, **other:** MEDICAL CARE, **W...gas:** Arco
68	Roscoe Blvd, to Panorama City, **E...gas:** Exxon, 76, **food:** Burger King, Carl's Jr, Denny's, Galpin Rest., Jack-in-the-Box, McDonald's, Shakey's Pizza, **lodging:** Holiday Inn Express, **other:** AutoZone, Ford/Lincoln/Mercury/Jaguar, Saturn, **W...gas:** Shell/diesel, **food:** Coco's, Mexican Grill, Tommy's Burgers, **lodging:** Motel 6
66	Sherman Blvd, Reseda, **E...gas:** Chevron, Mobil/diesel, LP, 76, Shell, **food:** KFC, **other:** Albertson's, Rite Aid, **W...gas:** Mobil, 76/diesel/24hr, **food:** Taco Bell, **other:** HOSPITAL, USPO
65	Victory Blvd, Van Nuys, **E...gas:** 76, Mobil/diesel, **food:** El Pollo Loco, Jack-in-the-Box, **other:** Office Depot, **E on Sepulveda...food:** Wendy's, **other:** Costco, PepBoys, **W on Victory...gas:** Arco/24hr
64	Burbank Blvd, **E...gas:** Chevron, Shell, **food:** Denny's, **lodging:** Best Western
63b	US 101, Ventura Fwy, no facilities
63a	Ventura Blvd(from nb), **E...gas:** Mobil, **food:** Denny's, Robinsons-May, **other:** Thrifty Food, mall, **W...gas:** Chevron, 76, **food:** McDonald's, **lodging:** Radisson
63a	Valley Vista Blvd(from sb), no facilities
61	Mulholland Dr, no facilities
59	Sepulveda Blvd, **W...**to Getty Ctr
57	Sunset Blvd, **E...gas:** Chevron/24hr, Shell, **other:** to UCLA, **W...lodging:** Holiday Inn, Luse Hotel
56	Waterford St, Montana Ave(from nb)
55c b	Wilshire Blvd, **E...**downtown, **W...gas:** Mobil, 7-11, **other:** HOSPITAL
55a	CA 2, Santa Monica Blvd, **E...gas:** Exxon, Mobil, 7-11, **food:** Chinese Cuisine, Jack-in-the-Box, Jamba Juice, NY Pizza, Starbucks, Winchell's, Yoshinoya, **W...gas:** 76/24hr, Shell/repair, 7-11, **lodging:** Best Western
54	Olympic Blvd, Peco Blvd(from sb), **E...gas:** 7-11, **food:** Pazzo Pizzaria, Subway, **W...food:** Panda Express, Starbucks, **other:** Marshall's
53	I-10, Santa Monica Fwy
52	Venice Blvd, **E...gas:** Chevron/service, Mobil, 76, Shell/diesel, 7-11, **food:** Carl's Jr, **other:** Winston Tire, **W...gas:** SP, **food:** FatBurger, **other:** services on Sepulveda
51	Culver Blvd, Washington Blvd, **E...food:** Dear John's Café, Domino's, **other:** **W...gas:** 76/repair
50b	CA 90, Slauson Ave, to Marina del Rey, **E...gas:** Arco/24hr, **food:** Del Taco, Shakey's Pizza, **other:** Circuit City, CompUSA, Firestone/auto, Goodyear/auto, Office Depot, Pic'n Sav Foods, transmissions, **W...gas:** 76, **food:** Denny's, **other:** Albertson's

Interstate 405

N ↑ ↓ S

Hawthorne

50a Jefferson Blvd(from sb), **E...food:** Coco's, Jack-in-the-Box, **other:** Rite Aid, **W...**to LA Airport

49 Howard Hughes Pkwy, to Centinela Ave, **E...gas:** Mobil/diesel, **food:** Sizzler, **lodging:** Ramada Inn, Sheraton, **other:** JC Penney, Macy's, Robinsons-May, mall, **W...gas:** Chevron, **food:** Dinah's Rest., Islands Burgers, On the Border, **lodging:** Extended Stay America, **other:** Radisson, Ford, Saturn, SavOn Drug, Howard Hughes Ctr, mall

48 La Tijera Blvd, **E...food:** El Pollo Loco, FatBurger, KFC, McDonald's, TGIFriday, **lodging:** Best Western, **other:** EZ Lube, 99c Store, Von's Foods, **W...gas:** Arco/24hr, Chevron/diesel/24hr, 76/Circle K, **food:** Buggy Whip Rest., **other:** Marie Callender's, USPO

47 CA 42, Manchester Ave, to Inglewood, **E...gas:** Chevron, 76/diesel/24hr, **food:** Carl's Jr, Steppin Up Rest., **lodging:** Best Western, Econolodge, **W...gas:** Arco, Shell, 76, **food:** Arby's, Burger King, Jack-in-the-Box, Randy's Donuts, **lodging:** Day's Inn, **other:** Chrysler/Jeep/Dodge, K-Mart

46 Century Blvd, **E...gas:** 76, **food:** Burger King, Casa Gamino Mexican, Flower Drum Chinese, Rally's, Subway, **lodging:** Best Western, Comfort Inn, Motel 6, Tiboli Hotel, **other:** AutoZone, **W...gas:** Arco/24hr, Chevron/diesel, 76/Circle K, Shell, **food:** Carl's Jr, Denny's, McDonald's, Taco Bell, **lodging:** Hampton Inn, Hilton, Holiday Inn, Marriott, Quality Hotel, Travelodge, Westin Hotel

45 I-105, Imperial Hwy, **E...gas:** Arco, Mobil/diesel, Shell, **food:** BBQ, El Pollo Loco, El Tarasco Mexican, Jack-in-the-Box, McDonald's, **other:** J&S Trasmissions, **W...food:** Proud Bird Rest.(1mi)

44 El Segundo Blvd, to El Segundo, **E...gas:** Arco, Chevron/24hr, **food:** Burger King, Christy's Donuts, HongKong Express, Jack-in-the-Box, Los Chorros Mexican, Pizza Hut, Rally's, Subway, Taco Bell, **other:** Albertson's, SavOn Drug, **W...food:** Denny's, **lodging:** Ramada Inn, **other:** Office Depot

43b a Rosecrans Ave, to Manhattan Beach, **E...gas:** 76, Mobil/diesel, Shell, **food:** El Pollo Loco, Pizza Hut, Starbucks, Subway, **other:** Albertson's, Best Buy, Food4Less, Home Depot, Michael's, Ross, SavOn Drug, **W...gas:** Arco, **food:** Carl's Jr, China Chef, Luigi's Rest., McDonald's, **other:** Costco/gas, Staples

42b Inglewood Ave, **E...gas:** Arco, **food:** Del Taco, Denny's, In-n-Out, Yoshinoya, **other:** Von's Foods, **W...gas:** Arco, Mobil, Shell/diesel/24hr, **other:** Drug Emporium, Goodyear/auto

42a CA 107, Hawthorne Blvd, **E...food:** Jack-in-the-Box, LA Wok, McDonald's, Papa John's, **lodging:** Best Western, Day's Inn, **other:** Freeway Drug, 99c Store, Radio Shack, **W...gas:** Arco/24hr, Mobil/diesel, Thrifty, Blimpie, Subway, Taco Bell, Yoshinoya, **other:** Goodyear, Robinson-May

40b Redondo Beach Blvd, Hermosa Beach, **E...gas:** Arco/24hr, Thrifty, **food:** Amigo's Tacos, ChuckeCheese, **other:** golf, **W...food:** Boston Mkt, RoundTable Pizza, **other:** Ralph's Foods, SavOn Drug, U-Haul

40a CA 91 E, Artesia Blvd, to Torrance, **W...gas:** Chevron, 76/24hr, **other:** Winchell's, Parts+, XpressLube/Burger King/Taco Bell

39 Crenshaw Blvd, to Torrance, **E...gas:** Arco/24hr, Chevron/24hr, Mobil/repair, Shell, 7-11, **food:** Burger King, Denny's, Pizza Hut, **other:** MEDICAL CARE, Ralph's Foods, **W...gas:** Mobil/diesel, Shell/Subway/diesel

38b Western Ave, to Torrance, **E...gas:** Arco, Chevron, Mobil/repair, 76/diesel, **food:** Del Taco, Denny's, Wendy's, Yorgo's Burgers, **other:** Albèrtson's, Toyota, **W...gas:** Mobil, **food:** Mill's Rest., **lodging:** Courtyard

38a Normandie Ave, to Gardena, **E...lodging:** Comfort Inn, **W...gas:** Shell/diesel, **food:** Carl's Jr, Great Steak Café, Hong Kong Express, StarBucks, Subway, Taco Bell, **lodging:** Extended Stay America, **other:** Goodyear, Office Depot

37b Vermont Ave(from sb), **W...lodging:** Holiday Inn, **other:** hwy patrol

37a I-110, Harbor Fwy, no facilities

36 Main St(from nb), no facilities

36mm weigh sta both lanes

35 Avalon Blvd, to Carson, **E...gas:** Arco/24hr, Chevron, Mobil, Shell, **food:** ChuckeCheese, Denny's, FoodCourt, Jack-in-the-Box, McDonald's, Pizza Hut, Shakey's Pizza, Sizzler, Subway, Tony Roma, **lodging:** Quality Inn, **other:** MEDICAL CARE, America's Tire, Firestone, Goodyear/auto, Ikea, JC Penney, PepBoys, Sears/auto, mall, **W...gas:** Arco/24hr, Mobil, Shell, **food:** Carl's Jr, El Charro, IHOP, **other:** Chrysler/Dodge/Jeep, Ford/Lincoln/Mercury, Isuzu, Kia, Ralph's Foods, USPO

34 Carson St, to Carson, **E...food:** Del Taco, **lodging:** Comfort Inn, **W...gas:** Mobil, 76/diesel/24hr, **food:** Carl's Jr, El Charro, IHOP, Jack-in-th-Box, Subway, **lodging:** Hilton

33b Wilmington Ave, **E...gas:** Arco/service, Chevron/repair/24hr, **food:** Carson Burgers, **W...gas:** Shell/Subway/Taco Bell/diesel, **other:** Chevrolet/Hyundai, Toyota

Carson

N ↑ ↓ **S**

33a Alameda St, no facilities

32d Santa Fe Ave(from nb), **E...gas:** Arco/24hr, **W...gas:** Chevron/24hr, Shell

32c b I-710, Long Beach Fwy, no facilities

32a Pacific Ave(from sb), no facilities

30b Long Beach Blvd, **E...gas:** 76, **W...gas:** Mobil, **other:** HOSPITAL, Toyota

30a Atlantic Blvd, **E...gas:** Chevron/diesel, Shell/Subway/diesel, **food:** Arby's, Black Angus, Denny's/24hr, El Patio, El Torito, Jack-in-the-Box, **other:** Mercedes, Staples, Target, Walgreen, **W...other:** HOSPITAL, Chrysler/Jeep, Nissan

29c Orange Ave(from sb), no facilities

29b a Cherry Ave, to Signal Hill, **E...gas:** Mobil/diesel, **food:** Fantastic Burgers, **other:** Ford, auto repair, **W...food:** John's Burgers, Charley Brown's Steaks/Lobster, Rib Café, **other:** BMW, Dodge, Firestone, Nissan

27 CA 19, Lakewood Blvd, **E...lodging:** Marriott, **W...gas:** Chevron, Shell/24hr, **food:** Spires Rest., Taco Bell, **lodging:** Holiday Inn, Residence Inn, **other:** HOSPITAL, Ford, Goodyear/auto, Kia, Plymouth

26b Bellflower Blvd, **E...gas:** Chevron, 76, **food:** Burger King, Carl's Jr, KFC, **other:** Chevrolet, Ford, K-Mart, Lowe's Whse, **W...gas:** Mobil/diesel, 76, **food:** Fish-Tale Rest., Hof's Rest., McDonald's, Quizno's, Wendy's, **other:** HOSPITAL, Borders Books, Circuit City, CompUSA, Goodyear/auto, Rite Aid/24hr, SavOn Drug, Sears, Target

26a Woodruff Ave(from nb), no facilities

25 Palo Verde Ave, **W...gas:** 76, **food:** Del Taco, Dr Wi Donuts, Pizza Hut/Taco Bell, Subway

24b Studebaker Rd

24a I-605 N, no facilities

23 CA 22 W, 7th St, to Long Beach, no facilities

22 Seal Beach Blvd, Los Alamitos Blvd, **E...gas:** Chevron/repair/24hr, Mobil, 76, **food:** Carl's Jr, KFC, Panda Chinese, Spagatini Grill, Winchell's, **other:** Albertson's, Goodyear/auto, Ralph's Foods, Rite Aid, Target, Winston Tire

21 CA 22 E, Garden Grove Fwy, Valley View St, **E...gas:** Mobil, Shell/diesel, **food:** Coco's, DQ, Maxwell's Seafood Rest., Sizzler, **other:** Chevrolet, Ford, Rite Aid, Von's Foods

19 Westminster Ave, to Springdale St, **E...gas:** Arco/24hr, Chevron/diesel, 76/Circle K, Thrifty, 7-11/24hr, **food:** Café Westminster, Carl's Jr, In-n-Out, KFC, La Casa Brita, McDonald's, Taco Bell, Yoshinoya, **lodging:** Motel 6, Travelodge, **other:** Albertson's, America's Tire, Home Depot, Kragen Parts, Radio Shack, Rite Aid, **W...gas:** Chevron/diesel/24hr, Shell/diesel/24hr, **food:** Pizza Hut, Subway, **lodging:** Best Western, Day's Inn

18 Bolsa Ave, Golden West St, **E...food:** Pizza Hut, Popeye's, **W...gas:** Chevron, Mobil, 76, Shell, **food:** Bennigan's, Coco's, El Torito, IHOP, Jack-in-the-Box, **other:** Best Buy, JC Penney, Jo-Ann Fabrics, Jon's Foods, Robinson-May, Sears/auto, mall

16 CA 39, Beach Blvd, to Huntington Bch, **E...gas:** Shell, **food:** Hof's Rest., Jack-in-the-Box, Mei's Chinese, **lodging:** BeachWest Inn, Princess Inn, Super 8, Westminster Inn, **other:** HOSPITAL, Buick/Pontiac/GMC, K-Mart, PepBoys, Toyota, **W...gas:** Arco, Mobil/service, 76, **food:** Arby's, Burger King, Diedrich's Coffee, El Torito, Jack-in-the-Box, Macaroni Grill, Marie Callender's, Popeye's, Starbucks, **lodging:** Holiday Inn, **other:** Barnes&Noble, Chevrolet, Chrysler/Jeep, Circuit City, Dodge, Ford/Lincoln/Mercury, Just Tires, Marshall's, Mitsubishi, OfficeMax, Plymouth, Subaru, Target, VW

15b a Magnolia St, Warner Ave, **E...gas:** Shell, **food:** Del Taco, Sizzler, **other:** CompUSA, **W...gas:** Chevron, Mobil, **food:** Bullwinkle's Rest., Carrow's, Magnolia Café, Tommy's Burgers, **lodging:** Ramada Inn, **other:** IGA Foods, SavOn Drug

14 Brookhurst Ave, Fountain Valley, **E...gas:** Arco/24hr, Chevron, Thrifty, **food:** Alberto's Mexican, Coco's, Del Taco, **lodging:** Courtyard, Residence Inn, **other:** Thompson's RV Ctr, **W...gas:** Chevron/service/24hr, Shell/diesel, **food:** Black Angus, Stix Chinese, Wendy's, **other:** MEDICAL CARE, Albertson's, Office Depot

12 Euclid Ave, **E...food:** Carl's Jr, George's Burgers, Souplantation, Taco Bell, **other:** HOSPITAL, Costco, Fry's Electronics, Office Depot, Staples, Tire Whse

11b Harbor Blvd, to Costa Mesa, **E...lodging:** La Quinta, **W...gas:** Arco, Chevron, Mobil, Shell/diesel, 7-11, **food:** Burger King, Denny's, Domino's, El Pollo Loco, IHOP, Jack-in-the-Box, KFC, LJ Silver, McDonald's, Subway, **lodging:** Costa Mesa Inn, Motel 6, Super 8, Vagabond Inn, **other:** MEDICAL CARE, Albertson's, Big O Tire, Cadillac, Chevrolet, Dodge/Acura, Ford/Lincoln/Mercury, Honda, Infiniti, JustTires, Mazda, Pontiac/Buick, Radio Shack, Rite Aid, Target, Von's Foods, Winchell's

11a Fairview Rd, **E...gas:** Shell, **other:** Barnes&Noble, Best Buy, Nordstrom's, Old Navy, **W...gas:** Chevron, Mobil, Shell, **food:** Del Taco, Jack-in-the-Box

10 CA 73, to CA 55 S(from sb), Corona del Mar, Newport Beach

9b Bristol St, **E...gas:** Chevron, Shell/24hr, **food:** Bombay Bicycle Club, Carrow's, Coco's, In-n-Out, Jack-in-the-Box, Maggiano's Rest., McDonald's, New Panda Chinese, Pizza Hut, Red Robin, Sizzler, **lodging:** Holiday Inn, Marriott Suites, Red Lion, Westin Hotel, **other:** MEDICAL CARE, Firestone/auto, Goodyear/auto, Office Depot, Michael's, Radio Shack, Rite Aid, Ross, Robinson-May, SavOn Drug, Sears/auto, Staples, Target, Von's Foods, mall, **W...gas:** Chevron, 76/diesel, Shell, 7-11, **food:** Del Taco/24hr, El Pollo Loco, Garf's Grill, McDonald's, Subway, **lodging:** DoubleTree Hotel, Hilton, Holiday Inn, **other:** PepBoys

9a CA 55, Costa Mesa Fwy, to Newport Bch, Riverside

8 MacArthur Blvd, **E...food:** Carl's Jr, Chicago Joe's, Food Court, Kokomo's Rest., McDonald's, Oasis Diner, **lodging:** Crowne Plaza Hotel, Holiday Inn, Embassy Suites, **other:** MEDICAL CARE, **W...gas:** Chevron, **food:** El Torito, Gulliver's Ribs, IHOP, **lodging:** Hilton, Marriott

(vertical text: Costa Mesa)

Interstate 405

N ↕ S

Irvine

7   Jamboree Rd, Irvine, **E...lodging:** Courtyard, Hyatt, Residence Inn, **E on Main St...gas:** Texaco, **food:** Burger King, China West, JambaJuice, **W...food:** Asiana Rest., Daily Grill, Inka Grill, **lodging:** Marriott

5   Culver Dr, **W...gas:** Chevron, Shell, **food:** Carl's Jr, Subway, **other:** MEDICAL CARE, Ralph's Foods, Rite Aid, Wild Oats Mkt

4   Jeffrey Rd, University Dr, **E...gas:** Chevron, **food:** El Cholo Cantina, El Pollo Loco, McDonald's, Stix Chinese, Taco Bell, Togo's, **other:** Office Depot, Ralph's Foods, SavOn Drug, **W...gas:** Mobil/diesel, **food:** IHOP, Rubino's Pizza, **other:** Parkview Drug, Ralph's Foods

3   Sand Canyon Ave, **E...**HOSPITAL

2   CA 133, to Laguna Beach, no facilities

1c   Irvine Center Dr, **E...food:** Dave & Buster's, Chang's Chinese Bistro, **other:** Barnes&Noble, **W...food:** Burger King

1b   Bake Pkwy, **W...**Toyota

1a   Lake Forest

0mm   I-405 begins/ends on I-5, exit 132.

Interstate 505(Winters)

N ↕ S

Winters

Exit #	Services
33	I-5. I-505 begins/ends on I-5.
31	CA 12A, no facilities
28	CA 14, Zamora, no facilities
24	CA 19, no facilities
21	CA 16, Woodland, to Esparto, **W...gas:** Guy's Food/fuel
17	CA 27, no facilities
15	CA 29A, no facilities
11	CA 128 W, Russell Blvd, **W...gas:** Chevron/24hr, **food:** Mexican Rest., RoundTable Pizza, **other:** MEDICAL CARE, Eagle Drug, IGA Foods
10	Putah Creek Rd, same as 11
6	Allendale Rd, no facilities
3	Midway Rd, **E...other:** RV camping
1c	Vaca Valley Pkwy, no facilities
1b	I-80 E. I-505 begins/ends on I-80.

Interstate 580(Bay Area)

E ↕ W

Exit #	Services
79	I-580 begins/ends, accesses I-5 sb.
76b a	CA 132, Chrisman Rd, to Modesto, **E...gas:** 76/diesel, **other:** RV camping(5mi)
72	Corral Hollow Rd, no facilities
67	Patterson Pass Rd, **W...gas:** Arco/diesel/24hr
65	I-205(from eb), to Tracy, no facilities
63	Grant Line Rd, to Byron, no facilities
59	N Flynn Rd, Altamont Pass, elev 1009, no facilities, **S...**Brake Check Area, many wind-turbines
57	N Greenville Rd, Laughlin Rd, Altamont Pass Rd, to Livermore Lab, **S...gas:** Shell, **lodging:** Ramada Ltd, **other:** Harley-Davidson
56	weigh sta both lanes
55	Vasco Rd, to Brentwood, **N...gas:** Chevron, QuikStop/diesel, Shell/diesel/deli, **food:** A&W/KFC, **S...gas:** Citgo/7-11, 76/diesel, **food:** Blimpie, Jack-in-the-Box, Taco Bell

Livermore

54   CA 84, 1st St, Springtown Blvd, Livermore, **N...gas:** 7-11, Springtown Gas/diesel, **lodging:** DoubleTree Hotel, Holiday Inn, Motel 6, Springtown Inn, **S...gas:** Chevron/24hr, Shell, 76/24hr, **food:** Applebee's, Arby's, Burger King, Chevy's Mexican, Chili's, Happi House, IHOP, Italian Express, McDonald's, StarBucks, Subway, Taco Bell, Togo's, **other:** American Tires, Longs Drug, Lowe's Whse, Mervyn's, Office Depot, Radio Shack, Ross, Safeway/gas, Target

52   N Livermore Ave, **S...gas:** Chevron/Jack-in-the-Box, Citgo/7-11, **food:** Baja Fresh, In-n-Out, Quizno's, **lodging:** Hawthorn Suites, **other:** Home Depot, Honda, Office Max, Schwab Tire, Wal-Mart/auto

51   Portola Ave, Livermore(no EZ eb return), **S...gas:** Chevron, **other:** HOSPITAL, JC's RV Ctr

50   Airway Blvd, Collier Canyon Rd, Livermore, **N...gas:** Bernard's Gas, **food:** Wendy's, **lodging:** Comfort Inn, Courtyard, Hampton Inn, Hilton Garden, Residence Inn, Towneplace Suites, **other:** Costco Whse/gas, **S...food:** Cattlemen's Rest., McDonald's, **lodging:** Extended Stay America, **other:** Chrysler/Plymouth/Jeep, Lincoln/Mercury, Mazda

48   El Charro Rd, Croak Rd, no facilities

47   Santa Rita Rd, Tassajara Rd, **S...gas:** Shell, **food:** Bakers Square, California Burger, Ole's Mexican, McDonald's, Subway, Taco Bell, **other:** Longs Drug, Acura, BMW, Cadillac, GMC, Hummer, Infiniti, Lexus, MiniCooper, Mitsubishi, Rose Pavilion, Saab, Saturn, Volvo

46   Hacienda Dr, Pleasanton, **N...gas:** Shell, **food:** Applebee's, Black Angus, Fuddruckers, Macaroni Grill, Mimi's, On the Border, **lodging:** AmeriSuites, **other:** Barnes&Noble, Best Buy, Ford, Old Navy, TJ Maxx, **S...food:** Red Robin, **other:** HOSPITAL, Borders Books, Sam's Club, Staples, Wal-Mart

45   Hopyard Rd, Pleasanton, **N...gas:** 76, Minimart, **lodging:** Hilton, Holiday Inn Express, **other:** Dodge, Goodyear, Nissan, Office Depot, Pak'n Sav, RV Ctr, U-Haul, Toyota, **S...gas:** Chevron, Shell/diesel, **food:** Burger King, Buttercup Pantry/24hr, Chevy's Mexican, Chili's, Denny's, Hungry Hunter, Lyon's Rest., Maestro's Italian, Nations Burgers, Pedro's Mexican, Starbucks, Taco Bell, **lodging:** Candlewood Suites, Courtyard, Hilton, Marriott, Motel 6, Ramada, Sheraton, Super 8, **other:** CompUSA, Home Depot, Mercedes

Pleasanton

CALIFORNIA
Interstate 580

44b I-680, N to San Ramon, S to San Jose, no facilities

44a Foothills Rd, San Ramon Rd, **N...gas:** Chevron, Shell, 76, Valero, **food:** Burger King, Carl's Jr, Hooters, India Prince Rest., KFC, McDonald's, Outback Steaks, Popeye's, RoundTable Pizza, Subway, Wendy's, **lodging:** Best Western, Radisson, **other:** Buick, Chevrolet, Ford, Honda, Isuzu, Kragen Parts, Mervyn's, Michael's, Ralph's Foods, Rite Aid, Ross, Target, **S...lodging:** Crowne Plaza, Residence Inn, Wyndham Garden, **other:** Chrysler/Plymouth, JC Penney, Macy's, Nordstrom's, mall

39 Eden Canyon Rd, Palomares Rd, **S...other:** rodeo park

37 Center St, Crow Canyon Rd, same as 35, **S...gas:** Arco/24hr, Chevron/diesel/, 76, **food:** Starbucks, Subway

35 Redwood Rd, Castro Valley, **N...gas:** Arco, Chevron, 76/diesel, Shell/diesel, **food:** KFC, McDonald's, RoundTable Pizza, Sizzler, Taco Bell, **other:** Longs Drug, NAPA, Rite Aid, Safeway

34 I-238 W, to I-880, CA 238, **W off I-238...food:** Jack-in-the Box, **other:** Plymouth/Dodge/Jeep

33 164th Ave, Miramar Ave, **E...gas:** Chevron/diesel, **lodging:** 580 Motel

32b 150th Ave, Fairmont, **E...other:** HOSPITAL, **W...gas:** Gas n' Food, Shell, 76, **food:** Denny's, **other:** Longs Drug, Macy's

32a Grand Ave(from sb), Dutton Ave, **W...gas:** Coast, **other:** Rite Aid

30 106th Ave, Foothill Blvd, MacArthur Blvd, **W...gas:** 76/24hr

29 98th Ave, Golf Links Rd, **E...gas:** Shell, **W...gas:** 76

27b Keller Ave, Mtn Blvd, **E...repair**

27ab Edwards Ave(from sb, no EZ return), **E...**US Naval Hospital

26a CA 13, Warren Fwy, to Berkeley, no facilities

26b Seminary Rd, **E...**Observatory/Planetarium, **W...gas:** Arco/24hr

25b a High St, to MacArthur Blvd, **E...gas:** 76, **food:** Subway, **other:** Albertson's, Kragen Parts, **W...gas:** 76, **other:** Walgreen

24 35th Ave(no EZ sb return), **E...gas:** Exxon, 76, **food:** Taco Bell, **W...gas:** Chevron, QuikStop, 76

23 Coolidge Ave, Fruitvale, **E...gas:** Shell/24hr, **food:** McDonald's, **other:** Longs Drug, Safeway, **W...gas:** 76

22 Park Blvd, **E...**Shell, **W...**Arco, Quickstop, **other:** HOSPITAL

21b Grand Ave, Lake Shore, **E...gas:** Chevron, 76/24hr, 7-11, **food:** Domino's, KFC, Subway, **other:** Albertson's, Lucky Foods, **W...gas:** Chevron/diesel/24hr

21a Harrison St, Oakland Ave, **E...gas:** 76

19d c Ca 24 E, I-980 W, to Oakland, no facilities

19b West St, San Pablo Ave, downtown

19a I-80 W, no facilities

18c Market St, to San Pablo Ave, downtown

18b Powell St, Emeryville, **E...gas:** 76, **food:** Burger King, Courtyard, Denny's, Lyon's Rest., Starbucks, Trader Joe's, **lodging:** Day's Inn, Woodfin Suites, **other:** Circuit City, Jo-Ann Fabrics, Old Navy, **W...gas:** Shell, **food:** Chevy's Mexican, **lodging:** Holiday Inn

18a CA 13, Ashby Ave, Bay St, no facilities

17 University Ave, Berkeley, **E...gas:** Coast/diesel, 76, **food:** Mermaid Cambodian Seafood, **lodging:** Ramada Inn

16 Gilman St, **E...gas:** Chevron, **other:** Walgreen, Golden Gate Fields

13 Buchanan St(from eb), no facilities

13 Albany Ave, no facilities

12 Central Ave(from eb), El Cerrito, **E...gas:** Shell, **W...**Costco/gas

11 Bayview Ave, Carlson Blvd, **E...gas:** 76

10b Regatta Blvd, **E...gas:** Golden Gate/diesel, **W...food:** Cafe Teatro, Quizno's, **other:** Long's Drug

10a S 23rd St, Marina Bay Pkwy, **E...gas:** Stop and Save/diesel

9 Harbour Way, Cutting Blvd, **E...gas:** Arco, **food:** El Caballo Mexican, **W...**Burger King

8 Canal Blvd, Garrard Blvd, **W...gas:** Chevron/diesel, **lodging:** Quality Inn

7b Castro St, to I-80 E, Point Richmond, downtown industrial

7a Western Drive(from wb), Point Molate, no facilities

5mm Richmond-San Rafael Toll Bridge

2a Francis Drake Blvd(from wb), to US 101 S, no facilities

1b Francisco Blvd, San Rafael, **E...gas:** 76, **food:** Azul Marisco's Mexican, Burger King, Café Mesa, Foodles' Café, Subway, Wendy's, **other:** Aamco, Home Depot, Dodge/Isuzu, **W...**USPO, to San Quentin

1a US 101 N to San Rafael, I-580 begins/ends on US 101.

Interstate 605(LA)

Exit #	Services
25	Huntington Dr. I-605 begins/ends.
24	I-210, no facilities
23	Live Oak Ave, Arrow Hwy, **E...**Santa Fe Dam, **W...**Irwindale Speedway
22	Lower Azusa Rd, LA St, no facilities
21	Ramona Blvd, **E...gas:** Mobil, **food:** Del Taco/24hr
20	I-10, E to San Bernardino, W to LA
19	Valley Blvd, to Industry, **E...gas:** Chevron, 76, **food:** McDonald's, **lodging:** Valley Inn
18	CA 60, Pamona Fwy, no facilities
17	Peck Rd, **E...gas:** Shell, **W...other:** Ford Trucks, Freightliner
16	Beverly Blvd, RoseHills Rd, no facilities
15	Whittier Blvd, **E...gas:** 76, Shell, 7-11, **food:** Carl's Jr, **lodging:** GoodNite Inn, **W...gas:** Chevron, **other:** Buick, Chrysler/Dodge, Ford, GMC, Honda, Isuzu, Jeep, Kia, Plymouth, Pontiac, Saturn, Toyota, Volvo
14	Washington Blvd, to Pico Rivera, no facilities
13	Slauson Ave, **E...gas:** Arco, Mobil, **food:** Denny's, **lodging:** Motel 6, **W...**HOSPITAL
12	Telegraph Rd, to Santa Fe Springs, **E...gas:** Chevron, Shell, **other:** st patrol
11	I-5, no facilities
10	Florence Ave, to Downey, **E...other:** Chevrolet, Honda, Sam's Club, Volvo

Oakland Area

Los Angeles Area

E W

N S

Interstate 605

N ↕ **S**

Los Angeles Area

9 Firestone Blvd, **E...gas:** 76, Shell, **food:** Chuck-eCheese, KFC, McDonald's, Norm's Burgers, Taco Bell, **lodging:** Best Western, **other:** BMW, Costco, Food4Less, Staples, VW/Audi, **W...gas:** Arco, Chevron/repair, 76/diesel, **food:** Starbucks, **other:** Dodge, Office Depot, Target

8 I-105, Imperial Hwy, **E...gas:** 76, **food:** KFC, Pizza Hut/Taco Bell, **other:** SavOn Drug, **W...gas:** Arco

7 Rosecrans Ave, to Norwalk, **E...gas:** Chevron, **W...food:** Carrow's Rest, **lodging:** Motel 6

6 Alondra Blvd, **E...gas:** Chevron, **lodging:** Spires Rest., **other:** Staples, **W...gas:** Shell/24hr, Texaco/Subway

5 CA 91, no facilities

4 South St, **E...other:** Macy's, Mervyn's, Nordstrom's, Robinsons-May, Sears/auto, mall, **W...gas:** 76/service, Shell/service, Texaco/diesel, UltraMar, **other:** Buick/GMC/Pontiac, Chrysler/Plymouth, Daewoo, Dodge, Ford, Honda, Hyundai, Infiniti, Isuzu, Saturn, Toyota, Volvo

3 Del Amo Blvd, to Cerritos, **E...food:** Del Taco, Duke's Burgers, **other:** Ralph's Foods, **W...gas:** Mobil

2 Carson St, **E...gas:** Arco, 76, Shell, **food:** Jack-in-the-Box, KFC, Little Caesar's, McDonald's, Mexican Rest., Popeye's, Sky Burgers, Spike's Rest., Taco Bell, Wienerschnitzel, **lodging:** Lakewood Inn, **other:** Chief Parts, Kragen Parts, **W...gas:** Chevron/diesel, Mobil, **food:** Denny's, Del Taco, El Pollo Loco, El Torito, FoodCourt, In-n-Out, Jack-in-the-Box, Roadhouse Grill, Starbucks, TGIFriday, **other:** Barnes&Noble, GNC, Lowe's Whse, Michael's, Old Navy, Radio Shack, Ross, Sam's Club, Staples, Wal-Mart SuperCtr/24hr

1 Katella Ave, Willow St, **E...food:** McDonald's, **other:** HOSPITAL

0mm I-605 begins/ends on I-405.

Interstate 680(Bay Area)

N ↕ **S**

Exit #	Services
71b a	I-80 E, to Sacramento, W to Oakland, I-680 begins/ends on I-80.
70	Green Valley Rd(from eb), Cordelia, **N...other:** Costco, Longs Drug, Safeway
69	Gold Hill Rd, **W...gas:** TowerMart/diesel
65	Marshview Rd, no facilities
63	Parish Rd, no facilities
61	Lake Herman Rd, **E...gas:** Arco/Jack-in-the-Box/diesel, **W...gas:** Gas City, Shell/Carl's Jr/diesel/24hr, **other:** vista point
60	Bayshore Rd, industrial park
58	I-780, to Benicia, toll plaza
56	Marina Vista, to Martinez, no facilities
55mm	Martinez-Benicia Toll Br
54	Pacheco Blvd, Arthur Rd, Concord, **W...gas:** 76/24hr, Shell/diesel/24hr

Concord

53b CA 4 W, to Richmond, Pittsburg, no facilities

53a CA 4 E, Concord, Pacheco, **E...food:** Peppermill Coffeeshop, Sullivan's Rest., Taco Bell, **lodging:** Sheraton, **other:** Ford, Hyundai, Infiniti/VW, Toyota, USPO, **W...gas:** Chevron/24hr, Exxon, 76, Shell/24hr, 7-11, **food:** Burger King, Carrow's Rest., Denny's, KFC, McDonald's, **other:** Barnes&Noble, Goodyear/auto, K-Mart, Kragen Parts, Longs Drug, Marshall's, Mervyn's, Target

51 Willow Pass Rd, Taylor Blvd, **E...food:** Benihana Rest., Denny's, El Torito, Grissini Italian, JJ North's Buffet, Krispy Kreme, Marie Callender's, Red Lobster, Tony Roma, **lodging:** Hilton, **other:** MEDICAL CARE, Auto Parts Club, Circuit City, CompUSA, Cost+, Office Depot, Old Navy, Trader Joe's, Willows Shopping Ctr, **W...food:** Baja Mexican, Tahoe Joe's, **other:** Firestone, JC Penney, Macy's, Sears/auto

50 CA 242(from nb), to Concord, no facilities

49 Gregory Lane, to Pleasant Hill, **E...gas:** Chevron, **lodging:** Extended Stay America, **other:** Best Buy, Jo-Ann Fabrics, **W...food:** Confetti Rest., Lyon's Rest., **lodging:** Courtyard, Summerfield Suites, **other:** Grand Auto Supply

48 Oak Park Blvd, Geary Rd, **E...gas:** Chevron, 7-11, **food:** Subway, **lodging:** Embassy Suites, Extended Stay America, **other:** Best Buy, **W...gas:** Chevron, Shell/diesel, **food:** Black Angus, Burger King, China Rest., Sweet Tomatos, Wendy's, **lodging:** Courtyard, Holiday Inn, **other:** Mazda/Subaru, Nissan, Staples, Volvo, Walgreen

47 N Main St, to Walnut Creek, **E...gas:** Chevron/Subway, Shell, **food:** Black Diamond Brewery/rest., Fuddrucker's, Jack-in-the-Box, Taco Bell, Vino Ristorante, **lodging:** Marriott, Motel 6, Walnut Cr Motel, **other:** Cadillac, Chrysler/Jeep, Harley-Davidson, Mercedes, Target, **W...gas:** 76/diesel/24hr, 7-11, **food:** Domino's, **other:** Honda, NAPA, OfficeMax

46b Ygnacio Rd, no facilities

CALIFORNIA
Interstate 680

N

S

San Ramon

Fremont

46a CA 24, to Lafayette, Oakland, no facilities

45 S Main St, Walnut Creek, **E...**HOSPITAL

43 Livorna Rd, no facilities

42b a Stone Valley Rd, Alamo, **W...gas:** Chevron, Shell/ diesel, 7-11, **food:** Subway, **other:** Safeway

41 El Pintado Rd, Danville, no facilities

40 El Cerro Blvd, no facilities

39 Diablo Rd, Danville, **E...gas:** 76/24hr, **other:** Albertson's, Mt Diablo SP(12mi), **W...gas:** Chevron, 76, **food:** Pizza Hut, Primo's Pizza, **other:** MEDICAL CARE

38 Sycamore Valley Rd, **E...gas:** Shell, **food:** Denny's, **lodging:** Best Western, **W...gas:** 76, Valero

36 Crow Canyon Rd, San Ramon, **E...gas:** Shell, **food:** Burger King, Carl's Jr, Chili's, **other:** HOSPITAL, Albertson's, Rite Aid, USPO, **W...gas:** Chevron/ repair/24hr, 76, Shell/autocare, Valero, **food:** Boston Mkt, Chipotle Mexican, In-n-Out, McDonald's, Taco Bell, TGIFriday, **lodging:** Sierra Suites, **other:** Harley-Davidson, Longs Drug, Safeway

34 Bollinger Canyon Rd, **E...food:** Subway, **lodging:** Marriott, Residence Inn, **other:** Borders Books, Target, Whole Foods, **W...gas:** Chevron/Foodini's, **food:** Applebee's, Chevy's Mexican, Marie Callender's, **lodging:** Courtyard, Homestead Village

31 Alcosta Blvd, to Dublin, **E...gas:** 76, 7-11, **W...gas:** Chevron, Shell, **food:** Chatillon Rest., Chubby's Rest., ChuckeeCheese, DQ, Mike's Pizza, McDonalds, Pizza Palace, Starbucks, Subway, Taco Bell, **other:** Albertson's, Walgreen

30 I-580, W to Oakland, E to Tracy, no facilities

29 Stoneridge, Dublin, **E...lodging:** Crowne Plaza, Hilton, Wyndham Garden, **W...food:** Black Angus, Taco Bell, **other:** Chrysler/Plymouth/Jeep, Circuit City, Honda, Macy's, Nordstrom's, Office Max, Safeway/gas, Sears, Target, mall

26 Bernal Ave, Pleasanton, **E...gas:** Shell/Jack-in-the-Box, **food:** Lindo's Mexican, Ring's Burgers, Vic's Bakery

22 Sunol Blvd, Castlewood Dr, Pleasanton, no facilities

21b a CA 84, Calvaras Rd, W to Dumbarton Bridge, Sunol, no facilities

20 Andrade Rd, Sheridan Rd(from sb), **E...gas/diesel/ 24hr**

19mm weigh sta nb

19 Sheridan Rd(from nb), no facilities

18 Vargas Rd, no facilities

16 CA 238, Mission Blvd, to Hayward, **E...gas:** Shell, **food:** McDonald's, **W...**HOSPITAL

15 Washington Blvd, Irvington Dist, **E...gas:** QuikStop

14 Durham Rd, to Auto Mall Pkwy, **W...gas:** 76/Circle K/Subway/24hr, Shell/Jack-in-the-Box, **other:** Fry's Electronics, Home Depot

San Jose

12 Mission Blvd, to I-880, Warm Springs Dist, **W...gas:** 76, Valero, **food:** Burger King, Carl's Jr, Denny's, Jack-in-the-Box, KFC, Little Caesar's, RoundTable Pizza, Starbucks, Taco Bell, **lodging:** Econolodge, Extended Stay America, Quality Inn, **other:** GNC, Albertson's, Lion's Foods, Longs Drug, Safeway, Walgreen

10 Scott Creek Rd, no facilities

9 Jacklin Rd, **E...food:** Bonfare Rest., **W...gas:** Shell

8 CA 237, Calaveras Blvd, Milpitas, **E...gas:** Shell/repair, 76, **food:** Flames CoffeeShop, Paradise Pizza, Sizzler, Subway, **lodging:** Day's Inn, **other:** SuperMkt, **W...gas:** Shell, **food:** Lyon's Rest., McDonald's, Red Lobster, **lodging:** Embassy Suites, Extended Stay America, **other:** MEDICAL CARE, Albertson's, Longs Drug, Mervyn's

6 Landess Ave, Montague Expswy, **E...gas:** Arco, Chevron, 76, **food:** Burger King, Jack-in-the-Box, McDonald's, Royal Taco, StrawHat Pizza, Taco Bell, Togo's, Wienerschnitzel, **other:** Albertson's, Home Depot, Rite Aid, Target, Walgreen

5 Capitol Ave, Hostetter Ave, **E...gas:** Shell, **food:** Carl's Jr, Popeye's, **other:** SaveMart Foods, **W...gas:** Valero, **food:** KFC, **other:** MEDICAL CARE

4 Berryessa Rd, **E...gas:** Arco/24hr, USA, Valero, **food:** Denny's, Lee's Sandwiches, McDonald's, Taco Bell, **other:** Albertson's, Longs Drug, Safeway

2b McKee Rd, **E...gas:** 76, Chevron, Shell, **food:** Burger King, Country Harvest Buffet, Donut Express, Pizza Hut, Quizno's, Sizzler, Starbucks, Togo's, Wienerschnitzel, **other:** Albertson's, PaknSave Foods, Walgreen, **W...gas:** World Gas, **food:** Baskin-Robbins, Foster's Freeze, McDonald's, RoundTable, Winchell's, **other:** HOSPITAL, Fabric Whse, Kohl's

2a Alum Rock Ave, **E...gas:** Shell/diesel/24hr, **W...gas:** 76/24hr, **food:** Carl's Jr

1d Capitol Expswy, no facilities

1c King Rd, Jackson Ave(from nb), **E...gas:** 76, Shell, 7-11, **food:** Jack-in-the-Box, Mi Pueblo Mexican, Taco Bell, **other:** Walgreen

1b US 101, to LA, SF, no facilities

1a (exits left from sb)I-680 begins/ends on I-280.

Interstate 710(LA)

Exit #	Services
23	I-710 begins/ends on Valley Blvd
22b a	I-10, no facilities
20c	Chavez Ave, no facilities
20b	CA 60, Pamona Fwy, **W...gas:** Shell
20a	3rd St, no facilities
19	Whittier Blvd, Olympic Blvd, **W...gas:** Shell, **food:** McDonald's
17b	Washington Blvd, Commerce, **W...gas:** Commerce Trkstp/diesel/rest.

E

W

CALIFORNIA

Interstate 710

E — Los Angeles Area — W

17a	Bandini Blvd, Atlantic Blvd, industrial
15	Florence Ave, **E...food:** KFC, **other:** Ralph's Foods, **W...**truck repair
13	CA 42, Firestone Blvd, **E...gas:** Arco, **food:** Krispy Kreme, Starbucks, **other:** Ford, Target
12b a	Imperial Hwy, **W...gas:** 76, Shell
11b a	I-105, no facilities
10	Rosecrans Ave, no facilities
9b a	Alondra Ave, **E...**Home Depot
8b a	CA 91, no facilities
7b a	Long Beach Blvd, **E...gas:** Mobil/repair, 76, **food:** Taco Bell, **W...gas:** Arco/24hr, **lodging:** Day's Inn
6	Del Amo Blvd, no facilities
4	I-405, San Diego Freeway
3b a	Willow St, **E...gas:** Chevron, **food:** Chee Chinese, **W...gas:** Mobil, **food:** Popeye's, **other:** Ralph's Foods
2	CA 1, Pacific Coast Hwy, **E...gas:** Arco/mart, Shell, UltraMar, **food:** Burger Express, Via Italia Pizza, **lodging:** LaMirage Inn, **other:** auto repair, **W...gas:** 76/service, Shell/Carl's Jr/diesel, Xpress Minimart, **food:** Alberta's Mexican/24hr, Golden Star Rest., Jack-in-the-Box, McDonald's, Tom's Burgers, Wienerschnitzel, Winchell's, **lodging:** SeaBreeze Motel, SeaBrite Motel
1d	Anaheim St, **W...gas:** Shell/LP/24hr, **other:** diesel repair
1c	Ahjoreline Dr, Piers B, C, D, E, Pico Ave, Long Beach, no facilities
1b	Pico Ave, Piers F-J, Queen Mary
1a	Harbor Scenic Dr, Piers S, T, Terminal Island, **E...lodging:** Hilton
0mm	I-710 begins/ends in Long Beach

Interstate 780(Vallejo)

E — Benicia — W

Exit #	Services
7	I-780 begins/ends on I-680.
6	E 5th St, Benicia, **N...gas:** Fast&Easy, **S...gas:** Citgo/7-11, GasCity/diesel, **other:** Big O Tire
5	E 2nd St, Central Benicia, **N...gas:** Chevron, **lodging:** Best Western, **S...food:** McDonald's, Pappa's Rest.
4	Southampton Rd, Benicia, **N...food:** Asian Bistro, Burger King, Country Waffle, Jamba Juice, Rickshaw Express, RoundTable Pizza, Starbucks, Subway, **other:** Ace Hardware, AutoZone, GNC, Radio Shack, Raley's Foods
3b	Military West, no facilities
3a	Columbus Pkwy, **N...gas:** Shell/Burger King/mart, **food:** Napoli Pizza/pasta, Subway, **S...**to Benicia RA
1d	Glen Cove Pkwy, **N...**Hwy Patrol, **S...food:** Baskin-Robbins, Taco Bell, **other:** Safeway
1c	Cedar St, no facilities
1b a	I-780 begins/ends on I-80.

Interstate 805(San Diego)

San Diego Area

Exit #	Services
28mm	I-5(from nb). I-805 begins/ends on I-5.
27	Sorrento Valley Rd, Mira Mesa Blvd, **E...gas:** Shell, **food:** Chili's, McDonald's, **lodging:** Courtyard, Holiday Inn Express, Wyndham Garden, **other:** Staples
26	Vista Sorrento Pkwy, no facilities
25b a	La Jolla Village Dr, Miramar Rd, **1 mi E...gas:** 76/diesel, **other:** Discount Tire, Firestone/auto, **W...food:** Chang's China Bistro, **lodging:** Embassy Suites, Marriott, **other:** HOSPITAL, Nordstom's, Sears, mall
24	Governor Dr, **2 mi W...gas:** Chevron, Exxon, Mobil, 76, **food:** Carl's Jr, **other:** Rite Aid
23	CA 52, no facilities
22	Clairemont Mesa Blvd, **E...gas:** Chevron, Mobil/Subway/diesel, 76, **food:** Arby's, Burger King, Carl's Jr, Coco's, McDonald's, Quizno's, Players Grill, Rubio's Grill, Souplantation, Starbucks, **other:** Food4Less, Ford, K-Mart, **W...gas:** Arco/24hr, **food:** Carrow's, Godfather's, Oriental Buffet, **lodging:** CA Suites, Day's Inn, Motel 6
21	CA 274, Balboa Ave, **E...gas:** Arco, Chevron, Exxon/diesel, 76, Shell, **food:** Applebee's, Islands Burger, Jack-in-the-Box, **other:** Albertson's, Balboa AutoCare, Chevrolet, Dodge, Saturn, SavOn Drug
20	CA 163 N, to Escondido, no facilities
20a	Mesa College Dr, Kearney Villa Rd, **W...**HOSPITAL
18	Murray Ridge Rd, to Phyllis Place, no facilities
17b	I-8, E to El Centro, W to beaches
16	El Cajon Blvd, **E...gas:** Arco/24hr, Emerald, **food:** Church's, Venice Pizza, **other:** Albertson's, **W...gas:** 76, **food:** Wendy's
15	University Ave, **E...gas:** Chevron, **food:** Subway, **other:** Radio Shack, **W...gas:** Arco/24hr, Exxon, **other:** SavOn Drug
14	CA 15 N, 40th St, to I-15, no facilities
13b	Home Ave, MLK Ave, **E...gas:** Arco/24hr
13a	CA 94, no facilities
12b	Market St, no facilities
12a	Imperial Ave, **E...gas:** UltraMar/diesel
11b	47th St, no facilities
11a	43rd St, **W...food:** Giant Pizza, **other:** Albertson's, AutoZone, SavOn Drug
10	Plaza Blvd, National City, **E...food:** DQ, Dragon Garden Chinese, Manila Seafood, McDonald's, Popeye's, Winchell's, **other:** HOSPITAL, AutoZone, Firestone/auto, Ralph's Foods, Well's Drug, **W...food:** Jimmy's Rest., **lodging:** Day's Inn

67

CALIFORNIA
Interstate 805

N ↑↓ S

San Diego Area

9   Sweetwater Rd, **E...gas:** Citgo/7-11, **lodging:** Sweetwater Inn, **W...gas:** Chevron/diesel, **food:** Carl's Jr, Casa Taco, Subway, Taco Bell, **other:** Circuit City, Food4Less, Longs Drug, Staples

8   CA 54, no facilities

7c   E St, Bonita Rd, **E...food:** Applebee's, **other:** Mervyn's, Robinson-May, mall, **W...gas:** Chevron, 76, Shell, **food:** Burger King, Love's Rest., **lodging:** La Quinta, Ramada Inn

7b a   H St, **E...gas:** Shell, **food:** China China, Jack-in-the-Box, Subway, Taco Bell, **other:** JC Penney, Longs Drug, Marshall's, Vons Foods, mall, RV camping

6   L St, Telegraph Canyon Rd, **E... gas:** Arco/repair, 76, **food:** McDonald's, Subway, **other:** HOSPITAL, Rite Aid, Von's Foods, Olympic Training Ctr, RV camping, **W...gas:** Mobil, 7-11

4   Orange Ave, no facilities

3   Main St, Otay Valley Rd, **E...gas:** Shell, **W...lodging:** Holiday Inn Express

2   Palm Ave, **E...gas:** Arco/24hr, Chevron/24hr, **food:** Carl's Jr, Subway, Taco Bell, **other:** MEDICAL CARE, Home Depot, Radio Shack, USPO, Von's Foods, Wal-Mart, **W...gas:** 76/diesel, **food:** KFC, McDonald's

1b   CA 905, **E...**Brown Field Airport, Otay Mesa Border Crossing

1a   San Ysidro Blvd, **E...gas:** Arco, Shell, **lodging:** Travelodge, Factory2U, Kragen Parts, Longs Drug, 99c Store, U-Haul, **W...gas:** Chevron, Exxon, Mobil, 76, **food:** Denny's, McDonald's, Si Senor Mexican, **lodging:** Motel 6,

I-805 begins/ends on I-5.

Interstate 880(Bay Area)

N ↑↓ S

Exit #   Services

46b a   I-80 W(exits left). I-80 E/580 W.

44   7th St, Grand Ave(from sb), downtown

42b a   Broadway St, **E...gas:** 76, **lodging:** Howard Johnson, Marriott, **W...**to Jack London Square

41a   Oak St, Lakeside Dr, downtown, **W...gas:** Shell/diesel

40   5th Ave, Embarcadero, **W...lodging:** Executive Inn, Homewood Suites, Motel 6

39b a   29th Ave, 23rd Ave, to Fruitvale, **E...gas:** Shell, **food:** Boston Mkt, Burger King, DonutStar, Starbucks, **other:** Albertson's, AutoZone, Big Lots, GNC, Office Depot, Radio Shack, **W...gas:** 7-11

38   High St, to Alameda, **E...lodging:** Coliseum Motel, $Inn, **other:** El Monte RV Ctr, **W...gas:** Shell/diesel, **food:** McDonald's, **other:** Home Depot

37   66th Ave, Zhone Way, **E...**coliseum

36   Hegenberger Rd, **E...gas:** Arco/24hr, Shell/diesel, **food:** Burger King, Denny's, Jack-in-the-Box/24hr, McDonald's, Sam's Hofbrau, Taco Bell, **lodging:** Comfort Inn, Day's Inn/rest., Holiday Inn, Motel 6, **other:** Pak'n Save Foods, GMC/Volvo, Freightliner, AutoParts Club, **W...gas:** Chevron, 76/Circle K/diesel,

Oakland Area

Super Stop/diesel, **food:** Carrows Rest., Francesco's Rest., Green Garden Buffet, Hegen Burger, Subway, **lodging:** Courtyard, Hilton, Park Plaza Motel, Ramada Inn, **other:** Goodyear, Harley-Davidson, to Oakland Airport

35   98th Ave, **W...**airport

34   Davis St, **W...gas:** Shell/Burger King, **food:** Starbucks, Togo's, **other:** Costco, Home Depot, Office Depot, Wal-Mart

33b a   Marina Blvd, **E...gas:** Valero, **food:** Jack-in-the-Box, La Salsa Mexican, Starbucks, **other:** HOSPITAL, Firestone/auto, Ford, Hyundai, Kia, Marshall's, Nissan, Nordstrom's, OfficeMax, Old Navy, **W...gas:** Flyers/diesel, **food:** DairyBelle, Denny's, Giant Burger, KFC/A&W, Mtn Mike's Pizza, **other:** USPO

32   Washington Ave(from nb), Lewelling Blvd(from sb), **W...gas:** Arco, 76, TechCo, **food:** Chili Palace, Hometown Buffet, Jack-in-the-Box, McDonald's, Papa Murphy's, Subway, **other:** Big Lots, Big O Tire, GNC, Longs Drug, 99Cent Store, Radio Shack, Safeway/24hr, SavMax Foods, SP Parts, Walgreen/24hr

31   I-238(from sb), to I-580, Castro Valley, no facilities

30   Hesperian Blvd, **E...gas:** 76, **food:** Bakers Square, KFC, Mr Pizza, Starbucks, Western Superburger, **other:** House of Fabrics, Kragen Parts, Target, Wheelworks Repair, **W...gas:** Arco, Chevron, 76, **food:** Black Angus, Carrow's Rest., KFC, McDonald's, Taco Bell, **lodging:** Hilton Garden, Minutes Motel, Vagabond Inn, **other:** Albertson's, Kragen Parts, Radio Shack

29   A St, San Lorenzo, **E...gas:** 76, **food:** McDonald's, **lodging:** Best Western, **other:** AllPro Parts, Costco, **W...gas:** 76/Circle K, **food:** Acapulco Mexican, Burger King, McDonald's, StrawHat Pizza, **lodging:** Day's Inn, Heritage Inn, **other:** Big O, Costco

28   Winton Ave, **W...gas:** Chevron, Valero/diesel, **food:** Applebee's, Marie Callendar's, **other:** Circuit City, Firestone/auto, Food Fair, JC Penney, Macy's, Macy's, Mervyn's, Old Navy, Ross, Sears/auto, mall

27   CA 92, Jackson St, **E...gas:** Valero/24hr, **food:** Bakers Square, Rickshaw Chinese, Subway, Taco Bell, **other:** Albertson's, Longs Drug, Rite Aid, Safeway, **W...**San Mateo Br

26   Tennyson Rd, **E...gas:** All American/diesel, 76, Shell, **food:** Jack-in-the-Box, KFC, **other:** Big Lots, Kragen Parts, Walgreen, **W...gas:** 76, **food:** Dairy Bell, **other:** HOSPITAL

24   Whipple Rd, Dyer St, **E...gas:** Chevron/24hr, 76, **food:** Denny's, McDonald's, Taco Bell, **lodging:** Motel 6, Super 8, **other:** CHP, FoodMaxx, Home Depot, PepBoys, Target, **W...gas:** QuikStop/24hr, 76, Shell, **food:** Applebee's, Burger King, Chevy's Mexican, Chili's, In-n-Out, IHOP, Jamba Juice, Krispy Kreme, La Salsa Mexican, Starbucks, Texas Roadhouse, TGIFriday, Togo's, Tony Roma's, **lodging:** Extended Stay America, Holiday Inn Express, **other:** Albertson's/SavOn, Best Buy, Borders Books, Lowe's, Michael's, OfficeMax, RadioShack, Wal-Mart/auto

Interstate 880

N ↕ **S**

23 Alvarado-Niles Rd, (same as 24) **E...gas:** 7-11, **lodging:** Crowne Plaza, **W...gas:** 76, Shell, **other:** Wal-Mart/auto

22 Alvarado Blvd, Fremont Blvd, **E...food:** Luciano European Café, Phoenix Garden Chinese, **lodging:** Motel 6, **other:** Albertson's/SavOn

21 CA 84 W, Dumbarton Br, Decoto Rd, **E...gas:** Citgo/7-11, **food:** McDonald's, **other:** Rite Aid, Walgreen

19 CA 84 E, Thornton Ave, Newark, **E...other:** Chevrolet, U-Haul, **W...gas:** Chevron/diesel/24hr, Shell, 7-11, Valero, **food:** Bakers Square, Carl's Jr, KFC, Mike's Pizza, Taco Bell, **other:** Big Lots, K-Mart

17 Mowry Ave, Fremont, **E...gas:** Chevron/diesel, QuikStop, 76/Circle K, Valero, **food:** Applebee's, Burger King, Country Way Rest., Denny's, Hungry Hunter, KFC, Mkt Broiler, Olive Garden, Starbucks, Subway, **lodging:** Extended Stay America, Best Western, Motel 6, Studio+ Suites, **other:** HOSPITAL, Albertson's, Cost+, Jo-Ann Fabrics, **W...gas:** 76, **food:** Arby's, Bombay Garden, El Burro Mexican, FreshChoice Rest., HomeTown Buffet, Jack-in-the-Box, Lyon's Rest., McDonald's, Red Robin, Sizzler, Subway, Taco Bell, **lodging:** EZ 8 Motel, Goodnight Inn, Holiday Inn Express, Homestead Suites, La Quinta, Marriott, Motel 6, Woodfin Suites, **other:** Circuit City, $Tree, Firestone, Ford, Goodyear/auto, Hancock Fabrics, JC Penney, Macy's, Marshall's, Mervyn's, Sears/auto, Staples, Target, mall

16 Stevenson Blvd, **W...gas:** Chevron, **food:** Carl's Jr, Chevy's Mexican, ChuckeCheese, Sizzler, Togo's, **lodging:** Hilton Garden, **other:** AAA, Costco, FoodMaxx, Ford, Harley-Davidson, Home Depot, JC Penney, Macy's, Mervyn's, Nissan, Pontiac/GMC, PepBoys, Saturn, mall

15 Auto Mall Pkwy, **E...gas:** Chevron, **W...gas:** Shell/diesel, **food:** Wendy's, **lodging:** Hawthorn Suites, **other:** BMW, Dodge/Isuzu, Honda, Kia, Kohl's, Lexus, Mercedes, Toyota

14mm weigh sta both lanes

13 Fremont Blvd, Irving Dist, **W...food:** McDonald's, **lodging:** GoodNite Inn, Homestead Village, La Quinta, Marriott

13b Warren St(from sb), **W...lodging:** Amerisuites, Courtyard, Hampton Inn

13a Gateway Blvd(from nb), **E...lodging:** Holiday Inn Express

12 Mission Blvd, **E...to I-680, gas:** 76, **food:** Denny's, Togo's, **lodging:** Quality Inn

10 Dixon Landing Rd, **E...gas:** Chevron, 7-11, **food:** Starbucks, **lodging:** Residence Inn

8b CA 237, Alviso Rd, Calaveras Rd, to McCarthy Rd,, Milpitas, **E...gas:** Arco, 76, 7-11, **food:** Chili's, Denny's, Marie Callender, RoundTable Pizza, **lodging:** Best Western, Inns of America, Travelodge, **other:** Albertson's, Big Lots, Kragen Parts, SaveMart Foods, Walgreen, **W on McCarthy Rd...gas:** Chev-

ron, **food:** Applebee's, Black Angus, HomeTown Buffet, In-n-Out, Macaroni Grill, McDonald's, On the Border, Taco Bell, **lodging:** Candlewood Suites, Crowne Plaza, Hampton Inn, Hawthorn Suites, Hilton Garden, Homestead Suites, **other:** Best Buy, Borders Books, Chevrolet, Michael's, OfficeMax, Ranch Mkt Foods, Ross, Wal-Mart/auto

8a Great Mall Parkway, Tasman Dr, **E...mall**

7 Montague Expswy, **E...gas:** Chevron, 76, Shell/diesel, **food:** Jack-in-the-Box, **lodging:** Sleep Inn, **other:** MEDICAL CARE, U-Haul, auto repair, **W...gas:** Chevron, **food:** Dave&Buster's, **lodging:** Beverly Heritage Hotel, Sheraton

5 Brokaw Rd, **W...other:** Ford Trucks, CHP

4d Gish Rd (nb only), **W...other:** auto/diesel repair/transmissions

4c b US 101, N to San Francisco, S to LA, no facilities

4a 1st St, **E...gas:** 76, Shell, **food:** Subway, **W...gas:** Chevron, 76, **food:** Cathay Chinese, Denny's/24hr, Empire Buffet, Genji Japanese, McDonald's, **lodging:** Adlon Hotel, Best Western, Comfort Inn, Day's Inn, Executive Inn, EZ 8 Motel, Holiday Inn Express, Homestead Suites, Vagabond Inn, Wyndham Garden

3 Coleman St,, **E...gas:** Valero/diesel, **food:** George's Rest.

2 CA 82, The Alameda, **W...gas:** Shell/repair, **food:** Cozy Rest., **lodging:** Bell Motel, Best Western, Comfort Inn, Friendship Inn, Santa Clara Inn, Valley Inn, **other:** Safeway, Santa Clara U

1d Bascom Ave, to Santa Clara, **W...gas:** Rotten Robbie/diesel, Valero, **food:** Burger King, Normandy House Pizza

1c Stevens Creek Blvd, San Carlos St, **E...gas:** Valero/diesel, Valley/diesel, **lodging:** Valley Park Hotel, **W...gas:** 76, **food:** Arby's, Burger King, Lyon's Rest., Teriyaki Rest., **other:** Audi/VW, Best Buy, Chevrolet, Firestone/auto, Goodyear/auto, Isuzu, Longs Drugs, Macy's, Mitsubishi, Nordstrom's, Safeway, Subaru

1b I-280. I-880 begins/ends on I-280, no facilities

1a Ca 17 to Santa Cruz.

N ↑↓ **S**

Ft Collins

Exit #	Services
299	Colorado/Wyoming state line
296	point of interest both lanes, no facilities
293	to Carr, Norfolk, no facilities
288	Buckeye Rd, no facilities
281	Owl Canyon Rd, no facilities
278	CO 1 S, to Wellington, **1/2 mi W...gas:** Conoco, Shell, **food:** Blimpie, Burger King/Taco Bell, Subway, **lodging:** Comfort Inn
271	Mountain Vista Dr, **W...**Anheiser-Busch Brewery
269b a	CO 14, to US 87, Ft Collins, **E...food:** McDonald's, **lodging:** Mulberry Inn; **other:** RV service, **W...gas:** Conoco, Phillips 66/diesel, **food:** Burger King, Denny's, Waffle House, **lodging:** Comfort Inn, Day's Inn, Holiday Inn, Motel 6, National 9 Inn, Plaza Inn, Ramada Inn, Super 8, **other:** to CO St U, stadium
268	Prospect Rd, to Ft Collins, **W...other:** HOSPITAL, Welcome Ctr, Sunset RV Ctr
267mm	weigh sta both lanes
266mm	**rest area both lanes, full(handicapped)facilities, info, phone, picnic tables, litter barrels, petwalk**
265	CO 68 W, Timnath, **W...gas:** Shell, **2-3 mi W...food:** Austin's Grill, Carrabba's, Golden Corral, Hunan Chinese, IHOP, Macaroni Grill, Outback Steaks, Papa John's, Quizno's, Subway, Texas Roadhouse, Village Inn Rest., **lodging:** Courtyard, Hampton Inn, Marriott, Residence Inn, Safeway/gas, Sam's Club
262	CO 392 E, to Windsor, **E...gas:** Conoco, Phillips 66/Subway/diesel, **food:** Arby's, McDonald's(3mi), **lodging:** AmericInn, Super 8, **W...other:** Scott RV Ctr
259	Airport Rd, **E...**Wal-Mart Depot, **W...**to airport, Harley-Davidson
257b a	US 34, to Loveland, **E...gas:** Shamrock/diesel/RV camping, **lodging:** Country Inn Suites, **W...gas:** Conoco/diesel, **food:** Arby's(2mi), Blackeyed Pea, Chili's, Cracker Barrel, IHOP, KFC/Taco Bell, LoneStar Steaks, McDonald's, Subway, Waffle House, Wendy's, **lodging:** Best Western, Comfort Inn, Fairfield Inn, Hampton Inn, Holiday Inn Express, Super 8(2mi), **other:** HOSPITAL, Prime Outlets/famous brands, Target, RV camping, museum, to Rocky Mtn NP
255	CO 402 W, to Loveland, no facilities
254	to CO 60 W, to Campion, **E...gas:** Johnson's Corner/diesel/café/motel/24hr, **lodging:** Budget Host, **other:** RV camping/service
252	CO 60 E, to Johnstown, Milliken, **W...gas:** Loaf'n Jug
250	CO 56 W, to Berthoud, no facilities
245	to Mead, no facilities
243	CO 66, to Longmont, Platteville, **E...gas:** Conoco, Shell, **food:** Blimpie, Scott's Rest., **other:** K&C RV Ctr, Outfitter RV Ctr, Yamaha/Suzuki, **W...**to Rocky Mtn NP, to Estes Park

Thornton

241mm	St Vrain River
240	CO 119, to Longmont, **E...gas:** Phillips 66/diesel, **food:** Carl's Jr, Wendy's, **lodging:** Best Western, **other:** Kia, **W...gas:** Conoco/Subway/diesel/24hr, Shell/diesel, **food:** Arby's, Burger King, DQ, McDonald's, Pizza Hut, Taco Bell, Waffle House, Wendy's, **lodging:** Best Western, Comfort Inn, Day's Inn, 1st Interstate Inn, Super 8, **other:** HOSPITAL, Del Camino RV Ctr, museum, to Barbour Ponds SP
235	CO 52, Dacono, **E...**Ford, **W...gas:** Conoco/diesel/LP, **food:** McDonald's, **other:** Harley-Davidson, to Eldora Ski Area
232	to Erie, Dacono, no facilities
229	CO 7, to Lafayette, Brighton, no facilities
228	E-470, tollway, to Limon, no facilities
225	136th Ave, no facilities
223	CO 128, 120th Ave, to Broomfield, **E...gas:** Conoco, Shell, Sinclair, **food:** Applebee's, Burger King, Café Mexico, Damon's, Fuddrucker's, Golden Gate Chinese, LoneStar Steaks, OutBack Steaks, Pizza Hut, Shari's, **lodging:** Day's Inn, Hampton Inn, Holiday Inn, Radisson, Sleep Inn, **other:** Albertson's, Checker's Parts, Discount Tire, **W...gas:** Conoco, Shamrock/diesel, **food:** Casa Loma Mexican, Chili's, Cracker Barrel, DQ, Jade City Chinese, Perkins, Starbucks, Subway, Village Inn Rest., Wendy's, **lodging:** Comfort Inn, Fairfield Inn, La Quinta, Super 8
221	104th Ave, to Northglenn, **E...gas:** Conoco, Phillips 66, Shamrock/diesel, **food:** Burger King, Denny's, IHOP, McDonald's, Sonic, Subway, Taco Bell, Taco John's, Texas Roadhouse, **other:** HOSPITAL, AutoZone, Big A Parts, Bigg's Foods, Home Depot, King's Sooper's, Target, **W...gas:** Citgo/7-11, Conoco, Shell/diesel, **food:** Applebee's, Bennigan's, Blackeyed Pea, Cinzinetti's Italian, Hop's Grill, McDonald's, Taco Bell, **lodging:** La Quinta, Ramada Ltd, **other:** Albertson's, Borders Books, Dodge, Firestone/auto, Goodyear/auto, Lowe's Whse, Marshall's, Mervyn's, Office Depot, Rite Aid, Ross, mall
220	Thornton Pkwy, **E...food:** Golden Corral, **lodging:** Crossland Suites, **other:** HOSPITAL, Sam's Club/gas, Wal-Mart Super Ctr/24hr, Thornton Civic Ctr, **W...gas:** Conoco, Shamrock
219	84th Ave, to Federal Way, **E...gas:** Conoco, Shamrock, **food:** Arby's, Bonanza, Dos Verdes Mexican, Goodtimes Grill, Subway, Taco Bell, Waffle House, **other:** Radio Shack Outlet, Walgreen, **W...gas:** Shamrock/diesel, **food:** Burger King, DQ, Pizza Hut, Tokyo Bowl Japanese, Village Inn Rest., **lodging:** Motel 6, **other:** HOSPITAL, CarQuest, Discount Tire

217   US 36 W(exits left from nb), to Boulder, **W...food:** Subway, **other:** Chevrolet, Toyota

216b a   I-76 E, to I-270 E, no facilities

215   58th Ave, **E...food:** McDonald's, Steak Escape, Taco John's, Wendy's, **lodging:** Quality Inn, **W...gas:** Conoco, Shamrock/diesel/LP, **lodging:** Super 8, **other:** Malibu FunPark

214c   48th Ave, **E...**coliseum, airport, **W...food:** Village Inn Rest., **lodging:** Best Western, Holiday Inn

214b a   I-70, E to Limon, W to Grand Junction, no facilities

213   Park Ave, W 38th Ave, 23rd St, downtown, **E...gas:** BP/McDonald's, Citgo/7-11, Shell, **food:** Burger King, Denny's, **lodging:** La Quinta, **other:** Goodyear, **W... lodging:** Regency Inn, Travelodge

212c   20th St, downtown, Denver, **W...food:** Pagliacci's Italian

212b a   Speer Blvd, **E...**downtown, museum, **W...gas:** Conoco, Shell, **lodging:** Ramada Inn, Residence Inn, Super 8, Travel Inn

211   23rd Ave, **E...**funpark

210c   CO 33(from nb), no facilities

210b   US 40 W, Colfax Ave, **W...food:** Denny's, KFC, **lodging:** Ramada Inn/rest., Red Lion Inn, **other:** Mile High Stadium

210a   US 40 E, Colfax Ave, **E...**civic center, downtown, U-Haul

209c   8th Ave, **E...lodging:** Motel 7, **other:** Bob's Auto Parts

209b   6th Ave W, US 6, **W...lodging:** Day's Inn

209a   6th Ave E, downtown, Denver, no facilities

208   CO 26, Alameda Ave(from sb), **E...gas:** BP, Shamrock/diesel, **food:** Burger King, Denny's, same as 207b

207b   US 85 S, Santa Fe Dr, **E...gas:** BP, Shamrock, **food:** Burger King, Denny's, **other:** Home Depot

207 a   Broadway, Lincoln St, **E...food:** Griff's Burgers, **other:** USPO

206b   Washington St, Emerson St, **E...other:** WildOats Mkt/café, **W...other:** HOSPITAL

206a   Downing St(from nb), no facilities

205b a   University Blvd, **W...**to U of Denver

204   CO 2, Colorado Blvd, **E...gas:** BP, Conoco, Shamrock, 7-11, **food:** Grisanti's Grill, KFC, Lazy Dog Café, Pizza Hut, Village Inn Rest., **lodging:** Day's Inn, Fairfield Inn, Ramada, **other:** Albertson's, Best Buy, CompUSA, **W... food:** A&W/KFC, Dave&Buster's, Denny's, Perkins, **lodging:** Cameron Motel, La Quinta, **other:** Ford

203   Evans Ave, **E...gas:** Shell, **food:** Denny's, KFC, **lodging:** Rockies Inn, **other:** Big O Tire, **W...lodging:** Cameron Motel, **other:** Ford

202   Yale Ave, **W...gas:** Shamrock

N ↕ S

Cherry Hills

201 US 285, CO 30, Hampden Ave, to Englewood, Aurora, **E...gas:** BP, Conoco/LP, Phillips 66, Shamrock, Shell, **food:** Applebee's, Benihana, Blackeyed Pea, Boston Mkt, Chicago Grill, Chili's, Domino's, Houlihan's, Jason's Deli, Le Peep's Café, McDonald's, Mexican Grill, NY Deli, No Frills Grill, On-the-Border, Piccolo's Café, Skillet's Rest., Starbucks, Subway, Uno Pizzaria, **lodging:** Embassy Suites, Hampden Lodge, Marriott, TownePlace Suites, **other:** Discount Tire, King's Sooper Foods, Walgreen, **W...gas:** Shell, **food:** Burger King

200 I-225 N, to I-70, no facilities

199 CO 88, Belleview Ave, to Littleton, **E...gas:** BP, Phillips 66, **food:** Harvest Rest., Off Belleview Grill, Sandwiches+, Tosh's Hacienda Rest., Wendy's, **lodging:** Hyatt Regency, Marriott, Wyndham, **W...gas:** Conoco, Shamrock/diesel, **food:** European Café, McDonald's, Mountainview Rest., Pappadeaux Café, Pizza Hut, Taco Bell, **lodging:** Day's Inn, Holiday Inn Express, HomeStead Village, Wellesley Inn

198 Orchard Rd, **E...food:** Del Frisco's Steaks, Shepler's, **W...gas:** Shell, **food:** Bayou Bob's Café, 4Happiness Chinese, Le Peep's Café, Quizno's, **lodging:** Hilton, **other:** HOSPITAL,

197 Arapahoe Blvd, **E...gas:** BP, Conoco, **food:** A&W, Applebee's, Brothers BBQ, Bennigan's, BlackJack Pizza, Burger King, Carrabba's, Country Dinner, DeliZone, Denny's, El Parral Mexican, GoldStar Chili, GrandSlam Steaks, Gunther Toody's Rest., IHOP, Jalapeno Mexican, Landry's Seafood, Outback Steaks, Pizza Hut, Red Lobster, Schlotsky's, Subway, Taco Cabana, TrailDust Steaks, Wendy's, **lodging:** Candlewood Hotel, Courtyard, Embassy Suites, Hampton Inn, Holiday Inn, Homestead Suites, La Quinta, MainStay Suites, Motel 6, Radisson, Sheraton, Sleep Inn, Summerfield Suites, Woodfield Suites, **other:** Big A Parts, Buick/Pontiac, Chrysler/Toyota, Discount Tire, Ford, GMC/Cadillac/Subaru, K-Mart, Lowe's Whse, Nissan, Target, USPO, **W...gas:** Phillips 66/diesel, 7-11, **food:** Arby's, Baker St Gourmet, Blackeyed Pea, Boston Mkt, Brooks Steaks, Burger King, Chevy's Mexican, DQ, GoodTimes Grill, Grady's Grill, KFC, Lamonica's Rest., Macaroni Grill, McDonald's, Red Robin, Ruby Tuesday, Stanford's Grill, Souper Salad, Taco Bell, TCBY, Uno Pizzaria, **lodging:** Residence Inn, **other:** Albertson's, Barnes&Noble, Firestone/auto, Goodyear/auto, Office Depot, OfficeMax

196 Dry Creek Rd, **E...food:** Vasil's Steakhouse, Landry's Seafood, Maggiano's Italian, **lodging:** Best Western, Bradford Suites, Country Inn Suites, Holiday Inn, Homestead Village, Quality Inn, Ramada Ltd, **other:** Studio+, **W...lodging:** Drury Inn

195 County Line Rd, **E...lodging:** Courtyard, Residence Inn, **W...food:** Alexander's Rest., Champp's Rest., Cucina Cucina, Starbucks, **lodging:** AmeriSuites, **other:** Barnes&Noble, Best Buy, Borders, CompUSA, Costco, Dillard's, Home Depot, JC Penney, Nordstrom's, OfficeMax

194 CO 470 W, CO 470 E(tollway), **1 exit W on Quebec... food:** Arby's, ClaimJumper, Country Buffet, LoneStar Steaks, McDonald's, TGIFriday, **lodging:** AmeriSuites, Comfort Suites, Fairfield Inn, **other:** Barnes&Noble, Circuit City, Firestone, Home Depot, PepBoys, Sam's Club, Wal-Mart/auto/gas

193 Lincoln Ave, to Parker, **E...food:** PanAsia Bistro, Hacienda Colorado, **lodging:** Hilton Garden, **W...gas:** Conoco/diesel, **food:** Chipotle Grill, Cili's, McDonald's, Pizza Hut/Taco Bell, Starbucks, Subway, **lodging:** Marriott, **other:** HOSPITAL, Discount Tire, Safeway

191 no facilities

190 Surrey Ridge, no facilities

188 Castle Pines Pkwy, **W...gas:** BP, King's Sooper/gas, Shell/24hr, **food:** Celtic Crossing, La Dolce Vita, Subway, Wendy's, Wild Bean Café, Wild West Wings, **other:** Safeway

187 Happy Canyon Rd, no facilities

184 Founders Pkwy, Meadows Pkwy, to Castle Rock, **E...gas:** Conoco/diesel, Shell/Carl's Jr/diesel, **food:** Applebee's, Goodtimes Grill, KFC/A&W, Red Robin, Outback Steaks, Sonic, Taco Bell, Wendy's, **other:** Starbucks, GNC, Goodyear, Home Depot, King's Sooper/24hr, Target, Walgreen, Wal-Mart SuperCtr/24hr, **W...gas:** Conoco/diesel, **food:** Blackeyed Pea, Chili's, Food Court, IHOP, McDonald's, Rockyard Café, **lodging:** Best Western, Comfort Inn, Day's Inn, Hampton Inn, Castle Rock Prime Outlet/famous brands

183 US 85 N(from nb), Sedalia, Littleton, no facilities

182 CO 86, Castle Rock, Franktown, **E...gas:** Conoco, Phillips 66/diesel, **food:** Little Caesar's, Mexicali Café, Nick&Willie's, **other:** st patrol, **W...gas:** Shell/diesel, **food:** Burger King, KFC, McDonald's, Shari's/24hr, Taco Bell, Village Inn Rest., Wendy's, **lodging:** Comfort Inn, Holiday Inn Express, Quality Inn, Super 8, **other:** Chrysler/Plymouth/Dodge/Jeep, NAPA

181 CO 86, Wilcox St, Plum Creek Pkwy, Castle Rock, **E... gas:** BP, Citgo/7-11, Shamrock/diesel, **food:** DQ, Duke's Rest., Hungry Heifer Steaks, New Rock Café, Nicolo's Pizza, Pino's Café, Pizza Hut, Subway, **lodging:** Castle Rock Motel, **other:** MEDICAL CARE, Autozone, Big A Parts, Ford/Lincoln/Mercury, Safeway, USPO

174 Tomah Rd, no facilities

173 Larkspur(from sb, no return), **1 mi W...gas:** Conoco/diesel/phone

172 South Lake Gulch Rd, Larkspur, **2 mi W...gas:** Conoco/diesel/phone

171mm rest area both lanes, full(handicapped)facilities, phone, picnic tables, litter barrels, petwalk

167 Greenland, no facilities

163 County Line Rd, no facilities

162.5mm Monument Hill, elev 7352

162mm weigh sta both lanes

161 CO 105, Woodmoor Dr, **E...gas:** BP, **lodging:** Falcon Inn, **W...gas:** Citgo/7-11, Conoco/diesel, **food:** Arby's, Boston Mkt, Burger King, DQ, McDonald's, Pizza Hut, Rosie's Diner, Starbucks, Subway, Taco Bell, Village Inn Rest., **other:** Big O Tire, Rite Aid, Safeway

Castle Rock

Interstate 25

158 Baptist Rd, **E...gas:** Shell/Popeye's/diesel/24hr, **food:** Jackson Creek Chinese, Subway, **other:** Ace Hardware, Home Depot, King's Sooper/24hr, **W...gas:** Shamrock/diesel

156b N Entrance to USAF Academy, **W...**visitors center

156a Gleneagle Dr, **E...**mining museum

153 InterQuest Pkwy, **E...lodging:** Residence Inn

151 Briargate Pkwy, **E...lodging:** Hilton Garden, **other:** Focus on the Family Visitor Ctr, to Black Forest

150b a CO 83, Academy Blvd, **E...gas:** Shamrock/Quizno's/diesel, Shell/diesel, **food:** Applebee's, Blimpie, Boston Mkt, Burger King, Capt D's, Chevy's Mexican, Chipotle Mexican, Country Buffet, Cracker Barrel, Denny's, Egg&I Café, Fazoli's, Grady's Grill, IHOP, Joe's Crabshack, KFC, Macaroni Grill, McDonald's, Mimi's Café, Olive Garden, On-the-Border, Panera Bread, Pizza Hut, Red Robin, Schlotsky's, Sonic, Souper Salad, Starbucks, Subway, Taco Bell, Village Inn Rest., Wendy's, **lodging:** Comfort Inn, Day's Inn, Drury Inn, Radisson, Red Roof Inn, Sleep Inn, Super 8, **other:** Advance Parts, Barnes&Noble, Best Buy, Big O Tire, Borders Books, Circuit City, CompUSA, Cub Foods, Dillard's, Firestone/auto, Home Depot, King's Soopers, NAPA, Office Depot, OfficeMax, PepBoys, Rite Aid, Sam's Club, Sears/auto, USPO, Wal-Mart SuperCtr/24hr, mall, to Peterson AFB, **W...**S Entrance to USAF Academy

149 Woodmen Rd, **E...gas:** Conoco/Subway/diesel, **food:** Carl's Jr, Carrabba's, **other:** Nissan, **W...gas:** Shell, **food:** Old Chicago Pizza, Outback Steaks, TGIFriday, Zio's Italian, **lodging:** Comfort Inn, Embassy Suites, Extended Stay America, Fairfield Inn, Hampton Inn, Holiday Inn Express, Microtel

148b a Corporate Ctr Dr(exits left from sb), Nevada Ave, **E...other:** Harley-Davidson, K&C RV Ctr, **W...**New South Wales Rest.

147 Rockrimmon Blvd, **W...gas:** Shell, **lodging:** Bradford Suites, Wyndham, to Rodeo Hall of Fame

146 Garden of the Gods Rd, **E...gas:** BP, Shell/diesel, **food:** Carl's Jr, Denny's, McDonald's, Taco John's, **lodging:** Econolodge, La Quinta, Aamco, **W...gas:** Citgo/7-11, Conoco, Phillips 66, Shamrock, **food:** Applebee's, Arby's, Blackeyed Pea, Hungry Farmer Rest., Margarita's, Quizno's, Subway, Taco Bell, Village Inn Rest., Wendy's, **lodging:** AmeriSuites, Day's Inn, Holiday Inn, Quality Inn, Super 8, **other:** to Garden of Gods

145 CO 38 E, Fillmore St, **E...gas:** Citgo/7-11, Shamrock, **food:** DQ, **lodging:** Budget Host, Ramada Inn, **other:** HOSPITAL, **W...gas:** Conoco/diesel, Shell/diesel, **food:** BBQ, Waffle House, **lodging:** Best Western, Central Inn, Motel 6

144 Fontanero St, no facilities

143 Uintah St, **E...gas:** Citgo/7-11, **other:** Uintah Fine Arts Ctr

142 Bijou St, Bus Dist, **E...other:** Firestone/auto, **W...gas:** Western Gas, **food:** Denny's, Antlers, **lodging:** Doubletree Hotel, Best Western, Le Baron Motel, RainTree Inn, Red Lion Hotel

141 US 24 W, Cimarron St, to Manitou Springs, **W...gas:** Conoco, Phillips 66, **food:** Burger King, Capt D's, McDonald's, Papa John's, Popeye's, Sonic, Subway, Taco John's, Texas Roadhouse, Waffle House, **lodging:** Holiday Inn Express, **other:** Acura, AutoZone, Buick/GMC/Pontiac, Chevrolet, Chrysler/Plymouth, Discount Tire, Ford, Hyundai, Infiniti, Isuzu, Lincoln/Mercury, Mazda, Mercedes, NAPA, Nissan, Office Depot, Saturn, Subaru/Saab/VW, Suzuki, Toyota, Volvo, Wal-Mart SuperCtr/24hr, to Pikes Peak

140b US 85 S, Tejon St, **W...gas:** Conoco, Circle K, access to same as 141

140a Nevada Ave, **E...lodging:** Chateau Motel, Colorado Springs Motel, Economy Inn, Howard Johnson, Chrysler/Jeep, **W...gas:** BP, Citgo/7-11, Shamrock, Shell/diesel, **food:** Burger King, Colima Mexican, KFC, Little Caesar's, McDonald's, Schlotsky's, Subway, Taco Bell, TCBY, Wienerschnitzel, Wendy's, **lodging:** American Inn, Chief Motel, Cheyenne Motel, Circle S Motel, Econolodge, Stagecoach Motel, **other:** Checker Parts, Safeway, USPO, Walgreen, access to auto dealers at 141

139 US 24 E, to Lyman, Peterson AFB, no facilities

138 CO 29, Circle Dr, **E...gas:** Conoco, Shell/diesel, **lodging:** Day's Inn/Mexican Rest., Sheraton, **other:** RV repair, airport, zoo, **W...gas:** Citgo/7-11, **food:** Arby's, Burger King, Carrabba's, Carl's Jr, Chili's, Denny's, Fazoli's, Outback Steaks, Papa John's, Village Inn Rest., Subway, **lodging:** Budget Inn, DoubleTree Hotel, Fairfield Inn, Hampton Inn, La Quinta, Quality Inn, Residence Inn, **other:** Batteries+, OfficeMax, Radio Shack, Target

135 CO 83, Academy Blvd, **E...**to airport, same as 132, **W...**Ft Carson

132 CO 16, Wide Field Security, **3 mi E on US 85...gas:** Shamrock, **food:** Arby's, Burger King, KFC, McDonald's, Papa John's, Pizza Hut, Subway, Taco Bell, Wendy's, **other:** AutoZone, Camping Country RV Ctr, Checker Parts, KOA, Wal-Mart SuperCtr/24hr

128 to US 85 N, Fountain, Security, **E...gas:** Citgo/7-11, Conoco/Subway/diesel, **lodging:** Ute Motel, **other:** USPO, **W...gas:** Tomahawk/Shell/diesel/rest./24hr/@, **lodging:** 1st Inn Gold, Super 8

125 Ray Nixon Rd, no facilities

COLORADO
Interstate 25

N ↑

S ↓

Pueblo

123   no facilities

122   to Pikes Peak Meadows, **W**...Pikes Peak Intn'l Raceway

119   Midway, no facilities

116   county line rd, no facilities

115mm rest area nb, full(handicapped)facilities, picnic tables, litter barrels, petwalk

114   Young Hollow, no facilities

112mm rest area sb, full(handicapped)facilities, picnic tables, litter barrels, petwalk

110   Pinon, **W...gas:** Sinclair/Subway/diesel/repair/@, **lodging:** Pinon Tree Inn

108   Bragdon, **E...gas:** racetrack, **W**...KOA

106   Porter Draw, no facilities

104   Eden, no facilities

102   Eagleridge Blvd, **E...gas:** Conoco/diesel, **food:** Burger King, Texas Roadhouse, **other:** Big O Tire, Home Depot, Kohl's, Sam's Club/gas, **W...gas:** Shell/Blimpie/diesel, **food:** Cactus Flower Mexican, Cracker Barrel, DJ's Steaks, IHOP, Village Inn Rest., **lodging:** Comfort Inn, Day's Inn, Econolodge, Hampton Inn, Holiday Inn, La Quinta, Motel 6, National 9 Inn, Wingate Inn, **other:** MEDICAL CARE, Tires+, Harley-Davidson, frontage rds access 101

101   US 50 W, Pueblo, **E...gas:** Conoco, **food:** Denny's, Ruby Tuesday, **lodging:** Sleep Inn, **other:** Barnes&Noble, Circuit City, JC Penney, OfficeMax, Ross, Sears/auto, Wal-Mart SuperCtr/24hr, U-Haul, mall, **W...gas:** Conoco/Blimpie, Phillips 66, Shamrock/diesel, **food:** Applebee's, Arby's, Blackeyed Pea, Boston Mkt, Burger King, Carl's Jr, Country Kitchen, DQ, Domino's, Fazoli's, Gaetano's Italian, Golden Corral, King's Table Buffet, McDonald's, Pizza Hut, Red Lobster, Subway, Taco Bell, Wendy's, **lodging:** Holiday Inn, Motel 6, Quality Inn, Super 8, Villager Lodge, **other:** Advance Parts, Albertson's, Batteries+, Checker Parts, Discount Tire, Dodge, Goodyear/auto, K-Mart, Lincoln/Mercury, Lowe's Whse, Toyota, frontage rds access 102

100b   29th St, Pueblo, **E...food:** Country Buffet, KFC, **other:** King's Sooper Foods, mall, tires, **W...gas:** Amoco, Shamrock, Sinclair, **food:** Sonic, **other:** Safeway

100a   US 50 E, to La Junta, **E...gas:** Conoco/LP, Phillips 66, Shamrock, **food:** Little Caesar's, McDonald's, Pizza Hut, Wendy's, **lodging:** Ramada Inn/rest., Rodeway Inn, **other:** AutoZone, Furr's Foods, Goodyear

99b a   Santa Fe Ave, 13th St, downtown, **W...gas:** Amoco, Wendy's, **lodging:** Best Western, Brambletree Inn, Travelers Motel, **other:** HOSPITAL, Chevrolet, Chrysler/Jeep, Ford/Subaru, Honda, Mazda, Nissan, Pontiac, VW

98b   CO 96, 1st St, Union Ave Hist Dist, Pueblo, **W...gas:** Conoco, **food:** Carl's Jr, **lodging:** Jubilee Inn, Marriott

98a   US 50E bus, to La Junta, **E...gas:** Shamrock/diesel/24hr, **W...gas:** Shell/diesel, **food:** Sonic

97b   Abriendo Ave, **W...food:** Wendy's, **lodging:** Best Western, **other:** auto repair

97a   Central Ave, **W...gas:** Shamrock, **food:** McDonald's, **other:** Jim's Automotive, Tire King

96   Indiana Ave, **W...gas:** Fuzzy's, **other:** HOSPITAL, Cobra Automotive

95   Illinois Ave(from sb), **W**...to dogtrack

94   CO 45 N, Pueblo Blvd, **E...other:** 5J's Auto Parts, **W...gas:** Citgo/7-11, Shamrock/diesel, **food:** Pizza Hut/Taco Bell, **lodging:** Hampton Inn, Microtel, **other:** Pueblo Greyhound Park, RV camping, fairgrounds, to Lake Pueblo SP

91   Stem Beach, no facilities

88   Burnt Mill Rd, no facilities

87   Verde Rd, no facilities

83   no facilities

77   Hatchet Ranch Rd, Cedarwood, no facilities

74   CO 165 W, Colo City, **E...gas:** Shamrock/deli/diesel/24hr, **other:** KOA, **W...gas:** Shell/Subway/diesel, **lodging:** Greenhorn Inn/rest., **rest area both lanes, full(handicapped)facilities, phone, vending, picnic tables, litter barrels, petwalk**

71   Graneros Rd, access to Columbia House, no facilities

67   to Apache, no facilities

64   Lascar Rd, no facilities

60   Huerfano, no facilities

59   Butte Rd, no facilities

56   Redrock Rd, no facilities

55   Airport Rd, no facilities

52   CO 69 W, to Alamosa, Walsenburg, **W...gas:** Loaf n' Jug/gas, Phillips 66/diesel/24hr, Western Gas, **food:** Alpine Rose Café(2mi), Carl's Jr(2mi), Pizza Hut, Subway(2mi), Tex' Mexican(1mi), **lodging:** Best Western, Budget Host, to Great Sand Dunes NM, San Luis Valley

50   CO 10 E, to La Junta, **W**...HOSPITAL, tourist info

49   Lp 25, to US 160 W, Walsenburg, **W...other:** Lathrop SP, to Cuchara Ski Valley

42   Rouse Rd, to Pryor, no facilities

41   Rugby Rd, no facilities

34   Aguilar, **E...gas:** BP/diesel/rest

30   Aguilar Rd, no facilities

27   Ludlow, **W**...point of interest

23   Hoehne Rd, no facilities

18   El Moro Rd, **W...rest area both lanes, full(handicapped)facilities, picnic tables, litter barrels, petwalk**

15   US 350 E, Goddard Ave, **E...food:** Burger King, **lodging:** Super 8, **other:** Big R Foods, Family$, **W...gas:** Shell, **food:** B Lee's Café, **lodging:** Frontier Motel/café

Walsenburg

Interstate 25

N **Trinidad**

14b a	CO 12 W, Trinidad, **E...CO Welcome Ctr, gas:** BP, Shell, **food:** McDonald's, Pizza Hut, Subway, Taco Bell, **W...gas:** Conoco, Phillips 66, Shamrock, **food:** DQ, Domino's, El Capitan Rest., Wonderful Chinese, **lodging:** Prospect Plaza Motel, **other:** Parts+, TrueValue, RV camping, to Trinidad Lake, Monument Lake
13b	Main St, Trinidad, **E...gas:** Conoco/diesel, **food:** Main St Cafe, McDonald's, Sonic, **lodging:** Villager Lodge, **other:** CarQuest, Safeway
13a	Santa Fe Trail, Trinidad, **E...lodging:** Best Western, **other:** HOSPITAL, RV camping
11	Starkville, **E...gas:** Shell/Wendy's/diesel/24hr/@, weigh/check sta, **food:** Bob & Earl's Rest., **lodging:** Budget Host/RV park, Budget Summit Inn/RV Park, to Santa Fe Trail, **W...food:** Country Kitchen, **lodging:** Holiday Inn, **other:** Big O Tire, Checker Parts, Chevrolet/Buick, Wal-Mart SuperCtr/gas/24hr
8	Springcreek, no facilities
6	Gallinas, no facilities
2	Wootten, no facilities
1mm	scenic area pulloff nb
0mm	Colorado/New Mexico state line, Raton Pass, elev 7834, weigh sta sb

Interstate 70

E **W** **Burlington**

Exit #	Services
447mm	Colorado/Kansas state line
438	US 24, Rose Ave, Burlington, **N...gas:** Conoco, Sinclair, **food:** DQ, **lodging:** Comfort Inn, Hi-Lo Motel, Sloan's Motel, Super 8, **other:** HOSPITAL, Buick/Pontiac/GMC, CarQuest, Chevrolet, Ford, Goodyear, NAPA, **S...gas:** Amoco/diesel/24hr
437.5mm	**Welcome Ctr wb, full(handicapped)facilities, info, phone, picnic tables, litter barrels, petwalk, historical site**
437	US 385, Burlington, **N...gas:** Conoco/diesel/rest./24hr, Phillips 66/Taco Bell/diesel/24hr, **food:** Arby's, Burger King, DQ, McDonald's, Pizza Hut, Route Steaks, Sonic, Subway/TCBY, **lodging:** Burlington Inn, Chaparral Motel, Comfort Inn, Sloan's Motel, Super 8, Western Motel, **other:** HOSPITAL, Alco, Ford/Lincoln/Mercury, Goodyear, Safeway, to Bonny St RA, **S...**RV camping
429	Bethune, no facilities
419	CO 57, Stratton, **N...gas:** Ampride/diesel/24hr, Conoco/diesel, **lodging:** Best Western, Claremont Inn/café, **other:** Marshall Ash Village Camping, Trails End Camping, auto museum
412	Vona, **1/2 mi N...**gas, phone
405	CO 59, Seibert, **N...**Shady Grove Camping, **S...gas:** Conoco/A&W/diesel/24hr
395	Flagler, **N...gas:** Conoco/diesel, **food:** Dairy King, Freshway Subs, **lodging:** Little England Motel, **other:** NAPA, camping, **S...gas:** Cenex/diesel **other:** Country Store/diesel/café, golf

Limon **Denver Area**

383	Arriba, **N...gas:** Phillips 66/diesel/café, lodging, **S...rest area both lanes full(handicapped)facilities, picnic tables, litter barrels, point of interest, petwalk,** RV camping
376	Bovina, no facilities
371	Genoa, **N...**point of interest, gas, food, phone, **S...**HOSPITAL
363	US 24, US 40, US 287, to CO 71, to Hugo, Limon, **13 mi S...**HOSPITAL
361	CO 71, Limon, **N...other:** Chrysler/Dodge/Jeep, **S...gas:** Conoco/diesel, /Flying J/diesel/rest./24hr, Phillips 66/Wendy's/diesel/@, **food:** DQ, Pizza Hut, **lodging:** Midwest Inn, Silver Spur Motel(1mi), Travel Inn, **other:** KOA, st patrol
360.5mm	weigh/check sta both lanes
359	to US 24, CO 71, Limon, **S...gas:** Phillips 66, Shell/Subway/diesel, Shamrock/diesel/24hr, **food:** Arby's, Country Fair Rest., Denny's, Fireside Family Rest., Golden China, McDonald's, **lodging:** Best Western, Comfort Inn, Econolodge, Safari Motel, Silver Spur Motel, Super 8, Tyme Square Inn, **other:** camping
354	no facilities
352	CO 86 W, to Kiowa, no facilities
348	to Cedar Point, no facilities
340	Agate, **1/4 mi S...**gas/diesel, phone
336	to Lowland, no facilities
332mm	**rest area wb, full(handicapped)facilities, info, phone, picnic tables, litter barrels, vending, petwalk**
328	to Deer Trail, **N...gas:** Phillips/diesel, **S...gas:** Corner Gas,
325mm	East Bijou Creek
323.5mm	Middle Bijou Creek
322	to Peoria, no facilities
316	US 36 E, Byers, **N...gas:** Sinclair, **lodging:** Budget Host, **other:** Thriftiway Foods, **S...gas:** Frontier/gas, **food:** Country Burger Rest., Stagecoach Steaks, **lodging:** Lazy 8 Motel(1mi), **other:** USPO
310	Strasburg, **N...gas:** Conoco/24hr, **lodging:** Strasburg Inn, **other:** Corner Mkt, Diesel repair, NAPA, KOA, RV camping, USPO
306mm	Kiowa , Bennett, **N...rest area both lanes, full(handicapped)facilities, phone, picnic tables, litter barrels, petwalk**
305	Kiowa(from eb), no facilities
304	CO 79 N, Bennett, **N...** gas, food
299	CO 36, Manila Rd, **S...gas:** Shamrock/diesel/24hr/@, phone

COLORADO
Interstate 70

E ↕ **W**

295 Lp 70, Watkins, **N...gas:** Shell/diesel/rest./@, **food:** Lulu's Steakhouse, **lodging:** Country Manor Motel, **other:** USPO

292 CO 36, Airpark Rd, no facilities

289 E-470 Tollway, 120th Ave, CO Springs, no facilities

288 US 287, US 40, Lp 70, Colfax Ave(exits left from wb), no facilities

286 CO 32, Tower Rd, no facilities

285 Airport Blvd, **N...**Denver Int Airport, **S...gas:** ✈/Flying J/Conoco/diesel/rest./24hr/@, **lodging:** Comfort Inn, Crystal Inn, **other:** Harley-Davidson

284 I-225 N(from eb), no facilities

283 Chambers Rd, **N...lodging:** AmeriSuites, Hilton Garden, Holiday Inn, Marriott, Sleep Inn, **S...gas:** Phillips 66, Shamrock/Taco Bell, **food:** Burger King, **lodging:** Extended Stay America, **other:** Subaru

282 I-225 S, to Colorado Springs, no facilities

281 Peoria St, **N...gas:** BP, Citgo/7-11, Conoco/Blimpie/diesel/LP/24hr, Phillips 66, **food:** Burger King, McDonald's, Village Inn Rest., **lodging:** Best Western/grill, Drury Inn, Executive Hotel, Park Inn, **S...gas:** BP, Shamrock/diesel, **food:** Airport Broker Rest., BBQ, Church's, Denny's, IHOP, KFC, Mexican Grill, Pizza Hut, Subway, Taco Bell, Waffle House, Wendy's, **lodging:** Airport Value Inn, La Quinta, Motel 6, Traveler's Inn, **other:** ARMY MED CTR, Goodyear/auto, auto/RV repair

Denver Area

280 Havana St, **N...lodging:** Embassy Suites, **other:** Office Depot

279 I-270 W, US 36 W(from wb), to Ft Collins, Boulder, no facilities

278 CO 35, Quebec St, **N...gas:** Sapp Bros/Sinclair/Burger King/diesel/@, TA/diesel/rest./24hr/@, **food:** Denny's, **lodging:** Best Western, Day's Inn, Hampton Inn, Quality Inn, **S...**Stapleton Airport, **gas:** Amoco, Phillips 66, **food:** Breakfast Shop, **lodging:** Courtyard, Holiday Inn/rest., Radisson, Red Lion Hotel

277 to Dahlia St, Holly St, Monaco St, frontage rd, no facilities

276b US 6 E, US 85 N, CO 2, Colorado Blvd, **S...food:** Silver Bullet Rest.

276a Vasquez Ave, **N...gas:** Pilot/Wendy's/diesel/24hr/@, **lodging:** Colonial Motel, Western Inn, **other:** Blue Beacon, Ford/Mack Trucks, **S...gas:** Citgo/7-11, **food:** Burger King, **other:** NAPA

275c York St(from eb), **N...food:** Family Kitchen Rest., **lodging:** Colonial Motel

275b CO 265, Brighton Blvd, Coliseum, no facilities

275a Washington St, **N...gas:** Citgo/7-11, **food:** Pizza Hut, **S...gas:** Conoco, **food:** McDonald's, Muneca Mexican, Quizno's, Subway

274b a I-25, N to Cheyenne, S to Colorado Springs, no facilities

273 Pecos St, **N...gas:** Safeway, **S...gas:** Conoco, Phillips 66/diesel, Circle K, **lodging:** Discount Hotel, **other:** transmissions

272 US 287, Federal Blvd, **N...gas:** Amoco, Sinclair, **food:** Burger King, Goodtimes Burgers, Hamburger Stand, Loco Pollo, McCoy's Rest., McDonald's, Pizza Hut, Subway, Taco Bell, Village Inn Rest., Wendy's, **lodging:** Motel 6, **other:** K-Mart, **S...gas:** Amoco, Conoco, 7-11, **food:** Popeye's, **lodging:** Howard Johnson/Las Palmeras Mexican

271b Lowell Blvd, Tennyson St(from wb), no facilities

271a CO 95, **S...**Wild Chipmunk Amusement Park

270 Sheridan Blvd, **S...gas:** Shamrock, **food:** Arby's, Oriental Rest., Sunrise Café, **other:** Target, U-Haul, funpark, mall

Denver Area

269b I-76 E(from eb), to Ft Morgan, Ft Collins, no facilities

269a CO 121, Wadsworth Blvd, **N...gas:** Citgo/7-11, Conoco, LuckyMart/diesel, **food:** Applebee's, Bennigan's, Country Buffet, Fazoli's, Goodberry's Rest., Gunther Toody's Diner, Kokoro Japanese, LoneStar Steaks, McDonald's, Ruby Tuesday, Schlotsky's, Starbucks, Taco Bell, Texas Roadhouse, **other:** Advance Parts, Costco/gas, Home Depot, Lowe's Whse, OfficeMax, Office Depot, Sam's Club, Tires+, Waldenbooks, mall, **S...other:** Discount Tire

267 CO 391, Kipling St, Wheat Ridge, **N...gas:** Amoco, Shell/Carl's Jr/diesel, 7-11, **food:** Burger King, Denny's, Furr's Dining, Subway, **lodging:** American Motel, Motel 6, **other:** Chevrolet/Cadillac, Chrysler/Plymouth/Jeep, **S...gas:** Conoco, **food:** Pizza Hut/Taco Bell, Village Inn Rest., **lodging:** Comfort Inn, Holiday Inn Express, Motel 6, Super 8, **other:** RV Ctr

266 CO 72, W 44th Ave, Ward Rd, Wheat Ridge, **N...gas:** Shell, **S...gas:** Shamrock, TA/diesel/rest./24hr/@, **lodging:** Quality Inn

265 CO 58 W(from wb), to Golden, Central City, no facilities

264 Youngfield St, W 32nd Ave, **N...gas:** Conoco, **food:** GoodTimes Burgers, **lodging:** La Quinta, **S...gas:** Amoco, Conoco, Shamrock, **food:** Chili's, DQ, McDonald's, Papa John's, Pizza Hut/Taco Bell, Starbucks, Subway, **other:** Camping World RV Ctr, Casey's RV Ctr, King's Sooper/24hr, Radio Shack, Walgreen, Wal-Mart

263 Denver West Blvd, **N...lodging:** Marriott/rest., **S...other:** Barnes&Noble, Wild Oats Mkt

262 US 40 E, W Colfax, Lakewood, **N...gas:** Sinclair, **food:** Arby's, **lodging:** Hampton Inn, **other:** Home Depot, Honda, Kohl's, NAPA, U-Haul, transmissions, **S...gas:** Conoco, Shell/diesel/LP, **food:** Outback Steaks, Wendy's, **lodging:** Courtyard, Day's Inn/rest., Holiday Inn Express, Residence Inn, **other:** Chevrolet, Lexus, Target, Toyota, RV Ctr

261 US 6 E(from eb), W 6th Ave, to Denver, no facilities

260 CO 470, to Colo Springs, no facilities

259 CO 26, Golden, **N...gas:** Conoco, **lodging:** Hampton Inn(2mi), **other:** Heritage Sq Funpark, **S...**Music Hall, to Red Rock Park

257mm runaway truck ramp eb

256 Lookout Mtn, **N...**to Buffalo Bill's Grave

Interstate 70

E ↑ ↓ W

254 Genesee, Lookout Mtn, **N**...to Buffalo Bill's Grave, **S**...gas: Conoco/LP, **food:** Chart House Rest., Genesee Town Cafe, Guido's Pizza, **other:** MEDICAL CARE, USPO

253 Chief Hosa, **S**...RV Camping, phone

252 (251 from eb), CO 74, Evergreen Pkwy, **S**...gas: BP, **food:** Burger King, El Rancho Rest., McDonald's, **lodging:** Quality Suites, **other:** Big O Tire, Home Depot, King's Sooper/deli, Wal-Mart/auto

248 (247 from eb), Beaver Brook, Floyd Hill, **S**...food: Gourmet Coffee, to Saddlerack Summit Rest., **other:** Floyd Hill Grocery/grill

244 US 6, to CO 119, to Golden, Central City , Eldora Ski Area, **N**...food: Kermit's Café Food/drink

243 Hidden Valley, no facilities

242mm tunnel

241b a rd 314, Idaho Springs West, **N**...gas: BP/McDonald's, Phillips 66, Sinclair, 7-11, Shell, **food:** A&W, BBQ, Beaujo's Pizza, Buffalo Rest., Café Expresso, JC Sweet's, King's Derby Rest., Marion's Rest., Subway, Taco Bell, **lodging:** Argo Motel, Club Hotel, Columbine Inn, Hanson Lodge, H&H Motel, Indian Springs Resort, King Henry's Motel, National 9 Motel, 6&40 Motel/rest., The Lodge, **other:** CarQuest, NAPA, Radio Shack, Safeway, USPO

240 CO 103, **N**...gas: Shell, **food:** 2 Bros Deli, Buffalo restraraunt, Paco's, Schezwan Chinese, Subway, same as 241, **S**...to Mt Evans

239 Idaho Springs, **N**...gas: Amoco, Phillips 66, **other:** Sandwich Mine Mkt, camping

238 Fall River Rd, to St Mary's Glacier, no facilities

235 Dumont(from wb), no facilities

234 Downeyville, Dumont, weigh sta both lanes, **N**...gas: Conoco/Subway/diesel, **food:** Burger King, Starbucks, **other:** ski rentals

233 Lawson(from eb), no facilities

232 US 40 W, to Empire, **N**...to Berthoud Pass, Winterpark/Silver Creek ski areas

228 Georgetown, **S**...gas: Conoco/diesel, Phillips 66, Shamrock/diesel, **food:** Red Ram rest., Subway, **lodging:** Georgetown Lodge, Super 8

226.5mm scenic overlook eb

226 Georgetown, Silver Plume Hist Dist, **N**...other: Buckley Bros Mkt, lodging, ski rentals

221 Bakerville, no facilities

220mm Arapahoe NF eastern boundary

218 no facilities

216 US 6 W, Loveland Valley, Loveland Basin, ski areas

214mm Eisenhower Tunnel, elev 11013

213mm parking area eb

205 US 6 E, CO 9 N, Dillon, Silverthorne, **N**...gas: Citgo/7-11, Conoco, Shell/GoodTimes/diesel, **food:** Denny's, Domino's, Old Dillon Inn Mexican, Quizno's, Mtn Lyon Café, Village Inn Rest., Wendy's/24hr, **lodging:** Day's Inn, 1st Interstate Inn, Hampton Inn/rest., Luxury Suites, Sheraton, Silver Inn, **other:** CarQuest, Chevrolet, Chrysler/Plymouth/Dodge, Ford/Mercury, Prime Outlets/famous brands, **S**...gas: Phillips 66/Taco Bell, Shamrock, **food:** Arby's, BBQ, Burger King, DQ, McDonald's, Pizza Hut, Ruby Tuesday, SweetPeas, Starbucks, Subway, **lodging:** Best Western, Comfort Suites, Super 8, **other:** City Mkt Foods, Dillon Stores/famous brands, Goodyear/auto, OfficeMax

203.5mm scenic overlook both lanes, phones

203 CO 9 S, to Breckenridge, Frisco, **S**...gas: Citgo/7-11, Shamrock, **food:** A&W, Back Country Brewery/rest., BBQ, ClaimJumper Rest., Country Kitchen, KFC, Papa John's, Pizza Hut, Starbucks, Subway, Taco Bell, TCBY, Tex's Café, **lodging:** Alpine Inn, Best Western, Holiday Inn, Luxury Inn, Microtel, Ramada Ltd, Summit Inn, **other:** MEDICAL CARE, Big O Tire, Discout tire, NAPA, Radio Shack, Safeway, Wal-Mart/Mcdonalds/drugs, to Breckenridge Ski Area, Tiger Run RV Resort

201 Main St, Frisco, **S**...gas: Conoco, **food:** A&W, Brewery Rest., KFC, Pizza Hut, Spruce Inn Steakhouse, **lodging:** Bighorn Reservations, Frisco Lodge, Pearl Head Lodge, Snowshoe Motel, Skyvue Motel, Woodbridge Inn, **other:** CHIROPRACTOR, Alpine Natural Foods, RV camping, to Breckenridge Ski Area

198 Officers Gulch, no facilities, emergency callbox

195 CO 91 S, to Leadville, **1 mi S**...gas: Conoco/diesel, **food:** Camp Hale Coffee, Endo's Café, **lodging:** Copper Lodging, East West Resort, Fox Pine Inn, Telemark Lodge, **other:** to Copper Mtn Ski Resort

190 **S**...rest area both lanes, full(handicapped)facilities, phone, picnic tables, litter barrels

189mm Vail Pass Summit, elev 10662 ft, parking area both lanes

180 Vail East Entrance, phone, services 3-4 mi S

176 Vail, **S**...gas: Amoco/diesel, **lodging:** Best Western, Vailglo, Holiday Inn, **other:** MEDICAL CARE, info, Craig's Mkt, **1 mi S**...gas: Amoco, **food:** Chicago Pizza

173 Vail Ski Area, **N**...gas: Phillips 66, Shell/diesel, 7-11, **food:** DQ, Domino's, May Palace Chinese, 1/2 Moon Chinese, McDonald's, Subway, Taco Bell, Wendy's, **lodging:** West Vail Lodge, **other:** City Mkt Foods, Safeway, Vail Drug, **S**...gas: Conoco/LP, **lodging:** Black Bear Inn, Day's Inn, Marriott Streamside Hotel, The Roost Lodge

171 US 6 W, US 24 E, to Minturn, Leadville, **N**...food: Leadville Café, **other:** NAPA

168 William J. Post Blvd, no facilities

Dillon

Idaho Spgrs

Vail

COLORADO
Interstate 70

E ▲
W ▼

Avon

167 Avon, **N...gas:** Conoco, Phillips 66, **food:** Pizza Hut, **other:** Goodyear, **S...food:** Burger King, China Garden, Denny's, Domino's, Quizno's, Starbucks, Subway, **lodging:** Avon Ctr Lodge, Beaver Creek Inn, Beaver Creek Condos, Christie Lodge, Comfort Inn, Seasons Hotel, **other:** City Mkt/drugs, Wal-Mart, to Beaver Creek/Arrowhead Skiing

163 Edwards, **S...rest area both lanes, full(handicapped) facilities, phone, picnic tables, litter barrel, RV dump, gas:** Conoco, Shell/diesel, **food:** Bartelli's Deli, Canac's Kitchen, Gashaus Rest., Gore Range Brewery, Marko's Pizza, Subway, Starbucks, Wendy's, **lodging:** Riverwalk Inn, **other:** to Arrowhead Ski Area

162mm scenic overlook both lanes

159mm Eagle River

157 CO 131 N, Wolcott, **N...**to gas, phone, to Steamboat Ski Area

Eagle

147 Eagle, **N...gas:** Shamrock/Taco Bell/diesel, **food:** Burger King, McDonald's, Mi Pueblo Mexican, Taco Bell, **lodging:** AmericInn, Comfort Inn, Holiday Inn Express, **other:** City Mkt Foods, **S...gas:** Amoco/Subway/diesel, Conoco/pizza, **food:** Eagle Diner, Subway, Wendy's, Gourmet China, **lodging:** Best Western, Prairie Moon Motel, **other:** Suburban Lodge, FoodTown Foods, **rest area both lanes, full(handicapped)facilities, info**

140 Gypsum, **S...gas:** Phillips 66/diesel, **food:** Columbine Mkt Deli, Mexican-American Café, **other:** auto/truck repair, airport, 3 mi S...River Dance Resort camping

134mm Colorado River

133 Dotsero, no facilities

129 Bair Ranch, **S...rest area both lanes, full(handicapped) facilities, picnic tables, litter barrels, petwalk**

128.5mm parking area eb

127mm tunnel wb

125mm tunnel

125 to Hanging Lake(no return eb), no facilities

123 Shoshone(no return eb), no facilities

122.5mm exit to river(no return eb), no facilities

121 to Hanging Lake, Grizzly Creek, **S...rest area both lanes, full(handicapped)facilities, picnic tables, litter barrels,**

119 **No Name, rest area both lanes, full(handicapped) facilities, RV camping, rafting**

118mm tunnel

116 CO 82 E, to Aspen, Glenwood Springs, **N...gas:** Amoco, Conoco/diesel, Shell/diesel, **food:** A&W, Fiesta Guadalajara, KFC, Mancinelli's Pizza, Pizza Hut, Smokin Willie BBQ, Subway, Tequila Rest., **lodging:** Village Inn Rest., Best Western, Glenwood Inn, Hampton Inn, Holiday Inn Express, Hotel Colorado, Hot Springs Motel, National Nine Inn, Ramada Inn, Silver Spruce Motel, Starlight Motel, **other:** Audi/VW, Land Rover, Mazda, Nissan, Saab, Suzuki, Toyota,

Glenwood Springs

Hot Springs Bath, **S...gas:** Conoco, Phillips 66/diesel, Sinclair, 7-11, **food:** Arby's, China Town, Domino's, Glenwood Sprs Brewpub, 19th St Diner, Quizno's, Taco Bell, Wendy's, **lodging:** Best Western, Frontier Lodge, Hotel Denver, **other:** MEDICAL CARE, City Mkt Foods, NAPA, Rite Aid, 2 mi S...Sell, Subway, Taco Bell, Wenys, Caravan Inn, Goodyear, Honda, Wal-Mart, to Ski Sunlight

115mm **rest area eb, full(handicapped)facilities, picnic tables, litter barrels**

114 W Glenwood Springs, **N...gas:** Amoco/diesel, Citgo/7-11, Shell, **food:** Burger King, CharBurger, DQ, Dos Hombres Mexican, Fireside Steaks, Hot stuff pizza, Los Desperados Mexican, Marshall Dillon Steaks, Oasis Mexican, Ocean Pearl Chinese, **lodging:** Affordable Inn, Best Value Inn, Budget Host, Colonial Inn, 1st Choice Inn, Holiday Inn, Motel 5, National 9 Inn, Ponderosa Motel, Red Mtn Inn, Super 8, Terra Vista Motel, **other:** Big O Tire, Chevrolet/Cadillac, Chrysler/Dodge/Plymouth, Ford, JC Penney, K-Mart, Lincoln/Mercury, Radio Shack, Sears, Staples, Taylor's RV Ctr, mall, **S...gas:** Conoco/Kum&Go/diesel, **lodging:** Quality Inn, **other:** Audi, VW

111 South Canyon, no facilities

109 Canyon Creek, no facilities

108mm parking area both lanes

105 New Castle, **N...gas:** Conoco/Subway/diesel, Kum&Go, Sinclair, **lodging:** Roadway Inn, **other:** City Mkt Foods/deli, KOA(4mi), **S...gas:** Phillips 66, **other:** Best Hardware

97 Silt, **N...gas:** Conoco/Blimpie/diesel/24hr, Phillips 66, **food:** Miners Claim Rest., Pizza Pro, Silt Café, **lodging:** Red River Inn(1mi), **other:** Reed's Auto Repair, to Harvey Gap SP, **S...lodging:** Heron's Nest RV Park

94 Garfield County Airport Rd, no facilities

90 CO 13 N, Rifle, **N...rest area both lanes, full(handicapped)facilities, phone, picnic tables, litter barrels, RV dump, NF Info, gas:** Amoco/24hr, Kum&Go/gas, Phillips 66/diesel, Texaco, **food:** KFC, **lodging:** Winchester Motel(1mi), **other:** HOSPITAL, USPO, **S...gas:** Conoco/diesel, Phillips 66/Subway, **food:** Burger King, McDonald's, TCBY, **lodging:** Buckskin Motel, Red River Inn/rest., Rusty Cannon Motel

87 to CO 13, West Rifle, **2 mi N...lodging:** Buckskin Motel, La Donna Motel, Shaler Motel, Winchester Motel, gas, food, phone

81 Rulison, no facilities

75 Parachute, **N...rest area both lanes, full(handicapped)facilities, info, phone, picnic tables, litter barrels, petwalk, gas:** Sinclair/diesel, Shell/diesel/24hr, **food:** Dragon Treasure Chinese, El Rio Mexican, Hong's Garden Chinese, Hot Stuff Pizza, Outlaws Rest., Subway, **lodging:** Holiday Inn Express, Super 8, Westgate Inn/rest., **other:** Napa parts, Radio Shack, USPO, **S...gas:** Conoco/Wendy's/diesel, **other:** Good Sam RV Park(4mi), True Value Hardware

COLORADO

Interstate 70

E

63mm	Colorado River
62	De Beque, **1 mi N...gas:** Conoco, **other:** Canyon Lake campground, food, lodging, phone, auto repair
50mm	parking area eastbound, Colorado River, tunnel begins eastbound
49mm	Plateau Creek
49	CO 65 S, to CO 330 E, to Grand Mesa, to Powderhorn Ski Area, no facilities
47	Island Acres St RA, **N...**CO River SP, RV camping, **S...gas:** Shamrock/diesel/24hr/@, **food:** Rosie's Rest./24hr, **other:** Fawn's Gift Shop, motel, RV camping
46	Cameo, no facilities
44	Lp 70 W, to Palisade, **3 mi S...**gas, food, lodging
43.5mm	Colorado River
42	US 6, Palisade, **1 mi S...**Fruitstand/store, gas, lodging, Grand River Winery
37	to US 6, to US 50 S, Clifton, Grand Jct, **1 mi S on US 6 bus...**gas: Conoco/diesel, Shamrock, Shell, **food:** Burger King, Dos Hombres Mexican, KFC, Little Caesar's, McDonald's, Papa Murphy's, Pizza Chef, Pizza Hut, Subway, Taco Bell, Texas Roadhouse, **lodging:** Best Western, **other:** MEDICAL CARE, Albertson's, Checker Parts, City Mkt Food/gas, KOA, Max Foods, Rite Aid, USPO, Walgreen, **2-3 mi S...gas:** Amoco, Phillips 66, **food:** Capt D's, Furr's Dining, **lodging:** Village Inn Rest., Wendy's, Western Sizzlin, Wienerschnitzel, Timbers Motel, **other:** AutoZone, Checker Parts, Chrysler/Plymouth/Dodge, Chevrolet, Discount Tire, Hastings Books, K-Mart, Wal-Mart SuperCtr/24hr
31	Horizon Dr, Grand Jct, **N...gas:** Shamrock, Shell/diesel, **food:** Coco's, Diorio's Pizza, Pepper's Rest., Village Inn Rest., Wendy's, **lodging:** Best Western, Comfort Inn, Grand Vista Hotel, Holiday Inn, La Quinta, Motel 6, Ramada Inn, **other:** Harley-Davidson, USPO, Zarlingo's Repair, **S...gas:** Conoco/Subway/diesel, Phillips 66, **food:** Applebee's, Burger King, Denny's, Pizza Hut, Taco Bell, **lodging:** Adams Mark Hotel, Best Western, Budget Host, Country Inn, Day's Inn/rest., Mesa Inn, Super 8, **other:** HOSPITAL, golf, to Mesa St Coll, CO NM
28	Redlands Pkwy, 24 rd, **N...**camping, **S...**recreational park/sports complex
26	US 6, US 50, Grand Jct, **S...gas:** Conoco/A&W/diesel/24hr/@, **food:** Otto's Rest., **lodging:** Westgate Inn/rest., **other:** Ford/Lincoln/Mercury, Mazda, Mercedes, Subaru, Toyota, Freightliner, radiators, **3-5 mi S...food:** BBQ, Carl's JR., Chili's, Golden Corral, McDonald's, Outback Steaks, Red Lobster, Taco Bell, Wendy's **lodging:** Hampton Inn, Hawthorn Suites, Holiday Inn Express, **other:** Centennial RV Ctr, JC Penney, Mervyn's, Mobile City RV Park, Sears/auto, mall

W

(side tab: Grand Junction)

19	US 6, CO 340, Fruita, **N...gas:** Amoco, Conoco/diesel, **food:** Burger King, Pizza Pro, **lodging:** Balanced Rock Motel, **other:** HOSPITAL, CarQuest, City Mkt Foods/24hr, NAPA, USPO, **S...Welcome Ctr both lanes, full(handicapped)facilities, phone, picnic tables, litter barrels, RV dump, petwalk, gas:** Conoco/Subway/diesel/24hr, Shell/Wendy's/diesel/24hr, **food:** McDonald's, **lodging:** Comfort Inn, Super 8, **other:** CO Mon Trading Co, camping, museum, to CO NM
17mm	Colorado River
15	CO 139 N, to Loma, Rangely, **N...**to Highline Lake SP, gas/diesel, phone
14.5mm	weigh/check sta both lanes, phones
11	Mack, **2-3 mi N...**gas/diesel, food
2	to Dinosaur Quarry Trail, Rabbit Valley, no facilities
0mm	Colorado/Utah state line

Interstate 76

E

Exit #	Services
184mm	Colorado/Nebraska state line
180	US 385, Julesburg, **N...gas:** ✈/Flying J/diesel/rest./24hr, Shell, **lodging:** Budget Host, **other:** HOSPITAL, **Welcome Ctr/rest area both lanes, full(handicapped)facilities, info, RV dump, S...gas:** Conoco/diesel
172	Ovid, **2 mi N...**gas, food
165	CO 59, Sedgewick, to Haxtun, **N...**gas/café
155	Red Lion Rd, no facilities
149	CO 55, Crook, to Fleming, **S...gas:** Sinclair/diesel/café
141	Proctor, no facilities
134	Iliff, no facilities
125	US 6, Sterling, **N...gas:** Cenex/diesel, **food:** Arby's, McDonald's, Taco Bell, Wendy's, **lodging:** Best Western, 1st Interstate Inn, **other:** HOSPITAL, N Sterling SP, museum, st patrol, **rest area both lanes(full handicapped)facilities, picnic tables, litter barrels, petwalk, vending, RV dump, S...gas:** Phillips 66/Quizno's/diesel, **food:** Country Kitchen, **lodging:** Ramada Inn, Super 8, Travelodge, Jellystone Camping
115	CO 63, Atwood, **N...gas:** Sinclair/diesel, **other:** HOSPITAL, **S...gas:** Amoco, **food:** Steakhouse
102	Merino, no facilities
95	Hillrose, no facilities
92	to US 6 E, to US 34, CO 71 S, no facilities

W

(side tab: Julesburg ... Sterling)

COLORADO

Interstate 76

E ← → **W**

Ft Morgan

90b a	CO 71 N, to US 34, Brush, **N...gas:** Shell/diesel/24hr/@, **food:** Pizza Hut, Wendy's, **lodging:** Best Western, **S...gas:** Conoco/diesel, **food: China Buffet,** McDonald's, **lodging:** Microtel
89	Hospital Rd, **S...**HOSPITAL, golf
86	Dodd Bridge Rd, no facilities
82	Barlow Rd, **N...gas:** Conoco/diesel, **food:** Maverick's Grill, **lodging:** Affordable Inn, Comfort Inn, **S...gas:** Phillips 66/diesel, **food:** Burger King, **other:** $Tree, Wal-Mart SuperCtr/diesel/24hr
80	CO 52, Ft Morgan, **S...gas:** Conoco/diesel/24hr, Shamrock, Shell/diesel, **food:** A&W, Arby's, DQ, KFC, McDonald's, Sonic, Subway/TCBY, Taco John's, **lodging:** Best Western/rest., Day's Inn, Super 8, **other:** HOSPITAL, AutoZone, Rite Aid
79	CO 144, to Weldona, **N...gas:** Shell/diesel
75	US 34 E, to Ft Morgan, **S...gas:** Conoco/A&W/diesel, **lodging:** motel
74.5mm	weigh sta both lanes
73	Long Bridge Rd, no facilities
66b	US 34 W(from wb), to Greeley
66a	CO 39, CO 52, Wiggins, to Goodrich, **N...**to Jackson Lake SP, **S...gas:** Sinclair/diesel, **other: rest area both lanes, full(handicapped)facilities, picnic tables, litter barrels, petwalk, phone, vending**
64	Wiggins, no facilities
60	to CO 144 E, to Orchard, no facilities
57	rd 91, no facilities
49	Painter Rd(from wb), no facilities
48	to Roggen, **N...gas:** Shell/diesel, **lodging:** I-76 Motel
39	Keenesburg, **S...gas:** Phillips 66/diesel, **lodging:** Fine Food Rest., Keene Motel
34	Kersey Rd, no facilities
31	CO 52, Hudson, **S...gas:** Amoco/diesel, Phillips 66/diesel, **food:** El Faro Mexican, Pepper Pod Rest., **other:** auto/truck repair, RV camping
25	CO 7, Lochbuie, **N...gas:** Shell/diese
22	Bromley, **N...**HOSPITAL, **S...**Barr Lake SP
21	144th Ave, no facilities
20	136th Ave, **N...**Barr Lake RV Park
18	(from wb)E-470 tollway, to Limon
16	CO 2 W, Sable Blvd, Commerce City, **N...gas:** Shell/Blimpie/diesel/24hr/@
12	US 85 N, to Brighton, Greeley, no facilities
11	96th Ave, **N...**trailer sales, **S...**diesel repair
10	88th Ave, **N...gas:** Conoco/Blimpie/diesel, **lodging:** Holiday Inn Express, Super 8, **S...**flea mkt
9	US 6 W, US 85 S, Commerce City, **S...gas:** Shell/diesel, **other:** GMC/Freightliner, st patrol
8	CO 224, 74th Ave(no EZ eb return), **1 mi N...**NAPA, **S...gas:** Shamrock/diesel, **lodging:** Crestline Motel
6b a	I-270 E, to Limon, to airport
5	I-25, N to Ft Collins, S to Colo Springs
4	Pecos St, no facilities

Denver Area (Denver Area)

3	US 287, Federal Blvd, **N...gas:** Shamrock/diesel, **S...food:** Taco House
1b	CO 95, Sheridan Blvd, no facilities
a	CO 121, Wadsworth Blvd, **N...gas:** Citgo/7-11, Conoco, LuckyMart/diesel, **food:** Applebee's, Bennigan's, Country Buffet, Fazoli's, Goodberry's Rest., Gunther Toody's Diner, Kokoro Japanese, LoneStar Steaks, McDonald's, Ruby Tuesday, Schlotsky's, Starbucks, Taco Bell, Texas Roadhouse, **other:** Advance Parts, Costco/gas, Home Depot, Lowe's Whse, OfficeMax, Office Depot, Sam's Club, Tires+, Waldenbooks, mall, **S...other:** Discount Tire
0mm	I-76 begins/ends on I-70, exit 169b.

Interstate 225(Denver)

Exit #	Services
12b a	I-70, W to Denver, E to Limon **N**
10	US 40, US 287, Colfax Ave, **E...gas:** Citgo/7-11, Shell, **food:** KFC, McDonald's, Waffle House, **other:** RV camping, **W...gas:** Conoco
9	Co 30, 6th Ave, **E...gas:** Conoco, **food:** Pizza Hut, **lodging:** Super 8, **W...gas:** Phillips 66/diesel, **other:** HOSPITAL
8	Alameda Ave, **E...food:** Benny's Cafe, Chili's, **other:** Foley's, JC Penney, Ross, Target, mall, **W...gas: S** Conoco/mart, Shell/repair, 7-11
7	Mississippi Ave, Alameda Ave, **E...food:** Arby's, Bennigan's, Chevy's, Chicago Grill, Chubby's Mexican, Denny's, DQ, Jason's Deli, Sonic, Subway, Uno Pizzaria, Village Inn, **lodging:** Best Western, Hampton Inn, La Quinta, **other:** Best Buy, Circuit City, Office Max, Target, Tires +, Wal-Mart
5	Iliff Ave, **E...food:** Applebee's, Carrabba's, Fuddrucker's, Hop's Rest., Joe's Crabshack, Outback Steaks, Sweet Tomato, **lodging:** Comfort Inn, Fairfield Inn, Motel 6, **W...gas:** Coastal, **food:** Dragon Boat Chinese
4	CO 83, Parker Rd, **E...lodging:** Radison, **other:** Cherry Creek SP, **W...gas:** Shell, **food:** DQ, Denny's, McDonald's, Pizza Hut, Taco Bell
2b	no facilities
2	DTC Blvd, Tamarac St, **W...gas:** BP, 7-11, **food:** Pizza Hut
0mm	I-225 begins/ends on I-25, exit 200.

Interstate 270(Denver)

Exit #	Services
4	I-70. **E**
3	**N...gas:** TA/Popeye's/Quizno's/Pizza Hut/diesel24hr/@, **S...** Sapp Bros/diesel/@,
2b a	US 85, CO 2, Vasquez Ave, **N...gas:** Conoco, **food:** Arby's, GoodTimes Grill, KFC, McDonald's, Pizza Inn, Wendy's
1b	York St, no facilities
1a	I-76 E, to Ft Morgan
1c	I-25 S, to Denver
0	I-25 N, to Ft Collins **W**

CONNECTICUT

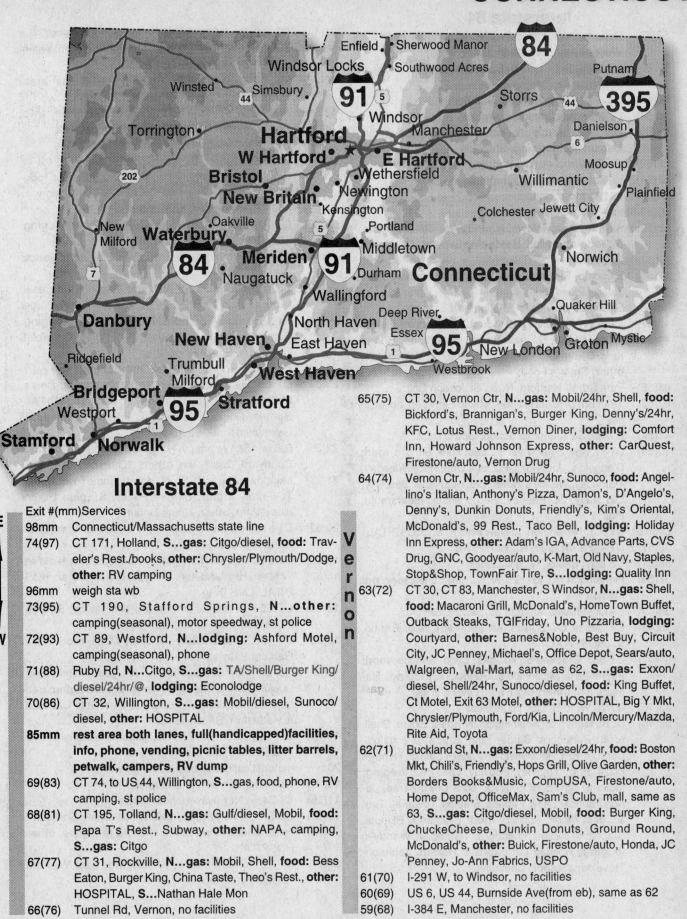

Interstate 84

Exit #(mm)Services

E

98mm Connecticut/Massachusetts state line

74(97) CT 171, Holland, **S...gas:** Citgo/diesel, **food:** Traveler's Rest./books, **other:** Chrysler/Plymouth/Dodge, **other:** RV camping

96mm weigh sta wb

73(95) CT 190, Stafford Springs, **N...other:** camping(seasonal), motor speedway, st police

W

72(93) CT 89, Westford, **N...lodging:** Ashford Motel, camping(seasonal), phone

71(88) Ruby Rd, **N...**Citgo, **S...gas:** TA/Shell/Burger King/diesel/24hr/@, **lodging:** Econolodge

70(86) CT 32, Willington, **S...gas:** Mobil/diesel, Sunoco/diesel, **other:** HOSPITAL

85mm **rest area both lanes, full(handicapped)facilities, info, phone, vending, picnic tables, litter barrels, petwalk, campers, RV dump**

69(83) CT 74, to US 44, Willington, **S...gas,** food, phone, RV camping, st police

68(81) CT 195, Tolland, **N...gas:** Gulf/diesel, Mobil, **food:** Papa T's Rest., Subway, **other:** NAPA, camping, **S...gas:** Citgo

67(77) CT 31, Rockville, **N...gas:** Mobil, Shell, **food:** Bess Eaton, Burger King, China Taste, Theo's Rest., **other:** HOSPITAL, **S...**Nathan Hale Mon

66(76) Tunnel Rd, Vernon, no facilities

Vernon

65(75) CT 30, Vernon Ctr, **N...gas:** Mobil/24hr, Shell, **food:** Bickford's, Brannigan's, Burger King, Denny's/24hr, KFC, Lotus Rest., Vernon Diner, **lodging:** Comfort Inn, Howard Johnson Express, **other:** CarQuest, Firestone/auto, Vernon Drug

64(74) Vernon Ctr, **N...gas:** Mobil/24hr, Sunoco, **food:** Angellino's Italian, Anthony's Pizza, Damon's, D'Angelo's, Denny's, Dunkin Donuts, Friendly's, Kim's Oriental, McDonald's, 99 Rest., Taco Bell, **lodging:** Holiday Inn Express, **other:** Adam's IGA, Advance Parts, CVS Drug, GNC, Goodyear/auto, K-Mart, Old Navy, Staples, Stop&Shop, TownFair Tire, **S...lodging:** Quality Inn

63(72) CT 30, CT 83, Manchester, S Windsor, **N...gas:** Shell, **food:** Macaroni Grill, McDonald's, HomeTown Buffet, Outback Steaks, TGIFriday, Uno Pizzaria, **lodging:** Courtyard, **other:** Barnes&Noble, Best Buy, Circuit City, JC Penney, Michael's, Office Depot, Sears/auto, Walgreen, Wal-Mart, same as 62, **S...gas:** Exxon/diesel, Shell/24hr, Sunoco/diesel, **food:** King Buffet, Ct Motel, Exit 63 Motel, **other:** HOSPITAL, Big Y Mkt, Chrysler/Plymouth, Ford/Kia, Lincoln/Mercury/Mazda, Rite Aid, Toyota

62(71) Buckland St, **N...gas:** Exxon/diesel/24hr, **food:** Boston Mkt, Chili's, Friendly's, Hops Grill, Olive Garden, **other:** Borders Books&Music, CompUSA, Firestone/auto, Home Depot, OfficeMax, Sam's Club, mall, same as 63, **S...gas:** Citgo/diesel, Mobil, **food:** Burger King, ChuckeCheese, Dunkin Donuts, Ground Round, McDonald's, **other:** Buick, Firestone/auto, Honda, JC Penney, Jo-Ann Fabrics, USPO

61(70) I-291 W, to Windsor, no facilities

60(69) US 6, US 44, Burnside Ave(from eb), same as 62

59(68) I-384 E, Manchester, no facilities

E ↑ **Hartford**

58(67) Roberts St, Burnside Ave, **N...lodging:** Holiday Inn, Wellesley Inn, **S...other:** Super Stop'n Shop

57(66) CT 15 S, to I-91 S, NYC, Charter Oak Br, no facilities

56(65) Governor St, E Hartford, **S...**airport

55(64) CT 2 E, New London, downtown

54(63) Old State House, **N...other:** Ford/Isuzu, Lincoln/Mercury, **S...lodging:** Sheraton

53(62) CT Blvd(from eb), **S...lodging:** Ramada Inn

52(61) W Main St(from eb), downtown

51(60) I-91 N, to Springfield

50(59.8) to I-91 S(from wb)

48(59.5) Asylum St, downtown, **N...lodging:** Crowne Plaza, **S...lodging:** Hilton, Holiday Inn Express, Residence Inn, **other:** HOSPITAL

47(59) Sigourney St, downtown, **N...**Hartford Seminary, Mark Twain House

46(58) Sisson St, downtown, UConn Law School

45(57) Flatbush Ave(exits left from wb), **N...**Shaw's Foods

44(56.5) Prospect Ave, **N...gas:** Exxon, Shell, **food:** Burger King, D'angelo's, Gold Roc Diner/24hr, McDonald's, **other:** Shaw's Foods

43(56) Park Rd, W Hartford, **N...**to St Joseph Coll

42(55) Trout Brk Dr(exits left from wb), to Elmwood, no facilities

41(54) S Main St, American School for the Deaf

40(53) CT 71, New Britain Ave, **S...gas:** Shell, Sunoco, **food:** D'angelo's, Joe's Grill, Pizzaria Uno, Ruby Tuesday, TGIFriday, Wendy's, **other:** Barnes&Noble, Best Buy, Old Navy, JC Penney, Radio Shack, Sears/auto, mall

39a(52) CT 9 S, Newington, to New Britain, **S...**HOSPITAL

39(51.5) CT 4, Farmington, **N...**HOSPITAL

38(51) US 6 W, Bristol, **N...gas:** Shell

37(50) Fienemann Rd, to US 6 W, **N...gas:** Shell, **lodging:** Marriott

36(49) Slater Rd(exits left from eb), **S...**HOSPITAL

35(48) CT 72, to CT 9(exits left from wb), New Britain, **S...**HOSPITAL

34(47) CT 372, Crooked St, **N...gas:** Citgo, Sunoco, **food:** Applebee's, McDonald's, Starbucks, **lodging:** Ramada Inn, **other:** Big Y Mkt, Lowe's Whse

33(46) CT 72 W, to Bristol, no facilities

32(45) Ct 10, Queen St, Southington, **N...gas:** Exxon, Shell, **food:** Bertucci's, Burger King, Chili's, D'angelo's, Denny's, KFC, McDonald's, Outback Steaks, Randy's Pizza, Ruby Tuesday, Subway, Taco Bell, **lodging:** Motel 6, **other:** HOSPITAL, CVS Drug, $Tree, Jo-Ann Fabrics, Shaw's Foods, Staples, TownFair Tire, **S...gas:** Mobil, Sunoco, **food:** Bickford's, Blimpie, Brannigan's Ribs, Friendly's, TGIFriday, Wendy's, **lodging:** Holiday Inn Express, Howard Johnson, Travelodge, **other:** Chevrolet

Waterbury

31(44) CT 229, West St, **N...gas:** Mobil, Sunoco/diesel/24hr, **S...gas:** Citgo, Gulf, **food:** Mack's Brick Oven, Valendino's Pizzaria, **lodging:** Residence Inn

30(43) Marion Ave, W Main, Southington, **N...**ski area, **S...gas:** Mobil/repair, **other:** HOSPITAL

42.5mm rest area eb, full(handicapped)facilities, info, phone, picnic tables, litter barrels, petwalk

29(42) CT 10, Milldale(exits left from wb), no facilities

28(41) CT 322, Marion, **S...gas:** Mobil, TA/diesel/24hr/@, **food:** Blimpie, Burger King, DQ, Dunkin Donuts, **lodging:** Day's Inn, **other:** MEDICAL CARE, radiators

27(40) I-691 E, to Meriden, no facilities

26(38) CT 70, to Cheshire, **N...food:** Silver Diner, **lodging:** Sheraton

25a(37) Austin Rd(from eb), **N...lodging:** Sheraton, Costco/gas

25(36) Scott Rd, E Main St, **N...gas:** Exxon, Gulf/diesel, **food:** Dunkin Donuts, **S...gas:** Mobil, **food:** Burger King, Friendly's, McDonald's, Nino's Rest., **lodging:** Ramada Inn, Super 8, **other:** BJ's Whse, Chevrolet, CVS Drug, Super Stop&Shop

24(34) Harpers Ferry Rd, **S...gas:** Getty, Shell/24hr

23(33.5) CT 69, Hamilton Ave, **N...food:** Bertucci's, Chili's, McDonald's, Ruby Tuesday, **other:** HOSPITAL, Barnes&Noble, Filene's, JC Penney, OfficeMax, Sears/auto, mall, **S...gas:** Shell

22(33) Baldwin St, Waterbury, **N...gas:** McDonald's, **lodging:** Courtyard, Quality Inn, **other:** HOSPITAL

21(33) Meadow St, Banks St, **N...food:** HomeTown Buffet, TGIFriday, **other:** Shaw's Foods, **S...gas:** Exxon/diesel/24hr, **other:** Home Depot

20(32) CT 8 N(exits left from eb), to Torrington, **N...gas:** Shell, **food:** McDonald's

19(32) CT 8 S(exits left from wb), to Bridgeport, no facilities

18(32) W Main, Highland Ave, **N...gas:** Exxon, **other:** HOSPITAL, CVS Drug

17(30) CT 63, CT 64, to Watertown, Naugatuck, **S...gas:** Mobil/diesel, **food:** Maples Rest.

16(25) CT 188, to Middlebury, **N...gas:** Mobil, **food:** Hilton Garden, Patty's Deli

15(22) US 6 E, CT 67, Southbury, **N...gas:** Mobil, **food:** Dunkin Donuts, Friendly's, McDonald's, **lodging:** Heritage Inn, Oaktree Inn, **other:** K-Mart/Little Caesar's, to Kettletown SP, **S...**Shell

14(20) CT 172, to S Britain, **N...gas:** Mobil/24hr, **food:** Thatcher's Rest., **other:** st police

20mm motorist callboxes begin eb, end wb

13(19) River Rd(from eb), to Southbury

11(16) CT 34, to New Haven, no facilities

10(15) US 6 W, Newtown, **S...gas:** Mobil/diesel, Shell/24hr, **food:** Blue Colony Diner/24hr, Pizza Palace, **other:** HOSPITAL

9(11) CT 25, to Hawleyville, **S...lodging:** Best Western, Hillside Inn, Microtel

Interstate 84

E / **W** / **D a n b u r y**

8(8) Newtown Rd, **N...gas:** Global, Mobil/diesel, **food:** Outback Steaks, **lodging:** Wellesley Inn, **S...gas:** BP, Shell, **food:** Bertucci's Italian, Boston Mkt, Burger King, Chili's, Denny's, Friendly's, Harold's Diner, McDonald's, Subway, Taco Bell, **lodging:** Best Western, Holiday Inn/rest., Quality Inn, **other:** Buick/Pontiac, Chrysler/Plymouth/Jeep/Kia, CVS Drug, GMC, Goodyear/auto, Radio Shack, Staples, Target, Wal-Mart

7(7) US 7N/202E, to Brookfield, New Milford, **1 exit N on Federal Rd...food:** Applebee's, **lodging:** Best Inn, **other:** Borders Books, Circuit City, Ford, Harley-Davidson, Home Depot, mall

6(6) CT 37(from wb), New Fairfield, **N...gas:** Shell, **other:** HOSPITAL, to Squantz Pond SP

5(5) CT 37, CT 39, CT 53, Danbury, **N...gas:** Exxon, **lodging:** Best Value Inn, **S...gas:** Exxon, Mobil, **food:** DeliSnack, Taco Bell, **other:** HOSPITAL, to Putnam SP

4(4) US 6 W/202 W, Lake Ave, **N...gas:** Amoco, Gulf/diesel, Shell/diesel, 7-11, **food:** McDonald's, **lodging:** Ethan Allen Inn, Super 8, Goodyear/auto, **S...**Sunoco, **lodging:** Residence Inn, to mall

3(3) US 7 S(exits left from wb), to Norwalk, **S...food:** Dave&Buster's, **other:** JC Penney, Lord&Taylor, Macy's, Sears/auto, mall

2b a(1) US 6, US 202, Mill Plain Rd, **N...gas:** Exxon, **food:** Desert Moon Café, Starbucks, **lodging:** Hilton Garden, **other:** Eckerd, Staples, **S...Welcome Ctr/ weigh sta, full(handicapped)facilities, info, picnic tables, litter barrels, petwalk,** to Old Ridgebury

1(0) Sawmill Rd, **N...**Hilton Garden

0mm Connecticut/New York state line

Interstate 91

N / **S**

Exit #	Services
58mm	Connecticut/Massachusetts state line

49(57) US 5, to Longmeadow, MA, **E...gas:** Citgo, Mobil, Valero, **food:** Friendly's, McDonald's, Rinaldi's Italian, **lodging:** Radisson, **W...food:** Cloverleaf Café

48(56) CT 220, Elm St, **E...gas:** Mobil, **food:** Arby's, Burger King, Denny's, Dunkin Donuts, Figaro Italian, Friendly's, McDonald's, Panera Bread, Ruby Tuesday, TGIFriday, Togo's, Wendy's, **other:** Filene's, Home Depot, Honda, Kohl's, Sears/auto, Target, same as 47

47(55) CT 190, to Hazardville, **E...gas:** Citgo, **food:** Bickford's, D'angelo, Domino's, Dunkin Donuts, Ground Round, Hazard Grille, KFC, McDonald's, Olive Garden, Pizza Hut, Quizno's, Red Lobster, Red Robin, Starbucks, Taco Bell, TCBY, **lodging:** Motel 6, Red Roof Inn, **other:** HOSPITAL, Advance Parts, AutoZone, Barnes&Noble, Bob's Store, CVS Drug, $Tree, Ford, Goodyear, JC Penney, Jo-Ann Fabrics, Michael's, OfficeMax, Radio Shack, Shaw's Foods, Staples, Stop&Shop Foods, Walgreen, mall, same as 48

46(53) US 5, King St, to Enfield, **E...gas:** Mobil, **food:** Astro's Rest., **W...lodging:** Super 8

45(51) CT 140, Warehouse Point, **E...gas:** Shell/Dunkin Donuts, **food:** Blimpie, Burger King, Cracker Barrel, Friendly's, Kowloon Chinese, Sofia's Pizza, **lodging:** Comfort Inn, **other:** Big Y Foods, Wal-Mart, to Trolley Museum, **W...gas:** Sunoco/diesel/24hr, **lodging:** Best Western

44(50) US 5 S, to E Windsor, **E...gas:** Sunoco/diesel, **food:** Dunkin Donuts, E Windsor Rest., Wendy's, **lodging:** Holiday Inn Express

49mm Connecticut River

42(48) CT 159, Windsor Locks, **E...**Longview RV Ctr, **W...gas:** Gulf, same as 41

41(47) Center St(exits with 39), **W...gas:** Shell/24hr, **food:** Ad Pizzaria, **lodging:** Howard Johnson

40(46.5) CT 20, **W...**Old New-Gate Prison, airport

39(46) Kennedy Rd(exits with 41), Community Rd, **W... gas:** Shell/diesel/24hr, **other:** K-Mart, Radio Shack, Stop&Shop Foods

38(45) CT 75, to Poquonock, Windsor Area, **E...gas:** Mobil/diesel, **food:** Beanery Rest., China Sea, Domino's, Dunkin Doughnuts, McDonald's, Subway, **other:** to Ellsworth Homestead, **W...lodging:** Courtyard, Hilton Garden, Marriott

37(44) CT 305, Bloomfield Ave, Windsor Ctr, **E...gas:** Mobil/diesel, **food:** McDonald's, **W...gas:** Gulf, **lodging:** Residence Inn

36(43) CT 178, Park Ave, to W Hartford, no facilities

35b(41) CT 218, to Bloomfield, to S Windsor, **E...**gas/diesel, food

35a I-291 E, to Manchester, no facilities

34(40) CT 159, Windsor Ave, **E...gas:** Shell/diesel, **W...gas:** Citgo/diesel, **lodging:** Flamingo Inn, **other:** HOSPITAL

33(39) Jennings Rd, Weston St, **E...other:** Buick/GMC, Mazda, Saturn, repair, **W...gas:** Exxon/diesel, Mobil, **food:** Burger King, Dunkin Donuts, McDonald's, Subway, **lodging:** Motel 6, Super 8, **other:** Champion Auto, Honda, Hyundai, Jaguar, Mitsubishi, Nissan, Toyota

32b(38) Trumbull St(exits left from nb), **W...**to downtown, **food:** Crowne Plaza, **lodging:** Sheraton, **other:** HOSPITAL, Goodyear

32a (exit 30 from sb), I-84 W, no facilities

29b(37) I-84 E, Hartford, no facilities

29a(36.5) US 5 N, CT 15 N(exits left from nb), **W...**downtown, **other:** HOSPITAL, capitol, civic ctr

28(36) US 5, CT 15 S(from nb), **W...gas:** Citgo, **food:** Burger King, Wendy's

27(35) Brainerd Rd, Airport Rd, **E...gas:** Shell/diesel, **food:** McDonald's, **lodging:** Day's Inn, **other:** Ford, to Regional Mkt

H a r t f o r d

CONNECTICUT
Interstate 91

N ↕ **S**

M e r i d e n

26(33.5) Marsh St, **E**...Silas Deane House, Webb House, CT MVD

25(33) CT 3, Glastonbury, Wethersfield, no facilities

24(32) CT 99, Rocky Hill, Wethersfield, **E**...**gas:** Gulf, Mobil, 7-11, **food:** Bickford's, Blimpie, Dakota Steaks, Mc-Donald's, On-the-Border, Subway, **lodging:** Hampton Inn, Howard Johnson, **W**...**gas:** Mobil, Shell/diesel, **food:** Bennigan's, China Star Buffet, D'angelo's, Denny's, Dunkin Donuts, Giovanni's Pizza, Ground Round, HomeTown Buffet, KFC, McDonald's, Priya Indian, Red Lobster, Sapporo Japanese, **lodging:** Motel 6, Ramada Inn, **other:** A&P, AutoZone, CVS Drug, Goodyear/auto, Lowe's Whse, Marshalls, Radio Shack, TownFair Tire, Walgreen, Wal-Mart

23(29) to CT 3, West St, Rocky Hill, Vet Home, **E**...**lodging:** Marriott, **other:** HOSPITAL, to Dinosaur SP, **W**...**gas:** Citgo/diesel, Mobil, **food:** Angelo's Pizza, D'angelo's, Subway, **lodging:** SpringHill Suites

22(27) CT 9, to New Britain, Middletown, no facilities

21(26) CT 372, to Berlin, Cromwell, **E**...**gas:** Sunoco/die-sel/repair, Wooster St Pizza, **lodging:** Comfort Inn, Radisson Inn/rest., **other:** Krauszer's Foods, **W**...**gas:** Citgo/diesel, Mobil/diesel, **food:** Blimpie, Burger King, Cromwell Diner/24hr, Dunkin Doughnuts, Luna Pizza, McDonald's, Oyama Japanese, **lodging:** Courtyard, Holiday Inn, Super 8, **other:** A&P, Fabric Place, Firestone/auto, Wal-Mart/drug

20(23) Country Club Rd, Middle St, no facilities

22mm **rest area/weigh sta nb, full(handicapped)facilities, info, phone, picnic tables, litter barrels, vending, RV dump, petwalk**

19(21) Baldwin Ave(from sb), no facilities

18(20.5) I-691 W, to Marion, access to same as 16 & 17, ski area

17(20) CT 15 N(from sb), to I-691, CT 66 E, Meriden, **W**...**gas:** BP, **food:** Getty, **lodging:** Best Western, Extended Stay America, Residence Inn

16(19) CT 15, E Main St, **E**...**gas:** Gulf/diesel, Mobil, Smart Stop, Valero, **food:** American Steaks, Gianni's Rest., Huxley's Café, NY Pizza, Olympos Diner, Subway, **lodging:** Candlewood Suites, Hampton Inn, Ra-mada Inn, The Inn, **other:** CVS Drug, Ford, Hancock Fabrics, Radio Shack, Volvo, **W**...**gas:** BP/diesel, Getty/diesel, Gulf/repair, Sunoco/diesel, **food:** Boston Mkt, Burger King, Dunkin Donuts, Friendly's, Great Wall Chinese, KFC, McDonald's, Taco Bell, Wendy's, **lodging:** Executive Suites, Howard Johnson, **other:** HOSPITAL, CarQuest, CVS Drug

15(16) CT 68, to Durham, **E**...golf, **W**...**lodging:** Courtyard, Fairfield Inn

15mm **rest area sb, full(handicapped)facilities, info, phone, picnic tables, litter barrels, petwalk**

14(12) CT 150(no EZ return), Woodhouse Ave, Wallingford, no facilities

---

N e w H a v e n

13(10) US 5(exits left from nb), Wallingford, **2 mi W on US 5**...to Wharton Brook SP

12(9) US 5, Washington Ave, **E**...**gas:** Citgo, Shell, Sunoco, Valero, **food:** Boston Mkt, Burger King, China Buffet, D'angelo, Dunkin Donuts, Friendly's, McDonald's, Quizno's, Rustic Oak Rest., Subway, Wendy's, **other:** CVS Drug, Stop&Shop Food, Walgreen, **W**...**gas:** Exx-on/diesel/24hr, Gulf, **food:** Athena II Diner, Danny's Pizza, Donato's Italian, Roy Rogers, **lodging:** Holiday Inn, **other:** BigY Foods

11(7) CT 22(from nb), North Haven, **E**...**gas:** Citgo, Sunoco, **food:** Hunan Chinese, **other:** AutoZone, JC Penney Outlet, Radio Shack, Stop&Shop Foods, TownFair Tire, USPO, same as 12

10(6) CT 40, to Cheshire, Hamden, no facilities

9(5) Montowese Ave, **W**...**gas:** Sunoco, **food:** McDonald's, Sbarro's, Subway, **other:** Barnes&Noble, BJ's Whse, Circuit City, Home Depot, OfficeMax, Target

8(4) CT 17, CT 80, Middletown Ave, **E**...**gas:** BP/diesel, Citgo/7-11, Exxon, Shell, Sunoco/24hr, **food:** Burger King, D'angelo, Dunkin Donuts, Exit 8 Diner, KFC, McDonald's, Taco Bell/Pizza Hut, **lodging:** Day's Inn, **other:** Advance Parts, Lowe's Whse, Wal-Mart, **W**...**gas:** Mobil/diesel

7(3) Ferry St(from sb), Fair Haven, no facilities

6(2.5) Willow St(exits left from nb), Blatchley Ave, **W**...**gas:** Shell

5(2) US 5(from nb), State St, Fair Haven, **E**...**food:** New Star Diner

4(1.5) State St(from sb), downtown

3(1) Trumbull St, downtown, **W**...Peabody Museum

2(.5) Hamilton St, downtown, New Haven, no facilities

1(.3) CT 34W(from sb), New Haven, **W**...HOSPITAL, down-town

0mm I-91 begins/ends on I-95, exit 48.

Interstate 95

Exit #   Services

112mm   Connecticut/Rhode Island state line

93(111) CT 216, Clarks Falls, **E**...**gas:** Shell/repair/24hr, to Burlingame SP, **W**...**gas:** Mobil, Republic/Citgo/die-sel/rest./@, **food:** McDonald's, Tim Horton, **lodging:** Budget Inn, Stardust Motel

92(107) CT 2, CT 49(no EZ nb return), Pawcatuck, **E**...**gas:** Shell, **other:** HOSPITAL, **W**...**lodging:** Randall's Inn/rest., RV camping

106mm **Welcome Ctr/rest area sb, full(handicapped)facil ities, phone, picnic tables, litter barrels, petwalk, vending**

91(103) CT 234, N Main St, to Stonington, **E**...HOSPITAL

N ↕ **S**

Interstate 95

90(101) CT 27, Mystic, **E…gas:** Mobil, **food:** Bickford's, Domino's, Friendly's, GoFish Rest., Jamm's Seafood, McDonald's, Newport Creamery, Peking Tokyo, Quizno's, Starbucks, Steak Loft, **lodging:** AmeriSuites, Econolodge, Hilton, Howard Johnson, Old Mystic Motel, Seaport Lodge, **other:** Mystic Factory Outlets, aquarium, **W…gas:** Mobil, Shell/Subway/ Dunkin Donuts/diesel, **food:** Ashby's Rest., Ground Round, Pizza Grille, **lodging:** Best Western, Comfort Inn, Day's Inn, Residence Inn, **other:** Chevrolet, Chrysler/Plymouth/Dodge, Ford, RV camping

100mm scenic overlook nb

89(99) CT 215, Allyn St, **W…**camping(seasonal)

88(98) CT 117, to Noank, **E…**MEDICAL CARE(7 am-11pm), airport, **W…food:** Octagon Steaks, Starbucks, **lodging:** Flagship Inn(3mi), Marriott, Sojourner Inn(3mi),

87(97) Sharp Hwy(exits left from sb), Groton, **E…**Griswold SP, airport

86(96) rd 184(exits left from nb), Groton, **W…gas:** Cory's Gas, Hess, Shell/diesel, **food:** Chinese Kitchen, Flanagan's Diner, Goodtimes Rest., IHOP, KFC, Rosie's Diner/24hr, Pancake House, Russel's Ribs, Taco Bell, **lodging:** Best Western, Clarion Inn/rest., Groton Suites, Morgan Suites, Super 8, **other:** Honda, Kohl's, Stop&Shop Foods, Wal-Mart, to US Sub Base

85(95) US 1 N, Groton, downtown, **E…gas:** Shell/diesel, **food:** Norm's Diner, **other:** NAPA

94.5mm Thames River

84(94) CT 32(from sb), New London, downtown

83(92) CT 32, New London, **E…**to Long Island Ferry

82a(90.5) frontage rd, New London, **E…other:** AutoZone, Brooks Drug, Goodyear, IGA Foods, Staples, TownFair Tire, same as 82, **W…food:** Chili's, ChuckeCheese, Outback Steaks, **lodging:** Fairfield Suites, Holiday Inn, SpringHill Suites, Marshall's, OfficeMax, ShopRite Foods, same as 82

82(90) New London, **E…food:** Pizza Hut, **other:** Staples, **W…gas:** Mobil, **food:** Dairy Rest., FoodCourt, Red Lobster, **lodging:** Fairfield Suites, Holiday Inn, **other:** Filene's, Home Depot, JC Penney, Macy's, Marshall's, Sears, Target, mall

81(89.5) Cross Road, **W…food:** Benoit's Rest., **other:** Bob's Store, BJ's Whse, Wal-Mart SuperCtr/24hr/McDonald's/drugs, Waterford Ind Park

80(89.3) Oil Mill Rd(from sb), **W…lodging:** Roadway Inn

76(89) I-395 N(from nb), to Norwich, no facilities

75(88) US 1, to Waterford, no facilities

74(87) rd 161, to Flanders, Niantic, **E…gas:** Citgo, Mobil, Sunoco/diesel/repair, **food:** Bickford's Rest., Burger King, Dunkin Donuts, KFC, Illiano's Grill, **lodging:** Best Value, Best Western, Day's Inn, Motel 6, Ramada Inn, Sleep Inn, Starlight Motel, **other:** Children's Museum, National Tire, **W…gas:** Shell, **food:** Kings Garden Chinese, McDonald's, Shack Rest., Wendy's, **other:** MEDICAL CARE, Brooks Drug, IGA Foods, Ford, True Value, RV camping

73(86) Society Rd, no facilities

72(84) to Rocky Neck SP, **2 mi E…**food, lodging, RV camping, to Rocky Neck SP

71(83) 4 Mile Rd, River Rd, to Rocky Neck SP, beaches, **1 mi E…**camping(seasonal)

70(80) US 1, CT 156, Old Lyme, **W…gas:** Shell/diesel, **lodging:** Old Lyme Inn/dining, **other:** MEDICAL CARE, A&P, Old Lyme Drug, Griswold Museum

78mm Connecticut River

69(77) US 1, CT 9 N, to Hartford, **W…food:** Saybrook Fish House, **lodging:** Comfort Inn/rest.

68(76.5) US 1 S, Old Saybrook, **E…gas:** Citgo/diesel, Mobil, **food:** Cloud 9 Deli, Emelio's Italian, Pat's Country Kitchen, Sully's Seafood, **other:** Chrysler/Plymouth/ Dodge/Jeep, Daewoo, Isuzu, **W…lodging:** Liberty Inn, **other:** Chevrolet/Nissan, Kia, Pontiac/Buick//GMC,. Toyota

67(76) CT 154, Elm St(no EZ sb return), Old Saybrook, **E… food:** Pasta Vita Itaian, same as 68

66(75) to US 1, Spencer Plain Rd, **1 mi E…gas:** Citgo/diesel/ 24hr, **food:** Aleia's Italian, Angus Steaks, Benny's Pizzeria, Cucu's Mexican, Dunkin Donuts/Baskin Robbins, Gateway Indian Cuisine, Luigi's Italian, Thai Cuisine, **lodging:** Day's Inn, Heritage Inn, Sandpiper Motel, Super 8, **other:** ABC Hardware, transmissions

74mm **rest area sb, full(handicapped)facilities, st police**

65(73) rd 153, Westbrook, **E…gas:** Exxon/Dunkin Donuts, **food:** Denny's, Subway, **lodging:** Sandpiper Hotel, Waters Edge B&B, Westbook Inn B&B, **other:** Honda, Old Navy, Westbrook Factory Stores/famous brands

64(70) rd 145, Horse Hill Rd, Clinton, no facilities

Interstate 95

N

↕

S

63(68) CT 81, Clinton, **E...gas:** Shell, **1 mi E on US 1...gas:** Citgo/diesel, Shell/diesel/LP, **food:** Friendly's, McDonald's, **other:** CVS Drug, **W...other:** Clinton Crossing Premium Outlets/famous brands

62(67) **E...**to Hammonasset SP, RV camping, beaches

66mm **service area both lanes, Mobil/diesel, McDonald's, atm**

61(64) CT 79, Madison, **E...gas:** Gulf, Shell, Sunoco, **food:** Panda House Chinese, Starbucks, Subway, **other:** CVS Drug

60(63.5) Mungertown Rd(from sb, no return), **E...**food, lodging

61mm East River

59(60) rd 146, Goose Lane, Guilford, **E...gas:** Citgo, Mobil/24hr, Shell/diesel, **food:** Dunkin Donuts, Friendly's, McDonald's, Rio Grande Steakhouse, Shoreline Diner, Wendy's, **lodging:** Comfort Inn, Tower Motel, **other:** Chevrolet/Pontiac, **W...**MEDICAL CTR

58(59) CT 77, Guilford, **on US 1 E...food:** Getty, Mobil, **other:** CVS Drug, to Whitfield Museum, **W...**st police

57(58) US 1; Guilford, **W...other:** Land Rover, Saab

56(55) rd 146, to Stony Creek, **E...lodging:** Advanced Motel, **W...gas:** Berkshire/diesel, Mobil, TA/diesel/rest./24hr/@, **food:** Dunkin Donuts, Dutchess Rest., Friendly's, USS Chowderpot, **lodging:** Best Value, Ramada Ltd, **other:** Stop&Shop Foods

55(54) US 1, **E...gas:** Sunoco, Thornton, **food:** Dunkin Donuts, Marco Pizzaria, McDonald's, Shoreline Rest., Vincent's Drive-In, **lodging:** Holiday Inn Express, Knight's Inn, Motel 6, **other:** Dodge, Ford, 7-11/24hr, Walgreen, **W...gas:** Citgo, Exxon/diesel, Mobil/diesel, **food:** Margarita's Mexican, Parthenon Diner/24hr, Su Casa Mexican, **lodging:** Day's Inn

54(53) Cedar St, Brushy Plain Rd, **E...gas:** Citgo/repair, Mobil, **food:** Dragon Chinese, Dunkin Donuts, Townhouse Rest., **other:** AAA, Chevrolet, Dodge, Mitsubishi, Staples, Subaru, **W...**Krauszer's Foods

52mm **service area both lanes, Mobil/diesel/24hr, McDonald's, atm**

52(50) rd 100, North High St, **E...other:** to Trolley Museum, **W...**st police

51(49.5) US 1, Easthaven, **E...gas:** Citgo, Hess, Sunoco, **food:** Boston Mkt, Chili's, Friendly's, McDonald's, **lodging:** Holiday Inn Express, **other:** Chevrolet, Hummer, Lexus, TJ Maxx, **W...gas:** Mobil, Gulf, **food:** Dunkin Donuts, Wendy's, **other:** AutoZone, Radio Shack, USPO

50(49) Woodward Ave(from nb), **E...gas:** Citgo, **other:** US Naval/Marine Reserve, Ft Nathan Hale

49(48.5) Stiles St(from nb), no facilities

48(48) I-91 N, to Hartford, no facilities

47(47.5) CT 34, New Haven, **E...gas:** Shell, **W...gas:** Mobil/diesel, **lodging:** Fairfield Inn, **other:** HOSPITAL

New Haven

46(47) Long Wharf Dr, Sargent Dr, **E...food:** Rusty Scupper Rest., **W...gas:** Mobil/diesel, **food:** Brick Oven Pizza, **lodging:** Fairfield Inn

45(46.5) CT 10(from sb), Blvd, same as 44, **W...food:** Getty, DQ, Dunkin Donuts, McDonald's

44(46) CT 10(from nb), Kimberly Ave, **E...lodging:** Super 8, **W...gas:** Getty, **food:** DQ, Dunkin Donuts, McDonald's, Wendy's, same as 45

43(45) CT 122, 1st Ave(no EZ return), West Haven, **W...gas:** BP, **other:** HOSPITAL, to U of New Haven

42(44) CT 162, Saw Mill Rd, **E...gas:** Mobil, **food:** Pizza Hut, **lodging:** Econolodge, **W...gas:** Shell, Mobil, 7-11, **food:** American Steaks, D'angelo's, Denny's, Dunkin Donuts, Friendly's, Pizza Hut, **lodging:** Best Western, **other:** Staples

41(42) Marsh Hill Rd, to Orange, no facilities

41mm **service area both lanes, gas: Mobil/diesel, food: McDonald's**

40(40) Old Gate Lane, Woodmont Rd, **E...gas:** Citgo/diesel, Gulf/diesel/24hr, Pilot/Wendy's/diesel/24hr, Shell, **food:** Bennigan's, Cracker Barrel, D'angelo's, Duchess Rest., Dunkin Doughnuts, Gipper's Rest., **lodging:** Best Value Inn, Comfort Inn, Mayflower Hotel, Milford Inn

39(39) US 1, to Milford, **E...gas:** Gulf/diesel, **food:** Athenean Diner, Friendly's, Hooters, Imo's Pizza, Pizzaria Uno, **lodging:** Howard Johnson, Super 8, **other:** Firestone/auto, Mazda/Volvo, Walgreen, **W on US 1...gas:** Mobil, **food:** Baskin-Robbins, Boston Mkt, Burger King, Chili's, Dunkin Donuts, KFC, Little Caesar's, Miami Subs, Mr Sizzzl, McDonald's, Nathan's Famous, Steak&Sword Rest., Subway, Taco Bell, Wendy's, **other:** Acura, Chrysler/Jeep, Filene's, JC Penney, Michael's, Old Navy, Rite Aid, Sears/auto, Stop&Shop Food, TownFair Tire, USPO, Waldbaum's Foods, mall

38(38) CT 15, Merritt Pkwy, Cross Pkwy, no facilities

37(37.5) High St(from nb, no EZ return), **E...gas:** Gulf, Shell, **lodging:** ShoreLine Motel, **other:** 7-11

35(37) Bic Dr, School House Rd, **E...gas:** Citgo, **food:** Subway, Wendy's, **lodging:** Fairfield Inn, **other:** Buick, Chevrolet, Chrysler/Jeep, Dodge, Ford/Lincoln/Mercury, Honda, Kia, K-Mart, Pontiac/Nissan, **W...lodging:** Red Roof Inn, SpringHill Suites

34(34) US 1, Milford, **E...gas:** Gulf, Shell, **food:** Denny's, Dunkin Donuts, Gourmet Buffet, McDonald's, Taco Bell, **lodging:** Devon Motel

33(33.5) US 1(from nb, no EZ return), CT 110, Ferry Blvd, **E...gas:** Shell/diesel, Sunoco, **food:** Marina Dock Rest., **other:** Jo-Ann Fabrics, Shaw's Foods, Staples, Stop&Shop Foods, Walgreen, **W...food:** Ponderosa, **other:** Home Depot, Marshalls, Wal-Mart SuperCtr/24hr

Milford

Interstate 95

N ↑
S ↓

Bridgeport

32(33) W Broad St, Stratford, **E...gas:** BP, **food:** Getty, **other:** Ford, repair, **W...gas:** Gulf, **food:** Dunkin Donuts

31(32) South Ave, Honeyspot Rd, **E...gas:** Gulf/diesel, **lodging:** Camelot Motel, Honeyspot Motel, **W...gas:** Citgo/diesel

30(31.5) Lordship Blvd, Surf Ave, **E...gas:** Shell/24hr, **food:** Ramada/rest., **other:** Harley-Davidson, Ryder, **W...gas:** Citgo/diesel

29(31) rd 130, Stratford Ave, Seaview Ave, **W...HOSPITAL**

28(30) CT 113, E Main St, Pembrook St, no facilities

27(29.5) Lafayette Blvd, downtown, **W...lodging:** Day's Inn, **other:** HOSPITAL, Bob's Store, Sears/auto, Barnum Museum

27a(29) CT 25, CT 8, to Waterbury, no facilities

26(28) Wordin Ave, downtown

25(27) CT 130(from sb, no EZ return), State St, Commerce Dr, Fairfield Ave, **E...food:** Getty, **other:** Mercedes, **W...gas:** Gulf, **food:** McDonald's

24(26.5) Black Rock Tpk, **E...food:** D'Angelo, **other:** Ford, Lexus, **other:** Staples, **W...other:** Ford/Nissan

23(26) US 1, Kings Hwy, **E...gas:** Sunoco/diesel, **food:** McDonald's, **other:** Home Depot

22(24) Round Hill Rd, N Benson Rd, no facilities

23.5mm service area both lanes, gas: Mobil/diesel, food: FoodCourt(sb), McDonald's/24

21(23) Mill Plain Rd, **E...gas:** Mobil, Shell, **food:** DQ, Grotto Rest., McDonald's, Subway, **lodging:** Fairfield Inn, **other:** Brooks Drug, Stop&Shop Food

20(22) Bronson Rd(from sb), no facilities

19(21) US 1, Center St, **E...**Southport Brewing Co, **W...gas:** Shell/Dunkin Donuts/diesel, **food:** Athena Diner, **lodging:** Tequot Motel, **other:** TownFair Tire

18(20) to Westport, **E...**Sherwood Island SP, beaches, **W...gas:** Citgo, Mobil, **food:** Bertucci's Pizza, Burger King, Carver's Ice Cream, Cedar Brook Café, McDonald's, Sherwood Diner, Subway, Woodie's Roadhouse, **other:** Toyota, Radio Shack, st police

17(18) CT 33, rd 136, Westport, **W...other:** FastStop Mart

16(17) E Norwalk, **E...gas:** Mobil, Shell/diesel, **food:** Baskin-Robbins/Dunkin Donuts, Eastside Café, Penny's Diner, Subway, **other:** Rite Aid

15(16) US 7, to Danbury, Norwalk, **E...gas:** Shell, **other:** Chevrolet, **W...gas:** Getty

14(15) US 1, CT Ave, S Norwalk, **E...**st police, **W...gas:** BP/diesel, Coastal, **food:** Angela Mia's Café, Pagano's Seafood, Pizza Hut, Post Road Diner, Silver Star Diner, **other:** HOSPITAL, Barnes&Noble, Circuit City, CompUSA, Firestone, GNC, ShopRite Foods, Stop&Shop

Norwalk

13(13) US 1(no EZ return), Post Rd, Norwalk, **W...gas:** Exxon, Mobil, Shell/24hr, **food:** American Steaks, Burger King, Driftwood Diner, Dunkin Donuts, Friendly's, IHOP, KFC, McDonald's, Pasta Fare Rest., Red Lobster, Wendy's, **lodging:** DoubleTree Hotel, **other:** Costco, Home Depot, Kohl's, LandRover, Old Navy, Radio Shack, ShopRite Foods, Staples, TownFair Tire, same as 14

12.5mm service area nb, Mobil/diesel, McDonald's

12(12) rd 136, Tokeneke Rd(from nb, no return), **W...food:** deli

11(11) US 1, Darien, **E...gas:** BP, **other:** Chevrolet, Lincoln/Mercury/Jaguar, **W...gas:** Exxon, **lodging:** Howard Johnson/rest., **other:** BMW

10(10) Noroton, **W...gas:** Citgo, Getty, Shell, **food:** Jake's Place

9.5mm service area sb, gas: Mobil/diesel, food: McDonald's

9(9) US 1, rd 106, Glenbrook, **E...food:** Indian Cuisine, **lodging:** Stamford Motor Inn, **W...gas:** Gulf, **food:** Blimpie, McDonald's, **other:** Aamco

8(8) Atlantic Ave, Elm St, **E...**U-Haul, **W...gas:** Exxon, Sunoco, **lodging:** Budget Inn, Marriott, Ramada Inn, **other:** HOSPITAL, Saturn

7(7) CT 137, Atlantic Ave, **E...lodging:** Westin Hotel, **W...lodging:** Marriott, **other:** JC Penney, mall, same as 8

6(6) Harvard Ave, West Ave, **E...gas:** Exxon, **food:** City Limits Diner, **lodging:** Fairfield Inn, **other:** Hyundai, USPO, **W...gas:** Getty, Shell/24hr, **food:** Boston Mkt, Corner Deli/pizza, Subway, Taco Bell, **lodging:** Stamford Hotel, Super 8, **other:** HOSPITAL, Firestone

5(5) US 1, Riverside, Old Greenwich, **W...gas:** Mobil, Shell/24hr, **food:** Italian Ristorante, McDonald's, Taco Bell, **lodging:** Howard Johnson, Hyatt Regency, **other:** MEDICAL CARE, A&P, Caldor, Edwards Drug, Staples

4(4) Indian Field Rd, Cos Cob, **W...lodging:** Howard Johnson, **other:** Bush-Holley House Museum

3(3) Arch St, Greenwich, **E...**Bruce Museum, **W...gas:** Shell, **other:** HOSPITAL

2mm weigh sta nb

2(1) Delavan Ave, Byram, no facilities

1mm Connecticut/New York state line

Stamford

CONNECTICUT
Interstate 395

N
↑
S

P
u
t
n
a
m

Exit #	Services
55.5mm	Connecticut/Massachusetts state line
100(54)	E Thompson, to Wilsonville, no facilities
99(50)	rd 200, N Grosvenor Dale, **E...**W Thompson Lake Camping(seasonal)
98(49)	to CT 12(from nb, exits left), Grosvenor Dale, same as 99
97(47)	US 44, to E Putnam, **E...food:** Dunkin Donuts, Empire Buffet, KFC, McDonald's, Subway, Wendy's, **other:** Advance Parts, $Tree, GNC, K-Mart/Little Caesar's, Radio Shack, Stop&Shop Foods, TJ Maxx, **W...gas:** Shell/diesel/repair/24hr, Sunoco, **other:** Wal-Mart
96(46)	to CT 12, Putnam, **W...food:** Annie's Buffet, Chance's Rest., **lodging:** King's Inn, **other:** HOSPITAL
95(45)	Kennedy Dr, to Putnam, **E...**Ford/Mercury, **W...**HOSPITAL
94(43)	Ballouville, **W...food:** Laurel House Rest., **lodging:** Holiday Inn Express
93(41)	CT 101, to Dayville, **E...gas:** Shell/diesel, **food:** Burger King, Bryan's Grill, China Garden, Dunkin Donuts, McDonald's, Subway, Zip's Diner, **other:** Stop&Shop, Wibberley Tire, **W...gas:** Mobil/diesel/24hr
92(39)	to S Killingly, **W...food:** Giant Pizza, **other:** Bonneville Drug, st police
91(38)	US 6 W, to Danielson, to Quinebaug Valley Coll, no facilities
90(36)	to US 6 E(from nb), to Providence, no facilities
35mm	**rest area both lanes, full(handicapped)facilities, gas: Mobil/diesel**
89(32)	CT 14, to Central Village, **E...gas:** Gulf, **other:** chevrolet/Jeep, RV camping, **W...gas:** Citgo/7-11/diesel/24hr, Sunoco/diesel/LP/repair, **food:** Grandma's Rest., Subway, **lodging:** Plainfield Motel/rest.
88(30)	CT 14A to Plainfield, **E...**RV camping, **1/2 mi W...gas:** Mobil
87(28)	Lathrop Rd, to Plainfield, **E...gas:** Shell/Domino's/diesel, **food:** Dunkin Donuts, HongKong Star Chinese, Subway, Wendy's, **lodging:** Holiday Inn Express, Plainfield Yankee Motel, **other:** Big Y Foods, Ford, Greyhound Park, Mazda, Radio Shack, **W...gas:** Citgo, **food:** McDonald's, O'Conner's rest., Pizza Place, **other:** CVS Drug
86(24)	rd 201, Hopeville, **E...**Hopeville Pond SP, RV camping
85(23)	CT 164, CT 138, to Pachaug, Preston, **E...other:** $Tree, Hidden Acres RV camping
84(21)	CT 12, Jewett City, **E...food:** Ruby Tuesday, **other:** Home Depot, Kohl's, Old Navy, Wal-Mart SuperCtr/24hr, **W...gas:** Citgo/7-11, Mobil/Pizza Hut/diesel, Shell/diesel, **food:** McDonald's, **other:** Val-U Foods
83a(20)	CT 169(from nb), Lisbon, **E...**RV camping

N
o
r
w
i
c
h

M
e
r
i
d
e
n

Exit #	Services
83(18)	rd 97, Taftville, **E...gas:** Getty/diesel, **other:** camping, repair, **W...gas:** Citgo/7-11
82(14)	to CT 2 W, CT 32 N, Norwichtown, **E...food:** Friendly's, **W...gas:** Citgo, Mobil/diesel, Shell/Dunkin Donuts/diesel, **food:** Illiano's Grill, McDonald's, Rena's Pizza, Subway, **lodging:** Comfort Suites, Courtyard, Rosemont Suites, **other:** Ace Hardware
81(14)	CT 2 E, CT 32 S, Norwich, **E...**HOSPITAL, to Mohegan Coll
80(12)	CT 82, Norwich, **E...gas:** Mobil, Shell/repair, **food:** Tim Horton, Burger King, Chinese Buffet, Dominic's Pizza, Friendly's, KFC/Taco Bell, McDonald's, Mr Pizza, Papa Gino's, Subway, Wendy's, **other:** Brooks Drug, Jo-Ann Fabrics, ShopRite Foods, Staples, TownFair Tire, **W...lodging:** Ramada Inn
79a(10)	CT 2A E, to Ledyard, **E...**to Pequot Res
8.5mm	**nb...st police, phone, sb...Mobil/diesel, rest area, full facilities**
79(6)	rd 163, to Uncasville, Montville, **1 mi E...gas:** Mobil/McDonald's/diesel, **food:** Dunkin Donuts, Friendly Pizza, Plan B Cafe, Subway, **other:** Beit Bro's Foods, Brooks Drug
78(5)	CT 32(from sb, exits left), to New London, RI Beaches
77(2)	CT 85, to I-95 N, Colchester, **1/2 mi E...gas:** Shell/diesel, Dunkin Donuts, **lodging:** Oakdell Motel
0mm	I-95. I-395 begins/ends on I-95, exit 76.

Interstate 691

E
↑
W

Exit #	Services
I-691 begins/ends on I-91, exit 18.	
12(12)	Preston Ave, no facilities
11(11)	I-91 N, to Hartford, no facilities
10(11)	I-91 S, to New Haven, CT 15 S, W Cross Pkwy
8(10)	US 5, Broad St, **N...gas:** Cumberland, Mobil/mart, Shell/diesel, **food:** Broad St Pizza, Chinese Gourmet, DQ
7(9)	Meriden(from wb), downtown, **S...gas:** Citgo
6(8)	Lewis Ave(from wb, no EZ return), to CT 71, **N...food:** Ruby Tuesday, **other:** HOSPITAL, Circuit City, Filene's, JC Penney, Lord&Taylor, Sears/auto, Target, mall, **S...**Citgo/7-11
5(7)	CT 71, to Chamberlain Hill(from eb, no EZ return), **N...other:** HOSPITAL, Best Buy, Target, mall, **S...gas:** Citgo/7-11
4(4)	CT 322, W Main St(no re-entry from eb), **N...gas:** Citgo, **food:** Dunkin Donuts, **other:** HOSPITAL
3mm	Quinnipiac River
3(1)	CT 10, to Cheshire, Southington, **N...food:** Tony's Pizza, Whole Donut
2(0)	I-84 E, to Hartford, no facilities
1(0)	I-84 W, to Waterbury, no facilities
I-691 begins/ends on I-84, exit 27.	

DELAWARE

Interstate 95

Exit #	Services
23mm	Delaware/Pennsylvania state line, motorist call-boxes for 23 miles sb
11(22)	I-495 S, DE 92, Naamans Rd, **E...food:** China Star, Harry's Grill(2mi), Wendy's, WaWa, **other:** Goodyear, JoAnn Fabrics, K-Mart, Sav-A-lot Foods, **W...gas:** Gulf/diesel, **food:** Crossroads Rest., KFC/Taco Bell, **lodging:** Howard Johnson Rest., Holiday Inn Select, **other:** Acme Foods, Eckerd, Home Depot, Radio Shack
10(21)	Harvey Rd(no nb return), no facilities
9(19)	DE 3, to Marsh Rd, **E...**to Bellevue SP, st police, **W...**Lamberti's Cafe, museum
8b a(17)	US 202, Concord Pike, to Wilmington, **W...** HOSPITAL, to gas, food, lodging
7b a(16)	DE 52, Delaware Ave, no facilities
6(15)	DE 4, MLK Blvd, **E...gas:** BP, **food:** Joe's Crabshack
5c(12)	I-495 N, to Wilmington, to DE Mem Bridge
5b a(11)	DE 141, to US 202, to New Castle, Newport, **E...lodging:** Quality Inn
4b a(8)	DE 1, DE 7, to Christiana, **E...food:** Don Pablo, FoodCourt, Houlihan's, Ruby Tuesday, **other:** Circuit City, CostCo, JC Penney, Lord&Taylor, Macy's, Michael's, Sears, Strawbridge, mall, **W...food:** Applebee's, ChiChi's, Chili's, Michael's Rest., **lodging:** Courtyard, Day's Inn, Fairfield Inn, Hilton Garden, Homestead Suites, Red Roof Inn, **other:** HOSPITAL, AAA, Borders Books, OfficeMax
3b a(6)	DE 273, to Newark, Dover, **E...gas:** BP/24hr, Exxon/diesel, **food:** Bertucci's, Bob Evans, Boston Mkt, Olive Grill Italian, Wendy's, **lodging:** Best Western, Hawthorn Inn, Residence Inn, **other:** Jo-Ann Fabrics, Staples, **W...gas:** Getty, Shell, 7-11, **food:** Denny's, Donut Connection, Pizza Hut, **lodging:** Comfort Inn, Hampton Inn, Holiday Inn/Oliver's Rest., McIntosh Inn
5mm	**service area both lanes(exits left from both lanes), info, gas:** Exxon/diesel, Sunoco, **food: Big Boy, Cinnabon, Roy Rogers, Sbarro's, Taco Bell, TCBY**
1b a(3)	DE 896, to Newark, to U of DE, Middletown, **W...gas:** Exxon, Gulf/diesel, Mobil, Shell/diesel/24hr, **food:** Boston Mkt, China Garden, Dunkin Donuts, 1st State Diner, Friendly's, Matilda's Rest., McDonald's, TGIFriday, **lodging:** Comfort Inn, Embassy Suites, Extended Stay America, Howard Johnson, Quality Inn, Sleep Inn, **other:** White Glove Carwash
1mm	toll booth, st police
0mm	Delaware/Maryland state line, motorist callboxes for 23 miles nb

Interstate 295(Wilmington)

Exit #	Services
15mm	Delaware/New Jersey state line, Delaware River, Delaware Memorial Bridge
14.5mm	toll plaza
14	DE 9, New Castle Ave, to Wilmington, **E...gas:** BP/24hr, Citgo, **other:** Advance Parts, Family$, Firestone/auto, Harley-Davidson/rest., Rite Aid, SuperFresh Foods, **W...gas:** Gulf, Shell, **food:** McDonald's, **lodging:** Motel 6, Roadway Inn, SuperLodge
13	US 13, US 40, to New Castle, **E...gas:** BP, Exxon/diesel, Hess, Sunoco/diesel, Shell, **food:** Burger King, Denny's, DogHouse, Dunkin Donuts, Golden Diner, IHOP, La Chiquita Mexican, McDonald's, Popeye's, Rascal's Seafood, 7-11, Subway, Taco Bell, **lodging:** Quality Inn, Red Rose Inn, **other:** Cottman Transmissions, Happy Harry's Drugs, PepBoys, Radio Shack, Rayco Repair, Sav-A-Lot, **W...gas:** Shell, **lodging:** Bridgeview Inn, **other:** Kia, Nissan
12	I-495, US 202, N to Wilmington
	I-295 begins/ends on I-95

Interstate 495

Exit #	Services
11mm	I-95 N. I-495 begins/ends on I-95.
5(10)	US 13, Phila Pike, Claymont, **W...gas:** BP, Exxon/diesel, Gulf, Sunoco, **food:** Arby's, Boston Mkt, McDonald's
4(5)	rd 3, Edgemoor Rd, no facilities
3(4)	12th St, no facilities
2(3)	rd 9A, Terminal Ave, Port of Wilmington, no facilities
1(1)	US 13, **E...gas:** Shell, WaWa, **food:** Denny's, Dunkin Donuts, Popeye's, Wendy's, **lodging:** Bridgeview Inn, **other:** Ford, Kia
0mm	I-95 S. I-495 begins/ends on I-95.

Talleyville
Wilmington
Stanton Newport
Newark Brookside
New Castle
Middletown
Townsend
Clayton Smyrna
Cheswold Leipsic
Dover
Little Creek
Camden
Rising Sun-Lebanon Bowers
Felton
Frederica
Harrington Milford
Farmington
Greenwood Ellendale
Milton Lewes
Bridgeville Rehoboth Beach
Georgetown
Seaford Millsboro
Bethel Bethany Beach
Laurel Frankford
Delaware
Selbyville Fenwick Island

FLORIDA
Interstate 4

Exit #	Services

132 I-95, S to Miami, N to Jacksonville, FL 400. I-4 begins/ends on I-95, exit 260b

129 to US 92(from eb, exits left), no facilities

126mm rest area eb, picnic tables, litter barrels, no facilities, no security

118 FL 44, to DeLand, **N...gas:** Shell/diesel, **lodging:** Howard Johnson, **other:** HOSPITAL, **S...gas:** Citgo/Subway(2mi)

116 Orange Camp Rd, Lake Helen, no facilities

114 FL 472, to DeLand, Orange City, **N...other:** KOA(1.5mi), Sunburst RV Park(.5mi), to Blue Sprgs SP

111b a Deltona, **N...gas:** Hess/diesel, RaceTrac, Shell, **food:** Baskin-Robbins/Dunkin Donuts, BBQ, Bob Evan's, Chick-fil-A, Chili's, Denny's, Fazoli's, KFC/A&W, McDonald's, Perkins, Pizza Hut, Quizno's, Ruby Tuesday, Steak'n Shake/24hr, **lodging:** Country Inn Suites, **other:** HOSPITAL, Lowe's Whse, Office Depot, Publix/deli, Tire Kingdom, Walgreen, **S...gas:** Chevron/repair, **food:** Wendy's, **other:** Albertson's, Family$

108 Dirksen Dr, DeBary, Deltona, **N...gas:** Chevron, **food:** Burger King, Shoney's, **lodging:** Hampton Inn, **other:** Publix, **S...gas:** Kangaroo, Shell, **food:** McDonald's, Waffle House, **lodging:** Best Western/rest.

104 US 17, US 92, Sanford, **N...**Featherlite RV Ctr, **S...gas:** Citgo/Subway

101b c rd 46, to FL 417 (toll), to Mt Dora, Sanford, **N...gas:** BP/Pizza Hut/diesel, Citgo/7-11, **other:** Chevrolet, Ford, **S...gas:** Chevron, Citgo/diesel, Mobil, RaceTrac, Speedway/diesel, Sunoco, **food:** Bennigan's, Burger King, Cracker Barrel, Denny's, Don Pablo, FoodCourt, Hops Grill, Joe's Crabshack, Logan's Roadhouse, McDonald's, Olive Garden, Orlando Alehouse, Outback Steaks, Red Lobster, Steak'n Shake, Waffle House, **lodging:** Comfort Inn, Day's Inn, Holiday Inn, SpringHill Suites, Super 8, **other:** HOSPITAL, BooksAMillion, Burdine's, Dillard's, $Tree, Eckerd, JC Penney, OfficeMax, Old Navy, Ross, Sears/auto, mall

101a b rd 46a, FL 417(toll), FL 46, Sanford , Heathrow, **S...lodging:** Marroitt, **S...other:** Acura, Honda, Sam's Club/gas

98 Lake Mary Blvd, Heathrow, **N...gas:** Shell, **food:** Mammolito's Pizza, Panera Bread, Stonewood Grill, **lodging:** Courtyard, **other:** Eckerd, Walgreen, Winn-Dixie, **S...gas:** BP/24hr, Chevron/24hr, Citgo/7-11, Mobil/diesel, **food:** Arby's, Bob Evans, Boston Mkt, Burger King, Checkers, Chevy's Mexican, Chick-fil-A, Chili's, Dunkin Donuts, Frank&Naomi's, Golden China, Japanese Steaks, KFC, Krystal, LongHorn Steaks, Macaroni Grill, McDonald's, Papa John's, Starbuck's, Steak'n Shake, Subway, Taco Bell, TGIFriday, Uno Pizzaria, Wendy's, **lodging:** Candlewood Suites, Extended Stay America, Hilton, Homewood Suites, La Quinta, MainStay Suites, **other:** Albertson's, Discount Parts, Goodyear, Home Depot, K-Mart, Olson Tire, Publix, Staples, Starbucks, Target, Tires+, USPO, Winn-Dixie, mall

95mm **rest areas both lanes, full(handicapped)facilities, phone, vending, picnic tables, litter barrels, petwalk, 24hr security**

94 FL 434, to Winter Springs, Longwood, **N...gas:** Hess/diesel, Mobil, **food:** Burger King, Imperial Dynasty, Kobe Japanese, Markham's Grill, Melting Pot Rest., Pizza Hut, Wendy's, **lodging:** Comfort Inn, **S...gas:** Mobil/diesel, Shell, **food:** Bonefish Grill, Boston Mkt, **lodging:** Candlewood Suites, **other:** HOSPITAL, 7-11

92 FL 436, Altamonte Springs, **N...gas:** Chevron, Citgo/7-11, Shell/diesel, **food:** Amigo's Rest, Bennigan's, Boston Mkt, Checker's, Chevy's Mexican, Chick-fil-A, ChuckeCheese, Cracker Barrel, Kobe Japanese, LongHorn Steaks, McDonald's, Olive Garden, Perkins, Pizza Hut, Popeye's, Red Lobster, Schlotsky's, Steak&Ale, Sweet Tomatoes, Taco Bell, TGIFriday, TropiGrill, WingHouse, **lodging:** Best Western, Day's Inn, Hampton Inn, Holiday Inn, Quality Suites, SpringHill Suites, Travelodge, **other:** Firestone/auto, Tire Kingdom, U-Haul, **S...gas:** BP, Citgo, Hess, Shell, **food:** Pizzaria Uno, Chili's, Denny's, Steak'n Shake, **lodging:** Embassy Suites, Hilton, Homestead Village, **other:** CompUSA, Marshall's, Michael's, Ross, TJ-Maxx, Sears/auto

90b a FL 414, Maitland Blvd, **N...gas:** Citgo/7-11/gas, **food:** Applebee's, **lodging:** Courtyard, Homewood Suites, Hotel Orlando, Studio+, Wellesley Inn, **S...**Maitland Art Ctr

88 FL 423, Lee Rd, **N...gas:** Citgo/7-11/gas, Shell, **food:** Arby's, Burger King, IHOP, LJ Silver/Taco Bell, McDonald's, Rhino Subs, Shell's Seafood, Sicilian Pizza, Waffle House, **lodging:** Comfort Inn, Holiday Inn, InTown Inn, La Quinta, Motel 6, Travelers Inn, **other:** Aamco, Eckerd, Firestone, Infiniti, **S...gas:** Chevron/diesel, Mobil/diesel, **food:** Denny's, Steak'n Shake, **lodging:** Park Inn, **other:** BMW

87 FL 426, Fairbanks Ave(no eb re-entry), **N...gas:** Hess/Blimpie/diesel, **1mi S...gas:** Chevron, Shell, **food:** Burger King, Steak'n Shake, Subway, Wendy's

86 Par Ave(from eb, no re-entry), **S...gas:** Shell

85 Princeton St, **S...gas:** Chevron, Shell, **other:** HOSPITAL

84 FL 50, Colonial Dr(from wb), Ivanhoe Blvd, **N...lodging:** Holiday Inn, **S...lodging:** Radisson, Travelers Hotel

83b US 17, US 92, FL 50, Amelia St(from eb), **N...lodging:** Holiday Inn

83a FL 526(from eb), Robinson St, **N...lodging:** Marriott

83 South St(from wb), downtown

82c Anderson St E, Church St Sta Hist Dist, downtown

82b Gore Ave(from wb), **S...**HOSPITAL, downtown

82a FL 408(toll), to FL 526, no facilities

81b c Kaley Ave, **S...gas:** Citgo, Sunoco, **other:** HOSPITAL

81a Michigan St(from wb), **N...gas:** Citgo/diesel

80b a US 17, US 441 S, US 92 W, **S...gas:** Amoco, Exxon, Mobil, RaceTrac, **food:** Denny's/24hr, Krystal/24hr, McDonald's, Subway, Wendy's, **lodging:** Day's Inn

Lake Mary

Orlando

FLORIDA

Interstate 4

79 FL 423, 33rd St, John Young Pkwy, **N...lodging:** Ramada Inn, **other:** Harley-Davidson, **S...gas:** Citgo/7-11, RaceTrac, Shell/diesel, **food:** Burger King, IHOP, KFC, McDonald's, **lodging:** Days Inn/rest.

78 Conroy Rd, **S...food:** McDonald's, Mimi's Cafe, **other:** BJ's Whse/gas, Home Depot, Macey's, Marshall's, Target, mall

77 FL 527, FL TPK(toll), no facilities

75b a FL 435, International Dr(exits left from both lanes), **N...gas:** Mobil, **food:** Cracker Barrel, Denny's, TGIFriday, **lodging:** AmeriSuites, Day's Inn, DoubleTree Motel, Fairfield Inn, Holiday Inn, Kobe Japanese, to Universal Studios, **S...gas:** Chevron, Citgo/7-11, **food:** Bamboo Rest., Steak&Ale, **lodging:** Court of Flags Hotel, Econolodge, Hampton Inn, Hilton Garden, Holiday Inn Express, Howard Johnson, International Gateway Inn, Knight's Inn, Lakefront Inn, Las Palmas Hotel, Motel 6, Rodeway Inn, Super 8, **other:** Belz Outlet/famous Brands, Office Depot

74b Universal Studios(from wb)

74a FL 482, Sand Lake Rd, **N...gas:** Citgo/7-11, Chevron, **food:** Chick-fil-A, Wendy's, **lodging:** Comfort Suites, Day's Inn, **other:** K-Mart, Publix, **S...gas:** BP, Chevron, Mobil, Shell, **food:** Burger King, Checker's, Denny's, Golden Corral, IHOP, Italianni's, King Henry's Feast, McDonald's, Morrison's Cafeteria, Perkins, Popeye's, TGIFriday, Tony Roma, Wendy's, **lodging:** Best Western, Courtyard, Comfort Inn, Crowne Plaza, Embassy Suites, Fairfield Inn, Holiday Inn, Howard Johnson, La Quinta, Marriott, Microtel, Peabody Hotel, Quality Inn, Residence Inn, Radisson Inn, Ramada Inn, Red Roof Inn, Wyndham Garden, **other:** HOSPITAL, Stouffer Resort, Walgreen, RV Park

72 FL 528 E(toll, no eb re-entry), to Cape Canaveral, **S...to airport

71 Central FL Pkwy(from eb), **S...gas:** Chevron, **food:** Wendy's, to SeaWorld

68 FL 535, Lake Buena Vista, **N...gas:** Chevron/24hr, Citgo/7-11, Shell/diesel, **food:** AleHouse, Black Angus Steaks, Burger King, Chevy's Mexican, Chili's, China Buffet, Denny's, Dunkin Donuts, Hooters, IHOP, Joe's Crabshack, Jungle Jim's Rest., Kobe Japanese, Macaroni Grill, McDonald's, Miami Subs, Olive Garden, Perkins, Pizza Hut, Pizzaria Uno, Red Lobster, Shoney's, Sizzler, Steak'n Shake, Subway, Taco Bell, TGIFriday, Tony Roma, Waffle House, **lodging:** Comfort Inn, Country Inn Suites, Courtyard,

Day's Inn, Doubletree, Embassy Suites, Fairfield Inn, Hampton Inn, Hilton, Homewood Suites, Hotel Orlando, Hyatt Hotel, Radisson, Residence Inn, Sheraton, SpringHill Suites, Summerfield Suites, Wyndham Hotel, **other:** Eckerd, Gooding's Foods, USPO, Walgreen, **S...gas:** Chevron, Citgo/7-11, **food:** Bahama Breeze, Bennigan's, Chick-fil-A, Golden Corral, Landry's Seafood, LoneStar Steaks, Wendy's, **lodging:** Courtyard, Fairfield Inn, Holiday Inn Resort, Marriott Village, SpringHill Suites, **other:** Premium Outlets, Walgreen

67 Fl 536, to Epcot, **N...DisneyWorld, **1 mi S...gas:** Citgo/7-11, **food:** Ponderosa, **lodging:** Holiday Inn, Marriott, **other:** Eckerd, Prime Outlet, to airport, multiple resorts

65 Osceola Pkwy, to FL 417(toll), **N...to DisneyWorld, Epcot, Animal Kingdom, and Wide World of Sports

FLORIDA

Interstate 4

64b a US 192, FL 536, to FL 417(toll), to Kissimmee, **N...gas:** 76/7-11, to DisneyWorld, MGM, **S...gas:** Citgo/7-11, Mobil/diesel, RaceTrac, **food:** Bennigan's, Boston Mkt, Cracker Barrel, Food Court, IHOP, Joe's Crabshack, KFC, Kobe Japanese, McDonald's, Ponderosa, Red Lobster, Shoney's, Steakhouse Foods, Subway, Waffle House, Wendy's, Western Sizzlin, **lodging:** Days Inn, Hampton Inn, Holiday Inn, Homewood Suites, Howard Johnson, Hyatt Hotel, Quality Suites, Radisson, Roadway Inn, Super 8, **other:** Camping World RV Service/supplies(3mi), Goodies Foods, Walgreen, factory outlet/famous brands

62 FL 417(toll, from eb), World Dr, **N...**to DisneyWorld, **S...**Celebration

58 FL 532, to Kissimmee, no facilities

55 US 27, to Haines City, **N...gas:** Citgo/7-11, Sunoco, **food:** Burger King, Cracker Barrel, Denny's, Johnnie's, McDonald's, NY Pizza, Waffle House, Wendy's, **lodging:** Comfort Inn, Day's Inn, Hampton Inn, Ramada Inn, Super 8, **other:** FL CampInn(5mi), **S...gas:** BP/diesel, Citgo/7-11, Marathon, RaceWay/24hr, Shell/diesel/service, **food:** BBQ, Bob Evans, Denny's, Grand China, GreenLeaf Chinese, Perkins/24hr, **lodging:** Best Western, Day's Inn, Holiday Inn Express, Howard Johnson, Red Carpet Inn, **other:** HOSPITAL, KOA, to Cypress Gardens

48 rd 557, to Winter Haven, Lake Alfred, **S...gas:** BP/diesel

46mm **rest area both lanes, full(handicapped)facilities, phone, vending, picnic tables, litter barrels, petwalk, 24hr security**

44 FL 559, to Auburndale, **N...other:** LeLynn RV Park, **S...gas:** Love's/Arby's/diesel/24hr, Shell/diesel, **other:** Fishhaven RV Park(3mi), Lelynn RV Park

41 FL 570 W toll, Auburndale, Lakeland, no facilities

38 FL 33, to Lakeland, Polk City, no facilities

33 rd 582, to FL 33, Lakeland, **N...gas:** Citgo/7-11, Exxon/24hr, **food:** Applebee's, Cracker Barrel, McDonald's, Wendy's, **lodging:** Baymont Inn, Econolodge, Hampton Inn, Jameson Inn, **other:** BMW, **S...gas:** BP, **food:** Ryan's, Waffle House, **lodging:** Baymont Inn, Hampton Inn, Howard Johnson, Relax Inn, **other:** HOSPITAL, Harley-Davidson, Lakeland RV Camp

32 US 98, Lakeland, **N...gas:** Chevron/diesel, Mobil/diesel, Shell/Blimpie, **food:** BBQ, Beef's Rest, Checker's, Chili's, China Coast, ChuckeCheese, Don Pablo, Dragon Buffet, Hooters, IHOP, KFC, LoneStar Steaks, McDonald's, Olive Garden, Piccadilly's, Pizza Hut, Red Lobster, Ruby Tuesday, Stacy's Buffet, Steak'n Shake/24hr, Subway, Taco Bell, TGIFriday, **lodging:** Lakeland Motel, La Quinta, Royalty Inn, Wellesley Inn, **other:** Barnes&Noble, Belk, Best Buy, Circuit City, Dillard's, $Tree, Food Lion, Goodyear/auto, Kash'n Karry, K-Mart, PepBoys, Tire Kingdom, Sam's Club/gas, Tire Kingdom, Walgreen, Wal-Mart SuperCtr/24hr(2mi), RV Ctr, **S...gas:** BP, Citgo/diesel, RaceTrac, **food:** Bob Evans, Burger King, Denny's, LJ Silver, McDonald's, Popeye's, Roadhouse Grill, Waffle House, Wendy's, **lodging:** Best Western/rest., Day's Inn, Holiday Inn, Motel

6, Ramada Inn, Red Carpet Inn, **other:** HOSPITAL, AutoZone, Chrysler/Plymouth/Dodge, Cost+ Foods, Family$, Home Depot, Office Depot, Radio Shack, U-Haul, Winn-Dixie, transmissions

31 FL 539, to Kathleen, Lakeland, **S...**hist dist

28 FL 546, to US 92, Memorial Blvd, Lakeland(from eb, no re-entry), no facilities

27 FL 570 E toll, Lakeland, no facilities

25 County Line Rd, **S...gas:** Citgo/diesel, Shell/Subway, **food:** McDonald's, Wendy's

22 FL 553, Park Rd, Plant City, **N...gas:** Chevrolet, **S...gas:** Shell/Subway/Taco Bell, Texaco/Blimpie, **food:** Arby's, Burger King, Denny's, Popeye's, **lodging:** Comfort Inn, Holiday Inn Express, **other:** RV Sales

21 FL 39, Alexander St, to Zephyrhills, Plant City, **S...gas:** BP/diesel, Shell, **food:** Red Rose Diner, **lodging:** Day's Inn, Ramada Inn/rest.

19 FL 566, to Thonotosassa, **N...gas:** BP, **S...gas:** RaceTrac, **food:** Applebee's, BBQ, BuddyFreddy's Rest., McDonald's, OutBack Steaks, Subway, Waffle House, **other:** HOSPITAL, $General, Publix

19mm weigh sta both lanes

17 Branch Forbes Rd, **N...gas:** Shell, United/diesel, **S...gas:** Chevron, Sparky's Gas/diesel

14 McIntosh Rd, **N...gas:** BP/diesel, **other:** Windward RV Park(2mi), **S...gas:** Citgo/7-11, RaceWay, **food:** Burger King, McDonald's, **other:** Bates RV Ctr, Encore RV Park

10 rd 579, Mango, Thonotosassa, **N...gas:** Flying J/CountryMkt/diesel/LP/24hr/@, Marathon, TA/Arby's/Popeye's/diesel/24hr/@, **food:** Bob Evans, Cracker Barrel, **other:** Camping World RV Service/supplies, Ford, Lazy Day's RV Ctr, Rally RV Park, **S...gas:** Shell/diesel, **food:** Hardee's, Subway, Wendy's, **lodging:** Masters Inn

9 I-75, N to Ocala, S to Naples, no facilities

7 US 92W, to US 301, Hillsborough Ave, **N on US 92W gas:** Chevron, Circle K, Citgo/diesel, **lodging:** Hard Rock Hotel, **N...food:** My's Oriental, **lodging:** Sheraton, to Busch Gardens, **S...gas:** BP, Citgo, **food:** Denny's, **lodging:** Baymont Inn, Holiday Inn Express, Red Roof Inn, **other:** ForeTravel RV, Holiday Travel RV, FL Expo Fair

6 Orient Rd(from eb), **N...**same as 7, **S...gas:** Exxon, Shell

5 FL 574, MLK Blvd, **N...food:** McDonald's, **S...gas:** BP, Citgo, Shell, **food:** Joe's NY Deli(2mi), Subway, Wendy's, **lodging:** Masters Inn

3 US 41, 50th St, Columbus Dr, **N...gas:** Shell/Subway, **lodging:** Bay Inn, Day's Inn, Milner Motel, **S...gas:** Exxon/diesel, GK/diesel, Shell, Sunoco/diesel, **food:** Burger King, Checker's, Church's, Eggroll King, McDonald's, Pizza Hut, Taco Bell, Wendy's, **lodging:** Howard Johnson, **other:** Discount Parts, Eckerd, Kash'n Karry

2 FL 569, 40th St, **N...gas:** Citgo/diesel/24hr, Shell/diesel, **lodging:** to Busch Gardens

1 FL 585, 22nd, 21st St, Port of Tampa, **S...gas:** BP/24hr, **food:** Burger King, Columbia Rest., McDonald's, **lodging:** Hilton Garden, **other:** brewery

0mm I-4 begins/ends on I-275, exit 45b.

Interstate 10

E
W

Jacksonville

Exit #	Services

363mm I-10 begins/ends on I-95, exit 351b.

362 Stockton St, to Riverside, **S...gas:** BP, Gate, **other:** HOSPITAL

361 US 17 S(from wb), downtown

360 FL 129, McDuff Ave, **S...gas:** BP, Chevron, **food:** Popeye's

359 Lenox Ave, Edgewood Ave(from wb), no facilities

358 FL 111, Cassat Ave, **N...gas:** BP/diesel, Chevron, Hess/Blimpie/diesel, Shell/subs/diesel, **food:** Burger King, McDonald's, Popeye's, **other:** AutoZone, GMC, **S...gas:** RaceTrac/24hr, Sunoco, **food:** Dunkin Donuts, Krispy Kreme, Taco Bell, **other:** Lowe's Whse, Winn-Dixie, transmissions

357 FL 103, Lane Ave, **N...gas:** Fuel Man, Hess/diesel, **food:** Andy's Sandwiches, **lodging:** Day's Inn, Quality Inn, Ramada Inn, **S...gas:** BP, Chevron, Texaco/diesel, **food:** Applebee's, Bono's BBA, Burger King, Cross Creek Steaks, Denny's, Hardee's, KFC, McDonald's, Piccadilly's, Shoney's, **lodging:** Diamond Inn, **other:** Battery Depot, Eckerd, Firestone, Home Depot, Office Depot, Pep Boys

356 I-295, N to Savannah, S to St Augustine, no facilities

355 Marietta, **N...gas:** Gate/diesel/24hr, Exxon, **S...gas:** Shell/diesel

351mm rest area eb, full(handicapped)facilities, phone, vending, picnic tables, litter barrels, 24hr security

350mm rest area wb, full(handicapped)facilities, phone, vending, picnic tables, litter barrels, 24hr security

351 FL 115, Chaffee Rd, to Cecil Fields, **N...gas:** Kangaroo/diesel/24hr, **other:** Rivers RV Ctr, **S...gas:** Chevron, KwikChek/gas, Shell/Subway/diesel/24hr, **food:** McDonald's, Wendy's, **lodging:** Hampton Inn

343 US 301, to Starke, Baldwin, **N...food:** Willard's BBQ, **S...gas:** Chevron, Citgo, Exxon, Pilot/Subway/diesel/24hr/@, Shell, TA/Arby's/diesel/rest./24hr/@, **food:** Burger King, McDonald's, Waffle House, **lodging:** Best Western, **other:** NAPA

336 FL 228, to Maxville, Macclenny, **N...HOSPITAL,** fireworks

335 FL 121, to Lake Butler, Macclenny, **N...gas:** BP/diesel, Citgo, **food:** Connie's Kitchen, Domino's, Hardee's, KFC, Larry's Subs, McDonald's, Pizza Hut, Subway, Taco Bell/TCBY, Waffle House, Wendy's, Woody's BBQ, **lodging:** Day's Inn, **other:** HOSPITAL, Advance Parts, $General, Food Lion, Radio Shack, Wal-Mart, Winn-Dixie, **S...gas:** RaceWay, Exxon/diesel, **food:** Burger King, China Garden, **lodging:** Econolodge, Travelodge

333 rd 125, Glen Saint Mary, **N...gas:** Citgo/diesel/24hr

327 rd 229, to Raiford, Sanderson, **1 mi N...gas**

Live Oak

324 US 90, to Olustee, Sanderson, **S... gas:** Citgo/diesel, to Olustee Bfd

318mm rest area both lanes, full(handicapped)facilities, phone, vending, picnic tables, litter barrels, petwalk, 24hr security

303 US 441, to Fargo, Lake City, **N...gas:** Chevron/diesel/24hr, **other:** KOA(1mi), Oaks'n Pines RV Park, **S...gas:** SuperTest/diesel, Shell/diesel, **lodging:** Day's Inn, **other:** HOSPITAL

301 US 41, to Lake City, **N...gas:** BP, Exxon/diesel, **other:** to Stephen Foster Ctr, **S...gas:** Shell, **other:** HOSPITAL

296b a I-75, N to Valdosta, S to Tampa

295mm rest area wb, full(handicapped)facilities, phone, vending, picnic tables, litter barrels, petwalk, 24hr security

294mm rest area eb, full(handicapped)facilities, phone, vending, picnic tables, litter barrels, petwalk, 24hr security

292 rd 137, to Wellborn, no facilities

283 US 129, to Live Oak, **N...gas:** Penn/diesel, to Boys Ranch, **S...gas:** Chevron, Shell, Texaco, **food:** Huddle House, Krystal, McDonald's, Subway, Taco Bell/TCBY, Waffle House, Wendy's, **lodging:** Best Western, Econolodge, Holiday Inn Express, Royal Inn, **other:** HOSPITAL, $Tree, Wal-Mart SuperCtr/gas/24hr

275 US 90, Live Oak, **N...**to Suwannee River SP, **S...other:** HOSPITAL, United 500/diesel/repair

271mm weigh sta both lanes

269mm Suwannee River

265mm rest areas both lanes, full(handicapped)facilities, phone, vending, picnic tables, litter barrels, petwalk, 24hr security

264mm weigh sta both lanes

262 rd 255, Lee, **N...gas:** Exxon/diesel, **food:** Kountry Kitchen, **other:** to Suwannee River SP, **S...gas:** Citgo/diesel/@, Texaco, **food:** Red Onion Grill

258 FL 53, **N...gas:** Amoco/Burger King/diesel24hr, Citgo/diesel/24hr, **food:** Waffle House, **lodging:** Day's Inn, Holiday Inn Express, Super 8, **other:** HOSPITAL **S... lodging:** Deer Wood Inn, **other:** Jellystone Camping, Madison Camping

251 FL 14, to Madison, **N...gas:** Texaco/Arby's, **other:** HOSPITAL

241 US 221, Greenville, **N...gas:** Texaco/DQ, **S...gas:** BP/diesel

FLORIDA

Interstate 10

234mm rest area both lanes, full(handicapped)facilities, phone, picnic tables, litter barrels, petwalk, 24hr security

233   rd 257, Aucilla, **N...gas:** Citgo, Shell/diesel

225   US 19, to Monticello, **N...**Campers World RV Park, **S...gas:** Amoco, Chevron/McDonald's, Exxon/Wendy's, Texaco/Arby's/diesel, **food:** Huddle House, **lodging:** Day's Inn, Super 8, **other:** Alligator Lake Camping, KOA, dogtrack

217   FL 59, Lloyd, **S...gas:** BP/diesel/24hr/@, Shell/Subway/diesel/@, **lodging:** motel

209b a   US 90, Tallahassee, **S...gas:** Citgo/diesel/24hr, 76, Shell, **food:** Cross Creek Rest., Subway, Waffle House, **lodging:** Best Western, **other:** Publix, Tallahassee RV Park

203   FL 61, to US 319, Tallahassee, **N...gas:** BP/diesel, Chevron, 76/Circle K, Shell, Texaco/diesel, **food:** Applebee's, Fuddrucker's, KFC, McDonald's, Pizza Hut, Popeye's, Subway, Taco Bell, TCBY, Waffle House, Wendy's, **lodging:** Motel 6, **other:** Albertson's, BooksAMillion, Discount Tire, Eckerd, Publix, Radio Shack, SteinMart, SuperLube, Wal-Mart SuperCtr/24hr(3mi), Winn-Dixie, **S...gas:** Citgo, **food:** Boston Mkt, Chick-fil-A, Don Pablo, Miami Subs, Osaka Japanese, Outback Steaks, Steak'n Shake, TGIFriday, Wings Grill, **lodging:** Cabot Lodge, Courtyard, Hilton Garden, Residence Inn, Studio+, **other:** HOSPITAL, Home Depot, Office Depot

199   US 27, Tallahassee, **N...gas:** MacKenzie, **food:** Burger King, Taco Bell, Waffle House, **lodging:** Best Inn, Comfort Inn, Fairfield Inn, Hampton Inn, Holiday Inn, Microtel, Villager Lodge, **other:** Big Oak RV Park(2mi), Sam's Club, **S...gas:** Amoco/24hr, BP, Chevron/diesel, Shell, 76/Circle K, USA, **food:** BBQ, Boston Mkt, Chick-fil-A, China Buffet, China Wok, Cracker Barrel, Crystal River Seafood, DQ, Hooters, Julie's Rest., KFC, Krispy Kreme, Longhorn Steaks, McDonald's, Melting Pot Rest., Miami Subs, Papa John's, Pizza Hut, Quizno's, Red Lobster, Roadhouse Grill, Shoney's, Starbucks, Steak&Ale, Subway, TCBY, Village Inn Rest., Whataburger, Wendy's, **lodging:** Cabot Lodge, Day's Inn, Econolodge, Howard Johnson, La Quinta, Motel 6, Ramada Inn, Red Roof Inn, Super 8, **other:** Albertson's, AutoZone, Barnes&Noble, Big 10 Tire, Firestone/auto, Dillard's, Publix, Walgreen, mall

196   FL 263, Tallahassee, **S...gas:** Chevron/diesel, Shell/diesel, **food:** Steak'n Shake, Waffle House, **lodging:** Sleep Inn, **2-5 mi S...food:** Applebee's, McDonald's, Subway, **lodging:** Colony Inn, Day's Inn, Lafayette Motel, Skyline Motel, **other:** Harley-Davidson, Home Depot, Lowe's Whse, RV camping, civic ctr, museum/zoo

194mm rest area both lanes, full(handicapped)facilities, phone, vending, picnic tables, litter barrels, petwalk, 24hr security

192   US 90, to Tallahassee, Quincy, **N...gas:** Citgo, Flying J/Conoco/diesel/LP/24hr/@, **lodging:** Howard Johnson, **S...gas:** Pilot/Subway/diesel/24hr/@, **food:** Waffle House, **other:** Lakeside RV Park(4mi)

181   FL 267, Quincy, **N...gas:** Exprezit/diesel, **other:** HOSPITAL, **S...gas:** Amoco/24hr, BP/diesel, **lodging:** Holiday Inn Express, to Lake Talquin SP

174   FL 12, to Greensboro, **N...gas:** Quality, Shell/Burger King/diesel, **other:** Beaver Lake Camping

166   rd 270A, Chattahoochee, **N...**to Lake Seminole SP, **S...gas:** Shell/diesel, **other:** KOA

161mm rest area both lanes, full(handicapped)facilities, phone, vending, picnic tables, litter barrels, petwalk, 24hr security

160mm Apalachicola River, central/eastern time zone

158   rd 286, Sneads, **N...**Lake Seminole, to Three Rivers SRA

155mm weigh sta both lanes

152   FL 69, to Grand Ridge, no facilities

142   FL 71, to Marianna, Oakdale, **N...gas:** Exprezit, Pilot/Arby's/diesel/24hr/@, **food:** BBQ, Burger King, KFC, Pizza Hut, Ruby Tuesday, Waffle House, **lodging:** Comfort Inn, Hampton Inn, Holiday Inn Express, Microtel, Super 8, **other:** HOSPITAL, Wal-Mart SuperCtr/diesel/24hr, to FL Caverns SP(8mi), **S...gas:** Chevron, Sunoco/diesel, TA/BP/diesel/rest./24hr/@, **food:** McDonald's, **lodging:** Best Western, **other:** Arrowhead Camping

136   FL 276, to Marianna, **N...gas:** Exprezit/diesel, **lodging:** Day's Inn(3mi), Executive Inn(3mi), **other:** HOSPITAL, to FL Caverns SP(8mi)

133mm rest area both lanes, full(handicapped)facilities, phone, picnic tables, litter barrels, petwalk, 24hr security

130   US 231, Cottondale, **N...gas:** Amoco/diesel, Chevron, **food:** Hardee's, Subway

120   FL 77, to Panama City, Chipley, **N...gas:** Exprezit, Exxon/Burger King, **food:** JJ's Kitchen, KFC, McDonald's, Taco Bell, Waffle House, Wendy's, **lodging:** Day's Inn/rest., Executive Inn, Holiday Inn Express, Super 8, **other:** HOSPITAL, Wal-Mart SuperCtr/gas/24hr, **S...gas:** Exprezit, **other:** Falling Water SRA

112   FL 79, Bonifay, **N...gas:** Chevron, Exxon/diesel, **food:** Blitch's Rest., Hardee's, McDonald's, Pizza Hut, Subway, Waffle House, **lodging:** Bonifay Inn, Economy Inn, Tivoli Inn, **other:** HOSPITAL, Hidden Lakes Camping, **S...**FL Springs Camping(8mi)

104   rd 279, Caryville, no facilities

Interstate 10

E ↕ W

96 FL 81, Ponce de Leon, **N**...to Ponce de Leon SRA, camping, **S**...gas: Amoco/diesel/24hr, Exprezit/Subway, Exxon/diesel, **other:** Ponce de Leon Motel/RV Park, **rest area both lanes, full(handicapped)facilities, phone, picnic tables, litter barrels, petwalk, 24hr security**

85 US 331, De Funiak Springs, **N**...gas: Amoco, Chevron/24hr, Texaco, **food:** Arby's, Burger King, McLain's Steaks, Pizza Hut, Subway, Waffle House, **lodging:** Comfort Inn, Day's Inn, Ramada Ltd, Sundown Inn, Super 8, **other:** HOSPITAL, Family$, Wal-Mart SuperCtr/gas/24hr, Winn-Dixie, winery, **S**...gas: BP, Emerald Express/diesel, Shell, **food:** Hardee's, KFC, McDonald's, **lodging:** Best Western

70 FL 285, to Ft Walton Bch, Eglin AFB, **N**...gas: RaceWay, **S**...gas: Citgo/Subway/diesel/24hr/@, **lodging:** Ramada Ltd, **other:** repair

60mm **rest area wb, full(handicapped)facilities, phone, vending, picnic tables, litter barrels, petwalk, 24hr security, weigh sta eb**

58mm **rest area eb, full(handicapped)facilities, phone, vending, picnic tables, litter barrels, petwalk, 24hr security**

56 FL 85, Crestview , Eglin AFB, **N**...gas: Amoco/diesel, Chevron, Exxon, Mobil, Shell/diesel, **food:** Applebee's, BBQ, Burger King, Capt D's, McDonald's, Pizza Hut, Popeye's, Ryan's, Subway, Taco Bell, **lodging:** Budget Host, Econolodge, **other:** HOSPITAL, Advance Parts, AutoZone, Publix, Walgreen, Wal-Mart SuperCtr/24hr, **S**...gas: Citgo/diesel, Exxon/Subway, **food:** Arby's, Cracker Barrel, Hardee's, LaBamba Mexican, Nim's Chinese, Shoney's, Waffle House, Wendy's, Whataburger, **lodging:** Comfort Inn, Day's Inn, Hampton Inn, Holiday Inn, Jameson Inn, Super 8, **other:** Chrysler/Dodge/Plymouth/Jeep, Ford/Mercury, museum, RV camping

45 rd 189, to US 90, Holt, **N**...gas: Chevron(1mi), **other:** to Blackwater River SP, Eagle Landing RV Park, **S**...gas: Amoco/diesel, River's Edge RV Park(1mi)

31 FL 87, to Ft Walton Beach, Milton, **N**...gas: Rolling Thunder/diesel/@, Shell/Quizno's/diesel, **food:** Waffle House, **lodging:** Holiday Inn Express, **other:** Blackwater River SP, Gulf Pines Camping, **S**...gas: Amoco, Shell/diesel, **lodging:** Comfort Inn, Red Carpet Inn

31mm **rest area both lanes, full(handicapped)facilities, phone, picnic tables, litter barrels, petwalk, 24hr security**

28 rd 89, Milton, **N**...HOSPITAL, **S**...Cedar Lakes RV Camping(2mi

26mm Blackwater River

26 rd 191, Bagdad, Milton, **N**...gas: Parade/Chester/diesel, **other:** HOSPITAL, **S**...gas: Chevron/DQ/Stuckey's, Petro/diesel, **other:** Pelican Palms RV Park

Crestview / Milton (left margin)

Pensacola (right margin)

22 N FL 281, Avalon Blvd, **N**...gas: Amoco/24hr, Exxon, **food:** McDonald's, Oval Office Café, **S**...gas: Texaco/Subway/diesel, **food:** Waffle House, **lodging:** Red Roof Inn, **other:** By the Bay RV Park(3mi)

18mm Escambia Bay

17 US 90, Pensacola, **N**...gas: BP, **S**...gas: Exxon, **food:** DQ, **lodging:** Ramada Inn/rest.

13 FL 291, to US 90, Pensacola, **N**...gas: Amoco, Chevron, Shell/diesel, **food:** Arby's, Barnhill's Buffet, Burger King, Capt D's, Denny's, McDonald's, Peking Garden, Shoney's, Subway, Taco Bell, TCBY, Waffle House, **lodging:** La Quinta, Motel 6, Shoney's Inn, Villager Inn, **other:** AutoZone, CVS Drug, Eckerd, Food World/24hr, **S**...food: Bennigan's, ChuckeCheese, Fazoli's, Piccadilly, Pizza Hut, Popeye's, Steak&Ale, Waffle House, Wendy's, Whataburger, **lodging:** Fairfield Inn, Hampton Inn, Holiday Inn Express, Motel 6, Red Roof Inn, Residence Inn, Super 8, **other:** HOSPITAL, Big 10 Tire, Firestone/auto, Goodyear/auto, JC Penney, McRae's, Mr Transmission, Sears/auto, U-Haul, mall

12 I-110, to Pensacola, Hist Dist, Islands Nat Seashore

10b a US 29, Pensacola, **N**...gas: Exxon, Fleet/diesel, **food:** Church's, Hardee's, Waffle House, **other:** Advance Parts, Carpenter's RV Ctr, Wal-Mart SuperCtr/gas/24hr, **S**...gas: RaceTrac, Shell, **food:** BBQ, Burger King, Denny's, IHOP, McDonald's, Ruby Tuesday, Subway, Waffle House, Wendy's, **lodging:** Comfort Inn, Day's Inn, Econolodge, Executive Inn, Holiday Inn Express, Howard Johnson, Hospitality Inn, Knight's Inn, Landmark Inn, Luxury Suites, Motel 6, Palm Court, Travelodge, **other:** Buick, Ford, Hill-Kelly RV Ctr, Isuzu, Jeep, Saturn, Toyota

7b a Fl 297, Pine Forest Rd, **N**...gas: Exxon/Krystal, **lodging:** Comfort Inn, Rodeway Inn, **other:** Albertson's, Tall Oaks Camping, **S**...gas: BP, Citgo, Texaco/diesel/café, **food:** BBQ, Burger King, Cracker Barrel, Hardee's, McDonald's, Ruby Tuesday, Subway, Waffle House, **lodging:** Microtel, Ramada Ltd, Sleep Inn, **other:** Food World/24hr, Big Lagoon SRA(12mi), museum

5 US 90 A, **N**...gas: Fleet/Subway/diesel, **other:** Albertson's/gas, **S**...Leisure Lakes Camping

4mm **Welcome Ctr eb, full(handicapped)facilities, info, phone, vending, picnic tables, litter barrels, petwalk, 24hr security**

3mm weigh sta both lanes

0mm Florida/Alabama state line, Perdido River

FLORIDA
Interstate 75

N ↑
S

| Exit # | Services |

472mm Florida/Georgia state line., Motorist callboxes begin sb.

470mm Welcome Ctr sb, full(handicapped)facilities, info, phone, vending, picnic tables, litter barrels, pet-walk

467 FL 143, Jennings, **E…gas:** Chevron, Texaco, **other:** Budget Lodge, **W…gas:** Amoco, Exxon/Burger King/diesel, **lodging:** Jennings House, Scottish Inn, **other:** Jennings Camping

460 FL 6, Jasper, **E…gas:** Amoco/Burger King, Exxon/Huddle House/diesel, Raceway, **lodging:** Day's Inn, **other:** HOSPITAL, **W…gas:** Shell/diesel, Texaco, **food:** Sheffield's Catfish, **lodging:** Scottish Inn, **other:** Suwanee River SP

451 US 129, Jasper, Live Oak, **E…gas:** Texaco/DQ/Subway/diesel, **other:** HOSPITAL, **W…gas:** Shell, **other:** Suwanee Music Park(4mi), to FL Boys Ranch

450mm weigh sta both lanes

447mm insp sta both lanes

443mm Historic Suwanee River

439 to FL 136, White Springs, Live Oak, **E…gas:** Gate/diesel, Shell/diesel, **food:** McDonald's, **lodging:** Scottish Inn, **other:** Kelly RV Park(5mi), Lee's Camping(3mi), to S Foster Ctr, **W…gas:** Express/diesel

435 I-10, E to Jacksonville, W to Tallahassee, no facilities

423 FL 47, to Ft White, Lake City, **E…gas:** Shell/diesel, **W…gas:** BP/diesel, Chevron/Little Caesar's, Exxon/diesel, Express, **lodging:** Motel 8, Super 8, **other:** Casey Jones Camping

427 US 90, to Live Oak, Lake City, **E…gas:** BP, B&B/Subway/diesel, Chevron/diesel/24hr, Exxon, Shell, **food:** Applebee's, Arby's, BBQ, Blimpie, Burger King, Cedar River Seafood, Cracker Barrel, Domino's, Fazoli's, Hardee's, IHOP, KFC, Krystal, McDonald's, Pizza Hut, Red Lobster, Ryan's, Ruby Tuesday, Steak&Shake, Sunny's BBQ, Taco Bell, Texas Roadhouse, Waffle House, Wendy's, Zaxby's, **lodging:** A-1 Inn, Day's Inn, Driftwood Inn, Executive Inn, Holiday Inn, Jameson Inn, Knight's Inn, Microtel, Ramda Ltd, Rodeway Inn, Scottish Inn, **other:** AutoZone, Belk, Discount Parts, Eckerd, Food Lion, Ford/Lincoln/Mercury, Goody's, JC Penney, K-Mart, Lowe's Whse, Publix, Radio Shack, Tire Kingdom, Toyota, Wal-Mart SuperCtr/gas/24hr, In&Out RV Park, mall, **W…gas:** BP, Chevron, Shell, Texaco/diesel, **food:** Bob Evans, Shoney's, Subway, Waffle House, **lodging:** American Inn, Best Western, Comfort Inn, Country Inn Suites, Econolodge, Gateway Inn, Guest Inn, Hampton Inn, Motel 6, Quality Inn, Travelodge, **other:** Chevrolet/Mazda, Chrysler/Plymouth/Dodge, FL Sports Hall of Fame, Travel Country RV, Wayne's RV Resort

414 US 41, US 441, to Lake City, High Springs, **E…gas:** Chevron/diesel/24hr, Pitstop/gas, Shell, **lodging:** Travelodge, **W…gas:** BP/diesel, Shell, **food:** Country Sta Rest, Huddle House, Subway, **lodging:** Diplomat Motel, Econolodge, **other:** antiques, tires, to O'Leno SP

413mm rest areas both lanes, full(handicapped)facilities, phone, vending, picnic tables, litter barrels, pet-walk

409mm Santa Fe River

404 rd 236, to High Springs, **E…gas:** Chevron/Shell/fruits/gifts, **W…**High Sprs Camping

399 US 441, to High Sprs, Alachua, **E…gas:** BP, **food:** BBQ, McDonald's, Pizza Hut, Subway, Waffle House, **lodging:** Comfort Inn, Quality Inn, Travelers Inn/RV Park, **W…gas:** Chevron, Citgo/Taco Bell/diesel, Exxon/Wendy's, Mobil, **food:** Kazbor's Grill, KFC, **lodging:** Day's Inn, Ramada Ltd

390 FL 222, to Gainesville, **E…gas:** Chevron/diesel, Exxon/McDonald's/diesel, Kangaroo/diesel, **food:** BBQ, Burger King, Schlotsky's(3mi), Wendy's, **other:** Publix, **W…gas:** BP/diesel, **food:** Crosscreek Steaks, **lodging:** Best Western, **other:** Buick, Chrysler/Jeep/Mercedes, Harley-Davidson, auto repair

387 FL 26, to Newberry, Gainesville, **E…gas:** Chevron, Citgo, Sunoco, Shell/diesel, **food:** BBQ, Boston Mkt, Burger King, Don Pablo's, Durango's Steaks, FoodCourt, LJ Silver, McDonald's, Perkins, Piccadilly's, Red Lobster, Rigatelli's Italian, Ruby Tuesday, Starbuck's, Subway, Wendy's, **lodging:** La Quinta, **other:** HOSPITAL, Belk, BooksAMillion, Borders Books, Eckerd, Dillard's, JC Penney, Office Depot, Sears/auto, to UFL, mall, **W…gas:** BP, Chevron/diesel, Exxon/diesel, Mobil/diesel/LP, **food:** Cracker Barrel, Domino's, Godfather's, GrillMasters Steaks, Hardee's, KFC, Krystal, Napolatanos Rest., Pizza Hut, Shoney's, Taco Bell, Tequila Mexican, Waffle House, Whataburger, **lodging:** Day's Inn, Econolodge, Fairfield Inn, Holiday Inn, Ramada Ltd, **other:** Circuit City, Discount Parts, $Tree, Home Depot, JiffyLube, JoAnn Fabrics, K-Mart, PepBoys, Publix, Walgreen, Winn-Dixie, tires/repair

384 FL 24, to Archer, Gainesville, **E…gas:** BP, Chevron/diesel/24hr, Citgo, Exxon/diesel, Shell, **food:** Atlanta Bread, BBQ, Bennigan's, Bob Evans, Burger King, Capt D's, Checker's, Chick-fil-A, Chili's, Hops Grill, KFC, LoneStar Steaks, McDonald's, Moe's Grill, Olive Garden, OutBack Steaks, Panera Bread, Papa John's, Pizza Hut, Rafferty's, Shoney's, Steak&Ale, Steak'n Shake, Subway, Taco Bell, Texas Roadhouse, TGIFriday, Waffle House, Wendy's, **lodging:** Cabot Lodge, Comfort Inn, Courtyard, Extended Stay America, Hampton Inn, Motel 6, Ramada Ltd, Red Roof Inn, Super 8, **other:** Albertson's, Barnes&Noble, Best Buy, CarQuest, $Tree, Eckerd, Firestone/auto, GNC, Goody's, Lowe's Whse, Michael's, OfficeMax, Old Navy, Publix, Radio Shack, Ross, Santa Fe Parts, Target, Wal-Mart, Winn-Dixie, **W…gas:** Mobil/diesel, **food:** Cracker Barrel, **lodging:** Baymont Inn, **other:** Sunshine RV Park, to Bear Museum

383mm rest areas both lanes, full(handiacpped)facilities, phone, vending, picnic tables, litter barrels, pet-walk, 24hr security

382 FL 121, to Williston, Gainesville, **E…gas:** Citgo/diesel/24hr, Mobil/diesel, **lodging:** Residence Inn(2mi), Travelodge, **W…gas:** BP/diesel, Chevron/diesel/24hr, Kangaroo, **food:** 43rd St Deli, **lodging:** Quality Inn, **other:** Fred Bear Museum

(margin: Lake City)

(margin: Gainesville)

N
S

374   rd 234, Micanopy, **E...gas:** BP, Chevron, **other:** antiques, fruit, to Paynes Prairie SP, **W...gas:** BP/repair, Citgo/diesel, Spirit Gas, **lodging:** Knight's Inn

368   rd 318, Orange Lake, **E...gas:** BP, Hi-Way Gas/RV, auto repair, Petro/Mobil/Wendy's/diesel/24hr/@, **food:** Jim's BBQ/gas, **other:** Grand Lake RV Park(3mi), **W...gas:** BP/diesel/repair, **other:** Encore RV Park(1mi), antiques

358   FL 326, **E...gas:** BP/diesel, Chevron, Mobil/McDonald's/diesel, Pilot/Arby's/diesel/24hr, Pilot/Wendy's/diesel/24hr/@, **other:** Liberty RV Ctr, **W...gas:** Chevron/DQ/diesel

354   US 27, to Silver Springs, Ocala, **E...gas:** BP/24hr, RaceTrac, SuperTest/diesel, **food:** BBQ, Burger King, Krystal, **lodging:** Payless Inn, **other:** fruits, **W...gas:** BP/diesel, Chevron, Shell/diesel/24hr, **food:** Damon's, Larenzo's Pizza, Penstripe Grill, Waffle House, **lodging:** Budget Host, Day's Inn/café, Howard Johnson, Knight's Inn, Ramada Inn, Travelodge, **other:** Arrowhead Campsites, Oaktree Village

352   FL 40, to Silver Springs, Ocala, **E...gas:** BP/diesel, Chevron, Citgo, RaceTrac/24hr, **food:** McDonald's, Pizza Hut/Taco Bell, Wendy's, **lodging:** Day's Inn/café, Economy Inn, Holiday Inn, Motor Inn/RV, Quality Inn, **other:** park, fruits, **W...gas:** Shell/diesel, **food:** Denny's, Golden Coast Buffet, Waffle House, **lodging:** Comfort Inn, Red Roof Inn, Super 8, **other:** Holiday TravL Park

350   FL 200 , to Hernando, Ocala, **E...gas:** Chevron, Citgo, RaceTrac, Shell/diesel, **food:** Applebee's, Arby's, Bella Luna Italian, Bennigans, Bob Evans, Burger King, Chick-fil-A, Chili's, El Toreo Mexican, Fazoli's, Grand Buffet, HongKong Chinese, Hooters, Hops Grill, Krystal, Lee's Chicken, LoneStar Steaks, McDonald's, Olive Garden, Outback Steaks, Papa John's, Perkins, Pizza Hut, Quincy's, Red Lobster, Ruby Tuesday, Shell's Rest., Shoney's, Sonic, Subway, Taco Bell, TGIFriday, Tokyo Japanese, Wendy's, Western Sizzlin, **lodging:** Country Inn Suites, Hampton Inn, Hilton, La Quinta, **other:** HOSPITAL, Advance Parts, Barnes&Noble, Belk, Chevrolet/Nissan/Mitsubishi, Circuit City, Discount Parts, Eckerd, $General, Goodyear/auto, Home Depot, JC Penney, Kia, K-Mart, Lowe's Whse, Pennzoil, PepBoys, Publix, Sears, Target, Tire Kingdom, Walgreen, Wal-Mart SuperCtr/24hr, Winn-Dixie, fruits, mall, **W...gas:** BP/24hr, Chevron/24hr, **food:** Burger King, Cracker Barrel, Dunkin Donuts, KFC, Steak'n Shake/24hr, Waffle House, **lodging:** Best Western, Courtyard, Fairfield Inn, **other:** Cadillac, Firestone/auto, KOA, Sam's Club, Camper Village, Pontiac

346mm   **rest area both lanes, full (handicapped)facilities, phone, vending, picnic tables, litter barrels, petwalk, 24hr security**

341   FL 484, to Belleview, **E...gas:** Chevron/fruit/24hr, Citgo/Dunkin Doughnuts, Exxon/diesel, Shell, **food:** BBQ, **lodging:** Microtel, **other:** museums, **W...gas:** BP/repair, Pilot/Arby's/DQ/diesel/24hr/@,

Ocala

Wildwood

  Texaco/diesel/rest./24hr, **food:** McDonald's, Waffle House

338mm   weigh sta both lanes

329   FL 44, to Inverness, Wildwood, **E...gas:** BP/repair, Gate/Steak'n Shake/diesel, Mobil/diesel, **food:** Burger King, Denny's, Johnnie's Rest., McDonald's, Waffle House, Wendy's, **other:** KOA, fruits, **W...gas:** Citgo/diesel/repair/24hr/@, Pilot/diesel/24hr/@, TA/BP/Pizza Hut/Subway/Popeye's/diesel/24hr/@, **food:** IHOP, KFC, Waffle House, **lodging:** Day's Inn/rest., Economy Inn, Super 8, Wildwood Inn

328   FL TPK(from sb), to Orlando, no facilities

321   rd 470, to Sumterville, Lake Panasoffkee, **E... gas:** Spirit/diesel/rest./24hr, **other:** Coleman Correctional, **W...gas:** BP/Hardee's/diesel, Chevron, **other:** Countryside RV Park

314   FL 48, to Bushnell, **E...gas:** BP/diesel, Chevron/A&W/24hr, Citgo, Mobil/DQ/Stuckey's, Shell/Subway, **food:** Four-Season Chinese, KFC/Taco Bell, McDonald's, Wendy's, **lodging:** Best Western, **other:** BlueBerry Hill RV Camp, Red Barn RV Camp, The Oaks Camp(1mi), Wal-Mart SuperCtr/24hr/gas, to Dade Bfd HS, **W...gas:** Shell/diesel, Sunoco/diesel, **food:** BBQ, McDonald's, Waffle House, **lodging:** Microtel

309   rd 476, to Webster, **E...**Breezy Oaks RV Park(1mi), Sumter Oaks RV Park(1mi)

307mm   **rest areas both lanes, full(handicapped)facilities, phone, coffee, vending, picnic tables, litter barrels, petwalk**

301   US 98, FL 50, to Dade City, **E...gas:** RaceTrac, Sunoco, **food:** Cracker Barrel, Denny's, McDonald's, Waffle House, Wendy's, **lodging:** Day's Inn, **other:** HOSPITAL, Winn-Dixie, **W...gas:** Chevron/Subway/diesel, Hess(3mi), **food:** Burger King, **lodging:** Best Western, Hampton Inn

293   rd 41, to Dade City, **W...gas:** Citgo(2mi), **other:** Travelers Rest Resort RV Park

285   FL 52, to Dade City, New Port Richey, **E...gas:** Flying J/Country Mkt/diesel/LP/24hr/@, **other:** HOSPITAL, tires, **W...gas:** Shell/diesel/24hr, **food:** Waffle House

279   FL 54, to Land O' Lakes, Zephyrhills, **E...gas:** Hess/Blimpie/Godfather's/diesel, RaceTrac, Shell, **food:** ABC Pizza, Applebee's, BBQ, Blimpie, Burger King, Carino's Italian, Pizza Hut/Taco Bell, Subway, Waffle House, Wendy's, **other:** Discount Parts, Ford, Kia, Publix, Walgreen, Winn-Dixie, Saddlebrook RV Resort(1mi), **W...gas:** BP, Circle K/diesel, Citgo/7-11/diesel, **food:** Cracker Barrel, Denny's, KFC, McDonald's, Outback Steaks, Remington's Steaks, Shanghai Chinese, **lodging:** Comfort Inn, Holiday Inn Express, Masters Inn, Sleep Inn, **other:** Kash'n Karry Foods, RV camping, USPO

FLORIDA

Interstate 75

N ↑↓ S

278mm rest areas both lanes, full(handicapped)facilities, phone, vending, picnic tables, litter barrels, petwalk, 24hr security

275 FL 56, no facilities

274 I-275(from sb), to Tampa, St Petersburg, no facilities

270 rd 581, Bruce B Downs Blvd, **E...gas:** Citgo/7-11, Hess/Blimpie/diesel, Mobil, Shell/diesel, **food:** Bennigan's, Boston Mkt, Burger King, Chick-fil-A, Chili's, Coldstone Creamery, DQ, Golden China, KFC, Krispy Kreme, Liang's Asian Bistro, McDonald's, Moe's SW Grill, Panera Bread, Papa John's, Quizno's, Ruby Tuesday, Starbuck's, Subway, Taco Bell, **lodging:** Holiday Inn Express, Wingate Inn, **other:** Circuit City, Home Depot, Walgreen, tires, **W...gas:** Citgo/711, Shell/Taco Bell, **food:** McDonald's, Olive Garden, Red Lobster, Selmon's Cafe, Stonewood Restaurants, **other:** Lowe's Whse

266 rd 582A, Fletcher Ave, **W...gas:** Citgo/7-11, Mobil, Shell/Subway, **food:** Bob Evans, Hooters, Wendy's, **lodging:** Courtyard, Extended Stay America, Fairfield Inn, Hampton Inn Suites, Hilton Garden, Residence Inn, Sleep Inn, **other:** HOSPITAL

Tampa

265 FL 582, Fowler Ave, Temple Terrace, **E...other:** Happy Traveler RV Park(1mi), flea mkt, **W...gas:** BP, Shell/diesel, 76, **food:** Burger King, Denny's, McDonald's, Perkins, Ryan's, **lodging:** Holiday Inn, La Quinta, Ramda Inn, Wingate Inn, to Busch Gardens

261 I-4, W to Tampa, E to Orlando, no facilities

260b a FL 574, to Mango, Tampa, **E...gas:** Chevron, RaceTrac, Shell/Subway, **food:** McDonald's(2mi), **other:** Walgreen, **W...gas:** BP, Citgo/diesel, Hess/diesel, Mystik/gas, **food:** NY Deli(2mi), **lodging:** Crowne Plaza Hotel, Hilton/rest, Residence Inn

257 FL 60, Brandon, **E...gas:** BP, Mobil, Texaco, **food:** Bennigan's, BuddyFreddy's Diner, Chili's, Domino's, Don Pablo, Grady's Grill, Macaroni Grill, Olive Garden, Outback Steaks, Red Lobster, TGIFriday, Waffle House, **lodging:** Holiday Inn Express, HomeStead Village, La Quinta, **other:** HOSPITAL, Aamco, Barnes&Noble, Best Buy, Chrysler/Plymouth/Dodge, Dillard's, Firestone, JC Penney, Jo-Ann Fabrics, K-Mart, Marshall's, MensWhse, Michael's, PepBoys, Sam's Club, Sears/auto, Staples, mall, **W...gas:** Citgo, Shell, **food:** BBQ, Bob Evans, Burger King, Hooters, McDonald's, Subway, Sweet Tomato, Wendy's, **lodging:** Baymont Inn, Best Western, Comfort Inn, Courtyard, Day's Inn, Fairfield Inn, Red Roof Inn, **other:** Chevrolet, Circuit City, Dodge, Harley-Davidson, Home Depot, Honda, Mitsubishi/Hyundai/Suzuki/Yamaha, Nissan, Office Depot, Pontiac/GMC, funpark

Brandon

256 FL 618 W(toll), to Tampa, no facilities

254 US 301, Riverview, **E...lodging:** Bianchi Motel(1mi), Costco/gas(1mi), **1mi W...gas:** Shell, 7-11/diesel, Circle K

250 Gibsonton Dr, Riverview, **1 mi E...gas:** BP, Chevron/diesel, Hess, Mobil, RaceWay, 7-11, **food:** Beef O'Brady's, Burger King, Godfather's, McDonald's, Subway, Taco Bell, Wendy's, **other:** Alafia River RV Resort, Hidden River RV Resort(4mi), **W...gas:** BP(1mi)

246 FL 672, Big Bend Rd, Apollo Bch, **1-2 mi E...gas:** 7-11, **food:** Blimpie, **3-5 mi W...gas:** Chevron, 7-11, **lodging:** Ramada Inn/rest.

240b a FL 674, Sun City Ctr, Ruskin, **E...Welcome Ctr, gas:** Chevron/24hr, **food:** BBQ, Bob Evan's, Burger King, Checker's, Denny's, Hungry Howie's, Pizza Hut, Taco Bell, Wendy's, **lodging:** Comfort Inn, Sun City Ctr Inn/rest., **other:** Kash'n Karry Foods, OilExpress, Radio Shack, Walgreen, Wal-Mart, SunLake RV Resort(1mi), to Little Manatee River SP, **W...gas:** Circle K/diesel, Hess/diesel, RaceTrac, **food:** KFC, McDonald's, Subway, **lodging:** Holiday Inn Express, **other:** Beall's, D&K Repair, Eckerd, NAPA, Publix

238mm rest area both lanes, full(handicapped)facilities, phone, vending, picnic tables, litter barrels, petwalk, 24hr security

229 rd 683, Moccasin Wallow Rd, to Parrish, **E...Little Manatee Sprs RV Park(10mi), W...other:** Fiesta Grove RV Park(3mi), Frog Creek RV Park(3mi), Terra Ceia RV Village(2mi), Winterset RV Park(3mi)

228 I-275 N, to St Petersburg, no facilities

224 US 301, to Bradenton, Ellenton, **E...gas:** BP, Chevron/24hr, RaceWay, Shell/diesel, **food:** Applebee's, Checker's, Food Court, McDonald's, Ruby Tuesday, Wendy's, **lodging:** Hampton Inn, Holiday Inn Express, Sleep Inn, **other:** Ace Hardware, K-Mart, Publix, Walgreen, USPO, Ellenton Garden Camping(1mi), Prime Outlets/famous brands, cleaners, **W...gas:** Pilot/Subway/diesel/@, **food:** Anna Maria, Crabtrap Seafood, Leverock's Seafood, Waffle House, **lodging:** Best Western, Day's Inn(3mi), Ellenton Inn, GuestHouse Inn, Ramada Ltd

Bradenton

220b a FL 64, to Zolfo Springs, Bradenton, **E...Lake Manatee SRA, W...gas:** BP/diesel, Chevron, Citgo/diesel/24hr, RaceTrac, 76/Circle K/diesel, Shell, **food:** BBQ, Burger King, Cracker Barrel, Denny's, KFC/LJ Silver, McDonald's, Subway, TCBY, Waffle House, Wendy's, **lodging:** Budget Inn, Comfort Inn, Day's Inn, Econolodge, Holiday Inn Express, Motel 6, **other:** HOSPITAL, Dream RV Ctr, Encore RV Resort(1mi), Wal-Mart SuperCtr/24hr

217b a FL 70, to Arcadia, **E...gas:** Hess/Blimpie/Godfather's/diesel/24hr, **other:** Kash'nKarry Foods, **W...gas:** BP/diesel/LP, Citgo/7-11, Exxon/diesel, Shell, 76/Circle K, **food:** Applebee's, Arby's, Bob Evans, Chick-fil-A, Daritino's Pasta, DQ, McDonald's, Hungry Howie's, Ritter's, Subway, **other:** Beall's, Eckerd, Lowe's Whse, Publix, Tire Kingdom, HorseShoe RV Park, Pleasant Lake RV Resort

Interstate 75

N ↑ ↓ S

Sarasota (vertical label)

213 University Parkway, to Sarasota, **E...gas:** Chevron/Subway/diesel, **food:** Chili's, China Coast, Pizza Hut, Ryan's Grill, **lodging:** Fairfield Inn, Holiday Inn, **other:** Publix, Walgreen, **W...food:** Altanta Bread, Carrabba's, Ruby Tuesday, Stonewood Grill, Wendy's, **lodging:** Comfort Suites, **other:** BJ's Whse, Eckerd, Staples, food court, **3-6 mi W...gas:** Chevron/24hr, Hess, **food:** Applebee's, Burger King, KFC, McDonald's, Ruby Tuesday, Taco Bell, **lodging:** Courtyard, Sleep Inn, SpringHill Suites, **other:** BJ's Whse/gas, Ringling Museum, dogtrack

210 FL 780, Fruitville Rd, Sarasota, **1 mi E...other:** Sun'n Fun RV Park(1mi), **W...gas:** BP/diesel/LP, BP/diesel, Chevron/24hr, Mobil/Blimpie/diesel, **food:** Applebee's, Bob Evans, Burger King, Checker's, Chick-fil-A, Don Pablo, KFC, Longhorn Steaks, McDonald's, Perkins, Subway, Taco Bell, **lodging:** AmericInn, **other:** Advance Parts, $Tree, Eckerd, GNC, Publix, Radio Shack, Sam's Club, Target, Tuffy Auto, Winn-Dixie

207 FL 758, Sarasota, **W...gas:** BP, Mobil/Subway/diesel/repair, Shell/Blimpie, **food:** Arby's, Auntie Pasta, BBQ, Checker's, Chili's, Bella Cucina Italian, MadFish Grill, McDonald's, Pizza Hut, Sarasota Ale House, Steak'n Shake, Taco Bell, **lodging:** Hampton Inn, **other:** HOSPITAL, $Tree, Goodyear/auto, Home Depot, Kash'n Karry, Publix, Radio Shack, Walgreen, Wal-Mart

205 FL 72, to Arcadia, Sarasota, **E...**Myakka River SP(9mi), **W...gas:** BP/A&W/LJ Silver/diesel, Citgo/7-11/diesel, Exxon/diesel, Mobil, **food:** Applebee's, Burger King, Chick-fil-A, McDonald's, Quizno's, Starbucks, Subway, Waffle House, Wendy's, **lodging:** Comfort Inn, Country Inn Suites, Holiday Inn Express(5mi), Ramada Ltd, **other:** Beach Club RV Resort(6mi), BMW, Eckerd, Land Rover, Lexus, Publix, Walgreen, Winn-Dixie, Windward Isle RV Park

200 FL 681 S(from sb), to Venice, Osprey, to Gulf Bchs

195 Laurel Rd, Nokomis, **E...gas:** BP/diesel, Stay'n Play RV Park(1mi), **food:** Fast Food Fast, **W...gas:** Citgo/7-11, Hess(3mi), **food:** Blimpie, Godfather's Pizza, **lodging:** Hampton Inn, Holiday Inn, **other:** Encore RV Park(2mi), Scherer SP(6mi)

193 Jaracanda Blvd, Venice, **W...gas:** Chevron/Subway/diesel/24hr, Citgo/Subway/diesel/24hr, Hess/Blimpie/Godfather's/diesel, Mobil, RaceTrac, **food:** Cracker Barrel, McDonald's, Ping's Chinese, Waffle House, **lodging:** Best Western, **other:** HOSPITAL

191 Englewood Rd, **W...other:** Venice Campground(1mi)

182 Sumter Blvd, to North Port, **W...gas,** food, lodging

179 Toledo Blade Blvd, North Port, no facilities

170 rd 769, to Arcadia, Port Charlotte, **E...gas:** Citgo/7-11/diesel, RaceTrac, **lodging:** Hampton Inn, Holiday Inn Express, **other:** Lettuce Lake Camping(7mi), Riverside Camping(5mi), **W...gas:** BP/Subway/DQ/

diesel, Hess/diesel, Chevron/diesel, Mobil/Blimpie/diesel, 76/Circle K, **food:** Burger King, Cracker Barrel, McDonald's, Taco Bell/Pizza Hut, Waffle House, Wendy's, **food:** Wingate Inn, **other:** HOSPITAL, Ace Hardware, Advance Parts, $General, Eckerd, GNC, Publix, USPO, Walgreen, Winn-Dixie

167 rd 776, Port Charlotte, no facilities

164 US 17, Punta Gorda, Arcadia, **E...gas:** Chevron/diesel, RaceTrac, Shell/diesel/24hr, **other:** $General, KOA(2mi), Winn-Dixie, **W...gas:** 76/Circle K, **food:** Fisherman's Village Rest., **lodging:** Best Western(2mi), Holiday Inn(2mi), SeaCove Motel(2mi), **other:** HOSPITAL, auto/tire repair

161 FL 768, Punta Gorda, **E...rest area both lanes, full(handicapped)facilities, phone, vending, picnic tables, litter barrels, petwalk, 24hr security,** Waters Edge RV Park(2mi), **W...gas:** BP/DQ/Subway/diesel, Pilot/Arby's/diesel/24hr/@, **food:** BBQ, Burger King, McDonald's, Pizza Hut, Waffle House, Wendy's, **lodging:** Day's Inn, Motel 6, **other:** Alligator RV Park(2mi), Encore RV Park(2mi)

160mm weigh sta both lanes

158 rd 762, **E...**Babcock-Wells Wildlife Mgt Area, **W...gas:** Pure/diesel(1mi), Tamiami RV Park(12mi)

143 FL 78, to Cape Coral, N Ft Myers, **E...gas:** Citgo/Lawhon's Foods/diesel, **other:** Upriver RV Park(1mi), **W...gas:** RaceTrac/diesel/24hr, **lodging:** Sunburst RV Resort

141 FL 80, Palm Bch Blvd, Ft Myers, **E...gas:** BP/diesel, Chevron/diesel, Exxon/diesel, **food:** Cracker Barrel, Waffle House, **lodging:** Comfort Inn, **W...gas:** Citgo, Hess/diesel, RaceTrac, **food:** BBQ, DQ, Hardee's, Juicy Lucy's Burgers, KFC(2mi), Perkins, Pizza Hut, Popey's(1mi), Subway, Taco Bell, **lodging:** Palm City Motel, **other:** MEDICAL CARE, BigLots, $General, Eckerd, Radio Shack, Tire/repair, North Trail RV Ctr, Publix, Radio Shack

139 Luckett Rd, Ft Myers, **E...other:** Cypress Woods RV Resort, Mark's RV Crt, **W...gas:** Pilot/Subway/diesel/24hr, **other:** Camping World RV Service/supplies, Lazy J's RV Park

138 FL 82, to Lehigh Acres, Ft Myers, **E...gas:** Hess/Subway/diesel, **W...gas:** Citgo, Sunoco

136 FL 884, Colonial Blvd, Ft Myers, **E...gas:** Home Depot, **W...food:** BP, Citgo/Subway, Shell/diesel, **food:** Bob Evans, Chick-fil-A, Wal-Mart SuperCtr/24hr/gas, **1-3 mi W...lodging:** Baymont Inn, Courtyard, Howard Johnson, La Quinta, Residence Inn, Super 8, Wellesley Inn, **other:** HOSPITAL

Ft Myers (vertical label)

FLORIDA

Interstate 75

131   Daniels Pkwy, to Cape Coral, **E...rest area both lanes, full(handicapped)facilities, phone, vending, picnic tables, litter barrels, petwalk, 24hr security, gas:** BP/Subway/diesel, **lodging:** WynStar Inn, airport, **W...gas:** Chevron Citgo/7-11/24hr, Exxon, Hess/diesel, RaceTrac/24hr, Shell/24hr, **food:** Arby's, BBQ, Bella rica Italian, Bob Evans, Burger King, Cracker Barrel, Denny's, McDonald's, New China, Taco Bell, Waffle House, Wendy's, **lodging:** Best Western, Comfort Suites, Country Inn Suites, Hampton Inn, Holiday Inn(4mi), Homewood Suites(4mi), Sleep Inn, **other:** HOSPITAL, American Van&Camper, C&C Tire/repair, Eckerd, Publix

128   Alico Rd, San Carlos Park, **1-3 mi W...gas:** Hess Gas, **food:** Dunkin Doughnuts, Pizza City, Subway, Wendy's

123   rd 850, Corkscrew Rd, Estero, **E...gas:** BP/diesel, Chevron, **food:** Chiburger, Jake's Rest., McDonald's, Perkins, **other:** Eckerd, Miromar Outlet/famous brands, Publix, TECO Arena, **W...gas:** Chevron, Citgo/7-11, Hess/Dunkin Doughnuts/diesel, **lodging:** Holiday Inn, **other:** Tire Choice, Koreshan St HS, Woodsmoke RV Park(4mi)

116   Bonita Bch Rd, Bonita Springs, **E...gas:** Chevron/diesel, **other:** Publix, **W...gas:** BP/McDonald's/24hr, Hess/diesel/24hr, **food:** Bob Evan's, Waffle House, **other:** Albertson's/gas, CVS Drug, Eckerd, Home Depot, Walgreen, **1-3 mi W...gas:** Shell/24hr, Sonoco, **food:** BBQ, Burger King, KFC, Perkins, Subway, Wendy's, **lodging:** AmericInn, Baymont Inn, Bonita Motel, Comfort Inn, Hampton Inn, Holiday Inn Express, **other:** Imperial Bonita RV Park, to gulf beaches

111   rd 846, Immokalee Rd, Naples Park, **E...gas:** Citgo/7-11, Mobil, **food:** Bob Evan's, Pizza Hut, **lodging:** Hampton Inn, **W...gas:** Shell/diesel, **food:** McDonald's, Pizza Hut, **lodging:** Fairways Motel(2mi), Vanderbilt Inn(5mi), **other:** HOSPITAL, Albertson's/gas, Eckerd, Publix, to Wiggins SP

107   rd 896, Pinebridge Rd, Naples, **E...gas:** BP/McDonald's/diesel/24hr, **other:** HOSPITAL, Publix, Walgreen, **W...gas:** Chevron/diesel24hr, RaceTrac, Shell/diesel/24hr, **food:** Applebee's, Burger King, IHOP, Perkins, Waffle House, **lodging:** Best Western, Clarion, Grand Inn(2mi), Hawthorn Suites, Hilton Garden(4mi), Spinnaker Inn, **other:** Harley-Davidson, Johnson Tire

101   rd 951, to FL 84, to Naples, **W...gas:** BP/Subway/diesel, Mobil/Subway/diesel/24hr, Shell/diesel/24hr, 76/Circle K/24hr, **food:** Burger King, Checker's, Cracker Barrel, Edy's Cafe/Subway, McDonald's, Taco Bell, Waffle House, **lodging:** Baymont Inn, Comfort Inn, Holiday Inn Express, Super 8, **other:** Mazda, Club Naples RV Ctr, Endless Summer RV Park(3mi), KOA

100mm   toll plaza both lanes

80   FL 29, to Everglade City, Immokalee, no facilities

71mm   Big Cypress Nat Preserve, hiking, no security

63mm   **W...rest area both lanes, full(handicapped)facilities, phone, vending, picnic tables, litter barrels, petwalk, 24hr security**

49   Gov't Rd, Snake Rd, Big Cypress Indian Reservation, **E...gas:** Mobil/diesel, **other:** museum

41mm   rec area eb, picnic tables, litter barrels

38mm   rec area wb, picnic tables, litter barrels

35mm   **W...rest area both lanes, full(handicapped)facilities, phone, vending, picnic tables, litter barrels, petwalk, 24hr security**

32mm   rec area both lanes, picnic tables, litter barrels

25mm   toll plaza wb, motorist callboxes begin/end

23   US 27, FL 25, Miami, South Bay, no facilities

22   NW 196th, Arvida Pkwy, **W...other:** Publix, same as 21

21   FL 84 W(from nb), Indian Trace, **W...gas:** Chevron(1mi), Citgo/diesel, **food:** Papa John's

19   I-595 E, FL 869(toll), Sawgrass Expswy, no facilities

15   Arvida Pkwy, Weston, Bonaventure, **W...gas:** Exxon, Mobil, **food:** Flanigan's Rest, Max's Grille, Pastability Ristorante, Subway, Wendy's, **lodging:** Courtyard, Residence Inn, **other:** HOSPITAL, USPO

13b a   Griffin Rd, **E...gas:** Shell/diesel, U-Gas, **food:** Burger King, DQ, Outback Steaks, Waffle House, **other:** Goodyear/auto, Publix, **W...gas:** Citgo/7-11, Thumb/gas, **food:** McDonald's, Ultimate Burrito, **other:** Home Depot, Honda, Nissan/Volvo, Toyota, Winn-Dixie/drug

11b a   Sheridan St, **E...gas:** Chevron, **food:** Cracker Barrel, **lodging:** Hampton Inn, Holiday Inn Express, **other:** HOSPITAL(3mi), BMW, Lincoln/Mercury, **W...gas:** Shell, **food:** Cihna One, DQ, McDonald's, Starbuck's, Subway, TGIFriday's, The Original PancakeHouse, **other:** GNC, Lowe's Whse, Publix

9b a   FL 820, Pine Blvd, Hollywood Blvd, **E...gas:** Shell, **food:** Chili's, Latin-American Grill, Macaroni Grill, **other:** BJ's Whse, Dodge, JC Penney, Mercedes, Walgreen, **W...gas:** BP, Chevron, Exxon, Mobil/diesel, **food:** KFC/Taco Bell, McDonald's, Quizno's, Sweet Tomatoe's, **lodging:** Grand Palms Motel, **other:** Tires+, USPO, Walgreen, Winn-Dixie

7b a   Miramar Pkwy, **E...gas:** Chevron, **food:** Dunkin Donuts/Baskin-Robbins, McDonald's, Pollo Tropical, Subway, Wendy's, **lodging:** Hilton Garden, Wingate Inn, **other:** Publix, USPO, **W...gas:** Shell, **other:** Eckerd, Home Depot, Walgreen

5   to FL 821(from sb), FL TPK(toll), no facilities

4   NW 186th, Miami Gardens Dr, **E...gas:** BP/24hr, Chevron/24hr, **food:** IHOP, McDonald's, Subway, **other:** Eckerd, GNC, Publix/deli

2   NW 138th, Graham Dairy Rd, **W...gas:** Mobil, Shell, **food:** DQ, McDonald's, Subway, Wendy's, **other:** HOSPITAL, GNC, Publix

1b a   I-75 begins/ends on FL 826, Palmetto Expswy, Multiple services on FL 826

Interstate 95

Exit #	Services
382mm	Florida/Georgia state line, St Marys River, motorist callboxes begin/end.
381mm	inspection sta both lanes
380	US 17, to Yulee, Kingsland, **E**...Hance's RV Camping/LP, GS Camping/LP, **W**...**gas**: BP/24hr, Shell/24hr, **lodging**: Day's Inn, Red Cricket Inn, Super 8
378mm	**Welcome Ctr sb, full(handicapped)facilities, phone, vending, picnic tables, litter barrels, petwalk, 24hr security**
376mm	weigh sta both lanes
373	FL 200, FL A1A, to Yulee, Callahan , Fernandina Bch, **E**...**gas**: Texaco/Krystal, **food**: Burger King, KFC/Pizza Hut, McDonald's, Taco Bell, Wendy's, **lodging**: Comfort Inn, Country Inn, Hampton Inn(3mi), Nassau Holiday Motel(3mi), **other**: Flash Foods/Krystal, King Orange/gas, Lofton Creek Camping(3mi), to Ft Clinch SP(16mi), **W**...**gas**: BP/diesel, Citgo/Subway, **food**: Waffle House
366	Pecan Park Rd, **E**...**gas**: BP/diesel, Citgo/diesel, **W**...Flea&Farmer's Mkt
363b a	Duval Rd, **E**...**gas**: Chevron, **W**...**gas**: BP, Chevron/A&W/Taco Bell, Shell/diesel, Sunoco/Subway, **food**: Denny's, Waffle House, Zaxby's, **lodging**: Admiral Benbow Inn, Clarion Hotel, Comfort Suites, Courtyard, Day's Inn, Fairfield Inn, Hampton Inn, Hilton Garden, Holiday Inn, Microtel, Quality Inn, Ramada Inn, Red Roof Inn, Residence Inn, Villager Lodge, Wingate Inn, **other**: RV Ctr
362b a	I-295 S , FL 9A, to Blount Island, Jacksonville
360	FL 104, Dunn Ave, Busch Dr, **E**...**gas**: Gate/diesel, **food**: Applebee's, Hardee's, Waffle House, **lodging**: Admiral Benbow Inn, Executive Inn, **other**: Sam's Club/gas, USPO, **W**...**gas**: BP, Hess, Shell, Texaco, **food**: Arby's, BBQ, Burger King, Capt D's, Dunkin Donuts, KFC, Krystal, Lee's Chicken, LJ Silver, McDonald's, New China, Pizza Hut, Popeye's, Quincy's, Rally's, Shoney's, Taco Bell, Wendy's, **lodging**: Best Western, Budget Inn, La Quinta, Motel 6, Red Carpet Inn, **other**: Aamco, Advance Parts, BigLots, $Tree, Eckerd, PepBoys, Publix, Radio Shack, Winn Dixie
358b a	FL 105, Broward Rd, Heckscher Dr, **E**...zoo, **W**...**lodging**: Best Value
357mm	Trout River
357	FL 111, Edgewood Ave, **W**...**gas**: BP/repair, Gas Express
356b a	FL 115, Lem Turner Rd, **E**...**food**: Hardee's, **other**: Publix, **W**...**gas**: BP/24hr, Hess, Shell/repair, Texaco/diesel, **food**: Burger King, Krystal, Popeye's, Rally's, Taco Bell, **other**: Advance Parts, 1 Stop Parts, Sav-A-Lot Foods, Tires+, Walgreen, flea mkt
355	Golfair Blvd, **E**...**gas**: BP, Shell, **W**...**gas**: Chevron/diesel, RaceTrac

Exit #	Services
354b a	US 1, 20th St, to Jacksonville, to AmTrak, MLK Pkwy, no facilities
353d	FL 114, to 8th St, **E**...**food**: McDonald's, **other**: HOSPITAL, **W**...**food**: Church's
353c	US 23 N, Kings Rd, downtown
353b	US 90A, Union St, Sports Complex, downtown
353a	Church St, Myrtle Ave, Forsythe St, downtown
352c	Monroe St(from nb), downtown
352b a	Myrtle Ave(from nb), downtown
351d	Stockton St, HOSPITAL, downtown
351c	Margaret St, downtown
351b	I-10 W, to Tallahassee, no facilities
351a	Park St, College St, HOSPITAL, to downtown, no facilities
351mm	St Johns River
350b	FL 13, San Marco Blvd, no facilities
350a	Prudential Dr, Main St, Riverside Ave(from nb), to downtown, **E**...**lodging**: Adam's Mark Hotel, Hilton
349	US 90 E(from sb), to beaches, downtown, **W**...**lodging**: Super 8
348	US 1 S(from sb), Philips Hwy, **W**...**lodging**: Scottish Inn, Super 8, **other**: Cadillac, Chevrolet, VW/Volvo
347	US 1A, FL 126, Emerson St, **E**...**gas**: Shell, **food**: Subway, **W**...**gas**: BP/diesel, Gate, Hess, **food**: McDonald's, Taco Bell, **lodging**: Emerson Inn, **other**: mall
346b a	FL 109, University Blvd, **E**...**gas**: BP, Hess/diesel, Shell, **food**: Capt D's, DQ, El Potro Mexican, Firehouse Subs, KFC, Krystal, Pizza Hut, Ying's Chinese, **other**: HOSPITAL, Firestone/auto, Goodyear/auto, 1 Stop Parts, Tire Kingdom, Winn-Dixie, **W**...**gas**: BP/diesel, RaceTrac, **food**: BBQ, Buckingham Grill, Burger King, Dunkin Donuts, Friendly's, IHOP, Ocean-Bay Seafood, Ryan's, Shoney's, Taco Bell, Waffle House, Wendy's, **lodging**: Comfort Lodge, Day's Inn, Ramada Inn, Red Carpet Inn, Super 8, **other**: Chrysler/Plymouth, U-Haul, auto repair
345	FL 109, University Blvd(from nb), **E**...**gas**: Chevron, Gate/diesel, Hess/Blimpie/Godfather's Pizza/diesel, **W**...**gas**: Chevron
344	FL 202, Butler Blvd, **E**...**food**: Dave&Buster's, **lodging**: Best Western, Econolodge, Holiday Inn Express, Inns of America, Marriott, Quality Inn/café, Ramada Inn, **other**: HOSPITAL, **W**...**gas**: BP, Shell, Texaco/diesel, **food**: Applebee's, Cracker Barrel, Hardee's, McDonald's, Waffle House, Wendy's, Whataburger/24hr, Zaxby's, **lodging**: Courtyard, Extended Stay America, Jameson Inn, La Quinta, Masters Inn, Microtel, Red Roof Inn, Studio+, Wingate Inn

FLORIDA

Interstate 95

341 FL 152, Baymeadows Rd, **E...gas:** BP/diesel, Chevron, Shell, **food:** Applebee's, Arby's, Chili's, Domino's, Hardee's, Roadhouse Grill, SouperSalad, Subway, Waffle House, **lodging:** AmeriSuites, Baymeadows Inn, Embassy Suites, Fairfield Inn, Holiday Inn, HomeStead Village, **other:** Food Lion, Publix, Tires+, **W...gas:** Exxon/diesel, Shell, Texaco/diesel, Kangaroo, **food:** Bennigan's, Bombay Bicycle Club, Burger King, Denny's, IHOP, KFC, McDonald's, Miami Subs, Pagoda Chinese, Pizza Hut, Red Lobster, Steak&Ale, Taco Bell, Wendy's, **lodging:** Best Inn, Comfort Inn, Homewood Suites, La Quinta, Motel 6, Residence Inn, Studio 6, **other:** Goodyear/auto, Office Depot

340 FL 115, Southside Blvd(from nb), **E on FL 115...gas:** Kangaroo, **food:** Longhorn Steaks, **other:** CompUSA, Home Depot, Target, same as 339

339 US 1, Philips Hwy, **E...gas:** Chevron, RaceTrac, **food:** Arby's, Buca Itatlian, Burger King, McDonald's, Mikado Japanese, Olive Garden, Ruby Tuesday, Taco Bell, Waffle House, **other:** Belk, Best Buy, Dillard's, Ford, Gayfer's, JC Penney, Parisian, Sears/auto, Toyota, mall, **W...gas:** BP

337 I-295 N, to rd 9a, to Orange Park, to Jacksonville Beaches, no facilities

335 St Andrews Rd

331mm **rest area both lanes, full(handicapped)facilities, phone, vending, picnic tables, litter barrels, petwalk, 24hr security**

329 rd 210, **E...gas:** Citgo/fruit, Pilot/McDonald's/diesel/24hr/@, TA/Shell/Subway/diesel/rest./@, **food:** Waffle House, **other:** KOA, **W...other:** fireworks

323 International Golf Pkwy, **E...gas:** Shell/Subway/diesel, **food:** Marvin's Steaks, NY Subs, **lodging:** Comfort Suites, Grand Villas Motel, **other:** World Golf Village

318 FL 16, Green Cove Sprgs, St Augustine, **E...gas:** BP/DQ, Gate/diesel/fruit, Kangaroo, Shell, **food:** Burger King, McDonald's, Huddle House, Subway, Waffle House, **lodging:** Country Inn, Econolodge, Holiday Inn Express, **other:** Belz Outlet, **W...gas:** Exxon, **food:** BBQ, Cracker Barrel, Denny's, FoodCourt, KFC, Ruby Tuesday, Shoney's, Taco Bell, Wendy's, **lodging:** Best Western, Day's Inn, Hampton Inn, Ramada Ltd, Scottish Inn, Super 8, **other:** Harley-Davidson, St Augustine Outlet Ctr, RV camping

311 FL 207, St Augustine, **E...gas:** BP/diesel, Chevron/24hr, Hess/Subway/diesel, Indian River Fruit/gas, **other:** HOSPITAL, Indian Forest RV Park(2mi), KOA(7mi), St Johns RV Park, flea mkt, to Anastasia SP, **W...gas:** Mobil/diesel, Shell, **lodging:** Comfort Inn

305 FL 206, to Hastings, Crescent Beach, **E...gas:** Citgo(2mi), Flying J/Country Mkt/diesel/24hr/@, **other:** Gore RV Ctr, to Ft Matanzas NM

302mm **rest areas both lanes, full(handicapped)facilities, phone, vending, picnic tables, litter barrels, petwalk, 24hr security**

298 US 1, to St Augustine, **E...gas:** BP/diesel, Citgo/gifts/fruit, Indian River Fruit/gas, Shell/diesel, **other:** to Faver-Dykes SP, **W...gas:** Hess/diesel/DQ, Mobil/diesel, Sunrise/gas, **food:** Waffle House

289 to FL A1A(toll br), to Palm Coast, **E...gas:** BP, Exxon/diesel, **food:** Cracker Barrel, Denny's, KFC, McDonald's, Pizza Hut, Wendy's, **lodging:** Hampton Inn, Microtel, Ocean-Hammock Resort, Sleep Inn, **other:** Beall's, Eckerd, Publix, Walgreen, **W...gas:** Shell, Kangroo, **food:** Baskin-Robbins/Dunkin Doughnuts, BBQ, Bob Evan's, Perkins, Ruby Tuesday, Steak'n Shake/24hr, Subway, Taco Bell, TCBY, **other:** Advance Parts, Ford, Home Depot, K-Mart, Tire Kingdom, USPO, Walgeen, Wal-Mart SuperCtr/24hr, Winn-Dixie

286mm weigh sta both lanes, phone

284 FL 100, to Bunnell, Flagler Beach, **E...gas:** BP, Chevron/diesel/24hr, Hess/diesel, Shell, **food:** BBQ, Burger King, Domino's, McDonald's, Oriental Garden, Popeye's, Subway, Woody's BBQ, **lodging:** Caribe Hotel, Holiday Inn Express, **other:** $General, Winn-Dixie, **W...gas:** BP/diesel, **food:** Highjacker's Rest., **other:** access to HOSPITAL, Chrysler/Plymouth/Dodge/Jeep

278 Old Dixie Hwy, **E...gas:** Citgo/7-11, **other:** Publix, Bulow RV Park(3mi), to Tomoke SP, **W...gas:** BP/diesel, **food:** Luigi's Pizza, **lodging:** Country Hearth Inn, **other:** Holiday Travel Park

273 US 1, **E...gas:** Chevron, Citgo, Mobil/Wendy's/diesel, RaceTrac, Shell/diesel, Valero/diesel, **food:** Denny's/24hr, Jackson Steaks(2mi), McDonald's, Waffle House, Wendy's, **lodging:** Comfort Inn, **other:** RV Ctr, **W...gas:** Exxon/Burger King, **food:** DQ, **lodging:** Best Value, Day's Inn, Econolodge, Scottish Inn, Super 8, **other:** Encore RV Park

268 FL 40, Ormond Beach, **E...gas:** Chevron, Shell, **food:** Applebee's, Bealls, Boston Mkt, Chili's, Chick-fil-A, Denny's/24hr, Dustin's BBQ, Papa John's, Schlotsky's, Steak'n Shake, Subway, Taco Bell, Waffle House, Wendy's, **lodging:** Sleep Inn, **other:** Beall's, K-Mart, Lowe's Whse, Publix, USPO, Wal-Mart SuperCtr/24hr, **W...gas:** Hess, Mobil/diesel, **food:** Cracker Barrel, McDonald's, **lodging:** Hampton Inn, Jameson Inn, **other:** HOSPITAL

265 LPGA Blvd,, Holly Hill, Daytona Beach, **E...gas:** Citgo/7-11, Shell/diesel, **food:** Subway(2mi), **W...other:** Dodge, Ford, Nissan

261b a US 92, to DeLand, Daytona Bch, **E...gas:** BP/diesel, Chevron/diesel, Citgo/7-11/diesel, Hess/Blimpie/diesel, Mobil, RaceWay/24hr, Shell/diesel, **food:** Alehouse, Bob Evans, Buca Italian, Burger King, Carrabba's, Checker's, Chick-fil-A, Cracker Barrel, Fazoli's, Friendly's, Hooters, Hops Grill, KFC, Krystal, Logan's

FLORIDA

Interstate 95

Daytona

Roadhouse, Longhorn Steaks, Olive Garden, Pizzaria Uno, Red Lobster, Roadhouse Grill, Ruby Tuesday, Shoney's, S&S Cafeteria, Subway, Taco Bell, Waffle House, **lodging:** Hampton Inn, Hilton Garden, Holiday Inn Express, La Quinta, Ramada Inn, Travelodge, **other:** HOSPITAL, Barnes&Noble, Best Buy, Circuit City, Dillard's, Dodge/Kia, Gayfer's, Home Depot, JC Penney, Marshall's, Michael's, OfficeMax, Old Navy, PepBoys, Ross, Sears/auto, Staples, SteinMart, Target, TJMaxx, Walgreen, mall, to Daytona Racetrack, **W...gas:** BP/diesel, Exxon, **food:** Denny's, IHOP, McDonald's, **lodging:** Day's Inn, Super 8, **other:** RV camping, museum

260b a I-4, to Orlando, FL 400 E, to S Daytona, **E...gas:** Chevron/diesel

256 FL 421, to Port Orange, **E...gas:** Citgo, Shell, **food:** BBQ, Bob Evans, Cick-fil-A, Denny's/24hr, Dustin's BBQ, Papa John's, Quizno's, Spruce Creek Pizza, **lodging:** Day's Inn, Hampton Inn, Holiday Inn, Palm Plaza Motel, **other:** Lowe's Whse, Target, Walgreen, **W...gas:** Citgo/7-11, Hess, Shell/diesel, **food:** McDonald's, Wendy's, Subway, **other:** Publix

249b a FL 44, to De Land, New Smyrna Beach, **E...gas:** Shell/diesel/fruit, **other:** HOSPITAL, **3 mi E...gas:** Citgo, **food:** Burger King, Denny's, KFC, McDonald's, **other:** GNC, Harley-Davidson, New Smyrna RV Camp, Publix, Wal-Mart, **W...gas:** Chevron/diesel,

244 FL 442, to Edgewater, **E...gas:** Chevron/diesel 24hr

231 rd 5a, Scottsmoor, **E...gas:** BP/Stuckey's/diesel, **other:** Crystal Lake RV Park

227mm **rest area sb, full(handicapped)facilities, phone, vending, picnic tables, litter barrels, petwalk, 24hr security**

225mm **rest area nb, full(handicapped)facilities, phone, vending, picnic tables, litter barrels, petwalk, 24hr security**

223 FL 46, Mims, **E...gas:** Chevron(2mi), **food:** McDonald's, **other:** Willow Lakes Camping, **W...gas:** BP, Shell/deli, **other:** KOA/LP, Seasons RV Camp

220 FL 406, Titusville, **E...gas:** BP/diesel, Shell/subs, **food:** KFC, McDonald's, Subway, Wendy's, **lodging:** Day's Inn, HighWay Inn, **other:** HOSPITAL, Advance Parts, Eckerd, Publix, Tires+, Walgreen, **W...gas:** Chevron/diesel

215 FL 50, to Orlando, Titusville, **E...gas:** BP/KFC/Pizza Hut/diesel, Circle K/gas, Shell/DQ/diesel, Sunoco/diesel, **food:** BBQ, Burger King, Denny's, Durango Steaks, McDonald's, Peking Buffet, Roadhouse Grill, Sunny's BBQ, Taco Bell, Waffle House, Wendy's, **lodging:** Best Western, Holiday Inn(3mi), Ramada Inn, **other:** Ford/Mercury, Lowe's Whse, Staples, Wal-Mart SuperCtr/gas/24hr, to Kennedy Space Ctr, **W...food:** Cracker Barrel, IHOP, **lodging:** Comfort Inn, Day's Inn, Hampton Inn, **other:** Great Outdoors RV Camp

212 FL 407, to FL 528 toll(from sb), no facilities

208 Port St John, no facilities

205 FL 528(wb toll), to Cape Canaveral, City Point, no facilities

202 FL 524, Cocoa, **E...gas:** Shell/diesel, **other:** museum, **W...gas:** BP/diesel, **lodging:** Day's Inn, Ramada Inn, Super 8

201 FL 520, to Cocoa Bch, Cocoa, **E...gas:** BP/diesel, Chevron, Pilot/Subway/diesel/@, **food:** IHOP, Olive Garden(6mi), Waffle House, **lodging:** Best Western, Budget Inn, **other:** HOSPITAL, **W...gas:** Chevron/diesel, Shell/Burger King, **food:** McDonald's, **lodging:** Holiday Inn Express, **other:** Sun Coast RV Ctr

195 FL 519, Fiske Blvd, **E...gas:** Citgo/7-11, Shell/diesel(1mi), **other:** Lowe's Whse, Space Coast RV Park

191 rd 509, to Satellite Beach, **E...gas:** Citgo/7-11, Hess/Blimpie/diesel, **food:** Bob Evans, Denny's, McDonald's, Perkins, Wendy's, **lodging:** Imperials Hotel, **other:** Eckerd, to Patrick AFB, **W...gas:** Chevron/diesel, **food:** Burger King, Cracker Barrel, Subway, **lodging:** Baymont Inn, **other:** Ross, Target, Wal-Mart SuperCtr/24hr/gas

183 FL 518, Melbourne, Indian Harbour Beach, **E...gas:** BP, Chevron, Citgo/7-11, RaceTrac/24hr, **other:** museum, **W...Flea Mkt**

180 US 192, to Melbourne, **E...gas:** BP/diesel, Circle K/gas, Citgo/7-11, Mobil/diesel, Sunoco/diesel, **food:** Denny's, IHOP, Olive Garden(3mi), Steak'n Shake/24hr(3mi), Waffle House, **lodging:** Budget Inn, Courtyard, Hampton Inn, Holiday Inn Express, Howard Johnson, Ramada Inn, York Inn, **other:** HOSPITAL, Sam's Club/gas, Saturn, Target(4mi), **W...gas:** Shell/diesel

176 rd 516, to Palm Bay, **E...gas:** Chevron/diesel, Citgo/7-11, **food:** Applebee's, Dunkin Donuts, Bob Evans, Chick-fil-A, Cracker Barrel, Denny's, Golden Corral, Taco Bell, Wendy's, **lodging:** Jameson Inn, Ramada Inn, **other:** Albertson's, BJ's Whse/gas, Chevrolet, $Tree, GNC, Wal-Mart SuperCtr/gas/24hr, **W...gas:** Citgo/7-11, **food:** Wendy's, **other:** Publix, Walgreen

173 FL 514, to Palm Bay, **E...gas:** Shell/diesel, **other:** HOSPITAL, Firestone/auto, Ford, Subaru, **W...gas:** BP/diesel, Hess, Shell, Sunoco/diesel, **food:** Arby's, BBQ, Burger King, IHOP, McDonald's, Subway, Taco Bell, Texas Roadhouse, Waffle House, Wendy's, Woody's BBQ, **lodging:** Motel 6, **other:** Advance Parts, BigLots, $General, Eckerd, Goodyear/auto, Home Depot, Publix, Russell Stover, Tire Kingdom, USPO, Walgreen

Interstate 95

N ⇕ **S**

168mm rest areas both lanes, full(handicapped)facilities, phone, vending, picnic tables, litter barrels, pet-walk, 24hr security, motorist aid callboxes begin nb/end sb

156 rd 512, to Sebastian, Fellsmere, **E...gas:** BP/DQ/diesel, Chevron/McDonald's, Mobil/diesel/LP(2mi), **food:** Subway(2mi), **other:** HOSPITAL, Encore RV Park, Sebastian Inlet SRA, Vero Bch RV Park(8mi)

147 FL 60, Osceola Blvd, **E...gas:** Chevron/repair, Citgo/diesel/24hr, Mobil/diesel, TA/diesel/24hr/@, 7-11, **food:** Waffle House, Wendy's, **lodging:** Best Western, Howard Johnson, Vero Bch Rsrt, **other:** HOSPITAL, NAPA, **W...gas:** Shell/diesel, **food:** Cracker Barrel, McDonald's, Steak'n Shake, **lodging:** Hampton Inn, Holiday Inn Express, **other:** Prime Outlets/famous brands

138 FL 614, Indrio Rd, **3 mi E...gas:** Chevron, **food:** McDonald's, **other:** Oceanographic Institute, citrus

133mm rest areas both lanes, full(handicapped)facilities, phone, vending, picnic tables, litter barrels, pet-walk, 24hr security

Ft Pierce

131b a FL 68, Orange Ave, **E...gas:** Valero/diesel, to Ft Pierce SP, **W...gas:** Flying J/CountryMkt/diesel/LP/24hr/@, **other:** Blue Beacon

129 FL 70, to Okeechobee, **E...gas:** Hess/diesel, RaceTrac, Sunoco/diesel, **food:** Applebee's, Gator's Rest., Golden Corral, Piccadilly's, Waffle House, **other:** HOSPITAL, Belk, Discount Parts, $Tree, Firestone/auto, Goodyear/auto, Home Depot, Radio Shack, Wal-Mart SuperCtr/gas/24hr, mall, **W...gas:** Chevron, Citgo/diesel, Exxon, Mobil/Subway, Pilot/Arby's/diesel/24hr/@, Shell/diesel, **food:** Burger King, Cracker Barrel, Denny's, KFC, McDonald's, Miami Subs, Red Lobster, Shoney's, Steak'n Shake, Waffle House, Wendy's, **lodging:** CrossRoads Inn, Day's Inn, Hampton Inn, Holiday Inn Express, Motel 6, Sleep Inn, Treasure Coast Inn, to FL TPK

126 rd 712, Midway Rd, **3-5 mi E...gas:** Bp, Mobil, Shell, **food:** Blimpie, Burger King

121 St Lucie West Blvd, **E...gas:** BP, Chevron/24hr, Citgo/7-11, Shell/Subway/diesel, **food:** Bob Evans, Burger King, Chili's, Friendly's, Little Italy Rest.(1mi), McCallaster's Deli, McDonald's, OutBack Steaks, Ruby Tuesday, Wendy's, **lodging:** Hampton Inn, SpringHill Suites, **other:** Publix/deli, USPO, Walgreen, **W...gas:** Mobil/diesel, **lodging:** MainStay Suites, Sheraton, **other:** PGA Village

118 Gatlin Blvd, to Port St Lucie, **E...gas:** BP/diesel/LP, Chevron/Subway/diesel, Shell/Subway/diesel, Sunoco, **food:** Burger King(2mi), Dunkin Doughnuts

110 FL 714, to Stuart, Palm City, no facilities

106mm rest areas both lanes, full(handicapped)facilities, phone, vending, picnic tables. litter barrels, pet-walk, 24hr security

102 FL 713, to Stuart, Palm City, no facilities

101 FL 76, to Stuart, Indiantown, **E...gas:** Chevron/24hr, Shell, Sunoco/diesel, **food:** Cracker Barrel, McDonald's, Wendy's, **other:** HOSPITAL, RV camping, **W...gas:** Shell/deli/diesel, **food:** DQ, Stuckey's

96 rd 708, to Hobe Sound, **E...**Dickinson SP(11mi), RV camping

Jupiter

87b a FL 706, to Okeechobee, Jupiter, **E...gas:** Chevron, Hess, Mobil, Shell, **food:** Applebee's, Burger King, China Dragon, City Grille, Duffy's Rest., Dunkin Donuts, Domino's, Gator's Rest, IHOP, KFC, McDonald's, Subway, **lodging:** Comfort Inn, Fairfield Inn, Wellesley Inn, **other:** HOSPITAL, Books-A-Million, Discount Parts, Dodge/Mazda, Eckerd, GNC, Home Depot, PepBoys, Publix, Tire Kingdom, Walgreen, Winn-Dixie, to Dickinson SP, Wal-Mart, Winn-Dixie, hist sites, museum, **W...gas:** Mobil/diesel, Sunoco, **other:** info, RV camping, to FL TPK

83 Donald Ross Rd, **E...**stadium

79c FL 809 S(from sb), **W...**to FL TPK, same services as 57b

79a b FL 786, PGA Blvd, **E...gas:** Sunoco, **food:** China Wok, Durango Steaks, **lodging:** Hampton Inn, Marriott, **other:** HOSPITAL, Loehmann's Foods, **W...gas:** Shell/diesel/24hr, **food:** Beacon St Café, **lodging:** DoubleTree Hotel, Embassy Suites, **other:** Publix

77 Northlake Blvd, to W Palm Bch, **E...gas:** Citgo, Hess, Shell/diesel, **food:** Applebee's, Arby's, Burger King, Checker's, KFC, McDonald's, Miami Subs, Taco Bell, Wendy's, **other:** HOSPITAL, Chevrolet, Chrysler/Jeep, Costco, Ford, Home Depot, Kia/Isuzu//Suzuki, K-Mart, Lincoln/Mercury, PepBoys, Pontiac/GMC, Staples, Suburu, VW/Mitsubishi, **W...gas:** Chevron, Citgo, Hess, Mobil/diesel, Shell, **food:** City Grille, Wendy's, **lodging:** Inns of America, **other:** Albertson's, OfficeMax, Publix

W Palm Beach

76 FL 708, Blue Heron Blvd, **E...gas:** BP/diesel, Shell, **food:** Wendy's, **other:** Honda, **W...gas:** Mobil, **food:** Burger King, Denny's, McDonald's, **lodging:** Motel 6, Super 8

74 FL 702, 45th St, **E...food:** Burger King, Hong Kong Café, IHOP, Subway, **lodging:** Day's Inn, Knight's Inn, **other:** HOSPITAL, Cadillac, Walgreen, **W...gas:** Mobil, RaceTrac, Sunoco, **food:** Cracker Barrel, Taco Bell, Wendy's, **lodging:** Courtyard, Red Roof Inn, Residence Inn, **other:** Harley-Davidson, Studio+, Goodyear/auto

71 Lake Blvd, Palm Beach, **E...gas:** BP, Mobil, **food:** McDonald's, Wendy's, **lodging:** Best Western, **other:** HOSPITAL, Best Buy, Burdine's, Dillard's, Firestone/auto, JC Penney, Lord&Taylor, Sears/auto, Target, mall, **W...food:** Red Lobster, Hooters, Jumbo China, Olive Garden, **lodging:** Comfort Inn, Wellesley Inn

Interstate 95

N ↑ ↓ **S**

70b a FL 704, Okeechobee Blvd, **E...gas:** Exxon, **lodging:** Marriott, **other:** Kravis Ctr, museum, **W...gas:** Chevron, Exxon/diesel, Hess, Shell/repair, **food:** Burger King, McDonald's, Shell's Rest., **other:** Chevrolet, Circuit City, CompUSA, Dodge, Lexus, Lincoln/Mercury, MensWhse, Mitsubishi

69 Belvedere Rd, **W...gas:** Shell, **food:** Burger King, Denny's, IHOP, Wendy's, **lodging:** Courtyard, Hampton Inn, Holiday Inn/rest., Motel 6, Radisson Suites, **other:** to airport

68 US 98, Southern Blvd, **E...food:** Mobil, John's Subs, **other:** Publix/deli, **W...lodging:** Hilton

66 Forest Hill Blvd, **E...food:** Havana Cafe

64 10th Ave N, **W...gas:** Citgo, Shell/diesel/24hr, **food:** Wendy's, **other:** Goodyear

63 6th Ave S, **W...HOSPITAL**

61 FL 812, Lantana Rd, **E...gas:** Shell, **food:** CrabHouse Rest., KFC, McDonald's, Subway, **lodging:** Motel 6, **other:** Beall's, Eckerd, Publix, **W...food:** Rosalita's Café, **other:** HOSPITAL, Costco Whse

60 Hypoluxo Rd, **E...gas:** BP, Mobil, Shell/diesel, **food:** Pizza Hut, Subway, Taco Bell, Wendy's, **lodging:** Best Western, Comfort Inn, Super 8, **other:** Sam's Club, Tires+, Tire Kingdom, U-Haul, **W...gas:** Hess, **food:** BBQ, Dunkin Doughnuts, Miami Subs

59 Gateway Blvd, **E...gas:** Shell/diesel, **W...gas:** Mobil, **food:** Ballpark Cafe, Blimpie, Carraba's, Chili's, McDonald's, Original Pancake House, Pete Rose Café, **lodging:** Hampton Inn, Holiday Inn, **other:** Target

57 FL 804, Boynton Bch Blvd, **E...gas:** Majestic Gas, **food:** KFC, **lodging:** Holiday Inn Express, **other:** HOSPITAL, USPO, **W...gas:** Chevron, Mobil, Shell/diesel, 7-11, **food:** Checker's, Krispy Kreme, Subway, TGIFriday, Waffle House, Wendy's, **other:** BJ's Whse/gas, Radio Shack, Winn-Dixie, **1mi W... food:** Steak'n Shake, **other:** Barnes&Noble, Office Depot, Old Navy, Publix, Wal-Mart SuperCtr/24hr

56 Woolbright Rd, **E...gas:** Shell/24hr, **food:** McDonald's, **other:** HOSPITAL, **W...gas:** Mobil/24hr, RaceTrac/24hr, **food:** Burger King, Cracker Barrel, Subway

52b a FL 806, Atlantic Ave, **W...gas:** Chevron, Mobil, Shell/diesel, **food:** Burger King, McDonald's, Miami Subs, **other:** Publix

51 rd 782, Linton Blvd, **E...gas:** Exxon, **food:** Abbey Rd Grill, DQ, McDonald's, OutBack Steaks, Polla Tropical, **other:** Chevrolet, Circuit City, Dodge, Ford, Home Depot, Nissan, OfficeMax, Ross, Target, **W...gas:** Shell, **other:** HOSPITAL

50 Congress Ave, **W...Homestead Hotel**

48b a FL 794, Yamato Rd, **E...gas:** Mobil, **food:** Panera Bread, **food:** Eckerd, **W...gas:** Chevron/Blimpie/diesel, **food:** Sal's Ristorante, The Grille, McDonald's, **lodging:** Guest Suites, Embassy Suites, Hampton Inn, SpringHill Suites, TownePlace Suites

45 FL 808, Glades Rd, **E on Frtg rd... lodging:** Fairfield Inn, **E...gas:** Shell, **food:** Alexandar's Rest, Mario's, Mon Ami Cafe, Subway, **other:** Barnes&Noble, Circuit City, Jamba Juice, PF Cahng's, WholeFoods Mkt, museum, **W...gas:** BP, **food:** Brewzzi Cafe, Chesapeake Seafood, Moe's SW Grill, **lodging:** Courtyard, Holiday Inn, Marriott, **other:** Rascal House Rest., Starbucks

44 Palmetto Park Rd, **E...gas:** Exxon/24hr, **food:** Denny's, Dunkin Doughnuts, Red's BBQ, Subway, Tomasso's Pizza, **other:** museums, **W...food:** McDonald's

42b a FL 810, Hillsboro Blvd, **E...gas:** BP, Texaco, Shell, **food:** McDonald's, Popeye's, Wendy's, **lodging:** Hampton Inn, Hilton, La Quinta, **other:** Advance Parts, **W...gas:** Chevron, Mobil/diesel, **food:** Denny's, **lodging:** Ramada Inn, Villager Lodge, Wellesley Inn, **other:** CompUSA, Eckerd, Home Depot, Wlagreen

41 FL 869(toll), SW 10th, to I-75, **E...gas:** Mobil, **food:** Cracker Barrel, **lodging:** Extended Stay America, **W...lodging:** Comfort Suites, Quality Suites

39 FL 834, Sample Rd, **E...gas:** BP, Hess, Mobil, Shell/diesel, **food:** Hops Grill(1mi), **other:** HOSPITAL, **W...gas:** Mobil/diesel, **food:** Arby's, Checker's, IHOP, McDonald's, Miami Subs, Subway, **other:** Eckerd, Family$, Harley-Davidson, Winn-Dixie

38b a Copans Rd, **E...gas:** BP, Mobil/7-11, **food:** McDonald's, **other:** Circuit City, Mercedes, PepBoys, Wal-Mart, **W...gas:** Pure, **other:** Home Depot, NAPA, NTB

36b a FL 814, Atlantic Blvd, to Pompano Beach, **E...gas:** RaceTrac, **food:** KFC/Taco Bell, Miami Subs, **other:** **1 mi W...gas:** BP, Mobil/diesel, Shell/repair, **food:** McDonald's, Polla Tropical, Ruby Tuesday, Wendy's, **other:** Chevrolet, Eckerd, Harness RaceTrack, Wal-Mart SuperCtr/24hr/gas, Winn-Dixie, USPO, to FL TPK, Power Line Rd has multiple services

33b a Cypress Creek Rd, **E...gas:** BP, Hess, **food:** Domino's, DownTown Pizzaria, Duffy's Diner, Jester's Grill, **lodging:** Extended Stay America, Hampton Inn, Westin Hotel, **W...gas:** Hess, Shell/repair, **food:** Arby's, Bennigan's, Burger King, Champp's Grill, Chili's, Hooters, Longhorn Steaks, McDonald's, Quizno's, StarLite Diner, Steak&Ale, SweetTomatoe's, Wendy's, **lodging:** La Quinta, Marriott, Sheraton Suites, **other:** GNC, Jaguar, Office Depot, OfficeMax

Pompano

Interstate 95

N ↕ S

Ft Lauderdale

32	FL 870, Commercial Blvd, Lauderdale by the Sea, Lauderhill, **E...food:** Wendy's, **lodging:** Crossland Suites, **W...gas:** BP, Mobil, Shell, Sunoco, **food:** Burger King, KFC, McDonald's, Waffle House, **lodging:** Best Western, Holiday Inn, Homestead Village, Red Roof Inn, Wellesley Inn
31b a	FL 816, Oakland Park Blvd, **E...gas:** BP, Chevron, Mobil/24hr, **food:** Denny's, Miami Subs, Wendy's, **other:** Lowe's Whse, **W...gas:** BP/diesel, Marathon, Shell, **food:** Burger King, Dunkin Doughnuts, IHOP, KFC, McDonald's, **lodging:** Day's Inn, **other:** Home Depot, Toyota, USPO, Walgreen
29b a	FL 838, Sunrise Blvd, **E...gas:** Mobil, Shell, **food:** Burger King, Popey's, **other:** Discount Parts
27	FL 842, Broward Blvd, Ft Lauderdale, **E...**HOSPITAL
26	I-595(from sb), FL 736, Davie Blvd, **W...gas:** BP, Hess, Mobil, **food:** Flannigan's Seafood, Miami Subs, Subway, Wendy's
25	FL 84, **E...gas:** Citgo/7-11, Mobil/diesel, RaceTrac/24hr, Sunoco, **food:** Domino's, Dunkin Donuts, Lil Red's Rest., Little Caesar's, McDonald's, Subway, Wendy's, **lodging:** Best Western, Hampton Inn, Holiday Inn Express, Motel 6, **other:** BigLots, Winn-Dixie, **W...lodging:** Ramada Inn, Red Carpet Inn, **other:** Ford Trucks
24	I-595(from nb), to I-75, **E...**to airport
23	FL 818, Griffin Rd, **E...lodging:** Sheraton, Wyndham Inn, **W...gas:** BP, Citgo/diesel, **lodging:** Courtyard
22	FL 848, Stirling Rd, Cooper City, **E...gas:** CF, Mobil, **food:** AleHouse Grill, Burger King, Dave&Buster's, Quizno's, McDonald's, Sal's Italian, Starlite Diner, Sweet Tomatoes, Taco Bell, TGIFriday, Wendy's, **lodging:** Comfort Inn, Hampton Inn, Hilton Garden, La Quinta, SpringHill Suites, **other:** Barnes&Noble, BigLots, BJ's Whse, Discount Parts, GNC, Home Depot, K-Mart/Little Caesar's, Marshall's, Michael's, OfficeMax, Old Navy, Ross, to Lloyd SP, same as 21, **1/2 mi W...gas:** Circle K, **food:** Dunkin Donuts, Miami Subs, Mr M Café, Subway, **other:** Eckerd, PepBoys, Tire Kingdom, Walgreen
21	FL 822, Sheridan St, **E...**same as 22, **W...gas:** Mobil, Shell, **food:** Atlantic Subs, Denny's, **lodging:** Day's Inn, Holiday Inn
20	FL 820, Hollywood Blvd, **E...lodging:** Howard Johnson, **W...gas:** BP, Chevron, Mobil, **food:** Boston Mkt, McDonald's, Taco Bell, Subway, **other:** HOSPITAL, Target
19	FL 824, Pembroke Rd, **E...gas:** Shell, **W...gas:** Mobil, Shell
18	FL 858, Hallandale Bch Blvd, **E...gas:** Amerika Gas, BP, Citgo/7-11, Exxon, **food:** Bakehouse Rest., BBQ, Burger King, Choice's Eatery, Church's, Denny's, IHOP, KFC, Little Caesar's, LJ Silver, McDonald's, Subway, Wendy's, **lodging:** Best Western, **other:** HOSPITAL, Goodyear/auto, Tire Kingdom, Walgreen, Winn-Dixie, **W...gas:** BP/Taco Bell, RaceTrac, **other:** Discount Parts

Miami

16	Ives Dairy Rd, **E...**HOSPITAL, mall, **W...gas:** BP, 7-11, **food:** Subway
14	FL 860, Miami Gardens Dr, N Miami Beach, **E...**HOSPITAL, Oleta River SRA, **1/2 mi W...gas:** BP, Chevron, Citgo/diesel, Marathon/diesel, **food:** Subway, **other:** BJ's Whse
12c	US 441, FL 826, FL TPK, FL 9, **E...gas:** Hess, **lodging:** Howard Johnson, Holiday Inn, **other:** HOSPITAL, **W...food:** Checker's
12b	US 441(from nb), same as 12c
12a	FL 868(from nb), FL TPK N, no facilities
11	NW 151st, **W...gas:** Sunoco, **food:** McDonald's, **other:** Discount Parts, Winn-Dixie, services on US 441 N
10b	FL 916, NW 135th, Opa-Locka Blvd, **W...gas:** BP, Chevron, Citgo, Mobil, QuikStop
10a	NW 125th, N Miami, Bal Harbour, **W...gas:** Shell, **food:** Burger King, Wendy's, **other:** U-Haul
9	NW 119th(from nb), **W...gas:** BP/McDonald's, **food:** KFC, **other:** AutoZone, Family$, Walgreen, Winn-Dixie
8b	FL 932, NW 103rd, **E...gas:** Exxon, Shell, **food:** 7-11, **W...gas:** Chevron, Marathon, Mobil, **food:** Dunkin Donuts
8a	NW 95th, **E...gas:** BP, **W...gas:** Mobil, Shell, **food:** Burger King, McDonald's, **other:** HOSPITAL, Discount Parts, Ford, SavALot Foods, Walgreen
7	FL 934, NW 81st, NW 79th, **E...gas:** Chevron/diesel, Citgo/diesel, **W...gas:** Exxon/diesel, **food:** Cafe China, Checker's, **lodging:** City Inn, **other:** Chrysler/Jeep, Lincoln/Mercury, Pontiac
6b	NW 69th(from sb), no facilities
6a	FL 944, NW 62nd, NW 54th, **W...gas:** Shell, **food:** Burger King, McDonald's, Subway, **other:** AutoZone, U-Haul, Winn-Dixie
4b a	I-195 E, FL 112 W(toll), Miami Beach, **E...**downtown, **W...**airport
3b	NW 8th St(from sb), no facilities
3a	FL 836 W(toll)(exits left from nb), **W...**HOSPITAL, to Orange Bowl, airport
2d	I-395 E(exits left from sb), to Miami Beach, no facilities
2c	NW 8th, NW 14th(from sb), Miami Ave, **E...**Port of Miami, **W...**to Orange Bowl
2b	NW 2nd(from nb), downtown Miami
2a	US 1(exits left from sb), Biscayne Blvd, downtown Miami
1b	US 41, SW 7th, SW 8th, Brickell Ave, **E...lodging:** Extended Stay America, Hampton Inn, Holiday Inn Express, **other:** Publix, Walgreen, **W...gas:** Shell, **food:** Papa John's
1a	SW 25th(from sb), downtown, to Rickenbacker Causeway, **E...lodging:** Hampton Inn, **other:** museum, to Baggs SRA
0mm	I-95 begins/ends on US 1., **1 mi S...gas:** Citgo, **food:** Quizno's

Interstate 275(Tampa)

N ↑ ↓ S

Exit #	Services
59mm	I-275 begins/ends on I-75, exit 274.
53	Bearss Ave, **E…gas:** Citgo, **W…gas:** BP, RaceTrac, Shell, **food:** BBQ, Burger King, Green Tea Chinese, McDonald's, Perkin's, Popey's, Subway, Wendy's, **lodging:** Quality Inn, **other:** Albertson's, BigLots, Eckerd, GNC, Publix, Radio Shack
52	Fletcher Ave, **E…gas:** BP, RaceTrac, **lodging:** Day's Inn, **other:** Cadillac, Cash'nCarry Foods, Saturn **W…gas:** BP, Citgo, **lodging:** Super 8, **other:** Jaguar
51	FL 582, Fowler Ave, **E…gas:** Citgo, Shell, **food:** Burger King, Denny's, Hop's Grill, McDonald's, Ponderosa, Steak'nShake, Subway, Waffle House, **lodging:** Howard Johnson, Quality Inn, **other:** Discount Parts, Family$, Office Depot, **W…lodging:** Motel 6, Value Lodge, **other:** Audi/Porsche, VW
50	FL 580, Busch Blvd, **E…gas:** Chevron, Exxon, Marathon, **lodging:** Comfort Inn, **other:** Busch Gardens, **W…food:** Burger King, KFC, **other:** Eckerd, Firestone, Goodyear, Home Depot, Wal-Mart/drug
49	Bird Ave(from nb), **W…gas:** Shell, **food:** Checker's, KFC, Wendy's, **other:** K-Mart
48	Sligh Ave, **E…gas:** BP, Sunoco, **W…gas:** Marathon, **other:** zoo
47b a	US 92, to US 41 S, Hillsborough Ave, **E…gas:** Citgo, Valero, **food:** Burger King, McDonald's, Wendy's, **other:** Advance Parts, **W…gas:** BP, 76
46b	FL 574, MLK Blvd, **E…gas:** BP, Chevron, **other:** Eckerd, Kash&Karry/drug, **W…gas:** Marathon, **food:** McDonald's, **other:** HOSPITAL
46a	Floribraska Ave, no facilities
45b	I-4 E, to Orlando, I-75, no facilities
45a	Jefferson St, downtown E
44	Ashley Dr, Tampa St, downtown W
42	Howard Ave, Armenia Ave, **E…gas:** Citgo, **W…gas:** BP, Shell/diesel, **food:** Popeye's
41c	Himes Ave(from sb), **W…**RJ Stadium
41b a	US 92, Dale Mabry Blvd, **E…gas:** BP, Exxon, Mobil, Shell, **food:** Alexander's Rest., Careno's Italian, Carrabba's, Hops Grill, Krystal, Pizza Hut, Ruby Tuesday, Village Inn Pancakes, **lodging:** Courtyard, **other:** MEDICAL CARE, Borders Books&Café, Office Depot, to MacDill AFB, **W…gas:** BP, Exxon/diesel, **food:** BBQ, Bennigan's, Blimpie, Burger King, Checker's, Chili's, Denny's, Dunkin Donuts, LongHorn Steaks, McDonald's, Quizno's, Sweet Tomatoes, Taco Bell, Tia's TexMex, Waffle House, Wendy's, **lodging:** Day's Inn, Howard Johnson, Westin Suites, **other:** Best Buy, Circuit City, Home Depot, Kash'nKarry, Wal-Mart
40b	Lois Ave, **W…gas:** Shell/diesel, **lodging:** DoubleTree Hotel, Sheraton
40a	FL 587, Westshore Blvd, **E…gas:** Citgo, Shell, **food:** Steak&Ale, Waffle House, **lodging:** Embassy Suites, Ramada Inn, **other:** JC Penney, **W…gas:** Shell, Crowne Plaza, **food:** Durango Steaks, **lodging:** Best Western, Marriott, SpringHill Suites

Tampa

St Petersburg

Exit #	Services
39b a	FL 60 W, **W…food:** Outback Steaks, **lodging:** Clarion, **2 mi W…lodging:** Day's Inn, to airport
32	Fl 687 S, 4th St N, to US 92(no sb re-entry), no facilities
31b	FL 688 W, Ulmerton Rd, to Largo, info, airport
31a	9th St N, MLK St N(exits left from sb), no facilities
30	FL 686, Roosevelt Blvd, no facilities
28	FL 694 W, Gandy Blvd, Indian Shores, **1-2mi W…food:** Bob Evans, Godfather's Pizza, **lodging:** La Quinta, **other:** Robert's RV Resort
26b a	54th Ave N, **E…gas:** Cracker Barrel, **W…gas:** Citgo, RaceTrac, **food:** Waffle House, **lodging:** Day's Inn, Landmark Rest., Ramada Inn, **other:** Harley-Davidson, NAPA
25	38th Ave N, to beaches, **W…gas:** Citgo/diesel, **food:** Burger King, Hardee's, **E…food:** McDonald's
24	22nd Ave N, **E…**Sunken Garden, **W…gas:** Citgo/7-11, RaceTrac, **other:** Home Depot, Lowe's Whse
23b	FL 595, 5th Ave N, **E…**HOSPITAL
23a	I-375, **E…**The Pier, Waterfront, downtown
22	I-175 E, Tropicana Fields, **E…**HOSPITAL
21	28th St S., downtown
20	31st Ave(from nb), downtown
19	22nd Ave S, Gulfport, **E…food:** Church's, **W…**Citgo, **other:** PriceBuster Foods
18	26th Ave S(from nb), no facilities
17	FL 682 W, 54th Ave S, Pinellas Bayway, **W…gas:** Citgo/7-11, Sunoco, **food:** Bob Evans, Burger King, McDonald's, Taco Bell, **lodging:** Bayway Inn, Park Inn, **other:** Eckerd, Publix, to Ft DeSoto Pk, St Pete Beach, same as 19
16	Pinellas Point Dr, Skyway Lane, to Maximo Park, **E…lodging:** Holiday Inn, **W…**marina
16mm	toll plaza sb
13mm	N Skyway Fishing Pier, **W…rest area both lanes, full(handicapped)facilities, phone, vending, picnic tables, litter barrels, petwalk**
10mm	Tampa Bay
7mm	S Skyway Fishing Pier, **E…rest area both lanes, full(handicapped)facilities, phone, vending, picnic tables, litter barrels, petwalk**
6mm	toll plaza nb
5	US 19, Palmetto, Bradenton, no facilities
2	US 41, Palmetto, Bradenton, no facilities
0mm	I-275 begins/ends on I-75, exit 228.

FLORIDA

Interstate 295(Jacksonville)

N ↕ S

Jacksonville

Exit #	Services
35b a	I-95, S to Jacksonville, N to Savannah. I-295 begins/ends on I-95, exit 362b.
33	Duval Rd, **W...**airport
32	FL 115, Lem Turner Rd, **E...food:** Cross Creek Steak, Subway, Wendy's, **other:** Home Depot, Radio Shack, Wal-Mart SuperCtr/24hr, **W...other:** Flamingo Lake Camping
30	FL 104, Dunn Ave, **E...gas:** Gate/diesel, Shell/24hr(1mi), **food:** McDonald's
28b a	US 1, US 23, to Callahan, Jacksonville, **E...gas:** Lil' Champ/gas, **W...gas:** BP/DQ/diesel, Chevron, RaceTrac/24hr
25	Pritchard Rd, **W...gas:** Kangaroo/diesel/24hr
22	Commonwealth Ave, **E...gas:** Sprint/diesel, **food:** Burger King, Hardee's, Waffle House, **lodging:** Holiday Inn, **other:** Winn-Dixie, dogtrack, **W...food:** Wendy's
21b a	I-10, W to Tallahassee, E to Jacksonville, no facilities
19	FL 228, Normandy Blvd, **E...gas:** BP/24hr, Shell/diesel, **food:** Burger King, Golden Corral, McDonald's, Sonic, Wendy's, **other:** Food Lion, Radio Shack, Walgreen, Wal-Mart SuperCtr/24hr, st patrol, **W...gas:** RaceTrac, Shell, **food:** Hardee's, McDonald's, Pizza Hut, Popeye's, Subway, **other:** Advance Parts, Eckerd, Family$, K-Mart, Publix, Radio Shack, Winn-Dixie
17	FL 208, Wilson Blvd, **E...gas:** BP/diesel, Hess/diesel, **food:** Hardee's, McDonald's(1mi), S&S Cafeteria, **other:** Advance Parts, Food Lion, **W...gas:** Kangaroo
16	FL 134, 103rd St, Cecil Field, **E...gas:** BP, Gate/diesel, Hess, Shell/24hr, **food:** Arby's, Burger King, Capt D's, Lucky Dragon Chinese, Popeye's, Wendy's, **lodging:** Hospitality Inn, **other:** Advance Parts, U-Haul, Wal-Mart, **W...gas:** BP, Chevron, Exxon/diesel, Shell, **food:** BBQ, DQ, Dragon Garden Chinese, Dunkin Donuts, El Potro Mexican, IHOP, KFC, McDonald's, Miami Subs, Mitoro Mexican, Pizza Hut, Rally's, Subway, Taco Bell, **other:** Aamco, Family$, Goodyear/auto, Publix, SavRite Foods, Walgreen, Winn-Dixie

Jacksonville

12	FL 21, Blanding Blvd, **E...gas:** BP, RaceTrac, Shell, **food:** Burger King, Larry's Subs, McDonald's, **other:** Acura, Best Buy, Cadillac, $General, Eckerd, Ford, Honda, Office Depot, Saturn, **W...gas:** BP, Chevron, Kangaroo, Shell, **food:** Arby's, Bennigan's, Chick-fil-A, Chili's, Chuck-eCheese, Cross Creek BBQ/steaks, Denny's, Jimmy Careno's, KFC, Longhorn Steaks, Los Toros Mexican, Olive Garden, Outback Steaks, Papa John's, Red Lobster, Steak&Ale, Taco Bell, Tony Roma, **lodging:** Country Inn, Hampton Inn, La Quinta, Motel 6, Red Roof Inn, Super 8, **other:** HOSPITAL, Circuit City, Dillard's, Discount Tire, Gayfer's, Home Depot, JoAnn Fabrics, Michael's, Sam's Club/gas, Sears/auto, Publix, Target, TJ-Maxx, Toyota, Walgreen, mall
10	US 17, FL 15, Roosevelt Blvd, Orange Park, **E...lodging:** Best Western, **W...gas:** BP, Chevron/diesel/24hr, RaceTrac, Shell, **food:** Coyote Grill, Cracker Barrel, Damon's, Krystal, LJ Silver, McDonald's, Pizza Hut, Quincy's, Sam's Seafood, Waffle House, Wendy's, **lodging:** Best Western, Comfort Inn, Day's Inn, Econolodge, Fairfield Inn, Holiday Inn, Quality Inn, Villager Lodge, **other:** Chrysler, Harley-Davidson, Honda, Nissan, VW
7mm	St Johns River, Buckman Br, no facilities
5b a	FL 13, San Jose Blvd, **E...gas:** Exxon/diesel/24hr, Lewis/gas, Shell, **food:** Applebee's, Arby's, Bob Evan's, Famous Amos, Popeye's, TCBY, **lodging:** Baymont Inn, Ramada Inn, **other:** Albertson's, Eckerd, Firestone/auto, Office Depot, Publix, Target, Walgreen, **W...gas:** BP, Gate(3mi), Shell(1mi), **food:** American Cafe, Baskin-Robbins, BBQ, Chili's, Golden China, Golden Corral, Hardee's, Kan-Ki Japanese, Krispy Kreme, Perkins, Pizza Hut, Schlotsky's, **other:** Barnes&Noble, BooksAMillion, Fresh Mkt, Marshal's, Michael's, NAPA, Radio Shack, SteinMart, TJMaxx, U-Haul, Wal-Mart
3	Old St Augustine Rd, **E...gas:** BP, Gate, Shell, **food:** Burger King, Denny's, Larry's Subs, Little China, Mandorin Chinese, McDonald's, Monks Rest, Pizza Hut, Taco Bell, **lodging:** Holiday Inn Express, **other:** $General, Eckerd, GNC, Publix/deli, Sing Food, Winn-Dixie, **W...gas:** Kangaroo, **food:** KFC/Pizza Hut, Subway, **other:** MEDICAL CARE, Lowe's Whse, Walgreen
0mm	I-295 begins/ends on I-95, exit 337.

GEORGIA

Interstate 16

Exit # Services

167b a W Broad, Montgomery St, Savannah, **N...gas:** BP, Chevron, Enmark, **lodging:** Comfort Suites, Courtyard, Econolodge(1mi), Howard Johnson, **S...food:** Burger King, KFC, Popeye's, Wendy's, I-16 begins/ends in Savannah.

166 US 17, Gwinnet St, Savannah, no facilities

165 GA 204, 37th St(from eb), to Ft Pulaski NM, Savannah College

164b a I-516, US 80, US 17, GA 21, no facilities

162 Chatham Pkwy, **S...gas:** Shell/Blimpie/diesel, **other:** Lexus, Toyota

160 GA 307, Dean Forest Rd, **N...gas:** Shell/Subway/diesel, Pilot/diesel/24hr/@, **food:** Ronnie's Rest., Waffle House

157b a I-95, S to Jacksonville, N to Florence

155 Pooler Pkwy, no facilities

152 GA 17, to Bloomingdale, no facilities

148 Old River Rd, to US 80, no facilities

144mm weigh sta both lanes

143 US 280, to US 80, **N...gas:** Citgo(2mi), **S...gas:** BP, El Cheapo/diesel/café/@, **other:** Black Creek Café/golf (3mi)

109

GEORGIA

Interstate 16

E ↕ **W**

Dublin · **Macon** · **Augusta**

Exit	Services
137	GA 119, to Pembroke, Ft Stewart, no facilities
132	Ash Branch Church Rd, no facilities
127	GA 67, to Pembroke, Ft Stewart, **N...gas:** El Cheapo/diesel, Shell/diesel, Oasis Camping(1mi), **S...gas:** Chevron/diesel/24hr, **food:** Huddle House
116	US 25/301, to Statesboro, **N...gas:** Chevron/diesel/24hr, **food:** PoJo's Deli, to GA S U, **S...gas:** Shell/diesel, **food:** Huddle House, **lodging:** Red Carpet Inn
111	Pulaski-Excelsior Rd, **S...gas:** Citgo/diesel, **food:** Grady's Grill, **other:** Beaver Run RV Park
104	GA 22, GA 121, Metter, **N...gas:** BP/diesel/24hr, Chevron/diesel, Exxon, Phillips 66, Shell/diesel, **food:** Burger King, DQ, Hardee's, Huddle House, KFC/Taco Bell, McDonald's, Subway, Village Pizza, Waffle House, Wendy's, Western Steer, **lodging:** Comfort Inn, Day's Inn, Holiday Inn Express, Metter Inn, **other:** HOSPITAL, Chevrolet, Rite Aid, to Smith SP, RV camping, **S...gas:** Citgo, Phillips 66/diesel, **other:** Ford
101mm	Canoochee River
98	GA 57, to Stillmore, **S...gas:** Amoco/diesel/24hr, Chevron/diesel
90	US 1, to Swainsboro, **N...gas:** BP, Citgo, Pure/diesel/rest., **food:** Oak Island Crabhouse, **other:** repair
87mm	Ohoopee River
84	GA 297, to Vidalia, **N...**truck sales
78	US 221, GA 56, to Swainsboro, **N...gas:** BP/diesel(1mi)
71	GA 15, GA 78, to Soperton, **N...gas:** Chevron/diesel/24hr
67	GA 29, to Soperton, **S...gas:** Chevron/diesel, Citgo/diesel, **food:** Huddle House
58	GA 199, Old River Rd, East Dublin, no facilities
56mm	Oconee River
54	GA 19, to Dublin, **1 mi N...gas:** Chevron
51	US 441, US 319, to Dublin, **N...gas:** Amoco/diesel/24hr, BP/Subway/diesel, Exxon/diesel, Pilot/diesel/@, Shell/24hr, **food:** Arby's, Buffalo's Café, Burger King, KFC, Krystal, McDonald's, Pizza Hut, Ruby Tuesday, Taco Bell/TCBY, Waffle House/24hr, Wendy's, **lodging:** Best Western, Comfort Inn, Day's Inn, Econolodge, Hampton Inn, Holiday Inn Express, Jameson Inn, Super 8, **other:** HOSPITAL, **S...gas:** Chevron, **food:** Cracker Barrel, **other:** Pinetucky Camping(2mi), antiques, to Little Ocmulgee SP
49	GA 257, to Dublin, Dexter, **N...gas:** Chevron/Friendly Gus, **3 mi N...gas:** Shell, **food:** BBQ, Huddle House, Waffle House, Zaxby's, **other:** HOSPITAL, **S...gas:** 257 Trkstp/diesel/@
46mm	**rest area wb, full(handicapped)facilities, phone, picnic tables, litter barrels, vending, petwalk, RV dump**
44mm	**rest area eb, full(handicapped)facilities, phone, picnic tables, litter barrels, vending, petwalk, RV dump**
42	GA 338, to Dudley, no facilities
39	GA 26, Montrose, to Cochran, no facilities
32	GA 112, Allentown, **S...gas:** Chevron/diesel, **food:** CJ's Grill
27	GA 358, to Danville, no facilities
24	GA 96, to Jeffersonville, **N...gas:** Citgo/diesel, **S...gas:** BP/diesel/24hr, **food:** Huddle House/24hr, **lodging:** Day's Inn, **other:** to Robins AFB, museum
18	Bullard Rd, Bullard, to Jeffersonville, no facilities
12	Sgoda Rd, Huber, **N...gas:** Marathon/diesel
6	US 23, US 129A, East Blvd, Ocmulgee, **N...gas:** BP, **food:** DQ, **lodging:** Day's Inn(2mi), **other:** to airport, GA Forestry Ctr, **S...gas:** Chevron/diesel Shell/diesel, **food:** Huddle House, Subway
2	US 80, GA 87, MLK Jr Blvd, **N...other:** HOSPITAL, Ocmulgee NM, conv ctr, **S...gas:** Marathon/diesel, Saf-T-Oil/diesel, to Hist Dist
1b	GA 22, to US 129, GA 49, 2nd St(from wb), **N...other:** HOSPITAL, coliseum
a	US 23, Gray Hwy(from eb), **N...gas:** BP, Citgo/diesel, Exxon, Flash/diesel, Marathon, Shell, **food:** Arby's, BBQ, Burger King, Central Park, DQ, El Sombrero Mexican, Golden Corral, HongKong Express, Huddle House, Krispy Kreme, McDonald's, Papa John's, Popeye's, Subway, Taco Bell, **other:** HOSPITAL, Isuzu, Kroger, Lincoln/Mercury, Mitsubishi, Radio Shack, U-Haul, Walgreen, transmissions, **S...gas:** Amoco, Conoco/diesel, Exxon, **food:** Burger King, Checker's, KFC, Krystal, Pizza Hut, Waffle House, Wendy's, Zaxby's, **other:** Pontiac, Staples, Tires+
0mm	I-75, S to Valdosta, N to Atlanta. I-16 begins/ends on I-75, exit 165 in Macon.

Interstate 20

E ↕ **W**

Exit #	Services
202mm	Georgia/South Carolina state line, Savannah River
201mm	**Welcome Ctr wb, full(handicapped)facilities, phone, vending, picnic tables, litter barrels, petwalk**
200	GA 104, Riverwatch Pkwy, Augusta, **N...gas:** Pilot/Wendy's/diesel/24hr/@, **lodging:** AmeriSuites, Courtyard, Quality Inn, Sleep Inn, **S...**auto repair
199	GA 28, Washington Rd, Augusta, **N...gas:** BP, RaceTrac/24hr, **food:** Applebee's, Burger King, Capt D's, Chick-fil-A, DQ, Damon's, Denny's, Huddle House, KFC, Krystal, McDonald's, Oldenburg Grill, Piccadilly's, Pizza Hut, Rhinehart's Seafood, Shogun Japanese, Waffle House, **lodging:** Day's Inn, Hampton Inn, Holiday Inn, Homewood Suites, La Quinta, Masters Inn, Radisson, Ramada Ltd, Scottish Inn, Sunset Inn, Shoney's Inn/rest., **other:** BMW/Infiniti, Hancock Fabrics, Hyundai, Lowe's Whse, Mazda, Mercedes, Toyota, **S...gas:** Amoco/24hr, Crown, 76/Circle K, Shell/diesel, **food:** Arby's, Blimpie, Bojangles, Carrabba's, China Rest., Church's, Domino's, Famous Dave's BBQ, Fazoli's, Hardee's, Hooters, Krispy Kreme, Kyoto Japanese, LoneStar Café, LJ Silver, McDonald's, Michael's Rest., Olive Garden, Outback Steaks, Red Lobster, Sonic, Subway, Taco Bell, T-Bonz Steaks, TGIFriday, Thai Jong Rest., Vallarta Mexican,

Interstate 20

E
↕
W

Waffle House, Wendy's, **lodging:** Econolodge, Fairfield Inn, Knight's Inn, Motel 6, Rodeway Inn, **other:** MEDICAL CARE, BooksAMillion, Dillard's, $General, Eckerd, FastLube, Goodyear/auto, Kroger, PepBoys, Publix, SteinMart

196b GA 232 W, **N...gas:** Amoco, Enmark, RaceTrac, 76, **food:** Applebee's, Arby's, Burger King, Checker's, China Pearl, Golden Corral, Krispy Kreme, Krystal, Ruby Tuesday, Ryan's, Salsa's Grill, Schlotsky's, Waffle House, Wendy's, **lodging:** Comfort Inn, Howard Johnson, Suburban Lodge, Travelers Inn, **other:** BiLo Foods, Home Depot, Lowe's Whse, OfficeMax, Sam's Club, Wal-Mart SuperCtr/24hr

a I-520, Bobby Jones Fwy, **S...gas:** Amoco, **other:** HOSPITAL, Best Buy, Circuit City, Target, Winn-Dixie, to airport

195 Wheeler Rd, **N...gas:** Chevron, **food:** O'Charley's, **S...gas:** BP, 76, Shell/24hr, **food:** Blimpie, **lodging:** Day's Inn, **other:** HOSPITAL, Harley-Davidson

194 GA 383, Belair Rd, to Evans, **N...gas:** Citgo/Taco Bell, Phillips 66/diesel, 76/Circle K/Blimpie/diesel, **food:** Burger King, Popeye's, Waffle House, **lodging:** Villager Lodge, **other:** Food Lion, Funsville Park, **S...gas:** Amoco/DQ/Stuckey's/diesel, Pilot/Subway/diesel/24hr/@, **food:** A&W/KFC, Cracker Barrel, Huddle House, Waffle House, **lodging:** Best Western, Econolodge, Hampton Inn, Quality Inn, Ramada Ltd, Wingate Inn

190 GA 388, to Grovetown, **N...gas:** Amoco/diesel, **food:** Waffle House, **S...gas:** Chevron/diesel, 76, KFC, **food:** McDonald's, Subway, TPS Grill

187mm weigh sta both lanes

183 US 221, Appling, to Harlem, **N...gas:** 76, **other:** Ford, **S...gas:** BP/diesel

182mm rest area both lanes, full(handicapped)facilities, phone, vending, picnic tables, litter barrels, RV dump, petwalk

175 GA 150, **N...gas:** Samuels/diesel/rest./24hr/@, **lodging:** Day's Inn, **other:** to Mistletoe SP

172 US 78, GA 17, Thomson, **N...gas:** BP/diesel, Chevron/diesel, **food:** Waffle House, **other:** Chrysler/Dodge/Jeep, Ford/Mercury, Pontiac/GMC, **S...gas:** Amoco/DQ/diesel/24hr, Bryants, RaceTrac/diesel, 76/Blimpie/Circle K, Shell/diesel, **food:** Amigo's Mexican, Arby's, Burger King, Denny's, Domino's, Hardee's, LJ Silver, McDonald's, Pizza Hut, Taco Bell, Waffle House, Wendy's, Western Sizzlin, **lodging:** Best Western, Econolodge, Holiday Inn Express, Howard Johnson, **other:** HOSPITAL, Advance Parts, AutoZone, BiLo Foods, Buick/Chevrolet/Cadillac, CVS Drug, Family$, Food Lion, K-Mart, Lowe's Whse

165 GA 80, Camak, no facilities

160 E Cadley Rd, Norwood, no facilities

154 US 278, GA 12, Barnett, no facilities

148 GA 22, Crawfordville, **N...gas:** Amoco/diesel, **other:** to Stephens SP, **S...gas:** Pure/diesel/rest./motel/repair/@

138 GA 77, Siloam, **S...gas:** Amoco/diesel, Exxon, **other:** HOSPITAL

130 GA 44, Greensboro, weigh sta, **N...gas:** Amoco/diesel/24hr, Exxon/Subway, **food:** McDonald's, Pizza Hut, Waffle House, Wendy's, Zaxby's, **lodging:** Jameson Inn, Microtel, Thrift Court, **other:** HOSPITAL, Motel(3mi), **S...gas:** Chevron/diesel/24hr

121 Buckhead, to Lake Oconee, **S...gas:** Phillips 66

114 US 441, US 129, to Madison, **N...gas:** Chevron/Subway, Citgo, Exxon, Pilot/diesel/24hr/@, RaceTrac, **food:** Arby's, Burger King, KFC, Krystal, McDonald's, Pizza Hut, Waffle House, Wendy's, Zaxby's, **lodging:** Comfort Inn, Day's Inn, Hampton Inn, **other:** HOSPITAL, BiLo Foods, Chevrolet/Pontiac/GMC, Ingles Foods, Wal-Mart/drugs, **S...gas:** TA/BP/Popeye's/Taco Bell/diesel/@, FuelMart/diesel, Texaco, **food:** Waffle House, **lodging:** Budget Inn, Holiday Inn Express, Ramada Inn, Super 8, **other:** RV camping

113 GA 83, Madison, **N...gas:** BP, **other:** HOSPITAL, st patrol

108mm rest area wb, full(handicapped)facilities, phone, picnic tables, litter barrels, vending, RV dump, petwalk

105 Rutledge, Newborn, **N...gas:** BP/diesel, **food:** Yesterday Café, **other:** Hard Labor Creek SP

103mm rest area eb, full(handicapped)facilities, phone, picnic tables, litter barrels, vending, RV dump, petwalk

101 US 278, no facilities

98 GA 11, to Monroe, Monticello, **4 mi N...gas:** Amoco, **food:** Blue Willow Inn/rest., Log Cabin Rest., Sycamore Grill, **S...gas:** BP, Chevron/diesel

95mm Alcovy River

93 GA 142, Hazelbrand Rd, **S...gas:** Exxon/diesel, Shell/24hr, **food:** Little Philly's Hoagies, Waffle House, **lodging:** Jameson Inn, **other:** HOSPITAL

92 Alcovy Rd, **N...gas:** Chevron/diesel, Circle K/diesel, **food:** BBQ, Chick-fil-A, Krystal, McDonald's, Pizza Hut, Waffle House, Wendy's, **lodging:** Best Western/rest., Cornerstone Lodge, Day's Inn, Econolodge, Holiday Inn Express, **S...HOSPITAL**

90 US 278, GA 81, Covington, **S...gas:** BP, Citgo, RaceTrac, Shell, **food:** Arby's, Bojangles, Burger King, Capt D's, Checker's, DQ, Hardee's, KFC, Nagano Japanese, Papa John's, Shoney's, Taco Bell/Pizza Hut, Waffle House, Zaxby's, **other:** Advance Parts, Chevrolet, $General, Eckerd, Ingles Foods, K-Mart, SaveRite Foods, Tire Depot

Madison

Thomson

GEORGIA

Interstate 20

88   Almon Rd, to Porterdale, **N...gas:** Chevron/diesel, **S... gas:** BP/Blimpie, **other:** Riverside Estates RV Camp, transmissions/repair

84   GA 162, Salem Rd, to Pace, **N...gas:** BJ's Whse/gas, **other:** Saturn, Super 1 RV Ctr, **S...gas:** BP/Amoco, Chevron/24hr, Phillips 66, RaceTrac, **food:** Burger King, China Kitchen, Hardee's, Los Bravos Mexican, QuikChick Express, Subway, Waffle House, **other:** Advance Parts, Eckerd, Medicine Shoppe, SaveRite Foods

83mm   parking area wb

82   GA 138, GA 20, Conyers, **N...gas:** Amoco, BP/diesel/repair, Speedway/diesel, **food:** Blimpie, ChuckeCheese, Cracker Barrel, Don Pablo, Golden Corral, IHOP, O'Charley's, On the Border, Outback Steaks, Red Lobster, Roadhouse Grill, Sonic, **lodging:** Conyers Inn, Day's Inn, Hampton Inn, Jameson Inn, La Quinta, Ramada Ltd, **other:** Chevrolet, Circuit City, Ford, Goody's, Home Depot, Kohl's, Michael's, NAPA, Office Depot, Old Navy, Staples, Tires+, U-Haul, Wal-Mart SuperCtr/24hr, **S...gas:** Chevron/24hr, QT, Shell/diesel, **food:** Arby's, Applebee's, Burger King, Capt D's, Checker's, Chili's, Chick-fil-A, Chihuahua Mexican, CiCi's, City Buffet, Donato's Pizza, Hooters, Huddle House, KFC, Krystal/24hr, LJ Silver, McDonald's, Milano Italian, Papa John's, Piccadilly's, Pizza Hut, Popeye's, Ruby Tuesday, Ryan's, Subway, Taco Bell, TCBY, Waffle House, Wendy's, **lodging:** InTown Inn, Suburban Lodge, **other:** Big 10 Tire, Cub Foods, Dodge, $General, Eckerd, Firestone/auto, GNC, Goodyear/auto, Honda, Jo-Ann Fabrics, Kroger/24hr, NTB, PepBoys, Publix, Radio Shack, Rite Aid, Target, Toyota, USPO, mall

80   West Ave, Conyers, **N...gas:** Exxon/diesel, Shell/ diesel, Speedway/diesel, **food:** Burger King, DQ, Domino's, Mrs Winner's, Subway, **lodging:** Holiday Inn, Richfield Lodge, **other:** Family$, Piggly Wiggly, **S...gas:** Exxon/diesel/24hr, **food:** Longhorn Steaks, McDonald's, Waffle House, **lodging:** Comfort Inn, **other:** Chrysler/Plymouth/Jeep, Ford, Hyundai, JustBrakes, Kia, Mitsubishi, Nissan

79mm   parking area eb

78   Sigman Rd, **N...gas:** Circle K/gas, **food:** Waffle House, **S...other:** Buick/Pontiac/GMC/Mazda, Crown RV Ctr, st police

75   US 278, GA 124, Turner Hill Rd, **N...gas:** BP/diesel, Citgo/diesel/24hr, **S...food:** Applebee's, Bugaboo Steaks, Chick-fil-A, KFC/Pizza Hut/Taco Bell, McDonald's, Olive Garden, **lodging:** AmeriSuites, **other:** Best Buy, Borders Books, Dillard's, JC Penney, Marshall's, Sears/auto, Staples, Tires+, mall

74   GA 124, Lithonia, **N...gas:** Chevron/24hr, Phillips 66, Shell, **food:** Capt D's, KFC/Taco Bell, McDonald's, Pizza Hut, Robert's Café, Waffle House, Wendy's, **S...gas:** Citgo/diesel/24hr, **food:** DQ, Krystal/24hr, Snuffy's Grille, Waffle House, **lodging:** Howard Johnson, **other:** CVS Drug, $General, Piggly Wiggly, Radio Shack

71   Hillandale Dr, Farrington Rd, Panola Rd, **N...gas:** Exxon/ diesel, QT/diesel, Shell/diesel, **food:** Burger King, C'est Bon Cajun, Checker's, Cracker Barrel, HotWings/pizza, KFC, McDonald's, Waffle House, Wendy's, **lodging:** Holiday Inn Express, Motel 6, Super 8, **S...gas:** BP/ diesel/24hr, Citgo, Shell, **food:** IHOP, New China, Philly Connection, Popeye's, Wendy's, **lodging:** Sleep Inn, **other:** NAPA AutoCare, Publix, Tires+, Walgreen

68   Wesley Chapel Rd, Snapfinger Rd, **N...gas:** Exxon/diesel, Shell/diesel, **food:** Blimpie, Capt D's, Checker's, Chick-fil-A, China Café, Church's, Hardee's, KFC, LJ Silver, Popeye's, Subway, Taco Bell, 3$ Café, Waffle House, Wendy's, **lodging:** Day's Inn, Motel 6, **other:** MEDICAL CARE, Ford, GNC, Goodyear/auto, Home Depot, Ingles Foods, Wal-Mart, **S...gas:** BP, Chevron/24hr, Shell/diesel, **food:** Burger King, DQ, McDonald's, Pizza Hut, **lodging:** Super Inn

67b a   I-285, S to Macon, N to Greenville

66   Columbia Dr(from eb, no return), **N...gas:** Citgo

65   GA 155, Candler Rd, to Decatur, **N...gas:** Amoco/24hr, Citgo, **food:** Blimpie, Dundee's Café, LJ Silver, Pizza Hut, Red Lobster, Supreme Fish Delight, Wendy's, **lodging:** Discover Inn, Econolodge, Howard Johnson, **other:** A-1 Foods, CVS Drug, U-Haul, **S...gas:** Chevron/24hr, Conoco, Circle K, Shell/diesel, **food:** Arby's, Burger King, Checker's, China Café, Church's, DQ, KFC, McDonald's, Rally's, Ruby Tuesday, Taco Bell, WK Wings, **lodging:** Best Western, Candler Inn, Ramada Ltd, Sunset Lodge, **other:** MEDICAL CARE, Advance Parts, Firestone/auto, JC Penney, Kroger, PepBoys, Winn-Dixie, mall

63   Gresham Rd, **S...gas:** Amoco/24hr, Citgo, Shell, **food:** Church's, **other:** auto repair

62   Flat Shoals Rd(from eb, no return), **N...gas:** Chevron, Shell

61b   GA 260, Glenwood Ave, **N...gas:** BP, Chevron, **food:** KFC

a   Maynard Terrace(from eb, no return), no facilities

60b a   US 23, Moreland Ave, **N...gas:** Exxon, **lodging:** Atlanta Motel, **S...gas:** BP/Chinese Rest./diesel, Shell, **food:** Checker's, KFC/Taco Bell, Krystal, LJ Silver, McDonald's, Mrs Winner's, Wendy's

59b   Memorial Dr, Glenwood Ave(from eb), no facilities

a   Blvd, Cyclorama, **N...gas:** Chevron/Blimpie/diesel, **other:** Confederate Ave Complex, MLK Site, **S...gas:** BP

58b   Hill St(from wb, no return), no facilities

a   Capitol St(from wb, no return), downtown, **N...**to GA Dome, **S...**Holiday Inn

57   I-75/85, no facilities

56b   Windsor St(from eb), stadium

a   US 19, US 29, McDaniel St, **N...gas:** Chevron

55b   Lee St(from wb), Ft McPherson, **S...gas:** BP, **food:** Church's, Popeye's, Taco Bell

a   Ashby St, **S...gas:** BP, Exxon, **food:** Taco Bell, **other:** Eckerd, Sears, mall

54   Langhorn St(from wb), to Cascade Rd

53   MLK Dr, to GA 139, **N...gas:** Shell/diesel, **other:** laundry, **S...gas:** BP

Interstate 20

52b a GA 280, Holmes Dr, High Tower Rd, **N...gas:** BP, **food:** Church's, McDonald's, **S...gas:** Exxon

51b a I-285, S to Montgomery, N to Chattanooga

49 GA 70, Fulton Ind Blvd, **N...gas:** Citgo/diesel/24hr, **food:** Capt D's, Hardee's, Mrs Winners, Subway, Wendy's, **lodging:** Fulton Inn, Masters Inn, Ramada Inn, Summit Inn, **S...gas:** Chevron, Citgo/diesel, Shell, **food:** Arby's, Las Cortas Mexican, McDonald's, Waffle House, **lodging:** Comfort Inn, Super 8, Travelodge

48mm Chattahoochee River

47 Six Flags Pkwy(from wb), **N...gas:** Amoco, **food:** Church's, Waffle House, **lodging:** La Quinta, Mark Inn, Sleep Inn, Wingate Inn, **other:** Arrowhead Camping, **S...lodging:** Comfort Inn, Day's Inn, **other:** Sam's Club, Six Flags Funpark

46b a Riverside Parkway, **N...gas:** Citgo, Marathon, QT, **food:** Waffle House, **lodging:** La Quinta, **other:** EZ Wash, **S...food:** Wendy's, **lodging:** Day's Inn, **other:** Sam's Club, Six Flags Funpark

44 GA 6, Thornton Rd, to Lithia Springs, **N...gas:** BP/24hr, Exxon/diesel, Phillips 66, RaceTrac, Shell, **food:** Burger King, Chick-fil-A, Courtini's Café, Hardee's, IHOP, Krystal, McDonald's, Shoney's, Subway, Taco Bell, Waffle House, Wendy's, **lodging:** Budget Inn, Hampton Inn, Knight's Inn, Shoney's Inn, Suburban Lodge, **other:** HOSPITAL, Chevrolet, CVS Drug, Ford, Kroger, Mazda, Nissan, VW, **S...lodging:** Country Inn Suites, Courtyard, Fairfield Inn, Motel 6, SpringHill Suites, **other:** Buick/GMC, Chrysler/Plymouth/Jeep, Dodge, KOA, Mitsubishi, Toyota, Wal-Mart SuperCtr/24hr, to Sweetwater Creek SP

42mm weigh sta eb

41 Lee Rd, to Lithia Springs, **N...gas:** Citgo/diesel, **food:** Hardee's, **other:** transmissions, **S...gas:** Shell, **food:** Blimpie, Waffle House

37 GA 92, to Douglasville, **N...gas:** Chevron, Citgo, RaceTrac, Shell/diesel/24hr, **food:** Arby's, BBQ, Burger King, Capt D's, Checker's, Chick-fil-A, Church's, Cracker Barrel, DQ, Hong Kong Buffet, Kenny's Rest., KFC, Krystal, McDonald's, Mrs Winner's, Papa John's, Pizza Hut, Subway, Taco Bell, Waffle House, Wendy's, **lodging:** Bilbo's Motel, Comfort Inn, Country Inn Suites, Day's Inn, Holiday Inn Express, Ramada Ltd, Super 8, **other:** HOSPITAL, Advance Parts, AutoZone, Dodge, $General, Gordy Tires, Kroger/24hr, **S...gas:** QT, RaceTrac, Shell/diesel, **food:** Pizza Hut, **other:** Aamco, Eckerd, Ingles Food, Winn-Dixie

36 Chapel Hill Rd, **N...**HOSPITAL, **S...gas:** BP/McDonald's/diesel/24hr, QT/24hr, Shell, **food:** Applebee's, Arby's, Blimpie, China Buffet, Hops Grill, Joe's Crabshack, Logan's Roadhouse, O'Charley's, Olive Garden, Outback Steaks, Rio Bravo, Souper Salad, TGIFriday, Waffle House, **lodging:** Hampton Inn, InTown Suites, Super 8, **other:** Borders, Circuit City, Dillard's, Eckerd, Firestone/auto, Marshall's, Michael's, OfficeMax, Old Navy, Sears/auto, Target, mall

Douglasville

34 GA 5, to Douglasville, **N...gas:** RaceTrac, Shell, **food:** Hooters, Huddle House, Waffle House, Zaxby's, **lodging:** Holiday Inn Express, Quality Inn, Sleep Inn, **other:** MEDICAL CARE, $Tree, Honda/Isuzu, Sam's Club, Wal-Mart SuperCtr/24hr, **S...gas:** Chevron/24hr, Circle K, Shell, **food:** BBQ, Burger King, Chili's, Chick-fil-A, China Café, CiCi's, DQ, Folks Rest., Golden Corral, KFC, Krystal, LJ Silver, McDonald's, Miano's Pasta, Papa John's, Pizza Hut, Red Lobster, Ruby Tuesday, Ryan's, Subway, Taco Bell, Taco Mac, Tokyo Steaks, Waffle House, Wendy's, **lodging:** Suburban Lodge, **other:** Advance Parts, Best Buy, Cub Foods, Eckerd, Food Depot, GNC, Goodyear/auto, Home Depot, Jo-Ann Crafts, K-Mart, Kroger, Lowe's Whse, PepBoys, Publix, Radio Shack, Rite Aid, USPO

30 Post Rd, **S...gas:** Shell/diesel

26 Liberty Rd, Villa Rica, **N...gas:** Shell/diesel, **S...gas:** Wilco/Hess/diesel/24hr/@, **food:** Leather's Rest., Subway, **lodging:** American Inn

24 GA 101, GA 61, Villa Rica, **N...gas:** BP, Exxon, QT, RaceTrac, Shell/diesel, **food:** Arby's, El Tio Mexican, Hardee's, KFC/Taco Bell, Krystal, McDonald's, New China Buffet, Pizza Hut, Romero's Italian, Subway, Waffle House, Wendy's, **lodging:** Best Western, Comfort Inn, Super 8, **other:** HOSPITAL, CVS Drug, Ingles Foods, Winn-Dixie, **S...gas:** QT, Shell/diesel, **other:** Wal-Mart SuperCtr/24hr, to W GA Coll

21mm Little Tallapoosa River

19 GA 113, Temple, **N...gas:** Flying J/diesel/LP/rest./24hr/@, Pilot/Subway/Wendy's/diesel/24hr/@, **food:** BBQ, Hardee's, **S...gas:** Shell/diesel

15mm weigh sta wb

11 US 27, Bremen, Bowdon, **N...gas:** Shell/diesel, **food:** Arby's, Hardee's(2mi), McDonald's, Pizza Hut, Subway, Wendy's, **lodging:** Day's Inn, Hampton Inn, Quality Inn, **other:** HOSPITAL, $General, Ingles, Publix, Wal-Mart/grill, **S...**Shell/diesel/24hr, Waffle House, John Tanner SP

9 Waco Rd, no facilities

5 GA 100, Tallapoosa, **N...gas:** Exxon/diesel, Shell/Blimpie/diesel, **food:** Waffle House **S...gas:** Citgo/Noble/diesel/24hr/@, Big O/diesel, Pilot/KFC/Taco Bell/diesel/24hr/@, **food:** DQ, Huddle House, Waffle King, **lodging:** Comfort Inn, **other:** to John Tanner SP

1mm **Welcome Ctr eb, full(handicapped)facilities, phone, vending, picnic tables, litter barrels, petwalk**

0mm Georgia/Alabama state line, Eastern/Central time zone

Interstate 59

N / S

Trenton

Exit #	Services

I-59 begins/ends on I-24, exit 167. For I-24, turn to Tennessee Interstate 24.

20mm I-24, W to Nashville, E to Chattanooga

17 Slygo Rd, to New England, **W...gas:** Citgo/diesel, **other:** KOA(2mi)

11 GA 136, Trenton, **E...gas:** Chevron/diesel, Citgo, Exxon/diesel, **food:** Asian Garden, Hardee's, McDonald's, Pizza Hut, Subway, **lodging:** Day's Inn, **other:** MEDICAL CARE, Advance Parts, CVS Drug, Family$, Ingles, Plymouth/Dodge, to Cloudland Canyon SP, **W...gas:** Amoco, Citgo, **food:** Huddle House, Krystal, Little Caesar's, Taco Bell, Wendy's, **other:** BiLo

11mm scenic area/weigh sta both lanes, litter barrels

4 Rising Fawn, **E...gas:** Citgo/diesel/24hr/@, **W...gas:** Amoco/diesel/24hr, Pilot/Subway/diesel/24hr/@, **other:** camping

0mm Georgia/Alabama state line, eastern/central time zone

Interstate 75

N / S

Ringgold

Exit #	Services

355mm Georgia/Tennessee state line

354mm Chickamauga Creek

353 GA 146, Rossville, **E...gas:** BP/24hr, Chevron, **lodging:** Knight's Inn, **W...gas:** Exxon/diesel/LP/24hr, Shell, **other:** carpet outlet

352mm Welcome Ctr sb, full(handicapped)facilities, info, phone, vending, picnic tables, litter barrels, petwalk

350 GA 2, Bfd Pkwy, to Ft Oglethorpe, **E...gas:** Exxon, Sav-A-Ton/diesel, **W...gas:** Exxon/diesel, RaceTrac/24hr, Shell, **other:** HOSPITAL, **3 mi W...gas:** Conoco/diesel/rest., **food:** BBQ Corral, Fazoli's, Taco Bell, **other:** KOA, Wal-Mart SuperCtr/24hr, to Chickamauga NP

348 GA 151, Ringgold, **E...gas:** Conoco, Golden Gallon/diesel, Shell/diesel, **food:** Hardee's, Krystal/24hr, KFC, McDonald's, Pizza Hut, Ruby Tuesday, Subway, Taco Bell, Waffle House, **lodging:** Best Western, Day's Inn, Holiday Inn Express, Super 8, **other:** Advance Parts, CVS Drug, Chevrolet, Chrysler/Plymouth/Jeep, Family$, Ingles, RV camping, **W...gas:** Chevron/24hr, Exxon, Texaco, **food:** Wendy's, **lodging:** Comfort Inn, **other:** Ford

345 US 41, US 76, Ringgold, **E...gas:** BP, **W...gas:** Citgo/diesel/rest./24hr, Chevron, Exxon/diesel/@, Golden Gallon/TCBY, **food:** Cochran's Rest, Waffle House

343mm weigh sta both lanes

341 GA 201, to Varnell, Tunnel Hill, **W...gas:** Chevron, Shell, **other:** carpet outlets

336 US 41, US 76, Dalton, Rocky Face, **E...gas:** Chevron/Blimpie, RaceTrac, Shell, **food:** Mr. Biscuit, Waffle House, **lodging:** Best Value Inn, Econolodge, **other:** HOSPITAL, Home Depot, Wal-Mart SuperCtr/24hr/gas, **W...gas:** BP/diesel, Phillips 66, **food:** Denny's, Los Pablos Mexican, Oyster Pub Rest, TaGin Chinese, Wendy's, **lodging:** Best Western/rest., Motel 6, Royal Inn, StayLodge Inn, Super 8, carpet outlets

Dalton

333 GA 52, Dalton, **E...gas:** BP/diesel, Chevron/24hr, Exxon/diesel, RaceTrac/diesel, Texaco, **food:** Applebee's, Burger King, Capt D's, Chick-fil-A, CiCi's, Cracker Barrel, Dairy Queen, Emperor Garden, Fuddrucker's, IHOP, Jimmy's Rest., JW's Rest., KFC, LJ Silver, Longhorn Steaks, Los Pablos Mexican, McDonald's, O'Charley's, Outback Steaks, Pizza Hut, Schlotsky's, Shoney's, Sonic, Steak'n Shake, Taco Bell, TCBY, Waffle House, Wendy's, **lodging:** Best Inn, Day's Inn, Hampton Inn, Travelodge, **other:** Chevrolet, Chrysler/Jeep, Ford, Isuzu, K-Mart, Kroger, Mr Transmission, Tanger Outlets/famous brands, Walgreen, **W...gas:** Shell/Texaco, **food:** Red Lobster, **lodging:** Comfort Inn, Courtyard, Country Inn Suites, Holiday Inn, Jameson Inn, Wellesley Inn, Wingate Inn, **other:** NW GA Trade/Conv Ctr

328 GA 3, to US 41, **E...gas:** BP/Blimpie/diesel, Pilot/Arby's/diesel/24hr/@, **food:** Mucho Mexico, Waffle House, Wendy's, **lodging:** Super 8, **W...**carpet outlets

326 Carbondale Rd, **E...**Chevron/diesel, Pilot/McDonalds/Subway/diesel/@, **W...**Citgo/diesel, Phillips 66/diesel

320 GA 136, to Lafayette, Resaca, **E...gas:** Flying J/Cookery/diesel/LP/rest./24hr/@, **other:** truckwash

319mm Oostanaula River, rest area sb, full(handicapped)facilities, phone, vending, picnic tables, litter barrels, petwalk

318 US 41, Resaca, **E...gas:** Hess/Wilco/DQ/Wendy's/diesel/24hr/@, **food:** Burger King, Hardee's, **lodging:** Knight's Inn, **W...gas:** Exxon/diesel, Right Stuff Gas, **lodging:** Best Inn, Budget Inn, Duffy's Motel, Knight's Inn, Smith Motel, Super 8

317 GA 225, to Chatsworth, **E...**New Echota HS, Vann House HS, **W...lodging:** Express Inn

315 GA 156, Redbud Rd, to Calhoun, **E...gas:** Citgo/diesel, Exxon, **food:** Waffle House, **lodging:** Scottish Inn, **other:** KOA(2mi), antiques, **W...gas:** BP/Subway/diesel, Chevron, Shell, Texaco/diesel, **food:** Arby's, Shoney's, **lodging:** Day's Inn, Best Value Inn, Howard Johnson, Ramada Ltd, **other:** HOSPITAL

Calhoun

312 GA 53, to Calhoun, **E...gas:** Shell/Texaco/diesel, **food:** Cracker Barrel, Denny's, **lodging:** Budget Host/rest., Quality Inn, Red Carpet Inn, **other:** Prime Outlets/famous brands, **W...gas:** BP/Arby's, Chevron/diesel, Citgo, Exxon, RaceWay, **food:** Bojangles, Burger King, Capt D's, Checker's, Chick-fil-A, China Cook, Dairy Queen, Domino's, Hickory House BBQ, Huddle House, IHOP, KFC, Krystal/24hr, Little Caesar's, LJ Silver, McDonald's, Pizza Hut, Ryan's, Subway, Taco Bell, Taylor's Rest., Waffle House, Wendy's, Zaxby's, **lodging:** Comfort Inn, Day's Inn, Guest Inn, Hampton Inn, Holiday Inn Express, Jameson Inn, **other:** Advance Parts, AutoZone, Chrysler/Jeep/Dodge, CVS Drug, $General, Goodyear/auto, Ingles, Kroger, Office Depot, Wal-Mart SuperCtr/gas/24hr

308mm rest area nb, full(handicapped)facilities, phone, picnic tables, litter barrels, vending, petwalk

306 GA 140, Adairsville, **E...gas:** Amoco/24hr, Citgo, Patty's/Texaco/diesel/24hr/@, QT/diesel, Shell, **food:** Wendy's, **lodging:** Travelodge, **W...gas:** BP/Subway, Cowboys/diesel, Exxon/diesel, **food:** Burger King, Hardee's, Taco Bell, Waffle House, **lodging:** Best Wetsern, Comfort Inn, Country Hearth Inn, Ramada Ltd, **other:** camping

Interstate 75

N
↑
↓
S

296 Cassville-White Rd, **E...gas:** Amoco/diesel, Pilot/Subway/diesel/@, TA/Burger King/Popeyes/Sbarro's/diesel/24hr/@, Texaco/Blimpie/24hr, **food:** McDonald's, **W...gas:** Chevron, Citgo, Shell, **food:** Waffle House/24hr, **lodging:** Budget Host/rest., Howard Johnson, Red Carpet Inn, Super 8, Travelodge, **other:** KOA

293 US 411, to White, **E...**Shell/diesel, Texaco, Scottish Inn, **W...gas:** Chevron/diesel, Citgo/diesel/24hr, **food:** Truckline Café, Waffle House, **lodging:** Courtesy Inn, Holiday Inn, **other:** RV camping, museum, st patrol

290 GA 20, to Rome, **E...gas:** Chevron/Subway/diesel, Cowboys/diesel, Exxon/diesel, **food:** Arby's, McDonald's, Morrell's BBQ, Wendy's, **lodging:** Best Western, Comfort Inn, Country Inn Suites, Motel 6, Ramada Ltd, Super 8, **W...gas:** BP, Texaco, Shell, **food:** Cracker Barrel, Pruitt's BBQ, Shoney's, Waffle House, **lodging:** Day's Inn, Hampton Inn, **other:** HOSPITAL, RV camping(7mi)

288 GA 113, Cartersville, **2 mi W...gas:** Amoco/24hr, BP/diesel, Exxon/diesel, **food:** Applebee's, Blimpie, Burger King, Chick-fil-A, Krystal/24hr, Mrs Winner's, Pizza Hut, Subway, Waffle House, **lodging:** Knight's Inn, Quality Inn, **other:** Kroger, to Etowah Indian Mounds(6mi)

286mm Etowah River

285 Emerson, **E...gas:** Shell/Texaco/24hr, **lodging:** Red Top Mtn Lodge, **other:** to Allatoona Dam, to Red Top Mtn SP

283 Emerson Allatoona Rd, Allatoona Landing Resort, camping

280mm Allatoona Lake

278 Glade Rd, to Acworth, **E...gas:** BP/Subway, Shell, **lodging:** Guesthouse Inn, **other:** to Glade Marina, **W...gas:** Chevron, Citgo, **food:** Burger King, Country Café, Dunkin Donuts, His&Hers Southern Buffet, Hong Kong Chinese, KFC, Krystal, Pizza Hut, Subway, Taco Bell, Waffle House, Western Sizzlin, **lodging:** Red Roof Inn, **other:** AutoZone, CVS Drug, Ingles, K-Mart, NAPA, Radio Shack

277 GA 92, **E...gas:** BP, Exxon/diesel, RaceTrac, Shell/diesel/24hr, **food:** Hardee's, Shoney's, Waffle House, **lodging:** Comfort Suites, Holiday Inn Express, Ramada Ltd, **W...gas:** Chevron/diesel, Shell/DQ/diesel, **food:** Bamboo Garden, Domino's, McDonald's, Ricardo's Mexican, Sonic, Waffle House, Wendy's, Zaxby's, **lodging:** Best Western, Day's Inn, Econolodge, Super 8, **other:** Advance Parts, CVS Drug, Publix

273 Wade Green Rd, **E...gas:** BP, Citgo/diesel, RaceTrac, **food:** Arby's, Burger King, China King, Del Taco/Mrs Winners, Dunkin Donuts, McDonald's, Papa John's, Pizza Hut/Taco Bell, Subway, Waffle House, **lodging:** Rodeway Inn, **other:** Eckerd, GNC, Goodyear/auto, Publix, **W...gas:** Amoco, Conoco, Shell/Blimpie/diesel

Marietta

271 Chastain Rd, to I-575 N, **E...gas:** Chevron, **food:** Cracker Barrel, **lodging:** Best Western, **lodging:** Comfort Inn, Extended Stay America, Fairfield Inn, Residence Inn, Suburban Lodge, Super 8, **other:** Circuit City, Goodyear, Outlets Ltd Mall, Studio+, Wal-Mart/auto, funpark, **W...gas:** Texaco/Subway/diesel, **food:** Arby's/Mrs Winners, Del Taco, Waffle House/24hr, Wendy's, **lodging:** Country Inn Suites, SpringHill Suites, Sun Suites, **other:** museum

269 to US 41, to Marietta, **E...gas:** Chevron/24hr, Shell, Texaco/diesel, **food:** Applebee's, Atlanta Bread, Burger King, Fuddrucker's, Grady's Grill, Happy China, Itpolotis Italian, Longhorn Steaks, Manhattan Bagel, McDonald's, New China, Olive Garden, Piccadilly's, Pizza Hut, Red Lobster, Rio Bravo Cantina, Starbucks, Subway, $3 Café, Waffle House, **lodging:** Holiday Inn Express, Econolodge, Red Roof Inn, Super 8, **other:** Barnes&Noble, Big 10 Tire, Firestone/auto, Home Depot, Macy's, Publix, Sears/auto, mall, **W...gas:** BP, Exxon, **food:** Chick-fil-A, Chili's, Cooker Rest., Golden Corral, Macaroni Grill, On-the-Border, Outback Steaks, Roadhouse Grill, Steak'n Shake, TGIFriday, **lodging:** Comfort Inn, Day's Inn, Hampton Inn, Ramada Ltd, Sleep Inn, **other:** Best Buy, Buick/Pontiac/GMC, Chevrolet, Mitsubishi, NTB, Office Depot, OfficeMax, Old Navy, Kia/Toyota, Target, mall, to Kennesaw Mtn NP

268 I-575 N, GA 5 N, to Canton, no facilities

267b a GA 5 N, to US 41, Marietta, **1/2 mi W...gas:** BP, Citgo, **food:** Burger King, McDonald's, Welcome Inn America, **other:** HOSPITAL

265 GA120, N Marietta Pkwy, **W...gas:** Chevron, Shell/diesel, **lodging:** Arrival Inn, Budget Inn, Crown Inn, Sun Inn, Suburban Lodge, Travelers Motel

263 GA 120, to Roswell, **E...gas:** Chevron/diesel/24hr, Shell/24hr, **other:** Harry's Farmers Mkt, cleaners, **W...gas:** Amoco, Exxon/diesel, **food:** Applebee's, Blackeyed Pea, Chili's, Dairy Queen, Hardee's, Longhorn Steaks, Piccadilly's, Subway, **lodging:** Best Western, Fairfield Inn, Hampton Inn, Marietta Motel, Mayflower Motel, Ramada Ltd, Regency Inn, Sheraton, Super 8, Wyndham Garden, **other:** DENTIST, U-Haul

261 GA 280, Delk Rd, to Dobbins AFB, **E...gas:** Exxon, RaceTrac, Shell/24hr, Texaco/diesel, **food:** Hardee's, KFC/Taco Bell, McDonald's, Papa John's, Spaghetti Whse, Waffle House, **lodging:** Courtyard, Drury Inn, Howard Johnson, Knight's Inn, Motel 6, Scottish Inn, Sleep Inn, Studio 6, Super 8, Travelers Inn, **W...gas:** Amoco, BP, Chevron/24hr, Shell/McDonalds/24hr, **food:** Cracker Barrel, D&B Rest., Waffle House, **lodging:** Best Inn, Comfort Inn, Fairfield Inn, Holiday Inn, La Quinta, Wingate Inn

GEORGIA

Interstate 75

N ↕ S

Atlanta Area

260 Windy Hill Rd, to Smyrna, **E...gas:** BP, Shell, **food:** Applebee's, Boston Mkt, Cooker, Fuddrucker's, Houston's Rest., LePeep Rest., NY Pizza, Pappasito's Cantina, Pappadeaux Seafood, Quizno's, Schlotsky's, Subway, TGIFriday, **lodging:** Clarion Suites, Econolodge, Hawthorn Suites, Hyatt, Marriott, Ramada Inn, Travelodge, **other:** CVS Drug, **W...gas:** Chevron, Citgo, Shell, Texaco/diesel, **food:** Arby's, Chick-fil-A, Fuddrucker's, McDonald's, Popeye's, Sub Shop, $3 Café, Waffle House, Wendy's, **lodging:** Best Western, Courtyard, Day's Inn, Hilton, Masters Inn, Red Roof Inn, **other:** HOSPITAL, Target

259b a I-285, W to Birmingham, E to Greenville, Montgomery, no facilities

258 Cumberland Pkwy, no facilities

257mm Chattahoochee River

256 to US 41, Northside Pkwy, no facilities

255 US 41, W Paces Ferry Rd, **W...gas:** Exxon/24hr, **E... gas:** Chevron, Shell/diesel, **food:** Caribou Coffee, Chick-fil-A, McDonald's, Dairy Queen, OK Café/24hr, Pero's Pizza, Steak'n Shake, Taco Bell, **other:** HOSPITAL, Publix

254 Moores Mill Rd, no facilities

252b Howell Mill Rd, **E...gas:** Texaco, **food:** Chick-fil-A, Domino's, Hardee's, McDonald's, **lodging:** Budget Inn, **other:** Eckerd, Goodyear, SaveRite Foods, **W...gas:** Exxon/diesel, **food:** Arby's, Green Derby Rest., KFC, Piccadilly, Sensational Subs, Taco Bell, US BBQ, Waffle House, Wendy's, **lodging:** Budget Inn, Holiday Inn, **other:** Kroger

252a US 41, Northside Dr, **W...gas:** BP, Waffle House, **food:** Krystal, **lodging:** Day's Inn, **other:** Firestone

251 I-85 N, to Greenville, no facilities

250 Techwood Dr(from sb), 10th St, 14th St, **E...lodging:** Travelodge

249d 10th St, Spring St(from nb), **E...gas:** BP, Chevron/24hr, **food:** Checker's, Domino's, Pizza Hut, Varsity Drive-In, **lodging:** Fairfield Inn, Regency Suites, Renaissance Hotel, Residence Inn, **W...food:** McDonald's, **lodging:** Courtyard, Comfort Inn, **other:** HOSPITAL, to GA Tech

249c Williams St(from sb), downtown, to GA Dome

249b Pine St, Peachtree St(from nb), downtown, **W...lodging:** Hilton, Marriott, **other:** HOSPITAL, KOA, Tanger Outlet/famous brands, Wal-Mart SuperCtr/gas/24hr, **W...gas:** BP/diesel, Phillips 66, RaceTrac/diesel, Texaco, **food:** Arby's, Burger King, Checker's, Chick-fil-A, Cracker Barrel, Dairy Queen, Denny's, KFC, McDonald's, Pizza Hut, Ryan's, Subway, Waffle House, Wendy's, **lodging:** Comfort Inn, $Wise Inn, Howard Johnson, Jameson Inn, Ramada Ltd, Red Roof Inn, Super 8, **other:** Buick/Pontiac/GMC, Tanger Outlet/famous brands

249a Courtland St(from sb), downtown, **W...lodging:** Hilton, Marriott, **other:** GA St U

248d Piedmont Ave, Butler St(from sb), downtown, **W... lodging:** Courtyard, Fairfield Inn, Radisson, **other:** HOSPITAL, Ford, MLK NHS

248c GA 10 E, Intn'l Blvd, downtown, **W...lodging:** Hilton, Holiday Inn, Marriott Marquis, Radisson

248b Edgewood Ave(from nb), **W...other:** HOSPITAL, downtown, hotels

248a MLK Dr(from sb), **W...st capitol, to Underground Atlanta

247 I-20, E to Augusta, W to Birmingham, no facilities

246 Georgia Ave, Fulton St, **E...lodging:** Hampton Inn, Holiday Inn Express, **other:** stadium, **W...gas:** Amoco, **food:** KFC, **other:** to Coliseum, GSU

245 Ormond St, Abernathy Blvd, **E...lodging:** Hampton Inn, Holiday Inn Express, **other:** stadium, **W...st capitol

244 University Ave, **E...gas:** Exxon, **W...gas:** Amoco, **food:** Mrs Winner's, **other:** Ford Trucks

243 GA 166, Lakewood Fwy, to East Point, no facilities

242 I-85 S, to airport

241 Cleveland Ave, **E...gas:** Chevron, **food:** Checker's, McDonald's, **lodging:** Palace Inn, **other:** K-Mart, **W...gas:** Shell, Texaco, **food:** Burger King, Church's, Krystal/24hr, **lodging:** American Inn, Day's Inn

239 US 19, US 41, **E...gas:** Chevron, **food:** Checker's, Waffle House, **W...gas:** Amoco, **food:** IHOP, Krystal, McDonald's, **lodging:** Best Western, **other:** USPO, to airport

238b a I-285 around Atlanta, no facilities

237a GA 85 S(from sb), **W...food:** Denny's, **lodging:** Day's Inn, Day's Lodge, King's Inn

237 GA 331, Forest Parkway, **E...gas:** Chevron, Exxon, Happy Store/gas, Shell, **food:** Burger King, McDonald's, Waffle House, **lodging:** Econolodge, Motel 6, Rodeway Inn, **other:** Farmer's Mkt, Chevrolet, **W...lodging:** Day's Inn, Ramada Ltd

Jonesboro

235 US 19, US 41, GA 3, Jonesboro, **E...gas:** Phillips 66, **food:** Hardee's, Waffle House, **lodging:** Super 8, **other:** K-Mart, RV Ctr, **W...gas:** Amoco, Marathon, RaceTrac/diesel, Shell, Texaco, **food:** Checker's, Dunkin Donuts, Folks Rest., Johnny's Pizza, KFC, Krystal, McDonald's, Red Lobster, Waffle House, **lodging:** Comfort Inn, Day's Inn, Econolodge, Holiday Inn Express, Shoney's Inn/rest. **other:** HOSPITAL, Cub Foods, Dodge, Office Depot

233 GA 54, Morrow, **E...gas:** BP, Chevron, Conoco/diesel, **food:** Cracker Barrel, Krystal/24hr, Mrs Winner's, Taco Bell, Waffle House, Wendy's, **lodging:** Best Western, Drury Inn, Fairfield Inn, Red Roof Inn, **other:** MEDICAL CARE, **W...gas:** Exxon/24hr, RaceTrac, Texaco/diesel, **food:** Bennigan's, China Café, Japanese Rest., KFC, LJ Silver, McDonald's, Pizza Hut, Shoney's, Waffle House, **lodging:** Hampton Inn, Quality Inn, **other:** Acura/Cadillac, Best Buy, Chevrolet, HobbyLobby, JiffyLube, Kroger, Nissan, OfficeMax, Toyota, mall

231 Mt Zion Blvd, **E...Honda, W...gas:** Citgo, Conoco, Exxon, **food:** Arby's, Blimpie, Chick-fil-A, Chili's, Del Taco, Longhorn Steaks, McDonald's, Mrs Winner's, On-the-Border, Papa John's, Philly Subs, Steak'n Shake, TGIFriday, Waffle House, Wendy's, **lodging:** Country Inn Suites, Extended Stay America, Howard Johnson Express, Sleep Inn, Sun Suites, **other:** Circuit City, Goody's, Home Depot, Michael's, NTB, Old Navy, Publix, Target

Interstate 75

N ↑ ↓ **S**

228 GA 54, GA 138, Jonesboro, **E...gas:** Exxon, RaceTrac/24hr, **food:** Applebee's, Arby's, Burger King, Chick-fil-A, CiCi's, Dairy Queen, Damon's, Frontera Mexican, Golden Corral, Gregory's Grill, Hardee's, IHOP, KFC, Krystal, LJ Silver, McDonald's, Piccadilly's, Philly Connection, Shoney's, Subway, Taco Bell, Waffle House, Wendy's, **lodging:** Best Western, Day's Inn, Comfort Inn, Holiday Inn Express, Motel 6, Ramada Ltd, Shoney's Inn, **other:** HOSPITAL, Bruno's Foods, Goodyear, K-Mart, Kroger, **W...gas:** Amoco/24hr, Chevron, Citgo/diesel, **food:** Waffle House, **other:** CarMax, Chrysler/Plymouth/Jeep

227 I-675 N, to I-285 E(from nb), no facilities

224 Hudson Bridge Rd, **E...gas:** BP, Citgo/24hr, Phillips 66, Texaco/Chick-fil-A/diesel, **food:** Dunkin Donuts, McDonald's, Subway, Waffle House, Wendy's, **lodging:** AmeriHost Inn, Eagle Landing Inn, **other:** HOSPITAL, CVS Drug, **W...**Teddy's Diner/24hr, Super 8

222 Jodeco Rd, **E...gas:** Amoco, Citgo/24hr, **food:** Hardee's, Waffle House, **W...gas:** BP, Chevron/diesel, **other:** KOA

221 Jonesboro Rd, **E...gas:** Flash/Chick-fil-A/diesel/24hr, **W...other:** flea market, KOA

218 GA 20, GA 81, McDonough, **E...gas:** Amoco, BP, **food:** Applebee's, Arby's, Burger King, Cracker Barrel, Dairy Queen, KFC, McDonald's, Mrs Winner's, Pizza Hut, Taco Bell, Up the Creek, Waffle House, Wendy's, **lodging:** Best Western, Budget Inn, Hampton Inn, Red Carpet Inn, **other:** Wal-Mart SuperCtr/24hr, **W...gas:** Shell/24hr, Speedway/diesel, **food:** Subway, Waffle House, **lodging:** Comfort Inn, Econolodge, HoJo's, Master's Inn

216 GA 155, McDonough, Blacksville, **E...gas:** Chevron/diesel, Shell, Texaco/diesel, **food:** BBQ(1mi), Blimpie, Waffle House, **lodging:** Day's Inn, Sunny Inn, Chevrolet/Pontiac, **other:** Ford/Lincoln/Mercury, **W...gas:** Amoco/diesel, BP/diesel, Citgo/diesel/24hr, Shoney's, Waffle House, **lodging:** Sleep Inn, Holiday Inn/rest.

212 to US 23, Locust Grove, **E...gas:** BP/Subway/diesel, Citgo, Exxon/diesel, Shell/diesel, **food:** Denny's, Hardee's, Huddle House, Waffle House, **lodging:** Executive Inn, Outlet Inn, Red Carpet, Scottish Inn, Travel Inn, **other:** Tanger Outlet/famous brands, **W...gas:** Chevron/diesel, **lodging:** Scottish Inn, Super 8

205 GA 16, to Griffin, Jackson, **E...gas:** BP, Citgo/diesel, **lodging:** BBQ, **W...gas:** Amoco, Chevron/diesel, Texaco/diesel

201 GA 36, to Jackson, Barnesville, **E...gas:** Sunshine/diesel/grill/24hr, TA/Subway/Taco Bell/diesel/24hr/@, Wilco/Hess/DQ/Wendy's/diesel/24hr/@, **food:** Huddle House, **other:** Blue Beacon, **W...gas:** BP, Flying J/Conoco/Hardee's/diesel/LP/24hr/@

198 Highfalls Rd, **E...gas:** Exxon(1mi), **other:** High Falls SP, **W...**High Falls RV Park

193 Johnstonville Rd, **E...gas:** BP

190mm weigh sta both lanes

Forsyth (vertical text)

188 GA 42, **E...gas:** Shell/24hr, **lodging:** Best Value Inn, Best Western, Super 8, **other:** to Indian Springs SP, RV camping

187 GA 83, Forsyth, **E... food:** El Tejado Mexican, **lodging:** Econolodge, New Forsyth Inn, Regency Inn, **W...gas:** Amoco/Blimpie, Citgo/diesel, Conoco/diesel, Exxon, Texaco, **food:** Burger King, Capt D's, Hardee's, McDonald's, Pizza Hut, Subway, Taco Bell, Waffle House, Wendy's, **lodging:** Day's Inn, Tradewinds Motel, **other:** Advance Parts, CVS Drug, Family$, Piggly Wiggly/24hr, Wal-Mart

186 Tift College Dr, Juliette Rd, Forsyth, **E...**Jarrell Plantation HS, KOA, **W...gas:** BP/diesel, Chevron, Shell/24hr, **food:** Dairy Queen, Hong Kong Café, Waffle House, **lodging:** Ambassador Inn, Hampton Inn, Holiday Inn/rest., **other:** HOSPITAL, Chrysler/Plymouth/Dodge, Ingles

185 GA 18, **E...**L&D RV Park, **W...gas:** Amoco/Waffle King/24hr, Texaco/diesel, **food:** Shoney's, **lodging:** Comfort Inn, **other:** Ford, st patrol

181 Rumble Rd, to Smarr, **E...gas:** BP/Subway/diesel/24hr, Shell/diesel/24hr

179mm **rest area sb, full(handicapped)facilities, phone, vending, picnic tables, litter barrels, petwalk**

177 I-475 S around Macon(from sb), no facilities

175 Pate Rd, Bolingbroke(from nb, no re-entry), no facilities

172 Bass Rd, **E...**funpark, **W...**to Museum of Arts&Sciences

171 US 23, to GA 87, Riverside Dr, **E...gas:** BP, Marathon/diesel, Shell, **food:** Cracker Barrel, Huddle House/24hr, **other:** Jack&Jill's Brewery

169 to US 23, Arkwright Dr, **E...gas:** Shell/24hr, **food:** Carrabba's, Logan's Roadhouse, Outback Steaks, Waffle House, Wager's Grill, **lodging:** Courtyard, Fairfield Inn, La Quinta, Red Roof Inn, Residence Inn, Sleep Inn, Super 8, **other:** Buick/Cadillac/GMC/Saturn, **W...gas:** Amoco/diesel, Chevron/24hr, Conoco/diesel, **food:** Applebee's, Burger King, Chick-fil-A, Chili's, Cracker Barrel, Dunkin Donuts, Hooters, KFC, Krystal, Longhorn Steaks, McDonald's, Papa John's, Papoulis' Gyros, Popeye's, Rio Bravo Cantina, Ryan's, Steak'n Shake, Subway, Taco Bell, Waffle House, WhataPizza, **lodging:** Hampton Inn, Holiday Inn, Quality Inn, Ramada Ltd, Shoney's Inn/rest., Studio+, Wingate Inn, **other:** HOSPITAL, Acura, Barnes&Noble, BMW/Mitsubishi, Chrysler/Jeep/Dodge, GNC, K-Mart, Kroger, Lexus, Pontiac, Publix, Radio Shack, Rite Aid, Volvo, same as 167

Macon (vertical text)

GEORGIA

Interstate 75

N
↑
↓
S

167 GA 247, Pierce Ave, **E...lodging:** Budget Inn Suites, **W...gas:** Amoco/Blimpie, BP/diesel, Chevron, Exxon, Marathon/Subway/diesel, Texaco/diesel, **food:** Applebee's, Arby's, Bennigan's, Capt D's, Denny's, Pizza Hut, Red Lobster, S&S Cafeteria, Shogun Japanese, SteakOut Rest., Texas Cattle Co, Waffle House, Wendy's, **lodging:** Ambassador Inn, Best Western/rest., Comfort Inn, Holiday Inn Express, Howard Johnson, **other:** Eckerd, Goodyear/auto

165 I-16 E, to Savannah, no facilities

164 US 41, GA 19, Forsyth Ave, Macon, **E...food:** Sid's Rest., **other:** hist dist, **W...gas:** BP, **other:** HOSPITAL, museum

163 GA 74 W, Mercer U Dr, **E...to Mercer U, W...gas:** Citgo, Marathon/diesel

162 US 80, GA 22, Eisenhower Pkwy, **W...gas:** Amoco, Chevron/24hr, Flash, **food:** Capt D's, Checker's, CityView Café, IHOP, LJ Silver, McDonald's, Mrs Winners, Subway, Taco Bell, Wendy's, **lodging:** Suburban Lodge, **other:** Advance Parts, FoodMax, Goodyear, Home Depot, Office Depot, PepBoys, Walgreen

160 US 41, GA 247, Pio Nono Ave, **E...gas:** Exxon/diesel, RaceTrac, **food:** Waffle House, **lodging:** Masters Inn, **W...gas:** BP, Enmark/diesel, **food:** Arby's, DQ, Gabby's Diner, KFC, King Buffet, McDonald's, Pizza Hut, Subway, Waffle House, **other:** Advance Parts, Eckerd, FoodMax, JiffyLube, USPO, same as 162

156 I-475 N around Macon(from nb), no facilities

155 Hartley Br Rd, **E...gas:** BP/KFC/Pizza Hut/diesel/24hr, Marathon/diesel, **food:** Wendy's, **other:** Kroger/gas, **W...gas:** Citgo, **food:** Subway, Waffle House, **lodging:** Ambassador Inn

149 GA 49, Byron, **E...gas:** Chevron/diesel, Shell/24hr, **food:** Burger King, Krystal, McDonald's, Pizza Hut, Shoney's, Waffle House, **lodging:** Best Western, Holiday Inn Express, Super 8, **other:** MidState RV Ctr, Peach Stores/famous brands, antiques, **W...gas:** BP, Citgo/diesel/24hr, Flash/diesel, Marathon, RaceTrac, **food:** Country Cupboard, DQ, Huddle House, Papa's Pizza, Popeye's, Subway, Waffle House, **lodging:** Comfort Inn, Day's Inn, Econolodge, Passport Inn, **other:** Chevrolet, Ford, NAPA

146 GA 247, to Centerville, **E...gas:** Exxon, Flash/diesel, Shell, **food:** Subway, Waffle House, **lodging:** Budget Inn, **other:** HOSPITAL, to Robins AFB, museum, **W...gas:** Pilot/Arby's/diesel/24hr/@, **lodging:** Royal Inn

145 new exit

142 GA 96, Housers Mill Rd, **E...gas:** Chevron/diesel, **other:** Ponderosa RV Park

138 Thompson Rd, **E...gas:** Phillips/Chester/diesel, **other:** HOSPITAL, **W...airport

P
e
r
r
y

136 US 341, Perry, **E...gas:** Amoco, Chevron/24hr, Flash, Shell/diesel, **food:** Arby's, BBQ, Burger King, Capt D's, Chick-fil-A, Hardee's, Hong Kong Buffet, Jalisco Grill, KFC, Krystal, McDonald's, Pizza Hut, Red Lobster, Sister's Café, Subway, Taco Bell, Waffle House, Wendy's, Zaxby's, **lodging:** Best Inn, Great Inn, Hampton Inn, Jameson Inn, Ramada Ltd, Super 8, **other:** HOSPITAL, Advance Parts, $Tree, Kroger,

Radio Shack, Wal-Mart SuperCtr/24hr, **W...gas:** BP, Chevron, Conoco/diesel, RaceWay/24hr, **food:** Angelina's Café, Applebee's, Green Derby Rest., **lodging:** Comfort Inn, Day's Inn, Econolodge, Holiday Inn/rest., Knight's Inn, Passport Inn, **other:** Ford, Crossroads Camping

135 US 41, GA 127, Perry, **E...gas:** BP/diesel, Exxon, Flash, Shell, Texaco, **food:** Cracker Barrel, Waffle House, **lodging:** Day's Inn, Red Carpet Inn, Relax Inn, Scottish Inn, Travelodge, **other:** Plymouth/Jeep/Dodge, GA Nat Fair, **W...food:** Mandarin Chinese, **other:** GA Patrol, Fair Harbor RV Park

134 South Perry Pkwy, **W...**Chevrolet/Buick/Pontiac/GMC, Priester's Pecans

127 GA 26, Henderson, **E...**Twin Oaks Camping, **W...gas:** Chevron, **lodging:** Henderson Lodge

122 GA 230, Unadilla, **E...gas:** Dixie, **other:** Chevrolet/Ford, **W...gas:** Phillips 66, **lodging:** Red Carpet

121 US 41, Unadilla, **E...gas:** BP, Shell, Texaco/DQ/Stuckey's, **food:** Cotton Patch Rest., Subway, **lodging:** Day's Inn, Economy Inn, Scottish Inn, **other:** $General, Southern Trails RV Resort, **W...gas:** Citgo/diesel/rest./24hr/@, **lodging:** Regency Inn

118mm rest area sb, full(handicapped)facilities, phone, vending, picnic tables, litter barrels, petwalk

117 to US 41, Pinehurst, **W...gas:** BP/diesel, Danfair, **lodging:** Budget Inn

112 GA 27, Vienna, **E...gas:** Pure, **W...gas:** BP/diesel, Marathon

109 GA 215, Vienna, **E...gas:** BP/diesel, **W...gas:** Citgo/diesel, El Cheapo, Shell, **food:** Huddle House/24hr, Popeye's, **lodging:** Knight's Inn, **other:** HOSPITAL

108mm rest area nb, full(handicapped)facilities, phone, vending, picnic tables, litter barrels, petwalk

104 Farmers Mkt Rd, Cordele, **E...lodging:** Cordele Inn, **W...gas:** Phillips 66/diesel

102 GA 257, Cordele, **E...gas:** Shell, **W...food:** Pecan House, **other:** HOSPITAL

101 US 280, GA 90, Cordele, **E...gas:** Exxon/diesel, Pilot/Arby's/diesel/24hr/@, Shell, **food:** Denny's, Golden Corral, Waffle House, **lodging:** Day's Inn, Ramada Inn, **other:** Ford/Lincoln/Mercury, st patrol, **W...gas:** BP/diesel, Chevron/24hr, Liberty, RaceWay/24hr, **food:** Burger King, Capt D's, Compadres Mexican, Cracker Barrel, Cutter's Steaks, Dairy Queen, Hardee's, KFC/Pizza Hut/Taco Bell, Krystal/24hr, McDonald's, Shoney's, Subway, Wendy's, **lodging:** Best Western, Comfort Inn, Deluxe Inn, Hampton Inn, Holiday Inn Express, Premier Inn, Super 8, **other:** CVS Drug, Family$, Radio Shack, Wal-Mart SuperCtr/24hr, to Veterans Mem SP, J Carter HS

99 GA 300, GA/FL Pkwy, **W...**to Chehaw SP

97 to GA 33, Wenona, **E...lodging:** Royal Inn, **other:** RV DR RV Park, **W...gas:** TA/BP/Popeye's/Pizza Hut/diesel/24hr/@, **other:** KOA

92 Arabi, **E...gas:** Chevron/Plantation House, Phillips 66, **lodging:** Budget Inn, **W...gas:** BP, **other:** Southern Gates RV Park

85mm rest area nb, full(handicapped)facilities, phone, vending, picnic tables, litter barrels, petwalk

C
o
r
d
e
l
e

Interstate 75

84 GA 159, Ashburn, **E...gas:** Shell/diesel, **W...gas:** A-1 Trkstp/diesel@, BP/Subway/diesel, **food:** Waffle King, **lodging:** motel/RV park

82 GA 107, GA 112, Ashburn, **W...gas:** BP, Chevron, Shorty's, **food:** Hardee's, Huddle House/24hr, Krystal, McDonald's, Pizza Hut, Shoney's, **lodging:** Best Western, Day's Inn, Ramada Ltd, Super 8, **other:** Chevrolet, Rite Aid, to Chehaw SP

80 Bussey Rd, Sycamore, **E...gas:** Exxon/Subway, Shell, **lodging:** Budget Inn/camping, **W...gas:** Chevron/diesel

78 GA 32, Sycamore, **E...**to Jefferson Davis Memorial Park(14mi)

76mm rest area sb, full(handicapped)facilities, phone, vending, picnic tables, litter barrels, petwalk

75 Inaha Rd, **E...gas:** Chevron, **W...gas:** BP/DQ/Stuckey's

71 Willis Still Rd, Sunsweet, **W...gas:** BP/diesel

69 Chula-Brookfield Rd, **E...gas:** Phillips 66, **lodging:** Red Carpet Inn, **other:** antiques

66 Brighton Rd, no facilities

64 US 41, Tifton, **E...gas:** Chevron, **other:** HOSPITAL, $General, Food Lion, **W...gas:** Citgo/diesel

63b 8th St, Tifton, **E...gas:** Flash, Texaco, **food:** Hardee's, KFC, Krystal, McDonald's, **lodging:** Budget Inn, **other:** Belk, JC Penney, Winn-Dixie, **W...food:** Split Rail Grill, same as 63a

63a 2nd St, Tifton, **E...gas:** BP, Chevron, **food:** Arby's, Burger King, Checker's, Denny's, King Buffet, Krystal, LJ Silver, McDonald's, Pizza Hut, Red Lobster, Subway, Taco Bell, Waffle House, **lodging:** Econolodge, Super 8, **other:** Advance Parts, Buick/Pontiac/Cadillac/GMC, FoodMax, **W...gas:** Shell/diesel, **lodging:** Comfort Inn, Family Inn

62 US 82, to US 319, Tifton, **E...gas:** BP, Citgo, Exxon/diesel, **food:** Applebee's, Charles Seafood, Country Buffet, Cracker Barrel, DQ, Golden Corral, Sonic, Waffle House, Western Sizzlin, Zaxby's, **lodging:** Courtyard, Hampton Inn, Masters Inn, Microtel, **other:** Advance Parts, Ford/Lincoln/Mercury, Pecan Outlet, **W...gas:** Amoco/Subway, RaceTrac/24hr, Shell/diesel, **food:** Burger King, Capt D's, Chick-fil-A, Longhorn Steaks, Shoney's, Waffle House, Wendy's, **lodging:** Day's Inn, Holiday Inn, Ramada Ltd, Rodeway Inn, **other:** Chevrolet, Chrysler/Jeep, Honda, Lowe's Whse, Mazda, Plymouth/Dodge, Radio Shack, Toyota, Wal-Mart SuperCtr/gas/24hr

61 Omega Rd, **W...gas:** Citgo/diesel, **food:** Waffle King, **lodging:** Motel 6, **other:** Pines RV Park

60 Central Ave, Tifton, **E...gas:** Chevron, **food:** Taj Mahal Rest., **W...gas:** Pilot/Subway/Steak'n Shake/diesel/@, **other:** Amy's RV Ctr, Blue Beacon

59 Southwell Blvd, to US 41, Tifton, no facilities

55 to Eldorado, Omega, **E...gas:** Chevron/Magnolia Plantation, **W...gas:** Pure/diesel

49 Kinard Br Rd, Lenox, **E...gas:** Dixie/diesel, **lodging:** Knight's Inn, **W...gas:** BP/diesel/24hr, Phillips 66/diesel, **food:** Blimpie

47mm rest area both lanes, full(handicapped) facilities, phone, vending, picnic tables, litter barrels, petwalk

45 Barneyville Rd, **E...** **lodging:** Red Carpet Inn

41 Rountree Br Rd, **W...**to Reed Bingham SP

39 GA 37, Adel, Moultrie, **E...gas:** Shell/McDonald's/diesel, **food:** DQ, Hardee's, Subway, Waffle House, **lodging:** Scottish Inn, Super 8, Villager Lodge, **W...gas:** BP, Citgo/Huddle House/diesel/@, **food:** Burger King, IHOP, Mama's Table, Taco Bell, Western Sizzlin, **lodging:** Day's Inn, Hampton Inn, **other:** Factory Stores/famous brands, to Reed Bingham SP

37 Adel, no facilities

32 Old Coffee Rd, Cecil, **W...gas:** Chevron

29 US 41 N, GA 122, Hahira, Sheriff's Boys Ranch, **E...gas:** Pure, **food:** Subway, **W...gas:** BP, Citgo/Blimpie/diesel, Sav-A-Ton/Apple Valley Café/diesel/24hr, **lodging:** Super 8

23mm weigh sta both lanes

22 US 41 S, to Valdosta, **E...gas:** BP, Shell/Subway/diesel, **other:** HOSPITAL, Chevrolet/Mazda, Chrysler/Jeep/Toyota, Ford/Lincoln/Mercury, golf, **W...gas:** Citgo/Burger King/DQ/Stuckey's, **lodging:** Day's Inn

18 GA 133, Valdosta, **E...gas:** Amoco, Chevron, Citgo, Exxon, Shell, Texaco/diesel, **food:** Applebee's, Arby's, BBQ, Burger King, Chick-fil-A, Country Buffet, Cracker Barrel, Denny's, El Potro Mexican, Fazoli's, Hardee's, Hooters, KFC, Krystal, Little Caesar's, Longhorn Steaks, McDonald's, Outback Steaks, Red Lobster, Ruby Tuesday, Steak'n Shake, Subway, Taco Bell, Texas Roadhouse, Waffle House, Wendy's, **lodging:** Clubhouse Inn, Country Inn Suites, Courtyard, Fairfield Inn, Hampton Inn, Holiday Inn, Howard Johnson, Jolly Inn, Quality Inn, Scottish Inn, **other:** Belk, Home Depot, JC Penney, Publix, Sam's Club, Target, Wal-Mart/auto, mall, **W...gas:** BP/diesel, Shell, **lodging:** Best Western, Sleep Inn, **other:** RiverPark Camping

16 US 84, US 221, GA 94, Valdosta, **E...gas:** Amoco, BP/diesel, Chevron, Citgo/Blimpie/diesel, Phillips 66, Shell/diesel, **food:** Aligatou Japanese, Burger King, IHOP, McDonald's, Pizza Hut, Shoney's, Sonic, Waffle House, Wendy's, **lodging:** Comfort Inn, Day's Inn, Guesthouse Inn, Motel 6, New Valdosta Inn, Quality Inn, Ramada Ltd, Super 8, **other:** to Okefenokee SP, **W...**Shell/Huddle House/diesel/24hr, Austin's Steaks, Comfort Inn, Knight's Inn

13 Old Clyattville Rd, Valdosta, **W...**Wild Adventures Park

11 GA 31, Valdosta, **E...gas:** Pilot/Subway/diesel/24hr/@, Wilco/Hess/diesel/24hr/@, **food:** Waffle House, **lodging:** Travelers Inn, **W...gas:** BP, Texaco

GEORGIA

Interstate 75

N

S

5   GA 376, to Lake Park, **E...gas:** Amoco, Chevron, Phillips 66, RaceTrac, Shell, Texaco, **food:** BBQ, Chick-fil-A, China Garden, Hardee's, Mama's Subs, Shoney's, Sonic, Subway, Waffle House, **lodging:** Guesthouse Inn, Holiday Inn Express, **other:** Family$, Travel Country RV Ctr, Winn-Dixie, **W...gas:** Citgo/Burger King/diesel, Shell/diesel, **food:** Cracker Barrel, McDonald's, Pizza Hut, Taco Bell, Wendy's, **lodging:** Day's Inn, Hampton Inn, Super 8, Travelodge, **other:** FSA/famous brands, SunCoast RV Ctr

3mm   **Welcome Ctr nb, full(handicapped)facilities, phone, vending, picnic tables, litter barrels, petwalk**

2   Lake Park, Bellville, **E...gas:** Shell, TA/BP/diesel/rest./24hr/@, Texaco/DQ, **food:** Arby's, **W...gas:** ♿Flying J/Conoco/diesel/LP/rest./24hr/@, **lodging:** Best Western

0mm   Georgia/Florida state line

Interstate 85

Exit #   Services

179mm   Georgia/South Carolina state line, Lake Hartwell, Tugaloo River

177   GA 77 S, to Hartwell, **E...gas:** BP/gifts/diesel, **food:** Dad's II Grill, **other:** to Hart SP, Tugaloo SP

176mm   Welcome Ctr sb, full(handicapped)facilities, info, phone, picnic tables, litter barrels, vending, petwalk

173   GA 17, to Lavonia, **E...gas:** RaceTrac/24hr, Shell/Texaco/diesel, **food:** La Cabana Mexican, McDonald's, Subway, Taco Bell, Waffle House, **lodging:** Best Western, Sleep Inn, **other:** $General, Rite Aid, **W...gas:** Chevron/diesel, Exxon, **food:** Arby's, Burger King, Hardee's, Pizza Hut, Waffle House, Wendy's, Shoney's Inn/rest., Zaxby's, **lodging:** Guesthouse Inn, **other:** Chrysler/Plymouth, Sunset Cmpgrnd(3mi), to Tugaloo SP

171mm   weigh sta nb

169mm   weigh sta sb

166   GA 106, to Carnesville, **E...gas:** Wilco/Hess/Wendy's/DQ/diesel/24hr/@, **W...gas:** Echo Trkstp/Country Kitchen/diesel/rest./24hr/@, **other:** repair

164   GA 320, to Carnesville, **E...gas:** Sunshine/Citgo/cafe/diesel/24hr/@

160mm   **rest area nb, full(handicapped)facilities, phone, vending, picnic tables, litter barrels, petwalk**

160   GA 51, to Homer, **E...gas:** Shell/Chester's/Subway/diesel/24hr/@, **W...gas:** ♿Flying J/Country Mkt/diesel/24hr/@, Petro/Pizza Hut/diesel/24hr/@, Blue Beacon

154   GA 63, Martin Br Rd, no facilities

149   US 441, GA 15, to Commerce, **E...gas:** Chevron, Citgo/diesel/rest./24hr, Shell, TA/76/diesel/rest./24hr/@, **food:** Agua Linda Mexican, Capt D's, Chinese Chef, Grand China, Pizza Hut/Taco Bell, Shoney's, Sonny's BBQ, Waffle House, Zaxby's, **lodging:** Admiral Inn, Day's Inn, Guest House Inn, Hampton Inn, Holiday Inn Express, Scottish Inn, **other:** HOSPITAL, KOA, Tanger Outlet/famous brands, Wal-Mart SuperCtr/gas/24hr, **W...gas:** BP/diesel, Phillips 66/diesel, RaceTrac/diesel, Texaco, **food:** Applebee's, Arby's, Burger King, Checker's, Chick-fil-A, Cracker Bar-

rel, DQ, Denny's, KFC, McDonald's, Pizza Hut, Ryan's, Subway, Waffle House, Wendy's, **lodging:** Comfort Inn, $Wise Inn, Howard Johnson, Jameson Inn, Ramada Ltd, Red Roof Inn, Super 8, **other:** Buick/Pontiac/GMC, Tanger Outlet/famous brands, tires

147   GA 98, to Commerce, **E...gas:** Citgo/Liberty Cafe/diesel/24hr/@, FuelMart/diesel, Flash/diesel, **other:** HOSPITAL

140   GA 82, Dry Pond Rd, **W...**Truck Repair

137   US 129, GA 11 to Jefferson, **E...gas:** BP, Shell, **food:** Arby's, McDonald's, Waffle House, Zaxby's, **lodging:** Comfort Inn, **other:** museum, **W...gas:** QT/diesel/24hr/@, **food:** Burger King, Waffle House, Wendy's, **other:** flea mkt

129   GA 53, to Braselton, **E...gas:** Shell/diesel, **food:** Papa's Pizza, Waffle House, **lodging:** Best Western, **W...gas:** BP/Subway/diesel, Pilot/McDonald's/diesel/24hr/@, **food:** Wendy's

126   GA 211, to Chestnut Mtn, **E...gas:** Shell/diesel, **W...gas:** BP/diesel, **food:** Chateau Elan Winery/rest., China Garden, Papa John's, **lodging:** Holiday Inn Express, The Lodge, **other:** Publics

120   to GA 124, Hamilton Mill Rd, **E...gas:** BP, QT/diesel, 76/Circle K, **food:** Buffalo's Café, Burger King, Dos Copas Mexican, Golden Palace Chinese, McDonald's, Millhouse Rest., Moe's Grill, Ninja's Steaks, Starbucks, Subway, Wendy's, Zaxby's, **other:** Home Depot, Publix/Deli, **W...gas:** Shell/Huddle House/diesel, **other:** Kroger(2mi)

115   GA 20, to Buford Dam, **W...gas:** Citgo, QT/diesel, RaceTrac, Texaco, **food:** Arby's, Bruster's, Burger King, Chang's Bistro, Chick-fil-A, Chili's, Longhorn Steaks, Macaroni Grill, McDonald's, O'Charley's, Olive Garden, On the border, Red Lobster, Subway, TGIFriday, Waffle House, **lodging:** Counrty Inn/Suites, Hampton Inn, Spring-Hill Suites, Wingate Inn, **other:** Best Buy, Borders Books, Circuit City, Dillard's, JC Penney, Michael's, OfficeMax, Target, mall, **1 mi W... gas:** Amoco, BP, Chevron, Flash, **food:** BBQ, Ryan's, Waffle House, **other:** $Tree, Honda, Liu's Korean Buffet, Lowe's Whse, Toyota, Wal-Mart SuperCtr/24hr, XpertTire, to Lake Lanier Islands

114mm   **rest area sb, full(handicapped)facilities, phone, vending, picnic tables, litter barrels, petwalk**

113   I-985 N(from nb), to Gainesville, no facilities

112mm   **rest area nb, full(handicapped)facilities, phone, vending, picnic tables, litter barrels, petwalk**

111   GA 317, to Suwanee, **E...gas:** Amoco, BP, Phillips 66/diesel, **food:** Applebee's, Arby's, Blimpie, Burger King, Cazadore's Mexican, Checker's, Chick-fil-A, Cracker Barrel, Del Taco/Mrs Winner's, Oriental Garden, Outback Steaks, Philly Connection, Pizza Hut, Subway, Taco Bell/Pizza Hut, Waffle House, Wendy's, **lodging:** Admiral Inn, Comfort Inn, Courtyard, Fairfield Inn, Holiday Inn, Howard Johnson Express, Red Roof Inn, Sun Suites, **other:** CVS Drug, Ingles, Publix, **W...gas:** Chevron/diesel/24hr, Exxon, Shell, **food:** A&W/KFC, Denny's, McDonald's, Waffle House, **lodging:** Day's Inn, Ramada Ltd, **other:** Wal-Mart SuperCtr/24hr/gas, flea mkt

109   Old Peachtree Rd, **E...gas:** QT/diesel/24hr, **W...**Waffle House, Home Depot

108   Sugarloaf Pkwy, **W...food:** Chick-fil-A, Hilton Garden, Holiday Inn, **other:** Gwinnett Civic Ctr, **W...**Bass pro Shop

Interstate 85

N ↕ **S**

Atlanta Area

107 GA 120, to GA 316 E, Athens, **E...other:** Mercedes, **W...gas:** Amoco/diesel, BP, Chevron, QT, **food:** McDonald's, **lodging:** La Quinta

106 Boggs Rd(from sb, no return), Duluth, **W...gas:** QT/diesel/24hr

104 Pleasant Hill Rd, **E...gas:** Chevron/24hr, Circle K, Citgo/LP, Exxon/diesel, Phillip 66, RaceTrac, **food:** Bahama Breeze, Burger King, Chick-fil-A, Cooker, Corky's Ribs/BBQ, Grady's Grill, Dunkin Donuts, Hardee's, Krispy Kreme, Macaroni Grill, O'Charley's, Popeye's, Restaurante Mexicano, Ruby Tuesday, Smokey Bones BBQ, TGIFriday, Waffle House, **lodging:** Candlewood Suites, Comfort Suites, Hampton Inn Suites, Holiday Inn Express, Marriott, **other:** Best Buy, CVS Drug, Eckerd, Goodyear/auto, Home Depot, Ingles, K-Mart, Office Depot, Publix, Winn-Dixie, **W...gas:** Amoco, BP/diesel, Phillips 66/diesel, Texaco/diesel, **food:** Applebee's, Arby's, Blackeyed Pea, Burger King, Chili's, Chipotle Mexican, Hooters, KFC, McDonald's, Mrs Winner's, Olive Garden, Pizza Hut, Red Lobster, Ryan's, Shoney's, Steak'n Shake, Subway, Taco Bell, Waffle House, Wendy's, **lodging:** AmeriSuites, Courtyard, Day's Inn, Extended Stay America, Fairfield Inn, Ramada Ltd, Sumner Inn, Wellesley Inn, Wingate Inn, **other:** BMW, Chevrolet, Dodge, Firestone/auto, Ford/Lincoln/Mercury, Honda, Kroger, Macy's, Mazda/Hyundai, Mitsubishi, Nissan, Sears/auto, mall

103 Steve Reynolds Blvd(from nb, no return), **E...gas:** QT/diesel/24hr(1mi), **W...gas:** QT, Shell, **food:** Dave&Buster's, Waffle House, **other:** Circuit City, Costco Whse, CompUSA, Goody's, Kohl's, Sam's Club

102 GA 378, Beaver Ruin Rd, **E...gas:** Shell/diesel, QT, **other:** Chevrolet, **W...gas:** Amoco/24hr, Citgo, QT/diesel/24hr(1mi),

101 Lilburn Rd, **E...gas:** QT/diesel, Shell, **food:** Burger King, McDonald's, Shoney's Inn/rest., Studio 1, Taco Bell, **lodging:** Suburban Lodge, Super 8, **W...gas:** BP/diesel, Chevron/24hr, Citgo, Exxon, **food:** Arby's, Blimpie, Dairy Queen, Hardee's, Little Caeser's, Mexican Rest., Mrs Winner's, Papa John's, Peach's Rest., Waffle House, Wendy's, **lodging:** Red Roof Inn, Villager Lodge, **other:** CarMax, Chrysler/Plymouth/Jeep, CVS Drug, Lowe's Whse, Outlet Mall, Winn-Dixie

99 GA 140, Jimmy Carter Blvd, **E...gas:** Amoco/24hr, Chevron, Exxon, Phillips 66/diesel, Texaco/diesel, **food:** Bennigan's, Burger King, Chili's, Cracker Barrel, Denny's, Dunkin Donuts, KFC, Krystal, LJ Silver, McDonald's, Morrison's Cafeteria, Pizza Hut, Sizzler, Steak&Ale, Taco Bell, Waffle House, Wendy's, **lodging:** Amberley Suites, Best Western, Comfort Inn, Courtyard, Clubhouse Inn, GuestHouse Inn, La Quinta, Motel 6, Northcross Inn, Quality Inn, Rodeway Inn, **other:** MEDICAL CARE, Circuit City, Cub Foods, CVS Drug, **1 mi E...food:** Crown, Dairy Queen, ChuckeCheese, Waffle House, IHOP, Subway, Mrs Winner's, Ryan's, El Amigo's Mexican, Japanese Steaks, PoFolks, **other:** Firestone/auto, Goodyear, K-Mart, U-Haul, **W...gas:** Chevron/24hr, Citgo,

Phillips 66, QT/diesel/24hr, **food:** Arby's, Barnacle's Grill, Blimpie, Hong King Buffet, Hooters, Pappadeaux Steak/seafood, RW GoodTimes Grill, Shoney's, Waffle House, Wendy's, **lodging:** Drury Inn, Comfort Inn, Country Inn Suites, **other:** AutoZone, Big 10 Tire, NTB, PepBoys

96 Pleasantdale Rd, Northcrest Rd, **E...food:** Burger King, **lodging:** Econolodge, Peachtree Inn, **other:** West Marine, **W...gas:** BP/diesel, QT/diesel, **food:** Boss Cafe, Waffle House, **lodging:** USA Economy Lodge, Howard Johnson

95 I-285, no facilities

94 Chamblee-Tucker Rd, **E...gas:** Amoco, Shell, **lodging:** Masters Inn, Travel Inn, **W...gas:** QT/diesel, Shell, Texaco/diesel, **food:** Dairy Queen, Waffle House, **lodging:** Motel 6, Red Roof Inn, **other:** to Mercer U

93 Shallowford Rd, to Doraville, **E...gas:** Shell, **food:** Waffle House, Pizza 2 U, **lodging:** Global Inn, **other:** Publix, U-Haul, **W...gas:** Citgo/Circle K, Shell/diesel, **lodging:** Quality Inn

91 US 23, GA 155, Clairmont Rd, **E...gas:** Chevron, Flash, **food:** Popeye's, IHOP, Waffle House, Mo's Pizza, **other:** CVS Drug, Firestone, Piggly Wiggly, **W...gas:** Amoco/diesel/24hr, BP, **food:** McDonald's, Roadhouse Grill, Waffle House, Williams Seafood Rest., **lodging:** Day's Inn, Marriott, Wingate Inn, **other:** NTB, Sam's Club

89 GA 42, N Druid Hills, **E...gas:** Amoco/24hr, QT/diesel/24hr, Crown Gas, **food:** Arby's, Burger King, Chick-fil-A, Grady's Grill, McDonald's, Mexican Rest., Miami Subs, Morrison's Cafeteria, Rally's, Taco Bell, Wall St Pizza, **lodging:** Courtyard, **other:** CVS Drug, Eckerd, Firestone/auto, Target, **W...gas:** BP/diesel, Chevron, Exxon, Hess/diesel, **food:** Applebee's, BBQ, Capt D's, Denny's, Dunkin Donuts, Folks Rest, Krystal, Waffle House, **lodging:** Hampton Inn, Radisson, Red Roof Inn, Travelodge

88 Lenox Rd, GA 400 N, Cheshire Br Rd(from sb), **E...lodging:** Baymont Suites, **W...food:** Pancho's Mexican

87 GA 400 N(from nb), no facilities

86 GA 13 S, Peachtree St, **E...gas:** Amoco, BP, **food:** Denny's, Wendy's, **lodging:** La Quinta, **other:** Brake-O, **W...lodging:** Ramada Inn, Sleep Inn

85 I-75 N, to Marietta, Chattanooga, no facilities

84 Techwood Dr, 14th St, **E...gas:** Amoco, BP/diesel, **food:** CheeseSteaks, La Bamba Mexican, Thai Cuisine, VVV Ristorante Italiano, **lodging:** Hampton Inn, Marriott, Sheraton, Travelodge, **other:** Woodruff Arts Ctr, **W...food:** AllStar Pizza, Blimpie, **lodging:** Courtyard, Villager Lodge, **other:** CVS Drug, Office Depot

I-85 and I-75 run together 8 miles. See Georgia Interstate 75, exits 243-249.

GEORGIA

Interstate 85

N ↑ S

Atlanta Area

77	I-75 S, no facilities
76	Cleveland Ave, **E...gas:** BP, Conoco, Hess, Phillips 66/Blimpie, **food:** Arby's, Burger King, Mrs Winner's/Del Taco, WK Wings Rest., **lodging:** American Inn, Day's Inn, **other:** HOSPITAL, CVS Drug, Kroger, Radio Shack, **W...other:** Advance Parts, Chevrolet, Honda
75	Sylvan Rd, **E...lodging:** Best Western, **W...lodging:** Mark Inn
74	Aviation Commercial Center
73b a	Virginia Ave, **E...gas:** Citgo/diesel, **food:** Hardee's, IHOP, KFC, Malone's Grill, McDonald's, Morrison's Cafeteria, Pizza Hut, Schlotsky's, Waffle House, Wendy's, **lodging:** Club Hotel, Courtyard, Drury Inn, Hilton, Renaissance Hotel, Red Roof Inn, Residence Inn, **W...gas:** Chevron/24hr, Texaco, **food:** Blimpie, Happy Buddha Chinese, Hardee's, KFC, Steak&Ale, Waffle House, Crowne Plaza, **lodging:** Country Inn Suites, Econolodge, Harvey Hotel, Holiday Inn, Howard Johnson, Ramada Plaza
72	Camp Creek Pkwy, no facilities
71	Riverdale Rd, Atlanta Airport, **E...food:** Ruby Tuesday, **lodging:** Comfort Suites, Courtyard, GA Conv Ctr, Microtel, Hampton Inn, Sheraton/grill, Sleep Inn, Sumner Suites, Super 8, Wingate Inn, **W...food:** Bennigan's, **lodging:** Comfort Inn, Day's Inn, Embassy Suites, Marriott, Quality Inn, Ramada, Super 8, Travelodge, Westin Hotel
69	GA 14, GA 279, **E...gas:** Chevron/24hr, **food:** Denny's, Waffle House, **lodging:** La Quinta, Radisson, **other:** CVS Drug, Goodyear/auto, **W...gas:** BP, Citgo, Conoco/diesel, Exxon/diesel, RaceTrac, Texaco, **food:** Arby's, Blimpie, Burger King, Cajun Crabhouse, Checker's, Church's, El Ranchero Mexican, KFC, Krystal, Longhorn Steaks, McDonald's, Pizza Hut, Red Lobster, ShowCase Eatery, Steak&Ale, Subway, Taco Bell, Wendy's, **lodging:** Baymont Inn, Day's Inn, Fairfield Inn, Red Roof Inn, **other:** Advance Parts, AutoZone, Cottman Transmissions, Family$, Kroger, Radio Shack, Target, U-Haul
68	I-285 Atlanta Perimeter, no facilities
66	Flat Shoals Rd, **W...gas:** BP, Chevron/diesel, Texaco/Blimpie, **food:** Supreme Fish Delight, Waffle House, **lodging:** Motel 6
64	GA 138, to Union City, **E...gas:** BP/Blimpie/diesel, **food:** Waffle House, **lodging:** Econolodge, Ramada Ltd, **other:** Buick/Pontiac/GMC, Chevrolet, Chrysler, Dodge, Ford, Honda, Kia/Nissan, Saturn, Toyota, **W...gas:** Chevron, QT, Shell, Texaco/diesel, **food:** Arby's, Burger King, Capt D's, China King, Corner Café, Cracker Barrel, IHOP, KFC, Krystal, La Fiesta Mexican, McDonald's, Papa John's, Pizza Hut, Subway, Taco Bell, Wendy's, **lodging:** Comfort Inn, Day's Inn, Holiday Inn Express, Microtel, Red Roof Inn, **other:** Aamco, Chevrolet, $Tree, Eckerd, Firestone, Goodyear/auto, Ingles, Kroger, NTB, PepBoys, Sears/auto, Wal-Mart, mall
61	GA 74, to Fairburn, **E...gas:** BP, Chevron, RaceTrac, Shell, **food:** Hickory House Rest., McDonald's, Waffle House, Wendy's, **W...gas:** Citgo/diesel, Marathon, Phillips 66/Blimpie/diesel, **lodging:** Efficiency Motel

Newnan

56	Collinsworth Rd, **W...gas:** BP, Marathon/Blimpie, **food:** Frank's Rest.
51	GA 154, to Sharpsburg, **E...gas:** BP/diesel, Phillips 66/Blimpie/diesel, **food:** Hardee's, **W...gas:** Chevron/diesel, Shell/Krystal/diesel, **food:** Waffle House
47	GA 34, to Newnan, **E...gas:** BP, Chevron/diesel, Citgo/Subway, Shell, Texaco, **food:** Applebee's, Arby's, Dunkin Donuts, Hooters, LongHorn Steaks, Red Lobster, Ruby Tuesday, Ryan's, Schlotsky's, Sprayberry's BBQ, Steak'n Shake, Texas Roadhouse, Waffle House, Wendy's, **lodging:** Hampton Inn, Jameson Inn, Springhill Suites, **other:** Circuit City, Goodyear, Goody's, Home Depot, Kohl's, Lowe's Whse, OfficeMax, Peachtree Stores/famous brands, Wal-Mart SuperCtr/24hr, **W...gas:** Exxon/diesel, HotSpot/diesel, Phillips 66, RaceTrac, **food:** Burger King, Chick-fil-A, Cracker Barrel, Golden Corral, Hardee's, IHOP, KFC, Krystal, O'Charley's, Taco Bell, Waffle House, Zaxby's, **lodging:** Best Western, Comfort Inn, Day's Inn, Holiday Inn Express, La Quinta, Motel 6, **other:** HOSPITAL, BJ's Whse, Chevrolet, Ford/Lincoln/Mercury, Hyundai, Michael's, Office Depot, Old Navy, Plymouth, Pontiac/Buick/GMC, Publix, Target, Tires+, Toyota
41	US 27/29, Newnan, **E...gas:** Pilot/diesel/24hr/@, **food:** Wendy's, **W...gas:** Amoco/diesel/24hr, BP/24hr, Flash/diesel, Phillips 66, **food:** Blimpie, McDonald's, Waffle House, **lodging:** Day's Inn, Ramada Ltd, Super 8
35	US 29, to Grantville, **W...gas:** BP/diesel, Phillips 66/diesel
28	GA 54, GA 100, to Hogansville, **E...gas:** Shell/diesel, **W...gas:** BP/diesel, Chevron/diesel, Noble's Trkstp/Janet's Rest./diesel/@, **food:** BBQ, McDonald's, Subway, Waffle House, Wendy's, **lodging:** Day's Inn, KeyWest Inn, **other:** Ingles, Flat Creek RV Park
23mm	Beech Creek
22mm	weigh sta both lanes
21	I-185 S, to Columbus, no facilities

LaGrange

18	GA 109, to Mountville, **E...gas:** Chevron/Domino's/diesel, **lodging:** Econolodge, **other:** to FDR SP, Little White House HS, **W...gas:** BP/diesel, Citgo, RaceTrac, Shell/Church's/diesel, **food:** Applebee's, Banzai Japanese, Burger King, Los Nopales Mexican, Ryan's, Subway, Waffle House, Wendy's, **lodging:** AmeriHost, Best Western, Holiday Inn Express, Jameson Inn, Super 8, **other:** Chrysler/Plymouth/Dodge/Jeep, Ford/Lincoln/Mercury, Home Depot, Honda, Hoofer's RV Park(3mi), JC Penney
14	US 27, to La Grange, **W...gas:** BP/24hr, Pure, Shell/Church's, **lodging:** Hampton Inn
13	GA 219, to La Grange, **E...gas:** Texaco Trkstp/diesel/24hr/@, **food:** Waffle House, **lodging:** Admiral Benbow, Day's Inn, **other:** truckwash, **W...gas:** BP/diesel, Pilot/Subway/diesel/24hr/@, **food:** McDonald's, **other:** HOSPITAL
10mm	Long Cane Creek
2	GA 18, to West Point, **E...gas:** BP, Shell/Church's/diesel/24hr, **food:** KFC, **lodging:** Travelodge, **W...to** West Point Lake, camping
.5mm	**Welcome Ctr nb, full(handicapped)facilities, phone, picnic tables, litter barrels, vending, petwalk**
0mm	Georgia/Alabama state line, Chattahoochee River, eastern/central time zone

122

Interstate 95

Exit #	Services
113mm	Georgia/South Carolina state line, Savannah River
111mm	**Welcome Ctr/weigh sta sb, full(handicapped)facilities, info, phone, vending, picnic tables, litter barrels, petwalk**
109	GA 21, to Savannah, Pt Wentworth, Rincon, **E...gas:** Enmark/diesel, Pilot/McDonald's/Subway/diesel/24hr/@, **food:** Waffle House, **lodging:** Country Inn Suites, Hampton Inn, **W...gas:** 76/Circle K/diesel, **food:** Island Grill, Wendy's, **lodging:** Holiday Inn Express, Quality Inn, Ramada Ltd, Savannah Inn, Sleep Inn, Super 8
107mm	Augustine Creek
106	Jimmy DeLoach Pkwy, no facilities
104	Savannah Airport, **E...gas:** BP, Shell/diesel, **food:** Waffle House, **lodging:** Fairfield Inn, Hawthorn Suites, Hilton Garden, Springhill Suites, **other:** to airport, **W...gas:** Shell/Subway, **food:** Arby's, Chick-fil-A, Hilliard's Rest., McSnack, Ruby Tuesday, Schlotsky's, Sonic, Zaxby's Café, **lodging:** Red Roof Inn, **other:** Home Depot, Wal-Mart SuperCtr/Radio Grill/gas/24hr
102	US 80, to Garden City, **E...gas:** BP, Enmark/diesel, **food:** Cracker Barrel, Huddle House, KFC, Krystal, McDonald's, Peking Chinese, Pizza Hut/Taco Bell, Waffle House, **lodging:** Best Western, Jameson Inn, Microtel, Ramada Ltd, Travelodge Suites, **other:** Food Lion, Family$, Russell Stover, Wait's RV Ctr, to Ft Pulaski NM, museum, **W...gas:** BP, Gate/diesel, Shell, **food:** BBQ, Burger King, Domino's, El Potro Mexican, Hardee's, Italian Pizza, Subway, Wendy's, Western Sizzlin, **lodging:** Comfort Inn, Econolodge, Holiday Inn, **other:** CarCare
99b a	I-16, W to Macon, E to Savannah, no facilities
94	GA 204, to Savannah, Pembroke, **E...gas:** BP/diesel, El Cheapo/24hr, Exxon, 76/Circle K, Shell/diesel, **food:** Cracker Barrel, Denny's, Hardee's, McDonald's, Perkins, Ruby Tuesday, Shoney's, Sonic, **lodging:** Best Value, Best Western, Clarion, Comfort Inn, Country Inn Suites, Day's Inn, Fairfield Inn, GuestHouse Inn, Hampton Inn, Holiday Inn Express, Howard Johnson, La Quinta, Quality Inn, Red Roof Inn, Roadway Inn, Shoney's Inn/rest., Sleep Inn, Wingate Inn, **other:** HOSPITAL, Chevrolet, Factory Stores, Wal-Mart SuperCtr/24hr/gas(2mi), **W...gas:** Chevron/diesel/24hr, Shell, **food:** Crabdaddy's Rest, El Potro Mexican, Hooters, Huddle House, Shellhouse Rest, Subway, Waffle House, **lodging:** Econolodge, Microtel, Red Carpet Inn, Super 8, Travelodge, **other:** Harley-Davidson, Bellaire Woods RV Park(2mi)
91mm	Ogeechee River
90	GA 144, Old Clyde Rd, to Ft Stewart, Richmond Hill SP, **E...gas:** BP(1mi), Chevron, Exxon, **food:** El Potro Mexican(1mi), Hardee's(1mi), **other:** Kroger/deli, Waterway RV Park(3mi), **W...gas:** Shell/diesel, **other:** Gore's RV Ctr
87	US 17, to Coastal Hwy, Richmond Hill, **E...gas:** Chevron/diesel/24hr, Phillips 66, RaceTrac, **food:** Denny's/24hr, Huddle House, Steamers Rest., Subway, Waffle House, **lodging:** Day's Inn, Motel 6, Royal Inn, Scottish Inn, Travelodge, **W...gas:** Exxon/McDonald's/diesel, Shell/diesel, Speedway/diesel, TA/LJSilver/Pizza Hut/Popey's/diesel/24hr/@, Shell/diesel, **food:** Arby's, Burger King, KFC/Taco Bell, Waffle House,

(left margin: Savannah)

	Wendy's, **lodging:** Econolodge, Hampton Inn, Holiday Inn Express, Ramada Inn, **other:** KOA
85mm	Elbow Swamp
80mm	Jerico River
76	US 84, GA 38, to Midway, Sunbury, **E...**hist sites, **W...gas:** BP/diesel, El Cheapo/diesel, **food:** Holton's Seafood, Huddle House, **other:** HOSPITAL, museum
67	US 17, Coastal Hwy, to S Newport, **E...gas:** BP, Chevron/Subway/diesel, Shell/McDonald's, **other:** Newport Camping(2mi), RiverFront RV Park, **W...gas:** BP
58	GA 99, GA 57, Townsend Rd, Eulonia, **E...gas:** BP/diesel, Citgo, **food:** Altman's Rest., **lodging:** Eulonia Lodge, **other:** MEDICAL CARE, **W...gas:** Chevron/diesel/24hr, Shell/diesel, **food:** Huddle House, **lodging:** Day's Inn, Knight's Inn, **other:** McIntosh Lake RV Park, Lake Harmony RV Camp
55mm	weigh sta both lanes, phone
49	GA 251, to Darien, **E...gas:** BP/diesel, Chevron/diesel/24hr, Citgo, **food:** Archie's Rest.(1mi), DQ, McDonald's, Waffle House, **lodging:** Ft King George Motel, **other:** Inland Harbor RV Park, Tall Pines RV Park, **W...gas:** BP, Mobil/diesel, Shell/diesel, **food:** BBQ, Burger King, Huddle House, KFC/Pizza Hut/Taco Bell, Ruby Tuesday, TCBY, Wendy's, **lodging:** Comfort Inn, Hampton Inn, Jaysen Inn, Super 8, **other:** Darien Outlets/famous brands, flea mkt
47mm	Darien River
46.5mm	Butler River
46mm	Champney River
45mm	Altamaha River
42	GA 99, **E...**to Hofwyl Plantation HS
41mm	**rest area sb, full(handicapped)facilities, info, phone, vending, picnic tables, litter barrels, petwalk**
38	GA 25, to US 17, N Golden Isles Pkwy, Brunswick, **E...gas:** Conoco, Racetrac, **food:** Applebee's, Capt D's, FoodCourt, Ruby Tuesday, **lodging:** Embassy Suites, Fairfield Inn, Holiday Inn, Jameson Inn, Microtel, **other:** HOSPITAL, **W...gas:** BP, Chevron, Flash, Shell/diesel, **food:** BBQ, Cracker's Seafood, Godfather's, Huddle House/24hr, Waffle House, **lodging:** Econolodge, Guest Cottage Motel, Quality Inn, **other:** Food Lion
36b a	US 25, US 341, to Jesup, Brunswick, **E...gas:** Chevron/diesel/24hr, Exxon/diesel, RaceTrac, Shell/diesel, **food:** Burger King, Cracker Barrel, IHOP, KFC, Krystal/24hr, McDonald's, Pizza Hut, Quizno's, Shoney's, Taco Bell, Waffle House, Wendy's, **lodging:** Baymont Inn, Day's Inn, Hampton Inn, Knight's Inn, Ramada Inn, Red Roof Inn, **other:** Newcastle RV Ctr, **W...gas:** El Cheapo/diesel, Mobil/diesel, **food:** Sunny's BBQ, Capt Joe's Seafood, Denny's, Huddle House/24hr, Larry's Subs, Matteo's Italian, Minh-Shun Chinese, Subway, Waffle House, **lodging:** Best Western, Comfort Inn, Holiday Inn, Motel 6, Sleep Inn, Super 8, **other:** $General, Family$, Suncoast RV Ctr, Winn-Dixie

(right margin: Brunswick)

GEORGIA

Interstate 95

N ↕ S

33mm	Turtle River
30mm	S Brunswick River
29	US 17, US 82, GA 520, S GA Pkwy, Brunswick, **E...gas:** BP, Exxon, Flash Foods/gas, Mobil, Phillips 66/Church's/diesel, Pilot/Steak'n Shake/Subway/diesel/24hr/@, Shell, **food:** BBQ, Huddle House, Krystal, McDonald's, **other:** Blue Beacon, **W...gas:** Citgo, Shell/diesel, ⊘Flying J/Conoco/Country Mkt/diesel/LP/24hr/@, Mobil, TA/BP/diesel/rest./24hr/@, **food:** Waffle House, **lodging:** Microtel, Super 8, **other:** $General, Golden Isles Camping
27.5mm	Little Satilla River
26	Dover Bluff Rd, **E...gas:** Mobil/diesel, **food:** Choo Choo BBQ
21mm	White Oak Creek
19mm	Canoe Swamp
15mm	Satilla River
14	GA 25, to Woodbine, **W...food:** BP, Sunshine/diesel/rest./24hr, **food:** Jack's BBQ, **lodging:** Stardust Motel(3mi)
7	Harrietts Bluff Rd, **E...gas:** Exxon/diesel, Shell/Subway, **food:** Huddle House, Jack's BBQ, **W...gas:** BP/diesel, **other:** Pappy's Pizza
6.5mm	Crooked River
6	Laurel Island Pkwy, **E...gas:** BP/Arby's/diesel/24hr, Cisco Express/gas, Cone/diesel/24hr, **other:** pecans
3	GA 40, to St Marys, **E...gas:** BP, Chevron, Enmark/diesel, Exxon/Krystal, Mobil, Shell/Subway, Texaco/Krystal, **food:** Applebee's, BBQ, Burger King, Chick-fil-A, Cucina Italian, DQ, Dynasty Chinese, KFC, McDonald's, Mo-joe's Cafe, Pablo's Mexican, Pizza Hut, Ponderosa, Shoney's, Taco Bell, Waffle House, Wendy's, Zaxby's, **lodging:** Best Western, Comfort Inn, Country Inn Suites, Day's Inn, Hampton Inn, Holiday Inn Express, Super 8, **other:** HOSPITAL, Chevrolet/Buick, Chrysler/Plymouth/Jeep, CVS Drug, $Tree, Ford/Mercury, Kia, K-Mart, Publix, Winn-Dixie, to Submarine Base, **W...gas:** Citgo/diesel, Exxon/diesel, Landover Trkstp/rest./diesel/@, RaceWay, **food:** Cracker Barrel, Waffle House, **lodging:** Econolodge, Howard Johnson, Jameson Inn, Ramada Inn, Scottish Inn
1	St Marys Rd, **E...Welcome Ctr nb, full(handicapped)facilities, phone, vending, picnic tables, litter barrels, petwalk, gas:** Cisco/Blimpie/DQ/LJ Silver/Mrs Winners/Pizza Hut/diesel/@, Shell/diesel, **food:** to Cumberland Is Nat Seashore, **W...gas:** BP/diesel, Chevron/diesel, Wilco/Hess/Wendy's/diesel/@, **other:** Country Oaks RV Park, KOA
0mm	Georgia/Florida state line, St Marys River

Interstate 185(Columbus)

N ↕ S

Exit #	Services
48	I-85. I-185 begins/ends on I-85.
46	Big Springs Rd, **E...BP, W...gas:** Shell
42	US 27, Pine Mountain, **E...gas:** BP, Shell/diesel, **food:** Waffle House, **other:** to Callaway Gardens, Little White House HS
34	GA 18, to West Point, **E...gas:** Shell/diesel/24hr
30	Hopewell Church Rd, Whitesville, **W...gas:** Amoco/diesel

Columbus

25	GA 116, to Hamilton, **W...**RV camping
19	GA 315, Mulberry Grove, **W...gas:** Chevron/diesel/24hr
14	Smith Rd, no facilities
12	Williams Rd, **W...Welcome Ctr, gas:** Amoco, Shell, **food:** Church's, **lodging:** Country Inn Suites
10	US 80, GA 22, to Phenix City, **W...**Springer Opera House
8	Airport Thruway, **E...gas:** Chevron, **food:** Blimpie, China Moon, Shoney's, **other:** Advance Parts, Circuit City, Home Depot, Sam's Club, Wal-Mart, **W...gas:** Amoco, Citgo, Crown, **food:** Applebee's, Burger King, Capt D's, Hardee's, IHOP, KFC, McDonald's, Outback Steaks, Subway, Taco Bell/Pizza Hut, **lodging:** Comfort Inn, Extended Stay America, Hampton Inn, Sheraton, **other:** Cub Foods, K-Mart, Office Depot
7	45th St, Manchester Expswy, **E...gas:** Chevron, **food:** Applebee's, Burger King, Chevy's Mexican, Krystal, Ruby Tuesday, **lodging:** Baymont Inn, Courtyard, Super 8, **other:** Chevrolet/Cadillac, Dillard's, mall, **W...gas:** Amoco, BP, Chevron, Crown, **food:** Arby's, China Express, Crystal River Seafood, Dunkin Donuts, Logan's Roadhouse, McDonald's, Pizza Hut, Ryan's, Sonic, Subway, Waffle House, Wendy's, **lodging:** Fairfield Inn, Holiday Inn, Sleep Inn, **other:** HOSPITAL
6	GA 22, Macon Rd, **E...food:** Burger King, China Buffet, KFC, Pizza Hut, Taco Bell, Waffle House, **lodging:** Best Western, Comfort Inn, Day's Inn, **other:** Eckerd, Ford, Nissan, U-Haul, **W...gas:** BP, Chevron, **food:** Capt D's, Denny's, Longhorn Steaks, McDonald's, **lodging:** Efficiency Lodge, LaQuinta, **other:** Honda, OfficeMax, Publix
4	Buena Vista Rd, **E...gas:** BP, **food:** Arby's, Burger King, Capt D's, Chef Lee Chinese, Church's, Krystal, McDonald's, Pizza Hut, Taco Bell, Waffle House, **other:** AutoZone, Firestone/auto, Jones Foods, Super$, **W...gas:** Chevron, Crown, Spectrum
3	St Marys Rd, **W...gas:** Amoco, BP/diesel, **food:** KFC, DQ, Hardee's
1b a	US 27, US 280, Victory Dr, **1-3 mi W...gas:** RaceTrac/24hr, **food:** Burger King, Denny's, KFC, McDonald's, Popeye's, **lodging:** Econolodge, Colony Inn, Day's Inn, Motel 6. I-185 begins/ends.

Interstate 285(Atlanta)

Exit #	Services
62	GA 279, Roosevelt Hwy, Old Nat Hwy, **N...gas:** BP, Chevron, **lodging:** La Quinta, **S...gas:** Exxon, Shell, **food:** Burger King, Checker's, China Cafeteria, Church's, Dock's Rest., KFC, Krystal, Longhorn Steaks, McDonald's, Mrs Winner's, Popeye's, Red Lobster, Taco Bell, Waffle House, Wendy's, **lodging:** Day's Inn, Fairfield Inn, Howard Johnson, Radisson, Red Roof Inn, **other:** AutoZone, Cottman Transmissions, Family$, U-Haul
61	I-85, N to Atlanta, S to Montgomery. **Services 1 mi N...see GA I-85, exit 71.**

124

Interstate 285

60 GA 139, Riverdale Rd, **N...lodging:** Microtel(2mi), **S...gas:** BP, Exxon, QT/Blimpie, Shell/diesel, Speedway/diesel, **food:** Burger King, Checker's, China Café, McDonald's, Waffle House, Wendy's, **lodging:** Best Western, Day's Inn, Ramada Inn, Travelodge, **other:** Family$

59 Clark Howell Hwy, **N...**air cargo

58 I-75, N to Atlanta, S to Macon(from eb), to US 19, US 41, Forest Park, to Hapeville, **S...gas:** Amoco, Chevron/24hr, **food:** Waffle House, **lodging:** Home Lodge Motel

55 GA 54, Jonesboro Rd, **N...lodging:** Super 8, **S...gas:** Amoco, Citgo/diesel, Phillips 66, RaceTrac, Shell/diesel, **food:** Alondra's Mexican/Chinese, Arby's, DaiLai Vietnamese, McDonald's, Waffle House, **other:** Home Depot

53 US 23, Moreland Ave, to Ft Gillem, **N...gas:** Amoco, Conoco/diesel, Speedway/diesel, **S...gas:** Citgo, Shell, TA/diesel/24hr/@, **food:** Popeye's, Wendy's, **lodging:** Economy Inn

52 I-675, S to Macon

51 Bouldercrest Rd, **N...gas:** Amoco/24hr, Pilot/Wendy's/diesel/24hr, **food:** Hardee's, KFC/Pizza Hut, WK Wings, **lodging:** DeKalb Inn, **other:** Family$, Wayfield Foods, **S...gas:** Chevron/diesel

48 GA 155, Flat Shoals Rd, Candler Rd, **N...gas:** Circle K, Marathon, Shell/diesel, **food:** Arby's, Checker's, DQ, KFC/Pizza Hut, McDonald's, Taco Bell, Waffle King, WK Wings, **lodging:** Econolodge, Great American Inn, Ramada Ltd, **S...gas:** QT, Foodmart, Shell

46b a I-20, E to Augusta, W to Atlanta

44 GA 260, Glenwood Rd, **E...gas:** Marathon, Super 8, **W...gas:** Shell, **food:** Church's, Mrs Winner's, **lodging:** Glenwood Inn

43 US 278, Covington Hwy, **E...gas:** Chevron/Subway/24hr, Citgo/diesel, **other:** U-Haul, **W...gas:** Amoco/24hr, Shell/diesel, **food:** Blimpie, Checker's, KFC/Taco Bell, Mrs Winner's, Wendy's, **lodging:** Best Inn, **other:** Advance Parts, Family$, Firestone/auto

42 Marta Station

41 GA 10, Memorial Dr, Avondale Estates, **E...gas:** QT, Shell/diesel, **food:** Applebee's, Arby's, Burger King, Church's, Hardee's, McDonald's, Steak'n Shake, Waffle House, Wendy's, **lodging:** Savannah Suites, **other:** Advance Parts, AutoZone, Circuit City, Office Depot, Radio Shack, **W...gas:** Mobil, **food:** KFC, Waffle King, **lodging:** Comfort Inn

40 Church St, to Clarkston, **E...gas:** Chevron, Citgo, Shell/diesel, **food:** Waffle House, **W...gas:** Shell, **other:** HOSPITAL

39b a US 78, to Athens, Decatur, no facilities

38 US 29, Lawrenceville Hwy, **E...gas:** Phillips 66, Shell, **food:** Waffle House, **lodging:** Knight's Inn, Super 8, **other:** HOSPITAL, **W...gas:** Amoco, Shell, **food:** Waffle House, **lodging:** Masters Inn, Red Roof Inn

37 GA 236, to LaVista, Tucker, **E...gas:** Chevron, Circle K, **food:** Checker's, Chili's, Folks Rest., IHOP, O'Charley's, Olive Garden, Piccadilly's, Schlotsky's, Steak&Ale, Waffle House, **lodging:** Comfort Suites, Country Inn Suites, **other:** Firestone, Target, **W...gas:** Amoco, BP/repair,

Citgo, Shell, **food:** Arby's, Blackeyed Pea, Blue Ribbon Grill, DQ, Fuddrucker's, Jason's Deli, McDonald's, Panera Bread, Philly Connection, Pizza Hut, Red Lobster, Taco Bell, Wendy's, **lodging:** Courtyard, Fairfield Inn, Holiday Inn, Radisson, **other:** Best Buy, $Tree, Goodyear/auto, JC Penney, Kroger, Macy's, Office Depot, OfficeMax, Publix, mall

33b a I-85, N to Greenville, S to Atlanta

34 Chamblee-Tucker Rd, **E...gas:** Chevron, Citgo, Phillips 66, Shell, **food:** Arby's/Mrs Winner's, Blimpie, Galaxy Diner, Hunan Chinese, KFC/Taco Bell, S&S Cafeteria, **lodging:** Day's Inn, **other:** Advance Parts, Eckerd, Goodyear, **W...gas:** Amoco, Citgo, **food:** AllStar Grill, LoneStar Steaks, McDonald's, Waffle House

32 US 23, Buford Hwy, to Doraville, **E...gas:** Amoco/24hr, **food:** Burger King, Checker's, Chick-fil-A, El Azteca Mexican, KFC/Pizza Hut, Krystal, LJ Silver, Mrs Winners, Steak'n Shake, Wendy's, **other:** Firestone/auto, Goodyear/auto, K-Mart, OfficeMax, Target, **W...gas:** Phillips 66/diesel, **food:** Arby's, McDonald's, Szechuan Garden, Taco Bell, Waffle House, **lodging:** Comfort Inn

31b a GA 141, Peachtree Ind, to Chamblee, **W...food:** Chick-fil-A, Piccadilly, Red Lobster, Waffle House, Wendy's, **other:** Acura, Audi/VW, Buick/Pontiac, Chevrolet, CVS Drug, Dodge, Firestone, Ford, GMC, Isuzu, Kia, Lexus, Mazda, Mitsubishi, Porsche, Saab, Toyota

30 Chamblee-Dunwoody Rd, N Shallowford Rd, to N Peachtree Rd, **N...gas:** Amoco, BP, Chevron, **food:** Burger King, DQ, Del Taco, Mrs Winners, Subway, Waffle House, **other:** Kroger, **S...gas:** Exxon, Phillips 66, Shell, Texaco, **food:** Blimpie, Bombay Grill, China Express, City Café, KFC, LJ Silver, Mad Italian Rest., Malone's Grill, Papa John's, Taco Bell, Wendy's, **lodging:** Holiday Inn Select

29 Ashford-Dunwoody Rd, **N...gas:** Amoco, BP, Exxon, **food:** Applebee's, Calif Pizza, Chequer's Grill, Burger King, Denny's, Food Court, Fuddrucker's, Houlihan's, Maggiano's Italian, Mrs Winner's, Subway, **lodging:** Fairfield Inn, Holiday Inn, Marquis Hotel, Marriott, **other:** Best Buy, Firestone/auto, Goodyear/auto, Home Depot, Kroger, Marshall's, Old Navy, mall, **S...**Chevron, Conoco, Arby's, Christina's Café, Hilton Garden, Holiday Inn, Residence Inn

28 Peachtree-Dunwoody Rd(no EZ return wb), **N...food:** Burger King, Chequer's Grill, **lodging:** Comfort Suites, Concourse Hotel, Courtyard, Hampton Inn, Holiday Inn Express, Marriott, Residence Inn, Westin, Wyndham Garden, **other:** Eckerd, Goodyear/auto, OfficeMax, Publix, mall, **S...**HOSPITAL

27 US 19 N, GA 400, **2 mi N...**LDS Temple

26 Glenridge Dr(from eb), Johnson Ferry Rd

GEORGIA

Interstate 285

Atlanta Area

25 US 19 S, Roswell Rd, Sandy Springs, **N...gas:** Amoco, BP, Chevron, Phillips 66, Shell/diesel, **food:** American Pie Rest., Boston Mkt, Burger King, Checker's, Chick-fil-A, Church's, El Azteca Mexican, El Toro Mexican, IHOP, Jason's Deli, KFC/Pizza Hut, Panera Bread, Rally's, Ruth's Chris Steaks, Starbucks, 3$ Café, Togo's/Dunkin Donuts, Waffle House, **lodging:** Comfort Inn, Hampton Inn, Homestead Suites, Suburban Lodge, Wyndham Garden, **other:** HOSPITAL, Firestone/auto, K-Mart, NAPA AutoCare, Office Depot, Tires+, **S...gas:** Chevron/24hr, Citgo, Shell, **food:** Mama's Café, TGIFriday, **lodging:** Day's Inn/rest.

24 Riverside Dr, no facilities

22 New Northside Dr, to Powers Ferry Rd, **N...gas:** Shell, **food:** Bennigan's, **S...gas:** Amoco, Chevron/24hr, **food:** Blimpie, Chevy's Mexican, McDonald's, On-the-River Café, SideLines Grill, Waffle House, Wendy's, **other:** Crowne Plaza, CVS Drug

21 (from wb), **N...gas:** Shell, **food:** HillTop Café, Homestead Village, **other:** BMW

20 I-75, N to Chattanooga, S to Atlanta(from wb), to US 41 N

19 US 41, Cobb Pkwy, to Dobbins AFB, **N...gas:** BP, Amoco/24hr, Chevron/24hr, Citgo, Shell, **food:** Arby's, BBQ, Burger King, Carrabba's, Checker's, ChuckeCheese, Crabhouse Rest., Denny's, Dunkin Donuts, Folks Rest., Hardee's, Indian Cuisine, Jilly's Ribs, KFC, McDonald's, Old Hickory House Rest., Olive Garden, Pizza Hut, Red Lobster, Steak&Ale, Steak'n Shake, Sizzler, Taco Bell, Waffle House, Wendy's, **lodging:** French Quarter Hotel, Hilton, Holiday Inn, Howard Johnson, Red Roof Inn, **other:** MEDICAL CARE, Cadillac, Buick/Pontiac/Subaru, Chevrolet/Saab, Circuit City, Eckerd, Honda, Target, **S...gas:** Amoco/24hr, Chevron/24hr, **food:** Buffalo's Café, El Toro Mexican, Malone's Grill, Ruby Tuesday, Schlotsky's, **lodging:** Courtyard, Hampton Inn, Homewood Suites, Sheraton Suites, Stouffer Waverly Hotel, Sumner Suites, **other:** A&P, Barnes&Noble, JC Penney, Macy's, Sears/auto, mall

18 Paces Ferry Rd, to Vinings, **N...lodging:** Fairfield Inn, La Quinta, **S...gas:** BP, QT/24hr, Shell, **food:** Atlanta Exchange Café, Blimpie, Mrs Winner's, Subway, **lodging:** Hampton Inn, Studio+, Wyndham, **other:** Eckerd, Goodyear/auto, Home Depot, Publix

16 S Atlanta Rd, to Smyrna, **N...food:** Waffle House, **lodging:** Holiday Inn Express, **S...gas:** Exxon, Pilot/KFC/Subway/diesel/24hr/2, Texaco/diesel, RV Ctr

15 GA 280, S Cobb Dr, **E...lodging:** Microtel, **other:** U-Haul, **W...gas:** Amoco, BP/diesel, Exxon/diesel, RaceTrac, **food:** Arby's/Mrs Winners/Taco Bell, Checker's, Church's, IHOP, Krystal/24hr, McDonald's, Monterrey Mexican, Subway, Waffle House, Wendy's, **lodging:** AmeriHost, Knight's Inn, Sun Suites, **other:** HOSPITAL

14mm Chattahoochee River

13 Bolton Rd(from nb)

12 US 78, US 278, Bankhead Hwy, **E...gas:** Citgo/diesel, Petro/diesel/rest./24hr/@, **food:** McDonald's, Mrs Winner's, **other:** Blue Beacon, **W...gas:** Amoco

10b a I-20, W to Birmingham, E to Atlanta(exits left from nb), **W...** to Six Flags

9 GA 139, MLK Dr, to Adamsville, **E...gas:** Amoco, Phillips 66, **food:** KFC, McDonald's, Mrs Winner's, **other:** Family$, Winn-Dixie, **W...gas:** Chevron

7 Cascade Rd, **E...gas:** Chevron, Marathon, **other:** Kroger, **W...gas:** Amoco, Phillips 66, **food:** Applebee's, KFC, McDonald's, Mrs Winner's, Pizza Hut, Starbucks, Subway, Wendy's, **other:** HOSPITAL, Eckerd, GNC, Home Depot, Publix, Radio Shack

5b a GA 166, Lakewood Fwy, **E...gas:** Shell, **food:** Burger King, Capt D's, Checker's, DQ, Piccadilly's, Taco Bell, **other:** Circuit City, Cub Foods, CVS Drug, Goodyear, K-Mart, Kroger, mall, **W...gas:** Amoco, Conoco, Shell/diesel/24hr, Texaco, **food:** Church's, KFC, Mrs Winner's, Pizza Hut, Wendy's, **lodging:** Deluxe Inn, **other:** AutoZone, CVS Drug, Family$

2 Camp Creek Pkwy, to airport, **E...gas:** Amoco, BP, Shell/24hr, **food:** Checker's, McDonald's, Mrs Winner's, **lodging:** Clarion

1 Washington Rd, **E...gas:** BP/diesel, **W...gas:** Chevron, **lodging:** Regency Inn

Interstate 475(Macon)

Macon

Exit #	Services
16mm	I-475 begins/ends on I-75, exit 177.

15 US 41, Bolingbroke, **1 mi E...gas:** Exxon/diesel/LP, Marathon/diesel

9 Zebulon Rd, **E...gas:** BP/Chin's Wok/24hr, Citgo, Shell/Pizza Hut/Taco Bell/24hr, Texaco/24hr, **food:** Buffalo's Café, Chick-fil-A, Fuddrucker's, Krystal, Margarita's Mexican, McDonald's, Papa John's, Sonic, Subway, Waffle House, Wendy's, **lodging:** Fairfield Inn, Jameson Inn, Sleep Inn, **other:** HOSPITAL, Kroger, Lowe's Whse, Radio Shack, USPO, **W...gas:** Citgo, Polly's Café

8mm **rest area nb, full(handicapped)facilities, phone, vending, picnic tables, litter barrels, petwalk**

5 GA 74, Macon, **E...food:** Waffle House, Harley-Davidson/Suzuki, **other:** to Mercer U, **W...gas:** Exxon/Subway/Taco Bell, Marathon, Phillips 66/Church's/diesel, **food:** Fazoli's, Wok&Roll Chinese, **lodging:** Family Inn, **other:** $General, Food Lion, Tires+, to Lake Tobesofkee

3 US 80, Macon, **E...gas:** Citgo/Subway, Marathon/diesel, RaceTrac, **food:** BBQ, Cracker Barrel, Golden Corral, McDonald's, Popeye's, Waffle House, **lodging:** Best Western, Comfort Inn, Day's Inn, Discovery Inn, Economy Inn, Hampton Inn, Holiday Inn, Quality Inn, Red Carpet Inn, Regency Inn, Rodeway Inn, Super 8, Travelodge, **other:** Wal-Mart SuperCtr/gas/24hr, **1 mi E...food:** Applebee's, Chick-fil-A, KFC, Krystal, DQ, Taco Bell, **other:** Best Buy, BooksAMillion, Chrysler/Plymouth, Circuit City, CVS Drug, Dillard's, Firestone/auto, Honda, JC Penney, Jo-Ann Fabrics, Kroger, Lowe's Whse, Nissan, Sam's Club/gas, Sears/auto, Target, Toyota, mall, **W...gas:** Conoco/diesel, Shell, **food:** Burger King, **lodging:** Econolodge, Knight's Inn, Scottish Inn

0mm I-475 begins/ends on I-75, exit 156.

N

S

Interstate 575

I-575 begins/ends on GA 5/515.

27   GA 5, Howell Br, to Ball Ground, no facilities

24   Airport Dr, no facilities

20   GA 5, to Canton, **E...gas:** Amoco, Krystal/24hr, **food:** Hardee's, McDonald's, Shoney's, **lodging:** Day's Inn, **other:** Wal-Mart/McDonald's, **W...gas:** Exxon/diesel, **food:** Cracker Barrel, Waffle House

19   GA 20 E, Canton, no facilities

17   GA 140, Canton, to Roswell, no facilities

16   GA 20, GA 140, **W...gas:** Exxon

14   Holly Springs, **E...food:** Chris' Pinecrest Rest., **lodging:** Pinecrest Motel, **W...gas:** Amoco, BP, Chevron, Exxon, RaceTrac, **other:** Kroger

11   Sixes Rd, **E...gas:** Chevron, Citgo, **W...gas:** Conoco

8   Towne Lake Pkwy, to Woodstock, **E...gas:** BP, Chevron, **food:** HotRod Café, McDonald's, 1904 House Rest., Waffle House, Waffle King/24hr, **other:** Ford

7   GA 92, Woodstock, **E...gas:** Exxon, RaceTrac, Shell, **food:** Arby's, Burger King, McDonald's, Mrs Winner's, Waffle House, **lodging:** MetroLodge, **W...gas:** Amoco, **food:** IHOP, **other:** Honda, Home Depot

4   Bells Ferry Rd, **W...gas:** Chevron, QT/24hr, **food:** Arby's, Subway, Waffle House, **other:** Eckerd

3   Chastain Rd, to I-75 N, **E...gas:** BP, **W...gas:** Amoco, Shell, **food:** Arby's, Cracker Barrel, Subway, Waffle House, Wendy's, **lodging:** Comfort Inn, **other:** to Kennesaw St Coll

1   Barrett Pkwy, to I-75 N, US 41, **E...gas:** Chevron/24hr, **food:** Burger King, Hickory Ham Café, KFC, Waffle House, **other:** Barnes&Noble, Publix, **W...gas:** Chevron, Shell, **food:** McDonald's, Applebee's, Fuddrucker's, Olive Garden, Starbucks, Subway, $3 Cafe, **lodging:** Comfort Inn, Crestwood Suites, Day's Inn, Econolodge, Holiday Inn Express, Ramada Ltd, Red Roof Inn, Super 8, **other:** Home Depot, Marshall's, mall

0mm   I-575 begins/ends on I-75, exit 268.

Interstate 675

Exit #	Services
10mm	I-285 W, to Atlanta Airport, E to Augusta. I-675 begins/ends on I-285, exit 52.

7   Ft Gillem, Anvil Block Rd, no facilities

5   Ellenwood Rd, to Ellenwood, no facilities

2   US 23, GA 42, **E...food:** El Puente Mexican, Mojoe's Café, **W...gas:** Speedway/diesel, **food:** Waffle House, **other:** Eckerd, Winn-Dixie

1   GA 138, to I-75 N, Stockbridge, **E...gas:** Chevron/24hr, Citgo/diesel, Exxon, Marathon, Shell, **food:** Arby's, Blimpie, Buffalo's Café, Burger King, Capt D's, Checker's, DQ, Golden Corral, Hong Kong Buffet, KFC, McDonald's, Papa John's, Pizza Hut, Ryan's, Taco Bell, Waffle House, Wendy's, Zaxby's, **lodging:** Comfort Inn, Holiday Inn Express, Motel 6, Ramada Ltd, Shoney's Inn, Suburban Lodge, **other:**

Advance Parts, Cub Foods, CVS Drug, Eckerd, Goodyear, Ingles Foods, Radio Shack, Wal-Mart SuperCtr/24hr, USPO, **W...gas:** RaceTrac, **food:** Applebee's, BBQ, Chick-fil-A, Damon's, Fazoli's, Frontera Mexican, IHOP, Krystal, LJ Silver, Morrison's Cafeteria, O'Charley's, Waffle House, **lodging:** Best Western, Day's Inn, Hampton Inn, **other:** HOSPITAL, Kroger, Tires+

I-675 N begins/ends on I-75, exit 227.

Interstate 985(Gainesville)

Exit #	Services
	I-985 begins/ends on US 23, 25mm.

24   to US 129 N, GA 369 W, Gainesville, **N...other:** HOSPITAL, GA Mtn Ctr, **S...gas:** Chevron/diesel, Citgo

22   GA 11, Gainesville, **N...gas:** BP, QT/24hr, **food:** Burger King, McDonald's, Waffle House, **lodging:** Best Western/rest., Masters Inn, Shoney's Inn/rest., **S...gas:** Citgo/diesel, Exxon, **food:** Huddle House, Waffle House

20   GA 60, GA 53, Gainesville, **N...food:** Hardee's, McDonald's, Mellow Mushroom Pizza, Mrs Winners, **lodging:** Day's Inn, Hampton Inn, Holiday Inn, Shoney's Inn/rest., **S...gas:** Citgo/diesel, **food:** Waffle House

16   GA 53, Oakwood, **N...gas:** Amoco, Citgo, **food:** Arby's, Baskin-Robbins/Dunkin Donuts, Burger King, DQ, El Sombrero Mexican, Hardee's, KFC, McDonald's, Pizza Hut, Subway, Taco Bell, Waffle House, **lodging:** Admiral Benbow Inn, Country Inn Suites, Jameson Inn, Shoney's Inn/rest., **other:** A&P, Chrysler/Jeep, Food Lion, RV Ctr, Sam's Club, **S...gas:** Amoco, Chevron, Citgo/diesel, Exxon, QT, **food:** Checker's, Mrs Winners, Waffle House, Wendy's, **lodging:** Comfort Inn, Goodyear/auto

12   Spout Springs Rd, Flowery Branch, **N...gas:** Amoco, **food:** Taco Bell, **S...gas:** BP/Subway, Chevron/diesel

8   GA 347, Friendship Rd, Lake Lanier, **N...gas:** Chevron, Phillips 66, **S...RV** Ctr

4   US 23 S, GA 20, Buford, **N...gas:** Amoco/24hr, RaceTrac/mart, Shell, **food:** Arby's, Burger King, Hardee's, Krystal, McDonald's, Shoney's, **other:** Big B Drug, Ingles Food, **S...gas:** Amoco/mart, Chevron, Speedway, **food:** Waffle House, **other:** $Tree, Lowe's Whse, Wal-Mart SuperCtr/24hr

0mm   I-985 begins/ends on I-85.

IDAHO
Interstate 15

Exit #	Services
196mm	Idaho/Montana state line, Monida Pass, continental divide, elev 6870
190	Humphrey, no facilities
184	Stoddard Creek Area, **E**...Historical Site, RV camping, **W**...Stoddard Creek Camping
180	Spencer, **E...food:** Opal Country Café, **other:** High Country Opal Store, **W...food:** Spencer Grill/RV Park
172	**E**...US Sheep Experimental Sta, no facilities
167	ID 22, Dubois, **E...gas:** Exxon/diesel/24hr, Phillips 66/diesel, **food:** Opal Mtn Cafe, **lodging:** Crossroads Motel, **other:** RV dump, Scoggins RV Park, USPO, **rest area both lanes, full(handicapped) facilities, phone, picnic table, litter barrels, petwalk, W**...to Craters NM, Nez Pearce Tr
150	Hamer, **E**...**other:** Goodyear, gas, food, phone
143	ID 33, ID 28, to Mud Lake, Rexburg, **W**...weigh sta both lanes
142mm	roadside parking, hist site
135	ID 48, Roberts, **E...gas:** Tesoro/diesel/LP, **food:** Amy's Place, **other:** Western Wings RV Park
128	Osgood Area, **E...gas:** Sinclair/diesel
119	US 20 E, to Rexburg, Idaho Falls, **E...gas:** Sinclair/diesel, **food:** Applebee's, Brownstone Rest., Chili's, Denny's, JB's, Jaker's Steaks&Fish, Outback Steaks, Smitty's Rest., **lodging:** Best Western, Comfort Inn, Day's Inn, Guesthouse Inn, LeRitz Hotel, Motel 6, Quality Inn/rest., Red Lion Hotel, Shilo Inn/rest., Super 8, **other:** KOA, LDS Temple, **W...gas:** Shell
118	US 20, Broadway St, Idaho Falls, **E...gas:** Phillips 66/diesel, **food:** Arctic Circle, Chili's, Domino's, JB's, Smitty's Pancakes, Wendy's, **lodging:** AmeriTel, Fairfield Inn, **other:** HOSPITAL, Buick/GMC, Ford, Harley-Davidson, Subaru, LDS Temple, **W...gas:** Chevron/diesel, Exxon, Flying J/diesel, Maverik, Phillips 66, **food:** Arby's, BBQ, Burger King, DQ, Hong Kong Chinese, Jack-in-the-Box, Little Caesar's, McDonald's, O'Brady's, Papa Murphy's, Pizza Hut, Subway, **lodging:** Comfort Inn, Motel 6, Motel West/rest., **other:** Albertson's, American RV Sales, AutoZone, RiteAid
113	US 26, to Idaho Falls, Jackson, **E...gas:** Sinclair/Dad's/diesel/24hr/@, Yellowstone/Exxon/diesel/motel/@, **other:** HOSPITAL, Targhee RV Park
108	Shelley, Firth Area, **3 mi E...gas:** Chevron, Stop'n Go/diesel, **other:** RV Park/dump
101mm	**rest area both lanes, full(handicapped)facilities, phone, picnic tables, litter barrels, petwalk, geological site**
98	Rose-Firth Area, no facilities
94.5mm	Snake River
93	US 26, ID 39, Blackfoot, **E...gas:** Chevron/24hr, ✈/Flying J/diesel/LP/24hr, Maverik, **food:** Arctic Circle, Domino's, Homestead Rest., KFC, Little Caesar's, McDonald's, Papa Murphy's, Pizza Hut, Subway, Taco Bell, Taco Time, Wendy's, **lodging:** Best Western, Super 8, **other:** Albertson's, Auto Zone, Checker Parts, Chrysler/Dodge/Ford/Lincoln/Mercury, Goodyear/auto, King's Discount, Radio Shack, RiteAid, Schwab Tire, Wal-Mart SuperCtr/24hr, **W**...Phillips 66, Riverside Boot/saddleshop(4mi)
90.5mm	Blackfoot River

89	US 91, S Blackfoot, **2 mi E...lodging:** Y Motel
80	Ft Hall, **W...gas:** Sinclair/diesel/rest./casino, **other:** Shoshone Bannock Tribal Museum
72	I-86 W, to Twin Falls, no facilities
71	Pocatello Creek Rd, Pocatello, **E...gas:** Chevron/Burger King, Phillips 66/diesel, Circle K, Shell/diesel/24hr, **food:** Applebee's, Frontier Pies, Jack-in-the-Box, Perkins, Sandpiper Rest., Subway, **lodging:** AmeriTel, Best Western, Comfort Inn, Holiday Inn, Quality Inn/rest., Super 8, **other:** HOSPITAL, KOA(1mi), **W...gas:** Exxon, **food:** DQ, Papa Kelsey's Pizza, Senor Iguana's Mexican, SF Pizza, Sizzler, **other:** RiteAid, WinCo Foods, **1 mi W on Yellowstone...food:** Arby's, Golden Corral, KFC, McDonald's, Papa Murphy's, Pizza Hut, Schlotsky's, Skipper's, Sonic, Taco Bell, TCBY, Wendy's, Winger's, **other:** Albertson's, AutoZone, Ford, Fred Meyer, Radio Shack, Walgreen
69	Clark St, Pocatello, **W...other:** HOSPITAL, to ID St U, museum
67	US 30/91, 5th St, Pocatello, **E...gas:** Exxon/24hr, **1-2 mi W...gas:** Cowboys, Phillips 66/diesel, Shell, Sinclair/diesel, **food:** Elmer's Dining, McDonald's, Papa Paul's Rest., Pizza Hut, Subway, Taco Bell, Tom's Burgers, **lodging:** Best Western, Econolodge, Rainbow Motel, Sundial Inn, Thunderbird Motel, **other:** HOSPITAL, Cowboy RV Park, Del's Foods, Old Fort Hall, Sullivan's RV Tents, museum
63	Portneuf Area, **W...other:** to Mink Creek RA, RV camp/dump
59mm	**rest area/weigh sta both lanes, full(handicapped)f acilities, phone, picnic table, litter barrel, vending, petwalk, hist site**
58	Inkom(from sb), **1/2 mi W...gas:** Sinclair/diesel/café, **other:** Pebble Creek Ski Area
57	Inkom(from nb), same as 58
47	US 30, to Lava Hot Springs, McCammon, **E...gas:** ✈/Flying J/Conoco/diesel/LP/rest./24hr/@, Chevron/A&W/Taco Time/diesel, **food:** Subway, **other:** to Lava Hot Springs RA, McCammon RV Park
44	Lp 15, Jenson Rd, McCammon, **E**...access to food
40	Arimo, **E...gas:** Sinclair/diesel/deli, repair
36	US 91, Virginia, no facilities
31	ID 40, to Downey, Preston, **E...gas:** Shell/Flags West/diesel/motel/café/24hr/@, **other:** Downata Hot Springs RV camping
25mm	**rest area sb, full(handicapped)facilities, phone, picnic tables, litter barrels, petwalk**
24.5mm	Malad Summit, elev 5574
22	to Devil Creek Reservoir, **E**...RV camping
17	ID 36, to Weston, to Preston, no facilities
13	ID 38, Malad City, **W...gas:** Chevron/Burger King, Phillips 66/Taco Time/diesel/café, **food:** Me&Lou's Rest., Papa Kelsey's Pizza/subs, **lodging:** Village Inn Motel, **other:** HOSPITAL, Chevrolet/Buick, carwash, True Value, **1 mi W...gas:** Conoco/diesel, **food:** Chat&Chew Café, **other:** Thomas Foods, 3R's Tire, museum, repair
7mm	**Welcome Ctr nb, full(handicapped)facilities, info, phone, picnic tables, litter barrels, vending, petwalk**
3	to Samaria, Woodruff, no facilities
0mm	Idaho/Utah state line

216 ID 77, ID 25, to Declo, **N...gas:** Phillips 66/Blimpie/diesel, **other:** HOSPITAL, to Walcott SP, **S...gas:** Shell/Jake'sCafé/diesel, **other:** Frenchman's RV Park(6mi)

215mm Snake River

211 ID 24, Heyburn, Burley, **N...gas:** Chevron/A&W/diesel, **food:** Sinclair/diesel/café, **lodging:** Tops Motel, **other:** HOSPITAL, Riverside RV Park, Country RV Village

208 ID 27, **N...gas:** Phillips 66/diesel/café, **lodging:** Super 8, **S...gas:** Chevron/Subway/diesel/24hr, Shell/Taco Bell, Sinclair, **food:** Arby's, Burger King, Eduardo's Mexican, George K's Chinese, Jack-in-the-Box, JB's, KFC, McDonald's, Perkins, Polo Café, Wendy's, **lodging:** Best Western, Budget Motel, **other:** HOSPITAL, Cal Store, JC Penney, Radio Shack, Wal-Mart SuperCtr/24hr, to Snake River RA, **1 mi S...gas:** Sinclair/diesel, **food:** Guadalajara Mexican, KFC, **lodging:** Starlite Motel, **other:** Buick/Pontiac/GMC, CarQuest, Checker Parts, Chrysler/Plymouth/Dodge/Jeep, Clete's Repair, Kelly Tire, Minico Parts, NAPA

201 ID 25, Kasota Rd, to Paul, no facilities

194 ID 25, to Hazelton, **S...gas:** Sinclair/diesel/café, **other:** RV camping

188 Valley Rd, to Eden, no facilities

182 ID 50, to Kimberly, Twin Falls, **N...gas:** Sinclair/diesel, **other:** Gary's RV Ctr/park/dump, **S...gas:** Travelers/Shell/Blimpie/Taco Bell, **lodging:** Amber Inn, Best Western, **other:** HOSPITAL, to Shoshone Falls scenic attraction

173 US 93, Twin Falls, **N...gas:** ✈/Flying J/Thad's/diesel/24hr/@, **lodging:** Day's Inn, **other:** KOA(1mi), Blue Beacon/24hr, to Sun Valley, **5 mi S...gas:** Chevron/diesel, Phillips 66, **food:** Applebee's, Arby's, Blimpie, Burger King, Carino's Italian, Chili's, Elmer's, IHOP, Jack-in-the-Box, JB's, KFC, Mandarin Chinese, McDonald's, Outback Steaks, Perkins, Quizno's, Shari's, Subway, Tomato's Grill, **lodging:** AmeriTel, Best Western, Comfort Inn, Holiday Inn Express, Motel 6, Shilo Inn, Super 8, Weston Inn, **other:** HOSPITAL, Barnes&Noble, Buick, Chevrolet/Pontiac/Cadillac, Costco/gas, Daewoo/Isuzu, Ford, Goodyear, Home Depot, JC Penney, Michael's, Mitsubishi, Nissan, OfficeMax, Old Navy, Scwab Tire, ShopKO, Target, WinCo Foods, Coll of S ID

171mm **rest area/weigh sta eb, full(handicapped)facilities, phone, vending, picnic tables, litter barrels, petwalk**

168 ID 79, to Jerome, **N...gas:** Chevron/diesel, ShellWendy's/diesel, Sinclair/Honker's/diesel, **food:** Burger King, Cindy's Rest., McDonald's, Pizza Hut, **lodging:** Best Western, Crest Motel, **other:** Brockman RV Ctr, Wal-Mart SuperCtr/gas/24hr, **2 mi N...food:** DQ, **lodging:** Holiday Motel, **other:** HOSPITAL, Chevrolet, **S...food:** Subway

165 ID 25, Jerome, **N...gas:** Sinclair/diesel, **lodging:** Holiday Motel, **other:** HOSPITAL, RV camping/dump

157 ID 46, Wendell, **1 mi N...other:** HOSPITAL, Intermountain RV Park, **S...gas:** Shell/Farmhouse Rest./diesel

155 ID 46, to Wendell, **N...**Intermountain RV Ctr/Park

147 to Tuttle, **S...other:** to Malad Gorge SP, High Adventure RV Park

Interstate 84

E	Exit #	Services
↕	**275mm**	Idaho/Utah state line, no facilities
	270mm	**rest area both lanes, full(handicapped)facilities, geological site, phone, picnic tables, litter barrels, petwalk**
	263	Juniper Rd, no facilities
	257mm	Sweetzer Summit, Sweetzer Summit, elev 5530
	254	Sweetzer Rd, no facilities
W	**245**	Sublett Rd, to Malta, **N...gas:** Sinclair/diesel/café, **other:** camping
	237	Idahome Rd, no facilities
	234mm	Raft River
	229mm	**rest area/weigh sta both lanes, full(handicapped)facilities, phone, picnic tables, litter barrels, petwalk**
	228	ID 81, Yale Rd, to Declo, no facilities
	222	I-86, US 30 E to Pocatello, no facilities

(Jerome)

IDAHO

Interstate 84

146mm	Malad River
141	US 26, to US 30, Gooding, **N...HOSPITAL**, **S...gas:** Phillips 66/diesel/café, Shell/diesel, Sinclair/diesel/ 24hr, **lodging:** Amber Inn, Hagerman Inn, **other:** RV camping
137	Lp 84, to US 30, to Pioneer Road, Bliss, **2 mi S...gas:** Sinclair/diesel/24hr, **lodging:** Y Inn Motel, **other:** camping
133mm	**rest area both lanes, full(handicapped) facilities, info, picnic tables, litter barrels, petwalk, phone(wb)**
129	King Hill, no facilities
128mm	Snake River
125	Paradise Valley, no facilities
122mm	Snake River
121	Glenns Ferry, **1 mi S...gas:** Sinclair, Tesoro, **lodging:** Redford Motel, **other:** Carmela Winery/rest., **other:** to 3 Island SP, RV camping
120	Glenns Ferry(from eb), same as 121
114	ID 78(from wb), to Hammett, **1 mi S...**access to gas/ diesel, to Bruneau Dunes SP
112	to ID 78, Hammett, **1 mi S...**gas/diesel, food, to Bruneau Dunes SP
99	ID 51, ID 67, to Mountain Home, **2 mi S...lodging:** Maple Cove Motel, camping
95	US 20, Mountain Home, **N...gas:** Chevron/KFC/ diesel/24hr, Pilot/Arby's/diesel/24hr/@, **food:** AJ's Rest., Jack-in-the-Box, **lodging:** Best Western, Sleep Inn, **S...food:** McDonald's, Smoky Mtn Pizza, **lodging:** Hilander Motel(1mi), Towne Ctr Motel(1mi), **other:** HOSPITAL, Wal-Mart SuperCtr/gas/24hr, to Mountain Home AFB, KOA
90	to ID 51, ID 67, W Mountain Home, **S...gas:** Chevron/ 24hr, Shell/Burger King/diesel, **lodging:** to Hilander Motel, Maple Cove Motel, Towne Ctr Motel, **other:** KOA, to Mountain Home AFB
74	Simco Rd, no facilities
71	Orchard, Mayfield, **S...gas:** Sinclair/diesel/StageStop Motel/rest./24hr, **other:** phone
66mm	weigh sta both lanes
64	Blacks Creek, Kuna Rd, historical site
62mm	**rest area both lanes, full(handicapped)facilities, OR Trail info, phone, picnic tables, litter barrels, vending, petwalk**
59b a	S Eisenman Rd, Memory Rd, no facilities
57	ID 21, Gowen Rd, to Idaho City, **N...food:** Jack-in-the-Box, McDonald's, Perkins, Subway, **lodging:** Northwest Lodge, **other:** Albertson's/gas, to Micron, **S...gas:** Chevron/24hr, **food:** Burger King, Food-Court, McDonald's, **other:** Boise Stores/famous brands, ID Ice World
54	US 20/26, Broadway Ave, Boise, **N...gas:** Chevron/ diesel/24hr, ✈/Flying J/Conoco/diesel/LP/24hr/@, **food:** Chili's, Hugo's Deli, Jack-in-the-Box, Subway, Wendy's, **lodging:** Courtyard, **other:** HOSPITAL, Big O Tire, Dowdie's Automotive, Goodyear/auto, Jo-Ann Fabrics, OfficeMax, Radio Shack, ShopKO, to Boise St U, **S...gas:** TA/Subway/Taco Bell/diesel/ rest./24hr/@, **lodging:** Shilo Inn, **other:** Kenworth, Mtn View RV Park

53	Vista Ave, Boise, **N...gas:** Citgo/7-11, Shell/Taco Bell, Sinclair, **lodging:** Extended Stay America, Fairfield Inn, Hampton Inn, Holiday Inn Express, Quality Inn, Super 8, **other:** Parts'n Stuff, museums, st capitol, st police, zoo, **S...gas:** Chevron/McDonald's/24hr, **food:** Denny's, Kopper Kitchen, **lodging:** Best Western, Comfort Inn, InnAmerica, Motel 6, Sleep Inn
52	Orchard St, Boise, **N...gas:** Shell/Taco Bell/diesel/24hr, **other:** Mazda/Nissan, GMC, **1-2 mi N...food:** Burger King, Jack-in-the-Box, McDonald's, Pizza Hut, Raedean's Rest., Wendy's
50b a	Cole Rd, Overland Rd, **N...gas:** Chevron/24hr, Circle K, Shell, **food:** Buster's Grill, Cancun Mexican, Eddie's Rest., McDonald's, Outback Steaks, Pizza Hut, Subway, Taco Bell, TCBY, **lodging:** Plaza Suites, **other:** Pontiac/ Buick, transmissions, **S...gas:** ✈/Flying J/Conoco/die-sel/rest./24hr/@, **food:** BBQ, Black Angus, Burger King, Carino's, ChuckaRama, Cracker Barrel, Jamba Juice, KFC, Little Mexico, McGrath's FishHouse, On the Border, Pollo Rey Mexican, Yen Ching Chinese, **lodging:** Ameri-Tel, Best Rest Inn, **other:** LDS Temple, Commercial Tire, Goodyear, Lowe's Whse, Wal-Mart SuperCtr/24hr
49	I-184(exits left from eb), to W Boise, **N...lodging:** Rode-way Inn, National 9 Inn, **other:** HOSPITAL
46	ID 55, Eagle, **N...gas:** Chevron/McDonald's/diesel/ 24hr, Shell/Taco Bell/diesel/24hr, **lodging:** Holiday Inn Express, **other:** MEDICAL CARE, **S...**Fiesta RV Park
44	ID 69, Meridian, **N...gas:** Chevron/diesel/24hr, Sinclair, **food:** Blimpie, Bolo's Eatery, DQ, Jack-in-the-Box, KFC, McDonald's, Pizza Hut, Quizno's, RoundTable Pizza, Shari's/24hr, Taco Bell, Taco Time, Under The Onion Steaks, **lodging:** Best Western, Microtel, **other:** MEDI-CAL CARE, Bodily RV Ctr, Home Depot, Schwab Tire, WinCo Foods, **S...gas:** Shell/diesel/24hr, **food:** JB's, **lodging:** Knotty Pine Motel, Mr Sandman Motel, **other:** Ford, Playground RV Park
38	Garrity Blvd, Nampa, **N...gas:** Chevron/diesel, **other:** Cadillac, Chevrolet/Pontiac/Buick/GMC, Chrysler/Dodge/ Jeep, Ford, Swiss Village Cheese, **S...gas:** Chevron/ diesel, Phillips 66/diesel, Shell/Taco Ole/diesel/24hr, **food:** McDonald's, **other:** MEDICAL CARE, Garrity RV Park
36	Franklin Blvd, Nampa, **N...food:** Jack-in-the-Box, Noodles Rest., **lodging:** Shilo Inn/rest., **S...gas:** Chevron/diesel/ 24hr, Shell/A&W/Taco Bell/diesel/RV dump/24hr, **lodg-ing:** Desert Inn, Sleep Inn, **other:** HOSPITAL, Mason Cr RV Park, Minor RV Ctr
35	ID 55, Nampa, **S...gas:** Shell/diesel, Denny's/24hr, **lodging:** InnAmerica, Shilo Inn, Super 8, **1 mi S...food:** Burger King, McDonald's, Pizza Hut, Taco Time, **lodging:** Budget Inn, Desert Inn, **other:** HOSPITAL
29	US 20/26, Franklin Rd, Caldwell, **N...gas:** ✈/Flying J/Conoco/diesel/LP/rest./24hr/@, **food:** Guesthaus Rest., **other:** RV camping, **S...gas:** Sinclair/diesel, **food:** Perkins/24hr, Sage Café, **lodging:** Best Inn, Best Western, **1-2 mi S on Cleveland/Blaine St...food:** McDonald's, Subway, Taco Time, **lodging:** Desert Inn, **other:** Albertson's/gas, Chrysler/Plymouth/Dodge/Jeep, Honda, NAPA, Rite Aid, Wal-Mart SuperCtr/24hr, to Simplot Stadium

IDAHO

Interstate 84

28	10th Ave, Caldwell, **N...gas:** Maverik/gas, **lodging:** I-84 Motel, **S...gas:** Chevron/24hr, 7-11, Tesoro, **food:** Carl's Jr, DQ, Jack-in-the-Box, Mr V's Rest., Pizza Hut, Wendy's, **lodging:** Holiday Motel/café, Sundowner Motel, **other:** HOSPITAL, Paul's Drug
27	ID 19, to Wilder, **1 mi S...gas:** Tesoro/diesel/24hr
26.5mm	Boise River
26	US 20/26, to Notus, **N...other:** Camp Caldwell RV Park, **S...gas:** Chevron/diesel
25	ID 44, Middleton, **N...gas:** Shell/diesel, **food:** Bud's Burgers/shakes, **S...**weigh sta eb
17	Sand Hollow, **N...food:** Sand Hollow Café, **other:** Country Corners RV Park
13	Black Canyon Jct, **S...gas:** Sinclair/diesel/motel/rest./24hr, phone
9	US 30, to New Plymouth, no facilities
3	US 95, Fruitland, **N...gas:** Shell/A&W/diesel, Texaco/diesel/24hr(3mi), **5 mi N...other:** Neat Retreat RV Park, to Hell's Cyn RA
1mm	**Welcome Ctr eb, full(handicapped)facilities, info, phone, picnic tables, litter barrels, petwalk**
0mm	Snake River, Idaho/Oregon state line

Interstate 86

Exit #	Services
63b a	I-15, N to Butte, S to SLC. I-86 begins/ends on I-15, exit 72.
61	US 91, Yellowstone Ave, Pocatello, **N...gas:** Exxon, Shell/diesel, Tesoro/diesel, **food:** Arctic Circle, Burger King, Chapala Mexican, Johnny B Goode's Diner, Lei's BBQ, Papa Murphy's, Pizza Hut, Subway, Super China, Wendy's, **lodging:** Motel 6, Ramada Inn, **other:** Budget RV Park, Checker Parts, Smith's Foods, **S...gas:** Flying J/Taco Bell/diesel/24hr, Phillips 66/diesel, **food:** Denny's, IHOP, Me&Lou's Rest., McDonald's, Red Lobster, Taco Bandido, **lodging:** Pine Ridge Inn, **other:** Dillard's, Ford, Grocery Outlet, Herb's RV, Home Depot, JC Penney, K-Mart, Michael's, Schwab Tire, ShopKO, TJ Maxx, Walgreen, Wal-Mart SuperCtr/24hr, diesel repair, mall
59mm	Portneuf River
58	US 30, W Pocatello, **N...**RV dump, **S...gas:** Stinker/diesel
56	**N...**Pocatello Air Terminal, **S...gas:** Exxon/diesel/24hr/@
52	Arbon Valley, **S...gas:** Sinclair/Bannock Peak/diesel/@, **other:** casino
51mm	Bannock Creek
49	Rainbow Rd, no facilities
44	no facilities
40	ID 39, American Falls, **N...gas:** Cenex/diesel, Sinclair, **food:** Pizza Hut, Sagebrush Rest., **lodging:** American Motel, **other:** HOSPITAL, Chevrolet/GMC, NAPA, Schwab Tire, to Am Falls RA, RV Park/dump, **S...gas:** Tesoro/diesel/café, **lodging:** Hillview Motel
36	ID 37, to Rockland, American Falls, **2 mi N...gas:** Shell/diesel/24hr, **lodging:** Falls Motel, **other:** HOSPITAL, **2 mi S...**Indian Springs RV Resort

(Interstate 84 continued)

33	Neeley Area, no facilities
31mm	**rest area wb, full(handicapped)facilities, phone, picnic table, litter barrel, petwalk, vending, hist site**
28	**N...other:** to Massacre Rock SP, Register Rock Hist Site, RV camping/dump
21	Coldwater Area, no facilities
19mm	**rest area eb, full(handicapped)facilities, phone, picnic table, litter barrel, petwalk, vending, hist site**
15	Raft River Area, **S...gas:** Sinclair, phone
1	I-84 E, to Ogden. I-86 begins/ends on I-84, exit 222.

Interstate 90

Exit #	Services
74mm	Idaho/Montana state line, Pacific/Mountain time zone, Lookout Pass elev 4680
73mm	scenic area/hist site wb
72mm	scenic area/hist site eb
71mm	runaway truck ramp wb
70mm	runaway truck ramp wb
69	Lp 90, Mullan, **N...gas:** Exxon/diesel/24hr, Yuppie Trails/diesel, **food:** Mullan Café, **lodging:** Lookout Motel(1mi), **other:** USPO, museum
68	Lp 90(from eb), Mullan, same as 69
67	Morning District, Morning District, no facilities
66	Gold Creek(from eb), no facilities
65	Compressor District, no facilities
64	Golconda District, no facilities
62	ID 4, Wallace, **S...gas:** Exxon, **food:** Pizza Factory, Sweet's Café, Wallace Café, **lodging:** Brooks Hotel, Stardust Motel, Sweet's Hotel, **other:** HOSPITAL, Depot RV Park, Excell Foods, Parts+, USPO, museum, repair
61	Lp 90, Wallace, **S...gas:** Conoco/diesel, Exxon, **food:** Silver Lantern Drive-In, Wallace Sta Rest./gifts, **lodging:** Best Western, Brooks Hotel/rest., Molly B-Damm Inn, **other:** Harvest Foods, info ctr, same as 62
60	Lp 90, Silverton, **S...lodging:** SilverLeaf Motel, **other:** RV camping
57	Lp 90, Osburn, **S...gas:** Shell/diesel/24hr, **other:** Blue Anchor RV Park, auto repair
54	Big Creek, **N...other:** Elk Creek Store/repair, hist site
51	Lp 90, Division St, Kellogg, **N...gas:** Conoco/diesel, **food:** Broken Wheel Rest., Trail Motel, **other:** HOSPITAL, Chevrolet/Pontiac/Buick/Cadillac, Chrysler/Dodge/Jeep, IGA Food, Radio Shack, Schwab Tire, Sunnyside Drug, **S...food:** In Cahoots Cafe, Veranda Rest., **other:** USPO, museum
50	Hill St(from eb), Kellogg, **N...lodging:** Sunshine Inn/café, Trail Motel, **other:** IGA Foods, NAPA, **S...gas:** Conoco **other:** Pac'n Sav Foods, Silver Mtn Ski/summer resort/rec area, museum
49	Bunker Ave, **N...gas:** Conoco/diesel, **food:** McDonald's, Sam's Drive-In, Subway, Taco Express, **lodging:** Silverhorn Motel/rest., Silver Ridge Suites, Sunshine Inn, **other:** HOSPITAL, **S...food:** Silver Mtn/Gondola Café, Zany's Café, **lodging:** Super 8, **other:** museum, RV dump

IDAHO

Interstate 90

E ← → **W**

48 Smelterville, **N...gas:** Silver Valley Car/trkstp/motel/café, **other:** RV Park, **S...lodging:** motel/café, **other:** Wayside Mkt Foods

45 Pinehurst, **S...gas:** Chevron/diesel, Conoco/diesel/24hr, **other:** Honda/Yamaha, Pinehurst RV Ctr, KOA, RV dump

43 Kingston, **N...gas:** Shell/diesel/24hr, **food:** Snakepit Café, **lodging:** Enaville Resort, RV camping, **S...gas:** Exxon

40 Cataldo, **N...food:** Cataldo Cafe, Mission Inn Rest., General Store, **S...** Kahnderosa RV Park

39.5mm Coeur d' Alene River

39 Cataldo Mission, **S...other:** Old Mission SP, Nat Hist Landmark

34 ID 3, to St Maries, Rose Lake, **S...gas:** Conoco/diesel, Texaco/diesel, **other:** Rose Lake Gen Store, White Pines Scenic Rte

32mm chainup area/weigh sta wb

31.5mm Idaho Panhandle NF, eastern boundary, 4th of July Creek

28 4th of July Pass Rec. Area, elev 3069, Mullan Tree HS, ski area, snowmobile area, turnout both lanes

24mm chainup eb, removal wb

22 ID 97, to St Maries, L Coeur d' Alene Scenic By-Way, Wolf Lodge District, Harrison, **1 mi N...**Wolf Lodge Campground, **S...other:** KOA, Squaw Bay Resort(7mi)

20.5mm Lake Coeur d' Alene

17 Mullan Trail Rd, no facilities

15 Lp 90, Sherman Ave, Coeur d' Alene, **N...other:** forest info, Lake Coeur D' Alene RA/HS, **S...gas:** Cenex, Exxon/diesel/24hr, Shell, Tesoro, **food:** Michael D's Eatery, Mike's Café, Roger's Ice Cream, **lodging:** BudgetSaver Motel, El Rancho Motel, Holiday Inn Express, Holiday Motel, Red Rose Motel, Sandman Motel, Star Motel, State Motel, Sundowner Motel, **other:** Buick/Pontiac/GMC, IGA Foods/24hr, NAPA

14 15th St, Coeur d' Alene, **S...gas:** TAJ Mart, **other:** Jordon's Grocery

13 4th St, Coeur d' Alene, **N...gas:** Citgo/7-11, Conoco/diesel, **food:** Baskin-Robbins, Bruchi's Café, Carl's Jr, DQ, Davis Donuts, Denny's, Godfather's, IHOP, KFC, Little Caesar's, Taco John's, Wendy's, **lodging:** Fairfield Inn, **other:** Hastings Books, Kelly Tire, NAPA, Radio Shack, Schuck's Parts, Schwab Tires, same as 12, **S...gas:** Exxon/diesel, **food:** Phothanh Vietnamese, Subway

12 US 95, to Sandpoint, Moscow, **N...gas:** Chevron, Exxon/diesel, Holiday/diesel, Shell, **food:** Applebee's, Arby's, Burger King, Chili's, Domino's, DragonHouse Chinese, FastBurger, McDonald's, Perkins, Pizza Hut, Pizza Shoppe, Red Lobster, Taco Bell, Tomato St Italian, **lodging:** Best Inn, Best Western, Budget Host, Comfort Inn, Coeur d'Alene Inn, Guesthouse Inn, Holiday Inn, La Quinta, Motel 6, Shilo Inn, Super 8, **other:** Alton's Tires, Buick/Pontiac/GMC, Cadillac/Isuzu, Dodge, Ford/Lincoln/Mercury, Fred Meyer, Home Depot, K-Mart, Office Depot, Safeway/gas, Schwab Tire, Tidyman's Food/24hr, Toyota, U-Haul, Walgreen, radiators, **S...gas:** Shell, **food:** Chopstix Express, Figaro's Italian, Mr Steak, Jack-in-the-Box, Schlotsky's, Shari's, TCBY, **lodging:** AmeriTel, **other:** HOSPITAL, Albertson's/gas, GNC, Rite Aid, ShopKO/drugs, Staples, same as 13

11 Northwest Blvd, **N...gas:** Shell/diesel, **other:** Lowe's Whse, **S...gas:** Exxon, Qwikstop/diesel, **food:** Outback Steaks, **lodging:** Blvd Motel/RV Park, Day's Inn, Garden Motel, **other:** HOSPITAL, Honda/Kia, RiverWalk RV Park

8.5mm **Welcome Ctr/weigh sta eb, rest area both lanes, full(handicapped)facilities, info, phone, picnic tables, litter barrels, petwalk**

7 ID 41, to Rathdrum, Spirit Lake, **N...gas:** Exxon/diesel, **food:** Papa Murphy's, Wendy's, **other:** Wal-Mart SuperCtr/gas/24hr, Couer d'Alene RV Park, Suzuki, **S...gas:** Chevron/diesel/24hr, **food:** Applebee's, Casey's Rest./brewery, DQ, KFC/A&W **lodging:** Holiday Inn Express, U-Haul, repair

6 Seltice Way, **N...gas:** Citgo/7-11, Exxon/RV dump, Shell, **food:** La Cabana Mexican, Pizza Hut, **other:** MEDICAL CARE, Chevrolet, NAPA, Nissan, Subaru, Super 1 Foods/24hr, Walgreen, **S...gas:** Conoco/diesel/LP, **food:** Arby's/Taco John's, Big Cheese Pizza, Denny's, EasyRider Café, Godfather's, Hot Rod Café, JambaJuice, Little Caesar's, McDonald's, NW foods, Papa Murphy's, Rancho Viejo Mexican, Subway, Taco Bell, Winger's Diner, **other:** Ace Hardware, Alton Tire, Shuck's Parts, Tidyman's Food/24hr, USPO

5 Lp 90, Spokane St, Treaty Rock HS, **N...gas:** Shell/diesel, Texaco, **food:** Andy's Rest., Boddy's Burger's, Bruchi's Rest., Domino's, Golden Dragon Chinese, Hunter's Steaks, Rob's Seafood/burgers, WhiteHouse Grill, **other:** CarQuest, Excell Foods, Mazda, Schwab Tire, Seltice RV Ctr, **S...gas:** Pacific Pride/diesel, **food:** MillTown Grill

2 Pleasant View Rd, **N...gas:** ✈/Flying J/Conoco/diesel/rest./LP/24hr/@, Shell, **food:** Burger King, McDonald's, Toro Viejo Mexican, **lodging:** Howard Johnson Express, **S...gas:** Exxon/Subway/diesel/24hr, **food:** Chocolate Factory/pizza/pasta, Jack-in-the-Box, Zip's Rest., **lodging:** Riverbend Inn/rest., Sleep Inn, **other:** GNC, Post Falls Outlets/famous brands, dogtrack

0mm Idaho/Washington state line

Interstate 184(Boise)

B **o** **i** **s** **e**

E ← → **W**

Exit #	Services
6mm	I-184 begins/ends on 13th St, downtown, **lodging:** Best Western, StateHouse Inn, **other:** Aamco, USPO
5	River St(from eb), **W...food:** McDonald's, **other:** Ford/Mercury
4.5mm	Boise River
3	Fairview Ave, to US 20/26 E, **W...lodging:** DoubleTree, Econolodge, Shilo Inn
2	Curtis Rd, to Garden City, **W...**HOSPITAL
1	Franklin Rd, **E...gas:** Chevron/Subway, Sinclair, **lodging:** Boise Motel, Plaza Suites, **other:** Acura/Honda, Buick/Pontiac, Dodge, **W...gas:** Sinclair, **food:** Burger King, Chili's, EatABurger, Jack-in-the-Box, Perkins, Sizzler, Starbucks, Wendy's, YenChing Chinese, **lodging:** AmeriTel, **other:** Circuit City, Costco, Dillard's, JC Penney, Mervyn's, Office Depot, Old Navy, Ross, Saturn, Target, mall
0mm	I-184 begins/ends on I-84, exit 49.

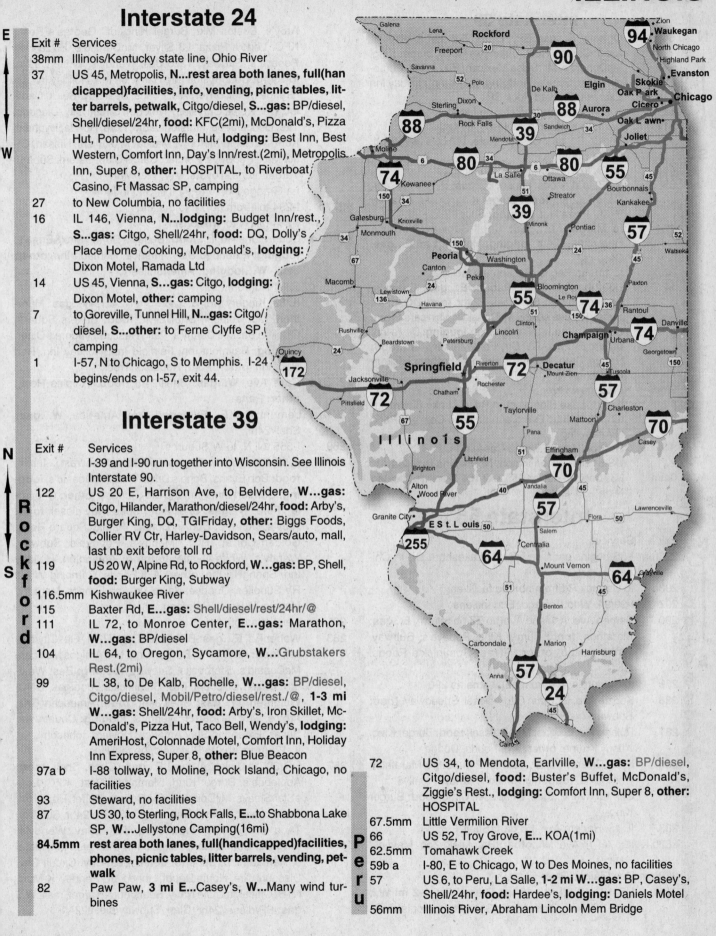

Interstate 24

E ↑ ↓ W

Exit #	Services
38mm	Illinois/Kentucky state line, Ohio River
37	US 45, Metropolis, **N...rest area both lanes, full(handicapped)facilities, info, vending, picnic tables, litter barrels, petwalk,** Citgo/diesel, **S...gas:** BP/diesel, Shell/diesel/24hr, **food:** KFC(2mi), McDonald's, Pizza Hut, Ponderosa, Waffle Hut, **lodging:** Best Inn, Best Western, Comfort Inn, Day's Inn/rest.(2mi), Metropolis Inn, Super 8, **other:** HOSPITAL, to Riverboat Casino, Ft Massac SP, camping
27	to New Columbia, no facilities
16	IL 146, Vienna, **N...lodging:** Budget Inn/rest., **S...gas:** Citgo, Shell/24hr, **food:** DQ, Dolly's Place Home Cooking, McDonald's, **lodging:** Dixon Motel, Ramada Ltd
14	US 45, Vienna, **S...gas:** Citgo, **lodging:** Dixon Motel, **other:** camping
7	to Goreville, Tunnel Hill, **N...gas:** Citgo/diesel, **S...other:** to Ferne Clyffe SP, camping
1	I-57, N to Chicago, S to Memphis. I-24 begins/ends on I-57, exit 44.

Interstate 39

N ↑ ↓ S

Rockford

Exit #	Services
	I-39 and I-90 run together into Wisconsin. See Illinois Interstate 90.
122	US 20 E, Harrison Ave, to Belvidere, **W...gas:** Citgo, Hilander, Marathon/diesel/24hr, **food:** Arby's, Burger King, DQ, TGIFriday, **other:** Biggs Foods, Collier RV Ctr, Harley-Davidson, Sears/auto, mall, last nb exit before toll rd
119	US 20 W, Alpine Rd, to Rockford, **W...gas:** BP, Shell, **food:** Burger King, Subway
116.5mm	Kishwaukee River
115	Baxter Rd, **E...gas:** Shell/diesel/rest/24hr/@
111	IL 72, to Monroe Center, **E...gas:** Marathon, **W...gas:** BP/diesel
104	IL 64, to Oregon, Sycamore, **W...**Grubstakers Rest.(2mi)
99	IL 38, to De Kalb, Rochelle, **W...gas:** BP/diesel, Citgo/diesel, Mobil/Petro/diesel/rest./@, **1-3 mi W...gas:** Shell/24hr, **food:** Arby's, Iron Skillet, McDonald's, Pizza Hut, Taco Bell, Wendy's, **lodging:** AmeriHost, Colonnade Motel, Comfort Inn, Holiday Inn Express, Super 8, **other:** Blue Beacon
97a b	I-88 tollway, to Moline, Rock Island, Chicago, no facilities
93	Steward, no facilities
87	US 30, to Sterling, Rock Falls, **E...**to Shabbona Lake SP, **W...**Jellystone Camping(16mi)
84.5mm	**rest area both lanes, full(handicapped)facilities, phones, picnic tables, litter barrels, vending, petwalk**
82	Paw Paw, **3 mi E...**Casey's, **W...**Many wind turbines

Peru

72	US 34, to Mendota, Earlville, **W...gas:** BP/diesel, Citgo/diesel, **food:** Buster's Buffet, McDonald's, Ziggie's Rest., **lodging:** Comfort Inn, Super 8, **other:** HOSPITAL
67.5mm	Little Vermilion River
66	US 52, Troy Grove, **E...** KOA(1mi)
62.5mm	Tomahawk Creek
59b a	I-80, E to Chicago, W to Des Moines, no facilities
57	US 6, to Peru, La Salle, **1-2 mi W...gas:** BP, Casey's, Shell/24hr, **food:** Hardee's, **lodging:** Daniels Motel
56mm	Illinois River, Abraham Lincoln Mem Bridge

ILLINOIS

Interstate 39

N ↕ S

54	Oglesby, **E...gas:** BP, Phillips 66/diesel, Shell/24hr, **food:** Cristo's Rest, Delaney's Rest., Burger King, McDonald's, Mr. Salsa Mexican, Pizza Grill, Pomodori Rest, Subway, **lodging:** Day's Inn, Holiday Inn Express, Starved Rock SP
52	IL 251, to La Salle, Peru, no facilities
51	IL 71, to Hennepin, Oglesby, no facilities
48	Tonica, **E...gas:** Casey's Store, Tonica/diesel, **food:** Noble Roman's
41	IL 18, to Streator, Henry, no facilities
35	IL 17, to Wenona, Lacon, **E...gas:** BP/diesel/24hr, Casey's(2mi), **food:** Burger King, Buster's Family Rest., Pizza Hut, **lodging:** Super 8
27	to Minonk, **E...gas:** Shell/Subway/Woody's Rest./diesel/24hr, **lodging:** Motel 6, **1 mi E...gas:** Casey's
22	IL 116, to Peoria, Benson, no facilities
14	US 24, to El Paso, Peoria, **E...gas:** Casey's, Freedom/diesel, Shell/diesel/24hr, **food:** DQ, Elm's Buffet, Hardee's/24hr, McDonald's, Monical's Pizza, Subway, Woody's Family Rest., **lodging:** Day's Inn, **other:** El Paso RV Ctr, Ford/Mercury, **W...food:** Range Cafe, **lodging:** Super 8, **other:** Hickory Hill Camping
9mm	Mackinaw River
8	IL 251, Lake Bloomington Rd, **E...**Lake Bloomington, **W...other:** Evergreen Lake, to Comlara Park, RV camping
5	Hudson, **1 mi E...gas:** Casey's
2	US 51 bus, Bloomington, Normal, no facilities
0mm	I-39 begins/ends on I-55, exit 164., Facilities located N on I-55, exit 165.

N o r m a l

Interstate 55

N ↕ S — C h i c a g o   A r e a

Exit #	Services
295mm	I-55 begins/ends on US 41, Lakeshore Dr, in Chicago.
293a	to Cermak Rd(from nb), no facilities
292	I-90/94, W to Chicago, E to Indiana
290	Damen Ave, Ashland Ave(no EZ nb return), **E...gas:** Marathon, **food:** Burger King, Popeye's, Subway, White Castle, **other:** $Tree, Dominick's Foods, GNC
289	to California Ave(from nb), same as 290
288	Kedzie Ave, **E...gas:** Citgo/diesel, Speedway, **food:** Subway
287	Pulaski Rd, **E...gas:** Mobil/diesel, **food:** Burger King, Krispy Kreme, **other:** Aldi Foods, Dodge
286	IL 50, Cicero Ave, **E...gas:** BP/24hr, Citgo, Marathon, Phillips 66, **food:** McDonald's, **other:** Family$
285	Central Ave, **E...gas:** BP/diesel, Citgo, **food:** Burger King
283	IL 43, Harlem Ave, **E...gas:** Shell
282b a	IL 171, 1st Ave, **W...other:** Brookfield Zoo, Mayfield Park
279mm	Des Plaines River
279b	US 12, US 20, US 45, La Grange Rd, **1-2 mi W...gas:** BP/24hr, Clark, Mobil, Shell, **food:** Applebee's, Arby's, Boston Mkt, Burger King, JC George's Rest., KFC, Ledo's Pizza, LJ Silver, McDonald's, Pizza Hut, Popeye's, Subway, Taco Bell, Wendy's, White Castle, **lodging:** Countryside Inn, Hampton Inn, Holiday Inn, La Grange Motel, **other:** Aldi Foods, Best Buy, Buick, Cadillac, Chevrolet, Chrysler/Plymouth, Circuit City, Discount Tire, Dodge/Jeep, Firestone/auto, Ford, Honda, Hyundai, Kohl's, Lincoln/Mercury, Mazda, Mitsubishi, Nissan, OfficeMax, PepBoys, Pontiac, Sam's Club, Saturn, Subaru, Target/drugs, Toyota, VW, Wal-Mart
a	La Grange Rd, to I-294 toll, S to Indiana
277b	I-294 toll(from nb), S to Indiana
a	I-294 toll, N to Wisconsin
276b a	County Line Rd, **E...food:** Bobak's Buffet, Max&Erma's, **lodging:** Extended Stay America, Ramada Inn, **other:** bank, **W...lodging:** AmeriSuites
c	Joliet Rd(from nb)
274	IL 83, Kingery Rd, **E...gas:** Shell/24hr, **W...gas:** Marathon, Mobil/diesel, Shell/24hr, **food:** Bakers Square, Chicken Basket, Denny's, Patio Rest., Salvadore's Diner, **lodging:** Baymont Inn, Fairfield Inn, Holiday Inn, Red Roof Inn, **other:** Ford, House of Trucks
273b a	Cass Ave, **W...gas:** Shell/24hr, **food:** Ripples Rest., **other:** Parts+
271b a	Lemont Rd, **E...**Extended Stay America, **W...gas:** Shell/24hr
269	I-355 toll N, to W Suburbs
267	IL 53, Bolingbrook, **E...gas:** 55 Trkstp/diesel/rest./24hr/@, **food:** Bob Evans, Bono's Drive-Thru, McDonald's, **lodging:** Comfort Inn, Ramada Ltd, Super 8, **other:** Chevrolet, Ford, **W...gas:** Shell/24hr, Speedway/diesel, **food:** Arby's, Denny's, Dunkin Donuts, Family Square Rest., Golden Corral, IHOP, Mendy's, Popeye's, Subway, Wendy's, White Castle, **lodging:** AmericInn, Holiday Inn, SpringHill Inn, **other:** Aldi Foods, Camping World RV Supplies, Goodyear/auto, Jo-Ann Fabrics, Mercury/Lincoln, U-Haul, Walgreen
265mm	weigh sta both lanes
263	Weber Rd, **E...gas:** BP/diesel, Citgo/7-11, GasCity/diesel, **food:** A&W/KFC, Burger King, Los Amigos Mexican, McDonald's, Starbucks, Subway, **lodging:** Best Western, **other:** Discount Tire, Dominick's Food/gas, GNC, Walgreen, **W...gas:** Shell/24hr, **food:** American Grill, Arby's, Cracker Barrel, Wendy's, **lodging:** Country Inn Suites, Extended Stay America, Howard Johnson
261	IL 126(from sb), to Plainfield, no facilities
257	US 30, to Joliet, Aurora, **E...gas:** Citgo, Shell, **food:** Applebee's, Burger King, Diamond's Rest., KFC, LoneStar Steaks, McDonald's, Old Country Buffet, Pizza Hut, Red Lobster, Samy's Grill, Steak'n Shake/24hr, Subway, Taco Bell, Texas Roadhouse, TGIFriday, Wendy's, **lodging:** Comfort Inn, Fairfield Inn, Hampton Inn, Motel 6, Ramada Ltd, Super 8, **other:** Best Buy, Circuit City, Discount Tire, Home Depot, Honda, JC Penney, K-Mart, NTB, OfficeMax, Old Navy, Sears/auto, Target, mall, **W...gas:** BP/diesel/24hr, Clark/Subway/diesel/24hr

Interstate 55

Joliet

253b a US 52, Jefferson St, Joliet, **E...gas:** Phillips 66, Shell/24hr, **food:** KFC/Pizza Hut, McDonald's, Wendy's, **lodging:** Best Western, Fireside Motel, Wingate Inn, **other:** HOSPITAL, Ford/Suzuki, Rick's RV Ctr, **W...gas:** BP/diesel/24hr, **food:** Baba's Rest., Burger King, DQ, Smile of Thai Rest., Subway(1mi), **other:** HOSPITAL, Chrysler/Plymouth/Dodge/Jeep, Goodyear

251 IL 59(from nb), to Shorewood, access to same as 253 W

250b a I-80, W to Iowa, E to Toledo, no facilities

248 US 6, Joliet, **E...gas:** Speedway/diesel/24hr, **lodging:** Manor Motel, **other:** Frank's Country Store, **W...gas:** BP/McDonald's, **food:** Ivo's Grill, Lone Star Rest.(2mi), **other:** to Ill/Mich Tr

247 Bluff Rd, no facilities

245mm Des Plaines River

245 Arsenal Rd, **E...other:** Joliet Army Ammunition Plant, Exxon/Mobil Refinery

241 to Wilmington, no facilities

241mm Kankakee River

240 Lorenzo Rd, **E...gas:** Phillips 66/diesel, **W...gas:** Citgo/diesel/rest./24hr, **lodging:** Motel 55

238 IL 129 S, Braidwood, to Wilmington, no facilities

236 IL 113, Coal City, **E...food:** Good Table Rest., **other:** Chrysler/Plymouth/Dodge/Jeep, **W...gas:** Clark/diesel, **2 mi W...gas:** Citgo, Mobil/diesel/24hr, Shell, **food:** McDonald's, Subway

233 Reed Rd, **E...gas:** Marathon, **lodging:** Sun Motel, **W...other:** antiques

227 IL 53, Gardner, **E...gas:** Casey's, Gardner Haus Rest., **W...gas:** BP/diesel/24hr

220 IL 47, Dwight, **E...gas:** Amoco/Burger King/diesel/24hr, Clark/diesel/24hr, **food:** Arby's, Dwight Chinese Rest., McDonald's, Pete's Rest., Subway, Classic Motel, **lodging:** Super 8

217 IL 17, Dwight, **E...gas:** Casey's, Shell/diesel/24hr, **food:** DQ, Rte 66 Rest., **other:** Chrysler/Plymouth/Dodge/Jeep, Family$, NAPA, RadioShack

213mm Mazon River

209 Odell, **E...gas:** BP, **food:** Wishing Well Café

201 IL 23, Pontiac, **1-3 mi E...gas:** Clark/24hr, **food:** DQ, **other:** Pontiac RV Ctr, 4H RV Camp(seasonal)

198mm Vermilion River

Pontiac

197 IL 116, Pontiac, **E...gas:** BP/Subway/diesel/24hr, Shell, **food:** Arby's, Baby Bull's Rest., Burger King, Buster's Rest., KFC/Taco Bell, LJ Silver, McDonald's, Wendy's, **lodging:** Comfort Inn, Fiesta Motel(1mi), Holiday Inn Express, Super 8, **other:** HOSPITAL, Aldi Foods, AutoZone, Chevrolet/Buick, Lincoln/Mercury/Dodge, Pontiac/Cadillac, Wal-Mart/auto, st police, **W...gas:** Citgo

193mm rest area both lanes, full(handicapped)facilities, phone, picnic tables, litter barrels, vending, petwalk

187 US 24, Chenoa, **E...gas:** Casey's, Phillips 66/McDonald's, Shell/Subway/diesel/24hr, **food:** Chenoa Family Rest., Super 8, **other:** Chevrolet

178 Lexington, **E...gas:** BP/Pizza Hut/diesel, Freedom/diesel, **W...**Chevrolet

177mm Mackinaw River

171 Towanda, **E...gas:** FastStop

167 Lp 55 S(exits left from sb), Veterans Pkwy, to Normal, **S...food:** to airport

165b a US 51B, to Bloomington, **E...gas:** BP/24hr, FS/diesel, Mobil/Arby's/diesel, Shell/Burger King/24hr, **food:** Denny's, Pizza Hut, Steak'n Shake, Uncle Tom's Pancakes, **lodging:** Best Western, Holiday Inn, Motel 6, Super 8, **other:** HOSPITAL, $General, to Ill St U, **W...**NAPA

164 I-39, US 51, N to Peru, no facilities

163 I-74 W, to Peoria, no facilities

Normal

160b a US 150, IL 9, Market St, Bloomington, **E...gas:** BP, Clark, Freedom/diesel, Pilot/Wendy's/diesel/24hr/@, Shell, Speedway/diesel, TA/diesel/rest./24hr/@, **food:** Arby's, Burger King, Cracker Barrel, Culver's, KFC, McDonald's, Subway, Taco Bell, **lodging:** Best Inn, Comfort Inn, Econolodge, Hawthorn Suites, Quality Suites, **other:** HOSPITAL, Aldi Foods, Blue Beacon, Family$, NAPA, **W...gas:** Citgo/diesel, **food:** Country Kitchen, Fiesta Ranchera, Ming's Wok, Steak'n Shake/24hr, **lodging:** Country Inn Suites, Hampton Inn, Ramada Ltd, Wingate Inn, **other:** Factory Stores/famous brands, Wal-Mart SuperCtr/gas/24hr

157b Lp 55 N, Veterans Pkwy, Bloomington, **N...gas:** Clark/24hr, FS, **food:** CJ's Rest., Froggy's Pad Rest., **lodging:** Parkway Inn/rest., Sunset Inn, **other:** HOSPITAL, to airport

a I-74 E, to Indianapolis, US 51 to Decatur

154 Shirley, no facilities

149 **W...rest area both lanes, full(handicapped)facilities, phone, picnic tables, litter barrels, vending, playground, petwalk**

145 US 136, McLean, **E...**RV Ctr, **W...gas:** Citgo, Dixie/Shell/diesel/rest./24hr, **food:** McDonald's, **lodging:** Super 8

140 Atlanta, **E...**camping, **W...gas:** Phillips 66/diesel, **food:** Country-Aire Rest., **lodging:** I-55 Motel

133 Lp 55, Lincoln, **2 mi E...gas:** Citgo, **lodging:** Budget Inn, **other:** HOSPITAL, Camp-A-While Camping

127 I-155 N, to Peoria, no facilities

ILLINOIS

Interstate 55

Lincoln

126	IL 10, IL 121 S, Lincoln, **E...gas:** Phillips 66/diesel/24hr, **food:** Cracker Barrel, KFC/Taco Bell, Steak'n Shake, Wendy's, **lodging:** Comfort Inn, Holiday Inn Express, Super 8, **other:** HOSPITAL, Russell Stover, **1 mi E...food:** A&W, Bonanza, Burger King, Hardee's, LJ Silver, McDonald's, **lodging:** Crossroads Motel, **other:** Aldi Foods, AutoZone, $General, Eagle Foods, Ford/Mercury, Radio Shack, Wal-Mart/auto
123	Lp 55, to Lincoln, **E...lodging:** Lincoln Inn, **other:** HOSPITAL
119	Broadwell, no facilities
115	Elkhart, **W...gas:** Shell/diesel
109	Williamsville, **E...gas:** Shell, **W...**New Salem HS
107mm	weigh sta sb
105	Lp 55, to Sherman, **W...gas:** BP, Shell, **food:** Cancun Mexican, DQ, Subway, **other:** to Prairie Capitol Conv Ctr, hist sites
103mm	**rest area sb, full(handicapped)facilities, phone, picnic tables, litter barrels, vending, petwalk**
102mm	Sangamon River
102mm	**rest area nb, full(handicapped)facilities, phone, picnic tables, litter barrels, vending, petwalk**
100b	IL 54, Sangamon Ave, Springfield, **W...gas:** BP/24hr, Shell/diesel, Speedway/diesel, **food:** Arby's, Burger King, Culver's, McDonald's, Sonic, Wendy's, **lodging:** Northfield Suites, **other:** Wal-Mart SuperCtr/gas/24hr, to Vet Mem
a	**E...gas:** Citgo/diesel, **other:** Kenworth/Ryder/Volvo Trucks
98b	IL 97, Springfield, **W...gas:** BP/24hr, Shell/diesel/24hr, **food:** Hardee's, McDonald's, Subway, Taco Bell, **lodging:** Best Rest Inn, Best Western, Parkview Motel, **other:** HOSPITAL, Goodyear, K-Mart, Walgreen, to Capitol Complex
a	I-72, US 36 E, to Decatur, no facilities

Springfield

96b a	IL 29 N, S Grand Ave, Springfield, **W...gas:** BP, Citgo/diesel/24hr, **food:** Burger King, Godfather's, **lodging:** Motel 6, Red Roof Inn, Super 8, **other:** AutoZone, Buick, Cub Foods, Dodge/Jeep, Ford/Lincoln/Mercury, Hyundai, Isuzu, JC Penney, Kia, Mazda, Mitsubishi, Pontiac/GMC/Subaru, Shop'n Save, Toyota, VW, museum
94	Stevenson Dr, Springfield, **E...**KOA(7mi), **W...gas:** BP, Mobil, **food:** Arby's, Bob Evans, Cheddar's, Denny's, Hooters, Little Caesar's, LJ Silver, Maverick Steaks, McDonald's, Outback Steaks, Pizza Hut, Red Lobster, Smokey Bones BBQ, Steak'n Shake, Subway, Taco Bell, Wendy's, **lodging:** Comfort Suites, Crowne Plaza, Day's Inn/rest., Drury Inn, Hampton Inn, Holiday Inn Express, Microtel, PearTree Inn, Signature Inn, Stevenson Inn, **other:** Cadillac, Chevrolet, CVS Drug, $General, Honda, Jo-Ann Fabrics, Radio Shack, Saturn, ShopKO, USPO

92b a	I-72 W, US 36 W, 6th St, Springfield, **W...gas:** Citgo/diesel/24hr, **food:** Arby's, Burger King, DQ, KFC, McDonald's, Subway, **lodging:** Super 8, Travelodge/rest., **other:** HOSPITAL, Walgreen
90	Toronto Rd, **E...gas:** BP/24hr, Qik-n-EZ/diesel, Shell, **food:** Burger King, Cracker Barrel, Hardee's, HenHouse, Hunan Chinese, McDonald's, Subway, **lodging:** Baymont Inn, Motel 6, Ramada Ltd, **other:** HOSPITAL
89mm	Lake Springfield
88	E Lake Dr, Chatham, **E...other:** to Lincoln Mem Garden/Nature Ctr, st police, **W...**KOA
83	Glenarm, **W...**JJ RV Park/LP(4mi)
82	IL 104, to Pawnee, **E...**to Sangchris Lake SP, **W...gas:** Mobil/Homestead/Subway/diesel/rest./24hr/@, **other:** antiques/crafts
80	Divernon, Hist 66, **W...gas:** Clark, Phillips 66/diesel, **food:** Bearden's Rest.
72	Farmersville, **W...gas:** Mobil/diesel/24hr, Shell/24hr, Subway/TCBY, **lodging:** Art's Motel/rest.
65mm	**rest area both lanes, full(handicapped)facilities, phone, picnic tables, litter barrels, vending, playground, petwalk**
63	IL 48, IL 127, to Raymond, no facilities
60	IL 108, to Carlinville, **E...other:** Kamper Kampanion RV Park, **W...gas:** Shell/diesel/LP/café, **lodging:** Holiday Inn/rest., **other:** to Blackburn Coll
56mm	weigh sta nb
52	IL 16, Litchfield, Hist 66, **E...gas:** Amoco/24hr, Casey's, Phillips 66/diesel, Shell/24hr, **food:** Ariston Café, Burger King, China Town, DQ, Denny's, Domino's, Gardens Rest., Hardee's, Jubelt's Rest., KFC, LJ Silver/A&W, Maverick Steaks, McDonald's, Pizza Hut, Ponderosa, Subway, Taco Bell, Wendy's, **lodging:** Baymont Inn, Best Value Inn, Comfort Inn, Super 8, **other:** HOSPITAL, Aldi Foods, Dodge, $General, Ford/Mercury, Goodyear/auto, IGA Foods, Kroger, Rainmaker Camping(8mi), Wal-Mart SuperCtr/gas/24hr, **W...**st police
44	IL 138, Mt Olive, to White City, **E...gas:** Mobil/diesel, **food:** Crossroads Diner, **lodging:** Budget 10 Motel
41	to Staunton, **E...**Classic Car Museum, **W...gas:** Casey's, Phillips 66/diesel/rest./24hr, **food:** DQ, Subway, **lodging:** Super 8, **other:** HOSPITAL
37	Livingston, New Douglas, **E...**Shady-Oak Camping(4mi), **W...gas:** BP/diesel/24hr, **food:** Country Inn, Gasperoni's Café
33	IL 4, Worden, to Staunton, **W...**gas
30	IL 140, Hamel, **E...**Innkeeper Motel/rest., **W...gas:** Shell, **food:** Earnie's Café, **other:** NAPA
28mm	**rest area both lanes, full(handicapped)facilities, phone, picnic tables, litter barrels, vending, petwalk**

Interstate 55

23 IL 143, Edwardsville, **E...gas:** Mobil/dieselmart, **other:** repair, **W...**Red Barn Camping(apr-oct)

20b I-270 W, to Kansas City, no facilities

a I-70 E, to Indianapolis, no facilities

I-55 S and I-70 W run together 18 mi

18 IL 162, to Troy, **E...gas:** BP/diesel/rest./24hr/@, Citgo/24hr, Pilot/Arby's/diesel/24hr/@, **food:** Burger King, China King, DQ, Imo's Pizza, Jack-in-the-Box, KFC, Little Caesar's, McDonald's, Moma Mia's Café, Perkins, Pizza Hut, Subway, **lodging:** Relax Inn, **other:** HOSPITAL, Family$, SuperValu Foods, USPO, **W...gas:** Phillips 66/diesel/24hr, **food:** China Garden, Cracker Barrel, Taco Bell, **lodging:** Ramada Ltd, Red Roof Inn, Super 8, Villager Lodge

17 US 40 E, to Troy, to St Jacob

15b a IL 159, Maryville, Collinsville, **E...gas:** Citgo, Phillips 66/diesel, Shell, **food:** Sharkey's Rest., **other:** Aldi Foods, Chevrolet, $General, Family$, Ford/Lincoln/ Mercury, **W...gas:** Conoco, **lodging:** Econolodge

14mm weigh sta sb

11 IL 157, Collinsville, **E...gas:** BP/24hr, Casey's, **food:** Denny's, Hardee's, LJ Silver, McDonald's, New China, Pizza Hut, Waffle House, Wendy's, **lodging:** Best Western, Howard Johnson, Motel 6, PearTree Inn, The Inn, Travelodge, **other: W...gas:** Motomart/diesel/24hr/@, **food:** Applebee's, Arby's, Bandana's BBQ, Bob Evans, Burger King, DQ, Ponderosa, Steak'n Shake, White Castle/24hr, **lodging:** Comfort Inn, Drury Inn, Fairfield Inn, Hampton Inn, Holiday Inn/rest., Quality Inn, Ramada Ltd, Super 8, **other:** Buick/Pontiac/GMC, Chrysler/Plymouth/ Dodge/Jeep, st police

10 I-255, S to Memphis, N to I-270

9 Black Lane(from nb, no return), **E...**Fairmount Race-Track

6 IL 111, Fairmont City, Great River Rd, **E...gas:** Phillips 66, **lodging:** Rainbo Motel, Royal Budget Inn, Cahokia Mounds SP, **W...**Horseshoe SP

5mm motorist callboxes begin at 1/2 mi intervals nb

4b a IL 203, Granite City, **E...gas:** Phillips 66/diesel/24hr, **lodging:** Western Inn, **W...gas:** Gateway/Pizza Hut/ Taco Bell/diesel/24hr/@, **food:** Burger King, **other:** Gateway Int Raceway

3 Exchange Ave, no facilities

2 I-64 E, IL 3 N, St Clair Ave, no facilities

2b 3rd St, no facilities

2a M L King Bridge, to downtown E St Louis, no facilities

1 IL 3, to Sauget(from sb), no facilities

I-55 N and I-70 E run together 18 mi

0mm Illinois/Missouri state line, Mississippi River

*(vertical text, left margin):* N S / E St Louis Area

Interstate 57

(vertical text): Chicago

Exit #	Services
358mm	I-94 E to Indiana, I-57 begins/ends on I-94, exit 63 in Chicago.
357	IL 1, Halsted St, **E...gas:** BP, Mobil, **other:** auto repair, **W...gas:** Marathon, Phillips 66, **food:** McDonald's, **oth- er:** Walgreen
355	111th St, Monterey Ave, **W...gas:** BP
354	119th St, no facilities
353	127th St, Burr Oak Ave, **E...gas:** Clark, Shell/Subway, Marathon, **food:** Burger King, McDonald's, Wendy's, **lodging:** Best Western, Plaza Inn, Super 8, **other:** HOSPITAL, Ace Hardware, Firestone, Ultra Foods, **W...gas:** BP/Amoco
352mm	Calumet Sag Channel
350	IL 83, 147th St, Sibley Blvd, **E...gas:** Citgo, Marathon/ diesel, **food:** Denver's Rest., **W...gas:** BP, Citgo
348	US 6, 159th St, **E...gas:** Clark, Marathon, **food:** Burger King, Taco Bell, USA Rest., White Castle, **lodging:** Holiday Inn Express, **other:** Firestone/auto, U-Haul, Walgreen, **W...gas:** Citgo/diesel, Mobil/diesel
346	167th St, Cicero Ave, to IL 50, **E...gas:** BP, Citgo/ diesel, **food:** Wendy's, **lodging:** Ramada Ltd, **W... gas:** Shell
345b a	I-80, W to Iowa, E to Indiana, to I-294 N toll to Wisconsin, no facilities
342a	Vollmer Rd, **E...gas:** Shell/24hr, **other:** HOSPITAL
340b a	US 30, Lincoln Hwy, Matteson, **E...gas:** BP/24hr, Citgo/diesel, Mobil, Shell, **food:** Applebee's, Benny's Steaks, Bistro 57, Bob Evans, Boston Mkt, Burger King, ChuckeCheese, Cracker Barrel, Denny's, Empire Buffet, Fazoli's, Fuddrucker's, IHOP, JN Michael's Grill, KFC, McDonald's, Old Country Buffet, Olive Garden, Pizza Hut, Red Lobster, Starbucks, Subway, Taco Bell, Wendy's, **lodging:** Baymont Inn, Country Inn Suites, Hampton Inn, Holiday Inn/rest., Matteson Motel, **other:** Aldi Foods, Best Buy, Circuit City, $Tree, Dodge, Dominick's Foods, Goodyear/auto, Home Depot, Isuzu, JC Penney, Jo-Ann Fabrics, K-Mart, OfficeMax, Sam's Club, Sears/auto, Target, Walgreen, Wal-Mart, mall, **W...other:** Buick, Chevrolet, Daewoo, Ford, Isuzu, Kia, Mitsubishi, VW
339	Sauk Trail, to Richton Park, **E...gas:** Shell, **food:** Bob's HotDogs, McDonald's, **other:** cinema
335	Monee, **E...gas:** BP/Subway, Petro/Mobil/diesel/rest./ Blue Beacon/24hr/@, Pilot/McDonald's/diesel/24hr/@, **food:** Burger King, Pizza Hut, **lodging:** Best Western, Country Host Motel, Holiday Inn Express, Super 8
332mm	**Prairie View Rest Area both lanes, full(handicap ped)facilities, info, phone, vending, picnic tables, litter barrels, petwalk**
330mm	weigh sta both lanes
327	to Peotone, **E...gas:** Casey's, Shell/Taco Bell/24hr, **food:** McDonald's
322	Manteno, **E...gas:** BP/McDonald's/24hr, Phillips 66/ Subway, **food:** Hardee's, KFC/Taco Bell, Monical's Pizza, Pizza Hut, **lodging:** Country Inn, Comfort Inn, Quality Inn, Welcome Inn, **other:** Harley-Davidson, **W...gas:** GasCity/diesel

Interstate 57

N↑S

K a n k a k e e

315   IL 50, Bradley, **E…gas:** Shell/Burger King/24hr, **food:** Cracker Barrel, LoneStar Steaks, Old Country Buffet, Piccolo's Rest., Pizza Hut, Red Lobster, Ruby Tuesday, TGIFriday, White Castle, **lodging:** Fairfield Inn, Hampton Inn, Holiday Inn Express, Lee's Inn, **other:** Barnes&Noble, $Tree, JC Penney, Michael's, Sears/auto, Staples, Target, mall, **W…gas:** BP/diesel, **food:** Applebee's, Arby's, Bakers Square, Boston Mkt, Coyote Canyon Steaks, Denny's, Hardee's, LJ Silver, McDonald's, Mongolian Buffet, Pizza Hut, Taco Bell, Ponderosa, Steak'n Shake, Subway, VIP's Rest., Wendy's, **lodging:** Motel 6, Northgate Motel, Quality Inn, Ramada Inn, Super 8, **other:** Aldi Foods, Buick/Nissan, Chevrolet, Honda, Hyundai, K-Mart, Lowe's Whse, Mazda, OfficeMax, RV Ctr, Wal-Mart/24hr, to Kankakee River SP

312   IL 17, Kankakee, **E…other:** Chrysler/Plymouth/Dodge, **W…gas:** BP, Shell/24hr, **food:** McDonald's, PoorBoy Rest., Subway, Uncle Johnni's Rest., Wendy's, **lodging:** Avis Motel, Day's Inn/rest., **other:** HOSPITAL, Walgreen, auto repair

310.5mm Kankakee River

308   US 45, US 52, to Kankakee, **E…**KOA(3mi), **W…gas:** Gas Depot, **lodging:** Economy Inn, Fairview Motel, Hilton Garden, **other:** airport

302   Chebanse, **W…gas:** BP

297   Clifton, **W…gas:** Phillips 66/DQ/diesel, **food:** Char-Grilled Cheeseburgers

293   IL 116, Ashkum, **E…gas:** BP/Noble Roman/diesel, **W…food:** Loft Rest., **other:** st police

283   US 24, IL 54, Gilman, **E…gas:** Apollo Trvl Ctr, BP/diner/diesel/24hr, Citgo/diesel, Shell, **food:** Burger King, DQ, McDonald's, Monical's Pizza, Red Door Rest., **lodging:** Budget Host, Super 8, Travel Inn, **other:** Pennzoil, **W…gas:** Phillips 66/Subway/diesel, **other:** R&R RV Ctr

280   IL 54, Onarga, **E…gas:** Casey's(1mi), Phillips 66, **other:** camping, **W…other** Lake Arrowhead RV camping

272   to Roberts, Buckley, no facilities

268.5mm **rest area both lanes, full(handicapped)facilities, vending, phone, picnic tables, litter barrels, pet-walk**

261   IL 9, Paxton, **E…gas:** Casey's, Citgo/diesel/24hr, **food:** Hardee's, Monical's Pizza, Pizza Hut, Subway, **other:** Chevrolet/Pontiac/Buick/GMC, **W…gas:** BP, Marathon, **food:** Country Garden Rest., Hot Stuff Pizza, **lodging:** Paxton Inn

C h a m p a i g n

250   US 136, Rantoul, **E…gas:** BP/rest./24hr, Phillips 66, **food:** Arby's, Hardee's, KFC/Taco Bell, LJ Silver, McDonald's, Monical's Pizza, Red Wheel Rest., **lodging:** Best Western, Day's Inn/rest., Rantoul Motel, Super 8, **other:** NAPA, camping, to Chanute AFB

240   Market St, **E…gas:** Citgo/diesel/rest., **other:** D&W Lake Camping, truck/tire repair

238   Olympian Dr, to Champaign, **W…gas:** Mobil/diesel, **food:** DQ, **lodging:** Microtel, **other:** RV/diesel repair

237b a   I-74, W to Peoria, E to Urbana, no facilities

235b   I-72 W, to Decatur, no facilities

235a   University Ave, to Champaign, **E…**HOSPITAL, U of Ill

229   to Savoy, Monticello, **E…gas:** Speedway/diesel

221.5mm **rest area both lanes, full(handicapped)facilities, phones, picnic tables, litter barrels, vending, pet-walk**

220   US 45, Pesotum, **W…gas:** Citgo, st police

212   US 36, Tuscola, **E…gas:** FuelMart/diesel, **W…gas:** BP/24hr, Citgo, Fleet/diesel/24hr, **food:** Amish Buffet, Burger King, DQ, Denny's, McDonald's, Monical's Pizza, Pizza Hut, Red Bar Buffet, Subway, **lodging:** AmeriHost, Holiday Inn Express, Super 8, **other:** Chevrolet/Pontiac/Buick/GMC, Firestone/auto, Ford, IGA Foods, Pamida, Tuscola Parts, Tuscola Stores/famous brands, camping

M a t t o o n

203   IL 133, Arcola, **E…gas:** Citgo/diesel, **other:** CampALot, **W…gas:** Clark, Shell/Subway/diesel/24hr, **food:** DQ, Dutch Kitchen, Hardee's, Hen House, Monical's Pizza, Subway/Noble Roman, **lodging:** Arcola Inn, Comfort Inn, Knight's Inn, Country Charm Amish, **other:** $General, NAPA, Rockome Gardens, Arcola Camping

190b a   IL 16, to Mattoon, **E…gas:** Citgo, **other:** HOSPITAL, to E IL U, Fox Ridge SP, **W…gas:** Amoco, BP/24hr, Clark, Phillips 66/Subway/24hr, **food:** Alamo Steaks, Arby's, Cody's Roadhouse, Cracker Barrel, DQ, El Vaquero Mexican, Fazoli's, Jubmo Buffet, McDonald's, Steak'n Shake/24hr, Taco Bell, Wendy's, **lodging:** Comfort Suites, Fairfield Inn, Hampton Inn, Ramada Inn/rest., Super 8, **other:** Aldi Foods, $General, Home Depot, JC Penney, Osco Drug, Sears/auto, Staples, Walgreen, Wal-Mart SuperCtr/gas/24hr, mall

184   US 45, IL 121, to Mattoon, **E…gas:** Citgo/Blimpie/diesel, **W…gas:** Marathon/diesel, Shell, **food:** McDonald's, Subway, **lodging:** Budget Inn, Knight's Inn, US Grant Motel, **other:** to Lake Shelbyville

177   US 45, Neoga, **E…gas:** BP/Subway/diesel, Citgo, **W…gas:** Phillips 66/diesel/24hr/@, Casey's(2mi)

166.5mm **rest area both lanes, full(handicapped)facilities, vending, phones, picnic tables, litter barrels, pet-walk, RV dump**

163   I-70 E, to Indianapolis, no facilities

I-57 S and I-70 W run together 6 mi

E f f i n g h a m

162   US 45, Effingham, **E…gas:** Moto/24hr, **lodging:** Budget Host, **W…gas:** Citgo, Phillips 66/Subway, Pilot/McDonald's/diesel/24hr/@, **food:** Trailways Rest., **lodging:** Effingham Motel/café, Lincoln Lodge, **other:** truck repair, Camp Lakewood(2mi)

160   IL 33, IL 32, Effingham, **E…gas:** BP, **food:** KFC, Little Caesar's, LoneStar Steaks, **lodging:** Comfort Inn, Hampton Inn, **other:** HOSPITAL, Aldi Foods, K-Mart, Kroger, Radio Shack, Walgreen, **W…food:** Flying J/diesel/24hr/@, Phillips 66, TA/Popeye's/Sbarro's/diesel/rest./@, **food:** A&W, Arby's, BBQ, Burger King/24hr, Cracker Barrel, Denny's, El Rancherito Mexican, KFC, LJ Silver, McDonald's, Ponderosa, Quizno's, Ryan's, Ruby Teusday, Steak'n Shake/24hr, Taco Bell, TGIFriday, Wendy's, **lodging:** Best Inn, Country Inn Suites, Hilton Garden, Holiday Inn Express, Keller Hotel, Ramada Ltd, Super 8, Travelodge Suites, **other:** Ford/Lincoln/Mercury, Wal-Mart SuperCtr/gas/diesel/24hr

Interstate 57

N ↕ S

159 US 40, Effingham, **E...gas:** BP/24hr, Clark, Dixie/Citgo/diesel/rest./24hr/@, Phillips 66/diesel/24hr, Speedway/diesel, **food:** China Buffet, Domino's, Hardee's/24hr, Niemerg's Rest., Papa John's, Subway, **lodging:** Abe Lincoln Motel, Comfort Suites, Day's Inn, Econolodge, Howard Johnson, Paradise Motel, **other:** Family$, Firestone, SavALot Foods, **W...gas:** Petro/Mobil/diesel/rest./24hr/@, **lodging:** Best Western, **other:** Blue Beacon

I-57 N and I-70 E run together 6 mi

157 I-70 W, to St Louis, no facilities

151 Watson, **5 mi E...**Percival Springs RV Park

150mm Little Wabash River

145 Edgewood, **E...gas:** Citgo

135 IL 185, Farina, **E...gas:** Shell/diesel/rest., **other:** Ford

127 to Kinmundy, Patoka, no facilities

116 US 50, Salem, **E...gas:** Clark/diesel, Huck's, Motomart/24hr, Shell, **food:** Austin Fried Chicken, Burger King, Hunan Garden, KFC, La Cabana Mexican, LJ Silver, McDonald's, Pizza Hut, Pizza Man, Subway, Taco Bell, Wendy's, **lodging:** Budget Inn, Continental Motel(2mi), Restwell Motel(1mi), **other:** AutoZone, Chrysler/Dodge/Jeep, MadPricer Foods, Radio Shack, Salem Parts, to Forbes SP, **W...gas:** Phillips 66/diesel, **food:** Applebee's, Arby's, Denny's, **lodging:** Comfort Inn, Salem Inn, Super 8, **other:** Chevrolet/Buick, Ford, Salem Tires, Wal-Mart SuperCtr/24hr/gas

114mm **rest area both lanes, full(handicapped)facilities, phones, picnic tables, litter barrels, vending, petwalk, playground**

109 IL 161, to Centralia, **W...gas:** Marathon/Biggie's Cafe/24hr

103 Dix, **E...gas:** Phillips 66/diesel, **lodging:** Scottish Inn, **other:** camping

96 I-64 W, to St Louis, no facilities

95 IL 15, Mt Vernon, **E...gas:** BP/diesel/24hr, Marathon, Mobil, Phillips 66, **food:** Burger King, Fazoli's, Hardee's, Hunan Chinese, KFC, LJ Silver, McDonald's, Papa John's, Pasta House, Pizza Hut, Steak'n Shake/24hr, Subway, Taco Bell, Wendy's, Western Sizzlin, **lodging:** Best Inn, Best Western, Drury Inn, Econolodge, Motel 6, Southgate Inn, Super 8, Thrifty Inn, Villager Lodge, **other:** HOSPITAL, AutoZone, Chevrolet, Country Fair Foods, CVS Drug, $Tree, Ford, Harley-Davidson, JC Penney, Jo-Ann Fabrics, K-Mart, Kroger, Radio Shack, Walgreen, **W...gas:** Hucks/diesel/rest./24hr/@, Shell/7-11/24hr, TA/Popeye's/diesel/24hr/@, **food:** Applebee's, Arby's, Burger King, Chili's, Cracker Barrel, LoneStar Steaks, McDonald's, Ryan's, Sonic, **lodging:** Comfort Inn, Day's Inn, Hampton Inn, Holiday Inn, Ramada Hotel, **other:** Cadillac/Pontiac/Buick/GMC, Fannie Mae Candies, Lowe's Whse, Outlet Mall/famous brands, Quality Times RV Park, Staples, Toyota, Wal-Mart SuperCtr/24hr

92 I-64 E, to Louisville, no facilities

83 Ina, **E...gas:** BP/diesel/deli/24hr, **W...**to Rend Lake

79mm **rest area sb, full(handicapped)facilities, info, vending, phones, picnic tables, litter barrels, petwalk, playground**

77 IL 154, to Whittington, **E...gas:** Shell/24hr, **other:** Holiday Trav-L Park, **W...lodging:** Best Western, Seasons at Rend Lake Lodge/rest., **other:** to Rend Lake, golf, Wayne Fitzgerrell SP

74mm **rest area nb, full(handicapped)facilities, vending, phones, picnic tables, litter barrels, petwalk, playground**

71 IL 14, Benton, **E...gas:** Amoco/24hr, BP/diesel, Citgo, **food:** Arby's, Hardee's, KFC/Taco Bell, Pizza Hut, Wendy's, **lodging:** Day's Inn/rest., Gray Plaza Motel, Motel Benton, Plaza Motel/rest., Super 8, **other:** HOSPITAL, AutoZone, KOA(1.5mi), Plaza Tire, **W...gas:** BP/Burger King/diesel, Shell/diesel/24hr, **food:** Bonanza, McDonald's, Subway, Taco John's, **other:** Big John Foods, CVS Drug, Wal-Mart SuperCtr/gas/drugs, to Rend Lake

65 IL 149, W Frankfort, **E...gas:** BP, Citgo/diesel/24hr, GasForLess, Shell, **food:** Hardee's, KFC, LJ Silver, Mike's Drive-In, Pizza Inn, Pancakes/24hr, Sonic, **lodging:** Gray Plaza Motel, **other:** HOSPITAL, CarQuest, $General, MadPricer Foods, **W...gas:** Casey's, **food:** Burger King, Triple E+ Steaks, McDonald's, **lodging:** American Classic Inn, **other:** Chevrolet/Pontiac, CVS Drug, $Tree, K-Mart, VF Factory Stores

59 to Herrin, Johnston City, **E...gas:** Citgo, Shell/24hr, **food:** DQ, Gibby's Grill, Hardee's, McDonald's, Subway, **other:** camping(2mi), **W...other:** HOSPITAL, camping

54b a IL 13, Marion, **E...gas:** Citgo, Phillips 66/24hr, **food:** Arby's, Fazoli's, Grand Buffet, Hardee's, KFC, LJ Silver, Papa John's, Pizza Hut, Subway, Tequila's Mexican, Wendy's, Western Sizzlin, **lodging:** Day's Inn, **other:** MEDICAL CARE, Aldi Foods, AutoZone, Chevrolet/Cadillac, Family$, Ford/Lincoln/Mercury/Hyundai, Kroger/gas, Plaza Tire, Radio Shack, SavALot Foods, USPO, **W...gas:** Amoco/24hr, BP/diesel/24hr, **food:** 17th Street BBQ, Applebee's, Backyard Burger, Bob Evans, Burger King, McDonald's, O'Charley's, Red Lobster, Ryan's, Sonic, Steak'n Shake, Taco Bell, **lodging:** Best Inn, Drury Inn, Fairfield Inn, Hampton Inn, Motel 6, Red Carpet Inn, Super 8, **other:** Buick/GMC/Pontiac/Mercedes, Chrysler/Plymouth/Dodge/Jeep, Dillard's, Harley-Davidson, Home Depot, Kia, Sam's Club/gas, Wal-Mart/auto, mall

53 Main St, Marion, **E...gas:** Shell/diesel, **food:** DQ, **lodging:** Motel Marion/camping, **other:** HOSPITAL, **W...gas:** Motomart/24hr, **food:** Cracker Barrel, Hide-Out Steaks, **lodging:** Comfort Inn, Comfort Suites, Holiday Inn Express

47mm weigh sta both lanes

45 IL 148, **1 mi E...gas:** King Tut's Food/diesel/24hr, **other:** Egyptian Hills Marina(9mi), camping, diesel repair

44 I-24 E to Nashville, no facilities

40 Goreville Rd, **E...other:** Ferne Clyffe SP, camping, scenic overlook, **W...gas:** Citgo/diesel/24hr

ILLINOIS

Interstate 57

36	Lick Creek Rd, no facilities
32mm	**Trail of Tears Rest Area both lanes, full(handicapped)facilities, info, phones, picnic tables, litter barrels, vending, petwalk, playground**
30	IL 146, Anna, Vienna, **W...gas:** Shell/diesel/rest./24hr, **other:** HOSPITAL, auto/tire repair
25	US 51 N(from nb, exits left), to Carbondale, no facilities
24	Dongola Rd, **W...gas:** Shell/diesel
18	Ullin Rd, **W...gas:** Citgo/diesel/24hr, **food:** Cheeko's Family Rest., **lodging:** Best Western, **other:** st police
8	Mounds Rd, to Mound City, **E...other:** K&K AutoTruck/diesel/repair
1	IL 3, to US 51, Cairo, **E...gas:** Amoco/diesel, BP/diesel, **lodging:** Belvedere Motel(2mi), Day's Inn, **other:** $General, Mound City Nat Cem(4mi), camping, **W...**camping
0mm	Illinois/Missouri state line, Mississippi River

Interstate 64

Exit #	Services
131.5mm	Illinois/Indiana state line, Wabash River
131mm	**Skeeter Mtn Welcome Ctr wb, full(handicapped) facilities, phone, vending, picnic tables, litter barrels, petwalk**
130	IL 1, to Grayville, **N...gas:** Shell/diesel/24hr, **food:** Subway, **lodging:** Best Western/rest., Super 8, **other:** museum, Beall Woods St Park, **S...gas:** Phillips 66/diesel
124mm	Little Wabash River
117	Burnt Prairie, **S...gas:** Marathon/diesel, **food:** Chuck-Wagon Charlie's Café, **other:** antiques
110	US 45, Mill Shoals, **N...gas:** FS/diesel, **other:** Barnhill Camping
100	IL 242, to Wayne City, **N...gas:** Marathon/diesel
89	to Belle Rive, Bluford, no facilities
86mm	**rest area wb, full(handicapped)facilities, phone, vending, picnic tables, litter barrels, petwalk**
82.5mm	**rest area eb, full(handicapped)facilities, phone, vending, picnic tables, litter barrels, petwalk**
80	IL 37, to Mt Vernon, **2 mi N...gas:** BP/Burger King/diesel/24hr, Marathon/diesel/24hr, **lodging:** Royal Inn, **other:** camping
78	I-57, S to Memphis, N to Chicago, no facilities
	I-64 and I-57 run together 5 mi. See Illinois Interstate 57, exit 95.
73	I-57, N to Chicago, S to Memphis, no facilities
69	Woodlawn, no facilities
61	US 51, to Centralia, Richview, **S...**access to gas, food
50	IL 127, to Nashville, **N...**to Carlyle Lake, **S...gas:** BP/24hr, Citgo/diesel/24hr, Conoco/diesel/rest., Shell/diesel/24hr, **food:** Hardee's(3mi), McDonald's, Subway, **lodging:** Best Western, Little Nashville Inn/rest., Derrick Motel/rest.(3mi), **other:** HOSPITAL

41	IL 177, Okawville, **S...gas:** Phillips 66/Burger King/diesel/24hr/@, **food:** DQ, Hen House/24hr, Golfer's Steakhouse, **lodging:** Original Springs Motel, Super 8, **other:** Toyo Tires/truck repair
37mm	Kaskaskia River
34	to Albers, **3 mi N...gas:** Casey's
27	IL 161, New Baden, **N...gas:** Shell/diesel/24hr, **food:** Good Ol' Days Rest., McDonald's, Outside Inn Rest., Subway, **other:** Chevrolet
25mm	**rest area both lanes, full(handicapped)facilities, info, phone, vending, picnic tables, litter barrels, petwalk**
23	IL 4, to Mascoutah, **N...food:** DQ, Hardee's, McDonald's
19b a	US 50, IL 158, **N...gas:** Motomart/24hr, **food:** Hero's Pizza/subs, **lodging:** Comfort Inn, **S...gas:** Citgo/diesel, **food:** Ivory Chopsticks Chinese, **other:** HOSPITAL, to Scott AFB
18mm	weigh sta eb
16	to O'Fallon, Shiloh, **N...food:** Dennys, **S...food:** Applebee's, Jonny Rocket's, Quizno's, St. Louis Bread Co., **lodging:** Holiday Inn Express, **other:** Dierbergs's Foods, Target
15mm	motorist callbox every 1/2 mile wb
14	O'Fallon, **N...gas:** QT, Shell/24hr, **food:** Japanese Garden, Steak'n Shake/24hr, **lodging:** Baymont Inn, Extended Stay America, Holiday Inn Express, Howard Johnson, Sleep Inn, **other:** Chevrolet, CVS Drug, Ford, Nissan/Cadillac, **S...gas:** Mobil, **food:** Chevy's Mexican, DQ, Emperor's Wok, Hardee's, Jack-in-the-Box, KFC, Lion's Choice, LoneStar Steaks, McDonald's, O'Charley's, Pepper's Rest., South Paul Cafe, Steak-Out, Taco Bell, Western Sizzlin, **lodging:** Econolodge, Ramada Ltd, **other:** BMW, Dierberg's Foods, Home Depot, Honda, Hyundai, Kia, Mazda, Mitsubishi, Sam's Club, Subaru, Suzuki, Toyota, VW, Wal-Mart/auto/24hr
12	IL 159, to Collinsville, **N...gas:** CFM/diesel, **food:** Applebee's, Bob Evans, Carlos O'Kelly's, Carrabba's, Damon's, HideOut Steaks, Houlihan's, Joe's Crabshack, Olive Garden, Red Lobster, TGIFriday, **lodging:** Best Western Camelot, Drury Inn, Fairfield Inn, Hampton Inn, Ramada Inn/rest., Super 8, **other:** Circuit City, Michael's, 1/2Price Store, Saturn, **S...gas:** BP/24hr, Mobil, Motomart/diesel/24hr, **food:** Boston Mkt, Burger King, Capt D's, Casa Gallardo, Chili's, Denny's, Fazoli's, Hardee's, IHOP, Longhorn Steaks, LJ Silver, Mazzio's, McDonald's, Old Country Buffet, Outback Steaks, Pasta House, Ponderosa, Popeye's, Rally's, Ramon's Mexican, Ruby Tuesday, Schlotsky's, Steak'n Shake, Taco Bell, **other:** AutoTire, Best Buy, Borders, Dillard's, Famous Barr, Firestone/auto, Goodyear, JC Penney, K-Mart, Kohl's, OfficeMax, Schnuck's Foods, Target, Walgreen, mall
9	IL 157, to Caseyville, **N...gas:** BP/24hr, Phillips 66/Subway/repair, **food:** Hardee's, Wendy's, **lodging:** Western Inn, **S...gas:** BP/diesel/repair, **food:** Cracker Barrel, DQ, Domino's, McDonald's, Pizza Hut/Taco Bell, **lodging:** Best Inn, Day's Inn, Motel 6, Quality Inn

ILLINOIS

Interstate 64

E **E S t   L o u i s W**

7	I-255, S to Memphis, N to Chicago, no facilities
6	IL 111, Kingshighway, **N...gas:** BP, Shell, **food:** Popeye's, **lodging:** Econo Inn
5.5mm	motorist callbox every 1/2 mi eb
5	25th St, no facilities
4	15th St, Baugh, no facilities
3	I-55 N, I-70 E, IL 3 N, to St Clair Ave, to stock-yards
2b a	3rd St, **S...gas**
1	IL 3 S, 13th St, E St Louis, **N...**Casino Queen
0mm	Illinois/Missouri state line, Mississippi River

Interstate 70

E **E f f i n g h a m** (left margin); **V a n d a l i a** (center margin)

Exit #	Services
156mm	Illinois/Indiana state line
155.5mm	weigh sta eb
154	US 40 W, **S...**South Fork Conv Mart
151mm	weigh sta wb
149mm	**rest area wb, full(handicapped)facilities, info, phone, picnic tables, vending, litter barrels, petwalk, camping**
147	IL 1, Marshall, **N...gas:** Jerry's Rest., **S...gas:** Casey's, Jiffy/diesel/24hr, Phillips 66/Arby's/diesel/@ , Shell/Subway, **food:** Burger King, DQ, McDonald's, Pizza Hut, Wendy's, **lodging:** Peak's Motel, Lincoln Motel(2mi), Super 8, **other:** Lincoln Trail SP, camping
136	to Martinsville, **S...gas:** BP/diesel/24hr
134.5mm	N Fork Embarras River
129	IL 49, Casey, **N...other:** RV service, KOA(seasonal), **S...gas:** Casey's, Citgo/DQ/diesel, Speedway, **food:** Hardee's, Joe's Pizza, KFC, McDonald's, Pizza Hut, **lodging:** Comfort Inn, Casey Motel(1mi)
119	IL 130, Greenup, **S...gas:** Amoco, BP/diesel, Phillips 66/Subway, **food:** DQ, Dutch Pan Rest., **lodging:** Budget Host, 5 Star Motel, **other:** MEDICAL CARE, Chevrolet, camping, hist sites
105	Montrose, **S...gas:** BP/diesel, Shell/delimart/24hr, **lodging:** Montarosa Motel/café
98	I-57, N to Chicago
	I-70 and I-57 run together 6 mi. See Illinois Interstate 57, exits 159-162.
92	I-57, S to Mt Vernon
91mm	Little Wabash River
87mm	**rest area both lanes, full(handicapped)facilities, info, phone, vending, picnic tables, litter barrels, playground, petwalk, RV dump**
82	IL 128, Altamont, **N...gas:** Casey's, Citgo/Stuckey's/Subway/24hr, Marathon, Speedway/diesel, **food:** McDonald's, **lodging:** Altamont Motel/rest., Knight's Inn, **other:** Fostoria Factory Outlet, **S...gas:** Phillips 66/diesel, **lodging:** Super 8

76	US 40, St Elmo, **N...gas:** Marathon, Phillips 66, **lodging:** Waldorf Motel, **other:** Timberline Camping(2mi)
71mm	weigh sta eb
68	US 40, Brownstown, **N...other:** Okaw Valley Kamping, Road Angel Camping, **S...**truck repair
63.5mm	Kaskaskia River
63	US 51, Vandalia, **N...food:** Chuck Wagon Café, LJ Silver, **lodging:** Day's Inn, **S...gas:** BP/Burger King/24hr, Clark, Marathon, **food:** Hardee's/24hr, KFC, McDonald's, Pizza Hut, Rancho Nuevo Mexican, Sonic, Subway, Wendy's, **lodging:** Jay's Inn, Mabry Motel, Travelodge, **other:** HOSPITAL, Aldi Foods, hist site
61	US 40, Vandalia, **S...gas:** Fastop/diesel, Phillips 66, **food:** KFC/Taco Bell, Ponderosa, **lodging:** Ramada Ltd, **other:** NAPA AutoCare, Wal-Mart
52	US 40, Mulberry Grove, **N...gas:** Citgo/diesel, **other:** Timber Trail Camp-In(2mi), tires/repair, antiques, **S...**Cedar Brook Camping(1mi)
45	IL 127, Greenville, **N...gas:** BP, Phillips 66/Domino's/diesel, Shell/diesel/24hr, **food:** Chang's Chinese, KFC/Taco Bell, Lu-Bob's Rest., Red Apple Rest., McDonald's, **lodging:** Best Western/rest., Budget Host, Super 8, 2 Acre Motel, **other:** HOSPITAL, Ford/Mercury, **S...**to Carlyle Lake, **food:** Circle B Steaks
41	US 40 E, to Greenville, no facilities
36	US 40 E, Pocahontas, **S... gas:** BP/diesel/24hr, Phillips 66/diesel/24hr, **lodging:** Lighthouse Lodge, Powhatan Motel/rest., Wickiup Hotel, Tahoe Motel(3mi)
30	US 40, IL 143, to Highland, **S...gas:** Shell/24hr, **food:** Blue Springs Café, **other:** Tomahawk RV Park(7mi)
26.5mm	**Silver Lake Rest Area both lanes, full(handicapped)facilities, phone, picnic tables, litter barrels, vending, petwalk**
24	IL 143, Marine, **3 mi S...food:** Ponderosa, **lodging:** Holiday Inn Express, **other:** HOSPITAL
23mm	motorist callboxes begin wb every 1/2mile
21	IL 4, Troy, **N...**gas/diesel/24hr
15b a	I-55, N to Chicago, S to St Louis, I-270 W to Kansas City
	I-70 and I-55 run together 18 mi . See Illinois Interstate 55, exits 1-18.
0mm	Illinois/Missouri state line, Mississippi River

ILLINOIS
Interstate 72

E ↕ W

Exit #	Services

1 mi E of I-72...food: McDonald's, Monical's Pizza, Pizza Hut, Texas Roadhouse, **other:** County Mkt Foods, Schnuck's Foods

182b a I-57, N to Chicago, S to Memphis, to I-74

176 IL 47, to Mahomet, no facilities

172 IL 10, Lodge, Seymour, no facilities

169 White Heath Rd, no facilities

166 IL 105 W, Market St, **N...**Ford/Mercury, **S...gas:** Mobil/diesel, **food:** Iron Horse Rest., **lodging:** Best Western, Foster Inn, **1 mi S...food:** Hardee's, McDonald's, Monical's Pizza, Pizza Hut, **other:** Chevrolet/Buick/Pontiac, Chrysler/Plymouth/Dodge/Jeep

165mm Sangamon River

164 Bridge St, **1 mi S...gas:** Mobil, **food:** DQ, Hardee's, McDonald's, Monical's Pizza, Pizza Hut, Subway, **other:** HOSPITAL

156 IL 48, Cisco, to Weldon, **S...**Friends Creek Camping(may-oct)(3mi)

153mm rest area both lanes, full(handicapped)facilities, phone, picnic tables, litter barrels, vending, petwalk

152mm Friends Creek

150 Argenta, no facilities

144 IL 48, Oreana, **N...gas:** Oasis Trkstp/diesel/24hr/@, **S...lodging:** Sleep Inn, **other:** HOSPITAL, Dodge, Honda

Decatur

141b a US 51 S, Decatur, **N...gas:** Shell, **food:** Applebee's, Cheddar's, Cracker Barrel, Country Kitchen, Hardee's, HomeTown Buffet, McDonald's, O'Charley's, Pizza Hut, Red Lobster, Steak'n Shake, Taco Bell, Texas Roadhouse, **lodging:** Baymont Inn, Comfort Inn, Country Inn Suites, Fairfield Inn, Hampton Inn, Ramada Ltd, Wingate Inn, **other:** Advance Parts, Bergner's, Buick/GMC, JC Penney, Lowe's Whse, Kohl's, Mitsubishi/Hyundai/Honda, Sears/auto, Staples, mall, **S...food:** Arby's, Burger King, China Buffet, Monical's Pizza, Panera Bread, Quizno's, Subway, **other:** Circuit City, Radio Shack, Sam's Club, Walgreen, Wal-Mart SuperCtr/24hr

138 IL 121, Decatur, **S...**HOSPITAL

133b a US 36 E, US 51, Decatur, **S...gas:** Citgo, Phillips 66/diesel, **lodging:** Day's Inn, Holiday Inn Select/rest.

128 Niantic, no facilities

122 Illiopolis, to Mt Auburn, **N...gas:** Citgo

114 Buffalo, Mechanicsburg, no facilities

108 Riverton, Dawson, no facilities

107mm Sangamon River

104 Camp Butler, **N...lodging:** Best Rest Inn, Park View Motel, **other:** golf(1mi)

103b a I-55, N to Chicago, S to St Louis, Il 97, to Springfield I-72 and I-55 run together 6 mi. **See IL I-55, exits 92-98.**

Springfield

97b a 6th St, I-55 S, **N...gas:** Shell, **food:** Heritage House Rest., McDonald's, **lodging:** Illini Inn, Ramada Inn, Super 8, Travelodge, **other:** Mr Lincoln's Camping/LP

93 IL 4, Springfield, **N...gas:** Hucks, **food:** Applebee's, Arby's, Bakers Square, Best Buffet Chinese, Burger King, Chili's, Damon's, Denny's, Grand Buffet, Lion's Choice Rest., LoneStar Steaks, Maverick Rest., McDonald's, Ned Kelly's Steaks, Old Country Buffet, Olive Garden, Panera Bread, Pasta House, Popeye's, Sonic, Taco Bell, TGIFriday, Wendy's, **lodging:** Com-

---

fort Inn, Courtyard, Fairfield Inn, Sleep Inn, **other:** Barnes&Noble, Batteries+, Best Buy, Circuit City, Cub Foods/24hr, Gordman's, Jo-Ann Crafts, K-Mart, Kohl's, Lowe's Whse, Michael's, Office Depot, OfficeMax, Sam's Club, Sears/auto, ShopKO, Staples, Target, Walgreen, Wal-Mart/auto, **S...gas:** Meijer/diesel, **food:** Bob Evans, Burger King, O'Charley's, Steak'n Shake, **lodging:** Hampton Inn, Staybridge Suites, **other:** Cadillac, Chevrolet, Chrysler/Plymouth/Dodge/Jeep, Ford, Honda, Saturn

91 Wabash Ave, to Springfield, **N...other:** Lincoln/Mercury/Mazda, Mr Battery, **S...**RV SuperCtr

82 New Berlin, **S...gas:** Phillips 66/A&W/diesel

76 IL 123, Alexander, to Ashland, no facilities

68 to IL 104, to Jacksonville, **2 mi N...gas:** BP, Clark, **food:** Hucks Food/gas, **other:** HOSPITAL

64 US 67, to Jacksonville, **N...food:** Classic Diner, **lodging:** Comfort Inn, **other:** Hopper RV Ctr, **2 mi N...gas:** Clark/diesel, **food:** DQ, McDonald's, Subway, **lodging:** Super 8, **other:** HOSPITAL, Harpers Food/gas

60 to US 67 N, to Jacksonville, **6 mi N...**HOSPITAL, gas, food, lodging

52 to IL 106, Winchester, **N...**golf, **2 mi S...**gas, food, lodging

46 IL 100, to Bluffs, no facilities

42mm Illinois River

35 US 54, IL 107, Griggsville, to Pittsfield, **4 mi N...**gas, food, lodging, **S...other:** HOSPITAL, camping(6mi), st police

31 New Salem, to Pittsfield, **5 mi S...**HOSPITAL, gas, food, lodging, camping

20 IL 106, Barry, **N...lodging:** Ice Market Inn, **other:** AppleBasket Farms, **S...gas:** Phillips 66/diesel/24hr, Shell/diesel/24hr, **food:** Wendy's

10 IL 96, Hull, to Payson, no facilities

4c b a US 36 W, I-172, to Quincy

0mm Illinois/Missouri state line, Mississippi River

Interstate 74

Exit #	Services

221mm Illinois/Indiana state line

220 Lynch Rd, Danville, **N...gas:** BP/diesel, Maraton(1mi), **food:** Big Boy, What's Cookin' Rest., **lodging:** Best Western, Comfort Inn, Danville Inn, Fairfield Inn, Holiday Inn Express, Redwood Inn, Super 8

Danville

216 Bowman Ave, Danville, **N...gas:** Citgo/diesel, Freedom, Mobil/diesel/24hr, **food:** Godfather's, KFC

215b a US 150, IL 1, Gilbert St, Danville, **N...gas:** Citgo/diesel, Speedway, **food:** Arby's, Hardee's, LJ Silver, McDonald's, Pizza Hut, Steak'n Shake, Subway, Taco Bell, **lodging:** Best Western, Day's Inn, **other:** HOSPITAL, Aldi Foods, Bass Tires, Ford/Lincoln/Mercury, **S...gas:** Clark, Speedway/diesel/24hr, **food:** Burger King, Monical's Pizza, **other:** AutoZone, Big R Foods, Buick/Pontiac/GMC, $General, Eagle Foods, Harley-Davidson, Forest Glen Preserve Camping(11mi)

214 G St, Tilton, no facilities

210 US 150, MLK Dr, **2 mi N...gas:** Marathon, **food:** Little Nugget Steaks, **other:** HOSPITAL, to Kickapoo SP, camping, **S...food:** PossumTrot Rest.

208mm Welcome Ctr wb, full(handicapped)facilities, info, phones, picnic tables, litter barrels, vending, petwalk

E ↕ W

Interstate 74

E

W

Urbana

| 206 | Oakwood, **N...gas:** Marathon/diesel/rest./24hr, **S...gas:** Marathon/diesel/24hr, @, Phillips 66/diesel/ @, Casey's(1mi), **food:** McDonald's, Oaks Grill |

200 IL 49 N, to Rankin, **N...**5 Bridges RV Park

197 IL 49 S, Ogden, **S...gas:** Phillips 66/diesel, **food:** Billy Bud's Steaks, Godfather's Pizza

192 St Joseph, **S...food:** DQ, **other:** antiques

185 IL 130, University Ave, no facilities

184 US 45, Cunningham Ave, Urbana, **N...lodging:** Park Inn, **S...gas:** Clark, Freedom/diesel/24hr, Speedway/Taco Bell, Shell, **food:** Cracker Barrel, Domino's, Longhorn Steaks, Ned Kelly's Steaks, Steak'nShake/24hr, **lodging:** Best Value Inn, Best Western, Eastland Suites, Motel 6, **other:** $General, Family$, Firestone/auto, NAPA, Sav-A-Lot

183 Lincoln Ave, Urbana, **S...gas:** Clark/diesel, Mobil, Speedway, **food:** Garden Rest., Seasons Rest., **lodging:** Holiday Inn/rest., Ramada Ltd, Sleep Inn, Super 8, **other:** HOSPITAL, to U of IL

182 Neil St, Champaign, **N...food:** Alexander's Steaks, Bob Evans, Chevy's Mexican, ChiChi's, Denny's, FoodCourt, Grandy's, McDonald's, Olive Garden, Subway, Taco Bell, **lodging:** Baymont Inn, Comfort Inn, Extended Stay America, La Quinta, Red Roof Inn, Super 8, **other:** Barnes&Noble, Chevrolet/Cadillac, Chrysler/Dodge/Jeep, JC Penney, Kohl's, Mercedes/ Volvo, Office Depot, Osco Drug, Sears/auto, mall, same as 181, **S...gas:** Mobil, **food:** Oakley's Rest.

181 Prospect Ave, Champaign, **N...gas:** Meijer/diesel/ 24hr, **food:** Applebee's, Bennigan's, Burger King, Cheddar's, Chili's, China Town, Culver's, Damon's, Fazoli's, HomeTown Buffet, LoneStar Steaks, O'Charley's, Old Country Buffet, Outback Steaks, Red Lobster, Ruby Tuesday, Ryan's, Steak'n Shake/ 24hr, Subway, Wendy's, **lodging:** Courtyard, Drury Inn, Extended Stay America, Fairfield Inn, **other:** Aamco, Advance Parts, Best Buy, Borders Books, Circuit City, $Tree, Hyundai, Kia, Lowe's Whse, Michael's, Mitsubishi, Sam's Club/gas, Staples, Target, Tires+, Wal-Mart/auto, same as 182, **S...gas:** Clark, Freedom/diesel, Mobil, Shell, **food:** Arby's, Dos Reales Mexican, Jimmy John's, KFC, LJ Silver, **lodging:** AmeriInn, Day's Inn, Econolodge, **other:** CarX, $General, NAPA, Nissan, Saturn, Subaru, RV/diesel repair

179b a I-57, N to Chicago, S to Memphis

174 Lake of the Woods Rd, Prairieview Rd, **N...gas:** BP/diesel, Casey's, Mobil/diesel, **food:** PickleTree Farm Rest., Subway, **other:** R&S RV Ctr, Tin Cup Camping, Lake of the Woods SP, **S...gas:** Citgo, **food:** McDonald's

172 IL 47, Mahomet, **N...** RV Sales, **S...gas:** Clark, Mobil, Shell/Domino's/diesel, **food:** Arby's, DQ, HenHouse Rest., Mahomet Garden Rest., Monical's Pizza, Peking House Chinese, Subway, **lodging:** Heritage Inn, **other:** Ace Hardware, CVS Drug, IGA Foods, NAPA

166 Mansfield, **S...gas:** BP

159 IL 54, Farmer City, **S...gas:** Casey's, **food:** Family Café, **lodging:** Budget Motel, Day's Inn, **other:** to Clinton Lake RA

156mm **rest area both lanes, full(handicapped)facilities, phone, picnic tables, litter larrels, vending, playground, petwalk**

152 US 136, to Heyworth, no facilities

149 Le Roy, **N...gas:** BP/diesel/24hr, Freedom, **food:** KFC, McDonald's, Roma Ralph's Pizza, Subway, **other:** Doc's Drug, $General, IGA Foods, to Moraine View SP, **S...gas:** Shell/ Woody's Rest./diesel/24hr, **lodging:** Super 8, **other:** Clinton Lake, camping

Bloomington

142 Downs, **N...gas:** BP/diesel/24hr, **food:** Pizza Hut

135 US 51, Bloomington, **N...gas:** Clarkdiesel, Huck's, Mobil/diesel, **food:** McDonald's, **other:** HOSPITAL, to IL St U, **S...gas:** Shell/diesel

134b Veterans Pkwy, Bloomington, **N...gas:** Clark/24hr, FS, **food:** CJ's Rest., Froggy's Rest., **lodging:** Parkway Inn/rest., Sunset Motel, **other:** airport

134a I-55, N to Chicago, S to St Louis, I-74 E

I-74 and I-55 run together 6 mi. See Illinois Interstate 55, exit 160b a.

127 I-55, N to Chicago, S to St Louis, I-74 W to Peoria

125 US 150, to Bloomington, Mitsubishi Motorway

123mm weigh sta wb

122mm weigh sta eb

120 Carlock, **N...gas:** BP/diesel/repair, **food:** Countryside Rest

114.5mm rest area both lanes, full(handicapped)facilities, vending, phone, picnic tables, litter barrels, petwalk

113.5mm Mackinaw River

112 IL 117, Goodfield, **N...gas:** Shell/Busy Corner/diesel, **other:** to Timberline RA, Jellystone Camping, Eureka Coll, Reagan Home

102b a Morton, **N...gas:** BP, Casey's, Citgo/Blimpie/diesel/ 24hr, Mobil/Arby's/diesel, **food:** Burger King, Country Kitchen, Cracker Barrel, Ruby Tuesday, Taco Bell, Wendy's, **lodging:** Best Western, Comfort Inn, Day's Inn, Holiday Inn Express, **other:** MEDICAL CARE, **S...gas:** Clark/24hr, Shell/Subway/diesel/24hr, **food:** China Dragon, KFC, McDonald's, Monical's Pizza, Quizno's, **other:** Chrysler/Dodge, CVS Drug, $Tree, Ford, K-Mart, Kroger

101 I-155 S, to Lincoln, no facilities

99 I-474 W, airport

98 Pinecrest Dr, no facilities

96 95c(from eb), US 150, IL 8, E Washington St, E Peoria, **N...gas:** Site, **food:** Monical's Pizza, Subway, Wendy's, **lodging:** Super 8

ILLINOIS

Interstate 74

E ↕ **W**

95b	IL 116, to Metamora, **N...lodging:** Hampton Inn
95a	N Main St, Peoria, **S...gas:** BP/24hr, **food:** Applebee's, Bob Evans, China Buffet, Godfather's, Hardee's, LJ Silver, Subway, **lodging:** Baymont Inn, Hotel East Peoria, Motel 6, **other:** Aldi Foods, Advance Parts, CVS Drug, $General, Goodyear/auto, Kroger, ShopKO, Walgreen
94	IL 40, RiverFront Dr, **S...gas:** Citgo/Burger King, Hucks/Godfather's/24hr, **food:** Papa John's, Steak'n Shake, Texas Roadhouse, **other:** Lowe's Whse, OfficeMax, Radio Shack, Wal-Mart SuperCtr/24hr
93.5mm	Illinois River
93b	US 24, IL 29, Peoria, **S...other:** Damon's, Sears, civic ctr
93a	Jefferson St, Peoria, **S...other:** Damon's, to civic ctr
92	Glendale Ave, Peoria, **S...other:** HOSPITAL, downtown
92a	IL 40 N, Knoxville Ave, Peoria, **S...lodging:** Holiday Inn, **other:** HOSPITAL
91b a	University St, Peoria, **1 mi N on Universtiy...**gas: BP, Phillips 66, **other:** AutoZone, Walgreen, Wal-Mart, to Expo Gardens, **S...**to Bradley U
90	Gale Ave, Peoria, **S...gas:** Speedway
89	US 150, War Memorial Dr, Peoria, **N on War Memorial...**gas: BP, Clark, Shell, **food:** Bob Evans, Burger King, Cheddar's, Denny's, Dunkin Donuts, IHOP, Ned Kelly's Steaks, Outback Steaks, Perkins/24hr, Pizza Hut, Red Lobster, Schlotsky's, Steak'n Shake, Subway, Wendy's, **lodging:** AmeriSuites, Best Western, Comfort Suites, Courtyard, Extended Stay America, Fairfield Inn, Holiday Inn, Red Roof Inn, Residence Inn, Sleep Inn, Super 8, The Inn, **other:** Chevrolet, Circuit City, Cub Foods, Famous-Barr, Firestone, JC Penney, Lowe's Whse, Pontiac/Cadillac, Sears/auto, Target, Tires+, U-Haul, Walgreen, mall
87b a	I-474 E, IL 6, N to Chillicothe, **E...**airport
82	Edwards Rd, Kickapoo, **N...gas:** Mobil/diesel/service, Shell/Subway/diesel, **food:** Jubilee Café, **other:** craft mall, to Jubilee Coll SP, **S...other:** USPO, Wildlife Prairie Park
75	Brimfield, Oak Hill, **N...gas:** Casey's, **food:** Jimall's Rest.
71	to IL 78, to Canton, Elmwood, no facilities
62mm	**rest area both lanes, full(handicapped)facilities, phone, picnic tables, litter barrels, vending, petwalk**
61.5mm	Spoon River
54	IL 97, Lewistown, **N...other:** TravL Park Camping(1mi), **S...gas:** Mobil/diesel(2mi)
51	Knoxville, **S...gas:** BP/diesel, Casey's, Citgo/diesel/24hr, **food:** Hardee's/24hr, McDonald's, Subway, **lodging:** Super 8
48b a	E Galesburg, Galesburg, **N...lodging:** Jumer's Hotel/rest., **S...gas:** Clark, Mobil/diesel, Phillips 66, **food:** DQ, KFC, Hardee's, McDonald's, Pizza Hut,

P e o r i a

G a l e s b u r g

M o l i n e

B e t t e n d o r f

	Subway, Taco Bell, Hy-Vee Foods, **lodging:** Days Inn, Economy 8, Galesburg Inn, Holiday Inn Express, Ramada Inn, Relax Inn, Super 8, Buick, **other:** Econo Foods, Firestone, Goodyear, to Sandburg Birthplace, Lincoln-Douglas Debates
46b a	US 34, to Monmouth, **N...other:** Nichol's Diesel Service, **3 mi S...food:** Applebee's, Golden Corral, **lodging:** Country Inn Suites, **other:** HOSPITAL
32	IL 17, Woodhull, **N...gas:** BP/diesel/@ , Shell, **food:** Woodhull Rest., **S...gas:** Mobil/diesel/rest./24hr/@ , **food:** Homestead Rest., **other:** Shady Lakes Camping(8mi)
30mm	**rest area wb, full(handicapped)facilities, vending, picnic tables, litter barrels, phones, playground, petwalk, RV dump**
28mm	**rest area eb, full(handicapped)facilities, vending, picnic tables, litter barrels, phones, playground, petwalk, RV dump**
24	IL 81, Andover, **N...**Gibson's RV Park(5mi)
14mm	I-80, E to Chicago, I-80/I-280 W to Des Moines
8mm	weigh sta wb
6mm	weigh sta eb
5b	US 6, Moline, **S...gas:** Citgo, **food:** Bender's Rest., Denny's, Harold's Rest., McDonald's, Omelet Shoppe, Skyline Rest., **lodging:** Best Western, Comfort Inn, Country Inn Suites, Exel Inn, Hampton Inn, Holiday Inn, Holiday Inn Express, La Quinta, Motel 6, Skyline Inn
5a	I-280 W, US 6 W, to Des Moines, no facilities
4b a	IL 5, John Deere Rd, Moline, **N...gas:** BP, **food:** Applebee's, Carlos O'Kelly's, Old Country Buffet, Ryan's, Steak'n Shake, Wendy's, **other:** Buick, Lowe's Whse, Staples, Tires+, Wal-Mart SuperCtr/24hr, **S...gas:** Citgo, Mobil, **food:** Arby's, Burger King, Denny's, LJ Silver, ChiChi's, New Mandarin Chinese, Pizza Hut, Subway, Taco Bell, Wendy's, Winner's Circle Rest., **lodging:** Best Western, Comfort Inn, Exel Inn, Fairfield Inn, **other:** Best Buy, Chevrolet, Eagle Foods, Firestone/auto, Food Fair, Ford, Goodyear/auto, JC Penney, OfficeMax, Sears/auto, ShopKO, mall
3	23rd Ave, Moline, **N...lodging:** Super 8
2	7th Ave, Moline, **S...lodging:** Signature Inn, **other:** Goodyear/auto, to civic ctr, riverfront
1	3rd Ave(from eb), Moline, **S...gas:** PetroStop, **lodging:** Radisson, **other:** Goodyear/auto
0mm	Illinois/Iowa state line, Mississippi River. **Exits 4-1 are in Iowa.**
4	US 67, Grant St, State St, Bettendorf, **N...gas:** BP, Phillips 66, Sinclair, **food:** Ross' Rest./24hr, **lodging:** Abbey Motel, Twin Bridges Motel, **other:** CarQuest, **S...food:** DQ, Village Inn Rest., **other:** $General, NAPA
3	Middle Rd, Locust St, Bettendorf, **S...gas:** BP, **food:** Bennigan's, Bishop's Cafeteria, Fortune Garden Chinese, MaidRite Café, McDonald's, Pizza Hut, Subway, Taco Bell, **lodging:** Econolodge, Holiday Inn, **other:** HOSPITAL, Goodyear/auto, ShopKO, Walgreen, mall

Interstate 74

E ↕ W

2 US 6 W, Spruce Hills Dr, Bettendorf, **N...gas:** BP/diesel, Phillips 66, **food:** Old Chicago Pizza, **lodging:** Courtyard, Heartland Inn, Signature Inn, The Lodge Hotel/rest., **other:** U-Haul, **S...food:** Applebee's, Bob Evans, Burger King, Country Kitchen, Godfather's, Hardee's, KFC, Panera Bread, Red Lobster, Subway, **lodging:** Day's Inn, Fairfield Inn, Hampton Inn, **other:** Cub Foods, Buick/Pontiac, Cadillac, Isuzu, Kohl's, Gordman's, Lowe's Whse, Sam's Club, st patrol

1 53rd St, Hamilton, **N...gas:** BP, **food:** Ruby Tuesday, **other:** Borders Books, Harley-Davidson, Michael's, Old Navy, Ultimate Electronics, **S...gas:** Phillips 66, **food:** Arby's, China Cafe, DQ, Golden Corral, IHOP, Krispy Kreme, Quizno's, Steak'n Shake, Village Inn Rest., Wendy's, **lodging:** Sleep Inn, **other:** MEDICAL CARE, Best Buy, Staples, Target, Wal-Mart SuperCtr/24hr/gas

0mm I-74 begins/ends on I-80, exit 298., **Exits 1-4 are in Iowa.**

Interstate 80

E ↕ W

Chicago Area

Exit #	Services
163mm	Illinois/Indiana state line

161 US 6, IL 83, Torrence Ave, **N...gas:** BP, **food:** Arby's, Bob Evans, Chili's, Dixie Kitchen, Hooters, IHOP, Olive Garden, On-the-Border, Oriental Palace, Wendy's, **lodging:** Comfort Suites, Day's Inn, Extended Stay America, Fairfield Inn, Red Roof Inn, Sleep Inn, Super 8, **other:** Best Buy, Chrysler/Plymouth/Jeep, Dominick's Foods, Firestone/auto, Home Depot, JustTires, K-Mart, PepBoys, Radio Shack, **S...gas:** Gas City, Marathon, Mobil, **food:** Al's Diner, Brown's Chicken/pasta, Burger King, Dunkin Donuts, Golden Crown Rest., McDonald's, Pappy's Gyro's, **other:** Auto Clinic, Chevrolet, OfficeMax, Saab, Sam's Club, SunRise Foods, Walgreen

160b I-94 W, to Chicago, tollway begins wb, ends eb

160a IL 394 S, to Danville, no facilities

159mm Oasis, **gas:** Mobil/diesel, **food:** Burger King, TCBY

157 IL 1, Halsted St, **N...gas:** Citgo/diesel, Clark, Marathon/diesel, **food:** Burger King, Yellow Ribbon Rest., **lodging:** Best Western, Comfort Inn, Econolodge, Hilton Garden, Holiday Inn Express, Motel 6, Park Inn, **S...gas:** Shell, Speedway, **food:** Applebee's, Arby's, Boston Mkt, Dunkin Donuts, Fannie May Candies, KFC, McDonald's, Popeye's, Shooter's Buffet, Subway, Taco Bell, Washington Square Rest., Wendy's, **lodging:** Rodeway Inn, Super 8, Villager Lodge, **other:** Chevrolet, $Tree, Firestone/auto, Goodyear/auto, Home Depot, Jewel-Osco, K-Mart, OfficeMax, PepBoys, Target

156 Dixie Hwy(from eb), **S...golf**

155 I-294 N, Tri-State Tollway, toll plaza, no facilities

154 Kedzie Ave(from eb), **N...gas:** Speedway, **S...HOSPITAL**

151b a I-57(exits left from both directions), N to Chicago, S to Memphis, no facilities

148b a IL 43, Harlem Ave, **N...gas:** Speedway/Subway/diesel, **food:** Burger King, Chicago Café, Cracker Barrel, Culver's, Papa John's, Quizno's, Wendy's, **lodging:** Baymont Inn, Comfort Suites, Fairfield Inn, Hampton Inn, Holiday Inn Select, Sleep Inn, Wingate Inn, **S...other:** Carmax, World Music Theatre, Windy City Camping

147.5mm weigh sta wb

145b a US 45, 96th Ave, **N...gas:** Gas City/Subway, **S...gas:** BP, Clark, Gas City/diesel, Shell/diesel/24hr, **food:** Burger King, DQ, Denny's, McDonald's(3mi), Mindy's Ribs, Morgan's Grill, Subway, White Castle, Wendy's, **lodging:** Super 8, **other:** camping(2mi)

143mm weigh sta eb

137 US 30, New Lenox, **N...food:** Les Bros Rest., **other:** K-Mart, **S...gas:** Speedway/diesel, **food:** Burger King, KFC, McDonald's, New Lenox Rest., Pizza Hut, Taco Bell, **other:** Eagle Foods, Jewel-Osco/gas, Walgreen

134 Briggs St, **N...gas:** Speedway, **other:** HOSPITAL, **S...gas:** Citgo/diesel, Clark

133 Richards St, no facilities

132b a US 52, IL 53, Chicago St, no facilities

131.5mm Des Plaines River

131 US 6, Meadow Ave, **N...to Riverboat Casino**

Joliet

130b a IL 7, Larkin Ave, **N...gas:** Citgo, Clark, Marathon/24hr, Shell/24hr, Speedway, Thornton/diesel, **food:** Bellagio Pizzaria, Bob Evans, Burger King, ChuckeCheese, Dunkin Donuts, Melrose Cafe, Pizza Hut, Steak'n Shake, Subway, Taco Bell, TCBY, Wendy's, White Castle, **lodging:** Comfort Inn, Holiday Inn Express, Microtel, Motel 6, Red Roof, Super 8, **other:** HOSPITAL, Aldi Foods, Chevrolet/Mitsubishi, Cub Food/drug, Ford, Goodyear/auto, K-Mart, NTB, PepBoys, Radio Shack, Sam's Club, Wal-Mart, to Coll of St Francis, **S...auto repair**

127 Houbolt Rd, to Joliet, **N...gas:** BP/deli, Citgo/7-11, **food:** Burger King, Cracker Barrel, McDonald's, Split-Second Deli, **lodging:** Fairfield Inn, Hampton Inn, Ramada Ltd, **other:** Harley-Davidson

126b a I-55, N to Chicago, S to St Louis, no facilities

125.5mm Du Page River

122 Minooka, **N...gas:** Citgo/diesel/24hr, **S...gas:** BP/24hr, Pilot/Arby's/diesel/24hr/@, **food:** DQ, McDonald's, Subway, Wendy's, **other:** SuperValu Foods

119mm **rest area wb, full(handicapped)facilities, vending, phones, picnic tables, litter barrels, playground, petwalk**

ILLINOIS

Interstate 80

E ↑ W

117mm	**rest area eb, full(handicapped)facilities, vending, phone, picnic tables, litter barrels, playground, petwalk**
112	IL 47, Morris, **N...gas:** BP/diesel/24hr, Citgo/diesel, **food:** Bellacino's, Chili's, **lodging:** Best Western, Comfort Inn, Day's Inn, Holiday Inn, **S...gas:** BP, Clark, Mobil, Shell/24hr, **food:** Burger King, Culver's, KFC, Maria's Ristorante, McDonald's, Morris Diner, Pizza Hut, Subway, Taco Bell, Wendy's, **lodging:** Morris Motel, Park Motel, Super 8, **other:** MEDICAL CARE, Aldi Foods, Chevrolet/Buick/Cadillac, Eagle Foods, Fisher Parts, Ford, Radio Shack, Walgreen, Wal-Mart SuperCtr/24hr, to Stratton SP
105	to Seneca, no facilities
97	to Marseilles, **N...food:** Taco Time, **S...other:** Prairie Lakes Resort/rest., to Illini SP, RV camping
93	IL 71, Ottawa, **N...gas:** Mobil/24hr, Shell/diesel/24hr, **other:** Skydive Chicago RV Park(2mi), **S...food:** Hank's Farm Rest., **other:** HOSPITAL
92.5mm	Fox River
90	IL 23, Ottawa, **N...gas:** BP/Subway, **food:** Cracker Barrel, Taco Bell, **lodging:** Hampton Inn, Holiday Inn Express, **other:** HOSPITAL, Buick/Pontiac/Cadillac, Ford/Lincoln/Mercury/Kia, Chrysler/Jeep, Honda, **S...gas:** BP/diesel/LP, Shell/24hr, **food:** China Inn, Country Kitchen, Dunkin Donuts, Hardee's, McDonald's, KFC, Ponderosa, **lodging:** Comfort Inn, Sands Motel, Super 8, Surrey Motel, Travelodge, **other:** Ace RV Ctr, Harley-Davidson, K-Mart, Kroger, USPO, Wal-Mart/drugs
81	IL 178, Utica, **N...**KOA(2mi), **S...gas:** BP, Shell/diesel, **food:** Duffy's Tavern(2mi), Jimmy Johns Sandwiches, **lodging:** Starved Rock Inn, **other:** Hickory Hollow Camping, to Starved Rock SP
79b a	I-39, US 51, N to Rockford, S to Bloomington, no facilities
77.5mm	Little Vermilion River
77	IL 351, La Salle, **S...gas:** FS/24hr, ✈/Flying J/Country Mkt/diesel/24hr/@, **food:** UpTown Grill, **lodging:** Daniels Motel, **other:** st police
75	IL 251, Peru, **N...gas:** BP, Crazy D's/diesel, Shell/diesel/rest./24hr, **food:** Arby's, Champ's Grill, McDonald's, Taco Bell, **lodging:** Comfort Inn, Econolodge, Motel 6, Super 8, Tiki Inn/RV Park/rest., **other:** antiques, **S...gas:** BP, **food:** Applebee's, Bob Evans, Culver's, DQ, Dunkin Donuts, Mi Margarita, Red Lobster, Steak'n Shake, Subway, Wendy's, **lodging:** Fairfield Inn, Ramada Ltd, **other:** HOSPITAL, AutoZone, Buick/Pontiac/GMC, Chevrolet/Mercedes, Chrysler/Jeep, EconoFoods, Goodyear/auto, Home Depot, HyVee Foods, JC Penney, Jo-Ann Fabrics, K-Mart, Mitsubishi, Nissan, Sears/auto, Staples, Target, Toyota, Walgreen, Wal-Mart/drugs, mall

P e r u

73	Plank Rd, **N...gas:** Sapp Bros/Burger King/diesel/@, **food:** Apple Barrel Rest., **other:** camping
70	IL 89, to Ladd, **S...lodging:** Motel Riviera, **3 mi S...gas:** Casey's, **food:** Hardee's, Pizza Hut, **other:** HOSPITAL
61	I-180, to Hennepin, no facilities
56	IL 26, Princeton, **N...gas:** Citgo, **lodging:** Super 8, **S...gas:** BP/24hr, Phillips 66, Shell, **food:** Big Apple Rest., Burger King, Country Kitchen, Culver's, KFC, McDonald's, Taco Bell, Wendy's, **lodging:** Comfort Inn, Day's Inn, Motor Lodge/rest., Princeton Motel, **other:** HOSPITAL, AutoZone, Chevrolet/Pontiac/Buick/Cadillac, $General, Pennzoil, Sullivan's Food/gas, Wal-Mart SuperCtr/gas/24hr
51.5mm	**rest area both lanes, full(handicapped)facilities, phone, picnic tables, litter barrels, vending, playground, petwalk, RV dump**
45	IL 40, **N...gas:** Marathon/diesel/rest., **lodging:** Day's Inn/rest., **other:** to Ronald Reagan Birthplace(21mi), **S...other:** Hennepin Canal SP, camping
44mm	Hennepin Canal
33	IL 78, Annawan, **S...gas:** Mobil/diesel, Phillips 66/diesel, **food:** Olympic Flame Rest., **lodging:** Holiday Inn Express, **other:** to Johnson-Sauk Trail SP
27	to US 6, Atkinson, **N...gas:** Casey's, Mobil/diesel/rest./24hr, **other:** Ford
19	IL 82, Geneseo, **N...gas:** BP, Citgo, Phillips 66/diesel/24hr, Shell, **food:** DQ, Hardee's, McDonald's, Pizza Hut, Subway, **lodging:** Deck Motel/diner, Oakwood Motel, Royal Motel, Super 8(2mi), **other:** HOSPITAL, $General, Ford, Hutchcraft RV Ctr, Wal-Mart/drugs, **S...food:** KFC
10	I-74, W to Moline, E to Peoria, no facilities
9	US 6, to Geneseo, no facilities
7	Colona, **N...gas:** Conoco/diesel/rest.
5mm	Rock River
4a	IL 5, IL 92, W to Silvis, **S...other:** to Quad City Downs, Lundeen's Camping
4b	I-88, IL 92, E to Rock Falls, no facilities
2mm	weigh sta both lanes
1.5mm	**Welcome Ctr eb, full(handicapped)facilities, info, phone, picnic tables, litter barrels, petwalk, scenic overlook**
1	IL 84, 20th St, Great River Rd, E Moline, **N...gas:** BP, **food:** Bridgeview Burgers, Brothers Rest., **other:** camping, **3 mi S...gas:** Citgo, **other:** camping
0mm	Illinois/Iowa state line, Mississippi River

E M o l i n e

Interstate 88

E ↕ W

Chicago Area

Exit #	Services
139.5mm	I-88 begins/ends on I-290.
139	I-294, S to Indiana, N to Milwaukee
138mm	toll plaza
137	IL 83 N, Cermak Rd, **N...lodging:** Rennaisance, Marriott, **other:** Nieman-Marcus
136	IL 83 S, Midwest Rd(from eb), **N...gas:** Costco/gas, **other:** Cost+, Nordstrom's, Old Navy
134	Highland Ave(no EZ wb return), **N...food:** Bennigan's, Buca Italian, Taylor Brewing Co, TGIFriday, **lodging:** Embassy Suites, Homestead Studios, Red Roof Inn, **other:** HOSPITAL, Circuit City, CompUSA, Firestone, JC Penney, mall, **S...food:** Parkers Ocean Grill
132	I-355 N(from wb)
131	I-355 S(from eb)
130	IL 53(from wb), no facilities
127	Naperville Rd, **S...food:** Bob Evans, Buona Beef, Chevy's Mexican, McDonald's, TGIFriday, Wendy's, **lodging:** Best Western, Day's Inn, Holiday Inn, Homestead Suites, **other:** Ford, Kia, Office Depot
125	Winfield Rd, **N...HOSPITAL, S...food:** Max&Erma's, Red Robin, Rockbottom Brewery, **lodging:** AmeriSuites
123	IL 59, **N...S...gas:** Mobil/diesel, **food:** Cracker Barrel, Steak'n Shake, Subway, Wendy's, White Hen Pantry, **lodging:** Country Inn Suites, Extended Stay America, Hawthorn Suites, Red Roof Inn, Sleep Inn
119	Farnsworth Ave, **N...gas:** BP, **food:** Jacaranda's Mexican, Papa Bear Rest., **lodging:** Best Western, Motel 6, **other:** Ford/Mercury/Lincoln/Mitsubishi, **S...gas:** Clark, Marathon, Phillips 66, Shell, **food:** Goody's Drive-Thru, McDonald's, Subway, Taco Bell, White Hen Pantry, **other:** Goodyear
118mm	toll plaza
117	IL 31, IL 56, to Aurora, Batavia, **N...gas:** Citgo, Marathon, **food:** A&W, Raimondo's Pizza, Tastee Freez, White Hen Pantry, **S...gas:** Mobil, Thornton's, **food:** Culver's, Denny's, Mayberry's Rest., McDonald's, Popeye's, Togo's/Baskin-Robbins/Dunkin Donuts, **lodging:** Baymont Inn, Howard Johnson, **other:** HOSPITAL, AutoZone, Firestone, GNC, Jewel/Osco, Radio Shack, U-Haul
115	Orchard Rd, **N...other:** Chrysler/Plymouth/Dodge/Jeep, Ford/Lincoln/Mercury, Isuzu, Nissan, Pontiac, Saturn, Subaru, **S...gas:** Citgo/7-11, **food:** Chili's, IHOP, Wendy's, **lodging:** Hampton Inn, **other:** Home Depot
114	IL 56W, to US 30(from wb, no EZ return), to Sugar Grove
109	IL 47(from eb, no EZ return), to Black Berry Hist Farm

DeKalb

Exit #	Services
94	Peace Rd, to IL 38, **N...HOSPITAL**
93mm	Dekalb Oasis/24hr both lanes, **gas:** Mobil/diesel, **food:** McDonald's
93mm	toll plaza
92	IL 38, IL 23, Annie Glidden Rd, to DeKalb, **N...lodging:** Super 8, **2-3 mi N...gas:** BP, Clark, **food:** Burger King, Happy Wok Chinese, Jct Rest., La Magaritas Mexican, McDonald's, Pagliai's Pizza, Pizza Hut, Pizza Villa, Taco Bell, Wendy's, Yen Ching Chinese, **lodging:** Baymont Inn, Best Western, Stadium Inn, Travelodge, **other:** Ford, Illini Tire, to N IL U
91mm	toll plaza
78	I-39, US 51, S to Bloomington, N to Rockford
76	IL 251, Rochelle, **N...gas:** BP/Blimpie/diesel, Casey's, Marathon, Shell, **food:** Olive Branch Rest., **other:** HOSPITAL, Dodge, Ford/Lincoln/Mercury, GMC, Goodyear
55	IL 26, Dixon, **N...gas:** BP/diesel, **food:** Pizza Hut, **lodging:** Comfort Inn, Quality Inn, Super 8, **1-2 mi N...gas:** Clark Gas, **food:** Hardee's, Hometown Pantry, **lodging:** Best Western, **other:** HOSPITAL, to Ronald Reagan Birthplace, to John Deere HS, to St Parks
54mm	toll plaza
44	US 30(last free exit eb), **N...gas,** food, lodging, camping
41	IL 40, Rock Falls, to Sterling, **1-2 mi N...gas:** Clark, Marathon, Mobil/24hr, Shell/deli, **food:** Arby's, Arthur's Deli, Bennigan's, Burger King, Culver's, First Wok Chinese, Hardee's, KFC, McDonald's, Perna's Pizza, Red Apple Rest., Subway, **lodging:** All Seasons Motel, Country Inn Suites, Holiday Inn, Super 8, **other:** HOSPITAL, AutoZone, Eagle Foods, Goodyear/auto, Harley-Davidson, Sav-A-Lot, Walgreen, Wal-Mart
36	to US 30, Rock Falls, Sterling, no facilities
26	IL 78, to Prophetstown, Morrison, **N...other:** to Morrison-Rockwood SP, camping, **S...gas:** Conoco/diesel
18	Erie, to Albany, no facilities
10	Hillsdale, to Port Byron, **S...gas:** Citgo/diesel, Phillips 66/diesel, **food:** Mama J's Rest.
6	IL 92 E, to Joslin, **1 mi S...other:** Sunset Lake Camping
2	Former IL 2, no facilities
1b a	I-80, W to Des Moines, E to Chicago
0mm	I-88 begins/ends on I-80, exit 4b. IL 5, IL 92, W to Silvis, to Quad City Downs, Lundeen's Camping

ILLINOIS
Interstate 90

E	Exit #	Services

0mm Illinois/Indiana state line, Chicago Skyway Tool Rd begins/ends

1mm US 12, US 20, 106th St, Indianapolis Blvd, **N...gas:** BP/diesel, Mobil, Shell/diesel, **S...food:** Burger King, Giappo's Pizza, KFC, McDonald's, **other:** Jewel-Osco, Larry's Repair

2.5mm **gas:** Skyway Oasis, **food:** McDonald's, **other:** toll plaza

3mm 87th St(from wb), no facilities

5mm 79th St, services along 79th St and Stoney Island Ave

5.5mm 73rd St(from wb), no facilities

6mm State St(from wb), no facilities

7mm I-94 N(mile markers decrease to IN state line)

I-90 E and I-94 E run together, **see Illinois Interstate 94, exits 43b thru 59a.**

84 I-94 W...Lawrence Ave, **N...gas:** BP

83b a Foster Ave(from wb), **N...gas:** BP, **food:** Checker's, Dunkin Donuts, **other:** Firestone/auto, Goodyear/auto, Walgreen

82c Austin Ave, to Foster Ave, no facilities

b Byrn-Mawr(from wb)

a Nagle Ave, no facilities

81b Sayre Ave(from wb)

a IL 43, Harlem Ave, **S...gas:** BP, Shell

80 Canfield Rd(from wb), **N...other:** Walgreen

79b a IL 171 S, Cumberland Ave, **N...gas:** Citgo/7-11, Mobil, **food:** Denny's, Hooters, McDonald's, Outback Steaks, Porter's Steaks, **lodging:** AmeriSuites, Holiday Inn, Marriott, **other:** Dominick's Foods, **S...food:** Bennigan's, Clarion, Rennaisance

0mm River Road Plaza, **N...food:** McDonald's, **lodging:** Marriott, Westin Hotel, **S...**Hyatt(mile markers increase to Rockford)

1mm I-294, I-190 W, to O'Hare Airport

2mm IL 72, Lee St(from wb), **N...lodging:** Extended Stay America, Quality Inn, Radisson, **other:** Studio+, **S...food:** McDonald's, **lodging:** Best Western, Holiday Inn Select, Ramada Plaza, Sheraton Gateway, Travelodge

5mm Des Plaines Oasis both lanes, **gas:** Mobil/diesel/24hr, **food:** McDonald's/24hr

6mm Elmhurst Rd(from wb), **S...gas:** Marathon, McDonald's, **lodging:** Best Western, Comfort Inn, Day's Inn, Hampton Inn, La Quinta, Microtel

7.5mm Arlington Hgts Rd, **N on Algonquin...gas:** BP, Shell, **food:** Denny's, Pappadeaux Rest., Yanni's Greek Rest., **lodging:** AmeriSuites, Courtyard, Motel 6, Radisson, Red Roof Inn, **other:** Sam's Club, **S...lodging:** Sheraton

11mm I-290, IL 53, **N...lodging:** Holiday Inn, **other:** mall, **S...lodging:** AmeriSuites, Extended Stay America, Residence Inn

13mm Roselle Rd(from wb), **N...**Medieval Times, **S...lodging:** Extended Stay America, **other:** BMW

16mm Barrington Rd(from wb), **N...lodging:** Hilton Garden, **1 mi S...lodging:** AmeriSuites, Hampton Inn

19mm IL 59, **N...lodging:** Marriott, **other:** to Poplar Creek Music Theatre

21mm Beverly Rd(from wb), no facilities

22mm IL 25, **N...food:** Milk Pail Rest., **lodging:** Day's Inn, **S...gas:** BP, Shell, Speedway/diesel, **food:** Arby's, Baker Hill Pancakes, Subway, **other:** HOSPITAL

24mm IL 31 N, **N...gas:** BP, Thornton's/diesel, **food:** Alexander's Rest., Bennigan's, Cracker Barrel, **lodging:** Baymont Inn, Crowne Plaza, Courtyard, Hampton Inn, Super 8, TownePlace Suites, **S...lodging:** Best Western

25mm toll plaza, phone

27mm Randall Rd, **N...food:** Jimmy's Charhouse, **lodging:** Country Inn Suites, **S...**HOSPITAL

32mm IL 47(from wb), to Woodstock, **N...other:** Prime Outlets/famous brands, Chevrolet

37mm US 20, Marengo, **N...gas:** Clark/diesel/24hr/@, Shell/diesel/repair/24hr/@, TA/BP/Burger King/Popeye's/diesel/rest./24hr/@, **food:** McDonald's, Wendy's, **other:** KOA, museums, to Prime Outlets at exit 32(6mi)

41mm Marengo-Hampshire toll plaza, phone

53mm Genoa Rd, to Belvidere, **N...**camping

55mm Belvidere Oasis both lanes, **gas:** Mobil/diesel/24hr, **food:** McDonald's/24hr, phone

56mm toll plaza

60.5mm Kishwaukee River

61mm I-39 S, US 20, US 51, to Rockford, **S...**funpark

63mm US 20, State St, **N...gas:** Phillips 66/Subway/diesel, **food:** Cracker Barrel, **lodging:** Baymont Inn, Best Western, Exel Inn, **other:** Time Museum, **S...gas:** BP, Citgo/diesel, Mobil/Blimpie/diesel, **food:** Arby's, Applebee's, BeefARoo, Burger King, Carlos O'Kelly's, Checker's, Cheddar's, ChiChi's, Chili's, Country Kitchen, DQ, Denny's, Don Pablo, Giovanni's Rest., HomeTown Buffet, KFC, Lino's Pizza, LoneStar Steaks, Machine Shed Rest., McDonald's, Old Chicago Grill, Old Country Buffet, Olive Garden, Outback Steaks, Panino's Drive-Thru, Perkins, Red Lobster, Ruby Tuesday, Ryan's, Steak'n Shake, Taco Bell, ThunderBay Grill, Tumbleweed Grill, Wendy's, **lodging:** Candlewood Suites, Comfort Inn, Courtyard, Extended Stay America, Fairfield Inn, Hampton Inn, Holiday Inn Express, Quality Suites, Ramada Inn/rest., Red Roof Inn, Residence Inn, Sleep Inn, Studio+, Super 8, **other:** HOSPITAL, Advance Parts, Aldi Foods, Barnes&Noble, Best Buy, Borders Books, Buick/Pontiac/GMC, Circuit City, CompUSA, Discount Tire, Dodge, $Tree, Home Depot, Iogli Foods, Jo-Ann Fabrics, K-Mart, Kohl's, Lowe's Whse, Marshalls, Michael's, Office Depot, OfficeMax, Old Navy, PepBoys, Sam's Club, Saturn, ShopKO, Target/drugs, Toyota/Lexus, Wal-Mart

66mm E Riverside Blvd, Loves Park, **1-2 mi S...gas:** BP/24hr, Citgo/diesel/24hr, Mobil/diesel, Phillips 66/diesel, **food:** A&W, Arby's, Basil Café, BeefARoo, Culver's, DQ, India

Interstate 90

E ↕ **W**

House, KFC, Little Caesar's, McDonald's, Sam's Ristorante, Subway, Wendy's, **lodging:** Day's Inn, **other:** Audi/Honda/Jaguar/Mercedes/Porsche/Subaru, Eagle Foods, to Rock Cut SP

75.5mm tollbooth, phone(mile markers decrease from W to E to Chicago)

3 Rockton Rd, no facilities

1.5mm **Welcome Ctr/rest area eb, full(handicapped)facilities, info, picnic tables, litter barrels, phone, petwalk, playground, RV dump**

1 US 51 N, IL 75 W, S Beloit, **S...gas:** Citgo/Subway/diesel/24hr, ✈/Flying J/Country Mkt/diesel/24hr/@, Shell/diesel, **lodging:** Knight's Inn, Ramada Inn, **other:** Ford/Lincoln/Mercury, GMC

0mm Illinois/Wisconsin state line

Interstate 94

Exit #	Services
77mm	Illinois/Indiana state line

I-94 and I-80 run together 3 mi. See Illinois Interstate 80, exit 161.

E ↕ **W**

74[160]b I-80/I-294 W

a IL 394 S to Danville, no facilities

73 b a US 6,159th St, **N...food:** Fuddrucker's, Outback Steaks, **other:** Chevrolet, Honda, Lincoln/Mercury, Nissan/Hyundai, Target, Tire Barn, Toyota, **S...gas:** Marathon, **food:** Fannie May Candies, Subway, **lodging:** Cherry Lane Motel, **other:** Aldi Foods, Buick/Pontiac, Ford, Stanfa Tire/auto

71b a Sibley Blvd, **N...gas:** Citgo, Mobil/diesel, **food:** McDonald's, Nicky's Gyros, Popeye's, Subway, **lodging:** Baymont Inn, **other:** Dominick's Foods, **S...gas:** BP, Shell, **food:** Dusty's Buffet, Wendy's, White Castle

70b a Dolton, no facilities

69 Beaubien Woods(from eb), Forest Preserve

68b a 130th St, no facilities

66b 115th St, **S...food:** McDonald's

a 111th Ave, **S...gas:** BP, Shell, **other:** Firestone

65 103rd Ave, Stony Island Ave, no facilities

63 I-57 S, no facilities

62 US 12, US 20, 95th St, **N...gas:** Citgo, Shell, **food:** Subway, Taco Bell, **S...gas:** Amoco

61b 87th St, **N...gas:** BP, Shell, **food:** Burger King, McDonald's, **S...other:** Cub Foods, Home Depot, Marshall's

a 83rd St(from eb), **N...gas:** Shell, **other:** st police

60c 79th St, **N...gas:** Mobil, Shell, **S...gas:** Citgo/diesel, **food:** Church's

b 76th St, **N...gas:** BP, Mobil, Shell, **other:** Walgreen/24hr, **S...food:** KFC, Popeye's

a 75th St(from eb), **N...gas:** BP, Mobil, Shell, **S...food:** KFC, Popeye's

59c 71st St, **N...gas:** BP, **S...food:** McDonald's

a I-90 E, to Indiana Toll Rd

(Chicago Area)

58b 63rd St(from eb), **N...gas:** Shell, **S...gas:** BP

a I-94 divides into local and express, 59th St, **S...gas:** BP

57b Garfield Blvd, **N...food:** Checker's, Chinese Kitchen, Popeye's, **other:** Trak Auto, Walgreen, laundry, **S...gas:** Mobil, Shell/24hr, **food:** Famous Burritos, Wendy's, **other:** HOSPITAL

a 51st St, **N...food:** McDonald's

56b 47th St(from eb)

a 43rd St, **S...gas:** Citgo/diesel, Econo

55b Pershing Rd, no facilities

a 35th St, **S...to New Comiskey Park

54 31st St, **S...HOSPITAL

53c I-55, Stevenson Pkwy, N to downtown, Lakeshore Dr

b I-55, Stevenson Pkwy, S to St Louis

52c 18th St, **N...gas:** Shell

b Roosevelt Rd, Taylor St(from wb), **N...gas:** Shell

a Taylor St, Roosevelt Rd(from eb), **N...gas:** Shell, **other:** Toyota, **S...gas:** Citgo

51h-i I-290 W, to W Suburbs

g E Jackson Blvd, to downtown

f W Adams St, to downtown

e Monroe St(from eb), downtown, **S...lodging:** Quality Inn, **other:** Walgreen

d Madison St(from eb), downtown, **S... lodging:** Quality Inn, **other:** Walgreen

c E Washington Blvd, downtown

b W Randolph St, downtown

a Lake St(from wb)

50b E Ohio St, downtown, **S...gas:** Marathon

a Ogden Ave, no facilities

49b a Augusta Blvd, Division St, **N...other:** Lexus, **S...gas:** BP, Shell, **food:** Pizza Hut

48b IL 64, North Ave, **N...gas:** BP, **other:** Home Depot, **S...gas:** BP, Shell, **other:** Volvo

a Armitage Ave, **S...gas:** Amoco, **other:** Jaguar, Volvo

47c b Damen Ave, **N...gas:** Citgo, car/vanwash

a Western Ave, Fullerton Ave, **N...gas:** Citgo, **food:** Burger King, Popeye's, **other:** Costco/gas, Home Depot, Target, **S...gas:** Marathon, **food:** KFC

46b a Diversey Ave, California Ave, **S...gas:** Mobil, **food:** IHOP/24hr, Popeye's

45c Belmont Ave, **N...food:** Wendy's

b Kimball Ave, **N...gas:** Marathon/diesel, **S...gas:** Marathon, **food:** Pizza Hut, Subway, Wendy's, **other:** Delray Farms Foods, Dominick's Foods, Radio Shack, Walgreen/24hr

a Addison St(from eb), no facilities

44b Pulaski Ave, Irving Park Rd, **N...gas:** BP, Mobil

ILLINOIS

Interstate 94

E	a	IL 19, Keeler Ave, Irving Park Rd, **N...gas:** BP, Shell/24hr, **other:** to Wrigley Field
	43c	Montrose Ave, no facilities
	b	I-90 W
	a	Wilson Ave, no facilities
W	42	W Foster Ave, **S...gas:** Citgo, Marathon
	41mm	Chicago River, N Branch
	41c	IL 50 S, to Cicero, to I-90 W
	b a	US 14, Peterson Ave, no facilities
	39b a	Touhy Ave, **N...gas:** BP/diesel, Shell, **lodging:** Radisson, **other:** Cassidy Tire, **S...gas:** BP, Citgo, Mobil/diesel, Shell, **food:** Burger King, Dunkin Donuts, Jack's Rest./24hr, **other:** Lee's Auto Parts, PepBoys
	37b a	IL 58, Dempster St, no facilities
	35	Old Orchard Rd, **N...gas:** BP, Shell, **food:** Bloomingdale's, Marshall Fields, **other:** HOSPITAL, Nissan, mall, **S...lodging:** Extended Stay America, Hampton Inn
C	34c b	E Lake Ave, **N...gas:** BP, **food:** Panda Express, Starbucks, **other:** Borders Books, GNC, Omaha Steaks, **S...gas:** BP, Shell, **food:** DQ
h	a	US 41 S, Skokie Rd(from eb)
i	33b a	Willow Rd, **S...gas:** BP, Shell, **food:** Starbucks, **other:** Dominick's Foods, Walgreen
c	31	E Tower Rd, **S...other:** BMW, Hummer, Jeep, Mercedes, Toyota,
a	30b a	Dundee Rd(from wb, no EZ return), **S...gas:** Citgo, Marathon, **food:** Bennigan's, Olive Garden, Japanese Steaks, **lodging:** Rennaisance
g	29	US 41, to Waukegan, to Tri-state tollway
o	50mm	IL 43, Waukegan Rd, **N...lodging:** Red Roof Inn, Embassy Suites, **other:** Home Depot
A	53mm	I-294 S
r	53.5mm	Deerfield Rd toll plaza, phones
e	54mm	Deerfield Rd, **W...lodging:** Marriott Suites
a	56mm	IL 22, Half Day Rd, **E...lodging:** Woodfield Suites
	59mm	IL 60, Town Line Rd, **E...**HOSPITAL
	60mm	Lake Forest Oasis both lanes, **gas:** Mobil/diesel, **food:** Wendy's/24hr, **other:** info
	62mm	IL 176, Rockland Rd(no nb re-entry), **E...other:** Harley-Davidson, to Lamb's Farm
	64mm	IL 137, Buckley Rd(from wb), **E...other:** to VA HOSPITAL, Chicago Med School
	67mm	IL 120 E, Belvidere Rd(no nb re-entry), **E...**HOSPITAL
	68mm	IL 21, Milwaukee Ave(from eb), **E...other:** HOSPITAL, Six Flags
	70mm	IL 132, Grand Ave, **E...gas:** Speedway/diesel, **food:** Burger King, Cracker Barrel, Culver's, IHOP, Joe's Crabshack, Little Caesar's, McDonald's, Ming's Chinese, Olive Garden, Outback Steaks, Subway, TCBY, **lodging:** Baymont Inn, Comfort Suites, Country Inn Suites, Grand Hotel, Extended Stay America, Hampton Inn, **other:** Six Flags Park,

W...gas: Mobil, Shell, **food:** Applebee's, Bakers Square, Boston Mkt, Chili's, Denny's, LoneStar Steaks, Max&Erma's, McDonald's, Pizza Hut, Pizzaria Uno, Red Lobster, Schlotsky's, Sizzler, Starbucks, Steak'n Shake, Taco Bell, TGIFriday, Wendy's, White Castle, **lodging:** Comfort Inn, Fairfield Inn, Holiday Inn, **other:** Circuit City, Dominick's Foods, Gurnee Mills Outlet Mall/famous brands, Home Depot, Honda, Hyundai, JC Penney, Jewel-Osco, Kohl's, Lincoln/Mercury, Michaels, OfficeMax, Sam's Club, Sears/auto, Target/drugs, VW, Wal-Mart/drugs

73.5mm	Waukegan toll plaza, phones
76mm	IL 173(from nb, no return), Rosecrans Ave, **E...**to IL Beach SP
1b	US 41 S, to Waukegan, **E...other:** Sky Harbor RV Ctr
a	Russell Rd, **W...gas:** Citgo/diesel/24hr, TA/Mobil/Pizza Hut/diesel/24hr/@, **other:** Peterbilt
0mm	Illinois/Wisconsin state line

Interstate 255(St Louis)

Exit # Services

I-255 begins/ends on I-270, exit 7.

E	30	I-270, W to Kansas City, E to Indianapolis
S	29	IL 162, to Glen Carbon, Granite City, to Pontoon Beach
t	26	Horseshoe Lake Rd, **E...**st police
	25b a	I-55/I-70, W to St Louis, E to Chicago, Indianapolis
L	24	Collinsville Rd, **E...gas:** BP/24hr, **food:** Jack-in-the-Box, **other:** Shop'n Save, **W...**Fairmount Racetrack
o	20	I-64, US 50, W to St Louis, E to Louisville, facilities 1 mi E off I-64, exit 9.
u	19	State St, E St Louis, **E...gas:** Clark, **lodging:** Western Inn, **other:** Holten SP
i	17b a	IL 15, E St Louis, Centreville, to Belleville, no facilities
s	15	Mousette Lane, **E...**HOSPITAL, **W...other:** GMC/Volvo Trucks
	13	IL 157, to Cahokia, **E...gas:** Casey's, **W...gas:** BP/24hr, QT, **food:** Burger King, Capt D's, China Express, DQ, Domino's, Hardee's, KFC, McDonald's, Pizza Hut, Ponderosa, Popeye's, Rally's, Taco Bell, **lodging:** Holiday Inn Express, **other:** Advance Parts, Aldi Foods, AutoZone, CarQuest, $General, GMC/Pontiac, Goodyear/auto, Schnuck's, Walgreen, Wal-Mart/drugs, Cahokia RV Parque(2mi)
	10	IL 3 N, to Cahokia, E St Louis, **W...gas:** Shell
	9	to Dupo, no facilities
	6	IL 3 S, to Columbia, **E...gas:** Citgo, Shell/24hr, **other:** Chevrolet
	4mm	**Missouri/Illinois state line, Mississippi River**
	3	Koch Rd, no facilities
	2	MO 231, Telegraph Rd, **N...gas:** Shell, **food:** Hardee's, McDonald's, Pizza Hut/Taco Bell, Steak'n Shake, **other:** Dierberg's Foods, $Tree, Wal-Mart SuperCtr/24hr, Jefferson Barracks Nat Cem, **S...gas:** CFM/diesel, **food:** DQ

N

S

Interstate 255

1d c US 50, US 61, US 67, Lindbergh Blvd, Lemay Ferry Rd, accesses same as I-55 exit 197, **N...food:** Arby's, Hooters, McDonald's, Old Country Buffet, Subway, **other:** Advance Parts, Costco/gas, Dillard's, Discount Tire, Ford, Sears/auto, mall, **S...gas:** Citgo, **food:** Jack-in-the-Box, Papa John's, White Castle, **other:** Firestone, Sam's Club

1b a I-55 S to Memphis, N to St Louis. I-255 begins/ends on I-55, exit 196.

Interstate 270(St Louis)
See Missouri Interstate 270(St Louis)

Interstate 294(Chicago)

Exit #   Services

I-294 begins/ends on I-94, exit 74. Numbering descends from west to east.

I-294 & I-80 run together 5 mi. See Illinois Interstate 80, exits 155-160.

5mm I-80 W, access to I-57

5.5mm 167th St, toll booth, phones

6mm US 6, 159th St, **E...gas:** BP, Citgo, Mobil, Shell, **other:** Aldi Foods, AutoZone, Walgreen, **W...gas:** Clark, Marathon, **food:** Burger King, Dunkin Donuts/Baskin-Robbins, Hung's Garden Chinese, KFC/Pizza Hut, Popeye's, Taco Bell, USA Rest., White Castle, **lodging:** Holiday Inn Express, **other:** Firestone/auto, Radio Shack, U-Haul, Walgreen

11mm Cal Sag Channel

12mm IL 50, Cicero Ave, **E...gas:** Citgo/7-11, Speedway, **food:** Onion Field Rest., **W...gas:** BP, Gas City/Subway/diesel/24hr, **food:** Boston Mkt, IHOP, Pizza Hut, Pizzaria Uno, Popeye's, Portillo's Dogs, Quizno's, Starbucks, **lodging:** Baymont Inn, Hampton Inn, **other:** Best Buy, Dominick's Foods, NTB, OfficeMax, PepBoys, Sears/auto

18mm US 12/20, 95th St, **E...gas:** Clark, **food:** Bennigan's, McDonald's, Papa John's, **other:** HOSPITAL, Buick, Honda, Mazda, Sears/auto, mall, **W...gas:** Citgo/7-11, Shell, Speedway/diesel, **food:** Arby's, Burger King, Denny's, George's Rest., Quizno's, Schoop's Burgers, Wendy's, **lodging:** Exel Inn, **other:** HOSPITAL, Jewel-Osco, Walgreen

20mm toll booth, phones

22mm 75th St, Willow Springs Rd, no facilities

23mm I-55, Wolf Rd, to Hawthorne Park, no facilities

25mm Hinsdale Oasis both lanes, **gas:** Mobil/diesel, **food:** Baskin-Robbins, Wendy's/24hr

28mm US 34, Ogden Ave, **E...zoo, W...gas:** BP, Shell/deli, **food:** Dunkin Donuts, McDonald's, Starbucks, **other:** HOSPITAL, Audi/Porsche, Firestone/auto, LandRover, Maserati, Rolls-Royce/Bentley/Ferrari/Lotus, Wild Oats Mkt

28.5mm Cermak Rd(from sb, no return)

29mm I-88 tollway, no facilities

30mm toll booth, phones

31mm IL 38, Roosevelt Rd(no EZ nb return), **E...gas:** Citgo/diesel, **lodging:** Hillside Manor Motel

32mm I-290 W, to Rockford(from nb), no facilities

34mm I-290(from sb), to Rockford, no facilities

38mm O'Hare Oasis both lanes, **gas:** Mobil/diesel, **food:** Burger King, TCBY

39mm IL 19 W(from sb), Irving Park Rd, **E... gas:** Clark, Marathon/diesel, **other:** 7-11, Walgreen, **1 mi E...gas:** BP/repair, Clark, **food:** DQ, Dunkin Donuts, McDonald's, Subway, Wendy's, **lodging:** Comfort Suites, **other:** Aldi Foods, **W...lodging:** Candlewood Suites, Day's Inn, Hampton Inn, Howard Johnson, Sheraton

40mm I-190 W, **E...services from I-90, exit 79...gas:** Mobil, **food:** McDonald's, **lodging:** Courtyard, Doubletree, Embassy Suites, Holiday Inn, Hotel Softel, Hyatt, Marriott, Radisson, Rosemont Suites, Westin

41mm toll booth, phones

42mm Touhy Ave, **W...gas:** Mobil/service, **food:** Tiffany's Rest., **lodging:** Comfort Inn

43mm Des Plaines River

44mm Dempster St(from nb, no return), **E...HOSPITAL, W...food:** Dunkin Donuts, Subway

46mm IL 58, Golf Rd, **E...gas:** Citgo/diesel, Shell, **food:** Omega Rest., Senoya Oriental, **other:** Best Buy, CVS Drug, Golf Mill Mall, Target, auto repair

49mm Willow Rd, **W...food:** TGIFriday, **lodging:** Baymont Inn, Doubletree Suites, Courtyard, Fairfield Inn, Motel 6, **1 mi W on Milwaukee...gas:** BP, **food:** Burger King, Denny's, McDonald's, **lodging:** Wingate Inn

53mm Lake Cook Rd(no nb re-entry), **E...Hyatt, lodging:** Embassy Suites

I-294 begins/ends on I-94.

Interstate 474(Peoria)

Exit #   Services

15 I-74, E to Bloomington, W to Peoria. I-474 begins/ends on I-74, exit 99.

9 IL 29, E Peoria, to Pekin, **N...gas:** Clark, Shell/Arby's, Thornton's, **food:** Creve Coeur Rest., Dan's Pizza, Pizza Hut, Taco John's, **lodging:** Ragon Motel, **other:** Riverboat Casino, **S...gas:** Casey's, Citgo/Subway/diesel, **food:** Denny's, McDonald's, **other:** Buick/Pontiac, Chrysler/Jeep/Dodge, Toyota

8mm Illinois River

6b a US 24, Adams St, Bartonville, **S...gas:** Clark/diesel, Shell/24hr, **food:** Hardee's, KFC, McDonald's, Tyroni's Café

5 Airport Rd, **S...gas:** Phillips 66

3a to IL 116, Farmington, **S...Wildlife Prairie Park**

0b a I-74, W to Moline, E to Peoria. I-474 begins/ends on I-74, exit 87.

INDIANA
Interstate 64

E ↑ ↓ W

New Albany

Exit #	Services
124mm	Indiana/Kentucky state line, Ohio River
123	IN 62 E, New Albany, **N...gas:** BP/24hr, Bigfoot/diesel, Speedway, Sunoco, **food:** DQ, **other:** Chevrolet, Firestone/auto, Goodyear/auto, Valu Mkt Foods, **S...gas:** BP, Marathon/diesel/24hr, Tobacco Road, **food:** Minny's Café, Subway/Noble Roman, Waffle Steak, **lodging:** Hampton Inn, Holiday Inn Express, **other:** HOSPITAL
121	I-265 E, to I-65(exits left from eb), no facilities, **N...**access to HOSPITAL
119	US 150 W, to Greenville, **1/2 mi N...gas:** Citgo/diesel, Marathon/Taco Bell, **food:** DQ, Papa John's, Sam's Family Rest., Tumbleweed Grill, **other:** Huber Winery, Rite Aid
118	IN 62, IN 64W, to Georgetown, **N...gas:** Marathon/diesel/24hr, Shell, **food:** Korner Kitchen, McDonald's, Pizza King, **lodging:** Motel 6, **other:** Thriftway Foods, **S...gas:** Marathon/diesel
115mm	**Welcome Ctr wb, full(handicapped)facilities, vending, phone, picnic tables, litter barrels**
113	to Lanesville, no facilities
105	IN 135, to Corydon, **N...gas:** Citgo/diesel, Shell/24hr, **food:** Big Boy, **lodging:** Quality Inn, **S...gas:** BP/diesel, Chevron, **food:** Arby's, Burger King, China Best Buffet, Cracker Barrel, Culver's, DQ, Hardee's, Hong Kong Chinease, KFC, Lee's Chicken, LJ Silver, McDonald's, O'Charley's, Papa John's, Pizza Hut, Ryan's, Subway/TCBY, Taco Bell, Waffle Steak/24hr, Wendy's, White Castle, **lodging:** Baymont Inn, Hampton Inn, Holiday Inn Express, Super 8, **other:** MEDICAL CARE, AutoZone, Chevrolet/Pontiac/Buick, $General, $Tree, Ford/Mercury, Radio Shack, WalMart SuperCtr/24hr, RV camping
100mm	Blue River
97mm	parking area both lanes, no facilities
92	IN 66, Carefree, **N...**Veringo Caves, **S...gas:** BP/Kathy's Kitchen/diesel/Days Inn, Citgo/food court/diesel/rest./24hr, Country Style Plaza/Shell/diesel/@, **food:** Country Style Rest., **lodging:** Day's Inn/rest./diesel, **other:** to Wyandotte Caves, Harrison Crawford SF
88mm	Hoosier Nat Forest eastern boundary
86	IN 37, to Sulphur, **N...**to Patoka Lake, **S...**gas, food, phone, scenic route
81.5mm	**no facilities**
80mm	**no facilities**
79	IN 37, to Tell City, St Croix, **S...**to Hoosier NF, Rec. Facilities, phone, to OH River Br
76mm	Anderson River
72	IN 145, to Birdseye, **N...**to Patoka Lake, **S...**gas, phone, St Meinrad Coll
63	IN 162, to Ferdinand, **N...gas:** Sunoco/diesel, **food:** Wendy's, **lodging:** Comfort Inn, **other:** Ferdinand SF, **S...**(8mi)Lake Rudolph RV Camping
58mm	**rest areas both lanes, full(handicapped)facilities, info, vending, picnic tables, litter barrels, phone**

Merrillville

Exit #	Services
57	US 231, to Dale, Huntingburg, **N...gas:** 231 Trkstp/diesel/rest./24hr/@, **S...gas:** Shell/diesel/24hr, **food:** Denny's, **lodging:** Baymont Inn, Budget Host(2mi), Motel 6, **other:** Lincoln Boyhood Home, Lincoln SP
54	IN 161, to Holland,Tennyson, no facilities
39	IN 61, Lynnville, **N...gas:** Shell, **food:** East LA Rest., **lodging:** Old Fox Inn/rest., **other:** Goodyear, **S...**museum(10mi)
32mm	Wabash & Erie Canal
29b a	I-164 S, IN 57 S, to Evansville, **N...gas:** Sunoco/Subway/TCBY/diesel
25b a	US 41, to Evansville, **N...gas:** ✈/Flying J/CountryMkt/diesel/24hr/@, Pilot/Wendy's/diesel/24hr/@, Pilot/diesel/24hr/@, **lodging:** Quality Inn, **other:** Blue Beacon, **S...gas:** BP/motel, Busler/diesel/24hr/@, **food:** Arby's, Denny's, McDonald's, **lodging:** Best Western, Best Inn, Comfort Inn, Gateway Inn, Holiday Inn Express, Super 8, **other:** st police, to U S IN
18	IN 65, to Cynthiana, **S...gas:** Motomart/diesel/24hr
12	IN 165, Poseyville, **S...other:** Chevrolet, New Harmonie Hist Area/SP
7mm	**Black River Welcome Ctr eb, full(handicapped)facilities, phone, picnic tables, litter barrels, petwalk**
5mm	Black River
4	4 IN 69 S, New Harmony, Griffin, **1 mi N...**gas/diesel, food, motel, antiques, **S...**Harmony St Park
2mm	Big Bayou River
0mm	Indiana/Illinois state line, Wabash River

Interstate 65

N ↑ S

Exit #	Services
262	I-90, W to Chicago, E to Ohio, I-65 begins/ends on US 12, US 20.
261	15th Ave, to Gary, **E...**Mack Trucks, **W...gas:** Marathon
259b a	I-94/80, US 6W, no facilities
258	US 6, Ridge Rd, **E...gas:** ExpressAmerica Gas, Speedway/diesel, **food:** Diner's Choice Rest., **W...gas:** Citgo, Marathon, Phillips 66
255	61st Ave, Merrillville, **E...gas:** Marathon, Speedway/diesel/24hr, Thornton, **food:** Arby's, Cracker Barrel, McDonald's, Pizza Hut/Taco Bell, Wendy's, **other:** Chevrolet, Chrysler/Jeep, Comfort Inn, $Inn, Lee's Inn, I-65 Repair, **1 mi W...gas:** Shell, **food:** Burger King, LJ Silver, Subway, **other:** HOSPITAL
253b	US 30 W, Merrillville, **W...gas:** Gas City/diesel/24hr, Meijer/diesel/24hr, Shell, Speedway/diesel, **food:** Applebee's, Arby's, Blimpie, Buffalo Wings, Denny's, Dunkin Donuts, Fannie May Candies, Hooters, House of Kobe, KFC, LoneStar Steaks, New Moon Chinese, Pizza Hut, Rio Bravo, Roma Pizza, Schlotsky's, Smokey Bones BBQ, Steak'n Shake, Subway, Texas Corral Steaks, Wendy's, White Castle, **lodging:** Courtyard, $Inn, Fairfield Inn, Hampton Inn, Holiday Inn Express, Radisson, Red Roof Inn, Residence Inn, **other:** Aldi Foods, CarQuest, Celebration Sta, Firestone, Ford/Lincoln/Mercury, Hyundai/Mitsubishi,

Interstate 65

Jo-Ann Fabrics, K-Mart, NTB, Saturn, Toyota, Walgreen, RV Ctr, transmissions

a US 30 E, **E...gas:** BP/diesel/24hr, Speedway, **food:** Bakers Square, Bennigan's, Bob Evans, Boston Mkt, Burger King, Casa Gallardo, Chili's, ChuckeCheese, DQ, Don Pablo, Heavenly Ham, Joe's Crabshack, McDonald's, New China Buffet, Old Country Buffet, Olive Garden, Pizzaria Uno, Popeye's, Red Lobster, Ruby Tuesday, Starbucks, Subway, Taco Bell, TGIFriday, Zel's Café, **lodging:** Day's Inn, Extended Stay America, Holiday Inn, Knight's Inn, La Quinta, Motel 6, Super 8, **other:** Barnes&Noble, Best Buy, Circuit City, Costco/gas, Dodge, Firestone/auto, Home Depot, JC Penney, Kia, Kohl's, Lowe's Whse, Michael's, Nissan, OfficeMax, Old Navy, Sam's Club/gas, Sears/auto, Target, Tire Barn, VW, **Wal-Mart**, mall

247 US 231, Crown Point, **W...gas:** Mobil/24hr, **other:** HOSPITAL, Vietnam Vet Mem

241mm weigh sta both lanes

240 IN 2, Lowell, **E...gas:** ✈/Flying J/Cookery/diesel/24hr/@, Mobil/Burger King, Pilot/diesel/24hr, **lodging:** Super 8, **W...**st police

234mm Kankakee River

231mm rest area both lanes, full(handicapped)facilities, phones, info, picnic tables, litter barrels, vending, petwalk

230 IN 10, Roselawn, **E...gas:** Crazy D's/diesel/rest./24hr, **W...gas:** Family Express, Shell/Subway, **food:** J&J Pizza, Rodeo Rest., **other:** CarQuest, CVS Drug, $General, Fagen Drug, Rose RV Ctr, TrueValue, RV camping

215 IN 114, Rensselaer, **E...gas:** Family Express/diesel/24hr, **food:** Arby's, KFC, McDonald's, **lodging:** Holiday Inn Express, Knight's Inn, **other:** HOSPITAL, **W...gas:** Grandma's/diesel/rest., Shell/24hr, **food:** Burger King, Trail Tree Rest., **lodging:** Economy Inn, **other:** tires/repair/towing/24hr

212mm Iroquois River

205 US 231, Remington, **E...gas:** Phillips 66/diesel, Shell, **other:** HOSPITAL, to St Joseph's Coll

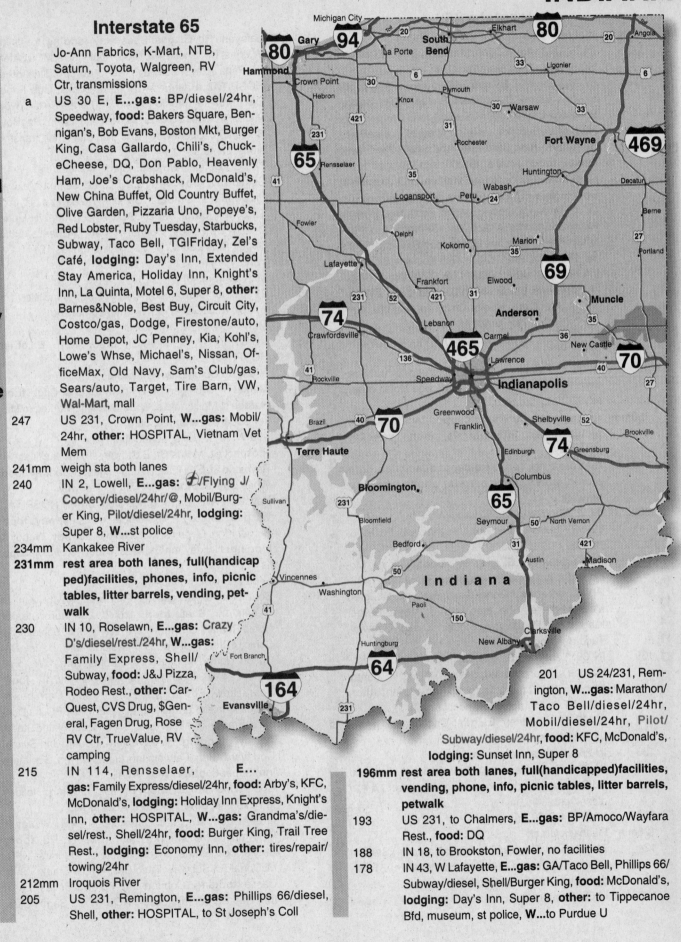

201 US 24/231, Remington, **W...gas:** Marathon/Taco Bell/diesel/24hr, Mobil/diesel/24hr, Pilot/Subway/diesel/24hr, **food:** KFC, McDonald's, **lodging:** Sunset Inn, Super 8

196mm rest area both lanes, full(handicapped)facilities, vending, phone, info, picnic tables, litter barrels, petwalk

193 US 231, to Chalmers, **E...gas:** BP/Amoco/Wayfara Rest., **food:** DQ

188 IN 18, to Brookston, Fowler, no facilities

178 IN 43, W Lafayette, **E...gas:** GA/Taco Bell, Phillips 66/Subway/diesel, Shell/Burger King, **food:** McDonald's, **lodging:** Day's Inn, Super 8, **other:** to Tippecanoe Bfd, museum, st police, **W...**to Purdue U

INDIANA

Interstate 65

N ↑ S

176mm	Wabash River
175	IN 25, Lafayette, **E...gas:** Marathon/24hr, **W...other:** HOSPITAL, **gas:** Marathon(1mi)
172	IN 26, Lafayette, **E...gas:** Meijer/diesel/24hr, **food:** Cracker Barrel, DQ, Steak'n Shake, White Castle, **lodging:** Baymont Inn, Budget Inn, Comfort Inn, Holiday Inn Express, Lee's Inn, Microtel, TownePlace Suites, **W...gas:** BP/diesel/24hr, Shell, Speedway/diesel, **food:** Arby's, Bob Evans, Burger King, Chick-fil-A, Chili's, China Garden, DQ, Damon's, Don Pablo, KFC, Logan's Roadhouse, McDonald's, Olive Garden, Outback Steaks, Pizza Hut, Porky's Rest., Spageddie's, Taco Bell, **lodging:** $Inn, Fairfield Inn, Hampton Inn, Homewood Suites, Knight's Inn, Radisson, Ramada Inn, Red Roof Inn, Signature Inn, Super 8, **other:** HOSPITAL, CVS Drug, $Tree, Marsh Foods, Buick/Nissan/Cadillac, Lowe's Whse, NAPA AutoCare, Sam's Club, Target, Wal-Mart SuperCtr/24hr, to Purdue U
168	IN 38, IN 25, Dayton, **E...gas:** BP/Piccadilly's/24hr, Mobil/diesel
158	IN 28, to Frankfort, **E...gas:** BP/diesel/24hr, Marathon, **2 mi W...lodging:** Lincoln Lodge Motel, **other:** HOSPITAL, camping
150mm	**rest area sb, full(handicapped)facilities, info, picnic tables, litter barrels, phone, vending, petwalk**
148mm	**rest area nb, full(handicapped)facilities, info, picnic tables, litter barrels, phone, vending, petwalk**
146	IN 47, Thorntown, no facilities
141	US 52 W(exits left from sb), Lafayette Ave, **E...**HOSPITAL
140	IN 32, Lebanon, **E...gas:** BP, **food:** Denny's, McDonald's, White Castle, **lodging:** Comfort Inn, HOSPITAL, **other:** AutoZone, Goodyear/auto, **W...gas:** McClure/diesel, Shell/diesel, **food:** Arby's, Burger King, KFC, Ponderosa, Steak'n Shake, Subway, Taco Bell, **lodging:** $Inn, Lee's Inn, Super 8
139	IN 39, Lebanon, **E...gas:** GA, **food:** Arni's Rest., Hardee's, Wendy's, **W...gas:** ✈/Flying J/Country Mkt/diesel/LP/24hr/@, **lodging:** Ramada Inn, **other:** HOSPITAL, Homemade Chocolates
138	to US 52, Lebanon, **E...gas:** Citgo/diesel, Shell/diesel, **other:** Chevrolet, Ford
133	IN 267, Whitestown, no facilities
130	IN 334, Zionsville, **E...gas:** Shell/diesel, Tobacco Rd/Subway, **food:** Burger King, **W...gas:** TA/BP/diesel/rest./24hr/@
129	I-865 E, US 52 E(from sb)
126mm	Fishback Creek
124	71st St, **1 mi E...gas:** BP, **food:** Hardee's, Steak'n Shake, **lodging:** Courtyard, Hampton Inn, Residence Inn, **W...**Eagle Creek Park
123	I-465, S to airport

Lebanon

121	Lafayette Rd, **E...gas:** Speedway, **lodging:** Lee's Inn, **W...gas:** BP, Shell/24hr, **food:** Applebee's, MCL Cafeteria, Papa John's, Subway, TCBY, **lodging:** $Inn, **other:** HOSPITAL, Batteries+, Borders Books, Cub Foods, Discount Tire, Firestone/auto, JC Penney, Kia/Toyota, Mercury/Lincoln/Mitsubishi, NAPA, Nissan, PepBoys, Sears/auto, Speedway Parts, Tire Barn, mall, transmissions, same as 119
119	38th St, Dodge, **W...gas:** Clark, Meijer's/diesel/24hr, Speedway, **food:** Arby's, KFC, La Bamba Mexican, McDonald's, Outback Steaks, Pizza Hut, Ryan's, Taco Bell, **other:** MEDICAL CARE, Dodge/Hyundai, Dominick's Foods, Honda, K-Mart, Michael's, Office Depot, Sears/auto, Tires+, mall, same as 121
117.5mm	White River
117	MLK St(from sb)
116	29th St, 30th St(from nb), Marian Coll, no facilities
115	21st St, **E...**HOSPITAL, **W...**museums, zoo
114	MLK St, West St, downtown
113	US 31, IN 37, Meridian St, to downtown, **E...other:** HOSPITAL
112a	I-70 E, to Columbus, no facilities
111	Market St, Michigan St, Ohio St, **E...gas:** Citgo, **food:** Hardee's, McDonald's, **W...other:** City Market, to Market Square Arena, museum
110b	I-70 W, to St Louis, no facilities
a	Prospect St, Morris St, E St(from sb), no facilities
109	Raymond St, **E...**HOSPITAL, **W...gas:** Speedway, **food:** White Castle, **other:** CVS Drug, Safeway
107	Keystone Ave, **E...lodging:** $Inn, **other:** HOSPITAL, **W...gas:** Citgo, Phillips 66/diesel, Speedway, **food:** Burger King, Denny's, McDonald's, Subway, Wendy's, **lodging:** Holiday Inn Express, **other:** U of Indianapolis
106	I-465 and I-74, no facilities
103	Southport Rd, **E...gas:** BP/McDonald's/24hr, Meijer/diesel/24hr, Shell, **food:** Arby's, Longhorn Steaks, Noble Roman, O'Charley's, Pizzaria Uno, Schlotsky's, Sonic, **other:** Aldi Foods, Firestone/auto, Harley-Davidson, Home Depot, Kohl's, Staples, Target, **W...gas:** Bigfoot/24hr, Citgo/7-11, Speedway/diesel/24hr, **food:** Beef&Brew, Bob Evans, Burger King, Carrabba's, Cheeseburger Paradise, Cracker Barrel, KFC, McDonald's, Steak'n Shake, Texas Roadhouse, Waffle Steak, Wendy's, **lodging:** Best Western, Country Inn Suites, Courtyard, $Inn, Fairfield Inn, Hampton Inn, Signature Inn, Super 8, **other:** HOSPITAL
101	CountyLine Rd, **W...food:** Blimpie, **lodging:** Holiday Inn Express, **other:** HOSPITAL, Kroger
99	Greenwood, **E...gas:** Citgo/diesel/24hr, **W...gas:** BP/Amoco, Marathon, Shell, Tobacco Rd, **food:** Arby's, Bob Evans, Byrd's Cafeteria, Denny's, KFC, McDonald's, Subway, Taco Bell, Waffle Steak, White Castle, **lodging:** Comfort Inn, InTown Suites, Lee's Inn, Red Carpet Inn, **other:** HOSPITAL, Sam's Club, Stout's RV Ctr

Indianapolis Area

Greenwood

Interstate 65

N ↑ ↓ S

95	Whiteland, **E...gas:** ✈/Flying J/CountryMkt/diesel/24hr@, Marathon/Kathy's Kitchen/diesel, **W...gas:** Pilot/Arby's/diesel/24hr/@, Pilot/McDonald's/diesel/24hr/@
90	IN 44, Franklin, **W...gas:** BP, Shell, **food:** Burger King, Franklin Gardens Rest., McDonald's, Subway, Waffle Steak, **lodging:** Carlton Lodge, Day's Inn/rest., Howard Johnson, Quality Inn, Super 8, **other:** HOSPITAL, golf
85mm	Sugar Creek
82mm	Big Blue River
80	IN 252, Edinburgh, to Flat Rock, **W...gas:** BP/diesel, Shell/diesel
76b a	US 31, Taylorsville, **E...gas:** Shell/diesel, Speedway/diesel, **food:** A&W/KFC, Burger King, Waffle Steak, **lodging:** Comfort Inn, **other:** HOSPITAL, **W...gas:** BP, Citgo/Subway/diesel, Thornton/diesel/café, **food:** Arby's, Cracker Barrel, Hardee's, Max&Erma's, McDonald's, Waffle Steak, **lodging:** Best Western, Hampton Inn, Holiday Inn Express, **other:** Edmundson RV Ctr, Goodyear, Harley-Davidson, Prime Outlets/famous brands, antiques, repair
73mm	**rest area both lanes, full(handicapped)facilities, phone, vending, info, picnic tables, litter barrels, petwalk**
68mm	Driftwood River
68	IN 46, Columbus, **E...gas:** BP/diesel/24hr, Bigfoot, Shell, Speedway/diesel, **food:** Burger King, McDonald's, Mexico Viejo, Riviera Diner, **lodging:** Courtyard, Holiday Inn/rest., Ramada Inn, Sleep Inn, Super 8, **other:** HOSPITAL, **W...gas:** Marathon, Swifty, **food:** Arby's, Bob Evans, Denny's, KFC/Pizza Hut, Taco Bell, Wendy's, **lodging:** Day's Inn, Knight's Inn, Travelodge, **other:** U-Haul, to Brown Co SP
64	IN 58, Walesboro, **W...gas:** Marathon, **food:** Kathy's Express Diner, **other:** to RV camping
55	IN 11, Seymour, to Jonesville, **E...gas:** BP
54mm	White River
51mm	weigh sta both lanes
50b a	US 50, Seymour, **E...gas:** Chevron, Marathon/diesel, Swifty, TA/BP/diesel/24hr/@, **food:** McDonald's, Waffle House, **lodging:** Day's Inn, Econolodge, Motel 6, Super 8, **other:** Tanger Outlet/famous brands, **W...gas:** BP, Shell/diesel, Speedway/diesel, Sunoco/diesel, **food:** Applebee's, Arby's, Bob Evans, Burger King, Cracker Barrel, Denny's, KFC, LJ Silver, McDonald's, Papa John's, Perkins, Pizza Hut, Rally's, Ryan's, Santa Fe Mexican, Steak'n Shake, Subway, Taco Bell, Tumbleweed Grill, Wendy's, **lodging:** Hampton Inn, Holiday Inn/rest., HomeTown Inn, Knight's Inn, Lee's Inn, **other:** HOSPITAL, Aldi Foods, AutoZone, Chevrolet/Buick/Pontiac/GMC, $General, Family$, Foods+, Ford/Lincoln/Mercury, GNC, Home Depot, JC Penney, Radio Shack, Staples, Wal-Mart SuperCtr/24hr

Columbus · Seymour (left vertical tab)

Scottsburg (right vertical tab)

41	IN 250, Uniontown, **W...gas:** UnionTown/diesel/rest./24hr, **other:** auto/truck repair
36	US 31, Crothersville, **E...gas:** Shell, **W...gas:** BP/pizza/subs
34a b	IN 256, Austin, **E...gas:** Bigfoot, **food:** Dairy Bar, **other:** to Hardy Lake, Clifty Falls SP, **W...gas:** Fuelmart/-A&W/diesel
29b a	IN 56, Scottsburg, to Salem, **E...gas:** BP/diesel, MotoMart, Speedway/diesel, **food:** Burger King, Cracker Barrel, KFC, Ponderosa, Sonic, Subway, Taco Bell, **lodging:** Holiday Inn Express, Mariann Motel/rest., **other:** HOSPITAL, CVS Drug, **W...gas:** Citgo/diesel, Shell, **food:** Arby's, LJ Silver, McDonald's, Pizza Hut, Roadhouse USA, Waffle Steak, Wendy's, **lodging:** Best Western, Hampton Inn, Super 8, **other:** Big O Tire, Jellystone Camping(4mi), Wal-Mart SuperCtr/24hr
22mm	**rest area both lanes, full(handicapped)facilities, info, phone, picnic tables, litter barrels, vending, petwalk**
19	IN 160, Henryville, **E...gas:** Bigfoot, Shell/24hr, Sprint/diesel, **food:** Schuler's Rest.
16	Memphis Rd, Memphis, **E...gas:** BP, Citgo/diesel, **W...gas:** Pilot/Arby's/diesel/24hr/@, **other:** Customers 1st RV Ctr.
9	IN 311, Sellersburg, to New Albany, **E...gas:** BP, Chevron, Shell, Swifty, **food:** Arby's, Cracker Barrel, DQ, Waffle Steak, **lodging:** Ramada Ltd, **other:** Carmerica Tires/service, Ford, O'Reilly Parts, st police, **W...gas:** DM/gas, **food:** Burger King, McDonald's, Taco Bell, **lodging:** Comfort Inn, **other:** city park
7	IN 60, Hamburg, **E...gas:** BP/diesel/24hr, **W...gas:** Citgo, **food:** KFC, **lodging:** Day's Inn
6b a	I-265 W, to I-64 W, New Albany, IN 265 E
5	Veterans Parkway, no facilities
4	US 31 N, IN 131 S, Clarksville, New Albany, **E...gas:** Thornton/Subway/diesel, **food:** White Castle, **lodging:** Crest Motel, **W...gas:** Speedway/diesel, **food:** Applebee's, Arby's, Blimpie, Bob Evans, Boston Mkt,

INDIANA

Interstate 65

Clarksville

Burger King, Capt D's, ChiChi's, Damon's, Denny's, Don Pablo, Fazoli's, Golden Corral, HomeTown Buffet, Hooters, Jerry's Rest., Little Caesar's, Logan's Roadhouse, LJ Silver, McDonald's, Mr Gatti's, O'Charley's, Outback Steaks, Papa John's, Pizza Hut, Rally's, Red Lobster, Steak'n Shake/24hr, Taco Bell, Texas Roadhouse, Wendy's, **lodging:** Best Western, Colonial Motel, $Inn, Hampton Inn, **other:** AutoZone, Buick/Pontiac/GMC, Circuit City, Dillard's, Firestone/auto, Ford, Hancock Fabrics, Home Depot, Honda, JC Penney, Kia, Kroger/deli, Mazda, Office Depot, OfficeMax, PepBoys, Premier RV Ctr, Sears/auto, Target, Toyota, USPO, Walgreen, Wal-Mart, mall

2 Eastern Blvd, Clarksville, **E...lodging:** Day's Inn, Motel 6, Super 8, **other:** U-Haul, **W...gas:** BP, Citgo/7-11, Shell, Tobacco Rd/gas, **food:** KFC, Omelet Shop, Ponderosa, **lodging:** Best Inn, Econolodge, Howard Johnson, Knight's Inn, Quality Inn

1 US 31 S, IN 62, Stansifer Ave, **W...food:** Derby Dinner House, **lodging:** Holiday Inn, Stansifer Hotel, **other:** HOSPITAL, Stinnett RV Ctr

0 Jeffersonville, **E...gas:** BP, Thornton, **food:** DQ, Hardee's, McDonald's, Waffle Steak, **other:** HOSPITAL, Chrysler/Jeep, Hyundai, Nissan, Walgreen, to Falls of OH SP, **W...food:** Hooters, Subway, **lodging:** Fairfield Inn, Ramada Inn, TownePlace Inn

0mm Indiana/Kentucky state line, Ohio River

Interstate 69

Exit #	Services
158mm	Indiana/Michigan state line
157	Lake George Rd, to IN 120, Fremont, Lake James, **E...gas:** Petro/Mobil/diesel/24hr/@, **lodging:** Lake George Inn, **other:** Western Star Trucks, **W...gas:** Pilot/Wendy's/diesel/24hr/@, Shell/Subway/diesel/24hr/@, **food:** McDonald's, Red Arrow Rest., **lodging:** Holiday Inn Express(1mi), Redwood Lodge, **other:** Prime Outlets/famous brands(1mi), fireworks
156	I-80/90 Toll Rd, E to Toledo, W to Chicago
154	IN 127, to IN 120, IN 727, Fremont, Orland, **E...food:** Herb Garden Rest., **lodging:** E&L Motel, Hampton Inn, Super 8, **W...gas:** Marathon/diesel, **lodging:** Budgeteer Motel, Holiday Inn Express, **other:** Prime Outlets/famous brands(2mi), to Pokagon SP, Jellystone Camping(4mi)
150	rd 200 W, to Lake James, Crooked Lake, **E...gas:** BP/diesel, **W...gas:** Shell, Pennzoil Gas, **other:** Marine Ctr
148	US 20, to Angola, Lagrange, **E...gas:** BP/Subway, Marathon/diesel, Speedway/diesel, **food:** McDonald's, Wendy's(1mi), **other:** HOSPITAL, **W...lodging:** Best Western
145mm	Pigeon Creek

N S (Ft Wayne)

Auburn

144mm	rest area sb, full(handicapped)facilities, info, phone, picnic tables, litter barrels, vending, petwalk
140	IN 4, Ashley, Hudson, to Hamilton, **1 mi W...gas:** Phillips 66
134	US 6, to Waterloo, Kendallville, **W...gas:** Marathon/diesel/24hr
129	IN 8, Auburn, to Garrett, **E...gas:** BP/diesel, Clark, GA, Marathon/diesel/24hr, Shell, Speedway/diesel, Ambrosia Rest., **food:** Applebee's, Arby's/24hr, Bob Evans, Burger King, DQ, Fazoli's, KFC, McDonald's, Pizza Hut, Ponderosa, Richard's Rest., Subway, Taco Bell, TCBY, Wendy's, Zesto Drive-In, **lodging:** Auburn Inn, Budget Inn, Comfort Suites, Country Hearth Inn, Holiday Inn Express, Ramada Ltd, Super 8, **other:** HOSPITAL, AutoZone, Chevrolet/Pontiac/Buick/RV Ctr, Chrysler/Jeep, $General, Ford, Kroger, Radio Shack, Staples, Wal-Mart SuperCtr/24hr, museum, **W...food:** Cracker Barrel, **other:** Home Depot
126	IN 11-A, to Garrett, Auburn, **E...**Kruse Auction Park, **W...**KOA
116	IN 1 N, Dupont Rd, **E...gas:** BP/Burger King, **lodging:** Comfort Suites, **W...gas:** BP/Elmo's/diesel, Speedway, **food:** Bob Evans, Ground Level Coffee, McDonald's(1mi), Trolley Grill, **lodging:** AmericInn, Sleep Inn, **other:** HOSPITAL
115	I-469, US 30 E, no facilities
112b a	Coldwater Rd, **E...gas:** BP/diesel/24hr, Marathon, Sunoco, **food:** Arby's, ChiChi's, Cork'n Cleaver, DeBrand's Chocolate, Hunan Chinese, Joe's CrabShack, Krispy Kreme, LoneStar Steaks, Old Country Buffet, Oriental Seafood Buffet, Papa John's, Red River Steaks/BBQ, Steak'n Shake, Taco Bell, Taco Cabana, Wendy's, Zesto Drive-In, **lodging:** AmeiSuites, Marriott, **other:** $Tree, Hall's Factory Steaks, Walgreen, Wal-Mart SuperCtr/24hr, **W...**DQ

Ft Wayne

111b a	US 27 S, IN 3 N, **E...gas:** Shell, **food:** Cap'n Cork Rest., Golden Corral, Sonic, **lodging:** Residence Inn, **other:** Honda, Infiniti, Kia, Nissan, Pontiac/GMC/Isuzu, Toyota, **W...gas:** BP/diesel, Marathon, Meijer/diesel/24hr, **food:** Applebee's, Cracker Barrel, Golden China, KFC, McDonald's, Sonic, Texas Roadhouse, Tumbleweed Grill, **lodging:** Baymont Inn, Courtyard, County Inn Suites, Day's Inn, **other:** $Inn, Fairfield Inn, Guesthouse Motel, Hampton Inn, Lee's Inn, Signature Inn, Studio+, Home Depot, Lowe's Whse, Sam's Club, VW
109b a	US 33, Ft Wayne, **E...gas:** BP, Citgo/Subway/diesel, Sunoco, **food:** Arby's, Liberty Diner, McDonald's, **lodging:** Best Inn, Comfort Inn, $Inn, Econolodge, Holiday Inn, Knight's Inn, Motel 6, Red Roof Inn, ValuLodge, **other:** HOSPITAL, to Children's Zoo
105b a	IN 14 W, Ft Wayne, **E...gas:** Meijer/diesel/24hr, Shell/Subway/diesel, Speedway/LP, **food:** Bob Evans, FlatTop Grill, Logan's Roadhouse, O'Charley's, Steak'n Shake, Subway, **lodging:** Klopfenstein Suites, **other:**

Interstate 69

N
↑
↓
S

102 HOSPITAL, Acura, Barnes&Noble, Best Buy, BMW, Cadillac, Chevrolet, Chrysler/Plymouth/Jeep, Daewoo, Dodge, Harley-Davidson, Hummer, Lexus, Kohl's, Lincoln/Mercury, Lowe's Whse, Mazda, Old Navy, Pontiac/Buick/GMC, Saab, Saturn, Staples, Subaru, Toyota, Volvo, Wal-Mart SuperCtr/24hr, to St Francis U, **W**...Corvette Museum

102 US 24, to Huntington, Ft Wayne, **E**...**food:** Subway(1mi), Taco Bell(1mi), **lodging:** Extended Stay America, Hampton Inn, **other:** HOSPITAL, to In Wesleyan U, **W**...**gas:** BP/24hr, Marathon, **food:** Applebee's, Arby's, Bob Evans, Capt D's, Carlos O'Kelly's, Coventry Tavern Rest., McDonald's, Outback Steaks, Pizza Hut, Tumbleweeds Grill, Wendy's, Zesto Drive-In, **lodging:** Best Western, Comfort Suites, Hilton Garden, Holiday Inn Express, **other:** Kroger, Scott's Foods, Walgreen, st police

99 Lower Huntington Rd, no facilities

96b a I-469, US 24 E, US 33 S, **E**...to airport

93mm **rest area sb, full(handicapped)facilities, info, phone, vending, picnic tables, litter barrels, pet walk**

89mm **rest area nb, full(handicapped)facilities, info, phone, vending, picnic tables, litter barrels, pet walk**

86 US 224, Markle, to Huntington, **E**...**gas:** Citgo/diesel(1mi), Marathon/24hr(1mi), Sunoco/Subway, **food:** DQ(1mi), E of Chicago Pizza, **lodging:** Sleep Inn, Super 8, **other:** HOSPITAL, antiques, **W**...to Huntington Reservoir

80mm weigh sta both lanes

78 IN 5, to Warren, Huntington, **E**...**gas:** Sunoco/diesel, **lodging:** Huggy Bear Motel, **W**...**gas:** Clark/Subway/diesel/24hr, Crazy D's/diesel/24hr, **food:** Hoosier-Land Rest., McDonald's, **lodging:** Ramada Ltd, Super 8, **other:** HOSPITAL, RV Camping, to Salmonie Reservoir

76mm Salamonie River

73 IN 218, to Warren, no facilities

64 IN 18, to Marion, Montpelier, **W**...**gas:** BP/Subway/diesel, Marathon/diesel, **food:** Arby's, **lodging:** Country Inn Suites, **other:** HOSPITAL, Harley-Davidson

60mm Walnut Creek

59 US 35 N, IN 22, to Upland, Gas City, **E**...**gas:** Citgo/Subway, **food:** Burger King, Cracker Barrel, **lodging:** B&B, Best Western, Super 8, **other:** Taylor U, **W**...**gas:** Marathon/diesel/24hr, McClure Trkstp/diesel/24hr/@, Shell/diesel, **food:** KFC/Taco Bell, **other:** IN Wesleyan

A n d e r s o n

55 IN 26, to Fairmount, **E**...**gas:** Marathon

50mm **rest area both lanes, full(handicapped)facilities, info, phone, picnic tables, litter barrels, vending, pet walk**

45 US 35 S, IN 28, to Alexandria, Albany, **E**...**gas:** Shell/Taco Bell/diesel/24hr, **other:** camping, **W**...camping

41 IN 332, to Muncie, Frankton, **E**...**gas:** Citgo/diesel, **other:** HOSPITAL, to Ball St U

34 IN 67, to IN 32, Chesterfield, Daleville, **E**...**gas:** Pilot/Subway/diesel/24hr/@, Shell/Burger King, **food:** Arby's, Taco Bell, White Castle, **lodging:** Budget Inn, **other:** HOSPITAL, Factory Shops/famous brands, **W**...**gas:** GA/diesel, Pilot/diesel/24hr/@, **food:** McDonald's, Subway, Wendy's, **lodging:** Super 8, **other:** flea mkt

26 IN 9, IN 109, to Anderson, **E**...**gas:** Meijer/diesel/24hr, **food:** KFC/A&W, Ryan's, **lodging:** $Inn, Hampton Inn, Quality Inn, **W**...**gas:** BP/24hr, Marathon, Shell, Red Barn Mkt/Noble Roman's/diesel, **food:** Applebee's, Arby's, Bob Evans, Burger King, ChiChi's, Cracker Barrel, Great Wall Chinese, Grindstone Charley's, La Charreada Mexican, Little Caesar's, LoneStar Steaks, McDonald's, Perkins, Pizza Hut, Red Lobster, Ruby Tuesday, Steak'n Shake, Taco Bell, TCBY, Texas Roadhouse, Waffle Steak, Wendy's, White Castle, **lodging:** Baymont Inn, Best Inn, Best Western, Comfort Inn, Econolodge, Holiday Inn, Lee's Inn, Super 8, **other:** HOSPITAL, Aldi Foods, Cadillac/GMC, Kohl's, OfficeMax, Old Navy, Payless Foods, Radio Shack, Target, Tire Barn, Toyota, Wal-Mart/auto, to Anderson U, to Mounds SP

22 IN 9, IN 67, to Anderson, **W**...**gas:** GA, **lodging:** Anderson Country Inn(1mi), **other:** HOSPITAL, st police

19 IN 38, Pendleton, **E**...**gas:** Marathon, **food:** Burger King, DQ, McDonald's, Subway

14 IN 13, to Lapel, **W**...**gas:** Pilot/Subway/diesel/24hr/@, **other:** camping

10 IN 238, to Noblesville, Fortville, **E**...outlet mall

5 IN 37 N, 116th St, Fishers, to Noblesville, **W**...**gas:** Shell/autocare, **food:** Hardee's, McDonald's, O'Charley's, Quizno's, Steak'n Shake, Wendy's, **other:** Target

INDIANA

Interstate 69

E ↕ W

3 96th St, **E...gas:** Meijer/diesel/24hr, Shell, VP/diesel, **food:** Applebee's, Bennigan's, Cracker Barrel, Golden Wok Chinese, Grindstone Charley's, McDonald's, Noble Roman's, Panera Bread, Qdoba Mexican, Red Rock Roadhouse, Ruby Tuesday, Steak'n Shake, Wendy's, **lodging:** Holiday Inn, Holiday Inn Express, Sleep Inn, Studio 6, **other:** Kohl's, Marsh Food/gas, PepBoys, Radio Shack, Sam's Club, Staples, Wal-Mart SuperCtr/24hr, **W...gas:** Marathon, **food:** Arby's, Bob Evans, Burger King, Panda Express, Peterson's Steaks/seafood, Schlotsky's, Taco Bell, **lodging:** Comfort Inn, Residence Inn, Staybridge Suites, **other:** Home Depot, Sam's Club/gas

1 82nd St, Castleton, **E...food:** Golden Corral, **lodging:** Clarion, $Inn, Extended Stay America, Omni Hotel, Super 8, **other:** HOSPITAL, Lowe's Whse, **W...gas:** BP, Speedway, **food:** Arby's, Burger King, Cancun Mexican, Castleton Grill, Charleston Rest., ChiChi's, China Dynasty, Denny's, Fazoli's, Hooters, IHOP, KFC, LJ Silver, McDonald's, Olive Garden, Pizza Hut, Red Lobster, Skyline Chili, Sonic, Starbucks, Steak'n Shake, Tony Roma, Wendy's, **lodging:** Best Western, Candlewood Suites, Day's Inn, Fairfield Inn, Hampton Inn, **other:** Aamco, Best Buy, Discount Tire, Goodyear/auto, Sears/auto, Tire Barn, mall

0mm I-465 around Indianapolis. I-69 begins/ends on I-465, exit 37, at Indianapolis.

Interstate 70

E ↕ W Richmond

Exit #	Services

156.5mm Indiana/Ohio state line, weigh sta

156b a US 40 E, Richmond, **N...gas:** Petro/Marathon/diesel/rest./24hr, Swifty, **lodging:** Fairfield Inn, Golden Inn, **other:** Blue Beacon, **S...gas:** Shell/mart, Speedway/mart, Sunoco, **food:** A&W/LJ Silver, Applebee's, Bob Evans, Burger King, Chili's, Cracker Barrel, Fazoli's, Golden Corral, KFC, McDonald's, O'Charley's, Pizza Hut, Ponderosa, Red Lobster, Ruby Tuesday, Ryan's, Steak'n Shake, Super China, Texas Roadhouse, White Castle, **lodging:** Best Western, Day's Inn, $Inn, Hampton Inn, Holiday Inn, Lee's Inn, Motel 6, **other:** Chevrolet/Cadillac, Chrysler/Jeep, $General, Firestone, Ford/Lincoln/Mercury, Goody's, Goodyear/auto, Hastings Books, Honda, JC Penney, Kroger, Lowe's Whse, Nissan, OfficeMax, Sav-A-Lot Foods, Sears/auto, Target, Tires+, U-Haul, Wal-Mart SuperCtr/24hr

153 IN 227, Richmond, to Whitewater, **2 mi N...**Grandpa's Farm RV Park(seasonal)

151b a US 27, Richmond, to Chester, **N...food:** Fricker's Rest., **other:** Best Buy RV Ctr, Dodge, Honda, KOA, **S...gas:** Meijer/diesel/24hr, Speedway, Shell, Sunoco/mart, **food:** Big Boy, Bob Evans, Burger King, Carver's Rest., McDonald's, Pizza Hut, Subway, Taco Bell, Wendy's, **lodging:** Comfort Inn, Super 8, **other:** HOSPITAL, Harley-Davidson

149 US 35, IN 38, Richmond, to Muncie, **N...**Love's/Hardee's/diesel/mart/24hr, **S...**Raper RV Ctr

148mm weigh sta both lanes

145 Centerville, **N...gas:** BP/DQ/Stuckey's, **lodging:** Super 8, **other:** Goodyear/repair

145mm Nolans Fork Creek

144mm **rest area both lanes, full(handicapped)facilities, info, vending, phone, picnic tables, litter barrels, petwalk**

141mm Greens Fork River

137 IN 1, to Hagerstown, Connersville, **N...**Amish Cheese, **S...gas:** Crazy D's/diesel/rest./24hr, GasAmerica/mart/24hr, Shell/mart/24hr, **food:** Burger King, McDonald's

131 Wilbur Wright Rd, New Lisbon, **S...gas:** Marathon/KFC/Taco Bell/diesel24hr, **other:** RV park

126mm Flatrock River

123 IN 3, Spiceland, to New Castle, **N...gas:** Speedway, **lodging:** Best Western(2mi), Day's Inn, Holiday Inn Express(3mi), **other:** HOSPITAL, Irwin RV Park(1mi), **S...gas:** BP/diesel/mart/@, ⚡/Flying J/CountyMkt/diesel/mart/24hr/@, **food:** Kathy's Kitchen

117mm Big Blue River

115 IN 109, to Knightstown, Wilkinson, **N...gas:** GA/diesel/rest./24hr, **food:** Burger King

107mm **rest area both lanes, full(handicapped)facilities, vending, phone, picnic tables, litter barrels, petwalk, RV dump**

104 IN 9, Greenfield, Maxwell, **N...gas:** GA/mart, **S...gas:** GA/diesel, Shell/mart, Sunoco/mart, Swifty/mart, **food:** Applebee's, Arby's, Bamboo Garden, Bob Evans, Burger King, Garfield's Rest., Hardee's, KFC, McDonald's, Pizza Hut, Steak'n Shake, Taco Bell, Waffle House, Wendy's, White Castle, **lodging:** Comfort Inn, $Inn, Holiday Inn Express, Lee's Inn, Super 8, **other:** Advance Parts, Aldi Foods, Big O Tire, CVS Drug, Home Depot, Marsh Foods, Radio Shack, Wal-Mart SuperCtr/gas/24hr

96 Mt Comfort Rd, **N...gas:** GA/mart, Pilot/diesel/mart/24hr, **food:** Burger King, Pizza Hut, Subway, **S...gas:** Shell/mart, **food:** McDonald's, **other:** KOA(seasonal), Mark's RV Ctr

91 Post Rd, to Ft Harrison, **N...gas:** Marathon/7-11, **food:** Big Boy, Cracker Barrel, Denny's, Joe's Crabshack, McDonald's, Outback Steaks, Steak'n Shake, Wendy's, **lodging:** Baymont Inn, InTown Suites, **other:** Lowe's Whse, st police, **S...gas:** BP/mart, Shell/mart, **food:** Hardee's, KFC/Taco Bell, Waffle Steak, **lodging:** Best Western, $Inn, Quality Inn, Super 8, Travelers Inn, **other:** CVS Drug, Home Depot, Marsh Foods

90 I-465(from wb), no facilities

89 Shadeland Ave, I-465(from eb), **N...gas:** Marathon, **food:** Bob Evans, Waffle House, **lodging:** Comfort Inn, Hampton Inn, Hawthorn Suites, Motel 6, **other:** Toyota, U-Haul, **S...gas:** BigFoot, Clark, Marathon, Shell/mart/24hr, Speedway/diesel, **food:** Arby's, Burger King, Cattle Co Steaks, 4Seasons Diner, McDonald's, Omelet Shop, Rally's, Red Lobster, Texas Roadhouse, Wendy's, **lodging:** Budget Inn, Day's Inn, Fairfield Inn,

Interstate 70

E ↕ **W**

Indianapolis Area

Holiday Inn/Damon's, Knight's Inn, La Quinta, Marriott, Ramada Ltd, **other:** Aamco, Buick, CVS Drug, Chevrolet, Dodge, Ford/Lincoln/Mercury

87 Emerson Ave, **N...gas:** BP/McDonald's, Speedway/mart, **S...gas:** Shell/mart

85b a Rural St, Keystone Ave, **N...fairgrounds, S...gas:** Marathon

83b(112) I-65 N, to Chicago

a(111) Michigan St, Market St, downtown, **S...food:** Hardee's

80(110a) I-65 S, to Louisville

79b Illinois St, McCarty St, downtown

a West St, **N...lodging:** Comfort Inn, **other:** HOSPITAL, to Union Sta, Govt Ctr, RCA Dome, zoo

78 Harding St, to downtown

77 Holt Rd, **S...gas:** Clark Gas, Shell/mart, **food:** McDonald's, Mr Dan's Rest., **other:** AllPro Parts

75 Airport Expswy, to Raymond St, **N...gas:** Marathon/mart, Speedway/mart, **food:** Cracker Barrel, Denny's, JoJo's Rest., Schlotsky's, Waffle Steak, **lodging:** Adam's Mark, Baymont Inn, Fairfield Inn, La Quinta, Motel 6, Red Roof Inn, Residence Inn, access to Day's Inn, Hilton, Holiday Inn, Ramada, **other:** to airport

73b a I-465 N/S, I-74 E/W

66 IN 267, to Plainfield, Mooresville, **N...gas:** BP/mart/24hr, Shell/mart, Speedway/diesel/mart, Thornton/diesel/mart, **food:** Arby's, Bob Evans, Burger King, Coachman Rest., Cracker Barrel, Golden Corral, Hog Heaven BBQ, Little Mexico, McDonald's, Perkins, Pizza King, Quizno's, Ritter's Custard, Sonic, Steak'n Shake, Subway, Wendy's, White Castle, **lodging:** AmeriHost, Comfort Inn, Day's Inn, $Inn, Hampton Inn, Holiday Inn Express, Lee's Inn, Super 8, **other:** Chateau Thomas Winery, Harley-Davidson

65mm **rest area both lanes, full(handicapped)facilities, info, vending, phone, picnic tables, litter barrels, petwalk**

59 IN 39, to Belleville, **N...gas:** Marathon/mart, **S...gas:** TA/Citgo/diesel/rest./24hr/@

51 rd 1100W, **S...other:** Koger's/diesel/mart, repair/towing/24hr

41 US 231, Cloverdale, to Greencastle, **N...food:** Long Branch Steaks, **lodging:** Midway Motel, **other:** HOSPITAL **S...gas:** BP/diesel/mart, Citgo/Subway/diesel/mart/24hr, Shell/mart, **food:** Arby's, Burger King, Chicago's Pizza, KFC, McDonald's, Taco Bell, Wendy's, **lodging:** Best Inn, Day's Inn, $Inn, Holiday Inn Express, Ramada Inn, Super 8, **other:** Clover Tire, Value Mkt Foods, to Lieber SRA

37 IN 243, to Putnamville, **S...gas:** Marathon/diesel/mart, **other:** to Lieber SRA

Terre Haute

23 IN 59, to Brazil, **N...gas:** Pilot/diesel/mart/24hr, **other:** HOSPITAL, **S...gas:** Pilot/Subway/diesel/mart, Shell/Brazil 70/diesel/rest./24hr/@, Sunoco/Rally's/diesel/mart, **food:** Burger King, **lodging:** Howard Johnson Express

15mm Honey Creek

11 IN 46, Terre Haute, **N...gas:** Pilot/Arby's/diesel/mart/24hr, Thornton/diesel, **food:** Burger King, McDonald's, airport, **S...KOA**

7 US 41, US 150, Terre Haute, **N...gas:** BP/mart, Marathon/diesel/mart, Thornton's/diesel, **food:** Applebee's, Arby's, Bob Evans, Burger King, Cracker Barrel, Fazoli's, Hardee's, IHOP, Little Caesar's, LoneStar Steaks, Pizza Hut, Quizno's, Schlotsky's, Steak'n Shake, Texas Roadhouse, Tumbleweed Mesquite Grill, **lodging:** Comfort Suites, $Inn, Drury Inn, Fairfield Inn, PearTree Inn, Signature Inn, Super 8, **other:** AutoZone, Chrysler/Dodge/Jeep, Daewoo, JiffyLube, S IN Tire, **S...gas:** JiffyMart/24hr, Marathon, Speedway/mart, Sunoco/mart, Thornton's/mart, **food:** Arby's, Burger King, ChiChi's, China Buffet, Garfield's Rest., Denny's, Hardee's, KFC, LJ Silver, McDonald's, Olive Garden, Outback Steaks, Papa John's, Ponderosa, Rally's, Red Lobster, Ritter's Custard, Ryan's, Sonic, Subway, Taco Bell, TGIFriday, Wendy's, **lodging:** Hampton Inn, Holiday Inn, Motel 6, **other:** HOSPITAL, Aldi Foods, BooksAMillion, Buick/Pontiac/Cadillac, Chevrolet/Hyundai/Nissan, Circuit City, Dodge, FashionBug, Ford/Kia, GMC/Mazda, Goodyear/auto, Jo-Ann Crafts, Kroger, Lowe's Whse, OfficeMax, Old Navy, Sam's Club, Saturn, Sears/auto, Staples, Toyota, Wal-Mart SuperCtr/gas/24hr

5.5mm Wabash River

3 Darwin Rd, W Terre Haute, **N...to** St Mary of-the-Woods Coll

1.5mm **Welcome Ctr eb, full(handicapped)facilities, info, picnic tables, litter barrels, phone, vending, petwalk**

1 US 40 E(from eb, exits left), W Terre Haute, to Terre Haute

0mm Indiana/Illinois state line

INDIANA
Interstate 74

Exit #	Services
171.5mm	Indiana/Ohio state line,
171mm	weigh sta wb
169	US 52 W, to Brookville, no facilities
168.5mm	Whitewater River
164	IN 1, St Leon, **N...gas:** Exxon, Shell/diesel, **food:** Christina's Rest., **S...gas:** BP/diesel
156	IN 101, to Sunman, Milan, **S...gas:** Exxon/diesel, **other:** Lee's Country RV Ctr(1mi)
152mm	**rest area both lanes, full(handicapped)facilities, phone, picnic tables, litter barrels, vending, pet-walk**
149	IN 229, to Oldenburg, Batesville, **N...gas:** Shell/diesel/24hr, Sunoco, **food:** China Buffet, McDonald's, Subway, Wendy's, **lodging:** Hampton Inn, **other:** $General, Kroger, Pamida, **S...gas:** BP, **food:** Arby's, DQ, KFC/Taco Bell, La Rosa's Pizza, Skyline Chili, Subway, Waffle House, **lodging:** Comfort Inn, Sherman House Inn/rest., **other:** HOSPITAL
143	to IN 46, New Point, **N...gas:** Petro/Marathon/Iron Skillet/diesel/rest./24hr/@, **S...gas:** Marathon
134b a	IN 3, to Rushville, Greensburg, **S...gas:** Bigfoot, BP/diesel, Shell/24hr, Speedway, Tobacco Rd/gas, **food:** Arby's, Big Boy, Burger King, Chili's, DQ, El Tapatio Mexican, Great Wall Chinese, KFC, McDonald's, Papa John's, Ponderosa, Subway, Taco Bell, Waffle House, Wendy's, **lodging:** Best Western, Fairfield Inn, Lee's Inn, Holiday Inn Express, Relax Inn, **other:** Advance Parts, Aldi Foods, AutoZone, Big O Tire, Chrysler, CVS Drug, $General, Ford/Mercury, Radio Shack, Staples, Wal-Mart SuperCtr/24hr
132	US 421(from eb), to Greensburg, no facilities
130mm	Clifty Creek
123	Saint Paul, **S...**camping
119	IN 244 E, to Milroy, no facilities
116	IN 44, to Shelbyville, Rushville, **N...gas:** Bigfoot/diesel, **S...gas:** BP, Marathon, Shell/24hr, Swifty, **food:** Applebee's, Arby's, Baskin-Robbins/Dunkin Donuts, Bellacino's, Bob Evans, Burger King, China Buffet, Denny's, Domino's, Golden Corral(1mi), King's Buffet, McDonald's, Papa John's, Pizza Hut, Ritter's Cafe, Subway, Taco Bell, Wendy's, **lodging:** Lee's Inn, Rasner Motel, **other:** HOSPITAL, Ace Hardware, Aldi Foods, Chevrolet/Nissan, CVS Drug, $General, Ford/Lincoln/Mercury, GNC, Goody's, IGA Foods, Kroger/gas, Marsh Food, NAPA, Osco Drug, Radio Shack, Wal-Mart SuperCtr/24hr/gas
115mm	Little Blue River
113mm	Big Blue River
113	IN 9, to Shelbyville, **N...gas:** CF/diesel, **food:** Cracker Barrel, **S...gas:** BP, Shell, **food:** Cow Palace(1mi), El Emparador Mexican, McDonald's, Waffle Steak, **lodging:** Comfort Inn, Day's Inn, Hampton Inn, Holiday Inn Express, Super 8, **other:** HOSPITAL, Buick/GMC, Chrysler/Plymouth, Ford/Lincoln/Mercury
109	Fairland Rd, **N...other:** Indiana Downs, **S...other:** Brownie's Marine, RV camping/funpark
103	London Rd, to Boggstown, no facilities
102mm	Big Sugar Creek
101	Pleasant View Rd, **N...gas:** Marathon, **food:** Chester Fried
99	Acton Rd, no facilities
96	Post Rd, **N...gas:** Marathon/Subway/diesel/24hr, **food:** McDonald's, **S...gas:** Shell/diesel, **food:** Wendy's, **other:** Chevrolet
94b a	I-465/I-74 W, I-465 N, US 421 N
	I-74 and I-465 run together 21 miles. **See Indiana Interstate 465, exits 2-16, and 52-53.**
73b	I-465 N, access to same facilities as 16a on I-465
73a	I-465 S, I-74 E, no facilities
71mm	Eagle Creek
66	IN 267, Brownsburg, **N...gas:** Phillips 66/24hr, Shell, **food:** Applebee's, Happy Wok, Hardee's, Steak'nShake, Subway, **lodging:** Holiday Inn Express, **other:** Big O Tire, **S...gas:** BP/diesel, Speedway/diesel, **food:** Arby's, Blimpie, Bob Evans, Burger King, China's Best, McDonald's, Papa Murphy's, Taco Bell, Wendy's, White Castle, **lodging:** Comfort Suites, Super 8, **other:** MEDICAL CARE, CVS Drug, $Tree, Ford, Kroger/gas, K-Mart, Radio Shack, Wal-Mart SuperCtr/24hr
61	to Pittsboro, no facilities
58	IN 39, to Lebanon, Lizton, no facilities
57mm	**rest area both lanes, full(handicapped)facilities, phone, picnic tables, litter barrels, vending, pet-walk**
52	IN 75, to Advance, Jamestown, **2 mi S...**gas, food, camping
39	IN 32, to Crawfordsville, **S...gas:** Crazy D's, **other:** antiques(1mi), to Wabash Coll
34	US 231, to Linden, **S...gas:** BP, GA, Marathon, Shell, **food:** Burger King, KFC, McDonald's, Sunshine Cafe(1mi), **lodging:** Comfort Inn, Day's Inn, Holiday Inn, Ramada Ltd., Super 8, **other:** HOSPITAL, KOA(1mi), Sugar Creek Campground(4mi)
25	IN 25, to Wingate, Waynetown, no facilities
22mm	**rest area both lanes, full(handicapped)facilities, phone, picnic tables, litter barrels, vending, pet-walk**
19mm	weigh sta both lanes
15	US 41, to Attica, Veedersburg, **1/2 mi S...gas:** Marathon, Phillips 66/Subway/diesel/24hr, **other:** to Turkey Run SP, camping
8	Covington, **N...gas:** Shell, **food:** Maple Corner Rest.(1mi), **other:** fireworks
7mm	Wabash River
4	IN 63, to Newport, **N...gas:** BP, Pilot/Arby's/diesel/24hr/@, **food:** Beefhouse Rest., Wendy's
1mm	**Welcome Ctr eb, full(handicapped)facilities, info, phone, picnic tables, litter barrels, vending, pet-walk**
0mm	Indiana/Illinois state line

Interstate 80/90

E ↕ W

Exit #	Services
157mm	Indiana/Ohio state line
153mm	toll plaza, litter barrels
146mm	**Booth Tarkington Service Area both lanes, Mobil/diesel, DQ, McDonald's, playground**
144	I-69, US 27, Angola, Ft Wayne, **N...gas:** Petro/Mobil/diesel/LP/24hr/@, Shell/Subway/diesel/24hr/@, Pilot/Wendy's/diesel/24hr/@, **food:** McDonald's, Red Arrow Rest., **lodging:** Redwood Lodge, Lake George Inn, **S...gas:** Marathon/diesel/24hr, **lodging:** Holiday Inn Express, **other:** Prime Outlets/famous brands, **services on IN 120 E...food:** Herb Garden Rest., **lodging:** E&L Motel, Hampton Inn, Super 8, **other:** Golf/rest., U-Haul/repair(1mi), **W...**to Pokagon SP, Jellystone Camping(7mi)
131.5mm	Fawn River
126mm	**Ernie Pyle Travel Plaza eb, Gene S Porter Travel Plaza wb, Mobil/diesel, Fazoli's, Hardee's, gifts, RV dump**
121	IN 9, Howe, to Lagrange, **N...gas:** Golden Buddha, **lodging:** Greenbriar Inn, Hampton Inn, Travel Inn, **other:** HOSPITAL(4mi), **2 mi N...food:** Applebee's, Golden Corral, DQ, Wendy's, **lodging:** Comfort Inn, Knight's Inn, Wood Motel, **S...gas:** Clark, **lodging:** Holiday Inn Express, Super 8, **other:** HOSPITAL(8mi)
120mm	Fawn River
108mm	**trucks only rest area both lanes**
107	US 131, IN 13, to Middlebury, Constantine, **N...gas:** Marathon/diesel, **food:** Country Table Rest.(1mi), McDonald's(4mi), **lodging:** PatchWork Quilt Inn(1mi), Plaza Motel, **other:** Tower Motel, **1 mi S...gas:** BP/Blimpie/diesel, **food:** Yup's DairyLand, **other:** KOA(apr-nov), **5 mi S...food:** DQ, Subway, **other:** Coachman RV Factory, Eby's Pines RV Park
101	IN 15, Bristol, to Goshen, **1 mi S...gas:** Citgo/7-11, Speedway/diesel, **food:** River Inn Rest., **other:** MEDICAL CARE, Eby's Pines Camping(3mi), bank
96	rd 17, E Elkhart, **2 mi S...gas:** BP/diesel, Citgo/7-11, Marathon, **food:** DQ, McDonald's, Subway
92	IN 19, to Elkhart, **N...gas:** Citgo/7-11, Phillips 66/Subway/diesel, **food:** Applebee's, Cracker Barrel, Perkins, Steak'n Shake, **lodging:** Best Western, Comfort Suites, Country Inn Suites, Diplomat Motel, Econolodge, Fairway Inn, Hampton Inn, Holiday Inn Express, Knight's Inn, Quality Inn, Sleep Inn, **other:** Aldi Foods, CVS Drug, GNC, K-Mart, Martin's Foods, Radio Shack, Tierra RV Ctr, **S...gas:** Clark, Marathon/diesel, **food:** Arby's, Bennigan's, Blimpie, Bob Evans, Burger King, Callaghan's Rest., Da Vinci's Pizza, King Wha Chinese, Lazy Bones Rest., McDonald's, Olive Garden, Red Lobster, Ryan's, Texas Roadhouse, **lodging:**

Elkhart (vertical label)

Budget Inn, Day's Inn, Ramada Inn, Red Roof Inn, Signature Inn, Super 8, Weston Plaza, **other:** HOSPITAL, CarQuest, $Tree, Holiday World RV, Wal-Mart SuperCtr/24hr, truck/RV repair, **1 mi S...gas:** Citgo, Shell, Speedway, Swifty, **food:** DQ, KFC, LJ Silver, Papa John's, Pizza Hut, Matterhorn Rest., Red Dragon Chinese, Taco Bell, Wendy's, **other:** Advance Parts, AutoZone, Family$, Osco Drug, Walgreen

91mm	Christiana Creek
90mm	**Henry Schricker Travel Plaza eb, George Craig Travel Plaza wb, BP/diesel, Arby's, Dunkin Donuts, Pizza Hut, RV dump, travelstore, USPO**
83	to Mishawaka, **1-2 mi N on IN 23W...gas:** BP/diesel, Citgo/7-11, Mobil, Phillips 66/Subway/diesel, **food:** Applebee's, Arby's, Famous Dave's, Olive Garden, Pizza Hut, Taco Bell, Wendy's, **lodging:** Carlton Lodge, Fairfield Inn, Hampton Inn, Holiday Inn Express, Super 8, **other:** Best Buy, CVS Drug, Kroger, JC Penney, Marshall Field, Michael's, Office Depot, Sears, Target, Walgreen, KOA(mar-nov), mall, **2 mi S on Grape Rd & Main St(off IN 23W)...gas:** Meijer/diesel/24hr, **food:** Arby's, Burger King, Chili's, LoneStar Steaks, Mancino's Pizza, McDonald's, Old Country Buffet, Outback Steaks, Papa Vino's Italian, Ryan's, Steak'n Shake, Subway, TGIFriday, **lodging:** Best Western, Courtyard, Extended Stay America, SpringHill Suites, **other:** Studio+, Barnes&Noble, Buick/GMC, Chrysler/Plymouth, Circuit City, Discount Tire, Hyundai, Jo-Ann Fabrics, Lowe's Whse, Sam's Club, Wal-Mart SuperCtr/24hr
77	US 33, US 31B, IN 933, South Bend, **N...gas:** Admiral, **food:** Arby's, Burger King, Damon's, Family Style Buffet, Fazoli's, Marco's Pizza, McDonald's, Panorama Rest., Papa John's, Pizza Hut, Ponderosa, Steak&Ale, Subway, **lodging:** Comfort Suites, Day's Inn, Hampton Inn, Motel 6, Ramada Inn, Super 8, **other:** AutoZone, Walgreen, **1 mi N on frtge rd...gas:** Meijer/diesel/24hr, Phillips 66, **food:** Burger King, McDonald's, **S...gas:** Marathon, **food:** Bob Evans, Denny's, Great Wall Chinese, King Gyro's, Perkins, Pizza King, Taco Bell, Wendy's, **lodging:** Best Inn,

South Bend (vertical label)

INDIANA

Interstate 80/90

Howard Johnson, Knight's Inn, Signature Inn, St Marys Inn, **other:** HOSPITAL, to Notre Dame St Joseph River

76mm	
72	US 31, to Niles, South Bend, **N...gas:** Pilot/Subway/diesel/24hr/@, **2 mi S on US 20...food:** 4 Seasons Rest., McDonald's, Ponderosa, Taco Bell, Wendy's, **lodging:** Day's Inn, Quality Inn, **other:** RV Ctr, to Potato Creek SP(20mi), airport, st police
62mm	eastern/central time zone line
56mm	**service area both lanes, BP/diesel, DQ, McDonald's, cookies, phone, RV dump, litter barrel**
49	IN 39, to La Porte, **N...lodging:** Hampton Inn, **S...lodging:** Cassidy Motel/RV park, **4mi S...gas:** Mobil/diesel, **lodging:** Blue Heron Motel, Holiday Inn Express, Super 8
39	US 421, to Michigan City, Westville, **5 mi N...lodging:** Hampton Inn, Holiday Inn, Knight's Inn, **other:** Premium Outlets/famous brands, **S...**Purdue U North Cent
38mm	**trucks only rest area both lanes, litter barrels**
31	IN 49, to Chesterton, Valparaiso, **N...food:** Hilton Garden, **lodging:** Econolodge(3mi), Super 8(3mi), **other:** Sand Creek RV Park(4mi), to IN Dunes Nat Lakeshore, **S...lodging:** Hampton Inn(8mi), **other:** Yellow Brick Rd Museum/gifts
24mm	toll plaza
23	Portage, Port of Indiana, **N...food:** Marko's Rest., **lodging:** Comfort Inn, Holiday Inn Express, **2 mi N...gas:** Marathon, Shell, **lodging:** Day's Inn, $Inn, Ramada Inn, Super 8, **S...gas:** Amoco, Marathon, **food:** Burger King, Dunkin Donuts, First Wok Chinese, KFC, McDonald's, Subway, Wendy's, **other:** Family$, GNC, Town&Country Mkt/24hr, USPO, Walgreen
22mm	**service area both lanes, info, gas: BP/diesel, food: Fazoli's, Hardee's, other: playground**
21mm	I-90 and I-80 run together eb, separate wb. **I-80 runs with I-94 wb. For I-80 exits 1 through 15, see Indiana Interstate 94.**
21	I-94 E to Detroit, I-80/94 W, US 6, IN 51, Lake Station, **N...gas:** Dunes Trkstp/diesel/@, ✈/Flying J/diesel/24hr/@, Pilot/diesel/24hr/@, TA/Subway/diesel/24hr/@, **food:** McDonald's, Ponderosa, Wing Wah Chinese, **other:** Aldi Foods, Buick, Parts+, truckwash, **S...gas:** Mobil, Pilot/Subway/diesel/24hr/@, Shell, **food:** Burger King, DQ, Ruben's Café, **other:** Walgreen
17	I-65 S, US 12, US 20, Dunes Hwy, to Indianapolis, no facilities
15	IN 53, Broadway, to Gary, no facilities
14a	Grant St, to Gary, **S...**HOSPITAL
10	IN 912, Cline Ave, to Gary, **N...**casino
5	US 41, Calumet Ave, to Hammond, **S...gas:** Marathon, Speedway, **food:** Arby's, Aurelio's Pizza, Dunkin Donuts, Johnel's Rest., KFC, McDonald's, Taco Bell, White Castle, **lodging:** American Inn, Ramada Inn, Super 8, **other:** Aldi Foods, AutoZone, Murray's Parts, Walgreen
3	IN 912, Cline Ave, to Hammond, to Gary Reg Airport, **S...gas:** Shell
1mm	toll plaza
1mm	US 12, US 20, 106th St, Indianapolis Blvd, **N...gas:** BP/diesel/24hr, Mobil, Shell/diesel, **other:** casino, **S...food:** Burger King, Giappo's Pizza, KFC, McDonald's, **other:** Jewel-Osco
0mm	Indiana/Illinois state line

Interstate 94

Exit #	Services
46mm	Indiana/Michigan state line
43mm	**Welcome Ctr wb, full(handicapped)facilities, info, phone, picnic tables, litter barrels, vending, petwalk**
40b a	US 20, US 35, to Michigan City, **N...food:** McDonald's, **other:** HOSPITAL, **S...gas:** Speedway/diesel
34b a	US 421, to Michigan City, **N...gas:** BP/diesel, Clark, Meijer/diesel/24hr, Mobil/diesel, Shell, Speedway/diesel, **food:** Applebee's, Arby's, Bob Evans, Buffalo Wings, Burger King, Chili's, Damon's, Denny's, El Brácero Mexican, Godfather's, KFC, King Gyro, McDonald's, Micro Brewery, Pizza Hut, Popeye's, Red Lobster, Ryan's, Schoop's Rest., Steak'n Shake, Subway, Taco Bell, Wendy's, **lodging:** Comfort Inn, Hampton Inn, Holiday Inn Express, Knight's Inn, Red Roof Inn, Super 8, Travel Inn, **other:** HOSPITAL, Aldi Foods, AutoZone, $Tree, JC Penney, Jo-Ann Fabrics, Lowe's Whse, OfficeMax, Parts+, Radio Shack, Wal-Mart/auto, **S...gas:** Gas City, **other:** Buick/Pontiac/GMC, Harley-Davidson
29mm	weigh sta both lanes
26b a	IN 49, Chesterton, **N...**to IN Dunes SP, Sand Cr Camping, **S...gas:** BP/White Castle, Shell/24hr, Speedway, **food:** Arby's, Burger King, Dunkin Donuts, KFC, Little Caesar's, LJ Silver, McDonald's, Pizza Hut, Subway, Taco Bell, Wendy's, **lodging:** Econolodge, Hilton Garden(3mi), Super 8, **other:** MEDICAL CARE, Jewel-Osco, K-Mart, Walgreen, to Valparaiso
22b a	US 20, Burns Harbor, **N...gas:** Steel City Express/diesel/@, TA/Subway/diesel/rest./24hr/@, **other:** Blue Beacon, **S...gas:** Mobil, Pilot/McDonald's/Subway/diesel/24hr/@, **other:** Camp-Land RV Ctr, Chevrolet, Chrysler/Dodge/Jeep, Ford/Mercury, Toyota

Exit # Services

E
S
o
u
t
h

B
e
n
d
W

E
W

Interstate 94

E

Portage

19   IN 249, Portage, to Port of IN, **N...gas:** Family Express/diesel, **S...gas:** Marathon/24hr, Shell/24hr, **food:** Denny's, **lodging:** Comfort Inn, Day's Inn, Hampton Inn, Holiday Inn Express, Ramada Inn, Super 8, **2 mi S...food:** Burger King, Subway, Wendy's

16   access to I-80/90 toll road E, I-90 toll road W, IN 51N, Ripley St

I-94/I-80 run together wb

15b   US 6W, IN 51, **N...gas:** ✈/Flying J/diesel/24hr/@ , Pilot/diesel/24hr/@ , TA/diesel/24hr/@ , **food:** McDonald's, **other:** Blue Beacon, **N on US 20...gas:** Dunes/diesel repair, **food:** Ponderosa, Wing Wah Chinese, **other:** Aldi Foods, Buick, Parts+, Pennzoil

a   US 6E, IN 51S, to US 20, **S...gas:** Mobil/diesel, Pilot/Subway/diesel/24hr/@ , Shell, **food:** Burger King, DQ, Reuben's Café

Gary Area

13   Central Ave(from eb), no facilities

12b   I-65 N, to Gary and toll road

a   I-65 S(from wb), to Indianapolis

11   I-65 S(from eb)

10b a   IN 53, Broadway, **N...gas:** Citgo, Marathon/24hr, **food:** Broadway BBQ, **S...gas:** BP/24hr, Citgo, **food:** DQ, Rally's

9b a   Grant St, **N...gas:** Citgo, **food:** Chicago Hotdogs, **other:** Walgreen, **S...gas:** Citgo, ✈/Flying J/Cookery/diesel/24hr/@ , Steel City/diesel/rest./24hr, **food:** Burger King, Church's, KFC, McDonald's, Subway, **other:** Aldi Foods, AutoZone, Firestone/auto, Ford, US Factory Outlets

6   Burr St, **N...gas:** BP/24hr, Pilot/Subway/diesel/24hr/@ , TA/Pizza Hut/Taco Bell/diesel/24hr/@ , **food:** Rico's Pizza, **S...gas:** Shell/diesel/24hr

5b a   IN 912, Cline Ave, **S...gas:** BP, Clark, Shell, Speedway/Subway, **food:** Arby's, DQ, Fannie May Candies, Jedi's Garden Rest., KFC, McDonald's, Pizza Hut, Popeye's, White Castle, **lodging:** Hammond Inn, Motel 6, Super 8, K-Mart, Radio Shack

3b a   Kennedy Ave, **N...gas:** Clark, Speedway, **food:** Burger King, Domino's, McDonald's, **other:** NAPA AutoCare, Walgreen, **S...gas:** Citgo, Speedway, **food:** Cracker Barrel, DQ, Firehouse Gyros, Squigi's Pizza, Subway, Wendy's, **lodging:** Courtyard, Fairfield Inn, Residence Inn, **other:** IN Welcome Ctr, Radio Shack

2b a   US 41S, IN 152N, Indianapolis Blvd, **N...gas:** Luke's, SavAStop, Shell, **food:** Arby's, Dunkin Donuts, Papa John's, Schoop's Burgers, Wheel Rest., Woodmar Rest., **other: S...gas:** Pilot/Subway/diesel/24hr/@ , Thornton, **food:** Blue Top Drive-In, Burger King, Steer Rest., Taco Bell, TopNotch Rest., **lodging:** AmeriHost, **other:** Aldi Foods, $General, K-Mart, Mr Transmission, Ultra Foods

1b a   US 41N, Calumet Ave, **N...gas:** BP/Subway/diesel, Gas City/diesel, Marathon, **other:** Dodge, Firestone/auto, Walgreen, **S...gas:** BP, Gas City, Marathon, Shell, **food:** Arby's, Boston Mkt, Burger King, Taco Bell, Wendy's, **other:** CVS Drug

0mm   Indiana/Illinois state line

Interstate 465(Indianapolis)

Exit #   Services

I-465 loops around Indianapolis. Exit numbers begin/end on I-65, exit 108.

53b a   I-65 N to Indianapolis, S to Louisville

52   Emerson Ave, **N...gas:** Shell/24hr, Speedway, **food:** Burger King, Domino's, KFC, LJ Silver, Subway, Taco Bell, Wendy's, **lodging:** Motel 6, **other:** HOSPITAL, CVS Drug, **S...gas:** Shell/repair, Speedway/diesel, **food:** Arby's, Blimpie, Dairy Queen, Donato's Pizza, Fazoli's, Hardee's, Hunan House, McDonald's, Papa John's, Pizza Hut, Ponderosa, Steak'n Shake, Subway, Waffle House, White Castle/24hr, **lodging:** Holiday Inn, InnAmerica, Red Roof Inn, Super 8, **other:** AutoZone, Goodyear/auto, K-Mart, Marsh Foods, Radio Shack, Walgreen

I-74 W and I-465 S run together around S Indianapolis 21 miles

49   I-74 E, US 421 S, no facilities

48   Shadeland Ave(from nb)

47   US 52 E, Brookville Rd, **E...gas:** Shell, **food:** Burger King

46   US 40, Washington St, **E...gas:** Marathon, **food:** Arby's, China Buffet, Italian Graden, Old Country Buffet, Perkins, Steak'n Shake, Subway, **other:** Ford, Osco Drug, Target, **W...gas:** Thornton's, **food:** Applebee's, Burger King, Bob Evans, ChiChi's, Don Pablo, Fazoli's, McDonald's, Pizza Hut, Pi's Chinese, Wendy's, **lodging:** Signature Inn, **other:** K-Mart, PepBoys, Pontiac/GM/Mazda, Suzuki

INDIANA

Interstate 465

Exit	Description
44b	I-70 E, to Columbus
a	I-70 W, to Indianapolis
42	US 36, IN 67 N, Pendleton Pike, **E...food:** Bennigan's, Hardee's, Papa's Rest., **lodging:** Days Inn, Sheraton, **W...gas:** Clark, Speedway, Thornton's, **food:** A&W/KFC, Arby's, Denny's, LJ Silver, McDonald's, Pizza Hut/Taco Bell, Subway, **other:** HOSPITAL, K-Mart/gas
40	56th St, Shadeland Ave, **E...gas:** Marathon, to Ft Harrison
37b a	I-69, N to Ft Wayne, IN 37, **W...other:** HOSPITAL, facilities on frontage rds
35	Allisonville Rd, **N...food:** Applebee's, Hardee's, LJ Silver, McDonald's, MCL Cafeteria, **lodging:** Courtyard, **other:** Best Buy, CompUSA, Firestone/auto, JC Penney, Jo-Ann Fabrics, Kohl's, Lazarus, Marshall's, Osco Drug, mall, **S...gas:** Shell, Speedway/diesel, **food:** Bob Evans, ChuckeCheese, Hop's Brewery, Papa John's, Perkins/24hr, White Castle, **lodging:** Signature Inn, **other:** Circuit City, Kroger, **S on 82nd...food:** PrimeTime Grill, **other:** Marsh Foods
33	IN 431, Keystone Ave, **N...gas:** BP/McDonald's, Marathon/diesel, Shell, **food:** Arby's, Bob Evans, Burger King, Steak&Ale, Subway, **lodging:** Motel 6, **other:** BMW, Chevrolet/Isuzu, Infiniti, Nissan, Toyota **S...food:** Cooker, Keystone Grill, **lodging:** AmeriSuites, Marriott, Sheraton, Westin Suites, **other:** Champ's, Kohl's, mall, **1 mi S on 82nd...food:** Applebee's, Boston Mkt, Chili's, Don Pablo, O' Charley's, Logan's Roadhouse, LoneStar Steaks, Pizzeria Uno, Prime Time Grill, Schlotsky's, Shell's Seafood, Subway, **other:** Barnes&Noble, OfficeMax
31	US 31, Meridian St, **N...lodging:** Residence Inn, Signature Inn, SpringHill Suites, Wyndham Garden, **other:** HOSPITAL, **S...gas:** Marathon, Shell/diesel, **food:** McDonald's
27	US 421 N, Michigan Rd, **N...food:** Dairy Queen, McDonald's, **lodging:** Red Roof Inn, **other:** Chevrolet, **S...gas:** BP, Marathon, Shell, Sunoco, **food:** Arby's, Bob Evans, Boston Mkt, ChiChi's, China Buffet, Denny's, IHOP, Max&Erma's, O'Charley's, Outback Steaks, Pizza Hut, Qdoba Mexican, Ruby Tuesday, Schlosky's, Steak'n Shake, Subway, Taco Bell, Texas Roadhouse, Wendy's, White Castle, Wildcat Brewing Co/rest., Yen Ching Rest.,
	lodging: Best Western, Comfort Inn, $Inn, Drury Inn, Embassy Suites, Extended Stay America, Fairfield Inn, Holiday Inn Select, HomeGate Inn, InTown Suites, Microtel, Quality Inn, Residence Inn, Signature Inn, Wellesley Inn, **other:** Aamco, Costco/gas, Cub Foods, CVS Drug, Discount Tire, $General, Firestone, Lowe's Whse, Office Depot, OfficeMax, PepBoys, Radio Shack, Staples, Wal-Mart SuperCtr/24hr
25	I-465 W, no facilities
23	86th St, **E...gas:** Shell/24hr, Speedway, **food:** Arby's, Burger King, Quizno's, **lodging:** MainStay Suites, Suburban Lodge, **other:** HOSPITAL
21	71st St, **E...gas:** Amoco, **food:** Galahad's Café, Hardee's, McDonald's, Steak'n Shake, Subway, **lodging:** Clarion Inn, Courtyard, Hampton Inn, **other:** DENTIST cleaners
20	I-65, N to Chicago, S to Indianapolis
19	56th St(from nb), **E...gas:** Citgo/7-11, Speedway/diesel
17	38th St, **E...gas:** BP, Marathon, Shell/24hr, **food:** ChiChi's, China Chef, DQ, Olive Garden, Subway, **lodging:** Day's Inn, **other:** Aamco, Circuit City, Home Depot, Kroger, Osco Drug, **W...food:** Arby's, Burger King, Chili's, Cracker Barrel, Don Pablo, McDonald's, Mtn Jack's Rest., Ruby Tuesday, Taco Bell, TGIFriday, **lodging:** Country Hearth Inn, Signature Inn, **other:** Marsh Foods, Target

I-74 E and I-465 run together around S Indianapolis 21 miles

Exit	Description
16b	I-74 W, to Peoria
a	US 136, to Speedway, **N...gas:** Bigfoot, BP, Shell, Thornton's/24hr, **food:** Applebee's, Blimpie, Burger King, Denny's, Dunkin Donuts, Grindstone Charlie's, Hardee's, KFC, LJ Silver, McDonald's, Rally's, Subway, Taco Bell, Wendy's, White Castle, **lodging:** $Inn, Motel 6, Red Roof, Super 8, **other:** Firestone, Goodyear, Kohl's, Kroger, Marsh Foods, MensWhse, Old Navy, Sears, Speedway Museum, **S...lodging:** Clarion
14b a	10th St, **N...gas:** Marathon, Shell, **food:** China Wok, Pizza Hut, Wendy's, **other:** HOSPITAL, Cub Food/24hr, Lowe's Whse, **S...gas:** BP, GA/Subway, Shell, Speedway/24hr, **food:** Arby's, Fazoli's, Hardee's, Little Caesar's, McDonald's, Noble Roman's, Pizza Hut, Rally's, Taco Bell, **other:** CVS Drug, $General

INDIANA

Interstate 465

13b a US 36, Rockville Rd, **N...gas:** Citgo/Burger King, **lodging:** Comfort Inn, Sleep Inn, Wingate Inn, **other:** Sam's Club, **S... gas:** Speedway/24hr, **food:** Bob Evans, **lodging:** Best Western

12b a US 40 E, Washington St, **N...gas:** BP, **food:** Burger King, Church's, Fazoli's, McDonald's, Papa John's, Taco Bell, White Castle, **other:** Advance Parts, AutoZone, $General, Family$, Kroger, Osco Drug, U-Haul, Walgreen, transmissions, **S...gas:** Bigfoot/24hr, Phillips 66/Noble Roman's/TCBY/diesel, Shell, Thornton/24hr, **food:** Arby's, Burger King, Hardee's, KFC, LJ Silver, McDonald's, Omelet Shoppe, Pizza Hut, Steak'n Shake, Wendy's, **lodging:** $Inn, **other:** Aamco, Goodyear, K-Mart, Radio Shack, Target, TireBarn

11b a Airport Expressway, **N...lodging:** Adam's Mark Hotel, Baymont Inn, Day's Inn, Extended Stay America, Motel 6, **S...gas:** BP, **food:** Burger King, **lodging:** Hilton, Holiday Inn, Ramada Inn

9b a I-70, E to Indianapolis, W to Terre Haute

8 IN 67 S, Kentucky Ave, **N...HOSPITAL, S... gas:** BP/diesel, Marathon, Speedway, Shell, **food:** Big Boy, Denny's, Hardee's, KFC

7 Mann Rd(from wb), **N...HOSPITAL**

4 IN 37 S, Harding St, **N...gas:** Mr Fuel/diesel, Pilot/Wendy's/DQ/diesel/24hr/@, **food:** Omelet Shoppe, **lodging:** Best Inn, $Inn, Super 8, **other:** Blue Beacon, **S...gas:** ⚡/Flying J/Conoco/diesel/LP/rest./24hr/@, Marathon, **food:** Hardee's, McDonald's, Taco Bell, Waffle&Steak, White Castle, **lodging:** Knight's Inn, **other:** Freightliner

2b a US 31, IN 37, **N...gas:** BP/24hr, **food:** Arby's, Burger King, Dutch Oven, Golden Wok, Hardee's, KFC, King Ribs, J's Burger, Laughner's Cafeteria, LJ Silver, McDonald's, MCL Cafeteria, Old Country Buffet, Papa John's, Pizza Hut, Ponderosa, Rally's, Steak&Ale, Steak'n Shake, Taco Bell, Wendy's, White Castle, **other:** Aldi Foods, AutoTire, AutoWorks, AutoZone, Chrysler/Jeep, CVS Drug, Dodge, $General, Family$, Firestone, Ford, Goodyear, Hancock Fabrics, Jo-Ann Fabrics, Kroger, Lincoln/Mercury, Marsh Foods, Office Depot, Osco Drug, Radio Shack, Save-A-Lot, Target, U-Haul, **S...gas:** Bigfoot, Shell, Sunoco/Subway, **food:** Applebee's, Bob Evans, Denny's, HH Smorgasbord, McDonald's, Red Lobster, Wendy's, **lodging:** Comfort Inn, Day's Inn, Holiday Inn Express, Quality Inn, Ramada Ltd, Red Roof Inn, Travelodge

53b a I-65 N to Indianapolis, S to Louisville

I-465 loops around Indianapolis. Exit numbers begin/end on I-65, exit 108.

Interstate 469(Ft Wayne)

Exit #	Services	
31c b a	I-69, US 27 S. I-469 begins/ends.	**N**
29.5mm	St Joseph River	
29b a	Maplecrest Rd, **W...gas:** BP/DQ/Subway/diesel	
25	IN 37, to Ft Wayne, **W...gas:** Meijer/diesel/24hr, **food:** Applebee's, Cracker Barrel, Kohl's, Wal-Mart SuperCtr/24hr, Steak'n Shake	
21	US 24 E, no facilities	
19b a	US 30 E, to Ft Wayne, **E...gas:** Sunoco/Taco Bell/diesel, **food:** Wendy's, **W...gas:** Citgo/diesel/mart, **food:** Arby's(2mi), KFC(1mi), Golden Gate Chinese, Richard's Rest., Zesto Drive-In, **lodging:** Holiday Inn Express, **other:** $General, Scott's Foods	**S**
17	Minnich Rd, no facilities	
15	Tillman Rd, no facilities	
13	Marion Center Rd, no facilities	
11	US 27, US 33 S, Ft Wayne, to Decatur, no facilities	
10.5mm	St Marys River	
9	Winchester Rd, no facilities	
6	IN 1, Ft Wayne, to Bluffton, **W...to airport**	
2	Indianapolis Rd, **W...to airport**	
1	Lafayette Ctr Rd, no facilities	
0b a	I-69, US 24 W, US 33 N, to Ft Wayne, Indianapolis. I-469 begins/ends.	

Indianapolis Area

Ft Wayne

165

IOWA
Interstate 29

N ↕ S

Sioux City (vertical side label)

Exit #	Services
152mm	Iowa/South Dakota state line, Big Sioux River
151	IA 12 N, Riverside Blvd, **E...gas:** Casey's, **other:** to Stone SP, Pecaut Nature Ctr
149	Hamilton Blvd, **E...gas:** Conoco, **lodging:** Hamilton Inn, **other:** AAA, to Briar Cliff Coll, **W...Iowa Welcome Ctr sb, full facilities,** Riverboat Museum
148	US 77 S, to S Sioux City, Nebraska, **W...gas:** Conoco/A&W/diesel, Phillips 66, **food:** McDonald's, Pizza Hut, Taco Bell, **lodging:** Marina Inn, Regency Inn, **other:** Ford, O'Reilly Parts
147b	US 20 bus, Sioux City, **E...food:** Arby's, Burger King, Chili's, Hardee's, KFC, Perkins/24hr, **lodging:** Best Western, Holiday Inn, Hilton Inn, **other:** HOSPITAL, Chevrolet, Staples, USPO, Walgreen,
a	Floyd Blvd, **E...gas:** Total, **W...**to Riverboat Casino
146.5mm	Floyd River
144 b	I-129 W, US 20 W, US 75 S, no facilities
a	US 20 E, US 75 N, to Ft Dodge, **1 mi E on Lakeport Rd...gas:** Amoco, Casey's, Shell, **food:** Applebee's, Burger King, Coyote Canyon Steaks, Garfield's Rest., Hardee's, KFC, LJ Silver, Nap's BBQ, Outback Steaks, Piccadilly's, Pizza Hut, Red Lobster, **lodging:** Comfort Inn, Fairfield Inn, Holiday Inn Express, **other:** Buick/Honda/Isuzu, HobbyLobby, Hy-Vee Foods/24hr, Jo-Ann Fabrics/crafts, Michael's, Sears/auto, Target, Younkers, mall
143	US 75 N, Singing Hills Blvd, **E...gas:** Cenex/@, Texaco/diesel/motel/café/24hr/@, **food:** McDonald's, **lodging:** AmericInn, Baymont Inn, Day's Inn, **other:** Sam's Club, Wal-Mart SuperCtr/gas/24hr, Sgt Floyd Mon, **W...gas:** Amoco/diesel/motel/café/24hr/@, **food:** Wendy's, Super 8, **other:** Kenworth/Peterbilt, truckwash
141	D38, Sioux Gateway Airport, **E...gas:** Casey's, Conoco, Phillips 66/diesel, Shell, **food:** China Taste, Godfather's, Steak Block Rest., Subway, **lodging:** Econolodge, **other:** Fairway Foods, mall, **W...lodging:** Motel 6, **other:** museum
139mm	**rest area both lanes, full(handicapped)facilities, phone, info, picnic tables, litter barrels, RV dump**
135	Port Neal Landing, no facilities
134	Salix, **E...gas:** Total, **W...**camping
132mm	weigh sta sb
127	IA 141, Sloan, **E...gas:** Amoco, Shell/diesel, **lodging:** Homestead Inn, WinnaVegas Inn, **3 mi W...**to Winnebago Indian Res/casino
120	to Whiting, **W...**camping
112	IA 175, Onawa, **E...gas:** Conoco/Subway/diesel/@, Phillips 66/diesel, Janz Rest., **food:** McDonald's, Michael's Rest., Oehler Bros Rest., **lodging:** Super 8, **other:** HOSPITAL, Chevrolet/Buick/GMC, Chrysler/Jeep/Dodge, Interchange RV Park, NAPA, Pamida, **2 mi W...other:** KOA, Lewis&Clark SP, Keelboat Exhibit
110mm	**rest area both lanes, full(handicapped)facilities, phone, info, picnic tables, litter barrels, petwalk, RV dump**
105	E60, Blencoe, 1/2 mi **E...gas:** TR's Gas
96mm	Little Sioux River
95	IA 301, Little Sioux, **E...gas:** G&N OneStop, **other:** Loess Hills SF(9mi), **W...**Woodland RV Camp
92mm	Soldier River
91.5mm	**rest area both lanes, litter barrels, no facilities**
89	IA 127, Mondamin, **1 mi E...gas:** Jiffy Mart/diesel
82	IA 300, F50, Modale, **1 mi W...gas:** Cenex
80mm	**rest area sb, full(handicapped)facilities, info, phone, picnic tables, litter barrels, RV dump**
78.5mm	**rest area nb, full(handicapped)facilities, info, phone, picnic tables, litter barrels, RV dump**
75	US 30, Missouri Valley, **E...Iowa Welcome Ctr(5mi), gas:** Sinclair, Texaco/diesel/24hr/@, **food:** Arby's, McDonald's, Subway, **lodging:** Hillside Motel(2mi), **other:** HOSPITAL(2mi), Ford/Mercury, to Steamboat Exhibit, **W...gas:** Amoco/diesel, Conoco/Kopper Kettle, **food:** Burger King, Oehler Bros Café, **lodging:** Day's Inn, Rath Inn, Super 8, **other:** Chevrolet/Pontiac/Buick, Chrysler/Jeep/Dodge
73.5mm	weigh sta both lanes
72.5mm	Boyer River
72	IA 362, Loveland, **E...gas:** Conoco/diesel, **W...**to Wilson Island SP(6mi)
71	I-680 E, to Des Moines, no facilities, **I-29 S & I-680 W run together 10 mi**
66	Honey Creek, **W...gas:** Phillips 66/diesel/LP/Iowa Feed&Grain Co Rest., **other:** camping
61b	I-680 W, to N Omaha, **I-29 N & I-680 E run together 10 mi, W...**Mormon Trail Ctr
a	IA 988, to Crescent, **E...gas:** Phillips 66, **other:** to ski area
56	IA 192 S(sb only, exits left), Council Bluffs, **E...lodging:** Super 7 Inn, **other:** HOSPITAL
55	N 25th, Council Bluffs, **E...gas:** Pump'n Munch, Sinclair/24hr, **lodging:** Travelodge
54b	N 35th St(from nb), Council Bluffs, **E on Broadway... food:** Arby's, Burger King, Wendy's, **lodging:** Best Western, **other:** Honda
a	G Ave(from sb), Council Bluffs, **E...gas:** Shell, **W...**auto repair
53b	I-480 W, US 6, to Omaha, no facilities
a	9th Ave, S 37th Ave, Council Bluffs, **E...gas:** Phillips 66, Shell, Total, **lodging:** Day's Inn, **W...other:** Harrah's Casino/hotel, RiverBoat Casino, camping
52	Nebraska Ave, **E...gas:** Conoco/diesel, **lodging:** Comfort Suites, **W...lodging:** AmeriStar Hotel/casino, Hampton Inn, Holiday Inn, **other:** RiverBoat Casino
51	I-80 W, to Omaha, no facilities
	I-29 and I-80 run together 3 miles. See Iowa Interstate 80, exits 1b-3.
48	I-80 E(from nb), to Des Moines, **E...**HOSPITAL

Council Bluffs (vertical side label)

Interstate 29

N ↑ ↓ S

47	US 275, IA 92, Lake Manawa, **E...gas:** Phillips 66, **other:** Iowa School for the Deaf
42	IA 370, to Bellevue, **W...other:** K&B Saddlery, to Offutt AFB, camping
38mm	**rest area both lanes, full(handicapped)facilities, phone, info, picnic tables, litter barrels, RV dump, petwalk**
35	US 34 E, to Glenwood, **E...lodging:** Western Inn(4mi), **W...gas:** Amoco/diesel, **lodging:** Bluff View Motel, **other:** Ford
32	US 34 W, Pacific Jct, to Plattsmouth, no facilities
24	L31, Bartlett, to Tabor, no facilities
20	IA 145, Thurman, no facilities
15	J26, Percival, **1-2 mi E...**gas/diesel
11.5mm	weigh sta nb
10	IA 2, to Nebraska City, Sidney, **E...**to Waubonsie SP(5mi), **W...gas:** Conoco/diesel/@, Sapp/diesel/rest./24hr/@, Shell/diesel/24hr/@, **lodging:** Super 8, **6 mi W on US 75...food:** A&W/Amigo's, Arby's, Burger King, McDonald's, Pizza Hut, Valentino's, **lodging:** Best Western, Day's Inn, **other:** CountryMart Foods, Pamida, Factory Stores of America/famous brands, to Arbor Lodge SP, camping(4mi)
1	IA 333, Hamburg, **1 mi E...gas:** Casey's/diesel, **food:** Pizza Hut, **lodging:** Hamburg Motel, **other:** HOSPITAL, Soda Fountain
0mm	Iowa/Missouri state line

Interstate 35

N ↑ ↓ S

Exit #	Services
219mm	Iowa/Minnesota state line
214	rd 105, to Northwood, Lake Mills, **W...Welcome Ctr both lanes, full(handicapped)facilities, picnic tables, litter barrels, vending, petwalk, RV dump,** Cenex/Burger King/diesel/24hr/@
212mm	weigh sta both lanes
208	rd A38, to Joice, Kensett, no facilities
203	IA 9, to Manly, Forest City, **W...gas:** Amoco/diesel, **other:** HOSPITAL, to Pilot Knob SP
202mm	Winnebago River
197	rd B20, **8 mi E...**Lime Creek Nature Ctr
196mm	parking area both lanes, litter barrels, no facilities
194	US 18, Clear Lake, to Mason City, **E...**HOSPITAL(8mi), **W...gas:** Casey's, Conoco/Taco John's/diesel/@, Kum&Go/@, Shell/Wendy's/diesel, **food:** Bennigan's, Burger King, Culver's, Dairy Queen, Denny's, KFC/Taco Bell, McDonald's, Perkins/24hr, Pizza Hut, Subway, **lodging:** AmericInn, Best Western/rest., Budget Inn, Lake Country Inn, Microtel
193	rd B35, Emery, to Mason City, **E...gas:** Amoco/diesel/24hr, **food:** Happy Chef/24hr, **lodging:** Super 8, **W...gas:** Phillips 66, **lodging:** Heartland Inn(3mi), **other:** Chevrolet, Ford, antiques, to Clear Lake SP
190	US 18, rd 27 E, to Mason City, no facilities
188	rd B43, to Burchinal, no facilities
182	rd B60, Swaledale, to Rockwell, no facilities

*(vertical text between columns: Clear Lake)*

IOWA

Interstate 35

N ↑↓ S

| 180 | rd B65, to Thornton, **2 mi W...gas:** Cenex/diesel, **other:** camping |

180   rd B65, to Thornton, **2 mi W...gas:** Cenex/diesel, **other:** camping

176   rd C13, to Sheffield, Belmond, no facilities

170   rd C25, to Alexander, no facilities

165   IA 3, to **lodging:** Hampton, Clarion, **E...gas:** Shell/diesel/rest., **lodging:** AmericInn, Hampton Motel, **other:** HOSPITAL(7mi)

159   rd C47, Dows, **2 mi W...**IA Welcome Ctr

155mm   Iowa River

151   rd R75, to Woolstock, no facilities

147   rd D20, to US 20 E, no facilities

144   rd 928, Williams, **E...gas:** Phillips 66/diesel/Boondocks Motel/@, **food:** TH Café, **lodging:** Best Western, **other:** RV camping, **W...gas:** ♪/Flying J/Conoco/diesel/rest./24hr/@

142b a   US 20, to Webster City, Ft Dodge, no facilities

139   rd D41, to Kamrar, no facilities

133   IA 175, Ellsworth, to Jewell, **W...gas:** Cenex, Kum&Go

128   rd D65, Randall, to Stanhope, **5 mi W...**Little Wall Lake Pk

124   rd 115, Story City, **W...gas:** Kum&Go/diesel/24hr/@, Texaco, **food:** DQ, Godfather's, Happy Chef/24hr, McDonald's, Subway, Valhalla Rest., **lodging:** Super 8, Viking Motel, **other:** Ford, Gookin RV Ctr, VF Factory Stores/famous brands, Whispering Oaks RV Park

123   IA 221, rd E18, to Roland, McCallsburg, no facilities

120mm   **rest area nb, full(handicapped)facilities, info, phone, picnic tables, litter barrels, vending, RV dump/scenic prairie area sb, no facilities**

119mm   **rest area sb, full(handicapped)facilities, phone, picnic tables, litter barrels, vending, RV dump**

116   rd E29, to Story, **7 mi W...**Story Co Conservation Ctr

113   13th St, Ames, **W...gas:** BP/Arby's/diesel/@, Kum&Go/Burger King/diesel, **food:** Starlite Village Rest., **lodging:** Best Western/rest., Holiday Inn Express, **other:** HOSPITAL, Harley-Davidson, to USDA Vet Labs, ISU

111b a   US 30, Ames, to Nevada, **E...**camping(11mi), **W...gas:** Shell/diesel/rest./@, **food:** Embers Rest., **lodging:** AmericInn, Comfort Inn, Country Inn Suites, Hampton Inn, Heartland Inn, Microtel, Super 8, **other:** to IA St U

109mm   S Skunk River

106mm   weigh sta both lanes

102   IA 210, to Slater, **3 mi W...food:** DQ

96   to Elkhart, **W...**to Big Creek SP(11mi), Saylorville Lake

94mm   **rest area both lanes, full(handicapped)facilities, info, phone, picnic tables, litter barrels, vending, petwalk**

A m e s (side label)

D e s M o i n e s (side label)

92   1st St, Ankeny, **W...gas:** BP/diesel/24hr, Kum&Go, QT, **food:** Applebee's, Arby's, Blue Sky Creamery, Burger King, Cazador Mexican, Duffy's Rest., Fazoli's, Happy Chef, KFC, Subway, Village Inn Rest., **lodging:** Best Western/rest., Day's Inn, Fairfield Inn, Heartland Inn, Super 8, **other:** Goodyear/auto, O'Reilly Parts, Staples, Tires+, auto repair, **1mi W...gas:** BP, Casey's, **food:** Golden Corral, LJ Silver, MaidRite Café, McDonald's, Pizza Hut, Taco John's, **other:** HOSPITAL, Hy-Vee Food/drug, NAPA

90   IA 160, Ankeny, **E...food:** Chip's Diner, **lodging:** AmericInn, Country Inn Suites, Holiday Inn Express, **W...gas:** Casey's, Phillips 66, **food:** B-bops Rest., Burger King, Chili's, Culver's, McDonald's, **other:** Chevrolet, Home Depot, Kohl's, Radio Shack, Target, Wal-Mart SuperCtr/24hr, to Saylorville Lake(5mi)

87b a   I-235, I-35 and I-80, no facilities

I-35 and I-80 run together 14 mi around NW Des Moines. See Iowa Interstate 80 exits 124-136.

72c   University Ave, **E...gas:** Phillips 66, **food:** Applebee's, Bakers Square, Cheddar's, Chili's, Cuco's Mexican, Don Pablo, KFC, Macaroni Grill, McDonald's, Outback Steaks, RockBottom Rest./brewery, **lodging:** Chase Suites, Courtyard, Fairfield Inn, Heartland Inn, Holiday Inn/Damon's, The Inn, Wildwood Lodge, **other:** MEDICAL CARE, Barnes&Noble, Best Buy, CompUSA, K-Mart, Kohl's, Lowe's Whse, Marshall's, SportMart, World Mkt, **W...gas:** Amoco, Kum&Go/Burger King, QT, **food:** Cracker Barrel, **lodging:** Baymont Inn, Best Western, Country Inn Suites, **other:** HOSPITAL

b   I-80 W no facilities

a   I-235 E, to Des Moines

71   new exit

69b a   Grand Ave, W Des Moines, no facilities

68.5mm   Racoon River

68   IA 5, **7 mi E...lodging:** Crystal Inn, Hampton Inn, **other:** to airport, to Walnut Woods SP

65   G14, Cumming, to Norwalk, **14 mi W...**John Wayne Birthplace, museum

61mm   North River

56   IA 92, to Indianola, Winterset, **W...gas:** Shell/diesel/café/@, Total/diesel, **other:** repair

56mm   Middle River

53mm   **rest area nb, litter barrels, no facilities**

52   G50, St Charles, St Marys, **14 mi W...**John Wayne Birthplace, museum

51mm   **rest area sb, litter barrels, no facilities**

47   rd G64, to Truro, no facilities

45.5mm   South River

43   rd 207, New Virginia, **E...gas:** Sinclair/diesel, **W...**Total/diesel/@

36   rd 152, to US 69, **3 mi E...**lodging

34   Clay St, Osceola, **W...**Lakeside Casino Resort/camping

IOWA

Interstate 35

N

33	US 34, Osceola, **E...gas:** BP/diesel, Casey's, Cenex/diesel/café/24hr/@, Kum&Go, Shell/diesel/rest./@, **food:** Family Table Rest., Hardee's, McDonald's, Pizza Hut, Subway, 3rd Rail Grill, **lodging:** Best Western, Blue Haven Motel(2mi), Super 8, **other:** HOSPITAL, Ford, Chrysler/Plymouth/Dodge/Jeep, Hy-Vee Foods, O'Reilly Parts, Pamida, st patrol, **W...food:** KFC/Taco Bell, **lodging:** AmericInn
32mm	**rest area both lanes, full(handicapped)facilities, phone, picnic tables, litter barrels, vending, pet-walk, RV dump**
30mm	weigh sta both lanes
29	rd H45, no facilities
22	rd 258, Van Wert, no facilities
18	rd J20, to Grand River, no facilities
12	rd 2, Decatur City, Leon, **E...gas:** Phillips 66, Shell/diesel/rest./@, **5 mi E...lodging:** Little River Motel, **other:** HOSPITAL
7.5mm	Grand River
7mm	**Welcome Ctr nb/rest area sb, full(handicapped)facilities, info, phone, picnic tables, litter barrels, vending, petwalk, RV dump**
4	US 69, Lamoni, to Davis City, **E...**to 9 Eagles SP(10mi), **W...gas:** BP/Kum&Go/diesel, Casey's(2mi), Cenex/diesel(2mi), **food:** Subway(2mi), **lodging:** Chief Lamoni Motel, Super 8, **other:** antiques, IA Welcome Ctr
0mm	Iowa/Missouri state line

Interstate 80

Exit #	Services
307mm	Iowa/Illinois state line, Mississippi River
306	US 67, to Le Claire, **N...Welcome Ctr wb (no trucks), full(handicapped)facilities, picnic tables, litter barrels, phone, petwalk, gas:** Phillips 66/diesel, **food:** Subway, **lodging:** Comfort Inn, Super 8, **other:** Slagle Foods, **1 mi N...gas:** BP, **food:** A&W(2mi), **other:** Buffalo Bill Museum, **S...gas:** BP/diesel
301	Middle Rd, to Bettendorf, no facilities
300mm	**rest area both lanes, full(handicapped)facilities, phone, picnic tables, litter barrels, vending, pet-walk, RV dump**

E **W**

Davenport

298	I-74 E, to Peoria, **S...other:** to HOSPITAL, st patrol
295b a	US 61, Brady St, to Davenport, **N...gas:** BP, to Scott CP, **S...gas:** BP, Shell, **food:** Country Kitchen, Cracker Barrel, McDonald's, ThunderBay Grille, Village Inn Rest., **lodging:** AmericInn, Best Western/rest., Baymont Inn, Casa Loma Suites, Country Inn Suites, Day's Inn, Exel Inn, Heartland Inn, Motel 6, Residence Inn, Super 8, Wickliffe Inn, **1-2 mi S...gas:** BP/diesel, Shell, **food:** Burger King, ChiChi's, Country Kitchen, Ground Round, Happy Joe's, Hardee's, Hooters, LoneStar Steaks, McDonald's, LJ Silver, Rudy's Tacos, Steak'n Shake, **lodging:** Holiday Inn, **other:** AutoZone, Acura, Dodge, Sears/auto, Toyota, mall

Iowa City

292	IA 130 W, Northwest Blvd, **N...gas:** Flying J/Conoco/Cookery/diesel/LP/rest./24hr/@, **other:** Interstate RV Park(1mi), Farm&Fleet, truckwash, waterpark, **S...gas:** BP/McDonald's, Fred's Gas/towing, Sinclair, **food:** Machine Shed Rest., **lodging:** Comfort Inn
290	I-280 E, to Rock Island, no facilities
284	Y40, to Walcott, **N...gas:** Pilot/Arby's/diesel/24hr/@, TA/IA 80/BP/Blimpie/DQ/Wendy's/diesel/24hr/@, Phillips 66/diesel, **food:** Gramma's Kitchen, SpeedCo Lube, **lodging:** Comfort Inn, Super 8, **other:** Blue Beacon, Goodyear, **S...gas:** Pilot/Subway/diesel/24hr/@, **food:** McDonald's, **lodging:** Day's Inn
280	Y30, to Stockton, New Liberty, no facilities
277	Durant, **2 mi S...**food
271	US 6 W, IA 38 S, to Wilton, no facilities
270mm	**rest area both lanes, full(handicapped)facilities, info, phone, picnic tables, litter barrels, vending, petwalk, RV dump**
268mm	weigh sta wb
267	IA 38 N, to Tipton, **N...other:** Cedar River Camping, **S...food:** The Cove Café
266mm	Cedar River
265	to Atalissa, **S...gas:** Phillips 66/diesel/rest./24hr/@
259	to West Liberty, Springdale, **S...gas:** BP/diesel/24hr, **lodging:** Econolodge, **other:** KOA
254	X30, West Branch, **N...gas:** BP/diesel, Casey's, **food:** HeynQtr Steaks, Main St Rest., **other:** Jack&Jill Foods, H Hoover NHS/museum, USPO, **S...gas:** Kum&Go, Phillips 66/diesel, **food:** McDonald's, **lodging:** Best Value
249	Herbert Hoover Hwy, **S...**golf
246	IA 1, Dodge St, **N...gas:** BP/A&W/diesel, Phillips 66, **lodging:** Quality Inn, **S...gas:** Sinclair, **lodging:** Travelodge
244	Dubuque St, Iowa City, **N...**Coralville Lake, **S...**HOSPITALS, to Old Capitol
242	to Coralville, **N...food:** River City Grille, **lodging:** Hampton Inn, Holiday Inn, **S...gas:** BP, Conoco **food:** Arby's, Big Mike's Subs, Burger King, Hardee's, KFC, LJ Silver, LoneStar Steaks, McDonald's, Old Chicago Pizza, Peking Buffet, Perkins/24hr, Pizza Hut, Subway, Taco Bell, Taco John's, **lodging:** Best Western, Big Ten Inn, Comfort Inn, Day's Inn, Econolodge, Fairfield Inn, Heartland Inn, Iowa Lodge, Motel 6, Red Roof Inn, Super 8, **other:** HOSPITAL, Toyota, Walgreen

IOWA

Interstate 80

E ↑ W

240 IA 965, to US 6, Coralville, N Liberty, **N...gas:** Conoco, Phillips 66/diesel, **food:** Culver's, McDonald's, Steak'n Shake, Village Inn Rest., Wendy's, **lodging:** AmericInn, Country Inn, ExpressWay Motel, Ramada Inn/rest., **other:** Colony Country Camping(3mi), Harley-Davidson, Kohl's, Wal-Mart SuperCtr/24hr, **S...gas:** BP, Conoco, Phillips 66/Blimpie, **food:** Applebee's(1mi), Bennigan's, Chili's, Old Country Buffet, Olive Garden, Red Lobster, **lodging:** Holiday Inn Express, **other:** Barnes&Noble, Best Buy, Dillard's, HyVee Foods, JC Penney, Old Navy, Sears/auto, Target, Tires+, U-Haul, Younkers, mall

239b I-380 N, US 218 N, to Cedar Rapids, no facilities

239a US 218 S, no facilities

237 Tiffin, **N...** Jon's Rest.,

236mm **rest area both lanes, full(handicapped)facilities, phone, picnic tables, litter barrels, vending, RV dump, petwalk**

230 W38, to Oxford, **N...other:** Sleepy Hollow Camping, Kalona Museum

225 US 151 N, W21 S, **N...**Amana Colonies, **lodging:** Comfort Inn, **S...Welcome Ctr, gas:** BP, Phillips 66/Made Rite, **food:** Colony Village Rest., Little Amana Rest., Old Yoke Rest., **lodging:** Day's Inn/rest., Econolodge, Holiday Inn, My Little Inn, Super 8

220 IA 149 S, V77 N, to Williamsburg, **N...gas:** BP, Phillips 66/diesel/@, **food:** Arby's, Landmark Rest., McDonald's, Pizza Hut, Subway, Taste Of China, **lodging:** Best Western, Crest Motel, Super 8, **other:** GNC, Tanger/famous brands, VF/famous brands, **S...lodging:** Day's Inn

216 to Marengo, **N...gas:** Kum&Go/diesel, **lodging:** Sudbury Court Motel(7mi), **other:** HOSPITAL

211 to Ladora, Millersburg, no facilities

208mm **rest area both lanes, full(handicapped)facilities, phone, vending, picnic tables, litter barrels, petwalk, RV Dump(eb)**

205 to Victor, no facilities

201 IA 21, to Deep River, **N...gas:** Phillips 66/diesel/24hr, Sinclair/Nick's Rest., **lodging:** Sleep Inn, **other:** RV camping, **S...gas:** KwikStar/diesel/rest./24hr/@

197 to Brooklyn, **N...gas:** BP/diesel/@, **food:** Brooklyn-80 Rest./24hr, **other:** RV camping

191 US 63, to Montezuma, **N...gas:** Sinclair, **S...gas:** Citgo/diesel/rest., FuelMart/diesel/rest., to Fun Valley Ski Area(13mi)

182 IA 146, to Grinnell, **N...gas:** Casey's, **food:** Country Kitchen, DQ(3mi), Hardee's(3mi), KFC, Taco Bell, Taco John's, HyVee, **lodging:** Country Inn, Day's Inn, Econolodge, Super 8, **other:** HOSPITAL(4mi), Chrysler/Plymouth/Dodge/Jeep, **S...**Fun Valley Ski Area

180mm **rest area both lanes, full(handicapped)facilities, phone, vending, weather info, picnic tables, litter barrels, petwalk, playground, RV dump(eb)**

179 IA 124, to Oakland Acres, Lynnville, no facilities

175mm N Skunk River

Newton

173 IA 224, Kellogg, **N...gas:** Phillips 66/Best Burger/diesel/rest./24hr, **other:** Rock Creek SP(9mi), **S...**Lake Pla-mor Camping, Pella Museum

168 SE Beltline Dr, to Newton, **1 mi N...gas:** Casey's/diesel, **food:** Arby's, Taco John's, **lodging:** Mid-Iowa Motel, **other:** Plymouth/Jeep, Rolling Acres Camping, Wal-Mart SuperCtr/gas/24hr

164 US 6, IA 14, Newton, **N...gas:** BP/diesel, Casey's, Kum&Go, Phillips 66/Subway/diesel, **food:** Country Kitchen, Culver's, KFC/Taco Bell, Perkins/24hr, Senor Tequila Mexican, **lodging:** Day's Inn, Holiday Inn Express, Radisson, Ramada Ltd, Super 8, **other:** HOSPITAL, museum, **S...lodging:** Best Western/rest., to Lake Red Rock

159 F48, to Jasper, Baxter, no facilities

155 IA 117, Colfax, **N...gas:** Colfax Trkstp/BP/McDonald's/diesel/@, **other:** antiques, **S...gas:** Casey's, Kum&Go/Subway/diesel/24hr/@, **lodging:** Comfort Inn

153mm S Skunk River

151 weigh sta wb

149 Mitchellville, no facilities

148mm **rest area both lanes, full(handicapped)facilities, phone, picnic tables, litter barrels, petwalk, vending, RV dump**

143 Altoona, Bondurant, **S...gas:** BP(2mi), Casey's, **lodging:** Settle Inn(2mi), **other:** HyVee Foods(2mi)

142b a US 65, Hubble Ave, Des Moines, **S...gas:** Bosselman/Sinclair/diesel/rest./24hr/@, Git'n Go, **food:** Burger King, Godfather's, Hardee's, KFC/Taco Bell, McDonald's, Pizza Hut, Subway/TCBY, Taco John's, **lodging:** Adventureland Inn, Country Inn, Heartland Inn, Holiday Inn Express, Howard Johnson Express, Motel 6, Settle Inn, **other:** Blue Beacon, Factory Outlet/famous brands, camping

141 US 6 W, US 65 S(from wb), Pleasant Hill, Des Moines, no facilities

137b a I-35 N, I-235 S, to Des Moines, no facilities
I-80 W and I-35 S run together 14 mi.

136 US 69, E 14th St, Camp Sunnyside, **N...gas:** BP/diesel, Phillips 66, **food:** Bonanza, Country Kitchen, Giselle's Rest., Okoboji Grill, **lodging:** Best Western/rest., Motel 6, Red Roof Inn, **other:** Volvo/GMC, **S...gas:** Casey's, Citgo/diesel(1mi), QT/Burger King/diesel/@, **food:** Arby's(1mi), Fazoli's, KFC, LJ Silver, McDonald's, Pizza Hut, Schlotsky's, Scornovacca's Pizza, Subway(1mi), Village Inn Rest., Wendy's, **lodging:** 14th St Inn, Ramada Ltd, **other:** Advance Parts, CarMax, CarX Muffler, Ford Trucks, Goodyear, MidState RV Ctr, Tires+

135 IA 415, 2nd Ave, Polk City, **N...other:** Harley-Davidson, diesel repair, **S...gas:** Git'n Go, QT, **other:** HOSPITAL, Earl's Tire, USPO(2mi), st patrol

133mm Des Moines River

131 IA 28 S, NW 58th St, **N...gas:** Casey's, QT, **food:** North-End Diner, Quizno's, Sonic, Tagliai's Pizza, **lodging:** Best Inn, Best Western, **other:** Acura, Goodyear/auto, HyVee Food, Infiniti, VW/Audi, **S...gas:** BP/diesel/24hr, Phillips 66, QT, Sinclair/diesel, **food:** Arby's, BBQ, Bennigan's, Burger King, Country Kitchen, Daytona's Grill, Denny's, Famous Dave's BBQ, KFC, McDonald's, Perkins, Pizza Hut, Shangrila Buffet, Village Inn Rest.,

Des Moines

IOWA

Interstate 80

E ↑ **W**

Wendy's, **lodging:** Comfort Inn, Day's Inn, Holiday Inn, Quality Inn, Red Roof Inn, Sheraton, Super 8, **other:** HOSPITAL, Best Buy, Chevrolet, Chrysler/Plymouth, Daewoo, Firestone/auto, Ford/Mitsubishi, Goodyear/auto, Isuzu, Lincoln/Mercury, Marshall's, NAPA Autocare, Nissan, Office Depot, Sears/auto, Suzuki, Toyota, Younker's, Walgreen, mall

129 NW 86th St, Camp Dodge, **N...gas:** Kum&Go, **food:** Burger King, McDonald's, Okoboji Grill, Village Inn Rest., **lodging:** Birchwood Creek Inn, Hilton Garden, **other:** Dahl's Foods, **S...gas:** BP, Phillips 66, **food:** Arby's, B-Bops Burgers, Culver's, Ember's Steaks, Friedrich's Coffee, Happy Joe's Pizza, **lodging:** Microtel, **other:** Walgreen

127 IA 141 W, Grimes, **N...gas:** BP/Blimpie/diesel/@, Phillips 66/Subway/diesel, **lodging:** AmericInn(3mi), to Saylorville Lake, **S...food:** Quizno's, **other:** Radio Shack, Target

126 Douglas Ave, Urbandale, **N...gas:** Pilot/diesel/rest./24hr/@, **S...gas:** Kum&Go/diesel, **food:** Dragon China, **lodging:** Day's Inn, Econolodge, Extended Stay America

125 US 6, Hickman Rd, **N...gas:** ✈/Flying J/Conoco/Cookery/diesel/LP/24hr/@, **S...food:** IA Machine Shed Rest., **lodging:** Clarion, Comfort Suites, Sleep Inn, **other:** GMC, Goodyear, Honda, Hyundai, to Living History Farms

124 (72c from I-35 nb), University Ave, **N...gas:** BP, Kum&Go/Burger King, QT, **food:** Baggi's Rest, Cracker Barrel, Rodeo Mexican, **lodging:** Baymont Inn, Best Western, Country Inn Suites, **other:** HOSPITAL, **S...gas:** Phillips 66, **food:** Applebee's, Bakers Square, Cheddar's, Chili's, Colton's Steaks, Cuco's Mexican, Don Pablo, KFC, Macaroni Grill, McDonald's, Outback Steaks, RockBottom Rest./brewery, **lodging:** Chase Suites, Courtyard, Fairfield Inn, Heartland Inn, Holiday Inn/Damon's, The Inn, Wildwood Lodge, **other:** MEDICAL CARE, Barnes&Noble, Best Buy, CompUSA, K-Mart, Kohl's, Lowe's Whse, Marshall's, World Mkt, I-80 E and I-35 N run together 14 mi

I-80 E and I-35 N run together 14 mi.

123b a I-80/I-35 N, I-35 S to Kansas City, I-235 to Des Moines, no facilities

122 (from eb)60th St, W Des Moines, no facilities

121 74th St, W Des Moines, **N...food:** West End Diner, **lodging:** Hampton Inn, Hawthorn Suites, **other:** Home Depot, HyVee Food/gas, SteinMart, Target, **S...gas:** BP, Kum&Go/Blimpie, **food:** Arby's, Burger King, McDonald's, Perkins, Taco John's, **lodging:** Candlewood Suites, Fairfield Inn, Quality Inn, Marriott, Motel 6, Wingate Inn

119mm **rest area both lanes, full(handicapped)facilities, info, vending, phone, picnic tables, petwalk, RV dump**

117 R22, Booneville, Waukee, **N...food:** Organic Farm Rest., **other:** Timberline Camping(2mi), **S...gas:** Kum&Go/24hr, **food:** Rube's Steaks

115mm weigh sta eb

D e s M o i n e s

---

113 R16, Van Meter, **1 mi S...gas:** Casey's
112mm N Racoon River
112mm Middle Racoon River
110 US 169, to Adel, DeSoto, **N...lodging:** Edgetowner Motel, **S...gas:** BP, Casey's, **other:** AirCraft Supermkt
106 F90, P58, **N...**KOA
104 P57, Earlham, **S...gas:** Casey's(2mi)
100 US 6, to Redfield, Dexter, no facilities
97 P48, to Dexter, **N...gas:** Casey's(2mi), camping
93 P28, Stuart, **N...gas:** BP/diesel/24hr, Conoco/diesel, .**food:** Burger King, McDonald's, Subway, AmericInn, Super 8, **other:** Jubilee Foods, NAPA, **S...gas:** Phillips 66/diesel, **food:** Country Kitchen, **lodging:** Stuart Motel
88 P20, Menlo, camping
86 IA 25, to Greenfield, Guthrie Ctr, **S...other:** to Preston/Spring Brook SP
85mm Middle River
83 N77, Casey, **1 mi N...gas:** Kum&Go, **other:** camping
80.5mm **rest area both lanes, full(handicapped)facilities, phone, picnic tables, litter barrels, vending, petwalk, RV dump**
76 IA 925, N54, Adair, **N...gas:** Amoco/diesel, Casey's/diesel, Kum&Go/diesel, Happy Chef/24hr, **food:** Mikey's Sandwiches, Subway, **lodging:** Adair Budget Inn, Super 8, **other:** camping
75 G30, to Adair, no facilities
70 IA 148 S, Anita, **S...**to Lake Anita SP(6mi)
64 N28, to Wiota, no facilities
61mm E Nishnabotna River
60 US 6, US 71, to Atlantic, Lorah, **S...gas:** Phillips 66/diesel/24hr, Shamrock, **food:** Valley County Cafe, **lodging:** Day's Inn
57 N16, to Atlantic, **S...**HOSPITAL(7mi)
54 IA 173, to Elk Horn, **6 mi N...Welcome Ctr, lodging:** AmericInn, **other:** Windmill Museum, gas, food
51 M56, to Marne, no facilities
46 M47, Walnut, **N...gas:** BP/McDonald's/24hr, **food:** Villager Buffet, **lodging:** Super 8, to Prairie Rose SP(8mi), **S...gas:** Kum&Go/diesel/24hr, **food:** Aunt B's Kitchen, **lodging:** Red Carpet Inn/RV Park, repair
44mm weigh sta both lanes
40 US 59, to Harlan, Avoca, **N...gas:** Conoco/Wings/Taco John/diesel/rest./24hr/@, **food:** Made Right, **lodging:** Motel 6, **other:** HOSPITAL(12mi), **S...gas:** Shell/diesel, **food:** Embers Rest., **lodging:** Avoca Motel, Capri Motel(1mi), **other:** Parkway Camping(2mi), Nishna Museum

IOWA

Interstate 80

39.5mm	W Nishnabotna River
34	M16, Shelby, **N...gas:** Shell/DQ/diesel, **food:** Cornstalk Rest., Country Pizza, **lodging:** Shelby Country Inn/RV Park
32mm	**rest area both lanes, litter barrels, no facilities**
29	L66, to Minden, **S...gas:** Phillips 66/A&W/diesel, **lodging:** Midtown Motel(2mi)
27	I-680 W, to N Omaha, no facilities
23	IA 244, L55, Neola, **S...gas:** Kum&Go/diesel, **other:** to Arrowhead Park, camping
20mm	**Welcome Ctr eb/rest area wb, full(handicapped)facilities, phone, picnic tables, litter barrels, vending, petwalk, RV dump**
17	G30, Underwood, **N...gas:** Phillips 66/Subway/diesel/24hr, **lodging:** Interstate 80 Inn/rest., Underwood Motel, **other:** truck/tire repair
8	US 6, Council Bluffs, **N...gas:** Coastal(1mi), Phillips 66/diesel(1mi), **lodging:** Chalet Motel(5mi), **other:** HOSPITAL, **S...**st patrol
5	5 Madison Ave, Council Bluffs, **N...gas:** BP, **food:** Burger King, FoodCourt, Great Wall Chinese, KFC, McDonald's, Panera Bread, Pizza Hut, Subway, **lodging:** Heartland Inn, **other:** MEDICAL CARE, Barnes&Noble, Dillard's, DrugTown, HyVee Food/drug, JC Penney, NTB, Old Navy, Sears/auto, Target, Walgreen, mall, **S...gas:** Conoco, Shell, **food:** DQ, Valentino's Rest., Village Inn Rest., **lodging:** Western Inn, **other:** No Frills Foods
4	I-29 S, to Kansas City, no facilities
3	3 IA 192 N, Council Bluffs, **N...**to Hist Dodge House, **S...gas:** Phillips 66/diesel/@, Shell/diesel, TA/Pizza Hut/diesel/24hr/@, **food:** Applebee's, Burger King, Beijing Chinese, Cracker Barrel, Dairy Queen, Fazoli's, Golden Corral, Gordman's, Hardee's, LJ Silver, McDonald's, Perkins/24hr, Red Lobster, Subway, Taco Bell, **lodging:** Comfort Inn, Day's Inn, Fairfield Inn, Motel 6, Settle Inn, **other:** Advance Parts, Aldi Foods, Chevrolet/GMC, Buick/Pontiac, Dodge, Ford/Lincoln/Mercury, Home Depot, Kia, Mazda, Nissan/Cadillac, OfficeMax, Plymouth/Jeep/Suzuki, Sam's Club/gas, Subaru, Toyota, TruckOMat, U-Haul, Wal-Mart SuperCtr/24hr, diesel repair
1b	S 24th St, Council Bluffs, **N...gas:** Casey's, Conoco, Pilot/Arby's/diesel/24hr, Sinclair, Sapp Bros/Shell/Burger King/diesel/rest., **lodging:** American Inn, Best Western, Country Inn, Super 8, **other:** Goodyear, RV camping, Peterbilt, SpeedCo, casino
1a	I-29 N, to Sioux City, no facilities
0mm	Iowa/Nebraska state line, Missouri River

Interstate 235(Des Moines)

Exit #	Services
15	I-80, E to Davenport
13	US 6, E Euclid Ave, **E...gas:** Coastal, Phillips 66, **food:** Burger King, Dragon House Chinese, Papa John's, Perkins, **other:** Hancock Fabrics, HyVee Foods, Radio Shack, Walgreen, **W...other:** NAPA
12	Guthrie Ave, **N...gas:** Coastal/diesel/mart, **other:** Jocko's Auto Parts
11	IA 163 W, E University Ave, Easton Dr, no facilities
10	US 65/69, E 14th, E 15th, **N...food:** DQ, **other:** Walgreen, **S...food:** McDonald's, **other:** HOSPITAL, st capitol, zoo
9	E 6th St, Penn Ave(from wb), **N...**HOSPITAL
8.5	3rd St, 5th Ave, **N...lodging:** Holiday Inn, **other:** HOSPITAL, **S...**Conv Ctr, **lodging:** Best Western, Embassy Suites, Park Inn, Marriott
8	Keo Way, **S...gas:** Git'n Go, **other:** HOSPITAL
7.5	Harding Rd(from wb)
7	MLK Blvd, Drake U, **S...**airport
6.5	31st St, Governor's Mansion
6	42nd St, Science & Art Ctr, **N...gas:** Git'n Go, **food:** Papa John's, Taco John's
5	56th St(from wb), **N...**golf
4	IA 28, 63rd St, to Windsor Heights, **S...**Hist Valley Jct, zoo
3	8th St, W Des Moines, **N...gas:** Kum&Go, **food:** B-Bop's Café, Blimpie, Burger King, **other:** NTB, Sam's Club/gas, Sears AutoCtr, Wal-Mart SuperCtr/24hr, **S...gas:** BP, Kum&Go, **food:** Classic Custard, Garcia's Mexican, Jimmy's American Café, **lodging:** Best Western, **other:** Ford
2	22nd St, 24th St, W Des Moines, **N...gas:** BP, Citgo, **food:** ChiChi's, ChuckeCheese, Famous Dave's BBQ, Hardee's, Hooters, LoneStar Steaks, McDonald's, Old Country Buffet, Taco Bell, Village Inn Rest., Zachary's Grill, **lodging:** Studio+, **other:** Firestone/auto, Goodyear/auto, Gordman's, Hancock Fabrics, Michael's, Office Depot, Walgreen
1	35th St, W Des Moines, **N...gas:** BP/diesel, **food:** Red Lobster, **other:** HyVee Foods, JC Penney, SteinMart, Target, Younker's, mall, **S...**MEDICAL CARE
0mm	I-235 begins/ends on I-80, exit 123.

Interstate 280(Davenport)

Exit #	Services
18b a	I-74, US 6, Moline, **S...gas:** Citgo, **food:** Bender's Rest., Denny's, Harold's Rest., McDonald's, Omelet Shoppe, Skyline Rest., **lodging:** Best Western, Comfort Inn, Country Inn Suites, Exel Inn, Hampton Inn, Holiday Inn, Holiday Inn Express, La Quinta, Motel 6, Skyline Inn
15	Airport Rd, Milan, **N...food:** MaidRite Café, **S...gas:** Mobil/diesel
11b a	IL 92, Rock Island, to Andalusia, **S...**Camelot Camping(apr-oct)
9.5mm	Iowa/Illinois state line, Mississippi River
8	rd 22, Rockingham Rd, to Buffalo
6	US 61, W River Dr, to Muscatine, **W...**food, camping
4	Locust St, rd F65, 160th St, **E...**HOSPITAL, to Palmer Coll, St Ambrose U, **W...gas:** Citgo/Subway/diesel/@
1	US 6 E, IA 927, Kimberly Rd, to Walcott, **E...**lodging, transmissions
0mm	I-280 begins/ends on I-80, exit 290.

172

Interstate 35

N ↕ S

K a n s a s C i t y A r e a

Exit #	Services
235mm	Kansas/Missouri state line
235	Cambridge Circle, **E…gas:** QT
234b a	US 169, Rainbow Blvd, **E…gas:** Phillips 66, **food:** Applebee's, Arby's, Burger King, McDonald's, Rosedale BBQ, Wendy's, **lodging:** Best Western, Day's Inn, **other:** KU MED CTR
233a	SW Blvd, Mission Rd, no facilities
233b	37th Ave(from sb), no facilities
232b	US 69 N, **E…gas:** QT, Phillips 66, **food:** McDonald's, Taco Bell
232a	Lamar Ave, **E…gas:** QT
231b a	I-635(exits left from nb), no facilities
230	Antioch Rd(from sb), **E…gas:** QT
229	Johnson Dr, **E…gas:** Shell, **food:** Arby's, Chili's, Papa John's, **other:** GNC, Home Depot, Marshall's, OfficeMax, Old Navy, Walgreen, Walnut Grove RV Park, **W…gas:** Phillips 66/diesel
228b	US 56 E, US 69, Shawnee Mission Pkwy, **W…food:** Burger King, Denny's, LJ Silver, Perkins, Pizza Hut, Steak'n Shake, Taco Bell, Wendy's
228a	67th St, **E…gas:** QT, Shell, **food:** Burger King, Chevy's Mexican, Denny's, Winstead's Rest., **lodging:** Comfort Inn, Drury Inn, Fairfield Inn, HomeStead Village, Quality Inn, **other:** BMW, K-Mart, VW, **W…gas:** Phillips 66, **other:** Jaguar, Land Rover, Mercedes, Porsche
227	75th St, **E…gas:** Circle K, Conoco, QT, **food:** McDonald's, Perkins, **lodging:** Wellesley Inn, **other:** HOSPITAL, Acura, JC Penney, Wal-Mart, **W…gas:** Citgo/7-11, QT/diesel, Shell, **food:** Ryan's, Sonic, Subway, Taco Bell, Wendy's, **lodging:** Hampton Inn
225b	US 69 S(from sb), Overland Pkwy, no facilities

O l a t h e

Exit #	Services
225a	87th St, **E…gas:** Amoco, Green Mill Rest., Tippen's Rest., **food:** Wendy's, **lodging:** Holiday Inn, **other:** Gomer's Foods, **W…gas:** Phillips 66, Shell, **food:** Arby's, Kahn Chinese, LongBranch Steaks, Mary's Place Gyros, Taco Bell, **other:** NTB, museum
224	95th St, **E…gas:** Amoco, Phillips 66, Shell, **food:** Applebee's, Burger King, China Buffet, Cielio's Italian, Denny's, Holiday Ham Café, Houlihan's, Italian Oven, KFC, McDonald's, Mimi's Café, Ming Palace, Mongolian BBQ, Old Chicago Pizza, On the Border, Pizza Hut, Ponderosa, Ruby Tuesday, Santa Fe Café, Steak&Ale, Taco Bell, TGIFriday, **lodging:** Comfort Inn, Day's Inn, Holiday Inn, La Quinta, Motel 6, Super 8, **other:** HOSPITAL, Advance Parts, Best Buy, CircuitCity, Dillard's, HyVee Foods, JC Penney, Nordstrom's, OfficeMax, Sam's Club, SteinMart, mall, **W…gas:** Conoco, Costco/gas
222b a	I-435 W & E, no facilities
220	119th St, **E…gas:** Conoco, Phillips 66, Shell, **food:** A&W, Burger King, Chevy's Mexican, China Café, Cracker Barrel, Gambucci's Italian, IHOP, Jersey Boyz Deli, Joe's Crabshack, La Mesa Mexican, LJ Silver, Machine Shed Rest., McDonald's, Rio Bravo Cantina, Ruby Tuesday, Schlotsky's, Souper Salad, Steak'n Shake, Subway, Tres Hombres Mexican, Wendy's, Zio's Italian, **lodging:** Comfort Suites, Fairfield Inn, Hampton Inn, Residence Inn, **other:** Aamco, Barnes&Noble, Dodge, GNC, Goodyear/auto, Home Depot, Honda, Hyundai, Mazda, OfficeMax, Old Navy, Radio Shack, Target, U-Haul, transmissions
218	135th, Santa Fe St, Olathe, **E…gas:** Shell, **food:** Backyard Burgers, Burger King, Corona Garden Mexican, Perkins, **other:** Ford, K-Mart, Osco Drug, **W…gas:** Amoco, Phillips 66, QT, **food:** Denny's, McDonald's, Ponderosa, Waffle House, Wendy's, **lodging:** Day's Inn, **other:** Chevrolet, Chrysler/Plymouth/Jeep, Kia, Mazda, Nissan, Pontiac/Buick/GMC, Saturn, Suzuki, Subaru, Toyota

Interstate 35

N / **S**

Ottawa / **Emporia** (left margin)

Wichita (right margin)

217	Old Hwy 56(from sb), same as 215
215	US 169 S, KS 7, Olathe, **E...gas:** Phillips 66/24hr, QT, **food:** Catfish Rest., Outback Steaks, **other:** Aldi Foods, Home Depot, Target, **W...gas:** Presto, Shell/Blimpie/24hr/@, **food:** Applebee's, Burger King, Chili's, FoodCourt, Red Lobster, McDonald's, Waffle House, Wendy's, **lodging:** Econolodge, Holiday Inn, Microtel, Sleep Inn, **other:** HOSPITAL, Chrysler/Jeep, Dillard's, Marshalls, mall
213mm	weigh sta both lanes
210	US 56 W, Gardner, **W...gas:** Phillips 66/diesel, **food:** KFC, McDonald's, Mr GoodSense Subs, Pizza Hut, Sonic, Subway, Taco Bell, Waffle House, **lodging:** Super 8
207	US 56 E, Gardner Rd, **E...**Olathe RV Ctr, **W...gas:** Conoco/diesel, Shell/diesel
202	Edgerton, no facilities
198	KS 33, to Wellsville, **W...gas:** Conoco
193	LeLoup Rd, Baldwin, no facilities
187	KS 68, Ottawa, **W...gas:** Shell/Texaco/diesel/24hr, **food:** DQ, **other:** Buick/GMC/Pontiac
185	15th St, Ottawa, no facilities
183b a	US 59, Ottawa, **W...gas:** BP, Citgo, Conoco/diesel, Phillips 66/diesel, **food:** Applebee's, Burger King, Country Kitchen, DQ, KFC, LJ Silver, McDonald's, Pizza Hut, Sirloin Stockade, Taco Bell, Wendy's, **lodging:** Comfort Inn, Day's Inn, Econolodge, Holiday Inn Express, Super 8, Travelodge, Village Inn Motel, Villager Lodge, **other:** Advance Parts, Chrysler/Plymouth/Dodge/Jeep, CountryMart Foods, $General, $Tree, Wal-Mart SuperCtr/gas/24hr
182b a	US 50, Eisenhower Rd, Ottawa, no facilities
176	Homewood, **W...**RV camping
175mm	**rest area both lanes, full(handicapped)facilities, phone, picnic tables, litter barrels, vending, pet-walk, RV dump**
170	KS 273, Williamsburg, **W...gas:** Shell/diesel/café, phone
162	KS 31 S, Waverly, no facilities
160	KS 31 N, Melvern, no facilities
155	US 75, Burlington, Melvern Lake, **E...gas:** BP, Subway/diesel?@, Shell/Wendy's/diesel/24hr/@, **food:** Country Pride Rest., **lodging:** Wyatt Earp Inn
148	KS 131, Lebo, **E...gas:** Casey's, Phillips 66/diesel/@, **food:** Lebo Grill, **lodging:** Universal Inn, **W...**to Melvern Lake
141	KS 130, Neosho Rapids, **E...**NWR(8mi)
138	County Rd U, no facilities
135	County Rd R1, **W...**RV camping/phone
133	US 50 W, 6th Ave, Emporia, **1-3 mi E...gas:** Casey's, **food:** McDonald's, Pizza Hut, **lodging:** Budget Host, **W...other:** RV Parking
131	KS 57, KS 99, Burlingame Rd, **E...gas:** Conoco/diesel, Phillips 66, **food:** DQ, Hardee's, Mr GoodSense Subs, **other:** Dillon's Food
130	KS 99, Merchant St, **E...gas:** Phillips 66/diesel, **food:** Subway, **lodging:** University Inn, **other:** Emporia St U
128	Industrial Rd, **E...gas:** Conoco, **food:** Burger King, Mazzio's, Pizza Hut, Subway, **lodging:** Econolodge, Ramada Inn, Motel 6, **other:** HOSPITAL, CarQuest, Dillon's Food, Goodyear/auto, Hastings Book, JC

	Penney, **W...gas:** Phillips 66/Wendy's/diesel, Shell, **food:** Applebee's, Golden Corral, McDonald's, MT Mike's Steaks, Starbuck's, Taco Bell, Village Inn Rest., **lodging:** Candlewood Suites, Fairfield Inn, Holiday Inn Express, **other:** Staples, Wal-Mart SuperCtr/24hr
127c	KS Tpk, I-335 N, to Topeka, no facilities
127b a	US 50, KS 57, Newton, **E...gas:** Conoco/diesel, ☮/Flying J/Conoco/diesel/rest./24hr/@, Phillips 66/diesel, Shell, **food:** Arby's, Carlos O'Kelly's, Chester Fried, China Buffet, Hardee's, **lodging:** Best Western/rest., Day's Inn, Super 8, **other:** Aldi Foods, Chevrolet/Pontiac/Buick, Chrysler/Dodge/Plymouth/Jeep/Toyota, $General, Ford/Lincoln/Mercury/Nissan, Napa, PriceChopper Foods, **W...**Emporia RV Park
127mm	I-35 and I-335 KS Tpk, toll plaza, I-35 S and KS tpk S run together
	I-35 S and KS Tpk S run together.
125mm	Cottonwood River
111	Cattle Pens
97.5mm	**Matfield Green Service Area(both lanes exit left), Phillips 66/diesel, McDonald's**
92	KS 177, Cassoday, **E...gas:** Fuel'n Service, phone
76	US 77, El Dorado N, **E...**El Dorado SP, **3 mi E...gas:** Casey's, Philips 66
71	KS 254, KS 196, El Dorado, **E...gas:** Phillips 66, **food:** Golden Corral, KFC, McDonald's, Pizza Hut, **lodging:** Best Western, Heritage Inn, Sunset Inn, Super 8, HOSPITAL, **other:** $General, Ford/Lincoln/Mercury, Pontiac/Buick/Cadillac, Radio Shack, Wal-Mart/24hr/auto
65mm	**Towanda Service Area(both lanes exit left), Phillips 66/diesel, McDonald's**
62mm	Whitewater River
57	21st St, Andover, **W...**golf, phone
53	KS 96, Wichita, **1 mi W...gas:** Conoco, **food:** McDonald's, Taco Bell, Wendy's, **lodging:** Courtyard, **other:** Acura, Lowe's Whse, Mercedes, Wal-Mart SuperCtr/24hr
50	US 54, Kellogg Ave, **E...**McConnell AFB, **W...lodging:** Comfort Inn, Clubhouse Inn, Day's Inn, Fairfield Inn, Hampton Inn, Hilton, Marriott, Residence Inn, Scotsman Inn, Studio+, Super 8, **other:** VA HOSPITAL, Wichita Suites, **1 mi E on Kellogg...gas:** Conoco/Wendy's/diesel, **food:** Burger King, IHOP, Subway, **other:** Acura, Buick/Infiniti, Lowe's Whse, Porsche/Jaguar, Wal-Mart SuperCtr/24hr, **W on Kellogg Ave...gas:** Coastal, **food:** Arby's, Carlos O'Kelly's, Denny's, Green Mill Rest., Hooters, KFC, LJ Silver, McDonald's, Old Chicago Pizza, Pizza Hut, Spangles Rest., Steak&Ale, Taco Bell, **lodging:** LaQuinta, Wichita Inn, Williamsburg Inn, **other:** Advance Parts, Barnes&Noble, Best Buy, Chevrolet/Cadillac, Chrysler/Plymouth, Circuit City, $General, Firestone/auto, Ford, Hancock Fabrics, Honda, JC Penney, Kia/Nissan, K-Mart, Lincoln/Mercury, Michael's, NTB, OfficeMax, PepBoys, Pontiac/GMC/Hyundai, Saturn, Sears/auto, Subaru/Isuzu, Target, Toyota, mall
45	KS 15, Wichita, **E...**Boeing Plant
44.5mm	Arkansas River
42	42 47TH St, I-135, to I-235, Wichita, **services on 47th St, E...gas:** Coastal, **food:** Potbelly's Rest., **lodging:** Best Western, Comfort Inn, Day's Inn, Holiday Inn Express, Red Carpet Inn, **W...gas:** Phillips 66, **food:**

Interstate 35

N ↑ S

Applebee's, Braum's, Burger King, DQ, Godfather's, KFC, LJ Silver, McDonald's, Pizza Hut, Quizno's, Spaghetti Jack's, Spangles Rest., Taco Bell, Taco Tico, **other:** Checker's Foods, Dillon's Foods, K-Mart, O'Reilly's Parts, Radio Shack

39	US 81, Haysville, **W...lodging:** Haysville Inn
33	KS 53, Mulvane, **E...**Mulvane Hist Museum, **W...** Wyldewood Winery
26mm	**Belle Plaine Service Area(both lanes exit left), gas: Phillips 66/diesel, food: McDonald's**
19	US 160, Wellington, **3 mi W...food:** Penny's Diner, **lodging:** OakTree Inn, Steakhouse Motel, Sunshine Inn, **other:** RV camping
17mm	toll plaza, I-35N and KS TPK N run together I-35 N and KS TPK N run together.
4	US 166, to US 81, South Haven, **E...gas:** Phillips 66/diesel, **lodging:** Economy Inn/rest., **W...**Oasis RV Park
1.5mm	weigh sta nb
0mm	Kansas/Oklahoma state line

Interstate 70

E ↕ W

K S   C i t y

Exit #	Services
423b	3rd St, James St, no facilities
423a	5th St, no facilities
422d c	Central Ave, service rd, no facilities
422b a	US 69 N, US 169 S, no facilities
421b	I-670, no facilities
421a	**S...**railroad yard
420b a	US 69 S, 18th St Expswy, no facilities
419	38th St, Park Dr, access to 10 motels
418b	I-635 N, **N...food:** McDonald's, Taco Bell, Wendy's, Dillard's, **other:** JC Penney, mall
418a	I-635 S, no facilities
417	57th St, no facilities
415a	KS 32 E(from eb), no facilities
415b	to US 40 W, State Ave, Kansas City, **N...gas:** Conoco, **food:** Alvardo's Café, Arby's, Capt D's, Perkins, McDonald's, Taco Bell
414mm	weigh sta wb, parking area both lanes, phone
414	78th St, **N...gas:** QT, **food:** Arby's, Burger King, Cracker Barrel, DQ, Hardee's, Lucky Chinese, Sonic, Wendy's, **lodging:** Microtel, **other:** HOSPITAL, Walgreen, **S...gas:** Conoco, **lodging:** American Motel, Comfort Inn
411b	I-435 N, access to Woodlands Racetrack, to KCI Airport
411a	I-435 S, no facilities
410	110th St, **N...**Cabella's, KS Speedway, last free exit wb before KS TPK
225mm	I-70 W and KS TPK run together, no facilities
224	KS 7, to US 73, Bonner Springs, Leavenworth, **N...gas:** Shell, **food:** KFC/Taco Bell, Mazzio's, Waffle House, Wendy's, **lodging:** Holiday Inn Express, **other:** museum, **S...gas:** Citgo, **food:** McDonald's, **other:** Ford, PriceChopper Foods, Wal-Mart SuperCtr/24hr
217mm	toll booth
209mm	**Lawrence Service Area(both lanes exit left), full facilities, Conoco/diesel, McDonald's**

T o p e k a

204	US 24, US 59, to E Lawrence, **S...gas:** Citgo, Conoco, **food:** Burger King, Sonic, **lodging:** Bismarck Inn, J-Hawk Motel, SpringHill Suites, **other:** O'Reilly Parts, outlet
203mm	Kansas River
202	US 59 S, to W Lawrence, **1 mi S...gas:** Phillips 66, **food:** Capt's Galley, Chili's, MT Mike's Steaks, **lodging:** Best Western, Day's Inn, Hampton Inn, Holiday Inn, Quality Inn, Ramada Inn, Travelodge, Super 8, **other:** HOSPITAL, Firestone/auto, to Clinton Lake SP, to U of KS
197	KS 10, Lecompton, Lawrence, **N...**Perry Lake SP, **S...**Clinton Lake SP,
188mm	**Topeka Service Area(both lanes exit left), full facilities, Conoco/diesel, Hardee's**
182	I-70 W(from wb), to Denver, no facilities
367mm	toll plaza
366	I-470 W, to Wichita, I-70 E and KS TPK E run together, no facilities
365	21st St, Rice Rd, no facilities
364b	US 40 E, Carnahan Ave, to Lake Shawnee, no facilities
364a	California Ave, **S...gas:** BP/diesel, Conoco, **food:** Burger King, McDonald's, Pizza Hut, Rosa's Mexican, Sonic, Subway, **other:** AutoZone, Dillon's Food/gas, Family$, Food4Less, Walgreen
363	Adams St, downtown
362c	10th Ave(from wb), **N...lodging:** Ramada Inn, **S...gas:** BP, **other:** st capitol
362b a	to 8th Ave, downtown, **N...lodging:** Capital Center Inn, **other:** to St Capitol
361b	3rd St, Monroe St, **N...gas:** BP, **lodging:** Ramada Inn
361a	1st Ave, **S...**Ryder
359	MacVicar Ave, no facilities
358b a	Gage Blvd, **S...gas:** gas/diesel, **food:** McDonald's, Wendy's, **other:** HOSPITAL
357b a	Fairlawn Rd, 6th Ave, **S...gas:** Conoco, Phillips 66, **food:** A&W, **lodging:** Best Western, Holiday Inn/rest., Motel 6, **other:** NAPA, zoo-rain forest
356b a	Wanamaker Rd, **N...lodging:** AmeriSuites, **other:** KS Museum of History, **S...gas:** BP, Phillips 66/diesel, Topeka/diesel/rest./24hr, **food:** Applebee's, Boston Mkt, Burger King, Chili's, ChuckeCheese, Coyote Canyon Café, Cracker Barrel, Denny's, Golden Corral, Good-Cents Subs, IHOP, McDonald's, Mesquite Grill, Old Country Buffet, Olive Garden, Panera Bread, Perkins, Pizza Hut, Red Lobster, Ruby Tuesday, Shoney's, Sirloin Stockade, Steak'n Shake, Taco Bell, Timberline Steaks, Wendy's, Winstead's Burgers, **lodging:** Candlewood Suites, Comfort Inn, Country Inn Suites, Courtyard,

KANSAS

Interstate 70

E ↑ W

Day's Inn, Fairfield Inn, Hampton Inn, Motel 6, Holiday Inn Express, Quality Inn, Residence Inn, Sleep Inn, Super 8, **other:** Barnes&Noble, Best Buy, Circuit City, Dillard's, Food4Less/24hr, Home Depot, JC Penney, Kohl's, Lowe's Whse, Office Depot, Sam's Club, Target, Wal-Mart SuperCtr/24hr, mall

355   I-470 E, to VA MED CTR, Topeka, air museum, **1 mi S...**same as 356

353   KS 4, to Eskridge, no facilities

351   frontage rd(from eb), Mission Creek, no facilities

350   Valencia Rd, no facilities

347   West Union Rd, no facilities

346   Carlson Rd, to Rossville, Willard, no facilities

343   frontage rd, no facilities

342   Eskridge Rd, Keene Rd, access to Lake Wabaunsee

341   KS 30, Maple Hill, **S...gas:** Amoco/diesel/café

338   Vera Rd, **S...gas:** Texaco/DQ/Stuckey's

336mm   rest area(exits left from both lanes), full(handicapped)facilities, phone, picnic tables, litter barrels, RV camping/dump, petwalk

335   Snokomo Rd, Skyline Mill Creek Scenic Drive, Paxico, no facilities

333   KS 138, Paxico, no facilities

332   Spring Creek Rd, no facilities

330   KS 185, to McFarland, no facilities

329mm   weigh sta both lanes

328   KS 99, to Alma, **S...**Wabaunsee Co Museum

324   Wabaunsee Rd, no facilities

322   Tallgrass Rd, no facilities

318   frontage rd, no facilities

316   Deep Creek Rd, no facilities

313   KS 177, to Manhattan, **N...gas:** DeDee's/diesel/café, **8 mi N...food:** Applebee's, Chili's, McDonald's, Schlotsky's, Village Inn Rest., **lodging:** Best Western, Comfort Inn, Fairfield Inn, Hampton Inn, Motel 6, Super 8, **other:** Jeep, Nissan, Sears/auto, to KSU

311   Moritz Rd, no facilities

310mm   rest area both lanes, full(handicapped)facilities, phone, picnic tables, litter barrels, petwalk, RV dump

307   McDowell Creek Rd, scenic river rd to Manhattan, no facilities

304   Humboldt Creek Rd, no facilities

303   KS 18 E, to Ogden, Manhattan, **8 mi N...lodging:** Hampton Inn, Super 8, to KSU

301   Marshall Field, to Ft Riley, **N...other:** Cavalry Museum, Custer's House, KS Terr Capitol

300   US 40, KS 57, Council Grove, **N...lodging:** Dreamland Motel, **S...**hist church

299   Flinthills Blvd, to Jct City, Ft Riley, **N...gas:** BP/diesel, **food:** Stacy's Rest., **lodging:** Econolodge, Great Western Inn, Red Carpet Inn, Super 8

298   Chestnut St, to Jct City, Ft Riley, **N...gas:** Shell/Burger King/diesel/24hr, **food:** BBQ, Cracker Barrel, Family Buffet, Taco Bell, **lodging:** Best Western, Holiday Inn Express, Super 8, **other:** $Tree, Wal-Mart SuperCtr/24hr

J c t   C i t y

296   US 40, Washington St, Junction City, **N...gas:** Citgo/diesel, Phillips 66, Shell/diesel/24hr, **food:** Country Kitchen, DQ, Denny's, El Cazador Mexican, KFC, McDonald's, Peking Chinese, Sirloin Stockade, Sonic, Subway, **lodging:** Budget Host/RV Park, Comfort Inn, Day's Inn, Ramada Ltd, **other:** Chevrolet/Pontiac, Food4Less/24hr

295   US 77, KS 18, Marysville, to Milford Lake, **N...gas:** Phillips 66/A&W/diesel/24hr, **lodging:** Motel 6, **other:** HOSPITAL

294mm   rest area both lanes, full(handicapped)facilities, phone, picnic tables, litter barrels, RV dump, petwalk

290   Milford Lake Rd, no facilities

286   KS 206, Chapman, **S...gas:** Citgo, **1 mi S...gas:** Casey's

281   KS 43, to Enterprise, **N...**4 Seasons RV Ctr/Park

277   Jeep Rd, no facilities

275   KS 15, to Clay Ctr, Abilene, **N...food:** DQ, **lodging:** Brookville Motel, Holiday Inn Express, **S...gas:** Amoco/diesel, Phillips 66/Taco Bell, **food:** Burger King, China Taste, Green Acres Rest., McDonald's, Pizza Hut, Sonic, Subway, **lodging:** Best Western, Day's Inn, Super 8, **other:** HOSPITAL, Alco/gas, AutoZone, Chevrolet/Pontiac/Buick, CountryMart Foods, $General, Ford/Lincoln/Mercury, Chrysler, Plymouth/Jeep/Dodge, to Eisenhower Museum

A b i l e n e

272   Fair Rd, to Talmage, **S...**Russell Stover Candy

266   KS 221, Solomon, **S...gas:** Total/diesel/rest./24hr/@

265mm   rest area both lanes, full(handicapped)facilities, phone, picnic tables, litter barrels, vending, petwalk

264mm   Solomon River

260   Niles Rd, New Cambria, no facilities

253mm   Saline River

253   Ohio St, **S...gas:** ♦/Flying J/Conoco/Country Mkt/diesel/LP/24hr/@, **other:** HOSPITAL, Harley-Davidson, Kenworth

252   KS 143, Salina, **N...gas:** Amoco/diesel/rest./24hr/@, Petro/Mobil/Phillips 66/Wendy's/Pizza Hut/diesel/@, **food:** Bayard's Café, DQ, McDonald's, Toucan's Mexican, **lodging:** Best Inn, Day's Inn, Holiday Inn Express, Motel 6, Salina Inn, Super 8, **other:** Blue Beacon, KOA, **S...gas:** Bosselman/Sinclair/Blimpie/diesel/24hr/@, **lodging:** Best Western, Travelodge

S a l i n a

250b a   I-135, US 81, N to Concordia, S to Wichita, no facilities

249   Halstead Rd, to Trenton, no facilities

244   Hedville, **N...**Sundowner West RV Park, **S...gas:** Phillips 66/diesel

238   to Brookville, Glendale, Tescott, no facilities

233   to Beverly, Juniata, no facilities

225   KS 156, to Ellsworth, **S...gas:** Shell/Texaco/diesel, **other:** Ft Harker Museum, Ft Larned HS

224mm   rest area both lanes, full(handicapped)facilities, phone, picnic tables, litter barrels, petwalk, RV dump

221   KS 14 N, to Lincoln, no facilities

219   KS 14 S, to Ellsworth, **S...gas:** Conoco/diesel, **other:** auto/truck repair

216   to Vesper, **S...gas:** Shell/DQ/Stuckey's

209   to Sylvan Grove, no facilities

206   KS 232, Wilson, **N...gas:** Conoco/rest., **other:** Wilson Lake(6mi), winery

Interstate 70

E

↕

W

199 KS 231, Dorrance, **N**...to Wilson Lake, **S...gas:** Agco

193 Bunker Hill Rd, **N...gas:** Total/diesel/Bearhouse Café/ 24hr, to Wilson Lake

189 US 40 bus, Pioneer Rd, Russell, no facilities

187mm **rest area both lanes, full(handicapped)facilities, phone, picnic tables, litter barrels, RV dump, pet-walk**

184 US 281, Russell, **N...gas:** Amoco/diesel/24hr, BP, Phillips 66/Mesquite Grill/diesel, **food:** Meridy's Rest., McDonald's, Pizza Hut, Sonic, Subway, **lodging:** AmericInn, Day's Inn, Russell Inn, Super 8, **other:** HOSPITAL, Dumler RV Park, JJJ RV Park, st patrol

180 Balta Rd, to Russell, no facilities

175 KS 257, Gorham, **1 mi N**...gas, food, phone

172 Walker Ave, no facilities

168 KS 255, to Victoria, **S...gas:** Ampride/diesel, to Cathedral of the Plains

163 Toulon Ave, no facilities

161 Commerce Parkway, no facilities

159 US 183, Hays, **N...gas:** Shamrock/diesel/24hr, **food:** Applebee's, Carlos O'Kelly's, Golden Corral, Quizno's, **lodging:** Comfort Inn, Fairfield Inn, **other:** Ford/ Lincoln/Mercury, Harley-Davidson, Plymouth/Dodge, Radio Shack, Toyota, Wal-Mart SuperCtr/gas/24hr, **S...gas:** BP/24hr, Conoco/Golden OX/diesel/24hr, Love's, Phillips 66/diesel, **food:** A&W, Arby's, Burger King, Country Kitchen, KFC, LJ Silver, McDonald's, MT Mike's Steaks, Pheasant Run Café, Pizza Hut, Pizza Inn, Sonic, Subway, Taco Bell, Vagabond Rest., Village Inn Rest., Wendy's, **lodging:** Best Western, Comfort Inn, Day's Inn, Econolodge, Hampton Inn, Holiday Inn, Motel 6, Super 8, **other:** HOSPITAL, Advance Parts, Chevrolet/Mazda, Chrysler, Firestone/auto, Hastings Books, JC Penney, NAPA, Radio Shack, SunMart Foods, Walgreen, mall, st patrol

157 US 183 S byp, to Hays, **S...lodging:** Gen Hayes Inn, **other:** museum, to Ft Hays St U

153 Yocemento Ave, no facilities

145 KS 247 S, Ellis, **S...gas:** Casey's, Shell, **food:** Alloway's Rest./TasteeFreez, **lodging:** Ellis House Inn, **other:** to Chrysler Museum, Railroad Museum, RV camping

140 Riga Rd, no facilities

135 KS 147, Ogallah, **N...gas:** Shell/Texaco/diesel, Schreiner/diesel/café, **other:** Goodyear, **S**...to Cedar Bluff SP(13mi)

132mm **rest area both lanes, full(handicapped)facilities, picnic tables, litter barrels, petwalk, RV dump**

128 US 283 N, WaKeeney, **N...gas:** Conoco/diesel/24hr, **lodging:** Budget Host, Super 8, **other:** HOSPITAL

127 US 283 S, WaKeeney, **N...gas:** Phillips 66/McDonald's/ diesel/24hr, **food:** DQ, Jade Garden Rest., Nobody's Rest., Pizza Hut, Real Country Cafe, **lodging:** KS Kountry Inn, Sundowner Motel, **S...gas:** BP/ diesel/rest./24hr, Conoco/Subway/diesel, **lodging:** Econolodge, **other:** KOA

120 Voda Rd, no facilities

115 KS 198 N, Banner Rd, Collyer, **N...gas:** Sinclair/diesel

107 KS 212, Castle Rock Rd, Quinter, **N...gas:** Phillips 66/ diesel, **lodging:** Budget Host/rest., **other:** HOSPITAL, Chevrolet, Sunflower RV Park, **S...gas:** Conoco/diesel/ 24hr, **food:** DQ

99 KS 211, Park, **1 mi N**...gas: Sinclair/diesel

97mm **rest area both lanes, full(handicapped)facilities, picnic tables, litter barrels, vending, petwalk, RV dump**

95 KS 23 N, to Hoxie, no facilities

93 KS 23, Grainfield, **N...gas:** Sinclair/diesel

85 KS 216, Grinnell, **S...gas:** Shell/Texaco/DQ/Stuckey's

79 Campus Rd, no facilities

76 US 40, to Oakley, **S...gas:** Shell/Texaco/diesel/café/ repair/24hr/@ , **lodging:** Best Value Inn, 1st Interstate Inn, **other:** HOSPITAL, Blue Beacon

70 US 83, to Oakley, **N...lodging:** Free Breakfast Inn, **S...gas:** Conoco/diesel, Phillips 66/diesel, **food:** Colonial Steaks, **other:** HOSPITAL, Hi-Plains RV Park, Prairie Dog Town, Fick Museum

62 rd 24, Mingo, **S...gas:** Ampride/diesel/24hr, phone

54 Country Club Dr, Colby, **1 mi N...lodging:** Country Club Motel, **other:** HOSPITAL, RV camping

53 KS 25, Colby, **N...gas:** Amoco/diesel, Conoco/DQ/ diesel, Phillips 66/Subway, **food:** Arby's, Burger King, DQ, KFC/Taco Bell, LJ Silver, McDonald's, MT Mike's Steaks, Pizza Hut, Sonic, Taco John's, **lodging:** Day's Inn, Holiday Inn Express, Motel 6, Quality Inn, Super 8, Welk-Um Inn, **other:** HOSPITAL, AutoZone, Dillon Food, $General, Ford/Lincoln/Mercury, Goodyear, Prairie Art Museum, Radio Shack, Wal-Mart, diesel repair, **S...gas:** Phillips 66/diesel, **food:** Quizno's, Starbucks, Village Inn Rest., **lodging:** Best Western, Comfort Inn, **other:** Chevrolet/Cadillac/Buick/Pontiac, outlets

48.5mm **rest area both lanes, full(handicapped)facilities, phone, picnic tables, litter barrels, RV dump, vending, petwalk**

45 US 24 E, Levant, no facilities

36 KS 184, Brewster, **N...gas:** Citgo/diesel

35.5mm Mountain/Central time zone

27 KS 253, Edson, no facilities

19 US 24, Goodland, **N...food:** Pizza Hut, **lodging:** Best Western, **other:** KOA, Plains Museum

17 US 24, KS 27, Goodland, **N...gas:** Conoco, Phillips 66/ diesel, Sinclair/DQ/diesel, **food:** McDonald's, Subway, Taco John's, Wendy's, **lodging:** Best Western/rest., Comfort Inn, Economy 9 Motel, Howard Johnson, Super 8, **other:** HOSPITAL, Pontiac/GMC, Wal-Mart SuperCtr/24hr, **S...gas:** Shamrock/A&W/diesel/24hr, Total/diesel, **other:** Mid-America Camping

Russell Hays Colby Goodland

KANSAS

Interstate 70

E ↕ **W**

12	rd 14, Caruso, no facilities
9	rd 11, Ruleton, no facilities
7.5mm	**Welcome Ctr eb/rest area wb, full(handicapped) facilities, info, phone, picnic tables, litter barrels, petwalk, vending, RV dump**
1	KS 267, Kanorado, no facilities
.5mm	weigh sta eb
0mm	Kansas/Colorado State Line

Interstate 135(Wichita)

N ↕ **S**

S a l i n a

Exit #	Services
95b a	I-70, E to KS City, W to Denver. I-135 begins/ends on I-70, exit 250. US 81 continues nb.
93	KS 140, State St, Salina, no facilities
92	Crawford St, **E...gas:** BP/diesel/@, Citgo, Shell, **food:** Blimpie, Braum's, Real Country Deli, Spangles, Taco Bell, Subway, Western Sizzlin, **lodging:** Best Western, Comfort Inn, Fairfield Inn, Holiday Inn, Super 8, **W...gas:** Phillips 66/diesel/@, **lodging:** Red Coach Inn
90	Magnolia Rd, **E...gas:** Phillips 66/diesel, Shell/24hr, **food:** Burger King, Carlos O'Kelly's, Chili's, China King, Coyote Canyon Café, Golden Corral, Hong Kong Buffet, IHOP, McDonald's, Mesquite Grill, Schlotsky's, Sonic, Subway, **lodging:** 1st Inn, Country Inn, **other:** Advance Parts, Buick/Subaru, Dillon's Foods/gas, $General, JC Penney, Sears/auto, mall, **W...gas:** Conoco
89	Schilling Rd, **E...gas:** Shell/Texaco, **food:** Applebee's, Burger King, Fazoli's, Pizza Hut, Red Lobster, Sonic, Tucson's Steaks, **lodging:** Candlewood Suites, Country Inn Suites, Hampton Inn, **other:** Aldi Foods, Cadillac/Chevrolet, Honda, Lowe's, OfficeMax, Sam's Club, Target, Wal-Mart SuperCtr/24hr, **W...gas:** Casey's, **lodging:** Baymont Inn
88	new exit, no facilities
86	KS 104, Mentor, Smolan, no facilities
82	KS 4, Falun Rd, Assaria, no facilities
78	KS 4 W, Lindsborg, **E...gas:** Shell/DQ/Stuckey's
72	US 81, Lindsborg, **4 mi E...other:** McPhearson St Fishing Lake, Maxwell WR, **W...other:** HOSPITAL, gas, food, lodging, phone, camping, museum
68mm	**rest areas(both lanes exit left), full(handicapped)facilities, phone, picnic tables, litter barrels petwalk, RV dump**

McPherson

65	Pawnee Rd, no facilities
60	US 56, McPherson, Marion, **W...gas:** Conoco/diesel, Phillips 66, **food:** Applebee's, Arby's, Braum's, KFC, McDonald's, Montana Mike's, Perkins, Pizza Hut, Subway, Taco Tico, **lodging:** Days Inn, Best Western, Red Coach Inn, Super 8, **other:** HOSPITAL, Autozone, Wal-Mart SuperCtr/24hr/auto
58	US 81, to Hutchinson, McPherson, no facilities
54	Elyria, no facilities
48	KS 260 E, Moundridge, **2 mi W...gas, food, phone
46	KS 260 W, Moundridge, **2 mi W...gas, food, phone
40	Lincoln Blvd., Hesston, **W...gas:** Sav-a-Trip/diesel/@, **food:** Pizza Hut, Sonic, Subway, **lodging:** Hesston Inn, **E...lodging:** AmericInn
34	N Newton, Avalene, KS 15, **E...other:** RV camping, **W...food:** Subway, **other:** Kaufman Museum

Newton

33	US 50 E, to Peabody, (from NB) no facilities
31	1st St, Broadway Ave, **E...gas:** Ampride/diesel, Conoco/diesel, Shamrock, Shell/diesel/motel, **food:** Applebee's, CJ's Pancake house, KFC, Red Coach Rest., **lodging:** Day's Inn, 1st Inn, Super 8, **other:** Chevrolet/Cadillac, Chrysler/Plymouth/Dodge/Jeep, Ford/Lincoln/Mercury, **W...food:** Braum's, **lodging:** Best Western
30	US 50 W, KS 15(exits left from nb), to Hutchinson, Newton, **W...gas:** Phillips 66, **food:** Sonic, **other:** HOSPITAL, AutoZone, Buick/Pontiac/GMC, Dillon's Foods/24hr, Wal-Mart SuperCtr/24hr
28	SE 36th St, **W...food:** Burger King, Subway, Taco Bell, **other:** Newton Outlets/famous brands
25	KS 196, to Whitewater, El Dorado, no facilities
23mm	**rest areas both lanes, full(handicapped)facilities, phone, picnic tables, litter barrels, vending, petwalk, RV dump**
22	125th St, no facilities
19	101st St, **W...other:** RV camping
17	85th St, **E...**Valley Ctr, KS Coliseum
16	77th St, **E...other:** Wichita Greyhound Park
14	61st St, **E...gas:** QT/Blimpie, Total, **food:** Applebee's, Cracker Barrel, Sonic, Spangles Rest., Taco Bell, Wendy's, **lodging:** Comfort Inn, **other:** Chevrolet, **W...gas:** Coastal/diesel/@, **food:** KFC, McDonald's, Wally's Cafe, **lodging:** Super 8, **other:** Goodyear/auto
13	53rd St, **W...gas:** Phillips 66, **food:** Country Kitchen, Red Coach Rest., **lodging:** Best Western, Day's Inn
11b	I-235 W, KS 96, to Hutchinson, no facilities
11a	KS 254, to El Dorado, no facilities
10b	29th St, Hydraulic Ave, no facilities
10a	KS 96 E, no facilities
9	21st St, **E...gas:** Amoco, **food:** Burger King, Wichita St U, **other:** Market Foods
8	13th St, no facilities
7b	8th St, 9th St, Central Ave., **E...**School of Medicine
6b	1st St, 2nd St, **E...**AutoZone, **W...**Chevrolet, Chrysler/Jeep
5b	US 54, US 400, Kellogg Ave, **1 mi E...gas:** Amoco, Total, **food:** McDonald's, Spangles Rest., Wendy's
5a	Lincoln St, **W...gas:** QT
4	Harry St, **1 mi E...gas:** QT, **food:** Church's Chicken, Denny's, Dunkin Donuts, McDonald's, Spangles Rest., Wendy's, **W...gas:** Amoco
3	Pawnee Ave, **E...gas:** QT, **W...food:** Burger King, Church's, Papa John's, Pizza Hut, Spangles, **lodging:** Pawnee Inn, **other:** Autozone, Dollar General
2	Hydraulic Ave, **E...gas:** QT, **W...food:** McDonald's, Subway
2mm	Arkansas River
1c	I-235 N, **2 mi W...**Hilton
1b a	US 81 S, 47th St, **E...gas:** Coastal, Conoco, **food:** Potbelly's Rest., **lodging:** Comfort Inn, Day's Inn, Holiday Inn Express, **W...gas:** Phillips 66, **food:** Applebee's, Braum's, Burger King, DQ/Super Wok, Godfather's, KFC, LJ Silver, McDonald's, Papa John's, Pizza Hut, Quizno's, Spaghetti Jack's, Spangles Rest., Subway, Taco Bell, Taco Tico, **lodging:** Best Western, Red Carpet Inn, **other:** Checker's Foods, Dillon's Foods/gas/diesel, K-Mart, O'Reilly's Parts, Radio Shack
0mm	I-135 begins/ends on I-35, exit 42.

Wichita

Interstate 24

Exit #	**Services**
93.5mm	Kentucky/Tennessee state line
93mm	**Welcome Ctr wb, full(handicapped)facilities, phones, picnic tables, litter barrels, vending, petwalk**
91.5mm	Big West Fork Red River
89	KY 115, to Oak Grove, **N...to Jeff Davis Mon St HS, S...gas:** Citgo/diesel, Pilot/Speedway/McDonald's/diesel/24hr/@
86	US 41A, to Ft Campbell, Pennyrile Pkwy, Hopkinsville, **N...gas:** Chevron/Taco Tico/diesel/24hr/@, **S...gas:** BP/Burger King/diesel/24hr, ⚡/Flying J/Conoco/Country Mkt/diesel/LP/24hr/@, Pilot/Subway/Wendy's/diesel/24hr/@, **food:** McDonald's, Waffle House, **lodging:** Baymont Inn, Best Western(8mi), Comfort Inn, Day's Inn, Econolodge, Fairfield Inn(8mi), Holiday Inn Express(9mi), Rodeway Inn(9mi)
79mm	Little River
73	KY 117, to Gracey, Newstead, no facilities
65	US 68, KY 80, to Cadiz, **S...gas:** Amoco, BP/diesel, Phillips 66/diesel/24hr, Shell/diesel/24hr, **food:** Bailey's Steaks/Seafood, Cracker Barrel, KFC, McDonald's, Wendy's, **lodging:** Holiday Inn Express, Knight's Inn, 7 Inn, Super 8, **other:** HOSPITAL, Chevrolet, antiques, golf, to NRA's
56	KY 139, to Cadiz, Princeton, **S...gas:** Chevron/diesel, **other:** Nat Rec Areas
47mm	Lake Barkley
45	KY 293, to Princeton, Saratoga, **S...gas:** Chevron/pizza/diesel, **lodging:** Regency Inn, **other:** RV Camping, to KY St Penitentiary
42	to W KY Pkwy eb, no facilities

Paducah

40	US 62, US 641, Kuttawa, Eddyville, **N...lodging:** Country Inn, Regency Inn, Relax Inn, **other:** camping, **S...gas:** BP/Wendy's/diesel/24hr, Huck's/diesel/24hr/@, Shell, **food:** Huddle House, Southwest grill, **lodging:** Day's Inn, Hampton Inn, **other:** W KY Factory Outlet, to Lake Barkley, KY Lake Rec Areas, camping
36mm	weigh sta both lanes, phones
34mm	Cumberland River
31	KY 453, to Grand Rivers, Smithland, **N...gas:** Amoco/diesel, **lodging:** Microtel, **S...gas:** BP/24hr, **food:** Miss Scarlett's, **lodging:** Best Western, Grand Rivers Resort(3mi), **other:** NRA's, camping
29mm	Tennessee River
27	US 62, to KY Dam, Calvert City, **N...gas:** BP, Chevron, Shell, **food:** Cracker Barrel, DQ, KFC, McDonald's, Waffle House, Willow Pond Rest., **lodging:** Cloverleaf Motel, Foxfire Motel, Super 8, **other:** KOA, **S...gas:** Coastal/diesel/rest./24hr, **lodging:** KY Dam Motel, **other:** Cypress Lakes Camp
25b a	to Calvert City, Carroll/Purchase Pkwy, services 1 mi N
16	US 68, to Paducah, **S...gas:** BP/diesel, Roadside, Southern Pride/diesel/24hr/@, **food:** Subway
11	rd 1954, Husband Rd, to Paducah, **N...gas:** Exxon/diesel, **lodging:** Best Western, **other:** Duck Creek RV Park
7	US 45, US 62, to Paducah, **N...gas:** Ashland/Subway/diesel, BP/diesel, Citgo, Pet-tro, Shell/diesel/24hr, **food:** A&W, Burger King, LJ Silver, Taco Bell, **lodging:** Quality Inn, **other:** HOSPITAL, **S... Welcome Ctr both lanes, full(handicapped)facilities, phones, vending, picnic tables, litter barrels, petwalk, gas:** BP/diesel, Shell, Scot Gas, **food:** Arby's, Golden Corral, Hardee's, KFC, Little Caesar's, Mardi Gras Café, McDonald's, Sonic, Taco John's, Waffle House, **lodging:** Denton Motel, Sunset Inn, **other:** FoodTown, K-Mart, Rite Aid, SuperValue Food/24hr

Interstate 24

E
W
Paducah

4 US 60, to Paducah, **N...gas:** Shell/diesel/24hr, **food:** Applebee's, Bob Evans, Burger King, Denny's, McDonald's, O'Charley's, Outback Steaks, Rafferty's, **lodging:** Courtyard, Day's Inn/rest., Drury Inn, Holiday Inn Express, Motel 6, Ramada Inn, Red Carpet Inn(1mi), **other:** Hancock Fabrics, KY Tobacco Outlet, **S...gas:** BP, Chevron/Domino's, Shell, **food:** Atlanta Bread Co, Capt D's, Chong's Chinese, ChuckeCheese, Cracker Barrel, Damon's, Denny's, El Chico's, Fazoli's, Godfather's, Hardee's/24hr, Logan's Roadhouse, Los Amigos, Olive Garden, Pasta House, Ponderosa, Pizza Hut, Red Lobster, Ruby Tuesday, Ryan's, Steak'n Shake, Subway, Taco Bell, Texas Roadhouse, TGIFriday, Wendy's, **lodging:** Best Inn, Comfort Suites, Drury Suites, Hampton Inn, Motel 6, PearTree Inn, Thrifty Inn, **other:** Advance Parts, Aldi Foods, BooksAMillion, Circuit City, Dillard's, Goody's, Goodyear, JC Penney, Lowe's Whse, Office Depot, OfficeMax, Sam's Club, Sears/auto, Wal-Mart SuperCtr/gas/24hr, Millsprings Funpark, mall

3 KY 305, to Paducah, **N...gas:** Citgo/diesel/24hr, **food:** Casa Mexicana, Huddle House/24hr, **lodging:** Comfort Inn/rest., Ramada Ltd, Super 8, **S...gas:** BP/diesel/24hr, Pilot/Subway/diesel/24hr/2, **food:** Waffle Hut, **lodging:** Baymont Inn, **other:** Fern Lake Camping, antiques

0mm Kentucky/Illinois state line, Ohio River

Interstate 64

E
W

Exit # Services
192mm Kentucky/West Virginia state line, Big Sandy River
191 US 23, to Ashland, **1-2 mi N...gas:** Exxon, GoMart, Marathon/diesel, **food:** Burger King, Hardee's, McDonald's, Pizza Inn, Subway, **lodging:** Holiday Inn Express(5mi), Ramada Ltd, **other:** HOSPITAL, Rite Aid
185 KY 180, Cannonsburg, **1-3 mi N...gas:** BP/diesel, Chevron, **food:** Arby's, Burger King, Hardee's, Subway, Taco Bell, Wendy's, **lodging:** Ashland Plaza, Budget Inn, Day's Inn, Fairfield Inn, Hampton Inn, Knight's Inn, **other:** st police, **S...**/Flying J/CountryMkt/diesel/24hr/@, Hidden Valley Camping
181 181 US 60, to Princess, **N...gas:** Citgo/diesel, **S...gas:** Marathon
179 rd 67, Industrial Parkway, no facilities
174mm **rest areas wb, full(handicapped)facilities, phone, vending, picnic tables, litter barrels, petwalk**
173mm **rest areas wb, full(handicapped)facilities, phone, vending, picnic tables, litter barrels, petwalk**

Grayson

172 rd 1, rd 7, Grayson, **N...gas:** Citgo/diesel, SuperQuik/diesel/24hr, **food:** A&W/LJ Silver, KFC, LJ Silver, Shoney's, Western Steer, **lodging:** American Inn, Day's Inn, Executive Inn, Holiday Inn Express, Knight's Inn, Travelodge, **other:** Chrysler/Plymouth/Jeep, Ford, K-Mart, SaveALot Foods, **S...gas:** BP, Chevron, Exxon, Marathon, Pilot/Wendy's/diesel/24hr/@, Speedway, **food:** Arby's, Burger King, China House, DQ, Hardee's, Little Caesar's, McDonald's, Pizza Hut, Subway, Taco Bell, **lodging:** Super 8, **other:** Advance Parts, AutoZone, CarQuest, $General, $Tree, Family$, Food Fair, Parts+, Rite Aid
161 US 60, to Olive Hill, **N...gas:** Citgo, **other:** to Carter Caves SP, camping, **S...gas:** Marathon/diesel/24hr, **lodging:** Spanish Manor Motel
156 rd 2, to KY 59, to Olive Hill, **S...gas:** BP(3mi), Citgo, Sunoco/diesel, DQ
148mm weigh sta both lanes
141mm **rest areas both lanes, full(handicapped)facilities, phone, vending, picnic tables, litter barrels, petwalk**
137 KY 32, to Morehead, **N...gas:** BP, **food:** DQ, **other:** Kroger, **S...gas:** BP, Chevron/Burger King/diesel/24hr, Exxon/diesel, **food:** Domino's, Hardee's, KFC, Lee's Chicken, McDonald's, Papa John's, Ponderosa, Shoney's, Subway, **lodging:** Best Western, Day's Inn, Holiday Inn Express, Mtn Lodge Motel, Ramada Ltd, Super 8, **other:** HOSPITAL, Buick/Pontiac, Food Lion, Goodyear, Radio Shack, Wal-Mart, st police
133 rd 801, to Sharkey, Farmers, **N...**Eagle Trace Golf/rest.(4mi), **S...gas:** BP/diesel, **lodging:** Comfort Inn
123 US 60, to Salt Lick, Owingsville, **N...gas:** Chevron/diesel
121 KY 36, to Owingsville, **N...gas:** BP/diesel, Citgo/diesel, Sunoco/diesel, **food:** DQ, McDonald's, Subway, **lodging:** Best Western, **other:** $General
113 US 60, to Mt Sterling, **N...gas:** Chevron/diesel/@
110 US 460, KY 11, Mt Sterling, **N...gas:** Chevron/repair/24hr, Shell/Krystal/diesel, **food:** Cracker Barrel, Fairfield Inn, Ramada Ltd, **other:** golf, **S...gas:** BP/diesel, Exxon/Subway, Marathon, Speedway/diesel, **food:** Applebee's, Arby's, Burger King, Golden Corral, Jerry's Rest., KFC, Lee's Chicken, LJ Silver, McDonald's, Rio Grande Mexican, Wendy's, **lodging:** Budget Inn, Day's Inn/rest., **other:** HOSPITAL, Family$, Ford/Mercury, **S on KY 686...gas:** Ashland, **food:** Hardee's, Little Caesar's, Pizza Hut, Taco Bell, Taco Tico, **other:** Advance Parts, Chevrolet, Chrysler/Plymouth/Dodge/Jeep, Ford, Wal-Mart SuperCtr/24hr
108mm **rest area wb, full(handicapped)facilities, phone, vending, picnic tables, litter barrels, petwalk**
101 US 60, no facilities
98.5mm **rest area eb, full(handicapped)facilities, phone, vending, picnic tables, litter barrels, petwalk**
98 KY 402(from eb), no facilities

Interstate 64

E ↕ **W**

Lexington

96b a KY 627, to Winchester, Paris, **N...gas:** BP/diesel, Citgo/diesel/rest., **S...gas:** Marathon/diesel, Speedway, **lodging:** Comfort Suites, Day's Inn, Hampton Inn, **other:** Chevrolet

94 KY 1958, Van Meter Rd, Winchester, **N...gas:** Chevron/24hr, Shell/diesel, **lodging:** Best Value Inn, Holiday Inn Express, **other:** flea mkt, **S...gas:** BP/diesel, Citgo, Marathon, Speedway/diesel, **food:** Applebee's, Arby's, Burger King, Cantuckee Diner, Capt D's, Domino's, Fazoli's, Golden Corral, Great Wall Chinese, JB Asian Grill, KFC, Little Caesar's, LJ Silver, McDonald's, Papa John's, Pizza Hut, Popeye's, Rally's, Sonic, Subway, Tacos Too, Waffle House, Wendy's, **lodging:** Best Western, Travelodge, **other:** HOSPITAL, Advance Parts, AutoZone, Chrysler/Plymouth/Dodge/Jeep, Family$, Ford/Mercury, K-Mart, Kroger, Lowe's Whse, Radio Shack, Wal-Mart SuperCtr/24hr, to Ft Boonesborough Camping

87 KY 859, Blue Grass Sta, no facilities

81 I-75 S, to Knoxville, no facilities

I-64 and I-75 run together 7 mi. See Kentucky Interstate 75, exits 113-115.

75 I-75 N, to Cincinnati, access to KY Horse Park

69 US 62 E, to Georgetown, **N...**antiques(mi), **S...**Equus Run Vineyards(2mi)

65 US 421, Midway, **S...gas:** Citgo/diesel, antiques

60mm **rest area both lanes, full(handicapped)facilities, phone, picnic tables, litter barrels, vending, petwalk**

55mm Kentucky River

53b a US 127, Frankfort, **N...gas:** Chevron/24hr, Shell/24hr, Speedway, **food:** A&W/LJ Silver, Applebee's, Big Boy, Burger King, Chili's, ChuckeCheese, Columbia Steaks, DQ, Fazoli's, Hardee's, KFC, McDonald's, O'Charley's, Pizza Hut, Shoney's, Steak'n Shake, Taco Bell, Wendy's, **lodging:** Day's Inn, Hampton Inn, Holiday Inn(4mi), Super 8(1mi), **other:** HOSPITAL, Advance Parts, Goodyear, Goody's, JC Penney, K-Mart, Kroger/24hr, Lowe's Whse, Office Depot, Radio Shack, Rite Aid, Wal-Mart SuperCtr/24hr, Ancient Age Tour, to KY St Capitol, st police, **S...gas:** BP, Marathon/diesel

Frankfort

48 KY 151, to US 127 S, **S...gas:** Chevron/24hr, Shell/Subway/diesel

58 US 60, to Frankfort, **N...gas:** BP/diesel, Chevron/diesel, Citgo/diesel, Shell, **food:** Arby's, KFC, Mkt Café, McDonald's, Sandy's Steaks, Tumbleweed's, White Castle, **lodging:** Best Western/rest., Blue Grass Inn, Fairfield Inn, University Lodge, **other:** Elkhorn Camping(5mi), Cadillac/Pontiac, Chevrolet/Nissan, Chrysler/Plymouth/Jeep, Ford/Lincoln/Mercury, Toyota, to KY St Capitol, KYSU, to Viet Vets Mem, transmissions

43 KY 395, Waddy, **N...gas:** ⛽/Flying J/Conoco/Country Mkt/diesel/LP/24hr/@, **S...gas:** Citgo/Stuckey's/diesel/rest./24hr

38.5mm weigh sta both lanes

35 KY 53, Shelbyville, **N...gas:** BP/diesel, Chevron/diesel, **food:** Cracker Barrel, KFC, McDonald's(1mi), Subway, **other:** Chevrolet, Ford/Mercury, Kroger/gas/deli, antiques, **S...gas:** Shell/Noble Roman's/diesel, **lodging:** Holiday Inn Express, **other:** golf

32b a KY 55, Shelbyville, **1-3 mi N...gas:** Shell, **food:** Arby's, Burger King, DQ, McDonald's, Pizza Hut, Wendy's, **lodging:** Best Western, Country Hearth Inn, Day's Inn, Shelby Motel, Probus Log Cabin, **other:** HOSPITAL, AutoZone, Buick/Pontiac/GMC, Wal-Mart SuperCtr/gas/24hr, **S...**Taylorsville Lake SP

29mm **rest area both lanes, full(handicapped)facilities, info, phone, picnic tables, litter barrels, vending, petwalk**

28 KY 1848, Veechdale Rd, Simpsonville, **N...gas:** Citgo, Pilot/Subway/diesel/24hr/@, **food:** Oasis Mkt/diner, **lodging:** Old Stone Inn, **other:** golf, **S...gas:** BP/diesel

19b a I-265, Gene Snyder Fwy, **N...**to Tom Sawyer SP

17 S Blankenbaker, **N...gas:** DM/diesel, **lodging:** Staybridge Suites, **S...gas:** BP, Chevron, Shell, Thornton's/Subway/diesel, **food:** Arby's, Big Boy, Back Yard Burger, Burger King, Cracker Barrel, HomeTown Buffet, KFC/A&W, King Buffet, Kingfish Rest., McDonald's, Ruby Tuesday, Subway, Taco Bell, Waffle House, Wendy's, **lodging:** Best Western Signature, Candlewood Suites, Comfort Suites, Country Inn Suites, Hilton Garden, Holiday Inn Express, MainStay Suites, Microtel, Sleep Inn, Super 8, **other:** Sam's Club/gas, Outlets Ltd

Louisville

15 Hurstbourne Lane, Louisville, **N...gas:** Amoco, BP/diesel, Chevron/diesel, Shell/diesel, **food:** Arby's, Bob Evans, Burger King, Carrabba's, Chili's, Don Pablo, Harper's Rest., LoneStar Steaks, Macaroni Grill, McDonald's, Olive Garden, Papa John's, Perkins, Sichuan Garden Chinese, Steakout, Subway, TGIFriday, Tumbleweed Mexican, Waffle House, **lodging:** AmeriSuites, Courtyard, Fairfield Inn, Holiday Inn, Red Roof Inn, **other:** Barnes&Noble, CompUSA, Kroger, Lowe's Whse, **S...gas:** BP/diesel, Shell, Meijer/diesel/24hr, Thornton's, **food:** Applebee's, Blimpie, Buc's Rest., China Star, ChuckeCheese, DQ, Damon's, Dillon's Rest., Macaroni Grill, O'Charley's, Piccadilly's, Shoney's, Shogun Japanese, Starbucks, Steak'n Shake, Wendy's, **lodging:** Day's Inn, Hampton Inn, Hurstbourne Hotel, Marriott, Radisson, Red Carpet Inn, **other:** Cadillac, Chevrolet/Subaru, Home Depot, Honda, Infiniti, Michael's, Mitsubishi, Pontiac/GMC, Radio Shack, Staples, Target, Town Fair Foods, Wal-Mart/drugs

KENTUCKY

Interstate 64

E ↕ W
Louisville

12b	I-264 E, Watterson Expswy, **1 exit N on US 60...gas:** Chevron, **food:** Alexander's Rest., CA Pizza, Denny's, Hop's Grill, Logan's Roadhouse, McDonald's, Outback Steaks, Rollo Pollo, Ruby Tuesday, Taco Bell, Wendy's, **other:** Acura, Best Buy, Dillard's, Ford, Galyan's, Goodyear/auto, JC Penney, Kohl's, Sears/auto, SteinMart, Suzuki, Towery's AutoCare, mall
12a	I-264 W, access to HOSPITAL
10	Cannons Lane, no facilities
8	8 Grinstead Dr, Louisville, **S...gas:** BP, Chevron, **other:** Southern Baptist Seminary, Presbyterian Seminary, Jim Porter's Rest.
7	US 42, US 62, Mellwood Ave, Story Ave, **N...gas:** Petroz
6	I-71 N(from eb), to Cincinnati, no facilities
5a	I-65, S to Nashville, N to Indianapolis, no facilities
5b	3rd St, Louisville, **N...food:** Hardee's, **food:** Joe's CrabShack, McDonald's, **lodging:** Ramada Inn, **S...lodging:** Galt House Hotel, **food:** Kingfish Rest., **other:** HOSPITAL
4	9th St, Roy Wilkins Ave, **S...**KY Art Ctr, science museum, downtown
3	US 150 E, to 22nd St, **S...gas:** Chevron, DairyMart, Shell, **food:** DQ, McDonald's, Subway, **other:** MEDICAL CARE
1	I-264 E, to Shively, **S...**airport, zoo
0mm	Kentucky/Indiana state line, Ohio River

Interstate 65

N ↕ S
Louisville

Exit #	Services
138mm	Kentucky/Indiana state line, Ohio River
137	I-64 W, I-71 N, I-64 E, **W...**to Galt House, downtown
136c	Jefferson St, Louisville, **E...**HOSPITAL, **W...gas:** Chevron, **food:** McDonald's, Papa John's, **lodging:** Clarion Inn, Doubletree Hotel, Hyatt, Quality Hotel, **other:** Tires+
136b a	Broadway St, Chestnut St, **E...other:** Ford/Lincoln/ Mercury, Tires+, HOSPITAL, **W...gas:** Speedway, Thornton, **food:** Taco Bell, **lodging:** Cumberland Motel, Day's Inn, Holiday Inn, Hyatt Hotel
135	W St Catherine, **E...gas:** BP/Amoco, Shell, **lodging:** Day's Inn
134b a	KY 61, Jackson St, Woodbine St, **W...gas:** BP/ Amoco, **lodging:** Day's Inn, Quality Inn, **other:** Harley-Davidson
133b a	US 60A, Eastern Pkwy, Taylor Blvd, **E...food:** Denny's, Papa John's, Pizza Mia, Subway, **W...gas:** BP/diesel, Shell, **food:** Cracker Barrel, McDonald's, **lodging:** Country Hearth Inn, **other:** U of Louisville, Churchill Downs, museum
132	Crittenden Dr(from sb), **E...food:** Denny's, same as 133

131b a	I-264, Watterson Expswy, **W...**Cardinal Stadium, Expo Center, airport
130	KY 61, Preston Hwy, **E on Ky 61...gas:** BP, DM, Speedway, Thornton, **food:** Blimpie, Bob Evans, Burger King, ChuckeCheese, Fazoli's, KFC, Lindy's Rest., McDonald's, Papa John's, Ponderosa, Rally's, Royal Garden Buffet, Subway, Taco Bell, Waffle House, Wendy's, **lodging:** Econolodge, Red Roof Inn, Super 8, **other:** Big O Tire, Chevrolet/Nissan, Chrysler/Plymouth, $General, Ford, PepBoys, Radio Shack, SavALot Foods, Staples, Tires+, U-Haul, Winn-Dixie
128	KY 1631, Fern Valley Rd, **E...gas:** BP/diesel, Bigfoot/ gas, Chevron, Thornton/Subway/diesel, **food:** Arby's, Big Boy, Golden Wall Chinese, Hardee's, McDonald's, Outback Steaks, Shoney's, Waffle House, White Castle, **lodging:** Holiday Inn, InTown Suites, Signature Inn, Thrifty Dutchman, **other:** Cottman Transmissions, Sam's Club, Walgreen, **W...**UPS Depot
127	KY 1065, outer loop, **E...**Texas Roadhouse, **W...food:** McDonald's, to Motor Speedway
125b a	I-265 E, KY 841, Gene Snyder Fwy
121	KY 1526, Brooks Rd, **E...gas:** BP/Amoco, Chevron, **food:** Arby's, Burger King, Cracker Barrel, **lodging:** Baymont Inn, Fairfield Inn, **W...gas:** BP/Blimpie/diesel, Pilot/Subway/Taco Bell/diesel/24hr/@, Shell/diesel, **food:** Waffle House, **lodging:** Comfort Inn, Hampton Inn, Holiday Inn Express, Quality Inn
117	KY 44, Shepherdsville, **E...gas:** BP, Shell/diesel, **food:** Denny's, Kitchen Rest., **lodging:** Best Western/rest., Day's Inn, **other:** KOA(2mi), **W...gas:** Amoco/diesel, Chevron/diesel/24hr, Speedway/diesel, **food:** Arby's, Backyard Burger, Burger King, DQ, El Tarasco Mexican, Fazoli's, LJ Silver, KFC, McDonald's, Mr Gatti's, Papa John's, Rio's Steaks, Sonic, Subway, Taco Bell, Waffle House, Wendy's, White Castle, **lodging:** Country Inn Suites, Hampton Inn, Motel 6, Super 8, **other:** $General, Family$, Kroger, NAPA, Rite Aid, Winn-Dixie
116.5mm	Salt River
116	KY 480, KY 61, **E...gas:** Love's/Subway/diesel/24hr/ @, Shell/diesel, **W...gas:** Marathon/diesel, **other:** Grandma's RV Park, Leisure Life RV Ctr
114mm	**rest area sb, full(handicapped)facilities, phone, vending, picnic tables, litter barrels, petwalk**
112	KY 245, Clermont, **E...gas:** Shell/diesel, **other:** Jim Beam Outpost, Bernheim Forest, to My Old Kentucky Home SP
105	KY 61, Lebanon Jct, **W...gas:** Shell/Subway/Noble Roman/diesel/24hr/@, 105 QuickStop/diesel
102	KY 313, to KY 434, to Radcliff, **E...**to Patton Museum

Interstate 65

94 US 62, Elizabethtown, **E...gas:** Exxon/diesel, Marathon, Shell, **food:** Denny's, Golden Corral, KFC/Taco Bell, Waffle House, White Castle, **lodging:** Day's Inn, Quality Inn, Super 8, **other:** KOA(1mi), **W...gas:** BP, Chevron/diesel/24hr, Speedway/diesel, Swifty, **food:** Blimpie, Burger King, BunBakers, Cracker Barrel, McDonald's, Mr Gatti's, Papa John's, Pizza Hut, Ryan's, Shoney's, Stone Hearth, Subway, TX Outlaw Steaks, Texas Roadhouse, Wendy's, **lodging:** Comfort Inn, Hampton Inn, Holiday Inn, Howard Johnson, Motel 6, Ramada Inn, **other:** HOSPITAL, Advance Parts, CVS Drug, $General, $Tree, Kroger/gas, Skagg's RV Ctr, st police

93 to Bardstown, to BG Pky, **E...**to My Old KY Home SP, Maker's Mark Distillery

91 US 31 W, KY 61, Elizabethtown, WK Pkwy, **E...gas:** Big T/Chevron/24hr, Citgo/diesel, Shell, **food:** LJ Silver, Omelet House, **lodging:** Budget Motel, Commonwealth Lodge, Howard Johnson, **other:** Ryder Trucks, to Lincoln B'Place, **W...gas:** Citgo, **food:** Denny's, Jerry's Rest./24hr, Lee's Chicken, **lodging:** Best Western, Rodeside Inn, **other:** HOSPITAL

90mm weigh sta both lanes

86 KY 222, Glendale, **E...gas:** Pilot/McDiner/diesel/24hr@, **other:** Glendale Camping, **W...gas:** Citgo/diesel/rest./24hr, Petro/diesel/rest./24hr/@, **lodging:** Economy Inn, **other:** Blue Beacon

83mm Nolin River

82mm **rest area sb, full(handicapped)facilities, phone, vending, picnic tables, litter barrels, petwalk**

81.5mm **rest area nb, full(handicapped)facilities, phone, vending, picnic tables, litter barrels, petwalk**

81 KY 84, Sonora, **E...gas:** BP, Davis Bros/diesel/rest./24hr/@, Citgo/diesel/rest., **other:** Blue Beacon, to Lincoln B'Place, **W...gas:** Shell

76 KY 224, Upton, **E...gas:** Chevron/diesel, **W...**to Nolin Lake

75mm eastern/central time zone

71 KY 728, Bonnieville, no facilities

65 US 31 W, Munfordville, **E...gas:** BP/Subway/diesel, Citgo/diesel, Marathon, **food:** County Fixen's Rest., DQ, Pizza Hut, McDonald's, Sonic, **lodging:** Super 8, **other:** $General, Family$, **W...gas:** Chevron/diesel/24hr, Shell, **food:** Cave Country Rest., to Nolin Lake

61mm Green River

58 KY 218, Horse Cave, **E...lodging:** Horse Cave Motel, **other:** HOSPITAL, **W...gas:** BP, Chevron/Pizza Hut/diesel/24hr, Marathon/repair, **food:** Bee's Rest./24hr, Subway, **lodging:** Budget Host/rest., Hampton Inn, **other:** Jent Factory Outlet, KOA, to Mammoth Cave NP

55mm **rest area sb, full(handicapped)facilities, phone, vending, picnic tables, litter barrels, petwalk**

53 KY 70, KY 90, Cave City, **E...gas:** Amoco/diesel, BP/Burger King, Chevron/diesel/24hr, JR/Subway, Shell, **food:** Country Kitchen, Cracker Barrel, DQ, Jerry's Rest., KFC, LJ Silver/A&W, McDonald's, Pizza Hut, Sahara BBQ/steaks, Taco Bell, Wendy's, **lodging:** Best Western, Comfort Inn, Day's Inn/rest., Howard Johnson, Quality Inn, Ramada Ltd, Super 8, **other:** HOSPITAL, Barren River Lake SP(24mi), **W...gas:** Shell, **other:** Onyx Cave, Mammoth Cave NP, Jellystone Camping

48 KY 255, Park City, **E...gas:** Shell/diesel/24hr, **lodging:** Parkland Motel, **other:** tire repair, **W...**to Mammoth Cave NP, Cedar Hill RV Park

43 Cumberland Pky(toll), to Barren River Lake SP

39.5mm **rest area nb, full(handicapped)facilities, phone, vending, picnic tables, litter barrels, petwalk**

38 KY 101, Smiths Grove, **W...gas:** BP/diesel, Chevron/diesel, Keystop, Shell, **food:** McDonald's, Bryce Motel, Victorian House B&B, **other:** $General, 7 Springs Park, RV camping

36 US 68, KY 80, Oakland, no facilities

30mm **rest area sb, full(handicapped)facilities, phone, vending, picnic tables, litter barrels, petwalk**

28 rd 446, to US 31 W, Bowling Green, **W...gas:** BP, Keystop/gas, Shell/Blimpie/24hr, **food:** Hardee's, Jerry's Rest., Wendy's, **lodging:** Best Western, Country Hearth Inn, Value Lodge, **other:** HOSPITAL, Corvette Museum, **3 mi W...**Camping World RV Supply, to WKYU

22 US 231, Bowling Green, **E...gas:** Citgo/diesel, MinitMart/gas, Shell, **food:** Cracker Barrel, Denny's, Domino's, Hardee's, Ryan's, Sonic, Waffle House, **lodging:** Best Western, Comfort Inn, Day's Inn, Econolodge, Fairfield Inn, Microtel, Ramada/rest., Super 8, **other:** USPO, **W...gas:** BP, Chevron/diesel, Exxon/TCBY, RaceWay, Shell/Blimpie/diesel, Speedway, **food:** Applebee's, Arby's, Beijing Chinese, Bob Evans, Buffalo Wings, Burger King, ChiChi's, CiCi's, Fazoli's, HomeTown Buffet, Hop's Grill, KFC, Krystal, Little Caesar's, LoneStar Steaks, Longhorn Steaks, McDonald's, MT Grille, C'Charley's, Olive Garden, Outback Steaks, Pizza Hut, Ponderosa, Quizno's, Rafferty's, Red Lobster, Santa Fe Steaks, Shoney's, Smokey Bones BBQ, Sonic, Steak'n Shake, Subway, Taco Bell, TGIFriday, Tumbleweed Grill, Waffle House, Wendy's, White Castle, **lodging:** Baymont Inn, Courtyard, Drury Inn, Hampton Inn, Motel 6,

Interstate 65

N ↑ S

Franklin

	Payless Inn, Scottish Inn, Travelodge, **other:** HOSPITAL, Advance Parts, Best Buy, BMW/Mercedes, Buick/GMC, Cadillac, Chevrolet, Chrysler/Jeep, CVS Drug, Daewoo, Dillard's, $General, Ford/Lincoln/Mercury, Goodyear, Home Depot, Honda, Hyundai/Isuzu/Subaru, JC Penney, K-Mart, KOA, Kroger/gas/24hr, Mazda, Nissan, Office Depot, Pontiac, Sears, Toyota, U-Haul, Winn-Dixie, mall
20	WH Natcher Toll Rd, to Bowling Green, access to W KY U, KY st police
6	KY 100, Franklin, **E...gas:** BP/diesel/24hr, Citgo/Blimpie/diesel/24hr/@, **W...gas:** Pilot/Subway/diesel/24hr/@, Pilot/diesel/24hr/@, **lodging:** Day's Inn, Super 8, **other:** HOSPITAL, KOA, PetroLube/tires/repair
4mm	weigh sta nb
2	US 31 W, to Franklin, **E...gas:** ♨/Flying J/Conoco/diesel/LP/rest./24hr/@, Keystop/Marathon/Burger King/diesel/24hr/@, **W...gas:** BP/Subway/diesel, **food:** Cracker Barrel, McDonald's, Richie's Steaks, Shoney's, Waffle House, **lodging:** Best Western, Comfort Inn, Franklin Inn, Hampton Inn, Holiday Inn Express, Kentucky Motel, **other:** HOSPITAL
1mm	**Welcome Ctr nb, full(handicapped)facilities, phone, vending, picnic tables, litter barrels, petwalk**
0mm	Kentucky/Tennessee state line

Interstate 71

N ↑ S

Exit #	Services
	Kentucky/Ohio state line, Ohio River
	I-71 and I-75 run together 19 miles. **See Kentucky Interstate 75, exits 175-192.**
77[173]	I-75 S, to Lexington, no facilities
75mm	weigh sta sb
72	KY 14, to Verona, **E...gas:** BP/diesel, Chevron/diesel, **other:** Oak Creek Camping(5mi)
62	US 127, to Glencoe, **E...gas:** 62 TrkPlaza/diesel/rest./@, **W...gas:** Marathon/diesel/rest., **lodging:** 127 Motel
57	KY 35, to Sparta, **E...gas:** Marathon/diese, **other:** Sparta RV Park(3mi), **W...gas:** BP/diesel, **lodging:** Ramada Inn, **other:** KY Speedway
55	KY 1039, **W...**KY Speedway
44	KY 227, to Indian Hills, **E...gas:** BP/LP, **W...gas:** Chevron/diesel/24hr, Citgo/diesel, Marathon/diesel, Shell, **food:** Arby's, Burger King, Hometown Pizza, KFC, LJ Silver, McDonald's, Subway, Taco Bell, Waffle House, **lodging:** Best Western, Day's Inn, Hampton Inn, Holiday Inn Express, Super 8, **other:** HOSPITAL, Chevrolet, Chrysler/Plymouth/Dodge, Ford/Mercury, $General, Factory Stores/famous brands, Kroger/gas, Rite Aid, Sav-A-Lot Foods, Wal-Mart SuperCtr/24hr, Carroll Butler SP
43.5mm	Kentucky River

Louisville

43	KY 389, to KY 55, English, no facilities
34	US 421, Campbellsburg, **W...gas:** Citgo/Subway/diesel, Marathon
28	KY 153, KY 146, to US 42, Pendleton, **E...gas:** Marathon/diesel, Paul's, Pilot/Subwaydiesel/24hr, **W...gas:** Pilot/McDonald's/diesel/24hr
22	KY 53, La Grange, **E...gas:** BP/24hr, Marathon/diesel, Speedway/Rally's, **food:** Burger King, Lucky Dragon Chinese, Papa John's, Ponderosa, Waffle House, Wendy's, **lodging:** Day's Inn, Holiday Inn Express, Luxbury Inn, **other:** HOSPITAL, Big O Tire, $General, Kroger/gas, Wal-Mart SuperCtr/24hr, **W...gas:** Chevron/diesel/24hr, Shell, Swifty, **food:** Arby's, Cracker Barrel, DQ, Hometown Pizza, KFC, LJ Silver, McDonald's, Subway, Taco Bell, **lodging:** Comfort Suites, Super 8, **other:** Chevrolet/Pontiac/Buick, NAPA, Rite Aid
18	KY 393, Buckner, **W...gas:** Citgo/diesel, **food:** Subway
17	KY 146, Buckner, **E...other:** Ford, **W...gas:** Shell/diesel, Thornton's/diesel/24hr, **other:** USPO, st police
14	KY 329, Crestwood, Pewee Valley, Brownsboro, **E...gas:** Chevron/24hr, Shell, **2 mi E...food:** DQ, Hometown Pizza, Subway
13mm	**rest area both lanes, full(handicapped)facilities, phone, vending, picnic tables, litter barrels, petwalk**
9b a	I-265, KY 841, Gene Snyder Fwy, **E...**to Sawyer SP
5	I-264, Watterson Expswy, **E...**to Sawyer SP
2	Zorn Ave, **E...**VA HOSPITAL, **W...gas:** BP, Chevron, **food:** Kingfish Rest., **lodging:** Ramada Inn, **other:** Art Museum
1b	I-65, S to Nashville, N to Indianapolis

Interstate 75

N ↑ S

Covington

Exit #	Services
193mm	Kentucky/Ohio state line, Ohio River
192	5th St(from nb), Covington, **E...gas:** BP, Chevron, Shell, Speedway, **food:** AllStar Chili, Big Boy, Burger King, GoldStar Chili, McDonald's, Perkins, Subway, Taco Bell, Waffle House, White Castle, **lodging:** Courtyard, Extended Stay America, Holiday Inn, Radisson, **other:** Ford/Lincoln/Mercury, Lexus, Subaru/VW, Riverboat Casino, **W...lodging:** Hampton Inn
191	12th St, Covington, **E...food:** Jillian's Rest., **other:** HOSPITAL, Dodge, museum, same as 192
189	KY 1072(from sb), Kyles Lane, **W...gas:** BP/diesel, Marathon/diesel, Shell/diesel, Speedway, **food:** Big Boy, Hardee's, Pizza Hut, Substation II, **lodging:** Day's Inn, Ramada Inn, **other:** SteinMart, Thriftway Foods, Walgreen, same as 188
188	US 25, US 42, Dixe Hwy, **W...lodging:** Day's Inn, Holiday Inn, Ramada, **other:** DENTIST, Kroger, same as 189

Interstate 75

N

S

F l o r e n c e

186   KY 371, Buttermilk Pike, Covington, **E...gas:** Ashland, BP/diesel, Citgo/diesel, **food:** DQ, DrawBridge Rest., Oriental Wok, Papa John's, **lodging:** Best Western, Cross Country Inn, **W...gas:** Ashland, BP, Shell, Sunoco/diesel, **food:** Arby's, Bob Evans, Burger King, Domino's, Fazoli's, GoldStar Chili, LJ Silver, McDonald's, Outback Steaks, Pizza Hut, Subway, **other:** CHIROPRACTOR, Drug Emporium, Remke Foods, Walgreen

185   I-275 E and W, **W...**to airport

184   KY 236, Donaldson Rd, to Erlanger, **E...gas:** BP/deli, Marathon, **food:** Double Dragon Chinese, Rally's, **W...gas:** Ashland/Subway, Marathon, Speedway, Sunoco, **food:** Waffle House, **lodging:** Comfort Inn, Day's Inn, Econolodge

182   KY 1017, Turfway Rd, **E...gas:** BP, **food:** Big Boy, Blimpie, Krispy Kreme, Lee's Chicken, Penn Sta Subs, Ryan's, **lodging:** Comfort Inn, Courtyard, Fairfield Inn, Ramada Ltd., Signature Inn, **other:** Big Lots, Office Depot, Winn-Dixie, funpark, **W...gas:** Meijer/diesel/24hr, **food:** Applebee's, Boston Mkt, Burger King, Cracker Barrel, Fuddrucker's, Italianni's Rest., Longhorn Steaks, Ming Garden Chinese, O'Charley's, Rafferty's, Ryan's, Schlotsky's, Shell's Rest., Steak'n Shake, Tumbleweeds Grill, Wendy's, **lodging:** AmeriSuites, Ashley Qtrs Hotel, Extended Stay America, Hampton Inn, Hilton Inn, Studio+ Suites, **other:** HOSPITAL, Best Buy, Biggs Foods, Home Depot, Kohl's, Lowe's Whse, Media Play, OfficeMax, Sam's Club, Turfway Park, Wal-Mart

181   KY 18, Florence, **E...gas:** Speedway, TA/Sunoco/Pizza Hut/Popeye's/diesel/rest./24hr/@, **food:** Goodfellow's Dining, Waffle House, **lodging:** Best Western, Cross Country Inn, **W...gas:** BP/diesel/Procare, Chevron, **lodging:** Microtel, Suburban Lodge, **other:** JC Penney, K-Mart, Dodge, Ford, Mazda, Nissan, Sears/auto, Toyota

180A   Mall Rd(from sb), **W...food:** Cathay Chinese, Chi-Chi's, ChuckeCheese, GoldStar Chili, China King, Hardee's, LoneStar Steaks, Old Country Buffet, Olive Garden, Subway, Taco Bell, **other:** Barnes&Noble, Home Goods, Jo-Ann Fabrics, Kroger/24hr, Lazarus, Mens Whse, Michael's, Sears/auto, Staples, Walgreen, mall, same as 180

180   US 42, US 127, Florence, Union, **E...gas:** BP/diesel, Speedway, Thornton, **food:** BBQ, Big Boy, Bob Evans, Burger King, Capt D's, Jalapeno's Mexican, LJ Silver, Main Moon Chinese, McDonald's, Pizza Hut, Rally's, Red Lobster, Substation II, Subway, WarmUps Café, Wendy's, **lodging:** Knight's Inn, Motel 6, Ramada Inn/rest., Super 8, **other:** Cadillac, funpark, **W...gas:** BP, Chevron/TCBY/diesel, Shell/diesel/24hr, Speedway, **food:** Arby's, Burger King, DQ, KFC, Little Caesar's, Perkins/24hr, Pizza Hut, Ponderosa, Waffle House, White Castle, Kroger/

deli, **lodging:** Budget Host, Holiday Inn, Travelodge, Wildwood Inn, **other:** AutoZone, Circuit City, CVS Drug, Michel Tire, NTB, PepBoys, Walgreen

178   KY 536, Mt Zion Rd, **E...gas:** BP/Rally's/diesel, Mobil, Shell/diesel, Sunoco/diesel, **food:** GoldStar Chili, Hometown Pizza, Jersey Mike's Subs, Margarita's Mexican, Steak'n Shake, Subway, **other:** VETERINARIAN, Goodyear/auto, MktPlace Foods, Valvoline

177mm   **Welcome Ctr sb/rest area nb, full(handicapped)facilities, phone, vending, picnic tables, litter barrels, RV dump**

175   KY 338, Richwood, **E...gas:** TA/BP/Taco Bell/diesel/rest./@, Pilot/Subway/diesel/@, **food:** Arby's, Burger King, White Castle/24hr, **lodging:** Holiday Inn Express, **other:** Florence RV Park, **W...gas:** BP/Wendy's, Pilot/Subway/diesel/24hr/@, Shell/diesel, **food:** GoldStar Chili, McDonald's, Snappy Tomato Pizza, Waffle House, **lodging:** Day's Inn/rest., Econolodge, **other:** to Big Bone Lick SP

173   I-71 S, to Louisville, no facilities

171   KY 14, KY 16, to Verona, Walton, **E...gas:** BP, Citgo/DQ, **food:** Waffle House, **W...gas:** ⚡/Flying J/Conoco/diesel/LP/rest./24hr/@, **other:** Blue Beacon, Dave's RV Ctr, Oak Creek Campground(1mi), to Big Bone Lick SP

168mm   weigh sta sb

166   KY 491, Crittenden, **E...gas:** BP, Citgo/diesel, Marathon/A&W/Taco Bell/diesel, **food:** McDonald's, **other:** Chrysler/Plymouth/Dodge, KOA(2mi), **W...gas:** Chevron, Shell/Subway/diesel, **food:** Burger King, Country Bumpkins Rest.

159   KY 22, to Owenton, Dry Ridge, **E...gas:** BP, Marathon/DQ, Shell/diesel, **food:** Arby's/24hr, Burger King, KFC/Taco Bell, LJ Silver, McDonald's, Pizza Hut, Subway, Waffle House, Wendy's, **lodging:** Country Inn Suites, Dry Ridge Inn, Microtel, Super 8, **other:** HOSPITAL, $General, Radio Shack, Wal-Mart SuperCtr/24hr, **W...gas:** Speedway/diesel, Sunoco/diesel, **food:** Country Grill, Cracker Barrel, Shoney's, **lodging:** Hampton Inn, Holiday Inn Express, **other:** Toyota, Dry Ridge Outlets/famous brands, Sav-A-Lot, Toyota

154   KY 36, Williamstown, **E...gas:** Citgo/diesel/LP, Shell/diesel, **food:** Chester Fried Chicken, Red Carpet Rest., **lodging:** Knight's Inn, **other:** HOSPITAL, to Kincaid Lake SP, **W...gas:** BP/diesel, Marathon/diesel, **food:** Sterling Rest., **lodging:** Best Value, Day's Inn, HoJo's

Interstate 75

N
↕
S

144 KY 330, to Owenton, Corinth, **E...gas:** Marathon, Noble's Trk Plaza/diesel/rest./@, **other:** Three Springs Camping, **W...gas:** BP, **food:** Hunter's Rest., Freeway Rest.

136 KY 32, to Sadieville, **W...gas:** Chevron

130.5mm weigh sta nb

129 KY 620, Delaplain Rd, **E...gas:** Pilot/Subway/diesel/24hr/@, **food:** Waffle House, **lodging:** Day's Inn, Motel 6, **W...gas:** Pilot/McDonald's/diesel/24hr/@, Shell/24hr

127mm **rest area both lanes, full(handicapped)facilities, phone, vending, picnic tables, litter barrels, petwalk**

126 US 62, to US 460, Georgetown, **E...gas:** BP, Chevron/24hr, Marathon, **food:** Applebee's, Big Boy, McDonald's, O'Charley's, **lodging:** Flag Inn, **other:** Lowe's Whse, Wal-Mart SuperCtr/gas/diesel/24hr, **W...gas:** BP, Shell/24hr, Speedway/A&W/diesel, **food:** Cracker Barrel, Fazoli's, KFC, Subway, Waffle House, Wendy's, **lodging:** Best Western, Comfort Suites, Country Inn Suites, Hampton Inn, Holiday Inn Express, Microtel, Shoney's Inn, Super 8, Winner's Circle Motel, **other:** HOSPITAL, Chevrolet/Pontiac/Buick, Ford, Dodge/Jeep, K-Mart/Little Caesar's, Outlets/famous brands, to Georgetown Coll, same as 125

125 US 460(from nb), Georgetown, **E...gas:** BP/diesel, Marathon, Shell, **lodging:** Econolodge, Flag Inn, Super 8, **other:** flea mkt, **W...gas:** DM, Swifty, **food:** Arby's, DQ, LJ Silver, Reno's Roadhouse, Taco Bell, Wendy's, **other:** Outlets/famous brands, Radio Shack, same as 126

120 rd 1973, to Ironworks Pike, KY Horse Park, **E...KY** Horse Park Camping, **W...gas:** Citgo/Stuckey's/diesel/pizza/24hr, **other:** HOSPITAL

118 I-64 W, to Frankfort, Louisville, no facilities

Lexington

115 KY 922, Lexington, **E...gas:** Exxon/diesel, Shell/Subway/24hr, **food:** Cracker Barrel, McDonald's, Waffle House, **lodging:** Knight's Inn, La Quinta, Sheraton, **other:** SaddleHorse Museum(4mi), **W...gas:** Chevron/diesel, **food:** Denny's, Post Rest., **lodging:** Embassy Suites, Holiday Inn, Marriott/rest., **other:** museum

113 US 27, US 68, to Paris, Lexington, **E...gas:** BP/diesel(2mi), Speedway, **food:** Waffle House, **lodging:** Ramada Inn, **W...gas:** Chevron/Subway/diesel/24hr, Shell, **food:** Fazoli's, LJ Silver, Siggy's Rest., Subway, **lodging:** Day's Inn, Catalina Motel, Red Roof Inn, **1 mi W...gas:** Shell, **food:** Burger King, Capt D's, Hardee's/24hr, Shoney's, **other:** Chevrolet, Chrysler/Plymouth/Jeep, Hall's RV Ctr, Kroger/deli, Northside RV Ctr, carwash, to UKY, Rupp Arena

Lexington

111 I-64 E, to Huntington, WV, no facilities

110 US 60, Lexington, **W...gas:** Shell, Speedway/diesel, Thornton/Subway/24hr, **food:** Arby's, Bob Evans, Cracker Barrel, Hardee's, International Buffet, McDonald's, Waffle House, Wendy's, **lodging:** Baymont Inn, Best Western, BlueGrass Suites, Comfort Inn, Country Inn Suites, Hampton Inn, HoJo's, Holiday Inn Express, Knight's Inn, Microtel, Motel 6, Quality Inn, Ramada Ltd, Signature Inn, Super 8, Wilson Inn

108 108 Man O War Blvd, **W...gas:** BP, Citgo/diesel, Meijer/diesel/24hr, Shell/Wendy's/24hr, Speedway, **food:** Applebee's, Arby's, Backyard Burger, Burger King, Carrabba's, Chick-fil-A, Damon's, Don Pablo, Fazoli's, GoldStar Chili, KFC/Pizza Hut, Logan's Roadhouse, Max&Erma's, McDonald's, Outback Steaks, Rafferty's, Ruby Tuesday, Steak'n Shake, Taco Bell, TGIFriday, Waffle House, Wnedy's, **lodging:** Courtyard, Hilton Garden, Sleep Inn, **other:** HOSPITAL, Barnes&Noble, Circuit City, Goody's, Kohl's, OfficeMax, Old Navy, Radio Shack, Target, Walgreen

104 KY 418, Lexington, **E...gas:** Exxon/Wendy's/diesel/24hr, Shell, **food:** Waffle House, **lodging:** Comfort Suites, Day's Inn, Econolodge, Red Roof Inn, Holiday Inn, **W...gas:** BP/diesel, Chevron, Speedway/Subway, **food:** Jerry's Rest., Wendy's, **other:** HOSPITAL, **4 mi W...food:** Hooters, KFC, Texas Roadhouse

99 US 25 N, US 421 N, no facilities

98mm Kentucky River

97 US 25 S, US 421 S, **E...gas:** Exxon/Huddle House/diesel/24hr, flea mkt, **W...RV** camping(2mi)

95 KY 627, to Boonesboro, Winchester, **E...gas:** BP/diesel, Love's/Arby's/diesel/24hr/@, **food:** Hall's Diner(6mi), McDonald's, **other:** Ft Boonesborough SP, camping, **W...gas:** Shell/Burger King/diesel/24hr

90 US 25, US 421, Richmond, **E...gas:** BP, Shell, **food:** Cracker Barrel, Outback Steaks(4mi), Western Sizzlin, **lodging:** Knight's Inn, La Quinta, Ramada Ltd, Red Roof Inn, **W...gas:** Citgo/24hr, Exxon/Arby's/diesel, Shell, Thorobred Gas, **food:** Big Boy, DQ, Hardee's, Pizza Hut, Subway, Waffle House, Wendy's, **lodging:** Day's Inn, Super 8, **other:** NTB, Pennzoil, antiques

Richmond

87 KY 876, Richmond, **E...gas:** Amoco/diesel/24hr, BP/diesel, Chevron/24hr, Citgo/diesel, Shell/diesel/24hr, Speedway/diesel, **food:** Arby's, Bojangles, Burger King, DQ, Denny's, Dunkin Donuts, Fazoli's, Hardee's, Hooters, KFC, Krystal/24hr, Little Caesar's, LJ Silver, McDonald's, Papa John's, Pizza Hut, Rally's, Red Lobster(2mi), Snappy Tomato Pizza, Subway, Taco Bell, Waffle House, Wendy's, **lodging:** Best Western, Econolodge, Holiday Inn, Quality Qtrs Inn, **other:** HOSPITAL, $General, Goodyear/auto, Winn-Dixie, to EKU, **W...gas:** BP/diesel, DM/24hr, **food:** Bob Evans, J Patrick's Grille, Ryan's, Steak'n Shake/24hr, **lodging:** Comfort Suites, Hampton Inn, Holiday Inn Express, Jameson Inn

Interstate 75

N
S

B e r e a

L o n d o n

82.5mm rest area both lanes, full(handicapped)facilities, phone, vending, picnic tables, litter barrels, pet-walk

77 77 KY 595, Berea, **E...food:** Artisan Cafe, **other:** HOSPITAL, to Berea Coll, **W...gas:** BP/Subway/24hr, Shell, **food:** Columbia Grill, **lodging:** Day's Inn, Holiday Inn Express

76 76 KY 21, Berea, **E...gas:** BP, Citgo/DQ/Stuckey's, DM/gas, Shell/Burger King, Speedway/diesel, **food:** Arby's, Dinner Bell Rest., KFC, Little Caesar's, LJ Silver, Mario's Pizza, McDonald's, Pizza Hut, Subway, WanTen Chinese/Thai, Wendy's, **lodging:** Holiday Motel, Howard Johnson, Knight's Inn, Super 8, **other:** HOSPITAL, $General, Ford, NAPA, Wal-Mart SuperCtr/24hr, tires, **W...gas:** BP, Chevron/24hr, Marathon/diesel, **food:** Lee's Chicken, Pantry Family Rest., **lodging:** Comfort Inn, Best Western, Econolodge, Fairfield Inn, Mtn View Motel, **other:** Chrysler/Plymouth/Dodge/Jeep, Oh! Kentucky Camping, Walnut Meadow Camping

62 US 25, to KY 461, Renfro Valley, **E...gas:** Shell/24hr, **food:** Hardee's, Waffle House, **lodging:** Country Hearth Inn, Heritage Inn, Renfro Valley Inn, **other:** KOA(2mi), **W...gas:** BP/Blimpie/24hr, Citgo/KFC/Wendy's/24hr, Shell/24hr, Marathon/Taco Bell, **food:** DQ, Denny's, Godfather's, McDonald's, Subway, **lodging:** Day's Inn, Econolodge, Mt Villa Motel, **other:** HOSPITAL, to Big South Fork NRA, Lake Cumberland

59 US 25, to Livingston, Mt Vernon, **E...gas:** BP, Marathon/diesel, Shell/diesel, **food:** Jean's Rest., Pizza Hut, **lodging:** Kastle Inn/rest., **other:** Nicely Camping, **W...gas:** Citgo, **lodging:** Super Sleep Inn

51mm Rockcastle River

49 KY 909, to US 25, Livingston, **W...gas:** Shell/diesel/24hr

41 KY 80, to Somerset, London, **E...gas:** Chevron, Marathon, Speedway, **food:** Arby's, Burger King, DQ, Ideal Rest., KFC, McDonald's, Pizza Hut, Rax, Sonic, **lodging:** Best Western, Day's Inn, Economy Inn, Holiday Inn Express, Park Inn, Red Roof Inn, Sleep Inn, Super 8, **other:** HOSPITAL, AutoZone, Chrysler/Jeep, DogPatch Trading, $General, Kroger/deli, Parsley's Tire/repair, Pontiac/GMC, Rite Aid, st police, **W...gas:** BP, BP/diesel/24hr/@, Chevron/McDonald's, Citgo/diesel/24hr, Shell/Subway/24hr, **food:** LJ Silver, Jerry's Rest., Patty's Buffet, Shiloh Roadhouse, Taco Bell, Waffle House, Wendy's, **lodging:** Budget Host, **other:** Westgate RV Camping

38 KY 192, London, **E...gas:** BP/diesel, Citgo/diesel, Shell/Arby's/diesel, Speedway/Rally's/diesel, **food:** Big Boy, Burger King, Capt D's, El Dorado Mexican, Fazoli's, Hardee's, Huddle House, Krystal, McDon-

C o r b i n

ald's, Pizza Hut, Ponderosa, Rockabilly Café, Ruby Tuesday, Taco Bell, **lodging:** Comfort Suites, Day's Inn, Hampton Inn, Holiday Inn Express, Ramada Ltd, **other:** HOSPITAL, Advance Parts, Goody's, Kroger, Office Depot, USPO, Wal-Mart SuperCtr/24hr, airport, camping, toll rd to Manchester/Hazard, Western Star Trucks, to Levi Jackson SP, **W...to** Laurel River Lake RA

34mm weigh sta. both lanes, truck haven

30.5mm Laurel River

29 US 25, US 25E, Corbin, **E...gas:** BP, Citgo/diesel/24hr, Exxon, Pilot/McDonald's/Subway/diesel/24hr/@, **food:** Arby's(2mi), KFC(2mi), Burger King, Shoney's, Taco Bell, Western Steer, Western Sizzlin, Best Western, **lodging:** Quality Inn/rest., Super 8, **other:** Goodyear, Blue Beacon, to Cumberland Gap NP, **W...gas:** BP/Krystal/diesel, Chevron/diesel, Shell/diesel/24hr, **food:** BBQ, Cracker Barrel, Taco Bell, **lodging:** Baymont Inn, Comfort Inn, Fairfield Inn, Hampton Inn, Knight's Inn, **other:** KOA, to Laurel River Lake RA

25 US 25W, Corbin, **E...gas:** Speedway/diesel, **food:** Burger King, Corbin Burgerhouse, Jerry's Rest., McDonald's, **lodging:** Country Inn Suites, Day's Inn, Holiday Inn Express, Landmark Inn, **other:** HOSPITAL, auto repair/tires, **W...gas:** BP/diesel, Exxon/Buddy's BBQ, Shell/24hr, **food:** Arby's, Reno's Roadhouse, Waffle House, **lodging:** Best Value, Best Western, Regency Inn, **other:** to Cumberland Falls SP

15 US 25W, to Williamsburg, Goldbug, **W...gas:** Chevron/diesel, Shell, **other:** Cumberland Falls SP

14.5mm Cumberland River

11 KY 92, Williamsburg, **E...gas:** BP/diesel, Exxon/diesel, Shell, **food:** Arby's, DQ, Hardee's, KFC, McDonald's, Pizza Hut, Subway, TCBY, **lodging:** Adkins Motel, Cumberland Inn, Scottish Inn, Super 8, **other:** Chevrolet, Chrysler/Plymouth/Dodge/Jeep, $General, Ford, NAPA, Sav-A-Lot Foods, U-Haul, mufflers/transmissions, **W...gas:** Shell/diesel, Pilot/Wendy's/diesel/@, **food:** BJ's Rest., Burger King, Krystal, LJ Silver, Ribeye Steaks, **lodging:** Day's Inn, Williamsburg Motel/RV Park, **other:** Wal-Mart SuperCtr/24hr, to Big South Fork NRA

1.5mm Welcome Ctr nb, full(handicapped)facilities, phone, vending, picnic tables, litter barrels, petwalk

0mm Kentucky/Tennesee state line

LOUISIANA
Interstate 10

Exit #	Services
274mm	Louisiana/Mississippi state line, Pearl River
272mm	West Pearl River
270mm	**Welcome Ctr wb, full(handicapped)facilities, info, phone, picnic tables, litter barrels, petwalk, RV dump**
267b	I-12 W, to Baton Rouge, no facilities
a	I-59 N, to Meridian, no facilities
266	US 190, Slidell, **N...gas:** Exxon/diesel, Shell/diesel, TA/Mobil/diesel/rest./24hr/@, Texaco, **food:** Arby's, Burger King, China Wok, CiCi's, Denny's, KFC, LoneStar Steaks, McDonald's, Pizza Hut, Shoney's, Taco Bell, Wendy's, **lodging:** Best Value Inn, Best Western, Day's Inn, Motel 6, Super 8, **other:** HOSPITAL, Harley-Davidson, PepBoys, Radio Shack, U-Haul, **S...gas:** Chevron/diesel/24hr, RaceTrac, **food:** Applebee's, Big Easy Diner, Cracker Barrel, Osaka Grill, Outback Steaks, Sonic, Waffle House, **lodging:** King's Lodge, La Quinta, Ramada Inn, **other:** HOSPITAL, Wal-Mart/auto, auto repair/transmissions, casino
265mm	weigh sta both lanes
263	LA 433, Slidell, **N...gas:** BP, Exxon, Shell, **food:** China Buffet, Ray's Rest., Waffle House, **lodging:** Comfort Inn, Hampton Inn, **other:** Chevrolet, Mitsubishi, **S...gas:** Fleet/Subway/diesel/@, Texaco/Domino's/diesel, **food:** McDonald's, Wendy's, **lodging:** Holiday Inn, **other:** Jeep, Ford/Lincoln/Mercury, Honda, Isuzu, Mazda, Nissan, Pontiac/Buick/GMC, Saturn, Toyota, Slidell Factory Outlet/famous brands, KOA(1mi)
261	Oak Harbor Blvd, Eden Isles, **N...gas:** Exxon/diesel, **food:** Phil's Marina Café, **lodging:** Sleep Inn, **S...gas:** BP/Subway/diesel
255mm	Lake Pontchartrain
254	US 11, to Northshore, Irish Bayou, **S...gas:** BP/diesel
251	Bayou Sauvage NWR, **S...**swamp tours
248	Michoud Blvd, no facilities
246b a	I-510 S, LA 47 N, S to Chalmette, N to Littlewood, **S...**6 Flags of NO
245	Bullard Ave, **N...gas:** Shell, **food:** Jame's Seafood, Kettle, Pizza Hut, Sonic, **lodging:** Comfort Suites, La Quinta, **other:** Daewoo, Honda, Hyundai, Mitsubishi, NAPA, **S...gas:** Exxon, Shell, **food:** Burger King, IHOP, KFC/Taco Bell, McDonald's, Shoney's, Subway, **lodging:** Hampton Inn, Motel 6, **other:** HOSPITAL, Buick/GMC, Circuit City, Ford, Home Depot, Nissan, PepBoys, Toyota
244	Read Blvd, **N...gas:** Shell, **food:** Lama's Seafood, McDonald's, TX BBQ, **other:** Office Depot, Rite Aid, Sam's Club, Walgreen, Wal-Mart, **S...gas:** Spur/diesel, **food:** Popeye's, Wendy's, **lodging:** Best Western, Day's Inn, Holiday Inn Express, **other:** HOSPITAL, Dillard's, Dodge/Jeep, Ford/Lincoln/Mercury, Goodyear/auto, Honda, Kia, Sears/auto, mall
242	Crowder Blvd, **N...gas:** Chevron, **S...gas:** Exxon, **food:** Papa John's, Rally's, Shoney's, Wendy's, **lodging:** La Quinta, **other:** Family$
241	Morrison Rd, **N...gas:** Shell, Spur, **food:** Burger King, **other:** Rite Aid
240b a	US 90 E, Chef Hwy, Downman Rd, **N...gas:** Amoco, Shell, Spur, **lodging:** Family Inn, Super 8, **other:** Chevrolet, Hyundai, U-Haul, **S...gas:** Chevron
239b a	Louisa St, Almonaster Blvd, **N...gas:** Spur, **food:** Burger King, McDonald's, Piccadilly's, Pizza Hut, Red Lobster, Wendy's, **lodging:** Howard Johnson, Knight's Inn, **other:** Firestone, K-Mart, PrecisionTune, Radio Shack, Toyota, Walgreen, Winn-Dixie, mall
238b	I-610 W(from wb)
237	Elysian Fields Ave, **N...gas:** Amoco/diesel
236b	LA 39, N Claiborne Ave, no facilities
a	Esplanade Ave, downtown
235a	Orleans Ave, to Vieux Carre, French Qtr, **S...lodging:** Day's Inn, Holiday Inn, Marriott, Sheraton, **other:** Winn-Dixie
234b	Poydras St, **N...**HOSPITAL, **S...**to Superdome, downtown
a	US 90A, Claiborne Ave, to Westbank, Superdome
232	US 61, Airline Hwy, Tulane Ave, **N...**Pennzoil, **S...gas:** Exxon, **food:** McDonald's, Piccadilly's, **other:** A&P, Chevrolet, Firestone, Radio Shack, Rite Aid, to Xavier U
231b	Florida Blvd, WestEnd
a	Metairie Rd, no facilities
230	I-610 E(from eb), to Slidell
229	Bonnabel Blvd, no facilities
228	Causeway Blvd, **N...gas:** Shell, **food:** Copeland's Rest., **lodging:** Best Western, Hampton Inn, Ramada Ltd, **S...gas:** Amoco, Exxon, Timesaver Gas, **food:** Denny's, Pasta Etc, Steak'n Egg/24hr, **lodging:** Courtyard, Extended Stay America, Holiday Inn, La Quinta, Quality Hotel, Residence Inn, Wyndham, **other:** MEDICAL CARE
226	Clearview Pkwy, Huey Long Br, **N...gas:** Chevron, Exxon, **food:** Ruby Tuesday, **lodging:** Sleep Inn, **other:** Sears, Target, **S...gas:** Chevron, Circle K, **food:** Burger King, Piccadilly's, Subway, **lodging:** Shoney's Inn, Sun Suites, **other:** HOSPITAL, Buick/GMC, Dillard's, mall
225	Veterans Blvd, **N...gas:** Chevron, Shell, Spur/diesel, **food:** Burger King, Denny's, McDonald's, Rouse's Foods, **lodging:** La Quinta, **other:** Aamco, Dodge, Honda, Radio Shack, Rite Aid, **S...gas:** Jubilee, Shell, **food:** Church's, Godfather's, N O Burgers, Piccadilly's, Popeye's, Rally's, Schlotsky's, Tiffin Pancakes, Wendy's, **lodging:** Holiday Inn, Sheraton, **other:** Acura, Best Buy, Chevrolet, CompUSA, GNC, Home Depot, Jo-Ann Fabrics, K-Mart, Michael's, Nissan, Office Depot, PepBoys, VW, Walgreen, Wal-Mart/auto
224	Power Blvd(from wb)

LOUISIANA

Interstate 10

223b a LA 49, Williams Blvd, **N...gas:** Exxon, Shell, Spur, **food:** Burger King, Church's, El Patio, Fisherman's Cove, Jade Palace, Pizza Hut, Popeye's, Rally's, Subway, Taco Bell, Tokyo Japanese, Wendy's, **lodging:** Fairfield Inn, **other:** AutoZone, Ford, Office Depot, OfficeMax, Rite Aid, **S...gas:** Exxon/diesel, Shell, **food:** Brick Oven, Burger King, Denny's, Jazz Seafood/steaks, McDonald's, Messina's Rest., Pizza Hut, Sonic, Subway, **lodging:** Best Western, Comfort Inn, Contempra Inn, Day's Inn, Extended Stay America, Holiday Inn, La Quinta, Plaza Inn, Travelodge, Wingate Inn, **other:** Advance Parts, Circuit City, Dillard's, Eckerd, Firestone/auto, Goodyear, Hyundai, NAPA, Radio Shack, U-Haul, mall

221 Loyola Dr, **N...gas:** Circle K, Exxon/diesel, Shell/diesel, Spur, **food:** Church's, McDonald's, Popeye's, Rally's, Subway, Taco Bell, **other:** Advance Parts, Sam's Club/gas, **S...gas:** Amoco, **food:** Rick's Café, Wendy's, **lodging:** Sleep Inn, **other:** airport, info

220 I-310 S, to Houma, no facilities

214mm Lake Pontchartrain

210 I-55N(from wb)

LOUISIANA

Interstate 10

E / **La Place** / **W**

209 I-55 N, US 51, to Jackson, **S...gas:** Chevron/24hr, Jet24/24hr, Pilot/Subway/diesel/24hr/@, Shell/diesel, **food:** Bully's Seafood, KFC/Taco Bell, McDonald's, Shoney's, Waffle House, Wendy's, **lodging:** Best Western, Day's Inn, Hampton Inn, Holiday Inn Express, La Place RV Camping

207mm weigh sta both lanes

206 LA 3188 S, La Place, **S...gas:** Shell, Texaco/diesel, **food:** McDonald's, SF Café, **lodging:** Millet Motel, **other:** HOSPITAL

194 LA 641 S, to Gramercy, **11-15 mi S...**plantations

187 US 61 S, to Gramercy, no facilities

182 LA 22, Sorrento, **N...gas:** Chevron/Popeye's, Shell/diesel, **S...gas:** Chevron/Subway/diesel, SJ/diesel, **food:** Coffeehouse, Huddle House, Lafitte's Café, McDonald's, Waffle House

181mm **rest area both lanes, full(handicapped)facilities, phone, picnic tables, litter barrels, RV dump, pet-walk**

179 LA 44, Gonzales, **N...gas:** Circle K, Mobil/diesel, **3 mi S...food:** Cabin Fine Cajun Food, Pelican Point Café

177 LA 30, Gonzales, **N...gas:** Citgo/USA/diesel/24hr/@, Shell, **food:** Burger King, Church's, Jack-in-the-Box, McDonald's, Shoney's, Taco Bell, Waffle House, **lodging:** Best Western, Budget Inn, Day's Inn, Holiday Inn, Quality Inn, Western Inn, White Rose Motel, **other:** HOSPITAL, **S...gas:** Chevron, Shell/diesel, **food:** Chili's, Cracker Barrel, Popeye's, Wendy's, **lodging:** Comfort Inn, **other:** Tanger/famous brands, Vesta RV Park

173 LA 73, Prairieville, to Geismar, **N...gas:** Shell/diesel, **S...gas:** Exxon, Mobil/Subway/diesel, **food:** Burger King, **other:** Twin Lakes RV Park(1mi)

166 LA 42, LA 427, Highland Rd, Perkins Rd, **N...gas:** Chevron/diesel, **food:** Church's, La Palmas Mexican, Ruffino's Rest., Sonic, Waffle House, **other:** Home Depot, funpark, **S...gas:** Shell/BBQ, Texaco

163 Siegen Lane, **N...gas:** Chevron/24hr, Exxon, RaceTrac, Shell, **food:** Arby's, Burger King, Canes Chicken, Chick-fil-A, Fazoli's, IHOP, McAlister's, McDonald's, Pizza Hut/Taco Bell, Shoney's, Subway, Waffle House, Whataburger, **lodging:** Baymont Inn, Holiday Inn, Microtel, Motel 6, **other:** Advance Parts, $Tree, Honda, Office Depot, Radio Shack, Target, **S...food:** Chili's, Joe's Crabshack, Subway, Wendy's, **lodging:** Courtyard, Residence Inn, **other:** BooksAMillion, Lowe's Whse, Sam's Club/gas, Wal-Mart SuperCtr/24hr

162 Bluebonnet Rd, **N...gas:** Chevron/diesel, **lodging:** Quality Suites, **S...gas:** RaceWay, **food:** Bennigan's, Burger King, Copeland's, J Alexander's, Logan's Roadhouse, Ralph&Kacoo's, **lodging:** AmeriSuites, **other:** Best Buy, CompUSA, Dillard's, JC Penney, McRae's, Sears/auto, Mall of LA

Baton Rouge

160 LA 3064, Essen Lane, **S...gas:** Chevron/24hr, Exxon, RaceTrac, **food:** Bamboo Garden, Burger King, Copeland's, McDonald's, Piccadilly's, Tomato Grill, Wendy's, **lodging:** Fairfield Inn, Springhill Suites, **other:** HOSPITAL, Albertson's, Tire Kingdom, Walgreen

159 I-12 E, to Hammond

158 College Dr, Baton Rouge, **N...gas:** Jubilee, **food:** Alabasha Café, Damon's, Fuddrucker's, Hooters, Jason's Deli, Macaroni Grill, On-the-Border, Ruby Tuesday, Starbucks, Waffle House, Wendy's, **lodging:** Best Western, Chase Suites, Corporate Inn, Extended Stay America, Homewood Suites, Marriott, **other:** HOSPITAL, Barnes&Noble, **S...gas:** Chevron/24hr, Shell, **food:** Burger King, Chili's, Gino's Pizza, IHOP, Koto Oriental, McDonald's, Ninfa's Mexican, Ruth's Chris Steaks, Seminola Grill, Starbucks, Taco Bell, **lodging:** Comfort Suites, Embassy Suites, Hampton Inn, Hawthorn Suites, Holiday Inn Express, Radisson, **other:** Albertson's, AutoZone, $Tree, Office Depot, Radio Shack, Rite Aid, SuperFresh Foods

157b Acadian Thruway, **N...gas:** Citgo, Shell, **food:** Denny's, Rib's Rest., **lodging:** Comfort Inn, La Quinta, Marriott, Rodeway Inn, **other:** HOSPITAL, **S...gas:** Exxon, Mobil, **food:** LoneStar Steaks, Outback Steaks, **lodging:** Courtyard, **other:** BooksAMillion, Eckerd

a Perkins Rd, **S...gas:** Shell/diesel, **other:** BooksAMillion, Wal-Mart/auto

156b Dalrymple Dr, **S...**to LSU

a Washington St, no facilities

155c Louise St(from wb), no facilities

b I-110 N, to Baton Rouge bus dist, airport

a LA 30, Nicholson Dr, Baton Rouge, downtown, **S...**to LSU

154mm Mississippi River

153 LA 1, Port Allen, **N...gas:** Chevron, Shell, Circle K, **food:** Church's, Popeye's, Sonic, **other:** AutoZone, IGA Foods, **S...gas:** RaceTrac, **food:** Waffle House, **lodging:** Days Inn

151 LA 415, to US 190, **N...gas:** Amoco, Cash's Trk Plaza/diesel/@, Chevron, Exxon/diesel, Pilot/diesel/24hr, RaceTrac, Shell/diesel/24hr, **food:** Burger King, Domino's, KFC/Taco Bell, McDonald's, Popeye's, Waffle House, Wendy's, **lodging:** Best Western, Chinese Inn/rest., Comfort Inn, Days Inn, Holiday Inn Express, Shoney's Inn, **other:** Cajun Country Camping(2mi), **S...gas:** Love's/Arby's/diesel/24hr, Shell/diesel/24hr, Texaco/diesel/24hr, **lodging:** Motel 6, Ramada Inn, Super 8

139 LA 77, Grosse Tete, **N...gas:** Shell/Subway/diesel, **other:** Chevrolet, **S...gas:** Tiger Trkstp/diesel/rest./@

137.5mm **rest area both lanes, full(handicapped)facilities, phone, picnic tables, litter barrels, petwalk, RV dump**

135 LA 3000, to Ramah, **N...gas:** Texaco

128mm emergency callboxes begin wb, about 1/2 mi intervals

Interstate 10

E
↑
↓
W

127 LA 975, to Whiskey Bay, no facilities

126.5mm Pilot Channel of Whiskey Bay

122mm Atchafalaya River

121 Butte La Rose, no facilities

117mm emergency callboxes begin eb, about 1/2 mi intervals

115 LA 347, to Cecilia, Henderson, **N...gas:** BP/diesel, Exxon/diesel/24hr, Texaco/diesel, **food:** Boudin's Rest., Landry's Seafood, **lodging:** Holiday Inn Express, **S...gas:** Chevron/DQ/diesel, Citgo, Exxon/Subway/diesel, Pilot/diesel/24hr/@, Shell, **food:** McDonald's, Waffle House

109 LA 328, to Breaux Bridge, **N...gas:** Shell/diesel, Texaco/Blimpie/diesel, **food:** Crawfish Kitchen, **S...gas:** Chevron/Popeye's, Mobil/Burger King/Domino's/diesel, Pilot/Arbys/diesel/24hr/@, Texaco, **food:** Church's, McDonald's, Mulate's Cajun Rest., Waffle House, Wendy's, **lodging:** Best Western, Sonan Motel

108mm weigh sta both lanes

103b I-49 N, to Opelousas

a US 167 S, to Lafayette, **N...gas:** Shell/diesel, **food:** Church's, **lodging:** Motel 6, Ramada Inn, **S...gas:** Chevron/diesel/24hr, RaceTrac, Shell, **food:** Checker's, ChopStix Chinese, Kajun Kitchen, KFC, McDonald's, Pizza Hut, Popeye's, Shoney's, Subway, Taco Bell, Waffle House, Wendy's, Western Sizzlin, **lodging:** Best Western, Comfort Suites, Fairfield Inn, Holiday Inn, Jameson Inn, La Quinta, Quality Inn, Super 8, TravelHost Inn, **other:** HOSPITAL, Albertson's/gas, $General, Firestone/auto, Ford, Home Depot, Rite Aid, Super 1 Foods/gas, VW, Wal-Mart SuperCtr/gas/24hr, transmissions

101 LA 182, to Lafayette, **N...gas:** Chevron/McDonald's, RideUSA, TA/Mobil/diesel/24hr/@, **food:** Arby's, Burger King, Pizza Hut, Waffle House, Whataburger, **lodging:** Red Roof Inn, **other:** Honda Motorcycles, **S...gas:** Circle K, Exxon, RaceTrac, Shell/diesel, **food:** Cracker Barrel, **lodging:** Calloway Inn, Day's Inn, **other:** HOSPITAL, Hyundai, Isuzu/Kia

100 Ambassador Caffery Pkwy, **N...gas:** Exxon/Subway/diesel/24hr, **S...gas:** Chevron/24hr, Citgo/24hr, RaceTrac/24hr, Shell/diesel, **food:** Burger King, McDonald's, Pizza Hut/Taco Bell, Sonic, Waffle House, Wendy's, **lodging:** Hampton Inn, Sleep Inn, Microtel, **other:** HOSPITAL, Goodyear

97 LA 93, to Scott, **N...**Christien Pt RV Park, **S...gas:** Shell/Church's/diesel/24hr, **lodging:** Howard Johnson, **other:** Harley-Davidson, KOA

92 LA 95, to Duson, **N...gas:** Texaco/diesel/casino/24hr, **S...gas:** Chevron/diesel, Exxon/diesel, **lodging:** Super 8

Lafayette

87 LA 35, to Rayne, **N...gas:** Chevron/diesel, Exxon/diesel/24hr, **food:** Burger King, Chef Roy's Café, Gabe's Café, McDonald's, **lodging:** Days Inn, **other:** RV camping, **S...gas:** Citgo/diesel, Mobil/diesel/24hr, Shamrock/diesel, Shell/Subway, **food:** DQ, Popeye's, **lodging:** Comfort Inn, **other:** HOSPITAL, Advance Parts, Eckerd, Family$, NAPA, Winn-Dixie

82 LA 1111, to E Crowley, **S...gas:** Chevron/diesel, Murphy USA/gas, Shamrock, **food:** Wendy's, **other:** HOSPITAL, $Tree, GNC, Radio Shack, Wal-Mart SuperCtr/24hr

80 LA 13, to Crowley, **N...gas:** Conoco/diesel/24hr, Shell/diesel, **food:** Rice Palace Rest., Waffle House, **lodging:** Best Western, Crowley Inn, **S...gas:** Circle K/24hr, Exxon/24hr, RaceTrac, Shamrock/diesel, **food:** Burger King, DQ, Domino's, El Dorado Mexican, Fezzo's Seafood/steaks, KFC, Lucky Wok Chinese, McDonald's, Mr Gatti's, Pizza Hut, PJ's Grill, Popeye's, Sonic, Subway, Taco Bell, **other:** AutoZone, Chrysler/Plymouth/Dodge/Jeep, $General, Ford/Mercury/Nissan, Nissan, Radio Shack, Rite Aid, U-Haul, Winn-Dixie

76 LA 91, to Iota, **S...gas:** Conoco/diesel/café/24hr

72 Egan, **S... food:** Cajun Connection Rest.

67.5mm **rest areas both lanes full(handicapped)facilities, phone, picnic tables, litter barrels, petwalk, RV dump**

65 LA 97, to Jennings, **N...gas:** Spur/diesel, **S...gas:** Phillips 66/diesel, **lodging:** Day's Inn, **other:** to SW LA St School

64 LA 26, to Jennings, **N...**Budget Inn, **S...gas:** Chevron, Citgo, Exxon, Fina, Jennings Trvl Ctr/diesel, Shamrock/diesel, **food:** Burger King, DQ, Denny's, McDonald's, Mr Gatti's, Pizza Hut, Popeye's, Shoney's, Sonic, Subway, Taco Bell, Waffle House, Wendy's, **lodging:** Comfort Inn, Holiday Inn, **other:** HOSPITAL, AutoZone, Chrysler/Jeep/Dodge, Goodyear/auto, HiLo Parts, Rite Aid, Wal-Mart SuperCtr/gas/24hr, bank

59 LA 395, to Roanoke, no facilities

54 LA 99, Welsh, **S...gas:** Chevron, Conoco/diesel, Exxon/diesel/24hr, **food:** Cajun Tails Rest., DQ, Subway

48 LA 101, Lacassine, **S...gas:** Citgo, Exxon

44 US 165, to Alexandria, **N...other:** Quiet Oaks RV Park(10mi), Grand Casino(22mi), **S...**Wood-n Treasures RV Park

Crowley

Jennings

191

LOUISIANA
Interstate 10

E

↑
W

Lake Charles *(vertical side label)*

43 LA 383, to Iowa, **N...gas:** Exxon/diesel/24hr, Loves/ Hardee's/diesel/24hr, **food:** Burger King, **lodging:** Howard Johnson, **S...gas:** Chevron/24hr, Conoco/ diesel, Shell, Texaco/diesel, **food:** Cajun Kwik Deli, Big Daddy's Rest., Fausto's Chicken, McDonald's, Subway, **other:** Factory Stores of America/famous brands

36 LA 397, to Creole, Cameron, **N...**Citgo, Jean Lafitte RV Park(2mi), **S...gas:** Chevron/diesel, Conoco/ diesel/RV dump/24hr, **other:** James Mobile Camping, casino

34 I-210 W, to Lake Charles, no facilities

33 US 171 N, **N...gas:** GasWay/diesel, RaceWay, Shamrock, **food:** Burger King, Church's, McDonald's, Subway, Taco Bell, **lodging:** Best Western, Comfort Inn, Day's Inn, La Quinta, **other:** AutoZone, Eckerd, O'Reilly Parts, Walgreen, to Sam Houston Jones SP, **S...lodging:** Holiday Inn Express, Motel 6, Treasure Inn

32 Opelousas St, **N...gas:** Exxon

31b US 90 E, Shattuck St, to LA 14, **S...gas:** Pakco/diesel, **food:** McDonald's, **lodging:** Econolodge

a US 90 bus, Enterprise Blvd, **S...gas:** BP/diesel/24hr, **food:** Popeye's

30b a LA 385, N Lakeshore Dr, Ryan St, **N...gas:** Chevron, **food:** Waffle House, **lodging:** Travel Inn/rest., **S...food:** Montana's Smokehouse, **lodging:** Harrah's Hotel/casino, Holiday Inn, Lakeview Motel

29 LA 385, **N...gas:** Chevron, **food:** Steamboat Bills Rest., Waffle House, **lodging:** Lakeview Motel, Travel Inn/rest., **S...lodging:** Best Suites, **other:** Players Island Casino/hotel

28mm Calcasieu Bayou, Lake Charles

27 LA 378, to Westlake, **N...gas:** Circle K/24hr, Fina, Shell, **food:** Burger King, DQ, Pizza Hut, **other:** to Sam Houston Jones SP, **S...gas:** Conoco/24hr, **lodging:** Inn at the Isle, **other:** Riverboat Casinos

26 US 90 W, Southern Rd, Columbia, **N...gas:** Circle K/gas

25 I-210 E, to Lake Charles, no facilities

23 LA 108, to Sulphur, **N...gas:** Circle K/gas, Citgo, Exxon, **food:** Burger King, McDonald's, Popeye's, Subway, Taco Bell, **lodging:** Comfort Suites, **other:** AllPro Parts, $General, Radio Shack, Wal-Mart SuperCtr/gas/24hr, **S...gas:** Citgo/diesel, **food:** Cracker Barrel, Waffle House, Winner's Choice Rest./24hr, **lodging:** Best Western, Crossland Suites, Holiday Inn Express, Super 8, **other:** Goodyear, casino

21 LA 3077, Arizona St, **N...gas:** Chevron, Conoco/ diesel, Exxon, **food:** A&W/KFC, Boiling Point Deli, DQ, Papa John's, **other:** $General, Ford, Kroger/gas, NAPA, Walgreen, **S...gas:** Chev⸺, Citgo/diesel, **other:** HOSPITAL, Hidden Ponds RV Park

Sulphur *(vertical side label)*

20 LA 27, to Sulphur, **N...gas:** Bayou Gas, Exxon/diesel/ 24hr, Shell, **food:** Bonanza, Burger King, Cajun Charlie's Rest./gifts, Cajun Cookery, Checker's, Hong Kong Chinese, McDonald's, Mr Gatti's, Popeye's, Subway, Taco Bell, Wendy's, **lodging:** Chateau Motel, Hampton Inn, Holiday Inn, **other:** Brookshire Foods, Family$, Firestone/auto, Goodyear/auto, InstaLube, **S...gas:** Pilot/diesel, Texaco/diesel, **food:** Pit Grill Cajun, Pizza Hut, Sonic, Waffle House, **lodging:** Fairfield Inn, La Quinta, Microtel, Wingate Inn, **other:** HOSPITAL, casino, to Creole Nature Trail

8 LA 108, Vinton, **N...gas:** Citgo/diesel, EZ/diesel, **other:** V RV Park

7 LA 3063, Vinton, **N...gas:** Delta/Exxon/diesel, **food:** Burger King, Lucky Delta Café, Subway

4 US 90, LA 109, Toomey, **N...gas:** Chevron/diesel, Exxon/diesel/24hr, Shell/diesel, **other:** casinos, **S...gas:** Exxon/diesel, **lodging:** Delta Downs Hotel/ casino, **other:** Pelican Palace RV Park

2.5mm weigh sta both lanes

1.5mm **Welcome Ctr eb, full(handicapped)facilities, phone, picnic tables, litter barrels, petwalk**

1 (from wb), Sabine River Turnaround, no facilities

0mm Louisiana/Texas state line, Sabine River

Interstate 12

Exit #	Services

E

↑
W

85c I-10 E, to Biloxi. I-12 begins/ends on I-10, exit 267.

b I-59 N, to Hattiesburg, no facilities

a I-10 W, to New Orleans, no facilities

83 US 11, to Slidell, **N...gas:** Chevron/diesel/24hr, Exxon/ diesel, **food:** Burger King, McDonald's, Waffle House, **other:** $General, SuperValu Foods, **S...gas:** Mardi Gras Trkstp/diesel, Shell, **lodging:** City Motel(3mi), **other:** HOSPITAL

80 Airport Dr, North Shore Blvd, **N...food:** IHOP, **other:** Target, **S...gas:** Chevron/24hr, Shell/diesel, **food:** Burger King, ChuckeCheese, McDonald's, Pizza Hut/ Taco Bell, Subway, Wendy's, **other:** Best Buy, Dillard's, Goodyear/auto, Home Depot, JC Penney, Mervyn's, Sam's Club/gas, Sears/auto, Wal-Mart SuperCtr/24hr, mall

74 LA 434, to Lacombe, **S...gas:** Spur/diesel(3mi)

65 LA 59, to Mandeville, **N...gas:** Chevron/Subway, Danny&Clyde's, Shell, **other:** Abbita Brew Pub, **S...gas:** Conoco/Burger King/diesel, Texaco/Domino's/ diesel, **other:** Winn-Dixie, to Fontainebleau SP, camping

63b a US 190, Covington, Mandeville, **N...gas:** Exxon, RaceTrac, Shell, **food:** Applebee's, Burger King, Copeland's Grill, Ground Pati Rest., IHOP, KFC, Osaka Japanese, Outback Steaks, Piccadilly's, Portofino Italian, Sonic, Subway, TGIFriday, Waffle House, Wendy's, **lodging:**

Interstate 12

E

W

Best Western, Comfort Inn, Courtyard, Hampton Inn, Holiday Inn, Mt Vernon Motel, Super 8, **other:** MEDICAL CARE, Albertson's, BooksAMillion, Circuit City, GNC, Home Depot, Nissan, Office Depot, Toyota, **Wal-Mart SuperCtr/24hr**, **S...other:** HOSPITAL, Chrysler/Plymouth, st police, to New Orleans via toll causeway

60.5mm **rest areas both lanes, full(handicapped)facilities, phone, picnic tables, litter barrels, petwalk**

59   LA 21, Madisonville, to Covington, **N...gas:** Chevron/Church's, Conoco/Burger King/diesel, Shell, **food:** McDonald's, **other:** HOSPITAL, **S...gas:** Shell/Domino's/diesel, **other:** Fairview Riverside SP

57   LA 1077, to Goodbee, Madisonville, **S...**Family RV Park, to Fairview Riverside SP

47   LA 445, to Robert, **1-3 mi N...other:** Hidden Oaks Camping, Jellystone Camping, Sunset Camping, to Global Wildlife Ctr

42   LA 3158, to Airport, **N...gas:** Amoco, Chevron/Stuckey's/diesel/24hr, **lodging:** Friendly Inn

40   US 51, to Hammond, **N...gas:** Chevron, RaceTrac, Shell/24hr, Texaco/diesel, **food:** Border Café, Burger King, China Garden, Church's, McDonald's, Pizza Hut, Quizno's, Ryan's, Taco Bell, Wendy's, **lodging:** Best Western, Comfort Inn, Supreme Inn, **other:** MEDICAL CARE, Dillard's, Rite Aid, Sears/auto, 'U-Haul, Walgreen, mall, **S...gas:** Petro/Mobil/diesel/rest./24hr/@, Pilot/Arby's/diesel/24hr/@, Shell, **food:** Waffle House, **lodging:** Colonial Inn, Ramada Inn, **other:** Blue Beacon, $General, **other:** HOSPITAL, KOA

38b a   I-55, N to Jackson, S to New Orleans

37mm   weigh sta both lanes

35   Pumpkin Ctr, Baptist, **N...gas:** Exxon, **other:** Punkin RV Park, **S...gas:** Chevron/24hr

32   LA 43, to Albany, **N...**Chevron, **1 mi S...gas:** Citgo/diesel, **other:** to Tickfaw SP

29   LA 441, to Holden, **N...gas:** Coastal/diesel, **other:** RV RestStop(1mi), st police

28mm **rest areas both lanes, full(handicapped)facilities, phone, picnic tables, litter barrels, petwalk**

22   LA 63, Livingston, to Frost, **N...gas:** Chevron/diesel, Conoco/diesel, Mobil

19   to Satsuma, no facilities

15   LA 447, to Walker, **N...gas:** Citgo, Shell/24hr, Texaco, **food:** Burger King, Church's, Domino's, Jack-in-the-Box, La Fleur's Seafood, McDonald's, Popeye's, Sonic, Subway, Waffle House, **other:** AutoZone, Rite Aid, **Wal-Mart SuperCtr/24hr**, Winn-Dixie, **S...gas:** Chevron, Fina/diesel, **other:** Rocky's RV Ctr

Hammond

Baton Rouge

10   LA 3002, to Denham Springs, **N...gas:** Chevron, Circle K, Exxon, RaceTrac, Shell/diesel, **food:** Arby's, Burger King, Cactus Café, Crawford's Cajun, KFC, McDonald's, Pizza Hut, Pepper's Rest., Popeye's, Ryan's, Subway, Waffle House, Wendy's, **lodging:** Best Western, Holiday Inn Express, **other:** Advance Parts, Firestone/auto, Home Depot, Radio Shack, Rite Aid, **S...gas:** Pilot/Subway/diesel, Shell, **food:** Piccadilly's, Shoney's, **lodging:** Day's Inn, Highland Inn, **other:** Dodge/Isuzu, Ford, KOA

8.5mm   Amite River

7   O'Neal Lane, **N...gas:** Mobil, **lodging:** Comfort Suites, **other:** HOSPITAL, Eckerd, HobbyLobby, Knight's RV Park, Office Depot, Toyota, **S...gas:** BP, Chevron/24hr, RaceTrac, Texaco/diesel, **food:** Blimpie, Burger King, China King, Fazoli's, LoneStar Steaks, McDonald's, Pizza Hut/Taco Bell, Popeye's, Sonic, Subway, Waffle House, Wendy's, **other:** $General, Radio Shack, Super Fresh Foods, Walgreen, **Wal-Mart SuperCtr/24hr**

6   Millerville Rd, **N...gas:** Chevron/24hr

4   Sherwood Forest Blvd, **N...gas:** Exxon, Shell/diesel, **food:** Bamboo House, Burger King, ChuckeCheese, Denny's, Egg Roll King, Jack-in-the-Box, McDonald's, Popeye's, Sonic, Subway, Waffle House, **lodging:** Crossland Suites, Red Roof Inn, Super 8, **other:** Piggly Wiggly, Rite Aid, **S...gas:** Chevron/24hr, Shell/24hr, **food:** Bayou Cajun Seafood, BBQ, Pasta Garden, Pizza Hut, Taco Bell, **lodging:** Calloway Inn, **other:** Harley-Davidson

2b   US 61 N, **N...gas:** Amoco, Chevron, Exxon/diesel, Mobil/diesel, Shell/24hr, Texaco, **food:** Applebee's, **Cracker Barrel**, McDonald's, Pizza Hut/Taco Bell, Shoney's, Subway, Taste of China, Wendy's, Wienerschnitzel, **lodging:** Hampton Inn, Holiday Inn, Microtel, Motel 6, Shoney's Inn, Sleep Inn, **other:** Acura/Infiniti, Albertson's, Dodge, $Tree, Ford/Lincoln/Mercury, Marshall's, Michael's, Nissan/Suzuki, PepBoys, SteinMart, Toyota, Walgreen, transmissions

a   US 61 S, **S...gas:** Chevron, Circle K/gas, Jubilee/diesel, **food:** Gustavo's Mexican, McDonald's, Waffle House, **lodging:** Deluxe Inn, Plantation Inn, **other:** Cadillac/Volvo, Chevrolet, Home Depot, Mitsubishi, Winn-Dixie

1b   LA 1068, to LA 73, Essen Lane, **N...gas:** Shell/diesel, **food:** Cane's Rest., McDonald's, **other:** HOSPITAL, Eckerd, Family$, Radio Shack

a   I-10(from wb). I-12 begins/ends on I-10, exit 159 in Baton Rouge.

LOUISIANA
Interstate 20

E ↑ **W**

Talulah

Exit #	Services
189mm	Louisiana/Mississippi state line, Mississippi River
187mm	weigh sta both lanes
186	US 80, Delta, **S...gas:** Chevron/Blimpie/diesel/24hr
184mm	**rest area both lanes, full(handicapped)facilities, phone, picnic tables, litter barrels, petwalk, RV dump**
182	LA 602, Mound, **S...food:** Winner's Circle Rest./OTB
173	LA 602, Richmond, no facilities
171	US 65, Tallulah, **N...gas:** Chevron, Shell/diesel, **food:** KFC, McDonald's, Subway, Wendy's, **lodging:** Day's Inn, Super 8, **other:** HOSPITAL, **S...gas:** Conoco/diesel, Love's/diesel/24hr/@, TA/Mobil/diesel/rest./24hr/@
164mm	Tensas River
157	LA 577, Waverly, **N...gas:** Tiger Trkstp/diesel/rest./24hr/@, **S...**Chevron/Subway/diesel/24hr/@, to Tensas River NWR
155mm	Bayou Macon
153	LA 17, Delhi, **N...gas:** Chevron/Taco Bell, Exxon, **food:** Burger King, DQ, Moby's Rest:, Pizza Hut, Sonic, Subway, **other:** HOSPITAL, **S...gas:** Shell, **lodging:** Best Western, Day's Inn
150mm	**rest area both lanes, full(handicapped)facilities, phone, picnic tables, litter barrels, petwalk, RV dump**
148	LA 609, Dunn, no facilities
145	LA 183, rd 202, Holly Ridge, no facilities
141	LA 583, Bee Bayou Rd, **N...gas:** Texaco/diesel
138	LA 137, Rayville, **N...gas:** Pilot/Wendy's/diesel/24hr/@, **food:** Burger King, McDonald's, **lodging:** Day's Inn, **other:** HOSPITAL, Chevrolet/Pontiac/Buick, Family$, Firestone, $General, Wal-Mart, **S...gas:** Citgo/Subway/diesel/24hr, Exxon, **food:** Popeye's, Waffle House, **lodging:** Ramada Ltd, **other:** Goodyear
135mm	Beouf River
132	LA 133, Start, **N...gas:** Exxon
128mm	Lafourche Bayou
124	LA 594, Millhaven, **N...gas:** EZ Mart/diesel, **other:** st police, to Arsage Wildlife Area
120	Garrett Rd, Pecanland Mall Dr, **N...gas:** Citgo/diesel, Shell, **food:** Applebee's, Gator's Rest., McAlister's, Olive Garden, Pizza Hut, Red Lobster, Zipp's Drive-Thru, **lodging:** Comfort Inn, Courtyard, Holiday Inn, Residence Inn, **other:** Dillard's, Firestone/auto, JC Penney, Sears/auto, mall, **S...gas:** Exxon/diesel, Kangaroo/diesel, **lodging:** Best Western, Day's Inn, **other:** Harley-Davidson, Hope's RV Ctr, Lowe's Whse, Pecanland RV Park, Sam's Club, Shilo RV Camp

Monroe

Exit #	Services
118b a	US 165, **N...food:** Copeland's Rest., IHOP, O'Charleys, **lodging:** Holiday Inn, La Quinta, **other:** Home Depot, Plymouth/Dodge, Goodyear, Target, to NE LA U, **S...gas:** Chevron, Citgo, Exxon, Shell, **food:** Burger King, McDonald's, **lodging:** Comfort Inn, Hampton Inn, Motel 6, Ramada Ltd
117b	LA 594, Texas Ave, no facilities
a	Hall St, Monroe, **N...**HOSPITAL, Civic Ctr
116b	US 165 bus, LA 15, Jackson St, **N...**HOSPITAL, **S...food:** Popeye's, **lodging:** Guesthouse Inn/rest.
a	5th St, Monroe, **N...gas:** Citgo/Circle K
115	LA 34, Mill St, **N...gas:** Citgo
114	LA 617, Thomas Rd, **N...gas:** RaceTrac, Shell, **food:** BBQ, Bennigan's, Burger King, Capt D's, Chick-fil-A, El Chico, Grandy's, KFC, Las Margaritas Mexican, McAlister's, McDonald's, Pizza Hut, Popeye's, Shoney's, Subway, Taco Bell, Waffle House, Wendy's, **lodging:** Shoney's Inn, Super 8, Wingate Inn, **other:** HOSPITAL, Office Depot, Rite Aid, Walgreen, Wal-Mart SuperCtr/gas/24hr, **S...gas:** Citgo/diesel, Exxon/diesel, Shell, **food:** Chili's, Cracker Barrel, Logan's Roadhouse, LoneStar Steaks, Outback Steaks, Sonic, Waffle House, **lodging:** Fairfield Inn, Holiday Inn Express, Jameson Inn, Red Roof Inn, Super 8
112	Well Rd, **N...gas:** Shell/diesel/24hr, Texaco/24hr, **food:** DQ, Flapjack's, McDonald's, Waffle House, **S...gas:** Pilot/Subway/Wendy's/diesel/24hr/@, **other:** Pavilion RV Park
108	LA 546, to US 80, Cheniere, **N...gas:** Exxon/diesel, Texaco/diesel
107	Camp Rd, rd 25, Cheniere, **N...**Sunset Cove RV Park
103	US 80, Calhoun, **N...gas:** Chevron/diesel/rest., Citgo/diesel, **lodging:** Avant Motel
101	LA 151, to Calhoun, **N...gas:** Texaco
97mm	**rest area wb, full(handicapped)facilities, phone, picnic tables, litter barrels, petwalk, RV dump**
95mm	**rest area eb, full(handicapped)facilities, phone, picnic tables, litter barrels, petwalk, RV dump**
93	LA 145, Choudrant, **S...gas:** Chevron
86	LA 33, Ruston, **N...gas:** Citgo, RaceWay, Shell/diesel, **food:** Cajun Café, Log Cabin Rest., Ryan's, Sonic, **lodging:** Comfort Inn, Day's Inn, Holiday Inn, Lincoln Motel, **other:** Buick/GMC, Chevrolet/Pontiac/Cadillac, Chrysler/Plymouth, Firestone, Ford/Lincoln/Mercury, Toyota, Wal-Mart SuperCtr/gas/24hr, **S...gas:** Texaco/diesel, **lodging:** Holiday Inn Express
85	US 167, Ruston, **N...gas:** Citgo/Subway, Exxon/A&W, Shell, **food:** Burger King, Capt D's, Huddle House, McDonald's, Peking Chinese, Shoney's, Wendy's, **lodging:** Econolodge, Hampton Inn, Ramada Inn, Relax Inn, **other:** Super 1 Foods, JC Penney, Radio Shack, **S...gas:** BP, Shell/diesel, **food:** Pizza Hut, **lodging:** Best Western, **other:** HOSPITAL

Ruston

Interstate 20

84 LA 544, Ruston, **N...gas:** Mobil/diesel, **S...gas:** Chevron, Citgo/24hr, Exxon, Shell/diesel, **food:** DQ, Johnny's Pizza, Pizza Inn, Quizno's, Subway, TCBY, Wendy's, **lodging:** Super 8

81 LA 141, Grambling, **S...gas:** Clark/Church's/diesel/24hr, Exxon, **other:** to Grambling St U

78 LA 563, Industry, **S...gas:** Texaco/diesel

77 LA 507, Simsboro, no facilities

69 LA 151, Arcadia, **S...gas:** BP/diesel, Exxon, Texaco, **food:** Country Folks Kitchen, McDonald's, Sonic, Subway, **lodging:** Day's Inn, Nob Hill Inn/rest., **other:** Arcadia Tire, Brookshire Foods, Factory Stores/famous brands, Fred's Drugs, NAPA

67 LA 9, Arcadia, **N...**to Lake Claiborne SP, **S...gas:** Texaco

61 LA 154, Gibsland, **S...gas:** Exxon(1mi)

58mm **rest area both lanes, full(handicapped)facilities, phone, picnic tables, litter barrels, petwalk, RV dump**

55 US 80, Ada, Taylor, no facilities

52 LA 532, to US 80, Dubberly, **N...**Exxon/Mom's Diner/diesel/24hr, **S...gas:** Citgo/diesel

49 LA 531, Minden, **N...gas:** Trucker's Paradise/diesel/rest./casino/24hr/@, Wal-Mart SuperCtr/gas/24hr(3mi)

47 US 371 S, LA 159 N, Minden, **N...gas:** Chevron/diesel, Mobil/diesel, Texaco/24hr, **food:** Golden Biscuit, **lodging:** Best Western, Exacta Inn/rest., Holiday Inn Express, Southern Inn, **other:** HOSPITAL, Ford/Lincoln/Mercury, **S...**B&B, to Lake Bistineau SP, camping

44 US 371 N, Dixie Inn, Cotton Valley, **N...gas:** Chevron, **food:** Crawfish Hole #2, Nicky's Cantina, **lodging:** Minden Motel(2mi), **other:** Family$

38 Goodwill Rd, Ammo Plant, **S...gas:** BP/Rainbow Diner/diesel/24hr, **other:** Interstate RV Park

36mm **rest area both lanes, full(handicapped)facilities, phone, picnic tables, litter barrels, petwalk, RV dump**

33 LA 157, Fillmore, **N...gas:** Phillips 66, **other:** Hilltop Camping(2mi), **S...gas:** Citgo, Pilot/Arby's/diesel/24hr/@, **other:** Lake Bistineau SP

26 I-220 W, Shreveport, **1 mi N...**facilities off of I-220

23 Industrial Dr, **N...gas:** Circle K, Exxon/Subway, Texaco/Popeye's/24hr, **food:** Barnhill's Buffet, Burger King, McDonald's, Sue's Kitchen, Taco Bell, **lodging:** Le Bossier Motel, **other:** st police, **S...gas:** Chevron/diesel, Road Mart/diesel, **lodging:** Quality Inn, **other:** RV SuperCtr

22 Airline Dr, **N...gas:** Chevron/McDonald's/diesel, Citgo/Circle K, Exxon/diesel, Mobil, **food:** Applebee's, Arby's, Backyard Burgers, Bennigan's, Burger King, Capt D's, Chili's, ChuckeCheese, DQ, Grandy's, IHOP, Little Caesar's, Luby's, Mr Gatti's, Mr Jim's Chicken, Pizza Hut, Popeye's, Red Lobster, Schlotsky's, Sonic, Taco Bell, Waffle House, **lodging:** Best Western, Crossland Suites, Isle of Capri Hotel, Super 8, **other:**

Albertson's/gas, BooksAMillion, Dillard's, Eckerd, Firestone/auto, Goodyear/auto, JC Penney, K-Mart, NAPA, Office Depot, Pep-Boys, Sears/auto, Walgreen, mall, **S...gas:** Texaco/diesel/24hr, Circle K, **food:** Church's, Darryl's Rest., Domino's, Outback Steaks, Popeye's, **lodging:** Baymont Inn, Microtel, Quality Inn, **other:** HOSPITAL, AutoZone, Fabrics+, Super1 Food, to Barksdale AFB

21 LA 72, to US 71 S, Old Minden Rd, **N...gas:** Circle K, Exxon, **food:** Burger King, Cowboy's Rest., El Chico, McDonald's, Morrison's Cafeteria, Ralph&Kacoo's, Subway, Whataburger, **lodging:** Hampton Inn, Holiday Inn, La Quinta, Residence Inn, Shoney's Inn/rest., **other:** Advance Parts, AutoZone, **S...gas:** RaceTrac, **food:** Dragon House Chinese, Waffle House, Wendy's, **lodging:** Day's Inn, Motel 6

20c (from wb), to US 71 S, to Barksdale Blvd

20b LA 3, Benton Rd, same as 21

a Hamilton Rd, Isle of Capri Blvd, **N...gas:** Circle K, Texaco/24hr, **food:** BBQ, **lodging:** Comfort Inn, **S...gas:** Chevron, **lodging:** Ramada/rest., **other:** casino

19b Traffic St, Shreveport, downtown, **N...other:** Chevrolet, casino

a US 71 N, LA 1 N, Spring St, Shreveport, **N...food:** Don's Seafood, **lodging:** Best Western, Holiday Inn

18b-d Fairfield Ave(from wb), downtown Shreveport, **N...other:** radiators, **S...**HOSPITAL

18a Line Ave, Common St(from eb), downtown, **S...gas:** Citgo, **other:** HOSPITAL

17b I-49 S, to Alexandria

a Lakeshore Dr, Linwood Ave, no facilities

16b US 79/80, Greenwood Rd, **N...**HOSPITAL, **S...gas:** Citgo, **food:** Burger King, El Chico, **lodging:** Travelodge

a US 171, Hearne Ave, **N...gas:** Citgo, **food:** Subway, **other:** HOSPITAL, **S...gas:** Exxon, Fina, Texaco/diesel, **food:** KFC, Krystal, **lodging:** Howard Johnson

14 Jewella Ave, Shreveport, **N...gas:** Citgo/diesel, Food-Fast, Texaco/diesel/24hr, **food:** Burger King, Church's, McDonald's, Popeye's, Subway, Taco Bell, Whataburger, **other:** Advance Parts, AutoZone, County Mkt Foods, Eckerd, Family$, Walgreen

13 Monkhouse Dr, Shreveport, **N...food:** Denny's, **lodging:** Best Value Inn, Day's Inn, Holiday Inn Express, Residence Inn, The Lodge, **S...gas:** Chevron, Exxon/Subway/diesel, Texaco/diesel, **food:** Waffle House, **lodging:** Best Western, Hampton Inn, Pelican Inn, Ramada, Super 8, **other:** to airport

LOUISIANA

Interstate 20

E ↕ **W**

11   I-220 E, LA 3132 E, to I-49 S

10   Pines Rd, **N...gas:** BP/diesel, **food:** DQ, Pizza Hut, Popeye's, Subway, **other:** Brookshire Foods, KOA, **S...gas:** Chevron/McDonald's, Exxon/diesel, Shell, **food:** Burger King, Church's, Cracker Barrel, Domino's, Dragon Chinese, Grandy's, IHOP, KFC, Nicky's Cantina, Subway, Taco Bell, Waffle House, Wendy's, Whataburger, **lodging:** Courtyard, Fairfield Inn, La Quinta, Holiday Inn, Jameson Inn, **other:** Chrysler/Dodge, Kroger, Radio Shack, USPO, Walgreen, Wal-Mart SuperCtr/gas/24hr

8   US 80, LA 526 E, **N...lodging:** Red Roof Inn, **other:** Freightliner, **S...gas:** Chevron/diesel, Petro/Mobil/diesel/rest./@ , Pilot/Wendy's/diesel/24hr/@ , Speedway, **food:** Crescent Landing Catfish Rest.(3mi), **other:** Blue Beacon

5   US 79 N, US 80, to Greenwood, **N...gas:** Kelly's/diesel/rest./24hr/@ , Texaco/diesel, **lodging:** Country Inn, Mid Continent Motel, **other:** Bounder RV Ctr

3   US 79 S, LA 169, Mooringsport, **S...gas:** Ⓔ/Flying J/Conoco/diesel/LP/rest./24hr/@ , Love's/Arby's/diesel/24hr/@

2mm   **Welcome Ctr eb, full(handicapped)facilities, phone, picnic tables, litter barrels, petwalk, RV dump**

1mm   weigh sta both lanes

0mm   Louisiana/Texas state line

Interstate 49

N ↕ **S**   **Shreveport**

Exit #   Services

I-49 begins/ends in Shreveport on I-20, exit 17.

206   I-20, E to Monroe, W to Dallas

205   King's Hwy, **E...food:** McDonald's, Piccadilly's, **other:** Dillard's, Sears/auto, mall, **W...gas:** Shamrock, **food:** Burger King, LJ Silver, Subway, Taco Bell, **other:** HOSPITAL

203   Hollywood Ave, Pierremont Rd, **W...gas:** Fina

202   LA 511, E 70th St, **W...gas:** Chevron, Circle K, **food:** Sonic, SC Chicken

201   LA 3132, to Dallas, Texarkana, no facilities

199   LA 526, Bert Kouns Loop, **E...gas:** Chevron/Arby's/diesel/24hr, Citgo, Exxon, RaceTrac, **food:** Burger King, KFC, Taco Bell, Wendy's, **lodging:** Comfort Inn, **other:** Home Depot, **W...gas:** Texaco/diesel, **food:** McDonald's, **other:** Brookshire Foods

196mm   Bayou Pierre

191   LA 16, to Stonewall, no facilities

186   LA 175, to Frierson, Kingston, no facilities

177   LA 509, to Carmel, **E...gas:** Eagles Trkstp/diesel/rest.

172   US 84, to Grand Bayou, Mansfield, no facilities

169   Asseff Rd, no facilities

162   US 371, LA 177, to Evelyn, Pleasant Hill, no facilities

---

Natchitoches

155   LA 174, to Ajax, Lake End, **W...gas:** Spaulding/diesel/@ , **other:** Country Livin' RV

148   LA 485, Powhatan, Allen, no facilities

142   LA 547, Posey Rd, no facilities

138   LA 6, to Natchitoches, **E...gas:** BP/Mkt Express, Exxon/Subway, RaceTrac, **food:** Shoney's, Wendy's, **lodging:** Best Western, Holiday Inn Express, Super 8(5mi), **other:** HOSPITAL, Albertson's(3mi), Wal-Mart SuperCtr/24hr(5mi), **W...gas:** Chevron/diesel, Citgo, Texaco/diesel, **food:** Burger King, Huddle House, McDonald's, Simpatico's Grille, **lodging:** Comfort Inn, Hampton Inn, Microtel, **other:** Nakatosh RV Park, to Kisatchie NF

132   LA 478, rd 620, no facilities

127   LA 120, to Cypress, Flora, **E...gas:** Citgo, **lodging:** Ryder Inn(10mi), **other:** to Cane River Plantations

119   LA 119, to Derry, Cloutierville, **E...**to Cane River Plantations

113   LA 490, to Chopin, **E...gas:** Phillips 66/diesel

107   to Lena, **E...**USPO

103   LA 8 W, to Flatwoods, **E...gas:** Texaco, **other:** to Cotile Lake, RV camping

99   LA 8, LA 1200, to Boyce, Colfax, **6 mi W...**Cotile Lake, RV camping

98   LA 1(from nb), to Boyce, no facilities

94   rd 23, to Rapides Sta Rd, **E...gas:** Rapides/diesel, **W...other:** I-49 RV Ctr

90   LA 498, Air Base Rd, **W...gas:** Chevron/diesel/24hr, Exxon/diesel, Mobil/diesel, Texaco/BBQ/diesel, **food:** Burger King, Cracker Barrel, McDonald's, **lodging:** La Quinta, Super 8, Travel Express Inn

86   US 71, US 165, MacArthur Dr, **1-2 mi W...gas:** Mobil, Texaco, **food:** Burger King, Ryan's, Shoney's, **lodging:** Clarion, Comfort Inn, Hampton Inn, Motel 6, Quality Inn, Travelodge, **other:** Super 1 Foods

85b   Monroe St, Medical Ctr Dr(from nb)

a   LA 1, 10th St, MLK Dr, downtown

84   US 167 N, LA 28, LA 1, Pineville Expswy(no ez return nb), no facilities

Alexandria

83   Broadway Ave, **E...**Fina, **1 mi W...gas:** Texaco, **food:** Wendy's, **other:** BooksAMillion, Harley-Davidson, Lowe's Whse, Target, Wal-Mart SuperCtr/24hr

81   US 71 N, LA 3250, Sugarhouse Rd, MacArthur Dr(from sb), **W...gas:** Phillips 66/diesel, same as 83

80   US 71 S, US 167, MacArthur Dr, Alexandria, **2-4 mi W...gas:** Chevron/diesel, Exxon, I-49 Trk Plaza/diesel, Mobil, **food:** Burger King, Carino's Italian, Chili's, Cuco's Mexican, KFC, Logan's Roadhouse, McDonald's, Outback Steaks, Pizza Hut, Sonic, Subway, Taco Bell, Western Sizzlin, **lodging:** Best Western, Clarion, Day's Inn, Hampton Inn, Holiday Inn, Ramada Ltd, Super 8, **other:** Albertson's, Dillard's, JC Penney, Sam's Club/gas, U-Haul, mall

73   LA 3265, rd 22, to Woodworth, **W...gas:** Exxon/Blimpie/diesel, **other:** LA Conf Ctr, to Indian Creek RA, RV camping

Interstate 49

N↑↓S

66	LA 112, to Lecompte, **E...gas:** Chevron/Burger King/diesel, **food:** Lea's Lunch, **W...**museum
61	US 167, to Meeker, Turkey Creek, **E...**to Loyd Hall Plantation(3mi)
56	LA 181, Cheneyville, no facilities
53	LA 115, to Bunkie, **E...gas:** Chevron/diesel/casino/ 24hr/@
46	LA 106, to St Landry, **W...**to Chicot SP
40	LA 29, to Ville Platte, **E...gas:** Exxon/diesel
35mm	**E...rest area/rec area both lanes, full(handicapped)facilities, picnic tables, litter barrels, vending, petwalk, RV dump**
27	LA 10, to Lebeau, no facilities
25	LA 103, to Washington, Port Barre, **W...gas:** Exxon, **other:** Family$
23	US 167 N, LA 744, to Ville Platte, **E...gas:** Chevron/ Subway/diesel, Texaco/diesel, **W...gas:** 167 Trkstop/ diesel/rest./casino/24hr/@, to Chicot SP
19b,a	US 190, to Opelousas, **W...**HOSPITAL, **1 mi W...gas:** Exxon/diesel, Mobil, **food:** Blimpie, Palace Café, Soileau's Café, **other:** RV camping
18	LA 31, to Cresswell Lane, **E...lodging:** Holiday Inn, **other:** Chrysler/Dodge/Jeep/Isuzu, Wal-Mart SuperCtr/diesel/24hr, **W...gas:** Chevron/diesel/24hr, Shamrock, Shell, **food:** Burger King, Creswell Lane, Domino's, McDonald's, Pizza Hut, Ryan's, Subway, Taco Bell, Wendy's, **lodging:** Best Western, Day's Inn, **other:** Eckerd, Express Lube, Family$, Firestone, Nissan, Pontiac/Buick/Cadillac, Rite Aid, TireWorld
17	Judson Walsh Dr, **E...gas:** Texaco/diesel, **W...food:** Ray's Diner, Ryan's
15	LA 3233, Harry Guilbeau Rd, **W...lodging:** Comfort Inn/rest., **other:** HOSPITAL
11	LA 93, to Grand Coteau, Sunset, **E...gas:** Chevron, Citgo/diesel/24hr, Exxon/Popeye's/diesel, **food:** Beau Chere Rest., **W...lodging:** Sunset Inn
7	LA 182, no facilities
4	LA 726, Carencro, **E...**Evangeline Downs Racetrack, Foreman RV Ctr, **W...gas:** Chevron, Citgo/Domino's, **food:** Burger King, McDonald's, **lodging:** Economy Inn
2	LA 98, Gloria Switch Rd, **E...gas:** Citgo/Blimpie/ diesel, **food:** Prejean's Rest., **other:** Stevens RV Ctr, Lowe's Whse, **W...gas:** Shell, **food:** Picante Mexican
1b	Pont Des Mouton Rd, **E...gas:** Exxon/diesel, **lodging:** Motel 6, Plantation Motel, Ramada Inn, **other:** Gauthier's RV Ctr, st police, **W...**Ford
a	I-10, W to Lake Charles, E to Baton Rouge, **US 167 S...gas:** Chevron/diesel/24hr, RaceTrac, Shell, **food:** Checker's, ChopStix Chinese, Kajun Kitchen, KFC, McDonald's, Pizza Hut, Popeye's, Shoney's, Subway, Taco Bell, Waffle House, Wendy's, Western

Lafayette **Opelousas**

Sizzlin, **lodging:** Best Western, Comfort Suites, Fairfield Inn, Holiday Inn, Jameson Inn, La Quinta, Quality Inn, Super 8, TravelHost Inn, **other:** HOSPITAL, Albertson's/gas, $General, Firestone/auto, Ford, Home Depot, Rite Aid, Super 1 Foods/gas, VW, Wal-Mart SuperCtr/gas/24hr, transmissions

I-49 begins/ends on I-10, exit 103.

Interstate 55

N↑↓S

Exit #	Services
65.5mm	Louisiana/Mississippi state line
65mm	**Welcome Ctr sb, full(handicapped)facilities, tourist info, phone, picnic tables, litter barrels, petwalk**
64mm	weigh sta nb
61	LA 38, Kentwood, **E...gas:** Chevron/diesel/24hr, Texaco, United/diesel, **food:** Jam Chicken, Sonic, **other:** HOSPITAL, Ford/Mercury, IGA Foods, **W...gas:** Exxon/Subway/diesel, Texaco/diesel/24hr, **other:** Chevrolet, Chrysler/Jeep/Dodge, Great Discovery Camping(3mi)
58.5mm	weigh sta sb
57	LA 440, Tangipahoa, **E...**to Camp Moore Confederate Site
54.5mm	**rest area nb, full(handicapped)facilities, phone, picnic tables, litter barrels, petwalk**
53	LA 10, Fluker, to Greensburg, **W...**HOSPITAL
50	LA 1048, Roseland, **E...gas:** Texaco/diesel/24hr
47	LA 16, Amite, **E...gas:** Chevron/Domino's/diesel, Citgo, Conoco, RaceTrac, **food:** Burger King, KFC, Master Chef, McDonald's, Pizza Hut, Popeye's, Sonic, Subway, Wendy's, **lodging:** Comfort Inn, **other:** HOSPITAL, AutoZone, Winn-Dixie, **W...gas:** Amite Trkstp/OysterGrill/diesel(2mi), **food:** Ardillo's, **lodging:** Colonial Motel, **other:** Ford
41	LA 40, Independence, **E...gas:** Conoco, **other:** HOSPITAL, **W...**Indian Cr Camping(2mi)
36	LA 442, Tickfaw, **E...gas:** Chevron/diesel, **other:** camping, to Global Wildlife Ctr(15mi)
32	LA 3234, Wardline Rd, **E...gas:** Spur, Texaco/diesel, **food:** Burger King, Chinese Cuisine, McDonald's, Murphy's Seafood, Wendy's, **lodging:** Best Western, **W...gas:** Chevron

LOUISIANA

Interstate 55

N ↑ S

Hammond

31	US 190, Hammond, **E...gas:** Chevron/diesel, Exxon/Subway/diesel, Pilot/diesel, Saver/diesel, United, **food:** Applebee's, Burger King, Chili's, Country Cookin Seafood, Cracker Barrel, Krystal, McDonald's, Pizza Hut, Shoney's, Sonic, Taco Bell, Waffle House, Wendy's, **lodging:** Executive Inn, Hampton Inn, Super 8, The Inn, **other:** HOSPITAL, Aamco, Advance Parts, AutoZone, BooksAMillion, Chrysler/Plymouth/Buick/Dodge, $General, $Tree, Eckerd, Lowe's Whse, Office Depot, OfficeMax, Radio Shack, Walgreen/24hr, Wal-Mart SuperCtr/ gas/24hr, Winn-Dixie, transmissions/repair
29b a	I-12, W to Baton Rouge, E to Slidell
28	US 51 N, Hammond, **E...gas:** RaceTrac, **food:** Catfish Charlie's, CiCi's, Don's Seafood Rest., Shoney's(2mi), **lodging:** Econolodge, Holiday Inn/rest., Ramada Inn/rest., Rockwood Inn, **other:** HOSPITAL, KOA, Mitchell RV Ctr
26	LA 22, Ponchatoula, to Springfield, **E...gas:** Amoco, Chevron/diesel, Conoco, Exxon/diesel, Shell, **food:** Burger King, China King, KFC, McDonald's, Popeye's, Sonic, Subway(1mi), Wendy's, **lodging:** Microtel, **other:** AutoZone, $General, Eckerd, Ford, NAPA, O'Reilly Parts, Winn-Dixie, **W...gas:** Texaco/ Domino's/diesel
23	US 51, Ponchatoula, no facilities
22	frontage rd(from sb), no facilities
15	Manchac, **E...food:** Middendorf Café, **other:** phone, swamp tours
7	Ruddock, no facilities
1	US 51, to I-10, Baton Rouge, La Place, **S...gas:** Chevron/24hr, Jet/Citgo/24hr, Shell/diesel, Speedway/Blimpie/Church's/diesel, **food:** Bully's Seafood, Burger King, KFC, McDonald's, Shoney's, Waffle House, Wendy's, **lodging:** Best Western, Holiday Inn Express, **other:** HOSPITAL, La Place RV Camping

I-55 begins/ends on I-10, exit 209.

Hammond / La Place

Interstate 59

See Mississippi Interstate 59

Interstate 220(Shreveport)

Exit #	Services
	I-220 begins/ends on I-20, exit 26.
17b	I-20, W to Shreveport, E to Monroe
a	US 79, US 80, **N...gas:** Exxon, Citgo/Circle K, RaceWay, **food:** Waffle House, **other:** LA Downs Racetrack, Hilltop RV Park(7mi), **S...gas:** Chevron/ diesel/mart, **food:** Huddle House
15	Shed Rd, no facilities
13	Swan Lake Rd, no facilities
12	LA 3105, Airline Dr, **N...**HOSPITAL, **S...gas:** Citgo, Exxon/diesel, Shamrock/diesel, Shell/Subway, **food:** Applebee's, Burger King, CiCi's, Grandy's, McDonald's, Quizno's, Sonic, Taco Bell, Wendy's, **lodging:** Best Western, **other:** Home Depot, Wal-Mart SuperCtr/24hr/gas, **1 mi S...gas:** Mobil, Circle K, **food:** Arby's, Chili's, ChuckeCheese, DQ, Mr Gatti's, Popeye's, **other:** HOSPITAL, BooksAMillion, Dillard's, Eckerd, NAPA, Office Depot, mall
11	LA 3, Bossier City, **N...other:** HOSPITAL, Buick/ Pontiac/GMC, Ford, Toyota/Lexus, Maplewood RV Park(3mi), **S...gas:** Chevron/McDonald's/diesel/ 24hr, **other:** Nissan
7b a	US 71, LA 1, Shreveport, **N...gas:** Citgo, Exxon/ diesel, Fina/diesel, **food:** Domino's, Sonic, Subway, Whataburger/24hr, **other:** Brookshire Foods, NAPA, **S...gas:** Chevron/24hr, RaceTrac, Texaco/ diesel/24hr, **food:** BBQ, Burger King, Church's, KFC, McDonald's, Sammy's Rest., Taco Bell, Howard Johnson/rest., **lodging:** Royal Inn, **other:** AutoZone, Eckerd, Family$, Kroger, Radio Shack, Rite Aid, repair/transmissions
5	LA 173, Blanchard Rd, **S...gas:** Citgo
2	Lakeshore Dr, no facilities
1a	Jefferson Paige Rd, **S...food:** Denny's, **lodging:** Best Value Inn, Best Western, Day's Inn, Ramada Inn, Super 8
b	I-20, E to Shreveport, W to Dallas. I-220 begins/ends on I-20, exit 11.

Shreveport

E ↕ W

Interstate 610(New Orleans)

	I-610 begins/ends on I-10
4	Franklin Ave(from eb), no facilities
3	Elysian fields, **N...**HOSPITAL, **S...gas:** Chevron, Shell, **food:** Burger King, McDonald's
2b	US 90, N Broad St, New Orleans St, no facilities
2c	Paris Ave(from wb, no return), **S...gas:** Shell/24hr, Spur, **food:** Popeye's
2a	St Bernard Ave(from eb), to LSU School of Dentistry, auto racetrack
1a	Canal Blvd, **S...gas:** Shell
1b	I-10, to New Orleans

I-610 begins/ends on I-10

E ↕ W

MAINE

Maine

Interstate 95

N ↑ ↓ S

Exit #(mm)Services

305mm   US/Canada border, Maine state line, US Customs. I-95 begins/ends.

63(304)   US 2, to Houlton, **E…other:** Houlton Airport, Ammex Duty Free Shop

303mm   Meduxnekeag River

62(302)   US 1, Houlton, **E…gas:** Irving/diesel/24hr, **food:** Burger King, KFC, McDonald's, Pizza Hut, **other:** HOSPITAL, Martin's Foods, Rite Aid, **W…rest area both lanes, full(handicapped)facilities, phone,**

Houlton

picnic tables, litter barrels, petwalk, gas: Citgo/ Subway/diesel, Exxon/diesel/LP, Irving/diesel, **food:** Tim Horton, York's DairyBar, **lodging:** Ivey's Motel, Shiretown Motel/rest., **other:** Chevrolet/Pontiac/Buick, Ford/Lincoln/Mercury, Shop&Save, Wal-Mart

301mm   B Stream

61(291)   US 2, to Smyrna, **E…lodging:** Brookside Motel/rest.

60(286)   Oakfield Rd, to ME 11, Eagle Lake, Ashland, **W…gas:** Irving/diesel, Mobil/diesel, **food:** A Place To Eat, Cross-Roads Café, Glen's Place

277mm   Mattawamkeag River, W Branch

59(276)   ME 159, Island Falls, **E…gas:** Citgo/LP, Mobil/diesel, **other:** Bishop's Mkt, **W…**to Baxter SP(N entrance), RV camping

58(264)   Sherman, to ME 11, **E…gas:** Mobil/diesel/rest., **W… gas:** Irving/diesel, **lodging:** Katahdin Valley Motel, **other:** to Baxter SP(N entrance)

57(259)   Benedicta(from nb, no re-entry), no facilities

252mm   scenic view nb

247mm   Salmon Stream

MAINE

Interstate 95

56(245) ME 157, to Medway, E Millinocket, **W...gas:** Irving/diesel, **lodging:** Gateway Inn, **other:** HOSPITAL, Pine Grove Camping(4mi), USPO, to Baxter SP(S entrance)

244mm Penobscot River

243mm **rest area both lanes, full(handicapped)facilities, phone, picnic tables, litter barrels, petwalk**

55(227) to US 2, ME 6, Lincoln, **4 mi E...**HOSPITAL, gas, food, lodging, RV camping

219mm Piscataquis River

54(216) ME 6, Howland, **E...gas:** Irving/95 Diner/diesel, **food:** Little Peters Rest., **other:** 95er Towing/repair, camping

201mm Birch Stream

53(200) ME 16(no nb re-entry), to LaGrange, no facilities

199mm rest area/weigh sta both lanes

52(197) ME 43, to Old Town, **E...**gas/diesel

196mm Pushaw Stream

51(193) Stillwater Ave, to Old Town, **E...gas:** Citgo/diesel, Irving/diesel, Mobil/diesel, **food:** Burger King, China Garden, DQ, Governor's Rest., KFC, McDonald's, Subway, Taco Bell, **lodging:** Best Western, **other:** Ames, IGA Foods, mall

50(190) Kelly Rd, to Orono, **2-3 mi E...**gas, food, lodging, camping

49(187) Hogan Rd, Bangor Mall Blvd, to Bangor, **E...gas:** Citgo, **food:** Denny's, **other:** HOSPITAL, Audi/VW, Chevrolet/Cadillac, Chrysler/Plymouth/Dodge, Daewoo/Suzuki, Firestone/auto, Ford, GMC/Isuzu, Honda/Nissan/Volvo, Mitsubishi/Hyundai/Mercedes/Saab/Subaru, Saturn, Sam's Club, **W...gas:** Citgo/diesel, Exxon/diesel, **food:** Applebee's, Arby's, Asian Palace, Bugaboo Creek Café, Burger King, China Wall, KFC, McDonald's, 99 Rest., Olive Garden, Oriental Jade, Papa Gino's, Paul's Rest., Pizza Hut, Pizzaria Uno, Red Lobster, Subway, Wendy's, **lodging:** Bangor Motel, Comfort Inn, Country Inn, Hampton Inn, **other:** Advance Parts, Best Buy, Borders Books, Goodyear/auto, Home Depot, JC Penney, Jo-Ann Fabrics, K-Mart, Lincoln/Mercury/Kia, Sears/auto, Shaw's Foods, Shop&Save, Staples, Target, Wal-Mart, mall

48a(186) Stillwater Ave, same as 49

48(185) ME 15, to Broadway, Bangor, **E...gas:** Irving, **food:** Tri-City Pizza, **other:** HOSPITAL, **W...gas:** Exxon, Mobil, **food:** China Light, DQ, Friendly's, Governor's Rest., KFC, Mamma Baldacci's, McDonald's, Pizza Hut, Subway, **other:** Firestone, Hannaford Foods, Mazda, Pontiac, Rite Aid

47(184) ME 222, Union St, to Ohio St, Bangor, **E...gas:** Citgo, Exxon, **W...gas:** Exxon, Mobil/diesel, **food:** Burger King, Dunkin Donuts, McDonald's, Nicky's Diner, Papa Gino's, Wendy's, **lodging:** Sheraton, **other:** Cadillac, Chrysler/Jeep, Hannaford's Foods, Radio Shack, Staples

46(183) US 2, ME 2, Hammond St, Bangor, **E...gas:** Exxon, Gulf, **food:** Corner Store, Papa Gambino's Pizza, Subway, **other:** NAPA

Bangor / Waterville

45b(182) US 2, ME 100 W, **W...gas:** Irving/diesel, Mobil/diesel, **food:** Dunkin Donuts, Ground Round, **lodging:** Day's Inn, Econolodge, Fairfield Inn, Holiday Inn, Howard Johnson, Motel 6, Ramada Inn, Super 8, Travelodge, **other:** RV camping

a I-395, to US 2, US 1A, Bangor, downtown

44(180) Cold Brook Rd, to Hampden, **E...**Citgo, **W...gas:** Citgo/diesel/24hr/@, **lodging:** Best Western, **other:** diesel repair

178mm **rest area sb, full(handicapped)facilities, info, phone, vending, picnic tables, litter barrels, petwalk**

177mm Soudabscook Stream

176mm **rest area nb, full(handicapped)facilities, info, phone, vending, picnic tables, litter barrels, petwalk**

43(174) ME 69, to Carmel, **E...gas:** Citgo/diesel, **W...**RV camping

42(167) ME 69, ME 143, to Etna, no facilities

41(161) ME 7, to E Newport, Plymouth, **E...**lodging, LP, **W...**RV camping

40(159) Ridge Rd(from sb), to Plymouth, Newport, no facilities

39(157) to US 2, ME 7, ME 11, Newport, **E...**HOSPITAL, **W...gas:** Citgo, Exxon, Irving/diesel/24hr, Mobil/diesel, **food:** Burger King, China Way, Dunkin Donuts, McDonald's, Sawyers Dairybar, Scotty's Diner, Subway, **lodging:** Lovley's Motel, **other:** MEDICAL CARE, CarQuest, Chrysler/Plymouth/Jeep, NAPA, Radio Shack, Rite Aid, Shop&Save, Wal-Mart SuperCtr/24hr

151mm Sebasticook River

38(150) Somerset Ave, Pittsfield, **E...gas:** Mobil, **food:** Subway, **other:** HOSPITAL, Chevrolet, Family$, NAPA, Rite Aid, Shop&Save Foods

147mm **rest area both lanes, full(handicapped)facilities, phone, picnic tables, litter barrels, petwalk**

37(137) Hinckley Rd, Clinton, **W...gas:** Citgo/diesel/LP

134mm Kennebec River

36(133) US 201, Fairfield, **E...gas: food:** Purple Cow Pancakes, **W...other:** Fairfield Creamery, Old NE CandleStore

35(132) ME 139, Fairfield, **E...gas:** Shell/deli, **W...gas:** Citgo/Subway/diesel

34(130) ME 104, Main St, Waterville, **E...gas:** Mobil, **food:** Arby's, Friendly's, Governor's Rest., McDonald's, Ruby Tuesday, Wendy's, **lodging:** Best Western, Comfort Inn, Holiday Inn, **other:** HOSPITAL, Advance Parts, Hannaford Foods, Home Depot, JC Penney, K-Mart, Mazda/VW, Mr Paperback, Radio Shack, Sears, Staples

129mm Messalonskee Stream

33(121) ME 11, ME 137, Waterville, Oakland, **E...gas:** Citgo/Burger King, Irving/diesel/24hr, Mobil, **food:** Angelo's Steaks, Applebee's, McDonald's, Pizza Hut, Subway, Thai Dish, Weathervane Seafood, **lodging:** Budget Host, Econolodge, Hampton Inn, **other:** HOSPITAL, Chevrolet/Pontiac/Buick, Cadillac/Toyota, Chrysler/Plymouth/Dodge/Jeep, Nissan, Mr Paperback, Rite Aid, Shaw's Food/gas/24hr, Wal-Mart/grill, **W...gas:** Exxon/diesel, Valero, **food:** China Express, **other:** CarQuest, Ford/Lincoln/Mercury

32(120) Lyons Rd, Sidney, no facilities

Interstate 95

N ↕ S

Augusta

117mm	rest area sb, full(handicapped)facilities, phone, vending, picnic tables, litter barrels, petwalk
113mm	rest area nb, full(handicapped)facilities, phone, vending, picnic tables, litter barrels, petwalk
31(106)	ME 27, ME 8, ME 11, Augusta, **E...gas:** Citgo, Getty, **food:** Capt's Seafood, Ground Round, Olive Garden, Panera Bread, **lodging:** Holiday Inn, **other:** Barnes&Noble, Home Depot, Old Navy, Sam's Club, Staples, Wal-Mart SuperCtr/24hr, **W...gas:** Irving/diesel/24hr, **food:** 99 Rest., Wendy's, **lodging:** Comfort Inn, **other:** Mitsubishi/Volvo, Vet Cem
105mm	Bond Brook
30(103)	US 202, ME 11, ME 17, ME 100, Augusta, **E...gas:** Citgo, Irving/diesel, Shell, **food:** Applebee's, Arby's, Burger King, Capitol Buffet, Damon's Subs, Domino's, DQ, Friendly's, KFC, McDonald's, Pizza Hut, Subway, Wendy's, **lodging:** Best Western, **other:** $Tree, K-Mart, Shaw's Foods, USPO, **W...gas:** Exxon, Getty, **food:** Bonanza, Margarita's Mexican, **lodging:** Best Inn, Econolodge, Motel 6, Super 8, **other:** CarQuest, Chrysler/Jeep/Nissan/Subaru, Dodge/Plymouth/Hyundai, Pontiac, Shop&Save/24hr, Sears/auto, Toyota
14	ME TPK/I-495. Maine Turnpike and I-95 run together nb, divide sb.
28(100)	ME 9, ME 126, to Gardiner, Litchfield, TOLL PLAZA, **W...gas**, last free nb exit
27(94)	US 201, to Gardiner, **E...gas/diesel, W...gas**, RV camping
26(88)	ME 197, to Richmond, **E...gas:** Citgo/diesel
25(81.5)	ME 125, Bowdoinham, no facilities
24(75)	ME 196, to Lisbon, Topsham, **E...gas:** Irving, **food:** Arby's, McDonald's, 99 Rest., Subway, Wendy's, **lodging:** Hannaford Foods, NAPA, Radio Shack, Rite Aid, mall
74.5mm	Androscoggin River
22(73)	US 1, Bath, **1 mi E on US 1...gas:** Gulf, Irving/diesel, Mobil/diesel, **food:** Dunkin Donuts, McDonald's, Thai House, **lodging:** Comfort Inn, Econolodge, MaineLine Motel, Travelers Inn, **other:** HOSPITAL, Chevrolet/Mazda, Ford
71mm	parking area southbound
21(68)	to Freeport(from nb), facilities 1 mi E on US 1
20(67)	ME 125, to Pownal, **E on US 1...gas:** Exxon, **food:** Arby's, Friendly's, McDonald's, Taco Bell, **other:** MEDICAL CARE, LL Bean, USPO, outlet mall/famous brands, **W...to** Bradbury Mtn SP
19(65)	Desert Rd, Freeport, **E...gas:** Citgo, **food:** Friendly's, **lodging:** Coastline Inn, Comfort Inn, Hampton Inn, Super 8, **other:** outlet mall/famous brands, RV camping
17(62)	US 1, Yarmouth, **E...rest area both lanes, full(handicapped)facilities, info, food:** Bill's Pizza, Muddy Rudder Rest., **lodging:** Best Western, **other:** Ford, Delorme Mapping, **W...gas:** Citgo/diesel, Shell, **food:** Bill's Pizza, McDonald's, Pat's Pizza, **lodging:** DownEast Village Motel, **other:** MEDICAL CARE, Shop&Save

Portland

16(59.5)	US 1, to Cumberland, Yarmouth, **W...gas:** Exxon, Mobil, **food:** 233 Grill, **lodging:** Brookside Motel, **other:** Rite Aid
15(55)	I-295 S, **US 1 S...gas:** Exxon/diesel, Gulf/diesel, Mobil, **food:** Dunkin Donuts, McDonald's, Moose Crossing Rest., **other:** Goodyear, Rite Aid, Shaw's Foods
54mm	toll booth
9(49)	I-495 N, to Lewiston, no facilities
8(48)	ME 25, to Portland, **E...gas:** Citgo, **food:** Applebee's, Burger King, ME Buffet, Subway, **lodging:** Ramada Ltd, **other:** BJ's Whse/gas, Jo-Ann Fabrics, Shaw's Foods, **W...gas:** Exxon, Mobil/diesel, Shell/Subway, **food:** DQ, Denny's, Friendly's, KFC, McDonald's, Pizza Hut, Verrillo's Rest., Wendy's, **lodging:** Howard Johnson, Motel 6, Super 8, Travelodge, **other:** Chrysler/Plymouth/Dodge/Jeep, DD Auto Parts, Ford/Hyundai, Home Depot, NAPA, Shop&Save, Tire Whse, VIP Auto
47mm	Stroudwater River
7b	to ME 25, Rand Rd, no facilities
7a(46)	to ME 22, Congress St, same as 7
7(43)	to US 1, Maine Mall Rd, S Portland, **E...gas:** Mobil, Shell/diesel, **food:** Burger King, Bugaboo Creek Steaks, Chili's, Friendly's, Great Wall Chinese, Ground Round, IHOP, LoneStar Steaks, Longhorn Steaks, Macaroni Grill, McDonald's, Old Country Buffet, Olive Garden, On the Border, Panera Bread, Pizza Hut, Pizzaria Uno, Ruby Tuesday, Tim Horton's, Weathervane Seafood, Wendy's, **lodging:** Coastline Inn, Comfort Inn, Day's Inn, Fairfield Inn, Hampton Inn, Residence Inn, Sheraton Tara, **other:** AAA, Best Buy, Borders Books, Circuit City, Filene's, Ground Round, Honda, JC Penney, Lexus/Subaru/Toyota, Macy's, Marshall's, OfficeMax, Sears/auto, Shaw's Foods, Shop'n Save, Staples, mall, **W...food:** Applebee's, **lodging:** AmeriSuites, Marriott, **other:** Target
6a(42)	I-295 N(from nb), to S Portland, Scarborough, **E...other:** HOSPITAL, Sam's Club, Wal-Mart(1mi)
41mm	Nonesuch River
6(39)	to US 1, **E...**Scarborough Downs Racetrack(seasonal)
5(36)	I-195 E, to Saco, Old Orchard Beach, no facilities
35mm	**E...lodging:** Holiday Inn Express/Saco Hotel Conference Ctr
33mm	Saco River

MAINE

Interstate 95

N↕S

Kittery (vertical text)

4(29)	ME 111, to Biddeford, **E...gas:** Irving/diesel, **food:** Wendy's, **lodging:** Comfort Inn, **other:** HOSPITAL, AutoZone, Ford, Shaw's Foods, Wal-Mart SuperCtr/24hr, **W...**Home Depot
25mm	Kennebunk River
3(24)	ME 35, Kennebunk Beach, **E...lodging:** Turnpike Motel
24mm	**service plaza both lanes, sb...Mobil/diesel, Burger King, Popeye's, TCBY, gifts, nb...Mobil/diesel, Burger King, Popeye's, TCBY, atm, gifts**
19.5mm	Merriland River
2(18)	ME 9, ME 109, to Wells, Sanford, **W...**to Sanford RA
6mm	Maine Tpk begins/ends, toll booth
4(5.8)	ME 91, to US 1, to The Yorks, **E...gas:** Irving/diesel, Mobil, Shell, **food:** Canellie's Deli, Foodee's Pizza, Norma's Cafe, Ruby's Grill, **other:** HOSPITAL, Family$, Ford, Shop&Save Foods, last exit before toll rd nb
5.5mm	weigh sta nb
5mm	York River
4mm	weigh sta sb
3mm	**Welcome Ctr nb, full(handicapped)facilities, info, phone, vending, picnic tables, litter barrels, petwalk**
2(2)	(2 & 3 from nb), US 1, to Kittery, **E...gas:** Citgo/Taco Bell/diesel, Getty, Mobil/diesel, **food:** Burger King, Clam Hut Diner, DQ, McDonald's, Quarterdeck Rest., Subway, Weathervane Seafood, **lodging:** Super 8, **other:** FSA/Tanger/famous brands, **W...gas:** Mobil
1	ME 103(from nb, no re-entry), to Kittery, **E...gas:** Citgo, Sunoco, **lodging:** Blue Roof Motel/diner, Day's Inn, NorthEaster Motel, Rex Motel, Super 8, **other:** Navy Yard
0mm	Maine/New Hampshire state line, Piscataqua River

Interstate 295

N↕S

Portland (vertical text)

Exit #(mm)Services
I-295 begins/ends on I-95, exit 15.

10	US 1, to Falmouth, **E...gas:** Exxon/diesel, Gulf/diesel, Mobil, **food:** Dunkin Donuts, McDonald's, Moose Crossing Rest., **other:** Goodyear, Rite Aid, Shaw's Foods
9mm	Presumpscot River
9	US 1 S, ME 26, to Baxter Blvd, **W...**The Diner
8	ME 26 S, Washington Ave, **E...other:** U-Haul
7	US 1A, Franklin St, **E...other:** CarQuest, NAPA
6b a	US 1, Forest Ave, **E...gas:** Mobil, **other:** HOSPITAL, AAA, Firestone/auto, Wild Oats Mkt, **W...food:** Arby's, Bleacher's Rest., Burger King, Pizza Hut, **other:** Hannaford Foods
5b a	ME 22, Congress St, **E...food:** Denny's, McDonald's, **lodging:** Fairfield Inn, **other:** HOSPITAL, **W...gas:** Citgo, Getty, Mobil/diesel, **food:** Ananias Italian, **lodging:** DoubleTree Hotel
3mm	Fore River

Lewiston (vertical text, right of I-95 column)

4	US 1 S, to Main St, to S Portland, facilities on US 1 away from exit
3	ME 9, to Westbrook St, **W...gas:** Irving/diesel, Mobil/diesel, **food:** Burger King, LoneStar Steaks, Olive Garden, Outback Steaks, TGIFriday, **other:** Chevrolet, Home Depot
2	to US 1 S, to S Portland, services on US 1, **E on US 1...gas:** Citgo/7-11, Exxon, Irving/diesel, Mobil, **food:** Dunkin Donuts, Governor's Rest., Tony Roma's, Yankee Grill, **lodging:** Best Western, Day's Inn, Quality Inn, **other:** Discount Tire
1	to I-95, to US 1, services on US 1, same as 2

I-295 begins/ends on I-95, exit 6a.

Interstate 495

Exit #(mm)Services
Maine Tpk begins/ends at exit 30 on I-95. I-495 portion of Maine Tpk begins/ends at 100mm.

14b(100)	I-95 S, ME 9, ME 126, to Gardiner
a	I-95 N
97.5mm	toll plaza
95mm	**service plaza nb, Mobil/diesel, Burger King, TCBY, atm, gifts**
82.5mm	Sabattus Creek
81mm	**service plaza sb, Mobil/diesel, Burger King, TCBY, atm, gifts**
13(78)	to ME 196, Lewiston, **W on ME 196...gas:** Getty, Mobil/diesel, Shell, Sunoco, **food:** Cathay Hut Chinese, Chalet Rest., D'angelo's, Dunkin Donuts, Fanny's Diner, Governor's Rest., KFC/Taco Bell, McDonald's, Wendy's, **lodging:** Motel 6, Ramada Inn, Super 8, **other:** HOSPITAL, Rite Aid, Shaw's Foods
76.5mm	Androscoggin River
12(73)	US 202, rd 4, rd 100, to Auburn, **E...gas:** Irving/Blimpie/Taco Bell/diesel, **food:** KnuckleHeads Buffet, **lodging:** Auburn Inn, **other:** HOSPITAL, RV camping, **W...**HOSPITAL
69mm	Royal River
64.5mm	toll plaza
11(61)	US 202, rd 115, rd 4, to ME 26, Gray, **E...gas:** Exxon, Gulf, Mobil, Shell, **food:** Dunkin Donuts, Subway, McDonald's, **other:** Rite Aid, Thriftway Foods
57mm	**service plaza nb, Mobil/diesel, Burger King, TCBY, atm, gifts**
56mm	**service plaza sb, Mobil/diesel, Burger King, TCBY, atm, gifts**
53mm	Piscataqua River
10(50)	to ME 26, ME 100 W, N Portland, **E...food:** Dunkin Donuts, Patty's Rest., **other:** HOSPITAL, Hannaford Foods
49mm	Presumpscot River
9(49)	I-95 N and S, to US 1

I-495 portion of Maine Tpk begins/ends at exit 9, 49mm.

Interstate 68

Exit #	Services
82c	I-70 W, to Breezewood. I-68 begins/ends on I-70, exit 1.
b	I-70 E, US 40 E, to Hagerstown
a	US 522, Hancock, **N**...Chevrolet, Chrysler/Dodge/ Jeep, **S**...gas: Lowest Price, Sheetz/24hr, **food:** Hardee's, Pizza Hut, Park'n Dine, Weaver's Rest., **lodging:** Hancock Motel, Super 8, **other:** $General, Happy Hills Camping, SavALot Foods
77	US 40, MD 144, Woodmont Rd, **S**...RV camping
75mm	runaway truck ramp eb
74mm	**Sideling Hill rest area/exhibit both lanes, full(ha ndicapped)facilities, vending, 1269 ft**
74	US 40, Mountain Rd(no return from eb), no facilities
73mm	Sideling Hill Creek
72mm	truck ramp wb
72	US 40, High Germany Rd, Swain Rd, **S**...gas: Amoco/ diesel
68	Orleans Rd, **N**...gas: Exxon/diesel
67mm	Town Hill, elevation 940 ft
64	MV Smith Rd, **S**...to Green Ridge SF HQ, scenic overlook, phone, 1040 ft
62	US 40, 15 Mile Creek Rd, **N**...Bill Meyer Wildlife Mgt Area
58.7mm	Polish Mtn, elevation 1246 ft
57mm	Town Creek
56mm	Flintstone Creek
56	MD 144, National Pike, Flintstone, **S**...gas: Sunoco, USPO
52	MD 144, Pleasant Valley Rd, National Pike, no facilities
50	Pleasant Valley Rd, **N**...lodging: Rocky Gap Lodge/ golf/rest., **other:** to Rocky Gap SP
47	US 220 N, MD 144, Old National Pike, Dehaven Rd(from wb), Bedford, same as 46
46	US 220 N, Dehaven Rd, Baltimore Pike, Naves Crossroads, **N**...food: Lindy's Rest., **lodging:** Cumberland Motel, MD Motel, **other:** Great Valu Foods, **S**...food: JB's SteakCellar, Mason's Barn Rest., Uncle Tucker's Pizza, **lodging:** Exit 46 Motel, Folcks Mill Inn/rest.
45	Hillcrest Dr, **S**...gas: BP/diesel
44	US 40A, Baltimore Ave, Willow Brook Rd, to Allegany Comm Coll
43d	Maryland Ave(from eb), **N**...HOSPITAL, USPO, **S**... gas: Liberty/Subway/diesel
c	(from wb), same as 43b
b	Maryland Ave, **N**...food: McDonald's, **lodging:** Holiday Inn, **S**...gas: Amoco, Citgo/diesel, **food:** Pizza Hut/ Taco Bell, Roy Rogers, Wendy's
a	to WV 28A, Beall St, Industrial Blvd, to Cumberland, **N**...gas: Sheetz
42	US 220 S, Greene St, Ridgedale, phone
41	Seton Dr(from wb)
41mm	Haystack Mtn, elev 1240 ft

Cumberland

40	US 220 S, to US 40A, Vocke Rd, La Vale, **N**...gas: BP, Citgo/diesel, Exxon, Mobil, **food:** Arby's, Bob Evans, Burger King, D'Atri Rest., Dairy Queen, Denny's, KFC, LJ Silver, McDonald's, Oriental Rest., Pizza Hut, Ruby Tuesday, Texas Grill, Wendy's, **lodging:** Best Western, Comfort Inn, Continental Motel, Slumberland Motel, Super 8, **other:** HOSPITAL, Advance Parts, CVS Drug, $General, Giant Foods, Ford, Harley-Davidson, Lowe's Whse, Staples, st police, **S**...food: ChiChi's, China Buffet, Ponderosa, **lodging:** OakTree Inn, **other:** $Tree, JC Penney, Kelly Tire, Martin Foods, Sears/auto, Trak Auto, Wal-Mart/drugs, mall
39	US 40A(from wb), same as 40
34	MD 36, to Westernport, Frostburg, **N**...gas: Amoco, Sheetz, **food:** Burger King, McDonald's, Pizza Hut, Pizza Outlet, **lodging:** Day's Inn, Hotel Gunter, Hampton Inn, **other:** HOSPITAL, $General, Food Lion, Rite Aid, **S**...to Dans Mtn SP
33	Midlothian Rd, to Frostburg, **N**...HOSPITAL, **S**...to Dans Mt SP
31mm	weigh sta eb
30mm	Big Savage Mtn, elevation 2800 ft
29	MD 546, Finzel, **N**...Mason-Dixon Camping(4mi/seasonal)
25.8mm	eastern continental divide, elevation 2610 ft
24	Lower New Germany Rd, to US 40A, **S**...to New Germany SP, to Savage River SF
23mm	Meadow Mtn, elevation 2780 ft
22	US 219 N, to Meyersville, **N**...gas: BP/diesel/24hr, Exxon, **food:** Burger King, Penn Alps Rest., Subway, **lodging:** Elliott House Inn, **other:** Hilltop Fruit Mkt, **S**...gas: Amoco, **lodging:** Holiday Inn
20mm	Casselman River
19	MD 495, to US 40A, Grantsville, **N**...gas: Exxon/diesel, Mobil, **food:** Penn Alps Rest., **lodging:** Casselman Motel/ rest., Elliott House Inn, **other:** Beachy's Drug, CarQuest, Chevrolet, USPO

MARYLAND

Interstate 68

15mm	Mt Negro, elevation 2980 ft
14mm	Keyser's Ridge, elevation 2880 ft
14b a	US 219, US 40 W, Oakland, **N...gas:** Citgo/diesel, Keyser's Ridge/Amoco/diesel/rest., **food:** McDonald's, repair
6mm	**Welcome Ctr eb, full(handicapped)facilities, info, phone, picnic tables, litter barrels, vending, petwalk**
4.5mm	Bear Creek
4mm	Youghiogheny River
4	MD 42, Friendsville, **N...gas:** Amoco/diesel, Citgo/diesel, **food:** Old Mill Rest., **lodging:** Yough Valley Motel, **other:** S&S Mkt, USPO, **S...lodging:** Sunset Inn, **other:** to Deep Creek Lake SP, camping
0mm	Maryland/West Virginia state line

Interstate 70

Exit # Services

I-70 begins/ends in Baltimore at Cooks Lane.

94	Security Blvd N, **S...gas:** Shell
91b a	I-695, **N off exit 17...gas:** Citgo/7-11, **food:** McDonald's, **lodging:** Day's Inn, Motel 6, Ramada, **other:** Best Buy, Firestone/auto, JC Penney, Old Navy, Sears/auto, Staples, mall
87b a	US 29(exits left from wb)to MD 99, Columbia, **2 mi S on US 40...gas:** Amoco/diesel, Shell, **food:** Burger King, Giardino's Italian, Lotte Oriental, McDonald's, Subway, Wendy's, **other:** Advance Parts, Chevrolet, Honda, Nissan, Pontiac/Isuzu/GMC/Volvo, Rite Aid, SuperFresh Food, Wal-Mart
83	US 40, Marriottsville(no EZ wb return), **2 mi S...lodging:** Turf Valley Hotel/Country Club/rest.
82	US 40 E(from eb), same as 83
80	MD 32, Sykesville, **N...golf, S...gas:** Citgo
79mm	weigh sta wb, phone
76	MD 97, Olney, **S...gas:** Citgo
73	MD 94, Woodbine, **N...gas:** Shell, **food:** McDonald's, Pizza Hut, **other:** Ramblin Pines RV Park(6mi), SuperMkt, **S...gas:** Amoco/diesel, Citgo
68	MD 27, Mt Airy, **N...gas:** Amoco/Blimpie/diesel/24hr, Citgo/7-11, Shell, **food:** Arby's, Burger King, Domino's, KFC, Ledo's Pizza, McDonald's, Pizza Hut, Roy Rogers, TCBY, **other:** Chrysler/Plymouth/Dodge/Jeep, Rite Aid, Safeway, SuperFresh Foods, Wal-Mart/auto, **S...gas:** Exxon/diesel/24hr, 4 Seasons Rest.
66mm	truckers parking area eb
64mm	weigh sta eb
62	MD 75, Libertytown, **N...gas:** Mobil/diesel, Shell, **food:** McDonald's, **other:** New Market Hist Dist
59	MD 144, no facilities
57mm	Monocacy River
56	MD 144, **N...gas:** Citgo, Sheetz, **food:** Beijing Chinese, Burger King, McDonald's, JR's Pizza, Roy Rogers, Taco Bell, Waffle House, **other:** $General, to Hist Dist
55	South St, no facilities
54	Market St, to I-270, **N...gas:** Costco, **lodging:** Travelodge, **S...gas:** Citgo, Exxon/diesel, Sheetz/24hr, Shell/24hr, SouStates/diesel, **food:** Bob Evans, Burger King, Checker's, Cracker Barrel, El Paso Cantina, Jerry's Rest., KFC, McDonald's, Pargo's Café, Peking Gourmet, Popeye's, Roy Rogers, Subway, Wendy's,

	Day's Inn/rest., **lodging:** Econolodge, Fairfield Inn, Hampton Inn, Holiday Inn Express, **other:** Aamco, Best Buy, Chrysler/Plymouth, Circuit City, Ford/Lincoln/Mercury/Isuzu, Honda, Hyundai/Buick, Kohl's, Lowe's Whse, OfficeMax, PrecisionTune, Sam's Club, Saturn, Sears/auto, Wal-Mart/auto, mall
53b a	I-270 S, US 15 N, US 40 W, to Frederick, no facilities
52b a	US 15 S, US 340 W, Leesburg, no facilities
49	US 40A(no EZ wb return), Braddock Heights, **N on US 40...gas:** Chevron, Citgo/diesel, Exxon/diesel, Freestate/diesel, Liberty/diesel, Shell/repair, Sunoco, 7-11, **food:** Arby's, BBQ, Bob Evans, Boston Mkt, Burger King, ChiChi's, Denny's, Fritchie's Rest., Ground Round, McDonald's, Mtn View Diner, Outback Steaks, Pizza Hut, Popeye's, Res Horse Rest., Red Lobster, Taco Bell, Wendy's, **lodging:** Comfort Inn, Holiday Inn, **other:** HOSPITAL, Ford/Subaru, Giant Eagle Foods, Goodyear, Home Depot, JC Penney, Merchant Tire, PepBoys, Toyota, st police, **S...to** Washington Mon SP, camping
48	US 40 E, US 340(from eb, no return), **1 mi N...same as** 49
42	MD 17, Myersville, **N...gas:** Exxon, Sunoco/diesel/24hr, **food:** Burger King, McDonald's, **other:** to Gambrill SP(6mi), Greenbrier SP(4mi), **S...gas:** BP/diesel
39mm	**rest area both lanes, full(handicapped)facilities, phone, vending, picnic tables, litter barrels, petwalk**
35	MD 66, to Boonsboro, **S...gas:** Sheetz, **other:** to Greenbrier SP, camping
32b a	US 40, Hagerstown, **1-3 mi N...gas:** BP/Blimpie, AC&T/24hr, Citgo/7-11, Exxon/diesel, **food:** Bob Evans, Burger King, DQ, Denny's, Ledo's Pizza, McDonald's, Pizza Hut, Quizno's, Red Horse Steaks, Subway, Taco Bell, Texas Roadhouse, **lodging:** Clarion, Comfort Suites, Day's Inn, Hampton Inn, Holiday Inn/rest., Quality Inn, Sheraton, Super 8, **other:** HOSPITAL, Chevrolet/Cadillac, Chrysler/Plymouth/Dodge, CVS Drug, Goodyear/auto, Martin Foods, Mercedes/Toyota, Nissan, Subaru/VW/Mazda, Weis Foods, **S...other:** Honda, Kia, Pontiac/Buick/GMC
29b a	MD 65, to Sharpsburg, **N...gas:** Exxon/diesel/24hr, Sheetz/24hr, Sunoco/diesel/24hr, **food:** FoodCourt, Longhorn Steaks, Pizza Hut, Subway, TCBY, **other:** HOSPITAL, Prime Outlets/famous brands, st police, **S...gas:** Shell/Blimpie/diesel/24hr, **food:** Burger King, Cracker Barrel, McDonald's, Waffle House, Wendy's, **lodging:** Sleep Inn, **other:** Safari Camping, to Antietam Bfd
28	MD 632, Hagerstown, **N...food:** Burger King, Chick-fil-A, Pizza Hut, Roy Rogers, Shoney's, Western Sizzlin, **S...** Jellystone Camping
26	I-81, N to Harrisburg, S to Martinsburg, no facilities
24	MD 63, Huyett, **N...gas:** Pilot/Subway/diesel/24hr, Sheetz(2mi), **S...lodging:** Red Roof Inn, **other:** KOA(2mi), C&O Canal
18	MD 68 E, Clear Spring, **N...gas:** BP, **food:** McDonald's, **S...gas:** Exxon/diesel, **food:** Wendy Hill Café
12	MD 56, Indian Springs, **S...gas:** Exxon/diesel, **other:** Ft Frederick SP
9	US 40 E(from eb, exits left), Indian Springs, no facilities
5	MD 615(no immediate wb return), **N...**Log Cabin Rest.(2mi)
3	MD 144, Hancock(exits left from wb), **S...gas:** ACT/diesel, BP/diesel/rest./24hr/@, **food:** Shive's Subs, Hardee's, Park'n Dine, Pizza Hut, Weaver's Rest., **lodging:** Hancock Motel, Super 8, **other:** Ford, NAPA, repair

MARYLAND

Interstate 70

E / W

1b US 522(exits left from eb), Hancock, **N...**Chevrolet, Chrysler/Dodge/Jeep, **S...gas:** Lowest Price/diesel, Sheetz/24hr, **food:** Park'n Dine, Pizza Hut, Weaver's Rest., **lodging:** Hancock Motel, Super 8, **other:** $General, Sav-A-Lot Foods, Happy Hills Camp

1a I-68 W, US 40, W to Cumberland, no facilities

0mm Maryland/Pennsylvania state line, Mason-Dixon Line

Interstate 81

N / S Hagerstown

Exit # Services

12mm Maryland/Pennsylvania state line

10b a Showalter Rd, **E...lodging:** Colonial Motel, Hampton Inn, **W...**Microtel

9 Maugans Ave, **E...gas:** Mobil, Sheetz, Shell/Domino's/diesel, **food:** Antrim House Rest., McDonald's, Pizza Hut, Taco Bell, Waffle House, **lodging:** Colonial Motel, Hampton Inn, **W...food:** Burger King, Family Time Rest., **lodging:** Microtel

8 Maugansville Rd(from sb, no re-entry), same as 9

7b a MD 58, Hagerstown, same as 6

6b a US 40, Hagerstown, **E...gas:** Exxon/diesel, Liberty, Shell, **food:** Roy Rogers, Wendy's, **lodging:** Clarion, Days Inn, Holiday Motel, Quality Inn, **other:** HOSPITAL, **W...food:** Arby's, IHOP, KFC, McDonald's, #1 Chinese, Pizzaria Uno, Ryan's, Subway, TGIFriday, Wendy's, **other:** Borders Books, Circuit City, $Express, Home Depot, OfficeMax, Trak Parts, Wal-Mart SuperCtr/24hr

5 Halfway Blvd, **E...gas:** AC&T/diesel/rest., Sheetz, Shell, **food:** Boston Mkt, Chick-fil-A, Dynasty Buffet, Fazoli's, Ground Round, Little Caesar's, McDonald's, Olive Garden, Outback Steaks, Pizza Hut, Popeye's, Red Lobster, Roy Rogers, Ruby Tuesday, Shoney's, Taco Bell, Wendy's, **lodging:** Holiday Inn Express, Motel 6, Plaza Hotel, Travelodge, **other:** CVS Drug, $Tree, Firestone/auto, Ford/Lincoln/Mercury, Hyundai, JC Penney, K-Mart, Lowe's Whse, Martin's Foods, Michael's, Sam's Club/gas, Sears/auto, Staples, Target, mall, **W...gas:** AC&T, Exxon

4 I-70, E to Frederick, W to Hancock, to I-68

2 US 11, Williamsport, **E...gas:** AC&T/diesel, **food:** Burger King, **W...gas:** Exxon, Shell/diesel, Sunoco/diesel/24hr, **food:** McDonald's, Waffle House, **lodging:** Red Roof Inn, **other:** KOA(4mi)

1 MD 63, MD 68, Williamsport, **E...gas:** Bowman/diesel, **other:** Jellystone, KOA, to Antietam Bfd, **W...**Citgo

0mm Maryland/West Virginia state line, Potomac River

Interstate 83

N / S

Exit # Services

38mm Maryland/Pennsylvania state line, Mason-Dixon Line

37 to Freeland(from sb)

36 MD 439, Bel Air, **5 mi W...**Morris Meadows Camping

35mm weigh/insp sta sb

33 MD 45, Parkton, **E...gas:** Exxon/diesel

31 Middletown Rd, to Parkton, golf

27 MD 137, Mt Carmel, Hereford, **E...gas:** Exxon/diesel, **other:** MEDICAL CARE, Graul's Foods, Hereford Drug, USPO

24 Belfast Rd, to Butler, Sparks

20 Shawan Rd, Hunt Valley, **E...gas:** Amoco, Exxon/diesel, 7-11, **food:** Beijing Rest., Burger King, Carrabba's, Cinnamon Tree Rest., McDonald's, Outback Steaks, Valley View Rest., Wendy's, **lodging:** Chase Suites, Courtyard, Econolodge, Embassy Suites, Hampton Inn, Hunt Valley Marriott, **other:** Giant Foods, Goodyear/auto, Sears/auto, Wal-Mart, mall

18 Warren Rd(from nb, no return), Cockeysville, **E...**Exxon, SS/diesel, Residence Inn

17 Padonia Rd, Deereco Rd, **E...**Amoco/diesel, Applebee's, Bob Evans, Chili's, Denny's, Macaroni Grill, Day's Hotel, Extended Stay America, Goodyear/auto, Rite Aid, USPO

16b a Timonium Rd, **E...**Sunoco/diesel, Steak&Ale, Holiday Inn, Red Roof Inn, Infiniti, Saab

14 I-695 N, no facilities

13 I-695 S, Falls Rd, HOSPITAL, st police

12 Ruxton Rd(from nb, no return), no facilities

10b a Northern Parkway, **E...**HOSPITAL, Exxon, Texaco

9b a Cold Spring Lane, no facilities

8 MD 25 N(from nb), Falls Rd

7b a 28th St, **E...**HOSPITAL, **W...**Baltimore Zoo

6 US 1, US 40T, North Ave, downtown

5 MD Ave(from sb), downtown

3 Chase St, Gilford St, downtown

2 Pleasant St(from sb), downtown

1 Fayette St, downtown Baltimore, I-83 begins/ends. **S...**Bennigan's, Mo's Seafood Rest.

Baltimore

Interstate 95

N / S

Exit # Services

110mm Maryland/Delaware state line

109b a MD 279, to Elkton, Newark, **E...gas:** Citgo/diesel, Petro/Iron Skillet/diesel/rest./24hr/@, Shell/diesel, **food:** Cracker Barrel, KFC/Taco Bell, McDonald's, Waffle House, **lodging:** Econolodge, Elkton Lodge, Hampton Inn, Knight's Inn, Motel 6, **other:** HOSPITAL, Blue Beacon, **W...gas:** TA/Mobil/Subway/diesel/24hr/@, 7-11, **other:** to U of DE

100 MD 272, to North East, Rising Sun, **E...gas:** Flying j/diesel/rest./LP/24hr/@, **food:** McDonald's, Schroeder's Deli, Wendy's, **lodging:** Crystal Inn, Holiday Inn Express, **other:** Eckerd, museum, st police, to Elk Neck SP, **W...gas:** Citgo, Mobil, **other:** zoo

96mm **Chesapeake House service area(exits left from both lanes), Exxon/diesel, Sunoco/diesel, Burger King, HotDogs, Pizza Hut, Popeye's, Starbucks, TCBY, gifts**

93 MD 275, to Rising Sun, US 222, to Perryville, **E...gas:** Exxon/diesel, Pilot/Subway/diesel/24hr/@, **food:** Denny's, KFC/Taco Bell, **lodging:** Comfort Inn, **other:** HOSPITAL, Prime Outlets/famous brands, Riverview Camping, **W...food:** CM Tuggs Diner, Crother's Mkt, **lodging:** Douglass Motel, **other:** st police

205

MARYLAND

Interstate 95

Aberdeen

92mm	weigh sta/toll booth
91.5mm	Susquehanna River
89	MD 155, to Havre de Grace(last nb exit before toll), **1-3 mi E...food:** McDonald's, MacGregor's Rest., **lodging:** Best Budget Inn, Super 8, Swede Suites, **other:** HOSPITAL, **W...**to Susquehanna SP
85	MD 22, to Aberdeen, **E...gas:** Amoco/24hr, Citgo/7-11, Crown/diesel, Enroy, Sunoco/diesel, Shell/diesel/24hr, **food:** Arby's, Bob Evans, Family Buffet, Golden Corral, Japan House, KFC, King's Chinese, Lee's Hunan, Little Caesar's, McDonald's, Olive Tree Italian, Papa John's, Subway, Taco Bell, Wendy's, **lodging:** Day's Inn, Econolodge/rest., Holiday Inn, Quality Inn/rest., Red Roof, Sheraton, Super 8, Travelodge, **other:** $Express, $General, $Tree, GNC, Klein's Foods, K-Mart, Mars Foods, Pontiac/Cadillac, Radio Shack, Rite Aid, Target, museum
81mm	**MD House service area(exits left from both lanes), Exxon/diesel, Sunoco/diesel, Big Boy, Cinnabon, Hotdog City, Roy Rogers, Sbarro's, TCBY, gifts**
80	MD 543, to Riverside, Churchville, **E...gas:** BP/Burger King, Citgo/7-11, Crown/A&W/diesel, Mobil/diesel, **food:** China Moon, Cracker Barrel, Krispy Kreme, McDonald's, Riverside Pizzaria, Ruby Tuesday, Waffle House, **lodging:** Country Inn, Extended Stay America, SpringHill Suites, Wingate Inn, **other:** Eckerd, Klein's Foods, Bar Harbor RV Park(4mi)
77b a	MD 24, to Edgewood, Bel Air, **E...gas:** Citgo/diesel, Exxon/Blimpie/diesel, Shell, **food:** Burger King, Denny's/24hr, Giovanni's Rest., Taco Bell, Vitali's Rest., **lodging:** Best Western, Comfort Inn, Day's Inn, Hampton Inn, Holiday Inn Express, Sleep Inn, **W...gas:** Exxon/diesel, Wawa, **food:** Chick-fil-A, KFC/Taco Bell, McDonald's, **other:** HOSPITAL, BJ's Whse, Target, Wal-Mart/drugs, Weis Foods
74	MD 152, Joppatowne, **E...gas:** BP/diesel, Citgo/High's/diesel, Exxon/diesel, **food:** Friendly's, KFC, IHOP, McDonald's, Venitian Palace, Wendy's, **lodging:** Edgewood Motel, Super 8, **other:** HOSPITAL, RV Ctr, Toyota(1mi)
70mm	Big Gunpowder Falls
67b a	MD 43, to White Marsh Blvd, US 1, US 40, **E on MD 7...gas:** BP/diesel, Crown/24hr, Enroy, Shell, Sunoco, **food:** Burger King, WhiteMarsh Diner, **other:** Best Buy, Dodge, Target, to Gunpowder SP, **W on White Marsh Blvd...gas:** Citgo/7-11, Exxon/diesel, **food:** Bayou Blues Café, Bertucci's, Chick-fil-A, Chili's, Don Pablo, Fuddrucker's, Lin's Chinese, McDonald's, Olive Garden, Red Brick Sta., Red Lobster, Ruby Tuesday, Taco Bell, TGIFriday, Wendy's, **lodging:** Hampton Inn, Hilton Garden, Residence Inn, **other:** Barnes&Noble, Giant Foods, GNC, Hecht's, IKEA, JC Penney, Lord&Taylor, Macy's, Old Navy, Sears/auto, Staples, USPO, mall, to Gunpowder SP
64b a	I-695(exits left), E to Essex, W to Towson
62	to I-895(from sb), no facilities
61	US 40, Pulaski Hwy, **E...gas:** BP, Texaco, Shell, **food:** McDonald's
60	Moravia Rd, **E...gas:** Citgo/diesel, **other:** Pontiac/GMC, Suzuki
59	Eastern Ave, **W...gas:** BP/diesel/24hr, Enroy Gas/diesel, Exxon, **food:** Broadway Diner, Wendy's, **other:** HOSPITAL, Home Depot

Baltimore

58	Dundalk Ave, **E...gas:** Citgo, Mobil
57	O'Donnell St, Boston St, **E...gas:** TÀ/Mobil/Subway/diesel/@, **food:** A&W, McDonald's, KFC, Sbarro's, **lodging:** Best Western, Rodeway Inn
56	Keith Ave, no facilities
56mm	McHenry Tunnel, toll plaza(north side of tunnel)
55	Key Hwy, to Ft McHenry NM, last nb exit before toll
54	MD 2 S, to Hanover St, **W...**downtown, HOSPITAL
53	I-395 N, to MLK, **W...**downtown, Oriole Park
52	Russell St N, **W...**HOSPITAL
51	Washington Blvd, no facilities
50.5mm	inspection sta nb
50	Caton Ave, **E...gas:** Crown Gas, Hess/diesel, Shell/24hr, **food:** McDonald's, McKenzie's Rest., **lodging:** Holiday Inn Express, **other:** Aldi Foods, Toyota, **W...**HOSPITAL
49b a	I-695, E to Key Bridge, Glen Burnie, W to Towson, to I-70, to I-83, no facilities
47b a	I-195, to MD 166, to BWI Airport, to Baltimore
46	I-895, to Harbor Tunnel Thruway, no facilities
43	MD 100, to Glen Burnie, **1 mi E on US 1...gas:** Citgo/diesel, Exxon/Wendy's, **lodging:** Best Western
41b a	MD 175, to Columbia, **E...gas:** Citgo, Exxon/diesel, Shell, TA/diesel/rest./24hr/@, **food:** Arby's, Burger King, Frank's Diner, High's Dairy, Jerry's Rest., McDonald's, **lodging:** Best Western, Budget Motel, Fairfield Inn, Holiday Inn, Super 8, **W...gas:** Crown Gas, Exxon, **food:** Applebee's, Bob Evans, McDonald's, Olive Garden, TGIFriday, **lodging:** Studio+, **other:** HOSPITAL, to Johns Hopkins U, Loyola U
38b a	MD 32, to Ft Meade, **2 mi E on US 1...gas:** BP, Enroy, Exxon, **food:** Burger King, McDonald's, Taco Bell, **lodging:** Comfort Inn, **other:** to BWI Airport
37mm	**Welcome Ctr both lanes, full(handicapped)facilities, info, phone, vending, picnic tables, litter barrels, petwalk, RV Dump**
35b a	MD 216, to Laurel, **E...gas:** Crown Gas, Exxon, **food:** McDonald's, **lodging:** Quality Inn, **other:** Weis Food/drug
34mm	Patuxent River
33b a	MD 198, to Laurel, **E...gas:** Exxon, **other:** HOSPITAL, **W...gas:** Exxon/Blimpie, Shell, **food:** Brass Duck Rest., McDonald's, **lodging:** Best Western
29	MD 212, to Beltsville, **W...gas:** Exxon/Blimpie/diesel, Shell, **food:** Magic Cue Rest., McDonald's, Wendy's, **lodging:** Fairfield Inn, Sheraton, **other:** CVS Drug, Giant Foods
27	I-495 S around Washington, no facilities
25b a	US 1, Baltimore Ave, to Laurel, College Park, **E...gas:** BP, Chevron, Citgo/7-11, Exxon/diesel, Shell/24hr, **food:** Arby's, Burger King, Danny's Burgers, Quizno's, El Mexicano, Jerry's Subs, McDonald's, Moose Creek Steaks, Pizza Hut, Quizno's, Wendy's, **lodging:** Holiday Inn, **other:** Goodyear, Rite Aid, US Agri Library, **W...gas:** BP/24hr, Shell, Barnside Diner/24hr, **food:** Baskin-Robbins/Dunkin Donuts, Starbucks, **lodging:** Day's Inn, Econolodge, Hampton Inn, Ramada Ltd, Super 8, **other:** GNC, Home Depot, Honda, Shoppers Foods, VW, to U of MD
23	MD 201, Kenilworth Ave, **E...lodging:** Marriott/rest., **1 mi W on Greenbelt...gas:** Shell, **food:** Boston Mkt, Checker's, KFC, McDonald's, Popeye's, TGIFriday's, TJ's Roadhouse, **lodging:** Courtyard, Residence Inn, **other:** Cadillac, CVS Drug, Giant Food/drug, Staples, Target
22	Baltimore-Washington Pkwy, **E...**to NASA
20b a	MD 450, Annapolis Rd, Lanham, **E...gas:** Mobil, **food:** Burger King, Jerry's Rest., McDonald's, Pizza Hut, Red Lobster, **lodging:** Best Western, Day's Inn/rest., Red Roof

Interstate 95

Inn, **other:** Ford/Kia, **W...gas:** BP, Chevron, Citgo/7-11/24hr, Shell, Sunoco/24hr, **food:** Bojangles, KFC, Popeye's, Wendy's, **lodging:** Ramada Inn, **other:** HOSPITAL, Chrysler/Dodge/Jeep, CVS Drug, Goodyear/auto, JustTires, Lincoln/Mercury, Nissan, Office Depot, Pontiac, Radio Shack, Safeway, Shoppers Foods, Staples

19b a US 50, to Annapolis, Washington, no facilities

17 MD 202, Landover Rd, to Upper Marlboro, **E...food:** Jasper's Rest., Outback Steaks, Ruby Tuesday's, **lodging:** DoubleTree Club Hotel, **other:** FedEx Center, **W...other:** Sam's Club, Sears/auto

16 Arena Dr, **W...**to Arena

15 MD 214, Central Ave, **E...lodging:** Extended Stay America, Hampton Inn/rest., **food:** ChuckeCheese, **other:** Circuit City, FedEx Center, to Six Flags, **W...gas:** Crown, Exxon/diesel, Shell/autocare, Sunoco/24hr, **food:** DQ, KFC, Jerry's Subs, McDonald's, Pizza Hut, Wendy's, **lodging:** Day's Inn/rest., **other:** Goodyear, Home Depot, NTB, Staples, U-Haul

13 Ritchie-Marlboro Rd, Capitol Hgts, no facilities

11 MD 4, Pennsylvania Ave, to Upper Marlboro, **W...gas:** Exxon, Shell, Sunoco, **food:** Applebee's, Arby's, IHOP, Pizza Hut, Starbucks, Taco Bell, Wendy's, **other:** CVS Drug, JC Penney, Marshall's, st police

9 MD 337, to Allentown Rd, **E...gas:** Crown, Shell/autocare, **food:** Bojangle's, Checkers, McDonald's, Popeye's, **lodging:** Holiday Inn Express, Motel 6, Ramada Inn, Super 8, **other:** HOSPITAL, Advance Parts, Family$, U-Haul, to Andrews AFB

7 MD 5, Branch Ave, to Silver Hill, **E...gas:** Exxon, Getty, Sunoco, **food:** Wendy's, **W...gas:** Shell/Subway/diesel, **lodging:** Day's Inn, **other:** HOSPITAL, Ford

4b a MD 414, St Barnabas Rd, Marlow Hgts, **E...gas:** Citgo, Exxon, **food:** Blackeyed Pea, Bojangles, Burger King, KFC, McDonald's, Outback Steaks, Wendy's, **other:** $Tree, Home Depot, Old Navy, Safeway, Staples, **W...gas:** Exxon/dieselDQ, Shell/autocare, **food:** McDonald's

3b a MD 210, Indian Head Hwy, to Forest Hgts, **E...gas:** Mobil, Shell, **food:** Danny's Burgers, Pizza Hut, Ranch House Rest., Taco Bell, **lodging:** Best Western, Oxon Hill Inn, **other:** Advance Parts, USPO, **W...gas:** BP/diesel/24hr, Crown Gas, Shell, 7-11, **food:** Burger King, Cici's Pizza, McDonald's, Wendy's, **other:** MEDICAL CARE, Radio Shack, Safeway

2b a I-295, N to Washingon, no facilities

0mm Maryland/Virginia state line, Potomac River, Woodrow Wilson Bridge

Interstate 97

Exit # Services

17 I-695. I-97 begins/ends on I-695.

16 MD 648, Ferndale, Glen Burnie, **E...gas:** BP, **food:** KFC, McDonald's, Quizno's, Wendy's, **other:** Giant Foods, **W...gas:** Mobil

15b a MD 176 W, Dorsey Rd, Aviation Blvd, **E...gas:** BP, **food:** KFC, Wendy's, **W...**to BWI

14b a MD 100, Ellicott City, Gibson Island, no facilities

13b a MD 174, Quarterfield Rd, **E...gas:** Citgo/7-11, Crown Gas, Exxon, **food:** Gary's Grill, WaWa, **W...gas:** Citgo/diesel, Shell/diesel, **other:** Shoppers Foods

12 MD 3, New Cut Rd, Glen Burnie, **E on Veterans Hwy...gas:** BP, Crown Gas, Enroy, **food:** KFC/Taco Bell, Wendy's, **other:** CVS Drug, **E...gas:** Exxon/24hr, Mobil, WaWa, **food:** Burger King, Domino's, Friendly's, Pizza Hut, Popeye's, Taco Bell, Wendy's, **other:** HOSPITAL, Giant Foods, Goodyear, Target, Walgreen, Wal-Mart

10b a Benfield Blvd, Severna Park, **E...gas:** Exxon/diesel, **lodging:** White Gables Motel, **other:** KOA, access to same as 12

7 MD 3, MD 32, Bowie, Odenton, **E...**motel

5 MD 178(no EZ sb return), Crownsville, no facilities

0mm I-97 begins/ends on US 50/301.

Interstate 270(Rockville)

Exit # Services

32 I-270 begins/ends on I-70, exit 53.

31b a MD 85, **N...gas:** Citgo/7-11, Exxon, Lowest Price, Sheetz, Shell/diesel, **food:** Applebee's, Arby's, Bob Evans, Burger King, Checker's, Golden Corral, Jerry's Rest., KFC/Taco Bell, LoneStar Steaks, McDonald's, Pargo's, Popeye's, Roy Rogers, Waffle House, Wendy's, **lodging:** Day's Inn, Holiday Inn, Holiday Inn Express, **other:** Best Buy, Borders Books, Chrysler, Circuit City, CVS Drug, Goodyear/auto, Home Depot, Lowe's Whse, OfficeMax, Sam's Club, Sears, Tires+, Wal-Mart/auto, **S...gas:** BP/Blimpie, **food:** Chico's Rest, Chipotle Mexican, Cracker Barrel, Macaroni Grill, McDonald's, Panda Express, TGIFriday, **lodging:** Comfort Inn, Courtyard, Extended Stay America, Fairfield Inn, Hampton Inn, MainStay Suites, Residence Inn, **other:** Honda, Toyota

30mm Monocacy River

28mm viewpoint wb

26 MD 80, Urbana, **N...gas:** Exxon, Citgo/7-11

22 MD 109, to Barnesville, Hyattstown, **S...lodging:** Comus Inn(3mi)

21mm weigh/insp sta both lanes

18 MD 121, to Clarksburg, Little Bennett Pk, Blackhill Pk, Boyds, **N...**gas, camping(seasonal)

16 MD 27, Father Hurley Blvd, to Damascus, **N...gas:** Chevron/diesel, Exxon, Mobil, **food:** Applebee's, Bob Evans, Burger King, McDonald's, Subway, TCBY, **lodging:** Extended Stay America, **other:** Best Buy, Borders Books, Giant Foods, Home Depot, Kohl's, Michael's, PepBoys, Starbucks, TJMaxx, Target, Wal-Mart, **S...gas:** BP, Citgo/7-11, Exxon, **food:** Burger King, Carrabba's, Chick-fil-A, McDonald's, Red Robin, Jasper's Rest., Longhorn Steaks, Ruby Tuesday, Subway, Taco Bell, Wendy's, **lodging:** Fairfield Inn, **other:** Eckerd

15b a MA 118, to MD 355, **N...gas:** Chevron/diesel, **food:** Burger King, **lodging:** Hampton Inn, **S...gas:** Amoco, Exxon/24hr, Mobil, **food:** Burger King, Pizza Hut, **other:** st police, tire/brake repair

13b a Middlebrook Rd(from wb), no facilities

MARYLAND

Interstate 270

11b a MD 124, Quince Orchard Rd, **N...gas:** Exxon, **food:** Boston Mkt, ChuckeCheese, McDonald's, Roy Rogers, Starbucks, Subway, **lodging:** Courtyard, Hilton, Holiday Inn, TownePlace Suites, **other:** Borders Books, CompUSA, CVS Drugs, Ford, JC Penney, Sam's Club, mall, **S...gas:** Shell/diesel, **food:** Chevy's Mexican, Chili's, Denny's, Friendly's, LoneStar Steaks, Starbucks, **lodging:** Motel 6, **other:** Advance Parts, Chevrolet/Hummer, Circuit City, Giant Foods, McGruder's Foods, Staples, Seneca Creek SP

10 MD 117, Clopper Rd(from wb), same as 11.

9b a I-370, to Gaithersburg, Sam Eig Hwy, **S...food:** access to Chinese Rest., India Bistro, Pizza Hut, Subway, **other:** Barnes&Noble, Festival Foods, Target, Weis Mkt

8 Shady Grove Rd, **S...lodging:** Marriott, Quality Suites, Residence Inn, Sleep Inn, SpringHill Suites, **other:** HOSPITAL, Barnes&Noble, Target

6b a MD 28, W Montgomery Ave, **N...lodging:** Woodfin Suites, **S...lodging:** Best Western

5b a MD 189, Falls Rd, no facilities

4b a Montrose Rd, **N...gas**, **S...st police**

2 I-270/I-270 spur diverges eb, converges wb

1 MD 187, Old Georgetown Rd, **S...gas:** Exxon, **food:** Hamburger Hamlet, **other:** HOSPITAL, CVS Drug, Giant Foods, GNC

1b a (I-270 spur)Democracy Blvd, **E...lodging:** Marriott, **W...gas:** Exxon/Shell/diesel, **other:** Hecht's, Nordstrom's, Sears, mall

0mm I-270 begins/ends on I-495, exit 35.

Interstate 495(DC)
See Virginia Interstate 495(DC)

Interstate 695(Baltimore)

Exit # Services

48mm Patapsco River, Francis Scott Key Br

44 MD 695(from nb), no facilities

43mm toll plaza

42 MD 151 S, Sparrows Point(last exit before toll sb), **E...gas:** Citgo/diesel

41 MD 20, Cove Rd, **W...gas:** North Point Fuel

40 MD 150, MD 151, North Point Blvd, no facilities

39 Merritt Blvd, **W...gas:** BP, **other:** Ford/Lincoln/Mercury, Hyundai, Mr. Tire, Suzuki

38b a MD 150, Eastern Blvd, to Baltimore, **E...gas:** Enroy Gas, **food:** Super Buffet, **W...food:** Applebee's, Checkers, Golden Corral, KFC, **other:** Chevrolet/Nissan, $Tree, Joann Fabrics, Shopper Foods, Staples

36 MD 702 S(exits left from sb), Essex, no facilities

35 US 40, **N...gas:** Citgo, WaWa/gas, **food:** Checkers, DQ, Dunkin Donuts, Hometown Buffet, McDonald's, Panda Express, Wendy's, **other:** Circuit City, $General, Harley-Davidson, Home Depot, NTB, Office Depot, Sam's Club, U-Haul, Wal-Mart/gas, same as 34

34 MD 7, Philadelphia Rd, **N...food:** Wendy's, **lodging:** Fairfield Inn, **S...gas:** Exxon, **other:** Walgreen, same as 35

33b a I-95, N to Philadelphia, S to Baltimore, no facilities

32b a US 1, Bel Air, **N...gas:** Exxon, 7-11, **food:** Denny's, Dunkin Donuts, Fisherman's Warf, IHOP, Krispy Kreme, McDonald's, Taco Bell, **other:** Giant Foods, K-Mart, Merchant Tire/auto, Toyota/Mazda, **S...gas:** Crown Gas, Getty, **food:** Carrabba's, McDonald's, Mr Crab, Subway, **other:** Goodyear/auto

31c MD 43 E(from eb), no facilities

31b a MD 147, Harford Rd, **N...gas:** BP/24hr, Citgo/7-11, Mobil, Shell/diesel, **other:** CVS Drugs, Chrysler/Plymouth, Goodyear, Honda, NAPA

30b a MD 41, Perring Pkwy, **N...food:** Burger King, Denny's, Roy Rogers, **other:** Chevrolet, Ford, Giant Foods, Home Depot, Office Depot, Ross, Safeway Foods, **S...other:** Dodge, Mazda

29b MD 542, Loch Raven Blvd, **S...gas:** BP, Crown, Hess, **food:** Bel Loc Diner, Hooters, Pizza Hut, Subway, **lodging:** Comfort Inn, Ramada Inn

29a Cromwell Bridge Rd, **S...lodging:** Holiday Inn

28 Providence Rd, **S...Citgo**

27b a MD 146, Dulaney Valley Rd, **N...Hampton NHS**, **S...gas:** Mobil/diesel, **food:** Rainforest Cafe, **lodging:** Sheraton, **other:** Hecht's, SuperFresh Food, mall

26b a MD 45, York Rd, Towson, **N...gas:** BP, Exxon/diesel, Friendly's, Shell, **S...gas:** Crown/diesel, Exxon, **food:** McDonald's, **other:** CompUSA, CVS Drug, Ford, Lexus

25 MD 139, Charles St, **S...HOSPITAL**

24 I-83 N, to York, no facilities

23b Falls Rd, , **N...gas:** Exxon/diesel

23a I-83 S, MD 25 N, Baltimore, no facilities

22 Greenspring Ave, no facilities

21 to Stevenson Rd, Park Hghts Rd, no facilities

20 MD 140, Reisterstown Rd, Pikesville, **N...gas:** Exxon, 7-11, **other:** Barnes&Noble, **S...gas:** BP, Mobil/Subway, Shell, **food:** McDonald's, Olive Branch Italian, **lodging:** Hilton Garden, Ramada Inn, **other:** Target

19 I-795, NW Expswy, no facilities

18b a MD 26, Randallstown, Lochearn, **E...gas:** Crown/diesel, HOSPITAL, **W...gas:** BP, Exxon, 7-11, Shell, **food:** Burger King, Sea Pride Crabhouse, Subway

17 MD 122, Security Blvd, **E...gas:** BP, **food:** Red Lobster, Wendy's, **lodging:** Day's Inn, Motel 6, Quality Inn, **other:** Chevrolet, Mitsubishi, Nissan, **W...gas:** Exxon, **food:** Bennigan's, McDonald's, **lodging:** Holiday Inn, **other:** Best Buy, Firestone, Ford, JC Penney, Staples, mall

16b a I-70, E to Baltimore, W to Frederick, no facilities

15b a US 40, Ellicott City, Baltimore, **E...food:** Burger King, ChuckeCheese, KFC, McDonald's, IHOP, **lodging:** Day's Inn, Comfort Inn, **other:** Dodge, Firestone, Lowe's Whse, Ross, Safeway Foods, Sam's Club/gas, U-Haul, **W...gas:** BP/diesel, Crown/24hr, Shell, **other:** Circuit City

14 Edmondson Ave, **E...gas:** Exxon, **food:** Royal Farms, **W...gas:** Citgo

13 MD 144, Frederick Rd, Catonsville, **W...gas:** BP, Crown/gas, 7-11, **food:** Dunkin Donuts, McDonald's/24hr, Subway

12c b MD 372 E, Wilkens, **E...HOSPITAL**

11b a I-95, N to Baltimore, S to Washington, no facilities

10 US 1, Washington Blvd, **E...food:** Wendy's, **lodging:** Beltway Motel/rest., **other:** Home Depot, **W...gas:** Exxon, **food:** Burger King

9 Hollins Ferry Rd, Lansdowne, **E...gas:** Mobil, Sunoco/diesel

8 MD 168, Nursery Rd, **N...gas:** Exxon, Shell, **food:** Burger King, KFC, McDonald's, Taco Bell, Wendy's, **lodging:** Motel 6

7b a MD 295, **N...to Baltimore**, **S...BWI Airport**

6b a Camp Mead Rd(from nb)

5 MD 648, Ferndale, gas, food, lodging

4b a I-97 S, to Annapolis, no facilities

3b a MD 2 N, Brooklyn Park, **S...gas:** Exxon, Hess, Shell, **food:** Bennigan's, Bob Evan's, Checker's, Chick-fil-A, ChuckeCheese, Denny's, KFC, Krispy Kreme, McDonald's, Taco Bell, **lodging:** Day's Inn, Hampton Inn, Holiday Inn, **other:** CompUSA, Giant Foods, Just Tires, Lowe's Whse, Target

2 MD 10, Glen Burnie, no facilities

1 MD 174, Hawkins Point Rd, **S...gas:** Citgo/deli/diesel

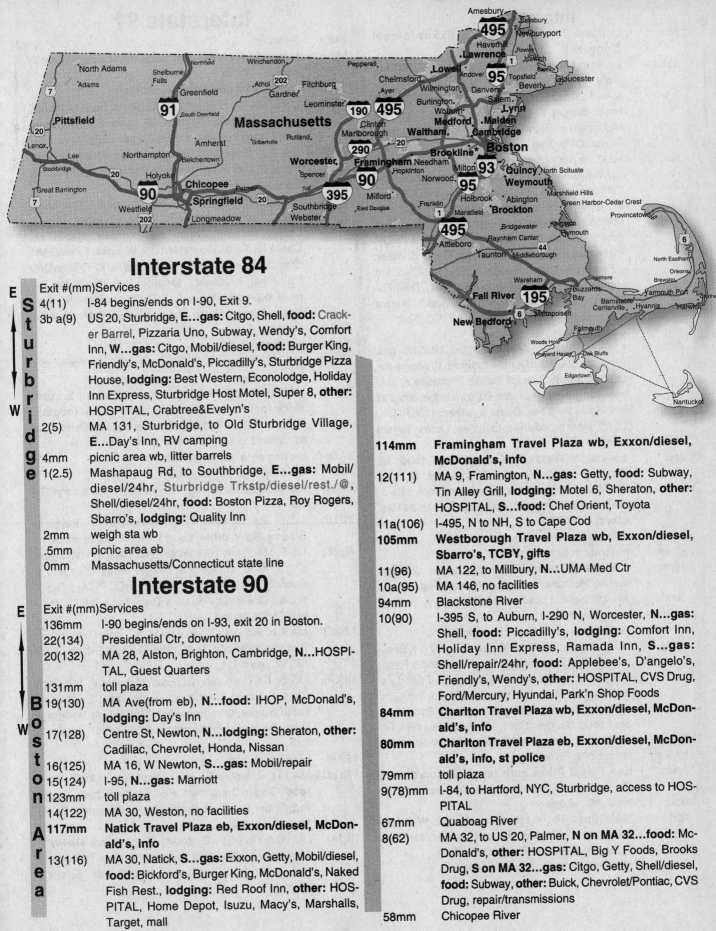

Interstate 84

Exit #(mm)Services

4(11)	I-84 begins/ends on I-90, Exit 9.
3b a(9)	US 20, Sturbridge, **E…gas:** Citgo, Shell, **food:** Cracker Barrel, Pizzaria Uno, Subway, Wendy's, Comfort Inn, **W…gas:** Citgo, Mobil/diesel, **food:** Burger King, Friendly's, McDonald's, Piccadilly's, Sturbridge Pizza House, **lodging:** Best Western, Econolodge, Holiday Inn Express, Sturbridge Host Motel, Super 8, **other:** HOSPITAL, Crabtree&Evelyn's
2(5)	MA 131, Sturbridge, to Old Sturbridge Village, **E…**Day's Inn, RV camping
4mm	picnic area wb, litter barrels
1(2.5)	Mashapaug Rd, to Southbridge, **E…gas:** Mobil/diesel/24hr, Sturbridge Trkstp/diesel/rest./@, Shell/diesel/24hr, **food:** Boston Pizza, Roy Rogers, Sbarro's, **lodging:** Quality Inn
2mm	weigh sta wb
.5mm	picnic area eb
0mm	Massachusetts/Connecticut state line

*(left margin, vertical: E ↑ Sturbridge ↓ W)*

Interstate 90

Exit #(mm)Services

136mm	I-90 begins/ends on I-93, exit 20 in Boston.
22(134)	Presidential Ctr, downtown
20(132)	MA 28, Alston, Brighton, Cambridge, **N…**HOSPITAL, Guest Quarters
131mm	toll plaza
19(130)	MA Ave(from eb), **N…food:** IHOP, McDonald's, **lodging:** Day's Inn
17(128)	Centre St, Newton, **N…lodging:** Sheraton, **other:** Cadillac, Chevrolet, Honda, Nissan
16(125)	MA 16, W Newton, **S…gas:** Mobil/repair
15(124)	I-95, **N…gas:** Marriott
123mm	toll plaza
14(122)	MA 30, Weston, no facilities
117mm	**Natick Travel Plaza eb, Exxon/diesel, McDonald's, info**
13(116)	MA 30, Natick, **S…gas:** Exxon, Getty, Mobil/diesel, **food:** Bickford's, Burger King, McDonald's, Naked Fish Rest., **lodging:** Red Roof Inn, **other:** HOSPITAL, Home Depot, Isuzu, Macy's, Marshalls, Target, mall
114mm	**Framingham Travel Plaza wb, Exxon/diesel, McDonald's, info**
12(111)	MA 9, Framington, **N…gas:** Getty, **food:** Subway, Tin Alley Grill, **lodging:** Motel 6, Sheraton, **other:** HOSPITAL, **S…food:** Chef Orient, Toyota
11a(106)	I-495, N to NH, S to Cape Cod
105mm	**Westborough Travel Plaza wb, Exxon/diesel, Sbarro's, TCBY, gifts**
11(96)	MA 122, to Millbury, **N…**UMA Med Ctr
10a(95)	MA 146, no facilities
94mm	Blackstone River
10(90)	I-395 S, to Auburn, I-290 N, Worcester, **N…gas:** Shell, **food:** Piccadilly's, **lodging:** Comfort Inn, Holiday Inn Express, Ramada Inn, **S…gas:** Shell/repair/24hr, **food:** Applebee's, D'angelo's, Friendly's, Wendy's, **other:** HOSPITAL, CVS Drug, Ford/Mercury, Hyundai, Park'n Shop Foods
84mm	**Charlton Travel Plaza wb, Exxon/diesel, McDonald's, info**
80mm	**Charlton Travel Plaza eb, Exxon/diesel, McDonald's, info, st police**
79mm	toll plaza
9(78)mm	I-84, to Hartford, NYC, Sturbridge, access to HOSPITAL
67mm	Quaboag River
8(62)	MA 32, to US 20, Palmer, **N on MA 32…food:** McDonald's, **other:** HOSPITAL, Big Y Foods, Brooks Drug, **S on MA 32…gas:** Citgo, Getty, Shell/diesel, **food:** Subway, **other:** Buick, Chevrolet/Pontiac, CVS Drug, repair/transmissions
58mm	Chicopee River

(left margin, vertical: E ↑ Boston Area ↓ W)

MASSACHUSETTS

Interstate 90

E / **W**

S p r i n g f i e l d

P i t t s f i e l d

56mm	**Ludlow Travel Plaza wb, Exxon/diesel, D'angelo's**
55mm	**Ludlow Travel Plaza eb, Exxon/diesel, McDonald's**
7(54)	MA 21, to Ludlow, **N...gas:** Gulf, Mobil, Sunoco, **food:** Burger King, Dunkin Donuts, Friendly's, McDonald's, Subway, **other:** HOSPITAL, Big Y Foods, CVS Drug, Jo-Ann Fabrics
6(51)	I-291, to Springfield, Hartford CT, **N...gas:** Pride/Subway/diesel, **food:** McDonald's, **lodging:** Motel 6, Plantation Inn, Ramada Inn, **other:** HOSPITAL, to Bradley Int Airport, Basketball Hall of Fame
5(49)	MA 33, to Chicopee, Westover AFB, **N...food:** Arby's, Burger King, Denny's, Friendly's, IHOP, Pizza Hut, Wendy's, Comfort Inn, Super 8, **other:** BJ's Whse, Big Y Foods, Chevrolet/Cadillac, Honda/Subaru, Stop&Shop Food/gas, TownFair Tire, U-Haul, World Mkt, mall, **S...food:** Admiral DW's Rest., **other:** Buick/Pontiac/GMC, Ford
46mm	Connecticut River
4(46)	I-91, US 5, W Springfield, to Holyoke, **US 5 N...gas:** Shell, **food:** Dunkin Donuts, **lodging:** Welcome Inn, **US 5 S...food:** Outback Steaks, Piccadilly's, Subway, **lodging:** Corral Motel, Econolodge, Knight's Inn, Springfield Inn, Super 8, **other:** HOSPITAL, BMW, Honda, Indian Motorcycles, Lexus, Toyota
41mm	st police wb
3(40)	US 202, to Westfield, **N...gas:** Mobil, **food:** NE Pizza, **lodging:** Country Court Motel, **S...gas:** Shell/Subway/diesel, **food:** Friendly's, Nick's Rest., Whip City Brewery/rest., **lodging:** Westfield Motel, **other:** HOSPITAL
36mm	Westfield River
35.5mm	runaway truck ramp eb
29mm	**Blandford Travel Plaza both lanes...Exxon/diesel, McDonalds, gifts, info, vending**
20mm	1724 ft, highest point on MA Tpk
14.5mm	Appalachian Trail
12mm	parking area both lanes, litter barrels
2(11)	US 20, to Lee, Pittsfield, **N...gas:** Citgo/7-11, Shell/diesel/24hr, Sunoco/repair, **food:** Athena's Rest., Blimpie, Burger King, Dunkin Donuts, Friendly's, McDonald's, Pizza Hut, **lodging:** Pilgrim Inn, Sunset Motel, Super 8, **other:** Brooks Drug, PriceChopper Foods, **S...gas:** Shell, Lee Plaza/diesel/Motel/rest., **other:** Prime Outlets/famous brands, NAPA
10.5mm	Hoosatonic River
8mm	**Lee Travel Plaza both lanes, Exxon/diesel, D'angelo's, TCBY, atm, bank, info, vending**
4mm	toll booth, phone
1(2)	MA 41(from wb, no return), to MA 102, W Stockbridge, the Berkshires, **N...lodging:** Pleasant Valley Motel, **other:** to Bousquet Ski Area
0mm	Massachusetts/New York state line

Interstate 91

N / **S**

G r e e n f i e l d

Exit #	Services
55mm	Massachusetts/Vermont state line, callboxes begin/end
54mm	parking area both lanes, picnic tables
28(51)	US 5, MA 10, Bernardston, **E...food:** Bella Notte Ristorante, **lodging:** Fox Inn, **W...gas:** Sunoco, **food:** Red House Pizzaria, **other:** RV camping
27(45)	MA 2 E, Greenfield, **E...gas:** Citgo, Mobil, Sunoco, **food:** Burger King, Denny's Pantry, Friendly's, McDonald's, **other:** HOSPITAL, CVS Drug
26(43)	MA 2 W, MA 2A E, Greenfield, **E...gas:** Citgo/diesel, Mobil, **food:** Applebee's, China Gourmet, Dunkin Donuts, **lodging:** GreenField Inn, **other:** HOSPITAL, Chevrolet, Ford/Lincoln/Mercury, **W...gas:** Exxon/24hr, Shell/24hr, **food:** Bickford's, Friendly's, KFC/Taco Bell/Pizza Hut, McDonald's, **lodging:** CandleLight Inn, Super 8, **other:** Big Y Foods, BJ's Whse, Family$, Home Depot, Nissan, Radio Shack, Staples, to Mohawk Tr
39mm	Deerfield River
37mm	weigh sta both lanes
25(36)	MA 116(from sb), S Deerfield, hist dist, camping, same as 24
24(35)	US 5, MA 10, MA 116, Deerfield(no EZ return), **E...gas:** Mobil, **food:** Chandler's Rest., Wolfy's Rest., **lodging:** Red Roof Inn, Whatley Inn, **other:** Yankee Candle Co, **W...gas:** Exxon/diesel/24hr, **food:** 24hr Diner
34.5mm	parking area nb, no facilities
23(34)	US 5(from sb), no facilities
22(30)	US 5, MA 10(from nb), N Hatfield, **W...**Diamond RV Ctr
21(28)	US 5, MA 10, Hatfield, **W...gas:** Sunoco, **lodging:** Stearns Motel, **other:** Long View RV Ctr, st police
20(26)	US 5, MA 9, MA 10(from sb), Northampton, **W...gas:** Citgo, **food:** Bickford's, Burger King, D'angelo's, Friendly's, McDonald's, **other:** HOSPITAL, Big Y Foods, Chevrolet/VW, CVS Drug, Ford, NAPA, Pontiac/GMC/Cadillac, VW
19(25)	MA 9, to Amherst, Northampton, **E...gas:** Getty, **food:** Webster's Fishook Rest., **other:** HOSPITAL, to Elwell SP, **W...gas:** Citgo
18(22)	US 5, Northampton, **E...gas:** Mobil/24hr, **lodging:** Clarion, Inn at Northampton, **W...gas:** Shell/24hr, **food:** Burger King, Friendly's, McDonald's, **lodging:** Best Western, Northampton Hotel, **other:** to Smith Coll
18mm	scenic area both lanes
17b a(16)	MA 141, S Hadley, **E...gas:** Citgo/diesel, Mobil/diesel, **food:** Dunkin Doughnuts, Real China, Subway, **lodging:** Super 8, **other:** Brooks Drug, Walgreen, **W...**to Mt Tom Ski Area
16(14)	US 202, Holyoke, **E...food:** Burger King, Denny's, Friendly's, McDonald's, **lodging:** Yankee Pedlar Inn/rest., **other:** HOSPITAL, to Heritage SP, **W...**Soldier's Home

Interstate 91

N / S Springfield

15(12) to US 5, Ingleside, **E...gas:** Shell, **food:** Cracker Barrel, Friendly's, Pizzaria Uno, Ruby Tuesday, **lodging:** Holiday Inn, **other:** HOSPITAL, Barnes&Noble, Best Buy, Circuit City, CompUSA, Filene's, JC Penney, Lord&Taylor, Old Navy, Sears/auto, Target, mall, **W...food:** Schermerhorn's Seafood

14(11) to US 5, to I-90(Mass Tpk), E to Boston, W to Albany, **E...HOSPITAL**

13b a(9) US 5 N, W Springfield, **E...gas:** Pride/diesel, **food:** Bickford's, B'Shara's Rest., Dougnut Dip, On the Border, Outback Steaks, Piccadilly's, Subway, **lodging:** Comfort Inn, Knight's Inn, Red Roof Inn, Residence Inn, Springfield Inn, Super 8, **other:** BMW, Home Depot, Honda/Lexus/Toyota, mall, **W...gas:** Citgo/diesel, Mobil, Sunoco/diesel, **food:** Arby's, Boston Mkt, Burger King, Calamari's Grill, ChiChi's, Chili's, D'angelo's, Empire Buffet, Friendly's, HomeTown Buffet, KFC, Longhorn Steaks, McDonald's, 99 Rest., Old Country Buffet, Pizza Hut, Wendy's, **lodging:** Best Western, Day's Inn, Econolodge, Hampton Inn, Knoll Motel, Quality Inn, Red Carpet Inn, **other:** Chrysler/Plymouth, Costco, Home Depot, Lincoln/Mercury, Mazda/Mercedes, Michael's, Nissan/Subaru, Stop&Shop Foods, Staples, TownFair Tire

12(8.5) I-391 N, to Chicopee, no facilities

11(8) Burney Ave(from sb), **E...gas:** Mobil, **other:** HOSPITAL

10(7.5) Main St(from nb), Springfield, **E...gas:** Mobil

9(7) US 20 W, MA 20A E(from nb), **E...food:** McDonald's

8(6.5) I-291, US 20 E, to I-90, **E...downtown, lodging:** Holiday Inn, **other:** HOSPITAL,

7(6) Columbus Ave(from sb), **E...lodging:** Marriott, Sheraton, **W...gas:** Pride/diesel/rest., **other:** to Basketball Hall of Fame

6(5.5) Springfield Ctr(from nb), **W...gas:** Pride Autotruck/diesel

5(5) Broad St(from sb), same as 4

4(4.5) MA 83, Broad St, Main St, **E...gas:** Citgo, Mobil/diesel, Shell/diesel, United, **food:** McDonald's, Wendy's, **other:** Buick/GMC, Hyundai, Saturn, **W...gas:** Sunoco/diesel, **lodging:** Hilton Garden

3(4) US 5 N, to MA 57, Columbus Ave, W Springfield, **E...gas:** Sunoco, **W...Chevrolet**

2(3.5) MA 83 S(from nb), to E Longmeadow, **E...food:** Friendly's

1(3) US 5 S(from sb), no facilities

0mm Massachusetts/Connecticut state line, callboxes

Interstate 93

Exit #   Services

47mm Massachusetts/New Hampshire state line, callboxes begin/end

48(46) MA 213 E, to Methuen, **E...HOSPITAL**

Methuen

47(45) Pelham St, Methuen, **E...gas:** Sunoco/24hr, **food:** Dunkin Donuts, McDonald's, Outback Steaks, **W...gas:** Getty, **food:** Fireside Rest., **lodging:** Day's Inn/rest., Guesthouse Inn, **other:** Chrysler/Plymouth/Jeep, Pontiac/Nissan

46(44) MA 110, MA 113, to Lawrence, **E...gas:** Getty, **food:** Burger King, Dunkin Donuts, McDonald's/24hr, PapaGino's, Pizza Hut/D'angelo, MktBasket Foods, **other:** HOSPITAL, **W...gas:** Citgo, Gulf, **food:** Dunkin Donuts, Jimmy's II Rest., Jackson's Rest., Millhouse Rest.

45(43) Andover St, River Rd, to Lawrence, **E...lodging:** Courtyard, Hawthorn Suites, Marriott, SpringHill Suites, Wyndham, **W...gas:** Mobil, **food:** Chateu Italian, **lodging:** Residence Inn, Tage Inn

44b a(40) I-495, to Lowell, Lawrence, **E...HOSPITAL**

43(39) MA 133, N Tewksbury, **E...gas:** Mobil/Dunkin Doughnuts/24hr

42(38) Dascomb Rd, East St, Tewksbury, no facilities

41(35) MA 125, Andover, st police

40(34) MA 62, Wilmington, no facilities

39(33) Concord St, **E...Shriners Auditorium**

38(31) MA 129, Reading, **W...gas:** Mobil, **food:** Burger King, Dunkin Donuts, Michael's Place Rest., 99 Rest.

37c(30) Commerce Way, Atlantic Ave, **W...lodging:** Residence Inn, **other:** Target

37b a(29) I-95, S to Waltham, N to Peabody, no facilities

36(28) Montvale Ave, **E...gas:** Mobil, **lodging:** Courtyard, **W...gas:** Citgo/diesel, Exxon/24hr, Getty, Shell, **food:** Bickford's/24hr, Friendly's, McDonald's, Polcari's Italian, **lodging:** Comfort Inn, Crowne Plaza Hotel, Howard Johnson, Sheraton/Spud's Rest., **other:** HOSPITAL, BJ's Whse, Nissan

35(27) Winchester Highlands, Melrose, **E...HOSPITAL**(no EZ return to sb)

34(26) MA 28 N(from nb, no EZ return), Stoneham, **E...gas:** Mobil, **food:** Friendly's, **other:** HOSPITAL

33(25) MA 28, Fellsway West, Winchester, **E...HOSPITAL**

32(23) MA 60, Salem Ave, Medford Square, **W...lodging:** AmeriSuites, **other:** HOSPITAL, to Tufts U

31(22) MA 16 E, to Revere(no EZ return sb), **E...gas:** Shell, **food:** Bertucci's, Subway, **lodging:** Howard Johnson Rest., **other:** Ford/Lincoln/Mercury, mall, st police, **W...gas:** Exxon, Mobil, **food:** Burger King, Dunkin Donuts, Pizza Hut, **other:** AutoZone, Dodge

30(21) MA 28, MA 38, Mystic Ave, Somerville, **W...gas:** Mr. C's Gas, **food:** Burger King, **other:** AutoZone, Lincoln/Mercury

Interstate 93

29(20)   MA 28(from nb), Somerville, **E...food:** 99 Rest., **lodging:** Tage Inn, **other:** Circuit City, Home Depot, K-Mart, Stop&Shop, mall, **W...same as 30, gas:** Gulf, **lodging:** Holiday Inn, **other:** Radio Shack, Stop&Shop

28(19)   Sullivans Square, Charles Town, downtown

27   US 1 N(from nb), no facilities

26(18.5) MA 28 N, Storrow Dr, North Sta, downtown

25   Haymarket Sq, Gov't Center

24(18)   Callahan Tunnel, **E...**airport

23(17.5) High St, Congress St, **W...lodging:** Marriott

22(17)   Atlantic Ave, Northern Ave, South Sta, Boston World Trade Ctr

21(16.5) Kneeland St, ChinaTown, no facilities

20(16)   I-90 W, to Mass Tpk, no facilities

19(15.5) Albany St(from sb), **W...gas:** Mobil/diesel, **other:** HOSPITAL

18(15)   Mass Ave, to Roxbury, **W...**HOSPITAL

17(14.5) E Berkeley(from nb), **E...**New Boston Food Mkt

16(14)   S Hampton St, Andrew Square, **W...gas:** Shell/24hr, **food:** Bickford's, **lodging:** Holiday Inn Express, **other:** Home Depot, K-Mart/Little Caesar's, Marshall's, OfficeMax, Old Navy

15(13)   Columbia Rd, Everett Square, **E...lodging:** Double-Tree Motel, **other:** JFK Library, to UMA, **W...gas:** Shell

14(12.5) Morissey Blvd, **E...**JFK Library, **W...gas:** Shell, **food:** D'angelo's, **lodging:** Howard Johnson, Ramada Inn, **other:** Stop&Shop Foods

13(12)   Freeport St, to Dorchester, **W...gas:** Citgo/7-11, **food:** Boston Mkt, **other:** CVS Drug, Dodge, Toyota

12(11.5) MA 3A S(from sb, no EZ return), Quincy, **E...gas:** Shell, **food:** Café Pacific, Domino's, **lodging:** Best Western, **W...gas:** Boston Mkt, Citgo/7-11, Exxon, Shell, Sunoco, **food:** Arby's, Bickford's, Ground Round, PapaGino's, Wendy's, **other:** AutoZone, CVS Drug, Ford/Lincoln/Mercury, Pontiac/GMC, Staples, Walgreen

11b a(11)to MA 203, Granite Ave, Ashmont, **W...food:** McDonald's

10(10)   Squantum Ave(from sb), Milton, **W...**HOSPITAL

9(9)   Adams St, Bryant Ave, to N Quincy, **W...gas:** Shell/repair

8(8)   Brook Pkwy, to Quincy, Furnace, **E...gas:** Global, Gulf/diesel, Mobil, **other:** Home Depot, Saturn

7(7)   MA 3 S, to Cape Cod(exits left from sb), Braintree, **E...lodging:** Marriott

6(6)   MA 37, to Holbrook, Braintree, **E...gas:** Mobil/24hr, **food:** Boardwalk Café, D'angelo's, Pizzaria Uno, TGI Friday, **lodging:** Sheraton/café, **other:** Circuit City, Filene's, Firestone/auto, Lord&Taylor, Macy's, Sears/auto, mall, **W...gas:** Sunoco, **food:** Ascari Café, **lodging:** Candlewood Suites, Extended Stay America, Hampton Inn, Holiday Inn Express, **other:** Barnes&Noble, Ford, Nissan, VW

5b a(4)   MA 28 S, to Randolph, Milton, **E...gas:** Citgo, Mobil/diesel, Shell/repair/24hr, **food:** D'angelo's, Domino's, Dunkin Donuts/Baskin-Robbins/Togo's, Friendly's, IHOP, Lombardo's Rest., Picadilly's Pub, Sal's Calzone Rest., Wong's Chinese, **lodging:** Holiday Inn/rest.

4(3)   MA 24 S(exits left from sb), to Brockton, no facilities

3(2)   MA 138 N, to Ponkapoag Trail, Houghtons Pond, no facilities

2b a(1)   MA 138 S, to Stoughton, Milton, **E...**golf, **W...gas:** Mobil, Shell/diesel, Sunoco, **food:** Baskin-Robbins, Dunkin Doughnuts

1(0)   I-95 N, S to Providence. I-93 begins/ends on I-95, exit 12.

Interstate 95

Exit #	Services

89.5mm   Massachusetts/New Hampshire state line, parking area sb

60(89)   MA 286, to Salisbury, beaches, **E...gas:** Mobil/diesel, **food:** Chubby's Diner, Lena's Seafood Rest., **other:** camping(seasonal)

59(88)   I-495 S(from sb), no facilities

58b a(78)MA 110, to I-495 S, to Amesbury, Salisbury, **E...gas:** Sunoco/diesel, **food:** China Buffet, Crossroads Pizza, Frankie's Café, Sylvan St Grille, Winner's Circle Rest., **other:** Dodge, Plymouth/Jeep, U-Haul, radiators, **W...gas:** Best Choice Gas/Domino's, Irving Gas, Mobil, **food:** Acapulco Mexican, Burger King, Dunkin Donuts, Friendly's, McDonald's, PapaGino's, Shorty's Diner, **lodging:** Fairfield Inn, **other:** Chevrolet/VW, Stop&Shop Foods

86mm   Merrimac River

57(85)   MA 113, to W Newbury, **E...gas:** Mobil/24hr, Shell/repair/24hr, Sunoco, **food:** Dunkin Donuts, Friendly's, Giuseppe's Italian, Jade Chinese, McDonald's, PapaGino's, Wendy's, White Hen Pantry/deli, **other:** HOSPITAL, Brooks Drug, GNC, K-Mart, MktBasket Foods, Radio Shack, Shaw's Foods, Walgreen

56(78)   Scotland Rd, to Newbury, **E...**st police

55(77)   Central St, to Byfield, **E...food:** Gen Store Eatery, Village Diner, **W...gas:** Prime/diesel/repair

54b a(76)MA 133, E to Rowley, W to Groveland, **E...food:** Agawam Diner, McDonald's, **W...**Old Town Tavern

75mm   weigh sta both lanes

53b a(74)MA 97, S to Topsfield, N to Georgetown

52(73)   Topsfield Rd, to Topsfield, Boxford, no facilities

51(72)   Endicott Rd, to Topsfield, Middleton, no facilities

50(71)   US 1, to MA 62, Topsfield, **E...gas:** Exxon/24hr, Mobil/24hr, **food:** Ristorante Italiano, **other:** Honda, **W...food:** Supino's Rest., **lodging:** Sheraton, **other:** CVS Drug, Hyundai, Staples, Stop&Shop, st police

49(70)   MA 62(from nb), Danvers, Middleton, **W...**same as 50

Interstate 95

N **S** Peabody

48(69) Hobart St(from sb), **W...food:** Italian Rest., Jake's Rest., **lodging:** Comfort Inn, Extended Stay America, Motel 6, **other:** Home Depot, Honda

47b a(68) MA 114, to Middleton, Peabody, **E...gas:** Exxon/diesel/24hr, Mobil, Shell, Sunoco, **food:** Dunkin Donuts, Friendly's, PapaGino's, **other:** Chevrolet, Dodge, Infiniti, Lowe's Whse, NTB, Subaru/Toyota, Wal-Mart, **W...food:** Chili's, McDonald's, TGIFriday, **lodging:** Motel 6, Residence Inn, TownePlace Suites, **other:** BigLots, Circuit City, Costco, Dodge, Home Depot, LandRover, Mazda, NAPA, Pontiac/Hyundai

46(67) to US 1, **W...gas:** Best, Gulf/diesel, Shell, Sunoco, **food:** Bel-Aire Diner, Burger King, **other:** Auto Parts+

45(66) MA 128 N, to Peabody, no facilities

44b a(65) US 1 N, MA 129, **E...gas:** Shell, **W...gas:** Shell, **food:** Bennigan's, Bertucci's, Bickford's, Carrabba's, Wendy's, **lodging:** Hampton Inn, Homewood Suites, SpringHill Suites, **other:** HOSPITAL

43(63) Walnut St, Lynnfield, **E...**to Saugus Iron Works NHS(3mi), **W...lodging:** Sheraton, **other:** golf

42(62) Salem St, Montrose, **E...gas:** Mobil, Prime, Sunoco, **food:** Paul's Pizza, **W...lodging:** Sheraton

41(60) Main St, Lynnfield Ctr, **E...gas:** Shell

40(59) MA 129, Wakefield Ctr, N Reading, **E...gas:** Exxon, **food:** HoneyDew Doughnuts, **W...other:** Chevrolet, diesel repair

39(58) North Ave, Reading, **E...gas:** Citgo, **lodging:** Best Western, **other:** Mazda/Isuzu/Volvo/Saab, **W...gas:** Exxon/repair, Shell/diesel/24hr, **food:** Chili's, **other:** HOSPITAL, Ford, Home Depot, Staples

38b a(57) MA 28, to Reading, **E...gas:** Gulf, Hess, Shell/repair, **food:** Bickford's, Boston Mkt, Burger King, China Moon, Dunkin Donuts, Ground Round, 99 Rest., PapaGino's, Subway, **other:** AutoZone, CVS Drug, Ford, GNC, Marshalls, Radio Shack, Shaw's Foods, **W...gas:** Exxon, Getty, Mobil, Shell, **food:** Dunkin Donuts, Harrow's Rest., McDonald's

37b a(56) I-93, N to Manchester, S to Boston, no facilities

36(55) Washington St, to Winchester, **E...gas:** Getty, **food:** Dunkin Donuts, FarEast Chinese, Italian Express, **lodging:** Crowne Plaza Hotel, **other:** AutoZone, Buick/Pontiac/GMC, CompUSA, Jaguar, Mitsubishi, Nissan, Staples, Toyota, **W...gas:** Shell, **food:** China Pearl, D'angelo's, Joe's Grill, McDonald's, 99 Rest., On the Border, Panera Bread, PapaGino's, Pizza Hut, Pizzaria Uno, TGIFriday, MktBasket Foods, **lodging:** Comfort Inn, Courtyard, Fairfield Inn, Hampton Inn, Red Roof Inn, **other:** CVS Drug, Hogan Tire, Kohl's, Lowe's Whse, Mkt Basket Foods, NTB, USPO, mall

35(54) MA 38, to Woburn, **E...lodging:** Radisson, **other:** HOSPITAL, **W...gas:** Mobil/diesel, Shell, **food:** Applebee's, Baldwin Park Grill, Dunkin Donuts, **lodging:** Sierra Suites, **other:** Stop&Shop Foods

34(53) Winn St, Woburn, no facilities

Boston Area

33b a(52) US 3 S, MA 3A N, to Winchester, **E...food:** Café Escadrille, ChuckeCheese, Outback Steaks, Papa-Razzi's, **lodging:** Summerfield Suites, **other:** HOSPITAL, CVS Drug, Honda, Marshalls, Michael's, **W...gas:** Citgo, Hess, **lodging:** Marriott, **other:** HOSPITAL, Porsche

32b a(51) US 3 N, MA 2A S, to Lowell, **E...gas:** Shell, **lodging:** Sheraton, **other:** Circuit City, **W...food:** Boston Mkt, Burger King, Chili's, McDonald's, Pizzaria Regina, Smokey's Café, TCBY, Victoria Sta Rest., **lodging:** Howard Johnson, **other:** Barnes&Noble, Dodge, Filene's, Lord&Taylor, Macy's, Sears/auto, mall

31b a(48) MA 4, MA 225, Lexington, **E...gas:** Mobil/repair, Shell, **food:** Alexander's Pizza, Bertucci's Pizza, **W...gas:** Exxon/24hr, Shell/24hr, **food:** Denny's, Friendly's, McDonald's, **lodging:** Bedford Motel, Best Western, Holiday Inn Express, Travelodge

30b a(47) MA 2A, Lexington, **E...gas:** Shell, **other:** HOSPITAL, **W...lodging:** Sheraton, **other:** to MinuteMan NP, Hanscom AFB

46.5mm travel plaza nb, Mobil/diesel/24hr, HoneyDew Doughnuts, McDonald's, gifts

29b a(46) MA 2 W, Cambridge, no facilities

28b a(45) Trapelo Rd, Belmont, **E...gas:** Exxon, Mobil, Shell, **food:** Burger King, Dunkin Donuts, Friendly's, McDonald's, PapaGino's, **other:** Osco Drugs, Star Mkt

27b a(44) Totten Pond Rd, Waltham, **E...gas:** Shell, **food:** D'angelo, Naked Fish Rest., **lodging:** Best Western, Courtyard, Holiday Inn Express, Homestead Suites Inn, Sheraton, Sierra Suites, Summerfield Suites, Westin Hotel, **W...food:** Bertucci's Rest., **lodging:** DoubleTree/rest., **other:** Costco, Home Depot

26(43) US 20, to MA 117, to Waltham, **E...gas:** Sunoco/diesel, **other:** HOSPITAL, **W...gas:** Mobil

25(42) I-90, MA Tpk, no facilities

24(41) MA 30, Newton, Wayland, **E...gas:** Mobil, **lodging:** Marriott

23(40) Recreation Rd(from nb), to MA Tpk, no facilities

22b a(39) Grove St, **E...lodging:** Holiday Inn, **other:** golf

38.5mm travel plaza sb, Mobil/diesel, McDonald's, gifts

21b a(38) MA 16, Newton, Wellesley, **E...HOSPITAL**, **W...food:** Pillar House Rest.

20b a(36) MA 9, Brookline, Framingham, no facilities

19(35) Highland Ave, Newton, Needham, **E...gas:** Gulf, Hess, **food:** D'angelo's, Dunkin Donuts, Ground Round, McDonald's, Mighty Subs, **lodging:** Sheraton/rest., **other:** Staples, **W...gas:** Highland/diesel, Shell/24hr, **food:** Bickford's, **other:** Chevrolet, Ford

MASSACHUSETTS
Interstate 95

N ↑↓ S — **Boston Area**

18(34)   Great Plain Ave, W Roxbury, no facilities

33.5mm parking area sb, phone, litter barrels

17(33)   MA 135, Needham, Wellesley, no facilities

32mm   truck turnout sb

16b a(31)MA 109, High St, Dedham, **W...gas:** Mobil/diesel

15b a(29)US 1, MA 128, **E...food:** Bickford's, Bugaboo Steaks, Chili's, Joe's Grill, Krispy Kreme, Panera Bread, PapaGino's, TGIFriday, Vinny T's Rest., **lodging:** Comfort Inn, Fairfield Inn, Holiday Inn, Residence Inn, **other:** Best Buy, BJ's Whse, Costco, Lincoln/Mercury, Nissan, OfficeMax, PepBoys, Speedy Repair, Star Foods, Volvo, **W...gas:** Shell/diesel/24hr, **food:** Burger King, Dunkin Donuts, Jade Chinese, McDonald's, **lodging:** Budget Motel, **other:** Aamco, Buick, Chrysler/Plymouth/Jeep, Hyundai, Mercedes, Pontiac

14(28)   East St, Canton St, **E...lodging:** Hilton

27mm   rest area sb, full(handicapped)facilities, phone, picnic tables, litter barrels

13(26.5) University Ave, no facilities

12(26)   I-93 N, to Braintree, Boston, motorist callboxes end nb

11b a(23)Neponset St, to Canton, **E...gas:** Citgo/repair, Sunoco/repair, **W...gas:** Gulf/diesel, **lodging:** Ramada Inn, Sheraton, **other:** HOSPITAL

22.5mm Neponset River

10(20)   Coney St(from sb, no EZ return), to US 1, Sharon, Walpole, **1 mi W on US 1...gas:** Shell, US/diesel, **food:** Beacon's Rest., Dunkin Donuts, Friendly's, IHOP, McDonald's, 99 Rest., Old Country Buffet, PapaGino's, Pizza Hut, Taco Bell, **lodging:** Best Western, **other:** Acura, Barnes&Noble, CVS Drug, Home Depot, Isuzu, Jo-Ann Fabrics, Kohl's, Lexus, OfficeMax, Old Navy, Stop&Shop Foods, mall

9(19)   US 1, to MA 27, Walpole, **W...gas:** Exxon, Mobil, Shell, Power Gas, **food:** Bickford's, Clyde's Roadhouse, **lodging:** Holiday Inn Express, Sharon Inn, **other:** BigY Food/drug, Wal-Mart, same as 10

8(16)   S Main St, Sharon, **E...food:** Dunkin Donuts, **other:** Brook's Drung, Shaw's Foods, whaling museum

7b a(13) MA 140, to Mansfield, **E...food:** Domino's, 99 Rest., Piccadilly Cafe, **lodging:** Comfort Inn, Courtyard, Holiday Inn, Red Roof Inn, Residence Inn, **other:** Stop&Shop Food, **W...gas:** Mobil, Shell, **food:** PapaGino's, **other:** Radio Shack

Attleboro

6b a(12) I-495, S to Cape Cod, N to NH, no facilities

10mm   Welcome Ctr/rest area both lanes, full(handicapped)facilities, info, phone, picnic tables, litter barrels, petwalk

9mm   truck parking area sb

5(7)   MA 152, Attleboro, **E...HOSPITAL, W...gas:** Gulf/diesel, **food:** Bill's Pizza, Piccadilly Rest., Wendy's, **other:** Brooks Drug, Radio Shack, Shaw's Foods

4(6)   I-295 S, to Woonsocket, no facilities

3(4)   MA 123, to Attleboro, **E...gas:** Shell/diesel, **other:** HOSPITAL, zoo

2.5mm   parking area/weigh sta both lanes, no restrooms, litter barrels, motorist callboxes

2b a(1)   US 1A, Newport Ave, Attleboro, **E...gas:** Cumberland, Mobil, Shell, Sunoco, **food:** McDonald's, Olive Garden, **lodging:** Holiday Inn, **other:** Bob's Store, Home Depot, K-Mart, Mazda, OfficeMax, Pontiac, Shaw's Foods

1(.5)   US 1(from sb), **E...lodging:** Day's Inn, **other:** Aamco, Brooks Drug, Volvo, **W...gas:** A+, Gulf, **food:** Burger King, McDonald's, Ponderosa, Taco Bell, **other:** Dodge, Mazda, Mitsubishi, Ro Jack's Foods

0mm   Massachusetts/Rhode Island state line

Interstate 195

Exit #   Services

N ↑↓ S

22(41)   I-495 N, MA 25 S, to Cape Cod. I-195 begins/ends on I-495, exit 1.

21(39)   MA 28, to Wareham, **N...gas:** Maxi/diesel/24hr, **food:** Zeadey's Rest., **S...gas:** Shell/diesel, **other:** HOSPITAL, **other:** NAPA, repair, **S...gas:** Mobil/Dunkin Doughnuts/diesel, Valero/diesel, **other:** HOSPITAL

37mm   rest area eb, info, phone, picnic tables, litter barrels, petwalk, boat ramp

36mm   Sippican River

20(35)   MA 105, to Marion, **S...**RV camping(seasonal)

19b a(31)to Mattapoisett, **S...gas:** Mobil

18(26)   MA 240 S, to Fairhaven, **1 mi S...gas:** Citgo/7-11, Gulf, Mutual, Shell, **food:** Applebee's, Blimpie, Burger King, D'angelo's, Dunkin Donuts, Fairhaven Chowder, Great Wall Chinese, McDonald's, 99 Rest., PapaGino's, Pasta House, Pizza Hut, Taco Bell, Uno Pizzaria, Wendy's, **lodging:** Hampton Inn, **other:** AutoZone, Brooks Drug, $Tree, GMC/Buick/Pontiac, GNC, K-Mart, Marshalls, Mazda, Radio Shack, Shaw's Foods, Stop&Shop Foods, Staples, TownFair Tire, Walgreen, Wal-Mart

25.5mm Acushnet River

17(24)   Coggeshall St, New Bedford, **N...gas:** Citgo/7-11, Sunoco, **food:** Dunkin Donuts, EndZone Café, McDonald's, same as 16

16(23)   Washburn St(from eb), **N...gas:** Shell, Sunoco, **food:** McDonald's

15(22)   MA 18 S, New Bedford, downtown, **S...**Whaling Museum, hist dist

14(21)   Penniman St(from eb), New Bedford, downtown

13b a(20)MA 140, **N...**airport, **S...gas:** Buttonwood/diesel, Sunoco, **food:** Dunkin Donuts, **other:** HOSPITAL, Buttonwood Park/zoo, CVS Drug, Honda, Shaw's Foods, VW

12b a(19)N Dartmouth, **S...gas:** Gulf, Hess, Mobil/diesel, **food:** Athens Pizzaria, Burger King, D'angelo's, Dunkin Donuts, Friendly's, Jimmy's Pizza, McDonald's, 99 Rest., Old Country Buffet, Panera Bread, PapaGino's, Peking Garden, Quizno's, Taco Bell, Texas Roadhouse, Wendy's, **lodging:** Comfort Inn, Residence Inn, **other:** Best Buy, Chevrolet, Firestone/auto, JC Penney, Lowe's Whse, Saturn, Sears/auto, Stop&Shop Food/gas, TownFair Tire, Toyota, USPO, mall, st police

11b a(17)Reed Rd, to Dartmouth, **2 mi S...gas:** Shell/24hr, **lodging:** Dartmouth Motel

Interstate 195

N

S

F a l l   R i v e r

10(16) MA 88 S, to US 6, Westport, **S...gas:** Mobil/diesel, Rte 6 Gas, **lodging:** Hampton Inn

9(15.5) MA 24 N(from nb), Stanford Rd, Westport, **S...gas:** Mobil/diesel, Rte 6 Gas, **food:** LePage's Seafood, Priscilla Rest., White's Rest., **lodging:** Hampton Inn

8b a(15) MA 24 S, Fall River, Westport, **N...gas:** Crosson Gas, **food:** Papa John's, **S...food:** Dunkin Donuts, Subway

7(14) MA 81 S, Plymouth Ave, Fall River, **N...gas:** Getty, **food:** Burger King, 99 Rest., Wendy's, **other:** CVS Drug, **S...gas:** Shell, **food:** Applebee's, McDonald's, **other:** Goodyear/auto, Walgreen

6(13.5) Pleasant St, Fall River, downtown

5(13) MA 79, MA 138, to Taunton, **S...gas:** Citgo/7-11, Hess, **food:** Denny's, Dunkin Doughnuts, **lodging:** Day's Inn

12mm Assonet Bay

4b a(10) MA 103, to Swansea, Somerset, **N...gas:** Getty, **food:** Rogers Rest., **other:** auto repair, **S...gas:** Shell/24hr, **food:** TKO Shea's Rest., **lodging:** Quality Inn

3(8) US 6, to MA 118, Swansea, Rehoboth, **N...gas:** Citgo/7-11, Hess, Shell/diesel, **food:** Burger King, D'angelo's, Dunkin Donuts, Friendly's, McDonald's, Ponderosa, Thai Taste, Tim Horton, **other:** BigLots, CarQuest, Firestone/auto, Hi-Lo Foods, Sears/auto, mall, **S...gas:** Cumberland/24hr, **food:** Anthony's Seafood, **lodging:** Swansea Motel

6mm **rest area eb, full(handicapped)facilities, phone, picnic tables, litter barrels, petwalk**

5.5mm parking area wb

2(5) MA 136, to Newport, **S...gas:** Mobil/24hr, Shell/24hr, **food:** Cathay Pearl Chinese, Domino's, Dunkin Donuts, McDonald's

3mm weigh sta both lanes

1(1) MA 114A, to Seekonk, **N...gas:** Exxon/diesel, Public, Shell/24hr, **food:** Athens Pizza, Newport Creamery, 99 Rest., **lodging:** Johnson&Wales Inn, Motel 6, **S...gas:** Mobil/24hr, Sunoco/diesel, **food:** Applebee's, Bickford's, Bugaboo Creek Steaks, Burger King, Chili's, China Wok, Cisco's Pizza, D'angelo's, Dunkin Donuts, Friendly's, McDonald's, Old Country Buffet, PapaGino's, Subway, Taco Bell, Testa's Italian, TGIFriday, Wendy's, **lodging:** Comfort Inn, Gateway Motel, Hampton Inn, Mary's Motel, Park Inn, Ramada Inn/rest., Town'n Country Motel, **other:** BigLots, Bob's Stores, Circuit City, Daewoo, GNC, Home Depot, Jiffy Lube, Michael's, PepBoys, Sam's Club, Staples, Stop&Shop Foods, Target, TownFair Tire, Volvo, Wal-Mart/drug

0mm Massachusetts/Rhode Island state line, **Exits 8-1 are in RI.**

8(5) US 1A N, Pawtucket, **S...gas:** Mobil/diesel, **food:** Subway, **other:** CVS Drug

7(4) US 6 E, CT 114 S, to Barrington, Seekonk, no facilities

6(3) Broadway Ave, **N...gas:** Speedy AutoService, **S...gas:** Shell, Sunoco/diesel

5(2.5) RI 103 E, Warren Ave, no facilities

4(2) US 44 E, RI 103 E, Taunton Ave, Warren Ave, **N...gas:** Exxon

3(1.5) Gano St, **S...lodging:** Radisson

2(1) US 44 W, Wickenden St, India Pt, downtown, **N...gas:** Shell/diesel

1(.5) Providence, downtown

0mm I-195 begins/ends on I-95, exit 20 in Providence, RI, **Exits 1-8 are in RI.**

Interstate 290

E

W

W o r c e s t e r

Exit #	Services
26b a(20)	I-495. I-290 begins/ends on I-495, exit 25.
25b a(17)	Solomon Pond Mall Rd, to Berlin, **N...food:** Bertucci's, TGIFriday, **food:** Olive Garden, **lodging:** Comfort Inn, **other:** Best Buy, Borders Books, JC Penney, Sears/auto, Target, mall, **S...**Solomon Pond Grill
24(15)	Church St, Northborough, no facilities
23b a(13)	MA 140, Boylston, **N...gas:** Citgo/diesel, Mobil, **food:** Dunkin Donuts, Other Place Rest.
22(11)	Main St, Worcester, **N...gas:** Exxon/24hr, Shell, **food:** Bickford's, Friendly's, McDonald's, Wendy's, **other:** HOSPITAL
21(10)	Plantation St(from eb), **N...lodging:** Best Western, **other:** Lowe's Whse, Staples, Stop&Shop, Target
20(8)	MA 70, Lincoln St, Burncoat St, **N...gas:** Charter/24hr, Exxon/Subway/24hr, Shell, Sunoco, **food:** Bickford's, Denny's, Dunkin Donuts, Friendly's, McDonald's, Papa Gino's, Taco Bell, Wendy's, **lodging:** Day's Inn, Econolodge, Holiday Inn, **other:** Auto Palace, CVS Drug, Radio Shack, Shaw's Food/24hr, Walgreen
19(7)	I-190 N, MA 12, no facilities
18	MA 9, Framington, Ware, Worcester Airport, **N...**HOSPITAL
16	Central St, Worcester, **N...food:** 99 Rest., **lodging:** Crowne Plaza, Hampton Inn, mall
14	MA 122, Barre, Worcester, downtown
13	MA 122A, Vernon St, Worcester, downtown
12	MA 146 S, to Millbury, no facilities
11	Southbridge St, College Square, **N...gas:** Shell/diesel, **food:** Wendy's, **S...gas:** Getty
10	MA 12 N(from wb), Hope Ave, no facilities
9	Auburn St, to Auburn, **E...gas:** Shell, **food:** Arby's, Bickford's, Wendy's, McDonald's, **lodging:** Baymont Inn, Comfort Inn, Holiday Inn Express, **other:** Acura, AutoZone, Firestone, Sears/auto, Shaw's Foods, Staples, mall
8	MA 12 S(from sb), Webster, **W...gas:** Shell, **lodging:** Best Western
7	I-90, E to Boston, W to Springfield. I-290 begins/ends on I-90.

MASSACHUSETTS
Interstate 395

N↑↓S

Exit #	Services
	I-395 begins/ends on I-90, exit 10.
7(12)	to I-90(MA Tpk), MA 12, **E...gas:** Shell, **food:** Piccadilly's, **lodging:** Best Western, Comfort Inn, Holday Inn Express
6b a(11)	US 20, **E...gas:** Gulf, **food:** Dunkin Donuts, KFC, **other:** Honda, Saab/VW, TCI Tires, truck repair, **W...gas:** Shell, BJ's Whse, **food:** Chuck's Steakhouse, Friendly's, **lodging:** Fairfield Inn, Hampton Inn, **other:** Ford/Mercury, Home Depot, Mitsubishi, Nissan, TJ Maxx, transmissions
5(8)	Depot Rd, N Oxford, no facilities
4b a(6)	Sutton Ave, to Oxford, **W...gas:** Mobil/24hr, **food:** Cumberland Farms, Dunkin Donuts, McDonald's, NE Pizza, Subway, **other:** Cahill's Tire/Repair, CVS Drug
3(4)	Cudworth Rd, to N Webster, S Oxford, no facilities
2(3)	MA 16, to Webster, **E...**Subaru, **W...gas:** Exxon/24hr, Getty, Mobil, Shell/24hr, **food:** Burger King, D'angelo/Papa Gino's, Empire Wok, Friendly's, Honey Dew Donughts, KFC, McDonald's, **other:** HOSPITAL, Brooks Drug, CVS Drug, Ford, PriceChopper Foods, Walgreen
1(1)	MA 193, to Webster, **E...**HOSPITAL, **W...gas:** Citgo/diesel, **food:** Golden Greek Rest., Wind Tiki Chinese, **other:** Goodyear
0mm	Massachusetts/Connecticut state line

Interstate 495

N↑↓S Amesbury

Exit #	Services
	I-495 begins/ends on I-95, exit 59.
55	MA 110(no return nb), to I-95 S, **E...gas:** Best Choice/Domino's, Mobil, Irving, **food:** Burger King, Friendly's, McDonald's, **lodging:** Fairfield Inn, **other:** Stop&Shop, Chevrolet/VW
54(118)	MA 150, to Amesbury, **W...**RV camping
53(115)	Broad St, Merrimac, **W...gas:** Gulf, **food:** Dunkin Donuts
114mm	**parking area sb, phone, restrooms, picnic tables, litter barrels**
52(111)	MA 110, to Haverhill, **E...**HOSPITAL, **W...gas:** Getty, Mobil/diesel, **food:** Dunkin Donuts, King's Roast Beef
110mm	parking area nb, phone, picnic tables, litter barrels
51(109)	MA 125, to Haverhill, **E...gas:** Citgo, Mobil, **food:** Bros Pizza, **other:** HOSPITAL, **W...food:** Burger King, Dunkin Donuts, Friendly's, McDonald's, Taco Bell, Wendy's
50(107)	MA 97, to Haverhill, **E...**HOSPITAL, **W...**Ford
49(106)	MA 110, to Haverhill, **E...gas:** Gulf, Sunoco/24hr, **food:** A1 Deli, Chunky's Diner, Dunkin Donuts, McDonald's, 99 Rest., PapaGino's, **lodging:** Best Western, Comfort Inn, **other:** Buick/Pontiac/GMC, Chevrolet, Chrysler/Plymouth, MktBasket Foods
105.8mm	Merrimac River
48(105.5)	MA 125, to Bradford, no facilities
47(105)	MA 213, to Methuen, **1-2 mi W...food:** Bugaboo Steaks, Burger King, ChuckeCheese, Joe's Grill, Macaroni Grill, McDonald's, Starbucks, TGIFriday, Wendy's, **other:** Borders Books, Brooks Drug, Home Depot, Marshalls, Old Navy, Wal-Mart, Methuen Mall, Stop&Shop Foods

Chelmsford

Exit #	Services
46(104)	MA 110, **E...gas:** Gulf, Sunoco/24hr, **other:** HOSPITAL, Ford/Lincoln/Mercury
45(103)	Marston St, to Lawrence, **W...other:** Chevrolet, Honda, Isuzu, Kia
44(102)	Merrimac St, to Lawrence, no facilities
43(101)	Mass Ave, no facilities
42(100)	MA 114, **E...gas:** Exxon, Gulf, Mobil, **food:** Denny's, Friendly's, Lee Chin Cninese, Pizza Hut, **lodging:** Hampton Inn, **W...gas:** Shell/diesel, 7-11, **food:** Burger King, Marathon Pizzaria, McDonald's, TCBY, Wendy's, **lodging:** Quality Inn, **other:** HOSPITAL, MktBasket Foods
41(99)	MA 28, to Andover, **E...food:** Dunkin Donuts, **other:** Chevrolet
40b a(98)	I-93, N to Methuen, S to Boston
39(94)	MA 133, to N Tewksbury, **E...gas:** Mobil/diesel/24hr, **food:** McDonald's, **lodging:** Extended Stay America, **W...gas:** Hess, **food:** Cracker Barrel, Wendy's, **lodging:** Fairfield Inn, Holiday Inn/rest., Ramada/rest., Residence Inn
38(93)	MA 38, to Lowell, **E...gas:** Shell, **food:** Applebee's, Burger King, Friendly's, IHOP, T-D Waffle, **lodging:** Motel 6, **other:** Home Depot, Honda/VW, Mazda, MktBasket Foods, **W...gas:** Shell/diesel, Sunoco, USA/diesel, **food:** Dunkin Donuts, Milan Pizza, McDonald's, Wendy's, **other:** MEDICAL CARE, Chevrolet/Pontiac/Buick/GMC, CVS Drug, K-Mart, Saturn, Staples
37(91)	Woburn St, to S Lowell, **W...gas:** Exxon
35c(90)	to Lowell SP, Lowell ConX, **1 mi W...food:** McDonald's, Outback Steaks, **lodging:** Courtyard, **other:** Shop&Save, Walgreen
35b a(89)	US 3, S to Burlington, N to Nashua, NH, no facilities
34(88)	MA 4, Chelmsford, **E...gas:** Mobil, Sunoco, **food:** Dunkin Donuts, Skip's Rest., 99 Rest., **lodging:** Radisson, **W...gas:** Shell, **food:** Ground Round, **lodging:** Best Western
33	MA 4, N Chelmsford(from nb), no facilities
88mm	motorist aid call boxes begin sb
87mm	**rest area both lanes, full(handicapped)facilities, phone, picnic tables, litter barrels, vending, petwalk**
32(83)	Boston Rd, to MA 225, **E...gas:** Exxon/24hr, Gulf/service, Mobil/24hr, **food:** Applebee's, B&B Café, Boston Mkt, Burger King, Chili's, D'angelo's, Dunkin Donuts, McDonald's, **other:** CVS Drug, MktBasket Foods, Osco Drug, to Nashoba Valley Ski Area
31(80)	MA 119, to Groton, **E...gas:** Mobil/diesel/24hr, **food:** Dunkin Donuts, Ken's Café, Subway
30(78)	MA 110, to Littleton, **E...gas:** Shell, **food:** HOSPITAL, **W...gas:** Citgo/diesel, Sunoco/diesel
29b a(77)	MA 2, to Leominster, **E...**to Walden Pond St Reserve
28(75)	MA 111, to Boxborough, Harvard, **E...gas:** Exxon/repair, **lodging:** Holiday Inn
27(70)	MA 117, to Bolton, **E...gas:** Mobil/diesel, **W...gas:** Mobil, **food:** Bolton Pizza, Hebert Ice Cream, **other:** RV camping(seasonal)
26(68)	MA 62, to Berlin, **E...**Best Western, **W...gas:** Exxon/24hr, Gulf/24hr, Shell/diesel
66mm	Assabet River
25b(64)	I-290, to Worchester, no facilities
25a	to MA 85, Marlboro, **E...food:** Burger King, Honeydew Donuts, 99 Rest., Piccadilly's

Interstate 495

N ↑ S

24b a(63) US 20, to Northboro, Marlboro, **E...gas:** Mikey/gas, Mobil, **food:** D'angelo's, Dunkin Donuts, Lakeside Rest., **lodging:** Holiday Inn/rest., **W...gas:** Exxon, Shell, **food:** Boston Mkt, China Taste, Longhorn Steaks, McDonald's, Panera Bread, PapaGino's, Starbucks, Subway, Tandoori Grill, Wendy's, **lodging:** Best Western, Embassy Suites, Homestead Suites, Radisson, **other:** GNC, OfficeMax, Victory Foods

23c(60) Simrano Dr, Marlboro, no facilities

23b a(59) MA 9, to Shrewsbury, Framingham, **E...gas:** Best Value Gas, Exxon/diesel, **food:** Red Barn Coffee, Wendy's, **lodging:** Red Roof Inn, **other:** Volvo, **W...gas:** Mobil/diesel/24hr, **food:** Burger King, Friendly's, McDonald's, Naked Fish Rest., Piccadilly's, **lodging:** Courtyard, Extended Stay America, Residence Inn, Sierra Suites, Studio+, Wyndham Hotel, **other:** HOSPITAL

22(58) I-90, MA TPK, E to Boston, W to Albany

21b a(54) MA 135, to Hopkinton, Upton, **E...gas:** Gulf, Mobil, **food:** Dino's Pizza, Dynasty Chinese, Golden Spoon Rest.

20(50) MA 85, to Milford, **W...gas:** Gulf/diesel/LP, Mobil, **food:** Cafe 85/deli, Wendy's, **lodging:** Baymont Inn, Day's Inn, Courtyard/rest, Fairfield Inn, Holiday Inn Express, **other:** HOSPITAL

19(48) MA 109, to Milford, **W...gas:** Mobil/Pizza Hut/diesel/24hr, Shell, **food:** Alamo Mexican, Applebee's, Bugaboo Cr Steaks, Burger King, D'angelo, Friendly's, KFC/Pizza Hut, McDonald's, PapaGino's, Richard's Grill, Taco Bell, **lodging:** Radisson/cafe, Tage Inn, **other:** CVS Drug, $Tree, Jo-Ann Fabrics, K-Mart, Radio Shack, Stop&Shop, Victory Foods

18(46) MA 126, to Bellingham, **E...food:** Chili's, McDonald's, **other:** Barnes&Noble, MktBasket Foods, Old Navy, Staples, **Wal-Mart**, Whole Foods Mkt, **W...gas:** Hess/Blimpie, Mobil/24hr, Sunoco/diesel, **food:** DQ, Dunkin Donuts, Outback Steaks, Pizzaria Uno, **other:** Home Depot

17(44) MA 140, to Franklin, Bellingham, **E...gas:** Mobil, Sunoco, **food:** Applebee's, Burger King, D'angelo's, Dunkin Donuts, Friendly's, KFC, Longhorn Steaks, Panera Bread, PapaGino's, Pipinelle's Rest., Pizza Hut, Subway, Taco Bell, Thai Cuisine, Wendy's, **other:** AutoZone, Buick/GMC, Chrysler/Jeep, CVS Drug, GNC, Marshalls, Radio Shack, Stop&Shop, **W...HOSPITAL,** BJ's Whse/gas, **food:** Piccadilly's, **lodging:** Residence Inn

16(42) King St, to Franklin, **E...gas:** Sunoco/24hr, **food:** Dunkin Donuts, Franklin Deli, Gold Fork Rest., Joe's Grill, McDonald's, Goodfella's Rest., McDonald's, **lodging:** Hampton Inn, **other:** Spruce Pond Creamery, **W...lodging:** Hawthorn Inn

15(39) MA 1A, to Plainville, Wrentham, **E...gas:** Mobil, **other:** HOSPITAL, **W...gas:** Mobil/diesel, **food:** Cracker Barrel, Dunkin Donuts, Ruby Tuesday, Uno Pizzaria, **other:** Premium Outlets/famous brands

14b a(37) US 1, to N Attleboro, **E...gas:** Mobil/D'angelo's/PapaGino's/diesel, **food:** Luciano's Rest., **lodging:** Arbor Inn, **W...gas:** Mobil

13(32) I-95, N to Boston, S to Providence, access to HOSPITAL

12(30) MA 140, to Mansfield, **E...food:** Wendy's, **other:** Home Depot, Shaw's Foods, Staples, **3 mi E...food:** 99 Rest., **lodging:** Comfort Inn, Courtyard, Holiday Inn, Red Roof Inn, Residence Inn, **other:** Stop&Shop Food

11(29) MA 140 S(from sb, no EZ return), **1 mi W...gas:** Gulf, **food:** Andrea's Pizza, Boston Pizza, Dunkin Donuts, Mandarin Chinese, McDonald's, **other:** $Tree, GNC, Radio Shack

10(26) MA 123, to Norton, **E...food:** Dunkin Doughnuts, **other:** McLaughlin RV Park, QuickStop, **W...HOSPITAL**

9(24) Bay St, to Taunton, **W...food:** Dunkin Donuts, Pizza Hut, Wendy's, **food:** Tedeschi Foods/deli, **lodging:** Extended Stay America, Holiday Inn, **other:** MEDICAL CARE, BJ's Whse

8(22) MA 138, to Raynham, **E...gas:** Mobil/diesel, **food:** Spartain's Rest., **W...gas:** Exxon/diesel, Mobil/24hr, Shell/diesel/repair, **food:** Bros Pizza, China Garden, Dunkin Doughnuts, Honeydew Donuts, La Casa Mia Rest., McDonald's, Pepperoni's Pizza, Subway, **other:** HOSPITAL

7b a(19) MA 24, to Fall River, Boston, **1/2 mi E...food:** Burger King

18mm weigh sta both lanes

17.5mm Taunton River

6(15) US 44, to Middleboro, **E...food:** Burger King, Dunkin Donuts, Fireside Grill, Friendly's, PapaGino's, **W...gas:** 44 Gas, Mobil/diesel, Shell/diesel, **lodging:** Fairfield Inn, Holiday Inn Express, **other:** Crossroads RV Ctr

5(14) MA 18, to Lakeville, **E...food:** Burger King, Dunkin Donuts, Fireside Grill, Friendly's, PapaGino's, **other:** MEDICAL CARE, CVS Drug, Kelly's Tire, Stop&Shop Food, **W...other:** Massasoit SP, RV camping(seasonal)

4(12) MA 105, to Middleboro, **E...gas:** Exxon/diesel/24hr, Mobil/diesel, Shell/24hr, Sunoco/24hr, **food:** DQ, Dunkin Donuts, McDonald's, Pappa Timmy's Pizza, Subway, **lodging:** Day's Inn, **other:** AutoZone, Brooks Drug, Chevrolet, Osco Drug

10.5mm parking area eb, picnic tables

10mm parking area wb, picnic tables

3(8) MA 28, to Rock Village, S Middleboro, **E...gas:** Citgo/diesel, **other:** Buds RV's, Fred's Repair, **W...gas:** Mobil/Dunkin Doughnuts, **food:** Fisher's Rest.

2(3) MA 58, W Wareham, **E...other:** Edaville Family Park, auto repair, to Myles Standish SF, **W...gas:** Citgo/7-11, **food:** Dapper Dan's Hotdogs, **other:** RV camping(seasonal)

2mm Weweantic River

1(0) I-495 begins/ends on I-195, MA 25 S.

MICHIGAN
Interstate 69

Exit #	Services
199	Lp 69(from eb, no return), to Port Huron, **S...gas:** Mobil/diesel, **other:** AutoZone, K-Mart, Sam's Club/gas
	I-69 E and I-94 E run together into Port Huron. **See Michigan Interstate 94, exit 274-275mm.**
198	I-94, to Detroit and Canada
196	Wadhams Rd, **N...gas:** Bylo/diesel, Marathon, Shell/Wendy's, **food:** Burger King, Hungry Howie's, McDonald's, Peking Kitchen, Subway, **other:** Carter's Foods, Wadham's Drugs, KOA, **S...golf**
194	Taylor Rd, **N...**RV camping
189	Wales Center Rd, to Goodells, **S...golf**
184	MI 19, to Emmett, **N...gas:** Citgo/diesel/rest./24hr, **S...gas:** Marathon/diesel/24hr
180	Riley Center Rd, **N...**RV camping
176	Capac Rd, **N...gas:** BP/McDonald's/diesel, **food:** Subway(2mi)
174mm	**rest area wb, full(handicapped)facilties, phone, picnic tables, litter barrels, vending, petwalk**
168	MI 53, Imlay City, **N...gas:** BP/diesel/24hr, Speedway/diesel, **food:** Big Boy, Burger King, DQ, Hungry Howie's, Jet's Pizza, Jimmy's Coney Island, Little Caesar's, Lucky's Steaks, McDonald's, Taco Bell, Wah Wong Chinese, Wendy's/Tim Horton, **lodging:** Day's Inn, M53 Motel, Super 8, **other:** AutoZone, Chevrolet/Pontiac, Chrysler/Plymouth/Dodge/Jeep, Farmer Jack's, Ford, GNC, IGA Foods, Pamida, **S...camping**
163	Lake Pleasant Rd, to Attica, no facilities
160mm	**rest area eb, full(handicapped)facilities, phone, picnic tables, litter barrels, vending, petwalk**
159	Wilder Rd, no facilities
158mm	Flint River
155	MI 24, Lapeer, **1 mi N...gas:** BP, Marathon/diesel, Meijer/diesel/24hr, **food:** Arby's, Burger King, DQ, Hot'n Now, KFC, Little Caesar's, McDonald's, Michael's Dining, Subway, Taco Bell, Tim Horton, Wendy's, **lodging:** Best Western, Fairfield Inn, **other:** HOSPITAL, K-Mart, Kroger, Radio Shack, SavALot, st police, **S...gas:** Mobil/diesel, Buick/Pontiac
153	Lake Nepessing Rd, **S...**to Thumb Correctional, camping, golf
149	Elba Rd, **S...food:** Woody's Pizza
145	MI 15, Davison, **N...gas:** Shell/diesel, Speedway, **food:** Apollo Rest., Arby's, Big Boy, Big John's Rest., Burger King, Country Boy Rest., Dunkin Donuts, Hungry Howie's, Italia Gardens, KFC, Little Caesar's, Lucky's Steaks, McDonald's, Subway, Taco Bell, **lodging:** Comfort Inn, **other:** AutoValue Parts, GNC, Kessel Foods, Pontiac/Buick/GMC, Radio Shack, Rite Aid/24hr, **S...gas:** Mobil/diesel
143	Irish Rd, **N...gas:** Shell/diesel, **S...gas:** Shell/McDonald's/24hr, 7-11
141	Belsay Rd, Flint, **N...gas:** BP/Wendy's, Shell/diesel/24hr, **food:** Country Kitchen, McDonald's, Taco Bell, **other:** MEDICAL CARE, Harley-Davidson, Kessel Foods, K-Mart, Wal-Mart/auto, **S...gas:** Sunoco/A&W/LJ Silver/diesel

139	Center Rd, Flint, **N...gas:** Marathon, Speedway/diesel, **food:** Applebee's, Boston Mkt, Halo Burger, McDonald's, Moikong Chinese, Old Country Buffet, Ponderosa, Subway, Tim Horton, Wendy's, **lodging:** Budget Host, **other:** Aldi Foods, Buick, Family$, Goodyear/auto, Home Depot, JC Penney, Jo-Ann Fabrics, Lowe's Whse, Mervyn's, OfficeMax, Old Navy, mall, **S...gas:** Meijer/diesel/24hr, **food:** Bob Evans, DQ, McDonald's, Walli's Rest., **lodging:** Super 8, **other:** MEDICAL CARE, FarmerJack's, Staples, Target, to IMA Sports Arena
138	MI 54, Dort Hwy, **N...gas:** BP/24hr, Speedway/diesel, Sunoco, **food:** Anna's Kitchen, Big John's Rest., Little Caesar's, Pumpernik's Rest., Toshi's Café, YaYa's Chicken, **other:** HOSPITAL, Rite Aid, **S...gas:** Speedway, Sunoco, **food:** Angelo's Coney Island, Arby's, Big John's Steaks, Burger King, Chester Fried, China Buffet, KFC, McDonald's, Red Roof Ribs, Subway, Taco Bell, **other:** Aamco, Advance Parts, AutoZone, Cadillac/Pontiac, $General, Goodyear, K-Mart, Radio Shack, Rite Aid, U-Haul, Walgreen
137	I-475, UAW Fwy, to Detroit, Saginaw
136	Saginaw St, Flint, **N...**HOSPITAL, U MI at Flint, **S...other:** ExpertTire, GMC
135	Hammerberg Rd, industrial area, **S...gas:** Sunoco/diesel
133b a	I-75, S to Detroit, N to Saginaw, US 23 S to Ann Arbor
131	MI 121, to Bristol Rd, **1/2 mi N on Miller Rd...gas:** Speedway, **food:** A&W, Big Boy, Burger King, Chili's, ChuckeCheese, Golden Moon Chinese, LJ Silver, Old Country Buffet, Outback Steaks, Ponderosa, Ryan's, Ruby Tuesday, Subway, Taco Bell, Valley Diner, **other:** Best Buy, Borders Books, Circuit City, Discount Tire, Dodge, Firestone/auto, Goodyear/auto, JC Penney, Jo-Ann Fabrics, Marshall Fields, Mervyn's, Michael's, Office Depot, Old Navy, Sears/auto, Target, mall
129	Miller Rd, **S...gas:** Speedway, **food:** Arby's, Burger King, McDonald's, Wendy's, **other:** Kroger/gas
128	Morrish Rd, **S...gas:** BP/24hr, **other:** Sports Creek Horse Racing
126mm	**rest area eb, full(handicapped)facilities, info, phone, picnic tables, litter barrels, petwalk**
123	MI 13, Lennon, to Saginaw, **N...gas:** Speedway/diesel
118	MI 71, Durand, to Corunna, **S...gas:** Marathon, Shell/diesel, **food:** Hardee's, McDonald's, Subway, **lodging:** Sunset Motel, **other:** MEDICAL CARE, Carter's Foods, Chevrolet/Pontiac, Family$, Radio Shack, Rite Aid
115mm	Shiawassee River
113	Bancroft, **S...gas:** BP/diesel, RV camping
105	MI 52, Perry, to Owosso, **S...gas:** Citgo/7-11, Phillips 66/Taco Bell, Sunoco/Subway/diesel, **food:** Burger King, Café Sports, 59er Diner, McDonald's, **lodging:** Heb's Inn, **other:** Family$, Ford, Rite Aid, RV camping, truck repair(1mi)
101mm	**rest area wb, full(handicapped)facilities, phone, picnic tables, litter barrels, petwalk**
98.5mm	Looking Glass River
98	Woodbury Rd, Shaftsburg, to Laingsburg, **S...**RV camping

MICHIGAN

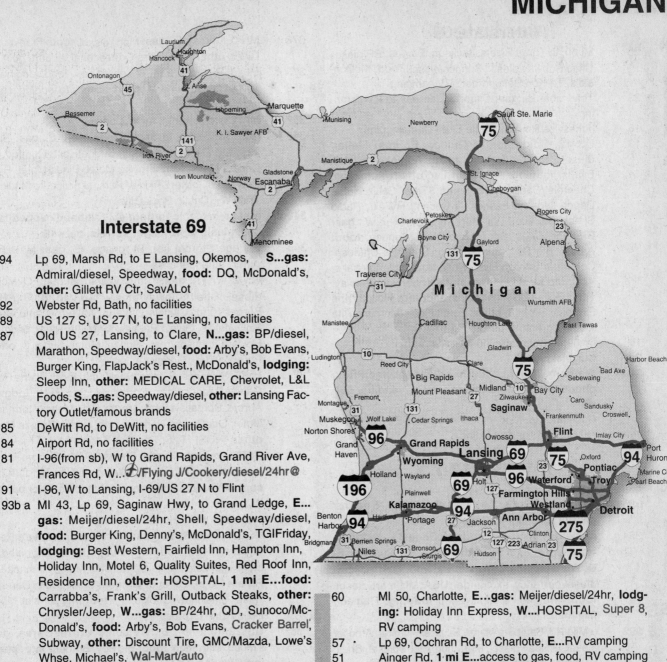

Interstate 69

N

S

Lansing

94 Lp 69, Marsh Rd, to E Lansing, Okemos, **S...gas:** Admiral/diesel, Speedway, **food:** DQ, McDonald's, **other:** Gillett RV Ctr, SavALot

92 Webster Rd, Bath, no facilities

89 US 127 S, US 27 N, to E Lansing, no facilities

87 Old US 27, Lansing, to Clare, **N...gas:** BP/diesel, Marathon, Speedway/diesel, **food:** Arby's, Bob Evans, Burger King, FlapJack's Rest., McDonald's, **lodging:** Sleep Inn, **other:** MEDICAL CARE, Chevrolet, L&L Foods, **S...gas:** Speedway/diesel, **other:** Lansing Factory Outlet/famous brands

85 DeWitt Rd, to DeWitt, no facilities

84 Airport Rd, no facilities

81 I-96(from sb), W to Grand Rapids, Grand River Ave, Frances Rd, W...✈/Flying J/Cookery/diesel/24hr@

91 I-96, W to Lansing, I-69/US 27 N to Flint

93b a MI 43, Lp 69, Saginaw Hwy, to Grand Ledge, **E...gas:** Meijer/diesel/24hr, Shell, Speedway/diesel, **food:** Burger King, Denny's, McDonald's, TGIFriday, **lodging:** Best Western, Fairfield Inn, Hampton Inn, Holiday Inn, Motel 6, Quality Suites, Red Roof Inn, Residence Inn, **other:** HOSPITAL, **1 mi E...food:** Carrabba's, Frank's Grill, Outback Steaks, **other:** Chrysler/Jeep, **W...gas:** BP/24hr, QD, Sunoco/McDonald's, **food:** Arby's, Bob Evans, Cracker Barrel, Subway, **other:** Discount Tire, GMC/Mazda, Lowe's Whse, Michael's, Wal-Mart/auto

95 I-496, to Lansing, no facilities

72 I-96, E to Detroit, W to Grand Rapids

70 Lansing Rd, **1 mi E...gas:** Citgo/diesel/rest./24hr/@, **other:** st police

68mm rest area nb, full(handicapped)facilities, phone, picnic tables, litter barrels, vending, petwalk

66 MI 100, to Grand Ledge, Potterville, **W...gas:** BP, Shell/Subway, **food:** McDonald's, to Fox Co Park

61 Lansing Rd, **E...gas:** Marathon/diesel, Mobil/diesel, **food:** Applebee's, **lodging:** Comfort Inn, **other:** AutoZone, Chevrolet, Chrysler/Jeep/Dodge, Wal-Mart SuperCtr/24hr, **W...gas:** Speedway, QD, **food:** Arby's, Big Boy, Burger King, Hot'n Now, KFC, Little Caesar's, McDonald's, Pizza Hut, Subway, Taco Bell, Top Chinese, Wendy's, **other:** HOSPITAL, Advance Parts, CarQuest, Family$, Ford/Mercury, Geldhof Tire/auto, Jo-Ann Fabrics, Pontiac/Buick/GMC, Radio Shack, SavALot

Marshall

60 MI 50, Charlotte, **E...gas:** Meijer/diesel/24hr, **lodging:** Holiday Inn Express, **W...HOSPITAL**, Super 8, RV camping

57 Lp 69, Cochran Rd, to Charlotte, **E...RV camping**

51 Ainger Rd, **1 mi E...**access to gas, food, RV camping

48 MI 78, Olivet, to Bellevue, **1 mi E...gas:** Citgo/Subway, **food:** Taco Bell, **other:** to Olivet Coll

42 N Drive N, Turkeyville Rd, **W...food:** Cornwell's Rest.(1mi)

41mm **rest area sb, full(handicapped)facilities, phone, picnic tables, litter barrels, petwalk**

38 I-94, E to Detroit, W to Chicago

36 Michigan Ave, to Marshall, **E...gas:** Mobil/diesel, Shell/Subway, **food:** Arby's, Burger King, McDonald's, Pizza Hut, Taco Bell, Wendy's, **lodging:** AmeriHost, **other:** HOSPITAL, AutoZone, Chevrolet, $Tree, GNC, K-Mart, Parts+, Radio Shack, Rite Aid, **W...lodging:** Arbor Inn, **other:** Chrysler/Dodge/Jeep

32 F Drive S, **3/4 mi E...gas:** Shell, **food:** Moonraker Rest.(3mi)

28mm **rest area nb, full(handicapped)facilities, phone, info, picnic tables, litter barrels, petwalk**

MICHIGAN

Interstate 69

N→S

25	MI 60, to Three Rivers, Jackson, **E...gas:** BP/diesel, Citgo/Subway/diesel, Sunoco/diesel, **food:** McDonald's, Te-Kon Rest., **other:** RV camping
23	Tekonsha, **E...gas:** Citgo, **W...**access to RV camping
16	Jonesville Rd, **W...**Waffle Farm Camping(2mi)
13	US 12, Coldwater, to Quincy, **E...gas:** Meijer/diesel/24hr, Speedway, **food:** Applebee's, Bob Evans, **lodging:** Red Roof Inn, **other:** AutoZone, Chevrolet/Cadillac, $General, $Tree, GNC, Home Depot, JJo-Ann Fabrics, N Country RV Ctr, Radio Shack, SavALot, Wal-Mart SuperCtr/24hr, **W...gas:** BP/24hr, Citgo, Speedway/diesel, Sunoco, **food:** Arby's, Big Boy, Burger King, Charlie's Chinese, Coldwater Garden Rest., Hot'n Now, Little Caesar's, KFC, McDonald's, Pizza Hut, Ponderosa, Subway, Taco Bell, TCBY, Wendy's, **lodging:** Holiday Inn Express, Super 8, **other:** Ford/Lincoln/Mercury, Rite Aid, Walgreen, st police
10	Lp 69, to Coldwater, no facilities
8mm	weigh sta nb
6mm	**Welcome Ctr nb, full(handicapped)facilities, phone, picnic tables, litter barrels, vending, petwalk**
3	Copeland Rd, Kinderhook, **W...gas:** BP
0mm	Michigan/Indiana state line

Interstate 75

Exit #	Services
395mm	US/Canada Border, Michigan state line, I-75 begins/ends at toll bridge to Canada
394	Easterday Ave, **E...food:** McDonald's, **lodging:** Holiday Inn Express, **other:** to Lake Superior St U, **W...Welcome Ctr/rest area, info, gas:** Holiday/diesel/currency exchange, USA Minimart/diesel, **food:** Freighter's Rest.(2mi), **lodging:** Ramada Inn(2mi)
392	3 Mile Rd, Sault Ste Marie, **E...gas:** Admiral, Amoco/diesel, Holiday/diesel, Marathon, Mobil/diesel, Shell, USA/diesel/24hr, **food:** Abner's Rest., Arby's, Burger King, Country Kitchen, Great Wall Chinese, Jeff's Café, KFC, La Senorita Mexican, Little Caesar's, Mancino's Pizza, McDonald's, Pizza Hut, Studebaker's Rest., Subway, Taco Bell, Wendy's, **lodging:** Best Western, Budget Host, Comfort Inn, Day's Inn, Hampton Inn, Kewadin Inn, King's Inn, Motel 6, Plaza Motel, Quality Inn, Skyline Motel, Super 8, **other:** HOSPITAL, Buick/Cadillac, Chevrolet/Pontiac, Family$, Glen's Mkt, JC Penney, Jo-Ann Fabrics, K-Mart, NAPA, OfficeMax, Radio Shack, Sav-A-Lot Wal-Mart, st police, Soo Locks Boat Tours
389mm	**rest area nb, full(handicapped)facilities, info, phone, picnic tables, litter barrels, petwalk**
386	MI 28, **3 mi E...**food, lodging, **W...**to Brimley SP, Clear Creek Camping(5mi)
379	Gaines Hwy, **E...**to Barbeau Area, camping

378	MI 80, Kinross, **E...gas:** Mobil/diesel, **food:** Frank&Jim's Diner, **other:** to Kinross Correctional, airport, golf
373	MI 48, Rudyard, **2 mi W...**gas/diesel, food, lodging
359	MI 134, to Drummond Island, access to lodging, camping
352	MI 123, to Moran, **5 mi W...**lodging
348	H63, St Ignace, to Sault Reservation, **E...gas:** Shell, **lodging:** Birchwood Motel, BudgetHost, Comfort Inn, Cedars Motel, NorthernAire Motel, Pines Motel, Rockview Motel, **other:** Tiki RV Park, st police, to Mackinac Trail, **W...**Castle Rock Gifts
346mm	**rest area/scenic turnout sb, full(handicapped)facilities, picnic tables, litter barrels, petwalk**
345	Portage St(from sb), St Ignace, **E...gas:** Marathon, **other:** other services
344b	US 2 W, **W...gas:** Citgo/diesel/rest./24hr, Holiday/diesel, Shell/Subway/diesel/24hr, **food:** Big Boy, Burger King, Clyde's Drive-In, Miller's Camp Rest., McDonald's, Suzi's Pasties, UpNorth Rest., **lodging:** Howard Johnson/rest., Sunset Motel, Super 8, **other:** Ford/Mercury, Goodyear
a	Lp 75, St Ignace, **E...gas:** Shell(1mi), **food:** Flame Rest., Gandy Dancer Rest., Northern Lights Rest., **lodging:** Aurora Borealis Motel, Moran Bay Motel, Normandy Motel, Quality Inn, Rodeway Inn, Straits Breeze Motel, **other:** HOSPITAL, Family$, Glen's Mkt, TrueValue, USPO, to Island Ferrys, Straits SP, KOA, st police
343mm	toll booth to toll bridge, **E...Welcome Ctr nb, full(handicapped)facilities, phone, picnic tables, litter barrels**, **W...**museum
341mm	toll bridge, Lake Huron, Lake Michigan
339	US 23, Jamet St, **E...gas:** Amoco, **food:** Audie's Rest., Big Boy, KFC, **lodging:** BudgetHost, Econolodge, LaMirage Motel, Motel 6, Parkside Motel, Ramada Inn, Riviera Motel, Super 8, **W...gas:** Shell, **food:** Darrow's Rest., Mackinaw Cookie Co, **lodging:** Chalet Motel, Holiday Inn Express
338	US 23(from sb), **E...Welcome Ctr/rest area, gas:** Amoco, Marathon, **food:** Big Boy, Burger King, Cheeping Chinese, DQ, Subway, **lodging:** Baymont Inn, Downing's Motel, Ramada Inn, Rodeway Inn, **other:** IGA Foods/supplies, same as 337, **W...lodging:** Bindel Motel, Chalet Motel, Ft Mackinaw Motel, Trails End Inn
337	MI 108(no EZ return to nb), Nicolet St, Mackinaw City, **E...gas:** Citgo/LP, **food:** Embers Rest., Mancino's Pizza, Mario's Ristorante, **lodging:** Anchor Inn, BeachComber Motel, BelAire Motel, Best Western, Budget Inn, Capri Motel, Cherokee Shores Inn, Chippewa Inn, Clarion, Day's Inn, Fairfield Inn, Friendship Inn, Grand Mackinaw Resort, Hamilton Lodge, Hampton Inn, Hawthorn Inn, Howard Johnson, King's Inn, Nicolet Inn, North Pointe Inn, Ottawa Motel, Quality Inn, Ramada Ltd, Starlite Inn, Sundown Motel, Surf Motel, Travelodge, **other:** KOA, Old Mill Creek SP, to Island Ferrys, **W...**Wilderness SP

Sault Ste Marie

Mackinaw City

Interstate 75

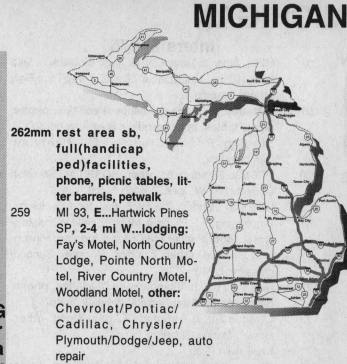

N ↑ ↓ S

336   US 31 S(from sb), to Petoskey

328mm   **rest area sb, full(handicapped)facilities, info, phone, picnic tables, litter barrels, petwalk**

326   C66, to Cheboygan, **E...gas:** Marathon, **other:** HOSPITAL, Sea Shell City/gifts

322   C64, to Cheboygan, **E...**HOSPITAL, LP, airport, st police

317mm   **rest area/scenic turnout nb, full(handicapped)facilities, info, phone, picnic tables, litter barrels, petwalk**

313   MI 27 N, Topinabee, **E...lodging:** Johnson Motel, gas, food, RV Park

311mm   Indian River

310   MI 33, MI 68, **E...lodging:** Holiday Inn Express, **other:** Jellystone Park(3mi), **W...gas:** Amoco/diesel, Shell/McDonald's/24hr, **food:** Burger King, Brown Trout Rest., Don's Burgers, Paula's Café, **lodging:** Coach House Motel, **other:** Ken's Mkt, to Indian River Trading Post/RV Resort, to Burt Lake SP

301   C58, Wolverine, **E...gas:** Marathon/diesel

297mm   Sturgeon River

290   Vanderbilt, **E...gas:** BP/diesel/LP/RV dump, **food:** Gateway Diner, **W...gas:** Mobil/diesel

287mm   **rest area sb, full(handicapped)facilities, info, phone, picnic tables, litter barrels**

282   MI 32, Gaylord, **E...gas:** Amoco/diesel, Clark, Holiday/24hr, Speedway/diesel, **food:** Arby's, Burger King, DQ, KFC, La Senorita Mexican, McDonald's, Quizno's, Subway, TCBY, Wendy's, **lodging:** Best Western, Comfort Inn, Quality Inn, Red Roof Inn, Glen's Foods, **other:** HOSPITAL, Harley-Davidson, Rite Aid, st police, **W...gas:** Citgo/diesel, Marathon/diesel, Mobil/diesel, Shell/diesel, **food:** BC Pizza, Big Boy, Bob Evans, China 1, Little Caesar's, Mancino's Pizza, Pizza Hut, Ponderosa, Taco Bell, **lodging:** Day's Inn, Hampton Inn, Super 8, **other:** Chrysler/Plymouth/Dodge, Dayton Tire, Home Depot, K-Mart, Save-A-Lot, Wal-Mart, RV camping

279mm   45th Parallel...halfway between the equator and north pole

279   Old US 27, Gaylord, **E...gas:** Marathon/Subway/diesel, Mobil/diesel, Shell, **food:** Burger King, Gobblers Rest., Mama Leone's, Willabee's Rest., **lodging:** Alpine Motel, Best Western(2mi), Brentwood Motel, Econolodge, Timberly Motel, **other:** Chevrolet, Chrysler/Jeep/Nissan, Ford/Lincoln/Mercury, Pontiac/Buick/GMC, RV Ctr, st police, **W...lodging:** Marsh Ridge Motel(2mi), KOA(3mi)

277mm   **rest area nb, full(handicapped)facilities, info, phone, picnic tables, litter barrels, petwalk**

270   Waters, **E...gas:** Mobil/diesel/rest., **W...food:** McDonald's, lodging, RV repair, to Otsego Lake SP

264   Lewiston, Frederic, **W...**access to food, lodging, camping

262mm   **rest area sb, full(handicapped)facilities, phone, picnic tables, litter barrels, petwalk**

259   MI 93, **E...**Hartwick Pines SP, **2-4 mi W...lodging:** Fay's Motel, North Country Lodge, Pointe North Motel, River Country Motel, Woodland Motel, **other:** Chevrolet/Pontiac/Cadillac, Chrysler/Plymouth/Dodge/Jeep, auto repair

256   (from sb), to MI 72, Grayling, access to same as 254

254   MI 72(exits left from nb, no return), Grayling, **1 mi W...gas:** Amoco, Admiral Gas, BP, Citgo/7-11, Mobil/diesel, Phillips 66, Shell, Speedway, **food:** A&W, Big Boy, Burger King, DQ, KFC, Little Caesar's, McDonald's, Patty's Diner, Pizza Hut, Subway, Taco Bell, Wendy's, **lodging:** Day's Inn, Holiday Inn, Super 7 Inn, **other:** HOSPITAL, Carquest, Family$, Ford/Lincoln/Mercury, Glen's Foods/24hr, K-Mart, NAPA, Rite Aid

251mm   **rest area nb, full(handicapped)facilities, info, phone, picnic tables, litter barrels, petwalk, vending**

251   4 Mile Rd, **E...**Jellystone RV Park, skiing, **W...gas:** Marathon/Arby's/diesel/24hr/@, **food:** Skyline Rest., **lodging:** Super 8

249   US 27 S(from sb), to Clare, no facilities

244   MI 18, Roscommon, **W...gas:** Sunoco/diesel/LP, **other:** N Higgins Lake SP, camping, museum

239   MI 18, Roscommon, S Higgins Lake SP, **E...other:** Ford/Mercury, gas, food, lodging, camping

235mm   **rest area sb, full(handicapped)facilities, phone, info, picnic tables, litter barrels, petwalk, vending**

227   MI 55 W, rd F97, to Houghton Lake, **5 mi W...**food

222   Old 76, to St Helen, **5 mi E...**food, lodging, camping

215   MI 55 E, West Branch, **E...gas:** Kimball/diesel, **food:** Coyle's Rest., **other:** HOSPITAL,

212   MI 55, West Branch, **E...gas:** Marathon/diesel, Shell/Subway, 7-11, **food:** Arby's, Big Boy, Burger King, Lumberjack Rest., McDonald's, Ponderosa, Taco Bell, Wendy's, **lodging:** Quality Inn/rest., Super 8, Tri Terrace Motel, **other:** HOSPITAL, Tanger Outlet/famous brands, st police, **W...gas:** BP/diesel, **other:** Lk George Camping

210mm   **rest area nb, full(handicapped)facilities, info, phone, picnic tables, litter barrels, petwalk, vending**

Grayling

Gaylord

MICHIGAN

Interstate 75

202 MI 33, Alger, to Rose City, **E...gas:** BP/Narski's Mkt/gerky(1/2mi), Mobil/diesel, Shell/Subway/Taco Bell, **other:** camping

201mm rest area sb, full(handicapped)facilities, phone, picnic tables, litter barrels, petwalk, vending

195 Sterling Rd, to Sterling, **E**...Riverview Camping(6mi)

190 MI 61, to Standish, **E...other:** HOSPITAL, Standish Correctional, **W...gas:** Amoco, Mobil

188 US 23, to Standish, **2-3 mi E...gas,** food, camping

181 Pinconning Rd, **E...gas:** Mobil, Shell/McDonald's/diesel, **food:** Pepper Mill Cheese, **lodging:** Pinconning Inn(2mi), **other:** camping, **W...gas:** Sunoco/diesel/rest./24hr

175mm rest area nb, full(handicapped)facilities, phone, picnic tables, litter barrels, petwalk, vending

173 Linwood Rd, to Linwood, **E...gas:** Mobil, **other:** Hoyle's Marina Camping

171mm Kawkawlin River

168 Beaver Rd, to Willard, **E...food:** Turkey Roost Rest.(3mi), **other:** to Bay City SP, **W...gas:** Mobil

166mm Kawkawlin River

164 to MI 13, Wilder Rd, to Kawkawlin, **E...gas:** Meijer Food/diesel/24hr, **food:** McDonald's, **lodging:** AmericInn

162b a US 10, MI 25, to Midland, **E**...HOSPITAL, st police

160 MI 84, Delta, **E...gas:** Mobil/Subway/diesel, Shell/Dunkin Donuts, **W...gas:** Amoco/diesel, Citgo/7-11, Speedway, **food:** Burger King, Howard Johnson Rest., KFC/Taco Bell, McDonald's, **lodging:** Best Value Inn, **other:** Bay Valley RV Park, to Saginaw Valley Coll

158mm rest area sb, full(handicapped)facilities, phone, picnic tables, litter barrels, vending, petwalk

155 I-675 S, to downtown Saginaw, **4 mi W...food:** OutBack Steaks, **lodging:** Hampton Inn, Super 8

154 to Zilwaukee, no facilities

153mm Saginaw River

153 MI 13, E Bay City Rd, Saginaw, **2-3 mi W**...lodging

151 MI 81, to Reese, **E...gas:** Sunoco/diesel, **food:** Burger King

150 I-675 N, to downtown Saginaw, **6 mi W...food:** OutBack Steaks, **lodging:** Hampton Inn, Super 8

149b a MI 46, Holland Ave, to Saginaw, **W...gas:** Admiral, Amoco, BP, Speedway/diesel, Sunoco, **food:** Arby's, Big Boy, Burger King, McDonald's, Taco Bell, Texan Rest., Wendy's, **lodging:** Best Western, Red Roof Inn, Rodeway Inn, **other:** HOSPITAL, Advance Parts, K-Mart, Save-A-Lot Foods

144b a Bridgeport, **E...gas:** Shell/Blimpie, Speedway/diesel/24hr, **lodging:** Heidelburg Inn, **W...gas:** Mobil, TA/diesel/rest./24hr/@, **food:** Arby's, Big Boy, Cracker Barrel, Little Caesar's, McDonald's, Peking City Chinese, Subway, Taco Bell, Wendy's, **lodging:** Baymont Inn, Day's Inn, Villager Lodge, **other:** MEDICAL CARE, Family$, IGA Food, Rite Aid, Radio Shack, st police

143mm Cass River

138mm weigh sta both lanes

136 MI 54, MI 83, Birch Run, **E...gas:** Mobil/diesel/24hr, Shell, **food:** Exit Rest., Halo Burger, KFC, Subway, **lodging:** Best Western, Comfort Inn, Hampton Inn, Holiday Inn Express, Super 8, **other:** CarQuest, Dixie Speedway, RV camping, **W...gas:** Amoco/Burger King, Citgo/7-11, Marathon, Sunoco/diesel, **food:** A&W, Arby's, Applebee's, Big Boy, Bob Evans, Coney Island, DQ, Little Caesar's, McDonald's, Schlotsky's, Taco Bell, Tony's Rest., Uno Pizzaria, Wendy's, **lodging:** Country Inn Suites, **other:** Chevrolet/Buick/Suzuki, Prime Outlet/famous brands

131 MI 57, Clio, to Montrose, **E...gas:** Shell, Sunoco, **food:** Arby's, Burger King, DQ, KFC, McDonald's, Subway, Taco Bell, **other:** AutoZone, Chevrolet, Chrysler/Plymouth, Dodge/Jeep, Farmer Jack's, Ford, K-Mart, Pamida, **W...gas:** Amoco/diesel, Mobil, **food:** Big Boy, Wendy's

129mm rest area both lanes, full(handicapped)facilities, phone, picnic tables, litter barrels, vending, petwalk

126 to Mt Morris, **E...gas:** BP/Burger King/diesel/24hr, **W...gas:** Amoco/diesel, carwash

125 I-475 S, UAW Fwy, to Flint

122 Pierson Rd, to Flint, **E...gas:** Amoco, Clark Gas, Marathon, **food:** Asia Buffet, KFC, McDonald's, Subway, Super 8, **other:** MEDICAL CARE, **W...gas:** Citgo, Meijer/diesel/24hr, Shell, **food:** Arby's, Big John's Steaks, Bob Evans, Burger King, Cracker Barrel, Denny's, Halo Burger, LJ Silver, Pizza Hut, Red Lobster, Taco Bell, Wendy's, YaYa Chicken, **lodging:** Baymont Inn, Great Western Inn, Ramada Inn, **other:** Discount Tire, Home Depot,

118 MI 21, Corunna Rd, **E...gas:** Sunoco, **food:** Badawest Lebanese, Big John's Steaks, Burger King, Coney Island, Hardee's, Little Caesar's, Taco Bell, YaYa Chicken, **other:** HOSPITAL, Advance Parts, $General, Rite Aid, **W...gas:** Amoco, Citgo, Mobil, Shell/Wendy's, Speedway, **food:** Domino's, Schlotsky's, **lodging:** Economy Motel, **other:** AutoZone, Buick, CarQuest, Farmer Jack's Foods, Home Depot, Lincoln/Mercury, Lowe's Whse, Rite Aid, Sam's Club/gas, Wal-Mart, st police

117b Miller Rd, to Flint, **E...gas:** Speedway/diesel, Sunoco/diesel, **food:** Applebee's, Arby's, Bennigan's, ChiChi's, Don Pablo, Fuddrucker's, KFC, LoneStar Steaks, McDonald's, Papa John's, Subway, **lodging:** Comfort Inn, Motel 6, Sleep Inn, **other:** K-Mart, NTB, Sav-A-Lot Foods, **W...gas:** Amoco/McDonald's, Marathon, **food:** Big Boy, Bob Evans, Burger King, Chili's, ChuckeCheese, Hooters, Mancino's Italian, Old Country Buffet, Olive Garden, Outback Steaks, Pizza Hut, Ryan's, Salvatori's Ristorante, Taco Bell, TCBY, Wendy's, **lodging:** Howard Johnson, Red Roof Inn, Super 8, **other:** MEDICAL CARE, Best Buy, Borders Books, Brake Depot, Circuit City, Dodge, Goodyear, JC Penney, Jo-Ann Fabrics, Marshall Field, Michael's, Office Depot, PepBoys, Radio Shack, Target, U-Haul, mall

Interstate 75

N ↑↓ S

117a I-69, E to Lansing, W to Port Huron

116 MI 121, Bristol Rd, **E...gas:** Amoco/24hr, Citgo, Speedway/diesel, **food:** Coney Island, KFC, McDonald's, **lodging:** Day's Inn, **other:** AutoZone, GM Plant, **W...gas:** Mobil/diesel, **other:** airport

115 US 23(from sb), **W on Hill Rd...gas:** Citgo, Meijer/diesel/24hr, Mobil, **food:** Maxie's Rest., McDonald's, **lodging:** AmericInn, Courtyard, Holiday Inn, Redwood Lodge, Residence Inn

111 I-475 N, UAW Fwy, to Flint

109 MI 54, Dort Hwy(no EZ return to sb), **1-2 mi E...food:** Big Boy, Damon's, Wendy's

108 Holly Rd, to Grand Blanc, **E...gas:** Sunoco, **food:** Subway, **lodging:** AmeriHost, **other:** BMW/Mercedes/Toyota, **W...gas:** Amoco/McDonald's., **other:** HOSPITAL,

106 Dixie Hwy(no nb return), Saginaw Rd, to Grand Blanc, **E...gas:** Clark

101 Grange Hall Rd, Ortonville, **E...other:** Holly RA, Jellystone Park, st police, **W...other:** to Seven Lakes/Groveland Oaks SP, RV camping

98 E Holly Rd, **E...gas:** Mobil/Subway/diesel/24hr, golf

95.5mm rest area both lanes, full(handicapped)facilities, picnic tables, litter barrels, info, phone, vending, petwalk

93 US 24, Dixie Hwy, Waterford, **E...Dodge, Saturn, 1-3 mi W...food:** Arby's, Big Boy, McDonald's, Taco Bell, Wendy's, **other:** MEDICAL CARE, Chrysler/Plymouth/Jeep, to Pontiac Lake RA

91 MI 15, Davison, Clarkston, **E...camping, W...gas:** Shell, **food:** Dugan's Rest., Mesquite Creek Café, Mrs B's Rest., **lodging:** Millwood B&B

89 Sashabaw Rd, **E...gas:** Shell/diesel, **other:** county park, **W...gas:** Amoco/24hr, **food:** E Ocean Chinese, McDonald's, Subway, **other:** Farmer Jack's Foods, GNC, Pine Knob Music Theatre

86mm weigh sta sb, parking area nb

84b a Baldwin Ave, **E...gas:** Shell/24hr, Sunoco/diesel, **food:** Big Boy, Joe's Crabshack, Wendy's, **other:** Best Buy, CompUSA, Costco/gas, $Castle, Kohl's, Michael's, OfficeMax, Old Navy, **W...gas:** Mobil/24hr, **food:** Chili's, McDonald's, Steak'n Shake/24hr, **other:** Borders Books, Great Lakes Crossing Outlet/famous brands, Marshall's

83b a Joslyn Rd, **E...gas:** Meijer/diesel/24hr, **other:** Jo-Ann Fabrics, Target, **W...food:** McDonald's, FoodTown/24hr, **other:** K-Mart/Little Caesar's, Outlets/famous brands

81 MI 24, Pontiac(no EZ return), **E...The Palace Arena, 1mi E...gas:** Amoco/24hr

79 University Dr, **E...gas:** Amoco, Domino's, **food:** Dunkin Donuts, Subway, **W...gas:** Speedway, **food:** Big Buck Brewery/steaks, Mtn Jack's Rest., McDonald's, Taco Bell, Wendy's/Tim Horton, **lodging:** AmeriSuites, Courtyard, Extended Stay America, Fairfield Inn, Hampton Inn, Holiday Inn, Motel 6, **other:** HOSPITAL, GM

Detroit Area

78 Chrysler Dr, **E...other:** Oakland Tech Ctr, Daimler-Chrysler

77b a MI 59, to Pontiac, **1 mi W on Opdyke...gas:** Fastrack/Tubby's/diesel, Shell, **other:** Wal-Mart/auto, Silver Dome Stadium

75 Square Lake Rd(exits left from nb), to Pontiac, **W...HOSPITAL**, St Mary's Coll

74 Adams Rd, no facilities

72 Crooks Rd, to Troy, **W...food:** Cooker, **lodging:** Embassy Suites, Northfield Hilton Inn

69 Big Beaver Rd, **E...food:** Champp's Grill, O'Grady's Grill, **lodging:** Drury Inn, Marriott, **other:** bank, **W...gas:** Amoco, Shell, 7-11/24hr, **food:** Coney Island, Denny's, Empire Szechuan, Papa Romano's Pizza, Ruth's Chris Steaks, TGIFriday, **other:** MEDICAL CARE

67 Rochester Rd, to Stevenson Hwy, **E...gas:** Clark, Mobil, Shell, **food:** Arby's, Big Boy, Burger King, Coney Island, Dunkin Donuts, KFC, Mr Pita, Pizza Hut/Taco Bell, Ram's Horn Rest., **other:** Discount Tires, Radio Shack, **W...food:** Mtn Jack's Steaks, **lodging:** Holiday Inn, Red Roof Inn, **other:** Belle Tire, repair

65b a 14 Mile Rd, Madison Heights, **E...gas:** Mobil, Shell, **food:** BeefCarver Rest., Bob Evans, Burger King, ChiChi's, Chili's, Country Oven, Denny's, Little Daddy's Grill, Logan's Roadhouse, McDonald's, Panera Bread, Steak&Ale, Taco Bell, Tubby's Subs, **lodging:** Motel 6, Red Roof Inn, **other:** MEDICAL CARE, Belle Tire, Borders Books, Circuit City, CompUSA, Dodge, Fannie May Candy, Ford, Goodyear/auto, JC Penney, Marshall Field, NTB, Office Depot, Sam's Club, Sears/auto, mall, **W...gas:** Mobil/Blimpie, **food:** Applebee's, Bennigan's, Big Fish Seafood, Coney Island, McDonald's, Ponderosa, White Castle, **lodging:** Courtyard, Day's Inn, Econolodge, Extended Stay America, Fairfield Inn, Day's Inn, Hampton Inn, Residence Inn, **other:** CVS Drug, FoodLand

63 12 Mile Rd, **E...gas:** Clark, Marathon, Speedway, **food:** Blimpie, Golden Wheel Chinese, Hacienda Azteca Mexican, Marinelli's Pizza, McDonald's, Red Lobster, TCBY, **other:** Home Depot, K-Mart, Radio Shack, transmissions, **W...gas:** Marathon/Dunkin Donuts, Speedway, **food:** Denny's, Chevrolet, Costco/gas

62 11 Mile Rd, **E...gas:** 7-11, Boodles Rest., **W...gas:** BP, Marathon/diesel, Mobil, **food:** DM, KFC, Pizza Hut, Taco Bell, Tim Horton, Tubby's Subs, **other:** Belle Tire

MICHIGAN
Interstate 75

61 I-696 E, to Port Huron, W to Lansing, to Hazel Park Raceway

60 9 Mile Rd, John R St, **E...gas:** Mobil/diesel, **food:** Burger King, China 1, McDonald's, Nick's Pizza, Subway, **lodging:** Guesthouse Hotel, **other:** DENTIST, Family$, Farmer Jack's, FashionBug, Rite Aid, **W...gas:** Mobil, **food:** Big Boy, Tubby's Subs, Wendy's

59 MI 102, 8 Mile Rd, **3 mi W...**st fairgrounds

58 7 Mile Rd, **W...gas:** Amoco/diesel

57 McNichols Rd, **E...food:** La Koney Rest./24hr, **W...gas:** BP

56b a Davison Fwy, no facilities

55 Holbrook Ave, Caniff St, **E...gas:** BP, Mobil, **W...food:** Grandy's Rest., KFC, Taco Bell

54 E Grand Blvd, Clay Ave, **W...gas:** Shell/autocare, **food:** Coney Island Rest.

53 b I-94, Ford Fwy, to Port Huron, Chicago

a Warren Ave, **E...gas:** Mobil, Shell, **W...gas:** Amoco

52 Mack Ave, **E...gas:** Shell, **food:** McDonald's, **W...** HOSPITAL

51c I-375 to civic center, downtown, tunnel to Canada

b MI 3(exits left from nb), Gratiot Ave, downtown

50 Grand River Ave, downtown

49b MI 10, Lodge Fwy, downtown

a Rosa Parks Blvd, **E...**Tiger Stadium, **W...gas:** Mobil, **other:** Firestone

48 I-96 begins/ends, no facilities

47b Porter St, **E...**bridge to Canada, DutyFree/24hr

a MI 3, Clark Ave, **E...gas:** Mobil

46 Livernois Ave, to Hist Ft Wayne, **E...gas:** Marathon, **food:** KFC/Taco Bell

45 Fort St, Springwells Ave, **E...gas:** BP/diesel, **W...gas:** Mobil, **food:** McDonald's

43b a MI 85, Fort St, to Schaefer Hwy, **E...gas:** Amoco, Sunoco, **W...gas:** Marathon, **other:** to River Rouge Ford Plant

42 Outer Dr, **W...gas:** BP/Subway/diesel, Mobil/diesel, **other:** K-Mart

41 MI 39, Southfield Rd, to Lincoln Park, **E...food:** A&W, Bill's Place Rest., **lodging:** Budget Inn, **W...gas:** Mobil/diesel, **food:** Dunkin Donuts, **lodging:** Sleep Inn, **other:** Buick

40 Dix Hwy, **E...gas:** BeeQuik/gas, BP, Citgo, Clark, Speedway, 7-11, **food:** Baffo's Pizza, Coney Island Diner, Ponderosa, **other:** MEDICAL CARE, Farmer Jack's, **W...gas:** Shell, Speedway, **food:** Big Boy, Burger King, Church's, DQ, Dunkin Donuts, LJ Silver, McDonald's, Pizza Hut, Rally's, Taco Bell, **lodging:** Holiday Motel, **other:** Firestone, CVS Drug, Foodland, Sears/auto

37 Allen Rd, North Line Rd, to Wyandotte, **E...gas:** Amoco, Mobil, Speedway, 7-11/24hr, **food:** Anita's Pizza, TCBY, Yum Yum Donuts, **lodging:** Ramada Inn, **other:** HOSPITAL, Sam's Club, transmissions, **W...food:** Arby's, Burger King, McDonald's, **lodging:** Baymont Inn, Cross Country Inn

36 Eureka Rd, **E...gas:** Speedway, **food:** Amigo's Mexican, Bob Evans, Denny's, Orleans Steaks, **lodging:** Ramada Inn, Super 8, **other:** Chevrolet, **W...gas:** Meijer/diesel/24hr, **food:** Bakers Square, Big Boy, Hooters, Mtn Jack's Steaks, Rio Bravo, Ruby Tuesday, Schlotsky's, Wendy's, **lodging:** Red Roof Inn, **other:** MEDICAL CTR, Borders Books, Costco, CVS Drug, Discount Tire, Home Depot, JC Penney, Kohl's, Mervyn's, Staples, mall

35 US 24, Telegraph Rd

34b Sibley Rd, Riverview, **W...gas:** Shell/Dunkin Donuts/Subway

a to US 24(from sb), Telegraph Rd, no facilities

32 West Rd, Woodhaven, to Trenton, **E...gas:** Citgo/diesel/rest., Meijer/diesel/24hr, Mobil/diesel/rest./24hr, Speedway/diesel, **food:** Bob Evans, Burger King, Church's/White Castle, Dunkin Donuts, KFC, LJ Silver, Panera Bread, Pizza Hut, Steak'n Shake, Subway, Taco Bell, **other:** Chevrolet, Chrysler/Plymouth/Dodge, Discount Tire, Firestone/auto, Ford, Home Depot, K-Mart, Kroger, Office Depot, Radio Shack, Target, **W...gas:** Amoco/24hr, Shell, **food:** Marco's Pizza, Millie's Rest., McDonald's, **lodging:** Best Western/rest., Knight's Inn, Holiday Inn Express, **other:** SavOn Drug

29 Gilbralter Rd, to Flat Rock, Lake Erie Metropark, **E...gas:** FasTrack/diesel, **food:** McDonald's, **other:** bank, **W...gas:** Marathon, **lodging:** Sleep Inn, **other:** Ford, st police

28 rd 85(from nb), Fort St, **E...**HOSPITAL

27 N Huron River Dr, to Rockwood, **E...gas:** Marathon, Rich, **food:** Benito's Pizza, Huron River Rest., Marco's Pizza, Ocean Duck Chinese, **other:** Rite Aid, **W...gas:** Speedway/diesel, **food:** Riverfront Rest.

26 S Huron River Dr, to S Rockwood, **E...gas:** Sunoco/diesel, **food:** Dick's Café, **other:** USPO

21 Newport Rd, to Newport, **E...gas:** Amoco/Taco Bell/24hr, **W...gas:** Mobil/Burger King/diesel/24hr

20 I-275 N, to Flint, no facilities

18 Nadeau Rd, **W...gas:** Pilot/Arby's/diesel/24hr/@, **other:** HOSPITAL, RV camping

15 MI 50, Dixie Hwy, to Monroe, **E...gas:** Shell, **food:** Bob Evans, Burger King, Dixie Skillet, Red Lobster, **lodging:** Cross Country Inn, Hampton Inn, Hometown Inn, Travel Inn, **other:** to Sterling SP, **W...gas:** Pilot/Subway/diesel/24hr/@, TA/BP/Popeye's/Quizno's/Pizza Hut/diesel/24hr/@, **food:** Beef Jerky Outlet, Big Boy, Cracker Barrel, Denny's, McDonald's, Wendy's, **lodging:** Holiday Inn Express, Knight's Inn, **other:** HOSPITAL, to Viet Vet Mem

14 Elm Ave, to Monroe, no facilities

13 Front St, Monroe, no facilities

11 La Plaisance Rd, to Bolles Harbor, **W...gas:** Amoco, Marathon/Taco Bell/diesel, Speedway, **food:** Burger King, McDonald's, Wendy's, **lodging:** AmeriHost, Comfort Inn, Harbor Town RV Resort, **other:** Outlet Mall/famous brands, st police

Interstate 75

10mm Welcome Ctr nb, full(handicapped)facilities, phone, info, picnic tables, litter barrels, vending, petwalk

9 S Otter Creek Rd, to La Salle, **W**...antiques

7mm weigh sta both lanes

6 Luna Pier, **E**...**gas:** Sunoco/Blimpie/McDonald's/diesel, **food:** Ganders Rest., Super 8

5 to Erie, Temperance, no facilities

2 Summit St, no facilities

0mm Michigan/Ohio state line

Interstate 94

Exit # Services

275mm I-69/I-94 begin/end on MI 25, **Pinegrove Ave in Port Huron**...**gas:** BP/24hr, Clark, Marathon, Shell/24hr, Speedway, **food:** Little Caesar's, McDonald's, Tim Horton, Wendy's, White Castle, **lodging:** Best Western, Day's Inn, Holiday Inn Express, **other:** Can-Am DutyFree, Family$, Honda, Rite Aid, tollbridge to Canada

274.5mm Black River

274 Water St, Port Huron, **N**...**Welcome Ctr/rest area wb, full facilities, food:** Cracker Barrel, **lodging:** Ramada Inn, **S**...**gas:** Bylo/diesel, Speedway/Taco Bell/diesel, **food:** Bob Evans, **lodging:** Comfort Inn, Fairfield Inn, Hampton Inn, Knight's Inn, **other:** Lake Port SP, RV camping

271 I-69 E and I-94 E run together eb, **E**...Lp I-69, to Port Huron

269 Dove St, Range Rd, **N**...**gas:** Speedway/diesel/24hr, **food:** Burger King, **lodging:** AmeriHost

266 Gratiot Rd, Marysville, **S**...**gas:** BP/diesel/24hr, **food:** Burger King, **1 mi S**...**gas:** Rich, Shell/24hr, **food:** Big Boy, 4Star Rest., KFC, Little Caesar's, McDonald's, Pelican Café, Pizza Hut, Taco Bell, **lodging:** Days Inn, Microtel, Super 8, **other:** HOSPITAL, AutoZone, Carter's Foods, CVS Drug, Goodyear, Rite Aid

262 Wadhams Rd, **N**...camping, **S**...**gas:** Marathon/diesel/showers/24hr

257 St Clair, Richmond, **S**...**gas:** BP/diesel, **other:** st police

255mm **rest area eb, full(handicapped)facilities, phones, info, picnic tables, litter barrels, petwalk**

251mm **rest area wb, full(handicapped)facilities, phones, info, picnic tables, litter barrels, petwalk**

248 26 Mile Rd, to Marine City, **N**...**gas:** BP/Amoco, **food:** McDonald's, **other:** Macomb Correctional, golf, **S**...**gas:** Citgo/7-11, Mobil, SpeedyQ/diesel

247mm Salt River

247 MI 19(from eb), New Haven, no facilities

243 MI 29, MI 3, Utica, New Baltimore, **N**...**gas:** Marathon, Meijer/diesel/24hr, Shell/Subway/diesel, Sunoco/diesel, **food:** Applebee's, Arby's, Burger

King, Gus Coney Island, McDonald's, Outback Steaks, Papa Romano's Pizza, Ruby Tuesday, Steak'n Shake, Texas Roadhouse, Town&Country Rest., Wendy's, White Castle/Church's/24hr, **lodging:** Chesterfield Motel, **other:** Belle Tire, GNC, Home Depot, K-Mart, Lowe's Whse, Michael's, NTB, Radio Shack, Staples, Target, Walgreen, **S**...**gas:** Marathon/diesel/24hr, Pilot/Subway/diesel/24hr/@, **food:** Big Boy, Hot'n Now, Taco Bell, LodgeKeeper, **other:** Chevrolet

241 21 Mile Rd, Selfridge, **N**...**gas:** Marathon/diesel, **food:** China King, Hungry Howie's, Quizno's, Subway, **other:** Advance Parts, CVS Drug, same as 240

240 to MI 59, **N**...**gas:** BP/Amoco, Citgo/7-11, Marathon, Speedway, **food:** Arby's, McDonald's, Tim Horton, **lodging:** Best Western, **other:** Ford, Wal-Mart/auto

237 N River Rd, Mt Clemens, **N**...**gas:** BP/diesel, Mobil/Subway/diesel, **food:** Damon's Grill, McDonald's, **lodging:** Comfort Inn, **other:** General RV Ctr, Gibralter Trade Ctr

236.5mm Clinton River

236 Metro Parkway, **S**...**food:** McDonald's

235 Shook Rd(from wb), no facilities

234b a Harper Rd, 15 Mile Rd, **N**...**gas:** Amoco/McDonald's, Citgo, Marathon, SpeedyQ, Sunoco/diesel/24hr, **food:** China Moon, Sorrento Pizza, Subway, **S**...**gas:** Mobil, **food:** China Moon, Little Caesar's, Subway

232 Little Mack Ave, **N**...**gas:** Sunoco, **food:** Bob Evans, **lodging:** Comfort Inn, Econolodge, Holiday Inn Express, Microtel, Red Roof Inn, Super 8, **S**...**gas:** BP/24hr, Meijer/diesel/24hr, Speedway/diesel, **food:** Cracker Barrel, IHOP, **lodging:** Baymont Inn, **other:** Circuit City, Home Depot, Jo-Ann Fabrics, K-Mart, same as 231

231 (from eb), MI 3, Gratiot Ave, **N**...**gas:** Shell, Speedway, Sunoco, **food:** Big Boy, Boston Mkt, Burger King, BBQ, ChuckeCheese, Denny's, McDonald's, Mtn Jack's Rest., Pizza Hut, **lodging:** Day's Inn, Georgian Inn, Knight's Inn, Red Roof Inn, Super 8, **other:** Discount Tire, Firestone/auto, Nissan, Sam's Club, Sears/auto, Target, Toyota, U-Haul, mall

MICHIGAN

Interstate 94

E ↑ ↓ W

230 12 Mile Rd, **N...gas:** Citgo/7-11, Marathon/diesel, **food:** Burger King, Outback Steaks, **other:** CVS Drug, Hyundai, Lincoln/Mercury, Marshall's, Wal-Mart, mall, **S...gas:** Marathon

229 I-696 W, Reuther Fwy, to 11 Mile Rd, **N...gas:** BP, **S... gas:** BP/dieselmart, Speedway

228 10 Mile Rd, **N...gas:** BP/24hr, Shell, **food:** Eastwind Chinese, Jet's Pizza, **other:** CVS Drug

227 9 Mile Rd, **N...gas:** Mobil, Speedway/diesel, Sunoco, **food:** McDonald's, Papa John's, Taco Bell, Wendy's, **other:** CVS Drug, Farmer Jack's, FM Drugs, Office Depot, **S...gas:** Mobil, **other:** Cadillac

225 MI 102, Vernier Rd, 8 Mile Rd, **S...food:** KFC, Wendy's, **other:** Kroger

224b Allard Ave, Eastwood Ave, no facilities

a Moross Rd, **S...gas:** Shell, **other:** Farmer Jack's

223 Cadieux Rd, **S...gas:** BP/Subway, Mobil, Shell, Sunoco, **food:** McDonald's, Taco Bell, Tubby's Subs, Wendy's

222b Harper Ave(from eb), **S...food:** Taco Bell

a Chalmers Ave, Outer Dr, **N...gas:** BP/Subway/diesel, Clark, Marathon, **food:** Coney Island, KFC, White Castle

220b Conner Ave, **N...gas:** BP, KwikFill/gas, **lodging:** Travel Inn

a French Rd, no facilities

219 MI 3, Gratiot Ave, **N...gas:** Citgo, Marathon/Subway, **food:** KFC, McDonald's, **other:** Family$, **S...gas:** BP/diesel

218 MI 53, Van Dyke Ave, **N...gas:** BP

217b Mt Elliott Ave, **S...gas:** Mobil, **food:** BBQ, KFC

a E Grand Blvd, Chene St, no facilities

216b Russell St(from eb), to downtown

a I-75; Chrysler Fwy, to tunnel to Canada

215c MI 1, Woodward Ave, John R St, no facilities

b MI 10 N, Lodge Fwy

a MI 10 S, downtown, tunnel to Canada

214b Trumbull Ave, to Ford Hospital

a (from wb)Grand River Ave, **N...gas:** Citgo

213b I-96 W to Lansing, E to Canada, bridge to Canada, to Tiger Stadium

a W Grand(exits left from eb), no facilities

212b Warren Ave(from eb), no facilities

a Livernois Ave, **S...gas:** Marathon/Subway/diesel

211b Cecil Ave(from wb), Central Ave, no facilities

a Lonyo Rd, **S...**Ford

210 US 12, Michigan Ave, Wyoming Ave, **N...gas:** Mobil/Pizza Hut, **S...gas:** BP/diesel, Citgo/diesel, **food:** YumYum Donuts

209 Rotunda Dr(from wb), no facilities

208 Greenfield Rd, Schaefer Rd, **N...gas:** Mobil, 7-11, **S...**River Rouge Ford Plant

207mm Rouge River

206 Oakwood Blvd, Melvindale, **N...gas:** Marathon, **food:** Oakwood Grill, **other:** Ford Plant, UPS, to Greenfield Village, **S...gas:** BP, Mobil, 7-11, **food:** Burger King, Domino's, Little Caesar's, O Henry's, Pizza Hut, Subway, YumYum Donuts, **lodging:** Best Western, Holiday Inn Express, **other:** Belle Tire, Smirnoff Distillery

205mm Largest Uniroyal Tire in the World

204b a MI 39, Southfield Fwy, Pelham Rd, **N...gas:** Marathon, Mobil, 7-11, **food:** Mancino's Pizza, Ponderosa, **other:** to Greenfield Village, **S...gas:** Mobil, BP, **1/2 mi S on Ecorse Rd...gas:** 7-11, **food:** Burger King, Dunkin Donuts, McDonald's

202b a US 24, Telegraph Rd, **N...gas:** Clark, Shell, **food:** Andoni's Rest., Burger King, KFC, Krispy Kreme, McDonald's, Pizza Hut, Taco Bell, Rally's, Ram's Horn Rest., Subway, Wendy's, **lodging:** Casa Bianca Motel, **other:** Rite Aid, **S...gas:** Marathon/diesel, **lodging:** Nu Haven Motel, **1/2 mi S...gas:** Amoco, Citgo, Mobil, Shell, **food:** Burger King, Hungry Howie's, Marina's Pizza/subs, Old Country Buffet, Pizza Hut, Red Lobster, Super China, YumYum Donuts, **lodging:** Quality Inn, **other:** CVS Drug, Radio Shack, U-Haul, Wal-Mart

200 Ecorse Rd,(no ez eb return), to Taylor, **N...gas:** Marathon/diesel, **food:** Granny's Rest., **S...gas:** BP/diesel, Speedway

199 Middle Belt Rd, **S...gas:** Amoco/diesel/24hr, **food:** Denny's, McDonald's, Wendy's, **lodging:** Day's Inn, Howard Johnson, Super 8

198 Merriman Rd, **N...food:** Bob Evans, **lodging:** Baymont Inn, Best Western, Clarion, Comfort Inn, Courtyard, Crowne Plaza Hotel, Doubletree Inn, Econolodge, Extended Stay America, Fairfield Inn, Hampton Inn, Hilton, Holiday Inn, Howard Johnson, Marriott, Motel 6, PearTree Inn, Sheraton, **S...**Wayne Co Airport

197 Vining Rd, no facilities

196 Wayne Rd, Romulus, **N...gas:** Shell, **food:** McDonald's, **S...gas:** Mobil/diesel, Speedway, **food:** Burger King

194b a I-275, N to Flint, S to Toledo

192 Haggerty Rd, **N...gas:** BP, Mobil/24hr, **food:** Burger King(2mi), Subway, **S...**Lower Huron Metro Park

190 Belleville Rd, to Belleville, **N...gas:** Meijer/diesel/24hr, Amoco/24hr, Marathon, **food:** Applebee's, Arby's, Big Boy, Cracker Barrel, McDonald's, Taco Bell, Wendy's, **lodging:** Hampton Inn, Holiday Inn Express, Red Roof Inn, **other:** Camping World RV Service/supplies, CVS Drug, $Tree, Farmer Jack's, Firestone/auto, Ford, Michal's RV Ctr, U-Haul, Wal-Mart, **S...gas:** Shell, **food:** Burger King, China King, Dimitri's Kitchen, Domino's, Subway, TCBY, **lodging:** Comfort Inn, Super 8, **other:** USPO

Interstate 94

E

W

Ann Arbor

187	Rawsonville Rd, **S...gas:** Mobil/diesel, Speedway/diesel, **food:** Burger King, Denny's, Hardee's, KFC, Little Caesar's, LoneStar Steaks, McDonald's, Pizza Hut, Subway, Tim Horton, Wendy's, **other:** $Tree, GNC, K-Mart, Radio Shack, Rite Aid
185	US 12, Michigan Ave(from eb, exits left, no return), to frontage rds, airport, no facilities
184mm	Ford Lake
183	US 12, Huron St, Ypsilanti, **N...gas:** Marathon/diesel, **other:** to E MI U, **S...food:** McDonald's, **lodging:** Marriott, **other:** HOSPITAL, Chevrolet/Pontiac/Buick/GMC, st police
181b a	US 12 W, Michigan Ave, Ypsilanti, **N...gas:** Meijer/diesel/24hr, Rich, Speedway, 7-11, **food:** Burger King, Taco Bell, **other:** HOSPITAL, Aamco, Busch's Food/24hr, Firestone, Jo-Ann Fabrics, Wal-Mart, **S...gas:** Shell, **food:** Chessy's Grill, McDonald's, Subway
180b a	US 23, to Toledo, Flint, no facilities
177	State St, **N...gas:** Amoco/24hr, Mobil, Shell, **food:** Azteca Mexican, Bennigan's, Burger King, Calif Pizza, Graham's Steaks, Macaroni Grill, Max&Erma's, Olive Garden, **lodging:** Best Western, Crowne Plaza Hotel, Comfort Inn, Courtyard, Fairfield Inn, Hampton Inn, Hilton, Holiday Inn Express, Red Roof Inn, Sheraton, Wolverine Inn, **other:** Firestone, JC Penney, Marshall Fields, Mitsubishi, Sears/auto, VW, World Mkt, mall, to UMI, **S...gas:** Clark/diesel, **food:** ChiChi's, Coney Island, McDonald's, Pizza Hut/Taco Bell, **lodging:** Motel 6, **other:** U-Haul
175	Ann Arbor-Saline Rd, **N...gas:** Shell, **food:** Applebee's, Old Country Buffet, Subway, **lodging:** Candlewood Suites, **other:** Mervyn's, Office Depot, mall, to UMI Stadium, **S...gas:** Meijer/diesel/24hr, **food:** Big Boy, Joe's Crabshack, McDonald's, Outback Steaks, TGIFriday, **other:** Best Buy, CompUSA, Jo-Ann Fabrics, Kohl's, OfficeMax, Target
172	Jackson Ave, to Ann Arbor, **N...gas:** Amoco, BP, Marathon, Shell, **food:** KFC, Schlotsky's, **other:** HOSPITAL, K-Mart, Kroger, Rite Aid, mall, **S...gas:** Sunoco/diesel, **food:** Weber's Rest., **lodging:** Best Western, **other:** Chevrolet/Pontiac/Cadillac, Ford
171	MI 14(from eb, exits left), to Ann Arbor, to Flint by US 23, no facilities
169	Zeeb Rd, **N...gas:** BP/24hr, **food:** Baxter's Deli, McDonald's, **S...gas:** Mobil, **food:** Arby's, Burger King, PB's Rest., Pizza Hut, Taco Bell, Wendy's
168mm	**rest area eb, full(handicapped)facilities, info, phone, picnic tables, litter barrels, vending, petwalk**
167	Baker Rd, Dexter, **N...gas:** Pilot/Subway/diesel/24hr/@, **S...gas:** Pilot/Arby's/diesel/24hr/@, TA/BP/diesel/rest./24hr/@, **food:** McDonald's, **other:** Blue Beacon

Jackson

162	Jackson Rd, Fletcher Rd, **S...gas:** Clark/Subway/diesel/24hr, **food:** Stiver's Rest.
159	MI 52, Chelsea, **N...gas:** Amoco/diesel/24hr, Mobil/diesel, Speedway, **food:** Big Boy, Chinese Tonite, KFC/Taco Bell, Little Caesar's, Main St Coney Island, McDonald's, Prego's Italian, Subway, Wendy's, **lodging:** Comfort Inn, Holiday Inn Express, **other:** HOSPITAL, Bridges RV Ctr, Chevrolet/Buick, Chrysler/Plymouth/Dodge/Jeep, CVS Drug, Farmer Jack's, Ford, Pamida
157	Jackson Rd, Pierce Rd, **N...**Gerald Eddy Geology Ctr
156	Kalmbach Rd, **N...**to Waterloo RA
153	Clear Lake Rd, **N...gas:** Marathon/diesel
151.5mm	weigh sta both lanes
150	to Grass Lake, **S...gas:** Phillips 66/Subway, **other:** RV camping
150mm	**rest area wb, full(handicapped)facilities, phone, picnic tables, litter barrels, vending, petwalk**
147	Race Rd, **N...**to Waterloo RA, camping, **S...**lodging
145	Sargent Rd, **S...gas:** BP/White Castle/diesel, Mobil/diesel/rest./24hr, **food:** McDonald's, Wendy's, Zig's Kettle/brewery, **lodging:** Colonial Inn, **other:** RV camping
144	Lp 94(from wb), to Jackson, same as 145
142	US 127 S, to Hudson, **3 mi S...gas:** Meijer/diesel/24hr, Speedway, **food:** Domino's, McDonald's, Wendy's, **other:** Advance Parts, Kroger, Parts+, Rite Aid
141	Elm Rd, **N...lodging:** Travelodge, **other:** Chevrolet/Dodge/Honda/Hyundai, **S...**HOSPITAL
139	MI 106, Cooper St, to Jackson, **N...**st police/prison, **S...gas:** Citgo/Subway, **other:** HOSPITAL
138	US 127 N, MI 50, Jackson, to Lansing, **N...food:** Gilbert's Steaks, Red Lobster, Yen Kang Chinese, **lodging:** Baymont Inn, Comfort Inn, Fairfield Inn, Hampton Inn, Holiday Inn, Super 8, **S...gas:** Admiral, Marathon, Shell/24hr, **food:** Big Boy, Bob Evans, Fazoli's, Ground Round, LJ Silver, Old Country Buffet, Outback Steaks, Pizza Hut, **lodging:** Country Hearth Inn, Motel 6, **other:** Best Buy, Circuit City, Kohl's, Lowe's Whse, Michael's, OfficeMax, Sears/auto, Target

MICHIGAN
Interstate 94

E ↕ W

137	Airport Rd, **N...gas:** Meijer/diesel/24hr, Shell/Taco Bell/24hr, 7-11, **food:** Burger King, Denny's, Hudson's Rest., McDonald's, Steak'n Shake/24hr, Subway, Wendy's, **other:** Bumper Parts, **S...gas:** BP/24hr, **food:** Cracker Barrel, Olive Garden, LoneStar Steaks, **other:** K-Mart, Sam's Club/gas, Staples
136	Lp 94, MI 60(from eb), to Jackson, no facilities
135mm	**rest area eb, full(handicapped)facilities, phone, picnic tables, litter barrels, vending, petwalk**
133	Dearing Rd, Spring Arbor, to Spring Arbor Coll
130	Parma, **S...gas:** Citgo/Trkstp/diesel/rest./24hr/@
128	Michigan Ave, **N...gas:** BP/Burger King/diesel/24hr, Marathon/diesel/24hr, **other:** Cracker Hill Antiques, RV camping
127	Concord Rd, **N...**St Julian's Winery, **S...**Harley's Antiques
124	MI 99, to Eaton Rapids, **S...**food, lodging
121	28 Mile Rd, to Albion, **N...gas:** Mobil, **food:** Arby's, **lodging:** Day's Inn, **S...gas:** FS/diesel/24hr, Marathon, Speedway/diesel/24hr, **food:** Burger King, Fresh'n Fast Café, KFC, McDonald's, Paradise Oriental, Pizza Hut, **lodging:** Knight's Inn, **other:** HOSPITAL, AutoZone, Chevrolet/Pontiac/Buick, $General, Family$, Felpausch Foods, Ford/Mercury, Radio Shack, Tire City, RV camping
119	26 Mile Rd, no facilities
115	22.5 Mile Rd, **N...gas:** Citgo/diesel/rest./24hr
113mm	**rest area wb, full(handicapped)facilities, phone, picnic tables, litter barrels, vending, petwalk**
112	Partello Rd, **S...gas:** Sunoco/diesel/24hr, **food:** Schuler's Rest.
110	Old US 27, Marshall, **N...gas:** Shell/Subway/diesel/24hr, **food:** Country Kitchen/24hr, **S...gas:** Citgo/diesel, **food:** Denny's, KFC, **lodging:** Holiday Inn Express, **other:** HOSPITAL, sheriff
108	I-69, US 27, N to Lansing, S to Ft Wayne, no facilities
104	11 Mile Rd, Michigan Ave, **N...gas:** Pilot/Taco Bell/diesel/24hr/@, Sunoco/Te-Khi Trkstp/rest./24hr/@, **S...gas:** Citgo/Subway/diesel/24hr, **lodging:** Quality Inn/rest.
103	Lp 94(from wb, no return), to Battle Creek, **N...**HOSPITAL, same as 104
102mm	Kalamazoo River
100	Beadle Lake Rd, **N...food:** Moonraker Rest., **S...gas:** Citgo/diesel, **other:** Binder Park Zoo
98b	I-194 N, to Battle Creek, no facilities
a	MI 66, to Sturgis, **S...gas:** Citgo/Blimpie/diesel, Meijer/diesel/24hr, **food:** Chili's, Schlotsky's, Steak'n Shake, **other:** Kohl's, Lowe's Whse, Michael's, Sam's Club, Staples, Wal-Mart/auto, same as 97

M
a
r
s
h
a
l
l

K
a
l
a
m
a
z
o
o

97	Capital Ave, to Battle Creek, **N...gas:** BP/24hr, Clark, **food:** Arby's, Lakeview Rest., LoneStar Steaks, McDonald's, Red Lobster, **lodging:** Comfort Inn, Knight's Inn, **S...gas:** Citgo, Shell/24hr, Sunoco/Subway/24hr, **food:** Applebee's, Bob Evans, Burger King, Canton Buffet, Cracker Barrel, Denny's, Don Pablo, Fazoli's, NY Burrito, Old Country Buffet, Pizza Hut, Steak'n Shake, Taco Bell, Wendy's, **lodging:** Appletree Inn, Battle Creek Inn, Baymont Inn, Day's Inn, Fairfield Inn, Hampton Inn, Motel 6, Super 8, **other:** Borders Books, Firestone/auto, Goodyear/auto, Harley-Davidson, JC Penney, K-Mart, Marshall Fields, Sears/auto, Target, mall
96mm	**rest area eb, full(handicapped)facilities, phone, picnic tables, litter barrels, vending, petwalk**
95	Helmer Rd, **N...gas:** Citgo/diesel, **other:** st police, **2 mi N...gas:** Meijer/diesel/24hr
92	Lp 94, to Battle Creek, Springfield, **N...gas:** Citgo/Arlene's Trkstp/diesel/rest./24hr/@, Shell/24hr, **other:** RV camping, to Ft Custer RA
88	Climax, **N...**Galesburg Speedway
85	35ᵗʰ St, Galesburg, **N...gas:** Shell/Burger King/diesel/24hr, **food:** McDonald's, **other:** Galesburg Speedway, to Ft Custer RA, **S...other:** Winery Tours, RV camping
85mm	**rest area wb, full(handicapped)facilities, phone, picnic tables, litter barrels, vending, petwalk**
81	Lp 94(from wb), to Kalamazoo, no facilities
80	Cork St, Sprinkle Rd, to Kalamazoo, **N...gas:** Citgo/diesel, Double Xpress, Speedway, **food:** Arby's, Burger King, Chicken Coop, Denny's, Godfather's, Hot'n Now, Perkins, Taco Bell, **lodging:** Best Western, Clarion Hotel, Fairfield Inn, Holiday Inn Express, Red Roof Inn, **S...gas:** BP/diesel/24hr, Speedway/diesel, **food:** Derk's Rest., Holly's Landing Rest., McDonald's, Subway/24hr, **lodging:** Day's Inn, Motel 6, Quality Inn
78	Portage Rd, Kilgore Rd, **N...gas:** Citgo, **food:** Hungry Howie's, Subway, Uncle Ernie's Pancakes, **lodging:** Hampton Inn, **other:** HOSPITAL, **S...gas:** Marathon, Shell/24hr, **food:** Angelo's Italian, Callahan's Rest., Gum Ho Chinese, McDonald's, Taco Bell, Theo&Stacy's Rest., **lodging:** Country Inn Suites, **other:** AutoValue Parts, museum
76b a	Westnedge Ave, **N...gas:** Meijer/diesel/24hr, Speedway/diesel, SuperDuper, **food:** Arby's, Bennigan's, Big Boy, Hong Kong Buffet, Hooters, Mancino's Eatery, Outback Steaks, Papa John's, Pappy's Mexican, Peter Piper Pizza, Pizza Hut, Quizno's, Steak'n Shake, Subway, Taco Bell, **lodging:** Quality Inn, **other:** Discount Tire, Goodyear/auto, Lowe's Whse, Office Depot, Rite Aid, **S...gas:** Shell/24hr, **food:** Applebee's, Burger King, Chili's, ChuckeCheese, Empire Chinese, Fazoli's, Finley's Rest., KFC, Little Caesar's, LJ Silver, Mtn Jack's

MICHIGAN

Interstate 94

Rest., McDonald's, Old Country Buffet, Olive Garden, Peking Palace, Pizza Hut, Qdoba Mexican, Red Lobster, Schlotsky's, Subway, Taco Bell, Wendy's, **lodging:** Holiday Motel, **other:** Barnes&Noble, Best Buy, Cadillac/Pontiac/Nissan, Circuit City, Fannie Mae Candies, Firestone/auto, Home Depot, JC Penney, Jo-Ann Fabrics, K-Mart, Kohl's, MktPlace Foods, Marshall Fields, Mervyn's, Michael's, OfficeMax, Old Navy, PepBoys, Radio Shack, Sears/auto, Target, Walgreen, WorldMkt, mall

75 Oakland Dr, no facilities

74b a US 131, to Kalamazoo, **N**...to W MI U, Kalamazoo Coll

72 Oshtemo, **N**...**gas:** Citgo/diesel, Speedway/diesel, **food:** Burger King, Culver's, McDonald's, Taco Bell, Wendy's, **lodging:** Hampton Inn, Saturn, **S**...**food:** Cracker Barrel, **lodging:** Fairfield Inn

66 Mattawan, **N**...**gas:** Speedway/Subway/diesel/24hr, **food:** Mancino's Italian, **other:** Rossman Auto/towing, **S**...**gas:** Shell

60 MI 40, Paw Paw, **N**...**gas:** BP/24hr, Speedway/diesel/24hr, **food:** Arby's, Big Boy, Burger King, Chicken Coop, McDonald's, Pizza Hut, Subway/TCBY, Taco Bell, Wendy's, **lodging:** Deerfield Inn, Quality Inn, **other:** HOSPITAL, Chrysler/Dodge/Jeep, Felpausch Foods, St Julian Winery, Warner Winery

56 MI 51, to Decatur, **N**...st police, **S**...**gas:** Citgo/diesel, Marathon/diesel/24hr

52 Lawrence, **N**...gas(1mi), **food:** Waffle House of America

46 Hartford, **N**...**gas:** Shell/diesel/24hr, **food:** McDonald's, Panel Room Rest.

42mm **rest area wb, full(handicapped)facilities, phone, picnic tables, litter barrels, vending, petwalk**

41 MI 140, Watervliet, to Niles, **N**...**gas:** BP/24hr, Citgo, **food:** Burger King, Chicken Coop, Taco Bell, Waffle House, **other:** HOSPITAL

39 Millburg, Coloma, Deer Forest, **N**...**gas:** Marathon/diesel, Speedway, **food:** McDonald's, **other:** RV Ctr, **1 mi N**...**gas:** BP/diesel, Westco/diesel, **food:** Pizza Hut, Subway

36mm **rest area eb, full(handicapped)facilities, phone, picnic tables, litter barrels, vending, petwalk**

34 I-196 N, US 31 N, to Holland, Grand Rapids, no facilities

33 Lp I-94, to Benton Harbor, **2-4 mi N**...airport, sheriff's dept

30 Napier Ave, Benton Harbor, **N**...**gas:** ⛽/Flying J/Wendy's/diesel/24hr/@, Shell/24hr, **lodging:** Super 8, **other:** HOSPITAL, Blue Beacon, **S**...**gas:** Chrysler/Dodge/Honda

Benton Harbor

29 Pipestone Rd, Benton Harbor, **N**... **gas:** Meijer/diesel/24hr, Speedway/diesel, **food:** Applebee's, Big Boy, Burger King, Denny's, Hacienda Mexican, Hardee's, IHOP, McDonald's, Pizza Hut, Red Lobster, Steak'n Shake, Subway, Texas Corral, **lodging:** Best Western, Courtyard, Motel 6, Red Roof Inn, **other:** MEDICAL CARE, Aldi Foods, Best Buy, $Tree, Ford/Lincoln/Mercury, Goodyear/auto, Home Depot, JC Penney, Jo-Ann Fabrics, Lowe's Whse, OfficeMax, Radio Shack, Sears, Staples, Walgreen, Wal-Mart SuperCtr/24hr, **S**...**gas:** Citgo/Blimpie/Taco Bell/diesel/24hr, **food:** Bob Evans, **lodging:** Comfort Suites, Holiday Inn Express

28 US 31 S, MI 139 N, to Niles, **N**...**gas:** Citgo/diesel, Speedway/diesel, **food:** Arby's, Burger King, Capozio's Pizza, Chicken Coop, Country Kitchen, DQ, Henry's Burgers, KFC, Little Caesar's, Pizza Hut, Subway, U-Buffet, Wendy's, **lodging:** Day's Inn/rest., Ramada Inn/rest., **other:** HOSPITAL, AutoZone, Chevrolet, $Tree, Firestone, M&W Tire, OfficeDepot, Old Navy, Rite Aid, Target, st police, **S**...**gas:** Marathon, **lodging:** Howard Johnson

27mm St Joseph River

27 MI 63, Niles Ave, to St Joseph, **N**...**gas:** Amoco/24hr, **food:** Nye's Apple Barn, **S**...Goodyear

23 Red Arrow Hwy, Stevensville, **N**...**gas:** Admiral, Amoco/TacoBell, Marathon/diesel, Mobil, Shell/diesel/24hr, **food:** Big Boy, Burger King, Cracker Barrel, DQ, Fireside Inn Rest., LJ Silver, McDonald's, Papa John's, Popeye's, Subway, **lodging:** Baymont Inn, Park Inn, Ray's Motel, Villager Lodge, **other:** Walgreen, **S**...**food:** Schuler's Rest., **lodging:** Hampton Inn

22 John Beers Rd, Stevensville, **N**...to Grand Mere SP, **S**...**gas:** Marathon/diesel

16 Bridgman, **N**...**gas:** Amoco/A&W/diesel/24hr, **other:** to Warren Dunes SP, **S**...**gas:** Speedway/diesel/24hr, **food:** McDonald's, Pizza Hut, Subway, **1/2 mi S**...**food:** Brian's Cove Rest., Chicken Coop Rest., Olympus Rest., Roma Pizza, **other:** Chevrolet/Buick

MICHIGAN

Interstate 94

E

12   Sawyer, **N...gas:** Citgo/diesel/rest./24hr, **S...gas:** TA/BurgerKing/Popeye's/Taco Bell/diesel/24hr/@, **lodging:** Super 8, **other:** USPO

6   Lakeside, Union Pier, **N...other:** St Julian's Winery, antiques, **S...**RV camping

4b a   US 12, New Buffalo, to Three Oaks, **N...food:** Pizza Hut, st police

W

2.5mm   weigh sta both lanes

1   MI 239, New Buffalo, to Grand Beach, **N...gas:** Shell, **lodging:** Best Western, Edgewood Motel, Holiday Inn Express, **S...gas:** New Buffalo/diesel/24hr, **food:** Arby's, Wendy's, **lodging:** Comfort Inn

.5mm   **Welcome Ctr eb, full(handicapped)facilities, info, phone, picnic tables, litter barrels, vending, petwalk**

0mm   Michigan/Indiana state line

Interstate 96

E

Exit #   Services

I-96 begins/ends on I-75, exit 48 in Detroit.

191   I-75, N to Flint, S to Toledo, US 12, to MLK Blvd, to Michigan Ave, no facilities

190b   Warren Ave, **N...gas:** Citgo, **S...gas:** Marathon

a   I-94 E to Port Huron

189   W Grand Blvd, Tireman Rd, **N...gas:** BP

188b   Joy Rd, **N...food:** Church's

a   Livernois, **N...gas:** Mobil, Shell, **food:** Burger King, KFC, McDonald's, **other:** Wendy's

187   Grand River Ave(from eb), no facilities

186b   Davison Ave, I-96 local and I-96 express divide, no exits from express

a   (from eb), Wyoming Ave

W

Detroit Area

185   Schaefer Hwy, to Grand River Ave, **N...gas:** BP/24hr, Mobil, **food:** Coney Island, McDonald's, **other:** CVS Drug, **S...gas:** Sunoco

184   Greenfield Rd, no facilities

183   MI 39, Southfield Fwy, exit from expswy and local, no facilities

182   Evergreen Rd, no facilities

180   Outer Dr, **N...gas:** BP/diesel/lube

180mm   I-96 local/express unite/divide

179   US 24, Telegraph Rd, **N...food:** Grand Buffet Chinese, Taco Bell, White Castle/Church's, **other:** Chevrolet, Family$, Goodyear, **S...gas:** BP, Marathon/diesel

178   Beech Daly Rd, **N...gas:** Sunoco

177   Inkster Rd, **N...food:** Panda Chinese, Subway, **lodging:** Super 8, **other:** Hancock Fabrics

176   Middlebelt Rd, **N...food:** Bob Evans, ChiChi's, IHOP, Olive Garden, **lodging:** Comfort Inn, Super 8, **other:** MEDICAL CARE, **S...gas:** Meijer/diesel/24hr, **food:** Boss Hog's BBQ, Logan's Roadhouse, **other:** Costco/gas, Home Depot, Marshall's, Wal-Mart

175   Merriman Rd, **N...gas:** Mobil, Speedway/diesel, **other:** CHIROPRACTOR, **S...gas:** Sunoco, **food:** Blimpie

174   Farmington Rd, **N...gas:** Mobil/diesel, Sunoco, **food:** Looney Bakery, **S...gas:** BP/Amoco, **food:** KFC, **other:** bank

173b   Levan Rd, **N...**HOSPITAL, to Madonna U

a   Newburgh Rd, no facilities

171mm   **I-275 and I-96 run together 9 miles**

170   6 Mile Rd, **N...food:** Andrea's Ristorante, Ground Round, Max&Erma's, **lodging:** Best Western, Courtyard, Holiday Inn, Marriott, **other:** mall, **S...gas:** BP, Mobil, **food:** Applebee's, Buca Italian, Charlie's Grille, Papa Vino's, **lodging:** Fairfield Inn, Residence Inn, TownePlace Suites, **other:** Barnes&Noble, CVS Drug, Office Depot

169b a   7 Mile Rd, **N...food:** Rio Bravo, LoneStar Steaks, **lodging:** Embassy Suites, **S...food:** Alexander's Rest., Bahama Breeze Rest., Bonfire Bistro, Champp's Rest., Cooker Rest., Del Rio Cantina, Macaroni Grill, **lodging:** AmeriSuites, **other:** Home Depot

167   8 Mile Rd, to Northville, **S...gas:** Meijer/diesel/24hr, Speedway, **food:** Benihana, Big Boy, Chili's, McDonald's, Kyoto Steaks, On-the-Border, Taco Bell, **lodging:** Hampton Inn, Hilton, Ramada Ltd, **other:** Best Buy, Costco/gas, Firestone, Home Depot, Kohl's, OfficeMax, Target, to Maybury SP

165   I-696, I-275, MI 5, Grand River Ave, **I-275 and I-96 run together 9 miles**

163   I-696(from eb), no facilities

162   Novi Rd, Novi, to Walled Lake, **N...gas:** BP, **food:** ChuckeCheese, McDonald's, Oaks Grill, Pizza Hut, Red Lobster, Subway, TooChez Rest, **lodging:** DoubleTree Hotel, Sheraton, **other:** HOSPITAL, Circuit City, Galyan's, JC Penney, Jo-Ann Fabrics, Kroger, Marshall's, OfficeMax, Sears/auto, WorldMkt, mall, **S...gas:** Mobil, **food:** Big Boy, Bob Evans, Boston Mkt, Grady's Rest., Kim's Chinese, Olive Garden, Red Robin, TGIFriday, Wendy's, **lodging:** Courtyard, Wyndham Garden, **other:** Borders Books, CompUSA, Mervyn's

161mm   **rest area eb, full(handicapped)facilities, phone, vending, picnic tables, litter barrels, petwalk**

160   Beck Rd, 12 Mile Rd, **N...**HOSPITAL, **S...other:** Home Depot, Kroger, to Maybury SP

159   Wixom Rd, Walled Lake, **N...food:** Wendy's, **lodging:** Baymont Inn, **other:** to Proud Lake RA, **S...gas:** Meijer/diesel/24hr, Mobil, Shell, **food:** Arby's, Burger King, KFC, McDonald's, Taco Bell, Togo's/Baskin-Robbins/Dunkin Donuts, **other:** Lincoln/Mercury, RV Ctr

155   New Hudson, to Milford, **N...**Ford, to RV camping, **S...gas:** Mobil, **food:** Putters Rest.

153   Kent Lake Rd, **N...**Kensington Metropark, **S...gas:** Mobil

151   Kensington Rd, **N...**Kensington Metropark, **S...**Island Lake RA, food, lodging

150   Pleasant Valley Rd, **S...**phone

148b a   US 23, N to Flint, S to Ann Arbor, no facilities

147   Spencer Rd, **N...gas:** Mobil, **other:** st police, **S...**to Brighton St RA

145   Grand River Ave, to Brighton, **N...gas:** BP, Shell/diesel, **food:** Arby's, Cracker Barrel, Outback Steaks, Pizza Hut, **lodging:** Courtyard, **other:** Cadillac/GMC, Ford/Mercury, **S...gas:** Clark/Subway/diesel, Meijer/diesel/24hr, **food:** Big Boy, Burger King, Chili's, DQ, KFC, Lil Chef, Little Caesar's, LoneStar Steaks, McDonald's, Red Robin, Taco Bell, Wendy's, **lodging:** Holiday Inn Express,

Interstate 96

E ↕ **W**

other: AAA, Farmer Jack's, Home Depot, Honda, Jo-Ann Fabrics, K-Mart, Mazda, Radio Shack, Staples, Target, USPO, mall, to Brighton Ski Area

141 Lp 96(from wb, no EZ return), to Howell, **N...gas:** Shell, Sunoco/diesel, **food:** Applebee's, Bob Evans, Little Caesar's, McDonald's, Mesquite Jct, TW's Italian, **lodging:** Grandview Inn, **other:** Chevrolet, **S...gas:** Speedway, **food:** Arby's, Big Boy, Taco Bell, Wendy's

141mm rest area wb, full(handicapped)facilities, phone, vending, picnic tables, litter barrels, petwalk

137 D19, Howell, to Pinckney, **N...gas:** Mobil, Shell/diesel, Speedway, **lodging:** Kensington Inn, Ramada Inn, **other:** HOSPITAL, Goodyear, Parts+, **S...food:** Benny's Grill, Country Kitchen, **lodging:** Best Western, **other:** Howell Auto Repair

135mm rest area eb, full(handicapped)facilities, vending, phone, picnic tables, litter barrels, petwalk

133 MI 59, Highland Rd, **N...gas:** Sunoco/McDonald's/diesel/, **food:** Texas Taco, **lodging:** AmeriHost, **other:** Factory Shops/famous brands

129 Fowlerville Rd, Fowlerville, **N...gas:** BP/rest./24hr, Shell/diesel, Sunoco/diesel, **food:** Big Boy, Fowlerville Rest., McDonald's, Subway, Taco Bell, Wendy's, **lodging:** Best Western, **S...gas:** Mobil, **other:** Chysler/Dodge/Jeep, **other:** Ford

126mm weigh sta both lanes

122 MI 43, MI 52, Webberville, **N...gas:** Mobil/diesel/24hr, **food:** Angel's Café, McDonald's, **other:** MI Brewing Co

117 Williamston, to Dansville, **N...gas:** Marathon, **1 mi N...gas:** Admiral, Speedway, **food:** Blimpie, DQ, Red Cedar Grill, Westside Deli, **S...gas:** Sunoco/diesel

111mm rest area wb, full(handicapped)facilities, phone, picnic tables, litter barrels, vending, petwalk

110 Okemos, Mason, **N...gas:** BP/24hr, Marathon, Sunoco, 7-11, **food:** Applebee's, Arby's, Big Boy, Burger King, Cracker Barrel, Hook's Grill, Little Caesar's, McDonald's, Stillwater Grill, Subway, **lodging:** Comfort Inn, Fairfield Inn, Hampton Inn, Holiday Inn Express, **other:** to stadium

L a n s i n g

106b a I-496, US 127, Lansing, to Jackson

104 Lp 96, Cedar St, Lansing, to Holt, **N...gas:** Admiral, Meijer/diesel/24hr, Shell, Speedway, **food:** Arby's, Blimpie, Bob Evans, Church's, Cuby Jack's Rest., Denny's, Hooters, KFC, LJ Silver, Mr Taco, Pizza Hut, Texas Roadhouse, Wendy's, White Castle, **lodging:** Best Western, Day's Inn, Econolodge, Governors Inn, Holiday Inn, Regent Inn, Super 8, **other:** HOSPITAL, Aldi Foods, Belle Tire, Cadillac, Chevrolet, Chrysler/Jeep, Dodge, GMC, Harley-Davidson, Hyundai, Lexus, Lincoln/Mercury, Mitsubishi, NTB, OfficeMax, Saab, Sam's Club, Target, Toyota, **S...gas:** Speedway/24hr, **food:** Buffalo's SW Café, Burger King, China East Buffet, Flapjack's Rest., McDonald's, Ponderosa, Subway, **lodging:** Ramada Ltd, **other:** CarQuest, Family$, Kroger, Lowe's Whse, NAPA

101 MI 99, MLK Blvd, to Eaton Rapids, **1-3 mi N...gas:** Meijer/diesel/24hr, QD, **food:** Arby's, **S...gas:** Speedway/Subway/diesel/24hr, Sunoco/diesel, **food:** McDonald's, Wendy's

98b a Lansing Rd, to Lansing, **S...gas:** Citgo/diesel/rest./24hr, **food:** Windsor Mtn Grill

97 I-69, US 27 S, S to Ft Wayne, N to Lansing

95 I-496, to Lansing

93b a MI 43, Lp 69, Saginaw Hwy, to Grand Ledge, **N...gas:** Meijer/diesel/24hr, Shell, Speedway/diesel, **food:** Burger King, Denny's, McDonald's, TGIFriday, **lodging:** Best Western, Fairfield Inn, Hampton Inn, Holiday Inn, Motel 6, Quality Suites, Red Roof Inn, Residence Inn, **other:** HOSPITAL, **1 mi N...food:** Carrabba's, Frank's Grill, Outback Steaks, **other:** Chrysler/Jeep, **S...gas:** BP/24hr, QD, Sunoco/McDonald's, **food:** Arby's, Bob Evans, Cracker Barrel, Subway, **other:** Discount Tire, GMC/Mazda, Lowe's Whse, Michael's, Wal-Mart/auto

92mm Grand River

91 I-69 N, US 27 N(from wb), to Flint

90 Grand River Ave, W...✈Flying J/Cookery/diesel/24hr/@, to airport

89 I-69 N, US 27 N(from eb), to Flint

87mm rest area eb, full(handicapped)facilities, phone, picnic tables, litter barrels, vending, petwalk

86 MI 100, Wright Rd, to Grand Ledge, **S...gas:** Mobil/McDonald's/diesel, Fleet/Subway/diesel/24hr/@

84 to Eagle, Westphalia, no facilities

79mm rest area wb, full(handicapped)facilities, info, phone, picnic tables, litter barrels, vending, petwalk

77 Lp 96, Grand River Ave, Portland, **N...gas:** BP/24hr, Marathon/diesel, Shell, Speedway/diesel, **food:** Arby's, Burger King, Little Caesar's, McDonald's, Oriental Star Chinese, Subway, **lodging:** Best Western, **other:** Family$, Rite Aid, Tom's Foods, **S...food:** Wendy's, **other:** Ford

76 Kent St, Portland, **N...gas:** Marathon/diesel(1mi), food

76mm Grand River

73 to Lyons-Muir, Grand River Ave, no facilities

69mm weigh sta both lanes

67 MI 66, to Ionia, Battle Creek, **N...gas:** Meijer/diesel/24hr(5mi), Pilot/Subway/diesel/24hr/@, **lodging:** AmeriHost, Midway Motel, Super 8, **other:** HOSPITAL, RV camping, st police

231

Interstate 96

E

W

Grand Rapids

64	to Lake Odessa, Saranac, **N**...Ionia St RA, **S**...I-96 Speedway
63mm	**rest area eb, full(handicapped)facilities, phone, picnic tables, litter barrels, petwalk, vending**
59	Clarksville, **N**...auto repair
52	MI 50, to Lowell, **N**...fairgrounds, **S**...**gas:** Marathon/Taco Bell/diesel(2mi), **other:** RV camping
46	rd 6, to rd 37, no facilities
46mm	Thornapple River
45mm	**rest area wb, full(handicapped)facilities, info, phone, picnic tables, litter barrels, vending**
43b a	MI 11, 28th St, Cascade, **N**...**gas:** Marathon/diesel, Meijer/diesel/24hr, **food:** Big Boy, Boston Mkt, Brann's Steaks, Burger King, Panera Bread, Pizza Hut, Shanghai Garden, Subway, Sundance Grill, Wendy's, **lodging:** Baymont Inn, Country Inn Suites, Crowne Plaza Hotel, Days Inn, Lexington Suites, **other:** Wal-Mart, **S**...**gas:** BP, Citgo, Shell, Speedway, **food:** Applebee's, Arby's, Blimpie, Bob Evans, Burger King, Cheddar's, Chili's, Damon's, Denny's, Dunkin Donuts, Grand Rapids Brewery, Hoffman House Rest., HongKong Garden, Hooters, IHOP, McDonald's, Olive Garden, Outback Steaks, Papa Vino's Italian, Perkins, Pizza Hut, Red Lobster, Rio Bravo, Steak'n Shake, Subway, Wendy's, **lodging:** Comfort Inn, Courtyard, Exel Inn, Extended Stay America, Hampton Inn, Hilton, Knight's Inn, Motel 6, Quality Inn, Red Roof Inn, **other:** Barnes&Noble, CarQuest, Circuit City, CompUSA, Home Depot, Jo-Ann Fabrics, Nissan/Acura/Audi/Subaru, NTB, OfficeMax, Sam's Club, Target, U-Haul
40b a	Cascade Rd, **N**...**gas:** BP, Marathon/diesel, 7-11/24hr, **food:** Subway, **other:** NAPA Autocare, **S**...**gas:** Shell, Speedway/diesel, **other:** HOSPITAL
39	MI 21(from eb), to Flint, no facilities
38	E Beltline Ave, to MI 21, MI 37, MI 44, **N**...RV camping, **S**...**food:** Duba's Dining, **other:** HOSPITAL
37mm	I-196(from wb, exits left), Gerald Ford Fwy, to Grand Rapids
36	Leonard St, **1-2 mi S**...**food:** Arby's, Blimpie, McDonald's, **other:** sheriff's dept
33	Plainfield Ave, MI 44 Connector, **N**...**gas:** BP, Meijer/diesel/24hr, Speedway, 7-11, **food:** Arby's, Big Boy, Blimpie, Burger King, Domino's, Fred's Pizza, Golden Dragon, Hungry Howie's, KFC, Little Caesar's, LJ Silver, McDonald's, Pizza Hut, Russ' Rest., Schlotsky's, Subway, Taco Bell, Wendy's, **lodging:** Grand Inn, Lazy T Motel, **other:** AutoZone, Belle Tire, Chevrolet, Chrysler/Plymouth/Jeep, Discount Tire, Dodge, Ford/Mercury, Goodyear/auto, NAPA, Nissan/VW, NTB, Plymouth/Jeep, Radio Shack, Rite Aid, U-Haul, Walgreen, transmissions, **S**...**gas:** Amoco/24hr, **food:** Denny's, Traditions Rest.
31mm	Grand River
31b a	US 131, N to Cadillac, S to Kalamazoo, **1 mi N**...**food:** McDonald's
30b a	Alpine Ave, Grand Rapids, **N**...**gas:** BP/24hr, Citgo/7-11, Marathon, Shell, **food:** Applebee's, Bennigan's, Blimpie, ChuckeCheese, Clock Rest., Cracker Barrel, Damon's, Fire Mtn Grill, Logan's Roadhouse, McDonald's, Old Country Buffet, Olive Garden, Outback Steaks, Perkins, Russ' Rest., Ryan's, Schlotsky's, Steak'n Shake, Subway, Taco Bell, TGIFriday, **lodging:** Hampton Inn, Holiday Inn Express, Swan Inn, **other:** Aldi Foods, Belle Tire, Best Buy, CarQuest, Circuit City, Discount Tire, Ford/Kia, Kia, Kohl's, Michael's, NAPA, OfficeMax, PepBoys, Radio Shack, Sam's Club, Target, Wal-Mart/auto, **S**...**gas:** Admiral/diesel, Gas4Less, Meijer/diesel/24hr, Speedway/diesel, **food:** Arby's, Burger King, Fazoli's, KFC, LJ Silver, McDonald's, Papa John's, Pizza Hut, Ponderosa, Wendy's, **lodging:** Motel 6, **other:** Goodyear/auto, Home Depot, Jo-Ann Fabrics, U-Haul
28	Walker Ave, **S**...**gas:** Meijer/diesel/24hr, **food:** Bob Evans, McDonald's, **lodging:** Amerihost, Baymont Inn
26	Fruit Ridge Ave, **N**...**gas:** Citgo/diesel, **S**...**gas:** Amoco/diesel
25mm	**rest area eb, full(handicapped)facilities, phone, picnic tables, litter barrels, petwalk**
25	8th Ave, 4Mile Rd(from wb), **S**...**gas:** Marathon/diesel, **lodging:** Wayside Motel
24	8th Ave, 4Mile Rd(from eb), **S**...**gas:** Marathon/diesel, **lodging:** Wayside Motel
23	Marne, **N**...**other:** tires, fairgrounds/raceway, **S**...**food:** Depot Café, Rinaldi's Café, **other:** USPO
19	Lamont, Coopersville, **N**...food, **S**...**food:** Sam's Joint Rest., **other:** LP
16	B-35, Eastmanville, **N**...**gas:** Amoco/Subway/TCBY/diesel, Fleet/diesel/24hr, Shell/Burger King/diesel, **food:** Arby's, Little Caesar's, McDonald's, Pizza Hut/Taco Bell, **lodging:** AmeriHost, **other:** Family RV Ctr, Prevo's Foods, Rite Aid, **S**...**gas:** Pacific Pride/diesel, **other:** RV camping
10	B-31, Nunica, **N**...**food:** Turk's Rest., **S**...**gas:** Mobil, **other:** RV camping, golf course/rest.
9	MI 104(from wb, exits left), to Grand Haven, Spring Lake, **S**...**gas:** Mobil, **other:** to Grand Haven SP
8mm	**rest area wb, full(handicapped)facilities, phone, picnic tables, litter barrels, vending, petwalk**
5	Fruitport(from wb, no return), no facilities
4	Airline Rd, **N**...**gas:** racetrack, **S**...**gas:** Speedway/diesel, Shell, Wesco/diesel, **food:** Burger Crest Diner, McDonald's, Subway, **other:** Fruitport Foods/24hr, Pleasure Island Water Park(5mi), USPO, to PJ Hoffmaster SP
1c	Hile Rd(from eb), **S**...**gas:** racetrack
b a	US 31, to Ludington, Grand Haven, **N**...**lodging:** Alpine Motel, Bel-aire Motel, Haven Motel, **other:** All Seasons RV, **2 mi N on Sherman Blvd**...**gas:** Westco/diesel, **food:** Applebee's, Arby's, Fazoli's, McDonald's, Old Country Buffet, Ruby Tuesday, Wendy's, **lodging:** Comfort Inn/rest., Ramada Inn, Super 8, **other:** HOSPITAL, Circuit City, GNC, Lowe's Whse, OfficeMax, Sam's Club, Staples, Target, Wal-Mart SuperCtr/24hr, **S**...**gas:** Mobil/diesel, **lodging:** AmeriHost, Best Western, Quality Inn, **other:** airport, racetrack

Muskegon

I-96 begins/ends on US 31 at Muskegon.

Interstate 196(Grand Rapids)

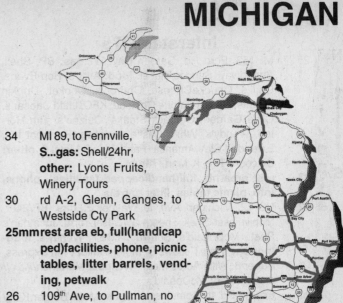

Exit # Services

81mm I-196 begins/ends on I-96, 37mm in E Grand Rapids.

79 Fuller Ave, **N**...sheriff's dept

78 College Ave, **S**...gas: DM/gas, McDonald's, **other:** HOSPITAL, Rite Aid, auto repair, museum

77c Ottawa Ave, downtown, **S**...Gerald R Ford Museum

b a US 131, S to Kalamazoo, N to Cadillac

76 MI 45 E, Lane Ave, **S**...gas: Amoco, **other:** Gerald R Ford Museum, John Ball Park&Zoo

75 MI 45 W, Lake Michigan Dr, **N**...to Grand Valley St U

74mm Grand River

73 Market Ave, **N**...to Vanandel Arena

72 Lp 196, Chicago Dr E(from eb), no facilities

70 MI 11(exits left from wb), Grandville, Walker, **S**...gas: BP/diesel, Shell/repair, Speedway, **other:** NAPA, USPO

69b a Chicago Dr, **N**...gas: Meijer/diesel/24hr, **food:** KFC, McDonald's, Papa John's, Perkins, Subway, **other:** Aldi Foods, AutoZone, $General, Radio Shack, Target, **S**...gas: Amoco, Clark Gas, Speedway, **food:** Arby's, Burger King, Get'm-n-Go Burger, Little Caesar's, Pizza Hut, Russ' Rest., Wendy's, **lodging:** Best Western, Holiday Inn Express

67 44th St, **N**...gas: Mobil/diesel, **food:** Burger King, Cracker Barrel, Steak'n Shake, **lodging:** Comfort Suites, **other:** AAA, Wal-Mart/auto, **S**...**other:** Circuit City, Lowe's Whse, Residence Inn(2mi)

65 new exit

62 32nd Ave, to Hudsonville, **N**...gas: BP/diesel/24hr, **food:** Arby's, Burger King, McDonald's, **lodging:** AmeriHost, **other:** Chevrolet, **S**...gas: Mobil/Subway/diesel/24hr, **lodging:** Super 8, **other:** Harley-Davidson

58mm rest area eb, full(handicapped)facilities, phone, picnic tables, litter barrels, vending, petwalk

55 Byron Rd, Zeeland, **N**...gas: 7-11, **food:** McDonald's, **3-5 mi N**...HOSPITAL, to Holland SP

52 16th St, Adams St, **2 mi N**...gas: Meijer/diesel/24hr, Speedway, **food:** Wendy's, **lodging:** Best Inn, Econolodge, **other:** HOSPITAL, **S**...gas: Mobil/Subway/diesel, **food:** Burger King

49 MI 40, to Allegan, **N**...gas: BP/McDonald's/diesel, **S**...gas: Tulip City/diesel/24hr/@, **food:** Rock Island Rest.

44 US 31 N(from eb), to Holland, **3-5 mi N**...lodging: Country Inn, **other:** HOSPITAL, gas, food

43mm rest area wb, full(handicapped)facilities, info, phone, picnic tables, litter barrels, vending, petwalk

41 rd A-2, Douglas, Saugatuck, **N**...gas: Marathon/diesel, Shell/Subway/diesel, **food:** Burger King, **lodging:** AmericInn, Holiday Inn Express, Timberline Motel(3mi), **other:** NAPA, Saugatuck RV Resort, to Saugatuck SP, **S**...lodging: Shangrai-la Motel

38mm Kalamazoo River

36 rd A-2, Ganges, **N**...gas: Shell, **lodging:** AmericInn

34 MI 89, to Fennville, **S**...gas: Shell/24hr, **other:** Lyons Fruits, Winery Tours

30 rd A-2, Glenn, Ganges, to Westside Cty Park

25mm rest area eb, full(handicapped)facilities, phone, picnic tables, litter barrels, vending, petwalk

26 109th Ave, to Pullman, no facilities

22 N Shore Dr, **N**...food: Seawolf Café, Tello's Ristorante, **other:** to Kal Haven Trail SP, RV camping

20 rd A-2, Phoenix Rd, **N**...gas: BP/diesel/24hr, Marathon/diesel, **food:** Arby's, Taco Bell, **lodging:** SouthHaven Motel, **other:** HOSPITAL, AutoZone, st police, **S**...gas: BP/diesel, **food:** Big Boy, McDonald's, Sherman's Dairybar, Wendy's, **lodging:** Hampton Inn, Holiday Inn Express, Lighthouse Inn, **other:** Wal-Mart SuperCtr/gas/24hr

18 MI 140, MI 43, to Watervliet, **N**...gas: Shell/diesel/24hr, **food:** Ma's Coffeepot Rest./24hr, **1-2 mi N**...gas: Speedway, **food:** Burger King, CT's Café, McDonald's, Pizza Hut, Platter's Diner, **lodging:** Budget Lodge, LakeBluff Motel, **other:** D&W Foods, Buick/Pontiac/Cadillac/GMC, Chevrolet, Chrysler/Dodge

13 to Covert, **N**...to Van Buren SP, RV camping

7 MI 63, to Benton Harbor, **N**...food: DiMaggio's Pizza, Vitale's Mkt/subs, **other:** RV camping

4 Riverside, to Coloma, **S**...gas: Marathon/diesel, **other:** KOA

2mm Paw Paw River

1 Red Arrow Hwy, **N**...Ross Field Airport

0mm I-94, E to Detroit, W to Chicago

I-196 begins/ends on I-94, exit 34 at Benton Harbor.

Interstate 275(Livonia)

Exit # Services

I-275 and I-96 run together 9 miles. **See Michigan Interstate 96, exits 165-170.**

29 I-96 E, to Detroit, MI 14 W, to Ann Arbor

28 Ann Arbor Rd, Plymouth, **E**...gas: BP/24hr, Shell, **food:** Atlantis Rest., Denny's, Dunkin Donuts, **lodging:** Day's Inn, Red Roof Inn, **W**...food: Bennigan's, Burger King, Steak&Ale, **lodging:** Quality Inn, **other:** Cadillac, K-Mart, Lincoln/Mercury

MICHIGAN

Interstate 275

N ← Livonia → **S**

25	MI 153, Ford Rd, Garden City, **W...gas:** BP, Shell, Speedway, Sunoco/diesel, **food:** Arby's, Bob Evans, Chili's, ChuckeCheese, Church's, Cooker, Dunkin Donuts, Hunan Empire Chinese, KFC, Little Caesar's, Olive Garden, Outback Steaks, Quizno's, Tim Horton, Wendy's, White Castle, **lodging:** Baymont Inn, Extended Stay America, Fairfield Inn, Motel 6, **other:** Discount Tire, K-Mart, Target
23	**rest area nb, full(handicapped facilities), phone, info, picnic tables, litter barrels**
22	US 12, Michigan Ave, to Wayne, **E...gas:** BP/24hr, Mobil/diesel, Shell, Speedway/diesel, **food:** Jonathan's Rest., McDonald's, Subway, TCBY, Wendy's, **lodging:** Day's Inn, Fellows Cr Motel, Holiday Inn Express, Super 8, Willo Acres Motel, **W...gas:** Marathon/A&W/diesel, **food:** McDonald's
20	Ecorse Rd, to Romulus, **W...gas:** Mobil/Burger King/diesel/24hr
17	I-94 E to Detroit, W to Ann Arbor, **E...**airport
15	Eureka Rd, **E...gas:** Shell, airport
13	Sibley Rd, New Boston, **W...**gas, food, hardware, to Lower Huron Metro Park
11	S Huron Rd, **1 mi W...gas:** Sunoco/Burger King/diesel, **food:** Jacob's Rest.
8	Will Carleton Rd, to Flat Rock, no facilities
5	Carleton, South Rockwood, **W...**food
4mm	**rest area sb, full(handicapped)facilties, phone, picnic tables, litter barrels**
2	US 24, to Telegraph Rd, **W...gas:** Marathon/diesel, lodging
0mm	I-275 begins/ends on I-75, exit 20.

Interstate 475(Flint)

N ← Flint → **S**

Exit #	Services
17.5mm	I-475 begins/ends on I-75, exit 125.
15	Clio Rd, **W...gas:** BP, **other:** Chevrolet, Northwoods RV Ctr
13	Saginaw St, **E...gas:** BP, **food:** DQ, McDonald's, Papa John's, Ponderosa, Taco Bell, **other:** Family$, Kroger/gas, **W...gas:** Clark, Sunoco, **food:** Burger King, KFC, Little Caesar's
11	Carpenter Rd, no facilities
10	Pierson Rd, no facilities
9	rd 54, Dort Hwy, Stewart Ave, **E...gas:** Citgo, **food:** McDonald's
8mm	Flint River
8b	Davison Rd, Hamilton Ave, no facilities
a	Longway Blvd, **W...food:** China 1 Buffet, **lodging:** Holiday Inn Express, **other:** HOSPITAL
7	rd 21, Court St, downtown Flint
6	I-69, W to Lansing, E to Port Huron
5	Alberton Rd(from sb), **E...gas:** Marathon
4	Hemphill Rd, Bristol Rd, **E...gas:** Speedway, **food:** Subway, **W...gas:** Speedway, **food:** Latina Rest., **other:** Kroger/gas
2	Hill Rd, **E...gas:** Speedway, **food:** Applebee's, Bob Evans, **lodging:** Wingate Inn, **other:** Ford, **W...gas:** Shell, Sunoco, **food:** Arby's, Bob Evans, **lodging:** Courtyard, Holiday Inn, Residence Inn
0mm	I-475 begins/ends on I-75, exit 111.

Interstate 696(Detroit)

E ← Detroit Area → **W**

Exit #	Services
	I-696 begins/ends on I-94.
28	I-94 E to Port Huron, W to Detroit, 11 Mile Rd, **E...gas:** BP/diesel, Speedway, 7-11
27	MI 3, Gratiot Ave, **N...gas:** BP, **food:** National Coney Island, **other:** Costco/gas, **S...gas:** BP, Mobil/McDonald's, **food:** White Castle, **other:** Goodyear/auto
26	MI 97, Groesbeck Ave, Roseville, **N...gas:** Mobil/diesel, **S...gas:** Marathon, **food:** Wendy's
24	Hoover Rd, Schoenherr Rd, **N...gas:** Sunoco, **food:** Burger King, KFC, **S...gas:** BP, Mobil, **food:** ChiChi's, Subway, Taco Bell, Tim Horton, **lodging:** Holiday Inn Express, **other:** CVS Drug, Kroger, Marshall's
23	MI 53, Van Dyke Ave, **N...gas:** BP, **food:** Arby's, Coney Island, Dunkin Donuts, McDonald's, **lodging:** Baymont Inn, **other:** MEDICAL CARE, Cadillac/Pontiac/GMC, Dodge, Jo-Ann Fabrics, radiators, **S...gas:** BP/24hr, **food:** Burger King, **other:** Chevrolet, Ford, Toyota, USPO
22	Mound Rd, no facilities
20	Ryan Rd, Dequindre Rd, **N...gas:** Marathon, **food:** IHOP, **lodging:** Knight's Inn, Red Roof Inn, **S...food:** Bob Evans, McDonald's, **lodging:** Comfort Suites, Ramada Ltd, **other:** Rite Aid, transmissions
19	Couzens St, 10 Mile Rd, **S...**Hazel Park Racetrack
18	I-75 N to Flint, S to Detroit
17	Campbell Ave, Hilton Ave, Bermuda, Mohawk, **S...gas:** Marathon/diesel
16	MI 1, Woodward Ave, Main St, **N...food:** Burger King, **other:** zoo
14	Coolidge Rd, 10 Mile Rd, **S...gas:** Mobil, Speedway, **food:** Dunkin Donuts, **food:** Jade Palace Chinese, Little Caesar's, LJ Silver, Pizza Hut, Subway, Taco Bell, Wendy's, **other:** CVS Drug, Farmer Jack's, Jo-Ann Fabrics
13	Greenfield Rd, **S...gas:** Mobil, Sunoco, **food:** Dunkin Donuts, **other:** Ford
12	MI 39, Southfield Rd, 11 Mile Rd, **S...gas:** Shell
11	Evergreen Rd, **S...lodging:** Residence Inn
10	US 24, Telegraph Rd, **N...gas:** BP, Marathon, **food:** Denny's, Seoul Garden Korean, **lodging:** Hampton Inn, Embassy Suites, **other:** Belle Tire, Best Buy, Chevrolet, Chrysler/Jeep, Circuit City, Dodge/Plymouth, $General, Farmer Jack's, Ford, Honda/Nissan/Isuzu, Hyundai, Jo-Ann Fabrics, K-Mart, Lexus, Lincoln/Mercury, Office Depot, Pontiac/Buick, USPO, mall, **S...gas:** Mobil, **lodging:** Courtyard, Hilton, Holiday Inn, Marriott
8	MI 10, Lodge Fwy, no facilities
5	Orchard Lake Rd, Farmington Hills, **N...gas:** Marathon, Mobil, Shell, **food:** Arby's, Hong Hua Chinese, Roberto's Rest., Ruby Tuesday, Starbucks, Steak&Ale, Steamer's Seafood, Subway, Wendy's, **lodging:** Comfort Inn, **other:** Discount Tire, to St Mary's Coll
1	(from wb), I-96 W, I-275 S, to MI 5, Grand River Ave

MINNESOTA

Interstate 35

Exit #	Services
260mm	I-35 begins/ends on MN 61 in Duluth.
259	MN 61, London Rd, North Shore, to Two Harbors, **W... gas:** Holiday/diesel, Spur, SA, **food:** Blackwoods Grill, Burger King, KFC, McDonald's, Perkins, Pizza Hut, Subway, Taco John's, Wendy's, **lodging:** Best Western
258	21st Ave E(from nb), to U of MN at Duluth, **W...food:** Perkins, **lodging:** Best Western, same as 259
256b	Mesaba Ave, Superior St, **E...gas:** ICO/DQ, **food:** Burger King, Grandma's Grill, Little Angie's Cantina, Red Lobster, Timberlodge Steaks, Tradewinds Rest., **lodging:** Canal Park Inn, Comfort Suites, Hampton Inn, Hawthorn Suites, Superior Lake Inn, **W...lodging:** Holiday Inn, Radisson
a	Michigan St, **E...**waterfront, **W...**HOSPITAL, downtown

255a	US 53 N, downtown, mall, **W...other:** Kia
b	I-535 spur, to Wisconsin, no facilities
254	27th Ave W, **W...gas:** BP/24hr, Holiday/Burger King/diesel, Spur/diesel, **food:** Embers Rest., Subway, **lodging:** Motel 6
253b	40th Ave W, **W...gas:** BP/diesel/24hr, **food:** Perkins/24hr, **lodging:** Comfort Inn, Super 8
a	US 2 E, US 53, to Wisconsin, no facilities
252	Central Ave, W Duluth, **W...gas:** Conoco/diesel, Holiday/diesel/24hr, **food:** Beaners Coffee, Giant Panda, KFC, McDonald's, Pizza Hut, Sammy's Café, Subway, Taco Bell, White Castle, **other:** K-Mart, Radio Shack, Super 1 Foods, Walgreen
251b	MN 23 S, Grand Ave, no facilities
a	Cody St, zoo, **E...lodging:** Allyndale Motel
250	US 2 W(from sb), to Grand Rapids, **1/2 mi W...gas:** Holiday/diesel, Mobil/diesel/LP, **food:** Blackwoods Grill, Country Kitchen, Wok'n Grill, **lodging:** AmericInn

235

N
↑
↓
S

249	Boundary Ave, Skyline Pkwy, **E...gas:** Holiday/McDonald's/diesel, **lodging:** Country Inn Suites, Sundowner Motel(1mi), **other:** to ski area, **W...rest area both lanes, full(handicapped) facilities, info, phone, picnic tables, litter barrels, vending, gas:** Phillips 66/diesel/24hr, **food:** Blackwoods Grill, Country Kitchen, **lodging:** Travelodge
246	MN 13, Midway Rd, Nopeming, **W...gas:** Armor/diesel, **food:** Dry Dock Rest.
245	MN 61, **E...food:** Buffalo House Rest./camping
242	rd 1, Esko, Thomson, **E...gas:** BP
239.5mm	St Louis River
239	MN 45, Scanlon, to Cloquet, **E...other:** Jay Cooke SP, KOA(May-Oct), **W...gas:** Conoco, **food:** Pantry Rest., Wood City Grille, **lodging:** Golden Gate Motel, **other:** HOSPITAL, Chevrolet, Pontiac/Buick, camping, diesel repair
237	MN 33, Cloquet, **1 mi W...gas:** BP/24hr, Conoco/diesel, Spur, **food:** Country Kitchen, Grandma's Grill, DQ, Hardee's, McDonald's, Perkins/24hr, Pizza Hut, Subway, Taco Bell, Taco John's, **lodging:** AmericInn, Super 8, **other:** HOSPITAL, Chrysler/Plymouth/Jeep, Family$, Ford/Mercury, NAPA, Super 1 Foods, Wal-Mart/24hr, White Drug
236mm	weigh sta both lanes
235	MN 210, Carlton, to Cromwell, **E...gas:** BP/diesel/rest., Armor Fuel, Spur/diesel/24hr, **food:** Backyard Grill, Embers Rest., **lodging:** AmericInn, Royal Pines Motel, **other:** to Jay Cooke SP, **W...other:** Black Bear Casino/Hotel/rest.
235mm	Big Otter Creek
233mm	Little Otter Creek
227	rd 4, Mahtowa, **E...**camping, **W...gas:** Conoco
226mm	**rest area nb, full(handicapped)facilities, phone, picnic tables, litter barrels, vending, petwalk**
220	rd 6, Barnum, **E...**camping, **W...gas:** BP/diesel/café/24hr, **lodging:** Northwoods Motel
219mm	Moose Horn River
218mm	Moose Horn River
216	MN 27(from sb, no EZ return), Moose Lake, **1-2 mi W...gas:** BP, Holiday/diesel, Phillips 66, **food:** Art's Café, DQ, Wyndtree Rest., **lodging:** AmericInn(4mi), Moose Lake Motel, **other:** HOSPITAL, Chevrolet/Buick/Pontiac, Super Valu Foods, to Munger Trail
214	rd 73(from nb, no EZ return), Moose Lake, **E...other:** Moose Lake SP(2mi), camping, **W...gas:** Conoco/Subway/diesel, **lodging:** AmericInn, **2 mi W...food:** Wyndtree Rest., **lodging:** Moose Lake Motel, **other:** HOSPITAL, Munger Trail, Red Fox Camping
209	rd 46, Sturgeon Lake, **E...gas:** Phillips 66, **W...lodging:** Sturgeon Lake Motel, **other:** Timberline Camping(3mi)

209mm	**rest area sb, full(handicapped)facilities, phone, picnic tables, litter barrels, vending, petwalk**
206.5mm	Willow River
205	rd 43, Willow River, **W...gas:** Citgo/diesel, **other:** camping(2mi), laundry
198.5mm	Kettle River
198mm	**rest area nb, full(handicapped)facilities, phone, picnic tables, litter barrels, vending, petwalk**
195	rd 18, rd 23 E, to Askov, **E...gas:** BP/diesel/café, **lodging:** Super 8, **other:** to Banning SP, camping, **W...**camping
191	MN 23, rd 61, Sandstone, **E...gas:** BP/diesel/LP, Conoco/diesel, **lodging:** Sandstone 61 Motel(2mi), **other:** MEDICAL CARE, Family Drug
184mm	Grindstone Rover
183	MN 48, Hinckley, **E...gas:** Conoco/Tobie's Rest., Holiday/diesel, **food:** Burger King, DQ, Hardee's, Subway, Taco Bell, **lodging:** Day's Inn, Grand Northern Inn, **other:** Chevrolet, flea mkt, to St Croix SP(15mi), **W...gas:** Mobil/24hr, Phillips 66/White Castle/diesel, **food:** Cassidy's Rest., **lodging:** Gold Pine Inn, **other:** Fire Museum
180	MN 23 W, rd 61, to Mora, no facilities
175	rd 14, Beroun, **E...gas:** BP/diesel
171	rd 11, Pine City, **E...gas:** SA/diesel, **food:** McDonald's, **other:** Chrysler/Dodge, **W...**camping
170mm	Snake River
169	MN 324, rd 7, Pine City, **E...gas:** BP/diesel, Holiday/diesel, **food:** A&W, DQ, Grizzly's Grill, KFC, Pizza Hut, Red Shed Rest., Subway, **other:** Ford/Mercury, Jubilee Foods, Pamida, Radio Shack, Wal-Mart, camping, **W...**to NW Co Fur Post HS
165	MN 70, Rock Creek, to Grantsburg, **E...gas:** Citgo/diesel, **lodging:** Chalet Motel, camping, **W...gas:** Total/diesel/café/24hr
159	MN 361, rd 1, Rush City, **E...gas:** Holiday/Burger King/diesel, **other:** HOSPITAL, Main St Mkt Foods, **W...**camping(2mi)
154mm	**rest area nb, full(handicapped)facilities, phone, picnic tables, litter barrels, vending, petwalk**
152	rd 10, Harris, **2 mi E...**gas/diesel
147	MN 95, North Branch, to Cambridge, **E...gas:** BP, Casey's, Conoco/diesel, Holiday/diesel, **food:** DQ, Domino's, KFC/Taco Bell, McDonald's, North Branch Café, Perkins, Pizza Hut, Subway, **lodging:** AmericInn, Oak Inn/rest., Super 8, **other:** MEDICAL CARE, CarQuest, Fisk Tire, NAPA, SuperValu Foods, to Wild River SP(14mi), **W...food:** Burger King, Denny's, **other:** Chevrolet, Chrysler/Plymouth/Dodge/Jeep, Ford, Tanger Outlet/famous brands
139	rd 19, Stacy, **E...gas:** BP, Phillips 66, **food:** Rustic Rest., **lodging:** Super 8(8mi), city park, **W...gas:** Conoco/pizza

Interstate 35

135 US 61 S, rd 22, Wyoming, **E...gas:** BP/diesel, **food:** Cornerstone Café, DQ, Pizza Zone, Subway, **other:** HOSPITAL, CarQuest, IGA Foods, **W...gas:** Citgo/diesel, **food:** McDonald's, Village Inn Rest., **other:** camping(10mi), golf

132 US 8(from nb), to Taylors Falls

131 rd 2, Forest Lake, **E...gas:** Amoco/24hr, Holiday/diesel, SA/diesel, **food:** Applebee's, Arby's, Burger King, Cheung Chinese, Hardee's, McDonald's, Perkins, Quack's Café, Taco Bell, White Castle, **lodging:** AmericInn, **other:** HOSPITAL, Champion Auto, Checker Parts, Kennedy Transmissions, OfficeMax, Rainbow Foods/24hr, Target, Tires+, Wal-Mart, **W...gas:** Holiday/diesel, **food:** Famous Dave's BBQ, Papa Murphy's, Quizno's, Starbucks, Wendy's, **lodging:** Country Inn Suites, **other:** Buick/Pontiac, Chevrolet/Cadillac, Chrysler/Plymouth/Dodge/Jeep, Cub Foods, Ford, GNC

131mm **rest area sb, full(handicapped)facilities, phone, picnic tables, litter barrels, vending, petwalk**

129 MN 97, rd 23, **E...**camping(6mi), **W...gas:** Conoco/pizza/diesel/24hr, **other:** camping(1mi)

128mm weigh sta both lanes

127 I-35W, S to Minneapolis. **See I-35W.**

123 rd 14, Centerville, **E...**Otter Lake RV Ctr, **W...gas:** Citgo/diesel, Marathon, Shell, **food:** DQ, Embers Rest., Kelly's Rest.

120 rd J(from nb)

117 MN 96, **E...gas:** Mobil, SA/diesel, **food:** Burger King, Casa Lupita Mexican, **lodging:** AmericInn, **other:** Goodyear/auto, NAPA, **W...gas:** BP, PDQ, **food:** Applebee's, Arby's/Sbarro's, Boston Mkt, Culver's, McDonald's, Subway, MEDICAL CARE, **other:** Cub Foods, Tires+, USPO, Walgreen

115 rd E, **E...gas:** BP, Conoco, SA/diesel, **food:** Jimmy's Panera Bread, Perkins, **lodging:** Holiday Inn Express, **W...gas:** KFC/Pizza Hut, **food:** McDonald's, Papa Murphy's, Quizno's, Wendy's, **other:** Festival Foods, GNC, Radio Shack, Target, Wal-Mart/auto

114 I-694 E(exits left from sb), no facilities

113 I-694 W, no facilities

112 Little Canada Rd, **E...gas:** Citgo, **W...gas:** Sinclair, **food:** Porterhouse Steaks

111b MN 36 W, to Minneapolis, no facilities

a MN 36 E, to Stillwater, no facilities

110b Roselawn Ave, no facilities

a Wheelock Pkwy, **E...gas:** BP, Mobil, **food:** Subway, **W...gas:** Sinclair/diesel

109 Maryland Ave, **E...gas:** Citgo, SA/diesel, **W...food:** Wendy's, **other:** K-Mart

108 Pennsylvania Ave, downtown

107c University Ave, downtown, **E...gas:** BP, **W...other:** HOSPITAL, to st capitol

107b a I-94, W to Minneapolis, E to St Paul. I-35 and I-94 run together.

106c 11th St(from nb), Marion St, downtown, **E...lodging:** Best Western, **other:** Sears/auto

106b Kellogg Blvd(from nb), downtown, **E...food:** MS Mud Grill, Subway, **lodging:** Holiday Inn, **other:** HOSPITAL

a Grand Ave, **E...**HOSPITAL

105 St Clair Ave, no facilities

104c Victoria St, Jefferson Ave, no facilities

b Ayd Mill Rd(from nb), no facilities

a Randolph Ave, no facilities

103b MN 5, W 7th St, **E...food:** Burger King, **W...gas:** SA/diesel, **other:** USPO

a Shepard Rd(from nb)

102mm Mississippi River

102 MN 13, Sibley Hwy, **W...gas:** BP, Holiday

101b a MN 110 W, **E...food:** Ziggy's Deli, **W...gas:** SA

99b I-494 W, no facilities

a I-494 E, no facilities

98 Lone Oak Rd, **E...lodging:** Homestead Suites, Microtel, **other:** Sam's Club, USPO, **W...gas:** BP, **food:** Costello's Coffee, Joe Senser's Grill, Magic Thai Café, **lodging:** Hampton Inn

97b Yankee Doodle Rd, **E...gas:** Holiday, **food:** Applebee's, Arby's, Blimpie, Burger King, Cattle Co Rest., Chili's, Culver's, DQ, Don Pablo's, Houlihan's, KFC, McDonald's, New China Buffet, Perkins, Pizza Hut, Red Robin, Taco Bell, **lodging:** Residence Inn, Springhill Suites, TownePlace Suites, **other:** MEDICAL CARE, Barnes&Noble, Byerly's Foods, Checker Parts, GNC, Kohl's, Michael's, Office Depot, OfficeMax, Old Navy, Rainbow Foods, Tires+, **W...gas:** BP, SA/diesel, **lodging:** Al Baker's Rest., Boston Mkt, Dragon Palace Chinese, **lodging:** Best Western, Extended Stay America

a Pilot Knob Rd, same as 97b, **E...gas:** Phillips 66, Hardee's, **lodging:** Best Western, SpringHill Suites, TownePlace Suites, **other:** Firestone, Goodyear, Wal-Mart, mall

94 rd 30, Diffley Rd, to Eagan, **W...gas:** Conoco

93 rd 32, Cliff Rd, **E...gas:** Shell, **food:** Subway, **W...gas:** Holiday/diesel, Mobil/diesel, **food:** Burger King, Bakers Square, Boston Mkt, Burger King, Cherokee Sirloin, DQ, Denny's, Dolittle's Café, Greenmill Rest., KFC, Little Caesar's, McDonald's, Subway, Taco Bell, Wendy's, **lodging:** Hilton, Holiday Inn Express, Sleep Inn, Staybridge Suites, **other:** Checker Parts, Target, USPO, Walgreen

N ↑↓ **S**

F a r i b a u l t

O w a t o n n a

92	MN 77, Cedar Ave, **E**...Zoo, **1 m W**...access to Cliff Rd services
90	rd 11, **E**...**gas:** KwikTrip, **W**...**gas:** Freedom
88b	rd 42, Crystal Lake Rd, **E**...**food:** Byerly's Rest., Ciatti's Grill, Millcreek Rest., **W**...**gas:** BP, PDQ, **food:** Arby's/Sbarro's, BBQ, Burger King, Ground Round, McDonald's, Old Country Buffet, Roadhouse Grill, Taco Bell, Vico's Café, **lodging:** Country Inn, Fairfield Inn, Hampton Inn, Holiday Inn, **other:** HOSPITAL, Home Depot, USPO, **1/2 mi W**...**gas:** Holiday/diesel, SA, **food:** Applebee's, Bakers Square, Champp's Café, ChiChi's, Chili's, ChuckeCheese, Godfather's, KFC, Kings Buffet, Macaroni Grill, Olive Garden, Outback Steaks, Papa John's, Red Lobster, Schlotsky's, Southern China Café, TGIFriday, **lodging:** InTown Suites, **other:** Barnes&Noble, Chevrolet, Circuit City, Cub Foods, Discount Tire, Goodyear/auto, JC Penney, K-Mart, Marshall Field, Mervyn's, Michael's, NTB, OfficeMax, Rainbow Foods, Sears/auto, Target, Tires+, Walgreen, mall
a	I-35W(from nb), N to Minneapolis. **See I-35W.**
87	Crystal Lake Rd, **W**...**gas:** KT, **other:** Buick, Ford/Lincoln/Mercury, Honda/Nissan, Saturn, Toyota, Beaver Mtn Ski Area
86	rd 46, **E**...**gas:** KT, SA/diesel, **food:** KFC, **other:** Harley-Davidson
85	MN 50, Sinclair, **E**...**gas:** BP/24hr, F&F/diesel, SA/diesel, **food:** Burger King, DQ, Lakeville Chinese, Pizza Hut, Subway, Taco Bell, **lodging:** Comfort Inn, **other:** MEDICAL CARE, Family Foods, Goodyear, **W**...**gas:** Holiday/diesel, **food:** ChartHouse Rest., Cracker Barrel, Perkins, **lodging:** AmericInn
84	185th St W(from sb), Orchard Trail, no facilities
81	rd 70, Lakeville, **E**...**gas:** Holiday/diesel, **food:** McDonald's, Subway, Tacoville, **lodging:** Motel 6, Super 8/rest., **other:** towing/repai
76	rd 2, Elko, **E**...**gas:** Phillips 66/diesel/LP, **W**...**food:** Glenno's Eatery/pizza, HeartThrop Café
76mm	**rest area sb, full(handicapped)facilities, phone, picnic tables, litter barrels, vending, petwalk**
69	MN 19, to Northfield, **E**...**gas:** Fuel&mart, **food:** Taco Bell(6mi), **8 mi E**...**lodging:** AmericInn, Country Inn, Super 8, **other:** Carleton Coll, St Olaf Coll, **W**...**gas:** Conoco/A&W/diesel/24hr, **food:** Embers Rest.
68mm	**rest area nb, full(handicapped)facilities, phone, picnic tables, litter barrels, vending, petwalk**
66	rd 1, to Dundas, **1 mi W**...**food:** Boonie's Grill

59	MN 21, Faribault, **E**...**gas:** Shell/diesel/rest., **lodging:** AmericInn, Day's Inn, Super 8, **2 mi E**...**gas:** Mobil, SA, **food:** A&W, Burger King, Hardee's, KFC, Peppermill Grill, Pizza Hut, Taco John's, **lodging:** Galaxie Inn, Lyndale Motel, **other:** Ford/Lincoln/Mercury, **W**...**other:** Go-Kart rides, camping
56	MN 60, Faribault, **E**...**gas:** BP, Mobil, **food:** Burger King, Great China Buffet, Hardee's, Perkins, Pizza Hut, Quizno's, Subway, Taco John's, **other:** HOSPITAL, Buick/Pontiac, Chevrolet, Chrysler/Plymouth/Jeep, Dodge, Family$, Goodyear/auto, Hy-Vee Foods, JC Penney, Jo-Ann Fabrics, Tires+, Wal-Mart, mall, **W**...**gas:** Petro/diesel, **food:** DQ, Happy Chef/24hr, **lodging:** Select Inn, **other:** Sakatah Lake SP, camping
55	(from nb, no return), **1 mi E**...**gas:** SA, KT, Mobil, **food:** Broaster Rest., Burger King, DQ, El Tequila Mexican, Great China Buffet, Hardee's, KFC, Pizza Hut, Subway, Taco John's, **lodging:** AmericInn, **other:** MEDICAL CARE, Ford/Mercury, Harley-Davidson
48	rd 12, rd 23, Medford, **W**...**food:** McDonald's, **other:** Outlet Mall/famous brands
45	rd 9, Clinton Falls, **W**...**gas:** KT/diesel, **food:** Green Mill Rest. Noble Romans, TimberLodge Steaks, Wendy's, **lodging:** Comfort Inn, Holiday Inn, **other:** Cabela's Sporting Goods, museum
43	rd 34, 26th St, Airport Rd, Owatonna, **W**...**lodging:** Ramada Inn, **other:** MEDICAL CARE
42b a	US 14 W, rd 45, Owatonna, to Waseca, **E**...**gas:** Sinclair/diesel/24hr, **food:** Kernel Rest., **other:** Bumper Parts, CashWise Foods, Chrysler/Dodge/Plymouth/Jeep, Ford/Lincoln/Mercury, **W**...**gas:** BP/diesel, **food:** Culver's, Happy Chef, McDonald's, Perkins, **lodging:** Best Budget Inn, Ramada Inn, Super 8, **other:** Wal-Mart SuperCtr/gas/diesel/24hr
41	Bridge St, Owatonna, **E**...**gas:** Mobil/diesel, **food:** Applebee's, Arby's, Burger King, DQ, KFC, Subway, Taco Bell, **lodging:** AmericInn, Country Inn Suites, **other:** HOSPITAL, **W**...**gas:** Mobil/diesel, **lodging:** Microtel, **other:** Target
40	US 14 E, US 218, Owatonna, **1 mi E on rd 6**...**gas:** Shell, **food:** El Tequila Mexican, Godfather's, Hardee's, Taco John's, **lodging:** Oakdale Motel, **other:** HOSPITAL, Hy-Vee Foods/24hr, Sterling Drug, WholesaleTire
38mm	Turtle Creek
35mm	**rest area both lanes, full(handicapped)facilities, phone, picnic tables, litter barrels, vending, petwalk**
34.5mm	Straight River
32	rd 4, Hope, **1/2 mi E**...camping, **1 mi W**...gas, food

Interstate 35

26	MN 30, Ellendale, to Blooming Prairie, **E...gas:** Cenex/diesel/rest./24hr, **W...gas:** BP/Mel's Diner/diesel/24hr
22	rd 35, Geneva, to Hartland, **1 mi E...**gas, food
18	MN 251, Clarks Grove, to Hollandale, **W...gas:** Phillips 66/diesel/LP, **other:** camping
13b a	I-90, W to Sioux Falls, E to Austin, **W...HOSPITAL**
12	US 65 S(from sb), Lp 35, Albert Lea, same as 11
11	rd 46, Albert Lea, **E...gas:** TA/McDonald's/Pizza Hut/diesel/24hr/@, **food:** Trails Rest., **lodging:** Comfort Inn, **other:** KOA(may-oct/6mi), **W...gas:** Conoco/diesel, Phillips 66, Shell/diesel, **food:** Burger King, China Buffet, Golden Corral, McDonald's, Osa Zamora Mexican, Perkins, Pizza Hut, Tienda Mexico, Trumble's Rest., Wendy's, **lodging:** Budget Host, Country Inn Suites, Day's Inn, Super 8, **other:** HOSPITAL, CarQuest, Buick/Pontiac/Cadillac/Honda, Ford, Home Depot, Mazda, NAPA, Nissan/VW, Toyota, Volvo, diesel repair, to Myre-Big Island SP
9mm	Albert Lea Lake
8	US 65, Lp 35, Albert Lea, to Glenville, **2 mi W...gas:** Cenex/24hr, Citgo, Holiday, **food:** DQ, Hardee's, KFC
5	rd 13, Twin Lakes, to Glenville, **3 mi W...**camping
2	rd 5, no facilities
1mm	**Welcome Ctr nb, full(handicapped)facilities, phone, picnic tables, litter barrels, vending, petwalk**
0mm	Minnesota/Iowa state line

Interstate 35W

Exit #	Services
41mm	I-35W begins/ends on I-35, exit 127.
36	rd 23, **E...gas:** BP/diesel, **W...gas:** Phillips 66/diesel, **food:** McDonald's, Subway, **other:** MEDICAL CARE, Kohl's, Target
33	rd 17, Lexington Ave, **E...gas:** BP, **1 mi E...food:** Burger King, McDonald's, **W...food:** Applebee's, Damon's, Green Mill Rest., Quizno's, Wendy's, **other:** Cub Foods, GNC, Home Depot, Michael's, Radio Shack, Wal-Mart
32	95th Ave NE, to Lexington, Circle Pines, **W...**Nat Sports Ctr
31b	Lake Dr, **E...gas:** Shell/diesel
a	rd J, 85th Ave NE(no EZ return to nb), no facilities
30	US 10 W, MN 118, to MN 65, no facilities
29	rd I, no facilities
28c b	rd 10, rd H, **W...gas:** BP, **food:** Best Steaks, Jake's Café, KFC, McDonald's, Mermaid Café, Perkins, Pizza Hut/Taco Bell, RJ Riches Rest., Subway, Saturn, **lodging:** AmericInn, Day's Inn, **other:** carwash

a	MN 96, no facilities
27b a	I-694 E and W
26	rd E2, **W...gas:** Phillips 66/diesel
25b	MN 88, to Roseville(no EZ return to sb), **E... gas:** SA/diesel, **lodging:** Courtyard, Fairfield Inn, Residence Inn, **W...gas:** Mobil, PDQ, **food:** Barley John's, Godfather's, Jake's Café, Main Event Rest., McDonald's, Perkins/24hr, Subway
a	rd D(from nb), same as 25b
24	rd C, **E...food:** Burger King, **lodging:** Holiday Inn, **W...lodging:** Comfort Inn, **other:** Chevrolet/Pontiac/GMC, Chrysler/Plymouth/Dodge/Jeep, Volvo
23b	Cleveland Ave, MN 36, **E...food:** India Palace Rest., Joe Senser's Rest., **lodging:** Day's Inn, Motel 6, Radisson, Super 8
a	MN 280, Industrial Blvd(from sb)
22	MN 280, Industrial Blvd(from nb), **E...lodging:** Sheraton
21b a	rd 88, Broadway St, Stinson Blvd, **E...**Ford Trucks, **W...food:** Burger King, Country Kitchen, Cousins Subs, McDonald's, Pizza Hut/Taco Bell, **other:** Home Depot, OfficeMax, Old Navy, Rainbow Foods/24hr, Target
19	E Hennepin(from nb)
18	US 52, 4th St SE, University Ave, to U of MN, **E...gas:** BP
17c	11th St, Washington Ave, **E...lodging:** Holiday Inn, **W...gas:** Mobil, **other:** HOSPITAL, Goodyear, to Metrodome
b	I-94 W(from sb)
a	MN 55, Hiawatha
16b a	I-94(from nb), E to St Paul, W to St Cloud, to MN 65
15	31st St(from nb), Lake St, **E...food:** McDonald's, Taco Bell, **other: W...**HOSPITAL
14	35th St, 36th St, no facilities
13	46th St, no facilities
13mm	Minnehaha Creek
12b	Diamond Lake Rd, no facilities
a	60th St(from sb), **W...gas:** Mobil, **other:** Cub Foods
11b	MN 62 E, to airport
a	Lyndale Ave(from sb), **E...gas:** Shell
10b	MN 62 W, 58th St, no facilities
a	rd 53, 66th St, no facilities
9c	76th St(from sb), no facilities
b a	I-494, MN 5, to airport

MINNESOTA

Interstate 35W

N ↕ **S**

8	82nd St, **W...food:** Bennigan's, Red Lobster, **other:** Chevrolet, Infiniti, Kia, Saturn, Suzuki, Toyota
7b	90th St, no facilities
a	94th St, **E...gas:** BP, Goodyear/auto, **W...lodging:** Holiday Inn
6	rd 1, 98th St, **E...gas:** Indian Joe's/gas, **food:** Bakers Square, Byerly's Rest., Caribou Coffee, New China, Starbucks, **other:** Ford, Gander Mtn, Walgreen, **W...gas:** SA/diesel, **food:** Burger King, Denny's, Subway
5	106th St, no facilities
5mm	Minnesota River
4b	113th St, Black Dog Rd, no facilities
a	Cliff Rd, **E...**Dodge, **W...**VW
3b a	MN 13, Shakopee, Canterbury Downs, **E...lodging:** Ramada Ltd
2	Burnsville Pkwy, **E...gas:** Citgo, Oasis Mkt/diesel, **food:** Bob's Café, **other:** MEDICAL CARE, AAA, mall, **W...gas:** BP, **food:** Embers Rest., Perkins, TimberLodge Steaks, **lodging:** Day's Inn, Prime Rate Motel, Red Roof Inn, Super 8, **other:** Best Buy
1	rd 42, Crystal Lake Rd, **See Minnesota Interstate 35, exit 88b.**
0mm	I-35W begins/ends on I-35, exit 88a.

Interstate 90

E ↕ **W**

Exit #	Services
277mm	Minnesota/Wisconsin state line, Mississippi River
275	US 14, US 61, to MN 16, La Crescent, **N...Welcome Ctr wb, full(handicapped)facilities, info, phone, picnic tables, litter barrels, vending, petwalk**
272b a	Dresbach, no facilities
270	Dakota, no facilities
269	US 14, US 61, to Winona, **N...other:** to OL Kipp SP/camping
266	rd 12, Nodine, **N...other:** Great River Bluff SP, OL Kipp SP, camping, **S...gas:** BP/Subway/diesel/24hr/@
261mm	weigh sta both lanes
257	MN 76, to Houston, Ridgeway, Witoka, **N...**gas, **S...**camping
252	MN 43 N, to Winona, **7 mi N...lodging:** AmeircInn, Best Western, Holiday Inn, Quality Inn, Super 8, **other:** HOSPITAL
249	MN 43 S, to Rushford, **N...other:** Peterbilt Trucks/repair, **S...**Ernie Tuff Museum
244mm	**rest area eb, full(handicapped)facilities, phone, picnic tables, litter barrels, vending, petwalk**
242	rd 29, Lewiston, no facilities
233	MN 74, to Chatfield, St Charles, **N...gas:** KT/LP/24hr, **food:** Pizza Factory, Subway, **other:** Whitewater SP, **S...gas:** Shell/Texaco/A&W/diesel, **food:** Amish Ovens Rest./bakery, **other:** RV dump/LP

229	rd 10, Dover, no facilities
224	rd 7, Eyota, no facilities
222mm	**rest area wb, full(handicapped)facilities, phone, picnic tables, litter barrels, vending, petwalk**
218	US 52, to Rochester, **8 mi N...food:** Old Country Buffet, **lodging:** Hampton Inn, Holiday Inn, Motel 6, Sleep Inn, **other:** Brookside RV Park, **S...gas:** Citgo, **other:** KOA(Mar-Oct)(1mi)
209b a	US 63, MN 30, to Rochester, Stewartville, **8-10 mi N...lodging:** Comfort Inn, Day's Inn, Hampton Inn, Holiday Inn, Super 8, **1 mi S...gas:** KwikTrip, **food:** DQ, **lodging:** AmericInn
205	rd 6, no facilities
202mm	**rest area eb, full(handicapped)facilities, phone, picnic tables, litter barrels, vending, petwalk**
193	MN 16, Dexter, **S...gas:** Phillips 66/Windmill Rest./diesel/24hr, **food:** Oasis Grill, Pinecone Rest., **lodging:** Budget Inn
189	rd 13, to Elkton, no facilities
187	rd 20, **S...**camping
183	MN 56, to Rose Creek, Brownsdale, **S...gas:** Freedom City Co-op/diesel/LP
181	28th St NE, no facilities
180b a	US 218, 21st St NE, to Austin, Oakland Place, **S...gas:** Shell, **lodging:** Austin Motel
179	11th Dr NE, to Austin, **N...gas:** Citgo/diesel/rest./24hr
178b	6th St NE, to Austin, downtown
178a	4th St NW, **N...food:** Culver's, Perkins, **lodging:** AmericInn, Day's Inn, Holiday Inn **S...gas:** BP, Conoco/Subway/diesel, Sinclair/diesel, **food:** A&W, Burger King, **other:** HOSPITAL, Goodyear
177	US 218 N, to Owatonna, Austin, Mapleview, **N...gas:** Holiday, **food:** Applebee's, KFC, King Buffet, Quizno's, **other:** Cashwise Food/gas/24hr, Hy-Vee Foods, JC Penney, BigK-Mart, Radio Shack, ShopKO, Staples, Target, mall, **S...gas:** Sinclair/McDonald's/diesel, **food:** Hardee's, **lodging:** Super 8
175	MN 105, rd 46, to Oakland Rd, **N...food:** Sportts Grill, **lodging:** Countryside Inn, **S...gas:** BP, Conoco/diesel, **food:** McDonald's(2mi), **lodging:** Downtown Motel(2mi), Sterling Motel(2mi), **other:** Chrysler/Plymouth/Dodge/Jeep, Ford/Mercury, camping
171mm	**rest area wb, full(handicapped)facilities, phone, picnic tables, litter barrels, petwalk**
166	rd 46, Oakland Rd, **N...other:** KOA/LP, golf(par3)
163	rd 26, Hayward, **S...gas:** Shell(4mi), Freeborn County Co-op, **food:** Pizza Hut(4mi), Trails Rest.(4mi), **other:** Myre-Big Island SP, camping
161mm	**rest area eb, full(handicapped)facilities, phone, picnic tables litter barrels, petwalk**
159b a	I-35, N to Twin Cities, S to Des Moines, no facilities

Interstate 90

E / **W** — Albert Lea / Fairmont

157   rd 22, Albert Lea, **S...gas:** Conoco/24hr, Mobil/Subway/diesel/24hr, **food:** Applebee's, Café Don'l, DQ, Herberger's, McDonald's, **lodging:** AmericInn, Holiday Inn Express, **other:** HOSPITAL, Chevrolet, Harley-Davidson, Hy-Vee Foods/24hr, Radio Shack, ShopKO, mall

154   MN 13, to US 69, to Manchester, Albert Lea, **N...gas:** SA/diesel, **3 mi S...lodging:** BelAire Motel

146   MN 109, to Wells, Alden, **S...gas:** BP/diesel/rest., Cenex, **other:** Tailfins Malt Shop

138   MN 22, to Wells, Keister, **S...camping**

134   MN 253, rd 21, to Bricelyn, MN Lake, no facilities

128   MN 254, rd 17, to Frost, no facilities

119   US 169, to Winnebago, Blue Earth, **S...gas:** Kwik-Trip/diesel, Shell/DQ/diesel, Sinclair/diesel, **food:** Country Kitchen, McDonald's, Pizza Hut, Subway, **lodging:** AmericInn, Budget Inn, Super 8, **other:** HOSPITAL, Wal-Mart/drugs, Jolly Green Giant, camping

118mm   **rest area both lanes, full(handicapped)facilities, phone, picnic tables, litter barrels, petwalk, playground**

113   rd 1, Guckeen, no facilities

107   MN 262, rd 53, to East Chain, Granada, **S...other:** Flying Goose Camping(May-Oct)(1mi)

102   MN 15, to Madelia, Fairmont, **S...gas:** Cenex/diesel, Conoco/Burger King/Subway/diesel(1mi), Phillips 66/diesel, SA/diesel/24hr, **food:** Burger King, China Rest., Happy Chef/24hr, KFC, McDonald's, Perkins, Pizza Hut, Ranch Family Rest.(1mi), Subway, **lodging:** Budget Inn, Comfort Inn, Holiday Inn, Super 8, **other:** HOSPITAL, Ace Hardware, CarQuest, Chrysler/Plymouth/Dodge/Jeep, Goodyear, K-Mart, Pontiac/Buick/GMC, camping

99   rd 39, Fairmont, no facilities

93   MN 263, rd 27, Welcome, **1/2 mi S...gas:** Cenex, camping

87   MN 4, Sherburn, **1 mi S...gas:** Cenex, **other:** HOSPITAL, camping

80   rd 29, Alpha, no facilities

73   US 71, Jackson, **N...gas:** Conoco/diesel, **food:** Burger King, **lodging:** Best Western/rest., Econolodge, Super 8, **other:** to Kilen Woods SP, **S...gas:** BP/DQ, **food:** Embers Rest., Pizza Ranch, Subway, **lodging:** Budget Host, Earth Inn, **other:** HOSPITAL, Park-Vu Motel, Chevrolet/Buick/Pontiac, Chrysler/Plymouth/Dodge/Jeep, to Spirit Lake, KOA(Apr-Oct)

72.5mm   W Fork Des Moines River

72mm   **rest area wb, full(handicapped)facilities, phone, picnic tables, litter barrels, vending, petwalk**

69mm   **rest area eb, full(handicapped)facilities, phone, picnic tables, litter barrels, vending, petwalk**

Worthington

64   MN 86, Lakefield, **N...HOSPITAL,** gas/diesel, food, camping

57   rd 9, to Heron Lake, Spafford, no facilities

50   MN 264, rd 1, to Brewster, Round Lake, **S...camping**

47   rd 53, eb only, no facilities

46mm   weigh sta eb

45   MN 60, Worthington, **N...gas:** BP/cafe/diesel, **S...gas:** Casey's, Shell/diesel/24hr, **food:** McDonald's, **lodging:** Budget Inn, Sunset Inn, camping

43   US 59, Worthington, **N...lodging:** Travelodge, **S...gas:** BP, Casey's, Cenex/diesel, Phillips 66/diesel, Shell, **food:** Arby's, Burger King, Country Kitchen, DQ, Godfather's, Ground Round, Happy Chef, KFC, McDonald's, Perkins/24hr, Pizza Hut, Subway, Taco John's, **lodging:** AmericInn, Budget Inn, Day's Inn, Holiday Inn Express, **other:** HOSPITAL, County Mkt Foods/24hr, Hy-Vee Foods, Chevrolet/Pontiac/Buick/Cadillac, Family$, Ford, JC Penney, Radio Shack, ShopKO, Wal-Mart SuperCtr/gas/24hr

42   MN 266, rd 25, to Reading, **S...lodging:** Super 8, **other:** Wal-Mart SuperCtr/gas/24hr

33   rd 13, to Wilmont, Rushmore, no facilities

26   MN 91, Adrian, **S...gas:** Cenex/diesel, **other:** camping

25mm   **rest area wb, full(handicapped)facilities, phone, picnic tables, litter barrels, petwalk**

24mm   **rest area eb, full(handicapped)facilities, phone, picnic tables, litter barrels, petwalk**

18   rd 3, Kanaranzi, Magnolia, **N...camping**

12   US 75, Luverne, **N...gas:** Casey's, Cenex/diesel, FuelTime/diesel, Phillips 66/diesel, Shell/diesel, Sinclair, **food:** China Rest., Country Kitchen, McDonald's, Pizza Hut, Subway, Taco John's, Tasty Drive-In, **lodging:** Comfort Inn, Cozy Rest Motel(1mi), Hillcrest Motel(2mi), **other:** HOSPITAL, Chevrolet/Pontiac/Buick/GMC, Chrysler/Dodge/Jeep, Jubilee Foods, NAPA, truckwash, to Blue Mounds SP, Pipestone NM, **S...food:** Magnolia Steaks, **lodging:** Super 8, **other:** Pamida

5   rd 6, Beaver Creek, **N...gas:** Shell/diesel

1   MN 23, rd 17, to Jasper, **N...other:** to Pipestone NM, access to gas/diesel

0mm   Minnesota/South Dakota state line, **Welcome Ctr/weigh sta eb, full(handicapped)facilities, info, phone, picnic tables, litter barrels**

MINNESOTA
Interstate 94

Exit #	Services
259mm	Minnesota/Wisconsin state line, St Croix River
258	MN 95 N, to Stillwater, Hastings, Lakeland, no facilities
257mm	weigh sta wb
256mm	**Welcome Ctr wb, full(handicapped)facilities, phone, picnic tables, litter barrels, vending, petwalk**
253	rd 15, Manning Ave, **S...other:** KOA, StoneRidge Golf, to Afton Alps SP, ski area
251	rd 19, Keats Ave, Woodbury Dr, **S...gas:** KT, SA, **food:** Burger King, DQ, FoodCourt, Subway, **lodging:** Extended Stay America, Holiday Inn Express, **other:** Outlets/famous brands, KOA
250	rd 13, Radio Dr, Inwood Ave, **N...**Machine Shed Rest., **S...gas:** Holiday, **food:** Blimpie, Don Pablo, Schlotsky's, Starbucks, Sunset Grill, Taco Bell, TGIFriday, Wendy's, **other:** Borders Books/Café, Champp's, Circuit City, CompUSA, Cub Foods, GNC, Hepner's Auto Ctr, Home Depot, Jo-Ann Crafts, LandsEnd Inlet, Mervyn's Calif, OfficeMax, Old Navy, Tires+
249	I-694 N & I-494 S, no facilities
247	MN 120, Century Ave, **N...food:** Denny's, Toby's Rest., **lodging:** AmericInn, Super 8, **other:** Harley-Davidson, Saturn, **S...gas:** SA, **food:** GreenMill Rest., McDonald's, **lodging:** Country Inn/rest., **other:** Chevrolet
246c b	McKnight Ave, **N...**3M
a	Ruth St(from eb, no return), **N...gas:** BP, Sinclair, **food:** Culver's, HoHo Chinese, Perkins, **other:** Firestone/auto, Michael's
245	White Bear Ave, **N...gas:** SA/Subway, **food:** Hardee's, Embers Rest., N China Buffet, **lodging:** Exel Inn, Ramada Inn, **S...gas:** BP, **food:** Arby's, Bakers Square, Burger King, Davanni's Pizza/subs, Ground Round, KFC/Pizza Hut, Krispy Kreme, McDonald's, Perkins, Taco Bell, **lodging:** Holiday Inn, **other:** Chrysler/Plymouth, Firestone/auto, JC Penney, Target
244	US 10 E, US 61 S, Mounds/Kellogg, no facilities
243	US 61, Mounds Blvd, **S...**River Centre
242d	US 52 S, MN 3, 6th St, **N...gas:** Holiday, **food:** Subway
c	7th St, **S...gas:** SA
b a	I-35E N, US 10 W, I-35E S(from eb)
241c	I-35E S(from wb)
b	10th St, 5th St, to downtown
a	12th St, Marion St, Kellogg Blvd, **N...lodging:** Best Western Kelly Inn, **other:** Sears, **S...gas:** BP, Holiday, SA, **lodging:** Savoy Inn, **other:** HOSPITAL, st capitol
240	Dale Ave, no facilities
239b a	Lexington Pkwy, Hamline Ave, **N...gas:** BP, **food:** Chevy's Mexican, Hardee's/24hr, **lodging:** Sheraton, **other:** HOSPITAL, Cub Foods, K-Mart, Target
238	Snelling Ave, **N...food:** Applebee's, McDonald's, Perkins, **lodging:** Sheraton, **other:** Target, **S...gas:** Citgo, **other:** Tires+, same as 239
237	Cretin Ave, Vandalia Ave, to downtown
236	MN 280, University Ave, to downtown
235b	Huron Blvd, **N...gas:** Citgo, **food:** Arnold's Burger Grill, **other:** HOSPITAL, U of MN
235mm	Mississippi River
235a	Riverside Ave, 25th Ave, **N...gas:** Winner, **food:** Starbucks, **S...food:** Perkins, Taco Bell
234c	Cedar Ave, downtown
234b a	MN 55, Hiawatha Ave, 5th St, **N...lodging:** Holiday Inn, **other:** to downtown
233b	I-35W N, I-35W S(exits left from wb)
a	11th St(from wb), **N...**downtown
231b	Hennepin Ave, Lyndale Ave, to downtown
a	I-394, US 12 W, to downtown
230	US 52, MN 55, 4th St, 7th St, Olson Hwy, **N...**Metrodome, **S...**HOSPITAL, Int Mkt Square
229	W Broadway, Washington Ave, **N...gas:** Holiday, Old Colony/diesel, **food:** Burger King, **S...food:** Taco Bell, Wendy's, **other:** Target
228	Dowling Ave N, no facilities
226	53rd Ave N, 49th Ave N, no facilities
225	I-694 E, MN 252 N, to Minneapolis, no facilities
34	to MN 100, Shingle Creek Pkwy, **N...food:** ChiChi's, Cracker Barrel, Denny's, Olive Garden, TGIFriday, **lodging:** AmericInn, Baymont Inn, Best Western, Comfort Inn, Country Inn Suites, Extended Stay America, Hilton, Motel 6, Super 8, **S...food:** Ground Round, India Passage, New King Buffet, Panera Bread, Perkins, Pizza Hut, Vallarta's Mexican, **lodging:** The Inn on the Farm, **other:** Best Buy, Circuit City, Ford, Kohl's, PepBoys, Target, Tires+
33	rd 152, Brooklyn Blvd, **N...food:** Culver's, **other:** Chevrolet, Dodge, Honda, Mazda, Pontiac, **S...gas:** BP, **food:** Embers Rest., **other:** Family$, Chrysler/Plymouth/Jeep, Rainbow Foods, Walgreen
31	rd 81, Lakeland Ave, **N...gas:** SA/diesel, **food:** DQ, Wagner's Drive-In, Wendy's, **lodging:** Ramada Inn, **S...lodging:** Budget Host, Super 8, **other:** Kennedy Transmissions
30	Boone Ave, **N...lodging:** Northland Inn/rest., Sleep Inn, **S...**Home Depot
29b a	US 169, to Hopkins, Osseo, no facilities
28	rd 61, Hemlock Lane, **N on Elm Creek...gas:** Citgo, **food:** Arby's/Sbarro's, Buca Café, ChuckeCheese, Don Pablo, Famous Dave's, Ground Round, Hop's Grill, Houlihan's, Joe's Crabshack, Krispy Kreme, Mongkok Asian, Olive Garden, Panera Bread, Qdoba Mexican, Red Lobster, Starbucks, TimberLodge Steaks, **lodging:** Hampton Inn, Staybridge Suites, **other:** Best Buy, Borders Books, Cub Foods, Jo-Ann Fabrics, Kohl's, Old Navy, Tires+, same as 215, **S...gas:** BP, **food:** Perkins/24hr, **lodging:** Travelodge

Interstate 94

E ↑ ↓ W

216	I-94 W and I-494, no facilities
215	rd 109, Weaver Lake Rd, **N...gas:** Citgo, SA/diesel, **food:** Burger King, Bakers Square, Cattle Co Steaks, Champp's, DQ, Don Pablo, Hop's Grill, J Cousineau's Rest., Joe's Crabshack, KFC, McDonald's, Old Country Buffet, Papa John's, Pizza Hut, Subway, Taco Bell, Wendy's, **lodging:** Hampton Inn, Staybridge Suties, **other:** MEDICAL CARE, Barnes&Noble, Cub Foods, GNC, Goodyear/auto, Kohl's, K-Mart, Old Navy, Tires+, USPO, Walgreen, mall, same as 28, **S...food:** Applebee's, Fuddrucker's
214mm	**rest area eb, full(handicapped)facilities, phone, picnic tables, litter barrels**
213	rd 30, 95th Ave N, Maple Grove, **N...gas:** SA/diesel, **S...gas:** Holiday/diesel, **food:** Culver's, McDonald's, Orient Buffet, Quizno's, **S...other:** Rainbow Foods, Sam's Club, Target, Wal-Mart/auto, KOA(2mi)
207	MN 101, Rogers, to Elk River, **N...gas:** Holiday/diesel, SA/diesel, TA/Citgo/diesel/24hr/@, **food:** Burger King, Denny's, Domino's, McDonald's, Pizza Hut, Subway, Taco Bell, Wendy's, **lodging:** Super 8, **other:** Camping World(off Rogers Dr), Target, **S...gas:** BP, Sinclair/diesel, **food:** Country Kitchen, DQ, Ember's Rest., Subway, **lodging:** AmercInn, **other:** Chevrolet
205.5mm	Crow River
205	MN 241, rd 36, St Michael, **S...gas:** SA/diesel, **3 mi S...gas:** Exxon, **food:** McDonald's
202	rd 37, Albertville, **N...gas:** Conoco/diesel, **food:** Burger King, Subway, **S...gas:** BP, Phillips 66, Shell, **lodging:** Riverwood Hotel/rest.
201	rd 19(rom eb), Albertville, St Michael, **N...other:** Albertville Outlets/famous brands, **S...gas:** BP
195	rd 75(from wb, no EZ return), Monticello, **N...gas:** Conoco/diesel, **food:** Hawk's Grill, Jam'n Go Café, **other:** HOSPITAL
193	MN 25, Monticello, to Buffalo, Big Lake, **N...gas:** Holiday/diesel, **food:** Burger King, Country Grill, DQ, KFC, Perkins, Taco Bell, Wendy's, **lodging:** AmericInn, **other:** AutoValue Parts, BMW, Cub Foods, Honda, K-Mart, Monticello RV Ctr, **S...gas:** BP, Conoco, SA/diesel, **food:** McDonald's, Subway, **lodging:** Best Western, Comfort Inn, Day's Inn, **other:** Checker Parts, Chevrolet, Ford/Mercury, Goodyear/auto, Lake Maria SP
187mm	**rest area eb, full(handicapped)facilities, phone, picnic tables, litter barrels, vending, petwalk**
183	rd 8, Hasty, to Silver Creek, Maple Lake, **N...**Northern RV/boat, **S...gas:** Marathon/diesel/rest./24hr/@, **other:** to Lake Maria SP, camping

St Cloud

178	MN 24, Clearwater, to Annandale, **N...gas:** Citgo/diesel, Holiday/24hr, Marathon/Pizza Hut, **food:** DQ, Burger King, Subway, **lodging:** Best Western, Budget Inn, Day's Inn, **other:** Eagle Trace Golf/grill, KOA(1mi), **S...gas:** Exxon/diesel, **food:** Longhorn Steaks, **other:** A-1 Acres Camping(1mi)
178mm	**rest area wb, full(handicapped)facilities, phone, picnic tables, litter barrels, petwalk, vending**
171	rd 7, rd 75, St Augusta, **N...gas:** Exxon/diesel, Holiday/diesel, **food:** McDonald's, Nathan B's Rest., **lodging:** AmericInn, Holiday Inn Express, Ramada Ltd, Travelodge, **other:** HOSPITAL, Toyota, **S...gas:** Conoco/diesel, **other:** Pleasureland RV Ctr
167b a	MN 15, to St Cloud, to Kimball, **4 mi N...gas:** SA/diesel, **food:** Applebee's, Arby's, Bakers Square, Chipotle Mexican, Embers Rest., McDonald's, Old Country Buffet, Outback Steaks, Perkins, Pizza Hut, Taco Bell, TimberLodge Steaks, **lodging:** Baymont Inn, Best Western, Comfort Inn, Country Inn Suites, Fairfield Inn, Holiday Inn, Quality Inn, Ramada Ltd, Radisson, Super 8, **other:** HOSPITAL, CashWise Foods, Kohl's, Sam's Club, ShopKO
164	MN 23, Rockville, to St Cloud, **2-3 mi N...**Taco Bell, **lodging:** Motel 6, Ramada Ltd
162.5mm	Sauk River
160	rd 2, St Joseph, to Cold Spring, **N...gas:** BP, SA, **lodging:** Super 8, **other:** Coll of St Benedict
158	rd 75(from eb), to St Cloud, same as 160, 3 mi N
156	rd 159, St Joseph, **N...**St Johns U, no facilities
153	rd 9, Avon, **N...gas:** Citgo, Shell/diesel, **food:** Neighbor's Rest., **lodging:** AmericInn, **S...other:** El Rancho Manana Camping, auto parts
152mm	**rest area both lanes, full(handicapped)facilities, phone, picnic tables, litter barrels, vending, petwalk**
147	MN 238, rd 10, Albany, **N...gas:** Holiday/diesel/24hr, Marathon, Shell/Subway/diesel, **food:** DQ, Hillcrest Rest., **lodging:** Country Inn Suites, **other:** HOSPITAL, IGA Food, **S...food:** KFC, **other:** Chrysler/Plymouth/Dodge/Jeep, NAPA
140	rd 11, Freeport, **N...gas:** Conoco/diesel, **food:** Charlie's Café, **lodging:** Ackie's Pioneer Inn, **other:** USPO, **S...**LP
137	MN 237, rd 65, New Munich, no facilities

Interstate 94

E ↑ / **W** ↓ (Fergus Falls / Alexandria / Moorhead / St Paul)

137mm	Sauk River
135	rd 13, Melrose, **N...gas:** Mobil/diesel, Phillips 66/Subway/diesel/24hr, **food:** Burger King, **other:** HOSPITAL, Ford, Jubilee Foods, NAPA, **S...gas:** Conoco/diesel, **food:** DQ, El Portal Mexican, **lodging:** Super 8, **other:** Save Foods
132.5mm	Sauk River
131	MN 4, Meire Grove, to Paynesville, no facilities
128mm	Sauk River
127	US 71; MN 28, Sauk Centre, **N...gas:** Casey's, Holiday/diesel, SA/24hr, **food:** DQ, Hardee's, McDonald's, Pizza Hut, Subway, **lodging:** AmericInn, BestValue Inn, Super 8, **other:** HOSPITAL, Coborn's Foods, Ford/Mercury, **S...gas:** BP/diesel/café/24hr, **other:** Chevrolet/Pontiac/Buick/Chrysler/Jeep, RV Service
124	Sinclair Lewis Ave(from eb), Sauk Centre, no facilities
119	rd 46, West Union, no facilities
114	MN 127, rd 3, Osakis, to Westport, **3 mi N...**gas/diesel, food, lodging, camping
105mm	**rest area wb, full(handicapped)facilities, phone, picnic tables, litter barrels, vending, petwalk**
103	MN 29, Alexandria, to Glenwood, **N...gas:** Citgo, F&F/diesel, Holiday, **food:** Burger King, Country Kitchen, Culver's, Dolittle's Café, Hardee's, KFC, McDonald's, Pizza Hut, Subway, Taco Bell, **lodging:** AmercInn, Best Inn, Comfort Inn, Day's Inn, SkyLine Motel, Super 8, **other:** HOSPITAL, Chevrolet/Cadillac/Mazda, OfficeMax, Target, Wal-Mart/24hr, **S...gas:** Conoco/diesel, **lodging:** Country Inn Suites, Holiday Inn, **other:** Buick/Pontiac/GMC
100mm	Lake Latoka
100	MN 27, no facilities
99mm	**rest area eb, full(handicapped)facilities, phone, picnic tables, litter barrels, vending, petwalk**
97	MN 114, rd 40, Garfield, to Lowery, no facilities
90	rd 7, Brandon, **2-3 N...**gas, food, camping, **S...camping, ski area**
82	MN 79, rd 41, Evansville, to Erdahl, **2 mi N...gas:** BP/diesel, **S...HOSPITAL, camping**
77	MN 78, rd 10, Ashby, to Barrett, **N...gas/diesel, food, camping, S...camping**
69mm	**rest area wb, full(handicapped)facilities, phone, picnic tables, petwalk, vending**
67	rd 35, Dalton, **N...camping, S...camping**
61	US 59 S, rd 82, to Elbow Lake, **N...gas:** Citgo/diesel/café/LP/24hr, **other:** HOSPITAL, camping(4mi), **S...camping**
60mm	**rest area eb, full(handicapped)facilities, phone, picnic tables, litter barrels, petwalk, vending**
57	MN 210, rd 25, Fergus Falls, **N...HOSPITAL**
55	rd 1, Fergus Falls, to Wendell, no facilities
54	MN 210, Lincoln Ave, Fergus Falls, **N...gas:** Cenex/diesel, F&F/diesel, Holiday, Tesoro, **food:** Applebee's, Burger King, Godfather's, KFC, McDonald's, Pizza Hut, Speedway Grill, Subway, **lodging:** AmericInn, Best Western, Comfort Inn, Day's Inn, Motel 7, Super 8, **other:** HOSPITAL, Chrysler/Jeep/Dodge, Ford/Lincoln/Mercury, Home Depot, JC Penney, K-Mart, Mazda, Parts+, Pontiac/GMC, Radio Shack, SunMart Foods, Target, Tires+, Toyota, mall, **S...food:** Mabel Murphy's Rest., **other:** Wal-Mart/drugs/24hr
50	rd 88, rd 52, to US 59, Elizabeth, to Fergus Falls, **N...gas:** AmStar/diesel/rest./24hr
38	rd 88, Rothsay, **S...gas:** Tesoro/diesel/café/24hr, Comfort Zone Inn
32	MN 108, rd 30, Lawndale, to Pelican Rapids, no facilities
24	MN 24, Barnesville, **N...food:** Tastee Freez, **1 mi S...gas:** Tesoro, Cenex/diesel, **food:** DQ
22	MN 9, Barnesville, **1 mi S...gas:** Tesoro, Cenex/diesel, **food:** DQ
15	rd 10, Downer, no facilities
8mm	Buffalo River
6	MN 336, rd 11, to US 10, Dilworth, no facilities
5mm	Red River weigh sta eb
2	rd 52, Moorhead, **1-2 mi N...gas:** Holiday/diesel, **food:** Bennigan's, Perkins, Speedway Grill, **lodging:** Guesthouse Motel, Travelodge, **other:** HOSPITAL, KOA, Target
2mm	**Welcome Ctr eb, full(handicapped)facilities, info, phone, picnic tables, litter barrels, vending**
1b	20th St, Moorhead(from eb, no return), no facilities
1a	US 75, Moorhead, **N...gas:** Phillips 66, **food:** Burger King, Papa Murphy's, Village Inn, **lodging:** Courtyard, **other:** SunMart Foods, **S...gas:** BP/24hr, Casey's, Citgo, **food:** Golden Phoenix Chinese, Hardee's, **lodging:** Day's Inn, Motel 75, Super 8, **other:** Osco Drug, Pontiac/GMC
0mm	Minnesota/North Dakota state line, Red River

Interstate 494/694

E ↑ / **W** ↓

Exit #	Services
I-494/I-694	loops around Minneapolis/St Paul.
71	rd 31, Pilot Knob Rd, **N...lodging:** Courtyard, Fairfield Inn, **S...lodging:** Holiday Inn Select, **food:** LoneOak Café, Sidney's Café(1mi)
70	I-35E, N to St Paul, S to Albert Lea
69	MN 149, MN 55, Dodd Rd, **N...food:** Ziggy's Deli
67	US 52, MN S, Robert Rd, **1 mi N...gas:** BP, Mobil, Holiday, **food:** Acre's Rest., Arby's/Sbarro's, Arnold's Burgers, Bakers Square, Bridgeman's Rest., Burger King, Godfather's, KFC, Old Country Buffet, Pizza Hut, Taco Bell, White Castle, **other:** MEDICAL CARE, Aamco, Best Buy, Buick/Pontiac, Chevrolet, Cub Foods, Dodge, Ford/Lincoln/Mercury, Jo-Ann Fabrics, Kia, K-Mart, Mazda, Nissan, Rainbow Foods/24hr, Sam's Club, Target, Toyota, VW, outlet mall, **S...gas:** PDQ

Interstate 494/694

E
↑
↓
W

| 66 | MN 3 N, MN 103 S, no facilities |
| 65 | 7ᵗʰ Ave, 5ᵗʰ Ave, no facilities |

64b a MN 56, Concord St, **N...gas:** Conoco/diesel, **lodging:** Best Western Drovers, **other:** Ford Trucks, Goodyear, Peterbilt, **S...lodging:** Golden Steer Motel/rest.

63mm Mississippi River

63c Maxwell Ave, no facilities

b a US 10, US 61, to St Paul, Hastings, **S...gas:** BP, SA, **lodging:** Boyd's Motel, Subway

62 Lake Rd, **N...lodging:** Country Inn Suites, **S...gas:** SA

60 Valley Creek Rd, **N...food:** Burger King, Cracker Barrel, McDonald's, Pizza Hut, Subway, **lodging:** Hampton Inn, **other:** Goodyear, **S...gas:** BP, SA/diesel/LP, **food:** Applebee's, Ciatti's Rest., Old Mexico Rest., Oriental Rest., Perkins, Pizza **lodging:** Red Roof Inn, **other:** Best Buy, Kohl's, Rainbow Foods/24hr, Target, Walgreen

58b a I-94, E to Madison, W to St Paul. **I-494 S begins/ends, I-694 N begins/ends**

57 rd 10, 10ᵗʰ St N, **E...**Wingate Inn, **W...gas:** Tom Thumb Superette, **food:** Burger King, KFC, **other:** K-Mart, Rainbow Foods/24hr, mall

55 MN 5, **W...gas:** BP/diesel, Holiday, **food:** Subway, **other:** st patrol

52b a MN 36, N St Paul, to Stillwater, **W...gas:** F&F/diesel

51 MN 120, **E...gas:** BP, Conoco, SA/diesel, **food:** Best Subs, Taco Bell, Zapata's Café

50 White Bear Ave, **E...gas:** Gas4Less, SA, **other:** K-Mart, **W...gas:** BP, Shell, **food:** Arby's, Applebee's, Bakers Square, Burger King, ChiChi's, Denny's, Dutch Rest., Godfather's, Hardee's/24hr, KFC, Old Country Buffet, Perkins/24hr, Red Lobster, Taco Bell, Wendy's, **lodging:** Best Western, Emerald Inn, **other:** Aamco, Best Buy, Goodyear, Jo-Ann Fabrics, Sears/auto, Tires+, mall

48 US 61, **E...gas:** Citgo, **food:** KFC, **other:** Acura/Honda/Buick, Chrysler/Dodge/Jeep, Ford, Isuzu, Mercury/Lincoln, Saturn, Subaru, Van Sales, **W...food:** Chili's, Gulden's Rest., McDonald's, Olive Garden, **lodging:** Best Western, NorthernAire Motel, **other:** HOSPITAL, Toyota, Audi/Porsche, Venburg Tire

47 I-35E, N to Duluth

46 I-35E, US 10, S to St Paul

45 rd 49, Rice St, **N...gas:** Mobil/diesel, Phillips 66, **food:** Taco Bell, **other:** Checker Parts, **S...gas:** Marathon, **food:** A&W, Burger King, Hardee's, Taco John's, **other:** Kath Parts

St Paul (vertical label)

43b Victoria St, **S...**Bob's Food Mkt

a Lexington Ave, **N...food:** Greenmill Rest., **lodging:** Hampton Inn, Hilton Garden, **S...gas:** BP/diesel, Conoco, Mobil/diesel, Sinclair, **food:** Blue Fox Grill, Burger King, Davanni's Pizza, Perkins, Wendy's, **lodging:** Holiday Inn, Super 8, **other:** Goodyear/auto, Kennedy Transmissions, Target

42b US 10 W(from wb), to Anoka, no facilities

a MN 51, Snelling Ave, **1 mi S...gas:** Shell, **food:** McDonald's, **lodging:** Country Inn Suites, Holiday Inn

41b a I-35W, S to Minneapolis, N to Duluth

40 Long Lake Rd, 10ᵗʰ St NW, no facilities

39 Silver Lake Rd, **N...gas:** BP, Sinclair, **food:** McDonald's, **other:** Ford, Snyder Drug, U-Haul

38b a MN 65, Central Ave, **N...gas:** Holiday/diesel, **food:** Subway, Shorewood Rest., **S...gas:** Ashland, SA, **food:** A&W/KFC, Arby's, Asia Rest., Buffalo Wild Wings, Cousins Subs, Denny's, Embers Rest., Flameburger Rest., Ground Round, La Casita Mexican, McDonald's, Papa John's, Subway/TCBY, Taco Bell, Ududi Indian Cuisine, Wendy's, White Castle, **lodging:** Best Western Kelly, Starlite Motel, **other:** GNC, Radio Shack, Target, Tires+, Welle Parts

37 rd 47, University Ave, **N...gas:** Holiday, Mobil, SA/diesel, Sinclair, **food:** Burger King, Cattle Co Rest., McDonald's, Zantigo's Rest., **other:** CarQuest, Cub Foods, Goodyear, Home Depot, Walgreen, **S...gas:** Bona Bros/repair, Shell

36 E River Rd, no facilities

35mm I-494 W begins/ends, I-694 E begins/ends

35c MN 252, **N...gas:** Holiday, SA

b a I-94 E to Minneapolis

34 to MN 100, Shingle Creek Pkwy, **N...food:** ChiChi's, Cracker Barrel, Denny's, Olive Garden, **lodging:** AmericInn, Baymont Inn, Best Western, Comfort Inn, Hilton, Super 8, **S...food:** Ground Round, India Passage, New King Buffet, Panera Bread, Perkins, Pizza Hut, Vallarta's Mexican, **lodging:** The Inn on the Farm, **other:** Best Buy, Circuit City, Ford, Kohl's, PepBoys, Target, Tires+

33 rd 152, Brooklyn Blvd, **N...food:** Culver's, **other:** Chevrolet, Dodge, Honda, Mazda, Pontiac, **S...gas:** BP, **food:** Embers Rest., **other:** Family$, Chrysler/Plymouth/Jeep, Rainbow Foods, Walgreen

Minneapolis (vertical label)

MINNESOTA

Interstate 494/694

E ↑ ↓ W

Minneapolis

31	rd 81, Lakeland Ave, **N...gas:** SA, Shell/diesel, **food:** DQ, Wagner's Drive-In, Wendy's, **lodging:** Ramada Inn, **S...lodging:** Budget Host, Super 8, **other:** Kennedy Transmissions
30	Boone Ave, **N...lodging:** Northland Inn/rest., Sleep Inn, **S...**Home Depot
29b a	US 169, to Hopkins, Osseo, no facilities
28	rd 61, Hemlock Lane, **N on Elm Creek...gas:** Citgo, **food:** Arby's/Sbarro's, Buca Café, Champp's Grill, ChuckeCheese, Don Pablo, Famous Dave's BBQ, Ground Round, Hop's Grill, Houlihan's, Joe's Crabshack, Krispy Kreme, Mongkok Asian, Old Country Buffet, Olive Garden, Panera Bread, Red Lobster, Starbucks, TimberLodge Steaks, **lodging:** Hampton Inn, Staybridge Suites, **other:** Best Buy, Byerly's Rest., Cub Foods, Jo-Ann Fabrics, Kohl's, Old Navy, Tires+, **S...gas:** BP, **food:** Perkins/24hr, **lodging:** Travelodge
27	I-94 W to St Cloud, I-94/694 E to Minneapolis
26	rd 10, Bass Lake Rd, **E...gas:** Conoco, **food:** Culver's, McDonald's, **lodging:** Extended Stay America, **other:** mall, **W...gas:** BP, Sinclair/LP, **lodging:** Hilton Garden
23	rd 9, Rockford Rd, **E...gas:** BP, Holiday, **food:** Chili's, **other:** Checker Parts, Lincoln/Mercury, Old Navy, Radio Shack, Rainbow Foods/24hr, Target, Walgreen, **W...gas:** Conoco, PDQ, **food:** Caribou Coffee, Cousins Subs, DQ, LeAnn Chin Chinese, Starbucks, Subway, TGIFriday
22	MN 55, **E...gas:** Holiday/diesel, **food:** Denny's, Green Mill Rest., McDonald's, **lodging:** Best Western Kelly, Radisson, Red Roof Inn, **W...gas:** Holiday/diesel, **food:** Arby's, Burger King, Davanni's Rest., Grandma's Grill, Mulligan's Grill, New Dynasty Chinese, Perkins, **lodging:** Comfort Inn, Day's Inn, Holiday Inn, **other:** Goodyear/auto, Tires+
21	rd 6, **E...gas:** BP/KwikTrip, **other:** Discount Tire, Home Depot
20	Carlson Pkwy, **E...gas:** Holiday/diesel, **food:** Subway, **W...food:** Italianni's Rest., **lodging:** Country Inn Suites
19b a	I-394 E, US 12 W, to Minneapolis, **1 mi E off of I-394...food:** Applebee's, Byerly's Rest., Godfather's, Uno Pizza, Wendy's, **other:** Best Buy, Borders Books, Circuit City, Ford, JC Penney, Jo-Ann Fabrics, OfficeMax, Marshall Field, Mazda, Mercedes/BMW, Saab, Sears/auto, Target, Tires+, mall, **1/2 mi W...gas:** BP, **food:** Bankok Bowl, BBQ, ChiChi's, Pizza Hut, **other:** MEDICAL CARE, Chevrolet, Lexus, Mitsubishi, Nissan
17b a	Minnetonka Blvd, **W...gas:** Mobil, **food:** Dunn Bros Coffee
16b a	MN 7, **1 mi W...food:** Davanni's Rest., Famous Dave's BBQ, Hopkins House Rest., Lund's Rest., McDonald's, Perkins, Subway, Taco Bell

Minneapolis

13	MN 62, rd 62, no facilities
12	Valleyview Rd, rd 39(from sb)
11c	MN 5 W, **N...lodging:** Extended Stay America, **other:** Land Rover, **S...other:** Chevrolet
b a	US 169 S, US 212 W, **N...food:** Don Pablo, **lodging:** AmeriSuites, Courtyard, Fairfield Inn, Hampton Inn, Residence Inn, **S...gas:** Phillips 66, **food:** Hop's Grill, **lodging:** Homestead Suites, SpringHill Suites, Towne-Place Suites, **other:** Cub Foods, Office Depot
10	US 169 N, to rd 18, no facilities
8	rd 28(from wb, no return), E Bush Lake Rd, no facilities
7b a	MN 100, rd 34, Normandale Blvd, **N...gas:** Shell/diesel, **food:** Burger King, Chili's, Embers Rest., Subway, TGI-Friday, **lodging:** Radisson, Select Inn, **S...gas:** Citgo, **lodging:** Country Inn Suites, Hilton Garden, Holiday Inn, Hotel Seville, Staybridge Inn
6b	rd 17, France Ave, **N...gas:** Mobil, **food:** Cattle Co Rest., Fuddrucker's, Macaroni Grill, Perkins, **lodging:** Best Western, Park Inn Suites, **other:** HOSPITAL, Circuit City, CompUSA, Office Depot, **S...food:** Denny's, Joe Senser's Grill, Olive Garden, **lodging:** Hampton Inn, **other:** Buick/Pontiac/GMC, Ford, Mercedes, Nissan
a	Penn Ave(no EZ eb return), **N...gas:** Citgo, **other:** Buick, Galyan's, Hyundai, Isuzu, **S...food:** Applebee's, Bennigan's, Edwardo's Café, Starbucks, Steak&Ale, Subway, **lodging:** Embassy Suites, **other:** Chevrolet, Chrysler/Pymouth/Jeep, Dodge, Kohl's, Rainbow Foods, Target
5b a	I-35W, S to Albert Lea, N to Minneapolis
4b	Lyndale Ave, **N...gas:** BP, Conoco, **food:** DQ, **lodging:** Hampton Inn, **other:** Best Buy, Borders, Honda, Mitsubishi, Radio Shack, Tires+, **S...gas:** Phillips 66, **other:** Acura, Lincoln/Mercury, Mazda, Subaru
a	MN 52, Nicollet Ave, **N...gas:** SA/diesel, **food:** Burger King, ChiChi's, **S...gas:** Mobil, Shell, **food:** Kwik Mart, Big Boy, McDonald's, **lodging:** Baymont Inn, Super 8, **other:** Home Depot
3	Portland Ave, 12th Ave, **N...gas:** Phillips 66, Sinclair, PDQ Mart, **food:** Arby's, BBQ, Ground Round, **lodging:** AmericInn, **S...gas:** BP, **food:** Denny's, Outback Steaks, Subway, **lodging:** Comfort Inn/rest., Holiday Inn Express, Microtel, **other:** SuperValu Foods, Walgreen, Wal-Mart
2c b	MN 77, **N...lodging:** Motel 6, **S...gas:** BP, SA, **lodging:** AmeriSuites, Best Western, Courtyard, Embassy Suites, Exel Inn, Marriott, Registry Hotel, Sheraton, Thunderbird Hotel, **other:** Nordstrom's, Sears, Mall of America
a	24th Ave, same as 2c b
1b	34th Ave, Nat Cemetary, **S...lodging:** Embassy Suites, Hilton, Holiday Inn
a	MN 5 E, **N...**airport
0mm	Minnesota River. I-494/I-694 loops around Minneapolis/St Paul.

246

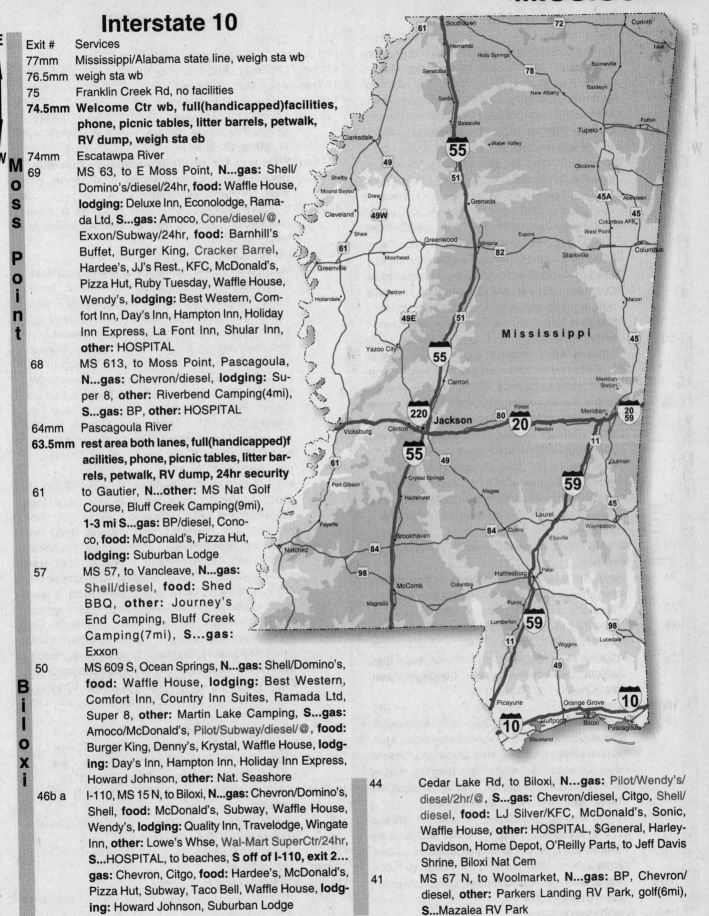

MISSISSIPPI

Interstate 10

Exit #	Services
77mm	Mississippi/Alabama state line, weigh sta wb
76.5mm	weigh sta wb
75	Franklin Creek Rd, no facilities
74.5mm	**Welcome Ctr wb, full(handicapped)facilities, phone, picnic tables, litter barrels, petwalk, RV dump, weigh sta eb**
74mm	Escatawpa River
69	MS 63, to E Moss Point, **N...gas:** Shell/Domino's/diesel/24hr, **food:** Waffle House, **lodging:** Deluxe Inn, Econolodge, Ramada Ltd, **S...gas:** Amoco, Cone/diesel/@, Exxon/Subway/24hr, **food:** Barnhill's Buffet, Burger King, Cracker Barrel, Hardee's, JJ's Rest., KFC, McDonald's, Pizza Hut, Ruby Tuesday, Waffle House, Wendy's, **lodging:** Best Western, Comfort Inn, Day's Inn, Hampton Inn, Holiday Inn Express, La Font Inn, Shular Inn, **other:** HOSPITAL
68	MS 613, to Moss Point, Pascagoula, **N...gas:** Chevron/diesel, **lodging:** Super 8, **other:** Riverbend Camping(4mi), **S...gas:** BP, **other:** HOSPITAL
64mm	Pascagoula River
63.5mm	**rest area both lanes, full(handicapped)facilities, phone, picnic tables, litter barrels, petwalk, RV dump, 24hr security**
61	to Gautier, **N...other:** MS Nat Golf Course, Bluff Creek Camping(9mi), **1-3 mi S...gas:** BP/diesel, Conoco, **food:** McDonald's, Pizza Hut, **lodging:** Suburban Lodge
57	MS 57, to Vancleave, **N...gas:** Shell/diesel, **food:** Shed BBQ, **other:** Journey's End Camping, Bluff Creek Camping(7mi), **S...gas:** Exxon
50	MS 609 S, Ocean Springs, **N...gas:** Shell/Domino's, **food:** Waffle House, **lodging:** Best Western, Comfort Inn, Country Inn Suites, Ramada Ltd, Super 8, **other:** Martin Lake Camping, **S...gas:** Amoco/McDonald's, Pilot/Subway/diesel/@, **food:** Burger King, Denny's, Krystal, Waffle House, **lodging:** Day's Inn, Hampton Inn, Holiday Inn Express, Howard Johnson, **other:** Nat. Seashore
46b a	I-110, MS 15 N, to Biloxi, **N...gas:** Chevron/Domino's, Shell, **food:** McDonald's, Subway, Waffle House, Wendy's, **lodging:** Quality Inn, Travelodge, Wingate Inn, **other:** Lowe's Whse, Wal-Mart SuperCtr/24hr, **S...**HOSPITAL, to beaches, **S off of I-110, exit 2...gas:** Chevron, Citgo, **food:** Hardee's, McDonald's, Pizza Hut, Subway, Taco Bell, Waffle House, **lodging:** Howard Johnson, Suburban Lodge
44	Cedar Lake Rd, to Biloxi, **N...gas:** Pilot/Wendy's/diesel/2hr/@, **S...gas:** Chevron/diesel, Citgo, Shell/diesel, **food:** LJ Silver/KFC, McDonald's, Sonic, Waffle House, **other:** HOSPITAL, $General, Harley-Davidson, Home Depot, O'Reilly Parts, to Jeff Davis Shrine, Biloxi Nat Cem
41	MS 67 N, to Woolmarket, **N...gas:** BP, Chevron/diesel, **other:** Parkers Landing RV Park, golf(6mi), **S...**Mazalea RV Park

247

MISSISSIPPI

Interstate 10

Gulfport

39.5mm Biloxi River

38 Lorraine-Cowan Rd, **N...gas:** Exxon/Subway, Shell/diesel, **food:** Capt Al's Seafood, Domino's, McDonald's, **5-7 mi S...gas:** Citgo, **food:** KFC, Subway, Waffle House, **lodging:** Coast Motel, Edgewater Inn, Gulf Beach Resort, Holiday Inn Express, Ramada Ltd, Super 8, **other:** HOSPITAL, Baywood Camping, Sand Beach RV Park, to beaches

34b a US 49, to Gulfport, **N...gas:** Chevron, MinuteStop, Texaco/diesel, **food:** Backyard Burger, Chili's, Chuck-eCheese, Cracker Barrel, Hardee's, O'Charley's, Papa John's, TGIFriday, Waffle House, **other:** Albertson's, Barnes&Noble, Chevrolet/Cadillac, Circuit City, Eckerd, Goody's, Honda, Office Depot, Old Navy, **S...gas:** Chevron, FastLane/diesel, Phillips 66, RacTrac, Shell/diesel, Texaco/diesel, **food:** Applebee's, Arby's/24hr, Burger King, Fazoli's, IHOP, KFC, KrispyKreme, McAlister's, McDonald's, Montana's Rest., Perkins, Piccadilly's, Schlotsky's, Shoney's, Sonic, Subway, Toucan's Mexican, Waffle House, Wendy's, **lodging:** Best Western, Comfort Inn, Day's Inn, Fairfield Inn, Guesthouse Inn, Hampton Inn, Holiday Inn, Holiday Inn Express, Motel 6, Villager Suites, **other:** HOSPITAL, Ford, Home Depot, Kia, Michael's, Nissan, OfficeMax, Prime Outlets/famous brands, Sam's Club, Wal-Mart SuperCtr/gas/24hr, transmissions

31 Canal Rd, to Gulfport, **N...gas:** Love's/Arbys/diesel/24hr, **S...gas:** /Flying J/Conoco/Cookery/diesel/LP/24hr, Texaco/Krystal/diesel/24hr, **food:** Waffle House, Wendy's, **lodging:** Crystal Inn, Econolodge

28 to Long Beach, **S...gas:** Chevron, Phillips 66

27mm Wolf River

24 Menge Ave, **N...gas:** Chevron/diesel, **S...gas:** Texaco, **other:** A1 RV Park, flea mkt, golf, to beaches

20 to De Lisle, to Pass Christian, **N...gas:** Spur

16 Diamondhead, **N...gas:** BP, Chevron/24hr, **food:** Burger King, DQ, Domino's, Subway, Waffle House, **lodging:** Diamondhead Inn, Ramada Inn, **other:** Diamondhead Foods, **S...gas:** Shell/diesel, **food:** Pizza Co, **lodging:** Comfort Inn

15mm Jourdan River

13 MS 43, MS 603, to Kiln, Bay St Louis, **N...**McLeod SP, **S...gas:** Chevron/diesel, Exxon/Subway/diesel, Pure, **food:** Waffles+ Rest., **3-7 mi S...food:** McDonald's, **other:** Casino Magic Inn/RV Park, **lodging:** Holiday Inn, Key West Inn, Studio Inn, Waveland Resort Inn, **other:** HOSPITAL, KOA, Nella RV Park

10mm parking area eb, litter barrels, no restroom facilities

2 MS 607, to Waveland, NASA Test Site, **S...Welcome Ctr both lanes, full(handicapped)facilities, phone, picnic tables, litter barrels, RV dump, petwalk, 24hr security, no trucks/buses,** to Buccaneer SP, camping, to beaches

1mm weigh sta both lanes

Interstate 20

Meridian

Exit # Services

I-20 W and I-59 S run together to Meridian

172mm Mississippi/Alabama state line

170mm weigh sta both lanes

169 Kewanee, no facilities

165 Toomsuba, **N...gas:** Shell/Subway, Texaco/ChesterFried/diesel, **S...gas:** FuelMart/Arby's/diesel/@, **other:** KOA(2mi)

164mm Welcome Ctr wb, full(handicapped)facilities, phone, vending, picnic tables, litter barrels, petwalk, RV dump, 24hr security

160 to Russell, **N...gas:** TA/BP/diesel/rest./24hr/@, **other:** Nanabe Cr Camping(1mi), **S...gas:** Amoco/diesel/rest.

157b a US 45, to Macon, Quitman, no facilities

154b a MS 19 S, MS 39 N, Meridian, **N...gas:** Amoco/diesel, BP/diesel, Shell, Texaco/Domino's, **food:** Applebee's, Backyard Burgers, Cracker Barrel, Krystal, Waffle House, **lodging:** Best Western, Day's Inn, Econolodge, Hampton Inn, Holiday Inn, Howard Johnson, Rodeway Inn, Super 8, **other:** Cadillac/Pontiac, Dodge/Subaru/Kia, Lincoln/Mercury, Mitsubishi, U-Haul, **S...gas:** Chevron, Conoco/diesel, **food:** CiCi's, Crescent City Grill, McDonald's, O'Charley's, Outback Steaks, Popeye's, Red Lobster, Ryan's, Taco Bell, **lodging:** Comfort Inn, Jameson Inn, Microtel, Scottish Inn, **other:** BooksAMillion, Dillard's, Ethridge RV Ctr, Harley-Davidson, JC Penney, Old Navy, Sears/auto, mall, same as 153

153 MS 145 S, 22nd Ave, Meridian, **N...gas:** BP, Shell, **food:** Arby's, Barnhill's Buffet, Burger King, Capt D's, Hardee's, KFC, McDonald's, Pizza Hut, Subway, Wendy's, Western Sizzlin, **lodging:** Relax Inn, Super Inn, **other:** HOSPITAL, Firestone, FoodMax, Ford/Nissan, Goodyear/auto, $General, Ford, Rite Aid, Sack&Save Foods, **S...gas:** Chevron/diesel, Conoco/diesel, Exxon/diesel, Shell, **food:** Depot Rest., Waffle House, **lodging:** Astro Motel, Baymont Inn, Best Western, Budget 8 Motel, Holiday Inn Express, Motel 6, Quality Inn, Sleep Inn, **other:** Buick, Chevrolet/Cadillac, Chrysler/Plymouth/Jeep, Honda, Suzuki, Lowe's Whse, Wal-Mart SuperCtr/gas/24hr

152 29th Ave, 31st Ave, Meridian, **N...gas:** Chevron/ChesterFried/diesel/24hr, **lodging:** Ramada Ltd, **S...lodging:** Royal Inn

151 49th Ave, Valley Rd, **N...tires, S...**stockyards

150 US 11 S, MS 19 N, Meridian, **N...gas:** Queen City Trkstp/diesel@, **other:** Okatibbee Lake, RV camping, **S...gas:** Stuckey's/Subway/diesel, Shell/diesel

131[149] I-59 S, to Hattiesburg. **I-20 E and I-59 N run together.**

129 US 80 W, Lost Gap, **S...gas:** Conoco/diesel/24hr/@, Spaceway/Grill King, RV dump

121 Chunky, no facilities

119mm Chunky River

115 MS 503, Hickory, no facilities

Interstate 20

E

N

S

W

109 MS 15, Newton, **N...gas:** Shell/Wendy's/diesel/24hr, **food:** Bo-Ro Rest., **lodging:** Thrifty Inn, **other:** lube, **S...gas:** Chevron/diesel/24hr, Conoco/diesel, **food:** Hardee's, KFC/Taco Bell, McDonald's, Pizza Hut, Sonic, Subway, **lodging:** Day's Inn, **other:** HOSPITAL, $General, Piggly Wiggly, Wal-Mart

100 US 80, Lake, Lawrence, **N...gas:** BP/diesel/rest.

96 Lake, no facilities

95mm Bienville Nat Forest, eastern boundary

90mm **rest area eb, full(handicapped)facilities, phone, picnic tables, litter barrels, petwalk, RV dump, 24hr security**

88 MS 35, Forest, **N...gas:** BP/Subway/diesel, Shell, **food:** KFC, McDonald's, Pizza Hut, Wendy's, **lodging:** AppleTree Inn, Comfort Inn, Day's Inn, Holiday Inn Express, Scott Motel, **other:** HOSPITAL, Chevrolet, Honda, Wal-Mart, **S...gas:** Chevron/diesel/24hr, **food:** Santa Fe Steaks

80 MS 481, Morton, no facilities

77 MS 13, Morton, **N...gas:** Phillips 66/diesel, **other:** HOSPITAL, to Roosevelt SP, RV camping

76mm Bienville NF, western boundary

75mm **rest area wb, full(handicapped)facilities, phone, picnic tables, litter barrels, petwalk, RV dump, 24hr security**

68 MS 43, Pelahatchie, **N...gas:** Chevron/Subway/ diesel/24hr, Conoco/diesel/rest./RV dump/24hr, **food:** Little Red Smokehouse, **other:** RV camping, **S...gas:** BP/diesel

B r a n d o n

59 US 80, E Brandon, **2 mi S...gas:** Conoco, Shell/ diesel

56 US 80, Brandon, **N...gas:** Texaco, **food:** BBQ, Burger King, CiCi's, Krystal, McDonald's, Popeye's, Taco Bell, **lodging:** Microtel, **other:** AutoZone, **S...gas:** Exxon, Mac's Gas, Shell/diesel, **food:** DQ, Sonic, Waffle House, **lodging:** Day's Inn, Red Roof Inn, **other:** to Ross Barnett Reservoir

54 Crossgates Blvd, W Brandon, **N...gas:** BP, Exxon, Phillips 66, **food:** Burger King, Domino's, Fernando's Mexican, KFC, Mazzio's, Papa John's, Pizza Hut, Popeye's, Subway, Waffle House, Wendy's, **lodging:** Ridgeland Inn, **other:** HOSPITAL, Buick/GMC, Chevrolet, Eckerd, Firestone/auto, Ford, Goodyear/ auto, Kroger, Wal-Mart SuperCtr/gas/24hr, **S...**Shell/ Domino's, Home Depot

52 MS 475, **N...gas:** Chevron, Conoco/diesel, **food:** Krystal(3mi), Waffle House, Wendy's(3mi), **lodging:** Quality Inn, Ramada Ltd, Super 8, **other:** Peterbilt, to Jackson Airport

48 MS 468, Pearl, **N...gas:** Conoco, MinuteStop/ diesel, Shell/diesel, **food:** Arby's, Bumpers Drive-In, Burger King, Cracker Barrel, Domino's, KFC, McDonald's, O'Charley's, Pizza Hut, Popeye's, Ryan's, Schlotsky's, Shoney's, Sonic, Waffle House, **lodging:** Best Western, Comfort Inn, Econolodge, Fairfield Inn, Hampton Inn, Holiday Inn Express, Jameson Inn, Motel 6, **other:** transmissions, **S...gas:** Chevron/diesel/24hr, Shell/diesel/24hr, **lodging:** Country Inn Suites, Day's Inn, La Quinta

J a c k s o n

47b a US 49 S, Flowood, **N...gas:** ✈/Flying J/ Conoco/CountryMkt/ diesel/LP/24hr/@, **food:** Western Sizzlin, **lodging:** Airport Inn, **2-3 mi S...gas:** Pilot/Krystal/Subway/ diesel/24hr/@, **food:** DQ, Waffle House, **lodging:** Day's Inn, Richland Inn, Super 8, **other:** Wal-Mart SuperCtr/gas/24hr, Magnolia RV Camping

46 I-55 N, to Memphis, no facilities

45b US 51, State St, to downtown, **N...gas:** Chevron, **other:** ExpressLube, **S...gas:** Speedway/ Hardee's/diesel, **other:** Nissan

a Gallatin St(from wb), to downtown, **N...gas:** Chevron, Petro/diesel/rest/@., **other:** Blue Beacon, **S...gas:** Pilot/McDonald's/diesel/@, **lodging:** Knight's Inn, **other:** Mazda, Toyota

44 I-55 S(exits left from wb), to New Orleans, no facilities

43b a Terry Rd, **N...gas:** Shell, **food:** BBQ, Kim's Seafood, Krystal, **lodging:** Tarrymore Motel

42b a Ellis Ave, Belvidere, **N...gas:** BP, Conoco, Shell, **food:** Burger King, Capt D's, Denny's, McDonald's, Popeye's, Waffle House, Wendy's, **lodging:** Best Western, Comfort Inn, Day's Inn, Econolodge, Ramada, SW Hotel, **other:** AutoZone, Chrysler/Plymouth/ Dodge, Family$, Firestone, Radio Shack, U-Haul, transmissions, zoo, **S...gas:** Conoco/diesel, Exxon/ diesel, Pump'n Save, **food:** DQ, **other:** Sack&Save Foods

41 I-220 N, US 49 N, to Jackson

40b a MS 18 W, Robinson Rd, **N...gas:** Phillips 66, Shell/ diesel, Spur, **food:** Arby's, China Buffet, El Chico, Krystal, Mazzio's, McDonald's, Piccadilly's, Pizza Hut, Popeye's, Wendy's, **lodging:** Day's Inn, Sleep Inn, **other:** CarCare, Home Depot, Office Depot, Sears/ auto, **S...gas:** Conoco, **food:** IHOP, Waffle House, **lodging:** Comfort Inn, **other:** HOSPITAL, Wal-Mart SuperCtr/gas/24hr

36 Springridge Rd, Clinton, **N...gas:** Mac's/Burger King, Shell, **food:** Backyard Burger, Bumpers Drive-In, Capt D's, China Garden, DQ, Mazzio's, McDonald's, Papa John's, Smoothie King, Subway, Taco Bell, Waffle House, Wendy's, **lodging:** Clinton Inn, Day's Inn, **other:** Avance Parts, Kroger/gas, Radio Shack, Walgreen, Wal-Mart SuperCtr/gas/24hr(2mi), **S...gas:** Exxon, Shell/diesel, **food:** Applebee's, Fazoli's, Pizza Hut, Popeye's, Shoney's, Xan's Diner, **lodging:** Comfort Inn, Hampton Inn, Holiday Inn Express, Ramada Ltd, Ridgeland Inn

MISSISSIPPI

Interstate 20

Exit	Services
35	US 80 E, Clinton, **N...gas:** Chevron/diesel, Phillips 66/diesel/rest., Shell/diesel, **food:** Backyard Burger, Chick-fil-A, McAlister's Deli, **lodging:** Ridgland Inn, **S...other:** Eagle Ridge RV Park
34	Natchez Trace Pkwy, no facilities
31	Norrell Rd, no facilities
27	Bolton, **N...gas:** Chevron, **S...gas:** BP/diesel
19	MS 22, Edwards, Flora, **N...other:** Askew Landing RV Camping, **S...gas:** BP/diesel, Phillips 66/DQ/Stuckey's, **lodging:** Relax Inn
17mm	Big Black River
15	Flowers, no facilities
11	Bovina, **N...gas:** Shell/diesel/24hr, **other:** RV camping
10mm	weigh sta wb
8mm	weigh sta eb
6.5mm	parking area eb
5b a	US 61, MS 27 S, **N...gas:** Shell/diesel, Zips/diesel, **food:** Sonic, **S...gas:** Texaco/Domino's/diesel, **food:** Bumpers Rest., Rowdy's Rest., **lodging:** Beechwood Inn, Comfort Inn, Jameson Inn, Scottish Inn, **other:** RV camping, same as 4a
4b a	Clay St, **N...gas:** Chevron, **lodging:** Bfd Inn/RV Park, Econolodge, Hampton Inn, Vicksburg Inn, **other:** HOSPITAL, KOA, to Vicksburg NP, **S...gas:** Shell/Domino's/diesel, **food:** China Buffet, Cracker Barrel, Dock Seafood, Pizza Inn, McAlister's, Waffle House, **lodging:** Beechwood Inn/rest., Comfort Inn, Holiday Inn Express, Jameson Inn, Scottish Inn, **other:** Chrysler/Jeep/Toyota, $General, Lincoln/Mercury, Outlet Mall/famous brands/deli, same as 5
3	Indiana Ave, **N...gas:** Texaco/Subway/diesel, **food:** Krystal, McDonald's, Waffle House, **lodging:** Best Western, Deluxe Inn, **other:** Chevrolet, Ford/Lincoln/Mercury, Honda, IGA Foods, Mazda, Rite Aid, **S...gas:** Shell, **food:** KFC, **lodging:** Best Inn, **other:** Buick/GMC/Pontica/Subaru, Family$, Sack&Save Foods
1c	Halls Ferry Rd, **N...gas:** Chevron/24hr, Exxon, **food:** Burger King, Sonic, **lodging:** Travel Inn, **other:** HOSPITAL, **S...gas:** FastLane/diesel, **food:** Capt D's, DQ, Goldie's BBQ, Hardee's, Piccadilly's, Pizza Hut, Popeye's, Ryan's, Shoney's, Subway, Taco Bell, Taco Casa, TCBY, Wendy's, **lodging:** Day's Inn, Fairfield Inn, Super 8, **other:** Dillard's, Home Depot, JC Penney, Kroger, USPO, mall
b	US 61 S, **S...gas:** BP, Chevron/Domino's, **other:** Mitsubishi, OfficeMax, Wal-Mart SuperCtr/24hr, same as 1c
a	Washington St, Vicksburg, **N...Welcome Ctr both lanes, full(handicapped)facilities, phone, gas:** Kangaroo/diesel, Shell/Subway/diesel, **food:** BBQ, **lodging:** AmeriStar Hotel, **other:** Isle of Capri RV Park, casino, transmissions, **S...food:** Waffle House, **lodging:** La Quinta, Ridgeland Inn
0mm	Mississippi/Louisiana state line, Mississippi River

Interstate 55

Exit #	Services
291.5mm	Mississippi/Tennessee state line
291	State Line Rd, Southaven, **E...gas:** 76/Circle K, **food:** BBQ, Best Pizza, Burger King, Exline's Pizza, McDonald's, Pizza Hut, Subway, Waffle House, **lodging:** Best Western, Comfort Inn, Holiday Inn Express, Quality Inn, **other:** Firestone/auto, Goodyear/auto, K-Mart, Kroger, MegaMkt Foods, Walgreen, **W...gas:** Exxon/diesel, **food:** El Patron Mexican, KFC, Mrs Winner's, Rally's, Wendy's, **other:** Fred's Drug, Rite Aid
289	MS 302, to US 51, Horn Lake, **E...gas:** 76/Circle K, Shell, **food:** Backyard Burger, Burger King, Chick-fil-A, Chili's, Danver's, Fazoli's, IHOP, Krystal, McDonald's, O'Charley's, Outback Steaks, Schlotsky's, Starbucks, Steak'n Shake, TGIFriday, **lodging:** Comfort Suites, Fairfield Inn, Hampton Inn, **other:** HOSPITAL, Aldi Foods, Chevrolet, Chrysler/Plymouth/Jeep, $Tree, Ford, Lowe's Whse, NAPA/repair, Office Depot, Pontiac/GMC, Wal-Mart SuperCtr/gas/24hr, **W...gas:** BP, Phillips 66/diesel, Shell/diesel, **food:** Applebee's, Arby's, Bob Evans, ChuckeCheese, Cracker Barrel, Great Wall Chinese, Hooters, KFC/Taco Bell, McDonald's, Mrs Winner's, Papa John's, Pizza Hut, Popeye's, Roadhouse Grill, Ryan's, Waffle House, Wendy's, **lodging:** Day's Inn, Drury Inn, Motel 6, Ramada Ltd, Sleep Inn, Super 8, **other:** Family$, Home Depot, Kroger, OfficeMax, Piggly Wiggly, Target, Walgreen
287	Church Rd, **E...gas:** Texaco/ChesterFried/diesel, **W...gas:** Shell/DQ/diesel, Texaco, **food:** McDonald's, Subway, Waffle House, **lodging:** Magnolia Inn, Super 8
285mm	weigh sta both lanes
284	to US 51, Nesbit Rd, **E...gas:** Chevrolet/GMC, **W...gas:** Citgo, Nesbit 1-Stop, **food:** Happy Daze Dairybar, **other:** USPO
280	MS 304, US 51, Hernando, **E...gas:** Exxon, **food:** Huddle House, Sonic, **lodging:** Day's Inn, Hernando Inn, **W...gas:** BP, Chevron/Subway/diesel, Shell/diesel, **food:** BBQ, Church's, McDonald's, Pizza Hut, Sonic, Wendy's, **lodging:** Super 8, **other:** Kroger/gas, NAPA, Piggly Wiggly, Memphis S Camping(2mi), to Arkabutla Lake
279mm	**Welcome Ctr sb, full(handicapped)facilities, phone, picnic tables, litter barrels, petwalk, RV dump, 24hr security**
276mm	**rest area nb, full(handicapped)facilities, phone, picnic tables, litter barrels, petwalk, RV dump, 24hr security**
273mm	Coldwater River
271	MS 306, Coldwater, **W...gas:** Amoco, **food:** Subway, **1-2 mi W...gas:** Citgo, Exxon/24hr, **other:** Lake Arkabutla, Memphis S RV Park
265	MS 4, Senatobia, **W...gas:** BP/Huddle House/diesel, Exxon, FuelMart/diesel, Shell/diesel, Texaco/diesel, **food:** KFC, McDonald's, Pizza Hut, Popey's, Sonic, Subway, Taco Bell, Waffle House, Wendy's, Western Sizzlin, **lodging:** Comfort Inn, Motel 6, **other:** HOSPITAL, CarQuest, $General, Fred's Drug, Goodyear/auto, NAPA, Piggly Wiggly, Pontiac/Buick/GMC, USPO

Interstate 55

N ↕ S

Batesville

257   MS 310, Como, **E...gas:** BP/diesel, **other:** N Sardis Lake

252   MS 315, Sardis, **E...gas:** Amoco/diesel, Chevron/diesel, **food:** BBQ, **lodging:** Lake Inn, Super 8, **other:** NAPA, to Kyle SP, Sardis Dam, RV camping, **W...gas:** BP/diesel, Shell/diesel, **food:** Sonic, **lodging:** Knight's Inn, **other:** HOSPITAL, $General, Fred's Drug

246   MS 35, N Batesville, **E...**to Sardis Lake, **W...gas:** Chevron, Shell/diesel

243b a   MS 6, to Batesville, **E...gas:** BP/diesel, Texaco/diesel, **food:** Backyard Burger, **other:** Lowe's Whse, Wal-Mart SuperCtr/gas/24hr, to Sardis Lake, U of MS, **W...gas:** Chevron/diesel, Exxon/diesel, FastLane/diesel, Phillips 66/diesel, Shell/diesel, **food:** Burger King, Capt D's, Cracker Barrel, DQ, Domino's, El Charro Mexican, Hardee's, Huddle House, KFC, McDonald's, Pizza Hut, Popeye's, Sonic, Subway, Taco Bell, Wendy's, Western Sizzlin, **lodging:** AmeriHost, Comfort Inn, Day's Inn, Hampton Inn, Ramada Ltd, **other:** HOSPITAL, Advance Parts, AutoZone, $General, Factory Stores/famous brands, Family$, Kroger, Radio Shack

240mm   **rest area both lanes, full(handicapped)facilities, phone, picnic tables, litter barrels, petwalk, RV dump, 24hr security**

237   to US 51, Courtland, **E...gas:** Pure/diesel/rest.

233   to Enid Dam, **E...**to Enid Lake, RV camping, **W...gas:** Benson's/groceries

227   MS 32, Oakland, **E...**to Cossar SP, Sunrise RV Park, **W...gas:** Chevron/diesel

220   MS 330, Tillatoba, **E...gas:** Conoco/diesel/@, **food:** All American Rest.

211   MS 7 N, to Coffeeville, **E...**Frog Hollow RV Park, **W...gas:** BP/diesel, Texaco/diesel

208   Papermill Rd, **E...**Grenada Airport

Grenada

206   MS 8, MS 7 S, to Grenada, **E...gas:** Exxon, RaceTrac, Shell/diesel, Texaco, **food:** BBQ/Steaks, Burger King, Domino's, Hong Kong Chinese, Jake&Rip's Café, La Cabana Mexican, McAlister's Deli, McDonald's, Pizza Hut, Pizza Inn, RagTime Grill, Shoney's, Subway, Taco Bell, Wendy's, Western Sizzlin, **lodging:** Best Western/rest., Comfort Inn, Day's Inn, Hampton Inn, Holiday Inn/rest., Jameson Inn, Super 8, **other:** HOSPITAL, AutoZone, Chrysler/Plymouth/Dodge, $General, Ford/Lincoln/Mercury, Toyota, USPO, Wal-Mart SuperCtr/24hr, to Grenada Lake/RV camping, **W...gas:** Exxon/HuddleHouse, **lodging:** Country Inn Suites, Hilltop Inn

204mm   parking area sb, phone, litter barrels

202mm   parking area nb, phone, litter barrels

199   S Grenada, to Camp McCain

195   MS 404, Duck Hill, **E...**to Camp McCain, **W...**Conoco/diesel

185   US 82, Winona, **E...gas:** Exxon, Shell/diesel, **food:** KFC, McDonald's, Pizza Hut, **lodging:** Budget Inn, Magnolia Lodge, Relax Inn, Western Inn, **other:** HOSPITAL, **W...gas:** Amoco/diesel/24hr/@, **food:** BBQ

174   MS 35, MS 430, Vaiden, **E...gas:** BP, Chevron/35/55/diesel/motel/24hr/@, Shell/diesel, **other:** NAPA, Vaiden Camping, **W...gas:** Texaco/Stuckey's/24hr, Interstate Grill, **other:** $General

173mm   **rest area sb, full(handicapped)facilities, phone, picnic tables, litter barrels, petwalk, RV dump, 24hr security**

164   to West, **W...gas:** West Trkstp/diesel/@

163mm   **rest area nb, full(handicapped)facilities, phone, picnic tables, litter barrels, petwalk, RV dump, 24hr security**

156   MS 12, Durant, **E...gas:** Shell/diesel, **lodging:** Durant Motel/rest., Super 8, **W...**HOSPITAL

150   **E...**Holmes Co SP, RV camping

146   MS 14, Goodman, **W...**to Little Red Schoolhouse

144   MS 17, to Pickens, **E...gas:** Shell/diesel/24hr/@, **food:** HomePlace Rest., J's Deli, **W...gas:** BP/diesel/rest., **other:** to Little Red Schoolhouse

139   MS 432, to Pickens, no facilities

133   Vaughan, **E...**to Casey Jones Museum

128mm   Big Black River

124   MS 16, to N Canton, no facilities

Canton

119   MS 22, to MS 16 E, Canton, **E...gas:** Amoco/Subway/diesel, BP, Chevron/Nancy's, Exxon/diesel, Shell, Texaco/Domino's/diesel, **food:** McDonald's, Pizza Hut, Popeye's, Sombrero Mexican, Wendy's, **lodging:** Best Western, Comfort Inn, Econolodge, Hampton Inn, Holiday Inn Express, **other:** HOSPITAL, Ford, to Ross Barnett Reservoir, **W...gas:** Chevron/KFC/diesel, Citgo/diesel, Love's/Arby's/diesel/24hr/@, **food:** Bumpers Drive-In, 2 Rivers Steaks

118   Nissan Parkway

112   US 51, Gluckstadt, **E...gas:** Exxon/Krystal/diesel, Kangaroo/Subway/diesel, **lodging:** Super 8

108   MS 463, Madison, **E...gas:** Shell/diesel, Texaco/Domino's/diesel, **food:** Backyard Burger, Burger King, Haute Pig Café, **other:** Wal-Mart SuperCtr/24hr

105b   Old Agency Rd, **E...gas:** Chevron/diesel, **other:** Pontiac/Buick/GMC

a   Natchez Trace Pkwy, no facilities

104   I-220, to W Jackson

MISSISSIPPI
Interstate 55

103 County Line Rd, **E...gas:** BP, Exxon/diesel, Speedway, **food:** Applebee's, Burger King, Chick-fil-A, Cuco's Mexican, Fuddrucker's, Grady's Grill, Hardee's, KFC, Krispy Kreme, Mazzio's, McDonald's, Popeye's, Roadhouse Grill, Ralph&Kacoo's Seafood, Ruby Tuesday, Subway, Taco Bell, Wendy's, **lodging:** Cabot Lodge, Day's Inn, Hilton Garden, Red Roof Inn, Shoney's Inn/rest., **other:** Acura, Dillard's, Goodyear, Isuzu, Mazda, Sam's Club, mall, to Barnett Reservoir, **W...food:** Olive Garden, Red Lobster, Subway, **lodging:** Comfort Suites, Drury Inn, Motel 6, **other:** Home Depot, Office Depot, Target

102b Beasley Rd, Adkins Blvd, **E...gas:** Phillips 66, **food:** Cracker Barrel, El Potrillo Mexican, LoneStar Steaks, OutBack Steaks, **lodging:** La Quinta, Super 8, **other:** BMW, Chrysler/Plymouth/Jeep, Ford, Lincoln/Mercury, Nissan, Toyota, **W...food:** McDonald's, **lodging:** Best Western, Fairfield Inn, InTown Suites, Jameson Inn, **other:** K-Mart, frontage rds access 102a

a Briarwood, **E...food:** Steam Room Grill, **lodging:** Extended Stay America, **W...food:** Capt D's, Chili's, ChuckeCheese, El Chico's, Hops Grill, Jiquilpan Mexican, Perkins, Popeye's, Red Lobster, Steak&Ale, Su Koon Chinese, **lodging:** Best Inn, Best Value Inn, Comfort Inn, Hampton Inn, **other:** Audi/VW, Chevrolet, Dodge, Jaguar/Saab, Mercedes

100 North Side Dr W, **E...gas:** BP, Chevron, Sprint Gas, **food:** Burger King, Dunkin Donuts, McAlister's Deli, McDonald's, Mo's SW Grill, Papa John's, Piccadilly's, Shoney's, SteakOut, Subway, Wendy's, Western Sizzlin, **other:** AutoZone, BooksAMillion, Eckerd, Goodyear/auto, Kroger, Office Depot, **W...gas:** Amoco, Exxon, Shell, **food:** Bennigan's, Broad St Café, Domino's, Hooters, IHOP, Pizza Hut, Waffle House, **lodging:** Holiday Inn, Knight's Inn, Super 8

99 Meadowbrook Rd, Northside Dr E(from nb)

98c b MS 25 N, Lakeland Dr, **E...gas:** Texaco, **lodging:** Parkside Inn, **other:** LaFleur's Bluff SP, **W...HOSPITAL,** museum, airport

a Woodrow Wilson Dr, downtown

96c Fortification St, **E...lodging:** Residence Inn, **W...HOSPITAL,** Bellhaven College

b High St, Jackson, downtown, **E...other:** Chevrolet, Infiniti, Lexus, Saturn, **W...gas:** Shell/diesel, Texaco/diesel, **food:** BBQ, Burger King, DQ, Dennery's, Popeye's, Shoney's, Taco Bell, Waffle House, Wendy's, **lodging:** Clarion, Day's Inn, Hampton Inn, Holiday Inn Express, Quality Inn, Red Roof, **other:** HOSPITAL, Honda, museum, st capitol

a Pearl St(from nb), Jackson, downtown, **W...access** to same as 96b

94 (46 from nb), I-20 E, to Meridian, US 49 S

45b[I-20]US 51, State St, to downtown, **N...gas:** Chevron

a Gallatin St(from sb), downtown, **S...gas:** Pilot/McDonald's/diesel/@ , **lodging:** Knight's Inn, **other:** Daewoo, Hyundai/Mazda, Nissan, Toyota

92c (44 from sb), I-20 W, to Vicksburg, US 49 N

b US 51 N, State St, Gallatin St

a McDowell Rd, **E...**Petro/diesel/@ , Pilot/McDonald's/diesel/@ , **lodging:** Knight's Inn, **W...gas:** Shell, Texaco/diesel, **food:** CiCi's, Waffle House, Wendy's, **lodging:** Super 8

90b Daniel Lake Blvd(from sb), **W...gas:** Shell, **other:** Harley-Davidson

a Savanna St, **E...lodging:** Econolodge, **W...gas:** Amoco, Shell, **food:** BoDon's Catfish, **lodging:** Save Inn

88 Elton Rd, **W...gas:** Chevron, Exxon/Subway/ChesterFried/diesel

85 Byram, **E...gas:** BP/diesel/24hr, Blue Sky, **food:** Double S Grill, **other:** Swinging Bridge RV Park, **W...gas:** Bar, Conoco/diesel, Spur, Texaco/diesel, **food:** McDonald's, Pizza Hut, Popeye's, Sonic, Subway, Taco Bell, Waffle House, Wendy's, **lodging:** Day's Inn, **other:** $General, PawPaw's Camper City, Super D Drug, Winn-Dixie

81 Wynndale Rd, **W...gas:** Conoco/diesel

78 Terry, **E...gas:** Conoco, Shell/Church's/diesel/24hr, **W...gas:** Mac's, **other:** $General, New Deal Food

72 MS 27, Crystal Springs, **E...gas:** Exxon/Subway/diesel, Phillips 66/diesel, **food:** McDonald's, Popeye's, **lodging:** Wisteria B&B, **other:** Ford/Lincoln/Mercury

68 to US 51, S Crystal Springs, no facilities

65 to US 51, Gallman, **E...gas:** Shell/DQ/Stuckey's

61 MS 28, Hazlehurst, **E...gas:** Amoco, Exxon/Subway, Phillips 66, Pump&Save, **food:** Burger King, KFC, McDonald's, Pizza Hut, Stark's Rest., Wendy's, Western Sizzlin, **lodging:** Day's Inn, Ramada Inn, Western Inn, **other:** HOSPITAL, Advance Parts, $General, Family$, Piggly Wiggly, Wal-Mart

59 to S Hazlehurst, no facilities

56 to Martinsville, no facilities

54mm **rest area both lanes, full(handicapped)facilities, phone, picnic tables, litter barrels, petwalk, RV dump, vending, 24hr security**

51 to Wesson, **W...gas:** Chevron/Country Jct/diesel/rest./RV camping/@

48 Mt Zion Rd, to Wesson, no facilities

42 to US 51, N Brookhaven, **E...gas:** Exxon/Church's, Phillips 66/diesel/@ , Shell, **lodging:** Della's Motel, **other:** HOSPITAL, **W...lodging:** Super 8

40 to MS 550, Brookhaven, **E...gas:** Amoco/Domino's, Exxon/Subway, Shell/diesel/24hr, **food:** BoBo Chinese, Burger King, CiCi's, Cracker Barrel, DQ, El Sombrero Mexican, KFC, Krystal, McDonald's, Pizza Hut, Popeye's, Shoney's, Sonic, Taco Bell, Wendy's, Western Sizzlin, **lodging:** Best Inn, Best Western, Comfort Inn, Day's Inn, Hampton Inn, Spanish Inn, **other:** HOSPITAL, AutoZone, CarQuest, Chevrolet, Chrysler/Plymouth/Dodge/Jeep, Fred's Drug, Ford/Lincoln/Mercury, Honda, Nissan, SaveALot Foods, Wal-Mart SuperCtr/gas/24hr

38 US 84, S Brookhaven, **1 mi E...gas:** Exxon/diesel, **W...gas:** Chevron/diesel/24hr

30 Bogue Chitto, Norfield, **E...gas:** Shell/BogueChitto/diesel/@

Interstate 55

N / S — McComb

24	Johnston Station, **E**...to Lake Dixie Springs
20b a	US 98 W, Summit, to Natchez, **E...gas:** BP/Ward'sBurgers/diesel, RaceWay, Shell/diesel, **W...gas:** Exxon/Subway/Stuckey's/diesel, Phillips 66/diesel
18	MS 570, Smithdale Rd, N McComb, **E...gas:** BP, **food:** Burger King, FoodCourt, McDonald's, Piccadilly's, Ruby Tuesday, **other:** HOSPITAL, JC Penney, Lowe's Whse, Sears/auto, Wal-Mart SuperCtr/24hr, mall, **W...gas:** Chevron/diesel, **food:** Arby's, **lodging:** Deerfield Inn, Hawthorn Inn, **other:** Ford/Lincoln/Mercury
17	Delaware Ave, McComb, **E...gas:** BP/Subway, Chevron/diesel, Exxon/Krystal, Pure, RaceWay, Shell/diesel, **food:** Burger King, China Gourmet, DQ, Golden Corral, Huddle House, McDonald's, Pizza Hut, Pizza Inn, Popeye's, Sonic, Taco Bell, Wendy's, **lodging:** Comfort Inn, Magnolia Inn, Super 8, **other:** HOSPITAL, AutoZone, $General, Eckerd, Family$, O'Reilly Parts, Winn-Dixie, **W...lodging:** Day's Inn, **other:** Chrysler/Plymouth/Dodge/Jeep, Toyota
15b a	US 98 E, MS 48 W, McComb, **1 mi E...gas:** Exxon/Subway, Quikmart/gas, Shell, **food:** Church's, Hardee's, KFC, **lodging:** Camellian Motel, Economy Inn, **W...gas:** BP/diesel
13	Fernwood Rd, **W...gas:** Conoco/Fernwood/diesel/rest./24hr/@, **lodging:** Fernwood Motel, **other:** golf, to Percy Quin SP
10	MS 48, Magnolia, **1 mi E...gas:** BP, Exxon, **food:** Subway, **other:** RV camping
8	MS 568, Magnolia, **E**...Pike Co Speedway
4	Chatawa, no facilities
3.5mm	**Welcome Ctr nb, full(handicapped)facilities, phone, picnic tables, litter barrels, petwalk, RV dump, 24hr security**
1	MS 584, Osyka, Gillsburg, **W**...RV camping
0mm	Mississippi/Louisiana state line

Interstate 59

N / S — Meridian

Exit #	Services
	I-59 S and I-20 W run together to Meridian
172mm	Mississippi/Alabama state line
	For exits 150 to Mississippi/Alabama state line, see Mississippi Interstate 20.
149mm	I-59 N and I-20 E run together 22 mi
142	to US 11, Savoy, **W**...to Dunns Falls
137	to N Enterprise, to Stonewall, no facilities
134	MS 513, S Enterprise, no facilities
126	MS 18, Pachuta, to Rose Hill, **E...gas:** Amoco/diesel/24hr, BP/diesel/24hr
118	to Vossburg, Paulding, no facilities
113	MS 528, to Heidelberg, **E...gas:** BP/JR's/diesel/24hr, Exxon/Subway/Pizza Inn/diesel, Stuckey's/pizza/diesel, Shell, **food:** Fly'n Pig BBQ
109mm	**rest area sb, litter barrels, no restrooms**
106mm	**rest area nb, litter barrels, no restrooms**
104	Sandersville, no facilities

Laurel / Hattiesburg

99	US 11, **E...gas:** T&B's/diesel, **lodging:** Magnolia Motel, **other:** KOA(1mi)
97	US 84 E, **E...gas:** Exxon/diesel, Kangaroo/Subway/diesel/24hr, **food:** Doc's Rest., Hardee's, **W...gas:** BP/diesel, Texaco/24hr, **food:** KFC, Vic's Biscuits/burgers
96b	MS 15 S, Cook Ave, no facilities
a	Masonite Rd, 4th Ave, no facilities
95d	(from nb), no facilities
c	Beacon St, Laurel, **E...gas:** Texaco, **W...gas:** Chevron, PumpSave Gas, **food:** BBQ, Burger King, Church's, McDonald's, Old Mexico, Popeye's, **lodging:** Town-House Motel/rest., **other:** Country Mkt Foods, Family$, JC Penney, USPO, XpertTire
b a	US 84 W, MS 15 N, 16th Ave, Laurel, **W...gas:** Amoco, Exxon/diesel, **food:** DQ, KFC, McAlister's Deli, McDonald's, Pizza Hut, Shoney's, Subway, Taco Bell, Waffle House, Wendy's, **lodging:** Comfort Suites, Econolodge, Executive Inn, Hampton Inn, Holiday Inn Express, Ramada Inn, Super 8, **other:** HOSPITAL, Advance Parts, $General, Piggly Wiggly
93	US 11, S Laurel, **W...gas:** Citgo/diesel, Exxon/Subway/diesel, Shell/diesel/24hr, **food:** Hardee's
90	US 11, Ellisville Blvd, **W...gas:** Dixie/diesel
88	MS 588, MS 29, Ellisville, **E...gas:** Chevron/diesel, FasTrac, **food:** Domino's, KFC, McDonald's, Pizza Hut, Subway, **other:** Food Tiger, Family$, NAPA, **W...gas:** Exxon/diesel, Shell, **food:** Glenda's Diner, **lodging:** Best Western
85	MS 590, to Ellisville, **W...food:** Red Barn Café
80	to US 11, Moselle, **E...gas:** BP/diesel
78	Sanford Rd, no facilities
76	**W**...Hattiesburg-Laurel Reg Airport
73	Monroe Rd, to Monroe, no facilities
69	to Glendale, Eatonville Rd, no facilities
67b a	US 49, Hattiesburg, **E...gas:** Exxon, Shell, Texaco/Krystal, **food:** Arby's, Burger King, Cracker Barrel, DQ, KFC, McDonald's, Pizza Hut, Taco Bell, Waffle House, **lodging:** Comfort Inn, Econolodge, Holiday Inn, Howard Johnson, Inn on the Hill, Motel 6, Ramada Ltd, Regency Inn, Scottish Inn, Super 8, **W...gas:** Amoco/diesel, MapleLeaf/diesel, Pure/diesel, RaceWay, Shell/Subway, Stuckey's/diesel, **food:** Sonic, Waffle House, Ward's Burgers, **lodging:** Best Western, Hawthorn Suites

MISSISSIPPI

Interstate 59

N
S

Hattiesburg

65b a	US 98 W, Hardy St, Hattiesburg, **E..gas:** Conoco, Exxon, Shell/diesel, Texaco, **food:** Applebee's, Buffalo Wings, Burger King, CiCi's, Domino's, Hong Kong Buffet, IHOP, KFC, Krystal, Lenny's Subs, Lucky Dogs Café, McDonald's, Mr Gatti's, Panino's Italian, Pizza Hut, Steak-Out, Subway, Taco Bell, Ward's Burgers, **lodging:** Day's Inn, Fairfield Inn, Western Motel, **other:** MEDICAL CARE, Eckerd, Goodyear/auto, Home Depot, S MS U, **W...gas:** Amoco/diesel, BP/Subway/diesel, Exxon/Domino's, Kangaroo, Shell, **food:** Backyard Burger, Burger King, Chili's, Copeland's Rest., Hardee's, La Fiesta Brava, LoneStar Steaks, Mandarin House, Mazzio's, McAlister's Deli, McDonald's, O'Charley's, Outback Steaks, Pizza Hut, Popeye's, Red Lobster, Ryan's, Schlotsky's, Taco Bell, Waffle House, Wendy's, **lodging:** Baymont Inn, Comfort Inn, Hampton Inn, Villager Lodge, **other:** HOSPITAL, Advance Parts, BooksAMillion, Dillard's, Firestone/auto, Goodyear/auto, JC Penney, Lowe's Whse, Office Depot, Radio Shack, Rite Aid, SaveRite Foods, Sam's Club/gas, Walgreen, Wal-Mart SuperCtr/24hr, mall
60	US 11, S Hattiesburg, **E...gas:** Shell/diesel, **W...gas:** Amoco/diesel, Kangaroo/Subway/diesel/24hr
59	US 98 E, to US 49, MS Gulf Coast, to Lucedale, Mobile, no facilities
56mm	**rest area both lanes, litter barrels, no restrooms**
51	MS 589, to Purvis, **2 mi W...gas:** Shell/diesel, **food:** Pizza Hut, to Little Black Cr Water Park
48mm	Little Black Creek
41	MS 13, to Lumberton, **W...gas:** Pure, **other:** $General, to Little Black Cr Water Park
35	Hillsdale Rd, **E...gas:** Pure/diesel, **lodging:** to Georgetowne Inn, to Lake Hillside Resort
32mm	Wolf River
29	MS 26, to Poplarville, **2 mi W...gas:** Kangaroo/diesel, **food:** Burger King
27	MS 53, to Poplarville, **W...gas:** Shell, **other:** Haciendas Camping(2mi)
19	to US 11, Millard, no facilities
15	to McNeill, **W...gas:** McNeill Trkstop/diesel/rest.
13mm	**rest area sb, litter barrels, no restrooms**
10	to US 11, Carriere, **E...gas:** Hilda's/diesel, **food:** Sherryl's Rest., **other:** Clearwater RV Camp(5mi)
8mm	**rest area nb, litter barrels, no restrooms**
6	MS 43 N, N Picayune, **W...gas:** Chevron/diesel, **food:** Paul's Pastries(3mi), **lodging:** Budget Host, Picayune Motel(1mi), **other:** HOSPITAL, Eckerd, Winn-Dixie

Picayune

4	MS 43 S, to Picayune, **E...food:** McDonald's, Ryan's, **other:** Chevrolet/Pontiac/Buick/Cadillac, Wal-Mart SuperCtr/gas/24hr, **W...gas:** BP/diesel, Exxon/diesel, Shell/diesel, Spur, Texaco/diesel, **food:** Burger King, Domino's, Godfather's, Hardee's, KFC, McDonald's, Papa John's, Pizza Hut, Popeye's, Shoney's, Taco Bell, Waffle House, Wendy's, **lodging:** Comfort Inn, Day's Inn, Heritage Inn, **other:** HOSPITAL, Advance Parts, AutoZone, Chrysler/Plymouth/Dodge/Jeep, Firestone/auto, Ford/Lincoln/Mercury, Radio Shack, Rite Aid, Winn-Dixie
3mm	**Welcome Ctr nb, full(handicapped)facilties, phone, vending, picnic tables, litter barrels, petwalk, RV dump**
1.5mm	weigh sta both lanes
1	US 11, MS 607, NASA, **W...gas:** Chevron/diesel
0mm	**Pearl River, Mississippi/Louisiana state line. Exits 11-1 are in Louisiana.**
11	Pearl River Turnaround. Callboxes begin sb.
5b	Honey Island Swamp, no facilities
a	LA 41, Pearl River, **E...gas:** Chevron/gifts
3	US 11 S, LA 1090, Pearl River, **W...gas:** Shell/Subway/diesel, **1 mi W...**Chevron/diesel/24hr, **food:** D&K Rest.
1.5mm	**Welcome Ctr sb, full(handicapped)facilities, info, phone, picnic tables, litter barrels, petwalk, RV dump**
1c b	I-10, E to Bay St Louis, W to New Orleans
a	I-12 W, to Hammond. I-59 begins/ends on I-10/I-12. **Exits 1-11 are in Louisiana.**

Interstate 220(Jackson)

Exit #	Services
11mm	I-220 begins/ends on I-55, exit 104.
9	Hanging Moss Rd, County Line Rd, **E...gas:** BP
8	Watkins Dr, **E...gas:** Shell, Spur
5b a	US 49 N, Evers Blvd, to Yazoo City, **E...lodging:** Star Motel, Family$, Sack&Save Foods, **W...gas:** Amoco, Exxon/Burger King/diesel, Shell/Subway/diesel, **other:** Penske
2b a	Clinton Blvd, Capitol St, **E...**to Jackson Zoo, **W...gas:** RaceWay, Shell, **food:** Burger King, McDonald's, Pizza Hut, Popeye's, Sonic
1b a	US 80, **E...gas:** Jubilee, **food:** BBQ, Capt D's, Denny's, KFC, Taco Bell, Wendy's, Western Sizzlin, **lodging:** Day's Inn, Econolodge, Sleep Inn, **W...gas:** BP, Exxon/Subway/diesel, **food:** Arby's, El Chico, Krystal, McDonald's, Piccadilly's, Pizza Hut, Popeye's, Ruby Tuesday, Wendy's, **other:** Dillard's, Ford, McRae's, Sears/auto, mall
0mm	I-220 begins/ends on I-20, exit 41.

E
W

Jackson

Interstate 29

N

↑

↓

S

Exit #	Services
124mm	Missouri/Iowa state line
123mm	Nishnabotna River
121.5mm	weigh sta both lanes
116	rd A, rd B, to Watson, no facilities
110	US 136, Rock Port, Phelps City, **E...gas:** Conoco/Subway/diesel, Shell/diesel, **lodging:** Rockport Inn, White Rock Motel(2mi), to NW MO St U, **W...gas:** Amoco/diesel/24hr, Phillips 66/diesel/24hr, **food:** McDonald's, Trails End Rest., **lodging:** Super 8, **other:** KOA
109.5mm	**Welcome Ctr sb, full(handicapped)facilities, info, phone, picnic tables, litter barrels, petwalk**
107	MO 111, to Rock Port, **W...lodging:** Elk Inn/RV Park/café
106.5mm	Rock Creek
102mm	Mill Creek
99	rd W, Corning, **E...gas:** Citgo/diesel
97mm	Tarkio River

92	US 59, Craig, to Fairfax, **W...gas:** Shell
90.5mm	Little Tarkio Creek
86.5mm	Squaw Creek
84	MO 118, Mound City, **E...gas:** Phillips 66/diesel, Shamrock/diesel, Sinclair, **food:** Hardee's, Quacker's Steaks, **lodging:** Audrey's Motel, Super 8, **other:** Dodge/Plymouth/Jeep, **W...gas:** King/Shell/Taco Bell/diesel/24hr/@, **other:** Big Lake SP(12mi)
82mm	**rest area both lanes, full(handicapped)facilities, phone, picnic tables, litter barrels, vending, petwalk**
79	US 159, Rulo, **E...gas:** Conoco/diesel/rest./24hr, **other:** RV camping/dump, **W...to** Big Lake SP(12mi), to Squaw Creek NWR(3mi)
78mm	Kimsey Creek
75	US 59, to Oregon, no facilities
67	US 59 N, to Oregon, no facilities
66.5mm	Nodaway River
65	US 59, rd RA, to Fillmore, Savannah, **E...gas:** Conoco/diesel, **other:** antiques

MISSOURI

Interstate 29

St Joseph

60	rd K, rd CC, Amazonia, **W...other:** Hunt's Fruit Barn, antiques
58.5mm	Hopkins Creek
56b a	I-229 S, US 71 N, US 59 N, to St Joseph, Maryville, no facilities
55mm	Dillon Creek
53	US 59, US 71 bus, to St Joseph, Savannah, **E...AOK** Camping, **W...gas:** Phillips 66/diesel
50	US 169, King City, St Joseph, **1-3 mi W on Cook Rd...gas:** Conoco/Domino's, **food:** Hardee's, LJ Silver, McDonald's, Ryan's, Taco Bell, Wendy's, **other:** Lowe's Whse, Wal-Mart SuperCtr/24hr
47	MO 6, Frederick Blvd, St Joseph, to Clarksdale, **E...gas:** Conoco, **food:** Country Kitchen, Grandma's BBQ, **lodging:** Day's Inn, Drury Inn, **W...gas:** Sinclair, Phillips 66/diesel, **food:** Applebee's, Carlos O'Kelly's, Cracker Barrel, Denny's, KFC, McDonald's, Perkins/24hr, Red Lobster, Sonic, Subway, Taco Bell, Whiskey Creek Steaks, **lodging:** Comfort Suites, Hampton Inn, Motel 6, Ramada Inn, Stoney Creek Inn, Super 8, **other:** HOSPITAL, Chevrolet/Mazda, Dillard's, Ford, Firestone/auto, Goodyear/auto, Sears, RV camp, **1 mi W on US 169...food:** Blimpie, Burger King, Church's, Fazoli's, Ground Round, Pizza Hut, Schlotsky's, Sonic, Taco Bell, **other:** Advance Parts, Aldi Foods, AutoZone, Cub Foods, Eckerd, Food4Less/drugs/24hr, Hastings Books, JC Penney, Jo-Ann Fabrics, Office Depot, Radio Shack, Walgreen
46b a	US 36, St Joseph, to Cameron, **1 mi W on US 169...gas:** BP, Phillips 66, Shell, **food:** Burger King, Godfather's, Pizza Hut, Taco John's, Wendy's, **other:** $General, Isuzu, Kia, Nissan, Save-A-Lot Foods, Wal-Mart SuperCtr/gas/24hr, to MO W St Coll
44	US 169, St Joseph, to Gower, **E...gas:** Phillips 66/Subway, **food:** BBQ, LP, **lodging:** Best Western, **other:** tires, **W...gas:** Shell/diesel/24hr/@, **food:** McDonald's, **other:** Chrysler/Jeep/Dodge, Food4Less, Goodyear, Harley-Davidson, Hyundai, Wal-Mart SuperCtr/gas/24hr
43	I-229 N, to St Joseph, no facilities
39.5mm	Pigeon Creek
35	rd DD, Faucett, **W...gas:** Farris/Phillips 66/Subway/diesel/motel/24hr/@, **food:** Oliver's Rest.
33.5mm	Bee Creek
30	rd Z, rd H, Dearborn, New Market, **E...gas:** Conoco/diesel/24hr
29.5mm	Bee Creek
27mm	**rest area both lanes, full(handicapped)facilities, phone, picnic tables, litter barrels, vending, pet-walk**
25	rd E, rd U, to Camden Point, **E...gas:** Phillips 66/diesel/rest.

Platte City

Kansas City

24mm	weigh sta both lanes
20	MO 92, MO 273, to Atchison, Leavenworth, **W...gas:** Phillips 66, **other:** to Weston Bend SP
19.5mm	Platte River
19	rd HH, Platte City(sb returns at 18), **E...antiques, W...gas:** Amoco, Casey's, Conoco, Phillips 66/diesel, **food:** DQ, Marko's Pizza, **lodging:** Comfort Inn, Super 8, **other:** Dodge, CarQuest, CountryMart Foods, Saturn, USPO, same as 18
18	MO 92, Platte City, **E...Basswood** RV Park, **W...gas:** Amoco, Conoco/KFC, QT/diesel, **food:** Burger King, McDonald's, Mr GoodCents Subs, Pizza Shoppe, Subway, Taco Bell, Waffle House, Wendy's, **lodging:** AmericInn, Comfort Inn, Super 8, **other:** Chevrolet/Pontiac/GMC, Ford, Saturn, same as 19
17	I-435 S, to Topeka
15	Mexico City Ave, **W...lodging:** Marriott
14	I-435 E(from sb), to St Louis
13	to I-435 E, **E...lodging:** Best Western, Comfort Suites, Extended Stay America, Fairfield Inn, Hampton Inn, Holiday Inn, Microtel, Radisson, **W...lodging:** Marriott, **other:** KCI Airport
12	NW 112th St, **E...gas:** Amoco, Conoco, **food:** Allie's Rest., **lodging:** Day's Inn, Hampton Inn, Hilton, Holiday Inn Express, Radisson, **W...lodging:** Econolodge
10	Tiffany Springs Pkwy, **E...gas:** Shell, **food:** Jade Garden, SmokeBox BBQ, Embassy Suites, Homewood Suites, **W...food:** Cracker Barrel, Ruby Tuesday, Wendy's, **lodging:** AmeriSuites, Chase Suites, Courtyard, Drury Inn, MainStay Suites, Ramada Inn, Residence Inn, Sleep Inn, **other:** Saturn, Toyota
9b a	MO 152, to Liberty, Topeka
8	MO 9, rd T, NW Barry Rd, **E...gas:** Total, **food:** Applebee's, Bob Evans, Boston Mkt, Chili's, Einstein Bros, 54th St Grill, Godfather's, Hooters, Kato Japanese, LoneStar Steaks, On the Border, Panera Bread, Pizza Hut/Taco Bell, Starbucks, Subway, Waid's Rest., Wendy's, Winstead's Rest., **other:** HOSPITAL, Barnes&Noble, Eckerd, HyVee Foods, Lowe's Whse, OfficeMax, Old Navy, SteinMart, Wal-Mart SuperCtr/24hr, **W...gas:** Citgo, Phillips 66, QT/diesel, **food:** Hardee's, LJ Silver/A&W, McDonald's, Minsky's Pizza, OutBack Steaks, Rainbow Oriental, Taco John's, **lodging:** Country Hearth Inn, Motel 6, Super 8, **other:** Tires+
6	NW 72nd St, Platte Woods, **E...gas:** Sinclair/diesel, **W...gas:** Phillips 66, Shell, **food:** Jazz Kitchen, Papa John's, Pizza Hut, Pizza Shoppe, Tasty Thai, **other:** IGA Foods, K-Mart/Little Caesar's
5	MO 45 N, NW 64th St, **W...gas:** Shell, **food:** Henhouse Deli, IHOP, McDonald's, O'Quigley's Grill, Silvio's Pizza, Subway, **other:** $General, GNC, Goodyear, Osco Drug, Radio Shack
4	NW 56th St(from nb), **W...gas:** Phillips 66, same as 5

Interstate 29

N / S

3c	rd A(from sb), Riverside, **W...gas:** QT, **food:** Argosy Café, Corner Café, Sonic, **lodging:** Skyline Inn, Super 8, **other:** USPO
b	I-635 S, no facilities
a	Waukomis Dr, rd AA(from nb), no facilities
2b	US 169 S(from sb), to KC, no facilities
a	US 169 N(from nb), to Smithville, no facilities
1e	US 69, Vivion Rd, **E...food:** Steak'n Shake, **other:** Chrysler/Plymouth, Chevrolet/Cadillac, Home Depot, Lincoln/Mercury, Mitsubishi, OfficeMax, PriceChopper Foods/24hr, **W...gas:** QT, **food:** McDonald's
d	MO 283 S, Oak Tfwy(from sb)
c	Gladstone(from nb), **E...food:** Arby's, Perkins, Pizza St Buffet, Ryan's, Smokehouse BBQ, Tippen's Café
b	I-35 N(from sb), to Des Moines
a	Davidson Rd, **E...gas:** Shell, **other:** O'Reilly Parts, **W...lodging:** Travelodge
8mm	I-35 N. I-29 and I-35 run together 6 mi.

See Missouri Interstate 35, exits 3-8a.

I-29 begins/ends on I-70.

Interstate 35

N / S

Exit #	Services
114mm	Missouri/Iowa state line
114	US 69, to Lamoni, **W...gas:** Conoco/diesel/24hr
113.5mm	Zadie Creek
110	weigh sta both lanes
106	rd N, Blythedale, **E...gas:** Conoco/fireworks, Phillips 66/diesel/café/motel/24hr, **other:** diesel repair, Eagle's Landing Motel, **W...gas:** Shell/diesel/24hr, **other:** camping
99	rd A, to Ridgeway, **5 mi W...**Eagle RV Camping
94mm	E Fork Big Creek
93	US 69, Bethany, **W...food:** Dos Chiquitos Mexican, **other:** RV dump
92	US 136, Bethany, **E...gas:** Conoco/diesel/24hr, Phillips 66/diesel/24hr, **food:** KFC/Taco Bell, McDonald's, **lodging:** Budget Inn, **W...gas:** Amoco/diesel, Casey's, Kum&Go/Wendy's/diesel, MFA Oil/diesel, **food:** Burger King, Country Kitchen, DQ, Pizza Hut, Subway, TootToot Rest., **lodging:** Best Western, Super 8, **other:** HOSPITAL, Chevrolet/Buick, Wal-Mart, **1 mi W...gas:** Ford/Lincoln/Mercury, **other:** Hy-Vee Foods
90mm	Pole Cat Creek
88	MO 13, to Bethany, Gallatin, **3 mi W...lodging:** Bethany Motel
84	rds AA, H, to Gilman City, **E...**Crowder SP(24mi)
81mm	**rest area both lanes, full(handicapped)facilities, phone, picnic tables, litter barrels, vending, petwalk**
80	rds B, N, to Coffey, no facilities
78	rd C, Pattonsburg, **W...gas:** Total/diesel, **other:** antiques

74.5mm	Grand River
72	rd DD, no facilities
68	US 69, to Pattonsburg, no facilities
64	MO 6, to Maysville, Gallatin, no facilities
61	US 69, Winston, Gallatin, **E...gas:** Shell/diesel/rest./24hr/@
54	US 36, Cameron, **E...gas:** Amoco/diesel/24hr, Cenex/diesel, Shell/Wendy's/diesel/24hr, **food:** McDonald's, Subway, **lodging:** Best Western, Comfort Inn, Crossroads Inn/RV Park, **W...gas:** Phillips 66, Shamrock, **food:** Burger King, DQ, Kettle Diner, KFC/Taco Bell, Pizza Hut, Sonic, Subway, **lodging:** Day's Inn, Econolodge, Holiday Inn Express, Super 8, **other:** HOSPITAL, Advance Parts, **other:** Chevrolet, CountryMart Foods, $General, Ford/Mercury, Goodyear, Radio Shack, Wal-Mart SuperCtr/24hr, W MO Corr Ctr
52	rd BB, Lp 35, to Cameron, **E...**MEDICAL CARE, **W...gas:** Casey's, same as 54
49mm	Brushy Creek
48.5mm	Shoal Creek
48	US 69, Cameron, **E...**Down Under RV Park, to Wallace SP(2mi), **W...gas:** Total, fireworks
40	MO 116, Lathrop, **E...gas:** Phillips 66/Country Café/diesel
35mm	**rest area sb, full(handicapped)facilities, phone, picnic tables, litter barrels, vending, petwalk**
34mm	**rest area nb, full(handicapped)facilities, phone, picnic tables, litter barrels, vending, petwalk**
33	rd PP, Holt, **E...food:** Rock Front Steaks, **W...gas:** Conoco/diesel, Phillips 66/diesel, **lodging:** Holt Steel Inn
30mm	Holt Creek
26	MO 92, Kearney, **E...gas:** Casey's/gas, Conoco/diesel, Shell/diesel, **food:** Kookie's Pizza, McDonald's, Sonic, **lodging:** Day's Inn, Super 8, **other:** CountryMart Foods, to Watkins Mill SP, **W...gas:** Conoco/diesel/24hr, **food:** Arby's, Burger King, Hunan Garden Chinese, Subway, **lodging:** Country Hearth Inn, Econolodge, **other:** Chevrolet, Family$, to Smithville Lake
22mm	weigh sta both lanes
20	US 69, MO 33, to Excelsior Springs, **E...**HOSPITAL
17	MO 291, rd A, **1 mi E...food:** Arby's, CiCi's, LJ Silver, Perkins, Ponderosa, **other:** Chevrolet, CountryMart Foods, Eckerd, Hy-Vee Foods, Liberty RV Ctr, Village Lodge, Walgreen, same as 16, **W...gas:** Phillips 66/diesel, **other:** KCI Airport

MISSOURI

Interstate 35

E → W

Liberty

16 MO 152, Liberty, **E...gas:** Conoco/diesel, Shell, **food:** A&W, Godfather's, Perkins, KFC, Little Caesar's, LJ Silver, Pizza Hut, Ponderosa, Subway, Taco Bell, **lodging:** Village Inn Rest., Wendy's, Super 8, **other:** HOSPITAL, Chevrolet, Firestone/auto, Ford, K-Mart, **W...gas:** Phillips 66, **food:** Applebee's, Backyard Burger, Bob Evans, Burger King, Chili's, Country Kitchen, Cracker Barrel, 54th St Grill, Golden Corral, LongHorn Steaks, McDonald's, Schlotsky's, SmokeStack BBQ, Steak'n Shake, Waffle House, **lodging:** Comfort Suites, Fairfield Inn, Hampton Inn, Holiday Inn, Express, **other:** Home Depot, Michael's, NAPA AutoCare, Target, Wal-MartSuperCtr/24hr

14 US 69(exits left from sb), Liberty Dr, Pleasant Valley, to Glenaire, **E...gas:** Conoco/diesel, Sinclair, Texaco, **other:** I-35 RV Ctr, **W...gas:** QT/diesel

13 US 69(from nb), to Pleasant Valley, **E...gas:** Phillips 66/diesel, Shell/A&W, Sinclair/24hr, **food:** KFC, McDonald's, **other:** auto repair, **W...gas:** QT/diesel

12b a I-435, to St Louis

11 US 69 N, Vivion Rd, **E...gas:** QT, **food:** Church's, McDonald's, Sonic, Stroud's Rest., same as 10

10 N Brighton Ave(from nb), **E...gas:** QT, **food:** Church's, McDonald's, Sonic, Stroud's Rest.

9 MO 269 S, Chouteau Trfwy, **E...gas:** Phillips 66, **food:** IHOP, Outback Steaks, Papa Murphy's, Popeye's, Subway, **other:** Food Festival, Harrah's Casino/rest., Radio Shack, Target, **W...gas:** Amoco, Wendy's

8c MO 1, Antioch Rd, **E...gas:** Citgo/7-11, Sinclair, **food:** Country Girl Rest., Domino's, **lodging:** Best Western, InnTown Inn, **W...gas:** Phillips 66, **food:** Catfish Rest., Waffle House

b I-29 N, US 71 N, KCI airport

I-35 S and I-29 S run together 6 mi

8a Parvin Rd, **E...gas:** Shell, **other:** O'Reilly Parts, **lodging:** Super 8, **W...lodging:** Travelodge

6b a Armour Rd, **E...gas:** Phillips 66/diesel, **food:** Arby's, Burger King, Capt D's, Denny's, McDonald's, **lodging:** Baymont Inn, Day's Inn, **other:** HOSPITAL, repair, to Riverboat Casino, **W...gas:** QT, Phillips 66, Shell, **food:** DQ, LJ Silver, Juanito's Mexican, Pizza Hut, Taco Bell, Wendy's, **lodging:** American Inn, Country Hearth Suites

Kansas City

5b 16th Ave, industrial district

a Levee Rd, Bedford St, industrial district

4.5mm Missouri River

4b Front St, **E...**Riverboat Casino/rest.

a US 24 E, Independence Ave, no facilities

3 I-70 E, US 71 S, to St Louis, no facilities

2n I-35 N and I-29 N run together 6 mi

2f Oak St, Grand-Walnut St, downtown, **E...lodging:** Super 8, **W...gas:** Conoco

Interstate 35

d Main-Delaware, Wyandotte St, downtown

c Broadway, downtown

a I-70 W, to Topeka

w 12th St, Kemper Arena

u I-70 E, to St Louis

1d 20th St(from sb), no facilities

c b 27th St, SW Blvd, W Pennway(from nb), **E...**HOSPITAL

a SW Trafficway(from sb), no facilities

0mm Missouri/Kansas state line

Interstate 44

E → W

Exit #	Services
290mm	I-44 begins/ends on I-55, exit 207 in St Louis.
290a	I-55 S, to Memphis
290c	Gravois Ave(from wb), 12th St, **N...gas:** Citgo, **S...food:** McDonald's
290b	18th St(from eb), downtown
289	Jefferson Ave, St Louis, **N...gas:** Citgo, Vickers, **food:** Subway, **lodging:** Holiday Inn Express, **S...food:** McDonald's
288	Grand Blvd, St Louis, **N...**HOSPITAL, **S...food:** Jack-in-the-Box
287b a	Kingshighway, Vandeventer Ave, St Louis, **N...gas:** Amoco, **S...gas:** Amoco, **other:** Chevrolet, Chrysler, Walgreen, to MO Botanical Garden
286	Hampton Ave, St Louis, **N...gas:** Mobil, Shell, **food:** Denny's, Jack-in-the-Box, McDonald's, Steak'n Shake, Subway, Taco Bell, **S...gas:** Shell, **food:** Burger King, Church's, Hardee's, Village Inn Rest., **lodging:** Holiday Inn, Red Roof Inn, **other:** museums, zoo
285	SW Ave(from wb, no EZ return), no facilities
284b a	Arsenal St, Jamieson St, no facilities
283	Shrewsbury(from wb), some services same as 282
282	Laclede Sta Rd, Murdock Ave(from eb), St Louis, **N...gas:** Amoco, Mobil, **food:** Pantera's Pizza, McDonald's, **other:** Subaru
280	Elm Ave, St Louis, **N...gas:** Amoco/repair, **food:** Steak'n Shake, **other:** Schnuck's Food/24hr, **S...gas:** Shell, **other:** Radiator King
279	(from wb), Berry Rd
278	Big Bend Rd, St Louis, **N...other:** HOSPITAL, Sam's Club, **S...gas:** Mobil/diesel, QT, Sinclair
277b	US 67, US 61, US 50, Lindbergh Blvd, **N...gas:** Shell, **food:** Hardee's, **lodging:** Best Western, **other:** HOSPITAL, Hancock Fabrics, Lowe's Whse, Target, Wal-Mart SuperCtr/24hr, **S...gas:** CFM/diesel, Shell, Vickers, **food:** Bob Evans, Burger King, Denny's, Longhorn Steaks, Steak'n Shake, St Louis Bread, Viking Rest., **lodging:** Comfort Inn, Day's Inn, Econolodge, Hampton Inn, Holiday Inn, **other:** CompUSA, Home Depot, Old Navy, WorldMkt
277a	MO 366 E, Watson Rd, access to same as 277b S
276b a	I-270, S Memphis, N to Chicago, no facilities
275	N Highway Dr(from wb), Soccer Pk Rd, **N...gas:** Texaco/diesel/rest./@

St Louis

Interstate 44

E ↕ **W**

274	Bowles Ave, **N...gas:** Shell/diesel, **S...gas:** Amoco, Citgo/diesel/24hr, QT, **food:** Bandana's BBQ, Cracker Barrel, Denny's, Krispy Kreme, McDonald's, Quizno's, Souper Salad, White Castle, **lodging:** Drury Inn, Econolodge, Fairfield Inn, Holiday Inn Express, Motel 6, PearTree Inn, Stratford Inn, **other:** Goodyear
272	MO 141, Fenton, Valley Park, **N...gas:** Motomart, **S...gas:** Citgo/7-11, Phillips 66, QT, Shell, **food:** Burger King, Krispy Kreme, McDonald's, Steak'n Shake, Subway, Taco Bell, **other:** Wet Willie's Waterslide
269	Antire Rd, Beaumont, no facilities
266	Lewis Rd, **N...other:** Rte 66 SP, golf
266mm	Meramec River
265	Williams Rd(from eb), no facilities
264	MO 109, rd W, Eureka, **N...gas:** Citgo/7-11, Shell, **food:** Burger King, DQ, KFC, McDonald's, Pizza Hut, Ponderosa, Smokers BBQ, Subway, Taco Bell, Wendy's, White Castle, **lodging:** Day's Inn, **other:** AutoTire, Byerly RV Ctr, Firestone, NAPA, Schnuck's Foods, to Babler SP, **S...gas:** QT/diesel/@, Shell
261	Lp 44, to Allenton, **N...gas:** Motomart/McDonald'sdiesel, **food:** Applebee's, China King, Country Kitchen, Denny's, KFC, Lion's Choice Rest., Steak'n Shake, **lodging:** Ramada Inn, Red Carpet Inn, Super 8, **other:** MEDICAL CARE, AutoZone, $Tree, GNC, Radio Shack, Wal-Mart SuperCtr/24hr, to Six Flags, same as 264, **S...gas:** Phillips 66/diesel/rest., Shell/diesel, **other:** Ford, KOA
257	Lp 44, Pacific, **N...lodging:** Comfort Inn, **S...gas:** Mobil/diesel/24hr, Motomart/24hr, Voss/diesel, **food:** Hardee's, KFC, McDonald's, Pizza Hut, Taco Bell, **lodging:** Holiday Inn Express, **other:** Buick/Chevrolet, Chrysler/Jeep/Dodge, IGA Foods, NAPA
253	MO 100 E, to Gray Summit, **S...gas:** Phillips 66, **lodging:** Best Western, Gardenway Motel
251	MO 100 W, to Washington, **N...gas:** Conoco/diesel/24hr, FuelMart/Blimpie/diesel/24hr, Mr Fuel/diesel, Phillips 66/Burger King/diesel, **food:** Tri-County Rest.
247mm	Bourbeuse River
247	US 50 W, rd AT, rd O, to Union, **N...other:** Harley-Davidson, **other:** Pin Oak Creek Camping, flea mkt, **S...**to Robertsville SP
242	rd AH, to Hist Rte 66
240	MO 47, St Clair, **N...gas:** Phillips 66/Taco Bell/diesel, Sinclair, **food:** Burger King, El Palenque Mexican, **other:** Reed RV Ctr, **S...gas:** Mobil/diesel, **food:** Hardee's, McDonald's, Subway, **lodging:** Budget Lodge, Super 8, **other:** $General, IGA Foods
239	MO 30, rds AB, WW, St Clair, **N...**repair, **S...gas:** Amoco
238mm	weigh sta both lanes
235mm	**rest area both lanes(both lanes exit left), full(handicapped)facilities, phone, picnic tables, litter barrels, vending, petwalk**

S u l l i v a n

R o l l a

230	rds W, JJ, Stanton, **N...lodging:** Stanton Motel, **S... food:** BS Boogie's Rest., **other:** KOA, Meramec Caverns Camping(3mi)
226	MO 185 S, Sullivan, **S...gas:** ✈/Flying J/ Conoco/Country Mkt/ diesel/LP/24hr/@, **S...gas:** Phillips 66/Burger King, **food:** Denny's, Golden Corral, Hardee's, KFC, Steak'n Shake, Taco Bell, **other:** O'Reilly Parts, Wal-Mart SuperCtr/24hr, KOA(1mi), to Meramec SP, same as 225
225	MO 185 N, rd D, Sullivan, **N...gas:** Mobil, Phillips 66/diesel, **food:** Domino's, **lodging:** Baymont Inn, Econolodge, Family Inn, Ramada Inn, Super 8, **other:** Chrysler/ Plymouth/Dodge/Jeep, Ford/Mercury, **S...gas:** Bobber/ diesel/café/@, Citgo, Capt D's, **food:** Jack-in-the-Box, McDonald's, Pizza Hut, Sonic, Subway, **lodging:** Sullivan Motel, **other:** HOSPITAL, Aldi Foods, Chevrolet/Buick, Goodyear, NAPA, same as 226
218	rds N, C, J, Bourbon, **N...gas:** Citgo/diesel, **lodging:** Budget Inn, **S...gas:** Mobil/24hr, **food:** HenHouse Rest., **other:** Suburban RV Ctr, Blue Sprgs Camping(6mi), Riverview Ranch Camping(8mi)
214	rd H, Leasburg, **N...gas:** Mobil/diesel, **S...other:** to Onandaga Cave SP(7mi), camping
210	rd UU, **S...food:** FeedLot Steaks, MO Hick BBQ, Mt Peasant Winery
208	MO 19, Cuba, **N...gas:** Phillips 66, Voss/diesel/rest./ 24hr/@, **food:** Country Kitchen, Huddle House, Kum&Get It Buffet, Pizza Hut, **lodging:** Best Western, Super 8, **other:** Blue Beacon, **S...gas:** Casey's, Delano/diesel, Mobil/Taco Bell/24hr, **food:** Burger King, East Sun Chinese, McDonald's, Pizza Pro, Sonic, Subway, **lodging:** Holiday Inn Express, **other:** Chevrolet/GMC, O'Reilly Parts, Wal-Mart/drugs, to Ozark Nat Scenic Riverways
203	rds F, ZZ, **N...**Blue Moon RV Park, **S...**Rosati Winery(2mi)
195	MO 8, MO 68, St James, Maramec Sprg Park, **N...gas:** Conoco/diesel, Mobil/Taco Bell/diesel, Phillips 66/diesel, **food:** John's Café, McDonald's, Pizza Hut, Subway, **lodging:** Comfort Inn, Economy Inn, **other:** Ford, NAPA, O'Reilly Parts, St James Winery, laundry, **S...gas:** Delano/ diesel, Phillips 66/diesel, S Gas, **food:** Burger King, **lodging:** Finn's Motel, **other:** CountryMart Foods, Pamida
189	rd V, **S...**antiques
186	US 63, MO 72, Rolla, **N...gas:** Sinclair, **food:** Steak'n Shake, **lodging:** Drury Inn, Hampton Inn, Sooter Inn, **other:** Lowe's Whse, **S...gas:** Amoco/24hr, Conoco, Mobil, Phillips 66, **food:** Denny's, Domino's, Donut King, Fortune Chinese, Lee's Chicken, St Louis Bread, Waffle House, **other:** HOSPITAL

MISSOURI

Interstate 44

E ← → **W** | **Rolla**

185   rd E, to Rolla, **S...gas:** Phillips 66, **food:** Arby's, DQ, Hardee's/24hr, Subway, Taco Bell, **other:** HOSPITAL, UMO at Rolla, st patrol

184   US 63 S, to Rolla, **N...lodging:** Comfort Inn, **S...gas:** MotoMart, Phillips 66, Shell, StationBreak, Shell, **food:** Arby's, Burger King, Domino's, El Rodeo Mexican, Golden Corral, Ground Round, KFC, Kyoto Japanese, Little Caesar's, LJ Silver, McDonald's, Papa John's, Pizza Hut, Pizza Inn, Shoney's, Sirloin Stockade, Subway, Taco Hut, Wendy's, Zeno's Steaks, **lodging:** Bestway Motel, Best Western, Chalet Motel, Day's Inn, Econolodge, Holiday Inn Express, Howard Johnson/rest., Interstate Motel, Ramada Inn, Super 8, Travelodge, Wayfarer Inn, Western Inn, **other:** HOSPITAL, Chevrolet, Ford/Lincoln/Mercury, Kroger, Wal-Mart, transmissions

179   rds T, C, to Doolittle, Newburg, **S...gas:** BP/24hr, **food:** Cookin' From Scratch Rest.

178mm rest area both lanes, full(handicapped)facilities, phone, picnic tables, litter barrels, vending, pet-walk

176   Sugar Tree Rd, **N...lodging:** Vernell's Motel, **S...** camping

172   rd D, Jerome, **N...**camping

169   rd J, no facilities

164mm Big Piney River

166   to Big Piney

163   MO 28, to Dixon, **N...gas:** Voss Truckport/diesel/café/repair/24hr/@, **food:** Ozark Crafts, **S...gas:** Conoco, **food:** Country Café, Sweetwater BBQ, **lodging:** Best Western, Day's Inn, Super 8, Village Lodge

161b a   rd Y, to Ft Leonard Wood, **N...gas:** Mobil, **food:** Aussie Jack's Café, Cracker Barrel, Jack's Diner, LJ Silver/A&W, Pizza Hut, Popeye's, Ruby Tuesday, Scottie's Custard, **lodging:** Comfort Inn, Fairfield Inn, Hampton Inn, Red Roof Inn, **other:** $Tree, Toyota, Wal-Mart SuperCtr/24hr, **S...gas:** Cenex, Total, **food:** Arby's, Capt D's, KFC, McDonald's, Papa John's, Pizza Hut, Subway, Taco Bell, Waffle House, Wendy's, **lodging:** Budget Inn, Econolodge, Holiday Inn Express, Motel 6, Ramada Inn, **other:** AutoZone, Dodge/Plymouth, $General, Firestone/auto, Ford/Lincoln/Mercury/Mazda, NAPA, Radio Shack

159   Lp 44, to Waynesville, St Robert, **N...food:** DQ, Sonic, **other:** IGA Foods, O'Reilly Parts, Covered Wagon RV Park(2mi), **S...gas:** Phillips 66/diesel, Shell/repair, **other:** Microtel, Ozark Motel, Cadillac/Chevrolet/GMC, Goodyear/auto, Pontiac, USPO

158mm Roubidoux Creek

156   rd H, Waynesville, **N...gas:** Citgo/diesel, **food:** Imperial Rest., McDonald's, Subway, **lodging:** Star Motel(1mi), **other:** $General, Smitty's Food/gas, Chevrolet/Buick, Covered Wagon RV Park(2mi)

153   MO 17, to Buckhorn, **N...gas:** Cenex/diesel, Citgo/diesel/rest., **food:** Ted Williams Steaks, **lodging:** Ft Wood Inn, **S...gas:** Shell/diesel, **other:** Glen Oaks RV Park

---

Lebanon

150   MO 7, rd P to Richland, no facilities

145   MO 133, rd AB, to Richland, **N...gas:** Conoco/diesel/rest./24hr, **S...**camping

143mm Gasconade River

140   rd N, to Stoutland, **S...gas:** Conoco, Phillips 66/diesel, **food:** Midway Chinese

139mm Bear Creek

135   rd F, Sleeper, no facilities

130   rd MM, **N...gas:** Phillips 66, **lodging:** Best Budget Inn, Best Western, Red Carpet Inn, **S...gas:** Phillips 66, **other:** HOSPITAL,

129   MO 5, MO 32, MO 64, Lebanon, to Hartville, **N...gas:** Conoco, Phillips 66/diesel, **food:** Applebee's, Bamboo Garden, Burger King, Country Kitchen, DQ, KFC, LJ Silver, McDonald's, Pizza Hut, Shoney's, Sonic, Subway, Taco Bell, Taco Hut, Wendy's, Western Sizzlin, **other:** Advance Parts, Aldi Foods, AutoZone, Chevrolet, Ford, IGA Foods, NAPA, O'Reilly Parts, Walnut Bowl Outlet, to Bennett Sprgs SP, **S...gas:** Amoco, Conoco/diesel, Shell, **food:** Blimpie, Candy's Custard, Capt D's, Hardee's, Pizza Hut, **other:** HOSPITAL, $Tree, Goodyear, Wal-Mart SuperCtr/24hr, to Lake of the Ozarks

127   Lp 44, Lebanon, **N...gas:** Conoco/diesel/rest./24hr, Phillips 66/diesel, **food:** Great Wall Chinese, Waffle House, **lodging:** Best Way Inn, Day's Inn, Econolodge, Hampton Inn, Holiday Inn Express, Scottish Inn, Super 8, **other:** Chicago Cutlery, Chrysler/Plymouth/Dodge/Jeep, Firestone, Ford/Lincoln/Mercury, Walnut Bowl Outlet, **S...other:** Buick/Pontiac/GMC/Cadillac, Harley-Davidson, Russell Stover

123   County Rd, **S...other:** Happy Trails RV Ctr, KOA

118   rds C, A, Phillipsburg, **N...gas:** Conoco/diesel, **S...gas:** Phillips 66

113   rds J, Y, Conway, **N...gas:** Phillips 66, **food:** Rockin Chair Café, **lodging:** Budget Inn, **other:** to Den of Metal Arts, **S...gas:** Conoco

111mm rest area both lanes, full(handicapped)facilities, phone, vending, litter barrels, picnic tables, pet-walk

108mm Bowen Creek

107   County Rd, no facilities

106mm Niangua River

100   MO 38, rd W, Marshfield, **N...gas:** Amoco, **food:** Tiny's BBQ, **other:** Chevrolet, Ford, Goodyear/auto, **S...gas:** Cenex, Citgo/diesel, Conoco/diesel, Phillips 66/diesel/24hr, Shell, **food:** Country Kitchen, DQ, KFC, LJ Silver/A&W, McDonald's, Pizza Hut, Sonic, Subway, Taco Bell, **lodging:** Holiday Inn Express, **other:** $General, PriceCutter Foods, Stanley Drug, Wal-Mart/auto

96   rd B, Northview, **N...**Paradise RV Park

89mm weigh sta both lanes

88   MO 125, Strafford, to Fair Grove, **N...gas:** Phillips 66/diesel/rest./24hr/@, TA/Subway/Taco Bell/diesel/24hr/@, **food:** McDonald's, **other:** Goodyear, truckwash, Paradise RV Park(4mi), **S...gas:** Citgo, Conoco/diesel, **lodging:** Super 8, **other:** Harter House Foods, Strafford RV Park

Interstate 44

E

↑↓

W

S p r i n g f i e l d

84 MO 744, **S**...Peterbilt

82b a US 65, to Branson, Fedalia, **S**...**gas:** Conoco/diesel, Phillips 66, **food:** Waffle House, **lodging:** American Inn, Village Inn, **other:** Truck World, st patrol, to Table Rock Lake, Bull Shoals Lake

80b a Springfield, rd H to Pleasant Hope, **N**...**gas:** Conoco/diesel/rest./24hr, Phillips 66, Shell, **food:** Waffle House, **lodging:** Day's Inn, Microtel, Motel 6, Super 8, **other:** to SWSU, **S**...**gas:** Conoco/diesel, Phillips 66, QT, Texaco, Total/diesel/LP, **food:** Andy's Café, Applebee's, Bob Evans, Burger King, Cracker Barrel, DQ, Denny's, Empire Asian, Fazoli's, Hardee's, Jade East Chinese, LJ Silver, KFC, McDonald's, Pizza Hut, Pizza Inn, Ruby Tuesday, Schlotsky's, Shoney's, Sonic, Steak'n Shake, Subway, Taco Bell, Village Inn Rest., Western Sizzlin, **lodging:** Bass Country Inn, Best Western, Comfort Inn, Day's Inn, Drury Inn, Econolodge, Economy Inn, Holiday Inn, Maple Inn, Ozark Inn, PearTree Inn, Plaza Inn, Ramada Inn, RainTree Inn, Red Lion Inn, Red Roof Inn, Sheraton, Solar Inn, **other:** HOSPITAL, AutoZone, Cottman Transmissions, Goodyear/auto, O'Reilly Parts, PriceCutter Foods, Radio Shack, U-Haul, Wal-Mart/auto, mall

77 MO 13, KS Expswy, **N**...**lodging:** Interstate Inn, **S**...**gas:** Phillips 66/diesel, QT, **food:** Arby's, Braum's, CiCi's, DQ, McDonald's, Papa John's, Papa Murphys, Pizza Inn, Subway, Taco Bell, Waffle House, Wendy's, **lodging:** Econolodge, **other:** Dillon's Foods, $Tree, GNC, Goodyear/auto, O'Reilly Parts, Radio Shack, Staples, Walgreen, Wal-Mart SuperCtr/24hr

75 US 160 W byp, to Willard, Stockton Lake, **S**...Conoco, The Café, Courtyard

72 MO 266, to Chesnut Expwy, **N**...Travelers RV Park, **1-2 mi S**...**gas:** Casey's, **food:** Hardee's, McDonald's, Taco Bell, Waffle House, **lodging:** Best Budget Inn, Best Inn

70 rds MM, B, **S**...**other:** Wilson's Creek Nat Bfd, KOA(1mi)

69 to US 60, Springfield

67 rds N, T, Bois D' Arc, **S**...to Republic, **gas:** Citgo/Ozarks/diesel/@, Conoco

66mm Pond Creek

64.6mm Dry Branch

64.5mm Pickerel Creek

61 rds K, PP, **N**...**gas:** Amoco, Cenex/diesel/rest./motel

58 MO 96, rds O, Z, Halltown, to Carthage, **S**...**gas:** Shell/diesel, **lodging:** Cook's Motel/café

57 to rd PP(from wb), no facilities

56.5mm Turnback Creek

56mm Goose Creek

52.5mm **rest area both lanes, full(handicapped)facilities, phone, picnic tables, litter barrels, vending, pet-walk**

49 MO 174E, rd CCW, Chesapeake, no facilities

46 MO 39, MO 265, Mt Vernon, Aurora, **N**...**gas:** Caseys, Phillips 66/diesel, TA/Conoco/diesel/rest./

J o p l i n

24hr/@, Sinclair/diesel/24hr/@, **food:** Bamboo Garden Chinese, Country Kitchen, Dalma's Rest., Hardee's, KFC, Mazzio's, McDonald's, Sonic, Taco Bell, **lodging:** American Inn, Budget Host, Super 8, **other:** Family$, O'Reilly Parts, Summer fresh Foods, **S**...**gas:** Total/diesel/rest., **lodging:** Comfort Inn, **other:** to Table Rock Lake, Stockton Lake

44 rd H, Mt Vernon, to Monett, **N**...**gas:** Citgo(2mi), **food:** Subway(1mi), **lodging:** Walnuts Motel, **other:** Mid-America Dental/Hearing

43.5mm Spring River

38 MO 97, to Stotts City, Pierce City, **N**...gas/repair, U of MO SW Ctr

33 MO 97 S, to Pierce City, **S**...**gas:** Sinclair/diesel

29 rd U, Sarcoxie, to La Russell, **N**...WAC RV Park, **S**...**gas:** Citgo/diesel, **lodging:** Sarcoxie Motel

29mm Center Creek

26 MO 37, Sarcoxie, to Reeds, **N**...truck/tire repair, **S**...**gas:** Amoco/gifts, **other:** Ford(2mi)

22 rd 100, **N**...RV parts, **S**...**gas:** Trkstp/diesel/rest./24hr/@

21mm Jones Creek

18b a US 71 N, MO 59 S, to Carthage, Neosho, **N**...**gas:** Phillips 66, **lodging:** BudgetWay Motel, **other:** Coachlight RV Park, **S**...**gas:** Total, **other:** George Carver Mon, Ballard's Camping

15 MO 66 W, Lp 44(from wb), Joplin, **N**...**lodging:** Tara Motel, Timber Motel

15mm Grove Creek

14mm Turkey Creek

11b a US 71 S, MO 249 N, to Neosho, Ft Smith, **S**...**gas:** ✈ /Flying J/Conoco/Country Mkt/diesel/LP/24hr/@ , **food:** Applebee's(3mi)

8b a US 71, Joplin, to Neosho, **N**...**gas:** Citgo, Conoco, Sinclair, **food:** Applebee's, Arby's, Benito's Mexican, Bob Evans, Braum's, Burger King, Capt D's, Casa Montez Mexican, CiCi's, Country Kitchen, Denny's, Grandy's, Great Wall Chinese, Gringo's Grill, IHOP, Jim Bob's Steaks, KFC, Kyoto Steaks, LJ Silver, MktPlace Deli, Memphis BBQ, McDonald's, Olive Garden, Outback Steaks, Pizza Hut, Red Lobster, Ruby Tuesday, Shoney's, Sonic, Steak'n Shake, Subway, Taco Bell, Timberline Steaks, Travetti's Italian, Waffle House, Wendy's, **lodging:** Baymont Inn, Best Western, Comfort Inn, Day's Inn, Drury Inn, Fairfield Inn, Hampton Inn, Holiday Inn, Howard Johnson, Motel 6, Ramada Inn, Select Inn, Solar Inn, Super 8, **other:** Chrysler/Plymouth/Dodge, Food4Less/24hr, Ford/Lincoln/Mercury, Hyundai, Jo-Ann Fabrics, Lowe's Whse, NAPA, Nissan/Mercedes, Office Depot, O'Reilly Parts, Pennzoil, Sam's Club/gas, Toyota, VW, Wal-Mart SuperCtr/24hr, **S**...**gas:** Citgo/diesel, Phillips 66/diesel, **food:** Cracker Barrel, Fazoli's, **other:** Microtel, Wheelen RV Ctr

MISSOURI

Interstate 44

E ↕ **W**

6   MO 86, MO 43 N, Joplin, to Racine, **1 mi N...gas:** Citgo, **food:** Arby's, McDonald's, Pizza Hut, **lodging:** Capri Motel, West Wood Motel, **other:** HOSPITAL, **S...**Goodyear, Harley-Davidson

5.5mm   Shoal Creek

4   MO 43 to Seneca, **N...gas:** Loves/Hardee's/diesel/24hr/@, **other:** Peterbilt, antiques, **S...gas:** Conoco/Subway/diesel/@, Petro/Blimpie/diesel/@, Pilot/Wendy's/diesel/24hr/@, **food:** McDonald's, **lodging:** Sleep Inn, **other:** KOA

3mm   weigh sta both lanes

2mm   **Welcome Ctr eb, rest area wb, full(handicapped)facilities, picnic tables, litter barrels, phones, vending**

1   US 400, US 166W, to Baxter Springs, KS, no facilities

0mm   Missouri/Oklahoma state line

Interstate 55

N ↕ **S**

St Louis

Exit #   Services

209mm   Missouri/Illinois state line at St. Louis, Mississippi River

209b   I-70 W to Kansas City

a   to Arch, Busch Stadium

208   7th St, downtown, **W...gas:** BP, **food:** Hardee's, Taco Bell, **lodging:** Adam's Mark Hotel, Drury Plaza, Marriott, Radisson, **other:** Ford Trucks

207c b   **W...**I-44 W, to Tulsa

a   Gravois St(from nb), **E...gas:** Citgo, **W...food:** A-1 Chinese Wok, Jack-in-the-Box

206c   Arsenal St, **E...**Anheuser-Busch Tour Ctr, **W...gas:** Shell

b   Broadway(from nb)

a   Potomac St(from nb)

205   Gasconade, **W...**HOSPITAL

204   Broadway, **E...gas:** Mobil/repair, **W...gas:** Clark, Sinclair, **food:** Crusoe's Rest., Hardee's, McDonald's, Pantera's Pizza, Pizza Hut, Wendy's, **other:** Radio Shack, Walgreen/24hr

203   Bates St, Virginia Ave, **W...gas:** BP, 7-11

202c   Loughborough Ave, **W...**Schnuck's Foods

b   Germania(from sb), no facilities

a   Carondelet(from nb)

201b   Weber Rd, no facilities

a   Bayless Ave, **E...gas:** BP, QT, Shell, **food:** McDonald's, **W...gas:** BP, Citgo/7-11, **food:** DQ, Jack-in-the-Box, Subway, Taco Bell, **other:** Goodyear

200   Union Rd(from sb), no facilities

199   Reavis Barracks Rd, **E...gas:** BP, Shell, **food:** Steak'n Shake/24hr, **other:** Fabric Whse

197   US 50, US 61, US 67, Lindbergh Blvd, **E...gas:** BP, Phillips 66, Shell, **food:** Arby's, KFC, Gingham's Rest., LJ Silver, McDonald's, Steak'n Shake, Subway, **lodging:** Holiday Inn, Super 8, **other:** Advance Parts, Best Buy, Circuit City, Chrysler/Dodge, Dillard's, Goodyear, JC Penney, K-Mart, Marshall's, mall, **W...food:** Bob Evans, Casa Gallardo's, Denny's, Pasta House, Ponderosa, Shoney's, **lodging:** Motel 6, Oak Grove Inn, **other:** Aldi Foods, Ford/Lincoln/Mercury, Honda, Hyundai, Mazda, Saturn

196b   I-270 W, to Kansas City, no facilities

a   I-255 E, to Chicago, no facilities

195   Butler Hill Rd, **E...gas:** Citgo, Phillips 66, **lodging:** Holiday Inn/rest., **W...gas:** Sinclair, **food:** Burger King, Hardee's, Pizza Hut/Taco Bell, Subway, Waffle House, **other:** Schnuck's Foods

193   Meramec Bottom Rd, **E...gas:** Citgo/7-11, Mobil, QT, **food:** Cracker Barrel, **lodging:** Best Western, **other:** Howard RV Ctr

191   MO 141, Arnold, **E...gas:** Citgo, Phillips 66, QT, **food:** Applebee's, BBQ, Burger King, Denny's, Emperor's Wok, Fazoli's, Hardee's, Jack-in-the-Box, LJ Silver, McDonald's, Steak'n Shake, Taco Bell, **lodging:** Drury Inn, Ramada Ltd, **other:** Eckerd, Kohl's, Schnuck's Foods, Shop'n Sav Foods, Wal-Mart/auto, mall, **W...gas:** Mobil, Phillips 66, **food:** Pasta House

190   Richardson Rd, **E...gas:** Citgo, QT, Shell/diesel, **food:** Domino's, DQ, Pizza Hut, Ponderosa, Sonic, Subway, Taco Bell, White Castle, **other:** Firestone, Ford, Mazda, SavALot Foods, **W...gas:** Shell/Blimpie/diesel, **food:** Burger King, McDonald's, Waffle House, **lodging:** Comfort Inn, **other:** Home Depot, Shnuck's Foods/24hr, Target, Walgreen, transmissions

186   Imperial, Kimmswick, **E...gas:** Shell, **food:** Southern Kitchen, Twisters, **W...**to Mastodon SP

185   rd M, Barnhart, Antonia, **W...gas:** Citgo/7-11, Citgo/diesel, **other:** KOA

184.5mm   weigh sta both lanes

180   rd Z, Pevely, to Hillsboro, **E...gas:** Mobil, **food:** BBQ, Burger King, KFC, Subway, **other:** $General, IGA Foods, **W...gas:** Mr Fuel, Phillips 66/McDonald's/diesel, **lodging:** Gateway Inn, Super 8, **other:** KOA(2mi)

178   Herculaneum, **E...gas:** QT/Wendy's/diesel, **W...**Chevrolet, Ford, Pontiac/Cadillac/Buick

175   rd A, Festus, **E...gas:** Phillips 66/diesel, **food:** Arby's, Bob Evans, Burger King, Dohack's, Fazoli's, McDonald's, Papa John's, Sonic, Steak'n Shake, Subway, Taco Bell, Wendy's, White Castle, **lodging:** Drury Inn, Holiday Inn Express, **other:** Advance Parts, Radio Shack, Schnuck's Foods, Toyota, Wal-Mart SuperCtr/gas/24hr, **W...gas:** Citgo/7-11/diesel, Mobil/diesel, **food:** Hardee's, Ruby Tuesday, Waffle House, **lodging:** Baymont Inn, **other:** Dodge, Lowe's Whse

174b a   US 67, Lp 55, Festus, Crystal City, **1 mi E...food:** Arby's, McDonald's, Ryan's, **lodging:** Twin City Motel, **other:** HOSPITAL, Wal-Mart SuperCtr/gas/24hr, same as 175

170   US 61, **W...gas:** Citgo/diesel/LP

162   rds DD, OO, no facilities

Interstate 55

N

S

Perryville

160mm	**rest areas both lanes, full(handicapped)facilities, picnic tables, litter barrels, phones, vending, petwalk**
157	rd Y, Bloomsdale, **E...gas:** Phillips 66, **W...gas:** Shamrock/diesel
154	rd O, no facilities
150	MO 32, rds B, A, to St Genevieve, **E...gas:** BP, **food:** DQ, **lodging:** Microtel(4mi), **other:** HOSPITAL, Hist Site(6mi), **W...other:** Pontiac/GMC, Hawn SP(11mi)
143	rds N, M, Ozora, **W...gas:** Shamrock/Subway/diesel/@, Sinclair, **lodging:** Family Inn/rest.
141	rd Z, St Mary, no facilities
135	rd M, Brewer, **E...**propane depot
129	MO 51, to Perryville, **E...gas:** MotoMart, Phillips 66/diesel, **food:** Burger King, KFC, McDonald's, Ponderosa, Taco Bell, **other:** HOSPITAL, Ford, **W...gas:** T-Rex, **food:** DQ, Kelly's Rest., **lodging:** Best Western, Comfort Inn, Super 8, **other:** Chevrolet/Pontiac/Buick, Chrysler/Plymouth/Dodge/Jeep, $Tree, KOA(1mi), Wal-Mart SuperCtr/24hr
123	rd B, Biehle, **W...gas:** Phillips 66, **food:** Country Kettle Rest./gifts
119mm	Apple Creek
117	rd KK, to Appleton, **E...food:** Sewing's Rest./repair
111	rd E, Oak Ridge, no facilities
110mm	**rest area both lanes, full(handicapped)facilities, picnic tables, litter barrels, phones, vending, petwalk**
105	US 61, Fruitland, **E...gas:** BP/diesel, Casey's, Rhodes/diesel, **other:** CarQuest, Trail of Tears SP(11mi), **W...gas:** D-Mart, **food:** Bavarian Rest., DQ, Pizza Inn, **lodging:** Drury Inn
99	US 61, MO 34, to Jackson, **E...**Holiday Lodge, Super 8, **W...other:** Wal-Mart SuperCtr/gas/24hr(4mi)
96	rd K, to Cape Girardeau, **E...gas:** BP, Citgo/diesel, **food:** Blimpie, Bob Evans, Burger King, Chuck-eCheese, Cracker Barrel, DQ, El Acapulco, Great Wall Chinese, Logan's Roadhouse, O'Charley's, Pizza Inn, Red Lobster, Ruby Tuesday, Ryan's, Steak'n Shake, Subway, Taco Bell, **lodging:** Drury Lodge/rest., Holiday Inn Express, PearTree Inn, Victorian Inn, **other:** HOSPITAL, Schnuck's Foods, Barnes&Noble, Best Buy, JC Penney, mall, **other:** AutoZone, Hastings Books, Sears, Walgreen, to SEMSU, **W...gas:** Shell/24hr, **food:** Lion's Choice, McDonald's, Outback Steaks, **lodging:** Drury Inn, Hampton Inn, **other:** Circuit City, Honda, Lowe's Whse, Sam's Club, Saturn, Staples, Target, Wal-Mart SuperCtr/24hr
95	MO 74 E, same as 96
93	MO 74 W, Cape Girardeau, no facilities

Miner

91	rd AB, to Cape Girardeau, **E...gas:** Phillips 66/diesel, **food:** Huddle House, **other:** Goodyear, Harley-Davidson, RV America, **W...** Capetown RV Ctr
89	US 61, rds K, M, Scott City, **E...gas:** Quick, Rhodes, **food:** Burger King, Pizza Pro, Sonic, Waffle Hut
80	MO 77, Benton, **W...gas:** BP, **food:** McDonald's, winery(8mi)
69	rd HH, Miner, to Sikeston, **E...**T&C RV Park(2mi), **W...gas:** Keller Trkstp/diesel/@, golf
67	US 60, US 62, Miner, **E...gas:** Breaktime/diesel, **lodging:** Best Western, Holiday Inn Express, Red Carpet Inn, **other:** T&C RV Park, **1-2 mi W...gas:** Citgo, Hucks, QuickChek, **food:** Bo's BBQ, Burger King, China Pearl, DQ, El Tapatio Mexican, Lambert's Rest., McDonald's, Pizza Hut, Pizza Inn, Sonic, Subway, Taco Bell, Taco John's, Wendy's, **lodging:** Country Hearth Inn, Drury Inn, Holiday Inn Express, PearTree Inn, Ramada Inn, Super 8, **other:** HOSPITAL, Aldi Foods, AutoZone, Chevrolet/Pontiac/Buick, GMC/Cadillac, Family$, Fisher Parts, Goodyear/auto, Pennzoil, Piggly Wiggly, Sikeston Outlets/famous brands
66b	US 60 W, to Poplar Bluff, **3 mi W on US 61/62...gas:** Breaktime, **food:** Applebee's, Arby's, DQ, El Bracero Mexican, Hardee's, KFC, McDonald's, Ryan's, Sonic, **lodging:** Day's Inn, **other:** Chrysler/Plymouth/Dodge/Jeep, $Tree, Ford/Lincoln/Mercury, Lowe's Whse, OfficeMax, Radio Shack, Wal-Mart SuperCtr/24hr
a	I-57 E, to Chicago, US 60 W
59mm	St Johns Bayou
58	MO 80, Matthews, **E...gas:** TA/Taco Bell/diesel/24hr/@, **W...gas:** ✈/Flying J/Conoco/diesel/LP/rest./RV dump/24hr/@
52	rd P, Kewanee, **E...gas:** BP/diesel, **W...gas:** Shamrock/diesel
49	US 61, US 62, New Madrid, **3 mi E...lodging:** Relax Inn, **other:** hist site
44	US 61, US 62, Lp 55, New Madrid, **E...**hist site
42mm	**Welcome Ctr nb/rest area both lanes, full(handicapped)facilities, picnic tables, litter barrels, phones, vending, petwalk**
40	rd EE, St Jude Rd, Marston, **E...gas:** Pilot/Arby's/diesel/24hr/@, **lodging:** Super 8, **W...gas:** BP/diesel, Breaktime/diesel, **lodging:** Budget Inn
32	US 61, MO 162, Portageville, **W...gas:** BP/diesel, Casey's, **food:** McDonald's, **lodging:** New Orleans Inn, **other:** diesel repair

MISSOURI

Interstate 55

27	rds K, A, BB, to Wardell, no facilities
19	US 412, MO 84, Hayti, **E...gas:** Breaktime/diesel, Conoco/Blimpie/diesel, Pilot/diesel/@, **food:** McDonald's, KFC/Taco Bell, Pizza Hut, **lodging:** Comfort Inn/rest., Holiday Inn Express, **other:** HOSPITAL, KOA(6mi), **W...gas:** BP/Subway, Conoco, R&P, **food:** Bavarian Haus Rest., DQ, Pizza Inn, **lodging:** Budget Inn, Drury Inn, **other:** Goodyear
17a	I-155 E, to TN, US 412, no facilities
14	rds J, H, U, to Caruthersville, Braggadocio, no facilities
10mm	weigh sta both lanes
8	MO 164, Steele, **E...gas:** Duckie's/diesel, **W...lodging:** Deerfield Inn
4	rd E, Cooter, to Holland, no facilities
3mm	**rest area both lanes, full(handicapped)facilities, picnic tables, litter barrels, phones, vending, petwalk**
1	US 61, rd O, Holland, **E...gas:** RaceWay/diesel, **W...gas:** Coastal/diesel
0mm	Missouri/Arkansas state line

Interstate 57

Exit #	Services
22mm	Missouri/Illinois state line, Mississippi River
18.5mm	weigh sta both lanes
12	US 60, US 62, MO 77, Charleston, **E...gas:** Sunshine Travel Ctr/diesel/@, **lodging:** Economy Motel, **W...gas:** Casey's, Sinclair/diesel, **food:** Apple Valley Buffet, KFC, **lodging:** Econolodge
10	MO 105, Charleston, **E...gas:** BP/Boomland/diesel, Pilot/Subway/diesel/24hr/@, **W...gas:** Casey's, **food:** China Buffet, DQ, McDonald's, Pizza Hut, **lodging:** Comfort Inn, **other:** CountryMart Foods, Plaza Tire
4	rd B, Bertrand, **E...**Jones Jct/diesel
1b a	I-55, N to St Louis, S to Memphis

I-57 begins/ends on I-55, exit 66.

Interstate 64

Exit #	Services
41mm	Missouri/Illinois state line, Mississippi River. I-64 and I-70 run together eb.
40b a	Broadway St, to Stadium, to the Arch, **N...lodging:** Sheraton, stadium, **S...other:** Dobb's Tire
c	(from wb), I-44 W, I-55 S
39c	11ᵗʰ St(exits left), downtown
39b	14ᵗʰ St, downtown, **N...lodging:** Sheraton, **S...gas:** BP
a	21ˢᵗ St, Market St(from wb), **N...lodging:** Drury Inn, Hampton Inn
38d	Chestnut at 20ᵗʰ St, **N...lodging:** Drury Inn, Hampton Inn

38c	Jefferson Ave, St Louis Union Sta, **N...**Joplin House
a	Forest Park Blvd(from wb), **N...gas:** Shell
37b a	Market St, Bernard St, Grand Blvd, **N...gas:** Shell, **food:** Del Taco, **lodging:** Courtyard, Hampton Inn, Hyatt, Drury Inn, Adam's Mark Hotel, Marriott
36d	Vandeventer Ave, Chouteau Ave, no facilities
36b a	Kingshighway, **N...lodging:** Best Western, **other:** HOSPITAL, **S...gas:** BP
34d c	Hampton Ave, Forest Park, **N...**museums, zoo, **S...gas:** BP, Mobil, **food:** Courtesy Diner, Hardee's, Imo's Pizza, Jack-in-the-Box, Steak'n Shake, Subway
34a	Oakland Ave, **N...gas:** BP, Del Taco, HOSPITAL
33d	McCausland Ave, **N... gas:** BP, **food:** Del Taco
33c	Bellevue Ave, **N...**HOSPITAL
33b	Big Bend Blvd, no facilities
32b a	Eager Rd, Hanley Rd, **S...gas:** Shell, **other:** Home Depot, Whole Foods Mkt
31b a	I-170 N, **N...gas:** Shell, **food:** Burger King, DQ, IHOP, KFC, Steak'n Shake, TGIFriday, Dillard's, Famous Barr, **other:** mall, **S...gas:** BP, **food:** Macaroni Grill, Subway, **other:** Borders Books, Circuit City, Dierberg's Foods, Goodyear, Target
30	McKnight Rd, no facilities
28c	Clayton Rd(from wb), no facilities
28b a	US 67, US 61, Lindbergh Blvd, **S...lodging:** Hilton, **other:** Shnuck's Foods, mall
27	Spoede Rd, no facilities
26	rd JJ, Ballas Rd, **N...**HOSPITAL, **S...**HOSPITAL
25	I-270, N to Chicago, S to Memphis
23	Mason Rd, **N...lodging:** Courtyard, Marriott, **other:** LDS Temple, hwy patrol
22	MO 141, **N...food:** Regatta Grille, **lodging:** Courtyard, Marriott, **other:** HOSPITAL, **S...food:** Pizza Hut
21	Timberlake Manor Pkwy, no facilities
20	Chesterfield Pkwy(from wb), same as 19b a
19b a	MO 340, Chesterfield Pkwy, **N...gas:** BP, Shell, **food:** Applebee's, Pizzaria Uno, **lodging:** DoubleTree Hotel, Hampton Inn, Residence Inn, **S...gas:** Mobil, **food:** Bahama Breeze Rest., Casa Gallardo's, **other:** Dillard's, mall
17	Boones Crossing, Long Rd, Chesterfield Airport Rd, **1 mi S...gas:** BP, Mobil, Phillips 66, **food:** Annie Gunn's Rest., Gator Flats Rest., Longhorn Steaks, McDonald's, O'Charley's, Old Country Buffet, Olive Garden, Red Lobster, Red Robin, SmokeHouse Rest., Steak'n Shake, Subway, **lodging:** Hampton Inn, Hilton Garden, **other:** Best Buy, $Tree, Ford, Lowe's Whse, Michael's, OfficeMax, Sam's Club, Target, Wal-Mart/auto, WorldMkt
14	Chesterfield Airport Rd(from eb), **S...gas:** Phillips 66, **lodging:** Comfort Inn
13mm	Missouri River, I-64 begins/ends.

Interstate 70

E
↕
W

Exit #	Services
252mm	Missouri/Illinois state line, Mississippi River
251a	I-55 S, to Memphis, to I-44, to downtown/no return
250b	Memorial Dr, downtown, Stadium, **S...gas:** Shell, **food:** McDonald's, **lodging:** Day's Inn
250a	Arch, Riverfront, Conv Center**N...lodging:** Econolodge, Embassy Suites, **S...lodging:** Drury Inn, Radisson, TWA Dome
249c	6th St(from eb), no facilities
249a	Madison St, 10th St, **N...gas:** Phillips 66/diesel
248b	St Louis Ave, Branch St, no facilities
248a	Salisbury St, McKinley Br, **N...**truck repair/24hr, **S...gas:** BP, Mobil/diesel
247	Grand Ave, **N...gas:** Phillips 66/diesel, **lodging:** Western Inn, **S...lodging:** Economy Inn
246b	Adelaide Ave, no facilities
246a	N Broadway, O'Fallon Park, **N...gas:** Phillips 66, **other:** Freightliner
245b	W Florissant, no facilities
245a	Shreve Ave, **N...**Pillsbury Factory, **S...gas:** BP
244b	Kingshighway, **3/4 mi S...food:** Burger King, McDonald's, Subway
244a	Bircher Blvd, Union Blvd, no facilities
243b	(243c from eb)Bircher Blvd, no facilities
243a	Riverview Blvd, no facilities
243	Goodfellow Blvd, **N...gas:** Shell
242b a	Jennings Sta Rd, **N...gas:** Shell/Texaco, **S...food:** McDonald's, **other:** transmission repair
241b	Lucas-Hunt Rd, **N...gas:** Shell, **3/4 mi S...gas:** Citgo, **food:** McDonald's
241a	Bermuda Rd, **S...gas:** Sinclair, **other:** HOSPITAL,
240b a	Florissant Rd, **N...gas:** BP/McDonald's, **food:** DQ, Sonic, Taco Bell, **other:** Schnuck's Foods, Walgreen
239	N Hanley Rd, **N...food:** Jack-in-the-Box, **S...gas:** Mobil, **food:** McDonald's
238c b	I-170 N, I-170 S, no return, no facilities
238a	**N...**Lambert-St Louis Airport, **S...lodging:** Renaissance Hotel
237	Natural Bridge Rd(from eb), **S...gas:** Phillips 66, Shell, **food:** Burger King, Denny's, Jack-in-the-Box, KFC, Pizza Hut, Steak'n Shake, Waffle House, Wendy's, DoubleTree, **lodging:** Days Inn, Holiday Inn, Renaissance, Travelodge
236	Lambert-St Louis Airport, **S...gas:** BP, **food:** BBQ, Big Boy, Coco's, Grone Cafeteria, Hardee's, Lombardo's Café Rafferty's Rest., Tiffany's Rest., **lodging:** Best Western, Day's Inn, Drury Inn/rest., Hampton Inn, Hilton Garden, Holiday Inn, Marriott, Motel 6
235c	Cypress Rd, rd B W, **N...**to airport

St Louis

235b a	US 67, Lindbergh Blvd, **N...gas:** Shell, **lodging:** Executive Intn'l Inn, Holiday Inn/café, Howard Johnson, **S...gas:** Shell, **food:** Lion's Choice Rest., Steak'n Shake, TGI-Friday, **lodging:** Congress Inn, Embassy Suites, Homestead Studios, Radisson, **other:** Chevrolet, Dillard's, Firestone, JC Penney, Sears/auto, mall
234	MO 180, St Charles Rock Rd, **N...gas:** Phillips 66, Shell, **food:** Applebee's, Casa Gallardo's, Fazoli's, Hardee's, Hatfield's/McCoy's Rest., LoneStar Steaks, LJ Silver, McDonald's, Old Country Buffet, Ponderosa, Red Lobster, Shoney's, Steak'n Shake, Taco Bell, Tony Bono's Rest., **lodging:** Knight's Inn, **other:** HOSPITAL, Best Buy, Circuit City, GrandPa's Food/drug, Honda, K-Mart, NTB, Office Depot, Sam's Club, Target, Walgreen/24hr, **S...**Isuzu
232	I-270, N to Chicago, S to Memphis, no facilities
231b a	Earth City Expwy, **N...lodging:** Candlewood Suites, Courtyard, Fairfield Inn, Sheraton, Studio+, **S...gas:** Mobil, **food:** Burger King, Dave&Buster's, Stage Left Café, Town Square Café, **lodging:** Holiday Inn, Doubletree Hotel, Wingate Inn, **other:** Harrah's Casino/Hotel, Riverport Ampitheatre
230mm	Missouri River
229b a	5th St, St Charles, **N...gas:** BP, Mobil/diesel, MotoMart, **food:** Burger King, Denny's, Jack-in-the-Box, KFC, McDonald's, Subway, Waffle House, **lodging:** Baymont Inn, Comfort Suites, Quality Inn, St Charles Inn, **other:** Walgreen/24hr, **S...gas:** Phillips 66, QT/diesel, **food:** Cracker Barrel, **lodging:** Best Western Noah's Ark, Day's Inn, Fairfield Inn, Howard Johnson, Ramada, Suburban Lodge, Townhouse Inn, **other:** JC Penney, malls, RV park
228	MO 94, to Weldon Springs, St Charles, **N...gas:** Citgo, Shell, **food:** Arby's, DQ, Hardee's, Imo's Pizza, LJ Silver, Papa John's, Pizza Hut, Steak'n Shake, Victoria's Creamery, Wendy's, **other:** Advance Parts, AutoValue, AutoZone, Chevrolet, Firestone, Radio Shack, Shop'n Save, Walgreen, Valvoline, **S...gas:** Mobil/diesel, Shell, **food:** ChuckeCheese, Fazoli's, Gingham's Rest., **lodging:** Best Western, Intown Suites, **other:** K-Mart, access to 227

St Charles

MISSOURI

Interstate 70

E ↑ ↓ W

St Peters

227 Zumbehl Rd, **N...gas:** Shell, **food:** Burger King, Culpepper's Grill, **lodging:** Econolodge, Super 8, **other:** Ford, Lowe's Whse, SavALot Foods, **S...gas:** Amoco, BP, Citgo, Mobil/FoodCourt, **food:** Applebee's, BBQ, Blackeyed Pea, Bob Evans, Boston Mkt, Capt D's, Chevy's Mexican, Golden Corral, Hardee's, Italian Ristorante, Jack-in-the-Box, Krieger's Grill, LoneStar Steaks, McDonald's, Mr Steak, Old Country Buffet, Popeye's, Subway, Taco Bell, **lodging:** Best Western, Comfort Inn, Red Roof Inn, TownePlace Suites, Travelodge, **other:** Deerborg's Foods/24hr, OfficeMax, Sam's Club, Schnuck's Foods/24hr, Wal-Mart/auto, access to 228

225 Truman Rd, to Cave Springs, **N...gas:** BP, Citgo, Shell, **food:** Taco Bell, Wendy's, **lodging:** Budget Motel, Hampton Inn, Knight's Inn, Motel 6, **other:** Buick/Pontiac, Cadillac, Lincoln/Mercury, Mazda, Saturn, Target, Toyota, U-Haul, **S...gas:** Conoco, Mobil, QT, **food:** Big Boy, Burger King, DQ, Denny's, El Mezcal Mexican, Fazoli's, Ground Round, IHOP, Jack-in-the-Box, Lion's Choice Rest., LJ Silver, McDonald's, Pasta House, Pizza Hut, Ponderosa, Red Lobster, Steak'n Shake, Subway, White Castle, **lodging:** Holiday Inn Select, **other:** HOSPITAL, Chrysler/Jeep, Dodge, Home Depot, Kia, K-Mart, Office Depot, OfficeMax, Shop'n Save, Target

224 MO 370 E, no facilities

222 Mall Dr, rd C, St Peters, **N...gas:** QT/diesel/24hr, **food:** Burger King, **other:** Chevrolet, Honda, Mitsubishi, Subaru, **S...gas:** Citgo, Mobil, **food:** Arby's, Bob Evans, Chili's, Domino's, Hardee's, Jack-in-the-Box, Joe's Crabshack, McDonald's, Olive Garden, Pizza Hut, Steak'n Shake, Subway, Taco Bell, Wendy's, **lodging:** Drury Inn, Extended Stay America, **other:** MEDICAL CARE, Aldi Foods, AutoZone, Best Buy, Circuit City, Costco/gas, Deerborg's Foods, Dillard's, Discount Tire, JC Penney, Nissan/Hyundai/VW, Schnuck's Foods, Sears/auto, Walgreen

220 MO 79, to Elsberry, **N...**Cherokee Lakes Camping(7mi), **S...gas:** BP, Citgo/7-11(1mi), **food:** Blimpie(1mi), Hardee's, McDonald's(1mi), Smokehouse Rest., Sonic, Subway

217 rds K, M, O'Fallon, **N...gas:** BP, QT, **food:** Blimpie, El Tio's Mexican, Burger King, Hardee's, Jack-in-the-Box, Ponderosa, Rally's, Taco Bell, Waffle House, **other:** AutoValue Parts, Firestone, Radio Shack, **S...gas:** Citgo/diesel, DirtCheap, Shell, **food:** Arby's, Bob Evans, Fazoli's, IHOP, KFC, Lion's Choice Rest., Longhorn Steaks, McDonald's, Pizza Hut, Steak'n Shake/24hr, Stefanina's Pizza, **other:** Aldi Foods, AutoZone, K-Mart/drugs, Lowe's Whse, Schnuck's Foods, Shop'n Save Foods, Walgreen, camping

216 Bryan Rd, **N...lodging:** Super 8, **other:** Ford, **S...gas:** Amoco, Casey's, Mobil, QT, **food:** Pantera's Pizza

214 Lake St Louis, **N...**Freedom RV Ctr(1mi), Hummer, **S...gas:** Phillips 66/diesel, Shell, **food:** Cutter's Rest., Denny's, Hardee's, Subway, **lodging:** Day's Inn, **other:** HOSPITAL, IGA Foods

212 rd A, **N...lodging:** Knight's Inn, Ramada Ltd, **S...gas:** Citgo/diesel, **food:** Arby's, Burger King, Imo's Pizza, Texas Willie's Steaks, Yaba's Pizza, **lodging:** Holiday Inn, **other:** Chrysler/Plymouth/Dodge/Jeep, Luxury Linens, Wentzville Outlets/famous brands

210b a US 61, US 40, to I-64 E, **S...gas:** Conoco, Phillips 66/diesel, Shell, **other:** HOSPITAL

209 rd Z(from wb), Church St, New Melle, no facilities

208 Pearce Blvd, Wentzville Pkwy, Wentzville, **N...gas:** Citgo, QT/diesel, **food:** Imo's Pizza, KFC, McDonald's, Palace Buffet, Pizza Hut, Steak'n Shake/24hr, Taco Bell, Waffle House, Wendy's, **other:** HOSPITAL, Chevrolet/Buick, Family$, Home Depot, Sav-A-Lot Foods, Radio Shack, Schnuck's Food, Walgreen, **S...gas:** Amoco, BP, Shell, **food:** Capt D's, Hardee's, KwanYin Chinese, Pantera's Pizza, Ruggeri's Italian, **lodging:** Super 8, **other:** $General, Pinewood RV Park, Plymouth/Dodge, Radio Shack, Thomas RV Ctr, Wal-Mart SuperCtr/24hr

204mm weigh sta both lanes

203 rds W, T, Foristell, **N...gas:** TA/diesel/rest./24hr/@, Mr Fuel/diesel, **lodging:** Best Western, diesel repair, **S...gas:** Phillips 66/diesel/café

200 rds J, H, F, Wright City, **N...gas:** Citgo/diesel, Shell/diesel, **food:** McDonald's, Ruiz Castillo's Mexican(1mi), **S...gas:** Phillips 66, **food:** Big Boy, **lodging:** Super 7 Inn, **other:** Volvo

199 (from wb), same as 200

198mm **rest area both lanes, full(handicapped)facilities, phone, picnic tables, litter barrels, petwalk**

193 MO 47, Warrenton, **N...gas:** Citgo, Phillips 66/diesel, **food:** Burger King, DQ, Jack-in-the-Box, McDonald's, Pizza Hut, Subway, Waffle House, **lodging:** Day's Inn, Super 8, **other:** Family$, Ford, Moser's Foods, Wal-Mart SuperCtr/24hr, **S...gas:** BP, Phillips 66/Blimpie/diesel, Shell/diesel/deli/24hr, **food:** Denny's, Hardee's, Imo's Pizza, KFC, Taco Bell, **lodging:** AmeriHost, BudgetHost, **other:** CarQuest, Chrysler/Plymouth/Dodge/Jeep, Kelly Tire, **1/2 mi on frontage rd...other:** Chevrolet/Pontiac, Outlet Ctr/famous brands

188 rds A, B, to Truxton, **S...gas:** ⚐/Flying J/Conoco/diesel/LP/24hr/@, **lodging:** Budget Inn

183 rds E, NN, Y, Jonesburg, **1 mi N...**KOA/LP, **S...gas:** BP, Phillips 66, Shell/diesel

179 rd F, High Hill, **S...lodging:** Budget Motel, Colonial Inn

175 MO 19, New Florence, **N...gas:** BP/Hardee's/diesel, Phillips 66/diesel/24hr, Shell/diesel/24hr, **food:** Maggie's Café, McDonald's, Pizza Cabin, **lodging:** Best Inn, Day's Inn, Best Inn, Super 8, **other:** Stone Hill Winery/gifts, U-Haul, auto repair, **S...**RV parking

Interstate 70

E

↕

W

170 MO 161, rd J, Danville, **N...gas:** Phillips 66, **other:** to Graham Cave SP, Kan-Do RV Park, **S...**Lazy Day RV Park

169.5mmrest area wb, full(handicapped)facilities, phone, vending, picnic tables, litter barrels, petwalk

168mm Loutre River

167mm rest area eb, full(handicapped)facilities, phone, vending, picnic tables, litter barrels, petwalk

161 rds D, YY, Williamsburg, **S...gas:** Conoco/diesel/café/24hr/@, **food:** Jumpstop Rest.

155 rds A, Z, to Calwood, **N...**antiques

148 US 54, Kingdom City, **N...gas:** BP, Phillips 66/Taco Bell/diesel, **lodging:** AmeriHost, **other:** to Mark Twain Lake, **S...gas:** Conoco/Subway/diesel/@, Gasper's/diesel/rest., Petro/Mobil/diesel/rest./24hr/@, Phillips 66/McDonald's/diesel, Shell, **food:** Denny's, Comfort Inn, Day's Inn, Red Carpet Inn, Super 8

144 rds M, HH, to Hatton, **S...other:** Crooked Creek Camping, Wilder RV Ctr, fireworks

137 rds DD, J, to Millersburg, Stephens, **S...food:** Dixie Chigger Cafe(3.5mi), **other:** Walnut Bowls Factory Outlet, to Little Dixie WA

133 rd Z, to Centralia, **N...other:** Loveall's RV

131 Lake of the Woods Rd, **N...gas:** BP, Phillips 66/Subway/diesel, **lodging:** Super 8, **other:** Harley Davidson, **S...gas:** Shell/diesel/24hr, **other:** RV Park

128a US 63, to Jefferson City, Columbia, **N...gas:** QT, **food:** Bob Evans, Burger King, Casa Grande Mexican, Cracker Barrel, Golden Corral, KFC, McDonald's, Pizza Hut, Schlotsky's, Steak'n Shake, Taco Bell, Wendy's, **lodging:** Fairfield Inn, Hampton Inn, Super 8, **other:** Aamco, Home Depot, KOA, Cottonwood's RV, **S...gas:** Breaktime/diesel, **food:** Sonic, Subway, **lodging:** Baymont Inn, Best Western, Candlewood Suites, Comfort Inn, Holiday Inn Express, Hawthorn Suites, Howard Johnson, La Quinta, Motel 6, Wingate Inn, **other:** HOSPITAL, Lowe's Whse, MegaMkt Foods, Nowell's Foods, Patricia's Foods, Sam's Club, Staples, Wal-Mart SuperCtr/24hr(1mi)

128 Lp 70(from wb), Columbia, **N...food:** Wendy's, **lodging:** Super 8, **S...gas:** Conoco/diesel, **lodging:** Best Western, Baymont Inn, Comfort Inn, Holiday Inn Express, **other:** HOSPITAL, same as 128a

127 MO 763, to Moberly, Columbia, **N...gas:** Breaktime/diesel, **food:** Honest John's Grill, McDonald's, Waffle House, **lodging:** Budget Host, Ramada, Travelodge, **other:** Acura, Chrysler/Dodge, $General, Harley-Davidson, Pontiac/Cadillac, Saturn, Toyota, **S...gas:** Phillips 66/diesel, **food:** DQ, Everett's Rest., Taco Bell, **lodging:** Econolodge, Super 7 Motel

Columbia

126 MO 163, Providence Rd, Columbia, **N...gas:** BP, **food:** BBQ, Country Kitchen, **lodging:** Best Value Inn, Quality Inn, Red Roof, **other:** Buick/GMC, Ford, Honda, same as 127, **S...gas:** BP, Breaktime/diesel, **food:** Burger King, DQ, McDonald's, Pizza Hut, Sonic, Subway, Taco Bell, **other:** HOSPITAL, Aldi Foods, AutoZone, Chevrolet/Nissan, Chrysler/Jeep, $General, Lincoln/Mercury, O'Reilly Parts

125 Lp 70, West Blvd, Columbia, **S...gas:** Breaktime/diesel, Conoco/diesel, Citgo, Phillips 66/diesel, Shell, **food:** Chevy's Mexican, Denny's, Domino's, El Maguey Mexican, Fazoli's, LJ Silver, Olive Garden, Outback Steaks, Perkins, Pizza Hut, Red Lobster, Ryan's, Wendy's, Western Sizzlin, Yen Ching Chinese, **lodging:** Deluxe Inn, Eastwood Inn, Econolodge, Howard Johnson/rest., Scottish Inn, **other:** Advance Parts, Chrysler/Plymouth/Subaru, Firestone/auto, Mitsubishi, Mr Transmissions, PriceChopper Foods, U-Haul, same as 124

124 MO 740, rd E, Stadium Blvd, Columbia, **N...gas:** BreakTime, **lodging:** Extended Stay America, **S...gas:** Phillips 66, **food:** Alexander's Steaks, Applebee's, Burger King, Great Wall Chinese, Hardee's, KFC, Little Caesar's, LJ Silver, McDonald's, Old Chicago Pizza, Pasta House, Pizza Hut, Red Lobster, Ruby Tuesday, Steak'n Shake, Sub Shop, Subway, Taco Bell, Wendy's, **lodging:** Baymont Inn, Day's Inn, Drury Inn, Holiday Inn/rest., Motel 6, Regency Inn, **other:** Circuit City, Dillard's, Ford, Isuzu, JC Penney, K-Mart, Radio Shack, Sears/auto, Toyota, Wal-Mart/auto, mall, to U of MO, same as 125

122mm Perche Creek

121 US 40, rd UU, Midway, **N...gas:** Conoco/diesel/rest./@, Phillips 66, **lodging:** Budget Inn, **other:** Goodyear, Flea Mkt/antiques, **S...**golf

117 rds J, O, to Huntsdale, **S...**Furniture World, repair

115 rd BB, Rocheport, **N...**Les Bourgeois Winery, to Katy Tr SP, **S...**antiques

114.5mm Missouri River

111 MO 98, MO 179, to Wooldridge, Overton, **S...gas:** Phillips 66/diesel

106 MO 87, Bingham Rd, to Boonville, **N...gas:** Conoco/diesel/rest., Phillips 66/diesel, **lodging:** Atlasta Motel/rest.

104mm rest area both lanes, full(handicapped)facilities, phone, picnic tables, litter barrels, vending, petwalk

E ↑ ↓ **W**

103 rd B, Main St, Boonville, **N...gas:** Breaktime, Phillips 66/diesel, **food:** Domino's, KFC, McDonald's, Sonic, Subway, Taco Bell, **lodging:** Day's Inn, QT Inn, Super 8, **other:** HOSPITAL, Wal-Mart/café, to Kay Tr SP, **S...gas:** BP/diesel, Conoco/diesel/24hr, **other:** Bobber Lake Camping

101 US 40, MO 5, to Boonville, **N...gas:** Pilot/Wendy's/diesel/24hr/@, **food:** A&W, Burger King, **lodging:** Comfort Inn, Holiday Inn Express, **other:** Russell Stovers Candy, **S...**Chrysler/Plymouth/Dodge/Jeep, **other:** to Lake of the Ozarks

98 MO 41, MO 135, Lamine, **N...**to Arrow Rock HS(13mi), **S...gas:** Conoco/diesel, Phillips 66, Shell/diesel/24hr, **food:** Dogwood Rest.

93mm Lamine River

89 rd K, to Arrow Rock, **N...**to Arrow Rock HS

84 rd J, **N...gas:** BP/DQ/Stuckey's, truck repair

78b a US 65, to Marshall, **N...gas:** Conoco/diesel, **other:** Lazy Days RV Park, **S...gas:** Breaktime/diesel

77mm Blackwater River

74 rds YY, **N...gas:** Shell/Texaco/diesel/rest./24hr/@, **lodging:** Betty's Motel, **S...gas:** BP/diesel/rest.

71 rds EE, K, to Houstonia, **N...**flea mkt

66 MO 127, Sweet Springs, **S...gas:** Phillips 66/diesel, Conoco/diesel, **food:** Brownsville Sta Rest., Sonic, Tastee Freez, **lodging:** People's Choice Motel, Super 8, **other:** HOSPITAL

65.5mm Davis Creek

62 rds VV, Y, Emma, no facilities

58 MO 23, Concordia, **N...gas:** TA/Subway/diesel/24hr/@, **food:** KFC/Taco Bell, McDonald's, **other:** $General, **S...gas:** Breaktime/diesel, Conoco, Shell, **food:** BBQ, Hardee's, Palace Rest., Pizza Hut, Taco John's, **lodging:** Best Western, Day's Inn, **other:** CountryMart Foods, NAPA

57.5mm rest area both lanes, full(handicapped)facilities, phone, picnic tables, litter barrels, vending, pet-walk

52 rd T, Aullville, no facilities

49 MO 13, to Higginsville, **N...gas:** BP, Pilot/McDonald's/Subway/diesel/24hr/@, **food:** China Buffet, McDonald's, Pizza Hut, Subway, **lodging:** Camelot Inn, Classic Motel(4mi), **other:** to Whiteman AFB, to Confederate Mem, **S...lodging:** Super 8/rest., **other:** Interstate RV Park

45 rd H, to Mayview, no facilities

43mm weigh sta both lanes

41 rds O, M, to Lexington, Mayview, no facilities

38 MO 131(from wb), Odessa, **S...gas:** BP, Shell, **food:** McDonald's, Sonic, Subway, Taco John's, Wendy's, **other:** camping, same as 37

37 MO 131, Odessa, **N...food:** Countryside Diner, **other:** Country Gardens RV Park, **S...gas:** BP/diesel, Shell, **food:** McDonald's, Morgan's Rest., Pizza Hut, Sonic, Subway, Taco John's, **lodging:** Odessa Inn, Parkside Inn, **other:** Chrysler/Plymouth/Dodge/Jeep, Ford, O'Reilly Parts, Prime Outlets/famous brands, Thriftway Foods, RV dump, same as 38

35mm truck parking both lanes

31 rds D, Z, to Bates City, Napoleon, **N...**I-70 Motel/RV Park, **S...gas:** BP/diesel

29.5mm Horse Shoe Creek

28 rd HF, Oak Grove, **N...gas:** TA/Conoco/Popeye's/Pizza Hut/diesel/24hr/@, **lodging:** Day's Inn, **other:** Blue Beacon, KOA, **S...gas:** QT/diesel/24hr/@, Petro/Blimpie/DQ/Wendy's/diesel/@, **food:** Hardee's, KFC/Taco Bell, McDonald's, Subway, Waffle House, **lodging:** Econolodge, Oak Grove Inn, **other:** Wal-Mart SuperCtr/24hr

24 US 40, rds AA, BB, to Buckner, **N...gas:** Phillips 66/diesel/rest., **lodging:** Comfort Inn, Travelodge, **other:** Country Campers RV Ctr, **S...gas:** Conoco/Subway/diesel/24hr/@, **food:** Sonic, **other:** GoodSam RV Park/LP, Trailside RV Ctr

21 Adams Dairy Pkwy, **N...**Nationwide RV Ctr(1mi), **S...gas:** Phillips 66/Burger King/diesel, **lodging:** Courtyard, Sleep Inn, **other:** Home Depot, **2 mi S...food:** Arby's, Burger King, Fazoli's, Ponderosa

20 MO 7, Blue Springs, **N...gas:** Phillips 66/diesel, Shamrock, Sinclair, **food:** Backyard Burger, Bob Evan's, Quizno's, Sonic, **lodging:** Motel 6, Ramada Ltd, Sleep Inn, Super 8, **other:** O'Reilly Parts, Osco Drug, PriceChopper Foods, Valvoline, Walgreen, **S...gas:** BP/diesel/24hr, QT, Shell, **food:** Applebee's, BBQ, Burger King, China Buffet, Clancy's, Denny's, Domino's, El Mezcal Mexican, Godfather's, Golden Corral, Jose Pepper's, KFC, LJ Silver, McDonald's, Subway, Thai Place, Texas Tom's Mexican, Village Inn Rest., Wendy's, Winstead's Burgers, **lodging:** Hampton Inn, Holiday Inn Express, Quality Inn, **other:** HOSPITAL, Advance Parts, Chevrolet, Firestone/auto, Hyundai, Office Depot, Radio Shack, Saturn, **1 mi S...food:** Arby's, Fazoli's, **other:** AutoZone, Goodyear/auto, HyVee Foods, NAPA, Wal-Mart/auto

18 Woods Chapel Rd, **N...gas:** BP, **lodging:** American Inn, Day's Inn, Interstate Inn, **other:** Harley-Davidson, **S...gas:** Conoco, Phillips 66/diesel, QT, **food:** Church's, KFC/Taco Bell, McDonald's, Pizza Hut, Taco John's, Waffle House, **other:** All Seasons RV, Ford, Hyundai, Nissan, same as 20

17 Little Blue Pkwy, 39th St, **N...food:** Applebee's, BBQ, Fazoli's, Hereford House, Joe's Crabshack, Macaroni Grill, O'Charley's, On the Border, **lodging:** Hilton Garden, **other:** mall entrance, **S...food:** Carrabba's, Hooters, IHOP, Kobe Steaks, Outback Steaks, Primo Ristorante, Wendy's, **lodging:** Holiday Inn Express, **other:** Costco, Lowe's Whse

Concordia

Independence

Interstate 70

E ⇅ **W**

Independence

16mm	Little Blue River
15b	MO 291 N, Independence, **1 exit N on 39th St...gas:** Conoco, QT, Phillips 66, **food:** Applebee's, Arby's, BBQ, Bob Evans, Burger King, Chevy's Mexican, Chili's, Denny's, 54th St Grill, Hops Grill, KFC, LJ Silver, LoneStar Steaks, Longhorn Steaks, Luby's, McDonald's, Mr GoodCents Subs, Souper Salad, Starbucks, TGIFriday, **lodging:** Fairfield Inn, Residence Inn, **other:** HOSPITAL, Albertson's, Barnes&Noble, Circuit City, Dick's Sports, Dillard's, Jo-Ann Fabrics, Kohl's, Marshall's, NTB, Sam's Club, Sears/auto, Target, Wal-Mart SuperCtr/24hr, mall
15a	I-470 S, MO 291 S, to Lee's Summit, no facilities
14	Lee's Summit Rd, **food:** AppleFarm Rest., Boston Mkt, Cracker Barrel, Olive Garden, Steak'n Shake, **lodging:** Budget Host, **other:** Home Depot
12	Noland Rd, Independence, **N...gas:** QT, Shell/diesel, **lodging:** Best Western, Super 8, **other:** Advance Parts, Firestone, K-Mart, Office Depot, OfficeMax, Osco Drug, Walgreen, U-Haul, transmissions, to Truman Library, **S...gas:** Phillips 66, **food:** Arby's, Burger King, Country Kitchen, Fuddrucker's, KFC/Taco Bell, KrispyKreme, McDonald's, Old Country Buffet, Red Lobster, Ruby Tuesday, Wendy's, **lodging:** American Inn, Comfort Inn, Crossland Inn, Red Roof Inn, **other:** Best Buy, $Tree, Old Navy, HyVee Foods, Tires+
11	US 40, Blue Ridge Blvd, Independence, **N...gas:** QT, Shell, **food:** A&W/LJ Silver, Burger King, McDonald's, Sonic, Subway, V's Italiano, **lodging:** Budget Host, Deluxe Inn, **other:** Radio Shack, Stadium RV Park, **S...gas:** BP, Citgo/7-11, Sinclair, **food:** Applebee's, Hong Kong Buffet, Old Country Buffet, Papa John's, Steak'n Shake, Taco Bell, **lodging:** Sports Stadium Motel, **other:** Cadillac, JC Penney, mall
10	Sterling Ave(from eb), same as 11
9	Blue Ridge Cutoff, **N...gas:** Conoco, **food:** Denny's/24hr, Wendy's, **lodging:** Adam's Mark Hotel/rest., Day's Inn, Drury Inn, Villager Lodge, **other:** HOSPITAL, **S...gas:** BP/24hr, Sinclair, **food:** Taco Bell, **lodging:** Holiday Inn, **other:** Sports Complex

Kansas City

8b a	I-435, N to Des Moines, S to Witchita, no facilities
7b	Manchester Trafficway, **S...**Ryder Trucks
7mm	Blue River
7a	US 40 E, 31st St, **N...lodging:** Sunset Inn, Villager Lodge, **S...lodging:** Economy Inn, SportsStadium Motel, Travelers Inn
6	Van Brunt Blvd, **N...gas:** Citgo/7-11, **S...gas:** BP, **food:** KFC, McDonald's, Pizza Hut, Taco Bell, **other:** VA HOSPITAL, Osco Drug
5c	Jackson Ave(from wb), no facilities
5b	31st St(from eb), no facilities
5a	27th St(from eb), no facilities
4c	23rd Ave, no facilities
4b	18th St, **N...gas:** Phillips 66/Wendy's/diesel
4a	Benton Blvd(from eb), Truman Rd, **N...gas:** Phillips 66/Wendy's/diesel, **other:** Advance Parts

Kansas City

3c	Prospect Ave, **N...gas:** Service Oil/diesel, **food:** Kate's BBQ, **S... food:** Bryant's Café, McDonald's, Church's
3b	Brooklyn Ave(from eb), **S...**same as 3c
3a	Paseo St, **S...gas:** BP, **other:** tires
2m	US 71 S, downtown
2l	I-670, to I-35 S, no facilities
2j	11th St, downtown
2g	I-29/35 N, US 71 N, to Des Moines, no facilities
2h	US 24 E, downtown
2e	MO 9 N, Oak St, **N...gas:** Conoco, **S...gas:** Shamrock, **lodging:** Comfort Inn
2d	Main St, downtown
2c	US 169 N, Broadway, downtown
2b	Beardsley Rd, no facilities
2a	I-35 S, to Wichita, no facilities
0mm	Missouri/Kansas state line, Kansas River

Interstate 270(St Louis)

N ⇅ **S**

Exit #	Services
15b a	I-55 N to Chicago, S to St Louis. I-270 begins/ends in Illinois on I-55/I-70, exit 20.
12	IL 159, to Collinsville, **N...gas:** Mobil/diesel, **food:** DQ, Hardee's, Ponderosa, **S...**HOSPITAL
9	IL 157, to Collinsville, **N...food:** Comfort Inn, **S...gas:** Phillips 66/24hr
7	I-255, to I-55 S to Memphis
6b a	IL 111, **N...gas:** BP/24hr, ⛽/Flying J/CountryMkt/ diesel/24hr/@, **food:** Hen House Rest., Sawyers Rest., **lodging:** Apple Valley Motel, Best Western, **S...food:** Denny's, McDonald's, **lodging:** Holiday Inn Express, Ramada Ltd, Super 8, to Pontoon Beach
4	IL 203, Old Alton Rd, to Granite City, no facilities
3b a	IL 3, **N...**Riverboat Casino, **S...food:** Hardee's, Waffle House, **lodging:** Chain of Rocks Motel, **other:** KOA
2mm	Chain of Rocks Canal
0mm	Illinois/Missouri state line, Mississippi River, motorist callboxes begin eb
34	Riverview Dr, to St Louis, **N...Welcome Ctr/rest area both lanes, full(handicapped)facilities, info, picnic tables, litter barrels, phones**
33	Lilac Ave, **N...**USPO, **S...gas:** Phillips 66/diesel, QT/ diesel/24hr, **food:** Hardee's
32	Bellefontaine Rd, **N...gas:** Mobil, Shell, **food:** Burger King, Denny's, McDonald's, Pizza Hut, Steak'n Shake, **lodging:** Econolodge, Motel 6, **other:** Advance Parts, Firestone, Schnuck's Foods, bank, **S...gas:** BP/24hr, **other:** Aldi Foods

Interstate 270

N ↑↓ S	

31b a   MO 367, **N...gas:** QT, **food:** Arby's, Jack-in-the-Box, **other:** HOSPITAL, **1 mi S...gas:** Phillips 66/diesel, **food:** Denny's, McDonald's, Taco Bell, **other:** Schnuck's Food/drug, Valvoline

30b a   Hall's Ferry Rd, rd AC, **N...gas:** Mobil, Phillips 66/diesel, QT/24hr, **food:** Applebee's, Hardee's, Lion's Choice Rest., Red Lobster, Taco Bell, White Castle, Wendy's, **lodging:** Super 8, **other:** Discount Tire, Target, **S...gas:** Conoco, Shell, Mobil, **food:** Church's, Cracker Barrel, IHOP, McDonald's, **other:** AutoZone, Buick, Home Depot, Hyundai, Jo-Ann Fabrics, Saturn, Shop'n Save Foods

29   W Florissant Rd, **N...food:** Jack-in-the-Box, **other:** Best Buy, Dierberg's Foods, K-Mart, Office Depot, **S...food:** Blackeyed Pea, Burger King, Krispy Kreme, Malone's Grill, McDonald's, Old Country Buffet, **other:** Circuit City, Saturn, Sam's Club, Wal-Mart

28   Elizabeth Ave, Washington St, **S...gas:** BP/24hr, **N...gas:** Sinclair, **food:** Jack-in-the-Box, Mrs O's Café, Pizza Hut, Subway, Taco Bell, **other:** Chevrolet, JC Penney, OfficeMax, Schnuck's Foods/24hr, Walgreen

27   New Florissant Rd, rd N, **N...gas:** BP, Shell, **food:** Pizza Palace

26b   Graham Rd, N Hanley, **N...gas:** Citgo/7-11, **food:** Denny's, Fazoli's, Hardee's, LJ Silver, Rosemari's Rest., **lodging:** Hampton Inn, Red Roof Inn, **other:** HOSPITAL, Mitsubishi, **S...food:** McDonald's, **lodging:** Day's Inn, **other:** $General, Hancock Fabrics

a   I-170 S, no facilities

25b a   US 67, Lindbergh Blvd, **N...gas:** Shell, Texaco, **food:** Arby's, Burger King, Hardee's, Imo's Pizza, Jack-in-the-Box, McDonald's, Papa John's, Rally's, Ruiz' Mexican, Taco Bell, Village Inn Rest., **lodging:** Baymont Inn, Fairfield Inn, InTown Suites, **other:** AutoZone, Cadillac, Ford, Goodyear, NAPA, Nissan, Schnuck's Foods, Toyota, Walgreen, **S...gas:** Citgo/7-11, Shell, Econolodge, Villa Motel, **other:** VW/Volvo

23   McDonnell Blvd, **E...food:** Bicycle Club Rest., Denny's, **lodging:** La Quinta, **W...gas:** BP, Phillips 66/diesel, QT, **food:** Arby's, Jack-in-the-Box, McDonald's, Steak'n Shake, **other:** Pontiac/GMC

22   MO 370 W, to MO Bottom Rd, no facilities

20c   MO 180, St Charles Rock Rd, **E...gas:** BP, Shell, **food:** Casa Gallardo's, Ground Round, Hardee's, McDonald's, Fazoli's, LJ Silver, Old Country Buffet, Ponderosa, Red Lobster, Shoney's, Steak'n Shake, Taco Bell, Tony Bono's Rest., **lodging:** Knight's Inn, **other:** HOSPITAL, Best Buy, Circuit City, K-Mart, Office Depot, Target, Walgreen/24hr, **W...gas:** BP/24hr, Citgo, Mobil, **food:** Bob Evans, Denny's, Olive Garden, Ryan's, Waffle House, **lodging:** Motel 6, Ramada Inn, Red Roof Inn, Super 8, **other:** Ford

20b a   I-70, E to St Louis, W to Kansas City

St Louis (vertical left margin)

17   Dorsett Rd, **E...gas:** BP, QT, **lodging:** Best Western, Drury Inn, Hampton Inn, **W...gas:** Mobil, Phillips 66, Shell, **food:** Arby's, Denny's, Fuddrucker's, McDonald's, Steak'n Shake, Subway, **lodging:** Baymont Inn

16b a   Page Ave, rd D, MO 364 W, **E...gas:** BP, CFM, Citgo/7-11, QT, Sinclair, **food:** Blimpie, Copperfield's Rest., Hardee's, Hooters, Malone's Grill, McDonald's, Stazio's Café, **lodging:** Comfort Inn, Courtyard, Holiday Inn, Red Roof Inn, Residence Inn, Sheraton

14   MO 340, Olive Blvd, **E...gas:** BP, Mobil, **food:** Denny's, McDonald's, Lion's Choice Rest., **lodging:** Drury Inn, **other:** HOSPITAL, Chevrolet, **W...food:** Bristol's Café, Culpepper's Café, TGIFriday, **lodging:** Courtyard

13   rd AB, Ladue Rd, no facilities

12b a   I-64, US 40, US 61, E to St Louis, W to Wentzville, **E...HOSPITAL**

9   MO 100, Manchester Rd, **E...gas:** BP, **food:** Café America, Houlihan's Rest, IHOP, Lion's Choice Rest., McDonald's, Famous Barr, Galyan's, Lord&Taylor, Nordstrom's, **other:** mall, **W...gas:** Shell, **food:** Applebee's, Casa Gallardo's Mexican, Olive Garden

8   Dougherty Ferry Rd, **S...gas:** Citgo/7-11, Mobil, **food:** McDonald's, **other:** HOSPITAL

7   Big Ben Rd, **N...HOSPITAL**

5b a   I-44, US 50, MO 366, E to St Louis, W to Tulsa

3   MO 30, Gravois Rd, **N...gas:** BP, Phillips 66, **food:** Bandana BBQ, Bob Evans, Rich&Charlie's Rest., TGIFriday, **lodging:** Best Western, Comfort Inn, Day's Inn, **S...Munzert Steaks**

2   MO 21, Tesson Ferry Rd, **N...gas:** Phillips 66, **food:** Calico's Rest., Olive Garden, Red Lobster, White Castle, **lodging:** Holiday Inn, **S...gas:** BP, CFM, Shell, **food:** Jack-in-the-Box, Wendy's, Dierberg's Foods

1b a   I-55 N to St Louis, S to Memphis

Interstate 435(Kansas City)

Exit #	Services
83	I-35, N to KS City, S to Wichita
82	Quivira Rd, Overland Park, **N...food:** Burger King, Old Chicago Pizza, Ponderosa, Taco Bell, **other:** HOSPITAL, **S...food:** McDonald's, Subway, Wendy's, **lodging:** Extended Stay America
81	US 69 S, to Ft Scott, no facilities
79	US 169, Metcalf Rd, **N...gas:** BP, Shell, **food:** Denny's, Dick Clark's Grill, Hooters, Tippin's Café, **lodging:** Clubhouse Inn, Embassy Suites, Hampton Inn, Red Roof Inn, Wyndham Garden, **other:** HOSPITAL, Chrysler/Dodge, **S...food:** McDonald's, **lodging:** Courtyard, Drury Inn, Marriott, PearTree Inn
77b a	Nall Ave, Roe Ave, **N...gas:** Amoco, Shell, **food:** DQ, On-the-Border, Panera Bread, Winstead's Grill, **lodging:** Fairfield Inn, **S...gas:** Amoco, **food:** Cactus Grill, McDonald's, Wendy's, **lodging:** AmeriSuites, Courtyard, Hilton Garden, Holiday Inn, Homestead Suites, Sheraton

Interstate 435

75b State Line Rd, **N…gas:** Amoco, Conoco, **food:** Applebee's, McDonald's, Waid's Rest., Wendy's, **other:** Buick/Cadillac, Ford, Goodyear, Infiniti, Lexus, Volvo, **S…**HOSPITAL, city park

a Wornall Rd, **N…gas:** QT, Shell, **other:** Chevrolet, Toyota, VW

74 Holmes Rd, **S…gas:** Amoco, Phillips 66, **food:** Burger King, Guacamole Grill, **lodging:** Courtyard, Extended Stay America

73 103rd St(from sb)

71b a I-470, US 71 S, US 50 E, no facilities

70 Bannister Rd, **E…gas:** Conoco, QT, **food:** Bennigan's, China Buffet, Luby's, McDonald's, Red Lobster, **other:** K-Mart, Sears/auto, mall, **W…food:** KFC/Taco Bell, LJ Silver/A&W, Old Country Buffet, Pizza Hut, **other:** Firestone/auto, Home Depot

69 87th St, Denny's, **E…food:** Darryl's, Denny's, IHOP, Luby's, McDonald's, Tippin's Café, **lodging:** Day's Inn, Motel 6, **other:** Best Buy, NTB, Suzuki, Wal-Mart SuperCtr/24hr, mall, **W…gas:** Amoco/diesel, **lodging:** Baymont Inn

67 Gregory Blvd, **W…**Nature Ctr, IMAX Theatre, zoo

66a 63rd St, **E…gas:** Shell, **food:** Applebee's, Waid's Rest., Wendy's

b MO 350 E, **W…food:** LC's BBQ, **lodging:** Relax Inn

65 Eastwood Tfwy, **W…gas:** Conoco, **food:** KFC, LC's BBQ, McDonald's, Peachtree Buffet, Pizza Hut, **lodging:** Relax Inn

63c Raytown Rd, Stadium Dr, **E…lodging:** Day's Inn, Sports Stadium Motel, Villager Lodge, **other:** Sports Complex

63b a I-70, W to KC, E to St Louis

61 MO 78, no facilities

60 MO 12 E, Truman Rd, 12th St, **E…gas:** Amoco/repair, Shamrock, **W…gas:** QT

59 US 24, Independence Ave, **E…gas:** QT, **food:** Hardee's, **lodging:** Queen City Motel(3mi), **other:** to Truman Library

57 Front St, **E…gas:** ✈/Flying J/Conoco/diesel/rest./24hr/@, **food:** Burger King, Taco Bell, **other:** Blue Beacon, **W…gas:** Phillips 66, QT, **food:** Denny's, KFC, McDonald's, Pizza Hut, Subway, Waffle House, Wendy's, lodging: Hampton Inn, Park Place Hotel, Smugglers Inn

56mm Missouri River

55b a MO 210, **E…gas:** Phillips 66/diesel, Shell, **lodging:** Red Roof Inn, other: Riverboat Casino, Ford/Volvo/GMC/Mercedes Trucks, **W…food:** Arby's, Denny's, McDonald's, **lodging:** Baymont Inn(2mi), Country Hearth Inn, Day's Inn

54 48th St, Parvin Rd, **E…**funpark, **W…gas:** QT, **food:** Alamo Mexican, Ponderosa, Waffle House, Wendy's, **lodging:** Best Western, Comfort Inn, Country Inn Suites, Crossland Suites, Holiday Inn, Super 8

52a US 69, **E…food:** A&W, KFC, **W…gas:** Amoco/repair, Coastal, Shell, **food:** McDonald's, Pizza Hut, Taco Bell, **other:** $General, Osco Drug, Sav-A-Lot Foods

52b I-35, S to KC

51 Shoal Creek Dr, no facilities

49b a MO 152 E, to I-35 N, Liberty, **E…food:** Applebee's, Bob Evans, Cracker Barrel, Golden Corral, Longhorn Steaks, Steak'n Shake, lodging: Best Western, Comfort Inn, Fairfield Inn, Hampton Inn, Holiday Inn Express, Super 8, Villager Inn

47 NE 96th St, no facilities

46 NE 108th St, no facilities

45 MO 291, NE Cookingham Ave, no facilities

42 N Woodland Ave, no facilities

41b a US 169, Smithville, **N…food:** Burger King, McDonald's, Sonic, lodging: Super 8

40 NW Cookingham, no facilities

37 NW Skyview Ave, rd C, **N…gas:** Total, **S…**golf

36 to I-29 S, to KCI Airport, **N…gas:** Total, **S…gas:** Amoco, lodging: Best Western, Comfort Suites, Fairfield Inn, Hampton Inn, Hilton, Holiday Inn Express, Microtel, Radisson, Wyndham Garden

31mm Prairie Creek

29 rd D, NW 120th St, no facilities

24 MO 152, rd N, NW Berry Rd, no facilities

22 MO 45, Weston, Parkville, no facilities

20mm Missouri/Kansas state line, Missouri River

18 KS 5 N, Wolcott Dr, **E…**to Wyandotte Co Lake Park

15b a Leavenworth Rd, **E…**Woodlands Racetrack

14b a Parallel Pkwy, **E…gas:** QT, **other:** HOSPITAL

13b a US 24, US 40, State Ave, **E…food:** Frontier Steaks, **W…other:** Cabela's Sporting Goods, KS Race Track

12b a I-70, KS Tpk, to Topeka, St Louis

11 Kansas Ave, no facilities

9 KS 32, KS City, Bonner Springs, **W…gas:** Phillips 66/diesel

8b Woodend Rd, **E…**Peterbilt

8.8mm Kansas River

8a Holliday Dr, to Lake Quivira, no facilities

6c Johnson Dr, no facilities

6b a Shawnee Mission Pkwy, **E…gas:** Amoco/diesel, **food:** Sonic, **other:** museum

5 Midland Dr, Shawnee Mission Park, **E…gas:** Conoco, Shell/Blimpie, **food:** Arizona's Grille, Barley's Brewhaus, Jose Pepper's Grill, Paula&Bill's Ristorante, Wendy's, **lodging:** Hampton Inn

3 87th Ave, **E…gas:** Amoco, Phillips 66, Shell, **food:** McDonald's, other: NY Burrito, Panera Bread, Sonic, Zarda BBQ, K-Mart, museum

2 95th St, no facilities

1b KS 10, to Lawrence

a Lackman Rd, **N…gas:** QT, Shell

0mm I-435 begins/ends on I-35.

Kansas City

Kansas City

MONTANA
Interstate 15

Exit #	Services
398mm	Montana/US/Canada Border
397	Sweetgrass, **W...rest area both lanes, full(handic apped)facilities, picnic tables, litter barrels, pet-walk, phone**, **gas:** Sinclair, **lodging:** Glocca Morra Motel/café, **other:** Duty Free
394	ranch access, no facilities
389	MT 552, Sunburst, **W...gas/diesel**, **food:** Kelly's Kitchen, **other:** Sunburst RV Park
385	Swayze Rd, no facilities
379	MT 215, MT 343, to Kevin, Oilmont, **W...food:** Four Corners Café
373	Potter Rd, no facilities
369	Bronken Rd, no facilities
366.5mm	weigh sta sb
364	Shelby, **E...**Lewis&Clark RV Park, **W...**airport
363	US 2, to Cut Bank, Shelby, **E...gas:** Exxon/Subway/diesel/24hr, Sinclair, **food:** Dash Drive-In, Dixie Inn Steaks, Pizza Hut, **lodging:** Comfort Inn, Crossroads Inn, Glacier Motel, O'Haire Motel, **1 mi E...other:** HOSPITAL, Albertson's, CarQuest, Ford/Mercury, GMC, Goodyear/auto, **W...food:** McDonald's, **other:** Pamida/drugs, to Glacier NP
361mm	parking area nb
358	Marias Valley Rd, to Golf Course Rd, **E...**camping
357mm	Marias River
352	Bullhead Rd, no facilities
348	rd 44, to Valier, **W...**Lake Frances RA(15mi)
345	MT 366, Ledger Rd, **E...**to Tiber Dam(42mi)
339	Conrad, **W...gas:** Cenex/diesel, Exxon/diesel, **food:** A&W/KFC, House of Pizza, Keg Rest., Main Drive-In, **lodging:** Conrad Motel, Northgate Motel, Super 8, **other:** HOSPITAL, Dan's Tires, IGA Foods, Olson's Drug, Parts+, Radio Shack, Chevrolet/Pontiac/Buick, Ford/Mercury, Pondera RV Park, RV Ctr/LP
335	Midway Rd, Conrad, **4 mi W...**HOSPITAL, gas, food, phone, lodging, RV camping
328	MT 365, Brady, **1 mi W...gas:** Mtn View Co-op/diesel, **other:** USPO, phone
321	Collins Rd, no facilities
319mm	**Teton River, rest area both lanes, full(handicapp ed)facilities, phones, picnic tables, litter barrels, petwalk**
313	MT 221, MT 379, Dutton, **W...gas:** Cenex/diesel, **food:** Dutton Café, **other:** USPO
302	MT 431, Power, no facilities
297	Gordon, no facilities
290	US 89 N, rd 200 W, to Choteau, **W...gas:** Exxon, Sinclair/diesel/LP/RV dump, **other:** USPO
288mm	parking area both lanes
286	Manchester, **W...**livestock auction, same as 290(2mi)
282	US 87 N(from sb), weigh sta, **E...gas:** Yellowstone Trkstp/diesel, **1-3 mi E...gas:** Exxon/A&W/Blimpie, **food:** McDonald's, **lodging:** Day's Inn, **other:** Wal-Mart
280	US 87 N, Central Ave W, Great Falls, **E...gas:** Conoco, ✈/Flying J/diesel/LP/24hr, **food:** Arby's, Double Barrel Diner, DQ, Ford's Drive-In, KFC, Taco John's, **lodging:** Adelweiss Motel, Alberta Inn, Day's Inn, Starlit Motel, **other:** NAPA, U-Haul/LP, Whalen Tire, to Giant Sprgs SP
280mm	Sun River
278	US 89 S, rd 200 E, 10th Ave, Great Falls, **E...gas:** Exxon/A&W, Sinclair/diesel, **food:** China Town, Classic 50's Diner, DQ, Elmer's Rest., Golden Corral, McDonald's, Quizno's, **lodging:** Airway Motel, Best Western, Budget Inn, Hampton Inn, Holiday Inn Express, Kanga Inn, **other:** Barnes&Noble, Dick's RV Park, Home Depot, OfficeMax, Smith's Food, **1-3 mi E...gas:** Cenex/diesel, Conoco, Holiday/diesel, Sinclair/diesel, **food:** Applebee's, Arby's, Burger King, Cattin's Rest., Country Kitchen, Del Taco, DQ, 4B's Rest., Fuddrucker's, Godfather's, Jaker's Rib/fish, JB's Rest., KFC, Little Caesar's, McDonald's, Ming's Chinese, Papa John's, Papa Murphy's, Pizza Hut, PrimeCut Rest., Sting Rest., Subway, Taco Bell, Taco John's, Wendy's, **lodging:** Comfort Inn, Fairfield Inn, Plaza Inn, Super 8, **other:** HOSPITAL, Albertson's, Checker Parts, Chevrolet/Cadillac/Toyota, County Mkt Food/24hr, Dodge/Hyundai/Suzuki/VW, Firestone/auto, Ford, Hancock Fabrics, Hastings Books, Herberger's, Honda, JC Penney, Jo-Ann Crafts, K-Mart, KOA(6mi), Lincoln/Mercury, McCollum RVs, NAPA, Osco Drug, Nissan, Plymouth/Jeep, Sears/auto, Target, TireRama, USPO, transmissions, to Malmstrom AFB
277	Airport Rd, **E...gas:** Conoco/diesel/café/casino/24hr, **lodging:** Crystal Inn
275mm	weigh sta nb
270	MT 330, Ulm, **E...gas:** Exxon/diesel/LP, **other:** USPO, **W...food:** Griffin's Rest., to Ulm SP
256	rd 68, Cascade, **1/2 mi E...gas:** Sinclair, **food:** Pizza Pro, **lodging:** Badger Motel/café, **other:** NAPA, Tom's Foods, USPO
254	rd 68, Cascade, **1/2 mi E...**same as 256
247	Hardy Creek, Hardy Creek, **W...**food, phone, RV camping
246.5mm	Missouri River
245mm	scenic overlook sb
244	Canyon Access, **2 mi W...**camping, food, RV camping, rec area

Interstate 15

N
↕
S

240	Dearborn, **E…**RV park, **W…food:** Dearborn Café, **other:** auto repair
250	local access, no facilities
239mm	**rest area both lanes, full(handicapped)facilities, phone, picnic tables, litter barrels, petwalk**
238mm	Stickney Creek
236mm	Missouri River
234	Craig, **E…food:** Trout Shop Café/lodge, **other:** rec area, boating, camping
228	US 287 N, to Augusta, no facilities
226	MT 434, Wolf Creek, Wolf Creek, **E…gas:** Exxon/diesel, **food:** Oasis Café, **other:** Lewis&Clark Canoes, MT Outfitters/flyshop/RV/motel, camping, **W…food:** Frenchman&Me Café, **other:** USPO
222mm	parking area both lanes
219	Spring Creek, Recreation Rd(from nb), Spring Creek, boating, camping
218mm	Little Prickly Pear Creek
216	Sieben, no facilities
209	**E…**to Gates of the Mtns RA, no facilities
205mm	turnout sb
202mm	weigh sta sb
200	MT 279, MT 453, Lincoln Rd, **W…gas:** Sinclair/Bob's Mkt/diesel, **food:** GrubStake Rest., **other:** Helena Campground(4mi), Lincoln Rd RV Park, to ski area

Helena

193	Cedar St, Helena, **E…**Helena RV Park(5mi), Home Depot, **W…gas:** Cenex/diesel, Conoco/diesel, Exxon/diesel, Sinclair/24hr, **food:** Applebee's, Arby's, Dragon Wall Chinese, Godfather's, Jade Garden Chinese, McDonald's, Perkins, Pizza Hut, Subway, Taco Bell, Taco John's, **lodging:** Blackstone Inn/casino, Wingate Inn, **other:** Albertson's/24hr, CarQuest, Checker Parts, Chevrolet, County Mkt Foods, Hastings Books, Kia, K-Mart, NAPA, ShopKO, Target, TireORama, USPO, radiator/transmissions
192b a	US 12, US 287, Helena, Townsend, **E…gas:** Conoco/diesel/24hr, **food:** Burger King, Golden Corral, Subway, **lodging:** Hampton Inn, **other:** D&D RV Ctr, Schwab Tire, Staples, Wal-Mart SuperCtr/24hr, st patrol, **other:** Buick/Cadillac/GMC, Chrysler/Jeep/Nissan, Ford/Lincoln/Mercury, Honda, Plymouth, Toyota, **W…gas:** Exxon/diesel, Sinclair/24hr, **food:** A&W/KFC, DQ, Frontier Pies, JB's, L&D Chinese, McDonald's, Overland Express Rest., Papa John's, Wendy's, **lodging:** Comfort Inn, Country Inn Suites, Day's Inn, Fairfield Inn, Holiday Inn Express, Jorgenson's Inn, Motel 6, Red Lion Inn, Shilo Inn, Super 8, **other:** HOSPITAL, Albertson's/gas, Country Harvest Foods, Dillard's, Goodyear/auto, Osco Drug, Safeway/gas
187	Clancy, **E…**RV camping, **W…gas:** Gen Store, **food:** Legal Tender Rest., to NF
182	Clancy, **E…**RV camping, **W…gas:** Gen Store, **food:** Legal Tender Rest., to NF

MONTANA
Interstate 15

178mm **rest area both lanes, full(handicapped)facilities, phone, picnic tables, litter barrels, petwalk**

176 Jefferson City, NF access, no facilities

174.5mm chain up area both lanes

168mm chainup area both lanes

164 rd 69, Boulder, **E...gas:** Exxon/diesel/casino/24hr, **food:** DQ, Elkhorn Café, Mtn Good Rest., **other:** Parts+, USPO, camping

161mm parking area nb

160 High Ore Rd, no facilities

156 Basin, **E...other:** Basin Cr Pottery, Merry Widow Health Mine/RV camping, **W...food:** Silver Saddle Café, **other:** camping

154mm Boulder River

151 to Boulder River Rd, Bernice, **W...**camping, picnic area

148mm chainup area both lanes

143.5mm chainup area both lanes

138 Elk Park, **W...other:** Sheepshead Picnic Area, wildlife viewing

134 Woodville, no facilities

133mm continental divide, elev 6368

130.5mm scenic overlook sb

129 I-90 E, to Billings, no facilities

I-15 S and I-90 W run together 8 mi

127 Harrison Ave, Butte, **N...gas:** Cenex/diesel, Conoco, **food:** Arctic Circle, DQ, Denny's, Derby Steaks, L&D Chinese, Papa John's, Taco John's, **lodging:** Day's Inn, Holiday Inn Express, Red Lion Inn, **other:** Checker Parts, Hastings Books, NAPA, Nissan/Toyota, Safeway, **S...gas:** Conoco/diesel, Exxon/diesel/24hr, Sinclair, **food:** A&W, Arby's, Burger King, 4B's Rest., Godfather's, KFC, McDonald's, Perkins, Pizza Hut, Ray's Rest., Silver Bow Pizza, Subway, Taco Bell, Wendy's, **lodging:** Comfort Inn, Hampton Inn, Ramada Inn, Super 8, **other:** Checker Parts, Chevrolet/Subaru, Chrysler/Plymouth/Dodge/Jeep, Ford/Honda, GMC/Buick/Cadillac/Pontiac, Herberger's, Honda, JC Penney, Jo-Ann Crafts, Lincoln/Mercury, Smith Foods, Staples, Wal-Mart SuperCtr/24hr, Whalen Tire

126 Montana St, Butte, **N...gas:** Cenex/diesel, **lodging:** Eddy's Motel, **other:** HOSPITAL, KOA, Safeway, Schwab Tire, **S...gas:** Conoco, Exxon/diesel

124 I-115(from eb), to Butte, City Ctr

122 Rocker, **N...gas:** ♨/Flying J/Arby's/diesel/LP/casino/24hr, **lodging:** Rocker Inn Motel, **other:** weigh sta both lanes, RV camping, **S...gas:** Conoco/4B's Rest./diesel/casino/24hr, **lodging:** Motel 6

I-15 N and I-90 E run together 8 mi

121 I-90 W, to Missoula, no facilities

119 Silver Bow, Port of MT Transportation Hub

116 Buxton, no facilities

112mm Continental Divide, elevation 5879

111 Feely, no facilities

109mm **rest area both lanes, full(handicapped)facilities, phone, picnic tables, litter barrels, petwalk**

102 rd 43, to Wisdom, Divide, **W...gas:** Sinclair, **other:** to Big Hole Nat Bfd

99 Moose Creek Rd, no facilities

93 Melrose, **W...food:** Melrose Café/grill/gas/diesel, Hitchin Post Rest., **other:** Sportsman Motel/RV Park, USPO

85.5mm Big Hole River

85 Glen, **E...**lodging, RV camping

74 Apex, Birch Creek, no facilities

64mm Beaverhead River

63 Lp 15, rd 41, Dillon, Twin Bridges, **E...gas:** Cenex/diesel/LP, Exxon/diesel/24hr, Phillips 66, **food:** KFC, McDonald's, Pizza Hut, Subway, **lodging:** Best Western/rest., Comfort Inn, GuestHouse Inn, Sundowner Motel, Super 8, **other:** HOSPITAL, KOA, Safeway/drug/gas, Schwab Tire, Chevrolet/Pontiac/Buick/Cadillac, museum, W MT Coll

62 Lp 15, Dillon, **E...gas:** Exxon, **food:** Arctic Circle, DQ, Sparky's Rest., Taco John's, **lodging:** Creston Motel, Crosswinds Motel/rest., Flyshop Inn, **other:** HOSPITAL, KOA, Southside RV Park, to WMT

60mm Beaverhead River

59 MT 278, to Jackson, **W...other:** Bannack SP, Countryside RV Park

56 Barretts, **E...**RV camping, **W...gas:** Big Sky Trkstp/diesel/24hr

52 Grasshopper Creek, no facilities

51 Dalys(from sb, no return), no facilities

50mm Beaverhead River

46mm Beaverhead River

45mm Beaverhead River

44 MT 324, **E...other:** Armstead RV Park, Beaverhead Flyshop, **W...other:** Clark Cyn Res, rec area, RV camping

38.5mm Red Rock River

37 Red Rock, no facilities

34mm parking area both lanes, litter barrels

29 Kidd, no facilities

23 Dell, **E...lodging:** Stockyard Inn, **other:** auto repair

16.5mm weigh sta both lanes

15 Lima, **E...gas:** Exxon/diesel, **food:** Jan's Café, **lodging:** Lee's Motel/RV Park, **other:** Big Sky Service/tires, I&J Mkt, USPO, ambulance, auto/tire repair

9 Snowline, no facilities

0 Monida, **E...**phone, to Red Rock Lakes

0mm Monida Pass, elevation 6870, Montana/Idaho state line

Interstate 90

Exit #	Services
509.5mm	weigh sta both lanes
554.5mm	Montana/Wyoming state line
549	Aberdeen, no facilities
544	Wyola, no facilities
530	MT 463, Lodge Grass, **1 mi S...gas:** Cenex/diesel/LP, lodging, phone
517.5mm	Little Bighorn River
514	Garryowen, **N...gas:** Conoco/Subway, **other:** Custer Bfd Museum, **S...other:** 7th Ranch RV camp
511.5mm	Little Bighorn River
510	US 212 E, **N...gas:** Exxon/KFC/diesel/café/gifts, **food:** Crows Nest Café, **other:** HOSPITAL, to Little Bighorn Bfd, **S...other:** Little Bighorn Camping/motel
509.3mm	Little Bighorn River
509	Crow Agency, **N...gas:** Conoco/24hr, **S...to** Bighorn Canyon NRA
503	Dunmore, no facilities
498mm	Bighorn River
497	MT 384, 3rd St, Hardin, **S...HOSPITAL**, visitors ctr, **2 mi S...lodging:** Lariat Motel, Western Motel, **other:** Casino Rest./lounge
495	MT 47, City Ctr, Hardin, **N...gas:** Shell/diesel, **food:** Purple Cow Rest., **other:** KOA, **S...gas:** Cenex, Conoco/Subway/diesel/LP/24hr, Exxon/diesel, Sinclair/KFC/diesel, **food:** DQ, KFC, McDonald's, Pizza Hut/Taco Bell, Taco John's, **lodging:** American Inn, Lariat Motel, Super 8, Western Motel, **other:** HOSPITAL, RV camping
484	Toluca, no facilities
478	Fly Creek Rd, no facilities
477mm	**rest area both lanes, full(handicapped)facilities, phone, picnic tables, litter barrels, petwalk**
469	Arrow Creek Rd, **N...food:** Rock Shop/Cafe
462	Pryor Creek Rd, no facilities
456	I-94 E, to Bismarck, ND, no facilities
455	Johnson Lane, **S...gas:** Exxon/A&W/Blimpie/diesel/24hr, Flying J/Conoco/diesel/LP/rest./24hr/@, **food:** Burger King, DQ, Jackpot Diner, Subway, **lodging:** Holiday Inn Express, **other:** RV Ctr(1mi)
452	US 87 N, City Ctr, Billings, **N...gas:** Conoco/Arby's/diesel/LP, Exxon/diesel, **lodging:** Best Western, Chevrolet, transmissions, **2-4 mi N on US 87...gas:** Cenex, Conoco, Holiday/diesel, **food:** Applebee's, Arby's, Burger King, DQ, Elmer's Pancakes, Godfather's, Guadalajara Mexican, Little Caesar's, McDonald's, Papa John's, Papa Murphy's, Peking Express, Pizza Hut, Subway, Taco Bell, Taco John's, Wendy's, **lodging:** Foothills Inn, Metra Inn, **other:** MEDICAL CARE, Albertson's, CarQuest, Champion Parts, Checkers Parts, County Mkt Foods, K-Mart, Radio Shack, Wal-Mart SuperCtr/24hr, **S...gas:** Cenex/diesel
451.5mm	Yellowstone River
450	MT 3, 27th St, Billings, **N...gas:** Conoco/diesel/24hr, Exxon/Subway, Sinclair/repair, **food:** Denny's, Hardee's, Perkins/24hr(1mi), Pizza Hut, **lodging:** Howard Johnson, Rimview Motel(2mi), Sheraton(1mi), War Bonnet Inn/rest., **other:** HOSPITAL, CarQuest, USPO, **S...KOA**, Yellowstone River Camping
447	S Billings Blvd, **N...gas:** Conoco/Subway/diesel/24hr, **food:** Burger King, 4B's Rest., McDonald's, **lodging:** Day's Inn, Extended Stay America, Hampton Inn, Sleep Inn, Super 8
446	King Ave, Billings, **N...gas:** Conoco, Holiday/diesel/LP/RV dump, **food:** Burger King, Country Harvest Buffet, Del Taco, Denny's, Fuddrucker's, Olive Garden, Outback Steaks, Perkins, Pizza Hut, Red Lobster, Taco John's, Texas Roadhouse, **lodging:** C'Mon Inn, Comfort Inn, Day's Inn, Fairfield Inn, Marriott, Quality Inn, Springhill Suites, Super 8, **other:** Best Buy, Chrysler/Plymouth/Kia, Costco/gas, Dodge, Ford, Kia, NAPA, Nissan, RV Repair, Shop-KO, Subaru/Hyundai, USPO, **N on King Ave...gas:** Exxon/Subway, Conoco, Sinclair, **food:** Applebee's, Cactus Creek Steaks, Famous Dave's, IHOP, McDonald's, Quizno's, Subway, Taco Bell, Wendy's, **other:** Albertson's, Barnes&Noble, Hastings Books, Home Depot, Lowe's Whse, Office Depot, OfficeMax, Old Navy, Target, Wal-Mart SuperCtr/24hr, mall, **S...gas:** Conoco/24hr, **food:** Cracker Barrel, Emporium Rest., **lodging:** Best Western, Billings Hotel, Fireside Inn, Holiday Inn, Kelly Inn, Motel 6, Ramada Ltd, Red Roof Inn
443	Zoo Dr, to Shiloh Rd, **N...Pierce** RV Ctr, zoo, **S...** Cenex/diesel, Harley-Davidson
439mm	weigh sta both lanes
437	E Laurel, **S...gas:** Sinclair/diesel/rest./casino/motel/24hr, **food:** Shotgun Willy's/grill, **other:** EZ Livin' RV Ctr
434	US 212, US 310, to Red Lodge, Laurel, **N...gas:** Cenex/diesel, Conoco/diesel, Exxon/diesel/24hr, **food:** Burger King, Hardee's, Pizza Hut, Subway, Taco John's, **lodging:** Howard Johnson, Super 8, **other:** IGA Foods, Chevrolet, Ford, **S...to** Yellowstone NP
433	Lp 90(from eb), no facilities
426	Park City, **S...gas:** Cenex/diesel/café/24hr, **food:** CJ's Motel, **other:** auto/tire repair

MONTANA

Interstate 90

E

W

419mm **rest area both lanes, full(handicapped)facilities, phone, picnic tables, litter barrels, petwalk**

408 rd 78, Columbus, **N**...Mtn Range RV Park, **S**...**gas:** Conoco/Big Sky Motel, Exxon/diesel/24hr, **food:** Apple Village Café/gifts, McDonald's, **lodging:** Super 8, **other:** HOSPITAL, IGA Foods, casino, museum, to Yellowstone

400 Springtime Rd, no facilities

398mm Yellowstone River

396 ranch access, no facilities

392 Reed Point, **N**...**gas:** Sinclair/diesel, **lodging:** Hotel Montana/rest., **other:** RV camping

384 Bridger Creek Rd, no facilities

381mm **rest area both lanes, full(handicapped)facilities, phone, picnic tables, litter barrels, petwalk**

377 Greycliff, **S**...**other:** Prairie Dog Town SP, KOA

370 US 191, Big Timber, **1 mi N**...**gas:** Conoco/diesel, Exxon, Sinclair/diesel, **lodging:** Grand Hotel, Lazy J Motel, **other:** Spring Creek RV Ranch(4mi), USPO

369mm Boulder River

367 US 191 N, Big Timber, **N**...**gas:** Exxon/diesel, Conoco/diesel, **food:** Country Skillet, Crazy Jane's Eatery/casino, **lodging:** Super 8, **other:** CarQuest, Chevrolet, hist site, visitor ctr

362 De Hart, no facilities

354 MT 563, Springdale, no facilities

343 Mission Creek Rd, no facilities

352 ranch access, no facilities

350 East End access, no facilities

340 US 89 N, to White Sulphur Sprgs, **S**...airport

337 Lp 90, to Livingston, **2 mi N**...**gas:** Exxon, **lodging:** motels

333mm Yellowstone River

333 US 89 S, Livingston, **N**...**food:** Pizza Hut, Taco John's, **lodging:** Best Western, Budget Host, Econolodge, Livingston Inn, Travelodge, **other:** HOSPITAL, Chevrolet, County Mkt Food/24hr, Ford/Lincoln/Mercury, Oasis RV Park, Pamida, Radio Shack, Western Drug, **S**...**gas:** Cenex/diesel, Conoco/diesel, Exxon/diesel, **food:** Hardee's, McDonald's, Subway, **lodging:** Comfort Inn, Super 8, **other:** Albertson's, KOA(10mi), Osen's RV Park, to Yellowstone

330 Lp 90, Livingston, **1 mi N**...**gas:** Yellowstone Trkstp/diesel/24hr/rest.

326.5mm chainup area both lanes

324 ranch access, no facilities

323mm chainup area wb

322mm Bridger Mountain Range

321mm turnouts/hist marker both lanes

319 Jackson Creek Rd, no facilities

319mm chainup area both lanes

316 Trail Creek Rd, no facilities

313 Bear Canyon Rd, **S**...**other:** Bear Canyon Camping

Livingston

Bozeman

309 US 191 S, Main St, Bozeman, **N**...**other:** Jeep/Subaru, Sunrise RV Park, **S**...**gas:** Exxon, Sinclair, **food:** Eastside Diner, MT AleWorks, **lodging:** Alpine Lodge, Best Western, Blue Sky Motel, Continental Motel, Ranch House Motel, Western Heritage Inn, **other:** HOSPITAL, Toyota/Mazda, RV service, Goodyear, to Yellowstone

306 US 191, N 7th, Bozeman, **N**...**gas:** Conoco, Sinclair, **N**...**food:** McDonald's, Panda Buffet, **lodging:** Best Value Inn, Fairfield Inn, Microtel, Park Inn, Ramada Ltd, Sleep Inn, Super 8, TLC Inn, **other:** RV supplies, ski area, **S**...**gas:** Conoco/Arby's/diesel, Exxon, Sinclair/diesel, **food:** Applebee's, DQ, Frontier Pies Rest., Hardee's, KFC, McDonald's, Papa John's, Subway, Taco Bell, Taco John's, Village Inn Pizza, Wendy's, **lodging:** Best Western, Bozeman/rest., Comfort Inn, Day's Inn, Hampton Inn, Holiday Inn, **other:** Big O Tire, CarQuest, County Mkt Foods, Firestone/auto, K-Mart, NAPA, U-Haul, Wal-Mart SuperCtr/24hr, Museum of the Rockies

305 MT412, N 19th Ave, **N**...**gas:** Exxon, **S**...**food:** A&W/KFC, Carino's Italian, Denny's, McKenzie River Pizza, **other:** Border's Books, Costco, Home Depot, Target, Smith's, UPS, USPO, **2-3 mi S**...**food:** Arby's, Bennigan's, Burger King, Perkins, Pizza Hut, Spanish Peaks Brewery/Italian Café, **lodging:** Best Western, Wingate Inn, **other:** Ford, museum

298 MT 291, MT 85, Belgrade, **N**...**gas:** Cenex/diesel, Conoco, Exxon/Subway/diesel, **food:** Burger King, DQ, McDonald's, Pizza Hut, **other:** Albertson's, IGA Foods, NAPA, **S**...**gas:** Flying J/Conoco/diesel/LP, **food:** Country Kitchen, **lodging:** Holiday Inn Express, La Quinta, Super 8, **other:** Harley-Davidson, Inter-West Tire, truckwash, to Yellowstone NP

292.5mm Gallatin River

288 Manhattan, **N**...**gas:** Conoco/diesel, **other:** RV camping

283 Logan, **S**...**other:** Madison Buffalo Jump SP(7mi)

279mm Madison River

278 MT 205, rd 2, Three Forks, Trident, **N**...Missouri Headwaters SP, **1 mi S**...**lodging:** Broken Spur Motel, Sacajawea Inn, **other:** camping, phone

277.5mm Jefferson River

274 US 287, to Helena, Ennis, **N**...**gas:** Conoco/diesel, Sinclair/diesel, **food:** Wheat MT Bakery/deli, **other:** to Canyon Ferry SP, Ft 3 Forks, **S**...**gas:** Exxon/Subway/diesel/24hr, **other:** Lewis&Clark Caverns SP, KOA(1mi), to Yellowstone NP

267 Milligan Canyon Rd, no facilities

261.5mm chain removal area

257mm Boulder River

256 MT 359, Cardwell, **S**...**gas:** Gas-Up/diesel, **other:** to Yellowstone NP, Lewis&Clark Caverns SP, RV camping

Belgrade

Interstate 90

E
W

Butte

249	rd 55, to rd 69, Whitehall, **S...gas:** Exxon/Subway/diesel/24hr, **food:** A&W/KFC, **lodging:** Chief Motel, Super 8, **other:** camping
241	Pipestone, **S...other:** Pipestone Camping(apr-oct), gas, phone
240.5mm	chainup area both lanes
238.5mm	runaway ramp eb
237.5mm	pulloff eb
235mm	parking area both lanes, litter barrels
233	Homestake, Continental Divide, elev 6393, no facilities
230mm	chain removal area both lanes
228	MT 375, Continental Dr, no facilities
227	I-15 N, to Helena, Great Falls, no facilities I-90 and I-15 run together 8 mi. **See Montana Interstate 15, exits 122-127.**
219	I-15 S, to Dillon, Idaho Falls, no facilities
216	Ramsay, no facilities
211	MT 441, Gregson, **3-5 mi S...**food, lodging, Fairmont RV Park(Apr-Oct)
210.5mm	parking area wb, Pintlar Scenic route info
208	rd 1, Pintler Scenic Loop, Georgetown Lake RA, Opportunity, Anaconda, **3-5 mi S...other:** HOSPITAL, gas, food, lodging, RV camp/dump, ski area
201	Warm Springs, **S...**gas/diesel, MT ST HOSPITAL
197	MT 273, Galen, **S...**to MT ST HOSPITAL
195	Racetrack, no facilities

Deer Lodge

187	Lp 90, Deer Lodge(no wb return), **2 mi S...**gas: Exxon, MRC/diesel/repair, **food:** A&W, Monte's Subs, Outlaw Cafe, Pizza Hut, **lodging:** Downtowner Motel, Scharf's Motel/rest., Western Motel, **other:** HOSPITAL, IGA Foods, Safeway/deli, Tow Ford Museum, Grant-Kohrs Ranch NHS, KOA(seasonal), Indian Creek RV Park(seasonal)(4mi), Schwab Tire
184	Deer Lodge, **S...**gas: Cenex/diesel, Conoco/diesel/casino, **food:** 4B's Rest., McDonald's, **lodging:** Super 8, **other:** Indian Cr Camping, **1 mi S...**gas: Exxon/diesel/casino, **food:** Pizza Hut, **lodging:** Downtowner Motel, Western Big Sky Inn, **other:** Safeway, Schwab Tire
179	Beck Hill Rd, no facilities
175mm	Little Blackfoot River
175	US 12 E(from wb), Garrison, **N...**phone, hist site, RiverFront RV Park
174	US 12 E(from eb), same as 175
170	Phosphate, no facilities
168mm	**rest area both lanes, full(handicapped)facilities, phone, picnic tables, litter barrels, petwalk**
166	Gold Creek, **S...other:** Camp Mak-A-Dream
162	Jens, no facilities

154	to MT 1(from wb), Drummond, **S...gas:** Cenex/diesel, Conoco/diesel, Exxon/diesel, Sinclair/diesel/24hr, **food:** Wagon Wheel Café/Motel, **lodging:** Sky Motel, **other:** Pintler Scenic Lp, Georgetown Lake RA, Goodtime RV Park(3mi)
153	MT 1(from eb), **N...other:** Garnet GhostTown, **S...food:** D-M Café, **lodging:** Drummond Motel, same as 154
150.5mm	weigh sta both lanes
143mm	**rest area both lanes, full(handicapped)facilities, phone, picnic tables, litter barrels, petwalk**
138	Bearmouth Area, **N...other:** Chalet Bearmouth Camp/rest., to gas, food, lodging
130	Beavertail Rd, **S...other:** to Beavertail Hill SP, rec area, camping(seasonal)
128mm	parking area both lanes, no facilities
126	Rock Creek Rd, **S...lodging:** Rock Creek Lodge/gas/casino, **other:** Ekstrom Camping/rest., rec area
120	Clinton, **1 mi N...gas:** Sinclair/diesel, **food:** Poor Henry's Café(1mi), **other:** USPO
113	Turah, **S...**Turah RV Park/gas
109.5mm	Clark Fork, Clark Fork
109mm	Blackfoot River
109	MT 200 E, Bonner, **N...gas:** Exxon/Arby's/Subway/diesel/casino/LP/24hr/@, **food:** River City Grill, **other:** USPO, banking, hist site
108.5mm	Clark Fork, Clark Fork

Missoula

107	E Missoula, **N...gas:** Ole's Mkt/Diner/Conoco/diesel/24hr, Sinclair, **food:** Kolb's Café/casino, **lodging:** Aspen Motel, **other:** diesel repair, **2 mi S...lodging:** Holiday Inn Express
105	US 12 W, Missoula, **S...gas:** Cenex/diesel/24hr, Conoco/diesel/24hr, Pacific Pride/diesel, Sinclair, **food:** Burger King, Finnegan's, Little Caesar's, McDonald's, McKay's Rest./casino, Pasta House, Pizza Hut, PressBox Café, Quizno's, Taco Bell, **lodging:** Best Western, Campus Inn, Creekside Inn, DoubleTree, Family Inn, Holiday Inn, Holiday Inn Express, Ponderosa Motel, Thunderbird Motel, **other:** Ace Hardware, Albertson's, Champion Parts, Flyshop, Jim's Casino, U of MT, Vietnam Vet's Mem
104	Orange St, Missoula, **S...gas:** Conoco, Sinclair, **food:** KFC, Pagoda Chinese, Subway, **lodging:** Budget Motel, Ramada Ltd., **other:** HOSPITAL, to City Ctr

MONTANA

Interstate 90

101	US 93 S, Reserve St, **N...gas:** Conoco/diesel, **food:** Cracker Barrel, Starbucks, **lodging:** Best Western, C'Mon Inn, Motel 6, **other:** ski area, **S...gas:** Cenex/diesel/LP, Conoco/24hr, Exxon/diesel/24hr, **food:** McDonald's, McKenzie River Pizza, Rowdy's Rest., Taco Time/TCBY, **lodging:** Best Inn, Comfort Inn, Hampton Inn, Microtel, Ruby's Inn/rest., Super 8, Travelers Inn, **other:** Bretz RV/Marine, KOA, casinos, diesel repair, **1 mi S...gas:** Conoco, Exxon/diesel, **food:** Arby's, Arctic Circle, Burger King, China Bowl, Fuddrucker's, Jimmy Carino's, Outback Steaks, Subway, Taco Bell, Wendy's, **other:** Albertson's, Barnes&Noble, Best Buy, Chevrolet, Costco/gas, Home Depot, Michael's, Old Navy, Staples, Target, Wal-Mart SuperCtr/24hr, mall
99	Airway Blvd, **S...lodging:** Wingate Inn, **other:** Chrysler/Plymouth/Dodge, Lincoln/Mercury, airport
96	US 93 N, MT 200W, Kalispell, **N...gas:** Conoco/diesel/rest./24hr/@, **lodging:** Day's Inn/rest., **other:** Jellystone RV Park, Peterbilt/Ford/Freightliner, to Flathead Lake & Glacier NP, **S...gas:** Sinclair/4B's/diesel/24hr/@, **lodging:** Redwood Lodge, **other:** RV repair
92.5mm	inspection sta both lanes
89	Frenchtown, **S...gas:** Conoco/diesel/café/24hr, Sinclair/rest./laundry, **other:** MEDICAL CARE, USPO, to Frenchtown Pond SP
85	Huson, **S...gas:** Sinclair/café, **other:** phone
82	Nine Mile Rd, **N...other:** Hist Ranger Sta/info, food, phone
81.5mm	Clark Fork
80mm	Clark Fork, Clark Fork
77	MT 507, Petty Creek Rd, Alberton, **S...access to** gas, food, lodging, phone
75	Alberton, **S...lodging:** MT Hotel, River Edge Motel/gas, **other:** MT Book Store, RV camp, casino
73mm	parking area wb, litter barrels
72mm	parking area eb, litter barrels
70	Cyr, no facilities
70mm	Clark Fork, Clark Fork
66	Fish Creek Rd, no facilities
66mm	Clark Fork, Clark Fork
61	Tarkio, no facilities
59mm	Clark Fork, Clark Fork
58mm	**rest area both lanes, full(handicapped)facilities, phone, picnic tables, litter barrels, petwalk, NF camping(seasonal)**
55	Lozeau, Quartz, no facilities
53.5mm	Clark Fork, Clark Fork
49mm	Clark Fork, Clark Fork
47	MT 257, Superior, **N...gas:** Cenex/24hr, Conoco/diesel, Sinclair/Durango's Rest., **lodging:** Bel-vue Motel, Big Sky Motel, Budget Host, **other:** HOSPITAL, IGA Food, Mineral Drug, NAPA, USPO, **S...gas:** Exxon/diesel/casino/mechanic/24hr

45mm	Clark Fork, Clark Fork
43	Dry Creek Rd, **N...**NP camping(seasonal)
37	Sloway Area, no facilities
34mm	Clark Fork, Clark Fork
33	MT 135, St Regis, **N...gas:** Conoco/diesel/rest./gifts, Exxon/pizza, Sinclair, **food:** Frosty Drive-In, Jasper's Rest., OK Café/casino, **lodging:** Little River Motel, St Regis Motel/camping, Super 8, **other:** KOA, Nugget Camground, St Regis, USPO
30	Two Mile Rd, **S...**fishing access
29mm	fishing access, wb
26	Ward Creek Rd(from eb), no facilities
25	Drexel, no facilities
22	Camels Hump Rd, Henderson, **N...other:** camping(seasonal), antiques(1mi)
18	DeBorgia, **N...food:** Pinecrest Rest./casino
16	Haugan, **N...gas:** Exxon/diesel/24hr, **lodging:** 10,000 Silver $/motel/rest./casino
15mm	weigh sta both lanes, exits left from both lanes
10	Saltese, **N...other:** Elk Glen's Store, **food:** MT Grill, **lodging:** Mangold's Motel, **other:** USPO, antiques
10mm	St Regis River
5	Taft Area, no facilities, access to Hiawatha Trail
4.5mm	**rest area both lanes, full(handicapped)picnic tables, litter barrels, petwalk, chainup/removal**
0	Lookout Pass, **other:** Lookout RV Park/deli/rest., access to ski area, info
0mm	Montana/Idaho state line, Mountain/Pacific time zone, Lookout Pass elev 4680

Interstate 94

Exit #	Services
250mm	Montana/North Dakota state line
248	Carlyle Rd, no facilities
242	MT 7(from wb), Wibaux, **S...rest area both lanes, full(handicapped)facilities, phone, picnic tables, litter barrels, gas:** Amsler's/diesel, Cenex/diesel, **food:** Tastee Hut, **lodging:** Budget Host, **other:** RV camping
241	MT 261(from eb), to MT 7, Wibaux, **S...gas:** Amsler's, Cenex, **lodging:** Budget Host, same as 242
241mm	weigh sta both lanes
236	ranch access, no facilities
231	Hodges Rd, no facilities
224	Griffith Creek, frontage road, no facilities
222.5mm	Griffith Creek
215	MT 335, Glendive, City Ctr, **N...gas:** Conoco, **food:** CC's Café, **lodging:** Comfort Inn, Day's Inn, King's Inn, Super 8, **other:** Glendive Camping(apr-oct), museum, **S...gas:** Exxon/diesel, Sinclair/diesel/repair, **food:** DQ, Hardee's, **lodging:** Best Western, Budget Motel, El Centro Motel, **other:** HOSPITAL, to Makoshika SP

MONTANA

Interstate 94

E Glendive W	
215mm	Yellowstone River
213	MT 16, Glendive, to Sidney, **N...gas:** Exxon/diesel, **other:** Green Valley Camping, st patrol, **S...gas:** Conoco/diesel, Sinclair/diesel, **food:** McDonald's, Pizza Hut, Subway, Taco John's, **lodging:** Best Western Downtown, Budget Host, Holiday Lodge, Parkwood Motel, **other:** Albertson's, Ford/Lincoln/Mercury, Radio Shack
211	MT 200S(from wb, no EZ return), to Circle, no facilities
210	Lp 94, to MT 200S, W Glendive, **S...gas:** Cenex, **food:** McDonald's, **other:** Chevrolet/Pontiac/Buick, Chrysler/Plymouth/Dodge/Jeep, Makoshika SP
206	Pleasant View Rd, no facilities
204	Whoopup Creek Rd, no facilities
198	Cracker Box Rd, **1 mi N...**Hess Arabians
192	Bad Route Rd, **S...rest area/weigh sta both lanes, full(handicapped)facilities, weather info, phone, picnic tables, litter barrels, camping, petwalk**
187mm	Yellowstone River
185	MT 340, Fallon, **S...food:** access to café, **other:** phone
184mm	O'Fallon Creek
176	MT 253, Terry, **N...gas:** Cenex/diesel, **lodging:** Diamond Motel, Kempton Hotel, **other:** HOSPITAL, Terry RV Oasis
170mm	Powder River
169	Powder River Rd, no facilities
159	Diamond Ring, no facilities
148	Valley Access, no facilities
141	US 12 E, Miles City, **N...other:** Big Sky RV Camping, casino(4mi), to KOA
Miles City	
138	MT 58, Miles City, **N...gas:** Cenex/diesel/24hr, Conoco, Exxon/diesel/24hr, **food:** A&W/KFC, DQ, 4B's Rest., Gallagher's Rest., Hardee's, Jewel's Steaks, Little Caesar's, McDonald's, Pizza Hut/Taco Bell, Subway, Taco John's, Wendy's, **lodging:** Best Western, Budget Inn, Day's Inn, Econolodge, Motel 6, **other:** HOSPITAL, Albertson's, Checker Parts, County Mkt Foods/24hr, Osco Drug, K-Mart, KOA, Wal-Mart/auto, casinos, **S...food:** Hunan Chinese, **lodging:** Comfort Inn, Guesthouse Inn, Holiday Inn Express, Super 8
137mm	Tongue River
135	Lp 94, Miles City(no EZ return), no facilities
128	local access, no facilities
126	Moon Creek Rd, no facilities
117	Hathaway, no facilities
114mm	**rest area eb, full(handicapped)facilities, phone, picnic tables, litter barrels, petwalk**
113mm	**rest area wb, full(handicapped)facilities, phone, picnic tables, litter barrels, petwalk, overlook**
106	Butte Creek Rd, to Rosebud, **N...**food, phone
103	MT 446, MT 447, Rosebud Creek Rd, no facilities
98.5mm	weigh sta both lanes
95	Forsyth, **N...gas:** Cenex, Exxon/diesel/24hr, **food:** Top That Eatery, **lodging:** Rails Inn Motel(1mi), MT Inn, **other:** Ford/Mercury, Yellowstone Drug, to Rosebud RA, **S...**camping
93	US 12 W, Forsyth, **N...gas:** Cenex, Exxon/diesel/24hr, **food:** Top That Eatery, **lodging:** Crestwell Inn, MT Motel, WestWind Motel, **other:** HOSPITAL, repair/tires
87	MT 39, to Colstrip, no facilities
82	Reservation Creek Rd, no facilities
72	MT 384, Sarpy Creek Rd, no facilities
67	Hysham, **1-2 mi N...**gas, phone, food, lodging
65mm	**rest area both lanes, full(handicapped)facilities, phone, picnic tables, litter barrels, petwalk**
63	ranch access, no facilities
53	Bighorn, access to phone
52mm	Bighorn River
49	MT 47, Custer, to Hardin, **S...food:** Ft Custer Café, **other:** to Little Bighorn Bfd, camping
47	Custer, **S...gas:** Conoco/diesel, **food:** Jct City Saloon/café, **lodging:** D&L Motel/café, **other:** Custer Food Mkt
41.5mm	**rest area wb, full(handicapped)facilities, phone, picnic tables, litter barrels, petwalk**
38mm	**rest area eb, full(handicapped)facilities, phone, picnic tables, litter barrels, petwalk**
36	Waco, frontage rd, no facilities
23	Pompeys Pillar, **N...other:** Pompeys Pillar Nat Landmark
14	Ballentine, Worden, **S...food:** Long Branch Café/casino
6	MT 522, Huntley, **N...**gas/phone, **food:** Sam's Café
0mm	I-90, E to Sheridan, W to Billings, I-94 begins/ends on I-90, exit 456.

NEBRASKA
Interstate 80

E ↕ **W**

Exit #	Services
455mm	Nebraska/Iowa state line, Missouri River
454	13th St, **N...gas:** BP/diesel, Kum&Go, Shamrock, **food:** Burger King, KFC, McDonald's, Subway, **lodging:** Comfort Inn, **S...gas:** Phillips 66/diesel, **other:** Doorly Zoo, Imax, stadium
453	24th St(from eb), no facilities
452b	I-480 N, US 75 N, to Henry Ford's Birthplace, Eppley Airfield
452a	US 75 S, no facilities
451	42nd St, **N...gas:** BP, Kwik Shop/gas, **S...gas:** Phillips 66, **food:** Burger King, McDonald's, Taco Bell, **other:** HOSPITAL, FastLube, Ford
450	60th St, **N...gas:** Conoco, Phillips 66/diesel, Shell, **other:** NAPA, to U of NE Omaha, **S...gas:** Phillips 66/diesel, **food:** Country Kitchen, **lodging:** Microtel
449	72nd St, to Ralston, **N...gas:** BP, **food:** Burger King, Grover St Grill., Perkins, Spezia Italian, **lodging:** Clarion, Hampton Inn, Holiday Inn/rest., Homewood Suites, Quality Inn, Ramada Inn, Red Lion Inn, Regency Inn, Super 8, Travelodge, **other:** HOSPITAL, **S...gas:** Phillips 66/diesel, **food:** Anthony's Steaks
448	84th St, **N...gas:** BP, KwikGas, Shell, **food:** Arby's, China Garden, Denny's, Farmhouse Café, Great Wall Chinese, Mangelson's Cafe, McDonald's, Subway, Taco Bell, **lodging:** Econolodge, **other:** EYECARE, Baker's Foods, Goodyear/auto, Hancock Fabrics, Mangelson's Crafts, NAPA AutoCare, ShopKO, **S...gas:** Phillips 66/diesel, QT, Shell, Sinclair, **food:** Wendy's, **other:** Acura/Isuzu/Kia, CarQuest, Chevrolet, Just Good Meats, U-Haul
446	I-680 N, to Boystown, no facilities
445	US 275, NE 92, l thru L St, **N...gas:** Cenex, **food:** Austin's Steaks, **lodging:** Clarion, Residence Inn, **other:** Nelsen's RV Ctr, Sam's Club, **S...food:** Village Inn Rest., **lodging:** Baymont Inn, Comfort Inn, Day's Inn, Econolodge, Hawthorn Suites, Holiday Inn Express, Howard Johnson, Kelly Inn, Motel 6, Super 8, **other:** Goodyear, NE Beef Co, **S on 108th...gas:** Conoco/diesel, QT/diesel, **food:** Arby's, Burger King, China 1, Hong Kong Café, McDonald's, Nebraska Cafe, Pizza Hut/Taco Bell, Sonic, Subway, Valentino's, Wendy's, **other:** Albertson's
444	Q St, **N...gas:** Cenex/diesel
442	126th St, Harrison St, **N...other:** Chrysler/Jeep, Toyota
440	NE 50, to Springfield, **N...gas:** Conoco, Sapp Bros, Shell/Subway/diesel/24hr/@, **food:** Azteca Mexican, Cracker Barrel, Hardee's, McDonald's, TH Café, **lodging:** Ben Franklin Motel, Budget Inn, Comfort Inn, Day's Inn, Ramada Ltd, **other:** HOSPITAL, Ford, truckwash, **S...gas:** BP/diesel, to Platte River SP
439	439 NE 370, to Gretna, **N...gas:** Phillips 66/diesel, **lodging:** Day's Inn, Suburban Inn, antiques, **S...HOSPITAL, museum**
432	US 6, NE 31, to Gretna, **N...gas:** Sinclair/diesel/rest./24hr, **food:** McDonald's, **lodging:** Super 8, **other:** GNC, Nebraska X-ing/famous brands, **S...gas:** ✈/Flying J/Conoco/diesel/LP/rest./24hr/@, **other:** KOA, to Schramm SP
431mm	**rest area wb, full(handicapped)facilities, info, phone, picnic tables, litter barrels, petwalk**
427mm	Platte River
426	to Ashland, **N...to Mahoney SP, museum**
425.5	**rest area eb, full(handicapped)facilities, phone, picnic tables, litter barrels, petwalk, vending**
420	NE 63, Ashland, **N...gas:** Conoco/diesel/café, **other:** RV camping, **S...gas:** Shell/diesel, **lodging:** Big Inn, **other:** to Platte River SP
416mm	weigh sta both lanes
409	US 6, to E Lincoln, Waverly, no facilities
405	US 77 N, 56th St, Lincoln, **S...gas:** Phillips 66, **other:** HOSPITAL, **1 mi S...food:** Misty's Rest., **lodging:** Howard Johnson, Motel 6, **other:** antiques
404mm	**rest area wb, full(handicapped)facilities, info, phone, picnic tables, litter barrels, vending, petwalk**
403	27th St, Lincoln, **S...gas:** Conoco/Wendy's/diesel, Phillips 66/Subway/diesel, **food:** Arby's, Cracker Barrel, Dairy Queen, Popeye's, Taco Inn, Wendy's, **lodging:** AmericInn, Best Western, Red Roof Inn, Settle Inn, Staybridge Suites, **other:** Chevrolet/Pontiac/Cadillac/GMC, Ford/Mazda, **1-3 mi S...gas:** Mobil, Phillips 66, Shell, **food:** Applebee's, Beacon Hill Rest., Burger King, Carlos O'Kelly's, DaVinci's Italian, Godfather's, Golden Corral, HyVee Foods, IHOP, King Kong Cafe, McDonald's, Papa John's, Ruby Teusday, Runza Rest., Schlotsky's, Sonic, Taco John's, Valentino's, **lodging:** Village Inn, Baymont Inn, Comfort Suites, Country Inn Suites, Fairfield Inn, Microtel, Ramada Ltd, Super 8, **other:** Culvers, $Tree, GNC, Haas Tire, Interstate Battery, Mazda, Michael's, Radio Shack, Sam's Club, ShopKO, Wal-Mart SuperCtr/24hr, to U NE, st fairpark
401b	US 34 W, **N...RV camping**
401a	I-180, US 34 E, to 9th St, Lincoln, no facilities
399	Lincoln, **N...gas:** BP/diesel/24hr, Phillips 66, **food:** Baskin-Robbins, McDonald's, NY Pizza, Perkins/24hr, Quizno's, TacoMaker, **lodging:** Airport Inn, Comfort Inn, Day's Inn, Hampton Inn, Holiday Inn Express, Horizon Inn, Motel 6, Ramada Inn, Sleep Inn, Travelodge, to airport, **S...gas:** Cenex, **lodging:** Econolodge, Economy Lodge, Inn4Less
397	US 77 S, to Beatrice, **S...gas:** Conoco, **lodging:** Congress Inn, Welcome Inn, **other:** Ford/Lincoln/Mercury
396	US 6, West O St(from eb), **S...gas:** Sinclair/diesel, **lodging:** Cobbler Inn, Red Carpet Inn, Senate Inn, Super 8, Travelodge, Welcome Inn, **other:** Lincoln/Mercury
395	US 6, NW 48th St, **N...gas:** Sinclair, **food:** Runza Rest., **other:** Ford/Freightliner Trucks, st patrol, **S...gas:** Shoemaker/Shell/Popeye's/diesel/@, **lodging:** Cobbler Inn, Senate Inn, Shoney's Inn, Super 8(2mi), Travelodge
388	NE 103, to Crete, Pleasant Dale, no facilities
382	US 6, Milford, no facilities
381mm	**rest area eb, full(handicapped)facilities, phone, picnic tables, litter barrels, petwalk, vending**

Omaha

Lincoln

Interstate 80

E ↕ W

York

379 NE 15, to Seward, **2-3 mi N...gas:** Phillips 66, **food:** McDonald's, Valentino's, **lodging:** Dandy Lion Inn, Super 8, **other:** HOSPITAL, antiques, **S...gas:** Shell/diesel,

375mm rest area wb, full(handicapped)facilities, info, phone, picnic tables, litter barrels, petwalk, vending

373 80G, Goehner, **N...gas:** Sinclair

369 80E, Beaver Crossing, **3 mi S...**HOSPITAL, food, RV camping

366 80F, to Utica, no facilities

360 93B, to Waco, **N...gas:** FuelMart/diesel/Roadeez Rest./@, **S...lodging:** Double Nickel Camping

355mm rest area wb, full(handicapped)facilities, info, phone, picnic tables, litter barrels, vending, petwalk

353 US 81, to York, **N...gas:** BP/diesel, Byco Fuel, SappBros/Sinclair/Subway/diesel/@, Shell/diesel, **food:** A&W/Amigo's, Arby's, Burger King, Country Kitchen, Golden Gate Chinese, KFC/Taco Bell, McDonald's, Taco John's, Wendy's, **lodging:** Budget Inn, Comfort Inn, Day's Inn, Quality Inn, Super 8, Yorkshire Motel, **other:** HOSPITAL, Buick/GMC, Chevrolet/Pontiac, Chrysler/Dodge, **S...gas:** Petro/Phillips 66/Iron Skillet/Pizza Hut/diesel/24hr/@, Shell/diesel/rest./24hr, **food:** Applebee's, **lodging:** 1st Inn, Holiday Inn, Blue Beacon

351mm rest area eb, full(handicapped)facilities, info, phone, picnic tables, litter barrels, petwalk, vending

348 93E, to Bradshaw, no facilities

342 342 93A, Henderson, **N...other:** Good Sam RV Park, antiques, **S...gas:** FuelMart/diesel, **food:** Eat'n Haus, **lodging:** 1st Interstate Inn, **other:** HOSPITAL, RV park

338 41D, to Hampton, no facilities

332 NE 14, Aurora, **N...gas:** Casey's, Shell/diesel, **food:** McDonald's(3mi), Pappy Jack's Rest., Pizza Hut(3mi), Subway(2.5), **lodging:** Budget Host(3mi), Hamilton Motel/rest., **other:** HOSPITAL, to Plainsman Museum, **S...gas:** Love's/Arby's/diesel/@, Sinclair/diesel

324 41B, to Giltner, no facilities

318 NE 2, to Grand Island, **S...other:** KOA

317mm rest area wb, full(handicapped)facilities, info, phone, picnic tables, litter barrels, vending, petwalk

315mm rest area eb, full(handicapped)facilities, info, phone, picnic tables, litter barrels, vending, petwalk

314mm Platte River

314 to Grand Island, **N...food:** Subway, Wendy's, **lodging:** Super 8

312 US 34/281, to Grand Island, **N...gas:** Bosselman/Sinclair/Max's/Subway/Taco Xpress/diesel/24hr/@, Phillips 66/Krispy Kreme, **lodging:** USA Inn/rest., **other:** HOSPITAL, Mormon Island RA, to Stuhr Pioneer Museum, **S...gas:** BP, **food:** Arby's, **lodging:** Holiday Inn/rest., Holiday Inn Express, **other:** Ford/Peterbilt, Hastings Museum(15mi)

305 40C, to Alda, **N...gas:** Sinclair/diesel/24hr, TA/Conoco/diesel/rest./24hr/@, **other:** Crane Meadows Nature Ctr/rest area

300 NE 11, Wood River, **S...gas:** Bosselman/Sinclair/Grandma Max's/Subway/diesel/24hr/@, **lodging:** motel/RV park

291 10D, Shelton, **N...other:** War Axe SRA

285 10C, Gibbon, **N...gas:** Ampride/diesel, **other:** Windmill SP, RV camping, **S...lodging:** Country Motel, **other:** Don's Repair

279 NE 10, to Minden, **N...gas:** Shell/diesel, **S...other:** Pioneer Village Camping

275mm The Great Platte River Road Archway Monument

Kearney

Interstate 80

E

↑
↓

W

272 NE 44, Kearney, **N...gas:** Cenex/diesel, Phillips 66/Subway/diesel, Shamrock, Shell/diesel, **food:** A&W/Amigo's, Arby's, Burger King, Carlos O'Kelly's, Country Kitchen, Dairy Queen, Fillmore's Rest, King's Buffet, McDonald's, Perkins/24hr, Pizza Hut, Red Lobster, Runza Rest., Spaghetti Shop, Taco Bell, Taco John's, USA Steaks, Valentino's Rest., Wendy's, **lodging:** AmericInn, Best Western, Budget Motel, Comfort Inn, Country Inn Suites, Day's Inn, Fairfield Inn, 1st Interstate Inn, Hampton Inn, Holiday Inn, Motel 6, Ramada Inn/rest., Super 8, Western Inn, Wingate Inn, Boogaart's Foods, **other:** HOSPITAL, Buick/Cadillac, Chevrolet/Mazda, Chrysler/Plymouth/Dodge/Jeep, $General, Pontiac, Goodyear, NAPA, Wal-Mart SuperCtr/24hr(3mi), Budget$ RV Park, Clyde&Vi's RV Park, to Archway Mon, U NE Kearney, Museum of NE Art, **S...gas:** BP, Shamrock/diesel, **food:** Grandpa's Steaks, Skeeter's BBQ, **lodging:** 1st Inn, Holiday Inn Express

271mm rest area wb, full(handicapped)facilities, info, phone, picnic tables, litter barrels, petwalk

269mm rest area eb, full(handicapped)facilities, info, phone, picnic tables, litter barrels, petwalk

263 rd 10 b, Odessa, **N...gas:** Sapp/Shell/diesel/rest./@, **other:** UP Rec Area, **S...food:** Aunt Lu's Rest.

257 US 183, Elm Creek, **N...gas:** Bosselman/Sinclair/Subway/Little Caesar/diesel/24hr/@, **lodging:** 1st Interstate Inn, **other:** Antique Car Museum, Nebraska Prarie Museum, Nebraska Tire, Sunny Meadows Camping, museum

248 Overton, **N...gas:** Mian Bros/BP/diesel/24hr/@, **food:** MB Rest.

237 US 283, Lexington, **N...gas:** Ampride/diesel/@, Conoco/KFC/Taco Bell/diesel/@, Phillips 66/diesel, **food:** A&W/Amigo's, Arby's, Burger King, Dairy Queen, McDonald's, Pizza Hut, Taquiera Mexican, Valarta Mexican, Wendy's, **lodging:** Budget Host, Comfort Inn, Day's Inn, 1st Interstate Inn, Gable View Inn, Holiday Inn Express, Minute Man Hotel, **other:** HOSPITAL, Advance Parts, Chevrolet/Pontiac/Buick, $General, Goodyear, SavALot Foods, Wal-Mart SuperCtr/24hr/café, museum, **S...gas:** Sinclair/diesel/@, **food:** Kirk's Café, **lodging:** Super 8, **other:** Goodyear, Wheels and Deals RV Ctr, to Johnson Lake RA

231 Darr Rd, **S...**truckwash/24hr

227mm rest area both lanes, full(handicapped)facilities, info, phone, picnic tables, litter barrels, vending, petwalk

222 NE 21, Cozad, **N...gas:** BP, Phillips 66/diesel, Sinclair, **food:** Burger King, Dairy Queen, El Paraiso Mexican, Pizza Hut, PJ's Rest., Subway, **lodging:** Best Value Inn, Motel 6, **other:** HOSPITAL, Alco, Ford, museum

211 NE 47, Gothenburg, **N...gas:** Shell/diesel/24hr/@, Sinclair/rest./diesel/@, **food:** China Red Chinese, Lasso Espresso, McDonald's, Mi Ranchito Mexican, Pizza Hut/Taco Bell, Runza Rest., **lodging:** Super 8,

Lexington (vertical sidebar)

Travel Inn, Western Motel, **other:** HOSPITAL, CarQuest, Pony Express Sta Museum(1mi), Chevrolet/Pontiac/Buick, truck permit sta, **S...**KOA/Sinclair

199 Brady, **N...gas:** Brady 1 Stop/DQ/diesel

194mm rest area both lanes, full(handicapped)facilities, phone, picnic tables, litter barrels, vending, petwalk

190 Maxwell, **N...gas:** Sinclair/diesel, **S...other:** to Ft McPherson Nat Cemetary, RV camping

181mm weigh sta both lanes, phones

179 to US 30, N Platte, **N...lodging:** La Quinta, **other:** RV camping, **S...gas:** ✈/Flying J/Conoco/CountryMkt/diesel/LP/24hr/@

177 US 83, N Platte, **N...gas:** BP/Subway, Conoco/diesel, Phillips 66/diesel/24hr, Shell/diesel, Sinclair/diesel, **food:** A&W, Amigo's Rest., Applebee's, Arby's, Baskin-Robbins/Blimpie/Dunkin Donuts, BBQ, Burger King, Dairy Queen, Hong King Chinese, KFC, McDonald's, Perkins/24hr, Pizza Hut, Quizno's, Roger's Diner, Runza Rest., Sonic, Subway, Valentino's, Village Inn Rest., Wendy's, Whiskey Creek Steaks, **lodging:** Best Western, Blue Spruce Motel, 1st Interstate Inn, Hampton Inn, Motel 6, Pioneer Motel, Quality Inn, Royal Colonial Inn, Sands Motel, Stockman Inn, **other:** Advance Parts, $General, Goodyear/auto, Harley-Davidson, Holiday TravL Park, JC Penney, ShopKO, Staples, SunMart Foods, Wal-Mart SuperCtr/gas/24hr, mall, museum, to Buffalo Bill's Ranch, **S...gas:** Conoco/Taco Bell/diesel/24hr/@, Phillips 66, Shell/diesel/rest./24hr, **food:** Hunan Chinese, **lodging:** Comfort Inn, Day's Inn, Holiday Inn Express, Ramada Ltd, Super 8, **other:** Cadillac, Chevrolet, Chrysler/Jeep, Dodge, Ford/Lincoln/Mercury, Honda, Toyota/Mazda, truck permit sta, to Lake Maloney RA

164 56C, Hershey, **N...gas:** Western/diesel/rest./24hr/@, **other:** Western Wear Outlet

160mm rest area both lanes, full(handicapped)facilities, info, phone, picnic tables, litter barrels, petwalk

158 NE 25, Sutherland, **N...lodging:** Park Motel(1mi), **S...gas:** Sinclair/diesel/24hr, **other:** RV camping

149mm Central/Mountain time zone

145 51C, Paxton, **N...gas:** Shell/diesel/24hr, **food:** Ole's Café, **lodging:** Day's Inn, **other** RV camping

133 51B, Roscoe, no facilities

132mm rest area wb, full(handicapped)facilities, info, phone, picnic tables, litter barrels, petwalk

126 US 26, NE 61, Ogallala, **N...gas:** BP, Phillips 66/diesel, Shell/diesel/24hr, Texaco/Burger King, **food:** Arby's/RV parking, Burger King, Country Kitchen, McDonald's, Mi Ranchito Mexican, Pizza Hut, Taco Bell, Taco John's, Valentino's, **lodging:** Best Western, Day's Inn, Gray Goose Lodge, Holiday Inn Express, **other:** HOSPITAL, Ace Hardware, Chevrolet/Buick, NAPA, Radio Shack, to Lake McConaughy, **S...gas:** Conoco/Subway/diesel, TA/diesel/rest./24hr/@, Phillips 66/diesel, **food:** Dairy Queen, KFC, Panda Chinese, Wendy's, **lodging:** Comfort Inn, Econolodge, 1st Interstate Inn, Super 8, **other:** $General, Open Corral RV Park, Pamida

124mm rest area eb, full(handicapped)facilities, info, phones, picnic tables, litter barrels, petwalk

N Platte (vertical sidebar)

Ogallala (vertical sidebar)

Interstate 80

E ↕ **W**

117	51A, Brule, **N...gas:** Happy Jack's/Sinclair/diesel/RV camping
107	25B, Big Springs, **N...gas:** Bosselman/Pilot/Sinclair/Grandma Max's/Little Caesar's/Subway/diesel/@, Total/diesel, **lodging:** Best Value, **other:** truckwash, **S...other:** McGreer's Camping
102	I-76 S, to Denver, no facilities
102mm	S Platte River
101	US 138, to Julesburg, no facilities
99mm	scenic turnout eb
95	NE 27, to Julesburg, no facilities
88mm	**Lodgepole Creek, rest area wb, full(handicapped)facilities, phone, picnic tables, litter barrels, vending, petwalk**
85	25A, Chappell, **N...gas:** Ampride, **other:** Chevrolet/Buick, Creekside Camping, USPO, wayside park
82.5mm	**rest area eb, full(handicapped)facilities, phone, picnic tables, litter barrels, vending, petwalk**
76	17F, Lodgepole, **1 mi N...**gas/diesel, lodging
69	17E, to Sunol, no facilities
61mm	**rest area wb, full(handicapped)facilities, phone, picnic tables, litter barrels, vending, petwalk**

Sidney

59	US 385, 17J, Sidney, **N...gas:** Conoco/KFC/Taco Bell/TCBY/diesel, Shell/diesel/24hr/@, **food:** Arby's, China 1 Buffet, KFC/Taco Bell, McDonald's, Mi Ranchito Mexican, Perkins, Quizno's, Runza Rest., Taco John's, **lodging:** AmericInn, Comfort Inn, Day's Inn, Motel 6, **other:** Cabela's SportsGear, $General, Lovers Leap Vinyards, Naddox RV Ctr, Pamida, Radio Shack, Wal-Mart SuperCtr/24hr, RV camping(2mi), golf, truck permit sta, **3 mi N...food:** KFC, Pizza Hut, **lodging:** Generic Motel, Sidney Motel, Super 8, **other:** HOSPITAL, RV camping, **S...gas:** Phillips 66/diesel, **lodging:** Holiday Inn/rest., **other:** truckwash
55	NE 19, to Sterling, Sidney, **2 mi N...lodging:** Ft Sidney Inn, Super 8
51.5mm	**rest area/hist marker eb, full(handicapped)facilities, phone, picnic tables, litter barrels, vending, petwalk**
48	to Brownson, no facilities
38	rd 17 b, Potter, **N...gas:** Cenex/diesel/LP, Shell, **other:** repair
29	53A, Dix, **1/2 mi N...**gas, food
25mm	**rest area wb, full(handicapped)facilities, phone, picnic tables, litter barrels, vending, petwalk**

Kimball

22	53E, Kimball, **N...lodging:** Day's Inn, **other:** KOA, golf
20	NE 71, Kimball, **N...gas:** Sinclair/diesel, **food:** Pizza Hut, Subway, **lodging:** Best Value, Day's Inn, 1st Interstate Inn, **S...food:** Burger King, **other:** HOSPITAL, truck permit sta., Twin Pines RV Park
18mm	parking area eb, litter barrel
10mm	**rest area eb, full(handicapped)facilities, info, phone, picnic tables, litter barrels, petwalk**
8	53C, to Bushnell, no facilities
1	53B, Pine Bluffs, **1 mi N...**RV camping
0mm	Nebraska/Wyoming state line

Interstate 680(Omaha)

Exit #	Services
29b a	I-80, W to Omaha, E to Des Moines. I-680 begins/ends on I-80, exit 27.
28	IA 191, to Neola, Persia, no facilities
21	L34, Beebeetown, no facilities
19mm	**rest area wb, full(handicapped)facilities, info, phone, picnic tables, litter barrels, petwalk**
16mm	**rest area eb, full(handicapped)facilities, info, phone, picnic tables, litter barrels, petwalk**
71	I-29 N, to Sioux City
66	Honey Creek, **W...gas:** Phillips 66/diesel/rest., **food:** Iowa Feed&Grain Co Rest.
3b a	I-29, S to Council Bluffs, IA 988, to Crescent, **E...gas:** Phillips 66, **other:** to ski area
1	County Rd, no facilities
14mm	Nebraska/Iowa state line, Missouri River, Mormon Bridge
13	US 75 S, Florence, **E...gas:** Shell/diesel, **food:** OJ's Mexican, Zesto Diner, **lodging:** Mormon Trail Motel, **other:** LDS Temple, Mormon Trail Ctr, **W...gas:** Phillips 66
12	US 75 N, 48th St, **E...gas:** Phillips 66, **food:** Burger King
9	72nd St, **3 mi E...food:** Famous Dave's BBQ, IHOP, Sonic, **other:** HOSPITAL, **W...**Cunningham Lake RA
6	NE 133, Irvington, **E...gas:** Conoco/diesel, **food:** Burger King
5	Fort St, **W...gas:** Sinclair, Shell, **other:** Wal-Mart/drugs, USPO
4	NE 64, Maple St, **E...gas:** BP/Amoco, **W...**Kum&Go, **food:** Burger King, KFC, McDonald's, Perkins, Pizza Hut, Runza, Subway, Taco Bell, **lodging:** Comfort Suites, La Quinta, Ramada Ltd, **other:** Albertson's, Champion Parts
3	US 6, Dodge St, **E...food:** Chang's Bistro, Macaroni Grill, Panera Bread, Steak'n Shake, TGIFriday, **lodging:** Hampton Inn, Marriott, **other:** MEDICAL CARE, Dodge, Ford, JC Penney, Mazda, Von Maur, **W...gas:** BP/Amoco, **food:** Blimpie, Boston Mkt, DQ, NY Burrito, **lodging:** Best Western, Crowne Plaza Motel, Super 8, **other:** Cadillac, Chevrolet, Nissan/Hyundai, Toyota
2	Pacific St, **E...gas:** BP/Amoco, Sinclair, **lodging:** Park Inn
1	NE 38, W Center Rd, **E...food:** Don&Millie's Rest., Garden Café, **W...gas:** Phillips, **food:** BBQ, Burger King, Wendy's
0mm	I-680 begins/ends on I-80, exit 446.

Omaha

N ↑ ↓ **S**

Exit #	Services
123mm	Nevada/Arizona state line, Pacific/Mountain time zone
122	Lp 15, Mesquite, **E...NV Welcome Ctr both lanes, full(handicapped)facilities**, **petwalk**, **gas:** Chevron/Subway/diesel/24hr, Shell/DQ, Sinclair/Arby's, **food:** Burger King, Golden West Rest./casino, Jack-in-the-Box, KFC, Los Lupes Mexican, Pizza Hut, Thunderbird Rest., **lodging:** Best Western, Budget Inn, Up Town Motel, **other:** AutoZone, Big O Tire, CarQuest, GNC, Great Outdoors RV, NAPA, Radio Shack, Rite Aid, Smith's Foods, USPO, diesel repair, museum, **W...gas:** Virgin River/76/diesel/LP/RV park, **food:** McDonald's, **lodging:** Holiday Inn, Eureka Motel/casino, Mesquite Springs Motel, Virgin River Hotel/casino
120	Lp 15, Mesquite, Bunkerville, **E...gas:** Arco/24hr, Chevron, Terribles, Shell/diesel, **food:** Carollo's Rest., McDonald's, Casablanca Resort/casino/RV Park, Oasis Resort/casino, Peppermill Resort/casino, Players Island Resort/casino, **lodging:** Valley Inn, **other:** USPO, **W...lodging:** Best Western
112	NV 170, Riverside, Bunkerville, no facilities
110mm	truck parking both lanes, litter barrels
100	to Carp, Elgin, no facilities
96mm	truck parking nb, litter barrels
93	NV 169, to Logandale, Overton, **E...lodging:** Best Western(10mi), **other:** Lake Mead NRA, Lost City Museum
91	NV 168, Glendale, **W...gas:** Chevron/diesel/rest.
90.5mm	Muddy River
90	NV 168(from nb), Glendale, Moapa, **W...gas:** Chevron/diesel/rest., **other:** Moapa Indian Reserv
88	Hidden Valley, no facilities
87.5mm	parking area both lanes, litter barrels
84	Byron, no facilities
80	Ute, no facilities
75	NV 169 E, Valley of Fire SP, Lake Mead NRA, **E...other:** casino, fireworks
64	US 93 N, Great Basin Hwy, to Ely, Great Basin NP, no facilities
60mm	livestock check sta sb
58	NV 604, Las Vegas Blvd, to Apex, Nellis AFB, no facilities
54	Speedway Blvd, Hollywood Blvd, **E...gas:** Petro/Mobil/diesel/24hr/@, **other:** Las Vegas Speedway
52	rd 215 W, no facilities
50	Lamb Ave(from sb), no facilities
48	Craig Rd, **E...gas:** Arco/24hr, Chevron/Subway/24hr, Mobil, Pilot/DQ/KFC/Pizza Hut/diesel/24hr, Shell, **food:** Burger King, Jack-in-the-Box, Speedway Grill, **lodging:** Best Western(2mi), Hampton Inn, Super 8, **other:** to Nellis AFB, **W...gas:** Citgo/7-11, **lodging:** Holiday Inn Express
46	Cheyenne Ave, **E...gas:** Arco/24hr, Citgo/7-11, Exxon, **lodging:** Ramada Inn/casino, **other:** NAPA, **W... gas:** Breeze-In/Jack-in-the-Box, Citgo/7-11, ✈/Flying J/diesel/LP/rest./24hr/@, **food:** Denny's, McDonald's, **lodging:** Comfort Inn, **other:** Blue Beacon, diesel repair
45	Lake Mead Blvd, **E...gas:** 7-11, McDonald's, **food:** Wendy's
44	Washington Ave(from sb), **E...lodging:** Best Western, casinos
43	D St(from nb), **E...**Best Western, same as 44, **W...**Office Depot
42b a	I-515 to LV, US 95 N to Reno, US 93 S to Phoenix, **E...**76, casinos, **W...gas:** Arco/24hr, Shell
41b a	NV 159, Charleston Blvd, **E...gas:** Arco/diesel, 7-11, **other:** antiques, **W...gas:** 76, Shell, **food:** Carl's Jr, Del Taco, McDonald's, Taco Bell, Wendy's, **other:** HOSPITAL, gifts
40	Sahara Ave, **E...**The Strip, **gas:** 76/diesel/rest./24hr, **lodging:** Las Vegas Inn/casino, Travelodge, **other:** LV Conv Ctr, Goodyear, RV Ctr, **W...gas:** Texaco/diesel/LP, 7-11, **food:** Denny's, **lodging:** Palace Station Hotel/casino, **other:** Lexus, Mazda, Mitsubishi, Mercedes
39	Spring Mtn Rd(from sb), **E...lodging:** Budget Suites, Frontier Hotel, **other:** Mirage, Treasure Island, **W...gas:** Arco/24hr, Circle K, United/diesel, **food:** Schlotsky's, **other:** EconoLube/Tune, Discount Tire, Firestone/auto, Goodyear/auto, Lexus, Mercedes, auto/transmission repair
38b a	Dunes Flamingo Rd, **E...**The Strip, **lodging:** Caesar's Palace, Flamingo Hilton, Monte Carlo, to UNLV, **W...gas:** Arco/24hr, Texaco, **food:** Burger King, Outback Steaks, Subway, Gold **lodging:** Coast Hotel, Palms Hotel, Rio Hotel, **other:** MEDICAL CARE, Terrible Herbst Wash/lube
37	Tropicana Ave, **E...lodging:** Excaliber Hotel, Mandalay Bay, MGM Grand, Motel 6, Tropicana Hotel, **other:** GMC/White/Volvo, airport, casinos, funpark, **W...gas:** Arco/24hr, Chevron/diesel, 76, Shell/Mr Subs, WildWest/diesel/LP, **food:** Burger King, IHOP, In-n-Out, Jack-in-the-Box, KFC, McDonald's, Taco Bell, Taco Cabana, Wendy's, **lodging:** Best Western, Budget Suites, Hampton Inn, Howard Johnson, Motel 6, Orleans Hotel, **other:** CarQuest, Honda Motorcycles, casino
36	Russell Rd, **E...gas:** Shell, McDonald's, **lodging:** Diamond Inn, Klondike Hotel, Pollyanna Motel, **other:** casinos, to airport, **W...gas:** Chevron/Herbst/diesel
34	to I-215 E, Las Vegas Blvd, to The Strip, McCarran Airport
33	NV 160, to Blue Diamond, Death Valley, **E...gas:** Arco/24hr, Chevron/McDonald's, Citgo/7-11/diesel, Mobil/diesel/LP, **other:** factory outlet/famous brands, **W...gas:** Chevron, TA/76/Burger King/diesel/LP/24hr/@, **food:** Jack-in-the-Box, Subway, **lodging:** Firebird Inn, **other:** Oasis RV Resort, Silverton Hotel/RV Resort/casino
27	NV 146, to Henderson, Lake Mead, Hoover Dam, **E...gas:** Arco, **2 mi E...other:** Wheelers RV/LP, factory outlets
25	NV 161, Sloan, **1 mi E...**Wheelers RV/service/LP
24mm	bus/truck check sta nb
12	NV 161, Jean, to Goodsprings, **E... Welcome Ctr nb, full facilities, info, gas:** Mobil/diesel, **other:** Gold Strike Casino/hotel/Burger King, USPO, skydiving, **W...other:** Nevada Landing Casino/Shell/diesel/24hr, NV Correctional
1	Primm, **E...gas:** Chevron, 76/diesel, **food:** Carl's Jr, Denny's, Johnnnie D's Rest., McDonald's, **other:** Buffalo Bill's Resort/casino, Primm Valley Resort/casino, Prima Donna RV Park, factory outlets, **W...gas:** Shell/diesel, **lodging:** Whiskey Pete's Hotel/casino/steaks
0mm	Nevada/California state line

Interstate 80

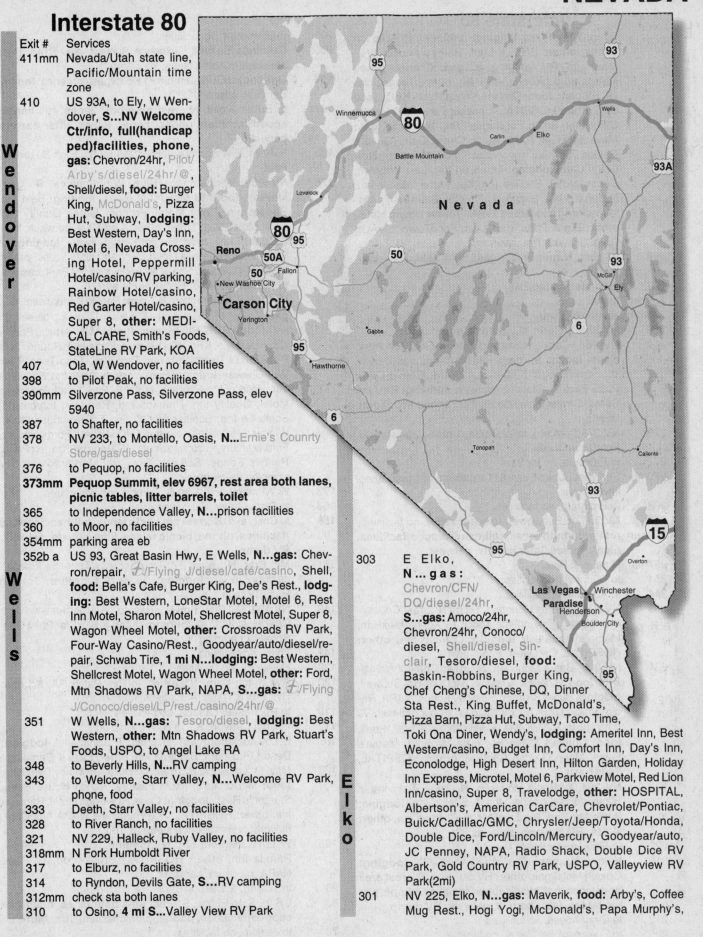

Wendover (side tab, left)

Wells (side tab, left)

Exit #	Services
411mm	Nevada/Utah state line, Pacific/Mountain time zone
410	US 93A, to Ely, W Wendover, **S...NV Welcome Ctr/info, full(handicapped)facilities, phone, gas:** Chevron/24hr, Pilot/Arby's/diesel/24hr/@, Shell/diesel, **food:** Burger King, McDonald's, Pizza Hut, Subway, **lodging:** Best Western, Day's Inn, Motel 6, Nevada Crossing Hotel, Peppermill Hotel/casino/RV parking, Rainbow Hotel/casino, Red Garter Hotel/casino, Super 8, **other:** MEDICAL CARE, Smith's Foods, StateLine RV Park, KOA
407	Ola, W Wendover, no facilities
398	to Pilot Peak, no facilities
390mm	Silverzone Pass, Silverzone Pass, elev 5940
387	to Shafter, no facilities
378	NV 233, to Montello, Oasis, **N...**Ernie's Counrty Store/gas/diesel
376	to Pequop, no facilities
373mm	**Pequop Summit, elev 6967, rest area both lanes, picnic tables, litter barrels, toilet**
365	to Independence Valley, **N...**prison facilities
360	to Moor, no facilities
354mm	parking area eb
352b a	US 93, Great Basin Hwy, E Wells, **N...gas:** Chevron/repair, Flying J/diesel/café/casino, Shell, **food:** Bella's Cafe, Burger King, Dee's Rest., **lodging:** Best Western, LoneStar Motel, Motel 6, Rest Inn Motel, Sharon Motel, Shellcrest Motel, Super 8, Wagon Wheel Motel, **other:** Crossroads RV Park, Four-Way Casino/Rest., Goodyear/auto/diesel/repair, Schwab Tire, **1 mi N...lodging:** Best Western, Shellcrest Motel, Wagon Wheel Motel, **other:** Ford, Mtn Shadows RV Park, NAPA, **S...gas:** Flying J/Conoco/diesel/LP/rest./casino/24hr/@
351	W Wells, **N...gas:** Tesoro/diesel, **lodging:** Best Western, **other:** Mtn Shadows RV Park, Stuart's Foods, USPO, to Angel Lake RA
348	to Beverly Hills, **N...**RV camping
343	to Welcome, Starr Valley, **N...**Welcome RV Park, phone, food
333	Deeth, Starr Valley, no facilities
328	to River Ranch, no facilities
321	NV 229, Halleck, Ruby Valley, no facilities
318mm	N Fork Humboldt River
317	to Elburz, no facilities
314	to Ryndon, Devils Gate, **S...**RV camping
312mm	check sta both lanes
310	to Osino, **4 mi S...**Valley View RV Park

Elko (side tab, right)

303	E Elko, **N...gas:** Chevron/CFN/DQ/diesel/24hr, **S...gas:** Amoco/24hr, Chevron/24hr, Conoco/diesel, Shell/diesel, Sinclair, Tesoro/diesel, **food:** Baskin-Robbins, Burger King, Chef Cheng's Chinese, DQ, Dinner Sta Rest., King Buffet, McDonald's, Pizza Barn, Pizza Hut, Subway, Taco Time, Toki Ona Diner, Wendy's, **lodging:** Ameritel Inn, Best Western/casino, Budget Inn, Comfort Inn, Day's Inn, Econolodge, High Desert Inn, Hilton Garden, Holiday Inn Express, Microtel, Motel 6, Parkview Motel, Red Lion Inn/casino, Super 8, Travelodge, **other:** HOSPITAL, Albertson's, American CarCare, Chevrolet/Pontiac, Buick/Cadillac/GMC, Chrysler/Jeep/Toyota/Honda, Double Dice, Ford/Lincoln/Mercury, Goodyear/auto, JC Penney, NAPA, Radio Shack, Double Dice RV Park, Gold Country RV Park, USPO, Valleyview RV Park(2mi)
301	NV 225, Elko, **N...gas:** Maverik, **food:** Arby's, Coffee Mug Rest., Hogi Yogi, McDonald's, Papa Murphy's,

E ↑ W

RoundTable Pizza, **lodging:** OakTree Inn, Shilo Inn Suites, **other:** GNC, K-Mart, Raley's Foods, Wal-Mart/auto, RV camping, **S...gas:** Conoco/diesel, Phillips 66/diesel/pizza/subs/RV dump, Texaco/diesel/RV park, **food:** Cimarron West Rest., KFC, Taco Bell, **other:** HOSPITAL, Checker Parts, IGA Foods, OfficeMax, Smith Foods/gas/24hr, **1/2 mi S...gas:** Maverik, Shell, **food:** Arctic Circle, Dairy Queen, Golden Phoenix Chinese, Los Sanchez Mexican, New China Café, **lodging:** American Inn, Best Western, Centre Motel, Esquire Inn, Key Motel, Manor Inn, National 9 Inn, Stampede 7 Motel, Stockmen's Motel/casino, Thunderbird Motel, Towne House Motel, **other:** Big A Parts, CarQuest, FoodTown, Sav-On Drug, Schwab Tire, casinos

Carlin

298	W Elko, **N...**repair, **S...gas:** Spirit Gas, RV camping
292	to Hunter, no facilities
285mm	tunnel
285mm	Humboldt River
282	NV 221, E Carlin, **N...**prison area
280	NV 766, Carlin, **N...other:** Desert Gold RV Park, diesel repair, **S...gas:** Pilot/Subway/diesel/24hr/@, Shell/Burger King/diesel, **food:** Chin's Cafe, Pizza Factory, State Café/casino, **lodging:** Best Inn Suites, Cavlier Motel, Comfort Inn, **other:** FoodTown, USPO
279	NV 278(from eb), to W Carlin, **1 mi S...** gas/diesel, FoodTown foods
271	to Palisade, no facilities
270mm	Emigrant Summit, elev 6114, parking area both lanes, litter barrels
268	to Emigrant, no facilities
261	NV 306, to Beowawe, Crescent Valley, no facilities
258mm	**rest area both lanes, full(handicapped)facilities, picnic tables, litter barrels, petwalk**
257mm	Humboldt River

Battle Mtn

254	to Dunphy, no facilities
244	to Argenta, no facilities
233	NV 304, to Battle Mountain, **1-2 mi N...gas:** Conoco/diesel/24hr, Exxon/24hr, **food:** El Aguila Mexican, Mama's Pizza/deli, **lodging:** Comfort Inn, **other:** HOSPITAL, CarQuest, FoodTown
231	NV 305, Battle Mountain, **N...gas:** Chevron/diesel/24hr, **food:** Hide-a-way Steaks, McDonald's, Subway, **lodging:** Super 8, **other:** Bestway Foods, NAPA, Radio Shack, USPO, **1 mi N...gas:** Conoco/diesel, ✈/Flying J/Exxon/Blimpie/diesel/casino/24hr/@, Shell, **food:** Donna's Diner, El Aguila Mexican, Mama's Pizza, Moon Garden Chinese, **other:** HOSPITAL, FoodTown
229	NV 304, W Battle Mountain, **N...gas:** ✈/Flying J/Blimpie/diesel/casino/24hr/@, Shell/diesel, **lodging:** Battle Mtn. Inn, Big Chief Motel, Comfort Inn, **other:** NAPA, RV camping, same as 231
222	to Mote, no facilities
216	Valmy, **N...gas:** 76/USPO/diesel/24hr, **lodging:** Golden Motel/grill, **other:** RV camping, **S...rest area both lanes, full(handicapped)facilities, phone, picnic tables, litter barrels, petwalk, RV dump**
212	to Stonehouse, no facilities
205	to Pumpernickel Valley, no facilities

Winnemucca

203	to Iron Point, no facilities
200	Golconda Summit, Golconda Summit, elev 5145, truck parking area both lanes, litter barrels
194	Golconda, **N...**Waterhole #1 Hotel/gas/groceries, **food:** Z Bar/Grill, **other:** USPO
187	to Button Point, **N...rest area both lanes, full(handicapped)facilities, phone, picnic tables, litter barrels, petwalk**
180	NV 794, E Winnemucca Blvd, **2-4 mi S...**High Desert RV Park
178	NV 289, Winnemucca Blvd, Winnemucca, **S...gas:** Maverik, **food:** El Mirador Mexican, **lodging:** Best Inn, Budget Inn, Cozy Motel, Frontier Motel, Quality Inn, Scott Motel, Valu Motel, **other:** CarQuest, carwash, **1 mi S...gas:** Shell, **food:** Burger King, Subway, **lodging:** La Villa Motel, Pyrenees Motel, Winners Hotel/casino, **other:** HOSPITAL, Radio Shack, Winnemucca RV Park, casinos, to Buckeroo Hall of Fame, same as 176
176	US 95 N, Winnemucca, **N...gas:** Pacific Pride/diesel, **S...gas:** Chevron/diesel/24hr, ✈/Flying J/Conoco/diesel/LP/rest./24hr/@, 76, Shell/diesel, **food:** A&W, Arby's, Burger King, Denny's, KFC, McDonald's, Pizza Hut, RoundTable Pizza, Sid's Rest., Subway, Taco Bell, Taco Time, Twin Wok Chinese, **lodging:** Best Western, Day's Inn, Economy Inn, Holiday Inn Express, Motel 6, Park Hotel, Pyrenees Motel, Quality Inn, Ramada Ltd, Red Lion Inn/casino, Santa Fe Inn, Scottish Inn, Super 8, Townhouse Motel, Winner's Hotel/casino, **other:** HOSPITAL, Ford/Mercury, Ford/Mercury, Goodyear/auto, JC Penney, Kragen Parts, Raley's Foods, Schwab Tire, Wal-Mart/auto/gas, RV camping, truck repair
173	W Winnemucca, **1 mi S...**airport, industrial area
168	to Rose Creek, **S...**prison area
158	to Cosgrave, **S...rest area both lanes, full(handicapped)facilities, phone, picnic tables, litter barrels, petwalk, RV dump**
151	Mill City, **N...gas:** TA/Arco/Subway/Taco Bell/diesel/casino/24hr/@, **lodging:** Super 8, **S...other:** Trading Post/RV park
149	NV 400, Mill City, **1 mi N...gas:** to TA/Arco/Subway/Taco Bell/diesel/24hr/@, **lodging:** Super 8, **S...** Star Point Gen. Sore/RV camping
145	Imlay, no facilities
138	Humboldt, no facilities
129	Rye Patch Dam, **N...other:** to Rye Patch RA, **S...gas:** Rye Patch Trkstp/Arco/diesel/café/24hr/@
119	to Rochester, Oreana, no facilities
112	to Coal Canyon, **S...**to correctional ctr

Lovelock

107	E Lovelock(from wb), **N...gas:** Exxon/diesel, **lodging:** Desert Plaza Inn, Ramada Inn, **other:** Lazy K Camping
106	Main St, Lovelock, **N...gas:** Chevron/diesel/LP, Two Stiffs, **food:** McDonald's, Pizza Factory, Ranch House Rest., Sturgon's Rest., **lodging:** Covered Wagon Motel, Ramada Inn, **other:** HOSPITAL, Ace Hardware, NAPA AutoCare, playground/restrooms, same as 105
105	W Lovelock(from eb), **N...lodging:** Lovelock Inn/rest., Ramda Inn, **other:** HOSPITAL, Brookwood RV Park, NAPA, museum, same as 106
93	to Toulon, **S...**airport
83	US 95 S, to Fallon, **S...rest area both lanes, full(handicapped)facilities, phone, picnic tables, litter barrels**
78	to Jessup, no facilities

Interstate 80

E

W

65	to Hot Springs, Nightingale, no facilities
48	US 50A, US 95A, to Fallon, E Fernley, **N...gas:** 76/diesel/rest./casino/@, **lodging:** Truck Inn/KFC/Pizza Hut, **other:** RV camping, tires, **S...gas:** Chevron/diesel/casino, Shell/Taco Bell/diesel/24hr/@, **food:** Domino's, Jack-in-the-Box, McDonald's, **lodging:** Best Western, Super 8, **other:** American Carcare, Goodyear/auto, Radio Shack, Scolari's Foods, Siverado Rest./casino, to Great Basin NP
46	US 95A, W Fernley, **N...gas:** Luv's/Arby's/diesel/@, **S...gas:** Pilot/DQ/Wendy's/diesel/24hr/@, **other:** Blue Beacon, Fernley RV Park, **1 mi S...gas:** Chevron, Exxon, **lodging:** Lazy Inn
45mm	Truckee River
43	to Pyramid Lake, Wadsworth, **N...gas:** 76/diesel/camping
42mm	**rest area wb, full(handicapped)facilities, phone, picnic tables, litter barrels, petwalk, check sta eb**
40	Painted Rock, no facilities
38	Orchard, no facilities
36	Derby Dam, no facilities
32	Tracy, Clark Station, no facilities
28	NV 655, Waltham Way, Patrick, no facilities
27mm	scenic view, eb
25mm	check sta wb
23	Mustang, **N...food:** Mustang Sta Café, **other:** RV camping, **S...**Chevron/diesel
22	Lockwood, no facilities
21	Vista Blvd, Greg St, Sparks, **N...gas:** Chevron/McDonald's, QwikStop, **food:** Del Taco, **lodging:** Fairfield Inn, **other:** HOSPITAL, **S...gas:** Petro/diesel/rest./24hr/@, **lodging:** Super 8
20	Sparks Blvd, Sparks, **N...gas:** Shell/diesel/24hr, **food:** Carl's Jr, Outback Steaks, Panda Express, **other:** water funpark, **S...gas:** Petro/diesel/rest./24hr/@, **lodging:** Super 8
19	E McCarran Blvd, Sparks, **N...gas:** Chevron/diesel, GoodCents, TA/76/diesel/rest./@, Winners Corner, **food:** Applebee's, Arby's, Black Bear Diner, Burger King, IHOP, Jack-in-the-Box, KFC, Kraig's Rest., Sierra Sid's, Wendy's, Wienerschnitzel, **lodging:** InnCal, Sunrise Motel, Windsor Inn, **other:** $Tree, Ford/Lincoln/Mercury/Isuzu, GNC, Jo-Ann Fabrics, Mervyn's, Radio Shack, Safeway, Sav-On Drug, Suzuki, Victorian RV Park, books, mall, **1 mi N on Prater Way...food:** El Pollo Loco, IHOP, Jack-in-the-Box, McDonald's, Pizza Hut, Sizzler, Subway, Taco Bell, **lodging:** Lariat Motel, **other:** Albertson's, Goodyear, Kragen Parts, LJ Silver, Longs Drugs, Target, **S...food:** Black Forest Rest., Denny's, **lodging:** McCarran House Hotel, Quality Inn, **other:** NAPA AutoCare
18	NV 445, Pyramid Way(from eb), Sparks, **N...gas:** Citgo/7-11, **lodging:** Courtyard, Silver Club Hotel/casino, **S...lodging:** Nugget Hotel/casino
17	Rock Blvd, Nugget Ave, Sparks, **N...gas:** Arco/24hr, Exxon, Winners, **other:** Kragen Parts, casinos, **S...lodging:** Nugget Hotel/casino
16	B St, E 4th St, Victorian Ave, **N...gas:** Arco/24hr, Winners, **lodging:** Motel 6, **other:** Rail City Ca-

Sparks

Reno

	sino, **S...gas:** Arco/diesel/24hr, Chevron/repair, **lodging:** Gold Coin Motel, Hilton
15	US 395, to Carson City, **1 mi N on McCarran Blvd...gas:** Chevron, Shell/diesel, **food:** Arby's, Burger King, Del Taco, Szechuan Chinese, Sonic, Subway, Taco Bell, TCBY, Wendy's, **other:** Home Depot, Kragen Parts, OfficeMax, Ross, Wal-Mart/auto, WinCo Foods, **S...food:** Bally's, **lodging:** Holiday Inn, 6 Gun Motel
14	Wells Ave, Reno, **N...lodging:** Motel 6, **S...gas:** Chevron, Shell, **food:** Carrow's Rest., Denny's, **lodging:** Day's Inn, Econolodge, Holiday Inn, **other:** Goodyear
13	US 395, Virginia St, Reno, **N...gas:** Shell, **food:** JimBoy's Taco's, **S...gas:** Chevron, Shell/diesel, **other:** HOSPITAL, NAPA, Walgreen, to downtown hotels/casinos, to UNVReno
12	Keystone Ave, Reno, **N...gas:** Arco/24hr, Citgo/7-11, **food:** Pizza Hut, **lodging:** Gateway Inn, Motel 6, **other:** Raley's Foods, Sav-On Drug, **S...gas:** Chevron, 76/diesel, Winter's Gas, **food:** Baskin-Robbins, Burger King, Ca Burger, Coffee Grinder Rest., Higgy's Pizza, Jack-in-the-Box, McDonald's, Port of Subs, Pierino Rest., Shakey's Pizza, Taco Bell, Wendy's, **other:** Harrah's, Hilton's, Albertson's, Allied Parts, Olson Tire, Radio Shack, 98 Cents Store, casinos, RV park
10	McCarran Blvd, Reno, **N...gas:** Arco/24hr, Citgo/7-11, Tesoro, **food:** Arby's, Baskin-Robbins, Burger King, Carl's Jr, Chili's, Del Taco, El Pollo Loco, Hacienda Mexican, IHOP, Jack-in-the-Box, KFC, McDonald's, Papa Murphy's, RoundTable Pizza, Schlotsky's, Starbucks, Taco Bell, **other:** MEDICAL CARE, Albertson's, Big O Tire, Kragen Parts, QuikLube/gas, Safeway, Sav-On Drug, ShopKO, Tires+, **S...gas:** Arco/24hr, Citgo/7-11, **lodging:** Summit Ridge Inn, **other:** Home Depot, K-Mart/Little Caesar's
9	Robb Dr, **N...gas:** 76, **other:** Scolari's Foods
8	W 4th St(from eb), Robb Dr, Reno, **S...**RV camping
7	Mogul, no facilities
6.5mm	truck parking/hist marker/scenic view both lanes
5	to E Verdi(from wb), **N...food:** Backstop Grill, Rattler Ridge Grill(2mi)
4.5mm	scenic view eb
4	Garson Rd, Boomtown, **N...gas:** Chevron/diesel/@, **lodging:** Boomtown Hotel/casino, **other:** RV park/dump
3.5mm	check sta eb
3	Verdi(from wb), no facilities
2.5mm	Truckee River
2	Lp 80, to Verdi, **N...gas:** Arco/diesel/24hr, **food:** Backstop Grill, Jack-in-the-Box, Taco Bell, **lodging:** Gold Ranch Hotel/casino
1	Gold Ranch Rd(from eb), to Verdi, no facilities
0mm	Nevada/California state line

NEW HAMPSHIRE
Interstate 89

N ↕ S

Lebanon

Exit #	Services
61mm	New Hampshire/Vermont state line, Connecticut River
20(60)	NH 12A, W Lebanon, **E...gas:** Mobil/24hr, Sunoco/24hr, **food:** Benning St Grill, Board&Basket, Brick Oven Pizza, Chili's, Domino's, Dunkin Donuts, KFC/Taco Bell, 99 Rest., Shorty's Mexican, Subway, **other:** Brooks Drug, GNC, Jo-Ann Fabrics, K-Mart, NE Soap&Herb, PowerHouse Mall/shops, Shaw's Foods, **W...gas:** Citgo/diesel/repair, **food:** Applebee's, Burger King, China Light, D'angelo, Denny's, Friendly's, Koto Japanese, Lantern Buffet, McDonald's, Panera Bread, Pizza Hut, 7 Barrel Brewery, TCBY, Weathervane Seafood, Wendy's, **lodging:** Economy Inn, Fireside Inn, **other:** Ames, AutoZone, Best Buy, BJ' Whse, Borders Books, CVS Drug, Home Depot, JC Penney, PriceChopper Foods, Radio Shack, Shaw's Foods, Staples, Wal-Mart
19(58)	US 4, NH 10, W Lebanon, **E...gas:** Exxon/diesel/24hr, Shell/Blimpie, **food:** China Station, **other:** Family$, Ford, Harley-Davidson, Honda, NAPA, P&C Foods, Radio Shack, **W...gas:** Sunoco
57mm	**Welcome Ctr/rest area/weigh sta sb, full(handicapped)facilities, phone, picnic tables, litter barrels, vending, petwalk, weigh sta nb**
18(56)	NH 120, Lebanon, **E...gas:** Getty/diesel/rest./24hr/@, **lodging:** Day's Inn, Residence Inn(2mi), **other:** Buick/Pontiac/GMC, Chevrolet/Cadillac/VW, Dodge/Mazda, Nissan/Jeep/Volvo, to Dartmouth Coll, **W...gas:** Citgo/diesel, Shell, **other:** HOSPITAL, U-Haul
17(54)	US 4, to NH 4A, Enfield, **E...food:** Riverside Grill, Shaker Museum, **other:** Tire Kingdom
16(52)	Eastman Hill Rd, **E...gas:** Exxon/Subway/diesel/24hr, **W...gas:** Mobil/diesel/24hr, **other:** Whaleback Ski Area
15(50)	Montcalm, no facilities
14(47)	NH 10(from sb), no facilities
13(43)	NH 10, to N Grantham, Grantham, **E...gas:** Gulf/diesel/Gen Store, **food:** Rusty Moose, **W...gas:** Mobil/repair
40mm	**rest area nb, full(handicapped)facilities, info, phone, picnic table, litter barrels, vending, petwalk**
12A(37)	Georges Mills, **W...other:** to Sunapee SP, food, phone, lodging, RV camping
12(34)	NH 11 W, New London, **2 mi E...gas:** Exxon/diesel, **lodging:** Maple Hill Country Inn, **other:** HOSPITAL
11(31)	NH 11 E, King Hill Rd, New London, **2 mi E...lodging:** Fairway Motel, food, **2 mi W...lodging:** Shaker Mtg House B&B
10(27)	to NH 114, Sutton, **E...**to Winslow SP, **1 mi W...**lodging, to Wadleigh SB
26mm	**rest area sb, full(handicapped)facilities, info, phone, picnic tables, litter barrels, vending, petwalk**

Concord

Exit #	Services
9(19)	NH 103, Warner, **E...gas:** Citgo/Subway/Pizza Hut/TCBY, Exxon, Mobil/diesel/24hr, **food:** Dunkin Donuts, Foothills Rest.(1mi), McDonald's, **other:** MktBasket Foods, Rollins SP, **W...**to Sunapee SP, ski area
8(17)	NH 103(from nb, no EZ return), Warner, **1 mi E...**gas, food, museum, to Rollins SP
15mm	Warner River
7(14)	NH 103, Davisville, **W...**Pleasant Lake Camping
12mm	Contoocook River
6(10)	NH 127, Contoocook, **1 mi E...gas:** Sunoco, **W... other:** Elm Brook Park, Sandy Beach Camping(3mi)
5(8)	US 202 W, NH 9(exits left from nb), Hopkinton, **W...**food, RV camping(seasonal)
4(7)	NH 103, Hopkinton(from nb, no EZ return), **E...**HorseShoe Tavern, gas
3(4)	Stickney Hill Rd(from nb), no facilities
2(2)	NH 13, Clinton St, Concord, **E...**HOSPITAL, food, **W...** NH Audubon Ctr
1(1)	Logging Hill Rd, Bow, **E...gas:** Mobil/24hr, **food:** Chen Yang Li Chinese, **lodging:** Hampton Inn
0mm	I-93 N to Concord, S to Manchester, I-89 begins/ends

Interstate 93

N ↕ S

Exit #	Services
2(11)	I-91, N to St Johnsbury, S to White River Jct. I-93 begins/ends on I-91, exit 19., no facilities
1(8)	VT 18, to US 2, to St Johnsbury, **2 mi E...**gas, food, lodging, camping
1mm	**Welcome Ctr nb, full(handicapped)facilities, info, phone, picnic tables, litter barrels, vending, petwalk**
131mm	Vermont/New Hampshire state line. **Exits 1-2 are in VT.**, Connecticut River
44(130)	NH 18, NH 135, **W...Welcome Ctr(8am-8pm)/scenic vista both lanes, full(handicapped)facilities, info, phone, picnic tables, litter barrels, petwalk**
43(125)	NH 135(from sb), to NH 18, Littleton, **1-2 mi W...** HOSPITAL, same as 42
42(124)	US 302 E, NH 10 N, Littleton, **E...gas:** Citgo, Cumberland, Gulf, Sunoco/24hr, **food:** Burger King, ClamShell Rest., Deluxe Pizza, Dunkin Donuts, Jing Fong Chinese, McDonald's, Oasis Italian, Pizza Hut, Subway, **other:** Brooks Drug, Medicine Shoppe, Parts+, Rite Aid, **W...gas:** Mobil, **food:** Applebee's, Asian Garden Chinese, **lodging:** Continental Inn, **other:** Aubuchon Hardware, Chevrolet/Buick/Pontiac, Chrysler/Dodge/Jeep, KOA, Shaw's Foods, Staples, Tire Whse, TJ Maxx, VIP Parts/repair, Wal-Mart/drug
41(122)	US 302, NH 18, NH 116, Littleton, **E...gas:** Irving/diesel/24hr, **lodging:** Eastgate Motel/rest., **E...other:** NE Tire
40(121)	US 302, NH 10 E, Bethlehem, **E...gas:** Exxon, **food:** Adair Rest., **lodging:** Angel Mtn B&B, Milborn Inn, **other:** Snowy Mtn Camping, to Mt Washington
39(119)	NH 116, NH 18(from sb), N Franconia, Sugar Hill, **W...**lodging

Littleton

Interstate 93

38(117) NH 116, NH 117, NH 142, NH 18, Sugar Hill, **E...lodging:** Franconia Village Hotel, **W...gas:** Mobil, **food:** DutchTreat Rest., Franconia Cafe, Village House Rest., **lodging:** Franconia Inn(2mi), **other:** Frost Museum, Kelley's FoodTown, USPO, camping, gifts, info

37(115) NH 142, NH 18(from nb), Franconia, Bethlehem, **E...lodging:** Canyonview Motel, Stonybrook Motel

36(114) NH 141, to US 3, S Franconia, **W...golf, food, lodging**

35(113) US 3 N(from nb), to Twin Mtn Lake, no facilities

112mm S Franconia, Franconia Notch SP begins sb

34c(111) NH 18, Echo Beach Ski Area, view area, info

34b Cannon Mtn Tramway, **W...other:** Boise Rock, Old Man Viewing, Lafayette Place Camping

109mm trailhead parking

108mm Lafayette Place Camping(from sb), trailhead parking

107mm The Basin, The Basin

34a US 3, The Flume Gorge, The Flume Gorge, info, camping(seasonal)

104mm Franconia Notch SP begins nb

33(103) US 3, N Woodstock, **E...gas:** Irving/diesel, **food:** Frescolones Pizza, Longhorn Palace Rest., Mountaineer Rest., Notchview Country Kitchen, **lodging:** Econolodge, Drummer Boy Motel, Indian Head Resort, Mt Coolidge Motel, Pemi Motel, Profile Motel, Red Doors Motel, **other:** Indian Head viewing, to Franconia Notch SP, **W...lodging:** Country Bumpkin Cottages/RV Park, Cozy Cabins, Mt Liberty Motel, White Mtn Motel, **other:** Clark's Trading Post, Cold Springs Camping

32(101) NH 112, Loon Mtn Rd, N Woodstock, **E...gas:** Irving, Mobil, Shell/diesel, **food:** Bill&Bob's Roast Beef, Burger King, Earl of Sandwich Rest., Emperor Chinese, Fratello's Rest., GH Pizza, Gypsy Café, House of Pancakes, McDonald's, Mr. W's Pancakes, NE Chowder, 7 Seas Seafood, Subway, **lodging:** Comfort Inn, Lincoln Sta Lodge, Loon Mtn Resort, Millhouse Inn/rest., Pollard Brook Resort, River Green Hotel, **other:** MEDICAL CARE, Big A Parts, GNC, Rite Aid, T&C Foods, USPO, to North Country Art Ctr, **W...gas:** Citgo, Mobil, **food:** Café Lafayette, Chalet Rest., Landmark II Rest., Peg's Café, Truant's Rest., **lodging:** Alpine Lodge, Autumn Breeze Motel, Carriage Motel, Woodstock Inn/rest., **other:** NAPA, USPO, candy/fudge/gifts

31(97) to NH 175, Tripoli Rd, **E...RV camping(seasonal)**, **W...KOA(2mi)**

30(95) US 3, Woodstock, **E...food:** Frannie's Place Café, **lodging:** Jack-O-Lantern Inn/rest., **other:** golf, **W...flea mkt, RV camping(seasonal)**

29(89) US 3, Thornton, **E...Pemi River RV Park, 1 mi W...lodging:** Gilcrest Motel

28(87) NH 49, Campton, **E...gas:** Citgo, Mobil, **food:** Mad River Rest., **other:** Family Store/deli, True Value, USPO, to ski area, RV camping, **W...gas:** Citgo/diesel, **food:** Sunset Grill, **lodging:** Scandinavi-Inn, **other:** Branch Brook Camping

27(84) Blair Rd, Beebe River, **E...food:** Country Cow Rest., **lodging:** Day's Inn, Red Sleigh Motel/chalets

26(83) US 3, NH 25, NH 3A, Tenney Mtn Hwy, **W on US 3...food:** McDonald's, **lodging:** Best Inn, Common Man Inn, Pilgrim Inn, **other:** HOSPITAL

25(81) NH 175(from nb), Plymouth, **W...gas:** Irving/diesel, Mobil, **food:** Biederman's Deli, Bierhaus Café, Bridgeside Diner, HongKong Garden, Subway, **lodging:** Deep River Motel, **other:** HOSPITAL, to Holderness School, Plymouth St Coll

24(76) US 3, NH 25, Ashland, **E...gas:** Cumberland, Irving/Subway/diesel, Mobil/diesel, **food:** Ashland Rest., Burger King, Common Man Diner, John's Cafe, **lodging:** Comfort Inn, **other:** Big A Parts, Bob's Foods, CarQuest, USPO, RV camp(4mi)

23(71) NH 104, NH 132, to Mt Washington Valley, New Hampton, **E...gas:** Citgo/diesel, Irving/diesel/24hr, **food:** Bobby's Grill, Dunkin Donuts, Rossi Italian, Subway, **other:** info, USPO, **W...food:** Homestead Rest.(2mi), **other:** Davidson's RV Park(2mi), ski area

NEW HAMPSHIRE
Interstate 93

N
↑
↓
S

Concord

22(62) NH 127, Sanbornton, **1-5 mi W...gas:** San Bornton Gen Store/diesel, **other:** HOSPITAL, gas/diesel, food, phone

61mm **rest area sb, full(handicapped)facilities, info, phone, picnic tables, litter barrels, vending, petwalk**

20(57) US 3, NH 11, NH 132, NH 140, Tilton, **E...gas:** Exxon/Subway/diesel/24hr, Irving/diesel/24hr, Mobil, **food:** Applebee's, Burger King, FoodCourt, Hong Kong Chinese, Kalliopee's Rest., KFC, McDonald's, Oliver's Rest., Pizzaria Uno, Tilt'n Diner, UpperCrust Pizza, Wendy's, **lodging:** Shalimar Resort(3mi), Super 8, **other:** BJ's Whse/gas, Home Depot, Lakes Region Outlet/famous brands, Shaw's Foods, Staples, VIP Auto, **W...lodging:** Black Swan B&B(2mi), Wayland Motel, **other:** Chrysler/Plymouth/Dodge, Ford/Nissan/Kia, MktBasket Foods, USPO, Wal-Mart/auto

56mm Winnipesaukee River

19(55) NH 132(from nb), Franklin, **W...gas:** Exxon, **other:** HOSPITAL, NH Vet Home, antiques

51mm **rest area nb, full(handicapped)facilities, phone, info, picnic tables, litter barrels, vending, petwalk**

18(49) to NH 132, Canterbury, **E...gas:** Sunoco, **other:** to Shaker Village HS

17(46) US 4 W, to US 3, NH 132, Boscawen, **4 mi W...** gas

16(41) NH 132, E Concord, **E...gas:** Mobil/diesel, **other:** Quality Cash Mkt

15W(40) US 202 W, to US 3, N Main St, Concord, **W...gas:** Citgo, Getty, Hess, **food:** Friendly's, **lodging:** Courtyard/café

15E I-393 E, US 4 E, to Portsmouth, no facilities

14(39) NH 9, Loudon Rd, Concord, **E...food:** Boston Mkt, Family Buffet, Panera Bread, Pizzaria Uno, **other:** AutoZone, Borders Books, $Tree, GNC, LLBean, MktBasket Foods, Osco Drug, Radio Shack, Shaw Foods/24hr, Shop'n Save Food, Staples, U-Haul, USPO, Walgreen, **1-2 mi E on Loudon Rd...gas:** Irving, Mobil, Shell/diesel, Sunoco, **food:** Applebee's, Burger King, Chili's, D'angelo, Dunkin Donuts, Friendly's, KFC, LJ Silver/Taco Bell, Longhorn Steaks, McDonald's, Olive Garden, OutBack Steaks, PapaGino, Ruby Tesday, Wendy's, **other:** Advance Parts, JC Penney, Sears/auto, Shaw's Foods, Wal-Mart SuperCtr/24hr, **W...gas:** Citgo, Gulf/diesel, Hess, Exxon/diesel, **food:** Domino's, Rainbow Buffet, Tea Garden Rest., **lodging:** Holiday Inn/Kansas City Steaks., **other:** Ames, Jo-Ann Fabrics, Marshalls, MktBasket Foods, Pill MktPlace, to state offices, hist sites, museum

13(38) to US 3, Manchester St, Concord, **E...gas:** Gulf, Mobil/diesel/24hr, Sunoco/diesel, **food:** Beefside Rest., Cityside Grille, Dunkin Donuts, Pizza Mkt, Red Blazer Rest., **other:** Chrysler/Plymouth, Outdoor RV

Manchester

Ctr, Saab, Volvo/Isuzu, **W...gas:** Hess, **food:** Burger King, Common Man Diner, D'angelo's, Hawaiian Isle Rest., KFC, McDonald's, **lodging:** Best Western, Comfort Inn, Fairfield Inn, **other:** HOSPITAL, BMW, Firestone, GMC, Goodyear/auto, NAPA

12N(37) NH 3A N, S Main, **E...gas:** Exxon/Dunkin Donuts, Irving/Subway/diesel/24hr, **lodging:** Day's Inn, **other:** Ford, Honda/Mazda/Saturn/VW, Suzuki, Toyota, **W...gas:** Mobil, **lodging:** Hampton Inn, **other:** HOSPITAL

12S NH 3A S, Bow Junction, **E...gas:** Citgo/diesel

36mm I-89 N to Lebanon, toll road begins/ends, no facilities

31mm **rest area both lanes, full(handicapped)facilities, info, phone, vending**

11(30) NH 3A, to Hooksett, toll plaza, phone, **4 mi E...gas:** Citgo Trkstp/diesel/rest.

28mm I-293(from sb), Everett Tpk, no facilities

10(27) NH 3A, Hooksett, **E...gas:** Irving/diesel, **food:** Wendy's, **other:** BJ's Whse, Home Depot, Kohl's, Staples, Target, **W...gas:** Exxon, Mobil/diesel, **food:** Big Cheese Pizza

26mm Merrimac River

9N S(24) US 3, NH 28, Manchester, **W...gas:** Manchester/diesel, Sunoco/diesel/24hr, **food:** Burger King, Happy Garden Chinese, KFC, Lusia's Italian, PapaGino's, Shorty's Mexican, **other:** HOSPITAL, Chrysler/Dodge/Jeep, Ford/Lincoln/Mercury, Mercedes

8(23) to NH 28a, Wellington Rd, **W...VA HOSPITAL,** Currier Gallery

7(22) NH 101 E, to Portsmouth, Seacoast, no facilities

6(21) Hanover St, Candia Rd, Manchester, **E...food:** Wendy's, **W...gas:** Citgo/diesel, Mobil/diesel, Shell/24hr

19mm I-293 W, to Manchester, to airport, to airport

5(15) NH 28, to N Londonderry, **E...gas:** Sunoco/diesel, **food:** Poor Boy's Diner, **3 mi E...gas:** Shell, **food:** Applebee's, Burger King, Pinkerton Tavern, **other:** Dodge/Jeep, Lincoln/Mercury, NAPA, Sullivan Tire, Victory Foods, Wal-Mart, **W...gas:** Exxon/deli/diesel, **lodging:** Sleep Inn, **other:** MEDICAL CARE

Derry

4(12) NH 102, Derry, **E...gas:** Citgo/diesel, Mobil/24hr, Mutual, Shell/24hr, Sunoco/diesel, **food:** Burger King, Cracker Barrel, Derry Rest., **other:** HOSPITAL, **W...gas:** Citgo/7-11, Exxon/diesel, Hess, Shell/diesel, **food:** Domino's, Happy Garden Chinese, McDonald's, PapaGino's, Wendy's, **other:** Chrysler/Plymouth, Ford, Home Depot, K-Mart, Mkt Basket Foods, Radio Shack, Shaw's Foods, USPO, VIP Auto, Walgreen

8mm weigh sta both lanes

3(6) NH 111, Windham, **E...gas:** Mobil/McDonald's, Sunoco/24hr, **food:** Dunkin Donuts, House of Pizza, **W...gas:** Exxon/diesel/24hr, Sunoco/24hr, **food:** Dunkin Donuts, Lobster Tail, **other:** Castleton Conference Ctr

2(3) to NH 38, NH 97, Salem, **E...lodging:** Red Roof Inn, **W...gas:** Mobil, **food:** KC Steaks, Lucy's Country Store/subs, Margarita's Cafe, **lodging:** Fairfield Inn, Holiday Inn

290

Interstate 93

1(2) NH 28, Salem, **E...gas:** Citgo/diesel, Exxon, Getty, **food:** Burger King, Chili's, Denny's, Friendly's, McDonald's, 99 Rest., **lodging:** Park View Inn, **other:** Barnes&Noble, Best Buy, DeMoula's Foods, Dodge/Nissan/Toyota, Filene's, Home Depot, JC Penney, K-Mart, Macy's, Marshall's, MktBasket Foods, NTB, Sears/auto, Shaw's Foods, Staples, Target, TownFair Rest., Walgreen, racetrack, mall

1mm **Welcome Ctr nb, full(handicapped)facilities, info, phone, picnic tables, litter barrels, vending, petwalk**

0mm New Hampshire/Massachusetts state line

Interstate 95

Exit #(mm)Services

17mm New Hampshire/Maine state line, Piscataqua River

7(16) Portsmouth, Port Authority, waterfront hist sites, **W...food:** Applebee's, Schoolhouse Rest., Wendy's, **lodging:** Courtyard, **other:** BJ's Whse/gas, K-Mart

6(15) Woodbury Ave(from nb), Portsmouth, **E...gas:** Gulf, Shell, **lodging:** Anchorage Inn

5(14) US 1, US 4, NH 16, The Circle, Portsmouth, **E...gas:** Gulf, Shell/diesel, **food:** Bickford's, Momma D's Rest., **lodging:** Anchorage Inn, Best Inn, Best Western, Holiday Inn, **other:** HOSPITAL, Pontiac/Cadillac/GMC, **W...gas:** Exxon, **food:** Dunkin Donuts, McDonald's, Pizza Hut, **lodging:** Hampton Inn, **other:** Ford, Home Depot, Mazda/VW, Nissan, Saturn

4(13.5) US 4(from nb), to White Mtns, Spaulding TPK, **E...HOSPITAL, W...**to Pease Int Trade Port

3a(13) NH 33, Greenland

3b(12) NH 101, to Portsmouth, **E...HOSPITAL, W...gas:** Mobil/diesel, Sunoco/diesel, TA/diesel/rest./24hr/@, **food:** McDonald's(1mi)

2(6) NH 51, to Hampton, **1 mi E on US 1...food:** McDonald's, **other:** HOSPITAL

5.5mm toll plaza

4mm Taylor River

1(1) NH 107, to Seabrook, toll rd begins/ends, **E...gas:** Getty, Sunoco, **food:** Applebee's, Burger King, D'Angelo's, KFC, McDonald's, Pizza Hut/Taco Bell, Road Kill Café, Subway, Wendy's, **lodging:** Hampshire Motel, **other:** AutoZone, CVS Drug, GNC, Jo-Ann Crafts, MktBasket Foods, NAPA, Radio Shack, Shaw's Foods, Staples, Wal-Mart, to Seacoast RA, **W...gas:** Citgo, **food:** Capt K's Seafood, McGrath's Dining, **lodging:** Best Western, **other:** Sam's Club, Seabrook Greyhound Pk

.5mm **Welcome Ctr nb, full(handicapped)facilities, phone, vending, picnic tables, litter barrels, petwalk**

0mm New Hampshire/Massachusetts state line

Interstate 293(Manchester)

Exit # Services

8(9) I-93, N to Concord, S to Derry. I-293 begins/ends on I-93, 28mm., no facilities

7(6.5) NH 3A N, Dunbarton Rd(from nb), no facilities

6(6) Singer Park, Manchester, **E...gas:** Sunoco, **food:** Hooters, **lodging:** Ramada Inn, **W...gas:** Mobil, Shell/diesel, **other:** HOSPITAL

5(5) Granite St, Manchester(from nb, no EZ return), **E...lodging:** Radisson, **W...gas:** Citgo/7-11, Exxon, **food:** Dunkin Donuts, **other:** HOSPITAL

4(4) US 3, NH 3A, NH 114A, Queen City Br, **E...gas:** Citgo/7-11, **lodging:** Queen City Inn, Thai Cuisine, **W on US 3...gas:** Hess/diesel, Z1 Gas, **food:** Applebee's, Bickford's, Burger King, Clam King, D'angelo's, DQ, KFC, McDonald's, Papa John's, Subway, Wendy's, **lodging:** Comfort Inn, Econolodge, **other:** Goodyear, Osco Drug, Subaru

3(3) NH 101, **W on US 3...food:** Carrabba's, China Buffet, Outback Steaks, Qacker's Rest., T-Bones Steaks, **lodging:** Wayfarer Inn, **other:** Bob's Store, CVS Drug, Macy's, Marshalls, Radio Shack, Stop'n Shop, Staples, VIP Auto, **S on US 3...**Hanpton Inn

2.5mm Merrimac River

2(2) NH 3A, Brown Ave, **S...gas:** Citgo/Subway/diesel, Citgo/7-11, Mobil/diesel, Shell/repair, **food:** Beijing Chinese, Kwikava, McDonald's, Rick's Café, **lodging:** Super 8, Tage Inn, **other:** Manchester Airport

1(1) NH 28, S Willow Rd, **N...gas:** Mobil/Pizza Hut/diesel, Sunoco/diesel, **food:** Bickford's, Boston Mkt, Burger King, Chili's, Friendly's, McDonald's, Panera Bread, PapaGino's, Taco Bell, Wendy's, Yee Dynasty Chinese, **lodging:** Fairfield Inn, Holiday Inn Express, Sheraton, **other:** HOSPITAL, AutoZone, Batteries+, Buick/Chevrolet, Circuit City, CVS Drug, $Tree, GMC, Harley-Davidson, Home Depot, Mercedes, Michael's, Nissan/Mitsubishi, OfficeMax, Osco Drug, PepBoys, Pontiac/Cadillac/Mazda, Radio Shack, Sam's Club, Stop'n Shop, Tire Whse, Town Fair Tire, U-Haul, VW, **S...gas:** Exxon/diesel, Shell, **food:** Antics Grill, Bertucci's, Bickford's, ChuckeCheese, FoodCourt, Ground Round, Longhorn Steaks, 99 Rest., Olive Garden, Pizzaria Uno, Ruby Tuesday, TGIFriday, **lodging:** Courtyard, TownePlace Suites, **other:** HOSPITAL, Barnes&Noble, Best Buy, Chrysler/Plymouth, Filene's, Ford, Honda, Hyundai, JC Penney, K-Mart, Lexus, NTB, Saturn, Sears/auto, Staples, Toyota, Wal-Mart, mall

0mm I-93, N to Concord, S to Derry. I-293 begins/ends on I-93.

NEW JERSEY
Interstate 78

E	Exit #	Services

E ↕ **W** / **Newark**

58b a US 1N, US 9N, NJ Tpk, no facilities

57 US 1S, US 9S, **S...lodging:** Day's Inn, Courtyard, Holiday Inn, Marriott, Ramada Inn, Sheraton, **other:** to Newark Airport, **3 mi S...lodging:** Day's Inn, Hampton Inn, Wyndham Garden

56 Clinton Ave, no facilities

55 Irvington(from wb), **N...gas:** BP, Hess/diesel, **food:** White Castle, **other:** HOSPITAL, PathMark Foods

54 Hillside, Irvington(from eb), **N...gas:** BP, **other:** HOSPITAL

52 Garden State Pkwy, no facilities

50b a Millburn(from wb), **N...gas:** BP, Exxon, Mobil, **other:** Firestone/auto, Home Depot, Lincoln/Mercury, USPO

49b (from eb), to Maplewood, same as 50b a

48 to NJ 24, NJ 124, to I-287 N, Springfield, no facilities

47mm I-78 eb divides into express & local, no facilities

45 NJ 527(from eb), Glenside Ave, Summit, no facilities

44 (from eb), to Berkeley Heights, New Providence, no facilities

43 (from wb), to New Providence, no facilities

41 to Berkeley Heights, Scotch Plains, no facilities

40 NJ 531, The Plainfields, **S...gas:** BP/24hr(1mi), **other:** HOSPITAL

36 NJ 651, to Warrenville, Basking Ridge, **N...gas:** Exxon/service/24hr, **food:** Dunkin Doughnuts, **other:** A&P, **S...gas:** Exxon

33 NJ 525, to Martinsville, Bernardsville, PGA Golf Museum, **N...food:** CIAO Italian, **lodging:** Courtyard, Somerset Hills Inn/rest., **S...gas:** Exxon

32mm scenic overlook wb

29 I-287, to US 202, US 206, I-80, to Morristown, Somerville, **S...HOSPITAL**

26 NJ 523 spur, to North Branch, Lamington, no facilities

24 NJ 523, to NJ 517, to Oldwick, Whitehouse, **2-3 mi S...gas:** Exxon/diesel/24hr, **food:** McDonald's, Readington Diner

20b a NJ 639(from wb), to Cokesbury, Lebanon, **S...gas:** Exxon/24hr, Shell/24hr, Sunoco, **food:** Bagelsmith Deli, Dunkin Donuts, Spinning Wheel Diner, **lodging:** Courtyard, **other:** to Round Valley RA

18 US 22 E, Annandale, Lebanon, **N...HOSPITAL**, same as 17, **S...Honda**

17 NJ 31 S, Clinton, **N...gas:** Amoco/24hr, Exxon, Hess/24hr, Mobil/24hr, **food:** Bagelsmith Deli, Dunkin Doughnuts/Baskin Robbins, Hibachi Japanese, King Buffet, McDonald's, **1 mi N...food:** TingHo Chinese, **other:** Chrysler/Plymouth/Dodge/Jeep/Ford, to Spruce Run RA

16 NJ 31 N(from eb), Clinton, **N...food:** King Buffet, McDonald's, A&P, bank, same as 17

15 NJ 173 E, to Pittstown, Clinton, **N...gas:** Citgo, Clinton Gas, Exxon, Shell/diesel/24hr, **food:** Subway, **lodging:** Holiday Inn Select, **other:** museum, **S...food:** Cracker Barrel, Frank's Pizza, **lodging:** Hampton Inn, **other:** HOSPITAL, $Tree, ShopRite Foods, TJMaxx, Wal-Mart/grill

13 NJ 173 W(from wb), **N...food:** Clinton Sta. Diner, Sherwood Crossing Rest., same as 12

12 NJ 173, to Jutland, Norton, **N...gas:** Citgo/Johnny's Rest./diesel, Exxon/diesel, **food:** Clinton Sta. Diner, **other:** to Spruce Run RA, **S...gas:** Shell/diesel, **food:** Bagelsmith Deli

11 NJ 173, West Portal, Pattenburg, **N...gas:** Coastal/24hr, Shell/diesel, **food:** Landslide Rest., Pizza Rest, **other:** Jugtown RV Park, to st police

8mm rest area both lanes, picnic tables, litter barrels, no restrooms

7 7 NJ 173, to Bloomsbury, West Portal, **N...RV** camping, **S...gas:** Citgo/Krispy Kreme/diesel/rest./24hr, Pilot/Subway/diesel/24hr/@, TA/Mobil/Buger King/diesel/rest./24hr/@

6 Warren Glen, Asbury(from eb), no facilities

4 4 Warren Glen, Stewartsville(from wb), no facilities

3.5mm weigh sta eb

3 US 22, NJ 173, to Phillipsburg, **N...gas:** PennJersey/diesel/rest./24hr/@, US/diesel/24hr, Getty, **other:** HOSPITAL, **1 mi N...gas:** Citgo/diesel, **food:** Applebee's, Almond Tree Rest., Burger King, Domino's, Key City Diner(3mi), McDonald's, Panera Bread, Perkins, Ponderosa, Ruby Tuesday, **lodging:** Clarion, Phillipsburg Inn, **other:** Circuit City, $Tree, Home Depot, Honda, Lowe's Whse, Michael's, ShopRite Foods, Staples, Stop 'n Shop, Target, Wal-Mart/auto, **S...other:** Chevrolet/Isuzu

0mm New Jersey/Pennsylvania state line, Delaware River

Interstate 80

Exit #	Services

E ↕ **W**

I-80 begins/ends at G Washington Bridge in Ft Lee, NJ.

73mm toll plaza eb

72b US 1 S, US 9, **N...food:** Red Oak Rest., **other:** Staples

72a US 46, NJ 4, **N...gas:** BP, Exxon/Subway, Getty, Gulf, Hess/diesel, Mobil, Sunoco, **food:** Bennigan's, **lodging:** Best Western, Holiday Inn, **S...gas:** Mobil, Shell, **lodging:** Courtesy Inn, Hilton

71 Broad Ave, Leonia, Englewood, **N...gas:** Gulf, **lodging:** Day's Inn, Executive Inn, **S...gas:** Shell

70b a NJ 93, Leonia, Teaneck, **N...gas:** Marriott, **other:** HOSPITAL

68b a I-95, N to New York, S to Philadelphia, to US 46, no facilities

67 to Bogota(from eb), no facilities

66 Hudson St, to Hackensack, **N...gas:** Getty

65 Green St, S Hackensack, **S...gas:** Exxon, **lodging:** Hilton

64b a NJ 17 S, to US 46 E, Newark, Paramus, **S...gas:** BP/24hr, Exxon, **food:** Baskin-Robbins, **lodging:** Crowne Plaza, **other:** PathMark Foods

63 NJ 17 N, **N...gas:** BP/24hr, Citgo, Gulf, Hess/diesel/24hr, **other:** HOSPITAL, CVS Drug, Harley-Davidson, Home Depot

62b a GS Pkwy, to Saddle Brook, **N...gas:** Shell, **lodging:** Howard Johnson, Marriott, **S...lodging:** Holiday Inn

NEW JERSEY

Interstate 80

61 NJ 507, to Garfield, Elmwood Park, **N**...Marcal Paper Co, **S**...**gas:** Sunoco

60 NJ 20, N to Hawthorne, **N**...**other:** HOSPITAL, Michelin/Cooper Tires

59 Market St(from wb), to Paterson, no facilities

58b a Madison Ave, to Paterson, Clifton, **S**...HOSPITAL

57c Main St(from wb), to Paterson, no facilities

57b a NJ 19 S, downtown Paterson, to Clifton, downtown Paterson

56b a Squirrelwood Rd, to Paterson, **S**...**gas:** Mobil

55b a Union Blvd(from wb, no EZ return), Totowa, **N**...**gas:** Sunoco/diesel, **S**...**lodging:** Holiday Inn

54 Minnisink Rd, to Paterson, **S**...**gas:** BP, **other:** Home Depot, JC Penney, Marshall's, Staples, mall

53 US 46 E, NJ 23(no eb return), **S**...**gas:** Exxon, Gulf, Mobil, Sunoco, **food:** Applebee's, Burger King, Hooters, McDonald's, Pizzaria Uno, Red Lobster, Ruby Steak 'n Ale, Tuesday, TGIFriday, Wendy's, **lodging:** Holiday Inn, Ramada Inn, Sheraton, **other:** Borders Books, Costco, Firestone/auto, Ford, Home Depot, Lord&Taylor, Macy's, Old Navy, Sears/auto, Target, mall

52 US 46, the Caldwells, no facilities

48 to Montville(from wb), Pine Brook, no facilities

47b US 46 W, to Montclair, **N**...**gas:** BP, **lodging:** Holiday Inn, **S**...**gas:** BP, Gulf, Mobil/diesel, Shell, **food:** Dakota Diner/24hr, Dunkin Donuts, Indian Cuisine, Italian Deli, McDonald's, Roy Rogers, Subway

47a I-280 E, to The Oranges, Newark, no facilities

45 to US 46, Lake Hiawatha, Whippany, **N**...**gas:** BP, Gulf, **food:** Bennigan's, Chili's, IHOP, Red Lobster, Taco Bell, Wendy's, **lodging:** Holiday Inn/rest., Howard Johnson, Ramada Ltd, Red Roof Inn, **other:** Drug Fair, K-Mart, ShopRite Foods, Staples, **services on US 46...food:** Applebee's, Boston Mkt, Burger King, Eccola Rest., Empire Diner, Outback Steaks, Perkins, **other:** CompUSA, Firestone/auto, PathMark Foods, **S...lodging:** Sheraton Tara

43b a I-287, to US 46, Boonton, Morristown, no facilities

42b a US 202, US 46, to Morris Plains, Parsippany, **N**...**gas:** Gulf, Hess, Shell, Sunoco, **food:** Fuddrucker's, TGIFriday, **lodging:** Courtyard, Day's Inn, Hampton Inn, **other:** Chrysler/Plymouth/Dodge, Ford/Daewoo, Pontiac, Subaru, same as 39

39 (38 from eb), US 46 E, to NJ 53, Denville, **N**...**gas:** Exxon, Gulf, Sunoco, **food:** Banzai Steaks, Blimpie, Burger King, Charlie Brown's Rest., Wendy's, **other:** HOSPITAL, BMW, Chevrolet, Discount Tire, Firestone, PathMark Foods, **S**...**gas:** Shell

293

Interstate 80

E ↑

37	NJ 513, to Hibernia, Rockaway, **N...gas:** Exxon/diesel, Shell/24hr, **food:** Damon's, Hibernia Diner, **lodging:** Best Western, Hampton Inn, **S...gas:** Mobil, **other:** HOSPITAL
35b a	to Dover, Mount Hope, **S...gas:** Exxon/24hr, **food:** Peking Garden, Sizzler, 13 Eateries, **lodging:** Hilton Garden, **other:** HOSPITAL, Acme Foods, Best Buy, JC Penney, Lord&Taylor, Macy's, Sears/auto, mall
34b a	NJ 15, to Sparta, Wharton, **N...gas:** Exxon/diesel, **food:** Donut Towne, McDonald's, Subway, **other:** HOSPITAL, Rite Aid, **S...food:** King's Chinese, Townsquare Diner, **other:** HOSPITAL, Costco, Home Depot, OfficeMax, ShopRite Foods
32mm	truck rest area wb, no facilities
30	Howard Blvd, to Mt Arlington, **N...gas:** Exxon/diesel/24hr, **food:** China City, Cracker Barrel, Davy's Hotdogs, IHOP, **lodging:** Courtyard, Holiday Inn Express, **other:** QuickChek Foods, truck parking
28	NJ 10, to Ledgewood, Lake Hopatcong, **S...gas:** Royal/diesel/repair, **food:** Cliff's Grill, **lodging:** Day's Inn, **other:** ShopRite Foods, Toyota, **1 mi S...gas:** Hess/diesel, Shell, **food:** Burger King, Blimpie, Boston Mkt, ChiChi's, Dunkin Donuts, McDonald's, Pizza Hut, Red Lobster, Roy Rogers, Subway, Taco Bell, TCBY, Wendy's, **lodging:** Day's Inn, **other:** ShopRite Foods, Toyota
27	US 206 S, NJ 182, to Netcong, Somerville, **N...gas:** Mobil/diesel, **food:** Perkins, **lodging:** Day's Inn, **other:** Ford, **S...gas:** Shell/diesel/24hr, **food:** Chili's, Longhorn Steaks, Macaroni Grill, Subway, Wendy's, **lodging:** Extended Stay America, **other:** Lowe's Whse, Michael's, Old Navy, Panera Bread, Sam's Club, TJMaxx, Wal-Mart
26	US 46 W(from wb, no EZ return), to Budd Lake, **S...gas:** Shell/diesel, same as 27
25	US 206 N, to Newton, Stanhope, **1-2mi N...gas:** Exxon/24hr, Shell/diesel, **food:** Dunkin Doughnuts, McDonald's, Subway, **lodging:** Wyndham Garden, **other:** ShopRite Foods, to Waterloo Village, Int Trade Ctr
23.5mm	Musconetcong River
21mm	**rest area both lanes, NO TRUCKS, scenic overlook(eb), phone, picnic tables, litter barrels, petwalk**
19	NJ 517, to Hackettstown, Andover, **N...RV camping, 1-2 mi S...gas:** Shell, **food:** Big Scoop Cafe, BLD's Rest., Panther Valley Inn/rest., **other:** HOSPITAL
12	NJ 521, to Blairstown, Hope, **N...food:** Maxwell House Rest., Nathan's Rest., **other:** Harley-Davidson, **1 mi S...gas:** Shell, **lodging:** Millrace Pond Inn, **other:** RV camping(5mi), Land of Make Believe, Jenny Jump SF
7mm	**rest area eb, full(handicapped)facilities, info, phone, picnic tables, litter barrels, vending, petwalk**
6mm	scenic overlook wb, no trailers

W ↓

Stanhope

4c	to NJ 94 N(from eb), to Blairstown, no facilities
4b	to US 46 E, to Buttzville, no facilities
4a	NJ 94, to US 46 E, to Portland, Columbia, **N...gas:** TA/BP/Taco Bell/diesel/24hr/@, **food:** McDonald's, Pizza Hut, **lodging:** Knight's Inn, **other:** RV camping, **S...gas:** Shell/diesel/24hr
3.5mm	Hainesburg Rd(from wb), accesses services at 4
2mm	weigh sta eb
1mm	**Worthington SF, S...rest area both lanes, restrooms, info, picnic tables, litter barrels, petwalk**
1	to Millbrook(from wb), **N...**Worthington SF
0mm	New Jersey/Pennsylvania state line, Delaware River

Interstate 95

Exit #	Services
124mm	New Jersey/New York state line, Geo Washington Br, Hudson River
123mm	Palisades Pkwy(from sb), no facilities
72(122)	US 1, US 9, US 46, Ft Lee, **E...gas:** Mobil, Shell, **lodging:** Courtesy Motel, Hilton
71(121)	Broad Ave, Leonia, Englewood, **E...gas:** Shell, **W...gas:** Gulf, **lodging:** Day's Inn, Executive Inn
70(120)	to NJ 93, , Leonia, Teaneck, **W...lodging:** Marriott
69(119)	I-80 W(from sb), to Paterson, no facilities
68(118)	US 46, Challenger Blvd, Ridgefield Park, **E...gas:** Exxon, **lodging:** Hampton Inn
	I-95 and NJ Turnpike run together sb
See NJ TPK, exits 7a through 18.	
	I-95 nb becomes I-295 sb at US 1.
67b a	US 1, to Trenton, New Brunswick, **E...gas:** Shell/24hr, **food:** Michael's Diner, **lodging:** Howard Johnson, Sleepy Hollow Motel, **other:** Acura, Dodge/Isuzu, Lincoln/Mercury, Mercedes, Toyota, Volvo, **1-3 mi W...gas:** BP/diesel/24hr, Mobil/Circle K/Blimpie/diesel, **food:** Applebee's, Asia Palace, Charlie Brown's Steaks, Chevy's Mexican, Chili's, Denny's, Hooters, Joe's Crabshack, Macaroni Grill, NY Deli, Olive Garden, On-the-Border, Pizza Hut, Princetonian Diner, Red Lobster, TGIFriday, Wendy's, **lodging:** AmeriSuites, Best Western, Extended Stay America, McIntosh Inn, Red Roof Inn, **other:** Barnes&Noble, Best Buy, BMW, Chevrolet, Circuit City, Drug Emporium, Firestone/auto, Home Depot, JC Penney, K-Mart, Lexus, Lord&Taylor, Lowe's Whse, Macy's, Marshall's, Mini, NTB, OfficeMax, PepBoys, Ross, Shop Rite Foods, Staples, TJ Maxx, Wal-Mart, mall
8	NJ 583, NJ 546, to Princeton Pike, no facilities
7b a	US 206, **W...gas:** Mobil/24hr, **food:** Lawrenceville Deli
5b a	Federal City Rd(sb only), no facilities
4b a	NJ 31, to Ewing, Pennington, **E...gas:** Exxon, **other:** ShopRite Foods(3mi), **W...gas:** Mobil/Blimpie/diesel
3b a	Scotch Rd, **E...gas:** Sunoco/diesel(2mi), **lodging:** Courtyard
2	NJ 579, to Harbourton, **E...gas:** Exxon(1mi), Mobil(1mi), **other:** Marrazzo's Mkt, 7-11, **W...gas:** BP
1	1 NJ 29, to Trenton, **2 mi W...**museum, st police
0mm	New Jersey/Pennsylvania state line, Delaware River

N ↑ **S**

Trenton

Turnpike

Exit #	Services

18(117) US 46 E, Ft Lee, Hackensack, last exit before toll sb

17(116) Lincoln Tunnel

115mm **Vince Lombardi Service Plaza nb...Sunoco/ diesel, Big Boy, Nathan's, Roy Rogers, TCBY, gifts**

114mm toll plaza, phone

16W(113) NJ 3, Secaucus, Rutherford, **E...gas:** Hess, Shell, **lodging:** Hilton, M Plaza Hotel, **W...lodging:** Sheraton, **other:** Meadowlands

112mm **Alexander Hamilton Service Area sb...Sunoco, Roy Rogers, gifts**

16E(112) NJ 3, Secaucus, **E...**Lincoln Tunnel

15W(109) I-280, Newark, The Oranges, no facilities

15E(107) US 1, US 9, Newark, Jersey City, **E...**Lincoln Tunnel

14c Holland Tunnel

14b Jersey City, no facilities

14a Bayonne, no facilities

14(105) I-78 W, US 1, US 9, **2 mi W...lodging:** Holiday Inn, Marriott, Radisson, **other:** airport

102mm **Halsey Service Area, Sunoco, Roy Rogers, other services in Elizabeth**

13a(102) Elizabeth, **E...**Ikea Furnishings, **W...lodging:** Hilton, Wyndham Garden

13(100) I-278, to Verrazano Narrows Bridge, no facilities

12(96) Carteret, Rahway, **E...food:** McDonald's, **lodging:** Holiday Inn

93mm **Cleveland Service Area nb...gas: Sunoco/diesel, food: Roy Rogers, TCBY, T Edison Service Area sb...gas: Sunoco/diesel, food: Big Boy, Dunkin Donuts, Roy Rogers, Starbucks, TCBY**

11(91) US 9, Garden State Pkwy, to Woodbridge, **E...**Home Depot

10(88) I-287, NJ 514, to Perth Amboy, **W...gas:** Hess/diesel, **lodging:** Holiday Inn, Ramada/rest.

9(83) US 1, NJ 18, to New Brunswick, E Brunswick, **E...gas:** Gulf, Hess/diesel, **food:** Grand Buffet, **lodging:** Motel 6, Ramada Inn, **other:** Eckerd, Radio Shack, **W...gas:** Exxon, **food:** Bennigan's, Fuddrucker's, **lodging:** Hilton, Howard Johnson Express

79mm Kilmer Service Area, **Kilmer Service Area nb...gas: Sunoco/diesel, food: Burger King, Sbarro's, Starbuck's, TCBY, other: gifts**

8a(74) to Jamesburg, Cranbury, **E...lodging:** Holiday Inn/rest., **W...lodging:** Courtyard

72mm **Pitcher Service Area sb...gas: Sunoco/diesel, food: Burger King, Cinnabon, Country Kitchen, Nathan's, Roy Rogers, Sbarro's Mexican, Starbuck's, TCBY**

8(67) NJ 33, NJ 571, Hightstown, **E...gas:** Exxon/diesel, Hess/diesel, Mobil, Shell, **food:** 8 Diner, Prestige Diner, **lodging:** Day's Inn, Ramada Inn, **other:** Thriftway Foods, **W...food:** Coach&4 Rest., **lodging:** TownHouse Motel

7a(60) I-195 W to Trenton, E to Neptune, no facilities

59mm **Richard Stockton Service Area sb...gas: Sunoco/diesel, food: Blimpie, Pizza Hut, Roy Rogers, Starbuck's, TCBY, Woodrow Wilson Service Area nb...gas: Sunoco, food: Roy Rogers**

Camden

7(54) US 206, to Bordentown, to Ft Dix, McGuire AFB, to I-295, Trenton, **Services W on US 206...gas:** Mobil/diesel, Petro/diesel/rest./24hr/@, Pilot/Wendy's/diesel/@, Sunoco, WaWa, **food:** Burger King, Denny's, **lodging:** Best Western/rest., Comfort Inn, Day's Inn/rest., Hampton Inn, Ramada Inn, **other:** RV Ctr

6(51) I-276, to Pa Turnpike, no facilities

5(44) to Mount Holly, Willingboro, **E...gas:** US gas/diesel, **food:** Applebee's, Cracker Barrel, Karma Rest., McDonald's, **lodging:** Best Western, Hampton Inn, Howard Johnson, **W...gas:** Exxon/diesel, GasWay, Mobil, **food:** Applebee's, Burger King, TGIFriday, **lodging:** Best Western, Econolodge, Holiday Inn Express, **other:** $Tree, Home Depot, Kohl's, Target

39mm **James Fenimore Cooper Service Area nb...gas: Sunoco/diesel, food: Burger King, Cinabon, Popeye's, Roy Rogers, TCBY, other: gifts**

4(34) NJ 73, to Philadelphia, Camden, **E...gas:** Exxon, Mobil/Circle K/diesel, 7-11, **food:** Bennigan's, Cracker Barrel, Chili's, Copperfield's Rest., Denny's, Macaroni Grill, McDonald's, Sage Rest., Wendy's, **lodging:** Candlewood Suites, Comfort Inn, Extended Stay America, Hampton Inn, Howard Johnson, McIntosh Inn, Studio+, Wyndham Hotel, **other:** Cadillac, Ford, Saturn, West Marine, **1-2 mi W...gas:** Exxon, Gulf/diesel, Hess, Mobil/diesel, Shell, Texaco, **food:** Bob Evans, Burger King, Dunkin Donuts, KFC, Pizza Hut, **lodging:** Courtyard, Day's Inn, DoubleTree Motel, Econolodge, Fairfield Inn, Laurel Place Inn, Hampton Inn, Motel 6, Radisson, Ramada Inn/rest., Red Roof Inn, Super 8, Track&Turf Motel, **other:** Lincoln/Mercury, Mazda, transmissions, to st aquarium

30mm Walt Whitman Service Area, **Walt Whitman Service Area sb...gas: Sunoco, food: Cinnabon, Roy Rogers, Nathan's, TCBY, other: gifts**

3(26) NJ 168, Atlantic City Expwy, Walt Whitman Br, Camden, Woodbury, **E...gas:** WaWa, **lodging:** Blemawr Motel, Comfort Inn, Holiday Inn, **other:** CVS Drug, **W...gas:** BP, Coastal, Valero, Xtra/diesel, **food:** Dunkin Donuts, Papa John's, Pizza Hut, Wendy's, **lodging:** Econolodge

2(13) US 322, to Swedesboro, **W...gas:** Shell/diesel

5mm **Barton Service Area sb...gas: Sunoco, Burger King, Nathan's, Pizza Hut, Starbuck's, TCBY, Fenwick Service Area nb...gas: Sunoco, food: TCBY**

NEW JERSEY

Turnpike

1(1.2)	Deepwater, **W...gas:** Mobil/diesel, Pilot/Subway/diesel/24hr/@, **lodging:** Comfort Suites, Friendship Motor Inn, Holiday Inn, Welsley Inn
1mm	toll road begins/ends
2(I-295)	I-295 N divides from toll road, I-295 S converges with toll road, no facilities
1(I-295)	NJ 49, to Pennsville, **E...gas:** Exxon, **food:** Burger King, McDonald's, **W...lodging:** Seaview Motel
0mm	New Jersey/Delaware state line, Delaware River, Delaware Memorial Bridge

Interstate 195

Exit #	Services
36	Garden State Parkway N. I-195 begins/ends on GS Pkwy, exit 99.
35b a	NJ 34, to Brielle, GS Pkwy S., Pt Pleasant, **2 mi S...gas:** Exxon/diesel/24hr, Getty, Sunoco/diesel
31b a	NJ 547, NJ 524, to Farmingdale, **N...food:** Mulligan's Grill, Woodside Grill, to Allaire SP
28b a	US 9, to Freehold, Lakewood, **N...gas:** Mobil/Circle K/diesel, **food:** ChapterHouse Cafe, Ivy League Rest., Lino's Pizza, Stewart's RootBeer, White Castle/24hr, **other:** bank, **S...gas:** Exxon/24hr, Getty, Gulf, Mobil/diesel/24hr, WaWa, **food:** Applebee's, Arby's, Boston Mkt, Burger King, Blimie, China Moon, Dunkin Doughnuts/Togo's, Jersey Mike's, McDonald's, Taco Bell, **lodging:** Capri Motel(3mi), **other:** GNC, K-Mart, Lowe's Whse, PathMark Foods, PepBoys, Radio Shack, Staples, Target
22	to Jackson Mills, Georgia, **N...**to Turkey Swamp Park, **2 mi S...food:** McDonald's, **other:** ShopRite Foods
21	NJ 526, NJ 527, to Jackson, Siloam, no facilities
16	NJ 537, to Freehold, **N...gas:** BP/24hr, Remington/diesel/LP, Sunoco, **food:** FoodCourt, Java Moon Café, Luigi's Pizza, S&S Deli, **other:** HOSPITAL, 6 Flags Outlet/famous brands, **S...gas:** Wawa/diesel/24hr, **food:** BellVictoria Pizzaria, Burger King, KFC, McDonald's, Millstone Rest., Red Cedar Pizza/Mexican, **other:** 6Flags Themepark
11	NJ 524, Imlaystown, **S...**to Horse Park of NJ
8	NJ 539, Allentown, **S...gas:** BP/repair, Mobil(1mi), **food:** American Hero Deli, **other:** Crosswicks HP
7	NJ 526(no eb return), Robbinsville, Allentown, **1 mi S...food:** La Piazza Ristorante
6	NJ Tpk, N to NY, S to DE Memorial Br, no facilities
5b a	US 130, **N...gas:** Delta/diesel, **food:** A Better Pizza, Ruster's Deli, ShrimpKing Rest., **other:** Harley-Davidson, **S...gas:** GardenState Fuel/diesel, **food:** Chick-fil-A, Chili's, Cracker Barrel, Savoy's Rest., Ruby Tuesday, Wendy's, **lodging:** Econolodge(4mi), **other:** BJ's Wholesale, Harry's Army Navy, Home Depot, Kohl's, Lowe's Whse, Michael's, Ross, USPO, Wal-Mart/auto, mall, to state aquarium
3b a	Hamilton Square, Yardville, **N...**HOSPITAL
2	US 206 S, S Broad St, Yardville, **N...gas:** 7-11, **food:** Taco Bell, **S...gas:** BP, Shell, **food:** Burger King, Ivy Rest., McDonald's, Wendy's, **other:** Acme Foods
1b a	US 206, **N...food:** Fortune House, Taco Bell, **S...other:** ShopRite Foods
0mm	I-295, I-195 begins/ends.

Interstate 287

Exit #	Services
68mm	New Jersey/New York state line
66	NJ 17 S, Mahwah, **1-3 mi E...gas:** Getty, Gulf, Mahwah Fuel/deli, Mobil/Subway/diesel, 17 Trkstp, **food:** Burger King, Mason Jar Rest., McDonald's, 17 Diner, **lodging:** Best Western, Comfort Inn, Courtyard, Doubletree, Homewood Suites, Sheraton, Wellesley Inn
59	NJ 208 S, Franklin Lakes, **W...food:** Blimpie, **other:** Super Stop'n Shop Foods
58	US 202, Oakland, **E...gas:** Mobil, **W...gas:** Exxon/24hr, **food:** Mike's Doghouse, **other:** ShopRite Foods
57	Skyline Dr, Ringwood, no facilities
55	NJ 511, Pompton Lakes, **E...other:** A&P, **W...gas:** Getty/diesel, **food:** Burger King, Dunkin Doughnuts, **other:** SuperFoodTown
53	NJ 511A, rd 694, Bloomingdale, Pompton Lakes, **E...gas:** Sunoco, Valero, **food:** Blimpie
52b a	NJ 23, Riverdale, Wayne, Butler, **E...gas:** BP, Mobil, Sunoco/diesel, **food:** Fuddrucker's(3mi), **lodging:** Welsley Motel(3mi), **other:** HOSPITAL, A&P, Buick/Pontiac/GMC, **W...gas:** Mobil, Shell/24hr, **food:** McDonald's, Ruppert's Rest.
47	US 202, Montville, Lincoln Park, **E...gas:** Exxon/24hr, **food:** Harrigan's Rest.
45	Myrtle Ave, Boonton, **W...gas:** Citgo, Exxon, **food:** Dunkin Donuts, McDonald's, Subway, **other:** A&P/24hr, Buick/GMC, Drug Fair, GNCc
43	Intervale Rd, to Mountain Lakes, **E...gas:** Shell, **W...**Dodge
42	US 46, US 202(from sb only), **W...gas:** Exxon, Shell, Sunoco, **food:** Applebee's, Dunkin Doughnuts, Fuddrucker's, McDonald's, Subway, **lodging:** Courtyard, Day's Inn, Embassy Suites, Garden Suites, Hampton Inn, **other:** Chrysler/Jeep/Pontiac/Subaru, Dodge, Ford, GNC
41b a	I-80, E to New York, W to Delaware Water Gap
40	NJ 511, Parsippany Rd, to Whippany, **W...gas:** Mobil, Shell/diesel, Woroco Gas, **food:** Frank&Son Pizza, Fuddrucker's(2mi), McDonald's, Wok's Chinese, Subway, **lodging:** Embassy Suites(1mi)
39b a	NJ 10, Dover, Whippany, **E...lodging:** Ramada Inn, **other:** PathMark Foods, **W...gas:** Mobil, **food:** Hong Kong Buffet, McDonald's, Wendy's, **lodging:** Hilton Garden, Marriott, Welsley Motel, **other:** Barnes&Noble, Buick/GMC/Isuzu, Stop'n Shop Foods
37	NJ 24 E, Springfield, no facilities
36b a	rd 510, Morris Ave, Lafayette, no facilities
35	NJ 124, South St, Madison Ave, Morristown, **E...food:** Friendly's, **W...lodging:** Best Western, HQ Plaza Hotel, **other:** HOSPITAL
33	Harter Rd, no facilities
33mm	**rest area nb, full(handicapped)facilities, phone, picnic tables, litter barrels, vending, petwalk**
30b a	to US 202, N Maple Ave, Basking Ridge, **E...food:** Ironwood Rest., **lodging:** North Maple Inn, **W...gas:** Gulf, **food:** Burger King, Friendly's, GrainHouse Rest., Thirsty Turtle Rest., **lodging:** Olde Mill Inn/rest.

Interstate 287

N ↕ **S**

26b a	rd 525 S, Mt Airy Rd, Liberty Corner, **3 mi E...gas:** Exxon/24hr, **lodging:**Courtyard, Summerset Hotel, **other:** Quick-Pik Foods
22b a	US 202, US 206, Pluckemin, Bedminster, **E...gas:** Exxon, **food:** Burger King, Golden Chinese, **other:** King's Foods, **W...gas:** Shell, **food:** Dunkin Donuts
21b a	I-78, E to NY, W to PA, no facilities
17	US 206(from sb), Bridgewater, **E...other:** Buick, **W...gas:** Hess, **food:** TGIFriday, **other:** Best Buy, Borders Books, Lord&Taylor, Macy's, OfficeMax, mall
14b a	US 22, to US 202/206, **E...gas:** Hess/diesel, **other:** Chevrolet/Lexus, **W...gas:** BP, **food:** Felix #9 Diner, Fuddrucker's, Red Lobster, **lodging:** Day's Inn, Red Bull Inn, **other:** Acura, Mercedes
13b a	NJ 28, Bound Brook, **E...gas:** BP/24hr, Mobil/diesel, **food:** Burger King, Costa del Sol Mexican, Dunkin Doughnuts, Good Time Buffet, Joey's Grill, King Lobster Buffet, Subway, **other:** ShopRite Foods, Walgreen, **W...food:** Applebee's, ChuckeCheese, McDonald's, **lodging:** Hilton Garden, **other:** HOSPITAL, Costco, Home Depot, Marshall's, Michael's, Old Navy, PepBoys, Target
12	Weston Canal Rd, Manville, **E...gas:** Shell, **W... food:** SportsTime Rest., **lodging:** Ramada Inn
10	NJ 527, Easton Ave, New Brunswick, **E...lodging:** Marriott, **W...gas:** BP, **lodging:** Courtyard, Holiday Inn, Doubletree, Hampton Inn, Staybridge Suites, **other:** HOSPITAL, Garden State Exhibit Ctr
9	NJ 514, River Rd, **W...lodging:** Embassy Suites, Sheraton
8.5mm	weigh sta nb
8	Possumtown Rd, Highland Park, no facilities
7	S Randolphville Rd, Piscataway, **E...gas:** Mobil
6	Washington Ave, Piscataway, **W...food:** Applebee's, BBQ, TGIFriday, Johnny Careno's, Longhorn Steaks, **other:** ShopRite Foods, same as 5
5	NJ 529, Stelton Rd, Dunellen, **E...gas:** Gulf, Mobil, Shell, Texaco/diesel, **food:** KFC, Piancone Ristorante, **lodging:** Ramada Ltd, **other:** Home Depot, NAPA, **W...gas:** Exxon, **food:** Burger King, Friendly's, Gianni Pizza, Grand Buffet, McDonald's, Red Lobster, Taco Bell, Uno Pizzaria, Wendy's, **lodging:** Best Western, Day's Inn, Motel 6, Holiday Inn, **other:** K-Mart, Lowe's Whse, OfficeMax, PathMark Foods, Pep Boys, Radio Shack, Staples, Stern's, Wal-Mart/auto
4	Durham Ave(no EZ nb return), S Plainfield, **E...gas:** Mobil/diesel, **other:** HOSPITAL
3	New Durham Rd(from sb), **E...gas:** Shell, **W...lodging:** Red Roof Inn, **other:** Walgreen
2b a	NJ 27, Metuchen, New Brunswick, **W...gas:** BP, Mobil, **other:** Costco
1b a	US 1, **1-2 mi N on US 1...gas:** Exxon/diesel, Getty, RaceWay, **food:** Bennigan's, Blimpie, Boston Mkt, ChiChi's, Dunkin Donuts, KFC, Macaroni Grill, McDonald's, Menlo Park Diner, Red Lobster, Ruby Tuesday, Sizzler, Steak&Ale, Uno Pizzaria, Wendy's,

Trenton (vertical, right margin)

White Castle, **lodging:** Lee's Motel, Roosevelt Motel, **other:** Best Buy, Drug Fair, Ford, Goodyear/auto, Macy's, Marshall's, Nordstrom's, Sears/auto, ShopRite Foods, Staples, Stern's, mall, **S...gas:** Shell, **food:** Applebee's, Boston Mkt, Burger King, ChuckECheese, Grand Buffet, McDonald's, **lodging:** Wellesley Inn, **other:** BJ's Whse, BMW, CompUSA, Home Depot, Infiniti, Mercedes, Office Depot, PepBoys, Stop&Shop Foods
I-287 begins/ends on NJ 440.

Interstate 295

Exit #	Services
67b a	US 1. I-295 nb becomes I-95 sb at US 1. See NJ I-95, exit 67b a.
65b a	Sloan Ave, **E...gas:** Exxon, **food:** Burger King, Subway, Taco Bell, Uno Pizzaria, **other:** CVS Drug, Goodyear, ShopRite Foods
64	NJ 535 N(from sb), to NJ 33 E, same as 63
63b a	NJ 33 W, rd 535, Mercerville, Trenton, **E...gas:** Mobil, **food:** Aladdin's Cafe, Applebee's, Boston Mkt, Lobster Dock, McDonald's, Pizza Hut, Popeye's, Vincent's Pizza, Wendy's, **other:** Ford/Lincoln/Mercury, auto repair, **W...gas:** Exxon/24hr, **food:** Dunkin Donuts, Golden Gate Diner/24hr, WaWa, **other:** Advance Parts
62	Olden Ave N(from sb, no return), **W...gas:** Delta
61b a	Arena Dr, White Horse Ave, **W...gas:** 7-11
60b a	I-195, to I-95, W to Trenton, E to Neptune, no facilities
58mm	scenic overlook both lanes
57b a	US 130, US 206, **E...gas:** Mobil, Shell/24hr, **food:** Burger King, Denny's, McDonald's, Rosario's Pizza, **lodging:** Best Western, Comfort Inn, Day's Inn, Econolodge, Hampton Inn, **other:** Acme Foods, **W...st police**
56	US 206 S(from nb, no return), to NJ Tpk, Ft Dix, McGuire AFB, **E...gas:** Sunoco, **lodging:** Day's Inn, Holiday Inn Express, same as 57
52b a	rd 656, to Columbus, Florence, **E...gas:** Petro/diesel/rest./24hr/@, Pilot/Wendy's/diesel/24hr/@
50mm	**rest area both lanes(7am-11pm), full(handicapped)facilities, phone, picnic tables, litter barrels, vending**
47b a	NJ 541, to Mount Holly, NJ Tpk, Burlington, **E...gas:** Exxon/diesel/24hr, GasWay, Mobil/diesel, **food:** Applebee's, Burger King, ChuckECheese, Cracker Barrel, FoodCourt, McDonald's, Taco Bell, TGIFriday, **lodging:** Best Western, Econolodge, Hampton Inn, Holiday Inn Express, Howard Johnson, **other:** MEDICAL CARE, $Express, Home Depot, Kohl's, OfficeMax, Sears, Target, mall, **W...gas:** Exxon, Gulf/repair, Hess/diesel, **food:** Checker's, Friendly's, Subway, Wedgewood Farms Rest., Wendy's, **other:** HOSPITAL, AutoZone, Acme Foods, K-Mart, Marshall's, Wal-Mart/auto

N ↕ **S** (right margin, Interstate 295)

N ↑↓ **S**

C h e r r y   H i l l

45b a to Mt Holly, Willingboro, **W...gas:** Mobil, **other:** HOSPITAL, auto repair

43b a rd 636, to Rancocas Woods, Delran, **W...gas:** Exxon/24hr, **food:** Carlucci's Rest.

40b a NJ 38, to Mount Holly, Moorestown, **W...gas:** Exxon/Subway/diesel/24hr, Mobil, **food:** Dunkin Doughnuts, FoodCourt, Perkins(3mi), **lodging:** Quality Inn(4mi), **other:** HOSPITAL, Acme Foods, Fall's Food, Target, U-Haul

36b a NJ 73, to NJ Tpk, Tacony Br, Berlin, **E...gas:** Exxon, Mobil/Circle K/diesel/24hr, **food:** Bennigan's, Bob Evans, Denny's, McDonald's, Sage Diner, Wendy's, **lodging:** Comfort Inn, Courtyard, Day's Inn, Econolodge, Fairfield Inn, Hampton Inn, Howard Johnson, Laurel Inn, McIntosh Inn, Radisson, Red Roof Inn, Super 8, Travelodge, Wingate Inn, **W...gas:** Amoco, Citgo, Shell, Texaco/diesel/24hr, **food:** Bertucci's, Boston Mkt, Burger King, Chick-fil-A, Don Pablo, Dunkin Donuts, KFC, McDonald's, Friendly's, Old Town Buffet, Panera Bread, Perkins, Pizza Hut, Ponderosa, Taco Bell, Togo's, Wendy's, **lodging:** Bel-Air Motel, Crossland Suites, Motel 6, Quality Inn, Rodeway Inn, Track&Turf Motel, **other:** Acura, Barnes&Noble, Best Buy, Chrysler, Circuit City, CompUSA, $Tree, Drug Emporium, Firestone/auto, Filene's, Ford, Goodyear/auto, Home Depot, Infiniti, K-Mart, Lexus, Loehmann's, Lord&Taylor, Lowe's Whse, Mitsubishi, NTB, OfficeMax, Old Navy, PepBoys, Ross, Sears/auto, ShopRite Foods, mall

34b a NJ 70, to Camden, Cherry Hill, **E...gas:** BP, Exxon/24hr, **food:** Big John's Steaks, Burger King, Dunkin Donuts, Friendly's, Korea Garden Rest., McDonald's, Pizzaria Uno, **lodging:** Extended Stay America, Marriott, Residence Inn, **other:** STS Tire/auto, **W...gas:** Mobil/repair/24hr, Shell/diesel, **food:** Denny's, Elephant & Castle, Old Country Buffet, Steak&Ale, **lodging:** Clarion, Hilton(3mi), Holiday Inn(3mi), Howard Johnson(4mi), **other:** HOSPITAL, Magaziner's Drug

32 NJ 561, to Haddonfield, Voorhees, **3 mi E...gas:** Mobil/diesel/24hr, **food:** Applebee's, FoodCourt, Fuddruckers, Olive Garden, **lodging:** Hampton Inn, Wingate Inn, **other:** HOSPITAL, USPO, **W...gas:** Shell, **food:** Burger King, **other:** Giant Foods, Ford

31 Woodcrest Station, no facilities

30 Warwick Rd(from sb), no facilities

29b a US 30, to Berlin, Collingswood, **E...gas:** BP, Gulf, Exxon, **food:** Church's, KFC, Wendy's, **other:** AutoZone, Drug Emporium, Home Depot, K-Mart, PathMark Foods, transmissions

28 NJ 168, to NJ Tpk, Belmawr, Mt Ephraim, **E...gas:** BP, Coastal/diesel, Shell/diesel, Xtra/diesel, Valero/diesel, **food:** Burger King, Club Diner, Dunkin Donuts, Italia Pizza, Wendy's, **lodging:** Bellmawr Motel, Comfort Inn, Econolodge, Holiday Inn, Howard Johnson, Super 8, **other:** $Land, Walgreen, **W...gas:** BP, Exxon/LP/24hr, **food:** McDonald's, Subway, Taco Bell, **lodging:** Budget Inn, **other:** AutoZone, CVS Drug

26 I-76, NJ 42, to I-676, Walt Whitman Bridge, Walt Whitman Bridge

25b a NJ 47, to Westville, Deptford, no facilities

24b a NJ 45, NJ 551(no EZ sb return), to Westville, **E...gas:** Getty, **other:** HOSPITAL, **W...**Chevrolet

23 US 130 N, to National Park, no facilities

22 NJ 644, to Red Bank, Woodbury, **E...gas:** Mobil, **1 mi W...gas:** Crown Point Trkstp/diesel/@, WaWa, **food:** Wendy's

21 NJ 44 S, Paulsboro, Woodbury, **W...food:** WaWa, Wendy's, **lodging:** Westwood Motor Lodge

20 NJ 643, to NJ 660, to National Park, Thorofare, **E...lodging:** Best Western, **W...lodging:** Red Bank Inn

19 NJ 656, to NJ 44, Mantua, no facilities

18b a NJ 667, to NJ 678, Clarksboro, Mt Royal, **E...gas:** BP/diesel, TA/Exxon/Buckhorn Rest./diesel/rest./@, **food:** Dunkin Donuts, KFC/Taco Bell, McDonald's, Wendy's, **other:** RV camping, **W...gas:** Shell/diesel

17 NJ 680, to Mickleton, Gibbstown, **W...gas:** Mobil, **food:** Burger King, **lodging:** Ramada Inn/rest, **other:** Advance Parts, Family$, GNC, Rite Aid, ShopRite Foods/FoodCourt

16b NJ 551, to Gibbstown, Mickleton, no facilities

16a NJ 653, to Paulsboro, Swedesboro, no facilities

15 NJ 607, to Gibbstown, no facilities

14 NJ 684, to Repaupo, no facilities

13 US 130 S, US 322 W, to Bridgeport(from sb, no return), no facilities

11 US 322 E, to Mullica Hill, no facilities

10 Ctr Square Rd, to Swedesboro, **E...gas:** Exxon/diesel, **food:** Applebee's, Dunkin Doughnuts/Baskin Robbins, McDonald's, Subway, WaWa/deli, Wendy's, **lodging:** Hampton Inn, Holiday Inn Select, **other:** Acme Foods/drug, Eckerd, **W...other:** Camping World RV Supplies/service

7 to Auburn, Pedricktown, **E...gas:** AutoTruck/diesel/rest./motel

4 NJ 48, Woodstown, Penns Grove, no facilities

3mm weigh sta nb

2mm **rest area nb, full(handicapped)facilities, info, phone, picnic table, litter barrels, vending**

2c to US 130(from sb), Deepwater, **W...gas:** All-American Plaza/Exxon/diesel/24hr/@, ⚡/Flying J/CountryMkt/diesel/LP/24hr/@, **other:** HOSPITAL

2b US 40 E, to NJ Tpk, **E...gas:** Mobil/diesel, Pilot/Subway/diesel/24hr/@, **lodging:** Comfort Inn, Econolodge, Friendship Motel, Holiday Inn Express, Quality Inn, Wellesley Inn

2a US 40 W(from nb), to Delaware Bridge

1c NJ 551 S, Hook Rd, to Salem, **E...lodging:** White Oaks Motel, **W...**HOSPITAL

1b US 130 N(from nb), Penns Grove, no facilities

1a NJ 49 E, to Pennsville, Salem, **E...gas:** Exxon/diesel/repair, **food:** Burger King, Cracker Barrel, KFC/Taco Bell, McDonald's, **lodging:** Hampton Inn, **W...gas:** Coastal, **lodging:** Seaview Motel

0mm New Jersey/Delaware state line, Delaware River, Delaware Memorial Bridge

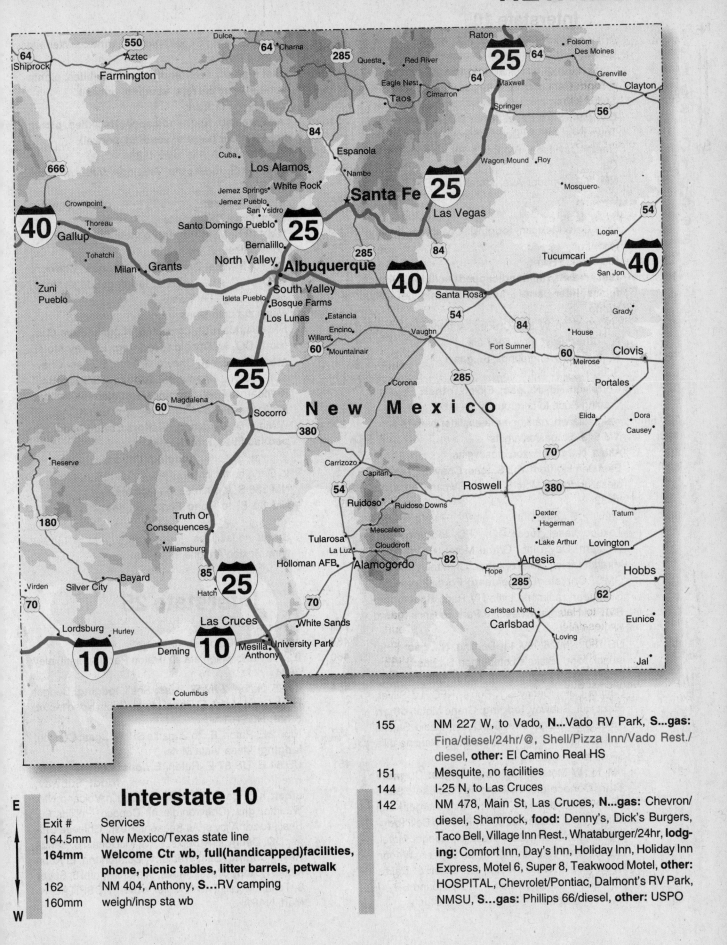

Interstate 10

E↕W

Exit #	Services
164.5mm	New Mexico/Texas state line
164mm	**Welcome Ctr wb, full(handicapped)facilities, phone, picnic tables, litter barrels, petwalk**
162	NM 404, Anthony, **S**...RV camping
160mm	weigh/insp sta wb

155	NM 227 W, to Vado, **N**...Vado RV Park, **S**...gas: Fina/diesel/24hr/@, Shell/Pizza Inn/Vado Rest./diesel, **other:** El Camino Real HS
151	Mesquite, no facilities
144	I-25 N, to Las Cruces
142	NM 478, Main St, Las Cruces, **N**...gas: Chevron/diesel, Shamrock, **food:** Denny's, Dick's Burgers, Taco Bell, Village Inn Rest., Whataburger/24hr, **lodging:** Comfort Inn, Day's Inn, Holiday Inn, Holiday Inn Express, Motel 6, Super 8, Teakwood Motel, **other:** HOSPITAL, Chevrolet/Pontiac, Dalmont's RV Park, NMSU, **S**...gas: Phillips 66/diesel, **other:** USPO

Interstate 10

E / **Las Cruces** / **W**

140 NM 28, Las Cruces, to Mesilla, **N...gas:** Phillips 66/diesel, **food:** Blake's Lotaburger, BurgerTime, Cracker Barrel, McDonald's, **lodging:** Baymont Inn, Best Western, Hampton Inn, La Quinta, SpringHill Suites, **other:** Wal-Mart SuperCtr/24hr, **N on Valley Dr...gas:** Shell/diesel, **food:** DQ, Domino's, Old Town Rest., **other:** Dodge, Toyota, VW, **S...other:** Harley-Davidson, RV Doc's RV Park, S&H RV Ctr

139 NM 292, Amador Ave, Motel Blvd, Las Cruces, **N...gas:** Pilot/Subway/diesel/24hr/@, TA/Burger King/Taco Bell/diesel/rest./24hr/@, **S...food:** Pit-Stop Café Mexican, **lodging:** Coachlight Inn/RV Park

138mm Rio Grande River

135.5mm **rest area eb, full(handicapped)facilities, picnic tables, litter barrels, petwalk, scenic view, RV dump**

135 US 70 E, to W Las Cruces, Alamogordo, **1 mi N...other:** Best View RV Park

132 **N...**to airport, fairgrounds, **S...gas:** Love's/Texaco/Subway/diesel/24hr/@

127 Corralitos Rd, **N...gas:** Exxon, **other:** Bowlin's Trading Post, to fairgrounds

120.5mm weigh sta wb, parking area eb, litter barrels

116 NM 549, **S...gas/café/gifts**

102 Akela, **N...gas:** Exxon/diesel/gifts

85 East Deming(from wb), **S...gas:** Chevron, Texaco/diesel, **lodging:** Motel 6, **other:** RV camping, same as 83

83 Deming, **S...gas:** Chevron/diesel, Fina, Save Gas, Texaco/diesel, **food:** DQ, KFC, **lodging:** Best Western, Day's Inn, Grand Motel, Holiday Inn, Mirador Motel, Motel 6, **other:** Chevrolet/Pontiac/GMC, Chrysler/Dodge/Jeep, Ford, Firestone, Goodyear, radiators, Little RV Park, Roadrunner RV Park, Wagon Wheel RV Park, to Rock Hound SP, st police

82b a US 180, NM 26, NM 11, Deming, **N... gas:** Fina/diesel, **food:** Blake's Lotaburger, **S...gas:** Exxon, Phillips 66, Shell/diesel, **food:** Burger King, Cactus Café, Denny's, K-Bob's, KFC, LJ Silver, Pizza Hut, Subway, **lodging:** Grand Motel, **other:** AutoZone, Budget Tire, CarQuest, Radio Shack, Wal-Mart SuperCtr/24hr, museum, to Pancho Villa SP, Rockhound SP

81 NM 11, W Motel Dr, Deming, **S...gas:** Chevron/24hr, Conoco/diesel, DemingTT/diesel, Save Gas, Shamrock/diesel, **food:** Arby's, Burger King, Burger Time, McDonald's, Sonic, Taco Bell, **lodging:** Balboa Motel, Best Western, Budget Motel, Grand Hotel/rest., Mirador Motel, Super 8, Wagon Wheel Motel, Western Motel/rest., **other:** 81 Palms RV Park, to Pancho Villa SP, Rock Hound SP

68 NM 418, **S...gas:** Savoy/diesel/rest./24hr

62 Gage, **S...gas:** Citgo/DQ/diesel, **other:** Butterfield Station RV Park

61mm **rest area wb, full(handicapped)facilities, picnic tables, litter barrels, vending, petwalk**

55 Quincy, no facilities

53mm **rest area eb, full(handicapped)facilities, picnic tables, litter barrels, vending, petwalk**

51.5mm Continental Divide, elev 4585

49 NM 146 S, to Hachita, Antelope Wells, no facilities

42 Separ, **S...gas:** Chevron/diesel, **other:** Bowlin's Continental Divide Gifts

34 NM 113 S, Muir, Playas, no facilities

29 no facilities

24 US 70, E Motel Dr, Lordsburg, **N...gas:** Chevron, Pilot/Arby's/diesel/24hr/@, **lodging:** Budget Motel, **other:** Range RV Park

23.5mm weigh sta both lanes

22 NM 494, Main St, Lordsburg, **N...gas:** Save Gas, **food:** DQ, McDonald's, **lodging:** Holiday Motel, **other:** CarQuest, Chevrolet, Ford, **S...gas:** Chevron, Exxon, Shamrock, **food:** KFC/Taco Bell, Kranberry's Rest., **lodging:** Best Western, Holiday Inn Express, Motel 10, Super 8, **other:** KOA

20b a W Motel Dr, Lordsburg, **Visitors Ctr/full(handicapped)facilities, info, N...gas:** Love's/Texaco/A&W/Subway/diesel/@, **lodging:** Day's Inn

15 to Gary, no facilities

11 NM 338 S, to Animas, no facilities

5 NM 80 S, to Road Forks, **S...gas:** USA/diesel/rest.

3 Steins, no facilities

0mm New Mexico/Arizona state line

Interstate 25

Exit #	Services

N / **S**

460.5mm New Mexico/Colorado state line

460 **E...**RV Park, weigh sta sb, Raton Pass Summit, elev 7834

454 Lp 25, Raton, **2 mi W...gas:** Shell, **lodging:** Budget Host, Capri Motel, El Portal Motel, Robin Hood Motel, **other:** HOSPITAL

452 NM 72 E, Raton, **E...**to Sugarite SP, **W...gas:** Conoco, **lodging:** Mesa Vista Motel

451 US 64 E, US 87 E, Raton, **E...gas:** Chevron/diesel, Shell/diesel, Total/diesel/24hr, **food:** Subway, **other:** Kick Back RV Park, to Capulin Volcano NM, **W...info, gas:** Chevron/diesel, Conoco, Phillips 66, Shell, **food:** Arby's, All Seasons Rest., Chinese Buffet, DQ, Denny's, K-Bob's, KFC, McDonald's, Sands Rest., **lodging:** Best Western/, Comfort Inn, El Kapp Motel, Holiday Classic Motel, Microtel, Motel 6, Super 8, Texan Motel, Travel Motel, **other:** HOSPITAL, K-Mart, NAPA

Interstate 25

N ↑↓ **S**

450 Lp 25, Raton, **W...gas:** Conoco/diesel, Phillips 66, Shamrock/diesel, **food:** K-Bob's, Pappa's Rest., Rainmaker Café, Sonic, **lodging:** Holiday Inn Express, Maverick Motel, Oasis Motel, Robin Hood Motel, Village Inn Motel, **other:** HOSPITAL, K-Mart, KOA, SuperSave Foods

446 US 64 W, to Cimarron, Taos, **4 mi W...**NRA Whittington Ctr, camping

440mm Canadian River

435 Tinaja, no facilities

434.5mm rest area both lanes, full(handicapped)facilit ies, weather info, picnic tables, litter barrels, petwalk

426 NM 505, Maxwell, **W...**to Maxwell Lakes

419 NM 58, to Cimarron, **E...gas:** Shell/diesel/24hr/@, **food:** Heck's Hungry Traveler Rest.

414 US 56, Springer, **E...gas:** Phillips 66/diesel, **food:** Dairy Delite Café

412 US 56 E, US 412 E, NM 21, NM 468, Springer, **1 mi E...gas:** Shamrock

404 NM 569, Colmor, Charette Lakes, no facilities

393 Levy, no facilities

387 NM 120, to Roy, Wagon Mound, **E...gas:** Chevron/diesel, Phillips 66/diesel

376mm rest area sb, full(handicapped)facilities, phone, picnic tables, litter barrels, petwalk, RV camp/dump

374mm rest area nb, full(handicapped)facilities, phone, picnic tables, litter barrels, petwalk, RV camp/dump

366 NM 97, NM 161, Watrous, Valmora, **W...**Santa Fe Trail, Ft Union NM, no facilities

364 NM 97, NM 161, Watrous, Valmora, no facilities

361 no facilities

360mm rest area both lanes, litter barrels, no facilities

356 Onava, no facilities

352 **E...**RV camping, **W...**airport

347 to NM 518, Las Vegas, **1-2 mi W...gas:** Fina/diesel, Phillips 66/Burger King, **food:** Arby's, DQ, Hillcrest Rest., K-Bob's, KFC, McDonald's, Pizza Hut, Taco Bell, **lodging:** Comfort Inn, Day's Inn, El Camino Motel, Super 8, Townhouse Motel, **other:** KOA, Storrie Lake SP, Las Vegas Civic Ctr

345 NM 65, NM 104, University Ave, Las Vegas, **E...**to Conchas Lake SP, **W...gas:** Fina/diesel, Shell/diesel, **food:** Arby's, Charlie's Cafe, DQ, Hillcrest Rest., KFC, McDonald's, Mexican Kitchen, Pizza Hut, Subway, Taco Bell, Wendy's, **lodging:** Budget Inn, Comfort Inn, El Camino Motel/rest., Palamino Motel, Plaza Hotel/rest., Sante Fe Trail Inn, Sunshine Motel, Townhouse Motel, **other:** HOSPITAL, Firestone, Hist Old Town Plaza

343 to NM 518 N, Las Vegas, **1 mi W...gas:** Chevron, Citgo, Fina, Phillips 66, **food:** Burger King, McDonald's, Taco Bell, Teresa's Mexican, **lodging:** Comfort Inn, Day's Inn, El Camino Motel, Plaza Motel, Santa Fe Trail Inn, Thunderbird Motel

L a s   V e g a s (vertical sidebar)

339 US 84 S, to Santa Rosa, Romeroville, **E...KOA, W...gas:** Shell/diesel

335 Tecolote, no facilities

330 Bernal, no facilities

325mm rest area both lanes, picnic tables, litter barrels, no restroom facilities

323 NM 3 S, Villanueva, **E...**to Villanueva SP, Madison Winery(6mi), RV camping

319 San Juan, San Jose, **3 mi E...gas/diesel, W...**Pecos River RV Camp/phone

307 NM 63, Rowe, Pecos, **W...**Pecos NM

299 NM 50, Glorieta, Pecos, **W...gas:** Fina/diesel(4mi), Shell(6mi), **food:** Renate's Rest., **other:** Glorieta Conf Ctr, Pecos NHP

297 Valencia, no facilities

294 Apache Canyon, **W...other:** KOA, Rancheros Camping(Mar-Nov)

290 US 285 S, to Lamy, S to Clines Corners, **W...other:** KOA, Rancheros Camping(Mar-Nov)

284 NM 466, Old Pecos Trail, Santa Fe, **W...gas:** Chevron/diesel, Sunset Gen Store, **lodging:** to Best Western, Desert Inn, Pecos Trail Inn, The Sands, **other:** HOSPITAL, museums

282 US 84, US 285, St Francis Dr, **W...gas:** Conoco/Wendy's/diesel, Giant, **food:** Church's

278 NM 14, Cerrillos Rd, Santa Fe, **W...lodging:** Sleep Inn, **other:** Santa Fe Outlets/famous brands, **1-4 mi W...gas:** Chevron/diesel/24hr, Conoco, Phillips 66/diesel, Shell, **food:** Applebee's, Arby's, Burger King, China Star, CiCi's, Denny's, Kettle, KFC, LJ Silver, Lotaburger, McDonald's, Olive Garden, Outback Steaks, Panda Express, Pizza Hut, Red Lobster, Schlotsky's, Sonic, Taco Bell, Village Inn Rest., **lodging:** Comfort Inn, Day's Inn, Fairfield Inn, Hampton Inn, Holiday Inn Express, Howard Johnson, La Quinta, Luxury Inn, Motel 6, Quality Inn, Ramada, Red Roof Inn, Santa Fe Lodge, Super 8, **other:** Albertson's, Best Buy, Buick/Pontiac, Chevrolet/GMC, Dillard's, Dodge, Firestone/auto, Ford, Honda/Isuzu, JC Penney, Los Campos RV Resort, PepBoys, Sam's Club, Sears/auto, Subaru, Target, VW, Walgreen, Wal-Mart, mall

276b a NM 599, to NM 14, to Madrid, **E...gas:** Phillips/diesel/24hr, **W...gas:** Conoco, Shell, **other:** Santa Fe Skies RV Park

271 CR 50F, La Cienega, **W...**Pinon RV Park(4mi), racetrack, museum

269mm rest area nb, full(handicapped)facilities, phone, picnic tables, litter barrels, petwalk

267 Waldo Canyon Rd, no facilities

S a n t a   F e (vertical sidebar)

N ↑↓ S

263mm	Galisteo River
259	NM 22, to Santo Domingo Pueblo, **W...gas:** Phillips 66/diesel, **other:** to Cochiti Lake RA
257	Budaghers, **W...**Mormon Battalion Mon
264	NM 16, Cochiti Pueblo, **W...**to Cochiti Lake RA
252	San Felipe Pueblo, **E...gas:** Phillips 66/diesel, **food:** San Felipe Casino/rest.
248	Algodones, no facilities
242	US 540, NM 44 W, NM 165 E, to Farmington, Aztec, **W...gas:** Chevron/diesel, Conoco/diesel, Phillips 66, Texaco/Burger King/diesel, **food:** Coronado Rest., Denny's, KFC, Lotaburger, McDonald's, Pizza Hut, Sonic, Subway, Taco Bell, Village Pizza, Wendy's, **lodging:** Day's Inn, Quality Inn, Super 8, **other:** to Coronado SP
240	NM 473, to Bernalillo, **W...gas:** Conoco/diesel, Fina, **food:** Abuelito's Kitchen, Range Café, **other:** KOA, to Coronado SP
234	NM 556, Tramway Rd, **E...gas:** Shamrock, **W...gas:** Phillips 66
233	Alameda Blvd, **E...gas:** Chevron/Burger King, **food:** Comfort Inn, **other:** Toyota, **W...gas:** Phillips 66/diesel, **food:** Carl's Jr, **lodging:** Holiday Inn Express, Ramada Ltd
232	Paseo del Norte, **E...lodging:** Motel 6, **other:** Lowe's Whse, **W...food:** Arby's, **lodging:** Courtyard, Marriott
231	San Antonio Ave, **E...food:** Cracker Barrel, Kettle, **lodging:** Howard Johnson, La Quinta, Quality Suites, Ramada, **other:** HOSPITAL, **W...lodging:** Baymont Inn, Crossland Suites, Hampton Inn, **other:** Mazda, VW
230	San Mateo Blvd, Osuna Rd, Albuquerque, **E...gas:** Chevron, Circle K, Conoco/diesel, **food:** Applebee's, Arby's, Bennigan's, Black-Eyed Pea, Bob's Burgers, Burger King, Carino's Itallan, Chili's, Hooters, KFC, LJ Silver, Lotaburger, McDonald's, Olive Garden, Pizza Hut/Taco Bell, Schlotsky's, Sizzler, Sonic, Subway, SweetTomato, Taco Cabana, Teriyaki Chicken, Village Inn Rest., Wendy's, Wienerschnitzel, Wild Oats Mkt, **lodging:** Wyndham, **other:** HOSPITAL, Buick/Pontiac/GMC, Mercedes, Nissan, Subaru/Isuzu, Firestone/auto, NAPA, PepBoys, **W...gas:** Shamrock, **food:** Whataburger, Motel 6
229	Jefferson St, **E...food:** Carrabba's, Landry's Seafood, Olive Garden, OutBack Steaks, **other:** HOSPITAL, same as 230, **W...food:** Chang's, Fuddrucker's, Jersey Jack's, Mimi's Café, Pappadeaux, Red Robin, Rockfish Café, Texas Land&Cattle Steaks, **lodging:** Drury Inn, Residence Inn
228	Montgomery Blvd, **E...gas:** Chevron/diesel, Texaco, **food:** Lotaburger, **lodging:** Best Western, **other:** HOSPITAL, Discount Tire, **W...food:** Arby's, Dickie's Smokehouse, IHOP, McDonald's, Panda Express, Starbucks, Wendy's, **lodging:** InTowne Suites
227b	Comanche Rd, Griegos Rd, **E...**UPS Depot
227a	Candelaria Rd, Albuquerque, **E...gas:** Chevron/rest., Circle K, Fina/Subway/diesel, Shell, TA/diesel/24hr/@, **food:** JB's, IHOP, Village Inn Rest., **lodging:** Comfort Inn, Clubhouse Inn, Fairfield Inn, Hilton, Holiday Inn, Rodeway Inn, Motel 6, Super 8, **W...food:** Waffle House, **lodging:** A-1 Motel, Red Roof Inn, **other:** Volvo
226b a	I-40, E to Amarillo, W to Flagstaff, no facilities
225	Lomas Blvd, **E...gas:** Chevron/7-11, **food:** JB's, Plaza Inn/rest., **other:** HOSPITAL, Chevrolet, Dodge, Ford, Saturn
224b	Grand Ave, Central Ave, **W...gas:** Chevron, **lodging:** Econolodge, **other:** HOSPITAL
224a	Lead Ave, Coal Ave, **E...gas:** Texaco, **food:lodging:** Crossroads Motel, **other:** HOSPITAL
223	Chavez Ave, **E...lodging:** Motel 6, **other:** sports facilities
222b a	Gibson Blvd, **E...gas:** Phillips 66, **food:** Applebee's, Burger King, Subway, Waffle House, **lodging:** Country Inn Suites, Courtyard, Hampton Inn, Hawthorn Suites, Quality Suites, Sleep Inn, University Inn, **other:** HOSPITAL, museum, **W...gas:** Fina/7-11, **food:** Church's, LotaBurger
221	Sunport(from nb), **E...lodging:** AmeriSuites, Wyndham, **other:** USPO, airport
220	Rio Bravo Blvd, Mountain View, **E...golf, 2 mi W...gas:** Shamrock, **food:** Burger King, Church's, McDonald's, Pizza Hut, Subway, Taco Bell, **other:** Albertson's, Family$, Walgreen
215	NM 47, **E...gas:** Conoco/diesel, **other:** to Isleta Lakes RA/RV Camping, casino, st police
214mm	Rio Grande
213	NM 314, Isleta Blvd, **W...gas:** Chevron/Subway/diesel/24hr
209	NM 45, to Isleta Pueblo, no facilities
203	NM 6, to Los Lunas, **E...gas:** Chevron/diesel/24hr, Shamrock, Shell/Wendy's/diesel, **food:** Benny's #2, McDonald's, Sonic, Village Inn Rest., **lodging:** Comfort Inn, Day's Inn, **other:** Chevrolet, Ford, Home Depot, **W...gas:** Phillips 66/Subway/diesel, **food:** Carino's Italian, Chili's, KFC, **lodging:** Western Skies Inn, **other:** Wal-Mart SuperCtr/24hr
195	Lp 25, Los Chavez, **1 mi E...food:** McDonald's, Pizza Hut/Taco Bell, **other:** Wal-Mart SuperCtr/gas/24hr
191	NM 548, Belen, **1 mi E...gas:** Conoco, **food:** KFC, McDonald's, Pizza Hut, Subway, **lodging:** Freeway Inn, Super 8, **other:** to Chavez SP, **W...food:** Casa de Mirada Rest./RV Park, Rio Grande Diner, **lodging:** Best Western, Holiday Inn Express, OakTree Inn
190	Lp 25, Belen, **1-2 mi E...gas:** Akins/diesel, Conoco/diesel, Mustang, **food:** Arby's, Casa de Pizza, Circle T Burger, KFC, McDonald's, Pizza Hut, TJ's Mexican, **lodging:** Freeway Inn, Hub Motel, Super 8, **other:** AutoZone, Big O Tire
175	US 60, Bernardo, **E...**Salinas NM, **W...other:** Kiva RV Park
174mm	Rio Puerco, no facilities

Side tab: **Albuquerque** / **Belen**

Interstate 25

N ▲
S ▼

169	**E**...La Joya St Game Refuge, Sevilleta NWR
167mm	**rest area both lanes, full(handicapped)facilities, picnic tables, litter barrels, vending, petwalk**
166mm	Rio Salado, no facilities
165mm	weigh sta nb/parking area both lanes
163	San Acacia, no facilities
156	Lemitar, **W**...Texaco/diesel/24hr/@
152	Escondida, **W**...to st police
150	US 60 W, Socorro, **W**...**gas:** Chevron, Circle K, Exxon/diesel, Phillips 66/diesel, Shell/diesel, **food:** Burger King, Denny's, Domino's, K-Bob's, KFC, Lotaburger, McDonald's, Pizza Hut, RoadRunner Steaks, Sonic, Subway, Taco Bell, Tina's Rest., **lodging:** Best Inn, Best Western, Economy Inn, Econolodge, El Camino Motel/rest., Holiday Inn Express, Payless Inn, Rio Grande Motel/rest., Sands Motel, San Miguel Inn, Super 8, **other:** Alco, Chevrolet/Pontiac/Buick, Chrysler/Dodge/Jeep, Ford/Mercury, NAPA, Radio Shack, Smith's Foods, to NM Tech
147	US 60 W, Socorro, **W**...**gas:** Chevron/diesel/RV dump, Conoco/LP, Shell/diesel, Texaco/diesel, **food:** Arby's, Armijo's Mexican, Denny's, KFC, Pizza Hut, **lodging:** Holiday Inn Express, Motel 6, Sands Motel, **other:** HOSPITAL, Parts+, TrueValue, Socorro RV Park, to airport
139	US 380 E, to San Antonio, **E**...**food:** Manny's Burgers, Owl Café, **other:** Bosque Del Apache NWR
124	to San Marcial, **E**...**other:** to Bosque del Apache NWR, Ft Craig
115	NM 107, **E**...**gas:** Truck Plaza/diesel/rest./24hr
114mm	**rest areas both lanes, full(handicapped)facilities, picnic tables, litter barrels, petwalk, RV parking, vending**
107mm	Nogal Canyon
100	Red Rock, no facilities
92	Mitchell Point, no facilities
90mm	La Canada Alamosa, La Canada Alamosa
89	NM 181, to Cuchillo, to Monticello, **4 mi E**...**gas:** Chevron, Monticello RV Park
83	NM 52, NM 181, to Cuchillo, **3 mi E**...**lodging:** Elephant Butte Inn/rest., Quality Inn, **other:** Lakeside RV Park, Elephant Butte SP
82mm	insp sta nb
79	Lp 25, to Truth or Consequences, **E**...**gas:** Chevron/diesel, Circle K, Phillips 66/diesel, **food:** China Buffet, DQ, Denny's, Hilltop Café, K-Bob's, KFC/Taco Bell, La Cocina Mexican, Los Arcos Steaks, McDonald's, Pizza Hut, Sonic, Subway, **lodging:** Ace Lodge, Best Western, Holiday Inn, Super 8, **other:** HOSPITAL, AutoZone, NAPA, USPO, to Elephant Butte SP
76	(75 from nb)Lp 25, to Williamsburg, **E**...**gas:** Chevron/24hr, Conoco/diesel, Shell/diesel, **food:** Café Rio, **lodging:** Rio Grande Motel, **other:** Shady Corner RV Park, USPO, city park, **1 mi E**...RJ RV Park

Socorro (vertical label)

71	Las Palomas, no facilities
63	NM 152, to Hillsboro, Caballo, **E**...Lakeview RV Park/diesel
59	rd 187, Arrey, Derry, **E**...to Caballo-Percha SPs
58mm	Rio Grande
51	rd 546, to Arrey, Garfield, Derry, no facilities
41	NM 26 W, Hatch, **1 mi W**...**gas:** Phillips 66/diesel/24hr, **food:** DQ, **lodging:** Village Plaza Motel, **other:** Chevrolet, Happy Trails RV Park
35	NM 140 W, Rincon, no facilities
32	Upham, no facilities
27mm	scenic view nb, picnic tables, litter barrels
26mm	insp sta nb
23mm	**rest area both lanes, full(handicapped)facilities, picnic tables, litter barrels, vending, petwalk**
19	Radium Springs, **W**...Leasburg SP, Fort Selden St Mon, RV camping
9	Dona Ana, **W**...**gas:** Chevron, Citgo, Conoco, **other:** Family$, RV camping
6b a	US 70, to Alamogordo, Las Cruces, **E**...**gas:** Phillips 66/diesel, Texaco, **food:** IHOP, Outback Steaks, Peter Piper Pizza, Pizzaria Uno, **lodging:** Century 21 Motel, Fairfield Inn, Super 8, **other:** HOSPITAL, K-Mart, Sam's Club, USPO, **W**...**gas:** Chevron, Shell, **food:** BurgerTime, DQ, Domino's, KFC, Lotaburger, McDonald's, Sonic, Subway, Taco Bell, Whataburger/24hr, **other:** MEDICAL CARE, Albertson's, AutoZone, Checker Parts, IGA Foods, Lowe's Whse, golf
3	Lohman Ave, Las Cruces, **E**...**gas:** Shamrock, Shell, **food:** Applebee's, Burger King, Cattle Baron Steaks, Carino's Italian, Chili's, Farley's Grill, Garduno's Italian, Golden Corral, Hooters, Jack-in-the-Box, KFC, Luby's, Pizza Hut, Popeye's, Red Lobster, Sonic, Twisters, Village Inn Rest., **lodging:** Hilton, **other:** Albertson's, Barnes&Noble, Dillard's, Discount Tire, Home Depot, JC Penney, OfficeMax, Sears/auto, Target, mall, **W**...**gas:** Conoco/diesel, **food:** Arby's, China Buffet, McDonald's, Subway, Wendy's, Wienerschnitzel, **other:** Best Buy, Hastings Books, Martin Tires, NAPA, PepBoys, Rainbow Foods, Walgreen, Wal-Mart SuperCtr/24hr
1	University Ave, Las Cruces, **E**...**other:** HOSPITAL, golf, museum, st police, **W**...**gas:** Conoco, **food:** Bennigan's, DQ, Lorenzo's Italian, McDonald's, **lodging:** Comfort Suites, Sleep Inn, **other:** Furr's Foods, Jo-Ann Fabrics, NMSU
0mm	I-25 begins/ends on I-10, exit 144 at Las Cruces.

Las Cruces (vertical label)

N
E
S
W

Tucumcari

Exit #	Services
373.5mm	New Mexico/Texas state line, Mountain/Central time zone
373mm	**Welcome Ctr wb, full(handicapped)facilities, phone, picnic tables, litter barrels, petwalk**
369	NM 93 S, NM 392 N, to Endee, no facilities
361	Bard, no facilities
358mm	weigh sta both lanes
356	NM 469, San Jon, **N...gas:** Citgo/Driver's Diner/diesel/24hr, to Ute Lake SP, **S...gas:** Phillips 66/diesel, Shell/diesel
343	ranch access, no facilities
339	NM 278, **N...**airport
335	Lp 40, E Tucumcari Blvd, Tucumcari, **N...gas:** Chevron, Conoco/diesel, Shell, **food:** Denny's, **lodging:** Best Western, Comfort Inn, Econolodge, Hampton Inn, Holiday Inn/rest., Howard Johnson, Motel 6, Super 8, **other:** to Conchas Lake SP, **S...**KOA
333	US 54 E, Tucumcari, **N...gas:** Love's/Chester Fried/Godfather's/diesel/@, **other:** Mtn Rd RV Park, **1 mi N...gas:** Shell, Circle K, **food:** Lotaburger, Pizza Hut, Sonic, **lodging:** Best Western, Comfort Inn, Holiday Inn, Palomino Motel, Relax Inn, Travelodge, **other:** K-Mart
332	NM 209, NM 104, 1st St, Tucumcari, **N...gas:** Chevron/Subway/diesel/24hr, Phillips 66, **food:** KFC, K-Bob's, Lotaburger, McDonald's, Pizza Hut, Sonic, **lodging:** Best Western, Comfort Inn, Day's Inn, Microtel, Travelers Inn, **other:** HOSPITAL, st police, to Conchas Lake SP
331	Camino del Coronado, Tucumcari, no facilities
329	US 54, US 66 E, W Tucumcari Ave, **N...gas:** Shell/diesel, **lodging:** Payless Motel, **other:** HOSPITAL, golf
321	Palomas, **S...gas:** Shell/DQ/Stuckey's/diesel
311	Montoya, no facilities
302mm	**rest area both lanes, full(handicapped)facilities, phone, picnic tables, litter barrels, petwalk, RV dump**
300	NM 129, Newkirk, **N...gas:** Phillips 66/diesel, **other:** to Conchas Lake SP
291	to Rte 66, Cuervo, **N...**Cuervo Gas/repair
284	no facilities
277	US 84 S, to Ft Sumner, **N...gas:** Chevron/diesel, **food:** DQ, Denny's, Golden Dragon Chinese, Silver Moon Café, **lodging:** Best Western, Budget Inn, Comfort Inn, Holiday Inn Express, La Quinta, Motel 6, Ramada Inn, **other:** Ford, KOA, **S...gas:** Love's/Carl's Jr/diesel/24hr/@, TA/Shell/Subway/diesel/24hr/@

Santa Rosa

Exit #	Services
275	US 54 W, Santa Rosa, **N...gas:** Phillips 66, Shell/Burger King, **food:** McDonald's, Rte 66 Rest., Santa Fe Grill, **lodging:** Best Western, Day's Inn, La Quinta, Travelodge, **other:** Donnie's RV Park, Santa Rosa Camping, **S...gas:** Chevron, Fina, Shell/diesel/24hr, **food:** Comet Drive-In, Joseph's Grill, Pizza Hut, **lodging:** American Inn, Laloma Motel, Sun'n Sand Motel, Sunset Motel, Super 8, Tower Motel, Western Motel, **other:** HOSPITAL, CarQuest, st police, USPO
273.5mm	Pecos River
273	US 54 S, Santa Rosa, **N...other:** Santa Rosa Lake SP, **S...gas:** Chevron, **food:** Mateo's Rest., **other:** repair
267	Colonias, **N...gas:** Shell/Stuckey's/rest.
263	San Ignacio, no facilities
256	US 84 N, NM 219, to Las Vegas, no facilities
252	no facilities
251.5mm	**rest area both lanes, full(handicapped)facilities, phone, picnic tables, litter barrels, petwalk, RV dump**
243	Milagro, **N...gas:** Chevron/diesel/café
239	no facilities
234	**N...gas:** Exxon/Flying C/DQ/diesel/gifts, **other:** repair/24hr
230	NM 3, to Encino, **N...other:** to Villanueva SP
226	no facilities
220mm	parking area both lanes, litter barrels
218b a	US 285, Clines Corners, **N...gas:** Phillips 66/diesel/24hr, Shell/diesel/24hr, **food:** Clines Corners Rest., **S...other:** to Carlsbad Caverns NP
208	Wagon Wheel, no facilities
207mm	**rest area both lanes, full(handicapped)facilities, picnic tables, litter barrels, petwalk**
203	**N...**Zia RV Park, **S...lodging:** El Vaquero Motel/rest.
197	to Rte 66, Moriarty, **S...gas:** Lisa's/diesel/rest./@, 1-2 mi S...same as 194, 196
196	NM 41, Howard Cavasos Blvd, **S...gas:** Circle K/diesel, Shell/Baja Taco, **food:** Lotaburger, Village Grill, **lodging:** Motel 6, Siesta Motel, **other:** Family$, USPO, to Salinas NM(35mi)
194	NM 41, Moriarty, **S...gas:** Chevron/24hr, Phillips 66/diesel, Rip Griffin/Pizza Hut/Subway/Taco Bell/diesel/24hr/@, **food:** Arby's, BBQ, El Comedor Rest., Mama Rosa's Rest., McDonald's, **lodging:** Day's Inn, Econolodge, Holiday Inn Express, Howard Johnson, Motel 6, Super 8, **other:** MEDICAL CARE, Chevrolet/GMC, I-40 RV Park, IGA Foods

Interstate 40

E ↕ **W**

Albuquerque

187	NM 344, Edgewood, **N...gas:** Conoco/diesel, **food:** DQ, **S...gas:** Exxon, Phillips 66/diesel, **food:** Mc-Donald's, **other:** MEDICAL CARE, Ford, Red Arrow Camping, Smith's Foods, USPO
181	NM 217, Sedillo, no facilities
178	Zuzax, **S...gas:** Chevron/diesel, **other:** Hidden Valley RV Park
175	NM 337, NM 14, Tijeras, **N...food:** Burger Boy(2mi), **other:** to Cibola NF, Turquoise Trail RV Park, **1 mi E...**auto/truck repair/24hr
170	Carnuel, no facilities
167	Central Ave, to Tramway Blvd, **S...gas:** Chevron/24hr, Fina/7-11, Phillips 66, Shell/Burger King, **food:** Einstein Bagels, KFC, Lotaburger, Mc-Donald's, Pizza Hut/Taco Bell, Starbucks, Waffle House, **lodging:** Best Western, Comfort Inn, Day's Inn, Econolodge, Howard Johnson, Motel 6, Trav-elodge, **other:** GNC, Goodyear/U-Haul/auto, KOA, Meyer's RV, Raley's Foods, Rocky Mtn RV/marine, Smith's/gas, to Kirtland AFB
166	Juan Tabo Blvd, **N...gas:** Chevron, Phillips 66, **food:** Blackeyed Pea, Burger King, Carrow's Rest., LJ Silver, McDonald's, Olive Garden, Oriental Buf-fet, Paul's Rest., Pizza Hut, Taco Bell, Twisters Diner, Village Inn Rest., Whataburger, Wendy's, **lodging:** Best Inn, Super 8, **other:** Albertson's, Discount Tire, Hastings Books, PepBoys, Radio Shack, Sav-On Drug, transmissions, **S...food:** Wienerschnitzel, **other:** Furr's Foods, Walgreen, KOA
165	Eubank Blvd, **N...gas:** Chevron, Phillips 66, Shell, **food:** JB's, Owl Café, Sonic, **lodging:** Day's Inn, Econolodge, Guesthouse Inn, Holiday Inn Express, Howard Johnson, Ramada Inn, **other:** Best Buy, Target, **S...gas:** Conoco, **food:** Burger King, Bob's Burgers, Boston Mkt, Taco Bell, Wendy's, **other:** Office Depot, Sam's Club/gas, Wal-Mart SuperCtr/24hr
164	Lomas Blvd, Wyoming Blvd, **N...gas:** Phillips 66/Subway, **other:** HOSPITAL, **S...other:** Ford, Dodge, Mazda/Toyota, Subaru, Kirtland AFB
162b a	Louisiana Blvd, **N...food:** Bennigan's, Buca Italian, Macaroni Grill, Japanese Kitchen, Steak&Ale, TGI-Friday, **lodging:** AmeriSuites, Marriott, Windrock Inn, **other:** Borders Books, Dillard's, JC Penney, Marshall's, Walgreen, **S...**atomic museum
161b a	San Mateo Blvd, Albuquerque, **N...gas:** Phillips 66/diesel, Shell/A&W, **food:** Boston Mkt, Burger King, Denny's, McDonald's, Pizza Hut, Quizno's, Starbucks, Taco Bell, Twisters Grill, Wendy's, **lodg-ing:** La Quinta, **other:** Circuit City, CompUSA, Old Navy, **S...gas:** Chevron

160	Carlisle Blvd, Albuquerque, **N...gas:** Shell, Conoco, Circle K, **food:** JB's, Lotaburger, Pizza Hut, Rudy's BBQ, Sonic, Village Inn Rest., Whata-burger, **lodging:** AmeriSuites, Candlewood Suites, Comfort Inn, Courtyard, Econolodge, Equus Hotel, Fairfield Inn, Hampton Inn, Hilton, Holiday Inn, Homestead Village, Motel 6, Quality Inn, Radisson, Residence Inn, Rodeway Inn, Super 8, Travelodge, **other:** BMW, Goodyear/auto, JC Penney, OfficeMax, Smith's Foods, Walgreen, **S...gas:** Shell/Subway/diesel, **food:** Burger King, **other:** HOSPITAL, K-Mart, Wild Oats Mkt
159b c	I-25, S to Las Cruces, N to Santa Fe, no facilities
159a	2nd St, 4th St, Albuquerque, **N...gas:** Chevron/24hr, Conoco, Love's/Subway/diesel, **food:** Furr's Café, **other:** U-Haul, **S...food:** Tony's Pizza, **lodging:** Vil-lage Inn Rest., Howard Johnson, **other:** Firestone
158	6th St, 8th St, 12th St, Albuquerque, **N...gas:** Love's/Subway/diesel, Phillips 66, **other:** U-Haul, **S...gas:** Chevron, **lodging:** Howard Johnson
157b	12th St(from eb), no facilities
157a	Rio Grande Blvd, Albuquerque, **S...gas:** Chevron/24hr, Shell, **lodging:** Best Western Rio Grande, Sheraton
156mm	Rio Grande River
155	Coors Rd, Albuquerque, **N...gas:** Chevron, Conoco/diesel, Shamrock/diesel/24hr, **food:** Applebee's, Arby's, Burger King, Chili's, Great Wall Chinese, IHOP, McDonald's, Papa Murphy's, Sonic, Sub-way, Twisters Burritos, Wendy's, **other:** Furr's Foods, Goodyear/auto, Home Depot, Radio Shack, Staples, Walgreen, Wal-Mart SuperCtr/24hr, **S...gas:** Chevron/24hr, Phillips 66/diesel, Shell, **food:** Arby's, Chico's Mexican, Del Taco, Denny's, Furr's Diner, Lotaburger, McDonald's, New China, Pizza Hut/Taco Bell, Subway, Village Inn Rest., **lodging:** Comfort Inn, Day's Inn, Holiday Inn Express, La Quinta, Motel 6, Motel 76, Red Roof Inn, Super 8, **other:** Checker Parts, Discount Tire, U-Haul, carwash
154	Unser Blvd, **N...gas:** Shamrock, **other:** to Petroglyph NM
153	98th St, **S...gas:** ♦/Flying J/Conoco/CountryMkt/diesel/LP/24hr/@, **food:** Tumbleweed Steaks(2mi), **lodging:** Microtel

NEW MEXICO
Interstate 40

E ↕ **W**

149	Central Ave, Paseo del Volcan, **N...other:** Enchanted Trails RV Camping, to Shooting Range SP, **S...gas:** Chevron/diesel/24hr, **food:** Tumbleweed Steaks(2mi), American RV Park
140.5mm	Rio Puerco River
140	Rio Puerco, **N...gas:** Exxon/diesel, **S...gas:** Conoco/diesel/rest./@, **other:** Rt 66 Casino
131	Canoncito, no facilities
126	NM 6, to Los Lunas, no facilities
120mm	Rio San Jose, Rio San Jose
117	Mesita, no facilities
114	NM 124, Laguna, **1/2 mi N...**Conoco/diesel
113.5mm	scenic view both lanes, litter barrels
108	Casa Blanca, Paraje, **S...gas:** Conoco/Casa Blanca/diesel/24hr, **food:** Taco Bell, **other:** Casa Blanca Mkt, casino
104	Cubero, Budville, no facilities
102	Sky City Rd, Acomita, **N...gas:** Acoma/diesel/24hr, **food:** Huwak'a Rest., **lodging:** Sky City Hotel, **other:** HOSPITAL, RV Park/laundry, casino, **S...rest area both lanes, full(handicapped)facilities, phone, picnic tables, litter barrels, petwalk**
100	San Fidel, no facilities
96	McCartys, no facilities
89	NM 117, to Quemado, **N...gas:** Citgo/Stuckey's, **S...**El Malpais NM
85	NM 122, NM 547, Grants, **N...gas:** Chevron/diesel/24hr, Conoco/diesel, Pump'n Save/gas, Shell/diesel, **food:** Denny's, Domino's, 4B's Rest./24hr, Lotaburger, Pizza Hut, Subway/TCBY, Taco Bell, **lodging:** Best Western, Comfort Inn, Day's Inn, Econolodge/rest., Holiday Inn Express, Motel 6, Super 8, **other:** HOSPITAL, AutoZone, Checker Parts, Chevrolet/Buick, Chrysler/Jeep/Dodge, Wal-Mart SuperCtr/24hr, **S...**Lavaland RV Park
81b a	NM 53 S, Grants, **N...gas:** Chevron, **food:** Burger King, KFC, McDonald's, **lodging:** Sands Motel, SW Motel, **other:** Ford/Lincoln/Mercury, NAPA, USPO, **S...other:** Cibola Sands RV Park, KOA, El Malpais NM
79	NM 122, NM 605, Milan, **N...gas:** Chevron, Love's/Subway/diesel/24hr/@, **food:** DQ, **lodging:** Crossroads Motel, **other:** Bar-S RV Park, **S...gas:** Petro/Mobil/diesel/24hr/@, **other:** st police
72	Bluewater Village, **N...gas:** Exxon/DQ/diesel
63	NM 412, Prewitt, **S...**to Bluewater SP, Grants West RV Camp
53	NM 371, NM 612, Thoreau, **N...gas:** Red Mtn Mkt&Deli, **other:** St Bonaventure RV camp
47	Continental Divide, 7275 ft, **N...gas:** Chevron, **other:** Continental Divide Trdg Post, **S...**USPO

Grants

44	Coolidge, no facilities
39	Refinery, **N...gas:** Pilot/diesel/24hr/@
36	Iyanbito, no facilities
33	NM 400, McGaffey, Ft Wingate, **N...other:** to Red Rock SP, RV camping, museum
26	E 66th Ave, E Gallup, **N...gas:** Chevron/diesel/24hr, **food:** Denny's/24hr, **lodging:** Sleep Inn, **other:** to Red Rock SP, RV parking/museum, st police, **S...gas:** Conoco/diesel, Fina/diesel, Mustang, **food:** Burger King, KFC, Lotaburger, McDonald's, Sonic, Wendy's, **lodging:** Best Western, Hacienda Motel, Roadrunner Motel, Super 8, **other:** HOSPITAL, Ortega Gifts
22	Montoya Blvd, Gallup, **N...rest area both lanes, full facilities, info, S...gas:** Armco/gas, Chevron, Conoco, Giant Gas, Phillips 66, Shell, Circle K, 7-11, **food:** Burger King, Carl's Jr, Church's, Earl's Rest., LJ Silver, McDonald's, Papa John's, Pedro's Mexican, Pizza Hut, Subway, Taco Bell, **lodging:** Best Western, El Capitan Motel, El Rancho Motel/rest., Redwood Lodge, **other:** Albertson's, Walgreen
20	US 666 N, to Shiprock, Gallup, **N...gas:** Giant/diesel, Phillips 66/diesel, Shell, **food:** Arby's, Burger King, CA Chinese, Church's, Cracker Barrel, DQ, Denny's, Furr's Café, Golden Corral, LotaBurger, McDonald's, Pizza Hut, Sizzler, Sonic, Taco Bell, Wendy's, **lodging:** Holiday Inn Express, Ramada Ltd, **other:** AutoZone, CarQuest, Chrysler/Plymouth/Dodge/Jeep, Family$, Firestone, JC Penney, K-Mart, NAPA, Nissan, PepBoys, Safeway, Wal-Mart SuperCtr/24hr, mall, radiators, **S...gas:** Exxon, Shell/diesel, **food:** El Dorado Rest., Lotaburger, Sonic, **lodging:** Best Value Inn, Best Western, Day's Inn, Economy Inn, Royal Holiday Inn, Shalimar Inn, Super 8, Thunderbird Motel, Travelodge, **other:** HOSPITAL, RV camping
16	NM 118, W Gallup, Mentmore, **N...gas:** Armco/diesel/24hr/@, Love's/Subway/diesel/24hr/@, Shell/Pizza Inn/diesel/24hr/@, TA/Blimpie/diesel/24hr/@, **food:** A&W, Howard Johnson, **other:** Blue Beacon, diesel repair, **S...gas:** Chevron/diesel, Conoco, Fina/Allsup's, Shell, **food:** Olympic Kitchen, Ranch Kitchen, Taco Bell, Virgie's Mexican, **lodging:** Best Western, Budget Inn, Comfort Inn, Day's Inn, Econolodge, Holiday Inn, Microtel, Motel 6, Red Roof Inn, Travelers Inn, Travelodge, **other:** USA RV Park
12mm	inspection sta eb
8	to Manuelito, no facilities
2mm	**Welcome Ctr eb, full(handicapped)facilities, phone, picnic tables, litter barrels, petwalk**
0mm	New Mexico/Arizona state line

Gallup

NEW YORK

Interstate 81

N ↑ S

Watertown

Interstate 81

N ↕ S

147mm rest area sb, full(handicapped)facilities, phone, picnic tables, litter barrels, vending, petwalk

43(146) US 11, to Kellogg Hill, no facilities

42(144) NY 177, Adams Center, Adams Center, **E...gas:** Mobil, Sunoco/diesel, **other:** Harley-Davidson, Polaris

41(140) NY 178, Adams, **E...gas:** Citgo/diesel, **food:** McDonald's, **1 mi E...food:** Tomacy's Rest., Chevrolet/Buick, Pontiac, Chrysler/Jeep/Dodge, Ford, NAPA, **W...**Stony Creek Marina

138mm South Sandy Creek

40(135) NY 193, to Ellisburg, Pierrepont Manor, no facilities

134mm parking area both lanes

39(133) Mannsville, no facilities

38(131) US 11, **E...lodging:** 81-11 Motel

37(128) Lacona, Sandy Creek, **E...gas:** Lacona Gas, **food:** J&R Diner, **lodging:** Harris Lodge, Lake Effect Inn, **W...gas:** Citgo, Sunoco/diesel, **food:** Subway, **lodging:** Salmon River Motel, **other:** KOA, **4 mi W...** Colonial Camping

36(121) NY 13(no immediate return sb or nb), Pulaski, **E...gas:** Agway/diesel, Citgo, **food:** C&M Diner, Ponderosa, **lodging:** Redwood Motel, Whitaker's Motel, **W...gas:** Mobil/diesel, Sunoco/diesel, **food:** Arby's, Burger King, McDonald's, **lodging:** Country Pizza Motel, Super 8, **other:** Aldi Foods, Chevrolet/Buick, Kinney Drug, NAPA, P&C Foods, Radio Shack, to Selkirk Shores SP, camping, fish hatchery

35(118) to US 11, Tinker Tavern Rd, **W...**Grandpa Bob's Animal Park

34(115) NY 104, to Mexico, **E...gas:** Sunoco/EZ/diesel/ 24hr/@, **2-12 mi W...gas:** Citgo, **lodging:** La Siesta Motel, Eis House, **other:** KOA, Salmon Country/Dowiedale/Jellystone Camping

33(111) NY 69, Parish, **E...gas:** Sunoco/diesel/24hr/@, **food:** Grist Mill Rest., **W...gas:** Mobil/diesel, **food:** Talk Town Rest., **lodging:** Montclair Motel, E Coast Resort, **other:** MEDICAL CARE, Up Country RV Park

32(103) NY 49, to Central Square, **E...gas:** Mobil/diesel, Sunoco/diesel, **food:** Golly's Rest., **other:** NAPA AutoCare, Pennzoil, **W...gas:** FasTrac/gas, **food:** Arby's, Burger King, McDonald's, Quinto's NY Pizza, **lodging:** Pine Grove Motel, **other:** Advance Parts, Ford, NAPA, Rite Aid, Wal-Mart SuperCtr/gas/24hr

101mm rest area sb, full(handicapped)facilities, phone, picnic tables, litter barrels, vending, petwalk

31(99) to US 11, Brewerton, **E...**Oneida Shores Camping, **W...gas:** Citgo, Mobil/diesel, Sunoco, **food:** Burger King, Castaways Rest., Little Caesar's, McDonald's, Sam's Lakeside Rest., Subway, **lodging:** BelAir Motel, Brewerton Motel, Holiday Inn Express, **other:** Kinney Drugs

30(96) NY 31, to Cicero, **E...gas:** Hess/diesel, Mobil, Sunoco, **food:** Arby's, Cracker Barrel, **W...gas:** Citgo/ diesel, Kwikfill, **food:** Frank's Café, Plainville Farms Rest., **other:** MEDICAL CARE, RV Ctr

29(93) I-481 S, NY 481, to Oswego, Syracuse, **1 mi W on US 11...gas:** Hess, Mobil, **food:** Burger King, Denny's, Dunkin Donuts, Friendly's, KFC, McDonald's, Papa John's, Perkins, Pizza Hut, Red Lobster, Taco Bell, Tully's Rest., **lodging:** Rodeway Inn, **other:** Advance

S y r a c u s e

Parts, AutoZone, Chrysler/Plymouth, Dodge, Eckerd, Firestone/auto, Ford/Lincoln/Mercury, Goodyear/auto, Home Depot, NAPA, PepBoys, PriceChopper Foods, VW/Porche/Audi, Wegman's Foods, mall

28(91) N Syracuse, Taft Rd, **E...**Eckerd, **W...gas:** Mobil

27(90) N Syracuse, **E...**airport

26(89) US 11, Mattydale, **E...gas:** Mobil, **food:** Doug's Fishfry, Friendly's, Hunan Empire, Paladino's Pizza, **lodging:** Red Carpet Inn, **other:** DENTIST, Advance Parts, Eckerd, Ford, Goodyear/auto, K-Mart, Michael's, Staples, **W...gas:** Hess/diesel, Kwikfill, **food:** Applebee's, Burger King, Denny's, KFC, McDonald's, Ponderosa, Subway, Taco Bell, Wendy's, **lodging:** Rest Inn, **other:** Aamco, Aldi Foods, Kost Tire, Lexus, Mazda, Toyota/VW

25a(88) I-90, NY Thruway, no facilities

25(87.5) 7th North St, **E...gas:** Pilot/McDonald's/diesel/24hr/@, **other:** auto repair, **W...gas:** Mobil, **food:** Bob Evans, Burger King, Colorado Steaks, Denny's, Friendly's, Ground Round, Jreck Subs, **lodging:** Day's Inn, Econolodge, Hampton Inn, Holiday Inn, Quality Inn, Ramada, Super 8, **other:** NAPA

24(86) NY 370 W, to Liverpool, **W...gas:** Hess, **other:** Best Buy, JC Penney, Kaufmann's, mall

23(86) NY 370 E, Hiawatha Blvd, **W...gas:** Hess, **other:** Best Buy, Borders Books, CompUSA, JC Penney, mall, same as 24

22(85) NY 298, Court St, no facilities

21(84.5) Spencer St, Catawba St(from sb), industrial area

20(84) I-690 W(from sb), Franklin St, West St, no facilities

19(84) I-690 E, Clinton St, Salina St, to E Syracuse

18(84) Harrison St, Adams St, **E...lodging:** University Hotel, **other:** HOSPITAL, CVS Drug, to Syracuse U, Civic Ctr

17(82) Brighton Ave, S Salina St, **W...gas:** KwikFill, Mobil

16a(81) I-481 N, to DeWitt, no facilities

16(78) US 11, to Nedrow, Onondaga Nation, **1-2 mi W...gas:** Hess, Mobil, **food:** McDonald's, Pizza Hut, Smoke Signals Diner

15(73) US 20, La Fayette, **E...gas:** Sunoco/diesel, **food:** Mama Mia Pizza, Nice'n Easy Deli, **other:** DENTIST, IGA Foods, NAPA, USPO, st police, **W...food:** McDonald's

70mm truck insp sta both lanes, phones

14(67) NY 80, Tully, **E...gas:** Sunoco/diesel, **food:** Nice'n Easy Deli, **lodging:** Best Western, **W...food:** Burger King

13(63) NY 281, Preble, **E...**to Song Mtn Ski Resort

60mm rest area nb, full(handicapped)facilities, phone, picnic tables, litter barrels, vending, petwalk

12(53) US 11, NY 281, to Homer, **W...gas:** Mobil/diesel/24hr, KwikFill, **food:** Applebee's, Burger King, Doug's Fishfry, Little Italy Pizzaria, Rusty Nail Rest., **lodging:** Budget Inn, **other:** HOSPITAL, to Fillmore Glen SP

11(52) NY 13, Cortland, **E...food:** Denny's, **lodging:** Comfort Inn, Quality Inn, **W...gas:** Mobil, Arby's, **food:** Bob Evans, China Moon, Friendly's, Little Caesar's, McDonald's, Subway, Taco Bell, Wendy's, **lodging:** Hampton Inn, Holiday Inn, **other:** Advance Parts, Eckerd, Family$, Jo-Ann Fabrics, Kost Tire, P&C Foods/24hr, Yellow Lantern Camping, museum

S y r a c u s e

Interstate 81

N
Cortland
S

10(50) US 11, NY 41, to Cortland, McGraw, **W...gas:** Agway/diesel, Citgo/Burger King/Pizza Hut/diesel/@, Mobil/Subway/diesel/24hr, Sunoco/diesel, **food:** Skyliner Diner, **lodging:** Cortland Motel, Day's Inn

45mm parking area nb, picnic tables

9(38) US 11, NY 221, **W...gas:** Citgo, Sunoco/diesel/24hr, XtraMart, **food:** NY Pizzaria, Taco Express, **lodging:** 3 Bear Inn/rest., Greek Peak Lodge, **other:** NAPA, Country Hills Camping

33mm **rest area sb, full(handicapped)facilities, phone, picnic tables, litter barrels, vending, petwalk**

8(30) NY 79, to US 11, NY 26, NY 206(no EZ return), Whitney Pt, **E...gas:** Hess, Kwikfill, Mobil/diesel/24hr, **food:** Aiello's Ristorante, Arby's, McDonald's, Subway, **lodging:** Point Motel, **other:** Chevrolet, NAPA, Parts+, Radio Shack, Strawberry Valley Farms(3mi), to Dorchester Park

7(21) US 11, Castle Creek, **W...gas:** Mobil

6(16) US 11, to NY 12, I-88E, Chenango Bridge, **E on US 11...gas:** Citgo/diesel, Exxon, Hess/Blimpie/diesel, KwikFill, Mobil, **food:** Arby's, Burger King, China Buffet, Denny's, Dunkin Donuts, Friendly's, King Grill, McDonald's, Pizza Hut, Ponderosa, Subway, Wendy's, **lodging:** Comfort Inn, Day's Inn, Motel 6, Quality Inn, **other:** Advance Parts, CVS Drug, Eckerd, Ford/Mazda, Giant Foods, Harley-Davidson, Kost Tire, Lowe's Whse, Radio Shack

15mm I-88 begins eb, no facilities

14mm **rest area nb, full(handicapped)facilities, phone, picnic tables, litter barrels**

5(14) US 11, Front St, **1 mi W...gas:** Mobil/diesel, **food:** Cracker Barrel, Nirchi's Pizza, **lodging:** Day's Inn, Econolodge, Fairfield Inn, Motel 6, Super 8

4(13) NY 17, Binghamton, no facilities

3(12) Broad Ave, Binghamton, **W...gas:** Exxon, **food:** KFC, Papa John's, **other:** CVS Drug, Giant Foods

2(8) US 11, NY 17, **1-2 mi W...gas:** Exxon, Lechner's/diesel, Pilot/Wendy's/diesel/24hr/@, TA/Sunoco/diesel/rest./@, Travelport/diesel, **food:** Arby's, Burger King, Far Out Pizza, McDonald's, Subway, **lodging:** Del Motel, Foothills Motel, Super 8, Thruway Motel

1(4) US 11, NY 7, Kirkwood, **1-2 mi W...gas:** Citgo, Mobil/diesel/24hr, Xtra, **lodging:** Kirkwood Motel, Wright Motel

2mm **rest area nb, full(handicapped)facilities, phone, picnic tables, litter barrels, vending, petwalk**

1mm weigh sta nb

0mm New York/Pennsylvania state line

Binghamton

Interstate 84

E
W

Exit #(mm)Services

71.5mm New York/Connecticut state line

21(68) US 6, US 202, NY 121(from wb), N Salem, same as 20

20(67.5) I-684, US 6, US 202, NY 22, **N...gas:** Mobil/24hr, Shell/diesel, **food:** Bob's Diner, Burger King, McDonald's, **lodging:** BelAire Motel, Heidi's Motel, **other:** Cadillac, Ford, Subaru

19(65) NY 312, Carmel, **S...food:** Applebee's, Friendly's, KFC, McDonald's, Wendy's, **other:** HOSPITAL, Home Depot, Kohl's, st police

18(62) NY 311, Lake Carmel, **S...**Bob's Towing/diesel

17(59) Ludingtonville Rd, **S...gas:** Hess/Blimpie/diesel/24hr, Sunoco, **food:** Lou's Deli, Tina's Rest.

56mm elevation 970 ft

55mm **rest area both lanes, full(handicapped)facilities, phone, vending, picnic tables, litter barrels, petwalk**

16(53) Taconic Parkway, N to Albany, S to New York, no facilities

15(51) Lime Kiln NY, **3 mi N...gas:** Mobil/24hr, **food:** Dunkin Donuts, Olympic Diner, **lodging:** Royal Inn

13(46) US 9, to Poughkeepsie, **N...gas:** Mobil/diesel, **food:** Boston Mkt, Burger King, Cracker Barrel, Denny's, Ruby Tuesday, Stanley's Eatery, Taco Bell, Wendy's, **lodging:** Courtyard, Hampton Inn, Hilton Garden, Holiday Inn, Homestead Suites, MainStay Suites, Residence Inn, Wellesley Inn, **other:** Sam's Club, Wal-Mart SuperCtr/24hr, **S...gas:** Hess/diesel/24hr, **food:** McDonald's, Pizza Hut, Subway

12(45) NY 52 E, Fishkill, **N...gas:** Coastal/diesel, Gulf, **food:** Friendly's, **S...gas:** Mobil, Sunoco/diesel, **food:** Dunkin Donuts, Hometown Deli, I-84 Diner/24hr, KFC

11(42) NY 9D, to Wappingers Falls, **1 mi N...gas:** Citgo/24hr, Mobil/diesel, Sunoco

41mm toll booth wb

40mm Hudson River

10(39) US 9W, NY 32, to Newburgh, **N...gas:** Citgo/diesel, Mobil, Shell, **food:** Burger King, Alexis Diner, McDonald's, Perkins, **lodging:** Budget Inn, Economy Inn, **S...gas:** Exxon/diesel, Sunoco/diesel, **food:** Subway, **lodging:** Travel Inn, Windsor Inn, **other:** HOSPITAL

8(37) NY 52, to Walden, **N...gas:** Citgo/diesel, Sunoco/24hr

7(36) NY 300, Newburgh, to I-87(NY Thruway), **N...gas:** Exxon/24hr, Mobil/24hr, **food:** McDonald's, Perkins, Taco Bell, Wendy's, **other:** MEDICAL CARE, AutoZone, KOA, Sears, mall, **S...gas:** Sunoco, **food:** Applebee's, Burger King, Cosimos Ristorante, Denny's, Gateway Diner, Neptune Diner, **lodging:** Clarion, Hampton Inn, Holiday Inn, Howard Johnson, Ramada Inn, Super 8, **other:** Auto Mall/dealers, Home Depot, Lowe's Whse, Nissan, Wal-Mart/auto

Newburgh

NEW YORK

Interstate 84

E 6(34) NY 17K, to Newburgh, **N...gas:** Mobil/24, Pilot/ Arby's/diesel/24hr, **food:** Airport Diner, **lodging:** Comfort Inn, Hampton Inn, **S...gas:** Exxon/diesel, **lodging:** Courtyard

5(29) NY 208, Maybrook, **N...gas:** Exxon/24hr, Mobil, **food:** Burger King, McDonald's, **other:** Eckerd, ShopRite Foods, **S...gas:** Stewarts, TA/diesel/ rest./@, **food:** Maybrook Diner, Pizza Hut, Subway, **lodging:** Rodeside Inn, Super 8, **other:** Blue Beacon, Winding Hills Camping

24mm **rest area wb, full(handicapped)facilities, phone, vending, picnic tables, litter barrels, petwalk**

4(19) NY 17, Middletown, **N...gas:** Getty, Mobil/24hr, Sunoco, **food:** Americana Diner, Applebee's, Boston Mkt, Charlie Brown Steaks, Denny's, Friendly's, Galleria Rest., KFC, McDonald's, Olive Garden, Red Lobster, Ruby Tuesday, Subway, Taco Bell, Wendy's, **lodging:** Howard Johnson, Middletown Motel, Super 8, **other:** HOSPITAL, Best Buy, Circuit City, Firestone/auto, Hannaford Foods, Home Depot, JC Penney, Lowe's Whse, Old Navy, Rite Aid, Sam's Club, Sears/auto, ShopRite Food, U-Haul, Wal-Mart SuperCtr/24hr, mall, **S...gas:** Getty/diesel, Mobil, **food:** El Bandido Mexican, Outback Steaks, TGIFriday, **lodging:** Courtyard, Hampton Inn, Holiday Inn, **other:** st police

17mm **rest area eb, full(handicapped)facilities, phone, vending, picnic tables, litter barrels, petwalk**

3(15) US 6, to Middletown, **N...gas:** Citgo/diesel/24hr, Mobil, **food:** Burger King, Colonial Diner, Ground Round, McDonald's, Perkins, Pizza Hut, Ponderosa, 6-17 Diner, Taco Bell, Wendy's, **other:** HOSPITAL, Acura/Honda, Chevrolet/Isuzu, Mazda, Subaru, **S...gas:** 84 Kwikstop, Sunoco/diesel, **lodging:** Day's Inn, Global Budget Inn, **other:** Chrysler/Jeep, Nissan/BMW/Suzuki, Kia, Toyota, transmissions

2(5) Mountain Rd, **S...**Delaney's Steaks

4mm elevation 1254 ft wb, 1272 ft eb

3mm parking area both lanes

1(1) US 6, NY 23, Port Jervis, **N...gas:** Sunoco/diesel, **food:** Arlene&Tom's Diner, KFC, **lodging:** Deerdale Motel, Painted Aprons Motel, **other:** Ford/Lincoln/Mercury, **S...gas:** Citgo/diesel, Exxon/diesel, Gulf/diesel, **food:** DQ, McDonald's, Ponderosa, **lodging:** Comfort Inn, **other:** HOSPITAL, ShopRite Foods, mall

0mm New York/Pennsylvania state line, Delaware River

Interstate 86

E Exit # Services

I-86 begins/ends on I-87, exit 16, toll booth

131(377) NY 17, **N...other:** Outlets/famous brands, **S...gas:** Exxon/Subway/diesel, Mobil, Sunoco, **food:** Blimpie, Chili's, McDonald's, TGIFriday's, Uno Pizzaria, **lodging:** American Budget Inn, **other:** BJ's Whse, Home Depot, Kohls, TJMaxx, Staples

130a(376) US 6, Bear Mtn, to West Point(from eb), **S...other:** BJ's Whse, Home Depot, Wal-Mart SuperCtr/24hr

130(376) NY 208, Monroe, Washingtonville, **N...gas:** Sunoco/ diesel, **lodging:** James Motel, Lake Anne Motel, **other:** Chrysler/Dodge/Jeep, Daewoo, Isuzu, st police, **S...gas:** Mobil/diesel, **food:** Burger King, Pizza Hut,

129(375) Museum Village Rd, **S...food:** Plum House Rest

128(374) rd 51(only from wb), Oxford Depot, no facilities

127(373) Greycourt Rd(from wb only), Sugar loaf, Warwick, no facilities

126(372) NY 94, Chester, Florida, **N...gas:** Mobil, Shell, Sunoco/ diesel, **food:** Lobster Pier Rest., McDonald's, Sunrise Diner, Wendy's, **S...lodging:** Holiday Inn Express, **other:** Radio Shack, Rite Aid, ShopRite Foods, funpark, **S...lodging:** Chester Inn, **other:** Black Bear Camping

125(369) NY 17M E, South St, **S...food:** Hacienda Mexican, Pizza Deli, **other:** HOSPITAL

124(368) NY 17A, NY 207, **N...gas:** Exxon/Subway/ diesel, Mobil/diesel, Sunoco/diesel, **food:** Burger King, Country Chicken, Friendly's, Dunkin Donuts, Goshen Diner, Pizza Hut, Plaza Diner, **other:** CVS Drug, **S...lodging:** Comfort Inn, **other:** Chrysler/Plymouth/Dodge/Jeep, Hyundai

122a(367) Fletcher St, Goshen, no facilities

122(364) rd 67, E Main St, Crystal Run Rd, **N...gas:** Mobil, **food:** El Bandido Rest., FoodCourt, Outback Steaks, Rusty Nail Rest., TGIFriday's, **lodging:** Courtyard, Hampton Inn, Holiday Inn, **S...gas:** Getty/diesel

121(363) I-84, E to Newburgh, W to Port Jervis, no facilities

120(363) NY 211, **N...gas:** Mobil, Sunoco, **food:** American Café, Olive Garden, **lodging:** Howard Johnson, Middletown Motel, Super 8, **other:** Best Buy, Cosimo's, Filene's, Hannaford's Foods, JC Penney, Sam's Club, Wal-Mart, **S...gas:** Getty, Mobil, **food:** Americana Diner, Arby's, Boston Mkt, Burger King, China Buffet, Denny's, Friendly's, Hana Japanese, KFC, Pizza Hut, Red Lobster, Wendy's, Taco Bell, **other:** AutoZone, Circuit City, Eckerd, Ford, Home Depot, Jo-Ann Fabrics, K-Mart, PriceChopper, ShopRite Foods, Staples, Stop&Shop Foods, U-Haul

119(360) NY 309, Pine Bush, **S...gas:** Best Gas/diesel

118a(358) NY 17M, Fair Oaks, no facilities

118(358) Circleville, **N...lodging:** Economy Inn, Heritage Motel, **S...gas:** Citgo, Exxon/diesel, Mobil, **food:** Raffael's Italian, Subway

116(355) NY 17K, Bloomingburg, **S...gas:** Citgo, Mobil, **food:** Gaudio Diner, Q-way Diner, **other:** Rainbow Valley Camping

113(350) US 209, Wurtsboro, Ellenville, **N...gas:** Mobil/diesel, Stewarts/gas, **food:** Giovanni's Café, **lodging:** Davidman Motel, Gold Mtn Chalet, Day's Inn, Valley Brook Motel, **other:** American Family Campground, Spring Glen Camping

112(347) Masten Lake, Yankee Lake, **S...food:** Potager Diner, **lodging:** ValleyBrook Motel, **other:** WonderWood Camping

111(344) (sb only), Wolf Lake, **S...gas:** Billy's/diesel

110(343) Lake Louise Marie, **N...food:** Dodge Inn Rest, **lodging:** Rock Hill Lodge

109(342) Rock Hill, Woodridge, **N...gas:** Exxon/diesel, **food:** Bernie's Diner, LandSea Rest., RockHill Diner, Rock Pizza, **lodging:** Rock Hill Lodge, Rosemond Motel, **other:** Hilltop Farms Camping, Lazy G Camping, **S...gas:** Mobil/diesel

Interstate 86

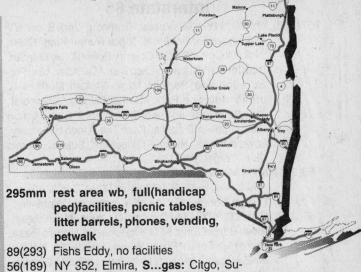

108(341) Bridgeville, same as 109

107(340) Thompsonville, **S...food:** Apollo FoodCourt, Hana Rest., Old Homestead Diner, **lodging:** Affordable Inn, Pines Motel, Raleigh Motel, **other:** Chevrolet, Chrysler/Plymouth/Dodge/Jeep, Toyota

106(339) (wb only), E. Broadway, **S...gas:** Mobil/diesel, **food:** Monitcello Cafe, **lodging:** Travel Inn, Econolodge, **other:** GMC Trucks

105(337) NY 42, Monticello, **N...gas:** Exxon/diesel, Mobil, Valero, **food:** Bro Bruno Diner, Blue Horizon Diner, Giovanni's Café, KFC, Kutshner's Cafe, McDonald's, **other:** Home Depot, ShopRite Foods, Wal-Mart SuperCtr/24hr, **S...gas:** Stewarts, **food:** Burger King, Monticello Diner, Pizza Hut, Wendy's, **lodging:** Econolodge, Ramada Ltd, **other:** NAPA

104(336) NY 17B, Raceway, Monticello, **S...gas:** Citgo, Exxon/diesel, **food:** Bean Bag Eatery, Kelly's Diner, Taco Maker, **lodging:** Best Western, Raceway Motel, Travel Inn, **other:** Swinging Bridge Camp, Woodstock Camping, airport

102(332) Harris, **S...other:** HOSPITAL, Swan Lake Camping

101(327) Ferndale, Swan Lake, **S...gas:** Exxon/diesel, **food:** McDonald's Burger King, Last Licks Cafe, Wendy's, **lodging:** Day's Inn, Inn by the Falls, Loncoln Motel

100(327) NY 52 E, Liberty, **N...gas:** Sunoco, **food:** Albert's Rest., Burger King, McDonald's, Taco Bell, Wendy's, **lodging:** Best Inn, Day's Inn, Econolodge, **S...gas:** Citgo, Exxon/diesel, Gulf, Mobil/24hr, **food:** Dunkin Donuts, Pizza Hut, **lodging:** Liberty Motel, Lincoln Motel, **other:** Eckerd, Ford/Lincoln/Mercury, Pontiac/Buick, Neversink River Camping, Swan Lake Camping, Yogi Bear Camping

99(325) NY 52 W, to NY 55, Liberty, **S...gas:** Exxon, Sunoco, **food:** Dairy Barn, **lodging:** Catskill Motel

98(321) Cooley, Parksville, **N...gas:** Mobil, **food:** Dari-King, W 17 Diner, **lodging:** Best Western, **other:** USPO

97(319) Morsston, no facilities

96(316) Livingston Manor, **N...food:** Catskill Rest., Tony's Pizza, **lodging:** Econo Motel, **other:** Covered Bridge Camping, Mongaup Pond Camping, **S...lodging:** DeBruce Inn, OZ B&B, Willowemac Motel

313mm rest area eb, full(handicapped)facilities, picnic tables, litter barrels, phones, vending, petwalk, truck insp. sta(eb)

94(311) NY 206, Roscoe, Lew Beach, **N...gas:** Exxon/diesel, Sunoco/diesel, **food:** 1910 Coffeshop, Ramondo's Diner, Roscoe Diner, **lodging:** Reynolds House Motel, Rockland House Motel, Roscoe Motel, Tennanah Lake Motel, **other:** Roscoe Camping, **S...gas:** Mobil/diesel, **other:** Beaverkill St Camping(8mi)

93(305) to Cooks Falls(from wb), no facilities

92(303) Horton, Cooks Falls, Colchester, **S...gas:** Sunoco/diesel, **food:** Riverside Café/lodge, **other:** Russell Brook Camping

90(297) NY 30, East Branch, Downsville, **N...gas:** Sunoco, **other:** Beaver-Del Camping, Catskill Mtn Camping, Oxbow Camping, Peaceful Valley Camping, **S...lodging:** E Branch Motel

295mm rest area wb, full(handicapped)facilities, picnic tables, litter barrels, phones, vending, petwalk

89(293) Fishs Eddy, no facilities

56(189) NY 352, Elmira, **S...gas:** Citgo, Sunoco/diesel, **food:** Hoss' Rest., McDonald's, Pizza Hut, **lodging:** Coachman Motel, Holiday Inn, Twain Motel, **other:** HOSPITAL

87a(288) NY 268(from wb), same as 87

87(284) NY 97, to NY 268, to NY 191, Hancock, Cadosia, **S...gas:** Getty, Mobil, Sunoco, **food:** Circle E Diner, Country Bakeshop/rest., Family Rest., Great Wall Chinese, McDonald's, Subway, **lodging:** Colonial Motel, Starlight Lake Inn, **other:** Buick/Chevrolet, NAPA, Parts+

276mm parking area wb, litter barrels

84(274) Deposit, **N...gas:** Citgo/diesel/24hr, Wheeler's, **food:** Wendy's, **lodging:** Deposit Motel, Laurel Bank Motel, Scott's Motel, **other:** Crystler/Jeep, st police

83(272) Depósit, Oquaga Lake, no facilities

82(270) NY 41, McClure, Sanford, **N...gas:** Sun/diesel, **other:** Kellystone Park, **S...lodging:** Alexander's B&B/diner, Chestnut Inn/rest., Scott's Family Resort, **other:** Guestward Camping(3mi)

265mm parking area eb, picnic tables, litter barrels

81(263) E Bosket Rd, no facilities

80(261) Damascus, **N...gas:** Exxon/diesel, **food:** Damascus Diner, **other:** Forest Hill Lake Park Camping

79(259) NY 79, Windsor, **N...gas:** Citgo, Sunoco/diesel, XtraMart, **food:** Subway, **other:** Lakeside Camping, **S...food:** Golden Oak Rest., Marian's Pizza

78(256) Dunbar Rd, Occanum, no facilities

77(254) W Windsor, **N...gas:** Mobil/diesel, **food:** McDonald's

76(251) Haskins Rd, to Foley Rd, no facilities

75(250) I-81 S, to PA(exits left from wb), **N...gas:** Exxon/diesel, **lodging:** Dell Motel

72(244) I-81 N, US 11, Front St, Clinton St, **S...food:** McDonald's, **other:** Advance Parts, K-Mart, antiques

71(242) Airport Rd, Johnson City, **S...gas:** Exxon

70(241) NY 201, Johnson City, **N...gas:** Exxon, Hess, **food:** Blimpie, ChiChi's, Christy's Grill, Friendly's, Great China Buffet, McDonald's, Pizza Hut, Ponderosa, Taco Bell, **lodging:** Best Inn, Best Western, Hampton Inn, Red Roof Inn, **other:** Giant Foods, JC Penney, Kaufmann's, Kost Tire, Wegman's Foods, mall, **S...** Home Depot

69(239) NY 17C, no facilities

238mm Susquehanna River

68(237) NY 17C, Old Vestal Rd, no facilities

Interstate 86

E
↕
W

Elmira

67(236) NY 26, NY 434, Vestal, Endicott, **2mi S on NY 434...gas:** Exxon/diesel, **food:** Burger King, China Wok, McDonald's, Old Country Buffet, Olive Garden, Red Lobster, Subway, Taco Bell, TGIFriday, Uno Pizzaria, **lodging:** Parkway Motel, SkyLark Motel/rest., **other:** Advance Parts, Barnes&Noble, Chevrolet, Chrysler/Plymouth/Jeep, $Tree, Ford, Grand Union Foods, Jo-AnnFabrics, Kost Tire, Lincoln/Mercury, Lowe's Whse, Nissan, OfficeMax, Subaru, Sam's Club, Target, Wal-Mart SuperCtr/24hr

66(231) NY 434, Apalachin, **S...gas:** KwikFill, Mobil/Subway/diesel, **food:** Blue Dolphin Diner, Donoli's Rest., Dunkin Donuts, McDonald's, **lodging:** Dolphin Inn

65(225) NY 17C, NY 434, Owego, **N...gas:** Mobil/diesel, **food:** Burger King, KFC, McDonald's, Nirchi's Pizza, Pizza Hut, Tony's Pizza, Wendy's, **lodging:** Holiday Inn Express, Treadway Motel/rest., **other:** $General, Hickories Park Camping, P&C Foods, Rite Aid

64(223) NY 96, Owego, **N...lodging:** DeepWell Motel, Sunrise Motel, **S...other:** Pennzoil/gas

222mm **rest area wb, full(handicapped)facilities, phone, vending, picnic Tables, litter barrels, petwalk**

63(218) Lounsberry, **S...gas:** Exxon/rest/diesel/@

62(214) NY 282, Nichols, **S...gas:** Citgo/Pizza Hut/diesel

212mm **rest area eb, full(handicapped)facilities, picnic tables, litter barrels, phone, vending, petwalk**

208mm Susquehanna River

61(206) NY 34, PA 199, Waverly, Sayre, **S...gas:** Citgo/24hr, KwikFill, **food:** McDonald's, **lodging:** Best Western/rest., **other:** Chevrolet/Buick, Joe's RV Ctr, Nissan

60(204) US 220, to Sayre, Waverly, **N...lodging:** O'brien's Inn, **S...gas:** Citgo, Mobil, **food:** Wendy's

59a(202) Wilawana, **S...gas:** Sunoco/Subway/diesel

59(200) NY 427, Chemung, **N...gas:** Dandy/diesel

199mm **rest area wb, full(handicapped)facilities, picnic tables, litter barrels, phone, vending, petwalk**

58(195) rd 2, Lowman, Wellsburg, **N...food:** W Diner, **lodging:** Red Jacket Motel, **S...other:** Gardiner Hill Campsites(4mi), Tillotson Farms Camping(5mi)

56(190) Jerusalem Hill, **S...gas:** Citgo/diesel, KwikFill, Sunoco/Subway, **food:** Hilltop Rest., McDonalds, Pizza Hut, **lodging:** Coachman Motel, Holiday Inn, Mark Twain Motel

54(186) NY 13, to Ithaca, no facilities

185mm I-86 begins ends., **S...gas:** Mobil, Sunoco, **food:** Dunkin Donuts, LJ Silver, Subway, Wendy's, **lodging:** Motel 6, Red Carpet Inn, **other:** Eckerd, K-Mart

52(184) NY 14, to Watkins Glen, **N...food:** Friendly's, **lodging:** Holiday Inn, Howard Johnson, Knight's Inn, **S...food:** Taste of China, **other:** SavALot Foods

52a(183) Commerce Ctr, same as 51

51(182) Chambers Rd, **N...gas:** Mobil/Subway/diesel, Sunoco/diesel, **food:** Lum's, McDonald's, Olive Garden, Outback Steaks, Red Lobster, Rico's Pizza, Ruby Tuesday, **lodging:** Country Inn Suites, Hilton Garden, Knights Inn, **other:** BonTon, Firestone, JC Penney, JoAnn Fabrics, Kaufman's, Sears/auto, mall, **S...food:** Applebee's, China Inn, Gino's Pizza, Larenzo's Rest., Old Country Buffet, Taco Bell, TGIFriday, Wendy's, **lodging:** Econolodge, Relax Inn,

Corning

other: Barnes&Noble, $Tree, Lowe's Whse, Michael's, Old Navy, Sam's Club, Staples, Top's Foods, Wal-Mart, museum

50(180) Kahler Rd, **N...**to Airport

49(178) Olcott Rd, Canal St, Big Flats, **N...**airport, antiques, **S...food:** Picnic Pizza, **other:** $General

48(171) NY 352, E Corning, **N...gas:** Citgo, **food:** Tag's Rest., **lodging:** Budget Inn, Gatehouse Motel

47(174) NY 352, Gibson, Corning, **N...lodging:** Radisson Inn, to HOSPITAL

46(171) NY 414, to Watkins Glen, Corning, **5mi N...other:** Ferenbaugh Camping, KOA, **S...gas:** Citgo/diesel, **lodging:** Comfort Inn, Day's Inn, Staybridge Suites, **other:** HOSPITAL, museums

45(170) NY 352, Corning, **S...food:** Bob Evans, Burger King, EnEn Chinese, Friendly's, McDonald's, Trixie's Diner, Wendy's, **lodging:** Fairfield Inn, Radisson, **other:** AutoZone, Chrysler/Plymouth/Dodge/Jeep, Eckerd

44(168) US 15 S, NY 417 W, Gang Mills, **N...lodging:** Best Western, Holiday Inn

43(167) NY 415, Painted Post, **N...gas:** Citgo, **food:** Burger King, Friendly's, Magic Wok, McDonald's, Pizza Hut, Ramblers Drive-In, **other:** AutoValue Parts, CarQuest, Eckerd, Firestone/auto, Jo-Ann Fabrics, **S...gas:** Sunoco, **food:** Denny's, **lodging:** Hampton Inn

167mm parking area wb, litter barrels

42(165) Coopers Plains, **N...**st police, **S...lodging:** Lampliter Motel

41(161) rd 333, Campbell, **N...other:** Camp Bell Camping(1mi), **S...gas:** Sunoco, **other:** Cardinal Campsites(6mi), antiques

160mm **rest area eb, full(handicapped)facilities, picnic tables, litter barrels, phone, vending, petwalk**

40(156) NY 226, Savona, **N...gas:** Mobil/Subway/diesel, **fo**-Savona Diner, **other:** Green Acres Camping

39(153) NY 415, Bath, **N...food:** Chat-a-Whyle Rest.(3mi), **lodging:** Holland American Country Inn, National Hotel, **S...other:** Babcock Hollow Camping(2mi)

38(150) NY 54, to Hammondsport, Bath, **N...gas:** Citgo, KwikFill, Mobil, Sunoco, **food:** Arby's, Burger King, Dunkin Donuts, McDonald's, Pizza Hut, Ponderosa, Subway, **lodging:** Budget Inn, Day's Inn, Super 8, **other:** HOSPITAL, Advance Parts, AutoValue Parts, Chrysler/Plymouth/Dodge/Jeep, Eckerd, Family$, Ford/Lincoln/Mercury, Hickory Hill Camping(3mi), K-Mart, Meyer's RV Ctr, NAPA, P&C Foods, Rite Aid, Top's Foods, museum, st police, winery, to Keuka Lake

147mm **rest area wb, full(handicapped)facilities, phone, picnic tables, litter barrels, vending, petwalk**

37(146) NY 53, to Prattsburg, Kanona, **S...gas:** Sunoco/diesel/rest./@, **food:** Hornet's Nest Rest., **other:** WagonWheel Camping(12mi)

36(145) I-390 N, NY 15, to Rochester, no facilities

35(138) Howard, **S...**to Lake Demmon RA, phone

34(130) NY 36, Hornell, Arkport, **N...gas:** Mobil/diesel, **other:** Stony Brook SP, Sun Valley Camping, **S...gas:** Gulf, **food:** Burger King(3mi), Country Kitchen, Friendly's(3mi), McDonald's, Ponderosa, Rupert's Rest., **lodging:** Comfort Inn(3mi), Day's Inn, Econolodge, Sunshine Motel, Super 8, **other:** Aldi, Chevrolet, Chrysler/Plymouth/Dodge/Jeep, Ford/Mercury, NAPA, Wal-Mart/auto, Wegman's Foods

Bath

Hornell

Interstate 86

E ← / → **W**

125mm scenic overlook eb, litter barrels

33(124) NY 21, to Alfred, Almond, Andover, **S...gas:** Mobil, **food:** Pizza Hut, **lodging:** Economy Inn, Saxon Inn Hotel, **other:** Lake Lodge Camping(8mi), Kanakadea Camping

117mm highest elevation on I-86, elev 2110 ft eb, 2080 ft wb

32(116) W Almond, no facilities

31(108) Angelica, **N...gas:** Citgo, **lodging:** Angelica Inn B&B

30(104) NY 19, Belmont, Wellsville, **N...**6-S Camping(3mi), **S...gas:** American Trkstp/Mobil/diner/24hr/@, **other:** Mothers Piknchikn Camping(6mi)

101mm rest area eb, full(handicapped)facilities, phone, picnic tables, litter barrels, vending, petwalk

29(99) NY 275, to Bolivar, Friendship, **S...gas:** Mobil, Sunoco, Miller &Brandes Gas, **food:** Subway

28(92) NY 305, Cuba, **N...food:** Moonwink's Rest., **lodging:** Coachlight Motel, **other:** Maple Lane RV Park, **S...gas:** Exxon, Sunoco/diesel, **food:** McDonald's, **other:** Giant Foods, HOSPITAL

27(84) NY 16, NY 446, Hinsdale, **N...**food, **S...**gas, lodging

26(79) NY 16, Olean, **S...gas:** Sunoco, **food:** Burger King, Wendy's, **other:** HOSPITAL

25(77) Buffalo St, Olean, **S...gas:** Citgo/diesel, **other:** HOSPITAL, **2 mi S on Constitution...gas:** UniMart, **food:** Applebee's, Burger King, Luigi's Pasta, Pizza Hut, **lodging:** Comfort Inn, Country Inn, Microtel, **other:** Advance Parts, BJ's Whse/gas, Home Depot, K-Mart, Radio Shack, Wal-Mart, St Bonaventure U

24(74) NY 417, Allegany, **1mi S...gas:** Mobil/diesel, **food:** Village Tastee, **other:** to St Bonaventure U

72mm rest area wb, full(handicapped)facilities, picnic tables, litter barrels, petwalk

23(68) US 219 S, **N...gas:** M&M/Subway/diesel

66mm Allegheny River

21(61) US 219 N, Salamanca, **S...food:** Red Garter Rest

20(58) NY 417, NY 353, Salamanca, **N...food:** Antone's Gas, Nafco Quickstop/Burger King, Seneca Hawk Petro, **food:** McDonald's/24hr, **lodging:** Holiday Inn Express, **other:** Rail Museum, Seneca-Iroquis Museum, **other:** casino

19(54) **S...other:** Allegany SP, Red House Area

18(51) NY 280, **S...other:** Allegany SP, Quaker Run Area

17(48) NY 394, Steamburg, **N...**gas, **other:** RV camping, **S...gas:** M&M/diesel/rest., **other:** camping

16(42) W Main St, Randolph, **N...gas:** Mobil/diesel, **food:** R&M Rest., lodging, **other:** RV parking

41mm rest area eb, phone, picnic table, litter barrel

15(40) School House Rd, no facilities

39mm rest area wb, phone picnic table, litter barrel

14(36) US 62, Kennedy, **N...gas:** Keystone Gas, **food:** Office Pizza/Subs, **S...**RV camping

32mm Cassadaga Creek

13(31) NY 394, Falconer, **S...food:** Burger King, Wendy's, **other:** Sugar Creek Stores, **lodging:** Budget Inn, Red Roof Inn

12(28) NY 60, Jamestown, **S...gas:** Mobil/McDonald's/diesel, **food:** Bob Evans, **lodging:** Comfort Inn, **other:** HOSPITAL, st police

Olean

Salamanca

Jamestown

11(25) to NY 430, Jamestown, **S...** gas, diesel, food, lodging

22mm Welcome Ctr/rest area eb, full(handicapped)facilities, picnic tables, litter barrels, petwalk, vending

10(21) NY 430 W, Bemus Point, no facilities

9(20) NY 430 E, **N...gas:** Mobil, **S...**gas, food, lodging

19mm Chautauqua Lake

8(18) NY 394, Mayville, **N...gas:** Mobil/diesel, lodging, **other:** RV camping

7(15) Panama, no facilities

14mm Pendergast Creek

10.5mm French Creek

6(9) NY 76, Sherman, **N...gas:** Mobil, **food:** Village Pizzeria, **other:** Ford, USPO

8mm French Creek

4(1) NY 430, Findley Lake, **N...food:** I-86 Express Rest., **lodging:** Holiday Inn Express, Peek'n Peak Motel, **S...**gas, food, lodging, **other:** RV camping, to Peek'n Peak Ski Area

0mm New York/Pennsylvania state line. Exits 3-1 are in PA.

3 PA 89, North East, Wattsburg, **N...**gas, food

1b a I-90, W to Erie, E to Buffalo. I-86 begins/ends on I-90, exit 37. I-390 begins/ends on I-86, exit 36.

Interstate 87

Exit #	Services

N ↑ / ↓ **S**

176mm US/Canada Border, NY state line, I-87 begins/ends.

43(175) US 9, Champlain, **E...**World Duty Free, **W...gas:** Peterbilt Trkstp/diesel/deli/24hr/@, **other:** repair

42(174) US 11 S, to Rouse's Point, Champlain, **E...gas:** Mobil, **food:** Chinese Eatery, Peppercorn Rest., Three Forks Pizza, **other:** Chevrolet/Pontiac(2mi), Kinney Drug, Rite Aid, Tops Foods, USPO, **W...gas:** Exxon/diesel, Irving/diesel, Mobil/diesel, Neverett Bros/Subway/diesel, **food:** McDonald's

41(167) NY 191, Chazy, **E...**st police, **W...**Miner Institute

162mm rest area both lanes, full(handicapped)facilities, info, phone, picnic tables, litter barrels, petwalk

40(160) NY 456, Beekmantown, **E...gas:** Mobil/diesel, **lodging:** Pt Auroche Lodge, Stonehelm Motel/café, **W...**Twin Ells Camping

39(156) NY 314, Moffitt Rd, Plattsburgh Bay, **E...gas:** Stewarts, **food:** Domenic's Rest., Gus' Rest., McDonald's, **lodging:** Pioneer Motel, Rip van Winkle Motel, Super 8, **other:** Plattsburgh RV Park, **W...other:** Shady Oaks Camping, to Adirondacks

Plattsburgh

NEW YORK

Interstate 87

N ↑↓ S

Plattsburgh

38(154) NY 22, NY 374, to Plattsburgh, **E...gas:** Mobil, Sunoco/24hr, **food:** Kinney Drug

37(153) NY 3, Plattsburgh, **E...gas:** Mobil, ShortStop/diesel, Sunoco, **food:** Burger King, Bootlegger Café, DQ, Domino's, IHOP, Jade Buffet, KFC, Little Caesar, Mangia Pizza, McDonald's, Pizza Hut, Subway, Wendy's, **lodging:** Comfort Inn, Holiday Inn, **other:** HOSPITAL, Aldi Foods, BigLots, Buick, Cadillac/Pontiac/GMC, Eckerd, Family$, Firestone/auto, Ford, Honda, Isuzu, Jo-Ann Fabrics, Kinney Drug, Michael's, P&C Foods, Radio Shack, Sam's Club, TJ Maxx, True Value, Wal-Mart SuperCtr/24hr, **W...gas:** Exxon, Mobil, Sunoco/Jreck/diesel, **food:** Applebee's, Butcher Block Rest., Friendly's, Lum's, Lindsey Rest., 99 rest., Ponderosa, **lodging:** Best Western, Baymont Inn, Day's Inn, Econolodge, Quality Inn, **other:** Advance Parts, AutoZone, K-Mart, Lowe's Whse, PriceChopper Foods, Sears/auto

151mm Saranac River

36(150) NY 22, Plattsburgh AFB, **E...gas:** Citgo, Mobil/diesel/24hr/@, **food:** Burger King(3mi), **W...other:** st police

146mm truck insp sta both lanes

35(144) NY 442, to Port Kent, Peru, **2-8 mi E...other:** Iroquois/Ausable Pines Camping, **W...gas:** Citgo/Sugar Creek Diner, Mobil/Subway/Dunkin Doughnuts/diesel, **food:** Cricket's Rest., McDonald's, **other:** Peru Drug, Tops Foods, USPO

143mm emergency phones at 2 mi intervals begin sb/end nb

34(137) NY 9 N, Ausable Forks, **E...gas:** Sunoco/diesel, **food:** Pleasant Corner Rest., Mac's Drive-in, Tastee-Freez, **W...other:** Prays Mkt, Ausable River RV Camping

136mm Ausable River

33(135) US 9, NY 22, to Willsboro, **E...gas/diesel, food, lodging, RV camping, to Essex Ferry

125mm N Boquet River

32(124) Lewis, **W...gas:** Getty/diesel/24hr/@, Pierce's Gas/diesel, **food:** Trkstp Diner

123mm rest area both lanes, full(handicapped)facilities, info, phone, picnic tables, petwalk

120mm Boquet River

31(117) NY 9 N, to Elizabethtown, Westport, **E...gas:** Mobil, **lodging:** HillTop Motel, **W...other:** HOSPITAL, st police

111mm rest area nb only, full(handicapped)facilities, phone, picnic tables, litter barrels, vending, petwalk

30(104) US 9, NY 73, Keene Valley, no facilities

99mm rest area both lanes, full(handicapped)facilities, phone, picnic tables, litter barrels, petwalk

29(94) N Hudson, **E...food:** Chuckwagon Rest., **other:** Jellystone Camping, **W...**Blue Ridge Falls Camping

28(88) NY 74 E, to Ticonderoga, Schroon Lake, **E...gas:** Sunoco/diesel, **food:** Birches Diner, **lodging:** Schroon Lake B&B, **other:** RV camp/dump, st police, services on US 9 parallel

83mm rest area both lanes, full(handicapped)facilities, phone, picnic tables, litter barrels, petwalk, vending

27(81) US 9(from nb, no EZ return), Schroon Lake, to gas/diesel, food, lodging

26(78) US 9(no EZ sb return), Pottersville, Schroon Lake, **E...lodging:** Lee's Corner Motel, **other:** Ideal Camping, Wakonda Camping, **W...gas:** Mobil, **food:** Black Bear Rest.

25(73) NY 8, Chestertown, **W...gas:** Mobil/diesel, **other:** RV camping

24(67) Bolton Landing, **E...**RV camping

66mm parking area sb, picnic tables, no facilities, Schroon River

64mm parking area nb, picnic tables, no facilities

23(58) to US 9, Diamond Point, Warrensburg, **W...gas:** Citgo/diesel, Mobil, **food:** McDonald's, **lodging:** Super 8, **other:** Ford/Mercury, RV camping, Central Adirondack Tr, ski area

22(54) US 9, NY 9 N, to Diamond Pt, Lake George, **E...gas:** Citgo, Mobil, **food:** Boardwalk Rest., Capri Pizzaria, China Wok, Dunkin Donuts, Gino&Tony's Café, Guiseppe's Rest., Jasper's Steaks, JT Kelly's Grill, KFC, Luigi's Italian, Mario's Italian, McDonald's, Pizza Hut, Subway, Taco Bell, Trattoria Siciliano, Trolley Steaks, **lodging:** Admiral Motel, Balmoral Motel, Balsam Motel, Blue Moon Motel, Brookside Motel, Cedarhurst Motel, Choice Inn, Econolodge, Ft Henry Resort, Georgian Lodge, Heritage Motel, Knight's Inn, Lakecrest Motel, Lakehaven Motel, Mohawk Cottages, Motel Montreal, Nordick's Motel/rest., Oasis Motel, O'Sullivan's Motel, Park Lane Motel, Quality Inn, 7 Dwarfs Motel, Sundowner Motel, Surfside Motel, Villager Motel, Windsor Lodge, **other:** Rexall Drug, USPO, **W...**parking area both lanes

21(53) NY 9 N, Lake Geo, Ft Wm Henry, **E on US 9...gas:** Mobil, Stewart's Gas, Sunoco, **food:** Adirondack Brewery, A&W, Barnsider Smokehouse, DQ, Mama Riso's Italian, Mountaineer Rest., Prospect Mt Diner, **lodging:** Best Western, Comfort Inn, Holiday Inn, Holly Tree Inn, Howard Johnson/rest., Nomad Motel, Northland Motel, Ramada Inn, Travelodge, Tiki Motel, Super 8, **W...gas:** Mobil/diesel/LP, **lodging:** Kathy's Motel

51mm Adirondack Park

20(49) NY 149, to Ft Ann, **E...gas:** Mobil/Subway, Sunoco/diesel, **food:** Coach House Diner, Frank's Italian, Logjam Rest., Meeting Place Rest., Montcalm Rest., Trading Post Rest., **lodging:** Day's Inn, French Mtn Motel, Mohican Motel, Rodeway Inn, Samoset Cabins, **other:** Ledgeview RV Park(3mi), Whipporwill/King Phillip/Lake George Camping(2mi), Factory Outlets/famous brands, funpark, st police

19(47) NY 254, Glens Falls, **E...gas:** Citgo, Getty, Hess/Blimpie, **food:** Burger King, China Buffet, Dunkin Donuts, FoodCourt, Friendly's, Ground Round, KFC/A&W, McDonald's, Mrs B's Café, NY Dogs, Old China Buffet, Olive Garden, Pizza Hut, Ponderosa, Queen Diner, Red Lobster, Silo Rest., Taco Bell, Wendy's, **lodging:** Econolodge, Sleep Inn, Welcome Inn, **other:** MEDICAL CARE, Advance Parts, AutoZone, BonTon, CVS Drug, Eckerd, Firestone/auto, Goodyear, Home Depot, JC Penney, Jo-Ann Fabrics, Radio Shack, Rite Aid, Sears, Staples, TJ Maxx, Wal-Mart, mall, **W...gas:** Mobil, Stewarts Gas, **lodging:** Ramada/rest., st police

Glens Falls

Interstate 87

N ↑ ↓ S

18(45) Glens Falls, **E...gas:** Citgo, Gulf/24hr, Hess/diesel/24hr, Mobil/24hr, **food:** Carl R's Café, Pizza Hut, Steve's Place Rest., Subway, **lodging:** Best Inn, Queensbury Hotel, **other:** HOSPITAL, CVS Drug, Hannaford Foods, U-Haul, **W...gas:** Stewarts, **food:** McDonald's, Super 8

43mm **rest area both lanes, full(handicapped)facilities, picnic tables, litter barrels, phone, vending, petwalk**

42mm Hudson River

17(40) US 9, S Glen Falls, **E...gas:** Citgo, Getty/Beaver's Diner/diesel, Gulf, Mobil/Subway/diesel/24hr, **food:** Dunkin Doughnuts, Wishing Well Rest., **lodging:** Budget Inn, Landmark Motel, Sara-Glen Motel, Sunhaven Motel, Swiss American Motel, Town&Country Motel, **other:** American RV Camp, **W...**Moreau Lake SP

16(36) Ballard Rd, Wilton, **E...other:** Coldbrook Campsites, golf, **W...gas:** Mobil, Stewarts, Sunoco/Scotty's Rest./diesel/24hr/@, **lodging:** Mt View Acres Motel, **other:** Alpin Haus RV Ctr, Ernie's Grocery

15(30) NY 50, NY 29, Saratoga Springs, **E...gas:** Hess/diesel/24hr, Mobil/Blimpie, **food:** Applebee's, Burger King, Denny's, Dunkin Doughnuts, FoodCourt, Friendly's, Gavano's Pizza, Golden Corral, KFC/Taco Bell, McDonald's, 99 Rest., Panera Bread, Ruby Tuesday, TGIFriday, Uno Pizzaria, **lodging:** Super 8, **other:** Barnes&Noble, Best Buy, BJ's Whse, Dodge, Eckerd, Ford/Mercury, Hannaford Foods, Home Depot, JC Penney, Lowe's Whse, Mazda, Old Navy, PriceChopper Foods, Sears/auto, Staples, Subaru, Target, Toyota, Wal-Mart SuperCtr/24hr, mall, **W... lodging:** Birches Motel, Gateway Motel, Residence Inn, Saratoga Motel, **other:** HOSPITAL

14(38) NY 9P, Schuylerville, **2 mi E...gas:** Mobil/Lakeside Mkt/deli, Stewart's Gas, **food:** Bayshore Rest./marina, Tropic Hut Rest., Waterfront Rest., **lodging:** Longfellow Inn/rest., Saratoga Springs Motel, **other:** Lee's RV Park, **2 mi W...gas:** Citgo/repair/LP, **lodging:** Holiday Inn, **other:** museum, racetrack

13(25) US 9, Saratoga Springs, **E...food:** Andy's Pizza, Chez Sophie Rest., DeLucia's Deli, Ripe Public House Rest.(1mi), Tomatoe Rest.(1mi), **lodging:** Maggiore's Motel, Post Road Lodge, **other:** Northway RV, Ballston Spa SP, **W...gas:** Mobil, StewartsMart, **food:** Packhorse Rest., **lodging:** Hilton Garden(1mi), Roosevelt Inn/rest., Thorobred Motel

12(21) NY 67, Malta, **E...gas:** Mobil/diesel, Sunoco, **food:** Dunkin Donuts, KFC/Taco Bell, Malta Diner, McDonald's, Subway, Tasty Chinese, **lodging:** Cocca's Motel, Fairfield Inn, Riviera Motel, **other:** MEDICAL CARE, CVS Drug, GNC, PriceChopper Foods, StewartsMart, st police, **W...**Saratoga NHP

11(18) Round Lake Rd, Round Lake, **E...food:** MyWay Cafe, **W...gas:** Citgo/diesel, Sunoco, **food:** CiderMill Rest.(3mi), Good Times Rest., GrandPrix Grill/Inn, **other:** StewartsMart

10(16) Ushers Rd, **E...gas:** Hess/diesel, Sunoco/diesel, **food:** Ferretti's Rest., **other:** Central Repair, **3 mi E... food:** Rusty Nail Rest., **W...other:** StewartsMart

14mm **rest area nb, full(handicapped)facilities, info, phone, picnic tables, litter barrels, vending, petwalk**

9(13) NY 146, Clifton Park, **E...gas:** Hess/diesel/24hr, USA/gas, **food:** Burger King, Chili's, Cracker Barrel, Pizza Hut, Red Robin, Sam's Pizzaria, Snyder's Rest., **lodging:** Comfort Suites, **other:** Advance Parts, Aldi Foods, Goodyear/auto, Home Depot, Kohl's, Lowe's Whse, Michael's, OfficeMax, **W...gas:** Mobil, Sunoco/diesel, **food:** Applebee's, Denny's, Dunkin Donuts, Friendly's, KFC, McDonald's, Outback Steaks, Quizno's, Ruby Tuesday, Starbucks, Taco Bell, TGIFriday, Wendy's, **lodging:** Best Western, Hampton Inn, **other:** AutoZone, BordersBooks, Chevrolet, CVS Drug, Eckerd, Firestone, Freedom RV Ctr, Hannaford Foods, JC Penney, Jo-Ann Fabrics, K-Mart, Marshall's, PriceChopper Foods, mall, st police

8a(12) Grooms Rd, to Waterford, **1-2 mi E on US 9...gas:** Getty, Gulf, **food:** 1/2 Moon Diner, Wendy's, **other:** Wal-Mart SuperCtr/24hr

8(10) Crescent, Vischer Ferry, **E...gas:** Hess/Blimpie/diesel/24hr, **food:** Krause's Rest.(2mi), McDonald's, **W...gas:** Coastal/Mr Subb/diesel/24hr, Sunoco/24hr, **food:** Pancho's Mexican, **other:** CVS Drug, StewartsMart

8mm Mohawk River

7(7) NY 7, Troy, **E on US 9 N...gas:** Hess/diesel, **lodging:** Hampton Inn, Holiday Inn Express, **other:** Acura, Buick/Pontiac, Dodge, $General, Eckerd, Ford, Prime Outlets/famous brands, Volvo, **E on US 9 S...gas:** Mobil, **food:** McDonald's, Subway, **other:** Cottman Transmissions, Infiniti, Marshall's, PriceChopper Foods

6(6) NY 2, to US 9, Schenectady, **E...gas:** Mobil, **food:** Applebee's, Circle Diner, Dakota Steaks, Ground Round, Krispy Kreme, Uno Pizzaria, Vanilla Bean Café, **lodging:** Cocca's Inn,**other:** Caldor, CVS Drug, Goodyear/auto, JC Penney, Lowe's Whse, Sam's Club, Staples, VW, Wal-Mart, same as 7, **W...gas:** Mobil/24hr, **food:** Bennigan's, Friendly's, Kings Buffet, Sebastian's Rest., Subway, **lodging:** Clarion, Microtel, Super 8, **other:** Target

5(5) NY 155 E, Latham, **E...food:** DeeDee's Rest., Philly's Grill, Vintage Pizza, **lodging:** Econolodge, **other:** USPO

Saratoga Sprgs (vertical left margin)

Albany (vertical right margin)

NEW YORK

Interstate 87

Albany

4(4) NY 155 W, Wolf Rd, **E on Wolf Rd...gas:** Hess/diesel, Mobil, Sunoco, **food:** Arby's, Ben&Jerry's, Burger King, ChiChi's, Denny's, Macaroni Grill, Maxie's Grill, McDonald's, 99 Rest., Olive Garden, Outback Steaks, Pizza Hut, Ponderosa, Real Seafood Co, Red Lobster, Subway, Weathervane Seafood, Wolf Rd Diner, **lodging:** Best Western, Courtyard, Hampton Inn, Holiday Inn, Marriott, Red Roof Inn, **other:** Chevrolet, CVS Drug, Firestone, Ford/Lincoln/Mercury, Hannaford Foods, **W...food:** Calaway Grill, Koto Japanese, **lodging:** Desmond Hotel, Wingate Inn, **other:** Engel's Farmer Mkt, to Heritage Park

2(2) NY 5, Central Ave, **E...gas:** Mobil, Sunoco, **food:** Wendy's, **lodging:** Scottish Inn, **other:** BJ's Whse, Jo-Ann Fabrics, Marshalls, Staples, Target, **E on Wolf Rd...gas:** Mobil, Sunoco, **food:** American Café, Applebee's, Bangkok Thai, Chili's, Dunkin Donuts, Emperor Chinese, Friendly's, IHOP, LJ Silver/Taco Bell, LoneStar Steaks, Papa Gino's, Starbucks, **lodging:** Econolodge, Cocca's Inn, Day's Inn, **other:** Barnes&Noble, Borders Books, Firestone/auto, Goodyear/auto, Macy's, OfficeMax, Sears/auto, mall, **W...gas:** Exxon, Mobil, **food:** BBQ, Butcher Block Grill, Delmonico's Steaks, Domino's, Empress Diner, Garcia's Mexican, Krause's Diner, Mr Subb, Papa John's, **lodging:** Ambassador Motel, Comfort Inn, Econolodge, Howard Johnson, Northway Inn, Quality Inn, Ramada Ltd, Super 8, **other:** AutoZone, Buick, Goodyear

1W(1) NY State Thruway(from sb), I-87 S to NYC, I-90 W to Buffalo, no facilities

1E(1) I-90 E(from sb), to Albany, Boston, no facilities

1S(1) to US 20, Western Ave, **on Western Ave...food:** Burger King, Denny's, TGIFriday, **lodging:** Holiday Inn Express, **other:** JC Penney, mall

1N(1) I-87 N(from nb), to Plattsburgh, no facilities

1N no facilities

NY State Thruway goes west to Buffalo(I-90), S to NYC(I-87), I-87 N to Montreal

24(148) I-90 and I-87 N, no facilities

23(142) I-787, to Albany, US 9 W, **E...gas:** 23 Trkstp/diesel/@, **lodging:** Econolodge, Quality Inn, to Knickerbocker Arena, **W...gas:** Stewarts, **lodging:** Econolodge

139mm parking area sb, phone, picnic tables, litter barrel

22(135) NY 396, to Selkirk, no facilities

21a(134) I-90 E, to MA Tpk, Boston, no facilities

127mm **New Baltimore Travel Plaza sb, Mobil/diesel, Big Boy, Mrs Fields, Roy Rogers, Starbucks, TCBY, atm, gifts, info, UPS**

21b(125) US 9 W, NY 81, to Coxsackie, **W...gas:** Trvl Plaza/diesel/motel/rest./24hr/@, Sunoco/diesel, **food:** McDonald's(5mi), Texarado Steaks, **lodging:** Best Western, Red Carpet Inn, **other:** Boat'n RV Whse

21(114) NY 23, Catskill, **E...gas:** Mobil, Sunoco/diesel/24hr, **lodging:** Catskill Motel/rest., Quality Inn, **other:** Home Depot, to Rip van Winkle Br, **W...food:** Anthony's Italian, LogSider Café, **lodging:** Astoria Motel, Budget Inn(3mi), Quality Inn, Rip van Winkle Motel, **other:** Indian Ridge Camping, to Hunter Mtn/Windham Ski Areas

103mm **Malden Service Area nb, Mobil/diesel, Carvel Ice Cream, Hotdogs, McDonald's, atm, gifts, phone, parking area sb**

20(102) NY 32, to Saugerties, **E...gas:** Getty, Mobil/diesel, Stewarts, **food:** King Buffet, McDonald's, Pizza Star, Starway Café, Subway, **other:** CarQuest, Chrysler/Plymouth/Dodge/Jeep, CVS Drug, Family$, **W...gas:** Hess/Blimpie, diesel, Sunoco/diesel, **food:** Johnny G's Diner, Land&Sea Grill, McDonald's, **lodging:** Catskill Mtn Lodge, Comfort Inn, Howard Johnson/rest., **other:** KOA(2mi), to Catskills

99mm parking area nb, phone, picnic tables, litter barrels

96mm **Ulster Travel Plaza sb, Mobil/diesel, Big Apple Bagel, Cinnabon, Nathan's, Roy Rogers, Mrs Fields, TCBY, atm, gifts, phone**

19(91) NY 28, Kingston, **E...gas:** Citgo/diesel, Mobil, **food:** Friendly's, Gateway Diner, Grand Buffet Rest., Picnic Pizza, **lodging:** Holiday Inn, Super 8, **other:** Advance Parts, Hannaford Foods, Radio Shack, Walgreen, **W...food:** Family Diner, International Diner, Roudigan's Steaks, **lodging:** Budget 19 Motel, Ramada Inn/rest., Skytop Motel/steaks, SuperLodge, **other:** Buick, Camper's Barn RV, Ford, Nissan, access to I-587, US 209

18(76) NY 299, to Poughkeepsie, New Paltz, **E...gas:** Citgo/diesel, Mobil, **food:** China Buffet, College Diner/24hr, **lodging:** Day's Inn, Econolodge, 87 Motel, Rocking Horse Ranch Resort, **other:** Cumberland Farms, to Mid-Hudson Br, **W...gas:** Sunoco/24hr, **food:** Burger King, Dunkin Donuts, Friendly's, McDonald's, Pasquale's Pizza, Pizza Hut, Subway, TCBY, **lodging:** Mohonk Lodge(6mi), Super 8, **other:** MEDICAL CARE, Advance Parts, Big A Parts, Eckerd, Radio Shack, Rite Aid, ShopRite Foods, Jellystone(9mi), KOA(10mi)

66mm **Modena service area sb, gas: Mobil/diesel, food: Arby's, Carvel's Ice Cream/bakery, Uno Pizzaria, McDonald's, other: atm, fax, gifts, UPS**

65mm **Plattekill Travel Plaza nb, gas: Mobil/diesel, food: Big Boy, Cinnabon, Nathan's, Roy Rogers, other: atm, gifts, info**

17(60) I-84, NY 17K, to Newburgh, **E...gas:** Getty/diesel, Sunoco/diesel/24hr, **food:** Burger King, Neptune Diner, Pizza Hut, Subway, **lodging:** Day's Inn, Holiday Inn, Howard Johnson/rest., **other:** Adams Foods, Caldor, Buick/Pontiac, Chevrolet/Cadillac, Dodge/Plymouth, Ford, Harley-Davidson, Lincoln/Mercury, NAPA, Nissan, Radio Shack, Rite Aid, ShopRite Foods, **W...gas:** Citgo/diesel, **E on NY 300...gas:** Exxon, Mobil, **food:** Applebee's, Cosimo's Rest., Denny's, Dunkin Donuts, King Buffet, McDonald's, Taco Bell, Wendy's, Yobo Oriental, **lodging:** Hampton Inn, Ramada Inn, Super 8, **other:** AutoZone, Discount Tire, Home Depot, Sears/auto, Wal-Mart/auto, Weis Foods, mall

16(45) US 6, NY 17, to West Point, Harriman, **W...gas:** Exxon/Subway/diesel, **lodging:** American Budget Inn, **other:** Chevrolet/Buick, Wal-Mart SuperCtr/24hr(1mi), Woodbury Outlet/famous brands, st police

34mm **Ramapo Service Area sb, gas: Sunoco/diesel/24hr, food: Carvel Ice Cream, Lavazza Coffee, McDonald's, other: atm**

Newburgh

NEW YORK

Interstate 87

33mm **Sloatsburg Travel Plaza nb, gas: Sunoco/diesel/ 24hr, food: Burger King, Dunkin Donuts, Sbarro's, TCBY, other: atm, gifts, info**

15a(31) NY 17 N, NY 59, Sloatsburg, **W...gas:** Citgo

15(30) I-287 S, NY 17 S, to NJ. I-87 S & I-287 E run together.

14b(27) Airmont Rd, Montebello, **E...lodging:** Holiday Inn, **W...gas:** Exxon/diesel, **food:** Airmont Diner, Applebee's, Friendly's, Pasta Cucina, Starbucks, Sutter's Mill Rest., Water Wheel Cafe, **lodging:** Wellesley Inn, **other:** HOSPITAL, DrugMart, ShopRite Foods, Walgreen, Wal-Mart

14a(23) Garden State Pkwy, to NJ, Chestnut Ridge

14(22) NY 59, Spring Valley, Nanuet, **E...gas:** Gulf, Shell/ diesel, **food:** Burger King, Denny's, McDonald's, Subway, **lodging:** Fairfield Inn, **other:** BMW, Car-Quest, Pergament, ShopRite Foods, Target, TJ Maxx, mall, **W...gas:** Citgo, **food:** ChuckeCheese, Dunkin Donuts, Great China, IHOP, KFC/Taco Bell, Red Lobster, Taco Bell, White Castle/Church's, **lodging:** Day's Inn, Hilton Garden, Nanuet Inn, **other:** Barnes&Noble, Daewoo, Home Depot, Macy's, Marshalls, NAPA, OfficeMax, Sears/auto, Staples, Stop'n Shop Foods, mall

13(20) Palisades Pkwy, N to Bear Mtn, S to NJ

12(19) NY 303, Palisades Ctr Dr, W Nyack, **E...Saturn, W...gas:** Mobil, **food:** Grill 303, **lodging:** Nyack Motel, **other:** Barnes&Noble, Best Buy, BJ's Whse, Circuit City, CompUSA, Dave&Buster's, Filene's, Home Depot, JC Penney, Jo-Ann's Etc, Lord&Taylor, Old Navy, Staples, ShopRite Foods, Target, mall

11(18) US 9W, to Nyack, **E...gas:** Mobil, **food:** Hilltop Rest, **lodging:** Best Western, **W...gas:** Quality Gas, Shell/ diesel, **food:** KFC, McDonald's, **lodging:** Super 8, **other:** HOSPITAL, J&L Repair/tire, Kia, Nissan

10(17) Nyack(from nb), same as 11

14mm Tappan Zee Br, Hudson River

13mm toll plaza

9(12) to US 9, to Tarrytown, **E...gas:** Hess, Shell/repair, **other:** Stop&Shop, **W...gas:** Mobil, **food:** El Dorado West Diner, **lodging:** Hilton, **other:** Honda/Subaru, Mavis Tire

8(11) I-287 E, to Saw Mill Pkwy, White Plains, **E...lodging:** Marriott

7a(10) Saw Mill River Pkwy S, to Saw Mill River SP, Taconic SP

7(8) NY 9A(from nb), Ardsley, **W...lodging:** Ardsley Acres Motel, **other:** HOSPITAL

6mm **Ardsley Travel Plaza nb, Sunoco/diesel, Burger King, Popeye's, TCBY, vending**

5.5mm toll plaza, phone

6ba (5) Stew Leonard Dr, to Ridge Hill, **W...other:** Costco, Home Depot, Stew Leonard's Farmfresh Foods

6(4.5) Tuckahoe Dr, Yonkers, **E...gas:** Getty/repair, **food:** Golden Jade Palace, McDonald's, Subway, **lodging:** Tuckahoe Motel, **other:** ShopRite Foods/drug, **W...gas:** Gulf, Mobil, **food:** Chinese Food, Domino's, Dunkin Donuts, Totanno's Italian, **lodging:** Holiday Inn, Regency Hotel

5(4.3) NY 100 N(from nb), Central Park Ave, White Plains, **E...gas:** Getty, Shell, Sunoco, **food:** Ground Round

4(4) Cross Country Pkwy, Mile Sq Rd, **E...gas:** Getty, **food:** Burger King, **other:** Ford/Lincoln/ Mercury/Subaru, Macey's, Sears/auto, **W...gas:** Shell/diesel/24hr, **food:** Burger King, Roy Rogers, **other:** Circuit City, TJ Maxx, to Yonkers Speedway

3(3) Mile Square Rd, **E...gas:** Stop&Shop, Foods, **other:** Circuit City, GNC, Macy's, Thriftway Drug, mall, **W...gas:** Getty, Shell/24hr

2(2) Yonkers Ave(from nb), Westchester Fair, **E...gas:** Mobil, **other:** Yonkers Speedway

1(1) Hall Place, McLean Ave, **E...other:** A&P Foods

0mm New York St Thruway and I-87 N run together to Albany, no facilities

14(11) McLean Ave, **E...gas:** Shell, **food:** Dunkin Donuts

13(10) E 233rd , NE Tollway, service plaza both lanes/Mobil

12(9.5) Hudson Pkwy(from nb), Sawmill Pkwy, no facilities

11(9) Van Cortlandt Pk S, no facilities

10(8.5) W 230th St(from sb), W 240th(from nb), **W...other:** Target

9(8) W Fordham Rd, **E...gas:** Gaseteria/diesel, **other:** HOSPITAL, Toyota

8(7) W 179th (from nb), **W...Roberto Clemente SP**

7(6) I-95, US 1, S to Trenton, NJ, N to New Haven, CT, no facilities

6(5) E 153rd St, River Ave, Stadium Rd, **E...Yankee Stadium**

5(5) E 161st, Macombs Dam Br, **E...Yankee Stadium**

3(3) E 138th St, Madison Ave Br, **E...gas:** Gaseteria/diesel

2(2) Willis Ave, 3rd Ave Br, **E...gas:** Mobil/diesel, **W...food:** McDonald's

1(1) Brook Ave, Hunts Point, **E...gas:** BP, Hess

0mm I-87 begins/ends on I-278.

Interstate 88

Exit #   Services

25a I-90/NY Thruway. I-88 begins/ends on I-90, exit 25a.

117mm toll booth (to enter or exit NY Thruway)

25(116) NY 7, to Rotterdam, Schenectady, **S...gas:** Citgo/ Friendly's/diesel/24hr, **3 mi S...gas:** Gulf, **food:** Burger King, Dunkin Donuts, McDonald's, Top's Diner, **lodging:** L&M Motel, Rotterdam Motel, **other:** Frosty Acres Camping

24(112) US 20, NY 7, to Duanesburg, **N...gas:** Mobil, **food:** Dunkin Donuts, **other:** st police, **S...gas:** Mobil, Stewarts, **food:** Duanesburg Diner

Interstate 88

E ← → **W**

Cobleskill

23(101) NY 30, to Schoharie, Central Bridge, **N...gas:** Mobil, Red Barrel, **other:** Hideaway Camping, Locust Park Camping, **S...lodging:** Holiday Inn Express, **2 mi S...gas:** Mobil, **food:** Dunkin Donuts, McDonald's, Hyland House B&B, **lodging:** Parrott House 1870 Inn, Wedgewood B&B

22(95) NY 7, NY 145, to Cobleskill, Middleburgh, **2-4 mi N... gas:** Hess/diesel, Mobil, **food:** Boreali's Diner, Burger King, Dunkin Doughnuts, McDonald's, **lodging:** Best Western, Holiday Inn Express(5mi), Holiday Motel, Howe Caverns Motel/rest., **other:** HOSPITAL, Twin Oaks Camping, to Howe Caverns, **S...st** police

21(90) NY 7, NY 10, to Cobleskill, Warnerville, **2 mi N...gas:** Hess, Mobil/diesel, **food:** Burger King, Pizza Hut, Sub Express, **other:** HOSPITAL, PriceChopper Foods, **3 mi N...food:** Delaney's Rest., **lodging:** Best Western, Gables B&B, **other:** Wal-Mart SuperCtr/24hr

20(87) NY 7, NY 10, to Richmondville, **S...gas:** Mobil/diesel/24hr, **food:** Reinhardt's Deli, Sub Express, **lodging:** Econolodge, **1 mi S...gas:** Sunoco/diesel, **other:** Hi-View Camping

79mm **rest area wb, full(handicapped)facilities, phone, vending, picnic tables, litter barrels, petwalk**

19(76) to NY 7, Worcester, **N...gas:** Stewarts, Sunoco/diesel, **other:** NAPA

73mm **rest area eb, full(handicapped)facilities, phones, vending, picnic tables, litter barrels, petwalk**

18(71) to Schenevus, **N...gas:** Citgo, **food:** Schenevus Rest.

17(61) NY 7, to NY 28 N, Colliersville, Cooperstown, **2 mi N... gas:** Mobil/diesel, **food:** Homestead Rest., Renae's Crossing Cafe, Taylor's, **lodging:** Best Western, Knott's Motel, Redwood Motel, **other:** to Baseball Hall of Fame

16(59) NY 7, to Emmons, **N...food:** Arby's, Burger King, Farmhouse Rest., Moore's Rest., Perrucci's Pizza, **lodging:** Larenzo Motel, Rainbow Inn, **other:** Eckerd, PriceChopper Foods, **1 mi N...food:** Arby's, Burger King, Pizza Hut, **S...food:** Brooks BBQ(4mi)

Oneonta

15 NY 28, NY 23, Oneonta, **N...food:** Friendly's, **other:** to Soccer Hall of Fame, **S...gas:** Citgo, Hess, Kwik-fill, Mobil, Red Barrel/Taco Bell, **food:** Applebee's, Burger King, Denny's, McDonald's, Neptune Diner/24hr, Subway, Wendy's, **lodging:** Budget Inn, Christopher's Lodge/rest., Holiday Inn, Super 8, Townhouse Motel, **other:** Aldi Foods, BJ's Whse, $Tree, Home Depot, JC Penney, Kost Tire, NAPA, OfficeMax, Wal-Mart SuperCtr/24hr

14(55) Main St(from eb), Oneonta, **N...gas:** Citgo, Kwikfill, Stewarts, Sunoco, **food:** Alfresco's Italian, Pepper Joe's Deli, **other:** CVS Drug, cleaners, **S...food:** Denny's, McDonald's, Taco Bell, Kountry Livin B&B, **other:** Subaru

13(53) NY 205, **1-2 mi N...gas:** Citgo, Hess, Mobil, **food:** Burger King, Duke Diner, Dunkin Donuts, McDonald's, Ponderosa, **lodging:** Celtic Motel, Hampton Inn, Maple Terrace Motel, Oasis Motor Inn, **other:** Chevrolet, Chrysler/Jeep, Honda/Mitsubishi, Nissan, Pontiac/Buick/GMC/Cadillac, Parts+, Rite Aid, to Susquehanna Tr, Gilbert Lake SP(11mi), camping

Binghamton

12(47) NY 7, to Otego, **S...gas:** Mobil/Red Barrel/diesel

43mm **rest area wb, full(handicapped)facilities, phone, picnic tables, litter barrels, vending, petwalk**

11(40) NY 357, to Unadilla,, Delhi, **N...KOA**

39mm **rest area eb, full(handicapped)facilities, phone, picnic tables, litter barrels, vending, petwalk**

10(38) NY 7, to Unadilla, **2 mi N...gas:** KwikFill, Red Barrel, **lodging:** Country Motel(5mi), **other:** Great American Foods, USPO, st police

9(33) NY 8, to Sidney, **N...gas:** Citgo/diesel, Hess/diesel, Mobil/diesel, **food:** Burger King, China Buffet, McDonald's, Pizza Hut, **lodging:** Algonkin Motel, Country Motel, Super 8, **other:** HOSPITAL, K-Mart/Little Caesar's, QuickWay Foods, Tall Pines Camping, USPO, **S...lodging:** Mason Inn(5mi)

8(29) NY 206, to Bainbridge, **N...gas:** Citgo, Mobil, Sunoco/Taco Bell/diesel/24hr, **food:** Bob's Family Diner, Olde Jericho Tavern, **lodging:** Algonkin Motel, Susquehanna Motel, **other:** Riverside RV Park, Parts+, to Oquage Creek Park, **S...lodging:** Mason Lodge(4mi)

7(22) NY 41, to Afton, **1-2 mi N...gas:** Mobil/24hr, Sunoco/diesel, Xtra, **food:** RiverClub Rest., Tempting Dish Rest., Vincent's Rest., **other:** Afton Golf/rest., Echo Lake Park, Kellystone Park, ValuRite Drug, Smith-Hale HS

6(16) NY 79, to NY 7, Harpursville, Ninevah, **S...gas:** Red Barrel/diesel, **other:** USPO

5(12) Martin Hill Rd, to Belden, **N...gas:** Exxon/diesel, **other:** Belden Manor Camping

4(8) NY 7, to Sanitaria Springs, **S...gas:** Hess/diesel

3(4) NY 369, Port Crane, **N...to** Chenango Valley SP, **S...gas:** Fastrac/diesel, KwikFill

2(2) NY 12a W, to Chenango Bridge, **N...gas:** Red Barrel Gas

1(1) NY 7 W(no wb return), to Binghamton, no facilities

0mm I-81, N to Syracuse, S to Binghamton. I-88 begins/ends on I-81.

Interstate 90

Exit #	Services

B24.5mm New York/Massachusetts state line

B3(B23) NY 22, to Austerlitz, New Lebanon, W Stockbridge, **N...gas:** Citgo/diesel, **food:** Depot 22 Rest., **S...gas:** Sunoco/diesel, **lodging:** Berkshire Spur Motel, **other:** Woodland Hills Camp

B18mm toll plaza, phone

B2(B15) NY 295, Taconic Pkwy, **1-2 mi S...gas**

B1(B7) US 9, NY Thruway W, to I-87, toll booth, phone

12(20) US 9, to Hudson, **1-3 mi S...gas:** Mobil/diesel/24hr, Sunoco/diesel, Xtra/24hr, **food:** McDonald's, **lodging:** Bel Air Motel, Blue Spruce Motel, **other:** to Van Buren NHS

18.5mm **rest area wb, full(handicapped)facilities, phone, picnic tables, litter barrels, vending, petwalk**

11(15) US 9, US 20, E Greenbush, Nassau, **N...gas:** Citgo/diesel, Hess/diesel, **food:** Daquiri's Rest., **other:** st police, **S...gas:** Mobil(2mi), **food:** Burger King, My Place Rest., Dewitt Motel, **lodging:** Econolodge, **other:** Grand Union, Rite Aid, USPO

E ↕ **W**

Interstate 90

10(10) Miller Rd, to E Greenbush, **1-3 mi S...gas:** Mobil, Stewarts, Sunoco, **food:** Dunkin Donuts, E Greenbush Diner, Pizza Hut, Ponderosa, Weathervane Seafood, **lodging:** Dewitt Motel

9(9) US 4, to Rensselaer, Troy, **N...gas:** Mobil, **food:** Applebee's, Ground Round, McDonald's, OffShore Pier Rest., **lodging:** Holiday Inn Express, **other:** $Tree, Grand Union Foods, Home Depot, Radio Shack, Staples, Wal-Mart, **1-2 mi S...gas:** Citgo/diesel, Mobil, Stewarts, **food:** Cracker Barrel, Denny's, Friendly's, Wendy's, **lodging:** Econolodge, Fairfield Inn, 4 Seasons Motel, Mt Vernon Motel

8(8) NY 43, Defreestville

7(7) Washington Ave(from eb), Rensselaer, no facilities

6.5mm Hudson River

6mm I-787, to Albany, no facilities

6(4.5) US 9, Northern Blvd, to Loudonville, **N...gas:** Stewarts/gas, **food:** Mr Subb, Ta-Ke Japanese, **lodging:** Red Carpet Inn, **other:** HOSPITAL, David's Fine Foods

5a(4) Corporate Woods Blvd, no facilities

5(3.5) Everett Rd, to NY 5, **S...gas:** Hess, **food:** Bob&Ron's Fishfry, Denny's, Friendly's, Gateway Diner, Ground Round, McDonald's, Subway, Pizza Hut, Popeye's, Taco Bell, **lodging:** Motel 6, Quality Inn, **other:** HOSPITAL, Advance Parts, AutoZone, Chevrolet, Chrysler/Jeep, CVS Drug, $Tree, Eckerd, Ford, Hannaford's Foods/24hr, Honda/Nissan, Mazda, PepBoys, Plymouth/Dodge, Pontiac, PriceChopper Foods, Radio Shack, Suzuki, multiple facilities on NY 5

4(3) NY 85 S, to Slingerlands, no facilities

3(2.5) State Offices, no facilities

2(2) Fuller Rd, Washington Ave, **S...food:** CrossGates Rest., Sunoco, **lodging:** Courtyard, CrestHill Suites, Extended Stay America, Fairfield Inn, Howard Johnson Express, TownePlace Inn, same as 1S

1N(1) I-87 N, to Montreal, to Albany Airport, no facilities

1S(1) US 20, Western Ave, **S...CrossGates Mall Rd, food:** Bugaboo Creek Steaks, FoodCourt, Hooters, Pizzaria Uno, **other:** Best Buy, Caldor, Filene's, Home Depot, JC Penney, Lord&Taylor, Macy's, Old Navy, Sam's Club, Wal-Mart, mall

24(149) I-87 N, I-90 E, no facilities

153mm **Guilderland Service Area eb, Sunoco/diesel, Ben&Jerry's, McDonald's, Mr Subb**

25(154) I-890, NY 7, NY 146, to Schenectady, **1 mi N...exit** 8 off I-890, Mobil

25a(159) I-88 S, NY 7, to Binghamton, no facilities

26(162) I-890, NY 5 S, Schenectady, no facilities

168mm **Pattersonville Service Area wb, Sunoco/diesel, Big Boy, Cinnabon, Roy Rogers, TCBY, Starbuck's, atm, fax, gifts, info, UPS**

172mm **Mohawk Service Area eb, Sunoco/diesel, Breyer's, McDonald's, fudge**

27(174) NY 30, Amsterdam, **N...gas:** Citgo, Mobil, **lodging:** Super 8/diner/24hr, Valleyview Motel, **1 mi N...lodging:** Best Western

28(182) NY 30A, Fonda, **N...gas:** Citgo/motel/diesel/rest./24hr, Getty/diesel, Gulf/repair, TA/rest/motel/diesel/24hr, **food:** McDonald's, Skip Dog's Grill, **lodging:** Holiday Inn(7mi), Riverside Motel, Super 8, Travelodge, **other:** HOSPITAL

184mm parking area both lanes, phones, litter barrels

29(194) NY 10, Canajoharie, **N...gas:** Gulf, Stewarts, **food:** McDonald's, Pizza Hut, **other:** $General, Rite Aid, **S...gas:** Getty/diesel, Sunoco, **lodging:** Econolodge(1mi), **other:** Chevrolet

210mm **Indian Castle Service area eb...gas: Sunoco/diesel, food: Big Boy, Mrs Fields, Roy Rogers, other: atm, gifts, UPS. Iroquois Service Area wb...gas: Sunoco/diesel, Burger King, Dunkin Donuts, Freshen's Frozen Treats, TCBY, gifts, UPS**

29a(211) NY 169, to Little Falls, HOSPITAL, to Herkimer Home

30(220) NY 28, to Mohawk, Herkimer, **N...gas:** Fastrac/diesel, Mobil/Subway/diesel, Stewarts, **food:** Applebee's, Burger King, Denny's, Friendly's, KFC/Taco Bell, McDonald's, Pizza Hut, Tony's Pizzaria, Waffle Works, **lodging:** Budget Motel, Herkimer Inn, Inn Towne, **other:** AutoZone, $Tree, Ford/Lincoln/Mercury, Goodyear, K-Mart, Rite Aid, Wal-Mart SuperCrt/24hr, **S...food:** Mohawk Sta Rest., **other:** Factory Depot, to Cooperstown(Baseball Hall of Fame)

227mm **Schuyler Service Area wb, Sunoco/diesel, Breyer's, Fresh Fudge, McDonald's, atm, st police**

31(233) I-790, NY 8, NY 12, to Utica, **N...gas:** Citgo/diesel, Fastrac, **food:** Burger King, **other:** Big Lots, BJ's Whse, $Tree, Eckerd, Lowe's Whse, PriceChopper Foods, Rite Aid, Wal-Mart SuperCtr/24hr(1mi W on frontage rd), **S...gas:** Hess/diesel, Sunoco/diesel, **food:** Delmonico's Steaks, Denny's, Dunkin Doughnuts, Friendly's, McDonald's, Pizza Hut, Taco Bell, Wendy's, **lodging:** A-1 Motel, Best Western, Happy Journey Motel, Motel 6, Red Roof Inn, Super 8

236mm I-790(from eb), to Utica, no facilities

237.5mm Erie Canal

238mm Mohawk River

32(243) NY 232, Westmoreland, **S...lodging:** Carriage House Motel, Quality Inn, **1 mi S...gas/diesel**

244mm **Oneida Service Area eb, Sunoco/diesel, Burger King, Cinnabon, Sbarro's, TCBY, atm, gifts**

250mm parking area eb, phones, picnic tables, litter barrel

Albany

Utica

NEW YORK
Interstate 90

33(253) NY 365, to Vernon Downs, Verona, **N...gas:** Citgo, SavOn Gas/diesel, Sunoco, **lodging:** Comfort Suites(6mi), Quality Inn(8mi), Turning Stone Resort/ casino, **other:** HOSPITAL, to Griffiss AFB, **S...gas:** SavOn Gas/diesel/repair, **lodging:** Super 8(3mi)

256mm parking area wb, phones, picnic tables, litter barrel

34(262) NY 13, to Canastota, **S...gas:** Mobil/diesel, SavOn/ diesel/24hr, **food:** Arby's, Canastota Rest., McDonald's, **lodging:** Days Inn, Graziano Motel/rest., Super 8(7mi), **other:** Boxing Hall of Fame, Verona Beach SP Camping

266mm Chittenango Service Area wb, Sunoco/diesel, Dunkin Donuts, Freshen's Treats, Sbarro's, TCBY, atm, gifts

34a(277) I-481, to Syracuse, Chittenango, no facilities

35(279) NY 298, The Circle, Syracuse, **S...gas:** Kwikfill, Mobil/repair, Sunoco/diesel, **food:** Burger King, Denny's, Dunkin Donuts, Joey's Italian, McDonald's, Pronto's Pizza, **lodging:** Candlewood Suites, Carrier Circle Inn, Comfort Inn, Courtyard, Day's Inn, Embassy Suites, Extended Stay America, Fairfield Inn, Hampton Inn, Holiday Inn, Howard Johnson Lodge, John Milton Inn, Marriott, Microtel, Motel 6, Ramada Ltd, Red Roof Inn, Residence Inn, Super 8, Wyndham Garden, **other:** Goodyear/auto, Speedy Transmissions

280mm Dewitt Service Area eb, Sunoco/diesel, McDonald's, ice cream

36(283) I-81, N to Watertown, S to Binghamton, no facilities

37(284) 7th St, Electronics Pkwy, to Liverpool, **N...lodging:** Best Western, **S...gas:** Hess/Godfather's/24hr, KFC/ Taco Bell, **lodging:** Holiday Inn, Homewood Suites, Knight's Inn, **1 mi S on 7th St...gas:** Mobil, **food:** Bob Evans, Burger King, Colorado Steaks, Denny's, Friendly's, Ground Round, Jreck Subs, **lodging:** Day's Inn, Econolodge, Hampton Inn, Quality Inn, Ramada Inn, Super 8, **other:** NAPA

38(286) NY 57, to Liverpool, Syracuse, **N...gas:** FasTrac, Hessmart, KwikFill, **food:** Hooligan's Grill, Kirby's Rest., Pier 57 Diner, Pizza Hut, **lodging:** Super 8, **other:** NAPA, **1 mi S...gas:** Mobil, Sunoco/24hr, **food:** Burger King, **other:** Onondaga Lake Park, Salt Museum

39(290) I-690, NY 690, Syracuse, **N...lodging:** Comfort Inn/ rest., **other:** Meyers RV Ctr

292mm Warners Service Area wb, Mobil/diesel/rest., McDonald's, Mama Iraldo's Café, ice cream

40(304) NY 34, to Owasco Lake, Weedsport, **N...**Riverforest RV Park, **S...gas:** Fastrac, KwikFill, Sunoco/diesel, **food:** Arby's, Arnold's Rest., DB's Drive-In, Old Erie Diner, **lodging:** Best Western, Day's Inn, Microtel, **other:** Big M Foods, NAPA

310mm Port Byron Service Area eb, Mobil/diesel/rest., Mama Iraldo's Café, McDonald's, ice cream

318mm parking area wb, picnic tables, phones

41(320) NY 414, to Cayuga Lake, Waterloo, **S...gas:** Mobil/ diesel, Petro/diesel/24hr/@, **food:** MaGee Country Diner, **other:** Waterloo Outlets/famous brands(3mi), NWR

324mm Junius Ponds Service Area wb, Sunoco/diesel, Dunkin Donuts, Mrs Fields, Roy Rogers, TCBY

42(327) NY 14, to Geneva, Lyons, **N...**RV camping, **S...gas:** Mobil/diesel, **lodging:** Relax Inn, **other:** Waterloo Outlets/famous brands(3mi)

337mm Clifton Springs Service Area eb, Sunoco/diesel, Roy Rogers, Sbarro's, TCBY, atm, gifts

43(340) NY 21, to Palmyra, Manchester, **N...**Hill Cumorah LDS HS(6mi), **S...gas:** Mobil/diesel/24hr, **food:** McDonald's, Steak-Out, **lodging:** Roadside Inn

44(347) NY 332, Victor, **S...gas:** Mobil/diesel, Sunoco/diesel, **food:** Di Pacific's Rest., KFC, McDonald's, Pizza Hut, Subway, **lodging:** Best Value Inn, Budget Inn, Econolodge, **other:** CVS Drug, KOA, st police

350mm Seneca Service Area wb, gas: Mobil/diesel, food: Burger King, Mrs Fields, Sbarro's, TCBY, other: atm, info, phone

45(351) I-490, NY 96, to Rochester, **N...lodging:** Hampton Inn, **S...gas:** KwikFill, **food:** Burger King, Chili's, Dede's Rest., Denny's, **lodging:** Exit 45 Motel, Microtel, **other:** Chevrolet

353mm parking area eb, phone, litter barrels

46(362) I-390, to Rochester, **N on NY 253 W...gas:** Citgo/diesel, Hess, **food:** McDonald's, Peppermints Rest., Tim Horton, Wendy's, **lodging:** Country Inn Suites, Day's Inn, Fairfield Inn, Marriott, Microtel, Red Carpet Inn, Red Roof Inn, Super 8

366mm Scottsville Service Area eb, gas: Mobil/diesel, food: Burger King, Dunkin Donuts, TCBY, other: atm, info

376mm Ontario Service Area wb, gas: Mobil/diesel/deli, food: McDonald's

47(379) I-490, NY 19, to Rochester, no facilities

48(390) NY 98, to Batavia, **N...lodging:** Comfort Inn, **S...gas:** Citgo, **food:** Bob Evans, **lodging:** Best Western, Day's Inn, Holiday Inn, Microtel, Park-Oak Motel, Red Carpet Inn, Sheraton, Super 8, **other:** OfficeMax, Wal-Mart/auto, **1 mi S on NY 63...gas:** Mobil, Sunoco, **food:** Arby's, Burger King, Denny's, McDonald's, Taco Bell, Perkins, Ponderosa, Red Dragon Chinese, Wendy's, **other:** Advance Parts, AutoZone, BJ's Whse, CarQuest, Chevrolet/Cadillac, CVS Drug, $Tree, GNC, Jo-Ann Fabrics, K-Mart, NAPA, Radio Shack, Top's Foods

397mm Pembroke Service Area eb, full(handicapped)facilities, gas: Sunoco/diesel, food: Burger King, Mrs Fields, Popeye's, Starbucks, TCBY, other: atm, gifts, phone, UPS

48a(402) NY 77, Pembroke, **S...gas:** Flying J/diesel/LP/rest./ 24hr/@, TA/Citgo/diesel/rest./24hr/@, **food:** Subway, **lodging:** Country Cottage Motel, Econolodge, 6 Flags Motel/RV Park

412mm Clarence Service Area wb, full(handicapped)facilities, gas: Sunoco/diesel, food: Burger King, Cinnabon, Nathan's Pizza Hut, TCBY, other: info, phone

49(417) NY 78, Depew, **1-2 mi N...gas:** Mobil, Sunoco, **food:** Applebee's, Arby's, Bennigan's, Boston Mkt, Burger King, ChiChi's, Cracker Barrel, Denny's, Don Pablo, Eatery Rest., Fazoli's, Golden Corral, KFC, McDonald's, Mighty Taco, Old Country Buffet, Perkins, Picasso's Pizza, Pizza Hut, Ponderosa, Protocol Rest., Red Lobster, Roadhouse Grill, Ruby Tuesday, Shogun Japanese, Spilio's Rest., Starbucks, Subway, Ted's Hotdogs, TGIFriday, Wendy's, **lodging:** Clarion, Econolodge, Fairfield Inn,

Interstate 90

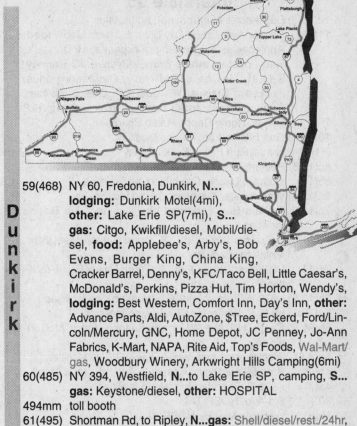

Holiday Inn Express, Microtel, Ramada Ltd, **other:** Acura, Barnes&Noble, Buick, Dodge, Eckerd/24hr, Firestone/auto, Ford, Home Depot, JC Penney, Jo-Ann Fabrics, K-Mart, Mitsubishi, NTB, OfficeMax, Saturn, Sears/auto, Target, TireMax, Top's Food/deli, Wal-Mart/auto, Wegman's Foods, mall, **S...gas:** Kwikfill, Mobil, **food:** Bob Evans, John&Mary's Cafe, Salvatore's Italian, **lodging:** Garden Place Hotel, Hospitality Inn, Howard Johnson, Red Roof Inn, Sleep Inn, **other:** Aamco, Top's Foods

419mm   toll booth

50(420)   I-290 to Niagara Falls, no facilities

50a(421) Cleveland Dr(from eb), no facilities

51(422)   NY 33 E, Buffalo, **S...**airport, st police

52(423)   Walden Ave, to Buffalo, **N...food:** Arby's, Bob Evans, Subway, TGIFriday, Tim Horton, Wendy's, **lodging:** Hampton Inn, Residence Inn, **other:** Aldi, Ford, Goodyear, Target, **S...gas:** Sunoco/diesel/rest./24hr/@, **food:** Alton's Rest., McDonald's, Milton's Rest., Olive Garden, Pizza Hut, **lodging:** Sheraton, **other:** Borders Books, Dodge, JC Penney, K-Mart, Niagara Hobby, Wegman's Foods, mall

52a(424) William St, no facilities

53(425)   I-190, to Buffalo, Niagara Falls, **N...food:** McDonald's, **lodging:** Holiday Inn Express

54(428)   NY 400, NY 16, to W Seneca, E Aurora, no facilities

55(430)   US 219, Ridge Rd, Orchard Park, to Rich Stadium, **S...gas:** KissMart, **food:** Arby's, Denny's, Ponderosa, Subway, Wendy's, **lodging:** Hampton Inn, **other:** Aldi, Home Depot, K-Mart

431mm   toll booth

56(432)   NY 179, Mile Strip Rd, **N...gas:** Citgo, Sunoco, **food:** Burger King, **lodging:** Econolodge, **other:** CVS Drug, Jubilee Foods, **S...gas:** Citgo, **food:** Applebee's, Boston Mkt, ChiChi's, ChuckeCheese, Garfield's Rest., McDonald's, Olive Garden, Outback Steaks, Pizza Hut, Red Lobster, Roadhouse Grill, Ruby Tuesday, Starbucks, Subway, TGIFriday, Wendy's, **other:** Aldi Foods, BJ's Whse, Firestone/auto, Home Depot, JC Penney, Jo-Ann Etc, OfficeMax, PepBoys, Sears/auto, Wegman's Foods, mall

57(436)   NY 75, to Hamburg, **N...gas:** Exit 57/diesel/rest., Mobil/diesel, **food:** Bob Evans, Denny's, McDonald's, Wendy's, **lodging:** Comfort Suites, Day's Inn, Red Roof Inn, Tallyho Motel, **other:** Chevrolet, Chrysler/Plymouth/Jeep/Mitsubishi, Dodge, Ford, GMC/Pontiac, Kia, **S...gas:** Kwikfill/diesel, Mobil, Stop&Gas, **food:** Arby's, Burger King, Camp Rd Diner, Pizza Hut, Subway, **lodging:** Holiday Inn, **other:** Goodyear/auto, USPO

442mm   parking area both lanes, phone, litter barrels

57a(445 to Eden, Angola, **2 mi N...gas:** Sunoco/diesel

447mm   Angola Service Area both lanes, full(handicapped) facilities, Mobil/diesel, Denny's, McDonald's, phone/fax, gifts

58(456)   US 20, NY 5, to Silver Creek, Irving, **N...gas:** Citgo, Kwikfill, **food:** Burger King, Aunt Millie's Rest., Sunset Grill, Tom's Rest., **other:** HOSPITAL, to Evangola SP

59(468)   NY 60, Fredonia, Dunkirk, **N...** **lodging:** Dunkirk Motel(4mi), **other:** Lake Erie SP(7mi), **S... gas:** Citgo, Kwikfill/diesel, Mobil/diesel, **food:** Applebee's, Arby's, Bob Evans, Burger King, China King, Cracker Barrel, Denny's, KFC/Taco Bell, Little Caesar's, McDonald's, Perkins, Pizza Hut, Tim Horton, Wendy's, **lodging:** Best Western, Comfort Inn, Day's Inn, **other:** Advance Parts, Aldi, AutoZone, $Tree, Eckerd, Ford/Lincoln/Mercury, GNC, Home Depot, JC Penney, Jo-Ann Fabrics, K-Mart, NAPA, Rite Aid, Top's Foods, Wal-Mart/gas, Woodbury Winery, Arkwright Hills Camping(6mi)

60(485)   NY 394, Westfield, **N...**to Lake Erie SP, camping, **S... gas:** Keystone/diesel, **other:** HOSPITAL

494mm   toll booth

61(495)   Shortman Rd, to Ripley, **N...gas:** Shell/diesel/rest./24hr, **other:** Lakeshore RV Park

496mm   New York/Pennsylvania state line

Interstate 95

Exit #	Services
32mm	New York/Connecticut state line
22(30)	Midland Ave(from nb), Port Chester, Rye, **W...gas:** BP, Shell, Sunoco, **other:** HOSPITAL, A&P, Home Depot, Staples
21(29)	I-287 W, US 1 N, to White Plains, Port Chester, Tappan Zee, no facilities
20(28)	US 1 S(from nb), Port Chester, **E...**Subaru
19(27)	Playland Pkwy, Rye, Harrison, no facilities
18b(25)	Mamaroneck Ave, to White Plains, **E...gas:** Shell, **other:** CVS Drug
18a(24)	Fenimore Rd(from nb), Mamaroneck, **E...gas:** Citgo
17(20)	Chatsworth Ave(from nb, no return), Larchmont, no facilities
19.5mm	toll plaza
16(19)	North Ave, Cedar St, New Rochelle, **E...food:** McDonald's, Taco Bell, **lodging:** Radisson, Residence Inn, **other:** Stop&Shop Foods, Toyota, **W...**HOSPITAL
15(16)	US 1, New Rochelle, The Pelhams, **E...gas:** Getty/diesel, PitStop/24hr, **food:** Thru-Way Diner, **other:** AutoZone, Costco, CVS Drug, Home Depot, NAPA, **W...**auto repair
14(15)	Hutchinson Pkwy(from sb), to Whitestone Br, no facilities
13(16)	Conner St, to Mt Vernon, **E...gas:** Gulf/diesel, **lodging:** Econolodge, **W...gas:** BP, **food:** McDonald's, **lodging:** Andrea Motel, **other:** HOSPITAL

NEW YORK

Interstate 95

E ↕ **W**

N Y C A r e a

12(15.5)	Baychester Ave(from nb), no facilities
11(15)	Bartow Ave, Co-op City Blvd, **E...gas:** Mobil, **food:** Applebee's, Burger King, Checker's, McDonald's, Red Lobster, **other:** Barnes&Noble, JC Penney, K-Mart, Marshalls, Old Navy, PathMark Foods, Popeye's, Staples, **W...gas:** BP, Gulf, Shell/mart, Sunoco/diesel, **food:** Eastern Wok, **other:** A&P Foods, Home Depot, Radio Shack
10(14.5)	Gun Hill Rd(from nb), no facilities
9(14)	Hutchinson Pkwy, **E...**JC Penny
8c(13.5)	Pelham Pkwy W, no facilities
8b(13)	Orchard Beach, City Island, no facilities
8a(12.5)	Westchester Ave(from sb), no facilities
7c(12)	Pelham Bay Park(from nb), Country Club Rd, no facilities
7b(11.5)	E Tremont(from sb), **E...gas:** Citgo/diesel/24hr, Mobil, **food:** diner
7a(11)	I-695(from sb), to I-295 S, Throgs Neck Br, no facilities
6b(10.5)	I-278 W(from sb), I-295 S(from nb), no facilities
6a(10)	I-678 S, Whitestone Bridge, no facilities
5b(9)	Castle Hill Ave, **W...gas:** Sunoco, **food:** McDonald's
5a(8.5)	Westchester Ave, White Plains Rd, no facilities
4b(8)	Bronx River Pkwy, Rosedale Ave, **W...gas:** Mobil
4a(7)	I-895 S, Sheridan Expsy, no facilities
3(6)	3rd Ave, HOSPITAL
2b(5)	Webster Ave, **E...**HOSPITAL
2a(4)	Jerome Ave, to I-87, no facilities
1c(3)	I-87, Deegan Expswy, to Upstate, no facilities
1b(2)	Harlem River Dr(from sb), no facilities
1a(1)	US 9, NY 9A, H Hudson Pkwy, 178th St, HOSPITAL
0mm	New York/New Jersey state line, Hudson River, Geo Washington Br

Interstate 190(Buffalo)

E ↕ **W**

N i a g a r a F a l l s

Exit #	Services
25.5mm	US/Canada Border, US Customs
25b a	R Moses Pkwy, NY 104, NY 265, Lewiston, no facilities
24	NY 31, Witmer Rd, **E...**st police
23	NY 182, Porter Rd, Packard Rd, **E...gas:** Sunoco, **food:** Burger King, DQ, **other:** Firestone/auto, K-Mart, NAPA, Prime Outlets/famous brands, U-Haul, **W...food:** Wendy's, **other:** Aldi Foods, Sam's Club, Wal-Mart
22	US 62, Niagara Falls Blvd, **E...food:** Bob Evans, Taco Bell, Timberlodge Steaks, **lodging:** Budget Host, Howard Johnson, Red Carpet Inn, **other:** Chevrolet/Buick/Pontiac, Ford, Jeep, Target, Top's Foods, Toyota, **W...lodging:** Econolodge, Scottish Inn, **other:** Home Depot
21b	NY 384, Buffalo Ave, R Moses Pkwy, **W...**Getty, NY SP, American Falls
a	La Salle Expswy
20.5mm	Niagara River East, toll booth
20b a	Long Rd, **E...lodging:** Budget Motel, **other:** Country Store

Interstate 190

19	Whitehaven Rd, **E...gas:** Getty, **other:** Top's Foods, KOA, **W...other:** Chevrolet
18b a	NY 324 W, Grand Island Blvd, **E...gas:** Mobil, **food:** Burger King, **W...**Beaver Island SP
17.5mm	Niagara River East
17	NY 266, toll booth
16	I-290 E, to I-90, Albany
15	NY 324, Kenmore Ave, **W...**U-Haul
14	Ontario St, **E...gas:** KwikFill, Mobil, **food:** McDonald's, Tim Horton, **other:** Advance Parts, **W...food:** Harry's Grille
11	NY 198, Buffalo, downtown
10mm	toll booth
9	Porter Ave, to Peace Bridge, Ft Erie
8	NY 266, Niagara St, downtown, **E...lodging:** Adam's Mark Hotel
7	NY 5 W, Church St, Buffalo, downtown
6	Elm St, **E...**HOSPITAL, downtown, **W...**HSBC Arena
5	Louisiana St, Buffalo, downtown
4	Smith St, Fillmore Ave, Buffalo, downtown
3	NY 16, Seneca St, **W...other:** Hutchins Auto Parts
2	US 62, NY 354, Bailey Ave, Clinton St, no facilities
1	Ogden St, **E...gas:** Sunoco, **food:** Wendy's, **lodging:** Best Value Inn, Holiday Inn Express, **other:** Volvo/GMC Trucks
.5mm	toll plaza nb
0mm	I-90. I-190 begins/ends on I-90, exit 53.

Interstate 287(NYC)

E ↕ **W**

N Y C A r e a

Exit#	Services
12	I-95, N to New Haven, S to NYC. I-287 begins/ends on I-95, exit 21.
11	US 1, Port Chester, Rye, **N...gas:** Amoco, Mobil, Sunoco, Shell, **food:** Burger King, Maryann 's Mexican, McDonald's, Port Chester Diner, Wendy's, **other:** HOSPITAL, A&P, Goodyear, Kohl's, Medallion Repair, Nissan, Staples
10	Bowman Ave, Webb Ave, no facilities
9N S	Hutchinson Pkwy, Merritt Pkwy, to Whitestone Br
9a	I-684, Brewster, no facilities
8	Westchester Ave, to White Plains, **S...other:** Nordstrom's, Westchester Mall Place
7	Taconic Pkwy(from wb), to N White Plains
6	NY 22, White Plains
5	NY 100, Hillside Ave, **S...gas:** Citgo, Getty, Mobil, **food:** Planet Pizza, **other:** Aamco
4	NY 100A, Hartsdale, **N...**HOSPITAL, **S...gas:** Amoco, **food:** Burger King, **other:** BMW, Dodge/Hyundai, Jaguar, Nissan/Mazda, Staples, Volvo
3	Sprain Pkwy, to Taconic Pkwy, NYC
2	NY 9A, Elmsford, **N...gas:** Amoco, Shell, Sunoco, **food:** Red Fox Diner
1	NY 119, Tarrytown, **N...lodging:** Marriott, **S...gas:** Exxon/diesel, Mobil, **lodging:** Extended Stay America, Hampton Inn

I-287 runs with I-87 N.

Interstate 290(Buffalo)

Exit #	Services
8	I-90, NY Thruway, I-290 begins/ends on I-90, exit 50.
7b a	NY 5, Main St, **N...gas:** Sunoco, **food:** La Nova Wings, Pizza Plant, Tim Horton, **S...gas:** Coastal, **food:** Sonoma Grille, **lodging:** Amherst Motel
6	NY 324, NY 240, **N...gas:** Getty, **lodging:** Courtyard, **other:** Cadillac, **S...other:** MEDICAL CARE, Chrysler/Dodge
5b a	NY 263, to Millersport, **N...gas:** Christino's Bistro, **lodging:** Hampton Inn, Marriott, Red Roof Inn, **S...gas:** Mobil, **lodging:** Homewood Suites, Motel 6, **other:** Nissan, Toyota, VW, Walgreen
4	I-990, to St U, no facilities
3b a	US 62, to Niagara Falls Blvd, **N...gas:** Citgo, Sunoco, **food:** Bob Evans, Max's Grill, Roadhouse Grill, **lodging:** Blvd Inn, Extended Stay America, Holiday Inn, Sleep Inn, Travelodge, **other:** Home Depot, Wal-Mart, **S...gas:** Mobil/mart, **food:** Applebee's, Don Pablo, Montana's Grill, Outback Steaks, Starbucks, Subway, Tim Horton, **other:** Barnes&Noble, Best Buy, Jo-Ann Fabrics, K-Mart, Target
2	NY 425, Colvin Blvd, **N...food:** KFC, McDonald's, Subway, Wendy's, **lodging:** Microtel, **other:** BJ's Whse, Family$, Goodyear/auto, Top's Foods, **S...gas:** Kwikfill, **food:** Old Town Bistro
1b a	Elmwood Ave, NY 384, NY 265, **N...gas:** Kwikfill, **lodging:** Microtel, **other:** Rite Aid, **S...gas:** Mobil/diesel/mart, **food:** Arby's, **other:** HOSPITAL
0mm	I-190. I-290 begins/ends on I-190 in Buffalo.

Interstate 390(Rochester)

Exit #	Services
20a b(76)	I-490. I-390 begins/ends on I-490 in Rochester
19(75)	NY 33a, Chili Ave, **N...food:** Wishing Well Rest., **S...gas:** Sunoco, **food:** Burger King, Subway, **lodging:** Day's Inn
18a b(74)	NY 204, Brooks Ave, **N...lodging:** Holiday Inn, **S...lodging:** Fairfield Inn, Motel 6, **other:** airport
17(73)	NY 383, Scottsville Rd, **W...gas:** Sunoco/Subway/diesel
16(71)	NY 15a, to E Henryetta, **S...lodging:** Courtyard, Hampton Inn, HOSPITAL
15(70)	I-590, Rochester,
14(68)	NY 15a, NY 252, **E...food:** Outback Steaks, Perkins, Tully's Rest., **other:** Staples, **W...gas:** Mobil, **food:** Boston Mkt, Krispy Kreme, Taco Bell, **lodging:** Holiday Inn, **other:** Barnes&Noble, Big Lots, Office Depot, Top's Foods
13(67)	Hylan Dr., **E...food:** Cracker Barrel, **lodgin:** Comfort Suites, Homewood Suites, **W...gas:** Mobil, **other:** Best Buy, Circuit City, Lowe's Whse, Pep Boys, Sam's Club, Target, Wal-Mart SuperCtr/24hr, mall
12(66)	I-90. NY Thruway, NY 253, **N on NY 253 W...gas:** Citgo/diesel, Hess, **food:** McDonald's, Peppermints Rest., Tim Horton, Wendy's, **lodging:** Country Inn Suites, Day's Inn, Fairfield Inn, Marriott, Microtel, Red Carpet Inn, Red Roof Inn, Super 8

11(62)	NY 15, NY 251, Rush, Scottsville, **S...food:** McDonald's, Wendy's, **lodging:** Cartwright Inn, Days Inn, Fairfield Inn, Red Roof Inn, RIT Inn
10(55)	US 20, NY 5, Avon, Lima, **N...food:** Tom Wahls Cafe, **lodging:** Cresthill Motel, Srtatford Motel, **S...gas:** Citgo/diesel, Mobil/diesel, **food:** Avon Cafe, Dutch Hollow Cafe, McDonald's, **lodging:** Avon Cedar Lodge, **other:** Crystler/Plymouth/Dodge/Jeep, Sugar Creek Camping
9(52)	NY 15, **N...gas:** Hess/Dunkin Doughnuts/diesel, **food:** Fratelli's Rest., Lakeville Rest., Tee&Gee Cafe, **S...other:** Buick/Pontiac/GMC
8(48)	US 20a, Geneseo, **N...food:** Arby's, **lodging:** Oak Valley Inn, **other:** Conesus Camping, **S...food:** Denny's, Dunking Doughnuts, KFC/Taco Bell, McDonald's, Wendy's, **lodging:** Day's Inn
7(39)	NY 63, NY 408, Geneseo, **S...gas:** Mobil, KwikFill, **food:** Brian's Diner, McDonald's, Millsrace Rest., **lodging:** Alligence B&B, Country Inn, Geneseo Hotel/Rest., Greenway Motel, **other:** Ridge Camping
38mm	rest area both lanes, full(handicapped)facilities, picnic tables, litter barrels, vending, petwalk
6(33)	NY 36, Mt Morris, Sonyea, **S...other:** The Ridge Camping, Letchworth Camping
5(26)	NY 36, Dansville, **N...gas:** Mobil/Subway, KwikFill, **food:** Arby's, Burger King, McDonald's, Pizza Hut, Subway, **other:** Advance Parts, Chevrolet, Ford/Lincoln/Mercuryt, Pontiac, Sav-A-lot Foods, Top's Foods, **S...gas:** TA/Mobil/Buckhorn Rest./@, **lodging:** Day's Inn
4(23)	NY 36, Dansville, **N...gas:** Citgo/diesel, **lodging:** Dansville Inn, Logan's Inn, **other:** HOSPITAL, Skybrook Camping, **S...other:** Sugar Creek Camping, Stonybrook Park Camping, Sunvalley Camping
3(17)	NY 15, NY 21, Wayland, **N...food:** Farmer's Kitchen Rest., **other:** Holiday Hill Campground(7mi), st patrol
2(11)	NY 415, Cohocton, Naples, **N...gas:** Mobil, **ohter:** Tumble Hill Camping(2mi)
1(2)	NY 415, I-390 begins/ends, Avoca, **N...truck/auto repair, **S...gas:** Mobil, **lodging:** Caboose Motel(3mi)

NEW YORK
Interstate 495(Long Island)

Exit #   Services

I-495 begins/ends on NY 25.

E

W

Long Island

73 rd 58, Old Country Road, to Greenport, Orient, **S...gas:** Coastal/diesel, **other:** Tanger/famous brands, **1 mi S...gas:** Exxon, Gulf, Mobil, **food:** Taco Bell, Wendy's, **other:** CVS Drug, Ford/Lincoln/Mercury, Nissan/Hyundai/Suzuki, Pergament, Tire Country, Waldbaum's

72 NY 25, Riverhead, Calverton(no EZ eb return), **S...lodging:** Ramada Inn/grill, **other:** Tanger/famous brands/foodcourt

71 NY 24, Calverton, to Hampton Bays, no facilities

70 NY 111, Manorville, to Eastport, **S...gas:** Mobil

69 Wading River Rd, to Wading River, Center Moriches, no facilities

68 NY 46, to Shirley, Wading River, no facilities

66 NY 101, Sills Rd, Yaphank, **N...**gas, food

64 NY 112, Medford, to Coram, **N...other:** Home Depot, King Kullen Foods, Sam's Club, **S...gas:** Amoco, Exxon, Gulf, 7-11, **lodging:** Gateway Inn, **other:** cinema

63 NY 83, **N...gas:** Hess, **S...gas:** Exxon, **food:** Churchill's Rest., **lodging:** Best Western

62 rd 97, to Blue Point, Stony Brook, **N...gas:** Gulf

61 rd 19, Holbrook, to Patchogue, **N...gas:** Mobil, **S...gas:** Exxon/diesel

60 Ronkonkoma Ave, **N...gas:** Exxon, **S...gas:** Shell

59 Ocean Ave, Ronkonkoma, to Oakdale, **S...gas:** Exxon

58 Old Nichols Rd, Nesconset, **N...gas:** Exxon, **food:** Hooters, **lodging:** Marriott, Wyndham Garden, **S...gas:** Amoco

57 NY 454, Vets Hwy, to Hauppauge, **N...gas:** Exxon/diesel, **food:** TGIFriday, **S... gas:** Amoco/24hr, Exxon, Gulf/diesel/24hr, Shell, **food:** Blue Dawn Diner, New Horizon Diner, Subway, **lodging:** Hampton Inn, **other:** Stop&Shop Foods

56 NY 111, Smithtown, Islip, **N...gas:** Exxon/Subway/Domino's/diesel, Mobil, **S...gas:** Mobil, **food:** Café La Strada, **lodging:** Holiday Inn Express

55 Central Islip, **N...gas:** Mobil, **S...gas:** Shell/diesel

54 Wicks Rd, **N...gas:** Amoco, **lodging:** Howard Johnson, Sheraton, **S...gas:** Mobil

53 Sunken Meadow Pkwy, Bayshore, to ocean beaches

52 rd 4, Commack, **N...gas:** Mobil/diesel, Shell/repair, **food:** Conca d'Oro Pizza, Ground Round, **lodging:** Hampton Inn, **other:** Costco

51.5mm parking area both lanes, phone, litter barrels

51 NY 231, to Northport, Babylon, no facilities

50 Bagatelle Rd, to Wyandanch, no facilities

49N NY 110 N, to Huntington, **N...lodging:** Marriott
   S NY 110 S, to Amityville

48 Round Swamp Rd, Old Bethpage, **S...gas:** Mobil/diesel, **food:** Old Country Pizza/deli, **lodging:** Rodeway Inn, **other:** USPO

46 Sunnyside Blvd, Plainview, **N...lodging:** Holiday Inn

45 Manetto Hill Rd, Plainview, Woodbury, no facilities

44 NY 135, to Seaford, Syosset, no facilities

43 S Oyster Bay Rd, to Syosset, Bethpage, **N...gas:** Mobil

42 Northern Pkwy, rd N, Hauppauge, no facilities

41 NY 106, NY 107, Hicksville, Oyster Bay, **S...gas:** Amoco, Mobil, Sunoco, **food:** Boston Mkt, Boulder Creek Steaks, Broadway Diner, Burger King, Dunkin Donuts, McDonald's, **lodging:** On the Border, Circuit City, Goodyear/auto, Sears/auto

40 NY 25, Mineola, Syosset, **S...gas:** Amoco, Exxon, Hess/diesel, Shell, 7-11, **food:** Burger King, Friendly's, IHOP, McDonald's, Nathan's Famous, Wendy's, **lodging:** Edgerton Motel, Hostway Motel, Howard Johnson, **other:** Home Depot, Kohl's, OffTrack Betting, Staples

39 Glen Cove Rd, **N...gas:** Mobil

38 Northern Pkwy E, Meadowbrook Pkwy, to Jones Beach

37 Willis Ave, to Roslyn, Mineola, **N...gas:** Exxon, Shell, **other:** repair, **S...gas:** Gulf,

36 Searingtown Rd, to Port Washington, **S...HOSPITAL**

35 Shelter Rock Rd, Manhasset, no facilities

34 New Hyde Park Rd, no facilities

33 Lakeville Rd, to Great Neck, **N...HOSPITAL**

32 Little Neck Pkwy, **N...food:** pizza

31 Douglaston Pkwy, **S...gas:** Amoco, **food:** Stern's, **other:** USPO, Waldbaum's Foods, mall

30 E Hampton Blvd, Cross Island Pkwy

29 Springfield Blvd, **S...gas:** Exxon, Texaco/repair, **food:** Chinese Rest., McDonald's

27 I-295, Clearview Expswy, Throgs Neck, **N...gas:** Gulf, 7-11, **food:** Blue Bay Diner, **other:** Rockbottom Drug

26 Francis Lewis Blvd, S

25 Utopia Pkwy, 188th St, **N...gas:** Citgo, Mobil, Sunoco, **S...gas:** Amoco, Gaseteria, Mobil, Shell/repair, Sunoco, **other:** Filene's Basement, Fresh Meadows, Goodyear, Radio Shack

24 Kissena Blvd, **N...gas:** Exxon/diesel, **food:** Dunkin Donuts, **S...gas:** Mobil

23 Main St, **N...food:** Palace Diner

22 Grand Central Pkwy, to I-678, College Pt Blvd, **N...gas:** Citgo, Mobil, **lodging:** Paris Suites, **S...gas:** Mobil, **lodging:** Best Western

21 108th St, **N...gas:** Gaseteria

19 NY 25, Queens Blvd, Woodhaven Blvd, to Rockaways, **N...other:** JC Penney, Macy's, Stern's, mall, **S...gas:** Amoco, **other:** Circuit City, Marshall's, Old Navy, Sears

18.5 69th Ave, Grand Ave(from wb), no facilities

18 Maurice St, **N...gas:** Amoco, **S...gas:** Gaseteria/Dunkin Donuts, **food:** McDonald's, **other:** diesel repair

17 48th St, to I-278, no facilities

16 I-495 begins/ends in NYC.

Interstate 26

E

↕

W

Exit #	Services
71mm	North Carolina/South Carolina state line
69mm	N Pacolet River
67.5mm	**Welcome Ctr wb, full(handicapped)facilities, phone, picnic tables, litter barrels**
67	US 74 E, to NC 108, Columbus, Tryon, **N...gas:** BP/Burger King/diesel, Exxon/diesel, Shell, **food:** Hardee's, KFC, McDonald's, Subway, Waffle House, Western Steer, **lodging:** Day's Inn, **other:** HOSPITAL, Food Lion
59	Saluda, **N...lodging:** Heaven's View Motel, **other:** camping, **S...gas:** BP/diesel/mart, Shell/mart, **food:** Apple Mill Rest./gifts, **other:** repair
56mm	Green River
54	US 25, to Greenville, E Flat Rock, access to Carl Sandburg Home
53.5mm	Eastern Continental Divide, 2130 ft
53	Upward Rd, Hendersonville, **N...gas:** Shell/diesel, **food:** Waffle House, **lodging:** Mtn Inn Suites, **other:** Dish Barn Giftshop, **S...gas:** Exxon/McDonald's/diesel, Shell/Pizza Inn, **food:** Burger King, Cracker Barrel, **lodging:** Holiday Inn Express, **other:** RV camping, to Carl Sandburg Home
49b a	US 64, Hendersonville, **N...gas:** Chevron, Shell/diesel/24hr, Texaco/diesel, **food:** Atlanta Bread Co, Chick-fil-A, Fazoli's, Jack-in-the-Box, Sonic, Waffle House, **lodging:** Best Western, Hampton Inn, Quality Inn, Ramada Ltd, **other:** HOSPITAL, CarQuest, $Tree, Ingles, Radio Shack, Staples, Wal-Mart SuperCtr/gas/24hr, World of Clothing, **S...gas:** Chevron/diesel, Exxon/diesel/LP, Shell/diesel, **food:** Applebee's, Arby's, Bojangles, Burger King, Checker's, City Grill, Denny's, Fatz Café, Hardee's, KFC, Krispy Kreme, LJ Silver, McDonald's, McGuffey's Café, Outback Steaks, Pizza Hut, Ryan's, Schlotsky's, Shoney's, Subway/TCBY, Taco Bell, Wendy's, **lodging:** Comfort Inn, Day's Inn, Red Roof Inn, **other:** HOSPITAL, Belk, BiLo Foods, CVS Drug, Goodyear/auto, Home Depot, JC Penney, K-Mart, Lowe's Whse, Parts+, mall
46mm	weigh sta both lanes, phones
44	US 25, Fletcher, **N...gas:** Exxon/diesel, **food:** Hardee's, Subway, **other:** HOSPITAL, flea mkt, **S...gas:** Citgo/diesel, Exxon/diesel, Shell/Bojangles/diesel/24hr, **food:** Bojangles, Burger King, Huddle House, **other:** Todd's RV/marine, to Uncle John's

Hendersonville

Asheville

41mm	**rest area both lanes, full(handicapped)facilities, phone, picnic tables, litter barrels, vending**
40	NC 280, Arden, **N...gas:** Exxon/diesel, Shell/Arby's/diesel, **food:** McDonald's, Pizza Hut, Tijuana Jct Mexican, Waffle House, **lodging:** Budget Motel, Comfort Inn, Day's Inn, Econolodge, Hampton Inn, Holiday Inn/rest., Sun Valley Motel, **other:** Honda/Acura/Kia, **S...gas:** BP/diesel, **food:** J&S Cafeteria, **lodging:** Fairfield Inn, **other:** Asheville Airport, BMW, Rutledg Lake Camping
37	NC 146, Skyland, **N...gas:** BP/diesel, Shell/McDonald's/diesel/24hr, **food:** Arby's, Shoney's, Waffle House, **lodging:** Quality Inn, **2 mi N on US 25...gas:** Exxon, **food:** BBQ, Bojangles, Sagebrush Steaks, Taco Bell, **other:** Advance Parts, Firestone/auto, NAPA, **S...food:** Cider Mill Rest.
34mm	French Broad River
33	NC 191, Brevard Rd, **N...other:** Saturn/Toyota, **2 mi N...gas:** Phillips 66, **other:** Asheville Farmers Mkt, Bear Creek RV Camp, **S...gas:** Citgo, HotSpot, Phillips 66/diesel, **food:** China Garden, Garfield's, Harbor Inn Seafood, LJ Silver, Los Volcanes, McDonald's, Ryan's, SouperSalad, Subway, Taco Bell, Texas Roadhouse, Waffle House, **lodging:** Baymont Inn, Comfort Suites, Country Inn Suites, Hampton Inn, Holiday Inn Express, Super 8, Wingate Inn, **other:** Belk, Dillard's, K-Mart, Ingles Foods, mall, to Blue Ridge Pkwy
32b a	I-40, E to Statesville, W to Knoxville
27mm	Patton Ave, see I-240(Asheville), exit 3a, 3b
25	rd 251, to UNCA
24	Elk Mtn Rd, Woodfin, no facilities
23	Merrimon Ave, N Asheville, **N...gas:** Exxon/diesel, **lodging:** Day's Inn, **other:** Food Lion, camping
21	New Stock Rd, **N...gas:** Citgo, **food:** Pizza Hut, **other:** Ingles
19a b	N US 25, W US 70, Marshall, **N...gas:** Shell/diesel, U-fillerup, **food:** Arby's, Bojangles, Burger King, KFC, McDonald's, Waffle House, **other:** Napa, **S...gas:** BP/diesel, Shell/diesel,
18	Weaverville(no EZ return from eb), no facilities
17	to Flat Creek, no facilities

Interstate 26

E

15	rd 197, to Jupiter, Barnardsville, no facilities
13	Forks of Ivy, **N...gas:** BP/diesel, **S...gas:** Exxon/diesel
11	rd 213, to Mars Hill, Marshall, **S...gas:** Chevron/diesel, Exxon/diesel, Shell/Subway/diesel, **food:** Hardee's, Mountain Harbor Seafood, Pizza Roma, Waffle House, **lodging:** Comfort Inn, **other:** Ford, Napa

W

9	Burnsville, Spruce Pine, no facilities
8mm	scenic overlook wb
7mm	runaway truck ramp eb
6mm	**Welcome Ctr/rest area eb, full (handicapped) facilities**
5.5mm	runaway truck ramp eb
5mm	Buckner Gap, elev. 3370
3	to US 23,, Wolf Laurel, no facilities
2.5mm	runaway truck ramp
0mm	North Carolina/Tennessee state line

Interstate 40

E

Wilmington

Exit #	Services
420mm	I-40 begins/ends at Wilmington, **Facilities on US 17, N...food:** Bob Evans, **other:** Chrysler/Jeep, Lincoln/Mercury/Isuzu, Home Depot, Kia, Nissan, Subaru/Saab/Audi, Toyota, VW, **S...gas:** Crown/diesel/24hr, Dodge's Store/gas, Exxon/diesel/24hr, Shell, **food:** Buffalo Wings, Burger King, Carrabba's, Chick-fil-A, Cracker Barrel, Hardee's, Hooters, IHOP, KFC, McDonald's, Ruby Tuesday, Sticky Fingers Rest., Taco Bell, Waffle House, Wendy's, **lodging:** Best Western, Day's Inn, Extended Stay America, Fairfield Inn, GreenTree Inn, Hampton Inn, Holiday Inn, Howard Johnson, Innkeeper, MainStay Suites, Motel 6, Ramada Inn, Rodeway Inn, Sheraton, Sleep Inn, Super 8, Wingate Inn, **other:** Advance Parts, AutoZone, Batteries+, Buffalo Tire/auto, Buick, Circuit City, Food Lion, Marshall's, OfficeMax, Saturn/Suzuki, Target, Wal-Mart SuperCtr/gas/24hr, **Facilities 2-4 mi S on NC 132...gas:** BP, Exxon/diesel, Scotsman, **food:** Applebee's, Bennigan's, Bojangles, Burger King, Checker's, Chili's, Domino's, Golden Corral, Golden Phoenix Chinese, Hardee's, KFC, McAlister's Deli, McDonald's, Outback Steaks, Perkins, Pier 20 Seafood, Rockola Café, Subway, Taco Bell, TCBY, Wendy's, **lodging:** Comfort Inn, Courtyard, Fairfield Inn, Holiday Inn Express, **other:** Barnes&Noble, Best Buy, Chevrolet, Chrysler/Plymouth, CVS Drug, $Tree, Ford, Harris-Teeter/24hr, Honda/Acura, Hyundai, K-Mart, Lowe's Foods, Lowe's Whse, Pontiac/GMC/Mercedes, Sam's Club
420b a	Gordon Rd, NC 132 N, **2 mi N...gas:** Citgo/diesel, Kangaroo/diesel, **food:** McDonald's, Perkins, Smithfield's Chicken/BBQ, KOA(4mi), **S...gas:** BP/diesel, Kangaroo/diesel, **food:** Subway
416	new interchange
414	to Brunswick Co beaches, Castle Hayne, **S...gas:** BP, Kangaroo, **food:** Hardee's
412	NE Cape Fear River

W

408	NC 210, **S...gas:** Exxon/diesel, **food:** Paul's Place Café, **other:** to Moore's Creek Nat Bfd/camping
398	NC 53, Burgaw, **2 mi S...food:** Andy's Rest., McDonald's, Skat's Café, Subway, **lodging:** Burgaw Motel, **other:** HOSPITAL, camping
390	to US 117, Wallace, no facilities
385	NC 41, Wallace, **N...gas:** Exxon, **food:** Mad Boar Rest., **lodging:** Holiday Inn Express, River Landing Cottages, **other:** camping, **2-3 mi S...to US 117, food:** Andy's Cafe, Hardee's, KFC/Taco Bell, McDonald's, **lodging:** Liberty Inn(4mi)
384	NC 11, Wallace, **S...lodging:** B&B
380	Rose Hill, **S...gas:** BP/diesel(1mi), Pure/grill, lodging(mi)
373	NC 903, Magnolia, **N...gas:** BP/diesel/24hr., **lodging:** B&B, **other:** HOSPITAL, Cowan Museum, **2 mi S...lodging:** B&B
369	US 117, Warsaw, no facilities
364	NC 24, to NC 50, Clinton, **rest area both lanes, full(handicapped)facilities, phone, picnic tables, litter barrels, vending, petwalk, 3 mi N...gas:** Wilco/Hess/Arby's/diesel/24hr/@, **lodging:** Country Squire Inn(7mi), Warsaw Inn, **S...gas:** Amoco/Bojangles/diesel, BP/diesel, Crown/24hr, Phillips 66/diesel/24hr, Shell/Texaco/diesel, **food:** KFC, McDonald's, Smithfield's BBQ, Subway, Waffle House, Wendy's, **lodging:** Day's Inn, Holiday Inn Express
355	NC 403, to US 117, to Goldsboro, Faison, **3 mi N...gas:** Exxon, Faison B&B
348	Suttontown Rd, no facilities
343	US 701, Newton Grove, **1 mi N...gas:** Exxon/diesel, to Bentonville Bfd
341	NC 50, NC 55, to US 13, Newton Grove, **1.5 mi N...gas:** Exxon/diesel, **food:** Hardee's, **S...gas:** BP/McDonald's, Shell, **food:** Smithfield BBQ, Subway
334	NC 96, Meadow, **S...gas:** BP(1mi)
328b a	I-95, N to Smithfield, S to Benson, no facilities
325	NC 242, to US 301, to Benson, **S...gas:** Citgo/diesel
324mm	**rest area both lanes, full(handicapped)facilities, phone, picnic tables, litter barrels, vending, petwalk, no overnight parking**
319	NC 210, McGee's Crossroads, **N...gas:** Citgo/DQ, Papa's Subs & Pizza, Shell/diesel/24hr, **other:** MEDICAL CARE, **S...gas:** Mobil, **food:** China Star Rest., Subway, Wendy's, **other:** Food Lion, Dollar General
312	NC 42, to Clayton, Fuquay-Varina, **N...gas:** Wilco/Hess/Wendy's/diesel/24hr, Phillips 66/diesel, **food:** Andy's Rest., China King, Cracker Barrel, Golden Corral, Smithfield BBQ, Wendy's, **lodging:** Best Western, Holiday Inn Express, Quality Inn, Super 8, **other:** CarQuest, Goodyear/auto, JustTires, Lowe's Whse, **S...gas:** Exxon/Burger King, BP/Amoco/Subway/diesel/24hr, BP/Burger King/24hr, Citgo/diesel, Shell/diesel, **food:** Bojangles, DQ, Domino's, Huddle House, Jumbo China, KFC/Taco Bell, McDonald's, Ribs-R-Us, Waffle House, **lodging:** Hampton Inn, Sleep Inn, **other:** CVS Drug, Food Lion

Interstate 40

E ↕ **W**

306 US 70, to Smithfield, Garner, Goldsboro, **1 mi N...gas:** Kangaroo/diesel, Shell/diesel

303 Jones Sausage Rd, Rd, **N...gas:** Shell/diesel, **food:** Bojangles, Burger King, **S...gas:** Shell/diesel, **food:** Smithfield BBQ, **S...gas** Shell/Texaco

301 I-440 E, US 64/70 E, to Wilson, no facilities

300b a Rock Quarry Rd, **S...gas:** BP/diesel, Exxon, **food:** Burger King, Hardee's, Subway

299 Person St, Hammond Rd, Raleigh(no EZ return eb), **1 mi N...gas:** BP, Shell/diesel, **lodging:** King's Motel, **other:** to Shaw U

298b a US 401 S, US 70 E, NC 50, **N...gas:** Shell, **lodging:** Red Roof Inn, **other:** Parts+, **S...gas:** BP, Citgo/diesel, Crown, Servco, **food:** Bojangles, Burger King, Domino's, KFC, **lodging:** Claremont Inn, Comfort Inn, Day's Inn, Innkeeper, **other:** Sam's Club, CarQuest

297 Lake Wheeler Rd, **N...gas:** Exxon, **food:** Burger King, **other:** HOSPITAL, Farmer's Mkt, **S...gas:** Citgo

295 Gorman St, **1 mi N...gas:** BP, Exxon/diesel, Shell, **food:** Hardee's, Subway, **other:** to NCSU, Reynolds Coliseum

293 US 1, US 64 W, to inner 440 Lp, Raleigh, **S...gas:** Exxon, **lodging:** Motel 6

291 Cary Towne Blvd, Cary, **1 mi S...food:** Burger King, DQ, Hardee's, Jersey Mike's Subs, McDonald's, Olive Garden, Ragazzi's, Taco Bell

290 NC 54, Cary, **1 mi N...gas:** Citgo, **2 mi S...gas:** Citgo, Shell, **lodging:** Hampton Inn

289 to I-440, Wade Ave, to Raleigh, **N...other:** HOSPITAL, museum, **S...**to fairgrounds

287 Harrison Ave, Cary, **N...**to Wm B Umstead SP, **S...gas:** Shell, **food:** Arby's, Burger King, McDonald's, Newton's SW Rest., Subway, Wendy's, **lodging:** Embassy Suites, Studio+

285 Aviation Pkwy, to Morrisville, Raleigh/Durham Airport, **N...lodging:** Hilton Garden

284 Airport Blvd, **N...food:** Chophouse Rest., to RDU Airport, **S...gas:** BP/diesel, Citgo/diesel, Exxon, Shell/diesel, **food:** Cracker Barrel, Jersey Mike's Subs, Quizno's, Schlotsky's, Texas Steaks, Waffle House, Wendy's, **lodging:** Baymont Inn, Courtyard, Day's Inn, Extended Stay America, Fairfield Inn, Hampton Inn, Holiday Inn Express, Microtel, La Quinta, Staybridge Suites, **other:** Prime Outlets/famous brands

283 I-540, to US 70, Aviation Pkwy, no facilities

282 Page Rd, **S...food:** McDonald's, **lodging:** Holiday Inn/rest., Sheraton/rest., Sleep Inn, Wellesley Inn, Wingate Inn, **other:** World Trade Ctr

281 Miami Blvd, **N...food:** Rudino's Grill, Wendy's, **lodging:** Best Western Crown Park, Marriott, Wyndham Garden, **S...gas:** BP, Shell, **lodging:** Clarion, Homewood Suites, Wellesley Inn

280 Davis Dr, **N...**to Research Triangle, **S...lodging:** Radisson Governor's Inn

279b a NC 147, Durham Fwy, to Durham, no facilities

278 NC 55, to NC 54, World Trade Ctr, Apex, Foreign Trade Zone 93, **N...gas:** Citgo, **food:** China 1 Rest., Waffle House, **lodging:** Doubletree Suites, Fairfield Inn, Innkeeper, La Quinta, Red Roof Inn, **S...gas:** Crown, Exxon/diesel, Mobil/diesel, **food:** Arby's, Bojangles, Burger King, Chick-fil-A, Fazoli's, Golden Corral, Hardee's, KFC, McDonald's, Miami Grill, O!Brian's, Papa John's, Pizza Hut, Schlotsky's, Subway, Taco Bell, Wendy's, **lodging:** Candlewood Suites, Courtyard, Crossland Suites, Hawthorn Suites, Homestead Village, Residence Inn, **other:** MEDICAL CARE, $Tree, Eckerd, Food Lion, transmissions/tires

276 Fayetteville Rd, **N...gas:** Exxon/diesel, Phillips 66/diesel, **food:** McDonald's, Quizno's, Ruby Tuesday, Rudino's Pizza, Souper Salad, Subs Etc, TCBY, Waffle House, Wendy's, **other:** Eckerd, GNC, Harris-Teeter, Kroger, to NC Central U

274 NC 751, to Jordan Lake, **1-2 mi N...food:** Burger King, McDonald's, Waffle House, Wendy's, **S...gas:** Citgo

273 NC 54, to Durham, UNC-Chapel Hill, **N...gas:** Shell/diesel, **S...gas:** BP/diesel, Shell/diesel, **food:** Hardee's, **lodging:** Best Western(2mi), Hampton Inn, Holiday Inn Express

270 US 15, US 501, Chapel Hill, Durham, **N...food:** Bob Evans, Bojangles, Outback Steaks, Philly Steaks, Tripp's Rest., **lodging:** Comfort Inn, Homewood Suites, **other:** HOSPITALS, Barnes&Noble, Best Buy, $Tree, Home Depot, OfficeMax, Old Navy, Marshall's, Michael's, Saab, Wal-Mart, to Duke U, **S...gas:** BP, Exxon, **food:** Applebee's, Golden Corral, Hardee's, McDonald's, Subway, Wendy's, **lodging:** Hampton Inn, Holiday Inn, Red Roof Inn, Sheraton, Siena Hotel, **other:** BMW, Chevrolet, CVS Drug, Lowe's Whse, Saturn, mall

266 NC 86, to Chapel Hill, **2 mi S...gas:** BP, Citgo, Exxon, Wilco/diesel, **food:** Subway, Zero's Subs, **other:** Harris-Teeter

263 New Hope Church Rd, no facilities

261 Hillsborough, **1.5 mi N...gas:** BP, Citgo/diesel, Shell, **food:** Hardee's, KFC, McDonald's, Pizza Hut, Waffle House, Wendy's

259 I-85 N, to Durham.

I-40 and I-85 run together 32 mi. See Interstate 85, exits 132-161.

227 to I-85 S, US 70.

NORTH CAROLINA
Interstate 40

E ↕ W

Greensboro (vertical side label)

226	McConnell Rd, **E...gas:** Shell/repair, **W...**Replacements LTD Outlet
224	NC 6, E Lee St, **W...gas:** BP/Blimpie/diesel, Phillips 66, **lodging:** Holiday Inn Express, to Coliseum, KOA
223	US 29 N, US 70, US 220, **W...**KOA
222	US 421 S, to Sanford, **E...gas:** Exxon, **food:** Arby's, Biscuitville, Burger King, Domino's, Golden Pizza, McDonald's, Szechuan Chinese, Subway, Wendy's, **other:** Advance Parts, BiLo, CVS Drug, Food Lion, Goodyear/auto
221	S Elm St, Eugene St, **E...gas:** Amoco, DM, Shell/diesel/24hr, **lodging:** Quality Inn, Super 8, **other:** CarQuest, Home Depot, **W...gas:** Chevron, Citgo/diesel, Crown, **food:** Bojangles, Sonic, **lodging:** Aggie Inn, Ramada Ltd, **other:** AutoZone, Family$, Food Lion
220	Randleman Rd, **E...gas:** Exxon, Shell/24hr, **food:** Cookout Drive-Thru, Mayflower Seafood, Waffle House, Wendy's, **lodging:** Cavalier Inn, **other:** K-Mart, **W...gas:** Amoco, Citgo, Crown, Shell, **food:** Arby's, BBQ, Biscuitville, Burger King, DQ, KFC, McDonald's, Pizza Hut, Substation II, Taco Bell, **lodging:** SouthGate Motel, **other:** Advance Parts, Harley-Davidson
219	I-85 S, to Charlotte, US 29, US 70, US 220, no facilities
218b a	US 220 S, to I-85 S, Freeman Mill Rd, no facilities
217b a	High Point Rd, Greensboro, **N...gas:** Exxon/diesel, Shell/diesel, **food:** Arby's, Bennigan's, Biscuitville, Burger King, Chili's, China King, Devereaux Dining, El Paraiso Restorante, Grady's Grill, Ham's Rest., Hooters, Jake's Diner/24hr, La Bamba Mexican, KFC, LoneStar Steaks, McDonald's, Mrs Winners, Olive Garden, Osaka Japanese, PoFolks, Stephen's Seafood, Subway, Taco Bell, **lodging:** Howard Johnson/rest., Park Lane Hotel, Red Roof Inn, Super 8, Travelodge, **other:** $General, Office Depot, **S...gas:** Crown, Shell/diesel, **food:** Bojangles, Burger King, Carrabba's, Cookout Café, Darryl's, Hoolihan's, Krispy Kreme, Kyoto Express, Libby Hill Seafood, Mamma Maria Italian, McDonald's, Nascar Café, Oh! Brian's, Pizza Inn, Sonic, Subway, Taco Bell, Tides Seafood, Waffle House, Wendy's, Wok'n Roll, **lodging:** Best Western, Comfort Inn, Day's Inn, Drury Inn, Econolodge, Fairfield Inn, Hampton Inn, Residence Inn, Sheraton, **other:** Aamco, Advance Parts, AutoZone, Belk, Borders Books, Dillard's, Discount Tire, Family$, JC Penney, Lowe's Foods, Merchant Tire/auto, NAPA, NTB, OfficeMax, PepBoys, Radio Shack, Sears/auto, mall
216	NC 6(from eb, exits left), to Greensboro Coliseum
214b a	Wendover Ave, **N...gas:** Citgo/diesel, Exxon/diesel, Shell/diesel, **food:** BBQ, Blimpie, Burger King, K&W Cafeteria, Ruby Tuesday, TCBY, Waffle House, **lodging:** Extended Stay America, Holiday Inn Express, Innkeeper, Microtel, **other:** BMW, Chevrolet, Chrysler, Dodge, Ford, Goodyear, Honda/Acura/Nissan, Isuzu/Subaru, Mercedes, Mitsubishi, Saab/Jaguar, Saturn, Staples, Volvo, **S...food:** Applebee's, Arby's, Bojangles, Chick-fil-A, Cracker Barrel, Fuddrucker's, Golden Corral, IHOP/24hr, Imperial Gourmet, Logan's Roadhouse, McDonald's, Red Lobster, Schlotsky's, Steak'n Shake, Subway, TGIFriday, Taco Bell, Tripp's Rest., Wendy's, **lodging:** AmeriSuites, Courtyard, Shoney's Inn/rest., Suburban Lodge, **other:** Best Buy, Circuit City, Ferrari, Goodyear, Harris-Teeter, Home Depot, K-Mart, Lowe's Whse, Porsche, Sam's Club, Wal-Mart SuperCtr/24hr
213	Jamestown, **N...gas:** BP/diesel, **food:** Damon's Ribs, **lodging:** Radisson, to Guilford Coll, **S...other:** Hecht's, Kohl's, Old Navy, Saturn, Target, same as 214
212	Chimney Rock Rd, no facilities
211	new exit
210	NC 68, to High Point, Piedmont Triad, **N...gas:** Phillips 66/diesel, **food:** Arby's, Hardee's, Mr Omelet, Wendy's, **lodging:** Day's Inn, Embassy Suites, Holiday Inn, Homewood Suites, Sleep Inn, **other:** Ford Trucks, Freightliner, to airport, **S...gas:** Exxon/diesel, **food:** Bojangles, McDonald's, Pizza Hut/Taco Bell, Shoney's, Subway, **lodging:** Best Western, Candlewood Suites, Comfort Suites, Hampton Inn, Innkeeper, Motel 6, Ramada Inn, Red Roof Inn, Studio+
208	Sandy Ridge Rd, **N...gas:** Wilco/Hess/diesel/@ , **other:** RV Country, **S...gas:** Citgo/diesel, Out Of Doors Mart/Airstream, **other:** Farmer's Mkt
206	Lp 40(from wb), to Kernersville, Winston-Salem, downtown
203	NC 66, to Kernersville, **N...gas:** BP/Amoco, Citgo/McDonald's/diesel, Shell/Subway/diesel, **food:** Capt Tom's Seafood, Clark's BBQ, Suzie's Diner, Waffle House, **lodging:** Sleep Inn, **other:** Ford, Merchant Tire/repair, **S...gas:** Shell/diesel, Holiday Inn Express
201	Union Cross Rd, **N...gas:** Exxon/diesel, QM, **food:** Burger King, China Café, **other:** CVS Drug, Food Lion
196	US 311 S, to High Point, no facilities
195	US 311 N, NC 109, to Thomasville, **S...gas:** Pure, Wilco/Hess/diesel
193c	Silas Creek Pkwy(from wb), same as 192
193b a	US 52, NC 8, to Lexington, **S...gas:** Citgo, Hess/diesel, Shell, **food:** Hardee's
192	NC 150, to Peters Creek Pkwy, **N...gas:** Shell, Wilco, **food:** Arby's, Bojangles, Burger King, Checker's, China Buffet, Country Roadhouse, IHOP, KFC, Little Caesar's, Monterrey Mexican, Old Country Buffet, Perkins, Pizza Hut, Red Lobster, Shoney's, Sonic, Taco Bell, Wendy's, **lodging:** Comfort Inn(1mi), Innkeeper, Knight's Inn, **other:** MEDICAL CARE, Acura/Subaru/Isuzu, Audi, AutoZone, Eckerd, Ford, Hyundai, Kroger, Lowe's Foods, Mazda, NAPA, Office Depot, PharMor Drug, Suzuki, VW, **S...gas:** BP, **food:** Libby Hill Seafood, McDonald's, K&W Cafeteria, Wendy's, **lodging:** Holiday Inn Express, **other:** Advance Parts, BiLo, Buick/BMW/Saturn, CVS Drug, Food Lion, Goodyear, Harris Teeter, Honda, K-Mart

Winston-Salem (vertical side label)

Interstate 40

E

W

190 Hanes Mall Blvd(from wb, no re-entry), **N...food:** McDonald's, O'Charley's, TGIFriday, Tripp's Rest., **lodging:** Day's Inn, **other:** HOSPITAL, Belk, Dillard's, Drug Emporium, Firestone, JC Penney, Marshall's, Sears/auto, mall, same as 189, **S...food:** Baja Fresh Grill, Bojangles, ChuckeCheese, Outback Steaks, Souper Salad, **lodging:** Comfort Suites, Microtel, Sleep Inn

189 US 158, Stratford Rd, Hanes Mall Blvd, **N...gas:** BP, Exxon, **food:** Bojangles, Chili's, Cozumel Mexican, McDonald's, O'Charley's, Olive Garden, Red Lobster, Sagebrush Steaks, Taco Bell, **lodging:** Courtyard, Fairfield Inn, **other:** HOSPITAL, Chevrolet, Hecht's, Jo-Ann Fabrics, OfficeMax, Michael's, NTB, mall, **S...gas:** BP, Shell, **food:** Applebee's, Burger King, Chick-fil-A, Copeland's Grill, Corky's BBQ, Dynasty Buffet, Fuddruckers, Hooters, Jason's Deli, Little Caesar's, LoneStar Steaks, Longhorn Steaks, Macaroni Grill, Schlotsky's, Subway, **lodging:** Extended Stay America, Hampton Inn, Holiday Inn, La Quinta, Sleep Inn, **other:** Barnes&Noble, Best Buy, Circuit City, Costco/gas, CVS Drug, Food Lion, Home Depot, Kohl's, Lowe's Whse, Sam's Club, Target

188 US 421, to Yadkinville, to WFU(no EZ wb return), Winston-Salem, **1/2mi N off US 421...gas:** BP/Amoco, Shell, **food:** Boston Mkt, Burger King, McDonald's, Waffle House, Wendy's, **other:** CVS Drug, $Tree, Kroger, Mercedes, Wal-Mart SuperCtr/24hr

184 to US 421, Clemmons, **N...gas:** Shell, Texaco, **food:** Bambini Italian, El Jinet Mexican, KFC, **lodging:** Holiday Inn Express, **S...gas:** BP/diesel, Citgo/diesel, Etna/diesel, Exxon/diesel, Texaco, **food:** Arby's, Brick Oven Pizza, Burger King, Cozumel Mexican, Cracker Barrel, Domino's, JB's Hotdogs, Mandarin Buffet, McDonald's, Mi Pueblo Mexican, Pizza Hut, Quizno's, Sagebrush Steaks, Schlotsky's, Sonic, Subway, Taco Bell, Tokyo Japanese, Waffle House, Wendy's, **lodging:** Holiday Inn, Super 8, Village Inn, **other:** Advance Parts, BiLo Foods, CarQuest, CVS Drug, Food Lion, K-Mart, Lowe's Foods, Merchant Tire, Parts+, Staples, USPO

182 Bermuda Run(from wb, no re-entry), Tanglewood, no facilities

182mm Yadkin River

180 NC 801, Tanglewood, **N...food:** Capt's Galley Seafood, **other:** Eckerd, Lowe's Foods, **S...gas:** BP/diesel, Citgo/Subway/diesel, Exxon, Shell, **food:** Bojangles, DQ, McDonald's, Wendy's, **other:** CVS Drug, Food Lion, Radio Shack

177mm **rest areas both lanes, full(handicapped)facilities, phone, vending, picnic tables, litter barrels, petwalk**

174 Farmington Rd, **N...gas:** Exxon/diesel, **other:** antiques, **S...other:** Furniture Gallery, vineyards

170 US 601, Mocksville, **N...gas:** Citgo/diesel/LP, Shell/diesel/ rest./24hr/@, **S...gas:** BP/diesel, Exxon, Shell/Taco Bell, **food:** Arby's, Bojangles, Burger King, China Grill, Dynasty Chinese, KFC, McDonald's, Pier 601 Seafood, Pizza Hut, Little Caesar's, Subway, Wendy's, Western Steer, **lodging:** Comfort Inn, Day's Inn, High-Way Inn, Scottish Inn, **other:** HOSPITAL, Advance Parts, CVS Drug, $General, Food Lion, Ford/Mercury, Goodyear/auto, Wal-Mart

168 US 64, to Mocksville, **N...gas:** Exxon/diesel, **other:** Lake Myers RV Resort(3mi), **S...gas:** BP

162 US 64, Cool Springs, **N...other:** Lake Myers RV Resort(5mi), **S...gas:** Shell, **other:** TravL Park

161mm S Yadkin River

154 to US 64, Old Mocksville Rd, **N...HOSPITAL, S...gas:** Citgo/diesel, **food:** Jaybee's Hotdogs, **lodging:** Hallmark Inn

153 US 64(from eb), **1/2 mi S...gas:** Citgo/diesel, **lodging:** Hallmark Inn, Jaybee's Hotdogs

152b a I-77, S to Charlotte, N to Elkin, no facilities

151 US 21, E Statesville, **N...gas:** Hess/diesel/24hr, PetroExpress/JerseyMike'sSubs/TCBY, **food:** Applebee's, Bojangles, Burger King, Chick-fil-A, Cracker Barrel, Golden Corral, Italian Oven, Jack-in-the-Box, KFC, K&W Cafeteria, Logan's Roadhouse, McDonald's, Mi Pueblo Café, Pizza Hut/Taco Bell, **lodging:** Pizza Inn, Red Lobster, Sagebrush Steaks, Schlotsky's, Wendy's, Day's Inn, Sleep Inn, **other:** Bi-Lo, Chevrolet/Cadillac, Chrysler/Jeep, CVS Drug, Home Depot, Lowe's Whse, Staples, Tire Kingdom, Wal-Mart SuperCtr/24hr, **S...gas:** Exxon, **food:** Lotus Pier Rest., Szechuan Chinese, Waffle House, **lodging:** Hampton Inn, Holiday Inn Express, Masters Inn, Super 8, Travelodge, **other:** VW, st patrol

150 NC 115, Statesville, **N...gas:** BP/diesel, Citgo, Shell, **food:** Amalfi's Italian, Little Caesar's, Ol'Bob's BBQ, **other:** CVS Drug, Food Lion, The Family RV Ctr, antiques, museum

148 US 64, NC 90, W Statesville, **N...gas:** Citgo/diesel, QP, **food:** Arby's, Burger King, KFC, McDonald's, Prime Sirloin, Shike Japanese, Subway, Village Inn Pizza, **lodging:** Economy Inn, **other:** CVS Drug, $General, Ingles Foods

146 Stamey Farm Rd, **S...gas:** Citgo/diesel/rest./24hr

144 Old Mountain Rd, **N...gas:** BP, Chevron/diesel, **food:** Troy's Rest., **S...gas:** BP/diesel, Shell/diesel

Clemmons

Statesville

NORTH CAROLINA
Interstate 40

E / **W** (directional arrow)

Hickory (vertical label)

143mm	weigh sta both lanes
141	Sharon School Rd, **N...gas:** Citgo, **other:** antiques
140mm	Catawba River
138	Oxford School Rd, to Catawba, **N...gas:** Exxon/diesel/24hr, **S...lodging:** B&B
136mm	**rest areas both lanes, full(handicapped)facilities, phone, picnic tables, vending, litter barrels, petwalk**
135	Claremont, **S...gas:** Shell, **food:** BoxCar Grille, Burger King, Hardee's, Rassie's Subs, **lodging:** Super 8, **other:** Lowe's Foods, RV Ctr
133	Rock Barn Rd, **N...gas:** Exxon/diesel, **S...gas:** Wilco/Subway/Taco Bell/diesel/24hr/@
132	new exit
131	NC 16, Conover, **N...gas:** BP/diesel, Shell/diesel, **lodging:** Holiday Inn Express
130	Old US 70, **N...food:** Jack-in-the-Box, Subway, **other:** $General, K-Mart, Lowe's Foods, NAPA AutoCare, **S...gas:** Citgo, Phillips 66, **other:** USPO
128	US 321, Fairgrove Church Rd, Hickory, **N...gas:** BP, Solo/diesel, **other:** HOSPITAL,Shell, McDonald's, Waffle House, to Catawba Valley Coll, **S...gas:** Citgo/diesel, Phillips 66, **food:** Arby's, Bennitt's Smokehouse, Harbor Inn Seafood, Nagano Japanese, Shoney's, Wendy's, **lodging:** Day's Inn, Ramada Inn, **other:** Dodge, Lincoln/Mercury, White/GMC/Volvo/Ford
126	to US 70, NC 155, **S...gas:** Citgo, Phillips 66, Shell, **food:** Applebee's, Asia Café Buffet, Bob Evans, IHOP, Libby Hill Seafood, McDonald's, Melting Pot Rest., O'Charley's, Olive Garden, Taco Bell, **lodging:** Holiday Inn Express, **other:** Barnes&Noble, Circuit City, $Tree, Office Depot, K-Mart, Lowe's Whse, Michael's, Sam's Club, Wal-Mart SuperCtr/24hr
125	Hickory, **N...gas:** Exxon/Subway/diesel/24hr, RaceTrac, **food:** Bojangles, Golden Corral, Peddler Rest., Rockola Café, Royal Palace Chinese, Texas Roadhouse, Tripp's Rest., Western Steer, **lodging:** Red Roof Inn, **other:** BMW/Mercedes, Chrysler/Jeep, **S...gas:** Servco/24hr, Shell/diesel, **food:** Buffalo's Rest., Burger King, Chick-fil-A, CiCi's, Cracker Barrel, El Sombrero Mexican, Fuddrucker's, Hardee's, Hooters, J&S Cafeteria, Kobe Japanese, Krispy Kreme, Longhorn Steaks, Outback Steaks, Ragazzi's Italian, Red Lobster, Ruby Tuesday, Sagebrush Steaks, Schlotsky's, Steak&Ale, Stockyard Grille, Waffle House, Wendy's, Zaxby's, **lodging:** Comfort Suites, Courtyard, Fairfield Inn, Hampton Inn, Holiday Inn Select, Jameson Inn, Sleep Inn, **other:** Aldi Foods, Belk, Food Lion, Ford, Home Depot, Honda, JC Penney, Kohl's, Lowe's Whse, Mazda, Mitsubishi, OfficeMax, Saturn, Sears/auto, Toyota, Volvo, VW, mall
123	US 70/321, to NC 127, Hickory, no facilities
121	new exit
119b a	Hildebran, **N...gas:** Shell/Subway/diesel, **food:** Hardee's, KFC, **other:** Furniture World Outlet
118	Old NC 10, **N...gas:** Exxon, Shell/diesel

Morganton (vertical label)

116	Icard, **S...gas:** Phillips/diesel/24hr, **food:** Burger King, Granny's Kitchen, **lodging:** Icard Inn/rest.
113	Connelly Springs, **N...gas:** Phillips 66/diesel, **other:** HOSPITAL, Ford, flea market
112	Mineral Springs Mtn Rd, Valdese, no facilities
111	Valdese, **N...food:** McDonald's
107	NC 114, to Drexel, no facilities
106	Bethel Rd, **S...gas:** Exxon/diesel, **lodging:** Rainbow Inn/rest.
105	NC 18, Morganton, **N...gas:** Chevron, **food:** Arby's, Coffeehouse, Fatz Café, McDonald's, Pizza Inn, Shoney's, Waffle House, Wendy's, Western Sizzlin, **lodging:** Hampton Inn, Red Carpet Inn, **other:** HOSPITAL, Joe's Tire, Pontiac/Cadillac/GMC, **S...**QM/diesel, Shell, El Paso Mexican, Sagebrush Steaks, Day's Inn, Holiday Inn/rest., Sleep Inn, to South Mtns SP
104	Enola Rd, **S...gas:** Citgo, **food:** Chick-fil-A, Jersey Mike's Subs, **other:** Belk, Food Lion, Goody's, Staples, st patrol
103	US 64, Morganton, **N...gas:** Exxon/diesel/24hr, Shell/diesel, Max' Mexican, Tastee Freez, Super 8, **S...gas:** Citgo, Phillips 66/diesel, RaceTrac, **food:** Butch's BBQ, Checker's, Denny's, Hardee's, KFC, Subway, Taco Bell, Tokyo Diner, **lodging:** Comfort Suites, **other:** Food Lion, Goodyear/auto, Goody's, Honda, Ingles Foods, Lowe's Whse, Radio Shack, Wal-Mart/drugs
100	Jamestown Rd, **N...gas:** BP/diesel/24hr, **other:** Ford/Mercury, **2 mi N...food:** KFC, Taco Bell, **lodging:** Eagle Motel
98	Causby Rd, to Glen Alpine, **S...**B&B/food
96	Kathy Rd, no facilities
94	Dysartsville Rd, no facilities
90	Nebo, **N...gas:** Exxon/diesel/rest., **other:** to Lake James SP, **S...gas:** BP/diesel, RV Ctr
86	NC 226, to Spruce Pine, Marion, **N...gas:** Exxon/diesel, **food:** Hardee's, KFC, **lodging:** Comfort Inn(3mi)
85	US 221, Marion, **N...lodging:** Comfort Inn(5mi), Hampton Inn, **other:** to Mt Mitchell SP, **S...gas:** BP/diesel, Shell/diesel/24hr, **food:** Sagebrush Steaks, **lodging:** Day's Inn, Super 8
83	Ashworth Rd, no facilities
82mm	**rest area both lanes, full(handicapped)facilities, phone, picnic tables, vending, litter barrels, petwalk**
81	81 Sugar Hill Rd, to Marion, **N...gas:** Amoco/24hr, BP/diesel, Chevron/diesel, Citgo, **other:** HOSPITAL, Chrysler/Plymouth/Dodge/Jeep, **2 mi N...food:** Burger King, McDonald's, **other:** Eckerd, Family$, Ingles Foods, **S...gas:** Shell/diesel/rest./24hr
76mm	Catawba River
75	Parker Padgett Rd, **S...gas:** Citgo/DQ/Stuckey's/diesel
73	Old Fort, Mtn Gateway Museum, **N...gas:** Citgo/diesel, **food:** Hardee's, **S...gas:** Exxon, Super Test/diesel, **food:** McDonald's, **other:** Parts+/repair
72	US 70(from eb), Old Fort, **N...**B&B

Interstate 40

E

W

71mm   Pisgah Nat Forest, eastern boundary

67.5mm truck rest area eb

66   Ridgecrest, no facilities

65   (from wb), to Black Mountain, Black Mtn Ctr, **N...lodging:** Super 8(2mi)

64   NC 9, Black Mountain, **N...gas:** Exxon, Shell/Subway/24hr, **food:** #1China, Pizza Hut, **lodging:** Super 8, BiLo/café, **other:** Chevrolet, $General, **S...gas:** Phillips 66, **food:** Arby's, Campfire Steaks, Denny's, Huddle House, KFC, McDonald's, Taco Bell, Wendy's, **lodging:** Comfort Inn, **other:** Eckerd, Ingles Foods, Radio Shack

63mm   Swannanoa River

59   Swannanoa, **N...gas:** BP, Citgo/Subway/TCBY, Exxon/diesel, Servco, Shell/diesel, **food:** Athens Pizza, BBQ, Burger King, **other:** Goodyear/auto, Harley-Davidson, Ingles Foods, KOA(2mi), Miles RV Ctr, to Warren Wilson Coll, **S...other:** Gant's Furniture Outlet

55   E Asheville, US 70, **N...gas:** BP, Citgo/Subway, Conoco, **food:** Arby's, Kountry Kitchen, Poseidon Seafood, Waffle House, Zaxby's, **lodging:** Day's Inn, Econolodge, Holiday Inn, Motel 6, Royal Inn, Super 8, **other:** VA HOSPITAL, Go Groceries, Top's RV park, to Mt Mitchell SP, Folk Art Ctr

53b a I-240 W, US 74, to Asheville, Bat Cave, **N...food:** KFC, J&S Cafeteria, McDonald's, **lodging:** Comfort Inn, **other:** Advance Parts, BiLo, CVS Drug, Eckerd, Hamrick's, **1-2 mi N on US 74...gas:** BP, Exxon/diesel, **food:** Applebee's, Burger King, Carrabba's, Chili's, Damon's, IHOP, O'Charley's, Olive Garden, Red Lobster, Subway, Waffle House, **lodging:** Courtyard, Day's Inn, Econolodge, Extended Stay America, Hampton Inn, Ramada Ltd, **other:** Circuit City, Home Depot, Ingles Foods, K-Mart, Office Depot, Sears/auto, mall, **S...gas:** BP/diesel/LP, Phillips 66, **other:** to Blue Ridge Pkwy

51   US 25A, Sweeten Creek Rd, **1/2 mi S...gas:** BP

50   US 25, Asheville, **N...gas:** Exxon/diesel, Shell/diesel, **food:** Arby's, Asaka Japanese, Chapala Mexican, LJ Silver, McDonald's, Pedro's Mexican, Pizza Hut, Popeye's, Subway, Texas Roadhouse, TGIFriday, Wendy's, **lodging:** Baymont Inn, Doubletree Inn, Holiday Inn Express, Howard Johnson, Plaza Motel, Sleep Inn, **other:** HOSPITAL, to Biltmore House, **S...gas:** Phillips 66/diesel, Servco/diesel, **food:** Atl Bread, Huddle House/24hr, **lodging:** Forest Manor Inn

47mm   French Broad River

47   NC 191, W Asheville, Farmer's Mkt, **N...other:** Asheville Speedway, **S...gas:** Phillips 66, **food:** Moose Café, Subway, Blackberry's Rest., **2 mi S...lodging:** Comfort Inn, Hampton Inn, Holiday Inn Express, Super 8, Wingate Inn

46b a I-26 & I-240 E, **2 mi N...**multiple facilities from I-240

A s h e v i l l e

44   US 74, W Asheville, **N...gas:** BP, Chevron/diesel, Conoco, Exxon, Servco, Shell/Substation II/24hr, **food:** Burger King, Cracker Barrel, El Chapala Mexican, Fatz Café, Pizza Hut, Popeye's, Szechuan Chinese, Waffle House, Wendy's, **lodging:** Best Western, Comfort Inn, Red Roof Inn, Sleep Inn, Super 8, Whispering Pines Motel, **other:** CarQuest, Chevrolet, Chrysler/Plymouth/Jeep, CVS Drug, Family$, Ingles Foods, Lowe's Whse, Mercedes/Mazda, **S...food:** McDonald's, Shoney's, Subway, Budget Motel, Ramada Inn, Home Depot, **1 mi S...gas:** Shell, **food:** BBQ, J&S Cafeteria, Subway, TCBY, **other:** Eckerd, Food Lion

41mm   weigh sta both lanes

37   E Canton, **N...gas:** BP, TA/Citgo/diesel/rest./24hr/@, **other:** Goodyear, **S...gas:** Exxon/diesel, Shell, **lodging:** Day's Inn, Plantation Motel, **other:** KOA, Big Cove Camping(2mi)

33   Newfound Rd, to US 74, **S...gas**

31   Canton, **N...food:** Sagebrush Steaks, **lodging:** Econolodge, **S...gas:** BP/diesel, Chevron/Stuckey's, Exxon/McDonald's/24hr, Shell/Arby's/diesel, **food:** Burger King, McDonald's, Pizza Hut(2mi), Subway(1mi), Taco Bell, Waffle House, **lodging:** Comfort Inn, **other:** Ingles Foods, Chevrolet/Pontiac/Buick, Ford, RV/truck repair

27   US 19/23, to Waynesville, Great Smokey Mtn Expswy, **3 mi S...gas:** Shell/Burger King, **food:** Papa's Pizza, Shoney's, Subway, Taco Bell, **other:** HOSPITAL, Food Lion, GNC, Lowe's Whse, Wal-Mart/drugs, to WCU(25mi)

24   NC 209, to Lake Junaluska, **N...gas:** Pilot/diesel/24hr/@, **lodging:** Midway Motel, **S...gas:** Citgo/diesel/24hr/@

20   US 276, to Maggie Valley, Lake Junaluska, **S...gas:** BP/diesel, Citgo, Exxon/diesel/café, **other:** Creekwood Farm RV Park, Pride RV Resort

16mm   Pigeon River

15   Fines Creek, **N...B&B**

12mm   Pisgah NF eastern boundary

10mm **rest area both lanes, full(handicapped)facilities, phone, vending, picnic tables, litter barrels, petwalk**

7   Harmon Den, no facilities

4mm   tunnel both lanes

0mm   North Carolina/Tennessee state line

NORTH CAROLINA
Interstate 77

N ↕ S

Elkin

Statesville

Exit #	Services
105mm	North Carolina/Virginia state line
105mm	**Welcome Ctr sb, full(handicapped)facilities, info, phone, vending, picnic tables, litter barrels, petwalk**
103mm	weigh sta both lanes
101	NC 752, to US 52, to Mt Airy, Greensboro, **E...lodging:** Hampton Inn, **other:** HOSPITAL(12mi),
100	NC 89, to Mt Airy, **E...gas:** Brintle's/Citgo/diesel/rest./24hr/@, Exxon/diesel, Marathon/Subway/diesel, Shell/diesel, **food:** Wagon Wheel Rest., **lodging:** Best Western, Comfort Inn(2mi), **other:** HOSPITAL(12mi), clothing outlet
93	to Dobson, Surry, **E...gas:** Citgo/diesel/diner, Shell/DQ/Stuckey's/diesel, **lodging:** Surry Inn, **other:** camping
85	NC 1138, CC Camp Rd, to Elkin, **W...gas:** Exxon/diesel, Shell/Blimpie/diesel, **3 mi W...food:** Burger King, Hardee's, KFC, McDonald's, **lodging:** Elk Inn
83	US 21 byp, to Sparta, no facilities
82.5mm	Yadkin River
82	NC 67, Elkin, **E...gas:** Amoco/diesel/24hr, BP/Case Knife Outlet/diesel, Chevron/diesel, Citgo/Subway, **food:** Arby's, Cracker Barrel, Jordan's Rest., **lodging:** Holiday Inn Express, **other:** Holly Ridge Camping(8mi), **W...gas:** Exxon/Baskin-Robbins/TCBY/diesel, **food:** Bojangles, Ham & Eggs Rest, McDonald's, New China, Shoney's, Waffle House, Wendy's, **lodging:** Comfort Inn, Day's Inn, Hampton Inn, Roses Motel, **other:** AutoValue Parts, Buick/Pontiac/GMC, D-Rex Drug, Family$, Food Lion
79	US 21 S, to Arlington, **E...gas:** Shell, **lodging:** Super 8, **W...gas:** Shell/Texaco/diesel, **food:** Sally Jo's Kitchen, **lodging:** Country Inn, **other:** auto repair
73b a	US 421, to Winston-Salem(20mi), **E...gas:** Shell/Subway/Krispy Kreme/diesel(1mi), **lodging:** Sleep Inn(8mi), Welborn Motel, Yadkin Inn
72mm	**rest area nb, full(handicapped)facilities, phone, vending, picnic tables, litter barrels, petwalk**
65	NC 901, to Union Grove, Harmony, **E...other:** Van Hoy Farms Camping, **W...gas:** BP/diesel, Citgo, Shell/Subway/TCBY/diesel/24hr, **food:** Burger Barn, Honey's Café, **other:** Fiddler's Grove Camping(2mi)
63mm	**rest area sb, full(handicapped)facilities, phone, vending, picnic tables, litter barrels, petwalk**
59	Tomlin Mill Rd, **W...gas:** Citgo
56.5mm	S Yadkin River
54	US 21, to Turnersburg, **E...gas:** Citgo, **W...gas:** Shell/diesel
51b a	I-40, E to Winston-Salem, W to Hickory, no facilities
50	E Broad St, Statesville, **E...gas:** BP, Citgo/diesel, Crown/diesel, Etna/diesel, Shell, **food:** Arby's, Bojangles, Burger King, China Buffet, Domino's, Hardee's, IHOP, McDonald's, Pizza Hut, Shoney's, TCBY, Village Inn Pizza, Wendy's, **lodging:** Fairfield Inn, Red Roof Inn, **other:** MEDICAL CARE, Belk, Eckerd, Harris-Teeter, JC Penney, JR Outlet, K-Mart, Radio Shack, Sears, USPO, Winn-Dixie, mall
49b a	US 70, G Bagnal Blvd, to Statesville, **E...gas:** BP, CircleK, Etna, Exxon, PDI, Shell/diesel, **food:** KFC, Waffle House, Best Western, **lodging:** Comfort Inn, Holiday Inn, Motel 6, Super 8, **other:** Buick/GMC/Cadillac, Camping World, Dodge, Ford, Honda, Lincoln/Mercury, Nissan, Subaru, Toyota, **W...gas:** Amoco/diesel, Chevron, Citgo, **lodging:** BestStay Inn, Microtel, Ramada Ltd.
45	to Troutman, Barium Springs, **E...KOA**, **W...gas:** Chevron/BBQ/diesel
42	US 21, NC 115, to Troutman, Oswalt, **E...gas:** Hess/Wilco/Subway/Taco Bell/TCBY/diesel/24hr/@, **W...other:** to Duke Power SP, camping
39mm	**rest area/weigh sta both lanes, full(handicapped)facilities, phone, picnic tables, litter barrels, petwalk, vending**
36	NC 150, Mooresville, **E...gas:** Accel/diesel, Exxon, Shell/24hr, **food:** Applebee's, Bob Evans, Burger King, Denny's, FatBoy's Cafe, Jack-in-the-Box, McDonald's, Peking Palace, Pizza Hut, Taco Bell, Texas Steaks, Waffle House, Wendy's, **lodging:** Day's Inn, Fairfeild Inn, Holiday Inn Express, Ramada Ltd, **other:** Belk, $tree, GNC, Goody's, Harris-Teeter, K-Mart, Staples, Suzuki, Wal-Mart SuperCtr/24hr, **W...gas:** BJ's Whse/gas, BP/diesel, Citgo/KrispyKreme/BBQ, Servco, Shell/diesel/24hr, **food:** Arby's, Chick-fil-A, Cracker Barrel, Golden Corral, Hardee's, Hooters, Kyoto Japanese, McDonald's, Monterrey Mexican, Subway, Texas Roadhouse, **lodging:** Hampton Inn, Sleep Inn, Super 8, Wingate Inn, **other:** Food Lion, Lowe's Whse, Tire Kingdom, Wallgreen
33	US 21 N, **E...gas:** Phillips 66/diesel, **food:** Mcdonald's, Subway, **other:** HOSPITAL, **W...gas:** BP, Citgo/diesel/24hr, **other:** Food Lion
30	Davidson, **E...gas:** Exxon/diesel, **other:** to Davidson College
28	US 21 S, NC 73, Cornelius, Lake Norman, **E...gas:** Amoco, Cashion's/diesel, Citgo/24hr, **food:** Acropolis Cafe, Bejing Chinese, Bojangles, Subway, **lodging:** Hampton Inn, Holiday Inn/rest., **W...food:** Burger King, El Cancun Mexican, Jersey Mike's Subs, KFC, Kobe Japanese, Lake Norman Brewing, Little Caesar's, LoneStar Steaks, Lotus 28 Chinese, McDonald's, Papa John's, Pizza Hut, Quizno's, Taco Bell, Wendy's, **lodging:** Best Western, Comfort Inn, Econolodge, Holiday Inn, Microtel, Quality Inn, **other:** Chrysler/Jeep, Dodge, Eckerd, Food Lion, Radio Shack, SteinMart
25	NC 73, Concord, Lake Norman, **E...gas:** Shell/diesel, Texaco, **food:** Atlanta Bread Factory, Burger King, Chili's, Fuddrucker's, Hops Rest., Longhorn Steaks, McDonald's, O'Charley's, US Subs, Wendy's, **lodging:** Country Suites, Hawthorn Suites, Ramada Ltd, **other:** MEDICAL CARE, Home Depot, Kohl's, Lowe's Whse, Old Navy, Target, Winn-Dixie, **W...gas:** 76/Circle K/Blimpie, **food:** Arby's, Bob Evans, Bojangles, Carrabba's, DQ, Outback Steaks, Subway, Taipei House, **lodging:** Candlewood Suites, Courtyard, Sleep Inn, **other:** Food Lion/deli, to Energy Explorium

Interstate 77

N ↕ S

Charlotte

23 NC 73, Huntersville, **E...gas:** BP, Citgo, Shell/24hr, **food:** Hardee's, Mama Mia Mexican, Palace of China, Subway, Waffle House, Wendy's, **lodging:** Holiday Inn Express, Red Roof Inn, **other:** MEDICAL CARE, $tree, Eckerd, Food Lion, Ford, Hancock Fabrics, Radio Shack, USPO, **W...gas:** Sam's Mart/diesel, **food:** Jonny Rocket's, **other:** BiLo, CVS Drug, Harris-Teeter

18 Harris Blvd, Reames Rd, **E...gas:** BP/Arby's, Phillips 66/Arby's/diesel, Shell/diesel, **food:** Bob Evans, Harris Grill, Jack-in-the-Box, Quizno's, Waffle House, **lodging:** Comfort Suites, Fairfield Inn, Hampton Inn, Hilton Garden, Suburban Lodge, **other:** HOSPITAL, to UNCC, Univ Research Park, **W...other:** Belk, Dillard's

16b a US 21, Sunset Rd, **E...gas:** Amoco/Circle K, **food:** Capt D's, Hardee's, KFC, McDonald's, Subway, Taco Bell, Waffle House, Wendy's, **lodging:** Best Stay Inn, Day's Inn, Super 8, **other:** AllPro Parts, AutoZone, Kerr Drug, Winn-Dixie, **W...gas:** Citgo, Shell/diesel/@, 76/Circel K, **food:** BBQ, Bojangles, Denny's, Domino's, Jack-in-the-Box, Waffle House, **lodging:** Microtel, Sleep Inn, Sunset Motel, **other:** CVS Drug, RV Ctr

13b a I-85, S to Spartanburg, N to Greensboro, no facilities

12 La Salle St, **W...gas:** Citgo/diesel, Shell/diesel

11b a I-277, Brookshire Fwy, NC 16, no facilities

10 Trade St, 5th St(from nb), **E...other:** to Discovery Place, **W...gas:** Citgo, **food:** Bojangles

10a US 21(from sb), Moorhead St, downtown

9 I-277, US 74, to US 29, John Belk Fwy, downtown, **E...**HOSPITAL, stadium

8 Remount Rd(from nb, no re-entry), no facilities

7 Clanton Rd, **E...gas:** Citgo/diesel, **food:** McDonald's, Waffle House, Wendy's, **lodging:** Day's Inn, Econolodge, Holiday Inn Express, Motel 6, Ramada, Super 8, **W...gas:** BP, Shell/diesel

6b a US 521, Billy Graham Pkwy, **E...gas:** Amoco/diesel, Citgo, 76/Circle K, Shell/diesel, Speedway/diesel, **food:** Arby's, Azteca Mexican, Bojangles, Buffalo Wings, Burger King, Checker's, China House, Harper's Rest., IHOP, KFC/Pizza Hut, Krispy Kreme, McDonald's, Shoney's, Steak&Ale, Three Pesos Mexican, Waffle House, Wendy's, **lodging:** Best Western, Comfort Inn, Day's Inn, Holiday Inn, Howard Johnson, Sterling Inn, **other:** CVS Drug, to Queens Coll, **W...gas:** Phillips 66, **food:** McDonald's, Wendy's, **lodging:** Clarion, Embassy Suites, Summerfeild Suites, La Quinta, Sleep Inn

5 Tyvola Rd, **E...gas:** Citgo/diesel, **food:** BBQ, Blackeyed Pea, Chili's, China King, Derby Diner, Hooters, LoneStar Steaks, McDonald's, Subway, **lodging:** Comfort Inn, Econolodge, Hampton Inn, Hilton, Marriott, Orchard Inn, Radisson, Residence Inn, Studio+, **other:** BiLo/24hr, Jaguar, Kia, Pontiac/GMC, Target, **W...lodging:** Extended Stay America, Wingate Inn, **other:** to Coliseum

Charlotte

4 Nations Ford Rd, **E...gas:** Amoco, Citgo, 76/Circle K/24hr, **food:** Shoney's, **lodging:** Best Inn, Innkeeper Inn, La Quinta, Motel 6, Ramada Ltd., Red Roof, Villager Lodge, **W...gas:** Shell/Burger King

2 (3 from sb), Arrowood Rd, to I-485(from sb), **E...gas:** Shell, **food:** Bob Evans, Chick-fil-A, Jack-in-the-Box, Japan Express, LJ Silver, McDonald's, Wendy's, **lodging:** AmeriSuites, Courtyard, Fairfield Inn, Staybridge Suites, TownePlace Suites, **W...food:** Bojangles, Ruby Tuesday, **lodging:** Hampton Inn, MainStay Suites, SpringHill Suites

1.5mm **Welcome Ctr nb, full(handicapped)facilities, info, phone, vending, picnic tables, litter barrels, petwalk**

1 Westinghouse Blvd, to I-485(from nb), **E...gas:** BP/diesel, Shell/diesel, **food:** Jack-in-the-Box, Subway, Waffle House, **lodging:** Super 8, **W...gas:** Shell/diesel, **food:** Burger King, McDonald's, **lodging:** Rodeway Inn, **other:** Sears

0mm North Carolina/South Carolina state line

Interstate 85

N ↕ S

Henderson

Exit #	Services
234mm	North Carolina/Virginia state line
233	US 1, to Wise, **E...gas:** Citgo/diesel, Wise Trkstp/Shell/diesel/rest./@, **food:** Budget Inn
231mm	**Welcome Ctr sb, full(handicapped)facilities, phone, picnic tables, litter barrels, petwalk**
229	Oine Rd, to Norlina, no facilities
226	Ridgeway Rd, **W...other:** to Kerr Lake, to St RA, no facilities
223	Manson Rd, **E...gas:** BP/diesel, **other:** camping, **W...**to Kerr Dam
220	US 1, US 158, Fleming Rd, to Middleburg, **E...gas:** Amoco/diesel, **W...gas:** Exxon/diesel, **lodging:** Chex Motel/rest.
218	US 1 S(from sb), to Raleigh, no facilities
217	Nutbush Bridge, **E...**same as 215 on US 158, **W...gas:** Exxon/diesel, **other:** Kerr Lake RA
215	US 158 BYP E, Henderson(no EZ return from nb), **E...gas:** Citgo/diesel, Shell, Winoco/diesel, **food:** BBQ, Burger King, Mystic Grill, PD Quix Burgers, Tastee Freez, 220 Seafood Rest., Subway, Waffle Pancakes, **lodging:** Budget Host, Comfort Inn, Howard Johnson, Scottish Inn, Travelodge, **other:** Food Lion, Goodyear/auto, Roses, services on US 158

NORTH CAROLINA
Interstate 85

N
S

214 NC 39, Henderson, **E...gas:** BP, Shell, **W...gas:** Amoco/diesel, Shell/HotStuff Pizza

213 US 158, Dabney Dr, to Henderson, **E...gas:** Amoco, Shell, **food:** Bamboo Garden, Bojangles, DQ, Denny's, KFC, McDonald's, Papa John's, Pizza Inn, Subway, Wendy's, **other:** CVS Drug, Eckerd, Food Lion, Goodyear/auto, Lowe's Foods, Radio Shack, Roses, Winn-Dixie, **W...gas:** Exxon, Shell, **food:** Golden Corral, Hurricanes Grill, **other:** Chevrolet/Buick, Chrysler/Plymouth/Dodge, $Tree, Ford/Lincoln/Mercury, K-Mart, Lowe's Whse, Pontiac, Staples, Tires+, same as 212

212 Ruin Creek Rd, **E...gas:** Shell/diesel, **food:** Cracker Barrel, Mazatlan Mexican, SiLo Rest., **lodging:** Day's Inn, **W...gas:** Amoco/Burger King, **food:** Gary's BBQ, Golden Corral, Western Sizzlin, **lodging:** Hampton Inn, Holiday Inn Express, Jameson Inn, Sleep Inn, **other:** HOSPITAL, Belk, Goody's, JC Penney, Wal-Mart SuperCtr/24hr, mall

209 Poplar Creek Rd, **W...**Vance-Granville Comm Coll

206 US 158, Oxford, **E...gas:** Citgo, **W...gas:** Shell/diesel, **food:** Tony's Rest., **other:** airport

O
x
f
o
r
d

204 NC 96, Oxford, **E...gas:** Amoco/diesel, **lodging:** Best Western, King's Inn, **other:** Honda, Pontiac/Buick/GMC, **W...gas:** Exxon/DQ/24hr, Shell/24hr, Texaco, Trade/diesel, **food:** Burger King, KFC, Little Caesar's, McDonald's, Pizza Hut, Subway, Taco Bell, Wendy's, Zeko's Italian, **lodging:** Ramada Inn, **other:** HOSPITAL, Byrd's Foods, GNC, Radio Shack, Wal-Mart

202 US 15, Oxford, **2 mi W...lodging:** Crown Motel

199mm **rest area both lanes, full(handicapped)facilities, phone, picnic tables, litter barrels, petwalk**

198mm Tar River

191 NC 56, Butner, **E...gas:** Amoco/diesel, BP, TradeMart/diesel, **food:** BBQ, Bojangles, Burger King, China Taste Rest., Domino's, KFC/Taco Bell, McDonald's, Pizza Hut, Subway, Wendy's, **lodging:** Comfort Inn, **other:** AutoValue Parts, Eckerd, Food Lion, Herbs4U, M&H Tires, to Falls Lake RA, **W...gas:** Exxon/diesel/24hr, Shell/diesel, **food:** Hardee's, **lodging:** Econolodge, Holiday Inn Express, Ramada Ltd, Sunset Inn, **other:** Goodyear/auto

189 Butner, no facilities

186b a US 15, to Creedmoor, no facilities

185mm Falls Lake

183 Redwood Rd, **E...lodging:** Day's Inn/gas/24hr, **food:** Redwood Café

182 Red Mill Rd, **E...gas:** Exxon/repair, **other:** Kenworth/Volvo Trucks

180 Glenn School Rd, **W...gas:** Heritage

179 E Club Blvd, **E...gas:** Exxon

178 US 70 E, to Raleigh, Falls Lake RA, Research Triangle, RDU Airport

177b c Avondale Dr, NC 55, same as 177a, **E...food:** Hong Kong Buffet, McDonalds, Golden Corral, **other:** Jiffy Lube

177a Durham, downtown, **W...gas:** Amoco, BP, Joy, Shell, **food:** American Hero Subs, Arby's, Dunkin Donuts, KFC, McDonald's, Pizza Hut, Shoney's, **lodging:** Chesterfield Motel, **other:** Advance Parts, Family$, K-Mart

176b a Gregson St, US 501 N, **E...other:** HOSPITAL, Belk, Museum of Life&Science, Sears/auto, mall

175 Guess Rd, **E...gas:** Shell/diesel, **food:** BBQ, Pizza Hut, **lodging:** Best Value Inn, Holiday Inn Express, Super 8, **W...gas:** BP/diesel, Etna, **food:** Bojangles, Honey's Diner/24hr, IHOP, JJ Fish &Chicken, Tokyo Express, Zero's Subs, **lodging:** Red Roof Inn, **other:** CVS Drug, Home Depot, Kroger

174a Hillandale Rd, **W...gas:** BP/diesel, **food:** El Corral, Papa's Grill, **lodging:** Courtyard, Hampton Inn, Howard Johnson, Shoney's Inn, **other:** MEDICAL CARE, Kerr Drug, Winn-Dixie

174b US 15 S, US 501 S(from sb), **E...lodging:** Forest Inn

D
u
r
h
a
m

173 US 15, US 501, US 70, Colemill Rd, W Durham, **E...gas:** BP, Exxon/diesel, Shell/Texaco, **food:** Arby's, BBQ, Bojangles, Burger King, Checker's, Chick-fil-a, KFC/Taco Bell, Cracker Barrel, DogHouse Rest., Domino's, Galley Seafood, Italian Garden Rest., McDonald's, Miami Subs, Subway, Taco Bell, Waffle House, Wendy's, **lodging:** Day's Inn, Fairfield Inn, Holiday Inn, Innkeeper, **other:** HOSPITAL, Autozone, Dodge/Jeep, Eckerd, Kroger, Rite Aid

172 NC 147 S, to US 15 S, US 501 S(from nb), Durham, from nb, no facilities

170 to NC 751, to Duke U(no EZ return from nb), **E...lodging:** Best Western/rest., Scottish Inn, Skyland Inn, **W...**to Eno River SP

165 NC 86, to Chapel Hill, **E...gas:** ExpressAmerica Trkstp/diesel/rest./@, **food:** Subway, **other:** Wal-Mart SprCtr/24hr., **W...gas:** BP/diesel

164 Hillsborough, **E...gas:** Amoco, Citgo/diesel, **food:** McDonald's, **lodging:** Holiday Inn Express, **W...gas:** Exxon/diesel, Shell, **food:** Bojangles, Canton House Chinese, Casa Ibarra Mexican, Domino's, Hardee's, KFC, Mayflower Seafood, Occoneechee Steaks, Öyster Bay Seafood, Pizza Hut, Subway, Waffle House, Wendy's, **lodging:** Microtel, Southern Country Inn, **other:** Braxton Tire, CarQuest, Chevrolet/Buick, Food Lion, Ford, Firestone/auto, GNC, Goodyear/auto, Lowe's Foods, Merchant Tire

163 I-40 E, to Raleigh. **I-85 S and I-40 W run together 30 mi**

161 to US 70 E, NC 86 N, no facilities

160 Efland, **W...gas:** BP/diesel, Exxon/diesel

158mm weigh sta both lanes

157 Buckhorn Rd, **E...gas:** BP/diesel, Petro/Mobil/Iron Skillet/diesel/rest./24hr/@, **W...gas:** Citgo, Exxon

154 Mebane, Oaks Rd, **E...gas:** Shell/Blimpie/diesel/24hr, **W...gas:** BP, Citgo, Exxon/diesel, Shell/diesel/24hr, **food:** Biscuitville, Bojangles, La Fiesta Mexican, McDonald's, Quizno's, Roma Pizza, Waffle House, Budget Inn/rest., **other:** MEDICAL CARE, Winn-Dixie

Interstate 85

N ↑ ↓ S

153 NC 119, Mebane, **E...gas:** BP/KFC/Taco Bell/Pizza Hut, Citgo, **food:** Cracker Barrel, Hibachi Rest., Jersy Mike's, **lodging:** Hampton Inn, Holiday Inn Express, **other:** Lowe's Whse, **W...gas:** Exxon/Burger King, **food:** Domino's, La Cocina Mexican, Subway, YumYum Chinese, **other:** CVS Drug, Food Lion

152 Trollingwood Rd, **E...gas:** Pilot/McDonald's/diesel/24hr/@, **W...gas:** Fuel City/diesel

150 Haw River, to Roxboro, **W...gas:** Hess/Wilco/DQ/Wendy's/diesel/24hr/@, ⚕/Flying J/Conoco/diesel/LP/rest./24hr/@, **lodging:** Best Western, **other:** Blue Beacon

148 NC 54, Graham, **E...gas:** BP/diesel/24hr, Exxon/diesel/24hr, QP, **food:** Waffle House, **lodging:** ComfortSuites, **W...lodging:** Ember's Motel, Travel Inn

147 NC 87, to Pittsboro, Graham, **E...gas:** BP, Servco/diesel, **food:** Arby's, Bojangles, Burger King, Domino's, Pizza Hut, Sagebrush Steaks, Subway, Wendy's, **other:** Advance Parts, Chevrolet, Family$, Food Lion, Ford, Goodyear, Plymouth/Jeep, Winn-Dixie, **W...gas:** Citgo/Etna/diesel, Exxon/diesel, Shell/diesel, **food:** BBQ&Ribs Rest., Biscuitville, Hardee's, McDonald's, Taco Bell, **other:** HOSPITAL, CVS Drug, Lowe's Foods

145 NC 49, Burlington, **E...gas:** BP/diesel, Shell/diesel, **food:** Capt D's, **lodging:** Microtel, Motel 6, Red Roof Inn, **W...gas:** BP, Hess, **food:** Arby's, Biscuitville, Bojangles, Burger King, Hardee's, KFC, Subway, Waffle House, **lodging:** Day's Inn, Holiday Inn, Scottish Inn, **other:** Dodge, $General, Eckerd, Food Lion, Radio Shack

143 NC 62, Burlington, **E...gas:** Citgo/Wendy's, **food:** Bob Evans, Hardee's, Waffle House, to Alamance Bfd, **W...gas:** Exxon, 76/Circle K, **food:** K&W Cafeteria, Libby Hill Seafood, Passion Grill, **lodging:** Ramada Inn, **other:** Cadillac, Chevrolet, Food Lion, Ford, Home Depot, Mitsubishi

141 to Burlington, **E...gas:** BP, Shell, Kangaroo, **food:** IHOP, Mayflower Seafood, Outback Steaks, **lodging:** Hampton Inn, **W...gas:** Crown, Phillips 66/diesel, Shell, **food:** Applebee's, Arby's, Biscuitville, Bojangles, Burger King, Chick-fil-A, Cracker Barrel, Golden Corral, KFC, Makita Indian Rest., McDonald's, Steak'n Shake/24hr, Taco Bell, **lodging:** Best Western, Country Suites, Courtyard, Super 8, **other:** HOSPITAL, Belk, Buick/GMC, Eckerd, Food Lion, Ford/Lincoln/Mercury, Isuzu, K-Mart/gas, Lowe's Foods, Mazda, Nissan, JC Penney, OfficeMax, Sears/auto, Wal-Mart SuperCtr/24hr, Winn-Dixie, mall, to Elon Coll

140 new interchange, no facilities

139mm **rest area both lanes, full(handicapped)facilities, phone, picnic tables,litter barrels, vending**

138 NC 61, Gibsonville, **W...gas:** Shell/diesel, TA/BP/Burger King/Popeye's/diesel/rest./@, **lodging:** Days Inn

135 Rock Creek Dairy Rd, **W...gas:** Citgo, Exxon, **food:** Jersey Mike's Subs, McDonald's, **other:** Food Lion

132 Mt Hope Church Rd, **W...gas:** Shell/diesel, Texaco, Wilco/Hess/Wendy's/diesel/24hr/@, **lodging:** Hampton Inn

131 to US 70, **I-85 N and I-40 E run together 30 mi.**

129 Youngsmill Rd, no facilities

128 Alamance Church Rd, no facilities

126b a US 421, to Sanford, no facilities

124 S Elm, Eugene St, no facilities

122 US 220, to Greenboro, Asheboro, access to I-40, no facilites

120 Groometown Rd, nb only, **W...gas:** Phillips 66/diesel/24hr

118 US 29 S, US 70 W, to High Point, Jamestown, **W...lodging:** Grandover Resort, **other:** HOSPITAL

115mm Deep River

113 NC 62, Archdale, **W...gas:** BP/diesel, **lodging:** Best Western, **E...gas:** Citgo/diesel,

111 US 311, to High Point, Archdale, **E...food:** Bamboo Garden, Big Guy Subs, Biscuitville, Bojangles, Hardee's, Little Caesar's, Subway, Wendy's, **lodging:** Innkeeper, **other:** CVS Drug, $General, Food Lion, Lowe's Foods/24hr, **W...gas:** BP/diesel/24hr, Citgo, Exxon/McDonald's, Phillips 66/diesel, Shell/diesel, **food:** Waffle House, **lodging:** Best Western, Comfort Inn, Fairfeild Inn, Hampton Inn, Holiday Inn Express, **other:** HOSPITAL, USPO, **2 mi W...food:** Bojangles, Burger King, Hardee's, KFC, Papa John's, Pizza Hut, SaltMarsh Annie's Seafood, Taco Bell, **other:** Advance Parts, Eckerd, Firestone, NAPA

108 Hopewell Church Rd, no facilities

106 Finch Farm Rd, **E...gas:** Exxon/diesel

103 NC 109, to Thomasville, **E...gas:** Citgo, Shell, **food:** Arby's, Cookout Burgers, Taco Bell, **other:** CVS Drug, Ingles Foods, K-Mart, Radio Shack, Wal-Mart SuperCtr/24hr, **W...gas:** BP/Subway/diesel, Coastal, Crown/24hr, Mobil, Texaco, Hess/Wilco, Sunoco, **food:** BBQ Shack, Biscuitville, Burger King, Captain Tom's, China Garden, Flashburger, Golden Corral, Hardee's, KFC, Loflin's Rest., Mazatlan Mexican, McDonald's, Mr Gatti's, Papa John's, PieZone Pizza, Pizza Hut, Sonic, Sunrise Grille, Waffle House, Wendy's, **lodging:** Howard Johnson, Quaility Inn, Ramada Ltd, Thomasville Inn(2mi), **other:** Advance Parts, AutoZone, Eckerd, Family$, Food Lion, Guy's Drug, Merchant's Tire, Walgreen, Winn-Dixie

Greensboro

Burlington

Thomasville

Interstate 85

N
S

102   Lake Rd, **W...gas:** Phillips 66/diesel, Shell/ KrispyKreme/diesel, **lodging:** Day's Inn/rest., **other:** HOSPITAL, Bapt Children Home

100mm   **rest area both lanes, full(handicapped)facilities, phone, vending, picnic tables, litter barrels, pet- walk**

96   US 64, to Asheboro, Lexington, **E...gas:** Exxon, **W...gas:** Chevron/diesel, Citgo(1mi), **lodging:** Qual- ity Inn(4mi), **other:** to Davidson Co Coll, NC Zoo

94   Old US 64, **E...gas:** Shell/Texaco

91   NC 8, to Southmont, **E...gas:** BP/diesel, Citgo, Phil- lips 66, Shell/diesel, **food:** Biscuit King, Capt'n Ste- ven's Seafood, KFC, McDonald's, Pizza Oven, Sonic, Subway, Wendy's, **lodging:** Comfort Suites, Super 8, **other:** Food Lion, High Rock Lake Camping(7mi), **W...gas:** Exxon/diesel, QM, **food:** Applebee's, Arby's, Burger King, Cracker Barrel, Golden Corral, Hardee's, Hunan Chinese, Little Caesar's, Taco Bell, Zaxby's, **lodging:** Country Hearth Inn, Holiday Inn Express, **other:** HOSPITAL, American Childrens Home, Belks, GNC, Goody's, Hamrick's, Ingles Foods, Wal-Mart

88   Linwood, **W...gas:** BP/diesel, **other:** HOSPITAL,

87   US 29, US 70, US 52(from nb), High Point, **W...lodging:** Best Western, **other:** HOSPITAL, mall

86   Belmont Rd, **W...gas:** Phillips 66/Bill's Trkstp/diesel/ rest./24hr/@

85   Clark Rd, to NC 150, no facilities

83   NC 150(from nb), to Spencer, no facilities

82   US 29, US 70(from sb), to Spencer, no facilities

81.5mm   Yadkin River

81   Spencer, **E...gas:** Exxon/diesel, **other:** camping

79   Spencer Shops St HS, Spencer, E Spencer, no facili- ties

76b a   US 52, to Albemarle, Salisbury, **E...gas:** BP, RaceTrac/24hr, Speedway, **food:** Applebee's, Athena Diner, China Rainbow, Golden Bee Rest., IHOP, Italy Café, Little Caesar's, LoneStar Steaks, Schlotsky's, Shoney's, **lodging:** Day's Inn, Happy Traveler Inn, Sleep Inn, Studio Suites, Super 8, **other:** Aldi Foods, Circuit City, CVS Drug, Dodge, Eckerd, Food Lion, GNC, Lowe's Whse, Staples, **W...gas:** Exxon/diesel, Servco, 76/diesel, Shell, **food:** Blue Bay Seafood, Bojangles, Burger King, Capt D's, Chick-fil-A, China Garden, Christo's Rest., Church's Chicken, Dunkin Donuts, El Cancun Mexican, Ham's Rest., Hardee's, KFC, McDonald's, O'Charley's, Out- back Steaks, Pizza Hut, Taco Bell, Village Inn Pizza, Waffle House/24hr, Wendy's, **lodging:** Budget Inn, Comfort Suites, Howard Johnson, **other:** HOSPITAL, Advance Parts, AutoZone, Family$, Firestone/auto, Goodyear/auto, K-Mart, Office Depot, USPO

Salisbury

75   US 601, Jake Alexander Blvd, **E...food:** Arby's, **lodg- ing:** Ramada Ltd, **other:** Dan Nicholas Park, **W...gas:** Amoco/24hr, BP, Citgo, Exxon/diesel, Shell/diesel, **food:** Casa Grande, Fire Mountain Grill, Ichiban Japanese, Ryan's, Sagebrush Steaks, Subway, Waffle House, Wendy's, **lodging:** Best Western, Day's Inn, Hampton Inn, Holiday Inn, **other:** Chevrolet/Cadillac, Chrysler/Plymouth/Jeep, Ford/Toyota, Honda/Kia, Nissan/Pontiac/GMC, Wal-Mart

74   Julian Rd, no facilities

72   Peach Orchard Rd, **W...airport**

71   Peeler Rd, **E...gas:** Shell/CW's Rest./diesel/rest./ 24hr/@, **W...gas:** Hess/Wilco/Bojangles/Subway/ diesel/24hr/@

70   Webb Rd, **E...flea mkt, W...st patrol**

68   US 29, US 601, to Rockwell, China Grove, no facili- ties

63   Kannapolis, **E...gas:** Pilot/Subway/diesel/@, **food:** Waffle House, **lodging:** Best Western, **3 mi W...gas:** Exxon/diesel, **food:** China Buffet, Hardee's, KFC, **other:** repair

60   Earnhardt Rd, Copperfield Blvd, **E...gas:** Exxon/ diesel(1mi), BP, **food:** Bojangles, Cracker Barrel, Kramer&Eugene's Café(1mi), Schlotsky's, Texas Roadhouse, **lodging:** Hampton Inn, Sleep Inn, **other:** HOSPITAL, **W...gas:** BP/diesel, **food:** Bob Evans, Ruby Tuesday, **other:** Sam's Club, Wal-Mart SuperCtr/24hr, visitor info

59mm   **rest area both lanes, full(handicapped)facilities, phone, vending, picnic tables, litter barrels, pet- walk**

58   US 29, US 601, Concord, **E...gas:** BP, Citgo, Crown/24hr, Exxon, Shell/diesel, Wilco/diesel, **food:** Applebee's, BearRock Café, Burger King, Capt D's, Chick-fil-A, China Orchid, El Cancun Mexican, El Val- larta Mexican, Golden Corral, Good Neighbor Chi- nese, Italian Oven, KFC, Little Caesar's, Longhorn Steaks, Mayflower Seafood, McDonald's, Mr C's Rest., O'Charley's, Pizza Hut, Schlotsky's, Shoney's, Subway, Taco Bell, Texas Steaks, Villa Maria Italian, Waffle House, Wendy's, **lodging:** Best Value, Colonial Inn, Holiday Inn Express, Mayfair Motel, Rodeway Inn, **other:** HOSPITAL, Belk, Cadillac, Chrysler/Plymouth/ Jeep, Eckerd, Food Lion, JC Penney, Sears/auto, U-Haul, mall, st patrol, **W...gas:** Phillips 66, **food:** CiCi's, Bojangles(2mi), Domino's, Hardee's(2mi), IHOP, Ryan's, **lodging:** Cabarrus Inn, Comfort Inn, Econolodge, Fairfield Inn, Mainstay Suites, Microtel, Park Inn, Studio 1 Suites, **other:** $General, Drug Em- porium, Eddie's Pizza/funpark, Harris-Teeter, Home Depot, JC Penney, OfficeMax, Target

Concord

Interstate 85

N ↑
| |
S ↓

55 NC 73, to Davidson, Concord, **E…gas:** Exxon/diesel, Shell, **food:** McDonald's, Waffle House, **W…gas:** Phillips 66/diesel, Shell/Texaco, 76/Circle K/diesel, **food:** Angelo's Fishhouse, Huddle House, **lodging:** Day's Inn

54 Kannapolis Pkwy, George W. Lyle Pkwy, new exit

52 Poplar Tent Rd, **E…gas:** Shell/diesel, **other:** to Lowe's Speedway, museum, **W…gas:** Exxon/24hr

49 Speedway Blvd, Concord Mills Blvd, **E…gas:** BP/McDonalds, Shelldiesel, Texaco, **food:** Arby's, BBQ, Bob Evans, Bojangles, Carrabbas, Chuckee Cheese, Hooters, Quizno's, Texas Roadhouse, Jack-in-the-Box, Subway, Wendy's, Zaxby's, **lodging:** Comfort Suites, Hampton Inn, Hawthorn Suites, Holiday Inn Express, Sleep Inn, SpringHill Suites, Suburban Lodge, Wingate Inn, **other:** Fleetwood RV camping(1.5mi), to Lowes Motor Speedway, **W…gas:** Citgo, **food:** Applebee's, Firemountain Grill, Olive Garden, On-the-Border, Panera Bread, Pizzaria Uno, Razzoo's cafe, Red Lobster, Roadhouse Grill, Steak'n Shake, TGI Friday, **other:** BooksAMillion, Discount Tire, Concord Mills Mall, Radio Shack

48 I-485, to US 29, no facilities

46 Mallard Creek Church Rd, **E…gas:** Wilco/diesel(1mi), **other:** Research Park, **W…gas:** Exxon/24hr, **food:** Subway(1mi)

45 Harris Blvd, **E…gas:** Phillips 66/diesel, **food:** Applebee's, BBQ, Bojangles, Burger King, Chili's, Chick-fil-A, Copeland's Rest., Hop's Grill, Houlihan's, Max&Erma's, McDonald's, Shoney's, Taco Bell, TGIFriday, Waffle House, **lodging:** Comfort Suites(1mi), Courtyard, Drury Inn, Hampton Inn, Hilton, Holiday Inn, Homewood Suites, Residence Inn, Sleep Inn, **other:** HOSPITAL, Best Buy, Food Lion, GNC, Hannaford's Foods, Kerr Drug, Kohl's, Lowe's Whse, Michael's, Office Depot, Old Navy, Radio Shack, Sam's Club, Walgreen, Wal-Mart/auto, mall, to UNCC, U Research Park, **2 mi W…gas:** Citgo, Shell, **food:** Longhorn Steaks, Macaroni Grill, McDonald's, Subway, Wendy's, **other:** Eckerd, Food Lion

43 to City Blvd, no facilities

41 Sugar Creek Rd, **E…gas:** RaceTrac, Shell/diesel, **food:** Bojangles, McDonald's, Taco Bell, Wendy's, **lodging:** Best Western, Best Value, Brookwood Inn, Continental Inn, Econolodge, Economy Inn, Microtel, Motel 6, Quality Inn, Red Roof Inn, **W…gas:** 76/Circle K, BP/diesel, Exxon/diesel, **food:** Shoney's, Texas Ranch Steaks, **lodging:** Comfort Inn, Day's Inn, Fairfield Inn, Holiday Inn Express, Ramada Inn, Rodeway Inn, Super 8

40 Graham St, **E…gas:** Exxon/diesel, **food:** Hereford Barn Steaks, **lodging:** Howard Johnson, **other:** Ford Trucks, UPS, **W…gas:** Citgo, **other:** Goodyear

Charlotte

39 Statesville Ave, **E…gas:** Pilot/Subway/diesel/24hr/@, **other:** CarQuest, carwash, **W…gas:** Citgo, Shell/diesel, **food:** Bojangles, **lodging:** Knight's Inn, **other:** auto repair

38 I-77, US 21, N to Statesville, S to Columbia, no facilities

37 Beatties Ford Rd, **E…gas:** Citgo, Phillips 66/diesel, Shell/diesel, **food:** Burger King, KFC/LJ Silvers, McDonald's, Subway, Taco Bell, Top's China, **other:** CVS Drug, Food Lion, **W…gas:** BP, **food:** McDonald's Cafeteria, **lodging:** Travelodge, **other:** funpark, to JC Smith U

36 NC 16, Brookshire Blvd, **E…gas:** BP/diesel, **food:** China City, **lodging:** Hornet's Rest Inn, **other:** HOSPITAL, repair, **W…gas:** Exxon, RaceTrac, Sunoco, **food:** Bojangles, Burger King, El Toro Mexican, Jack-in-the-Box

35 Glenwood Dr, **E…gas:** Citgo/Circle K, Shell/diesel, **lodging:** Innkeeper, Knight's Inn, **W…food:** Old Europe Rest., **other:** White/GMC

34 NC 27, Freedom Dr, **E…gas:** 76/Circle K, Amoco/diesel, BP, Walker/gas, **food:** Beauregard's Rest, Bojangles, Capt D's, IHOP, Mayflower Seafood, McDonald's, Pizza Hut, Ruby Palace Chinese, Shoney's, Subway, Taco Bell, Tung Hoy Chinese, Wendy's, **other:** MEDICAL CARE, Advance Parts, BiLo, Firestone, Goodyear, NAPA, Pizza Hut, Walgreen, **W…food:** IHOP, **lodging:** GuestHouse Suites, Howard Johnson, Quality Suites, Ramada Ltd, Villager Lodge, **other:** Jiffy Lube

33 US 521, Billy Graham Pkwy, **E…gas:** 76/Circle K/Blimpie/diesel, Crown/gas, **food:** Bojangles, Krystal, McDonald's, KFC/Taco Bell, Wendy's, **lodging:** Comfort Suites, Day's Inn, Economy Inn, Royal Inn, Sheraton, Springhill Suites, **other:** to Coliseum, airport, **W…gas:** Exxon/diesel, **food:** Cracker Barrel, Prime Sirloin, Waffle House/24hr, **lodging:** Best Value, Fairfield Inn, Hampton Inn, La Quinta, Microtel, Red Roof, Save Inn

32 Little Rock Rd, **E…gas:** Exxon, **food:** Hardee's, Waffle House, **lodging:** Courtyard, Econolodge, Holiday Inn, **other:** Toyota, tires, **W…gas:** Citgo/Circle K, Crown, Exxon, **food:** Arby's, Hardee's, Miguel's Mexican, Showmar's Rest., Shoney's, Subway, **lodging:** Best Western, Comfort Inn, Country Inn Suites, Motel 6, Shoney's Inn/rest., Wingate Inn, **other:** Eckerd, Family$, Food Lion

NORTH CAROLINA
Interstate 85

N ↕ S

30   I-485, no facilities

29   Sam Wilson Rd, **E…gas:** BP(1mi), **W…gas:** Shell/diesel

28mm   weigh sta both lanes

27.5mm Catawba River

27   NC 273, Mt Holly, **E…gas:** Citgo, Exxon/diesel, **food:** Arby's, Burger King, Capt's Seafood, Domino's, KFC, Niyoshi Japanese, Pizza Hut, Subway, Taco Bell, Waffle House, Wendy's, **other:** Chevrolet, Eckerd, Family$, Food Lion, NAPA, Radio Shack, Walgreen, **W…gas:** BP/diesel, Shell/Texaco/diesel, **lodging:** Holiday Inn Express

26   **E…gas:** Amoco, Citgo, **food:** Bojangles, Hardee's, McDonald's, New China, Papa John's, Western Sizzlin, **other:** Advance Parts, BiLo, Chrysler/Plymouth/Jeep, Ford, Winn-Dixie, **W…**Belmont Abbey Coll,

24mm   South Fork River

23   NC 7, McAdenville, **W…gas:** Exxon, Shell, World gas, **food:** Hillbilly's BBQ/Steaks, Hardee's, Hillbilly's BBQ/Steaks

22   Cramerton, Lowell, **E…food:** Applebee's, Burger King, Gator's Rest., Hooters, LJ Silver, Schlotsky's, Zaxby's, **other:** Chevrolet/Cadillac, Honda, Mazda, Kohl's, Lincoln/Mercury, Misubishi, Nissan, Sam's Club, U-Haul

21   Cox Rd, **E…gas:** Citgo/diesel, Exxon, **food:** Arby's, Boston Mkt, Chick-fil-A, Chili's, Don Pablo, Jackson's Cafeteria, Krispy Kreme, Longhorn Steaks, Max' Mexican Eatery, McDonald's, Peking Garden, Pizza Inn, Ryan's, Subway, **other:** Best Buy, BooksAMillion, BiLo/24hr, Dodge, $Tree, Hannaford's Foods, Harris-Teeter/24hr, Home Depot, K-Mart, Lowe's Whse, Michael's, OfficeMax, Old Navy, PepBoys, Tire Kingdom, Upton's, Wal-Mart, mall, **W…gas:** Exxon, Texaco, **food:** IHOP, **lodging:** Villager Lodge, Super 8, **other:** HOSPITAL, Harley-Davidson, Med Ctr Drug, Suzuki

20   NC 279, New Hope Rd, **E…gas:** Amoco, Shell, Shell/Texaco, **food:** Arby's, Burger King, Capt D's, Checker's, Hong Kong Buffet, Italian Oven, McDonald's, Morrison's Cafeteria, Pizza Hut, Red Lobster, Sake Japanese, Shoney's, Taco Bell, **lodging:** Holiday Inn Express, **other:** Advance Parts, Belk, Dillard's, Firestone/auto, JC Penney, K-Mart, NAPA, Office Depot, Sears/auto, Target, Winn-Dixie, mall, **W…food:** Bojangles, Cracker Barrel, Hickory Ham Café, KFC, Outback Steaks, Waffle House, **lodging:** Best Western, Comfort Inn, Courtyard, Fairfield Inn, Hampton Inn, Innkeeper, **other:** HOSPITAL, Circuit City

19   NC 7, E Gastonia, **E…gas:** World gas

17   US 321, Gastonia, **E…gas:** Exxon/diesel/LP, Servco, **food:** Los Arcos Mexican, **lodging:** Day's Inn, Midtown Motel, Villager Lodge, **W…gas:** Citgo/diesel, Perto Xprs/diesel, **food:** McDonald's, Waffle House, Wendy's, Western Sizzlin, **lodging:** Microtel, Motel 6

Gastonia *(vertical label)*

14   NC 274, E Bessemer, **E…gas:** Phillips 66, **food:** Burger King(1mi), **W…gas:** BP/Subway, Citgo/diesel, **food:** Bojangles, Waffle House, **lodging:** Howard Johnson Express

13   Edgewood Rd, Bessemer City, **E…**to Crowders Mtn SP, **W…gas:** Amoco, Exxon/diesel/24hr, **lodging:** Economy Inn

10b a   US 74 W, US 29, Kings Mtn, no facilities

8   NC 161, to Kings Mtn, **E…lodging:** Holiday Inn Express, **W…gas:** BP, **food:** KFC, McDonald's, Taco Bell, Waffle House, Wendy's, **lodging:** Comfort Inn, Travelodge, **other:** HOSPITAL, Chevrolet

6mm   **rest area sb, full(handicapped)facilities, phone, picnic tables, litter barrels, vending, petwalk**

5   Dixon School Rd, **E…gas:** Shell/Texaco/Subway/diesel, **food:** Classic Diner

4   US 29 S(from sb), no facilities

2.5mm   **Welcome Ctr nb, full(handicapped)facilities, info, phone, vending, picnic tables, litter barrels, petwalk**

2   NC 216, Kings Mtn, **E…**to Kings Mtn Nat Military Park, **W…gas:** Chevron

0mm   North Carolina/South Carolina state line

Interstate 95

Exit #   Services

N ↕ S

181mm   North Carolina/Virginia state line, **Welcome Ctr sb, full(handicapped)facilities, phone, picnic tables, litter barrels, vending, petwalk**

180   NC 48, to Gaston, Pleasant Hill, to Lake Gaston, **W…gas:** Pilot/Subway/diesel/24hr/@

176   NC 46, to Garysburg, **E…gas:** Texaco/Stuckey's, **other:** repair, **W…gas:** Shell, **food:** Aunt Sarah's, Burger King, **lodging:** Best Western

174mm   Roanoke River

173   US 158, Roanoke Rapids, Weldon, **E…gas:** BP/diesel, Shell/Blimpie, Texaco/diesel, **food:** Ralph's BBQ, Trigger's Steaks, Waffle House, **lodging:** Day's Inn, Interstate Inn, Orchard Inn, **other:** HOSPITAL, **W…gas:** BP/diesel, Exxon, RaceTrac, **food:** Arby's, Burger King, Cracker Barrel, Hardee's, KFC, Little Caesar's, McDonald's, Piccolowe's Rest., Pizza Hut, Ruby Tuesday, Ryan's, Shoney's, Subway, Taco Bell, Texas Steaks, Tokyo Sushi, Waffle House, Wendy's, **lodging:** Comfort Inn, Hampton Inn, Jameson Inn, Motel 6, Sleep Inn, **other:** Advance Parts, AutoZone, $General, Eckerd, Firestone/auto, Food Lion, Ford/Lincoln/Mercury/Honda, Piggly Wiggly, Wal-Mart SuperCtr/gas/24hr

171   NC 125, Roanoke Rapids, **W…gas:** Texaco/diesel, **lodging:** Holiday Inn Express, **other:** st patrol

Roanoke Rapids *(vertical label)*

Interstate 95

N ↕ S

168	NC 903, to Halifax, **E...gas:** Exxon/diesel, Shell/Burger King/diesel
160	NC 561, to Brinkleyville, **E...gas:** Exxon/24hr, **W...gas:** Citgo/diesel/rest.
154	NC 481, to Enfield, **E...gas:** Mobil, **W...other:** KOA(1mi)
152mm	weigh sta both lanes
150	NC 33, to Whitakers, **E...golf, W...gas:** BP/Subway/DQ/Stuckey's
145	NC 4, to US 301, Battleboro, **E...gas:** Amoco/diesel, Exxon, Shell/diesel, Texaco, **food:** BBQ, DQ, Denny's, Hardee's, Shoney's, Waffle House, Wendy's, **lodging:** Best Western/rest., Comfort Inn, Day's Inn, Deluxe Inn, Howard Johnson, Masters Inn, Quality Inn, Red Carpet Inn, Scottish Inn, Super 8, Travelodge
142mm	**rest area both lanes, full(handicapped)facilities, phone, picnic tables, litter barrels, vending, pet-walk**
141	NC 43, Red Oak, **E...gas:** Exxon/diesel/LP, Texaco/diesel, **W...gas:** BP/diesel, **lodging:** Econolodge
138	US 64, Rocky Mount, **5 mi E...lodging:** Comfort Inn, Courtyard, Hampton Inn, Holiday Inn, Residence Inn, **other:** HOSPITAL, to Cape Hatteras Nat Seashore
132	to NC 58, **E...gas:** Citgo/diesel, **1 mi W...gas:** Amoco/diesel
128mm	Tar River
127	NC 97, to Stanhope, **E...gas:** BP/diesel, **other:** airport
121	US 264, Wilson, **E...gas:** BP, Citgo/Subway, Kangaroo/diesel/LP, Shell, **food:** Aunt Sarah's, Hardee's, KFC/LJ Silver, Waffle House, **lodging:** Comfort Inn, **other:** HOSPITAL, **4 mi E...gas:** Shell/diesel, **food:** Applebee's, Arby's, Boston Mkt, Burger King, Chick-fil-A, Denny's, Golden Corral, Sonic, Subway, **lodging:** Hampton Inn, **other:** BooksAMillion, Eckerd, Jo-Ann Crafts, K-Mart, Lowe's Whse, Staples, Wal-Mart SuperCtr/24hr, **W...gas:** BP/Blimpie/diesel, **food:** Bojangles, Burger King, Cracker Barrel, McDonald's, **lodging:** Holiday Inn Express, Jameson Inn, Microtel, Sleep Inn, **other:** to Country Doctor Museum
119b a	US 264, US 117, no facilities
116	NC 42, to Clayton, Wilson, **E...gas:** Shell/diesel, HOSPITAL, **W...gas:** BP/diesel, **other:** Rock Ridge Camping
107	US 301, Kenly, **E...gas:** BP, Coastal/Subway, Exxon/McDonald's/diesel, Shell/diesel/24hr, **food:** BBQ, Burger King, Golden China, Nik's Pizza, Patrick's Rest., Waffle House, Willoughby's Seafood, **lodging:** Budget Inn, Deluxe Inn, Econolodge, **other:** Food Lion, Ford, Family$, IGA Food, Tobacco Museum

Wilson (side label)

106	Truck Stop Rd, Kenly, **W...gas:** TA/Wendy's/diesel/24hr/@, Wilco/Hess/diesel/24hr/@, **food:** Kenly Kitchen, Venero's Rest., Waffle House, **lodging:** Day's Inn, Super 8, **other:** Blue Beacon
105.5mm	Little River
105	Bagley Rd, Kenly, **E...gas:** Citgo/Stormin Norman/diesel/rest./24hr/@
102	Micro, **E...gas:** BP/repair, **W...gas:** Phillips 66, USPO
101	Pittman Rd, no facilities
99mm	**rest areas both lanes, full(handicapped)facilities, vending, phone, picnic tables, litter barrels, pet-walk, hist marker**
98	to Selma, **E...KOA**
97	US 70 A, Selma, to Pine Level, **E...gas:** Citgo/diesel/24hr, **food:** Denny's, Subway, **lodging:** Holiday Inn Express, **other:** J&R Outlet, **W...gas:** Amoco/diesel/24hr, BP/diesel, Exxon/diesel/24hr, Texaco/diesel, **food:** Bojangles, China Buffet, Golden Corral, Hardee's, KFC, McDonald's, Oliver's Rest., Pizza Hut, Shoney's, Waffle House, **lodging:** Comfort Inn, Day's Inn, Hampton Inn, Luxury Inn, Masters Inn, Regency Inn, Royal Inn, **other:** HOSPITAL
95	US 70, Smithfield, **E...lodging:** Log Cabin Motel/rest., Howard Johnson Express, Village Motel, **other:** Ava Gardner Museum, **W...gas:** Shell, Speedway/diesel, **food:** Bob Evans, Burger King, Cracker Barrel, Smithfield BBQ(2mi), Texas Roadhouse, **lodging:** Jameson Inn, Super 8, **other:** Harley-Davidson, Factory Outlets/famous brands
93	Brogden Rd, Smithfield, **W...gas:** Amoco/diesel, Shell
91.5mm	Neuse River
90	US 301, US 701, to Newton Grove, **E...gas:** Citgo/diesel, **food:** Roz's Rest., **lodging:** Travelers Inn, **other:** Holiday TravLPark, to Bentonville Bfd, **W...gas:** Phillips 66/diesel, **lodging:** Four Oaks Motel
87	NC 96, Four Oaks, no facilities
81b a	I-40, E to Wilmington, W to Raleigh
79	NC 50, to NC 27, Benson, Newton Grove, **E...gas:** BP, Citgo, **food:** Waffle House, **lodging:** Dutch Inn, **other:** Food Lion, **W...gas:** Coastal, Exxon, Mobil/McDonald's, **food:** Burger King, Domino's, McDonald's, KFC, Pizza Hut, Subway, **lodging:** Day's Inn, **other:** Family$, Lowe's Foods, Rite Aid

Selma (side label)

NORTH CAROLINA
Interstate 95

Dunn

77	Hodges Chapel Rd, **E...gas:** Pilot/Subway/diesel/24hr/@ , RV/truckwash
75	Jonesboro Rd, **W...gas:** Sadler/Shell/diesel/rest./24hr/@
73	US 421, NC 55, to Dunn, Clinton, **E...food:** Cracker Barrel, Wendy's, **W...gas:** Exxon/diesel, Chevron/diesel, Texaco, **food:** Bojangles, Burger King, Dairy Freeze, McDonald's(2mi), Sagebrush Steaks, Taco Bell, Triangle Waffle, **lodging:** Comfort Inn, Econolodge, Express Inn, Holiday Inn Express, Jameson Inn, Ramada Inn/rest., **other:** IGA Foods, museum
72	Pope Rd, **E...gas:** BP, **lodging:** Comfort Inn, Royal Inn, **W...gas:** BP, **food:** Brass Lantern Steaks, **lodging:** Budget Inn, Express Inn, **other:** Cadillac/GMC, auto repair
71	Longbranch Rd, **E...gas:** Citgo/Hardee's/Travel World/diesel/24hr, **W...**to Averasboro Bfd
70	SR 1811, **E...lodging:** Relax Inn
65	NC 82, Godwin, **W...other:** Children's Home
61	to Wade, **E...gas:** Citgo/diesel, **other:** KOA, **W...gas:** BP/Subway/diesel/24hr/@
58	US 13, to Newton Grove, **E...lodging:** Day's Inn/rest.

Fayetteville

56	Lp 95, to US 301(from sb), Fayetteville, **W...gas:** Shell, **lodging:** Budget Inn, **other:** HOSPITAL, to Ft Bragg, Pope AFB
55	NC 1832, **W...gas:** Exxon/diesel, Shell, **lodging:** Budget Inn
52	NC 24, Fayetteville, **W...other:** to Ft Bragg, Pope AFB, botanical gardens, museum
49	NC 53, NC 210, Fayetteville, **E...gas:** BP/diesel, Exxon, Texaco/diesel, **food:** Burger King, Denny's, McDonald's, Pizza Hut, Taco Bell, Waffle House, **lodging:** Day's Inn/rest, Deluxe Inn, Motel 6, Quality Inn, **W...gas:** BP/Subway/diesel, Exxon/diesel, Shell/diesel, **food:** Beaver Dam Seafood, Cracker Barrel, Shoney's, **lodging:** Best Western, Comfort Inn, Econolodge, Fairfield Inn, Hampton Inn, Holiday Inn, Innkeeper, Red Roof Inn, Sleep Inn, Sheraton, Super 8
48mm	**rest areas both lanes, full(handicapped)facilities, phone, picnic tables, litter barrels, vending, petwalk**
47mm	Cape Fear River
46b a	NC 87, to Fayetteville, Elizabethtown, **W...other:** HOSPITAL, Civic Ctr, to Agr Expo Ctr
44	Snow Hill Rd, **W...other:** Lazy Acres Camping, to airport
41	NC 59, to Hope Mills, Parkton, **E...gas:** Kangaroo/24hr, **W...gas:** BP, Spring Valley RV Park
40	Lp 95, to US 301(from nb), to Fayetteville, facilities on US 301(5-7mi)
33	US 301, St Pauls, **E...gas:** Amoco/diesel/repair/24hr

Lumberton

31	NC 20, to St Pauls, Raeford, **E...gas:** Amoco, BP, Mobil, Shell/Huddle House/diesel/24hr, **food:** Burger King, Hardee's, McDonald's, **lodging:** Day's Inn, **W...gas:** Citgo, Exxon/diesel
25	US 301, **E...gas:** BP/diesel
24mm	weigh sta both lanes
22	US 301, **E...gas:** Shell/DQ, **food:** Burger King, Denny's, Hardee's, Huddle House, John's Rest., Outback Steaks, Ruby Tuesday, Ryan's, Smithfield BBQ, Texas Steaks, Waffle House, Zaxby's, **lodging:** Best Western, Comfort Suites, Hampton Inn, Holiday Inn, Redwood Lodge, Super 8, **other:** $Tree, Goodyear/auto, Lowe's Foods, Lowe's Whse, Office Depot, OfficeMax, Wal-Mart SuperCtr/24hr, st patrol, **W...gas:** Circle B, Sun-Do/diesel, Texaco/Subway/diesel
20	NC 211, to NC 41, Lumberton, **E...gas:** Amoco, Citgo, Exxon/diesel, **food:** Carolina Steaks, Golden City Chinese, Hardee's, Little Caesar's, McDonald's, New China, Subway, Village Sta Rest., Waffle House, Western Sizzlin, **lodging:** Deluxe Inn, Howard Johnson, Quality Inn, Ramada Ltd, **other:** HOSPITAL, Food Lion/deli, K-Mart, **W...gas:** Texaco/diesel, **food:** BBQ, Cracker Barrel, LungWah Chinese, **lodging:** Comfort Inn, Country Inn Suites, Day's Inn/rest., Econolodge, Fairfield Inn, National 9 Inn
19	Carthage Rd, Lumberton, **E...gas:** BP/diesel, **food:** Mi Casita Mexican, **lodging:** Travelers Inn, **other:** auto repair, **W...gas:** Exxon/diesel, Texaco, **lodging:** Knight's Inn, Motel 6
18mm	Lumber River
17	NC 72, **E...gas:** BP/diesel, Citgo, Exxon/Huddle House/diesel, Mobil/diesel, Shell/Wendy's/diesel, **food:** Burger King, Hardee's, McDonald's, Old Foundry Rest., Subway, Waffle House, **lodging:** Budget Inn, Economy Inn, Southern Inn, **other:** AutoZone, Food Lion
14	US 74, Maxton, to Laurinburg, **W...gas:** BP/diesel, **lodging:** Exit Inn, **other:** Sleepy Bear's RV Camp
10	US 301, to Fairmont, no facilities
7	to McDonald, Raynham, no facilities
5mm	**Welcome Ctr nb, full(handicapped)facilities, phone, picnic tables, litter barrels, vending, petwalk**
2	NC 130, to NC 904, Rowland, no facilities
1b a	US 301, US 501, Dillon, **E...gas:** Exxon, Shell, **food:** Hot Tamale Rest., Pedro's Diner, Pedro's Ice Cream Fiesta, Sombrero Rest., **lodging:** Golden Triangle Motel, South-of-the-Border Motel, **other:** Pedro's Campground, Ford, **W...gas:** Shell/diesel, Sun-Do, **food:** Tarheel Diner, Waffle House, **lodging:** Budget Motel, Day's Inn, Holiday Inn Express
0mm	North Carolina/South Carolina state line

Interstate 240(Asheville)

Exit #	Services
9mm	I-240 begins/ends on I-40, exit 53b a.
8	Fairview Rd, **N...gas:** Shell/Blimpie, **food:** Burger King, J&S Cafeteria, KFC, Little Caesar's, Mandarin Chinese, McDonald's, Subway, **lodging:** Comfort Inn, **other:** Advance Parts, Bilo Foods, CVS Drug, Eckerd, Hamrick's, **S...food:** Pizza Now, **other:** Home Depot, Oakley Foods
7.5mm	Swannanoa River
7	US 70, **N...**U-Haul, **S...gas:** BP, Exxon/diesel, **food:** Applebee's, Burger King, Chili's, Cornerstone Rest., Damon's, East Buffet, Greenery Rest., IHOP, Joe's Crabshack, O'Charley's, Olive Garden, Outback Steaks, Philly Connection, Red Lobster, Rio Bravo, Subway, Taco Bell, Waffle House, **lodging:** Best Western, Country Inn, Courtyard, Day's Inn, Econolodge, Extended Stay America, Hampton Inn, Holiday Inn, Ramada Ltd, Spring Hill Suites, **other:** Belk, Circuit City, Firestone, Food Lion, Goody's, K-Mart, Lowe's Whse, Michael's, Office Depot, OfficeMax, Sears/auto
6	Tunnel Rd(from eb), same as 7
5b	US 70 E, US 74A, Charlotte St, **N...gas:** BP, Exxon, **food:** Fuddruckers, Two Guys Hogi, **S...lodging:** Best Western, Renaissance Motel, Civic Ctr
5a	US 25, Merrymont Ave, **N...gas:** Exxon/diesel, Shell, **food:** Bojangles, La Caterina, 3 Pigs BBQ, **S...lodging:** Interstate Motel
4c	Haywood St(no EZ return to eb), Montford, downtown
4b	Patton Ave(from eb), downtown
4a	US 19 N, US 23 N, US 70 W, to Weaverville, no facilities
3b	Westgate, **N...gas:** Servco, **food:** EarthFare Foods, **lodging:** Holiday Inn, **other:** CVS Drug, NTB
3a	US 19 S, US 23 S, W Asheville, **N...gas:** BP, Exxon, **food:** Arby's, Bojangles, Denny's, KFC/A&W, Krispy Kreme, Little Caesar's, LJ Silver, Mandarin Chinese, McDonald's, Pizza Hut, Ryan's, Taco Bell, Wendy's, **other:** Advance Parts, AutoZone, Best Foods, Bilo, Cadillac/Pontiac/GMC, Checker Parts, Goodyear/auto, Ingles, K-Mart, Radio Shack, Sam's Club/gas, **S...food:** Back Yard Burger
2	US 19, US 23, W Asheville, **N...gas:** Shell, **S...gas:** Eblen, Phillips 66, **other:** B&B Drug
1c	Amboy Rd(from eb), no facilities
1b	NC 191, to I-40 E, Brevard Rd, **S...other:** farmers mkt, camping
1a	I-40 W, to Knoxville, no facilities
0mm	I-240 begins/ends on I-40, exit 46b a.

Interstate 440(Raleigh)

Exit #	Services
16	I-40
15	Poole Rd, **W...gas:** Amoco/diesel, Citgo/diesel, **food:** Burger King, McDonald's, Subway
13b a	US 64, US 264 E, New Bern Ave, to Wilson, **1-2 mi E...gas:** Amoco, BP, Circle K, Exxon, Phillips 66(1mi), Shell, Speedway, Circle K, **food:** Arby's, Burger King, Checker's, Hardee's, K&S Cafeteria, McDonald's, Miami Subs, O!Brian's, Pizza Hut, Shoney's, Taco Bell, Treacher's Fish, Waffle House, Wendy's, **lodging:** Holiday Inn Express, Microtel, Red Roof Inn, Super 8, **other:** Firestone/auto, Ford, Hamrick's, K-Mart, Kroger, Food Lion, Radio Shack, RV Ctr, Winn-Dixie, **W...**HOSPITAL
12	Yonkers Rd, Brentwood Rd, no facilities
11b a	US 1, US 401, Capital Blvd N, **N...gas:** BP, Citgo, Shell, **food:** Applebee's(1mi), Bojangle's, Don Murray's BBQ, Perkins, Taco Bell, Waffle House, Wendy's, **lodging:** Comfort Inn, Country Inn, Day's Inn, Fairfield Inn, Holiday Inn, MainStay Inn, Sleep Inn, **other:** MEDICAL CARE, **S...gas:** Pontiac/GMC
10	Wake Forest Rd, **N...food:** Denny's, **lodging:** AmeriSuites, Red Roof Inn, **S...lodging:** Courtyard, Extended Stay America, Hampton Inn, Residence Inn, **other:** HOSPITAL
8b a	6 Forks Rd, North Hills, **N...gas:** Exxon, **food:** Bennigan's, **lodging:** Comfort Inn, **other:** Dillard's, Firestone/auto, Winn-Dixie
7b a	US 70, NC 50, Glenwood Ave, Crabtree Valley, **N...gas:** Amoco, BP, Exxon, **food:** McDonald's, Ruby Tuesday, **lodging:** Embassy Suites, Fairfield Inn, Holiday Inn, La Quinta, Marriott, Motel 6, Ramada Inn, Residence Inn, Sheraton, **other:** Barnes&Noble, Belk, Circuit City, Goodyear/auto, Hecht's, Sears/auto, mall
6	Ridge Rd(from nb), same as 7
5	Lake Boone Tr, **W...gas:** Phillips 66, **other:** HOSPITAL
4b a	to I-40 W, Wade Ave, **E...**bank, **W...**to I-40, RDU
3	NC 54, Hillsboro St, **E...gas:** Citgo, **lodging:** Ramada Inn, **other:** to Meredith Coll
2b a	Western Blvd, **E...**to NCSU, Shaw U, **W...**K-Mart
1d	Melbourne Rd(from sb), no facilities
1c	Jones-Franklin Rd, no facilities
1b a	I-40. I-440 begins on I-40. **1-2 mi W on Walnut St...gas:** Amoco, Shell, **food:** Hardee's, McDonald's, Olive Garden, Pizza Hut, Ryan's, Vicky's Seafood, **lodging:** Best Western, Candlewood Suites, Fairfield Inn, Holiday Inn, Motel 6, **other:** Michael's, mall

NORTH DAKOTA
Interstate 29

N ↑↓ S

Exit #	Services
218mm	North Dakota state line, US/Canada border. I-29 begins/ends.
217mm	US Customs sb
216mm	historical site nb, tourist info sb
215	ND 59, rd 55, Pembina, **E...gas:** Citgo/diesel, Gastrak/pizza/diesel/24hr, **food:** Depot Café, **other:** World DutyFree, museum
212	no facilities
208	rd 1, to Bathgate, no facilities
203	US 81, ND 5, to Hamilton, Cavalier, **W...**weigh sta both lanes
200	no facilities
196	rd 3, Bowesmont, no facilities
193	no facilities
191	ND 11, to St Thomas, no facilities
187	ND 66, to Drayton, **E...gas:** Cenex/diesel, **food:** Rte 66 Café, **lodging:** Motel 66, **other:** CarQuest, USPO
184	to Drayton, **2 mi E...gas:** gas/diesel/hardware, **other:** USPO, camping
180	rd 9, no facilities
179mm	**rest area both lanes(both lanes exit left), full(handicapped)facilities, phone, picnic tables, litter barrels, vending, petwalk**
176	ND 17, to Grafton, **10 mi W...**HOSPITAL, gas, food, lodging
172	no facilities
168	rd 15, Warsaw, to Minto, no facilities
164	no facilities
161	ND 54, rd 19, to Ardoch, Oslo, no facilities
157	no facilities
152	US 81, Manvel, to Gilby, **W...gas:** Co-op/diesel
145	US 81 bus, N Washington St, to Grand Forks, no facilities
141	US 2, Gateway Dr, Grand Forks, **E...gas:** Amoco/diesel/24hr, Conoco/McDonald's/diesel/@, Stamart, **food:** Burger King, Chinese Buffet, **lodging:** Budget Inn, Econolodge, Ramada Inn, Rodeway Inn, Select Inn, Super 8, **other:** AutoValue Parts, Checker Parts, Chrysler/Plymouth/Dodge/Jeep/Toyota, Ford/Lincoln/Mercury, to U of ND, **1 mi E...food:** DQ, Domino's, Hardee's, Taco John's, **other:** HOSPITAL, U-Haul, auto repair, **W...gas:** Simonson/diesel/café/24hr/@, Stamart/diesel/RV dump/@, **food:** Emerald Grill, Perkins, **lodging:** Settle Inn, **other:** Budget RV Ctr, port of entry/weigh sta, airport, to AFB
140	DeMers Ave, **E...gas:** Amoco, Conoco, Hilton Garden, **other:** HOSPITAL, Alerus Ctr, to U of ND
138	32nd Ave S, **E...gas:** Amoco, Holiday/Subway/diesel, Tesoro/diesel, **food:** Applebee's, Brannigan's, Buffalo Wild Wings, Burger King, ChiChi's, China Garden, Domino's, Grizzly's Steaks, Ground Round, McDonald's, Pizza Hut, Quizno's, Red Lobster, Taco Bell, Village Inn Rest., **lodging:** C'mon Inn, Comfort Inn, Country Inn Suites, Day's Inn, Fairfield

Grand Forks

Inn, Happy Host Inn, Holiday Inn Express, Lakeview Inn, Roadking Inn, **other:** Best Buy, Cadillac, Chevrolet, Chrysler/Toyota, Ford, Gordman's, Honda/Nissan, Hugo's Foods, JC Penney, Jo-Ann Fabrics, K-Mart, Marshall Field, Mazda, Michael's, OfficeMax, Old Navy, Osco Drug, Sam's Club, Sears/auto, Super 1 Foods, Target, Tires+, Wal-Mart, mall, **W...gas:** Conoco/Subway/diesel, **other:** Grand Forks Camping

130	ND 15, rd 81, Thompson, **1 mi W...**gas, food
123	CountyLine Rd, to Reynolds, **E...**to Central Valley School
118	to Buxton, no facilities
111	ND 200 W, to Cummings, Mayville, **W...other:** Big Top Fireworks, to Mayville St U
104	Hillsboro, **E...gas:** Cenex/Burger King/diesel/LP/24hr/@, Tesoro/diesel/24hr, Country **food:** Hearth Rest., **lodging:** Hillsboro Inn, Sunset View Motel, **other:** HOSPITAL, Ford/Mercury, Goodyear, bank, RV park
100	ND 200 E, ND 200A, to Blanchard, Halstad, no facilities
99mm	**rest area both lanes, full(handicapped)facilities, phone, picnic tables, litter barrels, vending, petwalk**
92	rd 11, Grandin, **E...gas:** Co-op/diesel, **W...gas:** Citgo/diesel/hardware
86	Gardner, no facilities
79	Argusville, no facilities
74.5mm	Sheyenne River
74mm	**rest area both lanes, full(handicapped)facilities, phone, picnic tables, litter barrels, vending, petwalk**
73	rd 17, rd 22, Harwood, **E...gas:** Cenex/pizza/diesel/café/24hr
69	rd 20, no facilities
67	US 81 bus, 19th Ave N, **E...**VA HOSPITAL, Hector Int Airport
66	12th Ave N, **E... gas:** Stamart Travel Plaza/diesel/24hr/@, Stop'n Go, **other:** HOSPITAL, to ND St U, **W...gas:** Cenex/diesel, **food:** Arby's, **lodging:** Microtel
65	US 10, Main Ave, W Fargo, **E...gas:** Simonson/diesel, Tesoro/diesel/24hr, **food:** BurgerTime, Kroll's Diner, **other:** Checker Parts, NAPA, OK Tire, U-Haul, transmissions, to Heritage Ctr, **W...gas:** Cenex/Subway/diesel, Simonson Gas, **food:** Embers Rest., Hardee's, Outback Steaks, **lodging:** Best Western, **other:** Aamco, CarQuest, Chevrolet/Buick/Cadillac/Honda, Chrysler/Dodge/Jeep, Cummins Diesel, Hyundai, Isuzu/Volvo/GMC, Kenworth, Mercury/Lincoln, Saturn, Subaru, Toyota
64	13th Ave, Fargo, **E...gas:** Amoco24hr, Cenex, Conoco/diesel, Kum&Go/gas, Phillips 66, Stamart/diesel, **food:** Acapulco Mexican, Applebee's, Arby's, Burger King, ChuckeCheese, DQ, GreenMill Rest., Ground Round, Hardee's, Perkins/24hr, Ponderosa, Quizno's, Subway, Taco John's, TCBY, Wendy's, **lodging:** Am-

Fargo

Interagency 29

N

S

Fargo

ericInn, Best Western, Comfort Inn, Country Suites, Econolodge, Hampton Inn, Motel 6, Motel 75, Super 8, **other:** MEDICAL CARE, CashWise Foods/24hr, Goodyear, SunMart Food, Tires+/transmissions, White Drug, **W...gas:** Amoco/24hr, Cenex, Tesoro, **food:** Applebee's, Blimpie, ChiChi's, Chili's, Culver's, Denny's, McDonald's, Fuddrucker's, Grandma's Saloon/deli, Godfather's, Hooters, Krispy Kreme, Kroll's Diner, LoneStar Steaks, Olive Garden, Paradiso Mexican, Pizza Hut, Red Lobster, Royal Fork Buffet, Schlotsky's, Taco Bell, Taco Time, TGIFriday, TimberLodge Steaks, Valentino's Ristorante, **lodging:** Comfort Inn, Day's Inn, Fairfield Inn, Holiday Inn Express, Kelly Inn, Ramada Inn, Red Roof Inn, Select Inn, **other:** Barnes&Noble, Best Buy, Chevrolet, GNC, Herberger's, Hornbacher's Foods, JC Penney, Jo-Ann Crafts, K-Mart, Kohl's, Lowe's Whse, Michael's, Office Depot, OfficeMax, Old Navy, Sam's Club, Sears/auto, SunMart Foods, Target, **Wal-Mart**, Walgreen, mall

63b a   I-94, W to Bismarck, E to Minneapolis

62   32nd Ave S, Fargo, **E...gas:** F&F/diesel, Tesoro, **food:** Country Kitchen, Papa John's, **other:** Ford, **W...gas:** Flying J/Conoco/diesel/LP/motel/24hr/@ , **other:** Goodyear/auto, Peterbilt, PleasureLand RV Ctr

60   52nd Ave S, to Fargo, **W...other:** Starr Fireworks

56   to Wild Rice, Horace, no facilities

54   rd 16, to Oxbow, Davenport, no facilities

50   rd 18, Hickson, no facilities

48   ND 46, to Kindred, no facilities

44   to Christine, **1 mi E...gas**

Fargo

42   rd 2, to Walcott, no facilities

40.5mm rest area both lanes, full(handicapped)facilities, phone, picnic tables, litter barrels, vending, petwalk

37   rd 4, Colfax, to Abercrombie, **E...**to Ft Abercrombie HS, **3 mi W...**gas

31   rd 8, Galchutt, **1 mi E...gas:** Cenex

26   to Dwight, no facilities

24mm   weigh sta both lanes

23b a   ND 13, Mooreton, to Wahpeton, **10 mi E...**HOSPITAL, ND St Coll of Science

15   rd 16, Great Bend, to Mantador, no facilities

8   ND 11, to Hankinson, Fairmount, **E...gas:** Mobil/diesel, **3 mi W...**camping

3mm Welcome Ctr nb, full(handicapped)facilities, phone, picnic tables, litter barrels, petwalk

2   rd 22, no facilities

1   rd 1E, **E...**Dakota Magic Casino/Hotel/rest./gas

0mm   North Dakota/South Dakota state line

Interstate 94

E

W

Exit #   Services

352mm   North Dakota/Minnesota state line, Red River

351   US 81, Fargo, **N...gas:** Conoco, Stop'n Go, Tesoro, **food:** Cousins Subs, Duane's Pizza, Great Harvest, Taco Shop, **other:** HOSPITAL, AutoZone, Hornbacher's Foods, Medicine Shoppe, **S...gas:** Philips 66/diesel, Stop'n Go/diesel, Tesoro, **food:** A&W/LJ Silver, Burger King, El Mariachi Mexican, Embers Rest., Happy Joe's Pizza, KFC, McDonald's, N American Steaks, Papa Murphy's, Pepper's Café, Subway, Taco Bell, **lodging:** Expressway Inn, Rodeway Inn, **other:** Hyundai/Nissan, K-Mart, USPO

NORTH DAKOTA
Interstate 94

E

W

350	25th St, Fargo, **N...gas:** Stop'n Go, **S...gas:** BP/diesel, Conoco/diesel, **food:** Dolittle's Grill
349b a	I-29, N to Grand Forks, S to Sioux Falls, facilities 1 mi N, exit 64
348	45th St, **N...Visitor Ctr/full facilities, gas:** BP, Petro/Mobil/diesel/LP/rest./24hr/@ , **food:** Bennigan's, IHOP, McDonald's, **lodging:** C'mon Inn, MainStay Inn, Ramada Inn, Sleep Inn, Wingate Inn, **1-2 mi N...gas:** Cenex, Stop'n Go, **food:** KFC, Olive Garden, Pizza Hut, Schlotsky's, **other:** Sam's Club, Target, Wal-Mart, **S...gas:** Tesoro/DQ/diesel, **food:** Old Chicago Pizza
347mm	Sheyenne River
346b a	W Fargo, to Horace, **S...gas:** Conoco/diesel
343	US 10, Lp 94, W Fargo, **N...gas:** BP, **food:** Highway Host Rest., Smoky's Steaks, **lodging:** Hi-10 Motel, **other:** Harley-Davidson, Pioneer Village
342	no facilities
341mm	weigh sta both lanes
340	to Kindred, no facilities
338	Mapleton, **N...gas:** Phillips 66/diesel
337mm	truck parking wb, litter barrels
331	ND 18, Casselton, to Leonard, **N...gas:** Phillips 66/diesel/café/motel, **other:** NAPA
328	to Lynchburg, no facilities
327mm	truck parking eb, litter barrels
324	Wheatland, to Chaffee, no facilities
322	Absaraka, no facilities
320	to Embden, no facilities
317	to Ayr, no facilities
314	ND 38, Buffalo, to Alice, **3 mi N...gas,** food
310	no facilities
307	to Tower City, **N...gas:** Mobil/diesel/café/repair/24hr, motel
304mm	**rest area both lanes(both lanes exit left), full(handicapped)facilities, info, phone, picnic tables, litter barrels, vending, petwalk**
302	ND 32, Oriska, to Fingal, **1 mi N...gas,** food
298	no facilities
296	no facilities
294	Lp 94, Valley City, to Kathryn, **N...HOSPITAL,** camping
292	Valley City, **N...gas:** Tesoro/diesel/café/24hr, **food:** Sabir's Rest., **lodging:** AmericInn, Super 8, Wagon Wheel Inn/rest., **other:** HOSPITAL, to Bald Hill Dam, camping, **S...other:** Ft Ransom SP(35mi)
291	Sheyenne River
290	Lp 94, Valley City, **N...gas:** Tesoro(1mi), **food:** Kenny's Rest., Pizza Hut, **lodging:** Bel Air Motel, Valley City Motel, **other:** HOSPITAL, Chrysler/Plymouth/Dodge, Pamida, **S...lodging:** Flickertail Inn
288	ND 1 S, to Oakes, no facilities
283	ND 1 N, to Rogers, no facilities
281	Sanborn, to Litchville, **1-2 mi N...gas,** food, lodging
276	Eckelson, **S...other:** Prairie Haven Camping/gas
275mm	continental divide, elev 1490
272	to Urbana, no facilities

Jamestown

269	Spiritwood, no facilities
262	Bloom, **N...**airport
260	US 52, Jamestown, **N...gas:** BP/diesel/café/@ , Stop'n Go, **lodging:** Starlite Motel, **other:** to St HOSPITAL, Chevrolet/Buick/Dodge, Harley-Davidson, camping
259mm	James River
258	US 281, Jamestown, **N...gas:** BP/24hr, Sinclair/diesel, **food:** Arby's, DQ, McDonald's, Taco Bell, Wagonmaster Rest., **lodging:** Comfort Inn, Day's Inn, Holiday Inn Express, Jamestown Motel, Ranch House Motel, **other:** HOSPITAL, Buffalo Herd/museum, Firestone/auto, Frontier Village/RV dump, Cadillac/GMC, CarQuest, Chrysler/Plymouth/Toyota/Jeep, Firestone/auto, Mazda, NW Tire, **S...gas:** Conoco/Subway/diesel/24hr, **food:** Applebee's, Burger King, Embers Rest., Grizzly's Rest., Paradiso Mexican, Perkins, Super Buffet, **lodging:** Dakota Inn, Super 8, **other:** Bob's RV Ctr, Ford, JC Penney, K-Mart/Little Caesar's, Sears, Wal-Mart/drugs, mall
257	Lp 94(from eb), to Jamestown, **N...**diesel repair
256	Lp 94, **S...other:** Wiest truck/trailer repair, **1 mi S...**KOA/RV dump
254mm	**rest area both lanes, full(handicapped)facilities, phone, picnic tables, litter barrels, petwalk, vending**
251	Eldridge, no facilities
248	no facilities
245	no facilities
242	Windsor, **1/4 mi N...**gas
238	Cleveland, to Gackle, **N...gas:** Prairie Oasis/café
233	no facilities
230	Medina, **1 mi N...gas:** Cenex/diesel/LP, **food:** C&R Dairy-Treat, **other:** Medina RV Park, USPO
228	ND 30 S, to Streeter, no facilities
224mm	**rest area wb, full(handicapped)facilities, phone, picnic tables, litter barrels, vending, petwalk, RV dump**
221	Crystal Springs, no facilities
221mm	**rest area eb, full(handicapped)facilities, phone, picnic tables, litter barrels, vending, petwalk, RV dump**
217	Pettibone, no facilities
214	Tappen, **S...**gas/diesel/food
208	ND 3 S, Dawson, **N...**RV camping, **1/2 mi S...**gas, food, to Camp Grassick, RV camping
205	Robinson, no facilities
200	ND 3 N, Steele, to Tuttle, **S...gas:** Cenex, Conoco/diesel/24hr, **food:** Lone Steer Motel/café/24hr/RV dump
195	no facilities
190	Driscoll, no facilities
182	US 83 S, ND 14, Sterling, to Wing, **S...gas:** Cenex/diesel/24hr/RV dump, **food:** Top's Café, **lodging:** Top's Motel(1mi)
176	McKenzie, no facilities
170	Menoken, **S...**to McDowell Dam, no facilities
168mm	**rest area both lanes, full(handicapped)facilities, phone, picnic tables, litter barrels, vending, petwalk**
161	Lp 94, Bismarck Expswy, Bismarck, **N...gas:** Cenex/diesel/24hr, **other:** KOA(1mi), **S...gas:** Tesoro/diesel/rest./24hr, **food:** McDonald's, **lodging:** Ramada Ltd, **other:** Capitol RV Ctr, Dakota Zoo

Interstate 94

E
Bismarck
W

159	US 83, Bismarck, **N...gas:** BP, Sinclair/diesel, **food:** A&W/LJ Silver, Applebee's, Arby's, Burger King, HongKong Chinese, KFC, Kroll's Diner, McDonald's, Paradiso Mexican, Perkins, Red Lobster, Royal Fork Buffet, Schlotsky's, Space Alien Grill, Taco Bell, **lodging:** AmericInn, Comfort Inn, Country Inn Suites, Fairfield Inn, Motel 6, **other:** Chevrolet, Dan's Foods, K-Mart, Sears, mall, **S...gas:** Conoco/diesel, Tesoro, **food:** DQ, Dominique's Rest., 83 Diner, Hardee's, Intn'l Rest., Pizza Hut, Starbucks, Steak Buffet, Subway, Taco John's, Wendy's, Woodhouse Rest., **lodging:** Best Western, Day's Inn, Kelly Inn, Select Inn, Super 8, **other:** HOSPITAL
157	Divide Ave, Bismarck, **N...gas:** Conoco/diesel/LP/24hr, **food:** Cracker Barrel, McDonald's, **S...gas:** Cenex/A&W, **other:** Econo Foods
156mm	Missouri River
156	I-194, Bismarck Expswy, Bismarck City Ctr, **1/2 mi S...lodging:** Colonial Motel, RiverTree Inn
155	to Lp 94(exits left from wb), Mandan, City Ctr, same as 153

Mandan

153	ND 6, Mandan Dr, Mandan, **1/2 mi S...gas:** Cenex/24hr, StaMart/diesel, Tesoro, **food:** Burger King, Bonanza, DQ, Dakota Farms Rest., Domino's, Godfather's, Hardee's, McDonald's, Pizza Hut, Subway, Taco John's, **lodging:** North Country Inn, **other:** CarQuest, Chevrolet, Ford/Mercury, Goodyear/auto, NAPA, Dacotah Centennial Park, Ft Lincoln SP(5mi)
152	Sunset Dr, Mandan, **N...gas:** Conoco, **lodging:** Best Western, Ridge Motel, **S...gas:** Tesoro/diesel/RV dump, **food:** Fried's Rest.
152mm	scenic view eb
147	ND 25, to ND 6, Mandan, **S...gas:** Sinclair/diesel/café/24hr
143mm	central/mountain time zone
140	to Crown Butte
135mm	scenic view wb, litter barrel
134	to Judson, Sweet Briar Lake, no facilities
127	ND 31, to New Salem, **N...**Knife River Indian Village(35mi), **S...gas:** Cenex/diesel, Tesoro/diesel, **lodging:** Sunset Inn/café, **other:** Food Pride, Golden West Shopping Ctr, Biggest Cow in the World
123	to Almont, no facilities
120	no facilities
119mm	**rest area both lanes, full(handicapped)facilities, phone, picnic tables, litter barrels, petwalk**
117	no facilities
113	no facilities
110	ND 49, to Glen Ullin, no facilities
108	to Glen Ullin, Lake Tschida, **3 mi S...**gas, food, lodging, camping
102	Hebron, to Glen Ullin, to Lake Tschida, **3 mi S...**gas, food, lodging, camping

Dickinson

97	Hebron, 2 mi N...gas, food, lodging
90	no facilities
84	ND 8, Richardton, N...gas: Cenex/diesel, **other:** HOSPITAL, to Assumption Abbey, Schnell RA
78	to Taylor, no facilities
72	Gladstone, no facilities
64	Dickinson, **S...gas:** Tesoro/diesel/rest./24hr, **other:** Firestone/auto, Ford/Lincoln/Mercury, Honda/Toyota, diesel repair
61	ND 22, Dickinson, **N...gas:** Cenex/diesel/24hr, Simonson/diesel, **food:** Applebee's, Arby's, Bonanza, Burger King, DQ, Ralphie's Grill, Taco Bell, Taco John's, Wendy's, **lodging:** AmericInn, Comfort Inn, Travelodge, **other:** Albertson's/24hr, Dan's Foods, Goodyear/auto, Herberger's, JC Penney, K-Mart, NAPA, Sears, Wal-Mart/24hr, **S...gas:** BP/Domino's, Cenex/diesel, Conoco/repair, Holiday/diesel/24hr, **food:** A&W/KFC, China Doll, Country Kitchen, Domino's, King Buffet, McDonald's, Perkins, Pizza Hut, Subway, **lodging:** Best Western, Budget Inn, Select Inn, Super 8, **other:** HOSPITAL, info
59	Lp 94, to Dickinson, **S...**to Patterson Lake RA, camping, **3 mi S...**facilities in Dickinson
51	South Heart, no facilities
42	US 85, Belfield, to Grassy Butte, Williston, **N...**T Roosevelt NP(52mi), **S...**info, gas: Conoco/diesel, Tesoro/diesel/24hr, **food:** DQ, **lodging:** Trapper's Inn/rest., **other:** NAPA
36	Fryburg, no facilities
32	**T Roosevelt NP, Painted Canyon Visitors Ctr, N...rest area both lanes, full(handicapped)facilities, phone, picnic tables, litter barrels, petwalk**
27	Lp 94, Historic Medora(from wb), T Roosevelt NP
24.5mm	Little Missouri Scenic River
24	Medora, Historic Medora, Chateau de Mores HS, T Roosevelt NP, **S...**visitors ctr
23	West River Rd, no facilities
22mm	scenic view eb
18	Buffalo Gap, **N...**Buffalo Gap Camping(seasonal)
12mm	**rest area eb, full(handicapped)facilities, phone, picnic tables, litter barrels, petwalk**
10	Sentinel Butte, Camel Hump Lake, **S...**gas
7	Home on the Range, no facilities
1	ND 16, Beach, **N...lodging:** Outpost Motel, **other:** camping, **S...gas:** Cenex/diesel/LP/24hr, ✈/Flying J/diesel/rest./24hr, **lodging:** Buckboard Inn, **other:** HOSPITAL, **Visitor/Welcome Ctr**
1mm	weigh sta both lanes, litter barrel
0mm	North Dakota/Montana state line

Interstate 70

E		

Exit # Services

225.5mm Ohio/West Virginia state line, Ohio River

225 US 250 W, OH 7, Bridgeport, **N...gas:** Marathon, StarFire Express/gas, Sunoco/24hr, **food:** Abbey's Rest., Dairy Queen, Papa John's, Pizza Hut, Wendy's, **other:** Advance Parts, AutoZone, Family$, Pennzoil, **S...gas:** Exxon, Gulf, **food:** Domino's

220 US 40, rd 214, **N...gas:** Citgo, Exxon/diesel, Sunoco, **lodging:** Hillside Motel(2mi), Holiday Inn Express(2mi), **other:** Aldi Foods, **S...gas:** Marathon/diesel, **food:** Undo's Pizza, Pizza Hut(1mi), **lodging:** Day's Inn

218 Mall Rd, to US 40, to Blaine, **N...gas:** BP/diesel, Citgo, Exxon, Marathon, **food:** Applebee's, Arby's, Big Boy, Buffalo Wings, Burger King, Denny's, Eat'n Park, Outback Steaks, Pizza Hut, Red Lobster, Steak'n Shake, Taco Bell, W Texas Steaks, **lodging:** Econolodge, Hampton Inn, Holiday Inn Express, Knight's Inn, Red Roof, Super 8, **other:** AutoZone, Chevrolet/Pontiac/Buick/Cadillac, Circuit City, Kroger, Lowe's Whse, Sam's Club, Staples, Wal-Mart/auto, **S...gas:** USA/diesel, **food:** Bob Evans, Bonanza, Cracker Barrel, Garfield's Rest., LJ Silver, LongHorn Steaks, McDonald's, Rax, **lodging:** Country Inn Suites, **other:** CVS Drug, Jo-Ann Fabrics, JC Penney, NTB, Sears/auto, mall

216 OH 9, St Clairsville, **N...gas:** BP, **S...gas:** Marathon

215 National Rd, **N...gas:** Citgo, **food:** Burger King, Subway, WenWu Chinese, **other:** NAPA, Riesbeck's Foods

213 OH 331, Flushing, **S...gas:** Citgo, Rich, Sunoco/diesel, **lodging:** Twin Pines Motel

211mm rest area both lanes, full(handicapped)facilities, phone, picnic tables, litter barrels, petwalk, vending

208 OH 149, Morristown, **N...gas:** BP/diesel, 208/diesel/rest., **food:** Schlepp's Rest., **lodging:** Arrowhead Motel(1mi), **other:** Ford/Mercury, **S...gas:** Marathon/diesel, **other:** Harley-Davidson, Barkcamp SP

204 US 40 E(from eb), National Rd, no facilities

202 OH 800, to Barnesville, **S...other:** HOSPITAL, gas/diesel, flea mkt

198 rd 114, Fairview, no facilities

193 OH 513, Middlebourne, **N...gas:** BP, FuelMart/diesel, Shell, **other:** fireworks

189mm rest area eb, full(handicapped)facilities, phone, picnic tables, litter barrels, petwalk, vending

186 US 40, OH 285, to Old Washington, **N...gas:** BP, **S...gas:** GoMart/diesel

180b a I-77 N, to Cleveland, to Salt Fork SP, I-77 S, to Charleston

178 OH 209, Cambridge, **N...gas:** BP/diesel, **food:** Bob Evans, Cracker Barrel, Grand Buffet, KFC, McDonald's, Rax, Ruby Tuesday, **lodging:** Best Western, BudgetHost, Comfort Inn, Day's Inn, Holiday Inn, **other:** HOSPITAL, Kroger/deli, **1 mi N...food:** Papa John's, Pizza Hut, Subway, Taco Bell, Wendy's, **other:** AutoZone, Buick/Pontiac/GMC/Cadillac, CVS Drug, Family$, **S...gas:** Pilot/Blimpie/diesel, **food:** Burger King, **lodging:** AmeriHost, **other:** $Tree, K-Mart/gas, Radio Shack, Wal-Mart SuperCtr/gas/24hr, Spring Valley RV Park(1mi)

176 US 22, US 40, to Cambridge, **N...gas:** Sunoco/diesel, **lodging:** Budget Inn, Deluxe Inn, **other:** Western Shop, RV camping, st patrol

173mm weigh sta both lanes

169 OH 83, New Concord, to Cumberland, **N...gas:** BP, **other:** RV camping, to Muskingum Coll

164 US 22, US 40, Norwich, **N...gas:** BP, **lodging:** Baker's Motel, museum

163mm rest area wb, full(handicapped)facilities, phone, picnic tables, litter barrels, petwalk, vending

160 OH 797, Airport, **N...gas:** Love's/Arby's/diesel/24hr/@, **S...gas:** BP, Exxon/Subway/diesel, Starfire, **food:** Denny's, McDonald's, Wendy's, **lodging:** Day's Inn, Holiday Inn, Red Roof Inn, **other:** st patrol

157 OH 93, Zanesville, **N...gas:** BP, **S...gas:** Marathon/Blimpie, Shell/diesel, **other:** KOA(1mi)

155 OH 60, OH 146, Underwood St, Zanesville, **N...info, food:** Bob Evans, Olive Garden, Red Lobster, Shoney's, Steak'n Shake, Tumbleweed Grill, **lodging:** Comfort Inn, Fairfield Inn, Hampton Inn, **other:** HOSPITAL, **other:** Pick'n Save Foods, **S...gas:** Exxon/diesel, **food:** Adornetto Café, Cracker Barrel, Subway, Wendy's, **lodging:** AmeriHost, Best Western, **other:** Old Mkt House Inn, Family$, Rite Aid

154 5th St(from eb)

153b Maple Ave(no EZ return from wb), **N...gas:** BP, **food:** Big Boy, Dairy Queen, Wendy's, **other:** HOSPITAL

a State St, **N...gas:** Speedway/diesel, **other:** Harley-Davidson, **S...gas:** BP

153mm Licking River

152 US 40, National Rd, **N...gas:** BP, Exxon/A&W/Blimpie, **food:** McDonald's, **lodging:** Super 8

142 US 40(from wb, no EZ return), Gratiot, **N...RV camping**

141 OH 668, US 40(from eb), to Gratiot, same as 142

132 OH 13, to Thornville, Newark, **N...Dawes Arboretum(3mi), S...gas:** BP, Shell, **other:** RV camping

131mm rest area both lanes, full(handicapped)facilities, phone, picnic tables, litter barrels, petwalk, vending

129b a OH 79, Hebron, to Buckeye Lake, **N...lodging:** AmeriHost, **S...gas:** BP/Duke/diesel/@, Citgo, Shell, **food:** Burger King, McDonald's, Pizza Hut/Taco Bell, Subway, Wendy's, **lodging:** Super 8, **other:** CarQuest, KOA(2mi), Blue Goose Marina(2mi)

126 OH 37, to Granville, Lancaster, **N...gas:** Citgo/diesel/@, Pilot/DQ/diesel/24hr/@, Starfire Express/diesel, **S...gas:** Sunoco/diesel, TA/BP/Sbarro's/Popeye's/diesel/24hr/@, **lodging:** Deluxe Inn, Red Roof Inn, **other:** truckwash, KOA(4mi),

122 OH 158, Kirkersville, to Baltimore, **N...lodging:** Regal Inn, **S...gas:** ✈/Flying J/CountryMkt/diesel/LP/24hr/@

118 OH 310, to Pataskala, **N...gas:** Speedway/diesel, Sunoco/DQ, **S...gas:** Duke's/diesel

112 OH 256, to Pickerington, Reynoldsburg, **N...gas:** BP, Shell, Sunoco/diesel, **food:** KFC, Logan's Roadhouse, McDonald's, O'Charley's, Panera Bread, TGIFriday, **lodging:** Country Inn Suites, Fairfield Inn, **other:** Sam's Club/gas, Tire Kingdom, Wal-Mart SuperCtr/24hr, **S...gas:** Speedway, **food:** Arby's, Boston Mkt, Cracker Barrel, Damon's, KFC, Longhorn Steaks, MT Steaks, Schlotsky's, Steak'n Shake, Wendy's, **lodging:** Best Western, Hampton Inn, Holiday Inn Express, **other:** Barnes&Noble, CVS Drug

Vertical labels: W, Blaine, Cambridge, Zanesville

OHIO

Interstate 70

110 Brice Rd, to Reynoldsburg, **N...gas:** Shell, Speedway, Sunoco, **food:** Arby's, Burger King, Bob Evans, ChiChi's, Gengi Japanese, Golden China, McDonald's, Max&Erma's, Pizza Hut, Popeye's, Roadhouse Grill, Ryan's, Subway, TeeJaye's Rest., Tim Horton, Waffle House, **lodging:** Best Western, Comfort Inn, Cross Country Inn, Extended Stay America, La Quinta, Ramada Inn, Red Roof, Super 8, **other:** Goodyear/auto, Home Depot, Pennzoil, **S...gas:** BP, Meijer/diesel/24hr, SA/diesel, Sunoco, **food:** Applebee's, Arby's, Asian Star, Boston Mkt, Burger King, China Paradise, KFC/Pizza Hut, McDonald's, Ponderosa, Ruby Tuesday, Skyline Chili, Chipotle Grill, Subway, Steak'n Shake, Taco Bell, Waffle House, Wendy's, White Castle, **lodging:** Comfort Suites, Day's Inn, Econolodge, Motel 6, **other:** Acura, Aldi, Circuit City, CVS Drug, Firestone/auto, GNC, Honda, Hyundai, JC Penney, Jo-Ann Fabrics, Kroger/deli, Lowe's Whse, Michael's, NTB, OfficeMax, Old Navy, Sam's Club, Sears/auto, Target, Toyota, mall

108b a I-270 N to Cleveland, access to HOSPITAL, I-270 S to Cincinnati

107 OH 317, Hamilton Rd, to Whitehall, **S...gas:** BP, Citgo/diesel, Sunoco/diesel, **food:** Arby's, Bob Evans, Burger King, McDonald's, Olive Garden, Red Lobster, Steak'n Shake, Subway, Taco Bell, **lodging:** Hampton Inn, Holiday Inn, InTown Suites, Howard Johnson, Knight's Inn, Residence Inn

105b a US 33, James Rd, to Lancaster, Bexley, **N...food:** Tat Italian, Wendy's

103 Livingston Ave, to Capital University, **N...gas:** BP, Speedway/diesel, Thornton, **food:** Domino's, Mr Hero Subs, Peking Chinese, Popeye's, Subway, Taco Bell, Wendy's, **S...gas:** Rich, Shell, **food:** McDonald's, Rally's, White Castle

102 Kelton Ave, Miller Ave, **S...**HOSPITAL

101a I-71 N, to Cleveland, no facilities

100b US 23, to 4th St, downtown

OHIO

Interstate 70

E

W

Columbus Area

99c	Rich St, Town St, **N...gas:** Sunoco, Ford
b	OH 315 N, downtown
a	I-71 S, to Cincinnati, no facilities
98b	Mound St(from wb, no EZ return), stadium, **N...gas:** Marathon, **S...food:** LJ Silver, McDonald's, Rally's
a	US 62, OH 3, Central Ave, to Sullivan, access to same as 98b
97	US 40, W Broad St, **N...gas:** Citgo, **food:** Arby's, Burger King, KFC, McDonald's, Pizza Hut/Taco Bell, Wendy's, White Castle, **lodging:** Day's Inn
96	Grandview Ave(from eb), no facilities
95	Hague Ave(from wb), **S...gas:** Sunoco
94	Wilson Rd, **N...DM/gas, S...gas:** BP, Pilot/Wendy's/diesel/24hr/@, Shell/24hr, Speedway/24hr, **food:** McDonald's, Waffle House, **lodging:** Econolodge, **other:** Buick, Sam's Club
93b a	I-270, N to Cleveland, S to Cincinnati
91b a	New Rome, to Hilliard, **N...gas:** Meijer/diesel/24hr, Shell, Speedway/diesel, **food:** Applebee's, Arby's, Big Boy, Burger King, Cracker Barrel, Fazoli's, KFC, McDonald's, Outback Steaks, Pizza Hut/Taco Bell, Salvi's Bistro, Schlotsky's, Skyline Chili, Tim Horton, Texas Roadhouse, White Castle, Wendy's, **lodging:** Comfort Suites, Cross Country Inn, Fairfield Inn, Hampton Inn, Hawthorn Inn, Motel 6, Red Roof Inn, **other:** Giant-Eagle Foods/gas, Ford, Sam's Club, Valvoline, Wal-Mart SuperCtr/24hr, **S...gas:** BP/diesel, Marathon/diesel, **food:** Bob Evans, Steak'n Shake, **lodging:** Best Western, Country Inn Suites, Hilton Garden, Microtel
85	OH 142, W Jefferson, to Plain City, no facilities
80	OH 29, to Mechanicsburg, **S...**hwy patrol
79	US 42, to London, Plain City, **N...gas:** Pilot/Subway/diesel/24hr/@, **food:** Waffle House, **S...gas:** Sunoco/24hr, Speedway/diesel/24hr, TA/BP/Popeye's/Pizza Hut/diesel/24hr/@, **food:** McDonald's, Taco Bell, Wendy's, **lodging:** Holiday Inn Express, Knight's Inn, **other:** HOSPITAL, truckwash
72	OH 56, Summerford, to London, **N...gas:** Shell/24hr, **4 mi S...**HOSPITAL, lodging
71mm	**rest area both lanes, full(handicapped)facilities, phone, picnic tables, litter barrels, vending, petwalk**
66	OH 54, South Vienna, to Catawba, **N...gas:** FuelMart/diesel, **S...gas:** Speedway/diesel, **other:** Crawford RV Park(1mi), Beaver Valley RV Park(3mi)

Springfield

62	US 40, Springfield, **N...gas:** Speedway, **lodging:** Harmony Motel, **other:** to Buck Creek SP, **S...**RV camping
59	OH 41, to S Charleston, **N...other:** HOSPITAL, Harley-Davidson, st patrol, **S...gas:** BP/diesel, Prime Fuel/diesel
54	OH 72, Springfield, to Cedarville, **N...gas:** BP/diesel, Shell, Speedway, Sunoco/diesel/24hr, **food:** A&W/LJ Silver, Arby's, Bob Evans, Cassano's Pizza/subs, Church's, Cracker Barrel, Denny's, Domino's, El Toro Mexican, Hardee's, KFC, Lee's Chicken, Little Caesar's, McDonald's, Panda Chinese, Perkins, Pizza Hut/Taco Bell, Rally's, Subway, Wendy's, **lodg-**

	ing: Comfort Suites, Day's Inn, Hampton Inn, Holiday Inn, Ramada Ltd, Red Roof Inn, Super 8, **other:** HOSPITAL, Aldi Foods, CVS Drug, Family$, Kroger/deli, Walgreen, **S...gas:** Certified/diesel, Swifty
52b a	US 68, to Urbana, Xenia, **S...**to John Bryan SP
48	OH 4(from wb), to Enon, Donnelsville, **N...**Enon RV Camp, **S...gas:** Speedway
47	OH 4(from eb), to Springfield, **5 mi N...**gas, food, lodging
44	I-675 S, to Cincinnati, no facilities
43mm	Mad River
41	OH 4, OH 235, to Dayton, New Carlisle, **N...gas:** BP/diesel, Sunoco/diesel, **food:** A&W/KFC, McDonald's, Wendy's
38	OH 201, Brandt Pike, **N...gas:** Shell, **S...gas:** Shell, **food:** Denny's, Waffle House, Wendy's, **lodging:** Comfort Inn, Travelodge, **other:** DENTIST
36	OH 202, Huber Heights, **N...gas:** Speedway/diesel/24hr, A&W/KFC, **food:** Applebee's, Big Boy, El Toro Mexican, Fazoli's, Pizza Hut, Ruby Tuesday, Steak'n Shake, Subway, Taco Bell, Uno Pizzaria, Waffle House, Wendy's, **lodging:** Super 8, **other:** Cub Foods/24hr, GNC, Kohl's, Lowe's Whse, Marshall's, Radio Shack, Saturn, Target, Wal-Mart/auto, **S...gas:** BP/diesel, Sunoco/diesel, **food:** Arby's, Bob Evans, Buffalo Wings, Burger King, Cadillac Jack's Grill, LJ Silver, McDonald's, TGIFriday, White Castle, **lodging:** Days Inn, Hampton Inn, Holiday Inn Express, **other:** CVS Drug, K-Mart, Kroger/gas
33 b a	I-75, N to Toledo, S to Dayton
32	Vandalia, **N...**to Dayton Intn'l Airport
29	OH 48, Englewood, to Dayton, **N...gas:** BP, Speedway, Sunoco/24hr, **food:** Arby's, Big Boy, Bob Evans, Perkins, Pizza Hut, Ponderosa, Skyline Chili, Taco Bell, Wendy's, **lodging:** Hampton Inn, Holiday Inn, Motel 6, Super 8, **other:** Advance Parts, Aldi Foods, McNulty RV Ctr, **S...gas:** Meijer/diesel/24hr, **food:** McDonald's, Waffle House, **lodging:** Comfort Inn, Cross Country Inn
26	OH 49 S, **S...gas:** Shell
24	OH 49 N, Clayton, to Greenville, **S...gas:** Sunoco/diesel/24hr, **other:** KOA(seasonal)
21	rd 533, Brookville, **N...**gas, **S...gas:** BP/diesel, Speedway/diesel, **food:** Arby's, Dairy Queen, KFC/Taco Bell, McDonald's, Rob's Dining, Waffle House, Wendy's, **lodging:** Day's Inn, Holiday Inn Express, **other:** Chevrolet, $General
14	OH 503, Lewisburg, to West Alexandria, **N...gas:** Sunoco/Subway/diesel, **lodging:** Super Inn, Super-Valu Foods, **S...gas:** Citgo/diesel
10	US 127, to Eaton, Greenville, **N...gas:** Marathon, TA/BP/Burger King/Subway/diesel/24hr/@, st patrol, **S...gas:** Pilot/DQ/diesel/24hr/@, **lodging:** Econolodge
3mm	**Welcome Ctr eb/rest area both lanes, full(handicapped)facilities, phone, vending, picnic tables, litter barrels, petwalk**
1	US 35 E(from eb), to Eaton, New Hope
0mm	Ohio/Indiana state line, Welcome Arch, weigh sta eb

Interstate 71

N ↕ **S**

Cleveland

Exit #	Services
247b	I-90 W, I-490 E. I-71 begins/ends on I-90, exit 170 in Cleveland.
a	W 14th, Clark Ave, no facilities
246	Denison Ave, Jennings Rd(from sb)
245	US 42, Pearl Rd, **E...gas:** BP, Sunoco, **other:** HOSPITAL, zoo
244	W 65th, Denison Ave, no facilities
242b a	W 130th, to Bellaire Rd, **W...gas:** Sunoco, **food:** Burger King(1/2mi)
240	W 150th, **E...gas:** Marathon, Speedway/diesel, **lodging:** Marriott, **W...gas:** BP/Subway/diesel, **food:** Burger King, MacKenzie's Grill, Somers Rest., Taco Bell, **lodging:** Baymont Inn, Holiday Inn
239	OH 237 S(from sb), **W...**to airport
238	I-480, Toledo, Youngstown, **W...**airport
237	Snow Rd, Brook Park, **E...gas:** BP, Citgo, Shell, **food:** Bob Evans, McDonald's, **lodging:** Best Western, Fairfield Inn, Holiday Inn Express, **W...**to airport
235	Bagley Rd, **E...food:** Bob Evans, **lodging:** Clarion, **W...gas:** BP/diesel, Shell, Speedway, **food:** Burger King, Damon's, Denny's, Friendly's, McDonald's, Olive Garden, Perkins, Pizza Hut, Taco Bell, **lodging:** Comfort Inn, Courtyard, Cross Country Inn, Motel 6, Radisson, Red Roof Inn, Residence Inn, Studio+, TownePlace Suites, **other:** HOSPITAL, Aldi Foods, GMC, K-Mart
234	US 42, Pearl Rd, **E...gas:** Shell, Speedway, Sunoco/diesel, **food:** Hunan Chinese, Katherine's Rest., Santo's Pizza, Wendy's, **other:** DENTIST, Audi/Porsche, Honda, Hyundai, Saturn, **W...gas:** Marathon/diesel, **food:** Buffalo Wings, Jennifer's Rest., Mad Cactus Café, **lodging:** Colony Motel, Day's Inn, Extended Stay America, La Siesta Motel, Murphy's Motel, Village Motel, **other:** Home Depot, Wal-Mart
233	I-80 and Ohio Tpk, to Toledo, Youngstown
231	OH 82, Strongsville, **E...gas:** Shell, **lodging:** Holiday Inn, Red Roof Inn, **W...gas:** BP/Subway/diesel, Marathon/diesel, Sunoco/diesel, **food:** Applebee's, Buca Italian, Demetrio's Rest., Longhorn Steaks, Macaroni Grill, Panera Bread, Rio Bravo, TGIFriday, **other:** Borders Books, Dillard's, Giant Eagle Foods, JC Penney, Jo-Ann Fabrics, Kohl's, OfficeMax, Sears/auto, Target, Tire Kingdom, mall
226	OH 303, Brunswick, **E...gas:** Shell/diesel/24hr, **food:** Denny's, Pizza Hut, **other:** Camping World RV Supplies/service, Chrysler/Plymouth/Jeep/Toyota, **W...gas:** BP, Marathon/diesel, Sunoco/diesel, **food:** Arby's, Bob Evans, Burger King, McDonald's, Mi-mi's Rest., Taco Bell, Wendy's, **lodging:** Howard Johnson, Sleep Inn, **other:** Ford, Giant Eagle Food, K-Mart
225mm	**rest area nb, full(handicapped)facilities, phone, picnic tables, litter barrels, petwalk**
224mm	**rest area sb, full(handicapped)facilities, phone, picnic tables, litter barrels, petwalk**
222	OH 3, **W...**st patrol

Ashland Mansfield

220	I-271 N, to Erie, Pa
218	OH 18, to Akron, Medina, **E...gas:** BP/diesel/24hr, Citgo/diesel, Shell/diesel, Sunoco/diesel, **food:** Alexandri's Rest., Blimpie, Burger King, Cracker Barrel, DQ, Hunan Dynasty, Medina Rest., **lodging:** Best Value, Best Western, Day's Inn, Holiday Inn Express, Super 8, **other:** $General, GMC, Mitsubishi, **W...food:** Arby's, Bob Evans, Buffalo Wings, Denny's, Pizza Hut, Wendy's, **lodging:** Cross Country Inn, Hampton Inn, Motel 6, Red Roof Inn, **other:** HOSPITAL, Dodge, Harley-Davidson, Honda, Pontiac/Buick/Cadillac, Tire Kingdom
209	I-76 E, to Akron, US 224 **W...gas:** Pilot/Subway/diesel/24hr, TA/BP/Burger King/Popeye's/diesel/24hr/@, **food:** McDonald's, Starbucks, **lodging:** Super 8, **other:** Blue Beacon, Chippewa Valley Camping(1mi)
204	OH 83, Burbank, **E...gas:** BP/diesel, Duke/Taco Bell/diesel, **W...gas:** Pilot/Wendy's/diesel/24hr, **food:** Bob Evans, Burger King, FoodCourt, McDonald's, **other:** HOSPITAL, Buick/Chevrolet/Pontiac, Chrysler/Jeep/Dodge, Prime Outlets/famous brands
198	OH 539, W Salem, **W...other:** Town&Country RV Park(2mi)
196mm	**rest area both lanes, full(handicapped)facilities, phone, vending, picnic tables, litter barrels, petwalk**
196	OH 301(from nb, no re-entry), W Salem, no facilities
191mm	weigh sta sb
186	US 250, Ashland, **E...gas:** Citgo, **food:** Perkins, Grandpa's Village/cheese/gifts, **other:** Hickory Lakes Camping(7mi), **W...gas:** TA/BP/diesel/rest./24hr/@, **food:** Bob Evans, Denny's, McDonald's, Wendy's, **lodging:** AmeriHost, Day's Inn, Holiday Inn Express, Super 8, **other:** HOSPITAL, st patrol, to Ashland U
176	US 30, to Mansfield, **E...lodging:** Econolodge, **other:** fireworks
173	OH 39, to Mansfield, no facilities
169	OH 13, Mansfield, **E...gas:** Exxon/diesel, **food:** Cracker Barrel, Steak'n Shake, **lodging:** AmeriHost, Baymont Inn, **W...gas:** Citgo, **food:** Arby's, Big Boy, Bob Evans, Burger King, McDonald's, Taco Bell, **lodging:** Super 8, Travelodge, **other:** HOSPITAL, st patrol
165	OH 97, to Bellville, **E...gas:** BP, Marathon/diesel/24hr, Speedway/diesel, **food:** Burger King, Dutchman Rest., McDonald's, **lodging:** Day's Inn, Comfort Inn, Ramada Ltd, **other:** to Mohican SP, **W...food:** Subway(2mi), Wendy's, **lodging:** Mid Ohio Motel

OHIO

Interstate 71

N ↑
S

151 OH 95, to Mt Gilead, **E...gas:** Duke/diesel/rest./24hr, Marathon, **food:** Gathering Inn Rest., McDonald's, Wendy's, **lodging:** Best Western, **other:** st patrol, **W...gas:** BP/diesel, Sunoco/diesel, **lodging:** Knight's Inn, **other:** HOSPITAL, M Camping, Mt Gilead SP(6mi)

149mm truck parking both lanes

140 OH 61, Mt Gilead, **E...gas:** Pilot/Arby's/diesel/24hr/@, **W...gas:** BP/Taco Bell, Sunoco/Subway, **food:** Ole Farmstead Rest.

131 US 36, OH 37, to Delaware, **E...gas:** ✈/Flying J/Conoco/diesel/LP/rest./24hr/@, Pilot/Subway/diesel/24hr/@, **food:** Burger King, **W...gas:** BP/diesel, Shell, **food:** A&W, Arby's, Bob Evans, Cracker Barrel, KFC, McDonald's, Subway, Taco Bell, Waffle House, Wendy's, White Castle, **lodging:** Day's Inn, Hampton Inn, Holiday Inn Express, **other:** HOSPITAL, Alum Cr SP

129mm weigh sta nb

128mm rest area both lanes, full(handicapped)facilities, phone, vending, picnic tables, litter barrels, petwalk

121 Polaris Pkwy, **E...gas:** BP/Blimpie, Shell/24hr, **food:** McDonald's, Polaris Grill, Skyline Chili, Steak'n Shake, **lodging:** Best Western, Wingate Inn, **other:** Polaris Ampitheatre, **W...gas:** Marathon/A&W, Meijer/diesel/24hr, **food:** Applebee's, Arby's, BajaFresh, Bob Evans, Carrabba's, Hoggy's Grille, Hop's Grill, Magic Mtn Grill, Martin's Italian, Max&Erma's, O'Charley's, Olive Garden, Panera Bread, Pizza Hut/Taco Bell, Quaker Steaks, Red Lobster, Starbucks, TGIFriday, Wendy's, **lodging:** Baymont Inn, Hilton Garden, Wellesley Inn, **other:** Barnes&Noble, Best Buy, GNC, JC Penney, Jo-Ann Fabrics, Kroger, Lowe's Whse, OfficeMax, Old Navy, Sears/auto, Target, Wal-Mart SuperCtr/24hr(3mi), mall

119 I-270, to Indianapolis, Wheeling

117 OH 161, to Worthington, **E...gas:** BP/diesel, Shell, Sunoco, **food:** Burger King, KFC, LJ Silver, LoneStar Steaks, Max&Erma's, Outback Steaks, Rally's, Red Lobster, Subway, TeeJaye's Rest., White Castle, **lodging:** Comfort Inn, Day's Inn, Holiday Inn Express, Knight's Inn, Motel 6, **other:** Advance Parts, Big Bear Foods, Firestone, Staples, **W...gas:** Shell, Speedway/diesel, **food:** Bob Evans, McDonald's, Pi's Chinese, Pizza Hut, Skyline Chili, Subway, Waffle House, Wendy's, **lodging:** Best Western, Clarion, Country Inn Suites, Cross Country Inn, Econolodge, Extended Stay America, Hampton Inn, Marriott, Ramada Ltd, Residence Inn, Super 8, **other:** Chevrolet, Giant Eagle/gas

116 Morse Rd, Sinclair Rd, **E...gas:** BP, Shell, Speedway, **food:** China 1st, McDonald's, Fairfield Inn, **other:** MEDICAL CARE, Buick, CVS Drug, **W...gas:** Sunoco, **food:** La Hacienda Real Mexican, TeeJaye's Rest., **lodging:** Cross Country Inn, Motel 6, Ramada Inn, NTB

Columbus Area

115 Cooke Rd, no facilities

114 N Broadway, **W...gas:** Sunoco

113 Weber Rd, **W...gas:** Speedway/diesel, **other:** CarQuest, NAPA

112 Hudson St, **E...gas:** BP, Shell, **food:** Wendy's, **lodging:** Holida Inn Express, **W...food:** Big Boy, **other:** Aldi Foods, Lowe's Whse, Tire Kingdom

111 17th Ave, **W...food:** McDonald's, **lodging:** Day's Inn

110b 11th Ave, no facilities

a 5th Ave, **E...gas:** Sunoco, **food:** White Castle, **W...gas:** Citgo, **food:** KFC/Pizza Hut, Wendy's, **other:** AutoZone

109a I-670, no facilities

108b US 40, Broad St, downtown, **W...**Honda

101a[70] I-70 E, US 23 N, to Wheeling

100b a[70] US 23 S, Front St, High St, downtown

106a I-70 W, to Indianapolis

b OH 315 N, Dublin St, Town St

105 Greenlawn, **E...gas:** BP, **food:** White Castle, Wild Bean Café, **other:** HOSPITAL

104 OH 104, Frank Rd, **W...**tires

101b a I-270, Wheeling, Indianapolis

100 Stringtown Rd, **E...gas:** BP, **food:** Bob Evans, Church's/White Castle, **lodging:** Best Western, Cross Country Inn, Hampton Inn, Holiday Inn Express, Hilton Garden, Microtel, Super 8, **W...gas:** Certified/diesel, Speedway/diesel, **food:** Applebee's, Arby's, Burger King, Capt D's, China Bell, Cracker Barrel, Damon's, Fazoli's, Hoggy's Rest., KFC, McDonald's, Perkins/24hr, Pizza Hut, Ponderosa, Rally's, Rancho Alegre Mexican, Roadhouse Grill, Ruby Tuesday, Starbucks, Subway, Taco Bell, TeeJaye's Rest., Tim Horton, Waffle House, Wendy's, **lodging:** Comfort Inn, Day's Inn, Motel 6, Red Roof Inn, Value Inn, **other:** Aldi Foods, All Tune/lube, Big Bear Food/drug, CVS Drug, GNC, Goodyear/auto, K-Mart, Kroger/24hr, NAPA, Radio Shack

97 OH 665, London-Groveport Rd, **E...gas:** Citgo/DM/Taco Bell, Sunoco/Subway, **food:** Arby's, McDonald's, Tim Horton/Wendy's, **other:** to Scioto Downs, **W...other:** Eddie's Repair

94 US 62, OH 3, Orient, **E...gas:** BP, **W...gas:** Sunoco

84 OH 56, Mt Sterling, **E...gas:** BP/Subway, Sunoco, **lodging:** Royal Inn, **other:** to Deer Creek SP(9mi)

75 OH 38, Bloomingburg, **E...**fireworks, **W...gas:** Sunoco

69 OH 41, OH 734, Jeffersonville, **E...gas:** ✈/Flying J/CountryMkt/diesel/24hr/@, **other:** Walnut Lake Camping, **W...gas:** BP, Shell/Subway/diesel, **food:** Arby's, TCBY, Wendy's, White Castle, **lodging:** AmeriHost, **other:** HOSPITAL, Outlets II/famous brands

68mm rest area both lanes, full(handicapped)facilities, phone, vending, picnic tables, litter barrels, petwalk

65 US 35, Washington CH, **E...gas:** Shell, TA/BP/Pizza Hut/Popeye's/diesel/24hr/@, TrueNorth/diesel, **food:** A&W/KFC, Bob Evans, Burger King, McDonald's, Taco Bell, LJ Silver, Waffle House, Wendy's, **lodging:** AmeriHost, Hampton Inn, **other:** HOSPITAL, Prime Outlets/famous brands, **W...lodging:** Budget Motel

Interstate 71

N ↑↓ **S**

58	OH 72, to Sabina, no facilities
54mm	weigh sta sb
50	US 68, to Wilmington, **E...food:** Werner's BBQ, **other:** HOSPITAL, **W...gas:** BP/DQ/diesel, Pilot/Subway/diesel/24hr, Shell/diesel/24hr, **food:** Dairy Queen, Max&Erma's, McDonald's, Wendy's, **lodging:** Budget Inn, Ramada Plaza
49mm	weigh sta nb
45	OH 73, to Waynesville, **E...gas:** BP, Marathon/diesel, **other:** HOSPITAL, 1000 Trails RV Park, **W...**Caesar Creek SP(5mi)
36	Wilmington Rd, **E...**to Ft Ancient St Memorial, RV camping
35mm	Little Miami River
34mm	**rest area both lanes, full(handicapped)facilities, scenic view, phone, vending, picnic tables, litter barrels, petwalk**
32	OH 123, to Lebanon, Morrow, **E...gas:** BP, Clark, **food:** Country Kitchen, **other:** Morgan's RV Park, **3 mi W...food:** Bob Evans, Skyline Chili, **lodging:** Knight's Inn
28	OH 48, S Lebanon, **E...lodging:** Countryside Inn(1mi), **W...other:** Lebanon Raceway(6mi), hwy patrol
25	OH 741 N, Kings Mills Rd, **E...gas:** Shell/Popeye's, Speedway/diesel, **food:** El Toro Mexican, McDonald's, Ruby Tuesday, Taco Bell, Outback Steaks, **lodging:** Comfort Suites, Kings Island Inn, Quality Inn, **other:** Harley-Davidson, **W...gas:** AmeriStop/Subway, BP, **food:** Arby's, Big Boy, Bob Evans, Burger King, DQ, Perkins, Pizza Hut, Skyline Chili, Waffle House, Wendy's, **lodging:** Best Western, Hampton Inn, Holiday Inn Express, Microtel, **other:** CVS Drug, GNC, Kroger
24	Western Row, King's Island Dr(from nb), **E...gas:** Sunoco, **lodging:** King's Island, **other:** Jellystone Camping
19	US 22, Mason Montgomery Rd, **E...gas:** Meijer/diesel/24hr, Shell, SA/diesel, Sunoco/24hr, **food:** United Dairy Farmers, Arby's, Big Boy, Bennigan's, Bob Evans, Boston Mkt, Cooker, Cracker Barrel, Fazoli's, Golden Corral, KFC, McDonald's, Olive Garden, Pizza Hut, Pizza Tower, Ponderosa, Taco Bell, TGIFriday, Wendy's, White Castle, **lodging:** Comfort Inn, Quality Inn, Signature Inn, SpringHill Suites, TownePlace Suites, **other:** AutoZone, Barnes&Noble, Best Buy, Circuit City, Chevrolet, Firestone/auto, GMC/Buick/Pontiac, Goodyear, Kohl's, Kroger, Lincoln/Mercury, Michael's, Michel's Tires, OfficeMax, Old Navy, Radio Shack, Target, Toyota, Wal-Mart/auto, Walgreen, **W...gas:** BP/diesel, Marathon/diesel/24hr, Shell, **food:** Applebee's, Burger King, Carrabba's, Chipotle Mexican, Copeland's Rest., Fuddrucker's, LoneStar Steaks, O'Charley's, RiverCity Grill, Steak'n Shake, Skyline Chili, Subway, Tumbleweed Grill, Waffle House, Wendy's, **lodging:** AmeriSuites, Baymont Inn, Best Western, Country Hearth Inn, Day's Inn, Marriott, Ramada Ltd, Red Roof Inn, **other:** Bigg's Foods, Home Depot, Lowe's Whse, Staples

Cincinnati

17b a	I-275, to I-75, OH 32, no facilities
15	Pfeiffer Rd, **E...**HOSPITAL, **W...gas:** BP, Shell/diesel, Sunoco/diesel/24hr, **food:** Applebee's, Bennigan's, Bob Evans, Buffalo Wings, Subway, **lodging:** Clarion, Courtyard, Embassy Suites, Hampton Inn, Holiday Inn Express, MainStay Suites, Ramada Inn, Red Roof Inn, Wingate Inn, **other:** Office Depot
14	OH 126, Reagan Hwy, Blue Ash, no facilities
12	US 22, OH 3, Montgomery Rd, **E...gas:** Shell/24hr, Sunoco, **food:** Arby's, Bob Evans, Jalapeno Café, KFC, LoneStar Steaks, LJ Silver, OutBack Steaks, Red Lobster, Ruby Tuesday, Subway, Taco Bell, TGIFriday, Wendy's, **lodging:** Hannaford Suites, Harvey Hotel, Sheraton, **other:** Dodge/Plymouth, Firestone, Goodyear, Hyundai, OfficeMax, PepBoys, Staples, **W...food:** Max&Erma's, McDonald's, Starbucks, **other:** Barnes&Noble, Dillard's, Firestone/auto, Parisian, mall
11	Kenwood Rd, **W...**HOSPITAL, same as 12
10	Stewart Rd(from nb), to Silverton, **W...gas:** Marathon/diesel
9	Redbank Rd, to Fairfax, **E...gas:** Mobil, Speedway, **W...gas:** Marathon
8	Kennedy Ave, Ridge Ave W, **E...gas:** Meijer/diesel, **lodging:** Red Roof Inn, **other:** Sam's Club, Target, **W...gas:** Exxon/Subway, Marathon/diesel, **food:** Denny's, Golden Corral, KFC, LJ Silver, McDonald's, Old Country Buffet, Pizza Hut, Rally's, Taco Bell, White Castle, Wendy's, **other:** Bigg's Foods, Circuit City, Ford, Goodyear, Home Depot, Office Depot, Tire Discounter, Wal-Mart, transmissions
7b a	OH 562, Ridge Ave E, Norwood, **1/2mi E...gas:** BP, **food:** Ponderosa, **other:** AutoZone
6	Edwards Rd, **E...gas:** Shell, Speedway, **food:** Boston Mkt, Buca Italian, Chang's China Bistro, Don Pablos, Fuddrucker's, GoldStar Chili, J Alexander's Rest., Longhorn Steaks, Max&Erma's, Starbucks, **other:** Drug Emporium, Old Navy, TJ Maxx, **W...gas:** Shell
5	Dana Ave, Montgomery Rd, **W...other:** Xavier Univ, Zoo
3	Taft Rd(from sb), U of Cincinnati
2	US 42 N, Reading Rd, **W...other:** HOSPITAL, downtown, art museum
1k j	I-471 S
1d	Main St, downtown
1c b	Pete Rose Way, Fine St, stadium, downtown
1a	I-75 N, US 50, to Dayton, no facilities
	I-71 S and I-75 S run together
0mm	Ohio/Kentucky state line, Ohio River

OHIO

Interstate 74

Exit #	Services
20	I-75(from eb), N to Dayton, S to Cincinnati, I-74 begins/ends on I-75.
19	Gilmore St, Spring Grove Ave, no facilities
18	US 27 N, Colerain Ave, no facilities
17	Montana Ave(from wb), **N...gas:** BP
14	North Bend Rd, Cheviot, **N...gas:** Citgo, Speedway/diesel, **food:** DQ, Happy Chinese, McDonald's, Perkins, Skyline Chili, Wendy's, **other:** Sam's Club/gas, Tires+, Walgreen, **S...gas:** BP, **food:** Bob Evans, **lodging:** TriStar Motel
11	Rybolt Rd, Harrison Pike, **S...gas:** BP, Meijer/gas, **food:** Angelo's Pizza, Dante's Rest., **lodging:** Imperial House Motel, **other:** Kohl's
9	I-275 N, to I-75, N to Dayton
8mm	Great Miami River
7	OH 128, Cleves, to Hamilton, **N...gas:** BP/diesel, Marathon/diesel, **food:** BierHaus Rest., Wendy's
5	I-275 S, to Kentucky
3	Dry Fork Rd, **N...gas:** Citgo, **S...gas:** Shell/diesel, **food:** Burger King, McDonald's, **other:** Chevrolet
2mm	weigh sta eb
1	New Haven Rd, to Harrison, **N...gas:** BP/diesel, **food:** Buffalo Wings, Cracker Barrel, GoldStar Chili, **lodging:** Comfort Inn, **other:** Biggs Foods, Ford, Home Depot, Tires+, **S...gas:** Marathon/diesel, Shell/24hr, Speedway/diesel, Sunoco, A&W/KFC, **food:** Arby's, Big Boy, Burger King, Jersey Mike Subs, McDonald's, Perkins, Pizza Hut, Skyline Chili, Taco Bell, Waffle House, Wendy's, White Castle, **lodging:** Holiday Inn Express, Quality Inn, **other:** Advance Parts, AutoZone, Big Lots, CVS Drug, Family$, Firestone, GNC, Goodyear/auto, K-Mart, Kroger, NAPA, Walgreen
0mm	Ohio/Indiana state line

Interstate 75

Exit #	Services
211mm	Ohio/Michigan state line
210	OH 184, Alexis Rd, to Raceway Park, **E...gas:** BP, **other:** FoodTown, **W...gas:** BP/diesel/24hr, Meijer/diesel/24hr, Pilot/Subway/diesel/24hr/@, **food:** Bob Evans, Burger King, Ground Round, McDonald's, Taco Bell, Wendy's, **lodging:** Comfort Inn, Hampton Inn, **other:** Ford Trucks
210mm	Ottawa River
209	Ottawa River Rd(from nb), **E...gas:** BP, Citgo, Sunoco, **food:** Little Caesar's, Marco's Pizza, **other:** VETERINARIAN, FoodTown, Rite Aid
208	I-280 S, to I-80/90, to Cleveland
207	Stickney Ave, Lagrange St, **E...gas:** BP, Citgo, Sunoco, **food:** McDonald's, Wendy's, **other:** Kash'nKarry Foods, Family$, K-Mart
206	to US 24, Phillips Ave, **W...**transmissions
205b	Burdan St, **E...**HOSPITAL
a	to Willys Pkwy, to Jeep Pkwy
204	I-475 W, to US 23, to Maumee, Ann Arbor
203b	US 24, to Detroit Ave, **W...gas:** BP/24hr, **food:** KFC, McDonald's, Rally's, **other:** Rite Aid, Sav-A-Lot Foods, U-Haul
a	Bancroft St, downtown

Exit #	Services
202	Washington St, Collingwood Ave(from sb, no EZ return), **E...gas:** BP, **other:** HOSPITAL, Art Museum, **W...food:** McDonald's
201b a	OH 25, Collingwood Ave, **W...**Toledo Zoo
200	South Ave, Kuhlman Dr, no facilties
200mm	Maumee River
199	OH 65, Miami St, to Rossford, **E...lodging:** Day's Inn
198	Wales Rd, Oregon Rd, to Northwood, **E...gas:** Shell/Subway/diesel/24hr, **food:** Pizza Hut, **lodging:** Comfort Inn, Microtel
197	Buck Rd, to Rossford, **E...gas:** Shell/diesel, **food:** Wendy's/Tim Horton, **W...gas:** BP/24hr, Sunoco/diesel, **food:** Denny's, McDonald's, **lodging:** Knight's Inn, Super 8
195	OH 795, Perrysburg, to I-80/90, OH Tpk(toll), **E...gas:** Barney's/Subway/diesel, BP/diesel, **lodging:** Courtyard
193	US 20, US 23 S, Perrysburg, **E...gas:** BP/diesel/24hr, Sunoco, **food:** Big Boy, Bob Evans, Burger King, Cracker Barrel, McDonald's, Panera Bread, Ralphie's, Shanghai Chinese, Subway, Taco Bell, Wendy's, **lodging:** Best Western, Day's Inn, Holiday Inn Express, **other:** GNC, Kohl's, K-Mart, Kroger/gas/24hr, KOA(7mi), **W...gas:** Marathon/diesel, **lodging:** Baymont Inn, **other:** AutoZone, Harley-Davidson
192	I-475, US 23 N(exits left from nb), to Maumee, Ann Arbor
187	OH 582, to Luckey, Haskins, no facilities
181	OH 64, OH 105, Bowling Green, to Pemberville, **E...gas:** Meijer/diesel/24hr, **W...gas:** BP, Citgo/Subway/diesel, Marathon, Speedway, Sunoco/diesel, **food:** Big Boy, Bob Evans, Burger King, ChiChi's, Domino's, El Zarape Mexican, Fricker's Rest., Hunan Buffet, McDonald's, Waffle House, Wendy's, **lodging:** Best Western, Buckeye Motel, Day's Inn, Quality Inn, Hampton Inn, **other:** HOSPITAL, bank, to Bowling Green U
179	US 6, to Fremont, Napoleon, **W...**museum
179mm	**rest area both lanes, full(handicapped)facilities, phone, picnic tables, litter barrels, vending, petwalk**
175mm	weigh sta nb
171	OH 25, Cygnet, no facilities
168	Eagleville Rd, Quarry Rd, **E...gas:** FuelMart/diesel
167	OH 18, North Baltimore, to Fostoria, **E...gas:** Petro/Mobil/diesel/rest./24hr/@, **food:** McDonald's, Pizza Hut, **other:** Blue Beacon, truck repair, **W...gas:** Sunoco/diesel, **lodging:** Crown Inn
165mm	Rocky Ford River
164	OH 613, to McComb, Fostoria, **E...other:** Shadylake Camping, to Van Buren SP, **W...gas:** Pilot/Subway/Taco Bell/diesel/24hr/@
162mm	weigh sta sb, phones
161	OH 99, **E...other:** Ford, camping, hwy patrol
159	US 224, OH 15, Findlay, **E...gas:** BP/diesel, Speedway/diesel, Swifty, **food:** Bob Evans, Burger King, Dakota Grill, KFC, McDonald's, Pizza Hut, Ponderosa, Ralphie's, Spaghetti Shop, Steak'n Shake, Taco Bell, Wendy's, **lodging:** Cross Country Inn, Ramada Inn, Rodeway Inn, Super 8, **other:** HOSPITAL, **W...gas:** Shell/diesel, **food:** China Garden, Cracker Barrel, Denny's, Outback Steaks, Waffle House, **lodging:** Country Hearth Inn, Hampton Inn, Holiday Inn Express

Interstate 75

N ↕ **S**

Lima (left vertical marker)

158 Blanchard River

157 OH 12, Findlay, **E...gas:** GA/diesel, Marathon/Blimpie/diesel, **lodging:** Day's Inn, **W...gas:** BP, Hwy Travel Ctr/diesel/24hr/@, **food:** Fricker's Rest., Pilgrim Rest., **lodging:** Econolodge

156 US 68, OH 15, to Carey, **E...**HOSPITAL

153mm rest area both lanes, full(handicapped)facilities, phone, picnic tables, litter barrels, vending, pet-walk

145 OH 235, Mt Cory, to Ada, **E...**TwinLakes Camping

142 OH 103, Bluffton, to Arlington, **E...gas:** Sunoco/diesel, **lodging:** Knight's Inn, **W...gas:** Marathon/diesel, Shell/diesel, **food:** Arby's, Burger King, KFC, McDonald's, Subway, Taco Bell, **lodging:** Comfort Inn, **other:** to Bluffton Coll

140 Bentley Rd, to Bluffton, no facilities

135 OH 696, to US 30, Beaverdam, to Delphos, **E...gas:** Pilot/diesel/24hr/@, **W...gas:** /Flying J/Cookery/diesel/LP/24hr/@, tires, truck repair

134 Napolean Rd(no nb re-entry), to Beaverdam

130 Blue Lick Rd, **E...gas:** Citgo/diesel, **food:** Blue Lick Pizza/subs, **lodging:** Ramada Inn

127b a OH 81, Lima, to Ada, **W...gas:** BP, Marathon/diesel, **food:** Waffle House, **lodging:** Comfort Inn, Day's Inn/rest., Econolodge

126mm Ottawa River

125 OH 309, OH 117, Lima, **E...gas:** BP/diesel, Speedway, **food:** Arby's, Big Boy, Bob Evans, Burger King, Capt D's, China Buffet, Cracker Barrel, Hunan Garden, McDonald's, Olive Garden, Pizza Hut, Ponderosa, Rally's, Ralphie's, Red Lobster, Ryan's, Skyline Chili, Subway, Taco Bell, TCBY, Texas Roadhouse, Wendy's, **lodging:** Hampton Inn, Holiday Inn, Motel 6, **other:** Ford/RV Ctr, Jo-Ann Fabrics, K-Mart, PharmX Drug, Ray's Foods, Sam's Club, Wal-Mart SuperCtr/24hr, **W...gas:** Shell, **food:** Damon's, Papa John's, Pomodoro Pizza, **lodging:** Super 8, **other:** HOSPITAL, $General, Sav-A-Lot Foods

124 4th St, **E...**hwy patrol

122 OH 65, Lima, **E...gas:** Speedway/diesel, **W...gas:** Shell/diesel/24hr, **other:** Freightliner, GMC, Mack , Volvo

120 Breese Rd, Ft Shawnee, **W...other:** Ace Hardware, Harley-Davidson, NAPA/repair

118 to Cridersville, **W...gas:** Fuelmart/Subway/diesel, Speedway/diesel, **food:** Dixie Ley Diner, **other:** $General

114mm rest area both lanes, full(handicapped)facilities, phones, picnic tables, litter barrels, vending, pet-walk

113 OH 67, Wapakeneta, to Uniopolis, no facilities

111 Bellefontaine St, Wahpakeneta, **E...gas:** L&G Trkstp/diesel/@, **lodging:** Day's Inn, **other:** KOA, **W...gas:** BP, Citgo, Shell, **food:** Arby's, Bob Evans, Burger King, Capt D's, Dairy Queen, El Azteca Mexican, KFC, Lamplighter Rest., Lucky Steer Rest., McDonald's, Pizza Hut, Ponderosa, Shanghai Grill, Taco Bell, Waffle House, Wendy's, **lodging:** Best Western, Holiday Inn Express, Super 8, Travelodge, **other:** Advance Parts, Family$, Neil Armstrong Museum, Radio Shack, st patrol

Sidney (right vertical marker)

110 US 33, to St Marys, Bellefontaine, **E...** hwy patrol, KOA

104 OH 219, Botkins, **W...gas:** Marathon/A&W/diesel/@, Sunoco/diesel, **lodging:** Budget Host

102 OH 274, to Jackson Ctr, New Breman, no facilities

99 OH 119, Anna, to Minster, **E...gas:** Citgo/diesel, 99 Trkstp/diesel/rest./@, **food:** Apple Valley Café, **W...gas:** GA, Sunoco/diesel, **food:** Subway, Wendy's, truckwash

94 rd 25A, Sidney, no facilities

93 OH 29, Sidney, to St Marys, **W...**Lake Loramie SP, RV camping

92 OH 47, Sidney, to Versailles, **E...gas:** Shell, Speedway/diesel, DM, **food:** Arby's, Subway, Wendy's, Winger's, **other:** HOSPITAL, AutoZone, CVS Drug, $General, NAPA, PharmX Drug, Sav-A-Lot Foods, **W...gas:** BP, Citgo/diesel, Sunoco, **food:** Bob Evans, Burger King, Cazador Mexican, El Monterrey Mexican, Highmarks Rest., KFC, McDonald's, Perkins, Pizza Hut, Ponderosa, Rally's, Taco Bell, Waffle House, **lodging:** Comfort Inn, Day's Inn, Econolodge, Holiday Inn/rest., **other:** Aldi Foods, Buick/Pontiac/GMC, Chevrolet, Dodge/Plymouth, $Tree, Ford/Lincoln/Mercury, Kroger, Radio Shack, Staples, Wal-Mart SuperCtr/gas/diesel/24hr

90 Fair Rd, to Sidney, **E...gas:** Sunoco/diesel, **other:** repair, **W...gas:** Marathon/DQ/diesel, **lodging:** Hampton Inn

88mm Great Miami River

83 rd 25A, Piqua, **W...gas:** Citgo/diesel, **lodging:** Red Carpet Inn, **other:** Chevrolet, Chrysler/Plymouth/Dodge/Jeep, Sherry RV Ctr, to Piqua Hist Area

82 US 36, Piqua, to Urbana, **E...gas:** BP, **food:** A&W/LJ Silver, Arby's, Blake's Buffet, China East, KFC, Pizza Hut, Taco Bell, Waffle House, Wendy's, **other:** MEDICAL CARE, Goodyear, Home Depot, Jo-Ann Fabrics, mall, st patrol, **W...gas:** Speedway, **food:** Bob Evans, Burger King, Cracker Barrel, El Sombrero Mex, McDonald's, Red Lobster, **lodging:** Comfort Inn, Howard Johnson, Ramada Ltd, **other:** Aldi Foods, JC Penney, Sears/auto, mall

81mm rest area both lanes, full(handicapped)facilities, phones, picnic tables, litter barrels, vending

78 rd 25A, **E...**HOSPITAL

Troy (right vertical marker)

74 OH 41, Troy, to Covington, **E...gas:** BP/diesel, **food:** China Garden, LJ Silver, McDonald's, Perkins, Pizza Hut, Subway, **other:** HOSPITAL, Goodyear/auto, PharmX Drug, Radio Shack, to Hobart Arena, **W...gas:** Meijer/diesel/24hr, Shell, Speedway/diesel, **food:** Applebee's, Big Boy, Bob Evans, Burger King, Crazy H Steaks, Dairy Queen, Fazoli's, Friendly's, KFC, Penn Sta, Skyline Chili, Steak'n Shake, Tego Bay Rest., **lodging:** Fairfield Inn, Hampton Inn, Holiday Inn Express, Knight's Inn, Residence Inn, **other:** AutoZone, County Mkt Foods, CVS Drug, Goodyear, Lowe's Whse, Staples, Tire Discounters, Wal-Mart

OHIO

Interstate 75

73	OH 55, Troy, to Ludlow Falls, **E...gas:** BP, Shell, **food:** Jersey Mike's Subs, Lincoln Sq Rest., Waffle House, Wendy's, **lodging:** Econolodge, HomeTown Inn, Super 8, **other:** HOSPITAL, Country Folks Gen Store
69	rd 25A, **E...gas:** DM/Taco Bell, Marathon, Starfire/diesel, **other:** Buick/Pontiac/GMC, Chrysler/Plymouth/Dodge, Ford
68	OH 571, Tipp City, to West Milton, **E...gas:** BP/dieselmart, Shell, Speedway, **food:** Burger King, Cassano's Pizza, Chin's Chinese, Domino's, Hong Kong Kitchen, McDonald's, Subway, Taco Bell, **other:** CVS Drug, Family$, Goodyear, Honda, **W...gas:** Citgo, Speedway/diesel, **food:** Arby's, Big Boy, Tipp' O the Town Rest., Wendy's, **lodging:** Heritage Motel, Holiday Inn Express
64	Northwoods Blvd, **E...gas:** Kroger/gas
63	US 40, Vandalia, to Donnelsville, **E...gas:** Speedway/diesel, **food:** Frischer's Rest., **lodging:** Crossroads Motel, **other:** auto repair, **W...gas:** BP/diesel, Shell, **food:** Arby's, Burger King, KFC, McDonald's, Pizza Hut, Taco Bell, Waffle House, Wendy's, **lodging:** Cross Country Inn, Travelodge(2mi), **other:** Rexall Drug
61b a	I-70, E to Columbus, W to Indianapolis, to Dayton Int Airport
60	Little York Rd, Stop 8 Rd, **E...food:** Damon's, Olive Garden, Red Lobster, Subway, **lodging:** Howard Johnson, Residence Inn, **other:** Discount Tire, Nissan, McNulty RV Ctr, NTB, Volvo/BMW/VW, **W...gas:** Sunoco, **food:** Arby's, Bennigan's, Bob Evans, Cracker Barrel, Don Pablo, El Rancho Grande Mexican, Golden Corral, Joe's Crabshack, LoneStar Steaks, Max&Erma's, O'Charley's, Outback Steaks, Ryan's, Skyline Chili, SmokeyBones BBQ, Wendy's, **lodging:** Comfort Inn, Country Inn Suites, Courtyard, Day's Inn, Extended Stay America, Fairfield Inn, Knight's Inn, Motel 6, Ramada Inn, Red Roof Inn, **other:** Sam's Club/gas
58	Needmore Rd, to Dayton, **E...gas:** BP/diesel, Shell/McDonald's, **food:** Big Boy, Hardee's, **lodging:** Best Western, **other:** Goodyear/auto, Tires UnLtd/repair, to AF Museum, **W...gas:** Marathon/diesel, Speedway/diesel, Sunoco/diesel/24hr, **food:** A&W/LJ Silver, Burger King, Capt D's, Cassano's Rest., Church's, Ma's Chinese, Sam's Pizza, Waffle House, **other:** Advance Parts, Kroger/gas
57b	Wagner Ford Rd, Siebenthaler Rd, Dayton, **E...gas:** Sunoco, **lodging:** Holiday Inn, **W...gas:** Speedway, **food:** Marion's Pizza, **lodging:** Day's Inn, Parkway Inn, **other:** Interstate Battery, Kelly Tire, Rite Aid, auto repair
a	Neva Rd, no facilities
56	Stanley Ave, Dayton, **E...gas:** Shell, **other:** trk repair, **W...gas:** Clark, **food:** Dragon City Chinese, GoldStar Chili, Great Steak Co, McDonald's, Rally's, Taco Bell, Wendy's, **lodging:** Dayton Motel, Plaza Motel, Royal Motel
55b a	Keowee St, Dayton, **E...**Arrow Batteries, **W...gas:** BP, **lodging:** Plaza Motel
54c	OH 4 N, Webster St, to Springfield, no facilities

54mm	Great Miami River
54b	OH 48, Main St, Dayton, **E...gas:** Chevrolet/Cadillac, **W...gas:** BP, **other:** HOSPITAL
a	Grand Ave(from sb), Dayton, downtown
53b	OH 49, 1st St, Salem Ave, Dayton, downtown, no facilities
a	OH 49, 3rd St, downtown
52b a	US 35, E to Dayton, W to Eaton
51	Edwin C Moses Blvd, Nicholas Rd, **E...**HOSPITAL, to U of Dayton, **W...gas:** BP/diesel, **food:** McDonald's, Wendy's, **lodging:** Econolodge, **other:** SunWatch Indian Village
50b a	OH 741, Kettering St, Dryden Rd, **E...gas:** Citgo, **W...gas:** Sunoco/Subway/diesel, **food:** TJ's Rest., **lodging:** Holiday Inn, Super 8
47	Central Ave, W Carrollton, Moraine, **E...gas:** Sunoco, **food:** Big Boy, Quizno's, Waffle House, **other:** Honda, auto repair, transmissions, **W...gas:** Ashland, Speedway, **food:** KFC, McDonald's, Pizza Hut, Taco Bell, Wendy's, **other:** USPO
44	OH 725, to Centerville, Miamisburg, **E...gas:** BP/diesel, Shell, Speedway, **food:** Big Boy, Blimpie, Burger King, ChiChi's, Dunkin Donuts, Fuddrucker's, Golden Corral, Hardee's, KFC, La Pinata Mexican, Max&Erma's, McDonald's, Ponderosa, Red Lobster, Skyline Chili, Wendy's, **lodging:** Comfort Suites, Courtyard, Doubletree Suites, Holiday Inn, Homewood Suites, Motel 6, Residence Inn, **other:** HOSPITAL, Best Buy, Circuit City, CompUSA, Firestone/auto, Goodyear/auto, Home Depot, Honda/Nissan/Mazda, JC Penney, Kia, Lazarus, Lowe's Whse, Michael's, Mitsubishi, OfficeMax, PepBoys, Pontiac, Sears/auto, Tire Discounters, Toyota, Wal-Mart, mall, **W...gas:** BP, Marathon, Shell, **food:** Bob Evans, Jersey Mike's Subs, LJ Silver, Perkins, **lodging:** Knight's Inn, Ramada Inn, Red Roof Inn, Signature Inn, Yankee Mill Inn, **other:** HOSPITAL, Aamco, $General, Ford
43	I-675 N, to Columbus
38	OH 73, Springboro, Franklin, **E...gas:** BP, Shell, Speedway, Sunoco/diesel, **food:** Arby's, Bob Evans, Chantrell's Rest., China Buffet, KFC/Taco Bell, LJ Silver, McDonald's, Papa John's, Perkins, Pizza Hut, Skyline Chili, Subway, Wendy's, **lodging:** Hampton Inn, Holiday Inn Express, **other:** K-Mart, Kroger, Radio Shack, **W...gas:** Exxon/diesel, Shell, **food:** Big Boy, Domino's, GoldStar Chili, **lodging:** Econolodge, Knight's Inn, **other:** AutoZone, $General, Marsh Foods, NAPA
36	OH 123, Franklin, to Lebanon, **E...gas:** Exxon/Wendy's/diesel/24hr/@, Pilot/Subway/Pizza Hut/diesel/@, **food:** McDonald's, Waffle House, **lodging:** Super 8, **W...gas:** BP, Marathon/White Castle
32	OH 122, Middletown, **E...gas:** BP, Duke, **food:** McDonald's, Waffle House, **lodging:** Best Western, Comfort Inn, Ramada Inn, Super 8, **other:** Ford/Mercury/Lincoln, Jeep, **W...gas:** Citgo, Meijer/diesel/24hr, Speedway, **food:** Applebee's, Big Boy, Bob Evans, Cracker Barrel, El Rancho Grande Mexican, KFC, LoneStar Steaks, McDonald's, O'Charley's, Old Country Buffet, Olive Garden, Ponderosa, Schlotsky's, Shell's Rest., Sonic, Steak'n Shake, Wendy's, **lodging:** Fairfield Inn, Hawthorn Inn, Holiday Inn Express, **other:** HOSPITAL, Buick/GMC/Pontiac, Goodyear/auto, Kohl's, Kroger, Lowe's Whse, Sears/auto, Target, Tire Discounters, mall

Interstate 75

N

S

29   OH 63, Monroe, to Hamilton, **E...gas:** Chevron/ WhiteCastle/diesel, Shell/diesel, Stony Ridge Trk Plaza/.diesel/@, **food:** Burger King, GoldStar Chili, Popeye's, Waffle House, Wendy's/Tim Horton, **lodging:** Day's Inn, Stony Ridge Inn, **W...gas:** BP/diesel, Speedway, Sunoco/diesel, **food:** McDonald's, Perkins, Sara Jane's Rest., **lodging:** Hampton Inn, **other:** flea mkt

27.5mm **rest area both lanes, full(handicapped)facilities, info, phone, picnic tables, litter barrels, vending, petwalk**

24   OH 129 W, to Hamilton, no facilities

22   Tylersville Rd, to Mason, Hamilton, **E...gas:** BP, Marathon, Sunoco, **food:** Arby's, Bob Evans, Burger King, Donato's Pizza, Dudley's Pizza, Fazoli's, GoldStar Chili, KFC, LJ Silver, McDonald's, Perkins, Pizza Hut, Skyline Chili, Taco Bell, Waffle House, Wendy's, **lodging:** Econolodge, **other:** Firestone, GNC, Home Depot, Kroger, Radio Shack, Tires+, bank, **W...gas:** Meijer/diesel/24hr, Shell, Speedway/diesel/24hr, **food:** O'Charley's, Steak'n Shake, **other:** Tire Discounters, Wal-Mart/auto

21   Cin-Day Rd, **E...food:** Big Boy, **lodging:** Holiday Inn Express, **W...gas:** Mobil/Subway/diesel, Shell, **food:** Waffle House, Skyline Chili, **lodging:** Knight's Inn

19   Union Centre Blvd, to Fairfield, **W...gas:** BP/Subway/ diesel, DM, Shell, **food:** Applebee's, Bob Evans, Buffalo Wings, Burger King, Great Steak Co, Max&Erma's, River City Grill, Roadhouse Grill, Skyline Chili, Uno Pizzaria, Wendy's, **lodging:** Marriott, Sleep Inn

16   I-275 to I-71, to I-74

15   Sharon Rd, to Sharonville, Glendale, **E...gas:** BP, Chevron, Marathon/diesel, Shell, Sunoco, **food:** BBQ, Big Boy, Bob Evans, Burbank's Rest., Pizza Hut, Skyline Chili, Waffle House, **lodging:** Best Western, Country Inn Suites, Fairfield Inn, Hampton Inn, Hilton Garden, Holiday Inn/rest., Motel 6, Ramada Inn, Red Roof Inn, Woodfield Suites, **other:** UPS, Valvoline, **W...gas:** Speedway, Sunoco, **food:** Capt D's, China Buffet, LJ Silver, McDonald's, Mexican Connection, Shogun Japanese, Subway, Taco Bell, Wendy's, **lodging:** Comfort Inn, Econolodge, Extended Stay America, Radisson, Residence Inn, Signature Inn, Super 8, **other:** Nissan

14   OH 126, to Woodlawn, Evendale, **E...GE** Plant, **W...lodging:** Quality Inn

13   Shepherd Lane, to Lincoln Heights, **E...GE** Plant, **W...food:** Taco Bell, Wendy's, **other:** Advance Parts

12   Wyoming Ave, Cooper Ave, to Lockland, no facilities

10a   OH 126, Ronald Reagan Hwy, **E...**Chevrolet
  b   Galbraith Rd(exits left from nb), Arlington Heights

9   OH 4, OH 561, Paddock Rd, Seymour Ave, to Cincinnati Gardens

8   Towne St, Elmwood Pl(from nb), no facilities

7   OH 562, to I-71, Norwood, Cincinnati Gardens, no facilities

6   Mitchell Ave, St Bernard, **E...gas:** Marathon, Shell, Speedway/diesel, **food:** KFC/Taco Bell, Wendy's, **lodging:** Holiday Inn Express, **other:** Walgreen, to Cincinnati Zoo, to Xavier U, **W...gas:** BP/Subway/

Cincinnati

diesel, **food:** McDonald's, Rally's, **other:** Family$, Ford, Honda, Kroger, Tires+

4   I-74 W, US 52, US 27 N, to Indianapolis, no facilities

3   to US 27 S, US 127 S, Hopple St, U of Cincinnati, **E...gas:** Marathon, **food:** White Castle, **lodging:** access to Day's Inn, **W...gas:** Shell, **other:** HOSPITAL

2b   Harrison Ave, industrial district, **E...**Ford Trucks, **W...gas:** BP, **food:** McDonald's

a   Western Ave, Liberty St(from sb)

1h   Ezzard Charles Dr, **W...lodging:** Holiday Inn

g   US 50W, Freeman Ave, **W...gas:** Site, **food:** Big Boy, Wendy's, **lodging:** Holiday Inn, **other:** Ford

f   7th St(from sb), downtown, **W...lodging:** Holiday Inn

e   5th St(from sb), downtown, **E...gas:** Crowne Plaza, **lodging:** Sheraton

1a   I-71 N, to Cincinnati, downtown, to stadium

0mm   Ohio/Kentucky state line, Ohio River

Interstate 76

E

W

Exit #   Services

242mm Ohio/Pennsylvania state line

Exits 232-235 are on the Ohio Turnpike.

235   I-680(from wb), to Youngstown

232   OH 7, to Boardman, Youngstown, **N...food:** DQ, Smaldino's Family Rest., **lodging:** Budget Inn, Day's Inn, Econolodge, Microtel, North Lima Inn, Super 8, **S...gas:** Shell/diesel, Speedway/diesel, **food:** Road House Diner, **lodging:** Davis Motel, Rodeway Inn, **other:** truck repair

60mm   I-76 eb joins Ohio TPK(toll), no facilities

57   to OH 45, Bailey Rd, to Warren, no facilities

54   OH 534, to Newton Falls, Lake Milton, **N...**RV camping, **S...gas:** BP, **other:** to Berlin Lake, camping

52mm   Lake Milton

48   OH 225, to Alliance, **N...**to W Branch SP, camping, **S...**to Berlin Lake

45mm   **rest area both lanes, full(handicapped)facilities, phone, picnic tables, litter barrels, petwalk**

43   OH 14, to Alliance, Ravenna, **N...**to W Branch SP, **S...gas:** Citgo/diesel, **other:** fireworks

38b a   OH 5, OH 44, to Ravenna, **N...gas:** BP, Speedway/diesel, **food:** Arby's, McDonald's, Wendy's, **other:** HOSPITAL, **S...gas:** Marathon/Circle K/Subway, **food:** Cracker Barrel, David's Rest., **other:** Giant Eagle Foods, auto repair, RV camping

33   OH 43, to Hartville, Kent, **N...gas:** BP/diesel, **food:** Bob Evans(2mi), Burger King(2mi), Pizza Hut, Salsita's Mexican, **lodging:** Alden Inn, Day's Inn, Hampton Inn, Holiday Inn, Ramada Inn, Super 8, Tallyho Inn, **other:** to Kent St U, **S...gas:** Speedway/diesel, **food:** McDonald's, Subway, Wendy's, **other:** RV camping

OHIO

Interstate 76

Akron

31	rd 18, Tallmadge, **1mi S...food:** Brimfield's Steaks, Pizza Serena
29	OH 532, Tallmadge, Mogadore, no facilities
27	OH 91, Canton Rd, Gilchrist Rd, **N...food:** Bob Evans, **S...gas:** Marathon/Subway/diesel, **food:** Hardee's, Wendy's, **lodging:** Best Western
26	OH 18, E Market St, Mogadore Rd, **N...gas:** Citgo/diesel, Shell, **S...food:** Arby's, McDonald's, Wendy's, **other:** $General
25b a	Martha Ave, General St, Brittain, **N...gas:** Citgo, **other:** Goodyear World Hdqtrs
24	Arlington St, Kelly Ave, **N...**Mercedes, Toyota
23b	OH 8, Buchtell Ave, to Cuyahoga, to U of Akron, to U of Akron
23a	I-77 S, to Canton, no facilities
22b	Wolf Ledges, Akron, downtown, **S...gas:** BP, **food:** McDonald's
22a	Main St, Broadway, downtown
21c	OH 59 E, Dart Ave, **N...**HOSPITAL
21b	Lakeshore St, Bowery St(from eb), no facilities
21a	East Ave(from wb), no facilities
20	I-77 N(from eb), to Cleveland, no facilities
19	Battles Ave, Kenmore Blvd, no facilities
18	I-277, US 224 E, to Canton, Barberton, interchange
17b a	OH 619, Wooster Rd, State St, to Barberton, **S...gas:** Sunoco, **other:** HOSPITAL, NAPA
16	Barber Rd, **S...gas:** Sunoco/diesel, **food:** Tomaso's Italian, **lodging:** Shamrock Motel, **other:** Chrysler/Jeep/Nissan/Suzuki
14	Cleve-Mass Rd, to Norton, **S...gas:** BP, Citgo, Marathon(2mi), **food:** Charlie's Rest., **lodging:** Berlin's Motel(2mi)
13b a	OH 21, N to Cleveland, S to Massillon, no facilities
11	OH 261, Wadsworth, **N...gas:** Speedway
9	OH 94, to N Royalton, Wadsworth, **N...gas:** DM, Marathon, **food:** Applebee's, Arby's, Bob Evans, Burger King, KFC, McDonald's, Pizza Hut, Ponderosa, Subway, Taco Bell, Wendy's, **lodging:** Holiday Inn Express, Ramada Ltd, **other:** Buehler's Foods, DrugMart, Goodyear/auto, K-Mart, NTB, Radio Shack, Wal-Mart SuperCtr/24hr, **S...gas:** BP/diesel, Citgo/DQ, Pennzoil, Sunoco, **food:** Casa Del Rio Mexican, Country Cafe, Denny's, **lodging:** Legacy Inn, **other:** AutoZone, Rite Aid
7	OH 57, to Rittman, Medina, **N...gas:** Marathon/diesel, **other:** HOSPITAL, airport
6mm	weigh sta both lanes
2	OH 3, to Medina, Seville, **N...food:** DQ, Hardee's, Subway, **lodging:** Comfort Inn, Hawthorn Suites, **other:** Maple Lakes Camping(seasonal), **S...gas:** Citgo/diesel, Sunoco, **other:** RV camping
1	I-76 E, to Akron, US 224, **W on US 224...gas:** Pilot/Subway/diesel/24hr/@, TA/Burger King/Popeye's/diesel/24hr/@, **food:** McDonald's, **lodging:** Super 8, **other:** Blue Beacon, SpeedCo, Chippewa Valley Camping(1mi)
0mm	I-76 begins/ends on I-71, exit 209.

Interstate 77

Cleveland

Exit #	Services
	I-77 begins/ends on I-90 exit 172, in Cleveland.
163c	I-90, E to Erie, W to Toledo
b	E 9th St, Tower City
162b	E 22nd St, E 14th St(from nb)
a	E 30th St, Woodland Ave, Broadway St(from nb), **W...**USPO
161b	I-490 W, E 55th, to I-71, **E...**HOSPITAL
a	OH 14(from nb), Broadway St
160	Pershing Ave(from nb), **W...**HOSPITAL
159b	Fleet Ave, **E...gas:** BP/Subway/diesel
a	Harvard Ave, Newburgh Heights, **W...gas:** BP/Subway/diesel/24hr, Marathon
158	Grant Ave, Cuyahoga Heights
157	OH 21, OH 17(from sb), Brecksville Rd, no facilities
156	I-480, to Youngstown, Toledo
155	Rockside Rd, to Independence, **E...gas:** Sunoco, **food:** Bob Evans, ChiChi's, Denny's, Frank&Pauly's Rest., **lodging:** Baymont Inn, Comfort Inn, Embassy Suites, Holiday Inn, Red Roof Inn, **W...gas:** BP/diesel, **food:** Applebee's, Damon's, Longhorn Steaks, **lodging:** AmeriSuites, Courtyard, Hampton Inn, Residence Inn, Sheraton
153	Pleasant Valley Rd, to Independence, 7 Hills
151	Wallings Rd, no facilities
149	OH 82, to Broadview Heights, Brecksville, **W...gas:** BP, **food:** Domino's, Laura's Kitchen, Pazzo's Café, **lodging:** Tallyho Motel
147	to OH 21, Miller Rd(from sb), no facilities
146	I-80/Ohio Tpk, to Youngstown, Toledo
145	OH 21(from nb), **E...gas:** BP/repair, Pilot/diesel, **food:** DQ, Wendy's, **lodging:** Brushwood Motel, Hampton Inn, Holiday Inn, Super 8
144	I-271 N, to Erie
143	OH 176, to I-271 S, **E...**to Coliseum, **W...gas:** Sunoco, **food:** Arabica Café, McDonald's, Subway
141mm	**rest area both lanes, full(handicapped)facilities, phone, picnic tables, litter barrels, vending, petwalk**
138	Ghent Rd, **2 mi E...lodging:** Hilton, Sheraton, **W...gas:** Citgo/diesel, **food:** Lanning's Rest., Vaccaro's Italian
137b a	OH 18, to Fairlawn, Medina, **E...gas:** BP, Citgo, Marathon, Shell, Speedway, **food:** Applebee's, Backyard Burger, Bob Evans, ChiChi's, Chili's, Cracker Barrel, Friendly's, Golden Corral, KFC, LoneStar Steaks, Macaroni Grill, Max&Erma's, McDonald's, Olive Garden, Ruby Tuesday, Starbucks, Steak'n Shake, Taco Bell, Wendy's, **lodging:** Courtyard, Fairfield Inn, Hampton Inn, Holiday Inn, Red Roof Inn, Super 8, **other:** Acme Foods, Best Buy, Borders Books, Ford, Home Depot, Jo-Ann Fabrics, Lowe's Whse, NTB, Old Navy, Sam's Club, Staples, Wal-Mart, **W...gas:** Citgo, **food:** Amazon Café, Bennigan's, Burger King, Damon's, Don Pablo, Eastside Mario's, Fuddrucker's, Outback Steaks, Thirsty Dog Brewing Co, TGIFriday, **lodging:** Best Western, Comfort Inn, Extended Stay America, Radisson, Residence Inn, Studio+
136	OH 21S, to Massillon, no facilities
135	Cleveland-Massillon Rd(from nb), no facilities
133	Ridgewood Rd, Miller Rd, **E...gas:** Citgo/diesel, **food:** Wendy's
132	White Pond Dr, Mull Ave, **E...**Jasper's Grille, golf

Interstate 77

N ↑↓ S

Akron

131   OH 162, Copley Rd, **E...gas:** Citgo, **other:** USPO, **W...gas:** BP/diesel/24hr, Marathon/diesel, **food:** McDonald's, Pizza Hut

130   OH 261, Wooster Ave, **E...gas:** BP, Citgo, **food:** Burger King, Church's, New China, Rally's, Subway, White Castle, **other:** Advance Parts, AutoZone, **W...food:** KFC, **other:** Chevrolet, Top's Foods, Toyota, U-Haul

129   I-76 W, to I-277, to Kenmore Blvd, Barberton

21a   East Ave(from nb), no facilities, I-77 S and I-76 E run together

b   Lakeshore(from sb), to Bowery St, no facilities

c   OH 59 E, Dart Ave, downtown, **E...HOSPITAL**

22a   Main St, Broadway St, downtown, **W...auto parts**

b   Grant St, Wolf Ledges, **W...gas:** BP, **food:** McDonald's

125b   I-76 E, to Youngstown, I-77 and I-76 run together

a   OH 8 N, to Cuyahoga Falls, U of Akron

124b   Lover's Lane, Cole Ave, no facilities

a   Archwood Ave, Firestone Blvd, no facilities

123b   OH 764, Wilbeth Rd, **E...to airport**

a   Waterloo Rd, **W...gas:** BP, **other:** Acme Foods

122b a   I-277, US 224 E, to Barberton, Mogadore

120   Arlington Rd, to Green, **E...gas:** Speedway/diesel, **food:** Applebee's, Church's, Denny's, Friendly's, IHOP, Mike's Ribs, Pizza Hut, Ryan's, Waffle House, White Castle, **lodging:** Comfort Inn, Holiday Inn Express, Red Roof Inn, **other:** Home Depot, Wal-Mart/auto, **W...gas:** BP, **food:** Bob Evans, Burger King, King Buffet, McDonald's, Subway, Taco Bell, TGIFriday, Wendy's, **lodging:** Day's Inn, Econolodge, Fairfield Inn, Hampton Inn, **other:** Buick/Pontiac/GMC, Chevrolet, Honda/Mazda, Sirpilla RV Ctr

118   OH 241, to OH 619, Massillon, **E...gas:** Speedway/diesel, **food:** Subway, **W...gas:** Citgo/DM, **food:** Arby's, McDonald's, Meneche Rest., Pancho's Mexican, **lodging:** Super 8, **other:** MEDICAL CARE

113   Akron-Canton Airport, **2 mi W...other:** Clay's RV, London Chocolate Factory

111   Portage St, N Canton, **E...gas:** TA/Marathon/diesel/rest./24hr/@, Sunoco/diesel, **food:** BrewHouse Grill, Burger King, Golden Corral, KFC, TrueValue, **other:** Begg's RV Ctr, **W...gas:** BP/diesel, **food:** Carrabba's, ChuckeCheese, Cracker Barrel, Don Pablo, IHOP, Joe's Crabshack, Longhorn Steaks, McDonald's, Pizza Hut, Quizno's, Red Robin, Taco Bell, Wendy's, **lodging:** Best Western, Microtel, Motel 6, **other:** BJ's Whse, Borders Books, DrugMart, Giant Eagle Foods, Goodyear/auto, Harley-Davidson, Home Depot, Lowe's Whse, Marshall's, OfficeMax, Old Navy, Sam's Club/gas, SteinMart, Wal-Mart/auto

109b a   Everhard Rd, Whipple Ave, **E...gas:** Citgo/Subway, Speedway/diesel, **food:** Blimpie, Burger King, Denny's, Fazoli's, McDonald's, Taco Bell, **lodging:** Comfort Inn, Fairfield Inn, Hampton Inn, Residence Inn, Super 8, **other:** $General, Ford, Saturn, **W...gas:** Marathon, **food:** Applebee's, Arby's, Bob Evans, Boston Mkt, Chang's Chinese, ChiChi's, Damon's, Donato's Pizza, Eastside Mario's, Eat'n Park, Friendly's, Fuddrucker's, Great Wall Chinese, HomeTown Buffet, Italian Oven, KFC, LoneStar Steaks, Manchu Café, Olive Garden, Outback Steaks, Panera Bread, Pizza Hut, Red Lob-

ster, TGIFriday, Thirsty Dog Grill, Wendy's, **lodging:** Best Suites, Day's Inn, Holiday Inn, Red Roof Inn, Sheraton, Super 8, **other:** B Dalton's, Best Buy, Circuit City, Dillard's, Firestone/auto, Goodyear/auto, Jo-Ann Crafts, Kohl's, Marc's Foods, Michael's, NTB, Radio Shack, Sears/auto, Target, mall

Canton

107b a   US 62, OH 687, Fulton Rd, to Alliance, **E...City Park, W...Pro Football Hall of Fame**

106   13th St NW, **E...HOSPITAL**

105b   OH 172, Tuscarawas St, downtown

a   6th St SW(no EZ return from sb), **W...HOSPITAL**

104   US 30, US 62, to E Liverpool, Massillon, no facilities

103   OH 800 S, **E...gas:** Citgo, Speedway, **food:** Arby's, Subway, Taco Bell

101   OH 627, to Faircrest St, **E...gas:** Citgo/Gulliver's 77 Plaza/diesel/rest./@, Marathon/McDonald's, **food:** Wendy's

99   Fohl Rd, to Navarre, **W...gas:** Shell, KOA(4mi)

93   OH 212, Bolivar, to Zoar, **E...gas:** Marathon, **food:** McDonald's, Pizza Hut, Wendy's, Zoar Tavern(3mi), **lodging:** Sleep Inn, **other:** Giant Eagle Foods, NAPA, to Lake Atwood Region, **W...gas:** Citgo/DQ

92mm   weigh sta both lanes

87   US 250W, to Strasburg, **2 mi E...food:** Arby's, Grinders, **W...gas:** Citgo/diesel, **food:** Hardee's, Lugnut Café, Manor Rest., McDonald's, **lodging:** Ramada Ltd, Twins Motel

85mm   rest areas both lanes, full(handicapped)facilities, info, phone, picnic tables, litter barrels, petwalk

83   OH 39, OH 211, Dover, to Sugarcreek, **E...gas:** BP, Marathon/Subway, Speedway/diesel, **food:** Bob Evans, Denny's, KFC, McDonald's, Shoney's, Wendy's, **lodging:** Hospitality Inn, **other:** HOSPITAL, Ford/Chrysler/Plymouth/Dodge/Jeep, Lincoln/Mercury/Nissan, RV American, **W...gas:** Marathon/DQ, **lodging:** Comfort Inn

81   US 250, to Uhrichsville, OH 39, New Philadelphia, **E...gas:** Marathon, **food:** Burger King, Denny's, El San Jose Mexican, Hong Kong Buffet, LJ Silver, McDonald's, Pizza Hut, Taco Bell, Texas Roadhouse, **lodging:** Budget Inn, Hampton Inn, Holiday Inn, Day's Inn, Motel 6, Schoenbrunn Inn, Super 8, Travelodge, **other:** Advance Parts, Aldi Foods, $General, Wal-Mart SuperCtr/24hr, **W...gas:** Eagle/diesel/rest./@

73   OH 751, to rd 21, Stone Creek, **W...gas:** Marathon

65   US 36, Port Washington, Newcomerstown, **W...gas:** BP, Duke/diesel/rest., Marathon/Wendy's/24hr, **food:** McDonald's, **lodging:** Hampton Inn, Super 8

64mm   Tuscarawas River

54   OH 541, rd 831, Kimbolton, to Plainfield, **W...gas:** BP, **food:** Jackie's Rest.

Interstate 77

47 US 22, to Cadiz, Cambridge, **E**...to Salt Fork SP(6mi), lodging, RV camping, **W**...**gas:** BP/repair, **other:** HOSPITAL, to Glass Museum, info

46b a US 40, Cambridge, to Old Washington, **W**...**gas:** BP/24hr, Exxon/Wendy's/diesel, FuelMart/diesel, Speedway/24hr, **food:** Burger King, Hunan Chinese, Lee's Rest., LJ Silver, McDonald's, Wally's Pizza, **lodging:** Long's Motel, **other:** Riesbeck's Food/deli

44b a I-70, E to Wheeling, W to Columbus

41 OH 209, OH 821, Byesville, **W**...**gas:** BP/diesel, **food:** McDonald's, **other:** IGA Foods, Family$

39mm **rest area nb, full(handicapped)facilities, phone, picnic tables, litter barrels, petwalk, vending**

37 OH 313, Buffalo, **E**...**gas:** BP/Subway, Duke/diesel, **food:** Buffalo Grill, **other:** truck repair, to Senecaville Lake

36mm **rest area sb, full(handicapped)facilities, phone, picnic tables, litter barrels, petwalk, vending**

28 OH 821, Belle Valley, **E**...**gas:** Sunoco/diesel, **food:** Marianne's Rest., **other:** USPO, to Wolf Run SP, RV camping

25 OH 78, Caldwell, **E**...**gas:** BP, Pilot/Arby's/diesel/24hr, Sunoco/Subway/diesel, **food:** Dairy Queen, Lori's Rest., McDonald's, **lodging:** Best Western, **other:** Chevrolet/Pontiac/Buick

16 OH 821, Macksburg, **E**...**food:** MiniMart Rest., **other:** antiques

6 OH 821, to Devola, **E**...**gas:** Exxon, **W**...HOSPITAL, BP/diesel/LP, RV camping

3mm **rest area nb, full(handicapped)facilities, info, phone, vending, picnic tables, litter barrels, petwalk**

1 OH 7, to OH 26, Marietta, **E**...GoMart/diesel/24hr, Dairy Queen, Damon's, Ryan's, Comfort Inn, Econolodge, Holiday Inn, Aldi Foods, Chevrolet/Cadillac, Chrysler/Plymouth, Dodge, Ford, IGA Foods, Harley-Davidson, Lowe's Whse, Pontiac/Buick, Toyota, Wal-Mart SuperCtr/24hr, **W**...**gas:** BP/diesel, Duke/diesel, Exxon, Marathon/diesel, Speedway, **food:** Applebee's, Bob Evans, Burger King, Capt D's, Chicago Pizza, Empire Buffet, LJ Silver, McDonald's, Napoli's Pizza, Papa John's, Pizza Hut, Rax, Shoney's, Subway, Taco Bell, Wendy's, **lodging:** Hampton Inn, Knight's Inn, Super 8, **other:** MEDICAL CARE, AutoZone, CVS Drug, Food4Less, Jo-Ann Crafts, K-Mart, Kroger/24hr, museum, st patrol

0mm Ohio/West Virginia state line, Ohio River

Interstate 80

Exit # Services

237mm Ohio/Pennsylvania state line

237mm **Welcome Ctr wb, full(handicapped)facilities, info, phone, picnic tables, litter barrels, vending, petwalk**

234b a US 62, OH 7, to Sharon, PA, Hubbard, **N**...**gas:** ✈/Flying J/Country Mkt/Magic Dragon Chinese/diesel/24hr/@, Shell/diesel/rest./motel/24hr/@, **food:** Arby's, Burger King, McDonald's, **other:** Blue Beacon, RV camping(2mi), tire repair, **S**...**other** Chevrolet

232mm weigh sta wb

229 OH 193, Belmont Ave, to Youngstown, **N**...**gas:** Speedway/diesel, **food:** Handel's Ice Cream, Sta Sq Rest., **lodging:** American Inn, Belmont Inn, Day's Inn, Hampton Inn, Holiday Inn, Knight's Inn, Super 8, TallyHotel, **other:** MEDICAL CARE, **S**...**gas:** Shell, **food:** Arby's, Asian Buffet, Armando's Italian, Bob Evans, Burger King, Cancun Mexican, Denny's, KFC, LJ Silver, McDonald's, Papa John's, Perkins/24hr, Pizza Hut, Sonic, Subway, Taco Bell, Wendy's, **lodging:** Comfort Inn, Econolodge, Quality Inn, **other:** Advance Parts, BigLots, Giant Eagle Foods, Goodyear/auto

228 OH 11, to Warren(exits left from eb), Ashtabula, no facilities

227 US 422, Girard, Youngstown, **N**...**gas:** Shell/diesel/24hr, **food:** Burger King, JibJab Hotdogs, Subway

226 Salt Springs Rd, to I-680(from wb), **N**...**gas:** BP/Subway/diesel, Sheetz/diesel/24hr, **food:** McDonald's, Waffle House, **S**...**gas:** Mr Fuel/diesel/24hr, Petro/Mobil/diesel/rest./24hr/@, Pilot/Arby's/diesel/24hr/@, **other:** Blue Beacon, SpeedCo, diesel repair

224b I-680(from eb), to Youngstown, no facilities

224a OH 11 S, to Canfield, no facilities

223 OH 46, to Niles, **N**...**gas:** Citgo/diesel, Pilot/McDonald's/diesel/24hr/@, **food:** Bob Evans, Burger King, IceHouse Rest., Salsita's Mexican, **lodging:** Comfort Inn, Howard Johnson, Youngstown Inn, **S**...**gas:** BP/diesel, FuelMart/diesel, Sunoco/Subway, TA/diesel/rest./24hr/@, **food:** Arby's, Cracker Barrel, McDonald's, Perkins, Roadhouse Cafe, Taco Bell, Wendy's, **lodging:** Best Western, Econolodge, Fairfield Inn, Hampton Inn, Motel 6, Sleep Inn, Super 8, **other:** Blue Beacon, Freightliner/24hr

221mm Meander Reservoir

219mm I-80 wb joins Ohio Tpk(toll), no facilities

For I-80 exits 2-218, see Ohio Turnpike.

Interstate 90

Exit # Services

243mm Ohio/Pennsylvania state line

242mm **Welcome Ctr/weigh sta wb, full(handicapped)facilities, info, phone, picnic tables, litter barrels, petwalk**

241 OH 7, to Andover, Conneaut, **N**...**food:** Burger King, McDonald's(2mi), **lodging:** Day's Inn, **other:** HOSPITAL, AutoZone, CVS Drug, Giant Eagle/deli, K-Mart, Evergreen RV Park, **S**...**food:** Beef&Beer Café

235 OH 84, OH 193, to Youngstown, N Kingsville, **N**...**gas:** Citgo/diesel, Grab and Go/gas, **lodging:** Dav-Ed Motel, **other:** Village Green Camping(2mi), **S**...**gas:** Speedway/Subway/diesel, TA/BP/Burger King/diesel/24hr/@, **food:** Kay's Place Dining, **lodging:** Kingsville Motel

228 OH 11, to Ashtabula, Youngstown, **N**...HOSPITAL(4mi)

223 OH 45, to Ashtabula, **N**...**gas:** ✈/Flying J/diesel/LP/rest./24hr/@, **food:** Mr C's, **lodging:** Comfort Inn, Holiday Inn Express, Sleep Inn, Travelodge, **other:** Buccaneer Camping, **S**...**gas:** BP/rest., Pilot/Subway/diesel, **food:** Burger King, McDonald's, **lodging:** Hampton Inn

218 OH 534, Geneva, **N**...**gas:** BP, Sunoco, **food:** Best Friends Rest., Geneva Rest., KFC, Lighthouse Grill, McDonald's, Pizza Hut, Season's Grille, Wendy's, **lodging:** Howard Johnson, **other:** HOSPITAL, Goodyear, truck service/diesel, KOA(8mi), Indian Creek Camping, to Geneva SP, **S**...**gas:** KwikFill/diesel/24hr, **other:** Kenisse's Camping

Interstate 90

E ↑ ↓ W

212 OH 528, to Thompson, Madison, **N...food:** JC's Diner, McDonald's, Potbelly's Rest., **S...gas:** Marathon/diesel, **other:** Heritage Hills Camping(4mi), radiators

205 Vrooman Rd, **S...gas:** BP/diesel, **food:** Capp's Eatery(1mi)

200 OH 44, to Painesville, Chardon, **N...HOSPITAL**, **S...gas:** BP/Subway/diesel, Sunoco/diesel, **food:** CK's Steakhouse, McDonald's, Red Hawk Grille, Waffle House, **lodging:** Quail Hollow Resort, **other:** Target, hwy patrol

198mm rest area both lanes, full(handicapped)facilities, phone, picnic tables, litter barrels, vending, petwalk

195 OH 615, Center St, Kirtland Hills, Mentor, **1-2mi N...gas:** BP, **food:** Yours Truly Rest., **lodging:** Best Western,

193 OH 306, to Mentor, Kirtland, **N...gas:** BP/Subway, Shell, Speedway, **food:** McDonald's, Ponderosa, **lodging:** Comfort Inn, Motel 6, Super 8, **S...gas:** Marathon, **food:** Burger King, Dino's Rest., Roadhouse Grill, **lodging:** Day's Inn/café, Red Roof Inn, Travelodge, **other:** HOSPITAL

190mm weigh sta eb

190 Express Lane to I-271(from wb), no facilities

189 OH 91, to Willoughby, Willoughby Hills, **N...gas:** BP/diesel, Shell/24hr, **food:** Bob Evans, Burger King, Café Europa, Cracker Barrel, Damon's, Eat 'n Park, Peking Chef, **lodging:** Courtyard, Fairfield Inn, Ramada Inn, Travelodge, **other:** HOSPITAL, CVS Drug, Walgreen

188 I-271 S, to Akron, no faiclities

187 OH 84, Bishop Rd, to Wickliffe, Willoughby, **N...lodging:** Clarion, Hampton Inn, **S...gas:** BP/diesel, Shell, Sunoco, **food:** Dairymart, Bakers Square, Burger King, Friendly's, Manhattan Deli, McDonald's, Quizno's, Sbarro's, Subway, TCBY, **lodging:** Erie Lake Lodge, Holiday Inn, **other:** HOSPITAL, CVS Drug, Chevrolet, Giant Eagle Foods, Marc's Foods, Mazda/VW, OfficeMax, Sam's Club

186 US 20, Euclid Ave, **N...gas:** Sunoco, **food:** Allegro Rest., Denny's, Joe's Crabshack, McDonald's, **lodging:** Clarion, Hampton Inn, **other:** DENTIST, Dodge/Saturn/Subaru, Ford, **S...gas:** Shell, **food:** Arby's, KFC, Pizza Hut, Popeye's, R-Ribs, Sidewalk Cafe, Taco Bell, Wendy's, Zanzibar Rest., **other:** CVS Drug, Firestone/auto, K-Mart, SaveAlot Foods

185 OH 2 E(exits left from eb), to Painesville, no facilities

184b OH 175, E 260th St, **N...gas:** Shell/autocare, **S...other:** Ryder Trucks, tires, transmissions

184a Babbitt Rd, same as 183, **S...gas:** BP, **other:** K-Mart

183 22nd St, **N...Pontiac**, **S...gas:** Sunoco/diesel/24hr, **other:** Forest City Parts

182b a E 200th St, E 185th St, **N...gas:** BP/24hr, **other:** Home Depot, Honda, Hyundai, **S...gas:** BP, Citgo/diesel, Marathon, Shell/24hr, Speedway, Sunoco, **food:** Shotz Grill, **other:** HOSPITAL

181b a E 156th St, **N...gas:** Marathon, **S...gas:** BP/24hr

180b a E 140th St, E 152nd St, no facilities

Cleveland

179 OH 283 E, to Lake Shore Blvd, no facilities

178 Eddy Rd, to Bratenahl, no facilities

177 University Circle, MLK Dr, **N...other:** Cleveland Lake SP, **S...other:** HOSPITAL, Rockefeller Park

176 E 72nd St, no facilities

175 E 55th St, Marginal Rds, **S...AAA**

174b OH 2 W, downtown, to Lakewood, downtown, Rock&Roll Hall of Fame

174a Lakeside Ave, no facilities

173c Superior Ave, St Clair Ave, downtown, **N...gas:** BP

173b Chester Ave, **S...gas:** BP

173a Prospect Ave(from wb), downtown

172d Carnegie Ave, downtown, **S...food:** Burger King, **other:** Cadillac/Hummer

172c b E 9th St, **S...other:** HOSPITAL, to Cleveland St U

172a I-77 S, to Akron, no facilities

171b a US 422, OH 14, Broadway St, Ontario St, **N...lodging:** Hilton Garden, **other:** to Stadium, to downtown

170c b I-71 S, to I-490, no facilities

170a US 42, W 25th St, **N...gas:** Sunoco, **S...gas:** Citgo

169 W 44th St, W 41st St, **N...HOSPITAL**

167b a OH 10, West Blvd, 98th St, to Lorain Ave, **N...HOSPITAL**, **S...gas:** BP/diesel

166 W 117th St, **N...gas:** BP/diesel, Shell, **other:** Forest City Parts, Home Depot, **S...food:** Chinese Cuisine, Church's/White Castle

165 W 140th St, Bunts Rd, Warren Rd, **N...gas:** Marathon, **other:** HOSPITAL

164 McKinley Ave, to Lakewood, no facilities

162 Hilliard Blvd(from wb), to Westway Blvd, Rocky River, **S...gas:** BP, Shell

161 OH 2, OH 254(from eb, no EZ return), Detroit Rd, Rocky River, no facilities

160 Clague Rd(from wb), **S...other:** HOSPITAL, same as 159

159 OH 252, Columbia Rd, **N...gas:** Speedway, **food:** Carrabba's, Cooker Grill, Dave & Buster's, Joe's Crabshack, Outback Steaks, Tony Roma's, **lodging:** Courtyard, TownePlace Suites, Super 8, **other:** MEDICAL CARE, DENTIST, **S...gas:** BP, **food:** Friendly's, Houlihan's, KFC, McDonald's, Taco Bell, **other:** CVS Drug, Mueller Tire, Tire Kingdom, Tops Foods

156 Crocker Rd, Bassett Rd, Westlake, Bay Village, **N...gas:** BP, Shell, **lodging:** Holiday Inn, Red Roof Inn, Residence Inn, **S...gas:** Marathon/diesel, **food:** Applebee's, Bob Evans, Max&Erma's, McDonald's, Subway, TGIFriday, Wendy's, **lodging:** Hampton Inn, **other:** HOSPITAL, Borders Books, CVS Drug, Giant Eagle, GNC, Jo-Ann Crafts, K-Mart, Marc's Foods, OfficeMax, Radio Shack, mall

OHIO

Interstate 90

153 OH 83, Avon Lake, **N...food:** Perkins, **other:** Wal-Mart/auto/gas, **2 mi N...gas:** Speedway, **food:** Burger King, McDonald's, **S...food:** Bob Evan's, IHOP, Panera Bread, Quizno's, Red Robin, Subway, Wendy's, **other:** Cosco/gas, CVS, Home Depot, Kohl's, Marshall's, Michael's, Old Navy, Target

151 OH 611, Avon, **N...gas:** BP/diesel, Pilot/Subway/diesel, **food:** McDonald's, Dianna's Deli, **lodging:** Fairfield Inn, **other:** Avon RV, Goodyear/auto, Harley Davidson, **S...gas:** BJ's Whse/gas

148 OH 254, Sheffield, Avon, **N...food:** Quaker Steak, **other:** Dodge, Ford, Mitsubishi, **S...gas:** BP, Speedway, **food:** Arby's, Burger King, China Star, Cracker Barrel, Donato's Pizza, KFC, McDonald's, Pizza Hut, Quizno's, Ruby Tuesday, Subway, Steak 'n Shake, Taco Bell, Weny's, **other:** Aldi Foods, CarCare USA, CVS, Giant Eagle, Sam's Club/gas, Tire Kingdom

147mm Black River

145 145 OH 57, to Lorain, I-80/Ohio Tpk E, Elyria, **1-2mi N...food:** Burger King, George's Rest., KFC, **other:** HOSPITAL, Chevrolet, $General, SaveAlot Food, U-Haul, **S...gas:** BP/McDonald's/diesel, Speedway, Shell, **food:** Applebee's, Arby's, Bennigan's, Blimpie, Bob Evans, Burger King, Country Kitchen, Denny's, Fazoli's, HomeTown Buffet, LoneStar Steaks, TGIFriday's, Pizza Hut, Red Lobster, Subway, Wendy's, **lodging:** Best Western, Comfort Inn, Country Inn, Day's Inn, Econolodge, Holiday Inn, Howard Johnson, Knight's Inn, Super 8, **other:** Best Buy, Dillard's, Firestone/auto, Goodyear/auto, Honda, JC Penney, Jo-Ann Fabrics, Lowe's Whse, Marc's Foods, Michael's, NTB, OfficeMax, Radio Shack, Sears/auto, Staples, TJMaxx, Wal-Mart/auto, mall

144 OH 2 W(from wb, no return), to Sandusky, **1 mi N on Broadway Ave...gas:** Marathon, Shell/24hr, **food:** McDonald's, **other:** HOSPITAL

143 I-90 wb joins Ohio Tpk, no facilities
For wb exits to Ohio/Indiana state line see Ohio Turnpike.

Interstate 270(Columbus)

Exit #   Services

55 I-71, to Columbus, Cincinnati

52b a US 23, High St, Circleville, **N...gas:** Speedway/diesel, Sunoco/Blimpie, Thornton/diesel, **food:** A&W/KFC, Arby's, Bob Evans, LJ Silver, McDonald's, Pizza Hut, Ponderosa, Roadhouse Grill, Skyline Chili, Wendy's, **other:** Kroger, Lowe's, Wal-Mart, **S...gas:** BP/diesel, **lodging:** Budget Inn, **other:** Kioto Downs

49 Alum Creek Dr, **N...gas:** Duke/diesel, Sunoco/diesel, **food:** A&W/KFC, Donato's Pizza, Subway, **S...gas:** BP/diesel, **food:** Arby's, McDonald's, Taco Bell, Wendy's, **lodging:** Comfort Inn, Sleep Inn

46b a US 33, Bexley, Lancaster, no facilities

43b a I-70, E to Cambridge, W to Columbus

41b a US 40, **E...gas:** BP, Shell, **food:** Bob Evans, Boston Mkt, Hooters, McDonald's, Outback Steaks, Rally's, Steak'n Shake, Texas Roadhouse, **other:** Walgreen, **W...gas:** Mobil, Speedway, **food:** Fuddruckers, Golden Corral, Hunan Chinese, LoneStar Steaks

39 OH 16, Broad St, **E...gas:** Meijer/diesel, Speedway/diesel, **food:** Arby's, Chipotle Grill, Church's, Quizno's, Waffle House, White Castle, **lodging:** Country Inn Suites, **other:** HOSPITAL, **W...gas:** Shell, **food:** Applebee's, **lodging:** Ramada Inn

37 OH 317, Hamilton Rd, **E...gas:** BP/diesel, Marathon, Speedway/diesel, Sunoco, **food:** Big Boy, Bob Evans, Burger King, Damon's, Hickory House Rest., KFC, McDonald's, **lodging:** Candlewood Suites, Holiday Inn Express, SpringHill Suites, **other:** Firestone, **W...lodging:** Comfort Inn, Concourse Hotel, Cross Country Inn, Hampton Inn

35b a I-670W, US 62, **E...gas:** Speedway/diesel, **food:** City BBQ, McDonald's, Tim Horton, **other:** CVS Drug, **W...**I-670

33 no facilities

32 Morse Rd, **E...gas:** Citgo/DM, Speedway/diesel, **food:** Donato's Pizza, **other:** Toyota, **W...gas:** BP, Shell, **food:** Applebee's, Cooker, HomeTown Buffet, McDonald's, Pizza Hut/Taco Bell, Wendy's, **lodging:** Extended Stay America, **other:** Best Buy, BMW, Circuit City, Jo-Ann Fabrics, Lowe's Whse, Sam's Club, Target, Wal-Mart SuperCtr/24hr, mall

30b a OH 161 E to New Albany, W to Worthington

29 OH 3, Westerville, **E...gas:** BP/diesel, **food:** Applebee's, Arby's, Chipotle Mexican, McDonald's, Fazoli's, Pizza Hut, Tim Horton, **lodging:** Cross Country Inn, Knight's Inn, **other:** CarQuest, Firestone/auto, Kroger, **W...gas:** Shell, Speedway/diesel, Sunoco/diesel, **other:** Aldi Foods

27 OH 710, Cleveland Ave, **N...gas:** Speedway, **food:** Wendy's, **lodging:** Signature Inn, **S...gas:** Sunoco, **food:** Bob Evans, McDonald's, O'Charley's, Steak'n Shake, TGIFriday, Tim Horton, **lodging:** Embassy Suites, Quality Inn, **other:** Home Depot

26 I-71, S to Columbus, N to Cleveland

23 US 23, Worthington, **N...gas:** Speedway, **food:** Alexander's, Bob Evans, Champ's Grill, Chipotle Mexican, El Acapulco, Fuddruckers, Gilbert's Steaks, Panera Bread, Ruth's Chris Steaks, **lodging:** AmeriSuites, Courtyard, Extended Stay America, Microtel, Motel 6, Homewood Suites, Red Roof Inn, Residence Inn, Sheraton, **S...gas:** BP, **food:** McDonald's

22 OH 315, no facitlites

20 Sawmill Rd, **N...gas:** BP, Marathon/diesel, **food:** McDonald's, Olive Garden, Taco Bell, Wendy's, **other:** Buick/Pontiac/GMC, Ford, Lincoln-Mercury, Mazda, NTB, Tire Kingdom, **S...gas:** Shell, Speedway, Sunoco, **food:** Applebee's, BajaFresh, Bob Evans, Boston Mkt, Burger King, Chili's, Don Pablo, Fuddrucker's, Golden Corral, Joe's Crabshack, KFC, Longhorn Steaks, Red Lobster, Ruby Tuesday, **lodging:** Hampton Inn, **other:** Barnes&Noble, Borders Books, Cadillac, Circuit City, Infiniti, Lowe's Whse, SteinMart, Toyota

17b a US 33, Dublin-Granville Rd, **E...gas:** Marathon, Sunoco, **food:** Bob Evans, Cooker, McDonald's, **lodging:** Embassy Suites, Wyndham Garden, **other:** BMW, CVS Drug, Kroger

15 Tuttle Crossing Blvd, **E...gas:** BP, Mobil, **food:** Bob Evans, Boston Mkt, Chang's Chinese, Cozymel's, Longhorn Steaks, Macaroni Grill, McDonald's, Pizza Hut/Taco Bell, Steak'n Shake, Wendy's, **lodging:** AmeriSuites, Baymont Inn, Drury Inn, Homewood Suites, Marriott, Staybridge Suites, Wellesley Inn, **other:** JC Penney, Sears/auto, mall, **W...gas:** Exxon/Subway/diesel, Shell, **food:** Uno Pizzaria, **other:** Best Buy, Wal-Mart/auto

C o l u m b u s

Interstate 270

13 Cemetery Rd, Fishinger Rd, **E...gas:** Shell, **food:** Burger King, Chili's, Damon's, Dave&Buster's, HomeTown Buffet, KFC, KrispyKreme, LoneStar Steaks, Skyline Chili, Spaghetti's, TGIFriday, **lodging:** Comfort Suites, Homewood Suites, **other:** Big Bear Foods, Lowe's Whse, NTB, Saturn, **W...gas:** BP, Mobil, Speedway, Sunoco, **food:** Bob Evans, Max&Erma's, McDonald's, Roadhouse Grill, Tim Horton, Wendy's, **lodging:** Hampton Inn, Motel 6, **other:** Nissan

10 Roberts Rd, **E...gas:** Marathon, **food:** Subway, Tim Horton, Wendy's, **W...gas:** Speedway, **food:** Waffle House, **lodging:** Holiday Inn, Royal Inn, Super 8, **other:** Kroger/gas

8 I-70, E to Columbus, W to Indianapolis

7 US 40, Broad St, **E...gas:** BP, Shell, Speedway, **food:** Arby's, Bob Evans, Boston Mkt, ChiChi's, TJ's Grill, Tumbleweed Grill, Wendy's, **other:** Chevrolet, Firestone/auto, NTB, Sears/auto, Staples, **W...gas:** Speedway/diesel, **food:** Arby's, Papa John's, Waffle House, **lodging:** Holiday Inn Express, **other:** Home Depot

5 Georgesville, **E...gas:** Citgo, Sunoco/diesel, **W...gas:** Sunoco, Thornton, **food:** Applebee's, Arby's, Bob Evans, Buffalo Wings, DQ, Fazoli's, LoneStar Steaks, McDonald's, O'Charley's, Pizzaria Uno, Red Lobster, Steak'n Shake, Tim Horton, Wendy's, White Castle, **other:** Hyundai/Isuzu, Kroger, Lowe's Whse, Toyota

2 US 62, OH 3, Grove City, **N...gas:** BP, **S...gas:** Shell, Speedway, Sunoco, **food:** Big Boy, Burger King, McDonald's, Tim Horton/Wendy's, Waffle House, **lodging:** Knight's Inn

0mm I-71.

Interstate 271(Cleveland)

Exit # Services

38mm I-271 begins/ends on I-90, exit 188.

36 Wilson Mills Rd, Mayfield, Highland Hts, **E...lodging:** Holiday Inn, **W...gas:** BP, Sunoco/diesel, Home Depot

34 US 322, Mayfield Rd, **E...gas:** BP, **other:** Giant Eagle Food, Walgreen, **W...food:** Bob Evans, Longhorn Steaks, McDonald's, Ponderosa, **lodging:** Baymont Inn, **other:** HOSPITAL, Best Buy

32 Brainerd Rd, Cedar Rd, **E...food:** Alexander's Rest., Champ's Grill

29 US 422 W, OH 87, Chagrin Blvd, Harvard Rd, **E...gas:** Gulf, **food:** Uno Café, **lodging:** Holiday Inn, Homestead Suites, Travelodge, **W...gas:** Shell, **lodging:** Embassy Suites, Marriott, Radisson

28 OH 175, Richmond Rd, Emery Rd, **E...gas:** BP, **food:** Country Kitchen, **other:** HOSPITAL, Lowe's Whse, **W...other:** BJ's Whse

27b I-480 W, no facilities

26 Rockside Rd, **E...gas:** Sunoco, **food:** Perkins, **lodging:** Red Roof Inn, **other:** Lowe's Whse

23 OH 14 W, Forbes Rd, Broadway Ave, **E...gas:** Sunoco, **food:** McDonald's, Pizza Hut, Subway, Taco Bell, Wendy's, **lodging:** Holiday Inn Express, **other:** OfficeMax, Sam's Club, **W...gas:** BP, **other:** HOSPITAL

21 I-480 E, OH 14 E(from sb), to Youngstown

19 OH 82, Macedonia, **E...gas:** Speedway, **W...gas:** Shell, Sunoco, **food:** Arby's, Burger King, Dairy Queen, Little Caesar's, Outback Steaks, Pizza Hut, Taco Bell, Wen-

dy's, **other:** CVS Drug, Giant Eagle Food, Home Depot, K-Mart/auto, Top's Foods

18 OH 8, Boston Hts, to Akron, **E...gas:** BP/Subway, Shell/diesel, Speedway, **food:** BBQ, Bob Evans, Denny's, **lodging:** Baymont Inn, Country Inn Suites, Knight's Inn, Motel 6, Travelodge, **W...food:** Applebee's, Ground Round, KFC, McDonald's, **other:** Kohl's, Wal-Mart/auto

12 OH 303, Richfield, Peninsula, no facilities

10 I-77, to I-80, OH Tpk(from nb), to Akron, Cleveland

9 I-77 S, OH 176(from nb), to Richfield, **E...gas:** Sunoco

8mm rest area both lanes, full(handicapped)facilities, phone, picnic tables, litter barrels, petwalk

3 OH 94, to I-71 N, Wadsworth, N Royalton, **W...gas:** Marathon

0mm I-271 begins/ends on I-71, exit 220.

Interstate 475(Toledo)

Exit # Services

20 I-75. I-475 begins/ends on I-75, exit 204.

19 Jackman Rd, Central Ave, **S...gas:** Shell, **other:** HOSPITAL

18b Douglas Rd(from wb), no facilities

a OH 51 W, Monroe St, no facilities

17 Secor Rd, **N...gas:** BP, Shell/diesel, **food:** Applebee's, Betsy Ross' Rest., Bob Evans, Boston Mkt, Burger King, KFC, **other:** MEDICAL CARE, Best Buy, Kroger, PharmX Drug, Walgreen, radiators, RV/auto repair, transmissions, **S...gas:** BP, **food:** Big Boy, Krispy Kreme, LJ Silver, McDonald's, Pizza Hut, Wendy's, **lodging:** Clarion Hotel, Comfort Inn, **other:** FoodTown, Home Depot, U of Toledo

16 Talmadge Rd(from wb, no return), **N...gas:** BP/diesel, Speedway, **food:** Arby's, ChiChi's, Panera Bread, **other:** JC Penney, Marshall Field, mall

15 Talmadge Rd(from eb, no return), no facilities

14 US 23 N, to Ann Arbor, no facilities

13 US 20, OH 120, Central Ave, **E...gas:** Speedway, **food:** Big Boy, Bob Evans, Burger King, McDonald's, Rally's, BMW, Daewoo, **other:** Ford, Honda, Isuzu, Kia, K-Mart, Lexus, Mitsubishi, Nissan, Saturn, Subaru, Toyota, **W...gas:** BP, Speedway

8b a OH 2, **E...gas:** BP/diesel, **food:** Don Pablo, Texas Roadhouse, **lodging:** Extended Stay America, Knight's Inn, Red Roof Inn, Residence Inn, **other:** HOSPITAL, Home Depot, Kohl's, Old Navy, to OH Med Coll **W...gas:** BP, Shell, Speedway, Sunoco/diesel, **food:** Arby's, Big Boy, Bob Evans, Boston Mkt, Burger King, Chili's, Cooker, Mancino's Pizza, McDonald's, New China, Pizza Hut, Rally's, Subway, Wendy's, **lodging:** Courtyard, Cross Country Inn, Fairfield Inn, **other:** Firestone/auto, Kroger, OfficeMax, Sam's Club/gas, Sears/auto, Target

OHIO

Interstate 475

6 Dussel Dr, Salisbury Rd, to I-80-90/tpk, **E...gas:** Barney's, BP, Speedway, **food:** Applebee's, Arby's, Burger King, Hop's Grill, Marie's Diner, Max&Erma's, McDonald's, Panera Bread, Wendy's, Subway, **lodging:** Country Inn Suites, Cross Country Inn, Fairfield Inn, Hampton Inn, Red Roof Inn, Studio+, Super 8, **W...gas:** BP, **food:** Bob Evans, Briarfield Café, Cracker Barrel, **lodging:** Ameri-Host

4 US 24, to Maumee, Napolean, **N...other:** HOSPITAL, Toledo Zoo

3mm Maumee River

2 OH 25, Perrysburg, to Bowling Green, **N...gas:** BP/diesel, Citgo/diesel, Shell, **food:** Café Marie, Charlie's Rest., Gino's Pizza, McDonald's, Papá John's, Subway, Wendy's, **other:** CVS Drug, Farmer Jack's Foods, Goodyear/auto, Young's RV Ctr, **S...gas:** Speedway/diesel, **food:** Bob Evans, Waffle House, **lodging:** Red Carpet Inn

0mm I-475 begins/ends on I-75, exit 192.

Interstate 480(Cleveland)

Exit# Services

42 I-80, PA Tpk, I-480 begins/ends, **S...gas:** BP, Marathon, Shell, Sheetz/24hr, **food:** Applebee's, Big Boy, Burger King, Denny's, McDonald's, Perkins, Ruby Tuesday, Steak'n Shake, **lodging:** Best Western, Comfort Inn, Fairfield Inn, Super 8, TownePlace Suites, **other:** Home Depot, Honda, Lowe's Whse, Nissan, Staples, Tire Kingdom, Top's Foods, **Wal-Mart**

41 Frost Rd, Hudson-Aurora, no facilities

37 OH 91, Solon, Twinsburg, **N...food:** Arby's, DQ, Pizza Hut, Taco Bell, **other:** Giant Eagle, **S...gas:** BP

36 OH 82, Aurora, Twinsburg, **N...gas:** BP/diesel, Super 8, **S...gas:** Marathon, **food:** Bob Evans, **Cracker Barrel**, Damon's, Donato's Pizza, McDonald's, Wendy's, **lodging:** Hilton Garden

26 I-271, to Erie, PA.

25a b c OH 8, OH 43, Northfield Rd, Bedford, **N...other:** Harley-Davidson, **S...food:** McDonald's, Rally's, White Castle

23 OH 14, Broadway Ave, **N...gas:** Gulf/diesel, **food:** Burger King, KFC

22 OH 17 Granger, Maple Hts, Garfield Hts, no facilities

21 Transportation Blvd, to E 98th St, **S...other:** Giant Eagle Foods, JoAnn Fabrics, **Wal-Mart**

20b a I-77, Cleveland, no facilities

17 (eb only)OH 176, Cleveland, no facilities

16 OH 94, to OH 176 S, State Rd, **S...gas:** BP, Sunoco/diesel, **other:** Kia

15 10 US 42, Ridge Rd, **N...gas:** BP, **food:** Applebee's, McDonald's, Ponderosa, Starbucks, **other:** Chevrolet, Lowe's Whse, Marc's Foods, TJMaxx, Top's Foods, **S...gas:** Speedway, **food:** Arby's, Donato's, **other:** K-Mart, Best Buy

13 Teideman Rd, Brooklyn, **N...gas:** Marathon, **S...gas:** BP, Speedway, **food:** Carrabba's, Cracker Barrel, Don Pablo's, Max&Erma's, Panera Bread, Schlotsky's, Steak 'n Shake, TGIFriday's, **lodging:** Extended Stay America, Hampton Inn

12 W 150th, W130th, Brookpark, **S...gas:** Marathon, Shell, **food:** Arby's, Big Boy, Bob Evans, Thursday's Grill, **lodging:** Day's Inn, Best Value, **other:** Acura, Dodge, Lexus, Tire Kingdom, Toyota

Youngstown

11 I-71, Cleveland, Columbus, no facilities

10 S rd 237, Airport Blvd, (wb only) no facilities

9 OH 17, Brookpark Rd, **N...lodging:** Hilton Garden, Knights's Inn, **other:** HOSPITAL, **S...**airport

7 (wb only)Clague Rd, to West Lake, no facilities

6 OH 252, to N Olmsted, **N...gas:** BP, Shell, **food:** Applebee's, Chili's, Galyan's, Harry Buffalo, Lonestar Steaks, Macaroni Grill, Red Robin, **lodging:** Candlewood Suites, Courtyard, Hampton Inn, Homestead Suites, Radisson, Studio+, **other:** Dillard's, Firestone, JC Penny, Michael's, Sears/auto, **Wal-Mart**, mall

3 Stearns Rd, no facilities

2 OH 10, Lorain Rd, to OH Tpk, **S...gas:** BP, Speedway, Sunoco, **food:** McDonald's

0mm OH 10, to Cleveland, I-480 begins/ends on exit 151, OH Tpk

Ohio Turnpike

Exit # Services

241mm Ohio/Pennsylvania state line

239mm toll plaza, phone

237mm Mahoning Valley Travel Plaza eb, Glacier Hills Travel Plaza wb, Sunoco/diesel/24hr, McDonald's, gifts, phone

235 I-680(from wb), to Youngstown, no facilities

232 OH 7, to Boardman, Youngstown, **N...gas:** Sheetz/24hr(1mi), **food:** DQ, Smaldino's Family Rest., **lodging:** Budget Inn, Comfort Lodge, Day's Inn, Econolodge, Holiday Inn Express, North Lima Inn, Ramada Ltd, Super 8, **S...gas: Penn Ohio Trksp/diesel/@**, **Pilot/diesel**, Shell/diesel, **food:** Road House Steaks,, **lodging:** Davis Motel, Liberty Inn, **other:** truck repair

218 I-80 E, to Youngstown. OH Tpk runs with I-76 eb, I-80 wb., Niles, no facilities

216 Lordstown(from wb), **N...**GM Plant

215 Lordstown(from eb), **N...**GM Plant

210mm Mahoning River

209 OH 5, to Warren, **N...gas:** ShortStop/diesel/rest.24hr/repair(3mi), **lodging:** Budget Lodge, **S...lodging:** Holiday Inn Express, Rodeway Inn, **other:** RV camping

197mm Portage Service Plaza wb, Bradys Leap Service Plaza eb, Sunoco/diesel/24hr, FoodCourt, McDonald's, gifts, phone

193 OH 44, to Ravenna, no facilities

192mm Cuyahoga River

187 OH 14 S, I-480, to Streetsboro, **S...gas:** Sheetz/24hr, **food:** Ruby Tueday, **lodging:** Comfort Inn, Fairfield Inn, Hampton Inn, Palms Motel, TownePlace Suites, Wingate Inn, **other:** Defer Tire, Firestone/auto, Home Depot, mall, **1 mi S...gas:** BP, Clark, DM/24hr, Shell, **food:** Arby's, Big Boy, Bob Evans, Brown Derby Roadhouse, Burger King, Burger Central, DQ, Denny's, Domino's, Golden Flame Steaks, KFC, LJ Silver, McDonald's, Mr Hero, New Peking Chinese, Perkins, Pizza Hut, Rally's, Subway, Taco Bell, **lodging:** Best Western, Holiday Inn Express, Microtel, Starlite Motel, Super 8, Wendy's, **other:** CVS Drug, $General, K-Mart, Save-A-Lot Foods, Staples, **Wal-Mart**, to Kent St U

180 OH 8, to I-90 E, **N...gas:** Marathon, **lodging:** Comfort Inn, Holiday Inn, **other:** Harley-Davidson, **S...gas:** BP/Subway/diesel, Starfire Express, **other:** to Cuyahoga Valley NRA

177mm Cuyahoga River

Ohio Turnpike

E ↑ **W**

173 OH 21, to I-77, **N...food:** My Place Rest., **lodging:** Howard Johnson, Scottish Inn, **other:** tires, **S...gas:** BP/repair, Pilot/Wendy's/diesel, **food:** DQ, Richfield Family Rest., **lodging:** Brushwood Motel, Holiday Inn, Super 8

170mm Towpath Service Plaza eb, Great Lakes Service Plaza wb, gas: Sunoco/diesel/24hr, food: Food-Court, Panera Bread, Pizza Hut, Wendy's, other: gifts, phone

161 US 42, to I-71, Strongsville, **N on US 42...gas:** Marathon/diesel, Shell, **food:** DairyMart, Jennifer's Rest., Mad Cactus Mexican, **lodging:** Colony Motel, Day's Inn, Extended Stay America, La Siesta Motel, Metrick's Motel, Murphy's Motel, Village Motel, **other:** Home Depot, Wal-Mart, **S on US 42...food:** Burger King, DQ, KFC, Nino's Italian, Olympia Treats, **lodging:** Elmhaven Motel, **other:** Dodge, NAPA, Staples

152 OH 10, to Oberlin, I-480, Cleveland, **N...gas:** BP, Marathon, Shell, Speedway/diesel, Sunoco/diesel, **food:** Kartel's Rest., McDonald's, **lodging:** Super 8, Travelodge, **other:** Giant-Eagle Foods, U-Haul, **S...gas:** BP, **other:** drive-in theatre(seasonal)

151 I-480 E(from eb), to Cleveland, airport

146mm Black River

145 OH 57, to Lorain, to I-90, Elyria, **N...gas:** BP/McDonald's/diesel, Speedway/diesel, Shell, **food:** Applebee's, Arby's, Blimpie, Bob Evans, Burger King, Country Kitchen, Denny's, Fazoli's, HomeTown Buffet, LoneStar Steaks, Pizza Hut, Red Lobster, Subway, Wendy's, **lodging:** Best Western, Comfort Inn, Day's Inn, Econolodge, Holiday Inn, **other:** Best Buy, Dillard's, Firestone/auto, Goodyear/auto, JC Penney, Jo-Ann Fabrics, Lowe's Whse, Michael's, NTB, Office-Max, Sears/auto, Staples, Wal-Mart/auto, mall, **S...gas:** Shell/24hr, Speedway/diesel, **lodging:** Howard Johnson, Super 8, **other:** HOSPITAL, Home Depot, laundry, st patrol

142 I-90(from eb, exits left), OH 2, to W Cleveland, no facilities

139mm Middle Ridge Service Plaza wb, Vermilion Service Plaza eb, Sunoco/diesel/24hr, Burger King, Food-Court, Panera Bread, Popeye's, Starbuck's, TCBY, gifts, phone, RV parking

135 rd 51, Baumhart Rd, to Vermilion, no facilities

132mm Vermilion River

118 US 250, to Norwalk, Sandusky, **N...gas:** DM/diesel, Marathon/diesel, Speedway, **food:** 4Monks Italian, McDonald's, Subway, **lodging:** Comfort Inn, Day's Inn, Hampton Inn, Motel 6, Red Roof Inn, Super 8, **5 mi N...food:** Perkins, Roadhouse Grill, **lodging:** Fairfield Inn, **S...food:** Maw's Place Cafe, Race Café, **lodging:** Colonial Inn, Homestead Inn/rest., **other:** Chevrolet, to Edison's Birthplace

110 OH 4, no facilities

100mm Erie Islands Service Plaza wb, Commodore Perry Service Plaza eb, gas: Sunoco/diesel/24hr, food: Burger King, Cinnabon, Max&Erma's, Sbarro's, Starbucks, other: phone

93mm Sandusky River

91 OH 53, to Fremont, Port Clinton, **N...food:** Z's Diner, **lodging:** Budget Inn, Day's Inn, **S...gas:** BP/diesel/24hr, **food:** Applebee's(2mi), **lodging:** Comfort Inn, Fremont Tpk Motel, Holiday Inn, **other:** HOSPITAL

81 OH 51, Elmore, Woodville, Gibsonburg, no facilities

80.5mm Portage River

77mm Blue Heron Service Plaza wb, Wyandot Service Plaza eb, Sunoco/diesel/24hr, Hardee's/chicken, phone

71 I-280, OH 420, to Stony Ridge, Toledo, **N...gas:** Petro/Mobil/diesel/rest./24hr/@, /Flying J/Conoco/diesel/rest./24hr/LP/@, **food:** Charter House Rest., Country Diner, **lodging:** Howard Johnson, Pizza Hut, Knight's Inn, Ramada Ltd, Stony Ridge Inn/truck plaza/diesel/@, **other:** Blue Beacon, **S...gas:** FuelMart/diesel/@, Pilot/diesel/24hr/@, TA/BP/Burger King/Taco Bell/diesel/24hr/@, **food:** McDonald's, Wendy's, **other:** truckwash

64 I-75 N, to Toledo, Perrysburg, no facilities

63mm Maumee River

59 US 20, to I-475, Maumee, Toledo, **N...gas:** Amoco, BP/diesel, Speedway/diesel, **food:** Arby's, Bob Evans, China Gate Rest., Church's, Dominic's Italian, Indian Cuisine, Max's Diner, McDonald's, Pizza Hut, **lodging:** Budget Inn, Econolodge, Holiday Inn, Motel 6, Quality Inn, **other:** Advance Parts, Goodyear/auto, Jo-Ann Fabrics, K-Mart/Little Caesar's, NAPA, Radio Shack, Savers Foods, Sears/auto, to Toledo Stadium, **S...gas:** Meijer/diesel/24hr, Speedway, **food:** Big Boy, ChiChi's, Fazoli's, Fricker's, Friendly's, Ralphie's Burgers, Red Lobster, Schlotsky's, Taco Bell, **lodging:** Best Western, Comfort Inn, Cross Country Inn, Day's Inn, Hampton Inn, Red Roof Inn, Super 8, **other:** Chevrolet, Ford/Lincoln/Mercury, Honda, Toyota

52 OH 2, to Toledo, **S...lodging:** Super 8, **other:** RV/truck repair

49mm service plaza both lanes, Sunoco/diesel/24hr, gifts/ice cream

39 OH 109, no facilities

34 OH 108, to Wauseon, **S...gas:** Shell/Subway/diesel/24hr/@, **lodging:** Arrowhead Motel, Best Western, Holiday Inn Express, Super 8, **other:** HOSPITAL, Toledo RV Ctr, Woods Trucking/repair(1mi), **2 mi S on US 20A...gas:** DM, Mobil, **food:** Burger King, McDonald's, Pizza Hut, Subway, Wendy's, **lodging:** Wauseon Motel, **other:** Wal-Mart/auto

25 OH 66, Burlington, **3 mi S...other:** Sauder Village Museum

24.5mm Tiffen River

21mm Indian Meadow Service Plaza both lanes, info, Sunoco/diesel/24hr, Hardee's/chicken, travel trailer park

13 OH 15, to Bryan, Montpelier, **S...gas:** Marathon/Subway/diesel, Pennzoil/diesel, **food:** Country Fair Rest., **lodging:** Econolodge, Rainbow Motel, Ramada Inn, **other:** Hutch's Diesel Repair

11.5mm St Joseph River

3mm toll plaza, phone

2 OH 49, to US 20, **N...gas:** Mobil/Subway/diesel, **food:** Burger King, **other:** info

0mm Ohio/Indiana state line

OKLAHOMA
Interstate 35

Exit #	Services
236mm	Oklahoma/Kansas state line
231	US 177, Braman, **E...gas:** Conoco/Grab'n Dash Deli/diesel/motel
230	Braman Rd, **W...gas:** Shell/diesel/tire repair
229mm	Chikaskia River
225mm	**Welcome Ctr sb, rest area nb, full(handicapped)facilities, phones, picnic tables, litter barrels, vending, petwalk**
222	OK 11, to Blackwell, Medford, Alva, Newkirk, **E...gas:** Conoco/diesel/rest., Phillips 66/diesel, Shell, **food:** Braum's, KFC/Taco Bell, Los Potros Mexican, McDonald's, Pizza Hut(2mi), Sonic(3mi), Subway, **lodging:** Comfort Inn, Day's Inn, Super 8(2mi), **other:** HOSPITAL, **W...gas:** Shell
218	Hubbard Rd, no facilities
216mm	weigh sta both lanes
214	US 60, to Tonkawa, Lamont, Ponka City, N OK Coll, **E...lodging:** Holiday Inn, **W...gas:** Phillips 66/diesel/rest., **lodging:** New Western Inn, **other:** Woodland RV Park
213mm	Salt Fork of Arkansas River
211	Fountain Rd, **E...gas:** Love's/Subway/diesel/24hr/@, **W...gas:** Coulter's Corner/gas
209mm	parking area both lanes, litter barrels
203	OK 15, Billings, to Marland, **E...gas:** Conoco/DQ/diesel/24hr
199mm	Red Rock Creek
195mm	parking area both lanes, no facilities, litter barrels
194b a	US 412, US 64 W, **E...other:** Cimarron Tpk(eb), to Tulsa, **W...to** Enid, Phillips U
193	to US 412, US 64 W(from nb), no facilities
191mm	Black Bear Creek
186	US 64 E, to Fir St, Perry, **E...food:** Subway/diesel, **food:** Braum's, KFC(2mi), McDonald's, Pizza Hut, Taco Mayo, **lodging:** Super 8, **other:** HOSPITAL, museum, **W...gas:** Conoco/diesel/24hr, **lodging:** Day's Inn
185	US 77, Perry, to Covington, **E...gas:** Phillips 66, **lodging:** Best Western/rest., **W...gas:** Shell/diesel/motel/rest./24hr, **other:** RV camping
180	Orlando Rd, no facilities
174	OK 51, to Stillwater, Hennessee, **E...gas:** Shell/diesel, **food:** Charlie's Chicken, **lodging:** Fairfield Inn(12mi), Holiday Inn(13mi), Motel 6(12mi), **other:** Lake Carl Blackwell RV Park
173mm	parking area sb, no facilities, litter barrels
171mm	parking area nb, no facilities, litter barrels
170	Mulhall Rd, no facilities
165mm	Cimarron River
157	OK 33, Guthrie, to Cushing, **E...gas:** Sinclair/diesel/repair, **W...gas:** Conoco, K&L/diesel, Love's/Subway/diesel/24hr, Shell/diesel, Total, **food:** Arby's, Braum's, Burger King, Carl's Jr(3mi), DQ, El Rodeo Mexican, KFC, McDonald's(3mi), **lodging:** Best Western, Interstate Motel, Sleep Inn, **other:** HOSPITAL, OK Terr Museum, Langston U, RV camping

Blackwell / **Guthrie** (side labels)

153	US 77 N(exits left from nb), Guthrie, **E...food:** McDonald's, Taco Mayo, **W...other:** Chrysler/Dodge/Jeep, Ford/Mercury, Pontiac/Buick
151	Seward Rd., **E...gas:** Conoco/diesel, Lazy E Arena(4mi), Pioneer RV park
149mm	weigh sta both lanes
146	Waterloo Rd, **E...gas:** Conoco/diesel/24hr, **1/2 mi W...gas:** Citgo/diesel
143	Covell Rd, no facilities
142	Danforth Rd(from nb), no facilities
141	US 77 S, OK 66E, to 2nd St, Edmond, Tulsa, **W...gas:** Conoco, Phillips 66/diesel, **food:** Coyote Café, Denny's, IHOP, KFC/Taco Bell, McDonald's, Western Sizzlin, **lodging:** Best Western, Hampton Inn, Holiday Inn Express, Stafford Inn, **other:** HOSPITAL
140	SE 15th St, Spring Creek, Arcadia Lake, Edmond Park, **W...food:** Braum's
139	SE 33rd St, **W...food:** Applebee's, **lodging:** Sleep Inn
138d	Memorial Rd, **W...other:** Enterprise Square USA
c	Sooner Rd(from sb), no facilities
b	Kilpatrick Tpk, no facilities
a	I-44 Tpk E to Tulsa

I-35 S and I-44 W run together 8 mi

137	NE 122nd St, to OK City, **E...gas:** Shell/diesel, Total/diesel, **lodging:** Travelodge, **W...gas:** Bosselman/diesel/24hr/@, ✈/Flying J/Conoco/CountryMkt/diesel/LP/24hr/@, Love's/Subway/Taco Bell/diesel/24hr/@, **food:** Cracker Barrel, McDonald's, Waffle House, **lodging:** Comfort Inn, Day's Inn, Motel 6, Quality Inn, Super 8, **other:** Abe's RV Park, Frontier City Funpark
136	Hefner Rd, **W...gas:** Conoco/Lil' Italy Rest./diesel, **food:** DQ, same as 137
135	Britton Rd, **E...gas:** Drivers/diesel
134	Wilshire Blvd, **E...gas:** Drivers/diesel, **food:** Braum's, **other:** Gordon Inland Marine, **W...lodging:** Executive Inn, **other:** Blue Beacon

I-35 N and I-44 E run together 8 mi

133	I-44 W, to Amarillo, **W...st** capitol, Cowboy Hall of Fame
132b	NE 63rd St(from nb), **1/2 mi E...gas:** Conoco/diesel, **food:** Braum's, **lodging:** Remington Inn
a	NE 50th St, Remington Pk, **W...other:** funpark, info, museum, zoo
131	NE 36th St, **W...gas:** Phillips 66/diesel/24hr, **other:** 45th Inf Division Museum
130	US 62 E, NE 23rd St, **E...gas:** Shell/Burger King, **W...to** st capitol
129	NE 10th St, **E...gas:** Conoco/McDonald's/diesel, Total, **W...food:** Tom's BBQ
128	I-40 E, to Ft Smith, no facilities
127	Eastern Ave, OK City, **W...gas:** Petro/diesel/rest./Blue Beacon/24hr/@, Pilot/Wendy's/diesel/24hr/@, Shell/diesel, **food:** BBQ, Waffle House, **lodging:** Best Western, Central Plaza Hotel, **other:** Blue Beacon, Lewis RV Ctr
126a	I-40, W to Amarillo, I-235 N, to st capitol
b	I-35 S to Dallas
125d	SE 15th St, **E...gas:** Conoco/diesel, Total/repair, **lodging:** Green Carpet Inn

Okla City (side label)

Interstate 35

b   SE 22nd St(from nb), no facilities

a   SE 25th, **E...food:** Denny's, McDonald's, Sonic, Taco Bell, Waffle House, **lodging:** Day's Inn, Guesthouse Suites, Plaza Inn, Royal Inn, Super 8, **W... gas:** Phillips 66

124b   SE 29th St, **W...food:** Mama Lou's Rest., **other:** McClain's RV Ctr, same as 125a

a   Grand Blvd, **E...**Shell, Courtesy Inn, **W...gas:** Sinclair, **food:** Cattle Rustler Steaks, Taco Mayo, **lodging:** Drover's Inn, Executive Inn

123b   SE 44th St, **E...gas:** Conoco, **food:** Sonic, **lodging:** BestValue Inn, **other:** MEDICAL CARE, **W...food:** DQ, Pizza 44, Subway, Taco Mayo, **other:** Family$, SavALot Foods, USPO

a   SE 51st St, **E...gas:** Conoco/diesel, **other:** Ryder Trucks, **W...**tires

122b   SE 59th St, **E...gas:** Shell/diesel/LP, **W...gas:** EZMart, Total/diesel, **other:** U-Haul

a   SE 66th St, **E...food:** Burger King, Casablanca Mexican, Luby's, McDonald's, Taco Bell, Village Inn Rest., **lodging:** Fairfield Inn, Ramada, Residence Inn, **other:** Best Buy, Cooper Tires, Dillard's, Firestone, Foley's, JC Penney, mall, **W...gas:** Citgo/7-11, **food:** Arby's

121b   US 62 W, I-240 E, **W...**to Will Rogers World Airport

a   SE 82nd St, **W...food:** Denny's, **lodging:** Green Carpet Inn, La Quinta

120   SE 89th St, **E...gas:** Total/diesel, **W...gas:** Love's/Subway/diesel/24hr, **food:** Carl's Jr, Tom's BBQ

119b   N 27th St, **E...gas:** Conoco, Shell/diesel, Circle K, **lodging:** Best Western, Luxury Inn/rest., **W...food:** Pickles American Grill, **other:** Harley-Davidson, Wholesale RV ctr

118   N 12th St, **E...gas:** Total, **lodging:** Super 8, **W...gas:** Phillips 66/diesel, Shell, **food:** Braum's, Dairy Queen, Fajita's Mexican, Grandy's, KFC, LJ Silver, Mazzio's, McDonald's, Taco Bell, Wendy's, Western Sizzlin, **lodging:** Best Western, Comfort Inn, Day's Inn, Motel 6, **other:** Family$

117   OK 37, S 4th St, **E...gas:** Shell, **other:** HOSPITAL, **W...gas:** Total, **food:** Mr Burger

116   S 19th St, **E...gas:** Conoco, **food:** BBQ, Braum's, Capt D's, Carl's Jr, DQ, McDonald's, Taco Bell, **lodging:** Microtel, **other:** Firestone/auto, Goodyear/auto, Ross, **W...food:** Burger King, **other:** $Tree, Kohl's, Tires+, Wal-Mart SuperCtr/24hr

114   Indian Hill Rd, **E...food:** Barry's Chicken Ranch, **other:** Kerr RV Ctr

113   US 77 S(from sb, exits left), Norman, no facilities

112   Tecumseh Rd, no facilities

110b a   Robinson St, **E...gas:** Petrostop, **food:** Hardee's, Krispy Kreme, Sonic, Taco Bell, Western Sizzlin, **lodging:** Day's Inn, Albertson's, **other:** HOSPITAL, Chrysler/Jeep, Ford, GMC/Pontiac, Honda, Hyundai, Lincoln/Mercury/Mazda, Subaru, Tires+, Toyota, **W...gas:** Conoco/Subway, 7-11/gas, **food:** Arby's, Blackeyed Pea, Braum's, Charleston's Rest., Cracker Barrel, Domino's, Little Mexico Rest., Outback Steaks, Ryan's, Santa Fe Grill, Taste of China, Waffle House, **lodging:** Holiday Inn, **other:** Kia/Isuzu

109   Main St, **E...gas:** Phillips 66, Shell, Texaco/diesel, **food:** Arby's, Braum's, CiCi's, Denny's, Furr's Cafeteria, Golden Corral, LJ Silver, Panera Bread, Prairie Kitchen, Subway, Taco Cabana, Waffle House, Wendy's, **lodging:** Econolodge, Guest Inn, Ramada Inn, Super 8, Thunderbird Lodge, Travelodge, **other:** AutoZone, Cadillac, Chevrolet, Dodge, Hastings Books, Lowe's Whse, Nissan, Target, Tires+, Wal-Mart SuperCtr/24hr, **W...gas:** Conoco/diesel, **food:** Applebee's, Burger King, Don Pablo, Chili's, Cracker Barrel, Marie Callender's, McDonald's, Olive Garden, On the Border, Piccadilly's, Red Lobster, Red River Steaks, Souper Salad, Village Inn Rest., **lodging:** Fairfield Inn, Hampton Inn, La Quinta, **other:** Barnes&Noble, Borders Books, Dillard's, IGA Foods, Michael's, OfficeMax, Old Navy, Ross, Saab, Sears/auto, SteinMart, mall

108b a   OK 9 E, Norman, **E...gas:** Citgo, Shell, Total, **food:** Arby's, Braum's, **lodging:** Thunderbird Lodge, Villager Lodge, **other:** to U of OK, **W...food:** IHOP, Jason's Deli, **lodging:** La Quinta, **other:** Home Depot

107mm   Canadian River

N (arrow pointing up and down, N at top, S at bottom)

Okla City

Norman

Interstate 35

N
↕
S

106	OK 9 W, to Chickasha, **W...gas:** Love's/Subway/diesel/24hr/@, Phillips 66/Burger King/diesel/@, **other:** Chevrolet
104	OK 74 S, Goldsby, **E...other:** Floyd's RV Ctr, **W...gas:** Shell/diesel, Total/diesel
101	Ladd Rd, no facilities
98	Johnson Rd, **E...gas:** Texaco/diesel, **other:** RV camping, **W...other:** muffler repair
95	US 77(exits left from sb), Purcell, **1-3 mi E...gas:** Conoco, **food:** Braum's, Carl's Jr, KFC, Mazzio's, Pizza Hut, Subway, **other:** HOSPITAL, Ford
91	OK 74, to OK 39, Maysville, **E...gas:** Conoco, Phillips 66/diesel, **food:** Carl's Jr, Casa Rosa Mexican, McDonald's, Ruby's Inn/rest., Subway, **lodging:** Econolodge, **other:** flea mkt, **W...gas:** Shell/Blimpie/diesel/24hr
86	OK 59, Wayne, Payne, no facilities
79	OK 145 E, Paoli, **E...gas:** Phillips 66
76mm	Washita River
74	OK 19, Kimberlin Rd, no facilities
72	OK 19, Paul's Valley, **E...gas:** Citgo, Total/diesel, **food:** Ballard's Drive-In, Braum's, Carl's Jr, Denny's, KFC/Taco Bell, McDonald's, Punkin's Catfish, Sonic, Subway, Taco Mayo, **lodging:** Day's Inn, Garden Inn, Relax Inn, Sands Motel, **other:** Buick/Pontiac/Cadillac/GMC, Chrysler/Dodge/Jeep, $General, Ford/Lincoln/Mercury, Wal-Mart/auto(1mi), **W...gas:** Love's/A&W/diesel/24hr/@, Phillips 66/diesel/24hr, **food:** Chaparral Steaks
70	Airport Rd, **E...**HOSPITAL
66	OK 29, Wynnewood, **E...**Kent's/Motel/diesel/rest., **W...gas:** Shell/diesel
64	OK 17A E, to Wynnewood, **E...**GW Exotic Animal Park
60	Ruppe Rd, no facilities
59mm	**rest area both lanes, full(handicapped)facilities, phone, picnic table, litter barrels, petwalk, RV dump**
55	OK 7, Davis, **E...gas:** Phillips 66/A&W/diesel/24hr/@, Total, **other:** to Chickasaw NRA, **W...gas:** Conoco/ChesterFried/diesel, **other:** Oak Hill RV Park, to Arbuckle Ski Area
54.5mm	Honey Creek Pass
54mm	weigh sta both lanes
51	US 77, Turner Falls, **E...lodging:** Arbuckle Mtn Motel, Mtnview Inn(3mi), **W...gas:** Sinclair/grill, **food:** Buffalo gap BBQ, **lodging:** Canyon Breeze Motel/RV Park, **other:** to Arbuckle Wilderness, Botanic Gardens
49mm	scenic turnout both lanes
47	US 77, Turner Falls Area, no facilities
46mm	scenic turnout both lanes
42	OK 53 W, Springer, Comanche, **W...gas:** Exxon/diesel
40	OK 53 E, Gene Autry, **E...gas:** Total/diesel/café/24hr, Gene Autry Museum(8mi)
33	OK 142, Ardmore, **E...gas:** Phillips 66/diesel/24hr, **food:** Ponder's Rest., Ryan's, **lodging:** Guest Inn, La Quinta, Super 8

Ardmore (vertical left margin)

32	12th St, Ardmore, **1 mi E...gas:** Phillips 66, **food:** Arby's, Braum's, Burger King, Carl's Jr, Fried Pies, Grandy's, KFC, LJ Silver, Pizza Hut, Taco Bell, Taco Bueno, **other:** HOSPITAL, Chevrolet, $General, Hastings Books, O'Reilly Parts, Staples, Toyota, Walgreen, Wal-Mart, **W...gas:** Love's/Godfather's/Subway/diesel/24hr/@, **food:** McDonald's, **lodging:** Microtel
31b a	US 70 W, OK 199 E, Ardmore, **E...gas:** Conoco/diesel/24hr, Shamrock/diesel, Shell/diesel, Sinclair/diesel, **food:** Applebee's, Burger King, Cattle Rustler Steaks, Denny's, El Chico's, Golden China, KFC, Little Caesar's, Mazzio's, McDonald's, Pizza Hut, Prairie Kitchen, 2Frogs Grill, **lodging:** Best Western, Comfort Inn, Dorchester Inn, Hampton Inn, Holiday Inn, Motel 6, **other:** AutoZone, Buy4Less/24hr, O'Reilly Parts, **W...gas:** Conoco/diesel, **other:** Cadillac, Chrysler/Dodge/Jeep, Ford/Lincoln/Mercury, Honda, Mazda, Nissan
29	US 70 E, Ardmore, **E...**to Lake Texoma SP
24	OK 77 S, **E...gas:** Sinclair, Total/diesel, **other:** Red River Livestock Mkt, to Lake Murry SP
22.5mm	Hickory Creek
21	Oswalt Rd, **W...**KOA
15	OK 32, Marietta, **E...gas:** Total/diesel, **food:** Carl's Jr, Denim's Rest., Pizza Hut, Robertson's Ham Sandwiches, Sonic, **lodging:** Lake Country Motel, **other:** HOSPITAL, $General, Ford, to Lake Texoma SP, **W...gas:** Phillips 66/Subway/24hr, Shell, **food:** BBQ
5	OK 153, Thackerville, **W...other:** Shorty's Foods, Indian Nation RV Park
3.5mm	**Welcome Ctr nb/rest area sb, full(handicapped)facilities, phone, picnic tables, litter barrels, vending, petwalk**
1	US 77 N, **E...gas:** Shamrock/diesel
0mm	Oklahoma/Texas state line, Red River

Interstate 40

E
↕
W

Exit #	Services
331mm	Oklahoma/Arkansas state line
330	OK 64D S(from eb), Ft Smith, no facilities
325	US 64, Roland, Ft Smith, **N...lodging:** Day's Inn, Travelodge, **other:** Cherokee Casino, **S...gas:** Citgo/diesel, Phillips 66, Pilot/Wendy's/diesel/24hr/@, Shell/diesel, **food:** KFC, McDonald's, Mazzio's, Sonic, Subway, **lodging:** Interstate Inn, **other:** $General, Marvin's Foods
321	OK 64b N, Muldrow, **N...food:** Sonic(1mi), **S...gas:** Curt's/diesel/Economy Inn, **other:** repair
316mm	**rest area eb, full(handicapped)facilities, info, phone, picnic tables, litter barrels, vending, petwalk, RV dump**
313mm	**Welcome Ctr wb, full(handicapped)facilities, info, phone, picnic tables, litter barrels, vending, petwalk, RV dump**
311	US 64, Sallisaw, **N...gas:** Phillips 66/diesel, **food:** Hardee's, KFC/Taco Bell, Pizza Hut, Simon's Pizza, Sonic, Subway, Taco Mayo, **lodging:** Econolodge, Motel 6, **other:** HOSPITAL, AutoZone, Pontiac, **1 mi N...food:** Lessley's Café, **other:** to Sallisaw RA, Brushy Lake SP(10mi), Sequoyah's Home(12mi)

Interstate 40

E↕W

Sallisaw

308 US 59, Sallisaw, **N...gas:** Citgo/diesel, Phillips 66/diesel, Sinclair, **food:** Arby's, Braum's, Dana's Rest., Mazzio's, McDonald's, Western Sizzlin, **lodging:** Best Western, Golden Spur Motel, McKnight Motel, Microtel, **other:** HOSPITAL, **Wal-Mart SuperCtr/gas/24hr**, to Blue Ribbon Downs, **S...gas: Shell/diesel**, **food:** Ole South Rest., **other:** Chevrolet, Chrysler/Plymouth/Dodge/Jeep, Ford, KOA, to Kerr Lake, repair

303 Dwight Mission Rd, **3 mi N...other:** Blue Ribbon Downs

297 OK 82 N, Vian, **N...gas:** Phillips 66, **lodging:** Siesta Motel, **other:** DENTIST, NAPA, to Tenkiller Lake RA

291 OK 10 N, to Gore, **N...other:** Greenleaf SP/RV dump(10mi), Tenkiller SP(21mi)

290mm Arkansas River

287 OK 100 N, to Webbers Falls, **N...gas: Love's/Subway/Taco Bell/diesel/24hr/@**, **food:** Charlie's Chicken, **lodging:** Sleepy Traveler Motel, **other:** parts/tires

286 Muskogee Tpk, to Muskogee, no facilities

284 Ross Rd, no facilities

283mm parking area both lanes, litter barrels

278 US 266, OK 2, Warner, **N...gas:** Phillips 66/diesel, **food:** Subway, **lodging:** Sleepy Traveler Motel, **other:** Auburn RV Park

270 Texanna Rd, to Porum Landing, **S...gas:** Sinclair

265 US 69 bus, Checotah, **N...food:** DQ, Pizza Hut, Sonic, **S...gas: Citgo/diesel/24hr**, **lodging:** Budget Inn, Travel Host, **other:** Chevrolet, Chrysler/Plymouth/Dodge/Jeep

264b a US 69, to Eufaula, **1 mi N...gas:** Citgo/diesel/24hr, ✈️**/Flying J/Conoco/Country Mkt/diesel/LP/24hr/@**, **food:** Charlie's Chicken, Simon's Pizza, **lodging:** Midway Inn, **other:** $General, **Wal-Mart**, auto repair

262 to US 266, Lotawatah Rd, **N...gas:** Phillips 66

261mm Lake Eufaula

259 OK 150, to Fountainhead Rd, **S...gas:** Shell/café, **lodging:** Lake Eufaula Inn, **other:** to Fountainhead SP

255 Pierce Rd, **N...KOA**

251mm rest area both lanes, no facilities

247 Tiger Mtn Rd, **S...other:** Quilt Barn/antiques

Henryetta

240b a US 62 E, US 75 N, Henryetta, **N...gas:** Conoco, Love's/diesel, Shell, Sinclair, **food:** Arby's, Braum's, DQ, Mazzio's, McDonald's, Sonic, Subway, Taco Mayo, **lodging:** Colonial Motel, Gateway Inn, LeBaron Motel, Relax Inn, **other:** Chrysler/Jeep, Ford, G&W Tire, **Wal-Mart**, **S...**Indian Nation Tpk

237 US 62, US 75, Henryetta, **N...gas: Citgo/diesel/24hr**, **Shell/diesel/24hr**, **food:** Pig Out Palace, **lodging:** Green Country Inn, Trail Motel, **other:** HOSPITAL, Henryetta RV Park(2mi), **S...food:** Hungry Traveler Rest., **lodging:** Super 8

231 US 75 S, to Weleetka, **N...gas:** Phillips 66/diesel/café, **food:** Cowpoke's Cafe

227 Clearview Rd, no facilities

221 US 62, OK 27, Okemah, **N...gas:** Conoco/diesel, Total/Subway/diesel/24hr, **food:** Mazzio's, Sonic, **other:** HOSPITAL, **S...gas:** Love's/A&W/Chester/**diesel/24hr**, Shell/diesel, **food:** Kellogg's Rest, **other:** truck repair

217 OK 48, to Bristow, Bearden, **S...gas**

216mm N Canadian River

212 OK 56, to Cromwell, Wewoka, **N...gas:** Conoco, **food:** BBQ, **S...gas:** Shell/diesel/cafe, to museum

208mm Gar Creek

202mm Turkey Creek

200 US 377, OK 99, to Little, Prague, **S...gas:** Citgo/diesel/24hr, Conoco/diesel/24hr, **Love's/Subway/diesel/24hr/@**, **food:** Robertson's Ham Sandwiches, **lodging:** Village Inn Motel/rest.

197mm rest area both lanes, full(handicapped)facilities, phone, picnic tables, litter barrels, petwalk

192 OK 9A, Earlsboro, **S...gas:** Shell/diesel, **food:** Biscuit Hill Rest., **lodging:** Rodeside Motel, **other:** CB Shop

189mm N Canadian River

186 OK 18, to Shawnee, **N...gas:** Citgo/diesel, Shell, **food:** Denny's, **lodging:** American Inn, Day's Inn, Motel 6, Ramada Inn, Super 8, **S...food:** Golden Corral, **lodging:** Colonial Inn, **other:** antique auto museum

Shawnee

185 185 OK 3E, Shawnee Mall Dr, to Shawnee, **N...food:** Chili's, Garcia's Mexican, Red Lobster, Taco Bueno, **other:** Dillard's, JC Penney, Sears/auto, **Wal-Mart/auto**, mall, **S...gas:** Phillips 66/diesel, **food:** Applebee's, Braum's, Charlie's Chicken, CiCi's, **Cracker Barrel**, Delta Café, Garfield's Rest., IHOP, Mazzio's, McDonald's, Schlotsky's(2mi), Sonic, **lodging:** Hampton Inn, **other:** Lowe's Whse, Staples

181 US 177, US 270, to Tecumseh, **S...lodging:** Budget Host, **other:** HOSPITAL

180mm N Canadian River

178 OK 102 S, Dale, **N...trailer sales**

176 OK 102 N, McLoud Rd, **S...gas:** Love's/Subway/diesel/**24hr**, **food:** Curtis Watson Rest.

172 Newalla Rd, to Harrah, **S...gas:** Shell

169 Peebly Rd, no facilities

166 Choctaw Rd, to Woods, **N...gas:** Love's/Subway/diesel/**24hr**, **other:** KOA, **S...gas: Anderson Trkstp/Phillips 66/diesel/@**, **other:** to Little River SP(11mi)

165 I-240 W(from wb), to Dallas, no facilities

162 Anderson Rd, **N...LP**

OKLAHOMA
Interstate 40

E

W

Okla City

Exit	Description
159b	Douglas Blvd, **N...gas:** Phillips 66, Total, **food:** Denny's, McDonald's, Sonic, Subway, Taco Bell, **other:** RV camping, **S...other:** Tinker AFB, HOSPITAL
159a	Hruskocy Gate, Hruskocy Gate, **N...gas:** Shell, **food:** China Grill, **lodging:** Executive Inn, **other:** Chrysler/Dodge, Family$, Firestone/auto, Nissan, U-Haul, same as 157, **S...**Gate 7, Tinker AFB
157c	Eaker Gate, Eaker Gate, Tinker AFB, same as 159
157b	Air Depot Blvd, **N...gas:** Conoco/diesel, Shell, **food:** Arby's, Golden Griddle Rest., IHOP, KFC, Pizza Inn, Santa Fe Steaks, Schlotsky's, Subway, Taco Mayo, **lodging:** Super 8, **other:** Chevrolet, Cottman Transmissions, Firestone, JC Penney, O'Reilly Parts, Walgreen, **S...**Gate 1, Tinker AFB
157a	SE 29th St, Midwest City, **N...gas:** Conoco/diesel, Shell, **lodging:** Planet Inn, **other:** O'Reilly Parts, **S...other:** Ford, Sam's Club
156b a	Sooner Rd, **N...gas:** Conoco, **food:** BBQ, Ray's Steaks, **lodging:** AmeriSuites, Comfort Inn, Hampton Inn, Holiday Inn Express, La Quinta, Studio 6, **other:** Home Depot, **S...lodging:** Motel 6, **other:** Chevrolet/Pontiac/GMC, Daewoo, Tires+, Toyota
155b	SE 15th St, Del City, **N...gas:** Shell, **other:** IGA Foods, **S...food:** Ashley's Rest.
155a	Sunny Lane Rd, Del City, **N...gas:** Conoco/Subway/U-Haul/diesel, **S...gas:** Shell, **food:** Braum's, Pizza Hut, Sonic
154	Reno Ave, Scott St, **N...gas:** Sinclair, **S...gas:** Phillips 66/diesel, 7-11/diesel
152	I-35 N, to Wichita, no facilities
127	Eastern Ave(from eb), Okla City, **N...gas:** Petro/Mobil/diesel/rest./@, JR's Trvl Crt/Wendy's/diesel/24hr/@, Shell, **food:** G Dale's BBQ, Waffle House, **lodging:** Best Western, Sunshine Inn, **other:** Blue Beacon, Lewis RV Ctr
151b c	I-35, S to Dallas, I-235 N, to downtown, st capitol
151a	Lincoln Blvd, **N...**Bricktown Stadium
150c	Robinson Ave(from wb), OK City, **N...food:** Spaghetti Whse, Zio's Italian, **lodging:** Westin Hotel, **other:** U-Haul, Ford
150b	Harvey Ave(from eb), downtown, **N...lodging:** Renaissance Hotel, Westin Hotel
150a	Walker Ave(from eb), **N...other:** Ford, Goodyear, **S...gas:** Phillips 66, transmissions
149b	Classen Blvd(from wb), to downtown, to downtown
149a	Western Ave, Reno Ave, **N...gas:** Total/Subway, **food:** McDonald's, Sonic, Taco Bell, **S...gas:** Conoco/diesel, Shell, **food:** Burger King, Popeye's
148c	Virginia Ave(from wb), to downtown, to downtown
148b	Penn Ave(from eb), **N...gas:** Shamrock, **S...other:** Isuzu/Ryder Trucks
148a	Agnew Ave, Villa Ave, **N...gas:** Phillips 66/diesel, **S...gas:** Conoco/diesel, **food:** BBQ, Braum's, **other:** Freddie's Tires
147c	May Ave, no facilities

Okla City

Exit	Description
147b a	I-44, E to Tulsa, W to Lawton, no facilities
146	Portland Ave(from eb, no return), **N...gas:** Shell/Subway/diesel, **other:** water funpark
145	Meridian Ave, OK City, **N...gas:** Conoco, Shell/diesel, **food:** Boomerang Grill, Denny's, McDonald's, Jin wei Aisan, On the Border, Outback Steaks, Shorty Small's Rest., **lodging:** Best Western, Builtmore Hotel, Day's Inn, Extended Stay America, Howard Johnson, Motel 6, Red Roof Inn, Residence Inn, Super 8, Travelers Inn, **S...gas:** Phillips 66/diesel, Sinclair, **food:** Arby's, Bennigan's, Burger King, Chili's, Cracker Barrel, Golden Palace Chinese, IHOP, Kona Ranch Steaks, Panera Bread, Quizno's, Rib Crib, Santa Fe Grill, Sonic, Taco Bueno, Tony Roma, Waffle House, Wendy's, Whataburger, **lodging:** AmeriSuites, Candlewood Suites, Clarion Hotel, Comfort Suites, Courtyard, Embassy Suites, Executive Inn, Hampton Inn, Hilton Garden, Holiday Inn Express, La Quinta, Lexington Suites, Motel 6, Ramada Ltd, Regency Inn, Sleep Inn, Wingate Inn
144	MacArthur Blvd, **N...gas:** Shell/diesel, **food:** Applebee's, Fire Mtn Steaks, Golden Corral, KFC, McDonald's, Sonic, Taco Cabana, **other:** HobbyLobby, Office Depot, Radio Shack, Wal-Mart SuperCtr/24hr, **S...food:** Ruby's Rest., **lodging:** Green Carpet Inn, Microtel, Super 10 Motel, Travelodge, **other:** Kenworth, Sam's Club
143	Rockwell Ave, **N...gas:** Shell, **lodging:** Rockwell Inn, **other:** Home Depot, McClain's RV Ctr, Tires+, **S...lodging:** Sands Motel/RV Park/LP, **other:** Rockwell RV Park
142	Council Rd, **N...gas:** Shell, Sinclair, **food:** Braum's, McDonald's, Subway, Taco Bell, Waffle House, Wendy's, **lodging:** Best Budget Inn, **S...gas:** TA/Burger King/diesel/24hr/@, **lodging:** Econolodge, **other:** Council Rd RV Park
140	Morgan Rd, **N...gas:** Pilot/McDonald's/diesel/24hr/@, TA/Phillips 66/Popeye's/diesel/24hr/@, **other:** Blue Beacon, **S...gas:** ⚡/Flying J/Conoco/diesel/LP/24hr/@, Love's/Subway/diesel/24hr/@, **food:** Ricky's Mexican, Sonic
139	Kilpatrick Tpk, no facilities
138	OK 4, to Yukon, Mustang, **N...food:** Denny's, Catcher's Grill, **lodging:** Super 8, **other:** Chrysler/Dodge/Jeep, **S...gas:** Conoco/diesel, Shell, **food:** Arby's, Burger King, Interurban Grill, Sonic, Subway, Homeland Foods, **lodging:** Best Western
137	Cornwell Dr, Czech Hall Rd, **N...**Albertson's
136	OK 92, to Yukon, **N...gas:** Shell, **food:** Braum's, Carl's Jr, Harry's Café, KFC, LJ Silver, McDonald's, Taco Mayo, Waffle House, Wendy's, **lodging:** Green Carpet Inn, Hampton Inn, **other:** AutoZone, Big Lots, Chevrolet, Big O Tire, Radio Shack, Rite Aid, Wal-Mart SuperCtr/gas/24hr, **S...food:** Alfredo's, Carino's Italian, Chili's, Jimmy's Egg Café, Quizno's, Rib Crib, Taco Bueno, **other:** HOSPITAL, Ford, Kohl's, Lowe's Whse, Staples
132	Cimarron Rd, **N...**Statuary World, **S...**airport
130	Banner Rd, **N...gas:** Shell/diesel/rest.

Interstate 40

E ↑
El Reno
↓ **W**

129mm weigh st both lanes

125 US 81, to El Reno, **N...gas:** Conoco, Love's/diesel, **food:** Serapio's Mexican, Taco Mayo, **lodging:** Economy Inn, Super 8, **other:** Chevrolet, Ford/Lincoln/Mercury, Plymouth, Pontiac/GMC/Buick, **S...**truck repair

123 Country Club Rd, to El Reno, **N...gas:** Conoco, Shamrock, Shell, **food:** Arby's, Braum's, Carl's Jr, KFC, Mazzio's, McDonald's, Pizza Hut, Subway, Taco Bell, **other:** HOSPITAL, Radio Shack, **Wal-Mart SuperCtr**/diesel/24hr, **S...gas:** Phillips 66/diesel, **food:** Denny's, Sirloin Stockade, **lodging:** Best Western, Comfort Inn, Day's Inn, Regency Motel, **other:** Family RV Park

119 Lp 40, to El Reno, no facilities

115 US 270, to Calumet, no facilities

111mm picnic area eb, picnic tables, litter barrels

108 US 281, to Geary, **N...gas:** Shell/Subway/diesel, **other:** KOA/Indian Trading Post, to Roman Nose SP, **S...gas:** Love's/diesel/@

105mm S Canadian River

104 Methodist Rd, no facilities

101 US 281, OK 8, to Hinton, **N...**to Roman Nose SP, **S...gas:** Henton Trkstp/Shell/Sonic/Microtel/diesel, **other:** picnic area, to Red Rock Canyon SP

95 Bethel Rd, no facilities

94.5mm picnic area wb, picnic tables, litter barrels

88 OK 58, to Hydro, Carnegie, no facilities

84 Airport Rd, **N...gas:** Shell/diesel, **lodging:** Holiday Inn Express, Travel Inn, **other:** Buick/Pontiac/GMC, Chevrolet/Cadillac, Chrysler/Plymouth/Dodge/Jeep

82 E Main St, Weatherford, **N...gas:** Conoco/diesel, Shell/Subway/diesel, **food:** Alfredo's Mexican, Arby's, Braum's, Carl's Jr, Jerry's Rest., KFC/Taco Bell, Mark Rest., Mazzio's, McDonald's, Pizza Hut, Sonic, Taco Bell, Taco Mayo, **lodging:** Best Western, Comfort Inn, Day's Inn, Scottish Inn, **other:** HOSPITAL, $General, O'Reilly Parts, Radio Shack, U-Haul, **Wal-Mart**, to SW OSU

80a W Main St(from eb), **N...gas:** Conoco/diesel, **food:** Casa Sota Mexican, **other:** Ford/Lincoln/Mercury

80 OK 54, Weatherford, **N...gas:** Shell, **lodging:** Economy Inn

71 Custer City Rd, **N...gas:** Love's/Subway/diesel/rest./@

69 Lp 40(from wb), to Clinton, **2 mi N...food:** Dairy Queen, **lodging:** Glancey's Motel/rest., Travel Inn

67.5mm Washita River

Clinton

66 US 183, Clinton, **S...gas:** Shell/diesel, **other:** Ford/Lincoln/Mercury, Chrysler/Dodge/Jeep, Wink's RV Park

65a 10th St, Neptune Dr, Clinton, **N...food:** Braum's, KFC, Lupita's Mexican, Pizza Hut, Subway, **lodging:** Day's Inn, Relax Inn, Super 8, **S...gas:** Phillips 66/diesel,

lodging: Clinton Inn

65 Gary Blvd, Clinton, **N...gas:** Conoco, Shell/diesel, **food:** Carl's Jr, DQ, LJ Silver, McDonald's, Pancake House, Rte 66 Rest, Taco Mayo, **lodging:** Best Western, MidTown Inn, Ramada Inn, Travelodge, **other:** HOSPITAL, K-Mart

62 Parkersburg Rd, **S...**Hargus RV Ctr

61 Haggard Rd, no facilities

57 Stafford Rd, no facilities

53 OK 44, Foss, **N...**to Foss RA, **S...gas:** Shell/diesel

50 Clinton Lake Rd, **N...other:** KOA/gas/LP/diesel

47 Canute, **S...gas:** Shell

Elk City

41 OK 34(exits left from eb), Elk City, **N...gas:** Love's/Subway/diesel, Shell, **food:** Home Cooking Café, **lodging:** Best Western, Day's Inn, Holiday Inn, Howard Johnson, Motel 6, Regency Inn, Travelodge, Super 8, **other:** HOSPITAL, Elk Run RV Park, Rte 66 Museum

40 E 7th St, Elk City, **N...food:** Portobello Grill, same as 41

38 OK 6, Elk City, **N...gas:** Conoco/diesel, Shell/diesel, **food:** Arby's, Denny's, LJ Silver, McDonald's, Western Sizzlin, **lodging:** Bedford Inn, Day's Inn, **other:** Elk Creek RV Park, **S...gas:** Phillips 66/diesel, **lodging:** Econolodge, Holiday Inn, Ramada Inn, **other:** to Quartz Mtn SP

34 Merritt Rd, no facilities

32 OK 34 S(exits left from eb), Elk City, no facilities

26 Cemetery Rd, **S...gas:** TA/Taco Bell/Subway/diesel/24hr/@

25 Lp 40, Sayre, **N...gas:** Shell/diesel, **lodging:** Western Motel(1mi), **other:** HOSPITAL, Ford

23 OK 152, Sayre, **S...gas:** Shell/diesel

22.5mm N Fork Red River

20 US 283, Sayre, **N...gas:** ✈/Flying J/Conoco/CountryMkt/diesel/24hr/@, **lodging:** AmericInn, **other:** to Washita Bfd Site(25mi)

14 Hext Rd, no facilities

13.5mm check sta both lanes, litter barrels

11 Lp 40, to Erick,, Hext, no facilities

10mm **Welcome Ctr/rest area both lanes, full(handicapped)facilities, phone, picnic tables, litter barrels, petwalk, RV dump**

7 OK 30, Erick, **N...lodging:** Comfort Inn, **S...gas:** Love's/A&W/Subway/diesel/@, **food:** Cowboy's Rest./Trading Post, **lodging:** Day's Inn

5 Lp 40, Honeyfarm Rd, no facilities

1 Texola, **S...gas:** gas/diesel/rest., **other:** RV camping

0mm Oklahoma/Texas state line

OKLAHOMA
Interstate 44

E ↕ W

Miami

Exit #	Services
329mm	Oklahoma/Missouri state line
321mm	Spring River
314mm	**Oklahoma Welcome Ctr, service plaza wb,** Phillips 66/diesel
313	OK 10, Miami, **N...gas:** Citgo/diesel, Conoco, Love's/Taco Bell/diesel/24hr, Phillips 66/diesel, **food:** Arby's, Lil Café, McDonald's, Okie Burger, Stables Rest., **lodging:** Best Western/rest., Deluxe Inn, Super 8, Townsman Motel, **other:** HOSPITAL, Miami RV Park, to NE OK A&M Coll, **S...other:** Chrysler/Plymouth/Dodge/Jeep
312mm	Neosho River
312mm	picnic area eb, phone, picnic table, litter barrel
310mm	picnic area wb, phone, picnic table, litter barrel
302	US 59, US 69, Afton, **3 mi S...**gas, **lodging:** Best Western, Grand Lake Country Inn, Shangri-La Inn, **other:** Bears Den Resort Camping
299mm	rest area eb, picnic table, litter barrel
289	US 60, Vinita, **N...gas:** Citgo, Phillips 66/Subway, **food:** Braum's, Carl's Jr, KFC, McDonald's, Pizza Hut, **lodging:** Holiday Inn Express, Vinita Inn, **other:** HOSPITAL, $General, Ford/Mercury, Super H Foods, Wal-Mart, st patrol
288mm	**service plaza both lanes,** Phillips 66/diesel/24hr, **McDonald's, phone**
286mm	toll plaza
283	US 69, Big Cabin, **N...gas:** Shell/diesel/rest./24hr, **lodging:** Super 8, **S...**truck repair
271mm	picnic area eb, picnic table, litter barrel
269	OK 28(from eb, no re-entry), to Adair, Chelsea, **S...gas:** Citgo, golf
269mm	rest area eb, picnic tables, litter barrel
256mm	rest area wb, picnic tables, litter barrel
255	OK 20, Claremore, to Pryor, **N...gas:** Citgo, **food:** Arby's, Carl's Jr, KFC, McDonald's, **lodging:** Best Western, Claremore Motel, Day's Inn, Super 8, **other:** HOSPITAL, to Rogers U, Will Rogers Memorial, museum, **S...gas:** Phillips 66
248	to OK 66, Port of Catoosa, no facilties
244mm	Kerr-McClellan Navigation System
241mm	Will Rogers Tpk begins eb, ends wb, phones
241	OK 66 E, to Catoosa, no facilities
240b	US 412 E, Choteau
240a	OK 167 N, 193rd E Ave, **N...gas:** Phillips 66/diesel/rest./24hr, SunMart/diesel/24hr, **food:** KFC, McDonald's, Pauline's Buffet, Pizza Hut, Taco Mayo, Waffle House, Wendy's, **lodging:** Super 8, Travelers Inn, **other:** KOA **S...gas:** Citgo, Phillips 66, QT, Shell/A&W/diesel, **food:** Mazzio's, Sonic, Subway, **other:** $General, Family$, Homeland Foods, NAPA, tires/repair
238	161st E Ave, **N...gas:** Shell/diesel/rest./24hr, **S...gas:** QT/diesel/24hr, **food:** Arby's, Burger King, **lodging:** Microtel, **other:** I-44 Auto Auction
236b	I-244 W, to downtown Tulsa, airport
a	129th E Ave, **N...gas:** ⚙/Flying J/Conoco/diesel/LP/rest./24hr/@, **S...food:** McDonald's

Tulsa

235	E 11th St, Tulsa, **N...gas:** Phillips 66, QT, **food:** Carl's Jr, Fajita Rita's, Lot-a-Burger, Sonic, Waffle House, **lodging:** Executive Inn, Stratford House Inn, Super 8, **other:** $General, May's Drug, O'Reilly Parts, **S...food:** Taco Bueno, **lodging:** National Inn, **other:** Whse Foods
234b	Garnett Rd, **N...food:** Mazzio's, **lodging:** Motel 6, Super 8, **S...gas:** QT/diesel, **food:** Braum's, Denny's, **lodging:** Econolodge, **other:** Whse Foods,
a	US 169, N to Owasso, to airport, S to Broken Arrow, no facilities
233	E 21st St(from wb), **S...gas:** Citgo, **food:** El Chico, **lodging:** Comfort Suites, **other:** MEDICAL CARE, K-Mart, Dean's RV Ctr
231	US 64, OK 51, to Muskogee, E 31st St, Memorial Dr, **N...gas:** Phillips 66, **food:** Whataburger, **lodging:** Day's Inn, Georgetown Plaza Motel, Ramada Inn, Travelodge, **other:** Homeland Foods, **S...gas:** Shell/A&W, **food:** Cracker Barrel, IHOP, McDonald's, Village Inn Rest., **lodging:** Courtyard, Embassy Suites, Extended Stay America, Fairfield Inn, Hampton Inn, Holiday Inn Express, Park Inn, Quality Inn, Super 8, **other:** Chevrolet, Chrysler, Nissan
230	E 41st St, Sheridan Rd, **N...gas:** Shell, **food:** Carl's Jr, On-the-Border, Quizno's, Subway, TGIFriday, Whataburger/24hr, **other:** Barnes&Noble, Circuit City, Goodyear/auto, Jo-Ann Fabrics, Michael's, Old Navy, **S...lodging:** Heritage Inn, **other:** Home Depot
229	Yale Ave, Tulsa, **N...gas:** Shell, **food:** McDonald's, **other:** Firestone, Foley's, Mervyn's, Ross, mall, **S...gas:** Phillips 66/diesel, QT/24hr, **food:** Applebee's, Arby's, Braum's, Denny's, Don Pablo, Outback Steaks, Red Lobster, Steak&Ale, Subway, Taco Bell, Taco Cabana, Village Inn Rest., **lodging:** Baymont Inn, Comfort Inn, Holiday Inn, Howard Johnson, Travelodge, **other:** HOSPITAL, Celebration Sta, Kia, Mazda
228	Harvard Ave, Tulsa, **N...gas:** Shell/diesel, **food:** Johnnie's Charcoal Buffet, Subway, **lodging:** Best Western, Towers Hotel, Tradewinds Motel, **S...gas:** Citgo, Phillips 66, **food:** Blimpie, Chili's, Chimi's Mexican, Jamil's Steaks, LoneStar Steaks, LJ Silver/A&W, Marie Callender's, McDonald's, Papa John's, Perry's Rest., Piccadilly's, Pizza Hut, Sol's Grill, Thai Rest., **lodging:** Holiday Inn Express, Ramada Inn, **other:** Albertson's, $Tree, Kelly Tire, K-Mart, SteinMart
227	Lewis Ave, Tulsa, **S...gas:** Shell, Sinclair, **food:** AZ Mexican Rest., El Chico, Goldie's Patio Grill, SteakStuffers USA, Wendy's, **other:** Tires+
226b	Peoria Ave, Tulsa, **N...food:** China Wok, Church's, CiCi's, Pizza Hut, Waffle House, **lodging:** Parkside Hotel, Super 8, **other:** Hancock Fabrics, **S...gas:** QT, Shell, **food:** Braum's, Burger King, **lodging:** Stratford House Inn, **other:** AutoZone, Buy4Less/24hr, $General, Food City
226a	Riverside Dr(from eb), **S...food:** Village Inn
225	Elwood Ave, **N...other:** Chevrolet, Ford
225	Arkansas River
224b a	US 75, to Okmulgee, Bartlesville, **N...gas:** Citgo, QT/diesel, **food:** KFC, Mazzio's, Subway, **other:** $General, Whse Mkt, **S...lodging:** Royal Inn, **other:** RV park
223c	33rd W Ave, Tulsa, **N...food:** Braum's, Domino's, **S...gas:** Phillips 66, **food:** Rib Crib BBQ, **other:** NAPA Autocare

Interstate 44

E
W

223b 51st St(from wb)

223a I-244 E, to Tulsa, downtown

222c (from wb), **S...lodging:** Value Inn

222b 55th Place, **N...lodging:** Capri Motel, Crystal Motel, **S...lodging:** Day's Inn, Economy Inn

222a 49th W Ave, Tulsa, **N...food:** Carl's Jr, Mama Lou's Rest., Monterey Café, **lodging:** Gateway Motel, Interstate Inn, Motel 6, **other:** $General, May Drug, Radio Shack, **S...gas:** Git'n Go, QT/Wendy's/diesel/24hr, **food:** Arby's, McDonald's, Village Inn Rest., Waffle House, **lodging:** Super 8, Buick/Pontiac/GMC, Volvo Trucks

221mm Turner Tkp begins wb, ends eb

218 Creek Tpk E(from eb)

215 OK 97, Sapulpa, to Sand Sprgs, **N...lodging:** Super 8, **S...gas:** Kum&Go, Phillips 66/diesel, **food:** Arby's, **other:** HOSPITAL, Chrysler/Jeep/Dodge

211 OK 33, to Kellyville, Drumright, Heyburn SP, **S...gas:** Phillip 66/diesel

207mm service plaza wb, **gas:** Phillips 66/diesel

205mm picnic area wb, litter barrels, picnic tables

204mm picnic area eb, litter barrels, picnic tables

197mm service plaza eb, gas: Phillips 66/diesel/24hr, **food:** McDonald's

196 OK 48, Bristow, **S...lodging:** Carolyn Inn, **other:** HOSPITAL

191mm picnic area wb, litter barrels, picnic tables

189mm picnic area eb, litter barrels, picnic tables

182mm toll plaza

179 OK 99, Stroud, to Drumright, **N...gas:** Citgo, **lodging:** Best Western/rest., **S...gas:** Phillips 66/Subway/diesel, **food:** Mazzio's, McDonald's, Sonic, Steak&Eggs Rest., Taco Mayo, **lodging:** Sooner Motel, **other:** HOSPITAL, auto/tire repair

178mm Hoback Plaza both lanes(exits left), gas: Phillips 66/diesel, **food:** McDonald's

171mm picnic area eb, litter barrels, picnic tables

167mm (from eb), **S...gas:** Phillips 66/diesel

166 OK 18, Chandler, to Cushing, **N...other:** Chrysler/Jeep/Dodge, **S...gas:** Phillips 66, **food:** DC Max Pizza, Swirleez Drive-In, **lodging:** Econolodge, Lincoln Motel, **other:** Chandler Tire, Ford

166mm picnic area wb, phones, litter barrels, picnic tables

158 OK 66, to Wellston, no facilities

157 (from wb), **N...gas:** Phillips 66/McDonald's/diesel, **other:** museum info

153mm picnic area both lanes, litter barrels, picnic tables

135mm Turner Tpk begins eb, ends wb

138d to Memorial Rd, to Enterprise Square

138a I-35, I-44 E to Tulsa, Turner Tpk, no facilities

I-44 and I-35 run together 8 mi. See Oklahoma Interstate 35, exits 134-137.

130 I-35 S, to Dallas, access to facilities on I-35 S

129 MLK Ave, Remington Park, **N...food:** County Line BBQ, **lodging:** Ramada Ltd, **other:** Cowboy Hall of Fame, **S...food:** McDonald's, **other:** Family$

128b Kelley Ave, OK City, **N...gas:** Conoco, Total/Subway/diesel, **food:** Sonic, **other:** Cowboy Hall of Fame

a Lincoln Blvd, st capitol, **S...lodging:** Comfort Inn, Oxford Inn

127 I-235 S, US 77, City Ctr, Broadway St, **N...gas:** Conoco, Shell, **lodging:** Holiday Inn, Santa Fe Inn, Travel Master Motel

126 Western Ave, **N...food:** Deep Fork Grill, Sonic, TapWorks Grill, **S...lodging:** Guest House Motel

125c NW Expressway(exits left from sb)

b Classen Blvd, OK City, **E...food:** IHOP, McDonald's, **lodging:** Courtyard, Hawthorn Suites, **W...gas:** Shell, **food:** Garcia's Mexican, **other:** Acura, Dillard's, Foley's, JC Penney, Old Navy, Ross, Wal-Mart SuperCtr/24hr, mall

a OK 3A, Penn Ave, to NW Expswy, **E...gas:** Shell, **food:** Braum's, **lodging:** Habana Inn, Homeland Foods, **W...gas:** Conoco/Burger King/diesel24hr

124 N May, **E...other:** Aamco, Ford, **W...gas:** Shell/Subway, **food:** San Marcos Mexican, **lodging:** Day's Inn, Ramada Ltd, Super 8, **other:** Dodge, O'Reilly Parts

123b OK 66 W, NW 39th, to Warr Acres, **W...food:** Burger King, Carl's Jr, Chinese Buffet, McDonald's, Quizno's, Rte 66 Rest., **lodging:** Carlyle Motel, Comfort Inn, Hospitality Inn, Villager Lodge, **other:** Pratt's Foods

a NW 36th St, no facilities

122 NW 23rd St, **E...gas:** Conoco, **food:** Arby's, Sonic, **other:** Big O Tire, Family$, **W...gas:** Conoco, 7-11/gas, **food:** Church's, EggRoll King, LJ Silver, Taco Mayo, **other:** Tires+,

121b a NW 10th St, **E...gas:** 7-11/gas, Shell, **other:** $General, Family$, Whittaker's Foods/24hr, antiques, fairgrounds, **W...gas:** Shell

120b a I-40, W to Amarillo, E to Ft Smith

119 SW 15th St, no facilities

118 OK 152 W, SW 29th St, OK City, **E...gas:** Conoco, 7-11, **food:** Burger King, Capt D's, Grandy's, KFC/Taco Bell, McDonald's, Sonic, Taco Bueno, **other:** AutoZone, $General, Grider's Foods, Walgreen, **W...gas:** Shell, **other:** U-Haul, transmissions

117 SW 44th St, **W...**auto repair

116b Airport Rd, **W...**airport

a SW 59th St, **E...gas:** Conoco, Shell, **W...**Will Rogers Airport

115 I-240 E, US 62 E, to Ft Smith

114 SW 74th St, OK City, **E...gas:** Phillips 66, Sinclair/repair, **food:** Braum's, Burger King, Capt D's, Taco Bell, **lodging:** Ramada Ltd, Villager Lodge, **other:** $General, RV/truckwash

113 SW 89th St, **E...gas:** Love's/Subway/diesel/24hr/@, Total/diesel, 7-11, **food:** McDonald's, Sonic, Taco Mayo

112 SW 104th St, **W...gas:** Shell/rest.

111 SW 119th St, **E...**Walker RV Ctr, **W...**American Dream RV Ctr

110 OK 37 E, to Moore, **E...gas:** Sinclair/diesel

109 SW 149th St, **E...food:** JR's Grill

108mm S Canadian River

Oklahoma City

OKLAHOMA

Interstate 44

E ↑↓ W

108	OK 37 W, to Tuttle, **W...gas:** Conoco/Subway/diesel, Phillips 66, **food:** Braum's, Carlito's Mexican, Carl's Jr, Little Caesar's, Mazzio's, **other:** MEDICAL CARE, $General, O'Reilly Parts, Wal-Mart
107	US 62 S(no wb return), to Newcastle, **E...gas:** Shamrock/KFC/diesel/24hr, **lodging:** Newcastle Motel, **other:** Newcastle RV, Walker RV
100mm	picnic area eb, picnic tables, litter barrels
99	H E Bailey Spur, rd 4, to Blanchard, Norman
97mm	toll booth, phone
95.5mm	picnic area wb, picnic tables, litter barrels
85.5mm	**service plaza, both lanes exit left, Texaco/diesel, McDonald's**
83	Chickasha, US 62, **W...gas:** Conoco/diesel, **food:** Subway, **other:** museum
80	US 81, Chickasha, **E...gas:** Conoco, Phillips 66/diesel, Shell/diesel, **food:** Burger King, Eduardo's Café, Western Sizzlin, **lodging:** Day's Inn, Delux Inn, Royal American Inn, **other:** HOSPITAL, Buick/Chevrolet/Pontiac/Cadillac, Chrysler/Plymouth/Dodge/Jeep, $Tree, GNC, Goody's, Wal-Mart/auto, **W...gas:** Conoco, Love's, Shell/diesel, **food:** Arby's, Braum's, Denny's, Domino's, El Rancho Mexican, KFC, LJ Silver, McDonald's, Peking Dragon, Pizza Hut, Sonic, Subway, Taco Bell, Taco Mayo, **lodging:** Best Western, Budget Motel, **other:** AutoZone, Eckerd, Family$, Firestone/auto, Ford/Lincoln/Mercury, Lightner's Foods/24hr, O'Reilly Parts, Radio Shack, Staples
78mm	toll plaza, phone
63mm	**rest area wb, picnic tables, litter barrels**
62	to Cyril(from wb)
60.5mm	**rest area eb, picnic tables, litter barrels**
53	US 277, Elgin, Lake Ellsworth, **E...gas:** Conoco/diesel, Total/pizza, **other:** Super H Foods, **W...gas:** Phillips 66/diesel
46	US 62 E, US 277, US 281, to Elgin, Apache, Comanche Tribe, last free exit nb
45	OK 49, to Medicine Park, **W...gas:** Love's/Subway/diesel/24hr/@, **food:** Burger King
41	Key Gate, to Ft Sill, Key Gate, **W...museum**
40c	Gate 2, to Ft Sill
40a	US 62 W, to Cache, **E...gas:** Fina, **W...lodging:** Super 8
39b	US 281(from sb), **W...lodging:** Ramada Inn
a	US 281, Cache Rd, Lawton, **1-3 mi W...gas:** Citgo/Circle K, Phillips 66, Total/diesel, **food:** Applebee's, Braum's, Chick-fil-A, Golden Corral, KFC, Ryan's, Subway, Wendy's, **lodging:** Baymont Inn, Day's Inn, Economy Inn, Holiday Inn, Super 8, Super 9 Motel, **other:** U-Haul, transmissions
37	Gore Blvd, Lawton, **E...gas:** Phillips 66, Sonic, **food:** Taco Mayo, Woody's Mexican, **lodging:** Howard Johnson, **other:** Comanche Nation Games, **W...food:** Arby's(3mi), Cracker Barrel, Mike's Grille, **lodging:** Ramada Inn(2mi), SpringHill Suites, **other:** Harley-Davidson, Lincoln/Mercury, Nissan
36a	OK 7, Lee Blvd, Lawton, **E...gas:** Phillips 66, **W...gas:** Fina/diesel/repair, Welch/diesel, Sun Country Gas/

C h i c k a s h a L a w t o n

	diesel, **food:** Big Chef Rest., KFC/Taco Bell, Leo&Ken's Rest., Salas Mexican, Sonic, **lodging:** Motel 6, **other:** HOSPITAL
33	US 281, 11th St, Lawton, **W...other:** HOSPITAL, gas, food, lodging, airport, to Ft Sill
30	OK 36, Geronimo, no facilities
20.5mm	**Elmer Graham Plaza, both lanes exit left, Texaco/diesel, McDonald's, info**
20	OK 5, to Walters, **E...food:** BBQ
19.5	toll plaza
5	US 277 N, US 281, Randlett, last free exit nb, **E...gas:** Shamrock/diesel
1	OK 36, to Grandfield, no facilities
0mm	Oklahoma/Texas state line, Red River

Interstate 240(Okla City)

E ↑↓ W

Exit #	Services
16mm	I-240 begins/ends on I-40.
14	Anderson Rd, **S...gas:** Conoco
11b a	Douglas Blvd, **N...**Tinker AFB
9	Air Depot Blvd, no facilities
8	OK 77, Sooner Rd, **N...gas:** Love's/Taco Bell/diesel/24hr/@, Phillips 66/Popeye's/diesel, **food:** McDonald's
7	Sunnylane Ave, **S...gas:** Total/A&W/diesel
6	Bryant Ave, no facilities
5	S Eastern Ave, no facilities
4c	Pole Rd, **N...food:** Burger King, Luby's, Taco Bell, Texas Roadhouse, **lodging:** Fairfield Inn, Ramada Inn, Residence Inn, **other:** Best Buy, Dillard's, Foley's, JC Penney, Tires+, mall
4b a	I-35, N to OK City, S to Dallas, US 77 S, US 62/77 N
3b	S Shields, **N...gas:** Total, **other:** Circuit City, Home Depot, **S...other:** Ford, Nissan, Saturn, Wal-Mart SuperCtr/24hr
a	S Santa Fe, **S...gas:** Shell, **food:** Chili's, IHOP, **other:** Buick, Chrysler/Jeep, Lowe's Whse, Staples, Wal-Mart SuperCtr/24hr
2b	S Walker Ave, **N...gas:** 7-11/gas, Shell, **food:** Rib Crib, **S...food:** ChuckeCheese, **other:** PepBoys
2a	S Western Ave, **N...gas:** Conoco, **food:** Burger King, House of Szechwan, Nino's Mexican, Taste of China, **other:** Tires+, **S...gas:** Citgo/7-11, **food:** Ashley's Rest./24hr, Grandy's, HomeTown Buffet, KFC, LJ Silver, McDonald's, Red Lobster, Steak&Ale, **lodging:** Holiday Inn Express, Quality Inn, **other:** Big O Tire, Chevrolet, Honda, Office Depot, Radio Shack
1c	S Penn Ave, **N...gas:** Conoco, **food:** Carl's Jr, Denny's, Don Pablo, Golden Corral, Harrigan's Rest., Hooters, Olive Garden, Outback Steaks, Pioneer Pies, Santa Fe Grill, Schlotsky's, Michael's, **S...gas:** Shell, **food:** Anna's Gyros, August Moon Chinese, Blackeyed Pea, Hunan Buffet, Mazzio's, McNear's Steaks, Pancho's Mexican, Papa John's, Subway, Taco Bueno, Wendy's, **other:** PharMor Drug, Radio Shack
b	S May Ave, **N...gas:** 7-11/gas, **food:** Capt D's, Jimmy's Egg Grill, Waffle House, **other:** Albertson's, **S...gas:** Phillips 66/diesel, Sinclair/diesel, **food:** Braum's, Burger King, Perry's Rest., **lodging:** Ramada Ltd, Villager Lodge
a	I-44, US 62, I-240 begins ends on I-44.

O k l a C i t y

Interstate 5

N

↕

S

Portland

Portland

Exit #	Services
308.5mm	Oregon/Washington state line, Columbia River
308	Jansen Beach Dr, **E...gas:** Chevron/24hr, **food:** Burger King, Starbuck's, Taco Bell, Waddles Rest., **lodging:** Courtyard, Oxford Suites, DoubleTree Suites, **other:** Safeway, **W...gas:** Arco, 76/diesel, **food:** BJ's Brewery, Damon's, Denny's, Joe's Cafe, McDonald's, Newport Bay Rest., Stanford's Rest., Subway, Tom's Pizza, **lodging:** DoubleTree Hotel, Holiday Inn Express, **other:** Barnes&Noble, Circuit City, CompUSA, Firestone, Home Depot, K-Mart, Office Depot, Old Navy, Staples, Target, mall
307	OR 99E S, MLK Blvd, Union Ave, Marine Dr, Expo Ctr, **E...food:** El Burrito, Elmer's Rest., Mo's Deli, Portland Cascade Grill, **lodging:** Best Western
306b	Interstate Ave, Delta Park, **E...gas:** 76, **food:** Burger King, Burrito House, Chinese Cuisine, Elmer's Rest., Shari's, **lodging:** Best Western, Day's Inn, **other:** Baxter Parts, Office Depot, OfficeMax, Portland Meadows
306a	Columbia(from nb), **W...gas:** 76, Shell/diesel, 7-11, **food:** Wendy's, Winchell's, **other:** Fred Meyer
305b a	US 30, Lombard St(from nb), same as 306a
304	Portland Blvd, U of Portland, **W...**Arco, Taco Time, Nite Hawk Cafe
303	Alberta St, Swan Island, **E...**HOSPITAL
302b	I-405, US 30 W, **W...**to ocean beaches, zoo
302a	Rose Qtr, City Ctr, **E...gas:** Shell, 7-11, **food:** McDonald's, **lodging:** Holiday Inn, Red Lion Inn, **other:** HOSPITAL, Ford, **W...food:** Cucina Cucina, **lodging:** Best Western, Ramada Inn, **other:** coliseum
301	I-84 E, US 30 E, facilities E off I-84 exits, no facilities
300	US 26 E(from sb), Milwaukie Ave, **W...lodging:** Hilton, Marriott
299b	I-405, no facilities
299a	US 26 E, OR 43(from nb), City Ctr, to Lake Oswego, no facilities
297	Terwilliger Blvd, **W...food:** Burger King, KFC, Starbucks, **other:** HOSPITAL, Fred Meyer, to Lewis and Clark Coll.
296b	Multnomah Blvd, no facilities
296a	Barbur, **W...gas:** Chevron/24hr, Shell, 7-11, **food:** Old Barn Rest., Szechuan Chinese, Subway, Taco Time, Wendy's, **lodging:** Capitol Hill Motel, Portland Rose Motel
295	Capitol Hwy, (from nb), **E...gas:** Shell, Pacific Pride/diesel, **food:** Dunkin Donuts, McDonald's, Round-Table Pizza, Starbucks, **lodging:** Hospitality Motel, Ranch Inn

OREGON

Interstate 5

294   OR 99W, to Tigard, **E...**Comfort Suites, **W...gas:** Arco/24hr, BP, Buster's BBQ, Shell, **food:** Arby's, Banning's Rest., Burger King, Carrow's Rest., Crab Bowl Rest., Italian Rest., KFC, King's Table, Mexican Rest., Newport Bay Rest., Subway, **lodging:** Day's Inn, Howard Johnson, Tigard Inn, Value Inn, Wayside Inn, **other:** Baxter Parts, Fred Meyer, Schwab Tire, U-Haul

293   Haines St, **W...other:** Ford

292   OR 217, Kruse Way, Lake Oswego, **E...gas:** Crowne Plaza, Shell, **food:** Applebee's, Chevy's Mexican, Chili's, Olive Garden, **lodging:** Fairfield Inn, Holiday Inn, Phoenix Inn, Residence Inn, **other:** LDS Temple, **W...**Chevron

291   Carman Dr, **W...gas:** Chevron, Shell, **food:** Burgerville, Houlihan's, Keystone Diner, Starbuck's, Subway, Sweet Tomato's, **lodging:** Courtyard, Sherwood Inn, Travelodge, **other:** Home Depot, Office Depot

290   Lake Oswego, **E...gas:** 76, **food:** Burger King, Carl's Jr., Denny's, Skipper's, Taco Bell, **lodging:** Red Roof Inn, Motel 6, **W...gas:** Arco, Chevron, 76/diesel, Shell, **food:** Fuddrucker's, JB's Roadhouse, Village Inn Rest., Wild Oat Cafe, **lodging:** Best Suites, Best Western, Quality Inn, Ramada Ltd., Red Roof Inn, Shilo Inn, **other:** Borders Books, CarQuest

289   Tualatin, **E...gas:** Shell, **lodging:** Sweetbrier Inn, **W...gas:** Arco/24hr, Chevron, Shell, **food:** Jack-in-the-Box, Lee's Kitchen, McDonald's, Quizno's, Wendy's, **lodging:** Century Hotel, **other:** HOSPITAL, Fred Meyer, K-Mart, Safeway, camping

288   I-205, to Oregon City, no facilities

286   Stafford, **E...gas:** 76/diesel/24hr, **food:** Cheyenne Deli, IHOP, Starbucks, Town Hero Sandwiches, Subway, **lodging:** Day's Inn, Super 8, **other:** Costco/gas, Mercedes, Office Depot, Pheasant Ridge RV Park, Target, **W...gas:** Exxon, **lodging:** Holiday Inn/rest., **other:** Camping World RV Service/supplies, Chevrolet, Dodge

283   Wilsonville, **E...gas:** 76/diesel, **food:** Applebee's, Arby's, Bullwinkle's Rest., DQ, Denny's, Domino's, Isleta Bonita Mexican, Izzy's Pizza, Jamba Juice, McDonald's, Papa Murphy's, Quizno's, Red Robin, Shari's/24hr, Subway, Taco Bell, TCBY, Wanker's Café, Wendy's, Wong's Chinese, **lodging:** Best Western, Comfort Inn, Snoozlnn, **other:** MEDICAL CARE, Fry's Electronics, GNC, Lamb's Foods, NAPA, Rite Aid, Scwab Tire, USPO, **W...gas:** Chevron, 7-11, **food:** Burger King/24hr, Chili's, Marvel's Pizza, New Century Chinese, **lodging:** Phoenix Inn, **other:** Albertson's, IGA Food, Walgreen

282.5mm   Willamette River

282   Charbonneau District, **E...food:** Charbonneau-on-the-Green Rest., **other:** Langdon Farms Golf

281.5mm   **rest area both lanes, full(handicapped)facilities, phone, info, picnic tables, litter barrels, petwalk, vending, coffee**

278   Donald, **E...gas:** Conoco/Circle K/diesel/RV Park, **W...gas:** Leather's/Shell/diesel/@, TA/Shell/diesel/rest./24hr/@, **other:** to Champoeg SP

275mm   weigh sta sb

274mm   weigh sta nb

271   OR 214, Woodburn, **E...gas:** Arco/24hr, Chevron/24hr, Exxon/diesel, 76/repair, Shell, **food:** Burger King, Country Cottage Rest., DQ, Denny's, Don Pedro's Express, KFC, McDonald's, Patterson's Rest., Shari's, Subway, Taco Bell, Wendy's, **lodging:** Best Western, Fairway Inn/RV Park, Super 8, **other:** Fairway Drug, Lind's Mkt, Trailer World, Wal-Mart SuperCtr/24hr, **W...gas:** Shell/diesel, **food:** Arby's, Elmer's Rest., Jack-in-the-Box, **lodging:** Hawthorn Suites, La Quinta, **other:** Chevrolet, Chrysler/Plymouth/Dodge/Jeep, Ford, Outlet/famous brands, Woodburn RV Park

263   Brooks, Gervais, **E...gas:** Astro Gas/LP, **other:** Brooks Mkt/deli, **W...gas:** Pilot/Subway/Taco Bell/diesel/24hr/@, **other:** Chalet Rest., Willamette Mission SP(4mi)

260b a   OR 99E, Salem Pkwy, Keizer, **2 mi E...**camping, **2 mi W...food:** Arby's, Carl's Jr., DQ, McDonald's, Sheri's Rest., Subway, **lodging:** Wittenburg Inn

259mm   45th parallel, halfway between the equator and N Pole

258   N Salem, **E...gas:** 76/Circle K, **food:** Figaro's Italian, Guesthouse Rest., McDonald's, Original Pancakes, **lodging:** Best Value, Best Western, **other:** Cottman Transmissions, Hwy RV Ctr, Roth's Foods, flea mkt, **W...gas:** Chevron, 76/Circle K, Pacific Pride/diesel, Shell/diesel, **food:** Hot Shots Grill, Jack-in-the-Box, **other:** Stuart's Parts, to st capitol

256   to OR 213, Market St, Salem, **E...gas:** Shell, **food:** Alberto's Mexican, Carl's Jr, Chalet Rest., China Faith, Denny's, Elmer's, El Mirador Mexican, Figaro's Italian, Jack-in-the-Box, Kyoto Japanese, Olive Garden, Outback Steaks, Skipper's, Taco Bell, **lodging:** Best Western, Cozzzy Inn, Crossland Suites, Tiki Lodge, **other:** Albertson's, American Tire, Best Buy, Bon-Ton, Borders Books, Fred Meyer/gas, Goodyear/auto, NAPA, Pic'n Save Foods, Ross, Safeway, Schwab Tires, Target, Walgreen, mall, **W...gas:** Arco/24hr, Chevron, Pacific Pride/diesel, Shell/diesel/24hr, **food:** Almost Home Rest., Baskin-Robbins, Canton Garden, DQ, McDonald's, Newport Bay Seafood, O'Callahan's Rest., Outback Steaks, Pietro's Pizza, Roger's 50's Diner, Subway, Tony Roma's, Village Inn, **lodging:** Holiday Lodge, Motel 6, Phoenix Inn, Quality Inn, Red Lion Hotel, Salem Inn, Shilo Inn, Super 8, **other:** Buick/GMC, Heliotrope Natural Foods, InStock Fabrics, Jack's IGA, Kia/Mazda/Isuzu, Nissan

253   OR 22, Salem, Stayton, **E...gas:** Chevron/repair, Shell/diesel, **food:** Burger King, Carl's Jr, Las Polomas Mexican, McDonald's, Shari's, Subway, **other:** $Tree, Home Depot, ShopKO, WinCo Foods, Salem Camping, to Detroit RA, **W...gas:** Shell/diesel, **food:** DQ, Denny's, Sybil's Omelet, **lodging:** Best Western,

OREGON

Interstate 5

N ↑ ↓ S

Comfort Suites, Economy Inn, Holiday Inn Express, Motel 6, Residence Inn, Travelodge, **other:** HOSPITAL, AAA, Chevrolet/Cadillac/Subaru, Chrysler/Plymouth, Costco/gas, Jeep/Pontiac, K-Mart/auto, Lowe's Whse, Roberson RV Ctr, Schwab Tire, Toyota, st police

252   Kuebler Blvd, **1-3 mi W...gas:** Arco/24hr, 76/24hr, **food:** Burger King, McDonald's, Neufeldt's Rest., Shari's/24hr, **lodging:** Phoenix Inn, **other:** HOSPITAL

249   to Salem(from nb), no facilities

248   Sunnyside, **E...food:** Burger King, Enchanted Forest Themepark, Thrillville funpark, Willamette Valley Vineyards, **other:** Forest Glen RV camping, **W...gas:** Pacific Pride/diesel

244   to Jefferson, no facilities

243   Ankeny Hill, no facilities

242   Talbot Rd, no facilities

241mm   **rest area both lanes, full(handicapped)facilities, info, phone, picnic tables, litter barrels, RV dump, petwalk**

240.5mm   Santiam River

240   Hoefer Rd, no facilities

239   Dever-Conner, Dever-Conner, no facilities

238   Scio, no facilities

237   Viewcrest(from sb), **W...**RV/truck repair

235   Millersburg, no facilities

234   OR 99E, Albany, **E...lodging:** Comfort Suites, Holiday Inn Express, **other:** Harley-Davidson, **W...gas:** Arco/24hr, Leather's Fuels, 76/diesel, Shell/diesel, **food:** Arby's, Burger King, China Buffet, DQ, Hereford Steer Rest., McDonald's, La Quinta, Lee's Wok, Original Breakfast Diner, Pizza Hut, Skipper's, Subway, Taco Bell, Wendy's, **lodging:** Bamboo Terrace Motel, Best Western/rest., Budget Inn, Day's Inn, Hawthorn Inn, Motel 6, Relax Inn, **other:** HOSPITAL, Big Lots, Costco/gas, K-Mart, Mervyn's, Chrysler/Jeep, Nissan, Lincoln/Mercury, RV camping, RV repair, to Albany Hist Dist

Albany

233   US 20, Albany, **E...gas:** Chevron/diesel/24hr, 76/diesel, **food:** Burgundy's Rest., LumYuen Chinese, **lodging:** Best Inn Suites, Motel Orleans, Phoenix Inn, **other:** Chevrolet/Toyota, Home Depot, Honda, Lassen RV Ctr, Mazda, RV camping, st police, **W...gas:** Shell, **food:** Abby's Pizza, AppleTree Rest., Baskin-Robbins, Burger King, Burgerville, Carl's Jr, Elmer's, Los Tequilos Mexican, McDonald's, Skipper's, Sweet Waters Rest., Taco Time, **lodging:** Valu Inn, **other:** HOSPITAL, Albertson's, Chrysler/Dodge/Jeep/Subaru/Hyundai, $Tree, Fred Meyer/gas/diesel, Goodyear, Jo-Ann Fabrics, Rite Aid, Schwab Tires, Schuck's Parts, Staples

228   OR 34, to Lebanon, Corvallis, **E...gas:** 76/diesel/24hr, **food:** Pine Cone Rest., **W...gas:** Arco/24hr, Chevron/A&W/diesel, Shell/CFN/diesel, 76, **other:** to OSU, KOA(5mi)

222mm   Butte Creek

216   OR 228, Halsey, Brownsville, **E...gas:** Pioneer Villa TrkStp/76/Blimpie/diesel/24hr/@, **lodging:** Best Western/rest., **other:** parts/repair/towing, **W...gas:** Shell/Subway/Taco Bell/diesel

209   to Jct City, Harrisburg, **W...food:** Hungry Farmer Café, **other:** Diamond Hill/GS RV Park

206mm   **rest area both lanes, full(handicapped)facilities, info, phone, picnic tables, litter barrels, petwalk**

199   Coburg, **E...gas:** Fuel'n Go/diesel, **lodging:** Country Squire Inn, Ingram Rv Ctr, **other:** Coburg Hills RV Park, **W...gas:** Shell/LP, TA/Shell/Truck'n'Travel Motel/diesel/rest./24hr/@, **other:** Destinations RV Ctr, Ford/Freightliner/GMC, Guaranty RV Outlet, Marathon RV Ctr, diesel repair, hist dist

197mm   McKenzie River

195b a   N Springfield, **E...gas:** Arco/24hr, Chevron/24hr, 76/Circle K/diesel/24hr, **food:** A&W, Applebee's, Denny's, ChinaSun Buffet, Elmer's Rest., FarMan Chinese, Gateway Chinese, HomeTown Buffet, IHOP, Jack-in-the-Box, KFC, McDonald's, Outback Steaks, Roadhouse Grill, Schlotsky's, Shari's/24hr, Sizzler, SweetRiver Grill, Taco Bell, **lodging:** Best Western, Clarion, Comfort Suites, Courtyard, Doubletree Hotel/rest., Gateway Inn, Holiday Inn Express, Motel Orleans, Motel 6, Pacific 9 Motel, Rodeway Inn, Travelodge, Shilo Inn/rest., Super 8, **other:** Circuit City, Sears/auto, Target, USPO, mall, st police, **W...other:** Costco/gas, ShopKO, to airport

Eugene

194b a   **E...**HOSPITAL, OR 126 E, Springfield, **W...**I-105 W, Eugene, **2 mi W...gas:** 76/repair, **food:** Trader Joe's, **lodging:** Red Lion Inn, **other:** Albertson's, Honda, mall

193mm   Willamette River

192   OR 99(from nb), to Eugene, **W...food:** Burger King, Wendy's, **lodging:** Best Western, Quality Inn

191   Glenwood, **W...gas:** 76/diesel, Shell/diesel/24hr, **food:** Denny's **lodging:** Motel 6, Phoenix Inn(2mi), **other:** RV camping

189   30th Ave S, **E...gas:** Shell/diesel/LP, **other:** Harley-Davidson, marine ctr, **W...gas:** Exxon/LP/24hr, **food:** Rainbow Mtn Rest., **other:** RV Ctr, Shamrock RV Park

OREGON

Interstate 5

N ↑ S

Exit	Description
188b a	OR 58, to Oakridge, OR 99S, **E...** Deerwood RV Caming, **W...gas:** Pacific Pride/diesel/rest./24hr, 76
186	to Goshen(from nb), no facilities
182	Creswell, **E...food:** Emerald Valley Rest.(1mi), golf, **W...gas:** Arco/24hr, Brown Dog Deli, 76/Taco Bell/diesel, Shell/diesel, **food:** Creswell Cafe, Figaro's Pizza, Mr Macho's Pizza, TJ's Rest., **lodging:** Best Western, Creswell Inn, Motel Orleans, **other:** Century Foods, Creswell Drugs, KOA, Kragen Parts, Sherwood Forest RV Park, Taylor's Travel Park
180mm	Coast Fork of Willamette River
178mm	**rest area both lanes, full(handicapped)facilities, phone, picnic tables, litter barrels, petwalk, coffee**
176	Saginaw, no facilities
175mm	Row River
174	Cottage Grove, **E...gas:** Chevron/diesel/repair/24hr, **food:** China Garden, Subway, Taco Bell, **lodging:** Best Western/rest., **other:** HOSPITAL, Chevrolet/Pontiac/Buick/GMC, Chrysler/Plymouth/Dodge/Jeep, Wal-Mart/auto, RV Ctr/camp, **W...gas:** Chevron, Mobil/diesel, 76/diesel, Shell/diesel, **food:** Arby's, Burger King, Carl's Jr, DQ(2mi), KFC, McDonald's, Vintage Inn Rest./24hr, **lodging:** City Ctr Motel, Comfort Inn, Holiday Inn Express, Relax Inn, **other:** HOSPITAL, Safeway, Mazda, Village Green Motel/RV Park
172	6th St, Cottage Grove Lake(from sb), **2 mi E...**Cottage Grove RV Park
170	to OR 99, London Rd(nb only), Cottage Grove Lake, **6 mi E...**Cottage Grove RV Park
163	Curtin, Lorane, **E...lodging:** Stardust Motel, **other:** Lucky Duck RV Park, Pass Creek RV Park, USPO, antiques, **W...gas:** 76
162	OR 38, OR 99 to Drain, Elkton, no facilities
161	Anlauf(from nb), no facilities
160	Salt Springs Rd, no facilities
159	Elk Creek, Cox Rd, no facilities
154	Yoncalla, Elkhead, no facilities
150	OR 99, to OR 38, Yoncalla, Red Hill, **W...other:** Trees of Oregon RV Park
148	Rice Hill, **E...gas:** Chevron/LP/24hr, Pacific Pride/diesel, Pilot/Subway/diesel/24hr/@ , **food:** Homestead Rest./24hr, Peggy's Rest., **lodging:** Best Western, Ranch Motel/rest., **other:** Rice Hill RV Park, **W...food:** K-R Drive-In
146	Rice Valley, no facilities
144mm	**rest area sb, full(handicapped)facilities, phone, picnic tables, litter barrels, petwalk**
143mm	**rest area nb, full(handicapped)facilities, phone, picnic tables, litter barrels, petwalk**
142	Metz Hill, no facilities
140	OR 99(from sb), Oakland, **E...food:** Tolly's Rest., **other:** Oakland Hist Dist
138	OR 99(from nb), Oakland, **E...food:** Tolly's Rest., **other:** Oakland Hist Dist
136	OR 138W, Sutherlin, **E...gas:** Chevron/A&W/diesel/24hr, 76/Subway/diesel, Shell/Subway/diesel, **food:** Burger King, McDonald's, Papa Murphy's, Pedotti's Italian, **lodging:** Sutherlin Inn, Town&Country Motel, Umpqua Regency Inn, **other:** I-5 RV Ctr, Schwab Tires, **W...gas:** Astro Gas/LP, Mobil/diesel, **food:** Dakota St Pizza, DQ, Taco Bell, **lodging:** Budget Inn, **other:** Hi-Way Haven RV Camp, Ray's Foods, diesel repair/towing
135	Wilbur, Sutherlin, **E...**muffler repair
130mm	weigh sta sb, phone
129	OR 99, Winchester, **E...**gas, food, camping, diesel repair, RV Ctr(1mi)
128mm	N Umpqua River, N Umpqua River
127	Stewart Pkwy, Edenbower Rd, N Roseburg, **E...lodging:** Motel 6, Super 8, **other:** Lowe's Whse, Mt Nebo RV Park, **W...gas:** Shell/Taco Maker/diesel, **food:** Applebee's, Carl's Jr, IHOP, Jack-in-the-Box, McDonald's, Subway, Taco Bell, **lodging:** Sleep Inn, **other:** HOSPITAL, Albertson's/gas, Big O Tire, Harley-Davidson, K-Mart, OfficeMax, Parkway Drug, Sears/auto, Sherm's Foods, Staples, Wal-Mart/auto
125	Garden Valley Blvd, Roseburg, **E...gas:** Chevron, 76/diesel, Shell/diesel/24hr, **food:** Brutke's Rest., Elmer's, Jack-in-the-Box, KFC, McDonald's, Taco Bell, WagonWheel Rest., **lodging:** Comfort Inn, Quality Inn, Windmill Inn/rest., **other:** Albertson's, CarQuest, Ford, GMC, NAPA, Rite Aid, transmissions, **W...gas:** Chevron/diesel, 76, Shell/LP/repair, **food:** Arby's, Burger King, Carl's Jr, IHOP, Izzy's Pizza, La Hacienda Mexican, Quizno's, Quicksilver Steaks, Rodeo Steaks, RoundTable Pizza, Sizzler, TomTom Rest., Wendy's, **lodging:** Best Western, Econolodge, **other:** MEDICAL CARE, BiMart, Fred Meyer, House of Fabrics, JC Penney, Sears/auto, Schuck's Parts, mall
124	OR 138, Roseburg, City Ctr, **E...gas:** Mobil/diesel, 76/diesel/24hr, Tesoro, **food:** Chi's Chinese, Denny's, HiHo Rest., **lodging:** Best Western, Dunes Motel, Holiday Inn Express, Holiday Motel, Travelodge, **other:** MEDICAL CARE, Chevrolet/Pontiac/Buick, Honda, Mazda, Rite Aid, Safeway, **W...gas:** Chevron, Shell/Subway, **food:** Charley's BBQ, Gay 90's Deli, KFC, Taco Time, **other:** HOSPITAL, Grocery Outlet
123	Roseburg, **E...other:** to Umpqua Park, camping, museum
121	McLain Ave, no facilities
120.5mm	S Umpqua River
120	OR 99 N(no EZ nb return), Green District, Roseburg, **E...lodging:** Shady Oaks Motel, **3 mi E...food:** HiHo Rest, **lodging:** Best Western, **W...**RV parts
119	OR 99 S, OR 42 W, Winston, **W...gas:** Chevron/A&W/diesel/24hr, Love's/Arby's/diesel/@ , **food:** McDonald's, Noah's Ark Rest., Papa Murphy's, Subway, **other:** PriceLess Foods, UPS, RV Park

Roseburg

Interstate 5

N
↑
↓
S

113	Clarks Branch Rd, Round Prairie, **W...lodging:** QuickStop Motel/mkt, **other:** On the River RV Park, diesel repair
112.5mm	S Umpqua River, S Umpqua River
112	OR 99, OR 42, Dillard, **E...other:** Rivers West RV park, **food:** Southfork Lodge Rest./store, **rest area nb, W...rest area sb, full(handicapped)facilities, phone, picnic tables, litter barrels, petwalk**
111mm	weigh sta nb
110	Boomer Hill Rd, no facilities
108	Myrtle Creek, no facilities
106	Weaver Rd, no facilities
103	Tri City, Myrtle Creek, **E...food:** Broaster House Diner, **W...gas:** Chevron/A&W/diesel/24hr, **food:** McDonald's
102	Gazley Rd, **E...**Surprise Valley RV Park(1mi)
101.5mm	S Umpqua River, S Umpqua River
101	Riddle, Stanton Park, **W...**camping
99	Canyonville, **E...food:** Burger King, Cow Creek Café/RV Park/casino, **lodging:** Riverside Motel, 7 Feathers Hotel/RV Park/casino, Valley View Motel, **other:** diesel/RV repair, **W...gas:** 7 Feathers Trk-stp/diesel/24/café/@, **lodging:** Best Western
98	OR 99, Canyonville, Days Creek, **E...gas:** 76/diesel, Shell/diesel/24hr, **food:** Bob's Country Jct Rest., **other:** NAPA, **lodging:** Leisure Inn, **W...other:** Bill's Tire, museum, auto repair
95	Canyon Creek, no facilities
90mm	Canyon Creek Pass, Canyon Creek Pass, elev 2020
88	Azalea, **W...other:** Azalea Gen Store/gas
86	Barton Rd, Quine's Creek, **E...gas:** Shell/diesel, **other:** Heaven on Earth Rest./RV camp
83	Barton Rd(from nb), **E...other:** Meadow Wood RV Park(3mi)
82mm	**rest area both lanes, full(handicapped)facilities, phone, picnic tables, litter barrels, petwalk**
80	Glendale, **W...gas:** Sawyer Sta/LP, **food:** Village Inn Rest.
79.5mm	Stage Road Pass, elev 1830
78	Speaker Rd, no facilities
76	Wolf Creek, **W...gas:** Exxon/diesel/24hr, Pacific Pride/diesel, 76/deli/diesel, **food:** Wolf Creek Inn Rest., **other:** Creekside RV park
74mm	Smith Hill Summit, elev 1730
71	Sunny Valley, **E...gas:** 76/diesel, **lodging:** Sunny Valley Motel, **W...other:** KOA
69mm	Sexton Mtn Pass, elev 1960
66	Hugo, **W...other:** Joe Creek Waterfalls RV Camping
63mm	**rest area both lanes, full(handicapped)facilities, phone, info, picnic tables, litter barrels, vending, petwalk**
61	Merlin, **E...other:** Beaver Creek RV Resort, Twin Pines RV Park, **W...gas:** Shell/diesel, **other:** Rouge Valley RV Ctr, repair

Grants Pass

58	OR 99, to US 199; Grants Pass, **W...gas:** Arco, Chevron, Gas4Less/U-Haul, 76/diesel, Shell/diesel/repair, Texaco/diesel, TownePump Gas, **food:** Angela's Mexican, Baskin-Robbins, Burger King, Carl's Jr, DQ, Della's Rest., Denny's, McDonald's, Muchos Gracias Mexican, Papa Murphy's, Pizza Hut, Rouge Rest., Sizzler, Skipper's, Subway, Taco Bell, Wendy's, **lodging:** Budget Inn, Comfort Inn, Hawk's Inn, Hawthorn Suites, La Quinta, Motel 6, Parkway Lodge, Regal Lodge, Riverside Inn, Royal Vue Motel, Shilo Inn, Sunset Inn, Super 8, SweetBreeze Inn, Travelodge, **other:** HOSPITAL, AutoZone, Chevrolet/Nissan/Honda, Chrysler/Dodge/Jeep, Jack's RV Resort, PriceChopper Foods, Radio Shack, Rouge Valley RV Park, Schwab Tire, ToolBox Repair, st police, towing
55	US 199, Redwood Hwy, E Grants Pass, **W...gas:** Arco/24hr, CFN/diesel, Exxon/diesel/LP/24hr, **food:** Applebee's, Abby's Pizza, Arby's, Carl's Jr, Elmer's, JJ North's Buffet, McDonald's, Shari's/24hr, Si Casa Flores Mexican, Subway, Taco Bell, Wild River Brewing Co, **lodging:** Best Western, Discovery Inn, Holiday Inn Express, Knight's Inn, **other:** HOSPITAL, Albertson's/gas, Big Lots, Big O Tire, Fred Meyer/gas/diesel, Grocery Outlet, JC Penney, Moon Mnt. RV Park, Rite Aid, RiverPark RV Park, Shuck's Parts, Siskiyou RV Ctr, Staples, Wal-Mart SuperCtr/24hr
48	Rogue River, Rogue River RA, **E...gas:** Chevron/diesel, Exxon/LP, Shell/diesel, **food:** Abby's Pizza, **W...food:** Betty's Kitchen, Karen's Kitchen, Tarasco Mexican, **lodging:** Bella Rosa Inn, Best Western, Rogue River Inn, Motel, Weasku Inn, **other:** Circle W RV Park, MktBasket Foods, Ridgeview RV Park
45b	**W...other: Valley of the Rogue SP/rest area both lanes, full(handicapped) facilities, phone, picnic tables, litter barrels, petwalk, camping**
45mm	Rogue River
45a	OR 99, Savage Rapids Dam, **E...other:** Cypress Grove RV Park
43	OR 99, OR 234, , to Crater Lake, Gold Hill, **E...food:** Red Barn Cafe, **lodging:** Lazy Acres Motel/RV Park

OREGON

Interstate 5

40 OR 99, OR 234, Gold Hill, **E...food:** Gold Hill Mkt/deli, **other:** to Shady Cove Trail, KOA, Lazy Acres Motel/RV Park, **W...**Dardanell's RV/Trailer Park/gas, **food:** Sammy's Rest.

35 OR 99, Blackwell Rd, Central Point, **2-4 mi W...**gas, food, lodging, st police, Jacksonville Nat Hist Landmark

33 Central Point, **E...gas:** Chevron, Pilot/Subway/Taco Bell/diesel/24hr/@, **food:** Burger King, KFC, Sheri's, **lodging:** Fairfield Inn, **other:** RV Ctr, RV camping, funpark, **W...gas:** 76/Circle K/diesel, Shell/diesel/24hr, **food:** Abbey's Pizza, BeeGee's Rest., LittleTown Hero Sandwiches, Little Caesar's, Mazatlan Grill, McDonald's, Pappy's Pizza, **other:** Albertson's

30 OR 62, to Crater Lake, Medford, **E...gas:** Arco/diesel, 76, Witham Trkstp/Chevron/rest./diesel/24hr/@, Gas4Less, Shell/diesel, **food:** Abby's Pizza, Applebee's, Arby's, Asian Grill, Carl's Jr, Chevy's Mexican, DQ, Denny's, Elmer's, IHOP, India Palace, Marie Callender's, McDonald's, Olive Garden, Papa John's, Pizza Hut, Quizno's, Red Robin, Schlotsky's, Si Casa Mexican, Sizzler, Starbucks, Subway, Taco Bell, Taco Delite, Thai Bistro, Wendy's, Williams Bakery, **lodging:** Best Western, Cedar Lodge, Comfort Inn, Hampot Inn, Motel 6, Reston Inn, Rogue Regency Hotel, Shilo Inn, ValliHai Inn, Windmill Inn, **other:** AAA RV, Albertson's, Aamco, Barnes&Noble, BiMart Foods, Chevrolet, Circuit City, Ford, Fred Meyer, Food4Less, Medford Oaks RV Park, NAPA, OR Tire, Radio Shack, River City RV Ctr, Safeway, Sears, USPO, st police, **W...gas:** Chevron/diesel, Shell/diesel, **food:** Burger King, Domino's, Jack-in-the-Box, KFC, King Wah Chinese, Red Lobster, Skipper's, Wendy's, **other:** HOSPITAL, JC Penney, Krecht's Parts, Mervyn's, Target, U-Haul, mall

27 Barnett Rd, Medford, **E...gas:** Exxon/diesel, Shell/24hr, **food:** DQ, Kopper Kitchen, **lodging:** Best Western, Day's Inn/rest., Economy Inn, Motel 6, **W...gas:** Chevron/24hr, Exxon/diesel, Gas4Less, 76/Circle K, Shell/diesel/24hr, **food:** Abby's Pizza, Apple Annie's, Burger King, Carl's Jr, HomeTown Buffet, Jack-in-the-Box, KFC, Kim's Chinese, McDonald's, McGrath's FishHouse, Pizza Hut, Rooster's Rest., Senor Sam's Mexican, Shari's, Starbucks, Subway, Taco Bell, Wendy's, Zach's Deli, **lodging:** Best Inn, Comfort Inn, Holiday Inn Express, Red Lion Inn, Royal Crest Motel, **other:** Ford/Mercury/Lincoln, Food4Less, Fred Meyer, Harry&David's, Hyundai, K-Mart, OfficeMax, Radio Shack, Saturn, Schwab Tires, Staples, Toyota, WinCo Foods

24 Phoenix, **E...gas:** Petro/diesel/rest./RV dump/24hr/@, Shell/diesel, **lodging:** PearTree Motel/rest./RV park, **other:** Peterbilt/GMC, **W...gas:** Exxon, 76/Circle K/diesel, **food:** Angelo's Pizza, Courtyard Café, Luigi's Café, McDonald's, Randy's Café, Subway, **lodging:** Bavarian Inn, Phoenix Motel, **other:** Ray's Foods, CarQuest, Holiday RV Park, Factory Stores/famous brands

22mm **rest area sb, full(handicapped)facilities, phone, picnic tables, litter barrels, vending, petwalk**

21 Talent, **W...gas:** Arco/diesel/24hr, Gas4Less, Talent's/diesel/rest./repair, **food:** Arbor House Rest., Expresso Café, Figaro's Italian, Senor Sam's Cantina, **lodging:** GoodNight Inn, **other:** American RV Resort, Wal-Mart/auto

19 Valley View Rd, Ashland, **W...gas:** Exxon/diesel/LP, Pacific Pride/diesel, 76/diesel, Shell/diesel, **food:** Burger King, El Tapatio Mexican, **lodging:** Best Western, Econolodge, La Quinta, Regency Inn/rest./RV Park, Stratford Inn, **other:** HOSPITAL, U-Haul

18mm weigh sta both lanes

14 OR 66, to Klamath Falls, Ashland, **E...gas:** Chevron, 76/diesel/LP, Shell/diesel, **food:** A&W/KFC, Denny's, OakTree Rest., **lodging:** Ashland Hills Inn/rest., Best Western, Holiday Inn Express, Relax Inn, Rodeway Inn, Vista Motel, Windmill Inn, **other:** Emigrant Lake Camping(3mi), KOA(3mi), Nat Hist Museum, **W...gas:** Arco/24hr, Astro, Mobil, 76/LP/24hr, **food:** Azteca Mexican, DQ, McDonald's, Omar's Rest(1mi), Pizza Hut, Taco Bell, Thai Rest., **lodging:** Knight's Inn/rest., Super 8, **other:** Albertson's, Rite Aid, Schwab Tire

11.5mm chainup area

11 OR 99, Siskiyou Blvd(no nb return), **2-4 mi W...gas:** Shell, **food:** BBQ, DQ, Figaro's Italian, Goodtimes Café, House of Thai, Little Caesar's, Omar's Rest., Senor Sam's Mexican, Subway, Wendy's, **lodging:** Best Western, Cedarwood Inn, Hillside Inn, Rodeway Inn, Stratford Inn, **other:** Radio Shack, Weisinger Brewery

6 to Mt Ashland, **E...lodging:** Callahan's Siskiyou Lodge/rest., **other:** phone, ski area

4mm Siskiyou Summit, elev 4310, brake check both lanes

1 to Siskiyou Summit(from nb), no facilities

0mm Oregon/California state line

Interstate 84

Exit #	Services	
378mm	Oregon/Idaho state line, Snake River	E

377.5mm **Welcome Ctr wb, full(handicapped)facilities, info, phone, picnic tables, litter barrels, vending, petwalk**

376 US 30, Ontario, to US 20/26, Payette, **N...gas:** Chevron/24hr, **food:** Burger King, Country Kitchen, DQ, Denny's, McDonald's, Taco Time, Wingers, **lodging:** Best Western, Colonial Inn, Holiday Inn, Motel 6, Sleep Inn, Super 8, **other:** Chrysler/Dodge/Plymouth/Jeep, K-Mart, Staples, Wal-Mart SuperCtr/24hr, st police, **S...gas:** Phillips 66, Pilot/Arby's/diesel/24hr/@, Shell, **food:** Domino's, Klondike Pizza, Rusty's Steaks, Sizzler, Subway, Taco Bell, Wendy's, **lodging:** Economy Inn, Holi-

E ↕ W

Interstate 84

day Motel/rest., OR Trail Motel, Stockmen's Motel, **other:** HOSPITAL, Commercial Tire, NAPA, Radio Shack, Schwab Tire, U-Haul, RV repair, 4 Wheeler Museum

374 US 30, OR 201, to Ontario, **N**...to Ontario SP, **S...gas:** Shell/diesel, **food:** North Star Café, **lodging:** Budget Motel, Carlile Motel, **other:** HOSPITAL, parts/repair

373.5mm Malheur River

371 Stanton Blvd, **2 mi S**...to correctional institution

362 Moores Hollow Rd, no facilities

356 OR 201, to Weiser, ID, **3 mi N**...Oasis RV Park

354.5mm weigh sta eb

353 US 30, to Huntington, **N**...weigh sta wb, **gas:** Farewell Bend Travel Plaza/diesel/rest./motel/@, **other:** to Farewell Bend SP, truck repair, RV camping, info

351mm Pacific/Mountain time zone

345 US 30, Lime, Huntington, **1 mi N**...gas, food, lodging, to Snake River Area

342 Lime(from eb), no facilities

340 Rye Valley, no facilities

338 Lookout Mountain, **N...other:** Oregon Tr RV Park

337mm Burnt River

335 to Weatherby, **N**...rest area both lanes, full(handicapped)facilities, Oregon Trail Info, picnic tables, litter barrels, vending, petwalk

330 Plano Rd, to Cement Plant Rd, **S**...cement plant

329mm pulloff eb

327 Durkee, **N...gas:** Oregon Tr Travel Ctr/Cenex/diesel/café/@

325mm Pritchard Creek

321mm Alder Creek

319 to Pleasant Valley, no facilities

317 to Pleasant Valley(from wb)

315 to Pleasant Valley, no facilities

306 US 30, Baker, **2 mi S...gas:** Chevron/diesel, **food:** DQ, **lodging:** Baker City Motel, Budget Inn, Friendship Inn, Lariat Motel/RV, OR Tr Motel/rest., Royal Motel, **other:** HOSPITAL, to st police, same as 304

304 OR 7, Baker, **N...gas:** Chevron/Burger King/TCBY/diesel, **lodging:** Super 8, Welcome Inn, **S...gas:** Shell/Blimpie/diesel/24hr, Sinclair/diesel/rest./24hr, **food:** DQ, Joltin Java, Klondike Pizza, McDonald's, Papa Murphy's, Pizza Hut, Subway, Sumpter Jct Rest., Taco Time, **lodging:** Best Western, Eldorado Inn, Quality Inn, Royal Motel, Western Motel, **other:** HOSPITAL, Albertson's, BiMart Foods, Ford/Lincoln/Mercury, Mel's Auto Parts, Mtn View RV Park(3mi), Paul's Transmissions, Rite Aid, Safeway, museum, to hist dist

302 OR 86 E to Richland, **S...other:** HOSPITAL, OR Tr RV Park/gas

298 OR 203, to Medical Springs, no facilities

297mm Baldock Slough

295mm **rest area both lanes, full(handicapped)facilities, info, phone, picnic tables, litter barrels, vending, petwalk**

289mm Powder River

287.5mm 45th parallel...halfway between the equator and north pole

286mm N Powder River

285 US 30, OR 237, North Powder, **N...gas:** Cenex/diesel/café, **lodging:** Powder River Motel, **S...other:** to Anthony Lakes, ski area

284mm Wolf Creek

283 Wolf Creek Lane, no facilities

278 Clover Creek, no facilities

273 Ladd Canyon, no facilities

270 Ladd Creek Rd(from eb, no return), no facilities

269mm **rest area both lanes, full(handicapped)facilities, info, phone, picnic tables, litter barrels, vending, petwalk**

268 Foothill Rd, no facilities

265 OR 203, LaGrande, **N**...airport, **S...gas:** ✈/Flying J/Exxon/TCBY/diesel/rest./@, **food:** SmokeHouse Rest., **lodging:** to Broken Arrow Lodge, Quail Run Motel, Travelodge, **other:** Radio Shack, RV camping, to E OR U

261 OR 82, LaGrande, **N...gas:** Chevron/diesel, Shell/diesel, Texaco/diesel, **food:** Denny's, Pizza Hut, Quizno's, Subway, Taco Bell, **lodging:** Howard Johnson, **other:** Chrysler/Plymouth/Dodge/Jeep, Ford/Lincoln/Mercury, Grocery Outlet, Shop'n Kart, Wal-Mart/drugs, LaGrande Rendezvous RV Resort, st police, **S... gas:** Exxon/diesel, 76/Subway/diesel, **food:** DQ, Klondike Pizza, Little Caesar's, McDonald's, Skipper's, Taco Time, Wendy's, Best Western, Sandman Inn, Super 8, **other:** HOSPITAL, Albertson's, Cottman Transmissions, Rite Aid, Safeway, Schuck's Parts, E OR U, Wallowa Lake

260mm Grande Ronde River

Interstate 84

E

↕

W

259	US 30 E(from eb), to La Grande, **1-2 mi S...gas:** Chevron, Exxon/Burger King/diesel, **food:** Foley Sta Rest., Greenwell Rest., Smokehouse Rest., **lodging:** Royal Motel, Stardust Lodge, **other:** same as 261
257	Perry(from wb), no facilities
258mm	weigh sta eb
256	Perry(from eb), no facilities
255mm	Grande Ronde River
254mm	scenic wayside
252	OR 244, to Starkey, Lehman Springs, **S...other:** Hilgard SP, camping, chainup area
251mm	Wallowa-Whitman NF, eastern boundary
248	Spring Creek Rd, to Kamela, no facilities
246mm	Wallowa-Whitman NF, western boundary
243	Summit Rd, Mt Emily Rd, to Kamela, Oregon Trail info, **2 mi N...other:** Emily Summit SP
241mm	Summit of the Blue Mtns, elev 4193
238	Meacham, **1 mi N...lodging:** Blue Mountain Lodge, **other:** Oregon Trail info
234	Meacham, **N...other:** Emigrant Sprs SP, RV camping
231.5mm	Umatilla Indian Reservation, eastern boundary
228mm	Deadman Pass, Oregon Trail info, **N...rest area both lanes, full(handicapped)facilities, phone, picnic table, litter barrel, petwalk, vending, RV dump**
227mm	weigh sta wb, brake check area, phone
224	Poverty Flats Rd, Old Emigrant Hill Rd, to Emigrant Springs SP, no facilities
223mm	wb viewpoint, no restrooms
221.5mm	eb viewpoint, no restrooms
220mm	wb runaway truck ramp
216	Mission, McKay Creek, **N...gas:** Pacific Pride/diesel, Shell/Arrowhead/diesel/@, **food:** Cody's Rest., **other:** Wildhorse Casino/RV Park
213	US 30(from wb), Pendleton, **3-5 mi N...gas:** Chevron/diesel, Exxon/deli, **lodging:** Budget Inn, Economy Inn, Pioneer Motel, Tapadera Budget Motel, Travelers Inn, **other:** HOSPITAL, Pendleton NHD
212mm	Umatilla Indian Reservation western boundary
210	OR 11, Pendleton, **N...gas:** Exxon, **other:** HOSPITAL, museum, **S...gas:** Pacific Pride/diesel, 76/diesel, Shell/diesel/LP, **food:** Kopper Kitchen, Shari's/24hr, **lodging:** Best Western, Holiday Inn Express, Motel 6, Red Lion Inn/rest., Super 8, **other:** Mtn View RV Park, st police

P
e
n
d
l
e
t
o
n

209	US 395, Pendleton, **N...gas:** Arco/24hr, **food:** A&W, Dean's Mkt/deli, Jack-in-the-Box, KFC, Taco Bell, **lodging:** Oxford Suites, Travelers Inn, Travelodge, **other:** HOSPITAL, Rite Aid, Safeway/24hr, Schuck's Parts, Wal-Mart SuperCtr/24hr, transmissions, **S...gas:** Exxon/diesel/24hr, Shell/diesel, **food:** Arby's, Burger King, Denny's/24hr, Klondike Pizza, McDonald's, Rooster's Rest., Subway, Wendy's, **lodging:** Econolodge, **other:** MEDICAL CARE, Chevrolet/Pontiac/Buick, Goodyear, Honda, K-Mart, Schwab Tire, Thompson RV Ctr, to Pilot Rock
208mm	Umatilla River
207	US 30, W Pendleton, **N...gas:** Chevron/diesel, Shell/diesel/LP, **food:** DQ, Godfather's, Taco Bell, **lodging:** Longhorn Motel, Oxford Suites, Tapadera Budget Motel, Vagabond Inn, **other:** Brooke RV Park, Lookout RV Park
202	Barnhart Rd, to Stage Gulch, **N...**Woodpecker Truck Repair, **S...gas:** Floyd's Truck Ranch/diesel/motel/café/@, **lodging:** 7 Inn, **other:** Oregon Trail info
199	Stage Coach Rd, Yoakum Rd, no facilities
198	Lorenzen Rd, McClintock Rd, **N...other:** trailer/reefer repair
193	Echo Rd, to Echo, Oregon Trail Site
188	US 395 N, Hermiston, **N...gas:** Chevron/diesel(1mi), Pilot/Subway/diesel/24hr/RV park/@, **5 mi N...food:** Denny's/24hr, Jack-in-the-Box, McDonald's, Shari's/24hr, **lodging:** Best Western, Economy Inn, Oxford Suites, **other:** HOSPITAL, **S...other:** Henrietta RV Park, Echo HS
187mm	**rest area both lanes, full(handicapped)facilities, phone, info, picnic tables, litter barrels, petwalk**
182	OR 207, to Hermiston, **N...other:** Buffalo Jct Gas, **5 mi N...gas:** Butter Creek/gas/diesel/RV park, **food:** McDonald's, Shari's
180	Westland Rd, to Hermiston, McNary Dam, **N...**trailer repair, **S...gas:** Shell/diesel
179	I-82 W, to Umatilla, Kennewick, WA
177	Umatilla Army Depot, no facilities
171	Paterson Ferry Rd, to Paterson, no facilities
168	US 730, to Irrigon, **8 mi N...other:** Oregon Trail info, Oasis RV Park
165	Port of Morrow, **S...gas:** Pacific Pride/diesel
164	Boardman, **N...gas:** Chevron/diesel, Shell/diesel, C&D Drive-In, Lynard's Cellar Café, Dodge City Motel, Riverview Motel, USPO, Boardman RV/Marina Park, bank, **S...**76/Taco Bell/diesel/24hr, Nomad Deli/24hr, Econolodge, NAPA Repair/parts, Sentry Foods
161mm	**rest area both lanes, full(handicapped)facilities, phone, picnic tables, litter barrels, vending, petwalk**
159	Tower Rd, no facilities
151	Threemile Canyon, no facilities

Interstate 84

E ↕ **W**

147 OR 74, to Ione, Heppner, Oregon Trail Site, Blue Mtn Scenic Byway, no facilities

137 OR 19, Arlington, **S...**Chevron, 76/diesel, Happy Canyon Chicken/pizza, Pheasant Grill, Arlington Motel, Village Inn/rest., Thrifty Foods, city park, Columbia River RV Park(1mi)

136.5mm view point wb, picnic tables, litter barrels

131 Woelpern Rd(from eb, no return), no facilities

129 Blalock Canyon, Lewis&Clark Trail, no facilities

123 Philippi Canyon, Lewis&Clark Trail, no facilities

114.5mm John Day River

114 **S...**to John Day River RA

112 **N...**John Day Dam

109 Rufus, **N...**John Day Visitor Ctr, **S...gas:** Pacific Pride/diesel, Shell/diesel, **food:** BBQ, Bob's T-Bone, Frosty's Café, Larry's Rest., **lodging:** Arrowhead Motel, Tyee Motel, Rufus Inn, **other:** RV camping

104 US 97, Biggs, **N...other:** Des Chutes Park Bridge, **S...gas:** Astro/diesel, Chevron, 76/diesel/24hr, Shell/diesel, **lodging:** Biggs Motel/café, Jack's Rest., Linda's Rest., Subway, Dinty's Motel, Riviera Motel, **other:** Maryhill Museum

100mm Deschutes River, Columbia River Gorge Scenic Area

97 OR 206, Celilo, **N...other:** Celilo SP, restrooms, **S...other:** Deschutes SP, Indian Village

88 **N...**to The Dalles Dam

87 US 30, US 197, to Dufur, **N...gas:** 76/Taco Bell/24hr, Shell/diesel, **food:** Big Jim's Drive-In, McDonald's, **lodging:** Comfort Inn, Inn at the Dalles, Shilo Inn/rest., **other:** Columbia Hills RV Park, Lone Pine RV Park, st police, **S...lodging:** Dalles Inn, Schwab Tire

85 The Dalles, **N...Riverfront Park, restrooms, phone, picnic tables, litter barrels, playground, marina, S...gas:** 76, **food:** BurgervilleUSA, Holstein's Coffee, **lodging:** Best Western, Oregon Motel, **other:** HOSPITAL, Fast Auto Repair, NAPA, camping, to Nat Hist Dist

83 (84 from wb)W The Dalles, **N...food:** Orient Café, Windseeker Rest., **other:** NAPA, Tire Factory, **S...gas:** Chevron, Exxon, Shell, **food:** Burger King, Cousins Rest., Denny's, McDonald's, Papa Murphy's, Skipper's, Subway, Taco Bell, Taco Time, **lodging:** Best Western, Day's Inn, Quality Inn, Shilo Inn, Tillicum Inn, Super 8, **other:** HOSPITAL, Albertson's, Chrysler/Plymouth/Dodge, $Store, Emporium, Fred Meyer, Jo-Ann Fabrics, K-Mart, Rite Aid, Safeway, Schuck's Parts, Staples

The Dalles

82 Chenowith Area, **S...gas:** Shell/diesel, **1-2 mi S... gas:** Astro/diesel/24hr, Exxon, **food:** Arby's, Burger King, Cousins Rest., KFC, Pietro's Pizza, Stooky's Café, Subway, Wendy's, Day's Inn, BiMart, **other:** Chevrolet/Pontiac/Buick/Jeep/Subaru, Ford/Isuzu/Nissan, Columbia River Discovery Ctr, museum, same as 84

76 Rowena, **N...other:** Mayer SP, Lewis & Clark info, windsurfing

73mm **Memaloose SP, rest area both lanes, full(handicapped)facilities, picnic tables, litter barrels, phone, petwalk, RV dump, camping**

69 US 30, Mosier, **S...gas:** Rte 30 Store

66mm **N...Koberg Beach SP, rest area wb, full facilities, picnic table, litter barrels**

64 US 30, OR 35, Hood River, to White Salmon, Gov't Camp, **N...gas:** Chevron, Shell/24hr, McDonald's, Riverside Grill, Taco Time, Best Western, marina, museum, st police, **S...gas:** Exxon, **food:** China Gorge Café

63 Hood River, City Ctr, **N...gas:** Shell/diesel, **other:** Visitor Ctr, **S...gas:** Exxon/diesel/24hr, 76, **food:** Burger King, China Gorge, Pasquale's Pizza, Pietro's Pizza, **lodging:** Hood River Hotel, **other:** HOSPITAL, USPO, same as 64

62 US 30, W Hood River, W Cliff Dr, **N...food:** Charburger, **lodging:** Columbia Gorge Hotel, Meredith Motel, Vagabond Lodge, **other:** FruitTree Gifts, **S...gas:** Chevron/diesel/LP, Shell/diesel/LP, **food:** Carolyn's Rest., DQ, McDonald's, Red Carpet Rest., Shari's/24hr, Subway, Taco Bell, **lodging:** Comfort Suites, Econolodge, Prater's Motel, Riverview Lodge, Stonehedge Inn, **other:** HOSPITAL, Chevrolet/Pontiac/Buick, Rite Aid, Safeway, Schwab Tire, Wal-Mart

Hood River

61mm pulloff wb

60 service rd wb(no return), no facilities

58 Mitchell Point Overlook(from eb)

56 **N...other:** Viento SP, RV camping, phone

55 Starvation Peak Tr Head(from eb), restrooms

54mm weigh sta wb

OREGON

Interstate 84

E ↕ **W**

P o r t l a n d

51	Wyeth, **S**...camping
49mm	pulloff eb
47	Forest Lane, Hermon Creek(from wb), camping
44	US 30, to Cascade Locks, **1-4 mi N...gas:** Chevron/LP, Shell/diesel, **food:** Charburger, **lodging:** Best Western, Br of the Gods Motel, Cascade Motel, Dolce Motel, Econolodge, **other:** to Bridge of the Gods, KOA, Stern Wheeler RV Park
43mm	weigh sta eb
41	Eagle Creek RA(from eb), to fish hatchery
40	**N...other:** Bonneville Dam NHS, info, to fish hatchery
37	Warrendale(from wb), no facilities
35	**S...other:** Ainsworth SP, scenic loop highway, waterfall area, Fishery RV Park
31	Multnomah Falls(exits left from both lanes), **S...lodging:** Multnomah Falls Lodge(hist site), camping
30	**S**...Benson SP(from eb)
29	Dalton Point(from wb)
28	to Bridal Veil(7 mi return from eb)
25	**N**...Rooster Rock SP
23mm	viewpoint wb, hist marker
22	Corbett, **2 mi S...gas:** Corbett Mkt, **lodging:** Chinook Inn/rest., **other:** Crown Point RV Camping
19mm	Columbia River Gorge scenic area
18	Lewis&Clark SP, to Oxbow SP, lodging, food, RV camping
17.5mm	Sandy River
17	Marine Dr, Troutdale, **N...food:** Wendy's, **lodging:** Holiday Inn Express, **S...gas:** Chevron/24hr, ✈/Flying J/Conoco/Burger King/diesel/LP/24hr/@, TA/Arco/Subway/diesel/24hr/@, **food:** Arby's, McDonald's, Shari's/24hr, Taco Bell, **lodging:** Best Value Inn, Motel 6, Phoenix Inn, **other:** Columbia Outlets/famous brands
16	238th Dr, Fairview, **N...gas:** Arco/diesel/24hr, **food:** Jack-in-the-Box, Yazzi's Rest., **lodging:** Travelodge, **other:** Wal-Mart/auto, **S...gas:** Chevron, **lodging:** Best Western, McMenamin Motel, Shilo Inn, **other:** HOSPITAL, Gresham RV Ctr(3mi)
14	207th Ave, Fairview, **N...gas:** Shell/A&W/Taco Bell/diesel, **food:** GinSun Chinese, **other:** Portland RV Park, Rolling Hills RV Park
13	181st Ave, Gresham, **N...gas:** Chevron, Tesoro, **food:** IHOP, **lodging:** Hampton Inn, **S...gas:** Arco/24hr, 76/Circle K, 7-11, **food:** Blimpie, Burger King, Jung's Chinese, McDonald's, PlumTree Rest., Shari's/24hr, Wendy's, **lodging:** Comfort Suites, Extended Stay America, Hawthorn Suites, Sheraton/rest., Sleep Inn, **other:** Candy Basket Chocolates, Safeway, auto repair
10	122nd Ave(from eb), no facilities
9	I-205, S to Salem, N to Seattle, to airport, (to 102nd Ave from eb)
8	I-205 N(from eb), to airport
7	Halsey St(from eb), Gateway Dist
6	I-205 S(from eb)
5	OR 213, to 82nd Ave, **N...lodging:** Capri Motel, Day's Inn, **1-3 mi N...gas:** 76, Shell, 7-11, **food:** Arby's, Domino's, Pizza Hut, **lodging:** Quality Inn, Shilo Inn, **S...food:** Elmer's Rest., **lodging:** Microtel
4	68th Ave(from eb), to Halsey Ave
3	58th Ave(from eb), **S...gas:** 76, HOSPITAL
2	43rd Ave, 39th Ave, Halsey St, **N...gas:** 76, Shell, **food:** McDonald's, Winchell's, **lodging:** Banfield Motel, Rodeway Inn, **other:** Rite Aid, **S...other:** HOSPITAL, Buick/Pontiac, Jeep, same as 1
1	33rd Ave, Lloyd Blvd, **N...gas:** 76, Pacific Pride/diesel, Shell, **food:** Burger King, **lodging:** Banfield Motel, Best Western, Holiday Inn, Red Lion Inn, Residence Inn, **other:** JC Penney, Rite Aid, **S...other:** Buick/GMC
0mm	I-84 begins/ends on I-5, exit 301.

Interstate 205(Portland)

P o r t l a n d   A r e a

N ↕ **S**

Exit #	Services
37mm	I-405 begins/ends on I-5. Exits 36-27 are in Washington.
36	NE 134th St(from nb), **E...gas:** Arco/diesel, **lodging:** Holiday Inn Express, University Inn, **other:** Fred Meyer, **W...gas:** Citgo/7-11, 76, TrailMart/diesel, **food:** Billygan's Roadhouse, Burger King, Burgerville, Jack-in-the-Box, McDonald's, Round Table Pizza, Taco Bell, **lodging:** Comfort Inn, Holiday Inn Express, Olympia Motel, Salmon Creek Inn, Shilo Inn, **other:** HOSPITAL, Albertson's, Hi-School Drugs, Zupan's Mkt, 99 RV Park
32	NE 83rd St, Andreson Rd, **W...gas:** Shell/diesel/24hr, **food:** Meadows Kitchen, Wendy's, **other:** Home Depot
30	WA 500, Orchards, Vancouver, **E...gas:** Shell/24hr, **food:** KFC, Burger King, Burgerville, Cisco's Rest., KFC, McDonald's, Subway, **other:** Albertson's, Rite Aid, Toyota, RV park, **W...gas:** Arco, Chevron/24hr, **food:** Chevy's Mexican, Golden Tent Rest., Moshi Japanese, Olive Garden, Outback Steaks, Red Lobster, Red Robin Rest., RoundTable Pizza, Skipper's, Shari's/24hr, Subway, Taco Bell, TCBY, TGIFriday, Tony Roma, **lodging:** Comfort Suites, Heathman Lodge, Holiday Inn Express, Residence Inn, Sleep Inn, Staybridge Inn, **other:** America's Tire, JC Penney, Meijer&Frank, Mervyn's, Nordstrom's, Pic'n Sav Food, Ross, Sears/auto, Target, mall, RV park
28	Mill Plain Rd, **E...gas:** Chevron/24hr, 76/Circle K, Shell/diesel, Shell/diesel, 7-11, **food:** Applebee's, Burger King, Burgerville, DQ, Elmer's Rest., Ghengis Khan Mongolian, Kings Buffet, McDonald's, Ming Chinese, Muchas Gracias Mexican, Papa's German

Interstate 205

Rest., Pizza Hut, Shari's, Taco Bell, Trader Joe's, **lodging:** Best Inn, Best Western, Extended Stay America, Guesthouse Inn, Phoenix Inn, **other:** Fred Meyer, Schuck's Parts; Schwab Tire, **W...gas:** Arco/24hr, Shell, **food:** Arby's, Jack-in-the-Box, Old Mill Bread, Subway, **other:** HOSPITAL, Chevrolet, Hyundai, Tire Factory, Wal-Mart/auto

27 WA 14, Vancouver, Camas, Columbia River Gorge, no facilities

25mm Oregonington state line. **Exits 27-36 are in Washington.**, Columbia River

24 122nd Ave, **E...food:** Burger King, China Wok, CoffeeHouse, McDonald's, Shari's, Subway, **lodging:** Comfort Suites, Courtyard, Fairfield Inn, Hilton Garden, Holiday Inn Express, La Quinta, Shilo Inn/rest., Silver Cloud Inn, Staybridge Suites, Super 8, **other:** Best Buy, Home Depot, **W...lodging:** Hampton Inn, Sheraton/rest.

23b a US 30 byp, Columbia Blvd, **E...gas:** Shell/diesel, **lodging:** Best Western, Econolodge, Red Lion Hotel, Travelodge, **other:** HOSPITAL, **W...gas:** Shell, **food:** Bill's Steaks, Elmer's Rest., **lodging:** Best Inn, Best Western, Clarion, Day's Inn, Holiday Inn, Ramada Inn, **other:** camping

22 I-84 E, US 30 E, to The Dalles, no facilities

21b I-84 W, US 30 W, to Portland, no facilities

21a Glisan St, **E...gas:** 76, **food:** Applebee's, Carl's Jr, Izzy's Pizza, Quizno's, Szechuan Chinese, **lodging:** Chesnut Tree Inn, **other:** Circuit City, Fred Meyer, Mervyn's, Office Depot, Ross, Tower Books, WinCo Foods, mall, **W...gas:** 76, **food:** Burger King, Elmer's Rest., McDonald's, **lodging:** Best Value Inn, Travelodge, **other:** Nissan

20 Stark St, Washington St, **E...food:** Elmer's Rest., McMenamin's Café, Newport Bay Café, Tony Roma's, **lodging:** Holiday Inn Express, **other:** Cottman Transmissions, mall, **W...gas:** 7-11, **food:** ChuckeCheese, Izzy's Pizza, McDonald's, Stark St Pizza, Taco Bell, Village Inn, **lodging:** Rodeway Inn

19 US 26, Division St, **E...gas:** Exxon, **food:** Burger King, **other:** HOSPITAL, Radio Shack, **W...gas:** Chevron/24hr, Shell/diesel, 7-11, **food:** Izzy's Pizza, McDonald's, Sizzler, Wendy's, **other:** Best Value Inn, Travelodge

17 Foster Rd, **E...gas:** 7-11, **W...gas:** Chevron, Shell, **food:** Arby's, Burger King, IHOP, McDonald's, New Copper Penny Grill, Wendy's, **lodging:** Econolodge, Home Depot

16 Johnson Creek Blvd, **W...gas:** Applebee's, **food:** Burger King, Carl's Jr, Denny's, Fuddrucker's, Old Chicago Pizza, Old Country Buffet, Outback Steaks, Papa Joe's, Ron's Café, Starbucks, Subway, Taco Bell, **other:** Best Buy, Fred Meyer, Home Depot, OfficeMax, RV Ctrs, Shuck's Parts

14 Sunnyside Rd, **E...gas:** 76, **food:** Baja FreshMex, Burger King, Domino's, Izzy's Pizza, KFC, McDonald's, McMenamin's Rest., Subway, Taco Time, Thai House, Wendy's, **lodging:** Best Western, Day's Inn, **other:** HOSPITAL, Office Depot, **W...gas:** 76/LP/24hr, **food:** Chevy's Mexican, Gustav's Grill, Olive Garden, Red Robin Rest., **lodging:** Courtyard, Monarch Hotel/rest., Sunnyside Inn/rest., **other:** Barnes&Noble, FabricLand, JC Penney, Mervyn's, Nordstrom's, Old Navy, Sears/auto, Target, World Mkt, mall

13 OR 224, to Milwaukie, **W...K-Mart**

12 OR 213, to Milwaukie, **E...gas:** Chevron/24hr, Shell, 7-11, **food:** Denny's, Elmer's, KFC, McDonald's, Skipper's, Taco Bell/24hr, Wendy's, **lodging:** Clackamas Inn, Cypress Inn, Hampton Inn, **other:** MEDICAL CARE, Fred Meyer, **W...lodging:** Comfort Suites

11 82nd Dr, Gladstone, **W...gas:** Arco/24hr, **food:** High Rock Steakery, Safeway, **lodging:** Oxford Suites

10 OR 213, Park Place, **E...other:** HOSPITAL, to Oregon Trail Ctr

9 9 OR 99E, Oregon City, **E...gas:** Arco/repair, 76, **food:** KFC, **other:** HOSPITAL, Clackamas Parts, GMC/Pontiac, Mazda, Subaru, Yamaha, **W...gas:** 76, **food:** HongKong Express, La Hacienda Mexican, McDonald's, Shari's, Subway, **lodging:** Budget Inn, Rivershore Hotel, **other:** Firestone/auto, Jo-Ann Fabrics, Michael's, Rite Aid

8.5mm Willamette River

8 OR 43, W Linn, Lake Oswego, **E...gas:** 76, museum, **W...gas:** Shell/diesel

7mm viewpoint nb, hist marker

6 10th St, W Linn St, **E...gas:** Chevron/LP, 76, Ixtapa Mexican, **food:** McDonald's, McMenamin's Café, Shari's/24hr, Thriftway, **other:** Willamette Coffeehouse, **W...food:** Bugatti's Pizza, Jack-in-the-Box, Subway, **other:** Albertson's

4mm Tualatin River

3 Stafford Rd, Lake Oswego, **W...other:** HOSPITAL, Wanker's Country Store/phone

0mm I-205 begins/ends on I-5, exit 288.

PENNSYLVANIA
Interstate 70

Exit #	Services

E ↕ **W**

171mm Pennsylvania/Maryland state line, **Welcome Ctr wb, full(handicapped)facilities, info, phone, vending, picnic tables, litter barrels, petwalk**

168 US 522 N, Warfordsburg, **N...gas:** Exxon/diesel, **S...**fireworks

163 PA 731 S, Amaranth, no facilities

156 PA 643, Town Hill, **N...gas:** Sunoco/Subway/diesel, **food:** 4 Seasons Rest., **lodging:** Day's Inn, **other:** Napa Care

153mm **rest area eb, full(handicapped)facilities, phone, picnic tables, litter barrels, vending, petwalk**

151 PA 915, Crystal Spring, **N...food:** CornerStone Family Rest., **other:** auto repair, **S...other:** Country Store/USPO

149 US 30 W, to Everett, S Breezewood(no immediate wb return), **3 mi S...food:** Denny's, McDonald's, **lodging:** Penn Aire Motel, Redwood Motel, Wildwood Motel

147 US 30, Breezewood, **Services on US 30...gas:** BP/diesel, Citgo, Exxon/diesel, Mobil/diesel/24hr, Sheetz/24hr, Shell, Sunoco/diesel/café, TA/diesel/ rest./24hr/@, Texaco/Subway, **food:** Arby's, Big John's Buffet, Bob Evans, Burger King, DQ, Denny's, Domino's, Family House Rest., Hardee's, KFC, McDonald's, Perkins, Pizza Hut, Taco Bell, Wendy's, **lodging:** Best Western, Breezewood Motel, Comfort Inn/rest., Econolodge, Holiday Inn Express, Penn Aire Motel, Quality Inn, Ramada Inn, Wiltshire Motel, **other:** museum

I-70 W and I-76/PA Turnpike W run together.

For I-70, I-76/PA Turnpike exits 75-146, see PENNSYLVANIA INTERSTATE 76/PA Tpk

58 PA Tpk. I-70 E and I-76/PA Turnpike E run together.

57 I-70 W, US 119, PA 66(toll), New Stanton, **N...food:** Exxon, Sheetz, Bob Evans, Donut Chef, Eat'n Park, KFC, McDonald's, Pagano's Rest., Pizza Hut, Subway, Wendy's, **lodging:** Comfort Inn, Day's Inn, Fairfield Inn, Howard Johnson, Quality Inn, Super 8, **S...gas:** BP/diesel, Sunoco/24hr, **food:** Cracker Barrel, TJ's Rest., **lodging:** New Stanton Motel

54 Madison, **N...KOA**

53 Yukon, no facilities

51b a PA 31, West Newton, no facilities

49 Smithton, **N...gas:** Citgo/diesel/@, Shell/Perkins/ diesel/@, **food:** Old Farmhouse Pizza

46b a PA 51, Pittsburgh, **N...gas:** BP/diesel, Exxon/24hr, **food:** Burger King, **lodging:** Sleeper Inn, **other:** Chevrolet/Pontiac/Buick/Cadillac/Kia, Harley-Davidson, **S...gas:** Crossroads/diesel/24hr, **lodging:** Holiday Inn, Knotty Pine Motel, Relax Inn

44 Arnold City, no facilities

43b a (43 from eb)PA 201, Fayette City, **N...**gas/diesel, **S...gas:** Exxon/24hr, Sunoco/24hr, **food:** Burger King, China Wok, Denny's, Eat'n Park, Hoss' Rest., KFC, LJ Silver, McDonald's, Ponderosa, Subway, Wendy's, **lodging:** Best Val-U Motel, **other:** Advance

---

Parts, $General, $Tree, Eckerd, Giant Foods, GNC, K-Mart, Lowe's Whse, Radio Shack, Staples, Wal-Mart SuperCtr/24hr

42a Monessen, no facilities

42 N Belle Vernon, **S...gas:** BP/McDonald's, Sunoco, **food:** Dairy Queen

41 PA 906, Belle Vernon, no facilities

40mm Monongahela River

40 PA 88, Charleroi, **N...gas:** Amoco, Crossroads/diesel, **food:** Subway, **other:** HOSPITAL

39 Speers, **N...food:** Loraine's Rest., **S...gas:** Exxon, camping

37b a PA 43, no facilities

36 Lover(from wb, no re-entry), no facilities

35 PA 481, Centerville, no facilities

32b a PA 917, Bentleyville, **N...food:** King of the Hill Steaks, **S... gas:** Amoco/diesel, Pilot/DQ/Subway/diesel/24hr, Sheetz/24hr, **food:** Burger King, McDonald's, **lodging:** Best Western, **other:** MEDICAL CARE, Advance Parts, Blue Beacon, $General, Ford, Giant Foods, Rite Aid

31 to PA 136, Kammerer, **N...lodging:** Carlton Motel, **food:** Carlton Kitchen

27 Dunningsville, **S...lodging:** Avalon Motel

25 PA 519, to Eighty Four, **S...gas:** Amoco/24hr, BP/diesel/ @, 7-11/diner

21 I-79 S, to Waynesburg. **I-70 W and I-79 N run together 3.5 mi.**

20 PA 136, Beau St, **N...KOA, S...**to Washington&Jefferson Coll

19b a US 19, Murtland Ave, **N...gas:** BP, **food:** Applebee's, Cracker Barrel, McDonald's, Ponderosa, Red Lobster, Texas Roadhouse, TGIFriday, **lodging:** SpringHill Suites, **other:** Aldi Foods, $Tree, Giant Eagle Foods, GNC, Lowe's Whse, Michael's, OfficeMax, Radio Shack, Sam's Club, Target, Toyota/Honda, Wal-Mart SuperCtr/24hr, **S...gas:** Amoco, BP/diesel, Sunoco, **food:** Arby's, Big Boy, Bob Evans, Burger King, Eat'n Park/24hr, Evergreen Chinese, Jade Garden Chinese, KFC, LJ Silver, Old Mexico, Papa John's, Pizza Hut, Shoney's, Taco Bell, **lodging:** Hampton Inn, Motel 6, **other:** HOSPITAL, Buick/Cadillac/GMC, $General, Firestone/auto, Home Depot, JC Penney, Jo-Ann Fabrics, K-Mart, Staples, Subaru, mall, st police

18 I-79 N, to Pittsburgh. **I-70 E and I-79 S run together 3.5 mi.**

17 PA 18, Jefferson Ave, Washington, **N...gas:** Crossroads/ diesel, Gulf, **food:** DQ, McDonald's, **other:** CarQuest, Family$, Rite Aid, **S...gas:** Sunoco, **food:** Burger King, 4Star Pizza, **other:** Advance Parts, Foodland

16 Jessop Place, **N...gas:** Citgo, **S...**auto/truck repair

15 US 40, Chesnut St, Washington, **N...food:** Stone-Crab Inn Rest., USA Steaks, Foodland, **S...gas:** BP, Crossroads/diesel, Sunoco/24hr, **food:** Bob Evans, China Buffet, Denny's, Eat'n Park/24hr, **other:** Hardee's, LJ Silver, McDonald's, Pizza Hut, Taco Bell, Wendy's, Day's Inn, Econolodge, Ramada Inn, Red Roof Inn, Eckerd, Sears/auto, mall

Interstate 70

E	
11	PA 221, Taylorstown, **N...gas:** Amoco/diesel, **other:** truck repair
6	to US 40, PA 231, Claysville, **N...gas:** Exxon, **other:** NAPA, **S...gas:** Petro/Citgo/Sbarro's/24hr
5mm	**Welcome Ctr eb, full(handicapped)facilities, phone, vending, picnic tables, litter barrels, pet-walk**
1	W Alexander, **S...gas:** Shell/diesel
W	
0mm	Pennsylvania/West Virginia state line

Interstate 76

Exit #	Service
E	
354mm	Pennsylvania/New Jersy state line, Delaware River, Walt Whitman Bridge
351	Front St, I-95(from wb), N to Trenton, S to Chester
350	Packer Ave, 7th St, to I-95(fromeb), **S...lodging:** Holiday Inn, **other:** to sports complex
349	to I-95, PA 611, Broad St
348	PA 291, W to Chester, **S...lodging:** Ramada Inn
347a	to I-95 S
W	
347b	Passyunk Ave, Oregon Ave, **S...other:** sports complex
346c	28th St, Vare Ave, Mifflin St(from wb)
346b	Grays Ferry Ave, University Ave, civic center, **N...food:** McDonald's, PathMark Foods, **S...gas:** BP/24hr, Hess

Philadelphia

346a	South St, no facilities
345	30th St, Market St, downtown
344	I-676 E, US 30 E, to Philadelphia(no return from eb)
343	Spring Garden St, Haverford
342	US 13, US 30 W, Girard Ave, Philadelphia Zoo, E Fairmount Park
341	Montgomery Dr, W River Dr, W Fairmount Park
340b	US 1 N, Roosevelt Blvd, to Philadelphia
339	US 1 S, **S...lodging:** Adams Mark Hotel, Holiday Inn
340a	Lincoln Dr, Kelly Dr, to Germantown
338	Belmont Ave, Green Lane, **N...other:** CVS Drug, **S...gas:** Sunoco, WaWa
337	Hollow Rd(from wb), Gladwyne
332	PA 23(from wb), Conshohocken, **N...lodging:** Marriott
331b a	I-476, PA 28(from eb), Conshohocken, to Chester
330	PA 320, Gulph Mills, **S...**to Villanova U
328	US 202 N, to King of Prussia, **N...gas:** Exxon/diesel, Mobil, WaWa, **food:** Charlie's Place Rest., Dunkin Donuts, Friendly's, Sizzler, TGIFriday, Uno Pizzaria, **lodging:** Econolodge, Holiday Inn, Howard Johnson, McIntosh Inn, **other:** JC Penney, Macy's, Sears/auto, Thrift Drug, mall, **S...**George Washington Lodge
327	US 202 S, Goddard Blvd, to Valley Forge, Valley Forge Park
326	I-76 wb becomes I-76/PA Tpk to Ohio

For I-76 westbound to Ohio, see I-76/PA Turnpike.

PENNSYLVANIA
Interstate 76/TPK

Exit #   Services
PA Tpk runs wb as I-276.

359 Pennsylvania/New Jersey state line, Delaware River Bridge

358 US 13, Delaware Valley, **N...gas:** WaWa, **lodging:** Day's Inn, Ramada Inn, **other:** Cadillac, U-Haul, **S...gas:** Bristol/diesel, Getty Gas, Mobil, Sunoco, **food:** Burger King, DeGrand Diner, Golden Eagle Diner, Italian Family Rest., McDonald's, Russo's Italian, **lodging:** Comfort Inn, Villager Lodge, **other:** Buick

352mm Neshaminy Service Plaza, wb...Welcome Ctr, gas: Sunoco/diesel/24hr, food: Burger King, Nathan's, other: Starbucks, eb...gas: Sunoco/diesel, food: Breyer's, HotDog Co, McDonald's, Nathan's

351 US 1, to I-95, to Philadelphia, **N...food:** Bob Evans, Ruby Tuesday, **lodging:** Courtyard, Hampton Inn, Holiday Inn, McIntosh Inn, **other:** Buick/Pontiac/Saturn/GMC, Home Depot, Sears/auto, Strawbridge's, Target, mall, **S...gas:** Amoco/24hr, Exxon/Subway, Sunoco/diesel, Texaco/diesel, **food:** Dunkin Donuts, Papa Yianni's Pizza, **lodging:** Comfort Inn, Howard Johnson, Knight's Inn, Neshaminy Inn, Radisson, Red Roof Inn, Sunrise Inn, **other:** Cadillac/Toyota

343 PA 611, Willow Grove, **N...gas:** Mobil, **food:** Chi-Chi's, **lodging:** Candlewood Suites(5mi), Courtyard, **S...gas:** Amoco/24hr, Hess/diesel, Mobil, Shell, Sunoco, 7-11, **food:** Bennigan's, China Garden, Domino's, Dunkin Donuts, Friendly's, McDonald's, Nino's Pizza, Ookaa Japanese, Williamson Rest., **lodging:** Hampton Inn, **other:** Best Buy, Firestone, Infiniti, PepBoys, Staples, transmissions

339 PA 309, Ft Washington, **N...gas:** Exxon, Mobil/Circle K/diesel, **food:** Friendly's, **lodging:** Best Western, Cherry Tree Hotel, Holiday Inn, **other:** BMW, Mercedes, Volvo

25A PA Tpk NE Extension, to I-476, no facilities

333 Germantown Pike, to Norristown, **N...gas:** Mobil/Circle K, **lodging:** SpringHill Suites, **other:** HOSPITAL, **S...gas:** Mobil/Circle K

328mm King of Prussia Service Plaza wb...Sunoco/diesel/24hr, Breyer's, McDonald's

PA Tpk runs eb as I-276, wb as I-76.

326 I-76 E, to US 202, I-476, Valley Forge, **N...gas:** Shell, **food:** Burger King, Cracker Barrel, Hooters, Hoss' Rest., **lodging:** Comfort Inn, Hampton Inn, MainStay Suites, Radisson, Sleep Inn, **S...gas:** Exxon, Mobil, Sunoco, WaWa, **food:** American Grill, CA Pizza, Chili's, Denny's, Houlihan's, McDonald's, **lodging:** Best Western, McIntosh Inn, Motel 6, Sheraton, **other:** Best Buy, Chevrolet, Costco, Crate&Barrel, Home Depot, JC Penney, Sears/auto, mall

325mm Valley Forge Service Plaza eb...gas: Sunoco/diesel/24hr, food: Burger King, Mrs Fields, Nathan's, TCBY, gifts

312 PA 100, to Downingtown, Pottstown, **N...other:** CarSense, Harley-Davidson, **S...gas:** Gulf/diesel, Sunoco/diesel/24hr, WaWa, **food:** Hoss' Rest., Red Robin, **lodging:** Best Western, Comfort Inn, Extended Stay America, Fairfield Inn, Hampton Inn, Holiday Inn Express, Residence Inn, Sheraton(6mi), **other:** HOSPITAL

305mm Camiel Service Paza wb...Sunoco/diesel/24hr, Mrs Fields, Nathan's, Roy Rogers, Sbarro's, Starbucks, TCBY, gifts

298 I-176, PA 10, to Reading, Morgantown, **N...lodging:** Economy Lodge, Heritage Motel/rest., **other:** HOSPITAL **S...food:** McDonald's, **lodging:** Holiday Inn

290mm Bowmansville Service Plaza eb...gas: Sunoco/diesel/24hr, food: Big Boy, Mrs Fields, Pizza Hut, Taco Bell, TCBY, other: gifts

286 US 322, PA 272, to Reading, Ephrata, **N...gas:** Citgo/Penn Amish Motel, Exxon/diesel, Shell/diesel, **food:** Zia Maria Italian, Zinn's Diner, **lodging:** Black Horse Lodge/rest., Penna Dutch Motel, **other:** Dutch Cousins Camping, **S...gas:** Turkey Hill, **lodging:** Comfort Inn, Holiday Inn, Red Carpet Inn

266 PA 72, to Lebanon, Lancaster, **N...gas:** Hess/diesel, Mobil/ChesterFried, **food:** Little Corner of Germany Café, **lodging:** Red Carpet Inn, Rodeway Inn, **S...food:** Hitz Mkt/deli, **lodging:** Hampton Inn, Holiday Inn Express, **other:** HOSPITAL, Mt Hope Winery

259mm Lawn Service Plaza wb...gas: Sunoco/diesel/24hr, food: Burger King, other: TCBY, RV dump

250mm Highspire Service Plaza eb...gas: Sunoco/diesel/24hr, food: Sbarro's

247 I-283, PA 283, to Harrisburg, Harrisburg East, Hershey, **N...gas:** Sunoco, **food:** Eat'n Park, Taco Bell, Wendy's, **lodging:** Best Western, Day's Inn, Rodeway Inn, **other:** facilities 3-5 mi N

246mm Susquehannah River

242 I-83, Harrisburg West, **N...gas:** BP, Hess, Mobil/diesel, **food:** Bob Evans, Eat'n Park, McDonald's, Pizza Hut, **other:** HOSPITAL, Comfort Inn, Day's Inn, Fairfield Inn, Holiday Inn, McIntosh Inn, Motel 6, **S...gas:** Keystone Trkstp/diesel/@, **lodging:** Day's Inn

236 US 15, to Gettysburg, Gettysburg Pike, Harrisburg, **N...gas:** Mobil, Shell, **food:** Isaac's Rest., McDonald's, Palumbo Pizza, Subway, **lodging:** Comort Inn, Econolodge, Hampton Inn/rest., Holiday Inn Express, Homewood Suites, **other:** HOSPITAL, U-Haul, **S...gas:** Sheetz/24hr, **food:** Burger King, Hoss' Steaks(1mi), McDonald's(1mi), Wendy's, **lodging:** Best Western, Wingate Inn, **other:** Giant Food/24hr

Interstate 76/TPK

Carlisle

226   US 11, to I-81, to Harrisburg, Carlisle, **N...gas:** BP, Petro/diesel/24hr/@, Citgo/diesel/24hr, /Flying J/diesel/LP/rest./24hr/@, Pilot/Wendy's/diesel/24hr, Shell/diesel, **food:** Arby's, BBQ, Big Boy/24hr, Bob Evans, Carelli's Subs, Eat'n Park, McDonald's, Middlesex Diner/24hr, Subway, Waffle House, Western Sizzlin, **lodging:** Appalachian Trail Inn, Best Western, Budget Host, Clarion, Hampton Inn, Holiday Inn, Howard Johnson, Quality Inn, Ramada Ltd, Roadway Inn, Super 8, **other:** HOSPITAL, Blue Beacon, Giant Foods, **S...gas:** Exxon/Taco Bell/24hr, Sheetz/24hr, **food:** Hoss' Rest., **lodging:** Motel 6, **other:** HOSPITAL, Chrysler/Jeep, U-Haul

219mm Plainfield Service Plaza eb...gas: Sunoco/diesel/24hr, food: Roy Rogers, other: TCBY, gifts

203mm Blue Mtn Service Plaza wb...gas: Sunoco/diesel/24hr, food: Nathan's, Hershy's IceCream, Roy Rogers, TCBY

201   PA 997, to Shippensburg, Blue Mountain, **S...lodging:** Johnnie's Motel/rest., Kenmar Motel

199mm Blue Mountain Tunnel

197mm Kittatinny Tunnel

189   PA 75, Willow Hill, **S...lodging:** Willow Hill Motel/rest.

187mm Tuscarora Tunnel

180   US 522, Ft Littleton, **N...gas:** BP/diesel, Shell/diesel, **food:** The Family Rest., **lodging:** Downes Motel, HOSPITAL

172mm Sideling Hill Service Plaza both lanes...gas: Sunoco/diesel/24hr, food: Big Boy, Burger King, TCBY, other: gifts

Breezewood

161   US 30, Breezewood, **Services on US 30...gas:** TA/diesel/rest./24hr/@, BP/diesel, Citgo/Dunkin Donuts, Exxon/diesel, Mobil/diesel/24hr, Sheetz/24hr, Shell, Sunoco/diesel/café, Texaco/Subway, **food:** Arby's, Big John's Buffet, Bob Evans, Bonanza, Burger King, DQ, Denny's, Domino's, Family House Rest., Hardee's, KFC, McDonald's, Perkins, Pizza Hut, Taco Bell, Wendy's, **lodging:** Best Western, Breezewood Motel, Comfort Inn/rest., Econolodge, Holiday Inn Express, Penn Aire Motel, Quality Inn, Ramada Inn, Wiltshire Motel, **other:** camping, museum, truck/tire repair

161mm I-70 W and I-76/PA Turnpike W run together

150mm roadside park wb

148mm Midway Service Plaza both lanes, eb...Sunoco/diesel/24hr, Cinnabon, Sbarro's, TCBY, gifts, wb... Sunoco/diesel/24hr, KFC, Sbarro's, Starbucks, TCBY, gifts

146   US 220, to I-99, Bedford, **N...gas:** Amoco/McDonald's/diesel/24hr, BP/diesel, Sheetz, **food:** Arena Rest., Denny's, Hoss' Rest., Pizza Hut, Wendy's, **lodging:** Best Western, Budget Host, Econolodge, Quality Inn, Super 8, Travelodge, **other:** to Shawnee SP(10mi), Blue Knob SP(15mi), **S...lodging:** Hampton Inn

142mm parking area wb

123mm Allegheny Tunnel

112mm Somerset Service Plaza both lanes, eb...gas: Sunoco/diesel/24hr, food: Big Boy, Roy Rogers, TCBY, other: gifts, wb...gas: Sunoco/diesel/24hr, food: Burger King, TCBY, other: gifts

110   PA 601, to US 219, Somerset, **N...gas:** KwikFill, Sheetz/24hr, **food:** Hoss' Rest., King's Rest., Pizza Hut, Taco Bell, **lodging:** $ Inn, Economy Inn, **other:** Advance Parts, Chrysler/Plymouth/Jeep, Ford/Lincoln/Mercury, **S...gas:** Exxon, Shell/diesel, **food:** Arby's, Bruester's Ice Cream, China Garden, Dunkin Donuts, Eat'n Park, Maggie Mae's Café, McDonald's, Pine Grill, Summit Diner, Wendy's, **lodging:** Best Western, Budget Host, Day's Inn, Hampton Inn, Holiday Inn, Knight's Inn, Ramada Inn, Super 8, **other:** Dodge, Eckerd, Harley-Davidson

91   PA 711, Donegal, **N...food:** Tall Cedars Rest./pizza, **S...gas:** BP/Hardee's/Pizza Hut, Exxon/diesel, Sunoco/diesel, **food:** DQ, **lodging:** Day's Inn, Donegal Motel, **other:** golf

78mm   service plaza wb...gas: Sunoco/diesel/24hr, food: McDonald's, lodging: Kings Family Rest.

I-70 E runs with I-76/PA Turnpike eb.

75   I-70 W, US 119, PA 66(toll), New Stanton, **S...gas:** BP/diesel, Exxon, Sheetz, Sunoco/24hr, **food:** Bob Evans, Cracker Barrel, Donut Chef, Eat'n Park, KFC, McDonald's/24hr, Pizza Hut, Subway, TJ's Rest., Wendy's, **lodging:** Budget Inn, Comfort Inn, Day's Inn, Fairfield Inn, Howard Johnson Express, New Stanton Motel, Ramada Inn, Super 8

74.6mm Hemphill Service Plaza eb...gas: Sunoco/diesel/24hr, food: Breyer's, McDonald's, other: atm

67   US 30, to Greensburg, Irwin, **N...gas:** BP/Blimpie/diesel, Sheetz/24hr, Shell, **lodging:** Motel 3, **other:** HOSPITAL, Ford, **S...gas:** Speedway, Sunoco/24hr, **food:** Angelo's Rest., Arby's, Bob Evans, Burger King, DQ, Denny's, Eat'n Park, KFC, LJ Silver, Los Compasinos Mexican, McDonald's, Pizza Hut, Royal China, Subway, Taco Bell, Teddy's Rest., Wendy's, **lodging:** Conley Inn, Holiday Inn Express, Penn Irwin Motel, **other:** Advance Parts, CarQuest, Giant Eagle Foods/24hr, Kohl's, Shop'n Save

PENNSYLVANIA
Interstate 76/TPK

Pittsburgh

61mm parking area eb

57 I-376, US 22, to Pittsburgh, Monroeville, **S...gas:** Amoco, BP, Citgo/diesel, **food:** Arby's, Burger King, ChiChi's, China Palace, Cooker Rest., Damon's, Denny's, Dunkin Donuts, Eat'n Park, LJ Silver, LoneStar Steaks, Max&Erma's, McDonald's, Marie's Italian, Outback Steaks, Pizza Hut, Red Lobster, Starbucks, Taco Bell, Wendy's, **lodging:** Day's Inn, Extended Stay America, Hampton Inn, Holiday Inn, King's Motel, Palace Inn, Radisson Inn, Red Roof Inn, SpringHill Suites, SunRise Inn, **other:** HOSPITAL, Buick/Jeep, Cadillac/Pontiac/GMC/Isuzu, Eckerd, Infiniti, Jo-Ann Fabrics, Marshall's, NTB, Office Depot, Old Navy, Radio Shack, Saturn, to Three Rivers Stadium

49mm Oakmont Service Plaza eb...Sunoco/diesel/24hr, Arby's, Hershey's Ice Cream, picnic tables, litter barrels, phone

48.5mm Allegheny River

48 A 28, to Pittsburgh, Allegheny Valley, New Kensington, **N...gas:** 76/24hr, **food:** Sam Morgan's Rest., **S...gas:** Exxon/diesel, **food:** Bob Evans, Bruster's Yogurt, Burger King, Denny's, Eat'n Park, Fuddrucker's, KFC, King's Rest., McDonald's, Ponderosa, Ripe Tomato, Subway, Taco Bell, Wendy's, **lodging:** Comfort Inn, Day's Inn, Holiday Inn Express, Super 8, Valley Motel, **other:** Advance Parts, Ford, Giant Eagle Food/drug/24hr

41mm parking area/call box eb

39 PA 8, to Pittsburgh, Butler Valley, **N...gas:** BP, Exxon/diesel, Sheetz/24hr, **food:** Bruno's Pizza, Eat'n Park, McDonald's, Venus Diner, **lodging:** Comfort Inn, **other:** Advance Parts, Jo-Ann Fabrics, Shop'n Save Foods, Wal-Mart/auto/drugs, mall, **S...gas:** BP, Sunoco/diesel, **food:** Arby's, Baskin-Robbins, Boston Mkt, Burger King, China Bistro, Denny's, Handel's Ice Cream, Hoss' Rest., KFC, McDonald's, Pizza Hut, Pizza Outlet, Quizno's, Subway, Taco Bell, Wendy's, **lodging:** Day's Inn, Econolodge, **other:** HOSPITAL, AutoZone, CVS Drug, Eckerd, Firestone/auto, Ford, Goodyear/auto, Radio Shack, Thrift Drug

31mm Butler Service Plaza wb...gas: Sunoco/diesel/24hr, food: Burger King, Mrs Fields, Popeye's, TCBY, other: gifts

Pittsburgh

28 to I-79, to Cranberry, Pittsburgh, **N...gas:** Amoco/24hr, Exxon/diesel, Sheetz, Sunoco/24hr, **food:** Arby's, Bob Evans, Boston Mkt, Burger King, Climo's Pizza/chicken, Denny's, Dunkin Donuts, Hardee's, LJ Silver, LoneStar Steaks, McDonald's, Perkins, Shoney's, Wendy's, **lodging:** AmeriSuites, Comfort Inn, Fairfield Inn, Hampton Inn, Holiday Inn Express, Motel 6, Red Roof Inn, Sheraton, Super 8, **other:** HOSPITAL, Giant Foods, Goodyear/atuo, Jo-Ann Fabrics, K-Mart, Phar-Mor Drug, Shop'n Save/24hr, Wal-Mart, mall, **S...gas:** BP/diesel, **food:** Gulf, Eat'n Park, Hot Dog Shop, **lodging:** Day's Inn, Residence Inn, **other:** Toyota

23.5mm pulloff eb

22mm Zelienople Service Plaza eb...Welcome Ctr, gas: Sunoco/diesel/24hr, food: Roy Rogers, Mrs Fields, TCBY, other: crafts, gifts

17mm parking area eb

13.4mm parking area eb

13mm Beaver River

13 PA 8, to Ellwood City, Beaver Valley, **N...lodging:** Alpine Inn, Beaver Valley Motel, Danny's Motel, HillTop Motel, Holiday Inn, Lark Motel, **other:** HOSPITAL, **S...food:** Giuseppe's Italian, **lodging:** Conley Inn/rest.

10 PA 60(toll), to New Castle, Pittsburgh, **S...**services(6mi), to airport

6mm pulloff eb

2mm pulloff eb

2 (from wb), no facilities

1.5mm toll plaza, phone, call boxes located at 1 mi intervals

0mm Pennsylvania/Ohio state line

Interstate 78

Allentown

Exit #	Services
77	Pennsylvania/New Jersey state line, Delaware River

76mm Welcome Ctr wb, full(handicapped)facilities, phone, vending, picnic tables, litter barrels, petwalk, toll booth wb

75 to PA 611, Easton, **N...gas:** TurkeyHill/gas, **food:** McDonald's, Perkins, **lodging:** Best Western, **S...gas:** Shell

71 PA 33, to Stroudsburg, no facilities

67 PA 412, Hellertown, **N...gas:** TurkeyHill/gas, **lodging:** Comfort Suites(3mi), **food:** Wendy's, HOSPITAL **S...gas:** Mobil/Subway, **food:** Burger King, McDonald's, Vassi's Drive-In, **other:** Chevrolet

60b a PA 309 S, Quakertown, **S...**Center Valley Motor Lodge

59 to PA 145(from eb), Summit Lawn, no facilities

58 Emaus St(from wb), no facilities

57 Lehigh St, **N...gas:** Hess/diesel, **food:** Arby's, IHOP, Queen City Diner, **lodging:** Day's Inn, Econolodge, **other:** Aldi Foods, CVS Drug, Family$, Home Depot, Dodge/Kia/Isuzu, Lincoln/Mercury, Whse Mkt Foods/24hr, **S...gas:** TurkeHill/gas, Getty/repair, Gulf, Sunoco, Mobil, Shell/diesel, **food:** Bennigan's, Bob Evans, Brass Rail Rest., Burger King, Domino's, Dunkin Donuts, Dynasty Chinese, Friendly's, Japanese Steaks, McDonald's, Papa John's, Perkins, Pizza Hut/Taco Bell, Subway, Wendy's, **other:** AA Parts, Acura, Audi/Mercedes, BonTon, Buick/GMC/Jeep/Saturn, Chevrolet/Pontiac/Saab, Chrysler, Food4Less, Ford/Hyundai/Honda, Hummer, Lehigh Tire, Mazda/Volvo, Mitsubishi, PharMor, Staples, SteinMart

55 PA 29, Cedar Crest Blvd, **S...**HOSPITAL

PENNSYLVANIA

Interstate 78

E

↕

W

54 US 222, Hamilton Blvd, **N...gas:** Hess, **food:** Ambassador Rest., Boston Mkt, Burger King, Carrabba's, Dunkin Doughnuts, Friendly's, Ice Cream World, Mango's Rest, McDonald's, Perkins, Subway, TGI-Friday, Wendy's, **lodging:** Comfort Inn, Holiday Inn Express, Howard Jhonson, **other:** Dorney Funpark, Laneco Foods, Office Depot, **S...gas:** Sunoco, WaWa/gas, **food:** Charcoal Drive-In, Hunan Chinese, Pizza Hut, Tom Sawyer Diner/24hr, **lodging:** Wingate Inn, **other:** Subaru, U-Haul, Valley Golf

51 to I-476, US 22 E, PA 33 N(eb only), Whitehall, no facilities

49b a PA 100, Fogelsville, **N...food:** Arby's, Cracker Barrel, Gyros King, LJ Silver, Orient Express, Pasta Connection, Pizza Hut, **lodging:** Comfort Inn, Hawthorn Inn, **other:** Eckerd, STS Tire/repair, **S...gas:** Shell, Sunoco/24hr, WaWa, **food:** Burger King, Damon's, Starlite Diner, Taco Bell, Yocco's Hotdogs, **lodging:** Cloverleaf Inn, Hampton Inn, Hilton Garden, Holiday Inn, Sleep Inn, **other:** Toyota, Clover Hill Winery, Vynecrest Winery, st police

45 PA 863, to Lynnport, **N...gas:** Exxon, Sunoco/diesel, **S...lodging:** Super 8

40 PA 737, Krumsville, **N...lodging:** Top Motel, **other:** Pine Hill RV Park(N to blinker, rgt onto Old Rte 22, 1.5 mi), Robin Hill RV Park(4mi), **S...gas:** Shell/diesel, **lodging:** Skyview Rest., **other:** to Kutztown U

I-79 and I-70 run together 3.5 mi. Exits 19-20.

35 PA 143, Lenhartsville, **3 mi S...**Robin Hill Park

30 Hamburg, **S...gas:** Getty/24hr, **food:** Subway

29b a PA 61, to Reading, Pottsville, **N...gas:** Mobil/diesel, **food:** Burger King, Dunkin Doughnuts/Baskin Robbins, Cracker Barrel, Wendy's, **lodging:** Microtel, **other:** Cabela's Outdoor, Harley-Davidson(8mi), st police, **S...other:** Schaeffer's RV(4mi)

23 Shartlesville, **N...gas:** Shell/diesel, Sunoco/Stuckey's/DQ, **lodging:** Dutch Motel, **other:** Appalachian Campsites, Martin RV Ctr, **S...food:** Blue Mtn Family Rest., **lodging:** Budget Motel, Haag's Motel/rest., **other:** antiques

19 PA 183, Strausstown, **N...gas:** Mobil, **S...gas:** Shell, **food:** C&C Pizza

17 PA 419, Rehrersburg, **N...gas:** Best/diesel, truck/tire repair

16 Midway, **N...gas:** Exxon/diesel, Sunoco/diesel, **food:** Blue Mtn Kitchen, Midway Diner, **lodging:** Comfort Inn, **S...**auto/truck repair

15 Grimes, no facilities

13 PA 501, Bethel, **N...gas:** Shell/diesel/24hr, **S...gas:** BP/diesel, Exxon/Subway/diesel

10 PA 645, Frystown, **N...other:** Boat'n RV Ctr, **S...gas:** Shell/diesel/24hr, All-American Trkstp/rest./diesel/24hr

6 (8 from wb, US 22)PA 343, Fredricksburg, **1 mi S...food:** Esther's Rest., **other:** Whse Mkt/fuel, KOA(3mi)

1 I-81. I-78 begins/ends on I-81, exit 89.

Interstate 79

Exit #   Services

I-79 begins/ends in Erie, exit 183.

N

↕

S

E

r

i

e

183b a PA 5, 12th St, Erie, **E...**HOSPITAL, **W...gas:** Sunoco, **food:** Bob Evans, Eat'n Park/24hr, Applebee's, KFC, Hooters, McDonald's, Serafini's Italian, Taco Bell, **lodging:** Clarion, Hampton Inn(2mi), **other:** Advance Parts, Aldi Foods, CVS Drug, $General, Eckerd, Giant Eagle Foods, to Presque Isle SP

182 US 20, 26th St, **E...gas:** Citgo, KwikFill, **other:** HOSPITAL, Advance Parts, Family$, Tops Food/24hr, **W...gas:** Citgo, Shell, **food:** Arby's, Burger King, Hoss' Rest., LJ Silver, McDonald's, Pizza Hut, Subway, Super Buffet, Aamco, AutoZone, CVS Drug, Eckerd, Ford, Giant Eagle, K-Mart

180 US 19, to Kearsarge, **E...food:** Arby's, ChiChi's, Don Pablo, Eat'n Park/24hr, KFC, LoneStar Steaks, Max&Erma's, McDonald's, Olive Garden, Outback Steaks, Ponderosa, Red Lobster, Roadhouse Grill, Wendy's, **lodging:** Fairfield Inn, Homewood Suites, **other:** HOSPITAL, Barnes&Noble, Borders Books, Cadillac, Chrysler/Plymouth/Jeep, Isuzu/Audi, JC Penney, Michael's, Sears/auto, SteinMart, mall, **W...gas:** Citgo/diesel, **other:** camping

178b a I-90, E to Buffalo, W to Cleveland, no facilities

174 to McKean, **E...**access to gas/diesel, phone, **W...**camping

166 US 6N, to Edinboro, **E...gas:** Citgo, Sheetz, **food:** Burger King, McDonald's, Perkins, Subway, Taco Bell, Wendy's, **lodging:** Edinboro Inn, Ramada Inn, **other:** $Tree, Radio Shack, Wal-Mart SuperCtr/24hr

163mm **rest area both lanes, full(handicapped)facilities, phone, vending, picnic tables, litter barrels, petwalk**

154 PA 198, to Saegertown, no facilities

N ↕ S

Meadville

147b a — US 6, US 322, to Meadville, **E...gas:** Citgo/diesel, Marathon, Sheetz/diesel/24hr, Sunoco, **food:** Applebee's, China Buffet, Cracker Barrel, Dairy Queen, Hoss' Rest., KFC, Perkins, Pizza Hut, Sandalini's Buffet, **lodging:** Day's Inn/rest., Holiday Inn Express, Motel 6, **other:** HOSPITAL, Advance Parts, Buick/Pontiac, Giant Eagle/24hr, **W...gas:** Sheetz, **food:** Burger King, King's Rest./24hr, McDonald's, Overlook Café, Pete's Rest., Ponderosa, Red Lobster, **lodging:** Super 8, Aldi Foods, **other:** AutoZone, Cadillac/GMC, Chevrolet, $Tree, Goodyear/auto, K-Mart, Nissan, SavALot, Staples, Toyota, Wal-Mart SuperCtr/24hr, to Pymatuning SP

141 — PA 285, to Geneva, **E...to** Erie NWR(20mi), **W...food:** Aunt Bee's Rest.

135mm rest area/weigh sta both lanes, full(handicapped)facilities, phone, vending, picnic tables, litter barrels, petwalk

130 — PA 358, to Sandy Lake, **E...gas:** Lakeway/diesel/rest./@, **other:** to Goddard SP, camping, **W...other:** HOSPITAL, to Pymatuning SP

121 — US 62, to Mercer, **E...gas:** Citgo, **W...gas:** Sunoco/diesel, **other:** st police

116b a — I-80, E to Clarion, W to Sharon, no facilities

113 — PA 208, PA 258, to Grove City, **E...gas:** BP, Citgo/diesel/24hr, **other:** HOSPITAL, **W...gas:** KwikFill/Subway, Sheetz/24hr, **food:** Eat'n Park/24hr, Elephant&Castle Rest., Hoss' Rest., King's Rest., McDonald's, Wendy's, **lodging:** Amerihost, Comfort Inn, Holiday Inn Express, **other:** KOA(3mi), Prime Outlets/famous brands

110mm rest area sb, full(handicapped)facilities, phone, vending, picnic tables, litter barrels, petwalk

107mm rest area nb, full(handicapped)facilities, phone, vending, picnic tables, litter barrels, petwalk

105 — PA 108, to Slippery Rock, **E...gas:** BP(3mi), **lodging:** Apple Butter Inn(3mi), Evening Star Motel/rest., **other:** Slippery Rock Camping, to Slippery Rock U

99 — US 422, to New Castle, **E...to** Moraine SP, **W...other:** Coopers Lake Camping, **other:** to Rose Point Camping

96 — PA 488, Portersville, **E...**Bear Run Camping, **W...food:** Brown's Country Kitchen

88 — (87 from nb), to US 19, PA 68, Zelienople, **1-2 mi W...gas:** Exxon/diesel/24hr, **food:** Burger King, DQ, Pizza Hut, Subway, **lodging:** Zelienople Motel, **other:** Goodyear, Indian Brave RV Camping

85 — (83 from nb), PA 528(no quick return), to Evans City, **E...**GoCarts, **W...other:** Pontiac/Buick

81mm picnic area both lanes, phone, picnic table, litter barrel

Pittsburgh

78 — (76 from nb, exits left from nb), US 19, PA 228, to Mars, access to I-76, PA TPK, **E...gas:** Citgo, **food:** Applebee's, McDonald's, Quizno's, **lodging:** Marriott, **other:** Kohl's, Lowe's, Staples, Target, Pittsburgh N Camping, **W on US 19...gas:** BP/diesel, Exxon/diesel/24hr, Gulf, 76, Sheetz/24hr, Sunoco/24hr, **food:** Arby's, Bob Evans, Boston Mkt, Burger King, Denny's, Eat'n Park, Hardee's, Hartner's Rest., King's Rest., LoneStar Steaks, LJ Silver, Max&Erma's, Papa John's, Perkins, Shoney's, Subway, TCBY, Wendy's, **lodging:** AmeriSuites, Comfort Inn, Fairfield Inn, Hampton Inn, Holiday Inn Express, Motel 6, Oak Leaf Motel, Red Roof Inn, Residence Inn, Sheraton, **other:** Barnes&Noble, Best Buy, CarQuest, GNC, Giant Eagle, Goodyear/auto, Home Depot, Jo-Ann Fabrics, K-Mart, OfficeMax, PepBoys, Shop'n Save/24hr, Toyota, Wal-Mart/drugs, mall

77 — to Cranberry, new exit

75 — US 19 S(from nb), to Warrendale, services along US 19

73 — PA 910, to Wexford, **E...gas:** BP/24hr, **food:** Eat'n Park, King's Family Rest./24hr, **lodging:** Best Inn, **other:** MEDICAL CARE, **W...gas:** Exxon/diesel/24hr, **food:** Carmody's Rest.

72 — I-279 S(from sb), to Pittsburgh

68 — Mt Nebo Rd, **W...**HOSPITAL, gas

66 — to PA 65, Emsworth, no facilities

65 — to PA 51, Coraopolis, Neville Island, **E...gas:** Gulf, **other:** Penske/Hertz Trucks

64.5mm Ohio River

64 — PA 51(from nb), to Coraopolis, McKees Rocks

60b a — PA 60, Crafton, **E...gas:** Exxon/diesel/24hr, **food:** King's Rest./24hr, **lodging:** Day's Inn, Econolodge, Motel 6, **other:** HOSPITAL, **W...gas:** Sunoco/24hr, **food:** Primanti Rest., **lodging:** Pittsburgh Motel, Red Roof Inn

59b — US 22 W, US 30(from nb), **W...**airport

59a — I-279 N, to Pittsburgh

57 — to Carnegie, **1-3 mi E...gas:** BP, Exxon, **food:** LJ Silver, McDonald's, TCBY, **lodging:** Shop'n Save, Ford, mall

55 — to Heidelberg, **1-2 mi E...gas:** Sunoco, **food:** Arby's, ChuckeCheese, DQ, Eat'n Park/24hr, Grand China, KFC, Little Caesar's, Old Country Buffet, Pizza Hut, Ponderosa, Subway, Taco Bell, Wendy's, **other:** HOSPITAL, Eckerd, Firestone/auto, Giant Eagle/24hr, Goodyear/auto, JC Penney, Jo-Ann Fabrics, K-Mart, Radio Shack, mall, **W...food:** LJ Silver, **food:** McDonald's

54 — PA 50, to Bridgeville, **E...gas:** BP/diesel, Exxon/diesel, **food:** Burger King, King's Rest./24hr, McDonald's, Wendy's, **lodging:** Comfort Inn, **other:** HOSPITAL, Chevrolet, Dodge, **W...gas:** Sunoco, **lodging:** Knights Inn

Interstate 79

50mm	**rest area/weigh sta both lanes, full(handicapped)facilities, phone, vending, picnic tables, litter barrels, petwalk**
48	South Pointe, **W...lodging:** Hilton Garden
45	to PA 980, Canonsburg, **E...gas:** Sheetz, **W...gas:** BP/24hr, Citgo, **food:** Hoss' Rest., KFC/Taco Bell, LJ Silver, McDonald's, Pizza Hut, Subway, Wendy's, **lodging:** Super 8, **other:** Advance Parts
43	PA 519, Houston, **E...gas:** Amoco/diesel, **W...gas:** Sunoco/24hr, HOSPITAL,
41	Race Track Rd, **E...food:** McDonald's, Wendy's, **lodging:** Comfort Inn, Holiday Inn, **W...gas:** BP/diesel, **other:** Trolley Museum
40	Meadow Lands(from nb, no re-entry), **W...other:** Trolley Museum(3mi), golf, racetrack
38	I-70 W, to Wheeling
	I-79 and I-70 run together 3.5 mi. See Pennsylvania Interstate 70, exits 19-20.
34	I-70 E, to Greensburg
33	US 40, to Laboratory, **W...gas:** Amoco, **other:** KOA
31mm	parking area/weigh sta sb
30	US 19, to Amity, **W...gas:** Exxon/Subway
23	to Marianna, Prosperity, no facilities
19	PA 221, to US 19, Ruff Creek, **W...gas:** Amoco/diesel
14	PA 21, to Waynesburg, **E...gas:** Amoco/diesel/24hr, **lodging:** Comfort Inn, **W...gas:** BP/diesel/24hr, Citgo/diesel, Exxon/Taco Bell/diesel, Sheetz, **food:** Burger King, DQ, Golden Corral, Hardee's, KFC, LJ Silver, McDonald's, Wendy's, **lodging:** Econolodge, Super 8, **other:** HOSPITAL, Chevrolet, CVS Drug, More4Less Foods, st police
7	to Kirby, no facilities
6mm	**Welcome Ctr/weigh sta nb, full(handicapped)facilities, phone, picnic tables, litter barrels, vending, petwalk**
1	Mount Morris, **E...gas:** Citgo/diesel/rest., **other:** Honda/Mazda, **W...gas:** BP/diesel, Marathon, **other:** Mt Morris Campground
0mm	Pennsylvania/West Virginia state line

Interstate 80

Exit #	Services
311mm	Pennsylvania/New Jersey state line, Delaware River
310.5	toll booth wb, phone
310	PA 611, Delaware Water Gap, **S...Welcome Ctr/rest area, full facilities, info, gas:** BP, Gulf/repair, **food:** Skillet Rest., Water Gap Diner, **lodging:** Glenwood Hotel/rest., Ramada Ltd, **other:** Christmas Factory Gifts
309	US 209 N, PA 447, to Marshalls Creek, **N...gas:** Exxon/diesel/24hr, Gulf, **food:** DQ, Wendy's, **lodging:** Shannon Motel, **other:** HOSPITAL
308	East Stroudsburg, **N...gas:** Shell, WaWa, **other:** HOSPITAL, **1 mi N...food:** Arby's, Burger King, China King, Friendly's, JR's rest., McDonald's, **other:** Eckerd, Goodyear/auto, K-Mart, NAPA, Radio Shack, ShopRite Foods, Wal-Mart SuperCtr/24hr, Weis Foods, **S...lodging:** Budget Motel, Super 8
307	PA 191, Broad St, **N...gas:** Gulf, **food:** KFC, McDonald's, **lodging:** Hampton Inn, **other:** HOSPITAL, same as 308
306	Dreher Ave(from wb, no EZ return), **N...gas:** Wawa, **other:** Buick
305	US 209, Main St, **N...gas:** Gulf, Mobil, **food:** Perkins/24hr, **lodging:** Clarion, **S...gas:** Exxon/24hr, **lodging:** Alpines Motel
304	(303 from eb)US 209, to PA 33, 9th St(no EZ return from wb), no facilities
302	PA 611, to Bartonsville, **N...gas:** Mobil/Subway/Pizza Hut/Taco Bell/diesel/24hr, Shell, **food:** McDonald's(3mi), Ponderosa(3mi), **lodging:** Comfort Inn, Howard Johnson, Knight's Inn, **other:** Goodyear
299	PA 715, Tannersville, **N...gas:** BP, Mobil, **lodging:** Ramada Ltd, **other:** The Crossing Factory Outlet/famous brands, **1-3 mi N...food:** Barley Creek Brewing, Friendly's, **lodging:** Chateau Inn/rest., **other:** camping, **S...gas:** Sunoco/24hr, **food:** Tannersville Diner, **lodging:** Day's Inn, Summit Resort, **other:** to Camelback Ski Area, to Big Pocono SP
298	PA 611(from wb), to Scotrun, **N...gas:** Shell, Sunoco/diesel, **food:** Anthony's Steaks, Plaza Deli, **lodging:** Scotrun Diner/motel, **other:** to Mt Pocono
295mm	**rest area eb, full(handicapped)facilities, phone, picnic tables, litter barrels, vending, petwalk**
293	I-380 N, to Scranton, no facilities
284	PA 115, to Wilkes-Barre, Blakeslee, **N...gas:** WaWa(1mi), **lodging:** Best Western, Blakeslee Inn(2mi), **other:** Fern Ridge Camping, st police, **S...gas:** Exxon/diesel, **other:** to Pocono Raceway

PENNSYLVANIA
Interstate 80

E

W

277 PA 940, to PA Tpk(I-476), to Pocono, Lake Harmony, Allentown, **N...gas:** BP/24hr, Shell, WaWa, **food:** Arby's, Burger King, Denny's/24hr, Gino's Pizza, Howard Johnson Rest., LJ Silver/A&W, McDonald's, **lodging:** Budget Inn, Comfort Inn, Econolodge, Mtn Laurel Resort, Ramada Inn

274 PA 534, **N...gas:** Hickory Run/Exxon/diesel/rest./24hr, Shell/Subway/diesel/24hr, **other:** camping, **S...other:** to Hickory Run SP(6mi)

273mm Lehigh River

273 PA 940, PA 437, to Freeland, White Haven, **N...gas:** BP, Mobil

270mm **rest area eb, full(handicapped)facilities, info, phone, picnic tables, litter barrels, vending, petwalk**

262 PA 309, to Hazleton, Mountain Top, **N...gas:** Shell, **food:** Evans Rest., Mary's Rest., Wendy's, **lodging:** Econolodge, MtnView Motel/rest., **other:** S...st police

260b a I-81, N to Wilkes-Barre, S to Harrisburg, no facilities

256 PA 93, to Nescopeck, Conyngham, **N...gas:** Pilot/Subway/diesel/24hr/@, Sunoco/repair, **lodging:** Lookout Motel, **S...gas:** Shell/diesel, **food:** Tom's Kitchen(2mi), **lodging:** Best Value Inn, Hampton Inn(4mi),\ HOSPITAL

251mm Nescopeck River

246mm **rest area/weigh sta both lanes, full(handicapped) facilities, weather info, phone, picnic tables, litter barrels, vending, petwalk**

242 PA 339, to Mainville, Mifflinville, **N...gas:** Shell/Blimpie/diesel/24hr, **food:** McDonald's, **lodging:** Super 8/rest., **S...gas:** Citgo/diesel

241mm Susquehanna River

Bloomsburg

241b a US 11, to Berwick, Lime Ridge, Bloomsburg, **N...lodging:** Red Maple Inn(2mi), **other:** HOSPITAL, **S...gas:** Shell, **food:** Kemler's Rest., Subway, **lodging:** Budget Host, **2-5 mi S...gas:** Coastal, Sheetz/24hr, Shell, **food:** Applebee's, Arby's, Burger King, Cap'n Jack's Rest., Chinese Cuisine, Dunkin Donuts, LJ Silver, McDonald's, Pizza Hut, Taco Bell, Terrapin's Cantina, Wendy's, **other:** Advance Parts, BigLots, Buick/Pontiac/GMC, Chevrolet/Cadillac, CVS Drug, Eckerd, Ford/Honda, Geo Grocery, Giant Foods, Kost Tire, Radio Shack, Staples, U-Haul, Wal-Mart

236 PA 487, to Bloomsburg, Lightstreet, **S...gas:** Sunoco, **food:** Denny's/24hr, **lodging:** Hampton Inn, Tennytown Motel(2mi), **other:** HOSPITAL, to Bloomsburg U

232 PA 42, Buckhorn, **N...gas:** Shell/diesel, TA/BP/Subway/diesel/rest./24hr/@, **food:** Buckhorn Rest., Burger King, Cracker Barrel, KFC, Perkins, Wendy's, Western Sizzlin, **lodging:** Buckhorn Inn, Econolodge, Quality Inn/rest., **other:** Home Depot, JC Penney, Sears, mall, **S...other:** Indian Head camping(3mi), Lowe's Whse, Wal-Mart SuperCtr/24hr

224 PA 54, to Danville, **N...gas:** BP/Subway/diesel/24hr, Mobil/DQ/diesel, **food:** Counrty Kitchen, **lodging:** Quality Inn, **S...gas:** Shell/diesel, **food:** Friendly's, McDonald's, Mom's Dutch Kitchen, **lodging:** Day's Inn, Hampton Inn, Key Motel, Red Roof Inn, **other:** HOSPITAL

219mm **rest area both lanes, full(handicapped)facilities, info, phone, picnic tables, litter barrels, vending, petwalk**

215 PA 254, Limestonevill, **N...gas:** Milton 32 Trkstp/diesel/rest./24hr, **S...gas:** Petro/Shell/diesel/rest./24hr/@

212b a I-180 W, PA 147 S, to Muncy, Williamsport, **N...gas:** Shell/diesel, **S...gas:** Sunoco/24hr(1mi)

210.5mm Susquehanna River

210b a US 15, to Williamsport, Lewisburg, **S...gas:** Citgo, **food:** Bonanza, **lodging:** Comfort Inn, Holiday Inn Express, **other:** HOSPITAL

199 Mile Run Rd, no facilities

194mm **rest area/weigh sta both lanes, full(handicapped)f acilities, phone, picnic tables, litter barrels, vending, petwalk**

192 PA 880, to Jersey Shore, **N...gas:** Citgo/diesel/24hr, **food:** Pit-Stop Rest., **S...gas:** Mobil, **other** truck repair

185 PA 477, Logantan, **N...gas:** Mobil, **other:** camping, **S...food:** Twilight Diner, RV Winter SP(12mi)

178 US 220, Lock Haven, **N...food:** Country Barn Rest., **other:** HOSPITAL(7mi), **5 mi N...gas:** Sheetz, **other:** Advance Parts, K-Mart, Wal-Mart SuperCtr/24hr, **S...gas:** Citgo/diesel

173 PA 64, Lamar, **N...gas:** Pilot/Subway/diesel/24hr, **food:** Cottage Rest., McDonald's, Perkins, **lodging:** Comfort Inn/rest., **S...gas:** Citgo, ✈/Flying J/Shell/Coutry Mkt/diesel/LP/@, TA/Mobil/Country Pride/Subway/diesel/rest./24hr/@, **food:** DQ

161 PA 26, US 220 S, to Bellafonte, **S...gas:** Shell/diesel/repair, **other:** KOA, to PSU

158 US 220 S, PA 150, to Altoona, Milesburg, **N...gas:** Bestway/diesel/rest./motel/24hr/@, BP/Subway, Citgo/diesel, TA/diesel/rest./24hr/@, **food:** McDonald's, Buckhorn Rest., **lodging:** Holiday Inn, **S...st police

147 PA 144, to Snow Shoe, **N...gas:** Citgo/diesel/24hr, Exxon/SnowShoe/diesel/repair/24hr, **food:** Snow Shoe Sandwich Shop, Subway, **other:** IGA Foods, repair

146mm **rest area both lanes, full(handicapped)facilities, phone, picnic tables, litter barrels, vending, petwalk**

138mm Moshanna River

133 PA 53, to Philipsburg, Kylertown, **N...gas:** KwikFill/motel/rest./diesel, Sunoco/LP, **food:** Roadhouse Rest., MktPlace Foods, **other:** USPO, diesel repair, Black Moshannon SP(9mi), **S...other:** HOSPITAL

Interstate 80

E ↕ W

D u   B o i s

123 PA 970, to Shawville, Woodland, **S...gas:** BP, Pacific Pride/diesel, **other:** st patrol

120mm Susquehanna River, W Branch

120 PA 879, Clearfield, **N...gas:** Sapp Bros/diesel/24hr/2, **food:** Aunt Lu's Café, **lodging:** Ramda Inn, **S...gas:** BP/Subway, Sheetz/24hr, **food:** Arby's, Burger King, Dutch Pantry, KFC/Pizza Hut/Taco Bell, McDonald's, **lodging:** Comfort Inn, Day's Inn, Holiday Inn Express, Super 8, **other:** HOSPITAL, K-Mart, Wal-Mart SuperCtr/24hr

111mm highest point on I-80 east of Mississippi River, 2250 ft

111 PA 153, to Penfield, **N...**to Parker Dam, to SB Elliot SP, **S...**HOSPITAL

101 PA 255, Du Bois, **N...gas:** BP/24hr, **other:** camping, **S...lodging:** Ramada Inn, **other:** HOSPITAL, st police, **1-2 mi S...gas:** Citgo, Sheetz/24hr, **food:** Arby's, Burger King, Eat'n Park/24hr, Hoss' Rest., Italian Oven, LJ Silver/A&W, McDonald's, Perkins/24hr, Ponderosa, Red Lobster, Ruby Tuesday, Subway, Taco Bell, Wendy's, **lodging:** Best Western, DuBois Manor Motel, Hampton Inn, **other:** BigLots, BiLo Foods, Eckerd, Goodyear/auto, JC Penney, K-Mart, Lowe's Whse, Old Navy, Sears, Shop'n Save Foods, Wal-Mart/drugs, mall

97 US 219, to Brockway, Du Bois, **S...gas:** Pilot/Arby's/diesel/24hr/@, Sheetz/diesel/24hr, **food:** Dutch Pantry Rest., Hoss' Rest.(2mi), Pizza Hut, **lodging:** Best Western, Du Bois Manor Motel(2mi), Holiday Inn, **other:** HOSPITAL, Advance Parts

87.5mm **rest area both lanes, full(handicapped)facilities, phone, picnic tables, litter barrels, vending, pet-walk**

86 PA 830, to Reynoldsville, no facilities

81 PA 28, to Brookville, to Hazen, **S...**to Brookville, hist dist(2mi)

78 PA 36, to Sigel, Brookville, **N...gas:** ✈/Flying J/Country Mkt/diesel/24hr/@, TA/BP/Blimpie/Taco Bell/diesel/rest./24hr/@, **food:** DQ, KFC, McDonald's, Pizza Hut, **lodging:** Howard Johnson, Super 8, **other:** Buick/Pontiac/Cadillac, NAPA, to Cook Forest SP, **S...gas:** Citgo/24hr, Sheetz, **food:** Arby's, Burger King, China Wok, Gilbert's Rest., Subway, **lodging:** Budget Host, Day's Inn, Holiday Inn Express, **other:** MEDICAL CARE

73 PA 949, Corsica, **N...other:** to Clear Creek SP, **S...**USPO

70 US 322, to Strattanville, **N...gas:** Exxon, Keystone/Shell/diesel/rest./24hr/@

64 PA 66 S, to New Bethlehem, Clarion, **N...**to Clarion U

C l a r i o n

62 PA 68, to Clarion, **N...gas:** BP/Subway/24hr, KwikFill/diesel, **food:** Arby's, Burger King, Eat'n Park, LJ Silver/A&W, McDonald's(2mi), Perkins/24hr, Pizza Hut, RRR Roadhouse Rest., Taco Bell, **lodging:** Comfort Inn, Day's Inn/rest., Holiday Inn/rest., Microtel, Quality Inn, Super 8, **other:** HOSPITAL, Advance Parts, Country Mkt/deli/24hr, $Tree, JC Penney, K-Mart, Staples, Wal-Mart SuperCtr/24hr, mall

61mm Clarion River

60 PA 66 N, to Shippenville, **N...gas:** Citgo, **other:** st police, to Cook Forest SP, camping

56mm parking area/weigh sta both lanes

53 to PA 338, to Knox, **N...gas/diesel, food:** Wolf's Den Rest., Wolf's Camping Resort, **S...other:** Good Tire Service

45 PA 478, to St Petersburg, Emlenton, **4 mi S...other:** Golf Hall of Fame

44.5mm Allegheny River

42 PA 38, to Emlenton, **N...gas:** Citgo/diesel/rest./motel/24hr, Exxon/Subway/diesel/24hr, **lodging:** Emlenton Motel, **other:** Gaslight RV Park, truck/RV repair

35 PA 308, to Clintonville, **N...gas/LP**

30.5mm **rest area both lanes, full(handicapped)facilities, phone, picnic tables, litter barrels, vending, pet-walk**

29 PA 8, to Franklin, Barkeyville, **N...gas:** Keystone/diesel, **food:** Arby's, Burger King, King's Rest., **lodging:** Comfort Inn, Day's Inn, Super 8, **S...gas:** Citgo/diesel/24hr, KwikFill/diesel/rest./24hr/@, TA/BP/Subway/diesel/rest./24hr/@, **other:** to Slippery Rock U

24 PA 173, to Grove City, Sandy Lake, **S...other:** HOSPITAL, Wendell August Forge/gifts(3mi)

19b a I-79, N to Erie, S to Pittsburgh, no facilities

15 US 19, to Mercer, **N...gas:** BP, **food:** Burger King, McDonald's, Olde Homestead Rest., **lodging:** Howard Johnson/rest., **other:** st police, camping, **2 mi S...food:** Iron Bridge Inn/rest.

PENNSYLVANIA
Interstate 80

E ↕ **W**

4b a PA 18, PA 60, to Sharon-Hermitage, New Castle, **N...gas:** Sunoco/Subway/diesel/24hr, **food:** Subway, **lodging:** Comfort Inn, Holiday Inn Express, Quality Inn, Radisson, Super 8, **S on PA 318...gas:** Citgo, **food:** DairyMart, DQ, MiddleSex Diner/24hr, **other:** AllPro Parts, antiques, museum

2.5mm Shenango River

1mm **Welcome Ctr eb, full(handicapped)facilities, phone, picnic tables, litter barrels, vending, petwalk**

0mm Pennsylvania/Ohio state line

Interstate 81

N ↕ **S**

Exit #   Services

233mm Pennsylvania/New York state line

232mm insp sta sb

230 PA 171, Great Bend, **E...gas:** Mobil/24hr, **W...gas:** Exxon/Arby's/diesel/24hr, Sunoco/diesel, **food:** Burger King, Dobb's Country Kitchen, McDonald's, Subway, **lodging:** Colonial Brick Motel/rest., **other:** Ford

223 PA 492, New Milford, **W...gas:** Gulf, Mobil/24hr, **food:** Green Gables Rest.

219 PA 848, to Gibson, **E...st police, W... gas:** Exxon/McDonald's/diesel, ⚘/Flying J/Country Mkt/diesel/24hr/@

217 PA 547, Harford, **E...gas:** Exxon/Subway/diesel/24hr/@, Sunoco/diesel/rest./24hr

211 PA 92, Lenox, **E...**Elk Mtn Ski Area, **W...gas:** Mobil/diesel/24hr, Shell/diesel, **food:** Bingham's Rest., **other:** Lenox Drug

209mm **Welcome Ctr sb, full(handicapped)facilities, phone, picnic tables, litter barrel, vending, petwalk**

206 PA 374, Lenoxville, to Glenwood, **E...**to Elk Mountain Ski Resort

203mm **rest area nb, full(handicapped)facilities, phone, picnic tables, litter barrels, vending, petwalk**

202 PA 107, to Fleetville, Tompkinsville, no facilities

201 PA 438, East Benton, **W...gas:** Mobil, **food:** North 40 Rest.

199 PA 524, Scott, **E...gas:** Amoco/diesel, Texaco/diesel/24hr, **W...gas:** Exxon/deli, **food:** Subway, **lodging:** Motel 81, **other:** to Lackawanna SP

197 PA 632, Waverly, **E...other:** Mr Z's Foods, Rite Aid, **W...gas:** Sunoco/24hr, Doc's Deli/24hr

194 US 6, US 11, to I-476/PA Tpk, Clarks Summit, **W... gas:** Shell/diesel, Sunoco/diesel, **food:** Burger King, Friendly's, Krispy Kreme, McDonald's, Pizza Hut, Sabatini's Rest., So-Journer Rest., Subway, Taco Bell, Wendy's, **lodging:** Comfort Inn, Hampton Inn, Nichols Village Inn, Ramada Inn, Summit Inn, **other:** Advance Parts, Eckerd, Kost Tire, Radio Shack, Weis Foods

Scranton

191b a US 6, US 11, to Carbondale, **E...gas:** Shell, **food:** Applebee's, Arby's, Burger King, China Buffet, ChuckeCheese, Denny's, Don Pablo, Fresno's SW Rest., Hawks Chocolates, LJ Silver, LoneStar Steaks, McDonald's, **other:** MEDICAL CARE, Nathan's Dogs, Old Country Buffet, Olive Garden, Perkins, Pizza Hut, Ruby Tuesday, Texas Steaks, TCBY, Wendy's, Quality Hotel, Aldi Foods, Borders Books, Circuit City, $Express, Firestone/auto, Home Depot, Hyundai, JC Penney, Jo-Ann Crafts, K-Mart, OfficeMax, PepBoys, Radio Shack, Sears/auto, Wal-Mart SuperCtr/24hr, Wegman's Foods, mall, **W...other:** to Anthracite Museum

190 Main Ave, Dickson City, **E...food:** Golden Corral, **lodging:** Fairfield Inn, Residence Inn, **other:** Best Buy, Lowe's Whse, Sam's Club, Staples

188 PA 347, Throop, **E...gas:** Sunoco/diesel, **food:** Big Boy, Boston Mkt, China World Buffet, McDonald's, Wendy's, **lodging:** Day's Inn, Econolodge, **other:** Advance Parts, Kost Tire, PriceChopper Foods, Radio Shack, st police, **W...gas:** Mobil, **food:** Burger King, Friendly's, **other:** Mazda

187 to I-84, I-380, US 6(no return from nb)

186 PA 435, Drinker St, **E...gas:** Mobil, **lodging:** Holiday Inn, **W...gas:** Citgo

185 Central Scranton Expwy, **W...**HOSPITAL

184 to PA 307, River St, **W...gas:** Citgo, Exxon, Mobil, **lodging:** Clarion, **other:** HOSPITAL, CVS Drug, $Tree, Gerrity Foods

182 Davis St, Montage Mtn Rd, **E...food:** Mugg's Rest., Rocket's Café, Stadium Club Rest., **lodging:** Comfort Suites, Courtyard, Hampton Inn, **W...gas:** Mobil, Sunoco/diesel, **food:** LJ Silver, McDonald's, Wendy's, **lodging:** Econolodge, Rodeway Inn, **other:** USPO

180 to US 11, PA 502, to Moosic, no facilities

178b a to US 11, Avoca, **E...food:** Damon's, **lodging:** Holiday Inn Express, **W...gas:** Petro/Sunoco/diesel/rest./24hr/@

175b a PA 315 S, to I-476, Dupont, **E...gas:** Mobil/diesel, Sunoco/24hr, **food:** Arby's, McDonald's, Perkins, **lodging:** Knight's Inn, Super 8, **other:** Chevrolet, **W...gas:** Getty, Pilot/Wendy's/diesel/24hr, **lodging:** Victoria Inn, **other:** Wal-Mart

170b a PA 115, PA 309, Wilkes-Barre, **E...gas:** Exxon/diesel, Sunoco/diesel, **lodging:** Best Western, **other:** to Pocono Downs, **W...gas:** Sunoco/24hr, **food:** Friendly's, LJ Silver, McDonald's, Perkins, Pizza Hut, TGIFriday, **lodging:** Candlewood Suites, Day's Inn, Hampton Inn, Holiday Inn, Red Roof Inn, **other:** HOSPITAL, Kia, BMW, Subaru, VW, mall

168 Highland Park Blvd, Wilkes-Barre, **W...gas:** Sheetz, **food:** Applebee's, Bennigan's, Bob Evans, Burger King, Chili's, Cracker Barrel, Ground Round, McDonald's, Olive garden, Outback Steaks, Pizzaria Uno, Red Robin, Wendy's, **lodging:** Best Western, Hilton Garden, Ramada Inn, Travelodge, **other:** Barnes&Noble, Best Buy, Lowe's Whse, Sam's Club/gas, Target, Wal-Mart SuperCtr/24hr, Wegman's Foods

Interstate 81

N ↕ **S**

165b a PA 309 S, Wilkes-Barre, **W...gas:** BP/diesel, Shell, **food:** Dunkin Donuts, Mark II Rest., McDonald's, Perkins, Taco Bell, **lodging:** Comfort Inn, Econolodge, **other:** Advance Parts, Eckerd, K-Mart

164 PA 29, Ashley, to Nanticoke, no facilities

159 Nuangola, **W...gas:** Amoco/24hr, Godfather's

157mm rest area/weigh sta sb, full(handicapped)facilities, vending, phone, picnic tables, litter barrels, petwalk

156mm rest area/weigh sta nb, full(handicapped)facilities, vending, phone, picnic tables, litter barrels, petwalk

155 to Dorrance, **E...gas:** Sunoco/diesel/24hr, **lodging:** Econolodge(2mi)

151b a I-80, E to Mountaintop, W to Bloomsburg

Hazleton

145 PA 93, W Hazleton, **E...gas:** Shell, Sunoco/diesel/24hr, TurkeyHill, **food:** Bonanza, Damon's, Friendly's, Ground Round, LJ Silver, McDonald's, Perkins, Pizza Hut, Rossi's Rest., Taco Bell, Wendy's, **lodging:** Best Western(2mi), Comfort Inn, Fairfield Inn, Forest Hill Inn, Ramada Inn, **other:** Aldi, Cadillac, Mazda, Plymouth/Jeep, **W...gas:** Shell, **food:** Top of the 80's Rest., **lodging:** Hampton Inn, **other:** st police

143 PA 924, to Hazleton, **E...lodging:** Hazleton Motel, **W...gas:** Exxon

141 PA 424, S Hazleton Beltway, **E...**Mt Laurel Motel

138 PA 309, to McAdoo, **2 mi E...lodging:** Pines Motel

135mm scenic area nb

134 to Delano, no facilities

132mm parking area/weigh sta both lanes

131b a PA 54, Mahanoy City, **E...other:** to Tuscarora/Locust Lake SP, **W...gas:** Exxon

124b a PA 61, to Frackville, **E...food:** Cracker Barrel, McDonald's, **lodging:** Holiday Inn Express, **other:** K-Mart, Sears/auto, mall, **W...gas:** Hess, Mobil/Taco Bell/24hr, **food:** Dutch Kitchen, Rocky's Pizza, Subway, **lodging:** Econolodge, Motel 6, **other:** HOSPITAL, Goodyear/auto, Plymouth/Dodge, Rite Aid, st police

119 High Ridge Park Rd, to Gordon, **E...lodging:** Country Inn Suites, **other:** HOSPITAL

116 PA 901, to Minersville, **E...food:** 901 Rest.

112 PA 25, to Hegins, **W...**camping

107 US 209, to Tremont, no facilities

104 PA 125, Ravine, **E...gas:** Exxon/diesel/24hr, **other:** Echo Valley Camping

100 PA 443, to Pine Grove, **E...gas:** Exxon, **food:** Arby's, McDonald's, **lodging:** Colony Lodge, Comfort Inn, Econolodge, **W...gas:** Shell/diesel/24hr

90 PA 72, to Lebanon, **E...gas:** Exxon, Hess, **food:** Subway, Wendy's, **lodging:** Day's Inn, **other:** KOA, Lickdale Camping, **W...lodging:** Red Carpet Inn

89 I-78 E, to Allentown

85b a PA 934, to Annville, **2 mi W...gas:** Mobil/rest., **other:** to Indian Town Gap Nat Cem

80 PA 743, Grantville, **E...gas:** Mobil/diesel, **lodging:** Econolodge, Hampton Inn, **W...gas:** Exxon, Shell, **lodging:** Comfort Suites, Holiday Inn, **other:** racetrack

79mm rest area/weigh sta both lanes, full(handicapped)facilities, phone, vending, picnic tables, litter barrels, petwalk

77 PA 39, to Hershey, **E...gas:** Exxon/diesel, Mobil/diesel, Pilot/Pizza Hut/diesel/24hr, **lodging:** Country Inn Suites, Ramada Ltd, Sleep Inn, **other:** to Hershey Attractions, st police, **W...gas:** Shell/Subway/diesel, TA/diesel/24hr/@, Wilco/Perkins/diesel/24hr, **food:** McDonald's, **lodging:** Comfort Inn, Daystop, **other:** Goodyear

72 to US 22, Linglestown, **E...gas:** Citgo/diesel, Hess, Shell/diesel, Sunoco/diesel, **food:** Applebee's, Burger King, El Rodeo Mexican, LJSilver, McDonald's, Malley's Rest., Old Country Buffet, Wendy's, **lodging:** Holiday Inn Express, L&M Motel, Quality Inn, **other:** Advance Parts, C&P Repair, Chrysler/Jeep, CVS Drug, Festival Foods, K-Mart, Toyota, U-Haul, **W...food:** Country Oven Rest., **lodging:** Best Western

70 I-83 S, to York, airport

69 Progress Ave, **E...food:** Cracker Barrel, **other:** st police, **W...food:** Western Sizzlin, **lodging:** Best Western, Red Roof Inn

67b a US 22, US 322 W, PA 230, Cameron St, to Lewistown, no facilities

66 Front St, **E...**HOSPITAL, **W...food:** McDonald's, Ponderosa, Wendy's, **lodging:** Day's Inn

65 US 11/15, to Enola, **1 mi E...gas:** Mobil/24hr, Sunoco/diesel/24hr, **food:** DQ, Eat'n Park, KFC, McDonald's, Subway, Wendy's, **lodging:** Quality Inn, **other:** Advance Parts, K-Mart, Radio Shack, Rite Aid

61 PA 944, to Wertzville, no facilities

59 PA 581, to US 11, to Harrisburg, **3 mi E...food:** Bob Evans, Burger King, Friendly's, McDonald's, Wendy's, **lodging:** Comfort Inn, Hampton Inn, Holiday Inn

57 PA 114, to Mechanicsburg, **1-2 mi E...food:** Arby's, Isaac's Rest., McDonald's, Pizza Hut, Taco Bell, **lodging:** Ramada Ltd

Harrisburg

N ↕ S

Carlisle

52b a US 11, to I-76/PA Tpk, Middlesex, **E...gas:** Citgo/diesel, ♿/Flying J/diesel/LP/rest./24hr/@, **food:** Bob Evans, Middlesex Diner/24hr, **lodging:** Appalachian Tr Motel, Clarion, Econolodge, Holiday Inn, Super 8, **W...gas:** Petro/diesel/rest./24hr/@, Pilot/Wendy's/diesel/24hr/@, Shell/diesel/24hr, Sunoco, **food:** Arby's, Big Boy/24hr, Carelli's Subs, Eat'n Park, Hoss' Rest., McDonald's, Subway, Waffle House, Western Sizzlin, **lodging:** Hampton Inn, Howard Johnson, Motel 6, Quality Inn, Ramada Ltd, Rodeway Inn, **other:** Giant Foods, Carlisle Camping

49 PA 74(no EZ sb return), **W...gas:** Getty, **food:** Burger King, LJ Silver, McDonald's, same as 48

48 PA 74, York St(no EZ nb return), **W...gas:** Gulf, Hess, KwikFill, **food:** Rillo's Rest., **other:** Ford/Mercury, OfficeMax, **1 mi W...food:** Burger King, LJ Silver, McDonald's, Pizza Hut, Taco Bell, **other:** CVS Drug, JC Penney, K-Mart, Lowe's Whse, Sears/auto

47 PA 34, Hanover St, **E...food:** Cracker Barrel, **lodging:** Sleep Inn, **W...gas:** Mobil

45 College St, **E...gas:** Mobil, Shell, **food:** Bonanza, Carelli's Subs, Friendly's, Great Wall Chinese, McDonald's, **lodging:** Day's Inn, Super 8, **other:** Eckerd, K-Mart, **W...HOSPITAL**

44 PA 465, to Plainfield, **W...gas:** Sheetz/24hr

38mm rest area both lanes, full(handicapped)facilities, phone, picnic tables, litter barrels, petwalk

37 PA 233, to Newville, **E...other:** Pine Grove Furnace SP, **W...**Col Denning SP

29 PA 174, King St, **E...gas:** Shell/diesel, Sunoco/24hr, **lodging:** Budget Host, **W...food:** Burger King(1mi), DQ, McDonald's(2mi), **lodging:** AmeriHost, **other:** Ford

24 PA 696, Fayette St, **W...gas:** Mobil/diesel

20 PA 997, Scotland, **E...gas:** Exxon/diesel, **food:** McDonald's, **lodging:** Comfort Inn, Super 8, **other:** JC Penney, Sears/auto, mall, **W...gas:** BP/diesel, Sunoco/24hr

Chambersburg

16 US 30, to Chambersburg, **E...gas:** Sheetz/24hr, **food:** Boston Mkt, DQ, KFC, Perkins, Popeye's, **lodging:** Day's Inn, **other:** Aldi Foods, $Express, Food Lion, Harley-Davidson, Nissan/Toyota, st police, **W...gas:** Hess/diesel, **food:** Burger King, Golden China, LJ Silver, McDonald's, Pizza Hut, Ponderosa, Taco Bell, **lodging:** Best Western(1mi), Sheraton, Travelodge(1mi), **other:** HOSPITAL, Advance Parts, Family$, Lincoln/Mercury, Sav-A-Lot Food

14 PA 316, Wayne Ave, **E...food:** Bob Evans, Cracker Barrel, **lodging:** Fairfield Inn, Hampton Inn, **W...gas:** Exxon/24hr, KwikFill, Sheetz, Shell/diesel, Sunoco, **food:** Applebee's, Arby's, Denny's, Pizza Hut, Red Lobster, Subway, Wendy's, **lodging:** Econolodge, Holiday Inn Express, Quality Inn, **other:** CVS Drug, Giant Foods, K-Mart, Staples, Weis Foods

12mm weigh sta sb

10 PA 914, Marion, no facilities

7mm weigh sta nb

5 PA 16, Greencastle, **E...gas:** Shell/diesel, TA/BP/diesel/24hr/@, **food:** Arby's, Buckhorn Rest., McDonald's, Subway, **lodging:** Castle Green Motel, Econolodge, Rodeway Inn, **other:** Whitetail Ski Resort, **W...gas:** Exxon/diesel, **food:** Antrim House Rest., Hardee's

3 US 11, **E...food:** Chef Family Rest., **lodging:** Comfort Inn

2mm Welcome Ctr nb, full(handicapped)facilities, phone, picnic tables, litter barrels, vending, petwalk

1 PA 163, Mason-Dixon Rd, **W...food:** Black Steer Rest., Mason-Dixon Rest., **lodging:** Econolodge, State Line Motel, **other:** Keystone RV

0mm Pennsylvania/Maryland state line, Mason-Dixon Line

Interstate 83

Exit # Services

Harrisburg

N ↕ S

51b a I-83 begins/ends on I-81, exit 70.

50b a US 22, Jonestown Rd, Harrisburg, **E...gas:** Shell, Sunoco, **food:** Applebee's, Arby's, Colonial Diner, LJ Silver, McDonald's, Old Coutry Buffet, Olive Garden, Pizza Hut, Red Lobster, Subway, Taco Bell, **other:** Aamco, Best Buy, Borders Books, Coscto/gas, CVS Drug, Goodyear/auto, Home Depot, Kohl's, Michael's, NTB, Old Navy, PepBoys, Sears/auto, Target, Tires+, Weis Foods, mall, **W...gas:** Citgo/7-11, Exxon, **food:** Friendly's, KFC, Outback Steaks

48 Union Deposit Rd, **E...gas:** Sunoco, **food:** Arby's, Burger King, Denny's, Evergreen Chinese, LoneStar Steaks, Panera Bread, Wendy's, **lodging:** Hampton Inn, Sheraton, **other:** HOSPITAL, Giant Foods, Staples, mall, **W...gas:** Shell, **food:** ChiChi's, Hardee's, McDonald's, OutBack Steaks, Rita's Drive-Thru, Subway, TGIFriday, Waffle House, Your Place Rest., **lodging:** Comfort Inn, Fairfield Inn, **other:** Lowe's Whse, Phar-Mor Drugs, Radio Shack, Weis Foods

47 (46b from nb), US 322 E, to Hershey, Derry St, **E...gas:** Hess Gas, **food:** Papa John's, **other:** Home Depot

46a I-283 S, to I-76/PA Tpk, **facilities E off I-283 S...gas:** Amoco, Exxon/diesel, Sunoco, **food:** Bob Evans, Capitol Diner, Doc Holliday's Steaks, Eat'n Park, Leed's Grill, McDonald's, **lodging:** Baymont Inn, Econolodge, Holiday Inn, Howard Johnson, Marriott, Red Roof Inn, Super 8, Travelodge, Wyndham, **other:** Buick, LandRover, VW/Audi

45 Paxton St, **E...gas:** Texaco, **food:** Burger King, Dunkin Donuts, Pizza Hut, Ponderosa, Santo's Pizza, S Philly Hoagies, Wendy's, **other:** Chrysler/Plymouth, JC Penney, Mazda/Subaru/Toyota, mall

44b 17th St, 19th St, **E...gas:** Pacific Pride/diesel, Sunoco, A+ Minimart, **food:** Benihana Japanese, Hardee's, Massimo's Pizza/subs, Royal Thai Rest., **other:** Big A Parts, Cadillac/GMC, Dodge, Firestone, Honda, Hyundai/Suzuki/Isuzu, Nissan, Pontiac

Interstate 83

N ↑↓ S

44a PA 230, 13th St, Harrisburg, downtown, **W...gas:** Chevrolet, **other:** Saturn

43 2nd St, Harrisburg, downtown, st capitol, **W...gas:** Crowne Plaza, **other:** HOSPITAL

42.5mm Susquehanna River

42 Lemoyne, **E...gas:** Hess, Mobil, Turkey Hill Gas/food, **food:** Burger King, KFC

41b Highland Park, **W...gas:** Mobil, **food:** KFC, Rascal's Pizza, Royal Subs, Weis Foods

41a US 15, PA 581 W, to Gettysburg, no facilities

40b New Cumberland, **W...gas:** Shell, **food:** JoJo's Pizza, McDonald's, Subway, **other:** $General

40a Limekiln Rd, to Lewisberry, **E...gas:** BP, Mobil, **food:** Bob Evans, Eat'n Park, McDonald's, Pizza Hut, **lodging:** Comfort Inn, Fairfield Inn, Holiday Inn, Rodeway Inn, Travelodge, **W...gas:** Hess/diesel, **lodging:** Motel 6, Travel Inn

39b I-76/PA Tpk

39a PA 114, Lewisberry Rd, **E...lodging:** Day's Inn

38 Reesers Summit, no facilities

36 PA 262, Fishing Creek, **E...gas:** Hess, **food:** Culhanes Steaks, **W...gas:** Shell

35 PA 177, Lewisberry, **E...food:** Hillside Café, **W...gas:** Mobil, **food:** Family Rest.

35mm parking area/weigh sta sb

34 Valley Green(from nb), same as 33

33 PA 392, Yocumtown, **E...gas:** Hess/Blimpie/diesel, Henry's Trkstop/diesel, Rutter's Gas, **food:** Alice's Rest., Burger King, Maple Donuts, McDonald's, Newberry Diner, **lodging:** Super 8, **other:** MEDICAL CARE, Eckerd, Family$, Radio Shack, SuperFresh Food, Thrift Drugs

33mm parking area/weigh sta nb

32 PA 382, Newberrytown, **E...gas:** Sunoco/diesel, Rutter's/diesel, **food:** Pizza Hut, **W...gas:** Exxon/diesel

28 PA 295, Strinestown, **W...gas:** Exxon/Rutter's/24hr, **food:** Wendy's

24 PA 238, Emigsville, **W...gas:** Mobil, **food:** Sibol's Steaks

22 PA 181, N George St, **E...gas:** Exxon/24hr, Getty, **lodging:** Comfort Inn, **W...gas:** Sunoco/24hr, **food:** LJ Silver, McDonald's, Wendy's, **lodging:** Day's Inn, Motel 6, Super 8, same as 21b

21b a US 30, Arsenal Rd, to York, **E...food:** Bob Evans, San Carlo's Rest., **lodging:** Day's Inn, Hampton Inn(2mi), Holiday Inn, Ramada Inn, Red Roof Inn, Sheraton, **other:** Pontiac, **W...gas:** Crown Gas, Exxon, Mobil, Texaco/diesel, **food:** Burger King, China Kitchen, Domino's, Dunkin Donuts, El Rodeo Mexican, Friendly's, Hardee's, Hooters, KFC, LoneStar Steaks, LJ Silver, McDonald's, Old Country Buffet, Pizza Hut,

York

Popeye's, Subway, Taco Bell, Wendy's, **lodging:** Holiday Inn, Motel 6, Super 8, **other:** Chevrolet/Subaru, Chrysler/Mitsubishi, CVS Drug, Harley-Davidson, NTB, PepBoys, Radio Shack, Staples, Weis Foods

19 PA 462, Market St, **E...gas:** Sunoco, **food:** Applebee's, Eat'n Park, Perkins, **lodging:** Quality Inn Suites, **other:** HOSPITAL, Nissan, Saturn, **W...gas:** Sunoco

18 PA 124, Mt Rose Ave, Prospect St, **E...gas:** Exxon, Mobil, Rutters, **food:** Sunoco/Pizza Hut, Burger King, Denny's, Little Caesar's, **lodging:** Budget Host, Spirit of 76 Motel, **other:** CVS Drug, K-Mart, Nello Tire, Weis Foods, **W...gas:** Mobil(1mi)

16b a PA 74, Queen St, **E...gas:** Mobil/24hr, **food:** Cracker Barrel, Pizza Hut, Ruby Tuesday, **lodging:** Country Inn Suites, **other:** Ford/Lincoln/Mercury, Giant Foods, **W...gas:** Exxon, **food:** Chap's Rest., McDonald's, Subway, Taco Bell, **other:** CVS Drug, Cadillac/BMW/Hyundai, CVS Drug, $General, Honda, Jo-Ann Fabrics, Weis Foods

15 (from nb)S George St, I-83 spur into York, **W...**HOSPITAL

14 PA 182, Leader Heights, **E...**Subway, **W...gas:** Exxon/Pizza Hut, Sunoco/diesel/24hr, **food:** McDonald's, **lodging:** Comfort Inn

10 PA 214, Loganville, **W...food:** Lee's Rest., Mamma's Pizza, **lodging:** Midway Motel, **other:** st police

8 PA 216, Glen Rock, **E...lodging:** Rocky Ridge Motel, **other:** Amish Farmers Mkt(2mi)

4 PA 851, Shrewsbury, **E...gas:** Crown/diesel/@, Mobil/diesel/24hr, **lodging:** Hampton Inn, **W...gas:** Exxon/diesel/24hr, **food:** Arby's, Coachlight Rest., KFC/Taco Bell, McDonald's, Subway, Wendy's, **other:** Advance Parts, CVS Drug, $Tree, Giant Foods/24hr, GNC, Radio Shack, Wal-Mart SuperCtr/24hr

2mm **Welcome Ctr nb, full(handicapped)facilities, phone, vending, picnic tables, litter barrels, petwalk**

0mm Pennsylvania/Maryland state line

PENNSYLVANIA
Interstate 84

E
W

Exit #	Services
54mm	Pennsylvania/New York state line, Delaware River
53	US 6, PA 209, Matamoras, **N...Welcome Ctr/both lanes, full(handicapped)facilities, phone, vending, picnic tables, litter barrels, petwalk, gas:** BP, Citgo, Go24, **food:** Apple Grill, Taco Palace, **lodging:** Apple Valley Motel, **other:** AutoZone, Tri-State Camping, **S...gas:** Mobil, **food:** McDonald's, Perkins, Subway, Wendy's, **lodging:** Best Western, Scottish Inn, **other:** Eckerd, Grand Union Foods, Home Depot, K-Mart, Wal-Mart, Riverbeach Camping
46	US 6, to Milford, **N...gas:** Mobil/24hr, **2 mi S...gas:** Citgo/diesel/24hr, Sunoco/diesel, **food:** Apple Valley Rest., **lodging:** Black Walnut B&B, Cliff Park Inn, Sherelyn Motel, Red Carpet Inn, Tom Quick Inn/rest.
34	PA 739, to Lords Valley, Dingmans Ferry, **S...gas:** Mobil, Sunoco/Taco Bell/diesel, **food:** China Dynasty, McDonald's, Pizza/pasta, **other:** Rite Aid, USPO
30	PA 402, to Blooming Grove, **N...**st police, to Lake Wallenpaupack
26	PA 390, to Tafton, **N...**Exxon/diesel, to Lake Wallenpaupack, **S...other:** to Promised Land SP
26mm	**rest area/weigh sta both lanes, full(handicapped)facilities, phone, vending, picnic tables, litter barrels, petwalk**
20	PA 507, Greentown, **N...gas:** Exxon/diesel, Mobil, **food:** John's Italian, **other:** Animal Park
17	PA 191, to Newfoundland, Hamlin, **N...gas:** Exxon/24hr, Howe's 84/diesel/24hr, **food:** Twin Rocks Rest., **lodging:** Comfort Inn/rest.
8	PA 247, PA 348, Mt Cobb, **N...gas:** Gulf, **other:** golf, **S...gas:** Mobil/diesel/24hr
4	I-380 S, to Mount Pocono, no facilities
2	PA 435 S, to Elmhurst, no facilities
1	Tigue St, **N...lodging:** Holiday Inn, **S...gas:** Mobil
0mm	I-84 begins/ends on I-81, exit 54.

Interstate 90

E
W

Exit #	Services
46mm	Pennsylvania/New York state line, **Welcome Ctr/weigh sta wb, full(handicapped)facilities, phone, vending, picnic tables, litter barrels, petwalk**
45	US 20, to State Line, **N...gas:** KwikFill/diesel/@, TA/Taco Bell/diesel/rest./@, **food:** McDonald's, Pizza Hut, **other:** Heritage Wine Cellars, **S...gas:** BP/Subway/diesel, **lodging:** Red Carpet Inn, **other:** Niagara Falls Info

Erie

41	PA 89, North East, **N...gas:** Shell, **lodging:** Super 8, Vineyard B&B, **S...**winery
37	I-86 E, to Jamestown, no facilities
35	PA 531, to Harborcreek, **N...gas:** TA/BP/diesel/rest./24hr/@, **food:** Pizza Hut, Subway, **lodging:** Rodeway Inn, **other:** Blue Beacon
32	PA 430, to Wesleyville, **N...gas:** Citgo, **S...other:** camping, st police
29	PA 8, to Hammett, **N...gas:** Citgo, **food:** Wendy's, **other:** HOSPITAL, **S...lodging:** Travelodge, **other:** Ford/Peterbilt, Cummins Repair
27	PA 97, State St, Waterford, **N...gas:** Citgo/diesel/24hr, Kwikfill, Petro, **food:** Arby's, Barbato's Italian, Big Boy, McDonald's, **lodging:** Best Western, Day's Inn, Red Roof Inn, TalleyHo Inn, **other:** HOSPITAL, **S...gas:** Pilot/Subway/diesel/24hr, Shell/diesel, **lodging:** Quality Inn, Super 8
24	US 19, Peach St, to Waterford, **N...gas:** Citgo/diesel, KwikFill, **food:** Applebee's, Burger King, China Garden, ChuckeCheese, Cracker Barrel, Damon's, Eat'n Park, Fazoli's, Longhorn Steaks, McDonald's, Old Country Buffet, Panera Bread, Ponderosa, QuakerSteak/lube, Taco Bell, TGIFriday, Valentino's, Wendy's, **lodging:** Courtyard, Motel 6, **other:** HOSPITAL, Advance Parts, Best Buy, Circuit City, Country Fair/deli, $Tree, Giant Eagle, Home Depot, Jo-Ann Fabrics, K-Mart, Kohl's, Lowe's Whse, Pontiac, Sam's Club, Staples, Target, VW, Wal-Mart/auto, Wegman's Foods, **S...gas:** Citgo, Sunoco, **food:** Bob Evans, **lodging:** Comfort Inn, Country Inn Suites, Econolodge, Hampton Inn, Holiday Inn Express, Microtel, Residence Inn
22b a	I-79, N to Erie, S to Pittsburgh, **3-5 mi N...**facilities in Erie
18	PA 832, Sterrettania, **N...gas:** Citgo/diesel/24hr, Shell/diesel/24hr, **food:** Burger King, **other:** Hill's Family Camping, to Presque Isle SP, **S...lodging:** Best Western
16	PA 98, to Franklin Center, Fairview, **S...other:** Follys Inn Camping(2mi), Mar-Jo-Dy Camping(5mi)
9	PA 18, to Girard, Platea, **N...gas:other:** Gulf, **other:** diesel repair, st police, **S...**lodging
6	PA 215, to Albion, East Springfield, **N...**lodging, **S...gas:** Sunoco
3	US 6N, to Cherry Hill, West Springfield, **N...**lodging on US 20, **S...gas:** BP/diesel/rest./repair/@/24hr
2.5mm	**Welcome Ctr/weigh sta eb, full(handicapped)facilities, info, phone, picnic tables, litter barrels, vending, petwalk**
0mm	Pennsylvania/Ohio state line

Interstate 95

N ↕ **S**

Exit #	Services
51mm	Pennsylvania/New Jersey state line, Delaware River
51	PA 32, to New Hope, **W**...Washington Crossing Hist Park
49mm	**Welcome Ctr sb, full(handicapped)facilities, vending, phone, picnic tables, litter barrels, petwalk**
49	PA 332, to Yardley, Newtown, **W**...lodging: Hampton Inn, **other:** HOSPITAL, to Tyler SP
46	US 1, Langhorne, Oxford Valley, **E**...HOSPITAL
44	US 1, PA 413, to Penndel, Levittown, **E**...gas: Shell/diesel/24hr, **food:** ChuckeCheese, Classic Steaks, Dunkin Donuts, Friendly's, Great American Diner, Panera Bread, Quizno's, Ruby Tuesday, Wendy's, **other:** HOSPITAL, Acura, Chevrolet/Buick, China Buffet, China Pearl, Chrysler, Dodge, $Tree, Drug Emporium, Ford, Goodyear/auto, Harley Davidson, Honda, Hyundai/Suzuki, Jeep, K-Mart, Lincoln/Mercury, Lowe's Whse, Marshalls, NTB, Radio Shack, Sam's Club, Subaru, VW/Volvo, Whse Mkt, **W**...gas: Mobil/diesel/24hr, **food:** Denny's, McDonald's, **other:** Toyota, U-Haul
40	PA 413, I-276(from nb), to Bristol Bridge, Burlington, **E**...food: Golden Eagle Diner/24hr, McDonald's, Taco Bell, **other:** HOSPITAL
37	PA 132, to Street Rd, **W**...gas: BP/24hr, Shell, Sunoco/diesel, **food:** Burger King, Denny's, IHOP, KFC, Wendy's, **other:** Firestone, GNC, PepBoys, Radio Shack
35	PA 63, to US 13, Woodhaven Rd, Bristol Park, **W**...gas: Coastal, Mobil, WaWa, **food:** Old Haven Pizza, **lodging:** Hampton Inn, **other:** HOSPITAL, Acme Foods, Hancock Fabrics, Home Depot, **1 mi W**...gas: BP, Exxon, Mobil, Sunoco, **food:** Arby's, Boston Mkt, Dynasty Buffet, Don Pablo, Dynasty Rest., Farm Buffet, KFC, McDonald's, Perkins, Pizza Hut, Taco Bell, Wendy's, **other:** CompUSA, JC Penney, Marshall's, Nordstrom's, NTB, OfficeMax, SuperFresh Foods, Wal-Mart, mall
32	Academy Rd, **W**...other: HOSPITAL, K-Mart
30	PA 73, Cottman Ave, **W**...gas: Sunoco
27	Bridge St, **W**...gas: Getty Gas, Eckerd, **other:** HOSPITAL
26	to NJ 90, Betsy Ross Brdg, **W**...gas: Sunoco, **food:** Burger King, McDonald's, Wendy's, **lodging:** Hampton Inn, **other:** Home Depot
25	Allegheny Ave, **W**...gas: Sunoco, Wawa, **other:** HOSPITAL
23	Lehigh Ave, Girard Ave, **W**...gas: Exxon, Shell, **food:** Dunkin Donuts, Pizza Hut, Ruby Tuesday, **other:** HOSPITAL, Radio Shack
22	I-676, US 30, to Central Philadelphia, Independence Hall, no facilities
20	Columbus Blvd, Penns Landing, **E**...gas: BP, Mobil, Sunoco, **food:** Burger King, Boston Mkt, Dave&Buster's, ChartHouse Rest., ChuckeCheese, Enginehouse Rest, Grand King Buffet, Hooters, McDonald's, **lodging:** Hyatt Hotel(1mi), **other:** Hyatt, Home Depot, OfficeMax, PepBoys, SavALot Foods, ShopRite Foods, Staples, Target, Wal-Mart
19	I-76 E, to Walt Whitman Bridge, **W on Oregon Ave**...gas: Shell, **food:** Burger King, Church's Chicken, McDonald's, Subway, Wendy's, **lodging:** Holiday Inn, **other:** Aldi, K-Mart, to stadium
17	PA 611, to Broad St, Pattison Ave, **W**...other: HOSPITAL, to Naval Shipyard, to stadium
15mm	Schuykill River
15	Enterprise Ave, Island Ave(from sb), no facilities
14	Bartram Ave, Essington Ave(from sb), no facilities
13	PA 291, to I-76 W(from nb), to Central Philadelphia, **E**...gas: Exxon/diesel, **lodging:** Day's Inn, Guest Quarters, Hilton, Residence Inn, Sheraton Suites, Westin Suites
12	**E**...Philadelphia Intl Airport
10	PA 291 E, **E**...lodging: Marriott, Rennaisance Hotel, **W**...lodging: Courtyard, Hampton Inn, Embassy Suites, Extended Stay America, Fairfield Inn, Microtel, Studio+
9b a	PA 420, to Essington, Prospect Park, **E**...gas: Coastal/diesel, **food:** Denny's, Shoney's, **lodging:** Comfort Inn, Econolodge, Holiday Inn, Motel 6, Radisson, Ramada Inn, Red Roof Inn
8	to Chester Waterfront, Ridley Park, **W on US 13**...gas: Sunoco, WaWa, **food:** McDonald's, **other:** Wal-Mart
7	I-476 N, to Plymouth, Meeting, no facilities
6	PA 352, PA 320, to Edgmont Ave, **1 mi E on US 13**...food: McDonald's, **other:** Wal-Mart, **W**...food: Edgmont Diner, **other:** HOSPITAL, to Widener U
5	Kerlin St(from nb), **E**...gas: BP
4	US 322 E, to NJ, to Barry Bridge, **W**...lodging: Highland Motel
3	(3 from nb, no EZ return)US 322 W, Highland Ave, **E**...gas: Sunoco/diesel/24hr, Ford/Lincoln/Mercury, Goodyear
2	PA 452, to US 322, Market St, **E**...gas: Getty, **W**...gas: Exxon, **food:** McDonald's
1	Chichester Ave, **E**...gas: Sunoco, **W**...gas: BP
0mm	**Pennsylvania/Delaware state line, Welcome Ctr/weigh sta nb, full(handicapped)facilities, phone, picnic tables, litter barrels, petwalk**

Levittown

Philadelphia Area

PENNSYLVANIA

Interstate 99

N
S

Altoona

Exit #	Services
	I-99 begins/ends on US 220 at Bald Eagle.
52	PA 350, **W...gas:** BP/Subway
48	PA 453, Tyrone, **W...gas:** Sheetz/diesel/24hr, **food:** Burger King, **other:** HOSPITAL
45	Tipton, Grazierville, **W...gas:** Exxon, **food:** Pizza Hut, **other:** HOSPITAL, Chrysler/Plymouth/Dodge/Jeep, DelGrosso's Funpark
41	PA 865 N, Bellwood, **E...**Ft Roberdeau HS, **W...gas:** Martin Gen Store/diesel, Sheetz/diesel
39	PA 764 S, Pinecroft, **W...**Oak Spring Winery
33	17th St, Altoona, **W...gas:** Sheetz/24hr, **food:** Hoss' Rest., Subway(2mi), **other:** Lowe's Whse, Railroader Museum, U-Haul
32	PA 36, Frankstown Rd, Altoona, **E...**Canoe Cr SP, **W...gas:** Sheetz, **food:** Dunkin Donuts, HongKong Buffet, McDonald's, Olive Garden, Papa John's, Perkins, Pizza Hut, Red Lobster, Subway, Wendy's, **lodging:** Day's Inn, Econolodge, Holiday Inn, Super 8, **other:** HOSPITAL, AutoZone, Big A Parts, Cadillac, CVS Drug, Daewoo, Dodge, Eckerd, Lincoln/Mercury, NAPA, Nissan, Radio Shack, Subaru
31	Plank Rd, Altoona, **E...food:** Fazoli's, Friendly's, Jethro's Rest., King's Rest., Outback Steaks, Ruby Tuesday, TGIFriday, **lodging:** Comfort Inn, Ramada Inn, **other:** Circuit City, Firestone/auto, Sam's Club, Target, Wal-Mart, **W...gas:** BP/Subway, food: Applebee's, Arby's, Burger King, Cracker Barrel, Denny's, Don Pablo, Eat'n Park, KFC, LJ Silver, Ponderosa, Taco Bell, **lodging:** Hampton Inn, Motel 6, **other:** Advance Parts, BiLo Foods, $General, Giant Eagle Foods, JC Penney, Kaufmann's, K-Mart, PharMor, Sears/auto, Staples, Trak Auto, Weis Foods
28	US 22, to Ebensburg, Holidaysburg, **1 mi E...food:** McDonald's
23	PA 36, PA 164, Roaring Spring, Portage, **E...gas:** Exxon/LittleCaesar's/24hr, Mobil/Blimpie/diesel, Sheetz/24hr, **food:** Lynn's Rest., **lodging:** Rax, Haven Rest Motel, **other:** HOSPITAL, Chrysler/Plymouth/Dodge/Jeep, truck repair
15	Claysburg, King, **W...**gas, food
10	to Imler, **W...**gas, food, Blue Knob SP(8mi)
7	PA 869, Osterburg, St Clairsville, **W...**gas, food
3	PA 56, Johnstown, Cessna, **E...gas:** BP/diesel
1	I-70/76. I-99 begins/ends on US 220. **E...gas:** Amoco, BP/Mcdonald's, Sheetz, **food:** Arena Rest., Denny's, Hoss' Rest, LJ Silver, Pizza Hut, Wendy's, **lodging:** Budget Host, Best Western, Econolodge, Hampton Inn, Quality Inn, Super 8, Travelodge

Interstate 476

E
W

Philadelphia

Exit #	Services
131	US 11, US 6. I-476 begins/ends on I-81.
122	Keyser Ave, Old Forge, Taylor, no facilities
121mm	toll plaza
115	I-81, PA 315, Wyoming Valley, Pittston, **W...gas:** Mobil, Pilot/Wendy's/diesel/24hr, Sunoco, **food:** Arby's, McDonald's, Perkins, **lodging:** Knight's Inn, Super 8, **other:** Chevrolet
112mm	toll plaza
105	PA 115, Wilkes-Barre, Bear Creek, **E...gas:** Amoco, Mobil/diesel, Texaco
103mm	parking area sb
100mm	parking areas both lanes
97mm	parking areas both lanes
95	I-80, PA 940, Pocono, Hazleton, **E...food:** Burger King, **W...gas:** Amoco/24hr, Texaco, WaWa, **food:** A&W/LJ Silver, Arby's, Gino's Pizza, Howard Johnson Rest., McDonald's, **lodging:** Comfort Inn, CountryPlace Inn, Day's Inn, Mtn Laurel Resort, Ramada Inn
90mm	parking area sb
86mm	Hickory Run Service Plaza both lanes, **gas:** Sunoco/diesel, **food:** Breyer's, McDonald's
74	US 209, Mahoning Valley, Lehighton, Stroudsburg, **W...gas:** Exxon/diesel, **food:** Subway
71mm	Lehigh Tunnel
56	I-78, US 22, PA 309, Lehigh Valley, **E...lodging:** Comfort Inn, Day's Inn, McIntosh Inn, Super 8
56mm	Allentown Service Plaza both lanes, **gas:** Sunoco/diesel, **food:** Big Boy, Nathan's, Pizza Hut, Roy Rogers, TCBY
44	PA 663, Quakertown, Pottstown, **E...lodging:** Best Western, Econolodge, Hampton Inn, Holiday Inn Express, Rodeway Inn, **other:** HOSPITAL
37mm	parking area sb
31	PA 63, Lansdale, **E...gas:** Amoco, Mobil, **lodging:** Best Western, Lansdale Motel
20	Germantown Pike W, to I-276 W, PA Tpk W
19	Germantown Pike E, no facilities
18b a	(18 from sb), Conshohocken, Norristown, **E...gas:** Mobil, Sunoco, **food:** Burger King, LoneStar Steaks, McDonald's, Outback Steaks, **other:** Toyota, **W... food:** Papa John's, Uno Pizzaria, Wendy's, **lodging:** Hampton Inn, **other:** BJ's Whse, Circuit City, Home Depot, Honda, Nissan, OfficeMax
16b a	(16 from sb), I-76, PA 23, to Philadelpia, Valley Forge
13	US 30, **E...gas:** Coastal, **food:** Campus Pizza, Villanova Diner, **other:** HOSPITAL, Radnor Drugs, USPO, Villanova Hardware
9	PA 3, Broomall, Upper Darby, **E...food:** Barnaby's Rest, **other:** HOSPITAL, PathMark Foods, carwash
5	US 1, Lima, Springfield, **N...**mall
3	Baltimore Pike, Media, Swarthmore, **E...**HOSPITAL, Swarthmore Coll
1	McDade Blvd, **E...gas:** Exxon, **food:** Dunkin Donuts, KFC, McDonald's
0mm	I-476 begins/ends on I-95, exit 7.

Interstate 95

Exit #	Services
43mm	Rhode Island/Massachusetts state line
30(42)	East St, to Central Falls, **E...food:** Dunkin Donuts, Subway
29(41)	US 1, Cottage St, **W...food:** D'angelo's, **other:** Firestone
28(40)	RI 114, School St, **E...gas:** Sunoco, **other:** HOSPITAL, Hyundai, to hist dist
27(39)	US 1, RI 15, Pawtucket, **E...gas:** Sunoco, **W...gas:** Shell/repair, Sunoco/diesel/24hr, **food:** Burger King, Dunkin Donuts, Ground Round, **lodging:** Comfort Inn, **other:** HOSPITAL
26(38)	RI 122, Lonsdale Ave(from nb), **E...other:** U-Haul
25(37)	US 1, RI 126, N Main St, Providence, **E...gas:** Hess, Shell, **food:** Chili's, **other:** HOSPITAL, Brooks Drug/24hr, CVS Drug, Shaw's Foods, **W...gas:** Gulf/diesel, Valero, **food:** Burger King, Chelo's Italian
24(36.5)	Branch Ave, Providence, downtown, **W...gas:** Mobil, **other:** Stop&Shop Foods
23(36)	RI 146, RI 7, Providence, **E...gas:** Mobil, **lodging:** Marriott, **other:** HOSPITAL, **W...**USPO
22(35.5)	US 6, RI 10, Providence, **E...food:** Dave&Buster's, **other:** mall
21(35)	Broadway St, Providence, **W...other:** Engle Tire, Goodyear/auto, Seedy Repair
20(34.5)	I-195, to E Providence, Cape Cod
19(34)	Eddy St, Allens Ave, to US 1(from sb), **W...food:** Wendy's, Dunkin Donuts, HOSPITAL
18(33.5)	US 1A, Thurbers Ave, **W...gas:** Shell, **food:** Burger King, **other:** HOSPITAL
17(33)	US 1(from sb), Elmwood Ave, **W...other:** Cadillac, Tires Whse
16(32.5)	RI 10, Cranston, **W...**Williams Zoo/park
15(32)	Jefferson Blvd, **E...gas:** Getty/diesel, Mobil, **food:** Bickford's, Bugaboo Steaks, Dunkin Donuts, **lodging:** Courtyard, Fairfield Inn, Motel 6, **W...other:** Ford Trucks, Ryder
14(31)	RI 37, Post Rd, to US 1, **W...gas:** Shell, HOSPITAL
13(30)	**1 mi E...**TF Green Airport, **lodging:** Hampton Inn, Holiday Inn Express, Homewood Suites, MainStay Suites, Masterhost Inn, Quality Suites, Residence Inn
12b(29)	RI 2, I-295 N(from sb), no facilities
12a	RI 113 E, to Warwick, **E...gas:** Shell/Dunkin Donuts/diesel, **lodging:** Crowne Plaza Hotel, **W...**mall
11(29)	I-295 N(exits left from nb), to Woonsocket, no facilities
10b a(28)	RI 117, to Warwick, **W...**HOSPITAL
9(25)	RI 4 S, E Greenwich, no facilities
8b a(24)	RI 2, E Greenwich, **E...gas:** Shell/diesel, **food:** China Buffet, Dunkin Donuts, McDonald's, Outback Steaks, Panera Bread, Ruby Tuesday, **lodging:** Extended Stay America, **other:** MEDICAL CARE, Dave's Mkt, Ro Jack's Foods, Walgreen, **W...gas:** Sunoco/diesel, **food:** Applebee's, Denny's, KFC, 99 Rest., PapaGino's, Weathervane Seafood, Wendy's, **lodging:** Comfort Suites, SpringHill Suites, **other:** Arlington RV, Best Buy, GNC, Goodyear/auto, Honda/Volvo, Jennings CarCare, Lowe's Whse, Mazda/Hyundai, Mitsubishi, Nissan, PepBoys, Pontiac/GMC/VW, Stop&Shop Foods, mall
7(21)	to Coventry, **E...gas:** Mobil/diesel, **W...food:** Applebee's, Cracker Barrel, Denny's, Wendy's, **lodging:** Hampton Inn, **other:** BJ's Whse/gas, auto repair
6a(20)	Hopkins Hill Rd, **W...**park&ride

RHODE ISLAND

Interstate 95

N ↕ S

6(18) RI 3, to Coventry, **W...gas:** Shell/diesel/24hr, Sunoco/diesel/repair, **food:** Dunkin Donuts, Mark's Grill, Tim Horton, **lodging:** Best Western, Super 8

5b a(15) RI 102, **W...gas:** R.I.'s Only Trkstp/diesel/24hr/@, **lodging:** Classic Motel

10mm rest area/weigh sta nb, weigh sta sb, phones

4(9) RI 3, to RI 165(from nb), Arcadia, **W...**Arcadia SP, camping

3b a(7) RI 138 E, to Kingston, Wyoming, **E...food:** Dunkin Donuts, McDonald's, Tim Horton, Wendy's, **other:** NAPA, Stop&Shop Food/gas, **W...gas:** Gulf, Exxon/Subway, Gulf, Mobil, Valero, **food:** Tim Horton, Bali Chinese, Bickford's, Village Pizza, **lodging:** Sun Valley Inn/rest., Wood River Inn Rest., **other:** Family$, NAPA, Ocean Drug

6mm **Welcome Ctr nb, full(handicapped)facilities, phone, picnic tables, litter barrels, vending, pet-walk**

2(4) Hope Valley, no facilities

1(1) RI 3, to Hopkinton, Westerly, **E...other:** HOSPITAL, to Misquamicut SP, RV camping, beaches

0mm Rhode Island/Connecticut state line, motorist call-boxes begin nb/end sb

Interstate 295 (Providence)

N ↕ S

Exit #   Services

2b a(4) I-95, N to Boston, S to Providence. I-295 begins/ends on I-95, exit 4 in MA. Exits 2-1 are in MA.

1b a(2) US 1, **E...food:** Friendly's, Hearth'n Kettle, Longhorn Steaks, 99 Rest., Panera Bread, TGIFriday, **other:** Best Buy, BJ's Whse, Borders, Circuit City, CompUSA, Filene's, JC Penney, Lord&Taylor, Lowe's Whse, Marshalls, Michael's, Office Depot, Old Navy, Sears/auto, Target, Wal-Mart, mall, **W...gas:** Exxon, Shell/Subway, **food:** Applebee's, **lodging:** Holiday Inn Express, Super 8, **other:** Ford, Dodge/Kia, Nissan, Toyota

0mm Rhode Island/Massachusetts state line. **Exits 1-2 are in MA.**

11(24) RI 114, to Cumberland, **E...gas:** Shell/diesel, **food:** Dunkin Donuts, Honeydew Donuts, **other:** CVS Drug, Dave's Foods, **W...food:** J's Deli, Sakis Pizza/subs, **other:** Tedeschi Foods, Diamond Hill Mkt, Diamond Hill SP

Providence

10(21) RI 122, **E...gas:** Gulf, Mutual Gas, **food:** Burger King, Dunkin Donuts, Jacky's Rest., Jim's Deli, McDonald's, Ronzio Pizza, **W...food:** Chicken Power, Fortune House Chinese, Subway, **other:** Brooks Drug, CVS Drug, Newport Creamery, Seabra Foods, True Value

20mm Blackstone River

19.5mm weigh sta both lanes, phone

9b a(19) RI 146, Woonsocket, Lincoln, **E...**mall, **2 mi W...gas:** Mobil, **other:** Chrysler/Plymouth, Honda, Isuzu

8b a(16) RI 7, N Smithfield, **W...gas:** Citgo/diesel/7-11, **food:** House of Pizza, Roost House Rest., Smith-Appleby House

7b a(13) US 44, Centerdale, **E...gas:** Valero, **food:** Isabella's Deli, **other:** HOSPITAL, NAPA, CarQuest, auto repair, **W...gas:** Exxon/Subway/diesel, Mobil, Shell, **food:** A&W, Applebee's, Burger King, Chelo's Grill, Chili's, D'angelo's, Dunkin Donuts, Hoho Chinese, KFC/Taco Bell, McDonald's, Panera Bread, PapaGino's, Pizza Hut, Pizzaria Uno, Subway, TinTsin Chinese, Wendy's, **other:** MEDICAL CARE, Brooks Drug, CVS Drug, Home Depot, Kohl's, Old Navy, Radio Shack, Staple's, Stop&Shop Foods, Target, TJ Maxx, to Powder Mill Ledges WR

6(10) US 6, to Providence, **E...gas:** Citgo/7-11, Mobil, Shell/Dunkin Donuts, **food:** Burger King, China Jade, Del's Deli, KFC, Luigi's Italian, McDonald's, Wendy's, **lodging:** Hi-Way Motel, **other:** AutoZone, BJ's Whse, Chevrolet/Buick, CVS Drug, Honda, Pontiac/GMC, Shaw's Foods, USPO, **W...lodging:** Bel-Air Motel

6b c(9) US 6 E Expswy, no facilities

5(8) RI Resource Recovery Industrial Park

4(7) RI 14, Plainfield Pk, **W...gas:** Mobil/diesel/24hr

3b a(4) rd 37, Phenix Ave, **E...**TF Green Airport

2(2) RI 2 S, to Warwick, **E...gas:** Exxon, **food:** Longhorn Steaks, Macaroni Grill, Pizzaria Uno, **other:** Filene's, JC Penney, Macy's, Marshalls, Radio Shack, mall, **W...gas:** Mobil, Shell, Sunoco, **food:** Bickford's, Chili's, ChuckeCheese, Dunkin Donuts, HomeTown Buffet, Kwikava, LoneStar Steaks, McDonald's, PapaGino's, Subway, Taco Bell, Wendy's, **other:** Brooks Drug, CompUSA, Dodge/Subaru, Home Depot, NAPA, OfficeMax, Sam's Club, Saturn, Sears/auto, Staples, TownFair Tire, Wal-Mart, mall

1(1) RI 113 W, to W Warwick, same as 2

0mm I-295 begins/ends on I-95, exit 11.

Landrum
26
85
Clover
25
221
29 Gaffney
178
Springfield
Spartanburg
York
Berea
Wade Hampton
Rock Hill
Greenville
Easley
385
Union
Chester
176
77
521
Pendleton
25
Fountain Inn
26
Whitmire
321
Belton
76
Great Falls
85
Laurens
21
Anderson
178
Newberry
76
Winnsboro
Greenwood
Lugoff
20
401
Calhoun Falls
Seven Oaks
★ Columbia
378
Springdale
Cayce
25
Sumter
95
Edgefield
178
601
221
1
321
St. Matthews
20
Aiken
Orangeburg
Brookdale
South Carolina
Williston
301
521
Kingstree
78
Bamberg
176
Barnwell
26
278
Ladson
Goose Creek
601
21
15
Fairfax
95
N Charleston
321
Hampton
Walterboro
Charleston
Mount Pleasant
17

Pageland
Bennettsville
1
15
Hartsville
52
Darlington
Dillon
Florence
Mullins
Lake City
378
Loris
501
Conway
Manning
701
Myrtle Beach
Murrells Inlet
Andrews
52
17A
Georgetown
Moncks Corner
17

Beaufort
Parris Island
21
Hilton Head Island

Interstate 20

	E ↕ W	

Exit #	Services
141b a	I-95, N to Fayetteville, S to Savannah. I-20 begins/ends on I-95, exit 160. **See Interstate 95, exit 160a for services.**
137	SC 340, to Timmonsville, Darlington, **S...gas:** Phillips/diesel
131	US 401, SC 403, to Hartsville, Lamar, **N... gas:** Exxon/diesel, Phillips 66/diesel/repair/rest./24hr/@, **other:** to Darlington Int Raceway
123	SC 22, Lamar, **N...gas:** BP, Lee SP
121mm	Lynches River
120	SC 341, Bishopville, Elliot, **N...lodging:** Bishopville Motel(3mi), **S...gas:** Exxon/diesel, **food:** Taste of Country Rest., **lodging:** Howard Johnson Express, **other:** HOSPITAL
116	US 15, Bishopville, to Sumter, Shaw AFB, **N...gas:** Shell/KFC/diesel/24hr, **food:** McDonald's, Pizza Hut, Subway(1mi), Waffle House, **lodging:** Econolodge, **S...gas:** Wilco/Hess/DQ/Wendy's/diesel/24hr/@
108	SC 34, to SC 31, Manville, **N...gas:** Shell/diesel, **S...gas:** Citgo/diesel
101	rd 329, no facilities
98	US 521, to Camden, **N...gas:** Citgo/diesel, Exxon/McDonald's, Shell, **lodging:** Fairfield Inn, **other:** HOSPITAL, **3-5 mi N...food:** Golden Corral, **lodging:** Colony Inn, Greenleaf Inn, Knight's Inn, **other:** Revolutionary War Pk

C o l u m b i a

96mm	Wateree River
93mm	**rest area both lanes, full(handicapped)facilities, phones, vending, picnic tables, litter barrels, petwalk**
92	US 601, to Lugoff, **N...gas:** Pilot/DQ/Subway/diesel/24hr/@, Shell/diesel, **food:** Hardee's, Waffle House, **lodging:** Day's Inn, Ramada Ltd, Travelodge, **other:** Camden RV Park(1mi), **2-3 mi N... lodging:** Best Western, KFC, McDonald's, Shoney's, Holiday Inn, **other:** Ford/Lincoln/Mercury
87	SC 47, to Elgin, **N...gas:** BP/diesel, Shell/diesel
82	SC 53, to Pontiac, **N...gas:** Shell, **S...other:** Clothing World Outlet
80	Clemson Rd, **N...gas:** Exxon/diesel, 76/Circle K, Shell/Bojangles, **food:** McDonald's, Waffle House, Zaxby's, **lodging:** Holiday Inn Express, **other:** CVS Drug, **S...other:** Chevrolet
76b a	Alpine Rd, to Ft Jackson, **N...**Sesquicentennial SP (76 from eb), I-77, N to Charlotte, S to Charleston

SOUTH CAROLINA
Interstate 20

E ↕ W

Exit	Services
74	US 1, Two Notch Rd, to Ft Jackson, **N...gas:** Amoco/24hr, Exxon, 76, **food:** Arby's, Burger King, Chili's, Denny's, Fazoli's, Hops Grill, IHOP, Lizard's Thicket, Outback Steaks, Ryan's, Waffle House, **lodging:** AmeriSuites, Best Western, Baymont Inn, Comfort Inn, Fairfield Inn, Hampton Inn, Holiday Inn, Microtel, Motel 6, Ramada Plaza, Red Roof Inn, Travelodge, **other:** Home Depot, USPO, U-Haul, to Sesquicentennial SP, **S...gas:** Hess/diesel, Exxon, Shell/diesel, **food:** Applebee's, BBQ, Bojangles, Capt D's, Church's, Santa Fe Mexican, Splendid China, **lodging:** Day's Inn, **other:** Advance Parts, Best Buy, Dillard's, Family$, Firestone/auto, Lowe's Whse, NAPA, Sears/auto, Staples, mall
73b	SC 277 N, to I-77 N, no facilities
a	SC 277 S, to Columbia, **S...HOSPITAL**
72	SC 555, Farrow Rd, no facilities
71	US 21, N Main, Columbia, to Blythewood, **N...gas:** Exxon/Subway/Pizza Hut/diesel/@, BP/diesel, **food:** McDonald's, **lodging:** Day's Inn, **other:** truckwash, **S...gas:** Shell
70	US 321, Fairfield Rd, **S...gas:** Exxon, ⊘/Flying J/Conoco/Hardee's/diesel/LP/24hr/@, **lodging:** Super 8
68	SC 215, Monticello Rd, to Jenkinsville, **N...gas:** Exxon/diesel, Shell, **S...gas:** Shell/diesel, **food:** Big Daddy's Café
66mm	Broad River
65	US 176, Broad River Rd, to Columbia, **N...gas:** Exxon, 76/Circle K, **food:** Applebee's, Bojangles, Great Wall Chinese, Monterrey Mexican, Rush's Rest., Subway, Waffle House, **lodging:** Economy Inn, **other:** Aamco, **S...gas:** Hess, RaceWay, **food:** Arby's, Capt Tom's Seafood, Church's, Golden Corral, Hooters, Julie's Place, KFC, Lizard's Thicket, McDonald's, Pizza Hut, Sandy's HotDogs, Taco Bell, Taco Cid, Wendy's, **lodging:** American Inn, Best Inn, InTowne Suites, Ramada Ltd, Royal Inn, **other:** Advance Parts, Belk, CVS Drug, Eckerd, Family$, Food Lion, Mr Transmission, PepBoys, mall
64b a	I-26, US 76, E to Columbia, airport, W to Greenville, Spartanburg
63	Bush River Rd, **N...gas:** 76/Circle K/diesel, **food:** Cracker Barrel, Steak-Out, Subway, **lodging:** Travelodge, **other:** CVS Drug, Hamrick's, **S...gas:** Citgo, **food:** El Chico, Fuddrucker's, Key West Grill, Villa Rest., Waffle House, **lodging:** Best Western, Courtyard, Knight's Inn, Sheraton, Sleep Inn
61	US 378, W Cola, **5 mi N...food:** Ryan's, Wendy's, **lodging:** Holiday Inn Express, **S...gas:** Amoco/diesel/24hr, 76(2mi), **food:** Waffle House, **other:** HOSPITAL, antiques
58	US 1, W Columbia, **N...gas:** Exxon, Shell/Subway/diesel, **food:** Waffle House, **2 mi S...gas:** Hess, **food:** Burger King, KFC, McDonald's, San Jose Mexican, **other:** Barnyard RV Park, to airport
55	SC 6, to Lexington, **N...gas:** Shell, **food:** Hardee's, **lodging:** Comfort Inn(2mi), Hampton Inn(2mi), Holiday Inn Express(3mi), **other:** CarQuest, **S...gas:** BP/diesel, Citgo, Depot/DQ, **food:** Bojangles, Fox's Pizza Den, Golden Town Chinese, McDonald's, Substation II, Subway, Waffle House, **lodging:** Ramada Ltd, **other:** CVS Drug, Piggly Wiggly
52.5mm	weigh sta wb
51	SC 204, to Gilbert, **N...gas:** Exxon/diesel, **S...gas:** Shell/Gertie's/diesel/24hr, Texaco/Subway/diesel/24hr/@
44	SC 34, to Gilbert, **N...gas:** Citgo/44Trkstp/diesel/rest./@
39	US 178, to Batesburg, **N...gas:** Exxon/diesel, **S...gas:** Citgo/diesel/24hr
35.5mm	weigh sta eb
33	SC 39, to Wagener, **N...gas:** BP/diesel, Shell/diesel, **food:** Huddle House
29	SC 49, no facilities
22	US 1, to Aiken, **S...gas:** BP/diesel, RaceTrac, 76/diesel, Shell/Blimpie/diesel, **food:** Hardee's, McDonald's, Waffle House, **lodging:** Day's Inn, Holiday Inn Express, **other:** Pine Acres RV Camp(5mi)
18	SC 19, to Aiken, **S...gas:** Exxon/Subway/diesel, Shell/Blimpie/diesel, **food:** Waffle House, **lodging:** Deluxe Inn, Guesthouse Inn, **other:** HOSPITAL
11	SC 144, Graniteville, no facilities
5	US 25, SC 121, **N...gas:** Bryants/diesel, 76/Blimpie/pizza/diesel/24hr, Shell/Bojangles/diesel/24hr, **food:** Burger King, Hardee's, Huddle House, Sonic, **lodging:** Sleep Inn, **other:** Winn-Dixie/24hr, **S...gas:** Citgo/Taco Bell/diesel, Speedway/diesel/24hr, **food:** Waffle House
1	SC 230, Martintown Rd, N Augusta, **S...gas:** 76/Blimpie/diesel/24hr, **food:** Tastee Freez, Waffle House, **other:** to Garn's Place
.5mm	**Welcome Ctr eb, full(handicapped)facilities, phone, picnic tables, litter barrels, vending, petwalk**
0mm	South Carolina/Georgia state line, Savannah

Interstate 26

E ↕ W

Exit #	Services
221	Meeting St, Charleston, **2 mi E...food:** Church's, KFC, **lodging:** Hampton Inn, **other:** Visitors Ctr, Family$, Piggly Wiggly
221b	US 17 N, to Georgetown, no facilities
	I-26 begins/ends on US 17 in Charleston, SC.
221a	US 17 S, to Kings St, to Savannah, **N...HOSPITAL**

Interstate 26

E

W

Charleston

N Charleston

220	Romney St(from wb), no facilities
219b	Morrison Dr, East Bay St(from eb), **N...gas:** Shell, Sam's Gas, **food:** Huddle House
219a	Rutledge Ave(from eb, no EZ return), to The Citadel, College of Charleston
218	Spruill Ave(from wb), N Charleston, no facilities
217	N Meeting St(from eb), no facilities
216b a	SC 7, Cosgrove Ave, **S...food:** Arby's, McDonald's, SunFire Grill, Wendy's, **other:** to Charles Towne Landing
215	SC 642, Dorchester Rd, N Charleston, **N...gas:** Hess/diesel, **lodging:** Howard Johnson, **S...gas:** Amoco/diesel, **food:** Alex's Rest./24hr
213b a	Montague Ave, Mall Dr, **N...food:** Piccadilly's, Red Lobster, **lodging:** Courtyard, Sheraton, **other:** Charles Towne Square, Firestone, **S...gas:** Amoco/diesel, Hess/Bojangles/diesel, **food:** Waffle House, **lodging:** Comfort Inn, Day's Inn, Embassy Suites, Extended Stay America, Hampton Inn, Hilton Garden, HomePlace Suites, Homestead Suites, Quality Inn, Ramada Inn, Suite 1, Super 8, Wingate Inn
212c b	I-526, E to Mt Pleasant, W to Savannah, airport
212a	Remount Rd(from wb, no EZ return), Hanahan, **N on US 52/78...gas:** Exxon, Hess/diesel, **food:** Burger King, KFC, McDonald's, Pizza Hut/Taco Bell, **other:** Dodge, Ford, Office Depot
211b a	Aviation Pkwy, **N on US 52/78...gas:** Amoco, Exxon, **food:** Arby's, Burger King, Capt D's, China Town, Church's, Grandy's, Huddle House, McDonald's, Old Country Buffet, Pizza Hut, Pizza Inn, Schlotsky's, Shoney's, Sonic, Subway, Tokyo Japanese, Wendy's, **lodging:** Masters Inn, Radisson, **other:** Aamco, Batteries+, $General, $Tree, Goodyear, PepBoys, Radio Shack, Sam's Club, **S...gas:** Citgo/diesel, El Cheapo/diesel, **food:** Waffle House, **lodging:** Best Western, Seagrass Inn, Travelodge
209	Ashley Phosphate Rd, to US 52, **N...gas:** Exxon, Kangaroo, **food:** Applebee's, Chick-fil-A, China Buffet, ChuckeCheese, Denny's, Don Pablo, Fazoli's, Hardee's, Hooters, Hops Grill, K&W Cafeteria, Krispy Kreme, Noisy Oyster Grill, Olive Garden, Outback Steaks, Perkins, Pizza Hut, Ryan's, Sticky Fingers Rest., Subway, Taco Bell, Waffle House, Wendy's, **lodging:** Clarion, Holiday Inn Express, Red Roof Inn, Residence Inn, Studio+ Hotel, Super 8, **other:** MEDICAL CARE, Barnes&Noble, Belk, Best Buy, BooksAMillion, Cicuit City, Dillard's, Firestone/auto, Home Depot, JC Penney, Lexus, Lowe's Whse, Mitsubishi, Nissan, OfficeMax, Sears/auto, Target, Toyota, Wal-Mart SuperCtr/24hr, mall, **S...gas:** Amoco, Hess, RaceWay, **food:** Bojangles, Cracker Barrel, Domino's, IHOP, Kobe Japanese, McDonald's, Waffle House, **lodging:** Fairfield Inn, Hampton Inn, Howard Johnson, InTowne Suites, La Quinta, Motel 6, Relax Inn, Sleep Inn
208	to US 52(from wb), to Goose Creek, Moncks Corner, no facilities

205b	US 78, to Summerville, **N...gas:** BP, Hess/diesel, **food:** Arby's, Atl Bread Co, Bruster's, Subway, Waffle House, Wendy's, **lodging:** Fairfield Inn, **other:** HOSPITAL, DENTIST, Charleston Southern U, **S...gas:** Speedway/diesel, **other:** KOA
204mm	rest area eb, full(handicapped)facilities, vending, phone, picnic tables, litter barrels, petwalk
203	College Park Rd, Ladson, **N...gas:** 76, Speedway/diesel, **food:** McDonald's, Waffle House, Wendy's, **lodging:** Best Western, Day's Inn, **S...other:** KOA(2mi)
202mm	rest area wb, full(handicapped)facilities, vending, phone, picnic tables, litter barrels, petwalk
199b a	US 17 A, to Moncks Corner, Summerville, **N...gas:** BP, Citgo/diesel, Hess/diesel, Pilot/McDonald's/diesel/24hr, **food:** KFC, Pizza Hut, Subway, **other:** Advance Parts, AutoZone, BiLo, Buick/Pontiac/GMC, CVS Drug, $General, Family$, Food Lion, Ford/Mercury, **S...gas:** 76/Circle K, Enmark/diesel, **food:** Applebee's, Bojangles, Burger King, China Town, Fazoli's, Hardee's, Huddle House, IHOP, Papa John's, Perkins/24hr, Ryan's, Shoney's, Waffle House, **lodging:** Comfort Inn, Econolodge, Hampton Inn, Holiday Inn Express, Sleep Inn, **other:** Belk, Chevrolet, Chrysler/Plymouth/Jeep, GNC, Home Depot, Lowe's Whse, Radio Shack, Staples, Target, Wal-Mart SuperCtr/24hr, Winn-Dixie
194	SC 16, to Jedburg, access to Foreign Trade Zone 21
187	SC 27, to Ridgeville, St George, **N...gas:** Phillips 66, **S...gas:** BP/diesel, **10 mi S...other:** Francis Beidler Forest
177	SC 453, to Holly Hill, Harleyville, **S...gas:** Shell/diesel/LP, **food:** Derrick's Kitchen, **lodging:** Ashley Lodge
174mm	weigh sta both lanes
172b a	US 15, to Santee, St George, **S...gas:** Horizon/Subway/diesel/24hr
169b a	I-95, N to Florence, S to Savannah, no facilities
165	SC 210, to Bowman, **N...gas:** Exxon/diesel, **S...gas:** BP/diesel/rest., Texaco/Blimpie/diesel/repair
159	SC 36, to Bowman, **N...gas:** Pilot/McDonald's/diesel/24hr/repair/@
154b a	US 301, to Santee, Orangeburg, **N...lodging:** Days Inn, **S...gas:** Exxon/Blimpie/diesel, Shell/diesel/24hr, **lodging:** Best Western(7mi), Holiday Inn(8mi), **other:** auto repair
152mm	rest area wb, full(handicapped)facilities, vending, phone, picnic tables, litter barrels, petwalk
150mm	rest area eb, full(handicapped)facilities, vending, phone, picnic tables, litter barrels, petwalk

E / W ←↑↓

149 SC 33, to Cameron, to SC State Coll, Orangeburg, Claflin Coll

145b a US 601, to Orangeburg, St Matthews, **S...gas:** Amoco/24hr, Exxon, Shell/Burger King, Speedway/diesel, **food:** Cracker Barrel, Fatz Café, Hardee's, KFC, McDonald's, Ruby Tuesday, Subway, Waffle House, **lodging:** Comfort Inn, Day's Inn, Fairfield Inn, Hampton Inn, Holiday Inn Express, Sleep Inn, Southern Lodge, **other:** HOSPITAL, other: Cadillac/Nissan, Chevrolet, Chrysler/Plymouth/Dodge, Nissan

139 SC 22, to St Matthews, **S...gas:** Phillips 66, Shell, Wilco/Hess/Arby's/diesel/24hr/@, **other:** Sweetwater Lake Camping(2.5mi)

136 SC 6, to North, Swansea, **N...gas:** BP, Exxon/diesel/LP/rest./24hr, **other:** auto/tire repair

129 US 21, **N...gas:** Shell/diesel

125 SC 31, to Gaston, **N...other:** Wolfe's Truck/trailer repair

123mm rest area both lanes, full(handicapped)facilities, vending, phone, picnic tables, litter barrels, petwalk

119 US 176, US 21, to Dixiana, **N...gas:** 76/Circle K/diesel, **S...gas:** Exxon, Shell/Subway/TCBY/diesel/@

116 I-77 N, to Charlotte, US 76, US 378, to Ft Jackson

115 US 176, US 21, US 321, to Cayce, **N...gas:** Coastal, RaceTrac/24hr, Texaco, **food:** Waffle House, **other:** Harley-Davidson, **S...gas:** Pilot/DQ/Wendy's/diesel/24hr/@, United/diesel/24hr, **food:** Bojangles, Great China, Hardee's, McDonald's, Subway, **lodging:** Ramada Ltd, **other:** Firestone, Piggly Wiggly

113 SC 302, Cayce, **N...gas:** Exxon, Texaco/diesel, **food:** Waffle House, **lodging:** Airport Inn, Best Western, Knight's Inn, Masters Inn, **other:** Peak's Tire, **S...gas:** Exxon, RaceTrac, 76/Circle K, **food:** Burger King, Denny's, Lizard's Thicket, Ryan's, Shoney's, Subway, Waffle House/24hr, **lodging:** Comfort Inn, Day's Inn, Sleep Inn, Travelodge, **other:** NAPA, airport

111b a US 1, to W Columbia, **N...gas:** Raceway/diesel, 76/Circle K, **food:** BBQ, Domino's, Dragon City Chinese, Hardee's, Maurice's BBQ, Ruby Tuesday, Sonic, Subway, TCBY, Waffle House, **lodging:** Holiday Inn, Super 8, **other:** CHIROPRACTOR, BiLo Foods, $Tree, Harlan Tire, JiffyLube, Kroger, Wal-Mart SuperCtr/gas/24hr, to USC, **S...gas:** Hess, **food:** Applebee's, Wendy's, **other:** CVS Drug, Lowe's Whse, U-Haul

110 US 378, to W Columbia, Lexington, **N...food:** BBQ, Burger King, Lizard's Thicket, McDonald's, Rush's Rest., Subway, Waffle House, Western Sizzlin, **lodging:** Day's Inn, Hampton Inn, Ramada/rest., **other:** MEDICAL CARE, CVS Drug, Eckerd, Food Lion, U-Haul, **S...gas:** 76/Circle K, **food:** Bojangles, Hardee's, Pizza Hut, **lodging:** Executive Inn, **other:** HOSPITAL

Columbia (left vertical text)

Columbia (right vertical text)

108 I-126 to Columbia, Bush River Rd, **N...gas:** Shell/diesel, **food:** Blimpie, Capt D's, Chick-fil-A, Hardee's, KFC, Royal China Buffet, Schlotsky's, Shoney's, Wendy's, **lodging:** Baymont Inn, Villager Lodge, **other:** Advance Parts, Firestone/auto, K-Mart, Office Depot, OfficeMax, mall, **S...gas:** RaceWay, Sunoco/diesel, **food:** Cracker Barrel, Royal Tahj Cuisine, **lodging:** Best Western, Courtyard, Day's Inn, Howard Johnson, **multiple facilities 1-3 mi N off I-126, Greystone Blvd, N...gas:** Amoco, Shell, **food:** Waffle House, **lodging:** Embassy Suites, Extended Stay America, Residence Inn, Studio+, **other:** Chrysler/Jeep, Dodge, Ford, GMC, Lincoln/Mercury, Honda, Kia, Mitsubishi, **S...Riverbanks Zoo

107b a I-20, E to Florence, W to Augusta, no facilities

106b a St Andrews Rd, **N...gas:** Exxon/Blimpie, **food:** ChuckeCheese, IHOP, Papa John's, **lodging:** Motel 6, **other:** DENTIST, BiLo Foods, Buick/Pontiac, CVS Drug, Eckerd, Infiniti, Jaguar, Kroger/deli, Nissan, **S...gas:** Hess/diesel, 76/Circle K, Shell, **food:** Bojangles, Domino's, Hilltop Rest., Maurice's BBQ, McDonald's, Old Country Buffet, Pizza Hut, Ryan's, Steak&Ale, TCBY, Thai Lotus, Waffle House, Wendy's, **lodging:** Red Roof Inn, Super 8, **other:** $General, Eckerd, Food Lion, NTB

104 Piney Grove Rd, **N...gas:** Speedway/diesel, Sunoco, **food:** Hardee's, Roadhouse Grill, San Jose Mexican, Waffle House, **lodging:** Comfort Inn, Knight's Inn, **other:** $General, to Subaru, RV/Marine Ctr, **S...gas:** Exxon/diesel, Shell, **lodging:** Comfort Suites, Microtel, **other:** Carmax, Land Rover, auto repair

103 Harbison Blvd, **N...food:** Applebee's, Hops Grill, **lodging:** Hampton Inn, Wingate Inn, **other:** Chevrolet, Home Depot, Hummer, Lowe's Whse, funpark, **S...gas:** Amoco/24hr, Exxon/Taco Bell, Hess/diesel, Shell, **food:** Bojangles, Blimpie, Carrabba's, Chili's, Chick-fil-A, Denny's, Fazoli's, LongHorn Steaks, Macaroni Grill, McAlister's Grill, McDonald's, Olive Garden, Outback Steaks, Roadhouse Grill, Ruby Tuesday, Rush's Rest., Shoney's, Sonic, Steak'n Shake, Sticky Fingers, Subway, Texas Roadhouse, Yamato Japanese, **lodging:** Comfort Suites, Country Inn Suites, Fairfield Inn, Suite 1, Holiday Inn Express, TownePlace Suites, Wingate Inn, **other:** MEDICAL CARE, Belk, Best Buy, BooksAMillion, Circuit City, Dillard's, Goodyear, Goody's, Marshall's, Michael's, OfficeMax, Old Navy, Publix, Rite Aid, Sam's Club, Saturn, Sears/auto, Staples, Target, Wal-Mart SuperCtr/24hr, mall

102 SC 60, Ballentine, Irmo, **N...lodging:** AmeriSuites, Wellesley Inn, **S...gas:** 76/Circle K, Exxon, Shell, **food:** Bellacino's Pizza, Maurice's BBQ, Papa John's, TCBY, Zaxby's, **other:** CVS Drug, Piggly Wiggly, same as 103

101b a US 76, US 176, to N Columbia, **1/2 mi N...gas:** Exxon/Subway/diesel, **food:** Blimpie, Fatz Café, Food Lion, **other:** Eckerd, Publix, **S...gas:** BP, 76, **food:** Waffle House, **other:** Toyota

Interstate 26

E ↕ W

97 US 176, to Ballentine, **N**...Woodsmoke Camping, **S**... **gas:** Exxon/diesel

94mm weigh sta wb, phones

91 SC 48, to Chapin, **S**...**gas:** BP/diesel, Exxon/diesel, Shell/diesel, **food:** Capital City Subs, Hardee's(3mi), McDonald's, Subway(2mi), Taco Bell, Waffle House, **other:** to Dreher Island SP

85 SC 202, Little Mountain, Pomaria, **S**...to Dreher Island SP

82 SC 773, to Prosperity, Pomaria, **N**...**gas:** Kangaroo/ Subway/diesel/24hr/@, **other:** Flea Mkt Campground

81mm weigh sta eb

76 SC 219, to Pomaria, Newberry, **2 mi S**...**gas:** BP, MurphyUSA, **food:** Burger King, Wendy's, **lodging:** Hampton Inn, Holiday Inn Express, **other:** Wal-Mart SuperCtr/gas/24hr, to Newberry Opera House

74 SC 34, to Newberry, **N**...**gas:** BP, Shell/diesel/ 24hr, **lodging:** Best Western/rest., **S**...**gas:** Shell/ diesel, **food:** Arby's, Bill&Fran's Café, Capt D's, Hardee's(2mi), McDonald's(2mi), Waffle House, **lodging:** Comfort Inn, Day's Inn, Economy Inn(2mi), Holiday Inn Express(2mi), **other:** HOSPITAL, to Nine-tySix HS

72 SC 121, to Newberry, **S**...**gas:** Citgo/Blimpie/diesel, **other:** HOSPITAL, to Newberry Coll

66 SC 32, to Jalapa, no facilities

63.5mm rest area both lanes, full(handicapped)facilities, phone, vending, picnic tables, litter barrels, pet-walk

60 SC 66, to Joanna, **S**...**gas:** Chevron, **other:** Magnolia Camping

54 SC 72, to Clinton, **N**...**gas:** Citgo/diesel/24hr, **S**...**gas:** Exxon/Blimpie/diesel, **other:** HOSPITAL, to Presbyterian Coll, Thornwell Home

52 SC 56, to Clinton, **N**...**gas:** Pilot/Subway/diesel/24hr/ @, **food:** Blue Ocean Rest., McDonald's, Waffle House, **lodging:** Comfort Inn, **S**...**gas:** Phillips 66/ diesel, Shell/diesel, **food:** Hardee's, Waffle House, Wendy's, **lodging:** Day's Inn, Ramada Inn, Travelers Inn(2mi), **other:** HOSPITAL

51 I-385, to Greenville(from wb), no facilities

45.5mm Enoree River

44 SC 49, to Cross Anchor, Union, no facilities

41 SC 92, to Enoree, **N**...**gas:** Valero

38 SC 146, to Woodruff, **N**...**gas:** Hot Spot/Shell/ Hardee's/diesel/24hr, **food:** Big Country Rest./ lounge

35 SC 50, to Woodruff, **S**...**gas:** Citgo/diesel/rest./24hr, **other:** HOSPITAL

33mm S Tyger River

32mm N Tyger River

28 US 221, to Spartanburg, **N**...**gas:** Citgo/AuntM's/ diesel/24hr, Shell/Subway/diesel/24hr, **food:** Burger King, Hardee's, Walnut Grove Seafood Rest., **other:** HOSPITAL, Pine Ridge Camping(3mi), to Walnut Grove Plantation

Spartanburg

22 SC 296, Reidville Rd, to Spartanburg, **N**... **gas:** BP/diesel, Exxon, **food:** Arby's, BBQ, Capri's Italian, Fuddrucker's(1mi), Hong Kong Express, Little Caesar's, McDonald's, Outback Steaks, Ryan's, Waffle House, Zaxby's, **other:** MEDICAL CARE, Advance Parts, Rite Aid, to Croft SP, **S**...**gas:** BP/diesel, **food:** Burger King, Denny's, Domino's, Hardee's, Subway, TCBY, Waffle House/24hr, **lodging:** Sleep Inn, Southern Suites, Super 8, **other:** Abbot Farms/ fruit, BiLo, BMW, CVS Drug, Eckerd, Harris-Teeter, Saturn, Toyota, Walgreen

21b a US 29, to Spartanburg, **N**...**gas:** BP, Crown/24hr, Exxon/Subway, Phillips 66, **food:** Burger King, Calzone's Rest., Checker's, Chick-fil-A, CiCi's, DQ, Dunkin Donuts, Firemountain Grill, Fuji's, Golden Corral, Hardee's, Hop's Grill, Jack-in-the-Box, Japanese Rest., KFC, LoneStar Steaks, LJ Silver, Moe's Grill, Mr Gatti's, O'Charley's, Old Country Buffet, Papa John's, Pizza Hut, Pizza Inn, Quincy's, Red Lobster, Substation II, Wendy's, **lodging:** Hilton Garden, **other:** Barnes&Noble, Belk, Circuit City, Dillard's, $General, Eckerd, Firestone/auto, Home Depot, JC Penney, Michael's, Office Depot, OfficeMax, Ross, Sears/auto, Wal-Mart SuperCtr/24hr, mall, **S**...**gas:** Citgo/diesel, Texaco/diesel, **food:** Applebee's, Aunt M's Café, Blimie, IHOP, McDonald's, Piccadilly's, Prime Sirloin, Shogun Japanese, Taco Bell, Thi Japanese, Waffle House, **other:** Advance Parts, Best Buy, Ingles, Lowe's Whse, Rite Aid, Sam's Club/gas, Target

19b a Lp I-85, Spartanburg, **N**...**gas:** Amoco, Phillips 66/ diesel, **food:** Cracker Barrel, **lodging:** Econolodge, Fairfield Inn, Radisson, Ramada Inn, Residence Inn, Quality Hotel, **S**...**lodging:** Bradford Hotel, Tower Motel

18b a I-85, N to Charlotte, S to Greenville

17 New Cut Rd, **S**...**gas:** Chevron/diesel, Sunoco/diesel, **food:** Burger King, Fatz Café, McDonald's, Waffle House, **lodging:** Comfort Inn, Day's Inn, Howard Johnson Express, Relax Inn

16 John Dodd Rd, to Wellford, **N**...**gas:** Citgo/diesel, **food:** Arby's, Aunt M's, **other:** Camping World RV Supply Ctr, Cunningham RV Park

15 US 176, to Inman, **N**...**gas:** FuelStop, 76/Circle K/ diesel, **food:** Waffle House, **other:** HOSPITAL **S**...**gas:** Exxon/Blimpie/diesel, **food:** Taco Bell(2mi)

10 SC 292, to Inman, **N**...**gas:** HotSpot/Shell/Subway/ diesel/24hr

9.5mm parking area both lanes, litter barrels

7.5mm Lake William C. Bowman, no facilities

SOUTH CAROLINA

Interstate 26

E ↕ W

5 SC 11, Foothills Scenic Dr, Chesnee, Campobello, **N...gas:** Kangaroo/Aunt M's Café/diesel/@, **S...gas:** Phillips 66

3mm **Welcome Ctr eb, full(handicapped)facilities, info, phones, picnic tables, litter barrels, vending, pet-walk**

1 SC 14, to Landrum, **S...gas:** BP/Burger King/diesel, HotSpot/gas(2mi), **food:** Denny's, Pizza Hut(1mi), Subway, **other:** BiLo Foods, $General, Ingles/café/gas/24hr

0mm South Carolina/North Carolina state line

Interstate 77

N ↕ S

Exit #	Services
91mm	South Carolina/North Carolina state line

90 US 21, Carowinds Blvd, **E...gas:** Petro Express, Shell, World Gas, **food:** Bojangles, Denny's, **lodging:** Day's Inn, **other:** HOSPITAL, RV Ctr, RV camping(4mi), **W...gas:** Citgo, Exxon/café, 76/Circle K/Wendy's/diesel, Petro, Rocket Stop, **food:** El Cancun Mexican, KFC, Mom's Rest., Shoney's, Slice's Italian, Wendy's, **lodging:** Comfort Inn, Holiday Inn Express, Motel 6, Ramada Inn, Sleep Inn, **other:** Carowinds Funpark, Carolina Pottery/outlet mall/famous brands

89.5mm **Welcome Ctr sb, full(handicapped)facilities, info, phone, vending, picnic tables, litter barrels, petwalk/weigh sta nb**

88 Gold Hill Rd, to Pineville, **W...gas:** Exxon/diesel, Shell/diesel, **other:** Dodge/Jeep, Ford, KOA

85 SC 160, Ft Mill, Tega Cay, **E...gas:** Exxon, **food:** Subway, Winn-Dixie/café, **other:** New Peach Stand, **W...gas:** BP/diesel, Crown, **food:** Burger King

84.5mm weigh sta sb

83 SC 49, Sutton Rd, no facilities

82.5mm Catawba River

82b a US 21, SC 161, Rock Hill, Ft Mill, **E...gas:** Exxon, Phillips 66, **food:** BBQ, IHOP, **lodging:** Holiday Inn/rest., **other:** Home Depot, museum, **W...gas:** Citgo, Exxon, Phillips 66, RaceTrac/diesel, Shell, Speedway, **food:** Arby's, Bojangles, Burger King, Capt's Galley Seafood, Chick-fil-A, CiCi's Pizza, Denny's, El Cancun Mexican, Godfather's, Hooters, Little Caesar's, LJ Silver, McDonald's, Outback Steaks, Pizza Hut, Pizza Inn, Sagebrush Steaks, Sake Steaks, Sakura Chinese, Shoney's, Subway, Taco Bell, TCBY, Waffle House, Wendy's, **lodging:** Bestway Inn, Best Western, Comfort Inn, Country Inn Suites, Courtyard, Day's Inn, Econolodge, Howard Johnson, Microtel, Quality Inn, Ramada/rest., Super 8, **other:** HOSPITAL, Advance Parts, Aldi, AutoZone, BiLo, Chevrolet, Chrysler/Jeep, Eckerd, Family$, Firestone/auto, Ford, Honda, K-Mart, Nissan, Office Depot, PepBoys, Toyota, U-Haul, Winn-Dixie, XpertTire

Rock Hill

79 SC 122, Dave Lyle Blvd, to Rock Hill, **E...gas:** BP, **food:** Applebee's, Chick-fil-A, Cracker Barrel, DQ, Hardee's, J&K Cafeteria, Longhorn Steaks, O'Charley's, Ryan's, Ruby Tuesday, **lodging:** Hampton Inn, Wingate Inn, **other:** Belk, Food Lion, Goody's, Honda, JC Penney, Lowe's Whse, Sears/auto, Staples, Tire Kingdom, Wal-Mart SuperCtr 24hr/drugs/gas/24hr, mall, **W...gas:** Citgo, **food:** Bob Evans, Chili's, McCallister's Deli, McDonalds, Midtown Rest., Panera Bread, Quizno's, Taco Bell, Wendy's, **lodging:** Hilton Garden, **other:** Lincoln/Mercury, Target, visitor ctr

77 US 21, SC 5, to Rock Hill, **E...gas:** BP/Subway/diesel, Citgo/diesel/24hr, **other:** to Andrew Jackson SP(12mi), **W...gas:** Cone/diesel, Exxon/diesel, Phillips 66/diesel, **food:** Bojangles, KFC, McDonald's, Subway, Waffle House, **other:** to Winthrop Coll

75 Porter Rd, **E...gas:** Citgo, Shell

73 SC 901, to Rock Hill, York, **E...gas:** Exxon/diesel, **W...gas:** Citgo(1mi), HOSPITAL

66mm **rest area both lanes, full(handicapped)facilities, phone, picnic tables, litter barrels, vending, pet-walk**

65 SC 9, to Chester, Lancaster, **E...gas:** BP/Blimpie/24hr, Shell/Texaco/diesel, **food:** Subway, Waffle House, **lodging:** Day's Inn, Econolodge, Relax Inn, **W...gas:** Exxon/diesel, **food:** Burger King, Country Omelet/24hr, Front Porch Cafe, KFC, McDonald's, **lodging:** Comfort Inn, Microtel, Ramada Ltd., Super 8, **other:** HOSPITAL

62 SC 56, to Fort Lawn, Richburg, no facilities

55 SC 97, to Chester, Great Falls, **E...gas:** Exxon/diesel, **food:** Home Place Rest., **W...HOSPITAL**

48 SC 200, to Great Falls, **E...gas:** Shell/Grand Central Rest./diesel/@, **W...gas:** Wilco/Hess/DQ/Wendy's

46 SC 20, to White Oak, no facilities

41 SC 41, to Winnsboro, **E...to Lake Wateree SP**

34 SC 34, to Winnsboro, Ridgeway, **E...gas:** AM,PM/diesel/24hr, **lodging:** Ridgeway Motel, **other:** camping(1mi), **W...gas:** Citgo/diesel/store, Exxon/Blimpie/diesel, **food:** Lois's Cafe, Waffle House, **lodging:** Day's Inn, Ramada Ltd.

27 Blythewood Rd, **E...gas:** BP/diesel, Exxon/Bojangles/diesel/24hr, **food:** Blythewood Pizza/subs, KFC, McDonald's, Oaks Farm/rest., Pizza Hut/KFC, Subway, Waffle House, Wendy's, WG's Wings, **lodging:** Comfort Inn, Holiday Inn Express, **other:** IGA Foods, **W...Food Lion**

24 US 21, to Wilson Blvd., **E...gas:** BP, Shell/Subway/diesel, **food:** Myer's BBQ

22 Killian Rd, no facilities

Interstate 77

19   SC 555, Farrow Rd, **E…gas:** BP, Exxon, Shell, **food:** Bojangles, Cracker Barrel, Wendy's, **lodging:** Courtyard, **other:** HOSPITAL, Longs Drug, **W…gas:** Shell/diesel, **food:** Waffle House, **other:** Carolina Research Pk, SC Archives

18   to SC 277, to I-20 W(from sb), Columbia, no facilities

17   US 1, Two Notch Rd, **E…gas:** BP/24hr, Kangaroo, 76/Circle K/diesel, **food:** Arby's, Burger King, Texas Roadhouse, Waffle House, **lodging:** Fairfield Inn, InTown Suites, Ramada Plaza, Wingate Inn, **other:** U-Haul, USPO, to Sesquicentennial SP, **W…food:** Chili's, Fazoli's, Hop's Grill, IHOP, Lizard's Thicket, Outback Steaks, Waffle House, **lodging:** AmeriSuites, Comfort Inn, Econolodge, Hampton Inn, Holiday Inn, Microtel, Quality Inn, Red Roof Inn, **other:** MEDICAL CARE, Home Depot

16b a   I-20, W to Augusta, E to Florence, Alpine Rd

15b a   SC 12, to Percival Rd, **W…gas:** El Cheapo/gas, Shell, **1/2 mi W…gas:** Exxon

13   Decker Blvd(from nb), **W…gas:** El Cheapo

12   Forest Blvd, Thurmond Blvd, **E…to Ft Jackson, W…gas:** BP/diesel, 76/diesel, Shell/diesel/24hr, **food:** Bojangles, Chick-fil-A, Fatz Café, Golden Corral, Hardee's, McDonald's, RedBone Rest., Steak&Ale, Subway, Wendy's, **lodging:** Extended Stay America, Super 8, **other:** HOSPITAL, $Tree, Sam's Club/gas, Wal-Mart SuperCtr/24hr, museum

10   10 SC 760, Jackson Blvd, **E…to Ft Jackson, 2 mi W…food:** Applebee's, Bojangles, Maurices BBQ, Ruby Tuesday, Subway, **lodging:** Econolodge, Liberty Inn

9b a   US 76, US 378, to Sumter, Columbia, **E…gas:** BP, Citgo, Hess/diesel, Sunoco/diesel, **food:** Capt D's, Chick-fil-A, China Chef, Domino's, KFC, McDonald's, Pizza Hut, Rush's Rest., Shoney's, Subway, Waffle House, **lodging:** Best Western, Comfort Inn, Country Inn Suites, Day's Inn, Hampton Inn, Holiday Inn Express, Sleep Inn, **other:** MEDICAL CARE, Advance Parts, Family$, Firestone/auto, Food Lion, Goodyear/auto, Interstate Batteries, Lowe's Whse, NAPA, Piggly Wiggly, Pontiac/GMC, Radio Shack, Tire Kingdom, U-Haul, USPO, Wal-Mart SuperCtr/gas/24hr/auto, **W…gas:** Corner Pantry/gas, 76/Circle K(1mi), **food:** CiCi's, Hardee's, Mark&Sue's, Sonic, Substation II, Wendy's, **lodging:** Economy Inn, **other:** HOSPITAL, $General, Eckerd, Target

6b a   Shop Rd, **W…to USC Coliseum, fairgrounds**

5   SC 48, Bluff Rd, **1 mi E…gas:** 76, **W…gas:** Shell/Burger King/diesel, **food:** Bojangles(2mi)

3mm   Congaree River

2   Saxe Gotha Rd, no facilities

1   US 21, US 176, US 321(from sb), Cayce, **W…**accesses same as SC I-26, exit 115.

0mm   I-77 begins/ends on I-26, exit 116.

(side bar: Columbia)

(side bar: Gaffney)

Interstate 85

Exit #	Services
106.5mm	South Carolina/North Carolina state line
106	US 29, to Grover, **W…gas:** Crown, Exxon/diesel, Wilco/Hess/DQ/Wendy's/diesel
104	SC 99, **E…gas:** Mr. Waffle/diesel/rest./24hr/@
103mm	**Welcome Ctr sb, full(handicapped)facilities, info, phone, picnic tables, litter barrels, vending, petwalk**
102	SC 198, to Earl, **E…gas:** JT/gas, BP/diesel, **food:** Hardee's, **W…gas:** Flying J/Conoco/diesel/LP/rest./24hr/@, Shell/Texaco/diesel, **food:** McDonald's, Waffle House
100mm	Buffalo Creek
100	SC 5, to Blacksburg, Shelby, **W…gas:** Speedway/Subway/diesel/24hr/@, Shell/Texaco/diesel
98	Frontage Rd(from nb), **E…food:** Broad River Café
97mm	Broad River
96	SC 18(from sb), **W…gas:** Kangaroo/diesel/@
95	SC 18, to Gaffney, **E…gas:** Citgo/24hr, Exxon/diesel, Kangaroo, Mr Petro/Mr Waffle, **food:** Aunt M's Rest., Fatz Café, **lodging:** Gaffney Inn, Shamrock Inn, **other:** HOSPITAL, Daewoo, to Limestone Coll
92	SC 11, to Gaffney, **E…gas:** Citgo, **food:** Applebee's, Blue Bay Seafood, Bojangles, Burger King, Chinese Buffet, Domino's, McDonald's, Pizza Hut, Ruby Tuesday, Ruby Tuesday, Ryan's, Sagebrush Steaks, Sonic, Subway, Super China, Taco Bell, Wendy's, Western Sizzlin, **lodging:** Holiday Inn Express, Jameson Inn, **other:** MEDICAL CARE, Advance Parts, Belk, BiLo, $Tree, Eckerd, Ford/Mercury, Ingles Foods, Radio Shack, Wal-Mart SuperCtr/24hr, to Limestone Coll, **W…gas:** Shell/Texaco/diesel, **food:** Waffle House, **lodging:** Comfort Inn, Day's Inn, to The Peach, Foothills Scenic Hwy
90	SC 105, SC 42, to Gaffney, **E…gas:** BP/DQ/diesel, Pilot/Arby's/diesel/24hr/@, **food:** Subway, Waffle House, **lodging:** Red Roof Inn, Sleep Inn, **W…gas:** Citgo/Burger King, **food:** Cracker Barrel, FoodCourt, Outback Steaks, **lodging:** Hampton Inn, **other:** Hamrick's, Prime Outlets/famous brands
89mm	**rest area both lanes, full(handicapped)facilities, phone, picnic tables, litter barrels, vending, petwalk**
87	SC 39, **E…other:** PineCone Camping(1.5mi), **W…other:** World of Clothing, fruit stand/peaches/fireworks

SOUTH CAROLINA
Interstate 85

N

S

Spartanburg

83   SC 110, **1 mi E...gas:** Hot Spot/gas, **food:** Subway, **W...gas:** Citgo/Mr Waffle/diesel/24hr, **other:** to Cowpens Bfd

82   Frontage Rd(from nb), no facilities

81   Frontage Rd(from sb), no facilities

80.5mm   Pacolet River

80   SC 57, to Gossett, no facilities

78   US 221, Chesnee, **E...gas:** Citgo/diesel, **food:** Hardee's, **lodging:** Motel 6, **other:** fruit stand, **W...gas:** BP, Exxon/Burger King/diesel, RaceTrac/diesel, **food:** BBQ, Burger King, McDonald's, Subway, Waffle House, Wendy's, **lodging:** Hampton Inn, Holiday Inn Express, **other:** Advance Parts, $General, Harley Davidson, Ingles Foods

77   Lp 85, Spartanburg, facilities along Lp 85 exits E

75   SC 9, Spartanburg, **E...food:** Denny's, **lodging:** Fairfield Inn, **1 mi E...gas:** Exxon, **lodging:** Best Western, Comfort Inn, Day's Inn, **W...gas:** BP/Burger King/LJSilver/diesel, Phillips 66, RaceTrac, **food:** Bruster's Ice Cream, Capri's Italian, Fatz Café, LJ Silver, McDonald's, Pizza Hut, Waffle House, Zaxby's, **lodging:** Hawthorn Inn, Jameson Inn, **other:** Advance Parts, CVS Drug, Grease Monkey Auto Repair, Ingles/gas, USPO

72   US 176, to I-585, **E...other:** to USC-S, Wofford/Converse Coll, **W...gas:** BP, RaceTrac, **other:** Masters RV Ctr

70b a   I-26, E to Columbia, W to Asheville

69   Lp 85, SC 41(from nb), to Fairforest, **E...lodging:** Hampton Inn, **other:** camping

68   SC 129(from sb), to Greer, no facilities

67mm   N Tyger River

66   US 29, to Lyman, Wellford, no facilities

63   SC 290, to Duncan, **E...gas:** 76/Circle K, Citgo/diesel, Exxon/Arby's, **food:** A&W/KFC, Atlanta Bread Co, Burger King, Denny's, Duke Sandwich, Jack-in-the-Box, Pizza Inn, Taco Bell, Thai Cuisine, Waffle House, **lodging:** Hampton Inn, Jameson Inn, Microtel, **W...gas:** Pilot/Wendy's/diesel/24hr/@, TA/BP/DQ/diesel/rest./@, Shell/Texaco, **food:** Arby's, BBQ, Bojangles, Hardee's, McDonald's, Waffle House, **lodging:** Comfort Inn, Day's Inn, Holiday Inn Express, Quality Inn, Travelodge, **other:** Sonny's RV Ctr

62.5mm   S Tyger River

60   SC 101, to Greer, **E...gas:** BP, Citgo/diesel, Grand/diesel, Phillips 66, **food:** Beaner's Grill, Subway, Theo's Diner, **W...gas:** Exxon/Burger King, **food:** Waffle House, **lodging:** Super 8

57   **W...other:** Greenville-Spartanburg Airport

56   SC 14, to Greer, **E...gas:** Spinx/diesel/DQ/@, Shell/Texaco/diesel, **W...gas:** Amoco/diesel, **other:** HOSPITAL

55mm   Enoree River

54   Pelham Rd, **E...gas:** BP/diesel, Citgo/diesel/24hr, **food:** Burger King, Corona Mexican, Waffle House, **lodging:** Best Western, Holiday Inn Express, **W...gas:** Amoco/diesel, Spinx/Exxon, **food:** Applebee's, Atlanta Bread Co, California Dreaming Rest., Chick-fil-a, China Wok, Hardee's, Jack-in-

Greenville

the-Box, Joe's Crabshack, J&S Cafeteria, Logan's Roadhouse, Macaroni Grill, Max&Erma's, Mayflower Seafood, McDonald's, Miami Grill, On the Border, Ruby Tuesday, Schlotsky's, Subway, Tony Roma, Wendy's, **lodging:** Comfort Inn, Courtyard, Extended Stay America, Fairfield Inn, Hampton Inn, MainStay Suites, Marriott, Microtel, Residence Inn, Wingate Inn, **other:** BiLo/24hr, CVS Drug, Goodyear/auto, Ingles, Radio Shack

52mm   weigh sta nb

51   I-385, SC 146, Woodruff Rd, **E...food:** Bob Evans, Bojangles, Chili's, Fatz Café, Fuddrucker's, IHOP, Midori's Café, Sticky Fingers, **lodging:** Hampton Inn, **other:** Goodyear/auto, Sam's Club/gas, Wal-Mart SuperCtr/24hr(1mi), **other:** VETERINARIAN, Best Buy, Lowe's Whse, **W...gas:** Amoco, BP, RaceTrac/24hr, Shell, **food:** Atl Bread Co, Capri's Italian, Cracker Barrel, Doughnut Connection, Jack-in-the-Box, McDonald's, Prime Sirloin, Remington's Rest., TGIFriday, Waffle House, **lodging:** Day's Inn, Embassy Suites, Fairfield Inn, Holiday Inn Express, La Quinta, Marriott(3mi), Microtel, **other:** BJ's Whse, CompUSA, Dillard's, Firestone/auto, Goody's, Home Depot, Lowe's Whse, Old Navy, Target, mall

48b a   US 276, Greenville, **E...food:** Waffle House, **lodging:** Red Roof Inn, Super 8, **other:** CarMax, Nissan, **W...gas:** BP, Exxon/diesel, **food:** Arby's, Bojangles, Burger King, Hooters, Jack-in-the-Box, McDonalds, Olive Garden, Ryan's, Taco Bell/Pizza Hut, **lodging:** Day's Inn, Embassy Suites, Valu-Lodge, **other:** Acura/Honda, BMW, BooksAMillion, Buick, Cadillac, Chrysler/Plymouth/Jeep, Daewoo/Suzuki, Dodge, Ford, Kia, Lexus, Lincoln/Mercury, Marshall's, Mazda, Mercedes, Michael's, Mini, Office Depot, OfficeMax, PepBoys, Pontiac/GMC, SteinMart, Toyota, Volvo, VW/Audi

46c   rd 291, Pleasantburg Rd, Mauldin Rd, **W...gas:** Shell/diesel, Spinx/Arby's, **food:** Jack-in-the-Box, Steak-Out, Subway, **lodging:** Garden Inn, InTowne Suites, Quality Inn, **other:** Aamco, BiLo/gas, CVS Drug, Tire Kingdom

46b a   US 25 bus, Augusta Rd, **E...gas:** BP, Chevron, Exxon, Phillips 66, **food:** Bojangles, Burger King, Waffle House, **lodging:** Camelot Inn, Holiday Inn, Motel 6, Southern Suites, **W...food:** Dixie Rest., Jack-in-the-Box, **lodging:** Economy Inn, Travelodge, **other:** Home Depot

44   US 25, White Horse Rd, **E...gas:** Spinx/Subway/diesel, **W...gas:** RaceTrac, **food:** McDonald's, BBQ, Quincy's, Waffle House, **other:** HOSPITAL

44a   SC 20(from sb), to Piedmont, no facilities

42   I-185 toll, US 29, to Greenville, **W...HOSPITAL**

40   SC 153, to Easley, **E...gas:** Exxon/diesel, **food:** Waffle House, **W...gas:** Exxon/diesel, RaceTrac, Shell/Texaco/diesel/24hr, **food:** Arby's, Burger King, Hardee's, KFC, Pizza Hut/Taco Bell, Subway, Zaxby's, **lodging:** Executive Inn, Super 8, **1 mi W...gas:** Shell, **food:** Little Caesar's, McDonald's, Sonic, **other:** BiLo Foods, Eckerd, GNC, Ingles Foods

SOUTH CAROLINA

Interstate 85

N ↕ S

A n d e r s o n

39   SC 143, to Piedmont, **E...gas:** Yates/diesel, **W... gas:** Marathon, Shell/diesel, **ohter:** Ace Hardware, antiques

35   SC 86, to Easley, Piedmont, **E...gas:** Pilot/McDonald's/diesel/24hr/@, **food:** Hardee's(1.5mi), Subway(1.5mi), **W...gas:** BP/grill/diesel

34   US 29(from sb), to Williamston, no facilities

32   SC 8, to Pelzer, Easley, **E...gas:** Shell/diesel

27   SC 81, to Anderson, **E...gas:** Amoco/diesel, BP/diesel, Citgo, Exxon, Pumper's Gas/diesel, **food:** Arby's, KFC/Pizza Hut, McDonald's, Waffle House, **lodging:** Holiday Inn Express, **other:** HOSPITAL **W...gas:** Anderson Travel Ctr/DQ/KrispyKreme/diesel/24hr.@, **food:** Charlie's Wings

23mm   **rest area sb, full(handicapped)facilities, phone, vending, picnic tables, litter barrels, petwalk**

21   US 178, to Anderson, **E...gas:** Shell/diesel/@, **2 mi E...food:** Applebee's, Chick-fil-a, Fazoli's, O'Charley's, Ruby Tuesday, **lodging:** La Quinta, Mainstay Suites, Quality Inn, Studio 1, Super 8, **other:** Publics/deli

19b a   US 76, SC 28, to Anderson, **E...gas:** Amoco/diesel, BP/diesel(1mi), Exxon/diesel, **food:** BBQ, Chick-fil-A, Chili's, DockMasters Seafood, Fuddruckers, Grand China, Hardee's, Texas Roadhouse, **lodging:** Day's Inn, La Quinta, Royal American Motel, **other:** Aldi Food, Buick/GMC, Chrysler/Plymouth, Russel Stover, **W...gas:** RaceTrac/diesel/24hr, **food:** Buffalo's Café, Cracker Barrel, Hooters, Outback Steaks, Paparazzi's Italian, Shrimp Shack, Waffle House, Wendy's, **lodging:** Comfort Suites, Country Inn Suites, Fairfield Inn, Hampton Inn, Holiday Inn Express, Jameson Inn, **other:** to Clemson U

18mm   **rest area nb, full(handicapped)facilities, phone, vending, picnic tables, litter barrels, petwalk**

15mm   Lake Hartwell

14   SC 187, to Clemson, Anderson, **E...gas:** FuelClub/diesel/24hr/@, **food:** Huddle House/24hr, **other:** KOA(1mi), **W...gas:** BP/diesel, **food:** Country Jack Kitchen, **lodging:** Budget Inn, **other:** to Clem Research Pk

12mm   Seneca River, Lake Hartwell

11   SC 24, SC 243, to Townville, **E...gas:** Exxon/diesel, Sunoco/diesel/24hr, **food:** Subway, **other:** Savannah River Scenic Hwy, **W...gas:** Shell/diesel, **food:** Circle's Cafe, **other:** GS RV Park(3mi)

9mm   weigh sta nb

4   SC 243, to SC 24, **E...gas:** Mobil/diesel/LP/rest./24hr/@, **other:** Thousand Trails Camping, **W...gas:** Marathon/Russell's Gen. Store

2   SC 59, to Fair Play, **E...camping, W...fireworks**

1   SC 11, to Walhalla, **W...food:** Gazebo Rest., **other:** fireworks, to Lake Hartwell SP

.5mm   **Welcome Ctr nb, full(handicapped)facilities, info, phone, picnic tables, litter barrels, vending, petwalk**

0mm   South Carolina/Georgia state line, Lake Hartwell, Tagaloo River

Interstate 95

N ↕ S

D i l l o n

F l o r e n c e

Exit #   Services

198mm   South Carolina/North Carolina state line

196mm   **Welcome Ctr sb, full(handicapped)facilities, info, phone, vending, picnic tables, litter barrels, petwalk**

195mm   Little Pee Dee River

193   SC 9, SC 57, Dillon, to N Myrtle Beach, **E...gas:** Amoco/24hr, Exxon, Speedway/diesel, **food:** Bojangles, Burger King, Golden Corral, Shoney's, Waffle House, Wendy's, **lodging:** Best Value Inn, Comfort Inn, Day's Inn/rest., Hampton Inn, Holiday Inn Express, Howard Johnson, Ramada Ltd, **other:** HOSPITAL **W...gas:** BP/diesel, **food:** Hubbard House, Waffle House, **lodging:** Econolodge, Super 8

190   SC 34, to Dillon, **E...gas:** BP/Stuckey's/DQ, **other:** repair, **W...gas:** Dillon Gas/diesel

181   SC 38, Oak Grove, **E...gas:** BP, ✈/Flying J/Conoco/diesel/LP/rest./24hr/@, Shell/Subway, **W...gas:** Wilco/Hess/DQ/Wendy's/diesel/@, **other:** auto/truck repair

175mm   Pee Dee River

172mm   **rest area both lanes, full(handicapped)facilities, phone, picnic tables, vending, litter barrels, petwalk**

170   SC 327, **E...gas:** BP, Pilot/Wendy's/diesel/24hr/@, **food:** McDonald's, **lodging:** Holiday Inn Express, **other:** to Myrtle Beach, Missile Museum, **W...gas:** Citgo/diesel

169   TV Rd, to Florence, **E...other:** KOA(1mi), Peterbilt, diesel repair, **W...gas:** Amoco, Petro/Exxon/diesel/rest./24hr/@, Texaco/diesel, **lodging:** Rodeway Inn, **other:** Blue Beacon

164   US 52, Florence, to Darlington, **E...gas:** Citgo, Exxon/Pizza Hut/diesel, RaceWay/24hr, Shell, **food:** Cracker Barrel, Denny's, Hardee's, Kobe Japanese, McDonald's, Ruby Tuesday, Waffle House, Wendy's, **lodging:** Best Western, Comfort Inn, Econolodge, Hampton Inn, Holiday Inn, Knight's Inn, Motel 6, Suburban Lodge, Super 8, **other:** HOSPITAL, Chrysler/Jeep, Pontiac/Buick, **W...gas:** Hess/diesel, Patlo/diesel/24hr, Pilot/Subway/Taco Bell/diesel/@, **food:** Arby's, Bojangles, Burger King, Fatz Café, KFC, Shoney's, **lodging:** Country Inn Suites, Day's Inn, Guesthouse Inn, Microtel, Ramada Inn, Sleep Inn, Thunderbird Inn, Wingate Inn, **other:** to Darlington Raceway

N ↕ **S**

160b I-20 W, to Columbia

a Lp 20, to Florence, **E...gas:** Shell/diesel, **food:** Burger King, Chick-fil-A, Huddle House, Morrison's Cafeteria, Outback Steaks, Pizza Hut, Red Lobster, Ruby Tuesday, Shoney's, Waffle House, Western Sizzlin, **lodging:** Courtyard, Fairfield Inn, Hampton Inn, Holiday Inn Express, Red Roof Inn, SpringHill Suites, **other:** Advance Parts, Belk, Chevrolet, $Tree, JC Penney, Sears/auto, Staples, Target, Wal-Mart/drugs, mall, **1-2 mi E...gas:** Exxon, Shell, **food:** Arby's, Hardee's, McDonald's, Percy&Willie's Rest., Subway, Taco Bell, Wendy's, **other:** BooksAMillion, Chevrolet/BMW/Isuzu, Circuit City, Lowe's Whse, Piggly Wiggly, CVS Drug, K-Mart, Firestone/auto, Nissan, NAPA, Nissan, Sam's Club, mall

157 US 76, Timmonsville, Florence, **E...gas:** BP/diesel, Exxon/McDonald's/diesel, Phillips 66, **food:** Swamp Fox Diner, Waffle House, **lodging:** Day's Inn, Howard Johnson Express, Villager Lodge, **W...gas:** Sunoco, **lodging:** Tree Room Inn/rest., Young's Plantation Inn/ Magnolia Dining Room, Swamp Fox Camping(1mi)

153 Honda Way, **W...**Honda Plant

150 SC 403, to Sardis, **E...gas:** BP/diesel, **lodging:** Budget Inn, **W...gas:** Exxon/diesel, **other:** Honeydew RV Camp

147mm Lynches River

146 SC 341, to Lynchburg, Olanta, **E...lodging:** Relax Inn

141 SC 53, SC 58, to Shiloh, **E...gas:** Exxon/diesel, **other:** DonMar RV Ctr, to Woods Bay SP, **W...gas:** Shell

139mm **rest area both lanes, full(handicapped)facilities, phone, vending, picnic tables, litter barrels, petwalk**

135 US 378, to Sumter, Turbeville, **E...gas:** BP, Citgo, **food:** Compass Rest., **lodging:** Day's Inn, Knight's Inn, **W...gas:** Exxon/diesel, **other:** Pineland Golf Course

132 SC 527, to Sardinia, Kingstree, no facilities

130mm Black River

122 US 521, to Alcolu, Manning, **E...food:** MD Fried Chicken(2mi), **lodging:** Manning Motel(3mi), **W...gas:** Exxon/diesel, **food:** Shrimper Rest.

119 SC 261, Manning, to Paxville, **E...gas:** Shell/24hr, TA/Amoco/Blimpie/LJS/Pizza Hut/Sbarro's/diesel/ 24hr/@, **food:** Huddle House, Mariachi's, Shoney's, Waffle House, Wendy's, **lodging:** Best Western, Comfort Inn, Holiday Inn Express, Ramada Ltd, **other:** HOSPITAL, Chrysler/Jeep/Dodge, Ford, **1 mi E...gas:** Exxon, **food:** Burger King, KFC, Sonic, Subway, **other:** CVS Drug, $General, Food Lion, Goodyear/auto, Radio Shack, Wal-Mart/drugs, to McDonald's(2mi), Campers Paradise RV Park, **W...gas:** Exxon/24hr, Horizon/diesel, **lodging:** Super 8, **other:** auto repair

S a n t e e

115 US 301, to Summerton, Manning, **E... gas:** Exxon/diesel, **lodging:** Carolina Inn, **W...gas:** Texaco/diesel/24hr, **food:** Georgio's Greek, **lodging:** Day's Inn, Econolodge, Sunset Inn

108 SC 102, Summerton, **E...gas:** BP/DQ/Stuckey's, **other:** TawCaw RV Parl(6m), **W...lodging:** Day's Inn, Deluxe Inn, Knight's Inn, Travelodge

102 US 15, US 301 N, to Santee, **E...lodging:** motel, **other:** RV camping, **W...gas:** Shell/diesel, **other:** to Santee NWR

100mm Lake Marion

99mm **rest area both lanes, full(handicapped)facilities, phone, info, vending, picnic tables, litter barrels, petwalk**

98 SC 6, Santee, to Eutawville, **E...gas:** BP, Chevron/LP, Citgo, **food:** Huddle House, KFC, Pizza Hut, Shoney's, **lodging:** Best Western, Day's Inn, Hampton Inn, Howard Johnson, Super 8, **other:** $General, Piggly Wiggly, Russell Stover Candy, Santee Outlets/famous brands, **W...gas:** BP/diesel, Citgo, Exxon, Hess/diesel, Horizon/ Pizza Hut/diesel/24hr, Shell/diesel, **food:** BBQ, Burger King, Cracker Barrel, Hardee's, Denny's, McDonald's, Waffle House, Wendy's, **lodging:** Budget Motel, Clark Inn/rest., Comfort Inn, Country Inn Suites, Economy Inn, Holiday Inn, Lake Marion Inn, **other:** BiLo, CarQuest, CVS Drug, Family$, Food Lion, NAPA, Radio Shack, USPO, to Santee SP(3mi)

97 US 301 S(from sb, no return), to Orangeburg, no facilities

93 US 15, to Santee, Holly Hill, no facilities

90 US 176, to Cameron, Holly Hill, **W...gas:** Exxon/diesel

86b a I-26, W to Columbia, E to Charleston, no facilities

82 US 178, to Bowman, Harleyville, **E...gas:** Amoco, Wilco Hess/Wendy's/DQ/diesel/24hr/@, **lodging:** Peachtree Inn, **W...gas:** Texaco/diesel

77 US 78, St George, to Bamberg, **E...gas:** Exxon/KFC, Shell/Subway/TCBY, **food:** Empire Asian, Georgio's Rest., Hardee's, McDonald's, Pizza Hut, Waffle House, Western Sizzlin, **lodging:** American Inn, Comfort Inn/RV park, Quality Inn, **other:** Chevrolet/Pontiac/GMC, CVS Drug, Family$, Food Lion, Ford, USPO, **W...gas:** BP, Texaco/diesel, **food:** Huddle House, Taco Bell, **lodging:** Best Western, Day's Inn, Southern Inn, Super 8

68 SC 61, Canadys, **E...gas:** Amoco, Citgo, Texaco/Subway/ diesel, **other:** to Colleton SP(3mi)

62 SC 34, **W...other:** Lakeside RV camping

57 SC 64, Walterboro, **E...gas:** BP/Subway/Pizza Hut/TCBY/ diesel/24hr, Exxon/diesel, Shell/DQ, Speedway, Texaco/ Blimpie/diesel, **food:** Burger King, Capt D's, Huddle House, Little Caesar's, Longhorn Steaks, McDonald's, Olde House Café, Taco Bell, Waffle House, Wendy's, **lodging:** Sleep Inn, Southern Inn, **other:** HOSPITAL, Advance Parts, AutoZone, BiLo, CVS Drug, Food Lion, GNC, K-Mart, Piggly Wiggly, Wal-Mart, **W...gas:** Amoco/ diesel, **lodging:** Super 8

SOUTH CAROLINA

Interstate 95

N ↕ S

53 SC 63, Walterboro, to Varnville, Hampton, **E...gas:** Amoco/McDonald's, Citgo/diesel, El Cheapo, Shell, Texaco, **food:** Burger King, Dairy Queen, KFC, Longhorn Steaks, McDonald's, Ruby Tuesday, Shoney's, Waffle House, **lodging:** Best Western, Comfort Inn/rest., Econolodge, Quality Inn, Ramada Inn, Rice Planter's Inn, Thunderbird Inn, **W...gas:** BP, **food:** Cracker Barrel, **lodging:** Day's Inn, Deluxe Inn, Hampton Inn, **other:** Green Acres Camping

47mm **rest area both lanes, full(handicapped)facilities, phone, vending, picnic tables, litter barrels, petwalk**

42 US 21, to Yemassee, Beaufort, no facilities

40mm Combahee River

38 SC 68, to Hampton, Yemassee, **E...gas:** Chevron, **W...gas:** BP/Subway/TCBY, Exxon, Shell/diesel, **food:** J's Rest., **lodging:** Palmetto Lodge/rest., Super 8

33 US 17 N, to Beaufort, **E...gas:** BP/diesel, Citgo, Exxon, Shell, Texaco/Subway/24hr, **food:** Denny's, McDonald's, TCBY, Waffle House, Wendy's, **lodging:** Best Western, Day's Inn/rest., Holiday Inn Express, Knight's Inn, **other:** KOA

30.5mm Tullifinny River

29mm Coosawhatchie River

28 SC 462, to Coosawhatchie, Hilton Head, Bluffton, **W...gas:** Amoco, Chevron/diesel, Citgo/Stuckey's/DQ, Exxon/diesel/rest.

22 US 17, Ridgeland, **E...food:** El Ranchito Mexican, **W...gas:** Shell, Plantation Inn, HOSPITAL

21 SC 336, to Hilton Head, Ridgeland, **W...gas:** Chevron/Blimpie/diesel/24hr, Citgo, Exxon, Texaco/diesel, **food:** Burger King, Hong Kong Chinese, Huddle House, Jasper's Porch Rest., KFC, Main St Pizza, Subway, Waffle House, **lodging:** Carolina Lodge, Comfort Inn/rest., Econolodge, Ramada Ltd, **other:** HOSPITAL, $General, Eckerd, Food Lion

18 SC 13, to US 17, US 278, to Switzerland, Granville, Ridgeland, no facilities

17mm parking area both lanes, litter barrels

8 US 278, Hardeeville, to Bluffton, **E...gas:** BP/Joker Joe's/diesel/24hr/@, Exxon, Shell/McDonald's, **food:** Huddle House, Wendy's, **W...gas:** Chevron/Subway, Kangaroo/24hr, **food:** KrispyKreme, Pizza Hut, TCBY, **lodging:** Ramada Ltd

5 US 17, US 321, Hardeeville, to Savannah, **E...gas:** El Cheapo, Exxon/Blimpie, Shell/24hr, **food:** KFC, Waffle House, **lodging:** Day's Inn, Economy, Sleep Inn, **other:** to Savannah NWR, **W...gas:** BP/diesel, Speedway/diesel, **food:** Burger King, McDonald's, New China Rest., Shoney's, Subway, Wendy's, **lodging:** Comfort Inn, Deluxe Inn, Holiday Inn Express, Howard Johnson Express, Knight's Inn, Scottish Inn, Super 8, **other:** NAPA, antiques

Hardeeville (vertical, left margin)

4.5mm **Welcome Ctr nb, full(handicapped)f acilities, info, phone, picnic tables, litter barrels, vending, petwalk**

3.5mm weigh sta both lanes

0mm South Carolina/Georgia state line, Savannah River

Interstate 385(Greenville)

Exit #	Services

N ↕ S

42 US 276, Stone Ave, to Travelers Rest., to Greenville Zoo, **E...other:** CarQuest, **W...gas:** Amoco, 1-2 mi **W...**multiple facilities on US 276, I-385 begins/ends on US 276.

40b a SC 291, Pleasantburg Dr, **E...gas:** Conoco, Speedway, **food:** Jack-in-the-Box, Jalisco Mexican, Little Caesar's, Lizard's Thicket, Pizza Hut, S&S Cafeteria, Sonic, Steak&Ale, Subway, Taco Casa, Wendy's, **other:** CVS Drug, to BJU, Furman U, **W...gas:** Shell, **food:** Domino's, Dragon Den Chinese, Krispy Kreme, **lodging:** Comfort Inn, Sleep Inn, **other:** Advance Parts, transmissions

39 Haywood Rd, **E...gas:** BP, Exxon/diesel, **food:** Domino's, LongHorn Steaks, Outback Steaks, Shoney's, **lodging:** AmeriSuites, Courtyard, GuestHouse Suites, Hilton, La Quinta, Quality Inn, Residence Inn, **other:** Firestone, **W...gas:** Crown, Shell, Texaco, **food:** Arby's, Applebee's, Bennigan's, Blackeyed Pea, Buffalo's Café, Burger King, Chili's, ChuckeCheese, CityRange Steaks, Don Pablo, Hardee's, Italian Mkt/grill, Jack-in-the-Box, Jason's Deli, Kanpai Tokyo, O'Charley's, Senor Wrap's, Steak'n Shake, Waffle House, Wendy's, **lodging:** Hampton Inn, Studio+, **other:** Barnes&Noble, Belk, Circuit City, Dillard's, Discount Tire, Goodyear, Harley-Davidson, JC Penney, NTB, Sears/auto, mall

37 Roper Mtn Rd, **E...other:** BiLo Foods, **W...gas:** Amoco, BP/diesel, Exxon/Pantry, RaceTrac, **food:** Atl Bread Co, Backyard Burger, Burger King, Capri's Italian, Cracker Barrel, Fazoli's, LoneStar Steaks, McDonald's, Miyabi Japanese, Rafferty's, Remington's Rest., Waffle House, **lodging:** Day's Inn, Crowne Plaza, Embassy Suites, Fairfield Inn, Holiday Inn Select, La Quinta, Travelodge, **other:** BJ's Whse, CompUSA, Goody's, Home Depot, Lowe's Whse, Old Navy, Target, mall

36b a I-85, N to Charlotte, S to Atlanta

Greenville

SOUTH CAROLINA

Interstate 385

N ↕ **S**

Simpsonville

35   SC 146, Woodruff Rd, **E...gas:** Amoco, BP, **food:** Applebee's, AZ Steaks, Bojangles, Boston Pizzaria, Burger King, Chick-fil-A, Chili's, DQ, Fazoli's, Hardee's, KFC, King Buffet, Little Caesar's, McAlister's Deli, Perkins, Ryan's, Schlotsky's, Sonic, Subway, Taco Bell, Topper's Rest., Waffle House, Wendy's, Zaxby's, **other:** Aldi Foods, BiLo Foods, $Tree, Publix, Staples, USPO, Wal-Mart SuperCtr/24hr, **W...gas:** Exxon/diesel, **food:** Burger King, Fatz Café, Fuddrucker's, IHOP, Midori's Rest., Monterrey Mexican, TCBY, Waffle House, **lodging:** Hampton Inn, **other:** Goodyear/auto, Hamrick's Outlet, funpark

34   Butler Rd, Mauldin, **E...gas:** Exxon, **food:** Arby's, **other:** CVS Drug, **W...gas:** Phillips 66, **lodging:** Super 8(3mi)

33   Bridges Rd, Mauldin, no facilities

31   I-185 toll(from sb), SC 417, to Laurens Rd, **E...gas:** Amoco, **food:** Hardee's, **other:** HOSPITAL, **W...gas:** BP, **food:** LJSilver, **lodging:** Masters Inn

30   I-185 toll(from nb), US 276, Standing Springs Rd, no facilities

29   Georgia Rd, to Simpsonville, **W...other:** MountainTop RV/Marine Ctr

27   Fairview Rd, to Simpsonville, **E...gas:** Amoco, Shell, **food:** Hardee's, McDonald's, **lodging:** Palmetto Inn, **other:** HOSPITAL, Advance Parts, BiLo Food, Chevrolet, $General, Rite Aid, **W...gas:** Amoco/Arby's, BP, **food:** Applebee's, AZ Steaks, Burger King, Cracker Barrel, Dragon Den Chinese, KFC, Ryan's, Pizza Hut, Taco Bell, Waffle House, Wendy's, **lodging:** Comfort Inn, Day's Inn, Hampton Inn, Holiday Inn Express, Microtel, **other:** $Tree, GNC, Ingles, Lowe's Whse, Radio Shack, Wal-Mart SuperCtr/gas/24hr

26   Harrison Bridge Rd(from sb), no facilities

24   Fairview St, Fountain Inn, **E...gas:** Phillips 66, **food:** Hardee's, Waffle House, **other:** carwash

23   SC 418, to Fountain Inn, Fork Shoals, **E...gas:** Exxon/Subway/diesel/24hr

22   SC 14 W, Old Laurens Rd, to Fountain Inn, no facilities

19   SC 14 E, to Gray Court, Owings, no facilities

16   SC 101, to Woodruff, Gray Court, no facilities

10   SC 23, to Ora, no facilities

9   US 221, to Laurens, Enoree, **E...gas:** Exxon/Subway/diesel/24hr, **food:** Waffle House, **lodging:** Budget Lodge, **W...**Wal-Mart Dist Ctr, **lodging:** Travel Inn

6mm   **rest area both lanes(both lanes exit left), full(handicapped)facilities, phone, vending, picnic tables, litter barrels, petwalk**

5   SC 49, to Laurens, Union, no facilities

2   SC 308, to Clinton, Ora, **W...other:** HOSPITAL, to Presbyterian Coll in Clinton

0mm   I-26 S to Columbia, I-385 begins/ends on I-26 at 52mm.

Interstate 526(Charleston)

E ↔ **W**

Charleston

Exit #   Services

33mm   I-526 begins/ends.

32   US 17, **N...gas:** Exxon, Hess, **food:** Subway, **lodging:** Day's Inn, Red Roof Inn, **other:** Advance Parts, CVS Drug, **1 mi N...gas:** Shell, **food:** Burger King, Chili's, IHOP, LongHorn Steaks, On The Border, TGIFriday, **other:** Barnes&Noble, Belk, Eckerd, Lowe's Whse, Old Navy, **S...gas:** Amoco, Speedway, **food:** Applebee's, Arby's, Chick-fil-A, China Buffet, Domino's, KFC, La Hacienda Mexicana, McDonald's, Papa John's, **other:** MEDICAL CARE, $General, Office Depot, Publix, USPO, VW, Wal-Mart, **1 mi S...gas:** Hess, 76, Shell, **food:** Hardee's, Huddle House, Outback Steaks, Shoney's, Wendy's, **lodging:** Comfort Inn, Day's Inn, Extended Stay America, Holiday Inn, Masters Inn, **other:** Cadillac/Chevrolet, Ford, Firestone/auto, Radio Shack, Staples

30   Long Point Rd, **N...gas:** Exxon, **food:** Bamboo Garden, Mo's Café, Sonic, Starbucks, Subway, Waffle House, **other:** Food Lion, Harris Teeter Foods, Charles Pinckney NHS

26mm   Wando River

24   Daniel Island, **S...**Queen Anne's Steaks/seafood, Hampton Inn

23b a   Clements Ferry Rd, no facilities

21mm   Cooper River

20   Virginia Ave(from eb), **S...gas:** Hess Depot, **other:** Marathon Refinery

19   N Rhett Ave, **N...gas:** Hess, **food:** Hardee's, **other:** Eckerd, Food Lion, **S...gas:** Amoco

18b a   US 52, US 78, Rivers Ave, **N...gas:** Amoco/diesel, Shell, **food:** McDonald's, **other:** Family$, Merchant Auto, NAPA, Piggly Wiggly, **S...lodging:** Catalina Inn

17b a   I-26, E to Charleston, W to Columbia

16   Montague Ave, Airport Rd, **S...food:** Wendy's, **lodging:** Embassy Suites, Hilton Garden

15   SC 642, Dorchester Rd, Paramount Dr, **N...gas:** BP, 76, **food:** Wendy's, **S...gas:** Amoco, Exxon, **food:** Burger King, Checker's, Huddle House, **lodging:** Super 8, **other:** Buick/Pontiac/GMC

14   Leeds Ave, **S...other:** HOSPITAL, boat marina

13mm   Ashley River

12   SC 61, Ashley River Rd, **N...food:** Chick-fil-A, McDonald's, O'Charley's, Quizno's, Sonic, **other:** HOSPITAL, Home Depot

11   Sam Rittenburg Blvd, **S...other:** Belk, Dillard's, JC Penney, Sears/auto, mall

10   US 17, SC 7, **services from US 17, E...gas:** BP, Shell, Speedway, **food:** Capt D's, Checker's, China Gourmet, CiCi's, McDonald's, Red Lobster, Ruby Tuesday, Taco Bell, **lodging:** Holiday Inn Express, Motel 6, **other:** Mazda, Mitsubishi, Piggly Wiggly, **W...gas:** Exxon, Hess, 76/Circle K, **food:** Waffle House, **lodging:** Econolodge, Hampton Inn, InTown Suites, **other:** Acura, Advance Parts, Chrysler/Plymouth/Jeep, Costco/gas, CVS Drug, Food Lion, Toyota

I-526 begins/ends on US 17.

Interstate 29

N

↑↓

S

Exit #	Services
253mm	South Dakota/North Dakota state line
251mm	**Welcome Ctr sb, full(handicapped)facilities, info, phone, picnic tables, litter barrels, petwalk**
246	SD 127, New Effington, to Rosholt, **3 mi W**...gas, food, Sica Hollow SP(24mi)
242	no facilities
235mm	weigh sta sb
232	SD 10, Sisseton, **E...gas:** Phillips 66/diesel/casino/24hr, **1-3 mi W...gas:** Cenex, Sinclair, **food:** A&W, American Hearth Rest., Country Kitchen, **lodging:** Holiday Motel, I-29 Motel, Viking Motel, **other:** Camp Dakotah, to Roy Lake SP(25mi), Ft Sisseton SP(35mi)
224	Peever, Sioux Tribal Hqtrs, **E...gas:** Cenex/diesel, **W**...Pickerel Lake(16mi)
213	SD 15, to Wilmot, **E...rest area both lanes, full (handicapped)facilities, phone, picnic tables, litter barrels, petwalk, RV dump, st patrol, 7 mi E**...gas, food, to Hartford Beach SP(17mi)
207	US 12, Summit, **E...gas:** Conoco/diesel/24hr, **W**...Blue Dog Fish Hatchery(15mi), Waubay NWR(19mi)
201	to Twin Brooks, no facilities
193	SD 20, to South Shore, Stockholm, no facilities
185	to Waverly, **4 mi W...other:** Dakota Sioux Casino/rest.
180	US 81 S, to Watertown, **5 mi W...other:** HOSPITAL, Bramble Park Zoo, airport

Watertown

177	US 212, Watertown, **E...gas:** Sinclair/Subway/diesel/café/24hr/@, **lodging:** Holiday Inn Express, **other:** Truckers QuikLube, **W...gas:** Conoco/diesel, **food:** Country Kitchen, McDonald's, **lodging:** Comfort Inn, Country Inn Suites, Day's Inn, Super 8, **other:** HOSPITAL, Redlin Art Ctr, **1-2 mi W...gas:** Amoco/diesel, Cenex/diesel, Conoco, Sinclair/diesel, **food:** Arby's, Burger King, China Buffet, Godfather's, Guadalajara Mexican, Hardee's, Little Caesar's, MacGregor's Steaks, Marguarite's Steaks, Papa John's, Pizza Hut, Subway, Taco John's, **lodging:** Best Western, Travelers Inn, **other:** Advance Parts, Buick/Nissan, Chrysler/Dodge/Plymouth/Jeep, EconoFoods, Firestone, Ford/Lincoln/Mercury, Goodyear/auto, Herberger's, Hy-Vee Foods, JC Penney, Jo-Ann Fabrics, K-Mart, Nissan, Osco Drug, ShopKO, Target, Tires+, Wal-Mart/drugs, mall, to Sandy Shore RA(10mi)
164	SD 22, to Castlewood, Clear Lake, **9 mi E...gas:** Cenex/diesel, **other:** HOSPITAL
161mm	**rest area both lanes, full(handicapped)facilities, phone, picnic tables, litter barrels, vending, petwalk, RV dump**
157	to Brandt, no facilities
150	SD 28, SD 15 N, to Toronto, **7 mi W**...gas, food, lodging, **24 mi W**...Lake Poinsett RA, SD Amateur Baseball Hall of Fame
140	SD 30, to White, Bruce, **W**...Oakwood Lakes SP(12mi)
133	US 14 byp, Brookings, **W**...to SD St U, museums, Laura Ingalls Wilder Home

SOUTH DAKOTA
Interstate 29

132   US 14, Lp 29, Brookings, **E...gas:** Cenex/Burger King/diesel, **lodging:** Fairfield Inn, Super 8, **W...gas:** Amoco, Citgo, Shell, **food:** Burger King, Country Kitchen, DQ, Guadalajara Mexican, Hardee's, KFC, King's Wok, Mad Jack's Food-Court, McDonald's, Papa John's, Papa Murphy's, Pavilion Grill, Perkins, Pizza Ranch, Subway, Zesto Drive-In, **lodging:** Brookings Inn, Comfort Inn, Quality Inn, **other:** HOSPITAL, Big O Tire, Chevrolet/Pontiac/Buick/Cadillac, $Discount, EconoFoods/24hr, K-Mart/Little Caesar's, Radio Shack, Wal-Mart/drugs, city park

127   SD 324, to Elkton, Sinai, no facilities

124mm   Big Sioux River

121   to Nunda, Ward, **E...rest area both lanes, full(handicapped)facilities, phone, picnic tables, litter barrels, vending, petwalk, RV dump, st patrol, W...**food, RV camping

114   SD 32, to Flandreau, **7 mi E...gas:** Cenex, Phillips 66, **lodging:** Sioux River Motel, **other:** Santee Tribal Hqtrs

109   SD 34, Colman, to Madison, **W...gas:** Conoco/diesel/rest., Shell/diesel/rest., **20 mi W...other:** to Lake Herman SP, Dakota St U, museum

104   to Trent, Chester, no facilities

103mm   parking area both lanes

98   SD 115 S, Dell Rapids, **3 mi E...food:** Pizza Ranch, **lodging:** Super 8, **other:** HOSPITAL

94   SD 114, to Baltic, **2 mi E...gas:** Citgo, **10 mi E...other:** to EROS Data Ctr, US Geological Survey

86   to Renner, Crooks, no facilities

84b a   I-90, W to Rapid City, E to Albert Lea

83   SD 38 W, 60th St, **E...gas:** ♦/Flying J/Conoco/Country Mkt/diesel/24hr/@, **other:** Freightliner Trucks, Harley-Davidson, Northview Campers, repair

81   SD 38 E, Russell St, Sioux Falls, **E...gas:** Amoco/24hr, Food'n Fuel, **food:** Burger King, Country Kitchen, Roll'n Pin Rest., **lodging:** Arena Motel, Best Western Ramkota/rest., Brimark Inn, Exel Inn, Kelly Inn, Motel 6, Ramada Inn, Sheraton, Sleep Inn, Super 8, **other:** Schaap's RV Ctr, st patrol

79   SD 42, 12th St, **E...gas:** Amoco/24hr, Cenex, Freedom, **food:** Burger King, Godfather's, Golden Harvest Chinese, KFC, McDonald's, Pizza Hut, Subway, Taco Bell, Taco John's, Wendy's, **lodging:** Nite's Inn, Ramada Ltd, **other:** HOSPITAL, BMW/Toyota, Chevrolet, K-Mart, Saturn, Walgreen, city park, to Great Plains Zoo/museum, **W...gas:** Cenex/diesel, Citgo, Phillips 66, **food:** Hardee's, **lodging:** Sunset Motel, Westwick Motel, **other:** Tower RV Park, Lemme Repair, Sioux Falls Tire, to USS SD Battleship Mem

78   26th St, Empire St, **E...gas:** Phillips 66/diesel, **food:** Bennigan's, ChuckeCheese, Cracker Barrel, Culver's, Dixie Bros Grill, Domino's, Granite City Rest., KFC, Outback Steaks, **lodging:** Hampton Inn, Holiday Inn Express, **other:** EconoFoods, Home Depot, Michael's, Sam's Club, USPO, **W...food:** DQ, Oscar's Coffee, Papa John's, Quizno's, **lodging:** Settle Inn, **other:** Hy-Vee Foods

77   41st St, Sioux Falls, **E...gas:** Amoco/24hr, Shell, Sinclair/diesel, SA/diesel, **food:** Andolini's Italian, Arby's, Burger King, Carlos O'Kelly's, ChiChi's, Chili's, China Express, Fry'n Pan Rest., Fuddrucker's, Green Mill Rest., KFC, LoneStar Steaks, MacGregor's Steaks, McDonald's, Nap's BBQ, Olive Garden, Perkins, Pizza Hut, Pizza Inn, Qdoba Mexican, Quizno's, Red Lobster, Schlotsky's, Subway, Szechwan Chinese, Taco Bell, Taco John's, TimberLodge Steaks, TGIFriday, Valentino's Rest., Wendy's, **lodging:** Best Western Empire, Comfort Suites, Fairfield Inn, Microtel, Radisson, Residence Inn, Super 8, **other:** Advance Parts, Barnes&Noble, Batteries+, Best Buy, Big O Tire, Checker Parts, Chrysler/Jeep/Mazda, Ford, Goodyear/auto, Hyundai/Nissan, JC Penney, OfficeMax, Radio Shack, Randall's Foods, Sears/auto, ShopKO, Target, Tires+, Toyota, Village Automotive, Walgreen, Wal-Mart SuperCtr/24hr, VW, Younkers, mall, **W...gas:** Citgo, Shell/diesel, **food:** Burger King, Denucci's Pizza, Godfather's, Little Caesar, Peking Chinese, Perkins/24hr, Subway, **lodging:** AmericInn, Baymont Inn, Day's Inn, Select Inn, **other:** USPO

75   I-229 E, to I-90 E

73   Tea, **E...gas:** Larry's Shell/diesel/café/24hr, **food:** Crabhouse Rest., **other:** U-Haul, antiques, **1.5mi W...**Red Barn Camping

71   to Harrisburg, Lennox, **W...**RV camping

68   to Lennox, Parker, no facilities

64   SD 44, Worthing, **1 mi E...gas:** Shell, **W...other:** Chevrolet/Pontiac/Buick

62   US 18 E, to Canton, **E...gas:** Conoco/pizza/diesel, **lodging:** Charlie's Motel, **other:** antiques(9mi), **W...**repair

59   US 18 W, to Davis, Hurley, no facilities

56   to Fairview, **E...**to Newton Hills SP(12mi)

53   to Viborg, no facilities

50   to Centerville, Hudson, no facilities

47   SD 46, Beresford, to Irene, **E...gas:** Casey's, Cenex/Burger King, Sinclair/diesel, **food:** Emily's Café, GoodTimes Pizza, **lodging:** Crossroads Motel, Super 8, **other:** Chevrolet, Fiesta Foods, **W...gas:** Cenex/diesel/24hr, camping

42   to Alcester, Wakonda, no facilities

40mm   parking area sb, litter barrel

Interstate 29

38	to Volin, **E**...to Union Co SP(7mi)
31	SD 48, Spink, to Akron, no facilities
26	SD 50, to Vermillion, **E**...**Welcome Ctr/rest area both lanes, full(handicapped)facilities, info, phone, picnic tables, litter barrels, petwalk, RV dump, W**...**gas:** Conoco/diesel/24hr, **6-7 mi W**...**gas:** Casey's/gas, Phillips 66, **food:** Amigo's Mexican, Burger King, Pizza Hut, Subway, Taco John's, **lodging:** Comfort Inn, Super 8, Travelodge, **other:** Hy-Vee Foods, to UofSD
18	Lp 29, Elk Point, to Burbank, **E**...**gas:** Amoco/diesel, Phillips 66/pizza/subs, **food:** Cody's Rest., Dairy Queen, **lodging:** HomeTowne Inn
15	to Elk Point, **1 mi E**...gas, food, lodging
9	SD 105, Jefferson, **E**...**gas:** Amoco/Choice Cut Rest.
4	McCook, **1 mi W**...**other:** KOA(seasonal), Adams Homestead/nature preserve
3mm	weigh sta nb
2	N Sioux City, **E**...**gas:** Ampride/diesel/rest./24hr, Cenex, **food:** Glass Palace Rest.(1mi), McDonald's, Taco John's, **other:** Dakota Valley Foods, Gateway Computers, USPO, **W**...**gas:** Casey's/gas, Citgo/Taco Bell, **lodging:** Comfort Inn, Econolodge, Hampton Inn, Super 8, **other:** to Sodrac Dogtrack
1	**E**...**other:** Dakota Dunes Golf Resort, **W**...**gas:** Citgo/diesel, **food:** Graham's Grill, **lodging:** Country Inn Suites
0mm	South Dakota/Iowa state line, Big Sioux River

Interstate 90

Exit #	Services
412.5mm	South Dakota/Minnesota state line
412mm	**Welcome Ctr wb/rest area eb, full(handicapped)facilities, info, phone, picnic tables, litter barrels, petwalk, RV dump(wb), weigh sta both lanes**
410	Valley Springs, **N**...Palisades SP(7mi), **S**...Beaver Creek Nature Area, gas, food
406	SD 11, Brandon, Corson, **S**...**gas:** BP/diesel, Gas n' Goodies, Sinclair/McDonald's/diesel, **food:** Dominos, DQ, Pizza Ranch, Subway, Taco John's, **lodging:** Holiday Inn Express, **other:** Jubilee, to Big Sioux RA
402	EROS Data Ctr, **N**...**other:** Jellystone RV Park
400	I-229 S, no facilities
399	SD 115, Cliff Ave, Sioux Falls, **N**...**gas:** Phillips 66/diesel, Sinclair/diesel, **food:** Cody's Grill, Frontier Village, **other:** Spader RV Ctr, KOA, **S**...**gas:** Cenex/diesel, Holiday/diesel, Pilot/Great American Rest/Subway/diesel/24hr/@, **food:** Burger King, McDonald's, Perkins, Taco John's, **lodging:** Cloud Nine Motel, Comfort Inn, Country Inn Suites, Day's Inn, Econolodge, Super 8, **other:** HOSPITAL, Blue Beacon, Goodyear, Kenworth, Peterbilt, Volvo
396b a	I-29, N to Brookings, S to Sioux City, no facilities
390	SD 38, Hartford, **N**...**other:** Camp Dakota RV Park, Goos RV Ctr, **S**...**gas:** Phillips 66/diesel, Buffalo Ridge/gas, **food:** Pizza Ranch
387	rd 17, Hartford, **N**...**gas:** Phillips 66/diesel
379	SD 19, Humboldt, **1 mi N**...**gas:** Mobil/diesel, Shell/diesel(1mi), **food:** Home Café/Grill, **other:** Town&Country Store
375mm	E Vermillion River
374	to SD 38, Montrose, **2 mi N**...gas, food, **5 mi S**...**other:** Battle Creek Res., Lake Vermillion RA, RV camping
368	Canistota, **4 mi S**...**lodging:** Best Western
364	US 81, to Yankton, Salem, **4 mi N**...**gas:** Cenex, Sinclair, **lodging:** Home Motel, **other:** RV camp
363.5mm	W Vermillion River
363mm	**rest area both lanes, full(handicapped)facilities, phone, picnic tables, litter barrels, vending, petwalk, RV dump, st patrol**
357	to Bridgewater, Canova, no facilities
353	Spencer, Emery, **S**...**gas:** TA/Subway/diesel/24hr/@
352mm	Wolf Creek
350	SD 25, Emery, Farmer, **N**...**other:** to DeSmet, Home of Laura Ingalls Wilder
344	SD 262, to Fulton, Alexandria, **S**...**gas:** Shell/diesel
337mm	parking area both lanes
335	Riverside Rd, **N**...RV camping
334.5mm	James River
332	SD 37 S, to Parkston, Mitchell, **N**...**gas:** Amoco/Burger King/24hr, Cenex/diesel/@, Phillips 66/Blimpie, Shell/I-90 TrvlCtr/Subway/diesel/24hr/@, **food:** Arby's, Bonanza, Burger King, Country Kitchen, Dairy Queen, Embers Rest., Hardee's, KFC, McDonald's, Perkins, Pizza Hut, Pizza Ranch, Twin Dragon Chinese, **lodging:** AmericInn, Best Western, Chief Motel, Comfort Inn, Corn Palace Motel, Day's Inn, Super 8, Thunderbird Motel, **other:** HOSPITAL, Advance Parts, Chrysler/Plymouth/Dodge, K-Mart, transmissions, **1-2 mi N**...**other:** to Corn Palace, Museum of Pioneer Life, RV camping, **S**...**gas:** Shell/Taco Bell/diesel/24hr, **food:** Culver's, Quizno's, **lodging:** Hampton Inn, Kelly Inn, **other:** Cabela's, $Tree, Radio Shack, Wal-Mart SuperCtr/gas/24hr

SOUTH DAKOTA
Interstate 90

E ↑ ↓ **W**

330 SD 37 N, Mitchell, weigh sta, **N...gas:** Cenex/24hr, Shell/diesel, **food:** Country Kitchen, **lodging:** Anthony Motel, Econolodge, Holiday Inn/rest., Motel 6, Siesta Motel, **other:** HOSPITAL, County Fair Foods, Jack's Campers/RV ctr., to Corn Palace, museum, **S...other:** Dakota RV Park

325 Betts Rd, **S...**RV camping

319 Mt Vernon, **1 mi N...gas:** Cenex

310 US 281, to Stickney, **S...gas:** Conoco/A&W/diesel/24hr, **other:** to Ft Randall Dam

308 Lp 90, to Plankinton, **N...gas:** Phillips 66/Al's Café/diesel, **lodging:** Cabin Fever Motel, Super 8, **other:** RV camping

301.5mm **rest area both lanes, full(handicapped)facilities, phones, picnic tables, litter barrels, RV dump**

296 White Lake, **1 mi N...gas:** Cenex/diesel, Shell, **lodging:** Bar-Z Motel, White Lake Motel

294mm Platte Creek

293mm parking area both lanes

289 SD 45 S, to Platte, **S...other:** to Snake Cr/Platte Cr RA(25mi)

284 SD 45 N, Kimball, **N...gas:** BP/tires, Phillips 66/diesel/24hr, **food:** Ditty's Diner, Frosty King Drive-In, Ponderosa Café, **lodging:** Super 8, Travelers Motel, **other:** RV Park, **S...lodging:** Kimball Motel

272 SD 50, Pukwana, **2 mi N...**gas, food, lodging, **S...other:** Snake/Platte Creek Rec Areas(25mi)

265 SD 50, Chamberlain, **N...gas:** BP/diesel, **food:** DQ, **lodging:** AmericInn, **3 mi N...food:** McDonald's, Subway, **lodging:** Bel Aire Motel, Hillside Motel, Lakeshore Motel, **other:** HOSPITAL, Honda, Lakota Museum, **S...gas:** Conoco/diesel, **other:** Happy Camper Park

264mm **rest area both lanes, full(handicapped)facilities, scenic view, info, phones, picnic tables, litter barrels**

C **263** Chamberlain, Crow Creek Sioux Tribal Hqtrs, **N...gas:** Sinclair/diesel, **food:** A&W, Anchor Grille, Casey's Café, McDonald's, Pizza Hut, Rainbow Café, Subway(1mi), Taco John's, **lodging:** The Plaza Motel/groceries/gas, Best Western(1mi), Bel Aire Motel, Hillside Motel, Lakeshore Motel, Riverview Inn, Super 8, **other:** Buche's IGA/deli

h
262mm Missouri River

a **260** SD 50, Oacoma, **N...gas:** BP/Burger King/diesel, Shell/diesel, **food:** Taco John's, **lodging:** Al's Oasis Motel, Cedar Shore Motel, Comfort Inn, Day's Inn, Holiday Inn Express, **other:** Chevrolet/Buick/Pontiac, Familyland Camping, Cedar Shore Resort, Hi Dri Camping, Old West Museum

m
b
e

251 SD 47, to Winner, Gregory, no facilities

r **248** SD 47, Reliance, **N...gas:** BP/diesel(1mi), **other:** Sioux Tribal Hqtrs, to Big Bend RA

l
241 to Lyman, no facilities

a **235** SD 273, Kennebec, **N...gas:** Conoco/diesel, **food:** Pony Express Café, **lodging:** Budget Host, Kings Inn, **other:** KOA

i
n

226 US 183 S, Presho, **N...gas:** Conoco/diesel, Sinclair-**food:** Norma's Drive-In Café, **lodging:** Coachlight Inn, Hutch's Motel/café, New Frontier RV park, **other:** museum

225 Presho, same as 226

221mm **rest area wb, full(handicapped)facilities, info, phone, picnic tables, litter barrels, RV dump, petwalk**

220 no facilities

218mm **rest area eb, full(handicapped)facilities, info, phone, picnic tables, litter barrels, RV dump, petwalk**

214 Vivian, no facilities

212 US 83 N, SD 53, to Pierre, **N...gas:** Phillips 66/diesel, **food:** Vivian Jct Rest., **other:** HOSPITAL(34mi)

208 no facilities

201 Draper, **N...**gas/diesel, **food:** Hilltop Café

194mm parking area both lanes

192 US 83 S, Murdo, **N...gas:** Amoco/diesel, HHH/diesel/@, Phillips 66, Sinclair/diesel, **food:** Buffalo Rest., Food Court, KFC, Murdo Drive-In, Star Rest., **lodging:** Anchor Inn, Best Western, Chuck's Motel, Day's Inn, Hospitality Inn, Lee Motel, Super 8, Tee-Pee Motel/RV Camp, **other:** Super Value Foods, camping, **S...lodging:** Landmark Country Inn, **other:** to Rosebud

M
u
r
d
o

191 Murdo, **N...**access to same as 192

190mm Central/Mountain time zone, Central/Mountain time zone

188mm parking area both lanes, litter barrels

183 Okaton, **S...**gas, Ghost Town

177 no facilities

172 to Cedar Butte, no facilities

170 SD 63 N, to Midland, **N...gas:** Shell, **other:** 1880's Town, KOA

167mm **rest area wb, full(handicapped)facilities, phones, picnic tables, litter barrels, RV dump, petwalk**

165mm **rest area eb, full(handicapped)facilities, phones, picnic tables, litter barrels, RV dump, petwalk**

163 SD 63, Belvidere, **S...gas:** BP/diesel/café, Sinclair/diesel, **lodging:** motel

152 Lp 90, Kadoka, **N...gas:** Phillips 66/diesel/rest./24hr/@, **S...lodging:** Best Western, Budget Host(2mi), Leewood Motel, **other:** Badlands Petrified Gardens, camping

150 SD 73 S, Kadoka, **N...food:** Jigger's, **lodging:** Dakota Inn/rest., **S...gas:** BP, Conoco/diesel, **food:** Happy Chef, Sidekicks Rest., **lodging:** Best Western, Budget Host, Downtowner Motor Inn, Ponderosa Motel/RV park, Super 8, **other:** to Buffalo Nat Grasslands

143 SD 73 N, to Philip, **15 mi N...**HOSPITAL

138mm scenic overlook wb

131 SD 240, **S...**to Badlands NP, **gas:** BP, Conoco(11mi), **lodging:** Badlands Inn/Best Value(9mi), Cedar Pass Lodge/rest.(9mi), **other:** Circle 10 Camping, Prairie Home NHS, KOA(11mi), Good Sam Camping

Interstate 90

129.5mm	scenic overlook eb
127	no facilities
121	no facilities
116	no facilities
112	US 14 E, to Philip, no facilities
110	SD 240, Wall, **N...gas:** BP/diesel, Exxon, Phillips 66/Subway, **food:** Cactus Café, DQ, Elkton House Rest., Subway, Wall Drug Rest., **lodging:** American Bison Inn, Best Value Inn, Best Western, Day's Inn, Econolodge, Elk Motel, Fountain Hotel, Hitching Post Motel, Homestead Motel, Kings Inn, Knight's Inn, Motel 6, Sunshine Inn, Super 8, The Wall Motel, Welsh Motel, **other:** NAPA, Wall Drug/gifts/rest., museum, **S...**to Badlands NP, RV camping
109	W 4th Ave, Wall, **1-2 mi N...**access to same as 110
107	Cedar Butte Rd, no facilities
101	rd T-504, Jensen Rd, to Schell Ranch, no facilities
100mm	**rest area both lanes, full (handicapped) facilities, info, phone, picnic tables, litter barrels, RV dump, vending, petwalk**
99.5mm	Cheyenne River
99	Wasta, **N...gas:** BP/diesel, **lodging:** Redwood Motel, **other:** Sunrise Campgrnd
90	173rd Ave, to Owanka, no facilities
88	rd 473(from eb, no re-entry), no facilities
84	167th Ave, **N...**Olde Glory Fireworks
78	161st Ave, New Underwood, **1/2 mi S...**gas, **lodging:** Jake's Motel, **other:** Steve's General Store
69mm	parking area both lanes
67	to Box Elder, Ellsworth AFB, **N...other:** museum
63	(eb only), to Box Elder, Ellsworth AFB
61	Elk Vale Rd, **N...gas:** ♨/Flying J/Conoco/CountryMkt/diesel/LP/RV dump/24hr/@, **other:** Langland RV Ctr, **S...food:** Arby's, McDonalds, **other:** KOA(seasonal)(3mi), transmissions
60	Lp 90(exits left from wb), to Mt Rushmore, Rapid City, **1-3 mi S...food:** KFC, LJ Silver, **lodging:** Holiday Inn Express, Stardust Motel, **other:** HOSPITAL, Nat Coll of Mines/Geology
59	La Crosse St, Rapid City, **N...gas:** BP/24hr, Phillips 66/A&W, Shell, **food:** Boston Pizza, Burger King, Denny's, Minerva's Rest., Outback Steaks, TGIFriday, **lodging:** Best Western, Country Inn Suites, Econolodge, Holiday Inn Express, Super 8, **other:** Sears/auto, mall, st patrol, **S...gas:** Cenex/diesel, Exxon/24hr, **food:** Golden Corral, McDonald's, MillStone Rest., Perkins/24hr, Schlotsky's, Sirloin Buffet, Subway, **lodging:** AmericInn, Comfort Inn, Day's Inn, Fair Value Inn, Foothills Inn, Microtel, Motel 6, Quality Inn, Ramada Inn, Rushmore Motel, Thrifty Motel, Thunderbird lodge, **other:** Sam's Club, Wal-Mart SuperCtr/gas/24hr
58	Haines Ave, Rapid City, **N...gas:** Conoco, Shell, **food:** Applebee's, Chili's, Fuddrucker's(mall), Hardee's, Red Lobster, Royal Fork Buffet, Su Casa Mexican, **lodging:** Red Roof Inn, Travelodge, **other:** Best Buy, Borders, Hancock Fabrics, Herbergers, JC Penney, Lowe's Whse, Target, Tires+, to Rushmore Mall, **S...gas:** Conoco, **food:** Taco John's, Wendy's, **other:** HOSPITAL, OfficeMax, ShopKO, same as 59
57	I-190, US 16, to Rapid City, to Mt Rushmore, **1 mi S on North St...**gas: Conoco, **lodging:** Best Western, Holiday Inn, Howard Johnson, Radisson, **other:** Albertson's
55	Deadwood Ave, **N...other:** Harley-Davidson, Lazy JD Camp(6mi), **S...gas:** Sinclair/Subway/diesel, **food:** A&W(2mi), Culver's(3mi), Wendy's, Windmill Rest., **lodging:** Best Western Sun Inn(3mi), **other:** Black Hills Dogtrack, Chevrolet, diesel repair
51	Black Hawk Rd, **N...other:** Three Flags Camping(1mi), **S...other:** Mid state RV Ctr(1mi), USPO
48	Stagebarn Canyon Rd, **N...other:** RV camping, **S...gas:** Sinclair/Stagebarn Plaza/food, **food:** Classick's Rest., Mike's Pizza, **lodging:** Super 8, **other:** MEDICAL CARE
46	Piedmont Rd, Elk Creek Rd, **N...food:** Elk Creek Steaks, **lodging:** Covered Wagon Resort, **other:** to Petrified Forest, camping, **S...gas:** Conoco/diesel/@
44	Bethlehem Rd, **S...lodging:** Bethlehem Lodge(6mi), Jack's RV(2mi), **other:** Bethlehem RV Park(2mi)
42mm	**rest area both lanes, full(handicapped) facilities, info, phones, picnic tables, litter barrels, RV dump, petwalk, vending**
40	Tilford, **N...**antiques
39mm	weigh sta eb
37	Pleasant Valley Rd, **N...other:** Elkview Camp, **S...other:** Bulldog Camping, Rush-No-More Camping
34	**S...other:** Black Hills Nat Cemetary, Catmandu Camping, No Name RV Park

SOUTH DAKOTA

Interstate 90

E → **Sturgis** ← **W**

32 SD 79, Sturgis, **N...gas:** BP, Conoco/Subway, Exxon/Phil-town Gen Store/diesel, **food:** Country Kitchen, Lynn's Country Mkt/café, Taco John's, **lodging:** Best Western, Lantern Motel, National 9 Inn, StarLite Motel, **other:** HOSPITAL, Ford/Lincoln/Mercury, Motorcycle SuperStore, Southside RV Park, to Bear Butte SP

30 US 14A W, SD 34E, to Deadwood, Sturgis, **N...gas:** Cenex/diesel, Conoco, Sinclair, **food:** Pizza Hut, McDonald's, Pizza Hut, Subway, Taco John's, **other:** CarQuest, Mr Tire, Pamida, Radio Shack, Day's End Camping, **S...gas:** RanchMart, Shell/Texaco/diesel, **food:** Burger King, DQ, McDonalds, Subway, **lodging:** Day's Inn, Super 8/rest., **other:** Chevrolet

23 SD 34 W, to Belle Fourche, Whitewood, **N...other:** Northern Hills RV Ctr, **S...gas:** BP, Phillips 66, **food:** Shea's Diner, **lodging:** Tony's Motel

17 US 85 S, to Deadwood, **9-12 mi S in Deadwood... food:** Cadillac Jack's Diner, 4Aces Buffet, Pizza Hut, Silverado Café, **lodging:** AmericInn, Best Western, Day's Inn, Holiday Inn Express, Palace Hotel, Super 8, White House Inn, Deadwood Gulch Resort, **other:** KOA, Winner's Casino

Spearfish

14 US 14A, Spearfish Canyon, **N...food:** Applebee's, **lodging:** Fairfield Inn, Holiday Inn/rest., Quality Inn, **S...gas:** BP/diesel, Conoco, **food:** Dairy Queen, KFC, Perkins, Pizza Ranch, **lodging:** All American Inn, Howard Johnson, Super 8, **other:** Ace Hardware, Ford/Lincoln/Mercury, K-Mart, auto museum, cinema, Mt View Camping, Chris' Camping

12 Spearfish, **S...gas:** Amoco, Conoco/diesel, Phillips 66/diesel, Sinclair/diesel, **food:** Arby's, Burger King, DQ, McDonald's, Millstone Rest., Papa Murphy's, Pizza Ranch, Subway, Wendy's, **lodging:** Day's Inn, Kelly Inn, **other:** HOSPITAL, Chevrolet/Buick/Pontiac, Black Hills St U, fish hatchery, same as 10

10 US 85 N, to Belle Fourche, **S...food:** Burger King, Cedar House Rest., DQ, Domino's, Golden Dragon Chinese, McDonald's, Subway, Taco Bell, Wendy's, **lodging:** Best Western, Day's Inn, **other:** Cadillac/GMC, Chevrolet/Buick/Cadillac, Jeep, Jo's Camping, KOA, Safeway/drug/gas, Thrift Foods, USPO, Wal-Mart, same as 12

8 McGuigan rd, W Spearfish, no facilities

2 1 mi N...McNenny St Fish Hatchery

1mm **Welcome Ctr eb, full(handicapped)facilities, info, phone, picnic tables, litter barrels, RV dump, petwalk**

0mm South Dakota/Wyoming state line

Interstate 229(Sioux Falls)

N ↑ **Sioux Falls** ↓ **S**

Exit #	Services
10b a	I-90 E and W. I-229 begins/ends on I-90, exit 400.
9	Benson Rd, **W...**Amoco/burgers/pizza
7.5mm	Big Sioux River
7	Rice St, **E...**winter sports, **W...**to stockyards
6	SD 38, 10th St, **E...**Citgo, Phillips 66, Applebee's, Arby's, Baxter Café, DQ, Domino's, Fry'n Pan Rest., Golden star Buffet, KFC, Pizza Hut, Quizno's, Taco Bell, Tomacelli's Italian, Budget Host, Suburban Motel, Super 8, Big O Tire, Checker Parts, Family\$, Hy-Vee Foods, K-Mart, Pronto Parts, ShopKO, Sunshine Foods, **W...**Amoco, Phillips 66/diesel/mart, Shell, Burger King, BurgerTime, Godfather's, Hardee's, LaBamba Mexican, Little Caesar's, Pizza Inn, Puerto Vallarta, Steak-Out, Subway, Taco John's, Wendy's, Rushmore Motel, Jim's Repair, Lewis Drug, Radio Shack, USPO
5.5mm	Big Sioux River
5	26th St, **E...**HOSPITAL, Shell/diesel, Cherry Creek Grill, Keg Chicken Café, McDonald's, city park
4	Cliff Ave, **E...**Philllips 66/TCBY/diesel, Sinclair/diesel, Runza Rest., Walgreen
3	SD 115, Lp 229, Minnesota Ave, **E...**city park, **1 mi W...**Sinclair, Burger King, Culver's, Famous Dave's BBQ, Hardee's, Little Caesar's, McDonald's, Subway, Holiday Inn, Dodge, GMC, Hy-Vee Foods, K-Mart, Lewis Drug, Mitsubishi/Toyota, Sunshine Foods, USPO
2	Western Ave, **E...**Shell, **W...**MEDICAL CARE, Cenex/diesel, Shell, Burger King, Champ's Café, China Buffet, Nap's BBQ, Pizza Hut, Valentino's Italian, Advance Parts, Goodyear/auto, Radio Shack
1.5mm	Big Sioux River
1c	Louise Ave, **E...**Homewood Suites, **W...**Amoco, Phillips 66/diesel, A&W, Burger King, McDonald's, Royal Fork Buffet, Wendy's, Honda/Mercedes, mall
1b a	I-29 N and S. I-229 begins/ends on I-29, exit 75.

Interstate 24

E ↑↓ W	Exit #	Services

Exit # **Services**

185b a I-75, N to Knoxville, S to Atlanta. I-24 begins/ends on I-75, exit 2 in Chattanooga.

184 Moore Rd, **S...food:** Chef Lin Buffet, Trovino's Italian, **other:** $Tree, K-Mart

183 (183a from wb), Belvoir Ave, Germantown Rd, no facilities

181a US 41 S, to East Ridge(from eb), **S...food:** Westside Grill, King's Lodge, **other:** Ford Trucks

181 Fourth Ave, to TN Temple U, Chattanooga, **N...gas:** Citgo/diesel, Conoco, Exxon/Blimpie/diesel, **food:** Bojangles, Burger King, Capt D's, Central Park, Hardee's, Krystal/24hr, Subway, Waffle House, **lodging:** Villager Lodge, **other:** BiLo, $General, Goodyear, Mr Transmission, Stop n' Save Foods, repair, **S...gas:** Citgo

180b a US 27 S, TN 8, Rossville Blvd, **N...other:** U-Haul, to Chickamauga, UT Chatt, **S...gas:** Fast TravelCtr/diesel, RaceTrac/diesel/24hr, **food:** KFC, **lodging:** Hamilton Inn, **other:** NTB

178 US 27 N, Market St, to Lookout Mtn, Chattanooga, **N...gas:** Amoco/diesel, Citgo, **lodging:** Day's Inn, Knight's Inn, Marriott, Ramada Inn, Staybridge Suites, **other:** Ford, Nissan, U-Haul, to Chattanooga ChooChoo, **S...food:** KFC, **lodging:** Comfort Suites, Hampton Inn, Motel 6

175 Browns Ferry Rd, to Lookout Mtn, **N...gas:** Citgo, Exxon/diesel, **lodging:** Best Value Inn, **other:** CVS Drug, $General, Food Lion, **S...gas:** Conoco/diesel, Shell/Texaco/diesel, **food:** Hardee's, McDonald's, Subway, **lodging:** Comfort Inn, Econolodge, Sleep Inn

174 US 11, US 41, US 64, Lookout Valley, **N...food:** Waffle House, **lodging:** Day's Inn, **other:** Racoon Mtn Camping(2mi), **S...gas:** BP/diesel/24hr, Exxon, Pure, **food:** BBQ, Cracker Barrel, Taco Bell, Waffle House, **lodging:** Baymont Inn, Best Western, Comfort Inn, Country Inn Suites, Hampton Inn, Holiday Inn Express, Knight's Inn, Ramada Ltd, Super 8, **other:** Ace Hardware, Lookout Valley Camping, st patrol

172mm **rest area eb, full(handicapped)facilities, phone, picnic tables, litter barrels, vending, petwalk**

171mm Tennessee/Georgia state line

169 GA 299, to US 11, **N...gas:** Fast/diesel/24hr, **S...gas,** BP/TCBY/diesel/24hr/@, Pilot/Subway/diesel/24hr/@, RaceTrac/24hr

167 I-59 S, to Birmingham, no facilities

167mm Tennessee/Georgia state line, Central/Eastern time zone

161 TN 156, to Haletown, New Hope, **N...gas:** BP(1mi), **S...gas:** Chevron/fireworks, **other:** On The Lake Camping

160mm Tennessee River/Nickajack Lake

159mm **Welcome Ctr wb/rest area eb, full(handicapped)facilities, phone, vending, picnic tables, litter barrels, petwalk**

158 US 41, TN 27, Nickajack Dam, **N...gas:** Shell, **S...gas:** BP/diesel/fireworks, **other:** Shellmound Camping

155 TN 28, Jasper, **N...gas:** Exxon/diesel, Citgo/diesel(1mi), **food:** Dairy Queen(1mi), Hardee's, Western Sizzlin, **lodging:** Acuff Country Inn, **S...HOSPITAL**

152 US 41, US 64, US 72, Kimball, S Pittsburg, **N...gas:** Amoco/fireworks, Scot/diesel, Phillips 66/fireworks, RaceTrac, **food:** A&W/LJ Silver, Arby's, Domino's, Hardee's, KFC, Krystal, McDonald's, Pizza Hut, Shoney's, Subway, Taco Bell, Waffle House, Wendy's, **lodging:** Budget Host, Comfort Inn, Day's Inn, Holiday Inn Express, **other:** HOSPITAL, BiLo, Chevrolet/Pontiac/Buick, $Tree, Goody's, Radio Shack, Wal-Mart SuperCtr/24hr, to Russell Cave NM, **3 mi S...other:** Lodge Cast Iron

143 Martin Springs Rd, **N...gas:** Chevron/diesel/fireworks

135 US 41 N, Monteagle, **N...gas:** Phillips 66/diesel/rest./24hr, Pure/diesel, **food:** BBQ, HappyLand Rest., **other:** AutoSure Parts, S Cumberland RV Park, **S...**Day's Inn

134 US 64, US 41A, to Sewanee, Monteagle, **N...gas:** Amoco/McDonald's, **other:** CVS Drug, to S Cumberland SP, **S...gas:** Citgo, Shell/diesel, **food:** Bluewater Lodge Rest., Hardee's, Lockheart's Rest, Pizza Hut, Smokehouse BBQ, Subway, Waffle House, **lodging:** Best Western, Regency Inn, **other:** $General, Firestone/U-Haul/auto, Monteagle Winery, Piggly Wiggly, to U of The South

133mm **rest area both lanes, full(handicapped)facilities, phone, picnic tables, litter barrels, vending, petwalk**

128mm Elk River

127 US 64, TN 50, to Winchester, Pelham, **N...gas:** Amoco, Phillips 66, Texaco/Stuckey's, **S...gas:** Exxon/diesel, **other:** to Tims Ford SP/RV camping

119mm trucks only parking area both lanes

117 to Tullahoma, USAF Arnold Ctr, UT Space Institute

116mm weigh sta both lanes

Left margin vertical text: Chattanooga · Monteagle

TENNESSEE
Interstate 24

E ↕ W

Manchester

114 US 41, Manchester, **N...gas:** BP/24 Truck Plaza/diesel/@, Marathon, Shell, **food:** O'Charley's, Ruby Tuesday, **lodging:** Comfort Inn, Holiday Inn Express, Ramada Ltd, Scottish Inn, Super 8, Trucker's Inn, **other:** Country Cabin Camping, Chrysler/Dodge/Toyota, KOA, Nissan, Toyota, Wal-Mart SuperCtr/gas/24hr, museum, **S...gas:** Exxon/24hr, RaceWay, **food:** Arby's, Burger King, Capt D's, KFC, Krystal, McDonald's, Pizza Hut, Taco Bell, Waffle House, Wendy's, **lodging:** Best Value, Country Inn Suites, Day's Inn, Knight's Inn, Red Roof Inn, Royal Inn, **other:** Advance Parts, AutoZone, BiLo Foods, Chevrolet, Family$, Ford/Lincoln/Mercury, Goodyear, Russell Stover, carwash

111 TN 55, Manchester, **N...gas:** BP, Chevron, Citgo/diesel/24hr, Co-op gas, **other:** to Rock Island SP, **S...gas:** BP, **food:** Hardee's, J&G Pizza/Steaks, Sonic, **other:** HOSPITAL, Gateway Tires, to Jack Daniels Dist HS, Old Stone Fort

110 TN 53, Manchester, **N...gas:** BP, Exxon/TCBY/24hr, Shell/diesel, **food:** Cracker Barrel, D Crockett's Roadhouse, Oak Rest., **lodging:** Ambassador Inn, Day's Inn, Hampton Inn, **S...gas:** Shell/diesel/24hr, **food:** Waffle House, **lodging:** Econolodge, **other:** HOSPITAL

110mm Duck River

Murfreesboro

105 US 41, **N...gas:** Busy Corner/BP/diesel/24hr/@, Shell/diesel, **food:** RanchHouse Rest., **S...gas:** Amoco, to Normandy Dam

97 TN 64, to Shelbyville, Beechgrove, **N...other:** auto parts/repair, **S...gas:** Phillips 66/diesel

89 Buchanan Rd, **N...gas:** Love's/McDonald's/diesel/@, Shell/Texaco/Outpost Rest/diesel, **S...gas:** Citgo/diesel/rest./24hr, **food:** Huddle House

84 Joe B. Jackson Pkwy, no facilities

81 US 231, Murfreesboro, **N...gas:** BP/diesel/24hr, Exxon, RaceWay/24hr, Shell, **food:** Arby's, Burger King, Cracker Barrel, King's Table Rest., Krystal, Parthenon Steaks, Ponderosa, Shanghai Chinese, Shoney's, Waffle House/24hr, Wendy's, **lodging:** Best Inn, Best Value, Guesthouse Inn, Knight's Inn, Ramada Ltd, Regal Inn, Scottish Inn, **other:** HOSPITAL, Dodge, Honda, Mazda, **S...gas:** Citgo/24hr, Express/diesel/24hr, Golden Gallon, Phillips 66/diesel/24hr/@, Shell/Texaco/24hr, **food:** BBQ, La Siesta Mexican, McDonald's, Pizza Hut/Taco Bell, Sonic, Subway, Waffle House, **lodging:** Howard Johnson, Quality Inn, Safari Inn, **other:** Gateway Tire, Toyota

78 TN 96, to Franklin, Murfreesboro, **N...gas:** BP, Phillips 66/Church's/White Castle/diesel, Shell/Jack-in-the-Box, Texaco/Burger King/24hr, **food:** Arby's, Applebee's, Backyard Burger, Bellacino's Pizza, Chick-fil-A, Cracker Barrel, Dairy Queen, Don Pablo, Fazoli's, IHOP, KFC, Luby's, McDonald's, OutBack Steaks, Red Lobster, Ryan's, Santa Fe Steaks, Starbucks, Steak'n Shake, Subway, Waffle House, Wendy's, **lodging:** Best Western, Comfort Inn, Country Inn Suites, Day's Inn, Garden Plaza Hotel, Hampton Inn, Holiday Inn, Microtel, Motel 6, Red Roof Inn, Sleep Inn, Super 8, Wingate Inn, **other:** BooksAMillion, Dillard's, HobbyLobby, Home Depot, JC Penney, Lowe's Whse, OfficeMax, Sears, Staples, Target, Wal-Mart SuperCtr/gas/24hr, mall, to Stones River Bfd, **S...gas:** BP/diesel/24hr, Chevron/24hr, Exxon/24hr, **food:** Corky's BBQ, Hardee's, O'Charley's, Sonic, Subway, Taco Bell, Waffle House, **other:** $General, Kohl's, Kroger, River Rock Outlet/famous brands, Sam's Club/gas, Walgreen

74b a TN 840, to Lebanon, Franklin, no facilities

70 TN 102, Lee Victory Pkwy, Almaville Rd, to Smyrna, **S...gas:** BP, Citgo/diesel/24hr, Express, Exxon, **food:** Dad's Rest., McDonald's, **lodging:** Deerfield Inn, **other:** Mapco Xpress

Nashville

66 TN 266, Sam Ridley Pkwy, to Smyrna, **N...gas:** Citgo/diesel/24hr, Shell/diesel, **food:** Chili's, Logan's Roadhouse, Sonic, Subway, **lodging:** Day's Inn, **other:** MEDICAL CARE, Kroger/gas, Nashville I-24 Camping(3mi), **S...food:** Cracker Barrel, O'Charley's, Ruby Tuesday, **lodging:** Fairfield Inn, Hampton Inn, Sleep Inn, **other:** I-24 Expo

64 Waldron Rd, to La Vergne, **N...gas:** Exxon/24hr, Marathon, Pilot/Subway/diesel/24hr/@, **food:** Arby's, Hardee's, Krystal/24hr, McDonald's, Waffle House, **lodging:** Comfort Inn, Holiday Inn Express, Super 8, **other:** Music City Camping(3mi), RV service, **S...gas:** Express/diesel/24hr, **lodging:** Sleep n' Go

62 TN 171, Old Hickory Blvd, **N...gas:** BP, Chevron, Citgo, Shell/diesel/24hr, TA/BP/Burger King/Popeye's/diesel/24hr/@, **food:** El Arroyo Mexican, Waffle House, **lodging:** Best Western

60 Hickory Hollow Pkwy, **N...gas:** BP, Citgo/24hr, Express, Shell, **food:** Applebee's, Arby's, Bailey's Grill, Burger King, ChuckeCheese, Courtyard Café, Cracker Barrel, KFC, Logan's Roadhouse, McDonald's, O'Charley's, Outback Steaks, Pizza Hut, Red Lobster, Subway, TGIFriday, Wendy's, **lodging:** Day's Inn, Fairfield Inn, Hampton Inn, Holiday Inn, Ramada Inn, **other:** MEDICAL CARE, Best Buy, Chevrolet, Circuit City, Dillard's, Dodge, Eckerd, Firestone/auto, Kroger, Mazda, NTB, Office Depot, mall, transmissions, **S...gas:** BP/diesel, Shell, **food:** Evergreen Chinese, IHOP, Olive Garden, Shoney's, Steak'n Shake, Waffle House/24hr, **lodging:** Knight's Inn, Quality Inn, Quarters Inn, Super 8, **other:** Acura, Goodyear, Home Depot, Target

59 TN 254, Bell Rd, same as 60

57 Haywood Lane, **N...gas:** Marathon, **food:** Hardee's, Pizza Hut, **other:** $General, Food Lion, Walgreen, **S...gas:** Phillips 66/diesel/24hr

56 TN 255, Harding Place, **N...gas:** Chevron/diesel, Exxon, Shell/diesel/24hr, **food:** Applebee's, Arby's, KFC, McDonald's, Pizza Hut/Taco Bell, Subway, Waffle House, Wendy's, White Castle/Church's, **lodging:** Capstone Inn, Drury Inn, Executive Inn, Motel 6, PearTree Inn, Suburban Lodge, Super 8, **other:** Sam's Club/gas, **S...gas:** Express, Shell, **food:** Burger King, Hooters, Jack-in-the-Box, Waffle House, **lodging:** Economy Inn, Motel 6, **other:** HOSPITAL

54b a TN 155, Briley Pkwy, **N...other:** to Opryland, Camping World RV Supplies, KOA

Interstate 24

Nashville

53	I-440 W, to Memphis, no facilities
52	US 41, Murfreesboro Rd, **N...gas:** BP, Shell, Texaco, **food:** Bennigan's, Denny's, Dunkin Donuts, Golden Corral, Krystal, Los Reyes Mexican, Piccadilly's, Pizza Hut, Red Lobster, Taco Bell, Waffle House, **lodging:** Budget Lodge, Day's Inn, Economy Inn, Econolodge, Holiday Inn Express, Howard Johnson, Quality Inn, Ramada Inn, Scottish Inn, **other:** CarQuest, Office Depot, bank, **S...food:** Jack-in-the-Box, **other:** Chevrolet, Dodge
52b a	I-40, E to Knoxville, W to Memphis, no facilities

I-24 and I-40 run together 2 mi. See Tennessee Interstate 40, exits 212-213.

50b	I-40 W, no facilities
48	James Robertson Pkwy, **N...gas:** Citgo, Shell, **S...gas:** Exxon, TA/Subway/diesel/24hr/@, **food:** Shoney's, **lodging:** Ramada Ltd, Stadium Inn, **other:** st capitol
47a	US 31E, no facilities
47	N 1st St, Jefferson St, **N...gas:** Express/diesel, **S...gas:** Conoco, **lodging:** Day's Inn, Knight's Inn, **other:** U-Haul

I-24 and I-65 run together. See Tennessee Interstate 65, exit 87 b a.

44b a	I-65, N to Louisville, S to Nashville, no facilities
43	TN 155, Briley Pkwy, Brick Church Pike, **N...gas:** Citgo, **food:** Little Barn BBQ, **other:** $General,
40	TN 45, Old Hickory Blvd, **N...gas:** Citgo/diesel, Shell/Subway/diesel, Phillips 66/diesel/24hr, **food:** Jack-in-the-Box, Hot Wings, **lodging:** Super 8
35	US 431, to Joelton, Springfield, **S...gas:** Amoco/diesel/24hr, BP/diesel/24hr, **food:** Mazatlan Mexican, McDonald's, Subway, **lodging:** Day's Inn, **other:** Family$, OK Camping
31	TN 249, New Hope Rd, **N...gas:** Shell, **food:** Taco Tico, **S...gas:** BP, Citgo/diesel/24hr, **food:** Buddy's ChopHouse, Survivor Grill, **other:** to Nashville Zoo
24	TN 49, to Springfield, Ashland City, **N...gas:** BP, Texaco, Williams/diesel/24hr, Express/diesel/24hr/@, **food:** BBQ, **other:** HOSPITAL, **S...gas:** Shell, **food:** Beefy's Hamburgers, Sonic, Subway
19	TN 256, Maxey Rd, to Adams, **N...gas:** BP/diesel, **S...gas:** Shell/deli/diesel/24hr
11	TN 76, to Adams, Clarksville, **N...gas:** Shell/diesel/24hr, **S...gas:** BP/diesel/24hr, Citgo/Subway/24hr, **food:** Don Poncho Mexican, McDonald's, Waffle House, **lodging:** Comfort Inn, Day's Inn, Holiday Inn Express, Super 8, **other:** HOSPITAL
9mm	Red River
8	TN 237, Rossview Rd, no facilities
4	US 79, to Clarksville, Ft Campbell, **N...gas:** BP/diesel/24hr, **food:** Cracker Barrel, **other:** Sam's Club/gas, Spring Creek Camping(2mi), Clarksville RV Ctr, **S...gas:** BP/diesel/24hr, Citgo/diesel, Exxon/Blimpie/diesel/24hr, Marathon/diesel, Texaco/diesel, **food:** Applebee's, Arby's, Burger King, Capt D's, ChiChi's, Church's/White Castle, DQ, Golden Corral, KFC, Krystal, Logan's Roadhouse, LJ Silver, Longhorn Steaks, McDonald's, O'Charley's, Olive Garden, Oriental Buffet, Outback Steaks, Ponderosa, Rafferty's,

Clarksville

Red Lobster, Ruby Tuesday, Ryan's, Santa Fe Steaks, Steak'n Shake, Sub's Grill, Suzie's Drive-Thru, Taco Bell, Uncle Bud's Catfish, Waffle House, Wendy's, **lodging:** Best Value, Best Western, Comfort Inn, Country Inn Suites, Day's Inn, Econolodge, Fairfield Inn, Hampton Inn, Holiday Inn, Microtel, Ramada Ltd, Red Roof Inn, Royal Inn, Shoney's Inn/rest., Super 8, Travelodge, Wingate Inn, **other:** Advance Parts, Goodyear/auto, K-Mart, Lowe's Whse, OfficeMax, Sears/auto, Target, Wal-Mart SuperCtr/gas/24hr, mall, winery, to Austin Peay St U, to Land Between the Lakes

1	TN 48, to Clarksville, Trenton, **N...gas:** Shell/diesel, **other:** Clarksville Camping, antiques, **S...gas:** BP, Exxon
.5mm	**Welcome Ctr eb, full(handicapped)facilities, phones, vending, picnic tables, litter barrels, petwalk**
0mm	Tennessee/Kentucky state line

Interstate 26

Exit #	Services	E
46	I-81, N to Bristol, S to Knoxville	
45	Eastern Star Rd, no facilities	
42	rd 75, to Bobby Hicks Pkwy, **N...gas:** Exxon/diesel, BP/diesel, **food:** Burger King, DQ, Papa John's, Pizza Hut, Taco Express, TCBY, McDonalds, Wendy's, **other:** Rite aid, $General, White's foods, **S...gas:** BP/diesel	
38	rd 354, to Boons Creek Rd, **N...food:** Bob Evans, **S...gas:** BP/24hr, Shell/diesel, **food:** Burger King, Cracker Barrel, El Matador Mexican, Kemosabee's Roadhouse, Wendy's, Waffle House, **lodging:** Jameson Inn	W
36	TN 381, to St of Franklin Rd, to Bristol, **N...gas:** BP/McDonald's, **food:** El Chico Mexican, Golden Corral, Logan's Roadhouse, Outback Steaks, Subway, **lodging:** Comfort Suites, **other:** Office Max, Radio Shack, Wal-Mart SuperCtr/gas, **S...gas:** Exxon(2mi), **food:** Atlanta Bread Co., Carrabba's, Chick-fil-a, Chili's, China Chef, Fuddruckers, IHOP, Wendy's, **lodging:** Hampton Inn(2mi), Sleep Inn, **other:** Barnes&Noble, Best Buy, Circuit City, Home Depot, K-Mart, Lowe's Whse, Old Navy, Ross	
35	US 11 E, US 19 N, to Roan St, **N...gas:** Citgo, **food:** Harbor House Seafood, Hardee's, Perkins, Sonic, **lodging:** Best Western, Holiday Inn, Ramada Ltd, Super 8, **other:** Ford, **S...gas:** Sunoco, **food:** Hooters, McDonald's, Ryan's, Shoney's, Subway, TCBY, **lodging:** Day's Inn, Fairfield Inn, Red Roof Inn, **other:** Walgreen	
33	rd 400, Unaka Ave, Watauga Ave, no facilities	
32	32 rd 91, Market St, **N...food:** DQ, McDonald's, **S...gas:** BP, **other:** museum	

Johnson City

TENNESSEE

Interstate 26

E
W

Erwin

31   US 321, TN 67, Elizabethton, **N...gas:** Shell/diesel, **food:** Schlotsky's, **S...gas:** BP/diesel, **food:** Arby's, Burger King, Jerry's Café, LJ Silver, **lodging:** Comfort Inn, Carnegie Hotel, **other:** Advance Parts, Food City, Kroger/24hr, E TN St Univ., Roan Mtn. SP

28   rd 359 N, Okolona Rd, **N...gas:** BP, Exxon/diesel, **lodging:** Budget Inn

23   rd 173, Unicoi Rd, **N...gas:** Phillips 66, **food:** Maple Grove Café, **lodging:** Budget Inn(3mi), **other:** Grandview Camping(7mi), **S...**Woodsmoke Camping

21   Tinker Rd, no facilities

19   Tinker Rd, no facilities

19   Main St, Erwin, **N...gas:** BP/24hr, Exxon/diesel, **food:** Amigo Mexican, Backwoods BBQ, Hardee's, KFC, Pizza Hut, Wendy's

18   TN 81, rd 107, Erwin, Jonesboro, **N...gas:** Shell/diesel/24hr, **food:** Huddle House/24hr, McDonald's, Sonic, **other:** HOSPITAL, **S...food:** River's Edge Pizza, **lodging:** Super 8

15   Jackson-Love Hwy, Erwin, Jonesboro, **N...gas:** Appco Gas/A&W/LJ Silver, **lodging:** Best Southern Motel(1mi), Holiday Inn Express, **other:** Nolichucky Gorge Camping(2mi)

13mm   S Indian Creek

12   US 19 W, rd 352, Temple Hill Rd, **N...gas:** Exxon(2mi)

10mm   S Indian Creek

9   Clear Brach Rd, **N...**Acorn Ridge RV Park

7.5mm   Scenic Overlook wb (no trucks)

5   Flagpond Rd, no facilities

1mm   Scenic Overlook eb (no trucks)

.5mm   brake check area

0mm   Tennessee/North Carolina state line

Interstate 40

E
W

Newport

Exit #	Services
451mm	Tennessee/North Carolina state line
451	Waterville Rd, no facilities

447   Hartford Rd, **N...gas:** Citgo/diesel, **S...gas:** Exxon/towing, **food:** River Co Deli, **other:** Fox Fire Camping, whitewater rafting

446mm Welcome Ctr wb, full(handicapped)facilities, phones, vending, picnic tables, litter barrels, petwalk, NO TRUCKS

443   Foothills Pkwy, to Gatlinburg, Great Smokey Mtns NP, **S...**camping

443mm   Pigeon River

440   US 321, to Wilton Spgs Rd, Gatlinburg, **N...gas:** Sunoco/diesel/rest./repair, **S...gas:** BP, **other:** Arrow Creek Camping(14mi), CrazyHorse Camping(12mi), Jellystone Camping(12mi)

439mm   Pigeon River

435   US 321, to Gatlinburg, Newport, **N...gas:** Exxon/diesel/24hr, Marathon/24hr, Shell, **food:** Arby's, Burger King, Capt D's, Hardee's, KFC, La Carreta Mexican, McDonald's, Pizza Hut, Pizza+, SageBrush Steaks, Shoney's, Subway, Taco Bell, **lodging:** Bryant Town Motel, Motel 6/RV park, **other:** HOSPITAL, Goodyear/auto, **S...gas:** Amoco, BP/TCBY,

food: Cracker Barrel, Ryan's, Shiner's BBQ, Waffle House/24hr, Wendy's, **lodging:** Best Western, Family Inn, Holiday Inn, **other:** CVS Drug, Sav-A-Lot, Wal-Mart SuperCtr/gas/24hr

432b a   US 70, US 411, US 25W, to Newport, **N...gas:** BP/diesel, Exxon/diesel/24hr, TimeOut Travel Ctr/diesel, Krystal, **food:** Lois' Country Kitchen, Rodeo Rest., Sonic, **lodging:** Budget Motel, Comfort Inn, Relax Inn, **other:** Chevrolet/Pontiac/Buick, Chrysler/Jeep/Dodge, Ford/Mercury, KOA, TMC Camping, **S...gas:** BP, Citgo/24hr, Shell/diesel, **lodging:** Family Inn/rest.

426mm rest area wb, full(handicapped)facilities, phone, vending, picnic tables, litter barrels, petwalk

425mm   French Broad River

424   TN 113, Dandridge, **N...gas:** BP/diesel

421   I-81 N, to Bristol, no facilities

420mm rest area eb, full(handicapped)facilities, phone, vending, picnic tables, litter barrels, petwalk

417   TN 92, Dandridge, **N...gas:** Marathon, Pilot/Subway/diesel/@, **food:** Hardee's, McDonald's, Perkins, **lodging:** Lake Suites, Tennessee Mtn Inn, **S...gas:** Shell/Wendy's/diesel, Texaco/KFC/diesel, **food:** Pt. Marina, Shoney's, Waffle House, **lodging:** Comfort Inn, Holiday Inn Express, Super 8

415   US 25W, US 70, to Dandridge, **S...gas:** Shell/diesel, **food:** Sonic(3mi)

412   Deep Sprgs Rd, to Douglas Dam, **N...gas:** Love's/Subway/diesel, Sunshine/diesel/@, **food:** Apple Valley Café, **S...gas:** TR Trkstp/Chevron/diesel

407   TN 66, to Sevierville, Pigeon Forge, Gatlinburg, **N...gas:** Citgo/Huddle House/diesel, **food:** McDonald's, **lodging:** Motel 6, KOA, **S...gas:** Amoco, BP/DQ/Pizza Inn, Exxon/diesel, Shell/Krystal/diesel, Shell/Subway/diesel, **food:** Ole Southern Rest., Wendy's, **lodging:** Best Western, Comfort Inn, Day's Inn, Holiday Inn Express, Quality Inn, Ramada Ltd, **other:** Chrysler/Jeep/Dodge, TN RV Ctr, Honda, RV camping, flea mkt, **3-10 mi S...gas:** Citgo, **lodging:** Clarion Inn, Comfort Inn, Ramada Ltd, Wingate Inn, **other:** Lee Greenwood Theatre, USPO, multiple services/outlets

402   Midway Rd, no facilities

398   Strawberry Plains Pk, Strawberry Plains Pk, **N...gas:** Amoco/diesel, BP/diesel, Exxon/Pizza Hut/diesel, Shell, **food:** McDonald's, Ruby Tuesday, Waffle House, Wendy's, **lodging:** Comfort Inn, Country Inn Suites, Hampton Inn, Holiday Inn Express, Ramada Ltd, Super 8, **S...gas:** Pilot/DQ/Subway/diesel/24hr/@, Pilot/diesel/24hr/@, **food:** Arby's, Burger King, Cracker Barrel, KFC, Krystal, Puleo's Grill, Taco Bell, **lodging:** Baymont Inn, Best Western, Fairfield Inn

395mm   Holston River

394   US 70, US 11E, US 25W, Asheville Hwy, **N...gas:** Mobil/diesel, **lodging:** Sunbeam Motel(2mi), **other:** $General, city park, **1 mi N...gas:** RaceTrac, **food:** Subway, Wendy's, **lodging:** Gateway Inn, **other:** Advance Parts, Food Lion, flea mkt, **S...gas:** Exxon, Shell/diesel, **food:** Waffle House/24hr, **lodging:** Day's Inn, **1 mi S...food:** China City, **lodging:** Family Inn/rest., **other:** CVS Drug, Kroger/gas, **other:** Walgreen

Knoxville

Interstate 40

E
↕
W

K n o x v i l l e

393   I-640 W, to I-75 N, no facilities

392   US 11 W, Rutledge Pike, **N...gas:** Shell/diesel, **food:** CookHouse Rest., **other:** $General, U-Haul, repair, **S...gas:** BP, **food:** BBQ, Hardee's, Shoney's, **lodging:** Family Inn, **other:** AutoValue Parts, transmissions, to Knoxville Zoo

390   Cherry St, Knoxville, **N...gas:** Pilot/diesel, Shell/diesel, Weigel's/Subway, **food:** Country Table Rest., Hardee's, **lodging:** Red Carpet Inn, **other:** Goodyear, **1 mi S...gas:** Amoco, Exxon, **food:** Arby's, KFC, Krystal, LJ Silver, Mrs Winner's, Subway, Wendy's, **lodging:** Budget Motel, Regency Inn, **other:** Advance Parts, AutoZone, Walgreen

389   US 441 N, Broadway, 5th Ave, **1/2 mi N...gas:** BP, Conoco, Star, **food:** Burger King, Capt D's, KFC, Krystal, Steak-Out, Subway, Taco Bell, Wendy's, **other:** CVS Drug, $General, Family$, Firestone, Kroger/deli/24hr, Radio Shack, Tires+, USPO, Walgreen/24hr, transmissions

388   US 441 S(exits left from wb), downtown, downtown, **S...gas:** BP, **lodging:** Radisson, **other:** to Smokey Mtns, to U of TN

387b   TN 62, 17th St, **N...gas:** Pilot, **lodging:** Best Inn, **1/2 mi S...lodging:** Hilton, Holiday Inn, **other:** Goodyear

387a   I-275 N, to Lexington, no facilities

386b a   US 129, University Ave, to UT, airport

385   I-75 N, I-640 E, no facilities

I-40 W and I-75 S run together 17 mi.

383   Papermill Rd, **N...lodging:** Holiday Inn/rest., **S...gas:** Amoco, BP, Citgo, Pilot/diesel, Spur Gas, **food:** Applebee's(1mi), Burger King, China Buffet, Darryl's, Dunkin Donuts, IHOP, Longhorn Steaks, McDonald's, Morrison's Cafeteria, Pizza Hut, Red Lobster, Regas Café, Ruby Tuesday, Showbiz Pizza, Taco Bell, Taco Rancho Mexican, Waffle House, Wendy's, Western Sizzlin, **lodging:** Econolodge, Howard Johnson, Super 8, **other:** Buick/GMC, Firestone, same as 380

380   US 11, US 70, West Hills, **S...gas:** BP, Citgo, Conoco, Pilot, Shell, Texaco/diesel, **food:** Arby's, Applebee's, Backyard Burger, Blackeyed Pea, Cancun Mexican, Checker's, Chick-fil-A, Chili's, China Buffet, Cozymel's Grill, Honeybaked Ham, KFC, Macaroni Grill, Michael's Prime Rib, Mr Gatti's, O'Charley's, Olive Garden, Papa John's, PlumTree Chinese, Schlotsky's, Subway, Taco Bell, Texas Roadhouse, Wendy's, **lodging:** Comfort Hotel, Extended Stay America, Howard Johnson, Quality Inn, Super 8, **other:** BiLo Foods, Borders Books, Dillard's, $General, Food Lion, Goody's, JC Penney, K-Mart, Kohl's, Office Depot, Old Navy, Staples, U-Haul, Walgreen, mall, st patrol, **1 mi S on Kingston Pike...gas:** Citgo/7-11, **food:** Morrison's Cafeteria, Central Park, Little Caesar's, **lodging:** Family Inn, **other:** Office Depot, Radio Shack

379   Bridgewater Rd, **N...gas:** Exxon/Subway, Pilot/diesel, Shell, **food:** McDonald's, Pizza Hut/Taco Bell, **lodging:** Red Carpet Inn, **other:** Sam's Club, Wal-Mart SuperCtr/24hr, **S...gas:** BP/diesel, Pilot/diesel, Texaco/diesel, **food:** Burger King, ChuckeCheese,

Don Pablo, Logan's Roadhouse, Mrs Winners, Old Country Buffet, Omelet House, Ryan's, Shoney's, Tony Roma, Wendy's, **lodging:** Family Inn, Holiday Inn, Scottish Inn, **other:** AutoZone, BooksAMillion, Buy4Less Foods, Cadillac, Firestone/auto, Ford, Dodge, GMC, Goodyear, Isuzu, Mitsubishi, Nissan, SuperX Drug

378   Cedar Bluff Rd, **N...gas:** Amoco/24hr, Pilot/Taco Bell, Texaco, **food:** Arby's, Burger King, Cracker Barrel, KFC, LJ Silver, McDonald's, Papa John's, Pizza Hut, Subway, Waffle House, Wendy's, **lodging:** Budget Inn, Econolodge, Hampton Inn, Holiday Inn, Ramada Inn, Sleep Inn, **other:** HOSPITAL, Food Lion, Walgreen, **S...food:** Applebee's, Bob Evans, Carrabba's, Corky's Ribs/BBQ, Denny's, Fazoli's, Famous Dave's, Friendly's, Grady's Grill, Hops Grill, IHOP, Outback Steaks, **lodging:** Best Western, Clubhouse Inn, Courtyard, Extended Stay America, Guesthouse Suites, Hilton Garden, La Quinta, Luxbury Best Western, Microtel, Red Roof Inn, Residence Inn, Signature Inn, **other:** Best Buy, Celebration Sta, Chevrolet, Chrysler, Circuit City, Ford, Jo-Ann Fabrics, Kia, Lowe's Whse, Michael's, Staples, Walgreen

376   I-140 E, TN 162 N, to Maryville, **N...to Oak Ridge Museum

374   TN 131, Lovell Rd, **N...gas:** Amoco, BP, Texaco/diesel, TA/diesel/rest./24hr/@, **food:** McDonald's, Taco Bell, Waffle House, **lodging:** Best Western, Knight's Inn, La Quinta, Travelodge, **other:** Passport RV Ctr, **S...gas:** Citgo, Pilot/Wendy's/diesel/24hr/@, Speedway, **food:** Arby's, Chili's, Krystal, McDonald's, Olive Garden, Ruby Tuesday, Shoney's, **lodging:** Candlewood Suites, Day's Inn/rest., Homewood Suites, Motel 6, **other:** CarMax, Goody's, Honda, Land Rover, Lexus, Mercedes, OfficeMax, Target, Toyota, Wal-Mart SuperCtr/24hr

373   Campbell Sta Rd, **N...gas:** Amoco, Shell/diesel, **lodging:** Comfort Suites, Country Inn, Ramada Ltd, Super 8, **other:** Buddy Gregg RV Ctr, **S...gas:** BP, Conoco/diesel, Pilot/diesel, **food:** Cracker Barrel, Wendy's, **lodging:** Baymont Inn, Holiday Inn Express

372mm   weigh sta both lanes

369   Watt Rd, **N...gas:** ⬧/Flying J/Conoco/diesel/LP/24hr/@, Speedco, **S...gas:** Exxon, Petro/Mobil/diesel/24hr/@, TA/BP/Burger King/Perkins/Pizza Hut/diesel/24hr/@, **other:** Blue Beacon

I-40 E and I-75 N run together 17 mi.

368   I-75 and I-40, no facilities

364   US 321, TN 95, Lenoir City, Oak Ridge, **N...gas:** Shell, **other:** Crosseyed Cricket Camping(2mi), **4-5 mi S...food:** KFC, Krystal, Ruby Tuesday

363mm   parking area wb, phone, litter barrel

362mm   parking area eb, phone, litter barrel

360   Buttermilk Rd, **N...**Soaring Eagle RV Park

E

W

Harriman

Crossville

Cookeville

356   TN 58 N, Gallaher Rd, to Oak Ridge, **N...gas:** BP/diesel, **food:** Huddle House, Simply Subs, **lodging:** Day's Inn, Family Inn/rest., Kings Inn, **other:** 4 Seasons Camping, **S...gas:** Citgo/diesel

355   Lawnville Rd, **N...gas:** Shell/diesel

352   TN 58 S, Kingston, **N...lodging:** Knight's Inn, **other:** NAPA, **S...gas:** Exxon/diesel, RaceWay, Shell, **food:** DQ, Hardee's, McDonald's, Pizza Hut, Sonic, Subway, Taco Bell, **lodging:** Comfort Inn, **other:** Marina RV Park, to Watts Bar Lake

351mm   Clinch River

350   US 70, Midtown, **S...other:** Lowe's Whse, Patterson RV Supplies

347   US 27, Harriman, **N...gas:** Phillips 66/Subway/diesel, **food:** Cancun Mexican, Hardee's, KFC, LJ Silver, McDonald's, Pizza Hut, Ruby Tuesday, Taco Bell, Wendy's, **lodging:** Best Western, **other:** to Frozen Head SP, Big S Fork NRA, **S...gas:** BP, Exxon, Shell/Krystal/diesel/24hr, **food:** Cracker Barrel, Reno's Grill, Shoney's, **lodging:** Holiday Inn Express, Super 8, **2-3 mi S...food:** Capt D's, Domino's, Subway, **other:** HOSPITAL, Advance Parts, Goody's, Kroger, Radio Shack, Wal-Mart SuperCtr/gas/24hr

340   TN 299 N, Airport Rd, no facilities

339.5mm   eastern/central time zone line, eastern/central time zone line

338   TN 299 S, Westel Rd, **N...gas:** BP/diesel, **S...gas:** Shell/diesel, E-WTrkstp/diesel/rest./24hr/@ , **other:** Top Mtn Camping

336mm   parking area/weigh sta eb, litter barrel

329   US 70, Crab Orchard, **N...gas:** BP/diesel, Exxon/mechanic, **other:** Lakes Camping

327mm   **rest area wb, full(handicapped)facilities, phone, picnic tables, litter barrels, petwalk, vending**

324mm   **rest area eb, full(handicapped)facilities, phone, picnic tables, litter barrels, petwalk, vending**

322   TN 101, Peavine Rd, Crossville, **N...gas:** BP/Bean Pot Rest., Exxon/Taco Bell/diesel, Phillips 66, **food:** Hardee's, McDonald's, **lodging:** Holiday Inn Express, **other:** Roam+Roost RV Campground, to Fairfield Glade Resort, **S...lodging:** Comfort Inn, Super 8, **food:** Cancun Mexican, **other:** HOSPITAL, Chesnut Hill Winery/rest., Cumberland Mtn SP

320   TN 298, Crossville, **N...** antiques, golf, winery, **S...gas:** BP/DQ/Pizza Hut/diesel, Shell/24hr, **food:** Catfish Cove Rest., Krystal(2mi), Wendy's(2mi), **other:** HOSPITAL, Factory Outlet/famous brands, antiques, auto repair

318mm   Obed River

317   US 127, Crossville, **N...gas:** BP/diesel, Citgo/diesel, Exxon/Subway/diesel/24hr, Shell/Blimpie/diesel, **food:** Huddle House, **lodging:** Best Western, La Quinta, Ramada Inn, **1-2 mi S...gas:** Citgo, Phillips 66/diesel, Sunoco, **food:** Cracker Barrel, Ponderosa, Ruby Tuesday, Ryan's, Schlotsky's, Shoney's, Taco Bell, Waffle House, Wendy's, **lodging:** Days Inn, Heritage Inn, Scottish Inn, Villager Lodge, **other:** HOSPITAL, Chevrolet/Cadillac, Chrysler/Plymouth/Dodge/Jeep, $Tree, GNC, Goodyear, Lowe's Whse, Staples, Wal-Mart SuperCtr/gas/24hr, to Cumberland SP

311   Plateau Rd, **N...gas:** Citgo/diesel, **S...gas:** BP/diesel, Exxon

306mm   parking area/weigh sta wb, litter barrels

301   US 70 N, TN 84, Monterey, **N...gas:** Phillips 66, Shell, **food:** Burger King, DQ, Subway

300   US 70, Monterey, **N...gas:** Citgo/diesel, **food:** Cup N' Saucer Rest., Hardee's

291mm   Falling Water River

290   US 70, Cookeville, **N...gas:** BP, **S...gas:** Citgo, **food:** Bella Vista Mexican, **lodging:** Alpine Inn

288   TN 111, to Livingston, Cookeville, Sparta, **S...gas:** Citgo, Mid Tenn Trkstp/diesel/@ , Phillips 66/Subway/diesel, **food:** Huddle House, **lodging:** Knight's Inn

287   TN 136, Cookeville, **N...gas:** BP/TCBY, Chevron/diesel, Citgo, Shell/diesel, **food:** Applebee's, Arby's, Burger King, Capt D's, Chick-fil-A, Chili's, China Star, Cracker Barrel, DQ, El Tapatio Mexican, Fazoli's, Golden Corral, Huddle House, IHOP, Jack-in-the-Box, King Buffet, Krystal, LJ Silver, Logan's Roadhouse, McDonald's, Mr Gatti's, Nick's Rest., O'Charley's, Outback Steaks, Pizza Hut, Ponderosa, Quizno's, Rafferty's, Red Lobster, Ryan's, Schlotsky's, Shoney's, Sonic, Steak'n Shake, Subway, Taco Bell, Waffle House, Wendy's, **lodging:** Best Value, Best Western, Comfort Suites, Day's Inn, Executive Inn, Hampton Inn, Holiday Inn/rest., Ramada Ltd, Super 8, **other:** Auto Value Parts, Cadillac/Honda, CVS Drug, $Tree, Firestone, Goody's, Harley-Davidson, JC Penney, K-Mart, Kroger, Lowe's Whse, OfficeMax, Radio Shack, Tires+, Toyota, Wal-Mart SuperCtr/24hr, mall, st patrol, transmissions, **S...gas:** Exxon/diesel, Pilot/Blimpie/diesel, **food:** Gondola Pizza, KFC, Waffle House, **lodging:** Baymont Inn, Country Inn Suites, Econolodge, **other:** Dodge

286   TN 135, Burgess Falls Rd, **N...gas:** BP, Exxon, RaceWay/diesel, Shell/diesel, **food:** Applebee's, Arby's, Hardee's, Steak'n Shake, Thai Cuisine, Waffle House, **lodging:** KeyWest Inn, **other:** HOSPITAL, Chrysler/Plymouth/Jeep, Goodyear, Kia/Mitsubishi, Mazda, Nissan, Toyota, U-Haul, to TTU, **S...gas:** Amoco/diesel, Citgo/diesel, **lodging:** Star Motor Inn/rest.

280   TN 56 N, Baxter, **N...gas:** Shell/diesel, **other:** Camp Discovery, Twin Lakes RV Park

276   Old Baxter Rd, **S...gas:** Citgo/diesel, **other:** fireworks

273   TN 56 S, to Smithville, **S...gas:** BP/diesel, Phillips 66, **food:** Rose Garden Rest., **lodging:** Timber Ridge Inn

268   TN 96, Buffalo Valley Rd, **S...** to Edgar Evins SP

267mm   Caney Fork River

267mm   **rest area both lanes, full(handicapped)facilities, info, phone, picnic tables, litter barrels, petwalk, vending**

266mm   Caney Fork River

263mm   Caney Fork River

258   TN 53, Gordonsville, **N...gas:** BP, Exxon/KFC/Taco Bell, Shell, **food:** Connie's BBQ, McDonald's, Timberloft Café, Waffle House, **lodging:** Comfort Inn, **other:** to Cordell Hull Dam, **S...gas:** Citgo/diesel, KeyStop/diesel, **lodging:** Courtyard Country Buffet

Interstate 40

254 TN 141, to Alexandria, no facilities

252mm parking area/weigh sta both lanes, picnic tables, litter barrels

245 Linwood Rd, **N...gas:** BP/diesel

239 US 70, Lebanon, **N...gas:** Citgo, RaceWay, **S...gas:** Phillips 66/diesel/rest/@

238 US 231, Lebanon, **N...gas:** BP, Express, Exxon, Shell, **food:** Applebee's, Arby's, BBQ, Cracker Barrel, Demo's Steaks, Gondola Rest., Hardee's, Jack-in-the-Box, McDonald's, Mrs Winner's, Pizza Hut, Ponderosa, Ryan's, Shoney's, Subway, Taco Bell, Waffle House, Wendy's, **lodging:** Best Western, Comfort Inn, Economy Inn, Guesthouse Inn, Hampton Inn, Holiday Inn Express, **other:** HOSPITAL, OfficeMax, Wal-Mart SuperCtr/24hr, **S...gas:** Citgo/diesel, Pilot/Subway/diesel/24hr/@, **food:** O'Charley's, Santa Fe Steaks, Sonic, **lodging:** Comfort Suites, Country Inn Suites, Day's Inn, Knight's Inn, Super 8, **other:** Prime Outlets/famous brands, flea mkt, to Cedars of Lebanon SP, RV camping

236 S Hartmann Dr, **N...food:** Jack-in-the-Box(2mi), Outback Steaks, **other:** Home Depot

235 TN 840 W, to Murfreesboro, no facilities

232 TN 109, to Gallatin, **N...gas:** Citgo, Express, Shell/diesel/24hr, **food:** Brewster's Grille, McDonald's, Sonic, Subway, Waffle House, Wendy's, **lodging:** Sleep Inn, **2 mi S...other:** Countryside Resort Camping

226 TN 171, Mt Juliet Rd, **N...gas:** BP/McDonald's/diesel, Express/diesel, Exxon/diesel, Shell/diesel/24hr, **food:** Arby's, Capt D's, **S...gas:** Express/diesel, **food:** Cracker Barrel, Ruby Tuesday, Waffle House, **lodging:** Microtel, **other:** to Long Hunter SP

221 TN 45 N, Old Hickory Blvd, to The Hermitage, **N...gas:** BP, Exxon, Express/diesel, RaceWay, Shell/24hr, **food:** Applebee's, DQ, Hardee's, IHOP, Jack-in-the-Box, Music City Café, O'Charley's, Waffle House, **lodging:** Best Inn, Comfort Inn, Holiday Inn Express, Suburban Lodge, **other:** HOSPITAL, CVS Drug, Kroger, Walgreen, **S...gas:** Phillips 66/White Castle, Shell/McDonald's

219 Stewart's Ferry Pike, **N...gas:** Express, **S...gas:** Express/Subway, Shell/diesel, **food:** Cracker Barrel, Uncle Bud's Catfish, Hacienda Mexican, Sal's Pizza, Waffle House, **lodging:** Best Value Inn, Best Western, Country Inn Suites, Day's Inn, Family Inn, Sleep Inn, **other:** $General

216 (216 c from eb)TN 255, Donaldson Pk, **N...gas:** BP/diesel, Citgo, Express, RaceWay, Shell/Subway/diesel/24hr, **food:** Arby's, Backyard Burger, BBQ, Burger King, Domino's, Jalisco's Cantina, KFC, Little Caesar's, McDonald's, New China, Papa John's, Pizza Hut/Taco Bell, Ruby Tuesday, Shoney's, Subway, Waffle House, Wendy's, **lodging:** Baymont Inn, Country Inn Suites, Drury Inn, Hampton Inn, Holiday Inn Express, Howard Johnson, Red Roof, Springhill Suites, Super 8, Wingate Inn, Wyndham Hotel, **other:** Advance Parts, K-Mart, Walgreen, **S...lodging:** Hotel Preston

216b a (from eb), **S...**Nashville Intn'l Airport

215b a TN 155, Briley Pkwy, to Opryland, **N...gas:** Shell, **food:** Denny's, Day's Inn, **lodging:** Econolodge, Embassy Suites, Holiday Inn, La Quinta, Marriott, Park Suite Hotel, Quality Inn, Rodeway Inn, Sheraton, **other:** bank, **2 mi N on Lebanon Pike...other:** to Camping World RV Service, KOA, Capt D's, Waffle House, Hampton Inn, **S...gas:** Shell, **lodging:** Clarion, Radisson, Royal Inn, Villager Lodge

213b I-24 W, no facilities

213a I-24 E/I-440, E to Chattanooga, no facilities

213 US 41(from wb), to Spence Lane, **N...gas:** Shell/diesel, **S...food:** Denny's, McDonald's, Red Lobster, Shoney's, Waffle House, Western Sizzlin, **lodging:** Day's Inn, Econolodge, Holiday Inn Express, Ramada Inn, Scottish Inn, Tudor Inn, same as 212

212 Fessler's Lane(from eb, no return), **N...**Harley-Davidson, **S...gas:** Shell/diesel, **food:** Burger King, Krystal, McDonald's, Mrs Winners, Sonic, Wendy's, same as 213

211mm Cumberland River

211b I-24 W, no facilities

211a I-24E, I-40 W, no facilities

210c US 31 S, US 41A, 2nd Ave, 4th Ave, **N...lodging:** Stouffer Hotel, **S...**museum

210b a I-65 S, to Birmingham, no facilities

209b a US 70 S, Charlotte Ave, Nashville, **N...lodging:** Holiday Inn, **other:** Chevrolet, Lincoln/Mercury, Nissan, Pontiac/GMC, Suzuki, Toyota, Country Music Hall of Fame, Conv Ctr, transmissions, **S...gas:** BP/diesel, Exxon, **food:** Burger King, Subway, White Castle, **lodging:** Comfort Inn, Guesthouse Inn, **other:** Chrysler/Plymouth

208b a I-65, N to Louisville, S to Birmingham, no facilities

207 28th Ave, Jefferson St, Nashville, TN St U, **N...gas:** Citgo, Phillips 66, **food:** Subway, Wendy's, **other:** Family$, **S...**HOSPITAL

206 I-440 E, to Knoxville, no facilities

205 46th Ave, W Nashville, **N...**Harley-Davidson, **S...gas:** Express, Shell, **food:** McDonald's, Mrs Winner's

204 TN 155, Briley Pkwy, **N...gas:** Exxon, Shell/diesel, **S...food:** Burger King, Church's/White Castle, Domino's, Jack-in-the-Box, KFC, Krystal, New China, Uncle Bud's Catfish, Waffle House, Wendy's, **lodging:** Baymont Inn, Best Western, Comfort Inn, **other:** AutoZone, CVS Drug, Ford, Goodyear/auto, Kroger, NTB, PepBoys, Walgreen

201b a US 70, Charlotte Pike, **N...gas:** Exxon, Shell/diesel/24hr, **food:** Cracker Barrel, Krystal, Subway, Super China, Waffle House, **lodging:** Super 8, **other:** $Tree, GNC, Lowe's Whse, Radio Shack, Wal-Mart SuperCtr/24hr, **S...lodging:** Howard Johnson/rest.

199 rd 251, Old Hickory Blvd, **S...gas:** BP, Express/Subway, **food:** Sonic, Waffle House, **other:** Sam's Club

TENNESSEE
Interstate 40

E ↕ W

D i c k s o n

196	US 70, to Bellevue, Newsom Sta, **N...gas:** Express, **food:** Shoney's, **S...gas:** BP, Express/diesel, Shell/diesel/24hr, **food:** Applebee's, Jack-in-the-Box, O'Charley's, Pizza Hut, Princeton's Grille, Ruby Tuesday, Sam's Grill, Sir Pizza, Sonic, Subway, Taco Bell, Waffle House, Wendy's, **lodging:** Hampton Inn, Microtel, **other:** MEDICAL CARE, Circuit City, Dillard's, $Tree, Firestone/auto, Home Depot, Michael's, Old Navy, Piggly Wiggly, Staples, USPO, Walgreen/24hr, mall
195mm	Harpeth River
192	McCrory Lane, to Pegram, **S...**Natchez Trace Pkwy
190mm	Harpeth River
188mm	Harpeth River
188	rd 249, Kingston Springs, **N...gas:** BP, Express/Blimpie/diesel, Shell/Arby's, **food:** McDonald's, Pizza Pro, Sonic, **lodging:** Best Western, Econolodge, Scottish Inn, **other:** USPO, **S...gas:** Petro/Chevron/Pizza Hut/diesel/showers/24hr/@
182	TN 96, to Dickson, Fairview, **N...gas:** Citgo/diesel, **lodging:** Deerfield Inn, Fairview Inn, **other:** M Bell SP(16mi), **S...gas:** BP/diesel, ⛽/Flying J/Conoco/Country Mkt/diesel/LP/24hr/@
175	TN 840, no facilities
172	TN 46, to Dickson, **N...gas:** BP/diesel/24hr, Citgo, Pilot/Wendy's/diesel/24hr/@, Shell, **food:** Arby's, Burger King, Cracker Barrel, McDonald's, Ruby Tuesday, Subway, Waffle House/24hr, Wang's China, **lodging:** Baymont Inn, Best Value, Comfort Inn, Econolodge, Hampton Inn, Knight's Inn, Motel 6, Ramada Ltd, Super 8, **other:** HOSPITAL, Chevrolet, KOA, to M Bell SP, **S...gas:** Phillips 66, Shell, O'Charley's, **lodging:** Day's Inn, Holiday Inn
170	**rest area both lanes, full(handicapped)facilities, phone, picnic tables, litter barrels, vending, petwalk**
166mm	Piney River
163	rd 48, to Dickson, **N...gas:** Phillips 66/Reed's/diesel, **S...gas:** Shell, **other:** Tanbark Camping
152	rd 230, Bucksnort, **N...gas:** Citgo, **food:** Rudy's Rest., **lodging:** Travel Inn
149mm	Duck River
148	rd 50, Barren Hollow Rd, to Turney Center, **S...gas:** Shell
143	TN 13, to Linden, Waverly, **N...gas:** Pilot/Arby's/diesel/24hr/@, Shell, **food:** Las Fuentes Mexican, Loretta's Kitchen, McDonald's, **lodging:** Best Western, Day's Inn, Holiday Inn Express, Super 8, **other:** KOA, **S...gas:** Exxon/diesel, Shell, **lodging:** Southside Motel/rest.
141mm	Buffalo River
137	Cuba Landing, **N...other:** TN River RV Park, **S...food:** Cuba Landing Rest./gas
133mm	Tennessee River
133	rd 191, Birdsong Rd, **N...lodging:** Lakeside RV Resort/marina(9mi)
131mm	**rest area both lanes, full(handicapped)facilities, phone, vending, picnic tables, litter barrels, petwalk**

J a c k s o n

126	US 641, TN 69, to Camden, **N...gas:** Exxon/Subway/TCBY/diesel, Phillips 66/North 40/diesel/rest./@, SugarTree Trkstp/diesel/@, Shell, **other:** tire/truck repair, to NB Forrest SP, **S...gas:** BP/diesel, Citgo/DQ/Stuckey's, Shell/diesel, **lodging:** Day's Inn/rest., **other:** HOSPITAL
116	rd 114, **S...other:** to Natchez Trace SP, RV camping
110mm	Big Sandy River
108	TN 22, to Lexington, Parkers Crossroads, **N...gas:** BP/McDonald's/24hr, Citgo/diesel/24hr, Phillips 66/diesel, **food:** Bailey's Rest., Dairy Queen, Subway/TCBY, **lodging:** Knight's Inn, **other:** USPO, city park, **S...gas:** Coastal, Exxon, Shell, **food:** Cotton Patch Rest., **lodging:** Best Western, **other:** HOSPITAL, RV camping, to Shiloh Nat Bfd(51mi)
103mm	parking area/weigh sta eb, litter barrels, phone
102mm	parking area/weigh sta wb, litter barrels
101	rd 104, **N...gas:** Exxon, 101 Travel Plaza/@, **other:** golf(3mi)
93	rd 152, Law Rd, **N...gas:** Phillips 66/diesel/deli/24hr, **S...gas:** Shell/diesel
87	US 70, US 412, Jackson, **N...gas:** Coastal/diesel, **S...gas:** Love's/Hardee's/diesel/24hr/@, Shell/diesel
85	Christmasville Rd, to Jackson, **N...gas:** BP/Subway/diesel, Exxon/diesel/24hr, **lodging:** Howard Johnson Express, **other:** $General, **S...gas:** Shell(1mi)
83	new exit
82b a	US 45, Jackson, **N...gas:** Shell, **food:** Cracker Barrel, **lodging:** Knight's Inn, Microtel, **other:** Batteries+, **S...gas:** BP, Citgo, RaceWay, **food:** Backyard Burger, Barley's Brewhouse, Burger King, Capt D's, China Palace, DQ, Folks Rest., KFC, Krystal, LJ Silver, McDonald's, Pizza Hut, Pizza Inn, Popeye's, Shoney's, Sonic, Subway, Suede's Rest., Taco Bell, Waffle House, Wendy's, **lodging:** Baymont Inn, Executive Inn, Ramada Ltd, Sheraton/rest., Super 8, **other:** Advance Parts, AutoZone, Belk, CarQuest, Firestone/auto, Goodyear/auto, JC Penney, Kroger/24hr, Office Depot, Radio Shack, Sears/auto, WaldenBooks, mall
80b a	US 45 Byp, Jackson, **N...gas:** BP/diesel, Exxon, **food:** Backyard Burger, Buffalo Wings, Chili's, Chick-fil-A, Corky's BBQ, Domino's, Fazoli's, 5&Diner, IHOP, Jason's Deli, KFC, Lenny's Subs, LoneStar Steaks, Longhorn Steaks, Peking Chinese, Perkins, Schlotsky's, Starbucks, Steak'n Shake, Wendy's, **lodging:** AmeriHost, Comfort Inn, Country Inn Suites, Jameson Inn, Red Roof Inn, **other:** Circuit City, Home Depot, Lowe's Whse, Nissan, Sam's Club/gas, Saturn, Wal-Mart SuperCtr/24hr, **S...gas:** BP, Citgo, Coastal/diesel, Phillips 66/diesel, 76, **food:** Applebee's, Arby's, Barnhill's Buffet, Burger King, Dunkin Donuts, El Chico's, Logan's Roadhouse, Madison's Rest., McDonald's, Mrs Winner's, O'Charley's, Pizza Hut, Sakura Japanese, Shakey's Custard, Sonic, Subway, Village Pizza, Waffle House, **lodging:** Best Western, Comfort Inn, Day's Inn, Econolodge, Fairfield Inn, Hampton Inn, Holiday Inn, Old Hickory Inn, **other:** HOSPITAL, Cadillac/Pontiac/Buick/Toyota, $General, Hancock Fabrics, Harley-Davidson, King Tires, K-Mart, to Pinson Mounds SP, Chickasaw SP

Interstate 40

E

W

79	US 412, Jackson, **S...gas:** BP/repair, Citgo/diesel, Exxon, **lodging:** Day's Inn, **other:** Jackson RV Park
78mm	Forked Deer River
76	rd 223 S, **S...other:** McKellar-Sites Airport, Whispering Pines RV Park
74	Lower Brownsville Rd, no facilities
73mm	**rest area both lanes, full(handicapped)facilities, info, phone, picnic tables, litter barrels, vending, petwalk**
68	rd 138, Providence Rd, **N...gas:** BP/diesel, **lodging:** Scottish Inn, **S...gas:** TA/Citgo/diesel/rest./24hr/@, **other:** Joy-O RV Park, truck repair
66	US 70, to Brownsville, **S...gas:** FuelMart/diesel/24hr, **lodging:** Motel 6
60	rd 19, Mercer Rd, no facilities
56	TN 76, to Brownsville, **N...gas:** BP, Citgo/Subway/diesel/24hr, **food:** DQ, KFC, McDonald's, Pizza Hut/Taco Bell, **lodging:** Best Western, Comfort Inn, Day's Inn, Holiday Inn Express, **S...gas:** BP/diesel, Exxon/Huddle House/diesel/24hr
55mm	Hatchie River
52	TN 76, rd 179, Koko Rd, to Whiteville, no facilities
50mm	weigh sta both lanes, phone
47	TN 179, to Stanton, Dancyville, **S...gas:** Exit 47 Trkstp/diesel/rest./24hr/@
42	TN 222, to Stanton, **N...lodging:** Countryside Inn, **S...gas:** Exxon/diesel, Pilot/Subway/diesel/@, **lodging:** Deerfield Inn
35	TN 59, to Somerville, **S...gas:** BP/diesel, **food:** Longtown Rest.
29.5mm	Loosahatchie River
25	TN 205, Airline Rd, to Arlington, **N...gas:** Chevron/diesel, Exxon/Subway/diesel, **other:** vistor ctr, **S...**Horizon/Backyard Burger/diesel
24	TN 385, rd 204, to Arlington, Millington, Collierville, no facilities
20	Canada Rd, Lakeland, **N...gas:** 76/diesel/24hr, Shell/McDonald's, **food:** Cracker Barrel, Waffle House, **lodging:** Day's Inn/rest., Relax Inn, Super 8, **S...gas:** Exxon/Subway/TCBY/diesel, **other:** Factory Outlet/famous brands/food court, **other:** KOA
18	US 64, to Bartlett, **N...gas:** Shell, **food:** Bob Evans, Buffalo Wings, Don Pablo, Hooters, Luby's, Memphis Pizza, Schlotsky's, Steak'n Shake, Waffle House, **lodging:** Country Inn Suites, Fairfield Inn, Holiday Inn Express, SpringHill Suites, **other:** Firestone, Goodyear/auto, Lowe's Whse, Pontiac/GMC, Sam's Club/gas, Wal-Mart SuperCtr/24hr, same as 16, **S...gas:** BP, Citgo/diesel, 76/Circle K, **food:** Backyard Burger, KFC, **other:** Kroger, Walgreen
16b a	TN 177, to Germantown, **N...gas:** 76, Shell, **food:** Alexander's Rest., Bahama Breeze, Burger King, Chili's, Chick-fil-A, IHOP, Joe's Crabshack, Logan's Roadhouse, Macaroni Grill, McDonald's, On-the-Border, Red Lobster, Sessel's Café, Taco Bell, Wendy's, **lodging:** AmeriSuites, Hampton Suites, Wellesley Inn, **other:** Barnes&Noble, Best Buy, Chevrolet, Chrysler/Plymouth/Dodge, Circuit City, Dillard's, Ford, Home Depot, Honda, JC Penney, Michael's, Office Depot, OfficeMax, Old Navy, Sears/auto, Target, Walgreen, mall, **S...gas:** Shell, **food:** Shogun Japanese, Waffle House, **lodging:** Best Inn, Comfort Suites, Microtel, Wingate Inn, **other:** Costco/gas
15b a	Appling Rd, **N...**BP, **1 mi N...gas:** Shell, **food:** Coletta's Italian, Suburban Lodge, **S...gas:** Chevron/diesel
14	Whitten Rd, **N...gas:** Express, 76/diesel, Shell/Burger King, **food:** Anna's Steaks, Quizno's, Sidecar Café, **other:** Harley-Davidson, **S...gas:** BP, Chevron/diesel, **food:** Backyard Burger, **lodging:** Travelers Inn
12	Sycamore View Rd, **N...gas:** Citgo/diesel, Phillips 66, **food:** Capt D's, Church's, Cracker Barrel, IHOP, KFC, Krystal, McDonald's, Mrs Winner's, Perkins, Ruby Tuesday, Shoney's, Sonic, Subway, Taco Bell, Waffle House, **lodging:** Baymont Inn, Drury Inn, Econolodge, Hampton Inn, Holiday Inn Express, Red Roof Inn, **other:** Walgreen, **S...gas:** Exxon, 76/diesel, **food:** Burger King, India Cuisine, Jimmy C's Café, Top's BBQ, Wendy's, **lodging:** Best Western, Comfort Inn, Day's Inn, Fairfield Inn, Hawthorn Inn, La Quinta, Memphis Inn, Motel 6, Ramada Inn, Super 8
10.5mm	Wolf River
10b a	(from wb)I-240 W around Memphis, I-40 E to Nashville, no facilities
12c	(from eb)I-240 W, to Jackson, I-40 E to Nashville, no facilities
12b	Sam Cooper Blvd(from eb), no facilities
12a	US 64/70/79, Summer Ave, **N...gas:** Express/diesel, Texaco/diesel, **food:** Luby's, Pappy&Jimmie's Rest., Waffle House, **lodging:** Ramada Inn, **other:** Ford, OfficeMax, U-Haul, mall, **S...gas:** Amoco, Exxon, **food:** Arby's, Great China, McDonald's, NamKing Chinese, Pizza Hut, Wendy's, Western Sizzlin, **other:** Firestone/auto, Fred's Drug, Goodyear/auto, Hancock Fabrics, K-Mart
10	TN 204, Covington Pike, **N...gas:** Amoco, **food:** McDonald's, Wendy's, **other:** Audi/VW, Buick, Cadillac, Chevrolet, Dodge, Honda, Hyundai, Isuzu/Mazda, Kia/Toyota, Mitsubishi, Nissan, Pontiac/GMC, Sam's Club, SuperLo Food/gas, Volvo
8b a	TN 14, Jackson Ave, **N...gas:** Citgo/diesel, 76, Sonic, **lodging:** Day's Inn, Sleep Inn, **other:** Raleigh Tire, **S...gas:** Citgo/diesel, **food:** Central Park, **other:** AutoZone, Family$, Kelly Tire, O'Reilly Parts, transmissions
6	Warford Rd, no facilities
5	Hollywood St, **N...gas:** BP, Shell, **food:** Burger King, **other:** Walgreen
3	Watkins St, **N...gas:** BP, Express/diesel, Oil City USA, **other:** U-Haul
2a	rd 300, to US 51 N, Millington, **N...other:** Meeman-Shelby SP
2	Smith Ave, Chelsea Ave, no facilities
1g f	TN 14, Jackson Ave, **N...lodging:** Rainbow Inn, **S...gas:** Express, **other:** Don's Transmissions

M e m p h i s

TENNESSEE

Interstate 40

E

1e	I-240 E, no facilities
1d c b	US 51, Danny Thomas Blvd, **N...other:** St Jude Research Ctr
1a	2nd St(from wb), downtown, downtown, **S...lodging:** Holiday Inn, Marriott, Sheraton, Wyndham Garden, **other:** Conv Ctr

W

| 1 | Riverside Dr, Front St(from eb), Memphis, **S...lodging:** Comfort Inn, **other:** Conv Ctr, Riverfront |
| 0mm | Tennessee/Arkansas state line, Mississippi River |

Interstate 55

N

Exit #	Services
13mm	Tennessee/Arkansas state line, Mississippi River
12c	Delaware St, Memphis, **W...lodging:** Super 8
b	Riverside Dr, downtown Memphis, **E...TN** Welcome Ctr
a	E Crump Blvd(from nb), **E...museum**
11	McLemore Ave, Presidents Island, industrial area

S

10	S Parkway, **1/2mi E...gas:** Conoco/diesel
9	Mallory Ave, industrial area
8	Horn Lake Rd(from sb), no facilities
7	US 61, 3rd St, **E...gas:** Amoco, Exxon/mart, **food:** BBQ, LotABurger, McDonald's, Taco Bell, **W...gas:** Citgo/Subway, Express/diesel, **food:** KFC, McDonald's, **lodging:** Rest Inn, Starliet Inn, **other:** CarQuest, Fuller SP, Indian Museum
6b a	I-240, no facilities
5b	US 51 S, Elvis Presley Blvd, to Graceland, **W...gas:** Citgo/diesel, Exxon, Phillips 66/diesel, **food:** Capt D's, Exline's Pizza, Kettle, KFC, Peking Chinese, Rally's, Taco Bellfs, **lodging:** American Inn, Day's Inn, Graceland Inn, Heartbreak Hotel, Motel 6, **other:** HOSPITAL, Advance Parts, Davis RV Ctr, Dodge, KOA, Walgreen, transmissions, to Graceland
a	Brooks Rd, **E...gas:** Express/diesel, Exxon, **food:** Popeye's, **lodging:** Airport Inn, Clarion, Travelodge, **other:** Toyota
3mm	**Welcome Ctr nb, full(handicapped)facilities, phone, vending, picnic tables, litter barrels, petwalk**
2b a	TN 175, Shelby Dr, Whitehaven, **E...gas:** Citgo/Subway, Conoco, Exxon, **lodging:** Shelby Inn, Super 8, **W...gas:** 76/mart, Shell, **food:** Burger King, CK's Coffee, Crumpy's Wings, Hook's Fish/chicken, **other:** Family$, Goodyear/auto, SaveALot Food, Seessel's Food/gas, U-Haul
0mm	Tennessee/Mississippi state line

(vertical label: Memphis)

Interstate 65

Exit #	Services
121.5mm	Tennessee/Kentucky state line
121mm	**Welcome Ctr sb, full(handicapped)facilities, phone, picnic tables, litter barrels, vending, petwalk**

N

| 119mm | weigh sta both lanes |
| 117 | TN 52, Portland, **E...gas:** Shell/diesel/fireworks, **other:** HOSPITAL, **W...gas:** Amoco, **other:** Jiffy Oil Trkstp/diesel/@, **lodging:** Budget Host, **other:** fireworks |

S

116mm	Red River
113mm	Red River
112	TN 25, Cross Plains, **E...gas:** Amoco/diesel, **food:** Sad Sam's Pizza, **W...gas:** Express/diesel, Exxon/diesel/24hr
108	TN 76, White House, **E...gas:** Keystop, Nervous Charlie's/diesel, **food:** Cracker Barrel, DQ, Hardee's, KFC/A&W, McDonald's, Sonic(1mi), Taco Bell, Waffle House, Wendy's, **lodging:** Comfort Inn, Holiday Inn Express, **other:** MEDICAL CARE, USPO, park/playground, **W...gas:** Amoco/diesel/24hr, **food:** BBQ, **lodging:** Day's Inn
104	TN 257, Bethel Rd, **E...gas:** Phillip 66/diesel/rest./24hr, **W...gas:** Shell, **other:** Owl's Roost Camping
98	US 31 W, Millersville, **E...gas:** Citgo/diesel, RaceWay, Shell/diesel, **food:** Waffle House, **lodging:** Holiday Rest Motel/RV park(2mi), **W...gas:** Amoco/diesel, **lodging:** Economy Inn, **other:** Nashville N Camping
97	TN 174, Long Hollow Pike, **E...gas:** BP, Exxon, Mapco, **food:** Arby's, Capt D's, Cracker Barrel, Domino's, KFC, McDonald's, Subway, Waffle House, Wendy's, **lodging:** Comfort Inn, Guesthouse Inn, Hampton Inn, Holiday Inn Express, Knight's Inn, Red Roof Inn, **other:** MEDICAL CARE, K-Mart, Kroger, Music City Outlets, **W...gas:** Shell/diesel, **food:** BBQ, Bob Evans, Dairy Queen, Hardee's, Jack-in-the-Box, Krystal/24hr, Poncho Villa Grill, Sonic, **lodging:** Baymont Inn, Motel 6, **other:** Eckerd
96	Two Mile Pky, **E...gas:** BP/diesel, Shell, **food:** Coach's Grill, Cooker, Copeland's Rest., Cracker Barrel, El Chico, Hooters, Krystal, Las Cebolla's Mexican, Las Palmas Mexican, McDonald's, Mr Gatti's, Mrs Winner's, O'Charley's, Papa John's, Pargo's Café, Pizza Hut, Rio Bravo, Schlotsky's, Subway, Uncle Bud's Catfish, Waffle House, Wendy's, **lodging:** Comfort Suites, Day's Inn, Quality Inn, Super 8, **other:** HOSPITAL, BooksAMillion, Cadillac, CVS, Dillard's, Firestone, Goodyear, Home Depot, JC Penney, Nissan, NTB, Sears/auto, Universal Tire, mall, **E on Gallatin...food:** Arby's, Burger King, Calhoun's Cafe, Checker's, Chick-fil-A, Chili's, ChuckeCheese, Fazoli's, IHOP, Krispy Kreme, LJ Silver/A&W, Logan's Roadhouse, Longhorn Steaks, Old Country

(vertical label: Nashville)

Interstate 65

Buffet, Olive Garden, Outback Steaks, Rafferty's, Red Lobster, Santa Fe Steaks, Starbucks, Steak'n Shake, Taco Bell, **other:** Best Buy, Chevrolet, Chrysler/Jeep, Circuit City, Goody's, Harley-Davidson, Honda, Isuzu, Lincoln/Mercury, Marshall's, Michael's, OfficeMax, Old Navy, Sam's Club/gas, Target, Walgreen, Wal-Mart/drugs, **W...gas:** Chevron, Phillips 66

95	TN 386, Vietnam Veterans Blvd(from nb)
92	TN 45, Old Hickory Blvd, **E...other:** HOSPITAL, to Old Hickory Dam
90	TN 155 E, Briley Pkwy, **E...**to Opreyland
90b a	US 31W, US 41, Dickerson Pike, **E...gas:** BP, Citgo/diesel, Express/diesel, Phillips 66, **food:** Arby's, Burger King, Capt D's, Domino's, KFC, Lee's Chicken, McDonald's, Mrs Winner's, Pizza Hut, Pizza Inn, Subway, Taco Bell, Waffle House, Wendy's, **lodging:** Colony Motel, Congress Inn, Day's Inn, Econolodge, Sleep Inn, Super 8, **other:** Advance Parts, AutoZone, Camping World RV Supply, CVS Drug, Family$, KOA, Kroger, Sam's Club, Walgreen
88b a	I-24, W to Clarksville, E to Nashville, no facilities
87b a	US 431, Trinity Lane, **E...gas:** Phillips 66/Blimpie, Pilot/Arby's/diesel, **food:** Krystal, White Castle/ Church's, **lodging:** Cumberland Inn, Delux Inn, **W...gas:** BP/diesel, Chevron, Exxon, Shell/24hr, Texaco, **food:** Burger King, Capt D's, Denny's, Jack-in-the-Box, Jack's BBQ, McDonald's, Ponderosa, Taco Bell, Waffle House, **lodging:** Baymont Inn, Day's Inn, Drury Inn, Econolodge, Hampton Inn, Holiday Inn Express, Knight's Inn, Liberty Inn, Motel 6, Quality Inn, Ramada Inn, Regency Inn, Super 8, **other:** Family$, to American Bapt Coll
86	I-24 E, to I-40 E, to Memphis
86mm	Cumberland River
85	US 41A, 8th Ave, **E...**to st capitol, **W...gas:** Exxon, Arby's, **food:** Krystal, McDonald's, Pizza Hut, Subway, Taco Bell, **other:** Cadillac/Honda
84b a	I-40, E to Knoxville, W to Memphis
209[I-40]	US 70, Charlotte Ave, Church St, **E...food:** McDonald's, **other:** Nissan, **W...gas:** Exxon, **food:** Burger King, White Castle, **lodging:** Best Western, Shoney's Inn
82b a	I-40, W to Memphis, E to Nashville
81	Wedgewood Ave, **W...gas:** BP, Exxon, **other:** U-Haul, **services on 8th Ave...gas:** Citgo, Cone/ diesel/, **food:** Burger King, Krystal, McDonald's, Mrs Winner's, **other:** $General, $Tree, Kroger, Walgreen
80	I-440, to Memphis, Knoxville

79	Armory Dr, **E on Powell...gas:** BP, Citgo, **food:** Applebee's, Rafferty's, Subway, Wendy's, **other:** CHIROPRACTOR, BMW, CarMax, CompUSA, Firestone/auto, Home Depot, Michael's, mall
78b a	TN 255, Harding Place, **E...gas:** Amoco, Express, Texaco, **food:** Cracker Barrel, Mama Mia's Italian, Santa Fe Grill, Waffle House, **lodging:** La Quinta, Red Roof Inn, Traveler's Rest Hist Home
74	TN 254, Old Hickory Blvd, to Brentwood, **E...food:** Capt D's, Shoney's, Waffle House, **lodging:** AmeriSuites, Hilton Suites, Holiday Inn, Steeplechase Inn, **W...gas:** BP, Exxon, Shell, Texaco/diesel, **food:** BBQ, Mazatlan Mexican, Mrs Winner's, O'Charley's, Papa John's, Pargo's Rest., Ruby Tuesday, Vittles Rest., Wendy's, **lodging:** Brentwood Suites, Courtyard, Extended Stay America, Hampton Inn, Studio+, **other:** USPO, Walgreen, **facilities on US 31...food:** Burger King, Little Caesar's, **other:** Eckerd, Harris-Teeter, OfficeMax
71	TN 253, Concord Rd, to Brentwood, no facilities
69	Moore's Lane, Galleria Blvd, **E...gas:** Express/diesel, **food:** Applebee's, Backyard Burgers, Cooker, Cozymel's, Houlihan's, Joe's Crabshack, Outback Steaks, Sonic, **lodging:** AmeriSuites, Homestead Suites, Red Roof Inn, Wingate Inn, **other:** Acura/ Lexus, Bruno's Foods, Circuit City, Home Depot, Mercedes, Michael's, Walgreen, **W...gas:** BP, Marathon, Shell/diesel, **food:** J Alexander's Rest., Buca Italian, Macaroni Grill, McDonald's, Pizza Hut/Taco Bell, Red Lobster, Rio Bravo, Schlotsky's, Stony River Steaks, Subway, **lodging:** Sleep Inn, **other:** Barnes&Noble, Best Buy, CompUSA, Dillard's, Infiniti, JC Penney, Sears/auto, Target, mall
68b a	Cool Springs Blvd, **E...lodging:** Embassy Suites, Marriott, **W...gas:** Exxon, Shell, **food:** Atl Bread, Carrabba's, Chili's, Jack-in-the-Box, Luby's, McDonald's, Ming Chinese, Off the Grill, Ruby Tuesday, Starbucks, TGIFriday, Wendy's, **lodging:** Country Inn Suites, Hampton Inn, **other:** MEDICAL CARE, Borders Books, Harley-Davidson, Harris-Teeter, Home Depot, Jo-Ann Fabrics, Kohl's, Kroger, Lowe's Whse, Marshall's, Sam's Club, Saturn, Staples, Walgreen, Wal-Mart SuperCtr/24hr, to Galleria Mall

TENNESSEE

Interstate 65

65	TN 96, Franklin, to Murfreesboro, **E...gas:** Exxon, Shell, **food:** Cracker Barrel, Sonic, Steak'n Shake, **lodging:** Baymont Inn, Comfort Inn, Day's Inn, Holiday Inn Express, Howard Johnson, Ramada Ltd, **other:** MEDICAL CARE, Buick/Pontiac/GMC/Kia, Chevrolet, Food Lion, Honda/Volvo, Hyundai, Walgreen, **W...gas:** BP/diesel, Express/diesel, Shell/diesel, **food:** Arby's, Backyard Burger, BBQ, Camino Real Mexican, ChopHouse Chinese, CiCi's, Hardee's, KFC, McDonald's, O'Charley's, Papa John's, Pizza Hut, Shoney's, Starbucks, Subway, Taco Bell, Waffle House, Wendy's, **lodging:** Best Western, Super 8, **other:** BiLo, Chrysler/Plymouth/Dodge, CVS Drug, $General, Eckerd, Ford/Mercury, Goody's, HobbyLobby, Home Depot, Kroger, Mazda, Nissan, SteinMart, Toyota, USPO, to Confederate Cem at Franklin
64mm	Harpeth River
61	TN 248, Peytonsville Rd, to Spring Hill, **E...gas:** TA/BP/diesel/rest./24hr/@, **W...gas:** Cone, Express/24hr, Shell, **other:** Goose Creek Inn/rest.
59b a	TN 840, no facilities
58mm	W Harpeth River
53	TN 396, Saturn Pkwy, to Spring Hill, Columbia, TN Scenic Pkwy
48mm	parking area/weigh sta nb, litter barrels
46	US 412, TN 99, to Columbia, Chapel Hill, **E...gas:** Chevron, **other:** Campers RV Park, **W...gas:** BP, Exxon/Burger King, Shell/diesel/rest., **food:** Cracker Barrel, Waffle House, **lodging:** Best Value Inn, Comfort Inn, Hampton Inn, Holiday Inn Express, Relax Inn, **other:** HOSPITAL
40.5mm	Duck River
37	TN 50, to Columbia, Lewisburg, **E...other:** HOSPITAL, TN Walking Horse HQ, **W...gas:** Shell/diesel, **lodging:** Richland Inn, **other:** to Polk Home
32	rd 373, Mooresville, to Lewisburg, **E...gas:** Exxon/diesel
27	rd 129, Cornersville, to Lynnville, **E...other:** Texas T Camping
25mm	parking area sb, litter barrels
24mm	parking area nb, litter barrels
22	US 31A, to Pulaski, **E...gas:** BP/diesel/rest./@, **food:** McDonald's, Subway, **lodging:** Econolodge, **W...gas:** Pilot/diesel, Shell/diesel/24hr, **other:** flea mkt
14	US 64, to Pulaski, **E...gas:** BP/diesel, Shell/diesel, **food:** Sands Rest., Sarge's Shack Rest., **lodging:** Super 8, **other:** KOA, to Jack Daniels Distillery, **W...**to David Crockett SP
6	rd 273, Bryson, **E...gas:** Phillips 66/diesel/rest./@, **lodging:** Best Value Inn
4mm	Elk River
3mm	**Welcome Ctr nb, full(handicapped)facilities, info, phone, picnic tables, litter barrels, petwalk**
1	US 31, rd 7, Ardmore, **E...gas:** Chevron/diesel/24hr, Exxon/Church's/diesel, **other:** antiques, **1-2 mi E...gas:** Shell/repair, **food:** DQ, Hardee's, McDonald's, Subway
0mm	Tennessee/Alabama state line

Interstate 75

Exit #	Services
161.5mm	Tennessee/Kentucky state line
161mm	**Welcome Ctr sb, full(handicapped)facilities, phone, vending, picnic tables, litter barrels, petwalk**
160	US 25W, Jellico, **E...gas:** Citgo, Exxon/Subway/diesel, Texaco/Stuckey's, **food:** KFC, **lodging:** Jellico Motel/rest., **other:** auto parts, **W...gas:** BP, Shell/Arby's/diesel, **food:** Hardee's, Wendy's, Subway, **lodging:** Best Western, Day's Inn/rest., **other:** HOSPITAL, Flowers Bakery, camping, fireworks, to Indian Mtn SP
156	new exit
144	Stinking Creek Rd, no facilities
141	TN 63, to Royal Blue, **E...gas:** Shell/Perkins/24hr, **W...gas:** Exxon/Stuckey's, Pilot/Subway/diesel/24hr/@, Shell/diesel, **food:** Dairy Queen, **lodging:** Comfort Inn, **other:** fireworks, to Big South Fork NRA
134	US 25W, TN 63, Caryville, **E...gas:** Exxon/diesel, Shell/24hr, **food:** Domino's, Pizza Hut, Waffle House/24hr, Western Sizzlin, **lodging:** Hampton Inn, Lakeview Inn/rest., Super 8, Thacker Christmas Inn, **other:** HOSPITAL, to Cove Lake SP, **W...gas:** BP, **food:** Shoney's, Scotty's Hamburgers, **lodging:** Budget Host
130mm	weigh sta both lanes, phones
129	US 25W S, Lake City, **E...gas:** BP, Sunoco, **other:** antiques, LP, **W...gas:** Citgo, Exxon/Subway/diesel/24hr, Shell, Texaco/Blimpie/diesel, **food:** Burger King, Cottage Rest., Cracker Barrel, KFC, McDonald's, **lodging:** Day's Inn, Blue Haven Motel, Lake City Motel, Lamb's Inn/rest., **other:** $General, same as 128
128	US 441, to Lake City, **E...gas:** BP, **other:** Coastal, Mountain Lake Marina(4mi), **W...gas:** Exxon/diesel/24hr, Shell, **food:** Cottage Rest., Subway, **lodging:** Blue Haven Motel, Lake City Motel, Lamb's Inn, **other:** $General, Hillbilly Mkt/deli, antique cars, to Norris Dam SP, same as 129
126mm	Clinch River
122	TN 61, Bethel, Norris, **E...gas:** Phillis 66, Shell, **other:** Fox Inn Camping, antiques, museum, **W...gas:** Citgo/diesel, Exxon/Subway/diesel/24hr, Marathon/diesel/24hr, Texaco, **food:** Burger King, Hardee's, Krystal/24hr, McDonald's, Waffle House, Wendy's, **lodging:** Best Western, Comfort Inn, Holiday Inn Express, Super 8, **other:** Big Pine Ridge SP

Interstate 75

N
S

Knoxville

117 TN 170, Racoon Valley Rd, **E…gas:** BP, Pilot/Burger King/Subway/diesel/24hr/@, **W…lodging:** Valley Inn, **other:** Vaughn Camping(2mi)

112 TN 131, Emory Rd, to Powell, **E…gas:** BP/diesel, Chevron, Pilot/DQ/Taco Bell/diesel/24hr/@, **food:** Aubrey's Rest., Buddy's BBQ, McDonald's, KFC, Krystal, Steak'n Shake, Wendy's, **lodging:** Country Inn Suites, Holiday Inn Express, **other:** CVS Drug, $General, Family$, Ingles, Toyota, **W…gas:** Exxon/24hr, Shell/diesel/24hr; **food:** Hardee's, Shoney's, Waffle House/24hr, **lodging:** Comfort Inn

110 Callahan Dr, **E…gas:** Coastal, Weigel's/gas, **lodging:** Knight's Inn, Quality Inn/rest., **other:** Honda, **W…gas:** BP, **food:** Burger King, Chick-fil-A, Chili's, Golden Corral, McDonald's, Wendy's, **lodging:** Scottish Inn, **other:** GMC/Volvo

108 Merchant Dr, **E…gas:** BP/diesel, Citgo/diesel, Pilot/diesel, Texaco/diesel, **food:** Applebee's, Cracker Barrel, Denny's, El Chico's, Logan's Roadhouse, O'Charley's, Pizza Hut, Sonic, Rafferty's, Ryan's, Waffle House, **lodging:** Comfort Inn, Day's Inn, Hampton Inn, Howard Johnson, Ramada Ltd, Sleep Inn, **other:** CVS Drug, Ingles, Valvoline, **W…gas:** Citgo, Exxon/Godfather's, Pilot/Conoco, Shell, **food:** Arby's, Burger King, Cancun Mexican, Capt D's, Darryl's Rest, Great American Steaks, IHOP, Mandarin House, McDonald's, Outback Steaks, Pizza Inn, Red Lobster, Subway, Waffle House/24hr, **lodging:** Clarion Inn, Econolodge, Family Inn, Motel 6, Super 8, **other:** Food Lion, Quaker Stake & Lube, Walgreen, **1 mi W on US 25W…food:** Arby's, Krystal, LJ Silver, Shoney's, Taco Bell, **other:** Advance Parts, CVS Drug, Firestone, K-Mart, Kroger

107 I-640 & I-75, no facilities

3b[I-640] US 25W, **N…gas:** Amoco, BP, Texaco/diesel, **food:** Hardee's, KFC, Krystal, LJ Silver, Mr Gatti's, Pizza Hut, Quincy's, Taco Bell, Wendy's, **other:** Chevrolet, CVS Drug, Firestone, Ford, K-Mart, Kroger, transmissions, same as 108

1[I-640] TN 62, Western Ave, **N…gas:** Cargo/diesel, RaceTrac, Shell/diesel, **food:** Central Park, Golden Corral, KFC, LJ Silver, McDonald's, Mixon's Deli, Ruby Tuesday, Shoney's, Subway, Taco Bell, Wendy's, **other:** CVS Drug, Kroger, Walgreen, **S…gas:** BP, **food:** Dad's Donuts, Domino's, Hardee's, Krystal, **other:** Advance Parts, USPO

I-75 and I-40 run together 17 mi. See Tennessee Interstate 40, exits 369 through 385.

84[368] I-40, W to Nashville, no facilities

81 US 321, TN 95, to Lenoir City, **E…gas:** BP/diesel, Exxon/Subway/diesel, Phillips 66, Shell/diesel, **food:** BelAir Grill, Burger King(1mi), Dinner Bell Rest., El Arriero Mexican, KFC, McDonald's, Shoney's, Waffle House, Wendy's, **lodging:** Crossroads Inn, King's Inn/rest., **other:** to Great Smokies NP, Ft Loudon Dam, **W…gas:** Citgo/diesel, Shell/diesel, Krystal, **food:** Ruby Tuesday, **lodging:** Comfort Inn, Econolodge, Ramada Ltd, **other:** Chevrolet, Pontiac/Buick/GMC

76 rd 324, Sugar Limb Rd, **W…**to TN Valley Winery

74mm Tennessee River

72 TN 72, to Loudon, **E…gas:** BP/McDonald's, Shell/Wendy's/diesel, **food:** BBQ, China King, **lodging:** Holiday Inn Express, Super 8, **other:** to Ft Loudon SP, **W…**Citgo, Marie's Kitchen, Knight's Inn, Express Camping

68 TN 323, to Philadelphia, **E…gas:** BP/diesel, **food:** cheese factory/store(2mi)

62 TN 322, Oakland Rd, to Sweetwater, **E…food:** Dinner Bell Rest., **W…other:** KOA

60 TN 68, Sweetwater, **E…gas:** Marathon, RaceWay, Shell/diesel, **food:** Burger King, KFC, McDonald's, Wendy's, **lodging:** Best Value Inn, Budget Host, Comfort Inn, Day's Inn, Super 8(2mi), **other:** HOSPITAL, to Lost Sea Underground Lake, **W…gas:** BP/diesel, Exxon/diesel, Phillips 66, **food:** BBQ, Cracker Barrel, **lodging:** Best Western, Quality Inn, **other:** flea mkt, to Watts Bar Dam

56 TN 309, Niota, **E…gas:** BP/Trkstop/diesel/rest./@, **other:** Country Music Camping, **W…**tires

52 TN 305, Mt Verd Rd, to Athens, **E…gas:** BP(1mi), Phillips 66, **other:** Overniter RV Park, **W…gas:** Exxon, **lodging:** Ramada Inn

Athens

49 TN 30, to Athens, **E…gas:** BP, Exxon, RaceWay, Shell/DQ/diesel/24hr, **food:** Applebee's, Burger King, Hardee's, KFC, Krystal, McDonald's, MexiWing, Monterrey Mexican, Shoney's, Subway, Waffle House, Wendy's, **lodging:** Day's Inn, Hampton Inn, Holiday Inn Express, Homestead Inn, Knight's Inn, Motel 6, Super 8, **other:** HOSPITAL, KOA, Russell Stover, to TN Wesleyan Coll, **W…gas:** Shell/diesel, **lodging:** Homestead Inn, **other:** Jeep, Pontiac/Buick/Cadillac/GMC

45.5mm **rest area both lanes, full(handicapped)facilities, phone, vending, picnic tables, litter barrels, petwalk**

42 TN 39, to Riceville, **E…gas:** Express/diesel, **food:** Callie's Kitchen, **lodging:** Relax Inn, Rice Inn(2mi)

36 TN 163, to Calhoun, no facilities

35mm Hiwassee River

33 TN 308, to Charleston, **E…gas:** Citgo, **other:** 33 Camping, **W…gas:** Shell/diesel/rest./24hr/@

TENNESSEE

Interstate 75

27 Paul Huff Pkwy, **1 mi E...food:** Applebee's, Central Park, CiCi's, DQ, Fazoli's, McDonald's, O'Charley's, Panera Bread, Ryan's, Steak'n Shake/24hr, Taco Bell, **lodging:** Jameson Inn, **other:** AutoZone, BooksAMillion, Buick/Pontiac, CVS Drug, Food Lion, Goodyear/auto, HobbyLobby, JC Penney, K-Mart, Lowe's Whse, OfficeMax, Sears, Staples, Wal-Mart SuperCtr/gas/24hr, mall, **W...gas:** BP/diesel, Conoco, Exxon, Shell, **food:** Denny's/24hr, Hardee's, Waffle House, Wendy's, **lodging:** Comfort Inn, EQ Motel, Hampton Inn, Ramada Ltd, Royal Inn, Super 8

25 TN 60, Cleveland, **E...gas:** BP, Chevron/diesel, RaceTrac, Shell/diesel, **food:** Burger King, Cancun Mexican, Cracker Barrel, Hardee's, McDonald's, Roblyn's Steaks, Schlotsky's, Shoney's, Waffle House, Wendy's, Zaxby's, **lodging:** Colonial Inn, Day's Inn, Douglas Inn, Econolodge, Economy Inn, Knight's Inn, Quality Inn, **other:** HOSPITAL, to Lee Coll, **W...gas:** Shell, **food:** TN Jack's Rest., **lodging:** Baymont Inn, Holiday Inn, Wingate Inn

23mm parking area/weigh sta nb

20 US 64 byp, to Cleveland, **1-3 mi E...gas:** Exxon, Shell, **food:** Golden Corral, Hardee's, McDonald's, Subway, Taco Bell, **other:** Chrysler/Jeep/Plymouth, Food Lion, Honda, Toyota, **W...gas:** Exxon/diesel/24hr, KOA(1mi)

16mm scenic view sb

13mm parking area/weigh sta sb, phone

11 US 11 N, US 64 E, Ooltewah, **E...gas:** Chevron, Citgo, RaceTrac, Shell, **food:** Arby's, Bohangles, Burger King, Hardee's, McDonald's, Subway, Taco Bell, Wendy's, **other:** MEDICAL CARE, BiLo, **W...gas:** Exxon/diesel, **food:** Krystal, Waffle House, **lodging:** Super 8, **other:** to Harrison Bay SP

7b a US 11, US 64, Lee Hwy, **W...gas:** Chevron, Shell, **food:** Waffle House, **lodging:** Best Inn, Best Western/rest., Day's Inn, Econolodge, Motel 6, Park Inn, Wellesley Inn, **other:** Harley-Davidson, Land Rover

5 Shallowford Rd, **E...food:** Alexander's, Arby's, Backyard Burgers, BBQ, Blimpie, Capt D's, Central Park, CiCi's, Country Place Rest., Famous Dave's, Hop's Grill, Krystal, Logan's Roadhouse, Macaroni Grill, McDonald's, Old Country Buffet, Pizza Hut, Schlotsky's, Steak'n Shake/24hr, Taco Bell, TGIFriday, **lodging:** Comfort Suites, Wingate Inn, **other:** MEDICAL CARE, Best Buy, BooksAMillion, Firestone/auto, FoodMaxx/24hr, Ford, FreshMkt Foods, Home Depot, Lowe's Whse, OfficeMax, Walgreen, Wal-Mart SuperCtr/24hr, **W...gas:** Exxon, Shell, **food:** Applebee's, Blimpie, Burger King, Cancun Mexican, Cracker Barrel, Domino's, El Chico's, Fazoli's, GlenGene Deli, Godfather's,

KFC, McDonald's, Ocean Ave Seafood, O'Charley's, Papa John's, Pizza Hut, Rio Bravo, Sonic, SteakOut Rest., Shoney's, Subway, Texas Roadhouse, Waffle House, Wendy's, **lodging:** Country Inn Suites, Day's Inn, Fairfield Inn, Guesthouse Inn, Hampton Inn, Holiday Inn, Holiday Inn Express, Homewood Suites, MainStay Suites, Ramada Ltd, Red Roof Inn, Sleep Inn, **other:** HOSPITAL, BiLo, CVS Drug, Goodyear, U of TN/Chatt

4a (from nb)Hamilton Place Blvd, **E...food:** DQ, El Meson Mexican, Grady's Grill, Olive Garden, Outback Steaks, Piccadilly's, Red Lobster, Ruby Tuesday, Sticky Fingers, **lodging:** Courtyard, **other:** Barnes&Noble, Circuit City, Dillard's, Goody's, JC Penney, Michael's, Old Navy, Sears/auto, Staples, mall

4 TN 153, Chickamauga Dam Rd, no facilities

3b a TN 320, Brainerd Rd, **E...gas:** Exxon, **food:** Subway

2 I-24 W, to I-59, to Chattanooga, Lookout Mtn

1.5mm **Welcome Ctr nb, full(handicapped)facilities, phone, vending, picnic tables, litter barrels, petwalk**

1b a US 41, Ringgold Rd, to Chattanooga, **E...gas:** BP, Exxon, **lodging:** Airport Inn, Best Value Inn, Comfort Inn, Crown Inn, Econolodge, Howard Johnson, Ramada Ltd, **other:** BiLo Foods, Family$, Shipp's RV Ctr/park, **W...gas:** Conoco/diesel, Pure, Shell/Texaco/diesel, **food:** Arby's, Burger King, Central Park Burger, Cracker Barrel, Hardee's, Krystal, LJ Silver/A&W, McDonald's, Pizza Hut, PortoFino Italian, Shoney's, Subway, Taco Bell, Teriyaki House, Uncle Bud's Catfish, Waffle House, **lodging:** Best Inn, Country Hearth Inn, Day's Inn, Holiday Inn Express, Super 8, Travelodge, Waverly Motel, **other:** Holiday Travel Park, U-Haul

0mm Tennessee/Georgia state line

Interstate 81

Exit #	Services
75mm	Tennessee/Virginia state line, **Welcome Ctr sb, full(handicapped)facilities, info, phone, vending, picnic tables, litter barrels, petwalk**
74b a	US 11 W, to Bristol, Kingsport, **E...lodging:** Day's Inn, Hampton Inn, **other:** HOSPITAL, **1-2 mi E...gas:** Shell, **food:** Burger King, KFC, LJ Silver, McDonald's, Pizza Hut, Shoney's, Taco Bell, Wendy's, **W...gas:** Exxon, **food:** Truby's Diner, **lodging:** Best Western
69	TN 394, to Blountville, **E...gas:** BP/Subway/diesel, **food:** Arby's, Burger King(1mi), **other:** Bristol Int Raceway

Interstate 81

N

S

Johnson City

66	TN 126, to Kingsport, Blountville, **E...gas:** Exxon/diesel, **W...gas:** Chevron/24hr, **food:** McDonald's, **other:** FSA/famous brands
63	rd 357, Tri-City Airport, **E...gas:** Exxon/Taco Bell/Krystal/diesel, Shell/Subway/diesel/24hr, **food:** Cracker Barrel, Wendy's, **lodging:** La Quinta, Sleep Inn, **other:** Hamrick's Clothing Outlet, **W...gas:** Phillips 66/diesel, **lodging:** Red Carpet Inn, **other:** $General, KOA, Sam's Club, Rocky Top Camping
60mm	Holston River
59	TN 36, to Johnson City, Kingsport, **E...gas:** Citgo/diesel, **lodging:** Super 8, **W...gas:** Amoco/LP, Exxon, Shell/diesel, Sunoco, **food:** Arby's, Burger King, Domino's, Fazoli's, Hardee's, HotDog Hut, Huddle House, Jersey Mike's Subs, La Carreta Mexican, Little Caesar's, McDonald's, Pal's Hot-Dogs, Perkins/24hr, Piccadilly's, Pizza Hut, Sonic, Subway, Wendy's, **lodging:** Comfort Inn, Holiday Inn Express, **other:** Advance Parts, CVS Drug, $Store, Firestone/auto, Ingles, USPO, to Warrior's Path SP
57b a	I-26 to Johnson City, ETSU, I-181 to Kingsport
56	Tri Cities Crossing, no facilities
50	TN 93, Fall Branch, **W...other:** auto auction, st patrol
44	Jearoldstown Rd, **E...gas:** BP, **W...other:** Exit 44 Mkt/gas
41mm	**rest area sb, full(handicapped)facilities, phone, vending, picnic tables, litter barrels, petwalk**
38mm	**rest area nb, full(handicapped)facilities, phone, vending, picnic tables, litter barrels, petwalk**
36	TN 172, to Baileyton, **E...gas:** Pilot/Subway/diesel/@, **other:** repair, **W...gas:** BP/diesel/24hr, Marathon/diesel/24hr/@, Shell/Subway/diesel/24hr, **lodging:** 36 Motel, **other:** Baileyton Camp(2mi)
30	TN 70, to Greeneville, **E...gas:** Exxon/DQ/Stuckey's/diesel
23	US 11E, to Greeneville, **E...gas:** BP/Wendy's, BP**other:** to Andrew Johnson HS, **W...gas:** Exxon/Taco Bell/diesel, Phillips 66/diesel/rest., **food:** McDonald's, NY Pizza/Italian, Tony's Rest., **lodging:** Comfort Inn, Super 8
21mm	weigh sta sb
15	TN 340, Fish Hatchery Rd, no facilities
12	TN 160, to Morristown, **E...gas:** Phillips 66, **W...gas:** Shell/diesel, **lodging:** Hampton Inn(12mi), Motel 6(6mi), **other:** to Crockett Tavern HS
8	US 25E, to Morristown, **E...gas:** Shell/diesel/repair, **food:** Sonic(2mi), **lodging:** Twin Pines Motel(3mi), **W...gas:** BP/diesel, **food:** Cracker Barrel, Hardee's, **lodging:** Holiday Inn/rest., Parkway Inn, Super 8, **other:** to Cumberland Gap NHP

4	rd 341, White Pine, **E...gas:** Exxon/diesel, Pilot/diesel/24hr, **food:** McDonald's/24hr, **lodging:** Crown Inn, **W...gas:** Citgo, Kwikshop, Shell/diesel, **food:** Huddle House/24hr, **lodging:** Day's Inn, Hillcrest Inn, **other:** to Panther Cr SP
2.5mm	**rest area sb, full(handicapped)facilities, phone, picnic tables, litter barrels, vending, petwalk**
1b a	I-40 E to Asheville, W to Knoxville. I-81 begins/ends on I-40, exit 421.

Interstate 640(Knoxville)

E

W

Knoxville

Exit #	Services
9mm	I-640 begins/ends on I-40, exit 393.
8	Millertown Pike, Mall Rd N, **N...gas:** Conoco/Backyard Burgers, Exxon/DQ/24hr, **food:** Applebee's, Burger King, Cracker Barrel, Don Pablos, KFC, McDonald's, Piccadilly's, Pizza Inn, Ruby Tuesday, Taco Bell, Texas Roadhouse, Wendy's, **other:** Circuit City, Dillard's, JC Penney, Kohl's, OfficeMax, Sam's Club, Sears/auto, Wal-Mart/auto, farmer mkt, mall, **S...gas:** Conoco, **food:** Subway, **other:** Food Lion, Home Depot, Lowe's Whse, PepBoys
6	US 441, to Broadway, **N...gas:** BP, Chevron, Conoco, Phillips 66, Pilot/diesel, **food:** Arby's, Austin's Steaks, Cancun Mexican, CiCi's, Fazoli's, Krispy Kreme, Larry's Subs, LJ Silver, McDonald's, Papa John's, Ruby Tuesday, Sonic, Subway, Taco Bell, **lodging:** Best Western, **other:** Advance Parts, AutoZone, Batteries+, CVS Drug, $General, Firestone, Goodyear, Kroger/24hr, NAPA, Target, Walgreen, **S...food:** Buddy's BBQ, Sam's Rest., Shoney's, YumYum Buffet, **other:** BiLo Foods, CVS Drug, Food City, K-Mart, NAPA, Office Depot, Walgreen
3a	I-75 N to Lexington, I-275 S to Knoxville
b	US 25W, Clinton Hwy, **N...gas:** Phillips 66, **other:** Chevrolet, Dodge, Ford, Nissan, facilities on frontage rds
1	TN 62, Western Ave, **N...gas:** Cargo/diesel, RaceTrac, Shell/diesel, **food:** Central Park, KFC, LJ Silver, McDonald's, Nixon's Deli, Ruby Tuesday, Shoney's, Sonic, Subway, Taco Bell, Wendy's, **other:** CVS Drug, Kroger, Walgreen, **S...gas:** BP, **food:** Hardee's, Krystal, **other:** Advance Parts, USPO
0mm	I-640 begins/ends on I-40, exit 385.

TEXAS
Interstate 10

O
r
a
n
g
e

Exit #	Services
880.5mm	Texas/Louisiana state line, Sabine River
880	Sabine River Turnaround, RV camping
879mm	**Welcome Ctr wb, full(handicapped)facilities, phone, picnic tables, litter barrels, vending, pet-walk**
878	US 90, Orange, **N...gas:** Mobil/diesel, **other:** air-boat rides, **S...other:** Western Store
877	TX 87, 16th St, Orange, **N...gas:** Chevron, Shamrock/diesel, **food:** Cajun Cookery, Gary's Café, Little Caesar's, Pizza Hut, Subway, Waffle House, **lodging:** Best Western, Day's Inn, Holiday Inn Express, Motel 6, Super 8, **other:** Buick/Pontiac/Toyota, $General, Eckerd, MktBasket/deli, Radio Shack, **S...gas:** Shell/diesel, **food:** Burger King, Church's, Cody's Rest., DQ, Jack-in-the-Box, McDonald's, Popeye's, Taco Bell, **other:** Buick/Pontiac, Cadillac/GMC, HEB Foods, Kroger, Modica Tires, O'Reilly Parts, Toyota
876	Adams Bayou, frontage rd, **N...gas:** Exxon, **food:** Cajun Cookery, Gary's Café, Waffle House, **lodging:** Best Western, Best Value Inn, Motel 6, Ramada Inn, Super 8, **S...gas:** Chevron/diesel, same as 877
875	FM 3247, MLK Dr, **N...food:** Luby's, **S...other:** HOSPITAL, Chrysler/Dodge/Plymouth/Jeep, RV Ctr
874	US 90, Womack Rd, to Orange, **S...HOSPITAL**, Oakleaf Park RV Park
873	TX 62, TX 73, to Bridge City, **N...gas:** Exxon/diesel/24hr, ⚡/Flying J/Conoco/diesel/LP/24hr/@, tires, **S...gas:** Pilot/Wendy's/diesel/24hr/@, Shamrock, Texaco/diesel, **food:** Jack-in-the-Box, Burger King, McDonald's, Waffle House
870	FM 1136, no facilities
869	FM 1442(from wb), to Bridge City, **S...**Lloyd RV Ctr
867	frontage rd(from eb), no facilities
866.5mm	**rest areas both lanes, full(handicapped)facilities, vending, picnic tables, litter barrels**
865	Doty Rd(from wb), frontage rd, no facilities
864	FM 1132, FM 1135, **N... food:** Burr's BBQ, **lodging:** Budget Inn
862c	Timberlane Dr(from eb), no facilities
b	Old Hwy(from wb), no facilities
a	Railroad Ave, no facilities
861d	TX 12, Deweyville, no facilities
c	Denver St, **N...gas:** Conoco/diesel
b	Lamar St(from wb), **N...gas:** Conoco/diesel
a	FM 105, Vidor, **N...gas:** Chevron/diesel, Shamrock, Shell, **food:** DQ, Domino's, McDonald's, Popeye's, Waffle House, **other:** Family$, Mktbasket Foods, Radio Shack, **S...gas:** Conoco, Exxon/diesel, **food:** Burger King, Church's, Great Wall Chinese, KFC, Pizza Hut, Sonic, Subway, Taco Bell, Whataburger, **other:** MEDICAL CARE, tires

B
e
a
u
m
o
n
t

860b a	Dewitt Rd, W Vidor, frontage rd, no facilities
859	Bonner Turnaround, no facilities
858b	Asher Turnaround, **N...other:** Boomtown RV Park, **S...food:** Denny's
a	Rose City East, **S...gas:** Chevron, Gateway/diesel, **food:** Denny's
857	Rose City, no facilities
856	Old Hwy, no facilities
855a	US 90 bus, to downtown, Port of Beaumont, no facilities
854	ML King Pkwy, Beaumont, **N...gas:** Conoco, **S...gas:** Exxon, Texaco, **food:** McDonald's, **other:** Chrysler/Jeep
853c	7th St, **N...gas:** Fina, **food:** Burger King, McDonald's, Ninfa's Mexican, Red Lobster, Waffle House, **lodging:** Holiday Inn, Scottish Inn, Super 8, Travel Inn, **other:** bank, same as 853b
b	11th St, **S...gas:** Conoco, Fina, **food:** Jack-in-the-Box, Luby's, **lodging:** Best Western, Interstate Inn, Motel 6, Quality Inn, Ramada Inn, **other:** HOSPITAL, Chevrolet/Cadillac/GMC
a	US 69 N, to Lufkin
852	Harrison Ave, Calder Ave, Beaumont, **N...gas:** Chevron/diesel/24hr, Texaco/diesel, **food:** BBQ, Bennigan's, Cajun Cookery, Casa Ole Mexican, Chili's, Olive Garden, Steak&Ale, **S...gas:** Chevron, **food:** Church's, McDonald's, **lodging:** Day's Inn, Econolodge, La Quinta, **other:** Chevrolet, transmissions
851	US 90, College St, **N...gas:** Exxon/diesel, RaceTrac, **food:** Acapulco Mexican, Carrabba's, China Border, Fujiyama Japanese, Golden Corral, Outback Steaks, Waffle House, **lodging:** Best Western, Comfort Inn, **other:** AutoZone, O'Reilly Parts, Pennzoil, Subaru/Suzuki, **S...gas:** Chevron/Burger King/24hr, Mobil, Shell, Texaco, **food:** DQ, IHOP, Jason's Deli, KFC, Pizza Hut, Taco Bell, Wendy's, Whataburger, **lodging:** Courtyard, Econolodge, Fairfield Inn, Hilton/rest., Motel 6, **other:** HOSPITAL, Discount Tire, Dodge, Eckerd, Firestone/auto, Ford/Lincoln/Mercury, GMC/Cadillac, Honda, Jeep, MktBasket Foods, Mazda, Mercedes, Mitsubishi, Nissan, NTB, Office Depot, Sam's Club/gas, U-Haul, Volvo, Walgreen
850	Washington Blvd(from wb), same as 851
849	US 69 S, Washington Blvd, to Port Arthur, airport, no facilities
848	Walden Rd, **N...gas:** Texaco, **food:** Pappadeaux Seafood, **lodging:** Holiday Inn/rest., La Quinta, **S...gas:** Chevron/Subway/diesel/24hr, Petro/Mobil/diesel/24hr/@, **food:** Carino's Italian, Cheddar's, Cracker Barrel, Jack-in-the-Box, Joe's Crabshack, Waffle House, **lodging:** Hampton Inn, Ramada Ltd, **other:** Blue Beacon
846	Brooks Rd(from eb), **S...other:** Gulf Coast RV Resort

Interstate 10

845 FM 364, Major Dr, no facilities

843 Smith Rd, no facilities

838 FM 365, Fannett, **N...gas:** Bar-H Store/gas/BBQ,
other: RV camping

837.5mm picnic areas both lanes, tables, litter barrels, handicapped accessible

833 Hamshire Rd, no facilities

829 FM 1663, Winnie, **N...gas:** Exxon/diesel, Mo-
bil/Burger King/diesel, Texaco/diesel/24hr, **food:**
McDonald's, Taco Bell, Whataburger/24hr, **lodging:** Holiday Inn Express, **S...gas:** Chevron/diesel,
Mobil/Subway/diesel, **food:** Cajun Cuisine, Hunan
Chinese, Jack-in-the-Box, Pizza Inn, Waffle House,
lodging: Best Western, Winnie Inn/RV Park,
other: HOSPITAL, Chevrolet, Ford, Chrysler/Jeep/
Dodge

828 TX 73, TX 124(from eb), to Winnie, **S...HOSPITAL,**
same as 829

827 FM 1406, no facilities

822 FM 1410, no facilities

819 Jenkins Rd, **S...gas:** Texaco/Stuckey's

817 FM 1724, no facilities

815mm weigh sta both lanes

813 TX 61(from wb), Hankamer, **N...gas:** Shell/diesel,
S...gas: Exxon/diesel, **food:** McDonald's

812 TX 61, Hankamer, **S...gas:** Exxon/diesel, **food:** DJ's
Diner

811 Turtle Bayou Turnaround, **S...gas:** Gator Jct/diesel,
food: Grandma's Diner, **other:** Ford, Turtle Bayou RV
Park

810 FM 563, to Anahuac, Liberty, **S...gas:** Chevron/Blimp-
ie/diesel, **other:** Ford

807 to Wallisville, **S...other:** Heritage Park

806 frontage rd(from eb), turnaround

805.5mm Trinity River

804mm Old, Lost Rivers

803 FM 565, Cove, Old River-Winfrey, no facilities

800 FM 3180, **N...gas:** Exxon/diesel

437

Interstate 10

E ↕ **W**

Baytown

797 TX 146, to Baytown, **N...gas:** Chevron, Conoco/ Subway/diesel, Shell/diesel, **food:** DQ, IHOP, McDonald's, Pizza Inn, Waffle House, **lodging:** Crystal Inn, Motel 6, Scanadian Inn, **other:** L&R RV Park, **S...gas:** Exxon, Mobil/Popeye's/diesel, RaceTrac/diesel, **food:** Jack-in-the-Box, **other:** HOSPITAL

796 frontage rd, **N...gas:** Chevron/Phillips/BP Chemical Refinery, no facilities

795 Sjolander Rd, no facilities

793 N Main St, **S...gas:** Citgo/KFC/diesel/24hr

792 Garth Rd, **N...gas:** Chevron/24hr, **food:** Burger King, Cracker Barrel, Denny's, Jack-in-the-Box, Red Lobster, Waffle House, Whataburger/24hr, **lodging:** Best Western, Baymont Inn, Hampton Inn, La Quinta, **other:** Chrysler/Jeep, Honda, Hyundai, Lincoln/Mercury, Nissan, Toyota, **S...gas:** RaceTrac, Shell, **food:** Cozumel Mexican, McDonald's, Outback Steaks, Pancho's Mexican, Piccadilly's, Pizza Hut/Taco Bell, Popeye's, Wendy's, **lodging:** Holiday Inn Express, **other:** HOSPITAL, Ford, Marshall's, Mervyn's, OfficeMax, Sears/auto, Vaughn RV Ctr, mall

791 John Martin Rd, no facilities

790 Wade Rd, no facilities

789 Thompson Rd, **N...gas:** Pilot/McDonald's/diesel, Shamrock, **lodging:** Super 8, **other:** Buick/Pontiac/ GMC, **S...gas:** TA/diesel/rest./24hr/@, **other:** truck repair

788.5mm rest area eb, full(handicapped)facilities, phone, picnic tables, litter barrels, petwalk

788 sp 330(from eb), to Baytown, no facilities

787 sp 330, Crosby-Lynchburg Rd, to Highlands, **N... gas:** Mobil/Domino's/diesel, **S...other:** to San Jacinto SP, camping

786.5mm San Jacinto River

786 Monmouth Dr, no facilities

785 Magnolia Ave, to Channelview, **N...gas:** Shell/diesel, **S...gas:** Phillips/diesel, same as 784

Houston

784 Cedar Lane, Bayou Dr, **N...gas:** Citgo, **lodging:** Budget Lodge, Ramada Ltd

783 Sheldon Rd, **N...gas:** Coastal/diesel, Shell, **food:** Burger King, Jack-in-the-Box, KFC, Pizza Hut, Pizza Inn, Popeye's, Sonic, Subway, Taco Bell, Whataburger, **lodging:** Best Western, Day's Inn, Leisure Inn, Super 8, Travelodge, **other:** Advance Parts, AutoZone, DiscountTire, Eckerd, Family$, Garland's Foods, Goodyear/auto, Radio Shack, **S...food:** Capt D's, McDonald's, Wendy's, **lodging:** Scottish Inn

782 Dell-Dale Ave, **N...gas:** Exxon, **lodging:** Dell Dale Motel, **other:** HOSPITAL, **S...gas:** Conoco/diesel

781b Market St, **N...lodging:** Holiday Inn, **other:** HOSPITAL

a TX 8, Sam Houston Pkwy

780 (779 from wb)Uvalde Rd, Freeport St, **N...gas:** Chevron/diesel, Mobil, Texaco, **food:** Cracker Barrel, IHOP, Jack-in-the-Box, KFC, Pancho's Mexican, Subway, Taco Bell, **other:** HOSPITAL, Office Depot, **S...gas:** Mobil/diesel, **food:** BBQ, Blackeyed Pea, Marco's Mexican, Whataburger, **other:** Circuit City, Home Depot, NTB, Sam's Club, U-Haul, Wal-Mart/ auto/24hr

778b Normandy St, **N...gas:** Conoco/diesel, Shell, **food:** Golden Corral, **S...gas:** Texaco/diesel, **lodging:** Scottish Inn

a FM 526, Federal Rd, Pasadena, **N...gas:** Chevron, Shell, **food:** BBQ, Blimpie, Jack-in-the-Box, KFC/ Taco Bell, LJ Silver, Pizza Hut, Popeye's, Wendy's, **lodging:** La Quinta, **other:** DiscountTire, Eckerd, HEB Foods, Radio Shack, Target, **S...gas:** Shell, **food:** Bennigan's, Chili's, Church's, Coney Island, Joe's Crabshack, McDonald's, Ninfa's Mexican, Pappa's Seafood, Peking Chinese, **other:** MEDICAL CARE, AutoZone, Family$, O'Reilly's Parts

776b John Ralston Rd, Holland Ave, **N...gas:** Citgo, Mobil, **food:** Luby's, **lodging:** Best Western, **other:** Kroger/deli/24hr, NTB, Walgreen, **S...**same as 778

a Mercury Dr, **N...gas:** Conoco, Shamrock/diesel, **food:** Burger King, E China Rest., Island Gourmet Seafood, McDonald's, Pizza Inn, **lodging:** Day's Inn, Fairfield Inn, Hampton Inn, Premier Inn, **S...gas:** Shamrock, Shell/diesel, **food:** DQ, Steak&Ale, **other:** bank

775b a I-610, no facilities

774 Gellhorn(from eb) Blvd, Anheuser-Busch Brewery

773b McCarty St, **N...gas:** Mobil/diesel, Shell, **S...food:** Don Chile Mexican

a US 90A, N Wayside Dr, **N...gas:** Chevron, Exxon, **food:** Jack-in-the-Box, Whataburger/24hr, **S...gas:** Coastal/diesel, Shell, **food:** BBQ, Church's, diesel repair

772 Kress St, Lathrop St, **N...gas:** Conoco, Exxon, **S... food:** Burger King, 7 Mares Seafood

771b Lockwood Dr, **N...gas:** Chevron/diesel, **food:** McDonald's, **other:** Family$, **S...gas:** Phillips 66/diesel, Shell/diesel

a Waco St, **N...food:** Frenchey's Chicken

770c US 59 N, no facilities

b Jenson St, Meadow St, Gregg St, no facilities

a US 59 S, to Victoria, no facilities

769c McKee St, Hardy St, Nance St, downtown, no facilities

a Smith St(from wb), to downtown

768b a I-45, N to Dallas, S to Galveston, no facilities

767b Taylor St, no facilities

a Studemont Dr, Yale St, Heights Blvd, **N...gas:** Chevron, **S...gas:** Shell/diesel

766 (from wb), Heights Blvd, Yale St, same as 767a

765b N Durham Dr, N Shepherd Dr, **N...gas:** Shamrock/ gas, **food:** Wendy's, **lodging:** Howard Johnson

Interstate 10

E ↑ ↓ **W**

a   TC Jester Blvd, **S...gas:** Exxon/diesel, Texaco/diesel

764   Westcott St, Washington Ave, Katy Rd, **N...food:** Denny's, **lodging:** Comfort Inn, **S...gas:** Chevron, **food:** IHOP

763   I-610, no facilities

762   Silber Rd, Post Oak Rd, **N...food:** Aubrey's Ribs, Red Robin, **other:** Dodge, **S...gas:** Shell, **food:** Jack-in-the-Box, **lodging:** Holiday Inn, Ramada Inn, **other:** Chevrolet, carwash

761b   Antoine Rd, **N...food:** Country Harvest Buffet, Hunan Chinese, **S...gas:** Shell, **food:** Blue Oyster Grill, Denny's, Papa John's, Whataburger/24hr, **lodging:** La Quinta, Wellesley Inn, **other:** NTB

a   Wirt Rd, Chimney Rock Rd, **N...food:** Capt Penny's Seafood, **S...gas:** Chevron, Exxon/TCBY, Shell, **food:** El Tiempo Cantina, 59 Diner, McDonald's, Planter's Seafood, Steak&Ale

760   Bingle Rd, Voss Rd, **S...gas:** Exxon/diesel, Texaco/diesel, **food:** Goode Co Café, Marie Callender, Mason Jar Rest., Pappy's Café, Redwood Grill, SaltGrass Steaks, Southwell's Burgers, Sweet Tomatos, TX BBQ, Ugo's Italian, **other:** HOSPITAL, DENTIST

759   Campbell Rd(from wb), same as 758b

758b   Blalock Rd, Campbell Rd, **N...food:** Ciro's Italian, Fiesta Foods, Sonic, **other:** Adam's Automotive, LubeStop, Mail It, cleaners, **S...gas:** Chevron/McDonald's/diesel, Exxon, Texaco, **other:** HOSPITAL, Kroger, Walgreen

a   Bunker Hill Rd, **N...gas:** Exxon, **food:** CiCi's, **other:** Best Buy, Costco, Lowe's Whse, Michael's, PepBoys, Radio Shack, **S...gas:** Texaco/diesel, Circle K, **food:** Charlie's Burgers, Guadalajara Mexican, Quizno's, Subway, **lodging:** Day's Inn, Howard Johnson, Super 8, **other:** Ford, Goodyear/auto, Marshall's, Nissan, Ross, Target

757   Gessner Rd, **N...gas:** Exxon, **food:** BBQ, Bennigan's, Chili's, DQ, McDonald's, Schlotsky's, Wendy's, Whataburger/24hr, **other:** MEDICAL CARE, BrakeCheck, Eckerd, Home Depot, Honda, Kroger, NAPA, OfficeMax, Sam's Club/gas, U-Haul, Wal-Mart, **S...gas:** Shell, Texaco/diesel, **food:** Fuddrucker's, Jack-in-the-Box, Jason's Deli, Macaroni Grill, Olive Garden, Pappasito's, Papadeaux Seafood, Taste of TX Rest., **lodging:** Radisson, Sheraton, **other:** HOSPITAL, Circuit City, Cost+, Foley's, Ford, Goodyear, Mervyn's, Office Depot, Sears/auto, mall

756   TX 8, Sam Houston Tollway, no facilities

755   Willcrest Rd, **N...other:** Discount Tire, Kia, Mazda, NTB, **S...gas:** Citgo/diesel, Exxon/McDonald's/24hr, Texaco, **food:** China Buffet, Denny's, IHOP, Steak&Ale, **lodging:** La Quinta

754   Kirkwood Rd, **N...other:** Lincoln/Mercury, Saturn, same as 753b, **S...gas:** Chevron/diesel, Shell/24hr, **food:** Carrabba's, IHOP/24hr, Kingfish Mkt, Mesa Grill, Original Pasta Co, Subway, Taco Cabana, **lodging:** Extended Stay America, Hampton Inn, **other:** Chevrolet, Subaru

753b   Dairy-Ashford Rd, **N...other:** Buick, Chrysler/Dodge, Infiniti, K-Mart, Lexus, Nissan, Toyota, Volvo, **S...gas:** Exxon/TCBY/diesel, Shamrock, **food:** Beck's Prime Rest., Subway, TX Cattle Steaks, Whataburger, **lodging:** Courtyard, Guesthouse Inn, **other:** Audi/Porsche, Cadillac, Mitsubishi, Pontiac/GMC/Suzuki

a   Eldridge Rd, **N...gas:** Conoco/diesel, **lodging:** Omni Hotel, **S...gas:** Shamrock/24hr, **other:** Pennzoil

751   TX 6, to Addicks, **N...gas:** Texaco, **food:** Cattlegard Rest., Waffle House, **lodging:** Drury Inn, Holiday Inn, Red Roof Inn, **other:** Sam's Club/gas, **S...gas:** Exxon, Chevron, Conoco/diesel, Texaco/diesel, **food:** Blimpie, DQ, Denny's/24hr, El Yucatan Mexican, Jack-in-the-Box, Wendy's, **lodging:** Bradford HomeSuites, Hearthside Extended Stay, La Quinta, Motel 6, Super 8, **other:** JiffyLube, **other:** USPO, carwash

748   Barker-Cypress Rd, **S...food:** Cracker Barrel, Lulu's Buffet, **lodging:** Fairfield Inn, **lodging:** TownePlace Inn, **other:** Chrysler/Plymouth/Jeep, Dodge, Hoover RV Ctr, Hyundai, VW

747   Fry Rd, **N...gas:** Chevron, Phillips 66, Shamrock/diesel, Shell/24hr, **food:** Bennigans, Burger King, Church's, DQ, Denny's, Godfather's, McDonald's, Pizza Hut, Sonic, Souper Salad, Subway, Taco Bell, Victor's Mexican, Whataburger, **other:** MEDICAL CARE, Goodyear, HEB Food/gas, Home Depot, Sam's Club/gas, Walgreen, Wal-Mart/auto, **S...gas:** Chevron, Citgo, Shell, **food:** Baskin-Robbins, Boston Mkt, Capt Tom's Seafood, El Chico, Fazoli's, IHOP, Jack-in-the-Box, Ninfa's Café, Omar's Mexican, Orient Express, Outback Steaks, Quizno's, Wendy's, **other:** Albertson's, Ford, Lowe's Whse, Radio Shack, Target

Houston

TEXAS

Interstate 10

E ↑ W

745   Mason Rd, **S...gas:** Chevron/24hr, Exxon/24hr, Shamrock, Shell/24hr, **food:** Babin's Seafood, BBQ, Blackeyed Pea, Burger King, Carino's Italian, Carrabba's, Chick-fil-A, Chili's, CiCi's, DQ, Fuzzy's Pizza, Hartz Chicken, Jack-in-the-Box, Jason's Deli, KFC, Landry's Seafood, Little Caesar's, LJ Silver, Luby's, McDonald's, Monterey Mexican, Papa John's, Pizza Hut, SaltGrass Steaks, Schlotsky's, SpagEddie's, Subway, Taco Bell, Taco Cabana, Taquiera Mexican, TCBY, Whataburger/24hr, **lodging:** Sleep Inn, **other:** CarQuest, Discount Tire, Dodge, Eckerd, Firestone/auto, Goodyear/auto, HEB Food/gas, K-Mart, Kroger, Randall's Food, Walgreen, transmissions

743   TX 99, Grand Pkwy, Peek Rd, **S...gas:** Texaco/diesel, **food:** A&W, Popeye's, **lodging:** Best Western, Comfort Inn, Holiday Inn Express, Super 8, **other:** Chevrolet, Kroger

741   (742 from wb)Katy-Fort Bend County Rd, Pin Oak Rd, **S...gas:** Chevron, Mobil/diesel/24hr, **food:** ChuckeCheese, Fuddruckers, Jack-in-the-Box, Red Lobster, TGIFriday, **other:** HOSPITAL, Chrysler/Jeep, Discount Tire, Katy Mills Outlet/famous brands, Outdoor World, Wal-Mart SuperCtr/24hr

740   FM 1463, **N...food:** McDonald's, Sonic, **other:** Yamaha, **S...gas:** Chevron, **food:** RainForest Café, **other:** Books-A-Million, Pyle RV Ctr

737   Pederson Rd, **S...other:** Holiday World RV Ctr

732   FM 359, to Brookshire, **N...gas:** Exxon/diesel, Phillips 66/diesel/rest./24hr, Shell, **lodging:** Executive Inn, **other:** KOA, **S...gas:** Chevron/diesel, Citgo/diesel, Exxon/Burger King/diesel/24hr, **food:** Jack-in-the-Box, **other:** Ford Trucks, truckwash

731   FM 1489, to Koomey Rd, **N...gas:** Exxon/diesel, Shell, **food:** Villa Fuentes Mexican, **lodging:** Brookshire Motel, Travelers Inn, **other:** KOA

730mm   picnic areas(both lanes exit left), tables, litter barrels

729   Peach Ridge Rd, Donigan Rd, no facilities

726   Chew Rd(from eb), **S...golf**

725   Mlcak Rd(from wb), no facilities

724mm   weigh sta wb

723   FM 1458, to San Felipe, **N...gas:** Knox/Subway/diesel/24hr, **other:** to Stephen F Austin SP, **S...other:** Outlet Ctr/famous brands, Food Court

721   (from wb), **S...**to Outlet Ctr

720a   Outlet Ctr Dr, **S...**Outlet Ctr/famous brands

720   TX 36, to Sealy, **N...gas:** Shell/diesel, **food:** DQ, Hartz Chicken, McDonald's, Sonic, Tony's Rest., **other:** Chevrolet/Pontiac/Buick/GMC, Jones RV Ctr, **S...gas:** Chevron/diesel/24hr, Mobil/diesel, Shell/diesel/24hr, **food:** Hinze's BBQ, Hunan Chinese, KFC/Taco Bell, Omar's Mexican, Pizza Hut, Subway, Whataburger/24hr, **lodging:** Best Western, Holiday Inn Express, Rodeway Inn, **other:** Bill's Foods, Chrysler/Plymouth/Dodge/Jeep, Radio Shack, Wal-Mart

718   US 90(from eb), to Sealy, no facilities

716   Pyka Rd, **N...gas:** Sealy Trk Plaza/diesel/rest./showers/24hr/@

713   Beckendorff Rd, no facilities

709   FM 2761, Bernardo Rd, no facilities

704   FM 949, no facilities

701mm   picnic area wb, tables, litter barrels

699   FM 102, to Eagle Lake, **N...other:** Happy Oaks RV Park, antiques, **S...other:** Eagle Lake SP(14mi)

698   Alleyton Rd, **N...food:** BBQ, **S...gas:** Shell/Taco Bell/diesel, **other:** Chrysler/Jeep/Dodge, Ford

697mm   Little Colorado River

696   TX 71, Columbus, **N...gas:** Chevron/diesel/24hr, Shell/diesel, **food:** Burger King, DQ, Denny's, Guadalajara Mexican, Jack-in-the-Box, Pizza Hut, Schobel's Rest., Whataburger, **lodging:** Columbus Inn, Holiday Inn Express, **other:** HOSPITAL, Buick/Chevrolet, HEB Foods, Radio Shack, Wal-Mart/drugs, **S...gas:** Mobil/Church's/Subway/diesel, Shamrock/diesel, **food:** McDonald's, Sonic, **lodging:** Country Hearth Inn, **other:** Columbus RV Park

695   TX 71(from wb), to La Grange

693   FM 2434, to Glidden, no facilities

692mm   **rest areas both lanes, full(handicapped)facilities, vending, phone, picnic tables, litter barrels, RV dump, petwalk**

689   US 90, to Hattermann Lane, **N...**Motorcoach RV Park

682   FM 155, to Wiemar, **N...gas:** Chevron, Exxon/diesel, Shell/diesel, **food:** BBQ, DQ, Quizno's, **lodging:** Super 8, **other:** HOSPITAL, $General, **S...other:** Buick/Chevrolet

678mm   E Navidad River

677   US 90, **N...food:** Nannie's Café, **other:** Fostoria Glass, OutPost Art Gallery

674   US 77, Schulenburg, **N...gas:** Chevron/diesel, Exxon/diesel, **food:** BBQ, McDonald's, **lodging:** Executive Inn, Oak Ridge Motel/rest., **other:** Ford, **S...gas:** Exxon, Phillips 66/diesel, Shamrock/Subway, Shell/diesel, **food:** Burger King, DQ, Frank's Rest., Guadalajara Mexican, Whataburger, **other:** Schulenberg RV Park

672mm   W Navidad River

668   FM 2238, to Engle, no facilities

661   TX 95, FM 609, to Flatonia, **N...gas:** Mobil, **food:** BBQ, **S...gas:** Exxon/24hr, Shamrock, Shell/Grumpy's Rest./motel, **food:** DQ, McDonald's, **lodging:** Sav-Inn

657.5mm   picnic areas both lanes

653   US 90, **N...gas:** Shell/diesel

649   TX 97, to Waelder, no facilities

642   TX 304, to Gonzales, **N...other:** Kactus Korral RV Park(2mi)

637   FM 794, to Harwood, no facilities

632   US 90/183, to Gonzales, **N...gas:** Love's/Subway/diesel/24hr, **lodging:** Coachway Inn(2mi), **S...other:** to Palmetto SP, camping

Interstate 10

E ↕ W

630mm San Marcos River

628 TX 80, to Luling, **N...gas:** Shamrock/24hr, **food:** DQ, **other:** HOSPITAL, Riverbend RV Park, **S... gas:** Shell

625 Darst Field Rd, no facilities

624.5mm Smith Creek

623mm Allen Creek

621mm rest areas both lanes, full(handicapped)faciliti es, phone, picnic tables, litter barrels, vending, petwalk

620 FM 1104, no facilities

617 FM 2438, to Kingsbury, no facilities

616mm truck weigh sta both lanes

614.5mm Mill Creek

612 US 90, no facilities

611mm Geronimo Creek

610 TX 123, to San Marcos, **N...gas:** Exxon/diesel, Chevron/Subway/diesel, **food:** K&G Steaks, Los Cucos Mexican, Luby's, Subway, **lodging:** Comfort Inn, Holiday Inn, **other:** Tire Whse, **S...gas:** Shamrock/diesel, **food:** Taco Cabana, **other:** HOSPITAL, River Shade RV

609 TX 123, Austin St, **S...gas:** Mobil/diesel, **other:** Chevrolet

607 TX 46, FM 78, to New Braunfels, **N...gas:** Texaco/ Jack-in-the-Box/diesel, **food:** Huddle House, **lodg ing:** Alamo Inn, **S...gas:** Exxon/DQ/diesel, **food:** BBQ, Hong Kong Chinese, Kettle, McDonald's, Soilitas Mexican, **lodging:** Best Western, Super 8, **other:** Chrysler/Plymouth/Dodge

605 FM 464, **N...other:** Twin Pines RV Park, **S...gas:** EZ Gas/24hr

605mm Guadalupe River

604 FM 725, to Lake McQueeney, **N...**RV park

603 US 90 E, US 90A, to Seguin, **N...other:** Explorer USA RV Sales, **S...other:** S Texas RV Super-Store

601 FM 775, to New Berlin, **N...gas:** Mobil/Subway/ diesel/24hr

600 Schwab Rd, no facilities

599 FM 465, to Marion, no facilities

599mm Santa Clara Creek

597 Santa Clara Rd, no facilities

595 Zuehl Rd, no facilities

594mm Cibolo Creek

593 FM 2538, Trainer Hale Rd, **N...gas:** Citgo/DQ/ diesel/24hr, **S...gas:** Exxon/diesel/rest./24hr

593mm Woman Hollering Creek

591 FM 1518, to Schertz, **N...gas:** Exxon/diesel/rest./ motel/repair/24hr, **other:** camping

590.5mm rest areas both lanes, full(handicapped)faciliti es, phone, picnic tables, litter barrels, petwalk, RV dump

589mm Salitrillo Creek

589 Pfeil Rd, Graytown Rd, no facilities

587 LP 1604, Randolph AFB, to Universal City, no facilities

San Antonio

585.5mm Escondido Creek

585 FM 1516, to Con-verse, **N...gas:** Texa-co/Church's/diesel/motel, **food:** Winfield's Rest., **S... other:** Peterbilt/GMC/Freight-liner

585mm Martinez Creek

583 Foster Rd, **N...gas:** ✈/Flying J/Conoco/diesel/LP/ rest./24hr/@, Shamrock/24hr, **food:** Jack-in-the-Box/24hr, **lodging:** Holiday Inn Express, Hillcrown Inn, **other:** truckwash, **S...gas:** TA/Chevron/Burger King/Pizza Hut/Popeye's/diesel/24hr/@

582.5mm Rosillo Creek

582 Ackerman Rd, Kirby, **N...gas:** Pilot/Arby's/diesel/ 24hr, **S...gas:** Petro/Mobil/diesel/24hr/@, KFC/Pizza Hut/Taco Bell, **food:** Wendy's, **lodging:** Relay Station Motel, **other:** Blue Beacon, Petrolube

581 I-410, no facilities

580 LP 13, WW White Rd, **N...gas:** Chevron, Fina, **food:** Hailey's Rest./24hr, Wendy's, **lodging:** Comfort Inn/ rest., Motel 6, Scotsman Inn, **other:** RV camping, **S... gas:** Exxon/diesel, **food:** BBQ, McDonald's, Mexican Rest., Pizza Hut, **lodging:** Econolodge, Quality Inn, Super 8, **other:** Ford/Freightliner, Volvo, tires

579 Houston St, **N...gas:** Shamrock, **lodging:** Ramada Ltd, **S...gas:** Chevron, **lodging:** Day's Inn, Passport Inn

578 Pecan Valley Dr, ML King Dr, **N...gas:** Phillips 66, **S...gas:** Shell/diesel

577 US 87 S, to Roland Ave, **S...food:** Whataburger/ 24hr, **other:** transmissions

576 New Braunfels Ave, Gevers St, **S...gas:** Shamrock, **food:** McDonald's, Taco Snack

575 Pine St, Hackberry St, **S...food:** Little Red Barn Steaks

574 I-37, US 281, no facilities

573 Probandt St, **N...food:** Miller's BBQ, **S...gas:** Conoco, Shamrock, **other:** to SA Missions HS

572 I-10 and I-35 run together 3 miles

TEXAS

Interstate 10

See TX I-35, exits 153-155a b.

570   I-10 and I-35 run together 3 miles

569c   Santa Rosa St, downtown, to Our Lady of the Lake U

568   spur 421, Culebra Ave, Bandera Ave, **S...**to St Marys U

567   Lp 345, Fredericksburg Rd(from eb upper level accesses I-35 S, I-10 E, US 87 S, lower level accesses I-35 N)

566b   Hildebrand Ave, Fulton Ave, **S...gas:** Exxon, 7-11, **lodging:** Galaxy Motel

a   Fresno Dr, **N...gas:** Exxon, Shamrock, **food:** McDonald's

565c   (from wb), access to same as 565 a b

b   Vance Jackson Rd, **N...food:** Miller's BBQ, **lodging:** Econolodge, Quality Inn, **S...gas:** Exxon, Texaco, **lodging:** La Quinta

a   Crossroads Blvd, Balcone's Heights, **N...gas:** Exxon, Texaco/diesel, **food:** Denny's, Whataburger, **lodging:** Comfort Suites, Rodeway Inn, **S...food:** Dave&Buster's, McDonald's, **lodging:** Sumner Suites, Super 8, **other:** Firestone/auto, Mazda, RV Ctr, Target, Toyota, mall, transmissions

564b a   I-410, facilities off of I-410 W, Fredericksburg Rd

563   Callaghan Rd, **N...gas:** Mobil, **food:** Las Palapas Mexican, Subway, TGIFriday, **lodging:** Embassy Suites, Marriott, **other:** CHIROPRACTOR, Ford, Lexus, Malibu Grand Prix, Mazda, Sun Harvest Foods, Toyota, **S...gas:** Exxon, **food:** Mama's Rest., **other:** Lowe's Whse

561   Wurzbach Rd, **N...gas:** Mobil/diesel, Phillips 66, **food:** Bennigan's, Fuddrucker's, Golden Corral, Jason's Deli, Pappasito's Cantina, Popeye's, Sea Island Shrimphouse, TX Land&Cattle, **lodging:** AmeriSuites, Homewood Suites, Ramada Ltd, Wyndham, **other:** MEDICAL CARE, Albertson's, HEB Food/gas, Eckerd/24hr, **S...gas:** Texaco/diesel, **food:** Alamo Café, Arby's, Benihana, Church's, Denny's, IHOP, Jack-in-the-Box, Luby's, McDonald's, Pizza Hut, Sombrero Rosa Café, Taco Bell, Taco Cabana, Tony Roma, Wendy's, **lodging:** Candlewood Suites, Drury Inn, Hawthorn Suites, Holiday Inn Express, La Quinta, Motel 6, Residence Inn, Sleep Inn, Thrifty Inn

560b   frontage rd(from eb), **N...food:** Water St Seafood, **other:** Chrysler/Plymouth, Kia, Nissan

a   Huebner Rd, **N...food:** BBQ, Champ's, Macaroni Grill, On the Border, SaltGrass Steaks, **other:** Borders, Land Rover, Old Navy, Ross, cinema, **S...gas:** Exxon, Shell/Jack-in-the-Box, **food:** Burger King, Cracker Barrel, Jim's Rest., **lodging:** AmeriSuites, Day's Inn, Hampton Inn, Homestead Village, **other:** Cadillac/Hummer

559   Lp 335, US 87, Fredericksburg Rd, **N...food:** Carrabba's, Chili's, Outback Steaks, Joe's Crabshack, Logan's Roadhouse, **other:** Buick/GMC, **S...gas:** Texaco, **food:** Krispy Kreme, Acura

558   De Zavala Rd, **N...gas:** Chevron, Exxon/diesel, **food:** BBQ, McDonald's, Sonic, Subway, Taco Cabana, **lodging:** Best Western, Howard Johnson, Radford Inn, Super 8, **other:** Barnes&Noble, Chevrolet, HEB Food/gas, Home Depot, Marshall's, OfficeMax, Target, **S...food:** IHOP, Schlotsky's, TGIFriday, Whataburger, Zio's Italian, **other:** Discount Tire, Wal-Mart SuperCtr/24hr

557   Spur 53, Univ of TX at San Antonio, **N...other:** Jaguar/Mazerati/Ferrari, **S...other:** Costco/gas

556b   frontage rd, **S...lodging:** Motel 6

a   to Anderson Lp, **S...lodging:** Comfort Inn, **other:** to Seaworld

555   La Quintera Pkwy, no facilities

554   Camp Bullis Rd, **N...gas:** Citgo, **other:** Russell Park, **S...gas:** Shell, **lodging:** Rodeway Inn, Motel 6(2mi)

551   Boerne Stage Rd(from wb), to Leon Springs, same as 550

550   FM 3351, Ralph Fair Rd, **N...gas:** Shamrock/Pico's/diesel, **S...gas:** Texaco/Domino's/diesel, **food:** Las Palapas Mexican, Macaroni Grill, Starbucks, **other:** GNC, HEB Foods

546   Fair Oaks Pkwy, Tarpon Dr, **S...gas:** Chevron/diesel/café, Exxon/diesel/café, **other:** Hoover RV Ctr

543   Boerne Stage Rd, to Scenic LP Rd, **N...gas:** Citgo/diesel/24hr, **food:** Alamo Café, Copeland's Seafood/steaks, ICaverns Inn/rest., **other:** Chevrolet, Chrysler/Dodge/Jeep, Ford, Pontiac/Buick/GMC, Alamo Fiesta RV Park, Ancira RV Ctr, Wal-Mart SuperCtr/24hr, to Cascade Caverns

540   TX 46, to New Braunfels, **N...gas:** Exxon/Taco Bell/diesel, Texaco/diesel/24hr, **food:** Burger King, Church's, DQ, Denny's, Little Caesar's, Margarita's Café, Pizza Hut, Quizno's, Shanghai Chinese, Sonic, Taco Cabana, Wendy's, **lodging:** Best Western, Holiday Inn Express, Key to the Hills Motel, **other:** HEB Food/gas, Walgreen, **S...Chili's,** Home Depot

539   Johns Rd, **S...gas:** Shamrock/diesel/LP, **food:** Pico's Chicken, **lodging:** Tapatio Springs Motel(4mi)

538mm   Cibolo Creek

537   US 87, to Boerne, **2 mi N...gas:** Chevron, Shamrock, **food:** La Hacienda Rest., Maque's Mexican, Pete's Place, Pico's Chicken, Subway, **lodging:** Key to the Hills Motel

533   FM 289, Welfare, **N...food:** Po-Po Family Rest., **other:** Top of the Hill RV Park(1mi)

532mm   Little Joshua Creek

531mm   picnic area wb, tables, litter barrels

530mm   Big Joshua Creek

529.5mm   picnic area eb, tables, litter barrels

527   FM 1621(from wb), to Waring

526.5mm   Holiday Creek

Interstate 10

E

W

Kerrville Ozona

Junction

Sonora

524	TX 27, FM 1621, to Waring, **N...**VETERINARIAN, **S...gas:** Chevron/diesel, Texaco/24hr, **food:** DD Family Rest.
523.5mm	Guadalupe River
523	US 87 N, to Comfort, **N...gas:** Chevron/McDonald's/diesel, **S...gas:** Exxon/diesel/24hr, Texaco/diesel, **food:** DQ, **lodging:** Inn at Comfort, **other:** USA RV Park
521.5mm	Comfort Creek
520	FM 1341, to Cypress Creek Rd, no facilities
515mm	Cypress Creek
514mm	**rest areas both lanes, full(handicapped)facilities, vending, phone, picnic tables, litter barrels, petwalk, playground**
508	TX 16, Kerrville, **N...gas:** Exxon/diesel, **other:** Chevrolet/Pontiac/Buick/Cadillac, RV camping, **S...**Chamber of Commerce, **gas:** Chevron/Subway/diesel, Shamrock/diesel, TC/diesel, Shell/McDonald's/diesel/24hr, **food:** Acapulco Mexican, BBQ, Cracker Barrel, DQ, Denny's, Luby's, Schlotsky's, **lodging:** Best Western, Budget Inn, Comfort Inn, Day's Inn, Econolodge, Hampton Inn, Holiday Inn Express, Motel 6, Super 8, YoYo Ranch Hotel, **other:** HOSPITAL, Home Depot, Kerrville RV Ctr, Lowe's Whse, **1-2 mi S...food:** Burger King, Jack-in-the-Box, KFC, Pizza Hut/Taco Bell, **other:** AutoZone, $General, Firestone, Hastings Books, HEB Foods, Pennzoil, Walgreen, to Kerrville-Schreiner SP
505	FM 783, to Kerrville, **S...gas:** Exxon/diesel, **3 mi S on TX 27...lodging:** Inn of the Hills, **food:** Chili's, DQ, Pizza Hut, Sonic, Taco Casa, Wal-Mart SuperCtr/24hr, **other:** Classic Car Museum
503.5mm	scenic views both lanes, litter barrels
501	FM 1338, **N...other:** Buckhorn RV Resort, **S...other:** KOA(2mi)
497mm	picnic area both lanes, tables, litter barrels
492	FM 479, **S...**Lone Oak Store
490	TX 41, no facilities
488	TX 27, Mountain Home, to Ingram, no facilities
484	Midway Rd, no facilities
477	US 290, to Fredericksburg, no facilities
476.5mm	service rd eb
472	Old Segovia Rd, no facilities
465	FM 2169, to Segovia, **S...gas:** Phillips 66/diesel, **food:** Safari Rest., **lodging:** Best Western, **other:** RV camping
464.5mm	Johnson Fork Creek
462	US 83 S, to Uvalde, no facilities
461mm	picnic area eb, tables, litter barrels
460	(from wb), to Junction, no facilities
459mm	picnic area wb, tables, litter barrels
457	FM 2169, to Junction, **N...gas:** Texaco/diesel, **S... lodging:** Day's Inn/rest., **other:** RV camping
456.5mm	Llano River

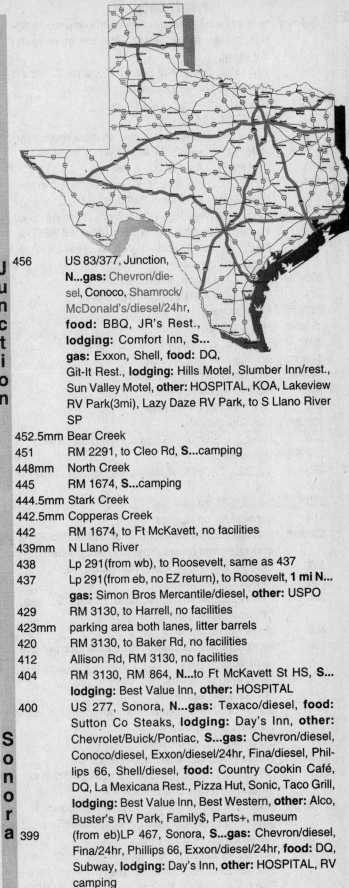

456	US 83/377, Junction, **N...gas:** Chevron/diesel, Conoco, Shamrock/McDonald's/diesel/24hr, **food:** BBQ, JR's Rest., **lodging:** Comfort Inn, **S... gas:** Exxon, Shell, **food:** DQ, Git-It Rest., **lodging:** Hills Motel, Slumber Inn/rest., Sun Valley Motel, **other:** HOSPITAL, KOA, Lakeview RV Park(3mi), Lazy Daze RV Park, to S Llano River SP
452.5mm	Bear Creek
451	RM 2291, to Cleo Rd, **S...**camping
448mm	North Creek
445	RM 1674, **S...**camping
444.5mm	Stark Creek
442.5mm	Copperas Creek
442	RM 1674, to Ft McKavett, no facilities
439mm	N Llano River
438	Lp 291(from wb), to Roosevelt, same as 437
437	Lp 291(from eb, no EZ return), to Roosevelt, **1 mi N... gas:** Simon Bros Mercantile/diesel, **other:** USPO
429	RM 3130, to Harrell, no facilities
423mm	parking area both lanes, litter barrels
420	RM 3130, to Baker Rd, no facilities
412	Allison Rd, RM 3130, no facilities
404	RM 3130, RM 864, **N...**to Ft McKavett St HS, **S... lodging:** Best Value Inn, **other:** HOSPITAL
400	US 277, Sonora, **N...gas:** Texaco/diesel, **food:** Sutton Co Steaks, **lodging:** Day's Inn, **other:** Chevrolet/Buick/Pontiac, **S...gas:** Chevron/diesel, Conoco/diesel, Exxon/diesel/24hr, Fina/diesel, Phillips 66, Shell/diesel, **food:** Country Cookin Café, DQ, La Mexicana Rest., Pizza Hut, Sonic, Taco Grill, **lodging:** Best Value Inn, Best Western, **other:** Alco, Buster's RV Park, Family$, Parts+, museum
399	(from eb)LP 467, Sonora, **S...gas:** Chevron/diesel, Fina/24hr, Phillips 66, Exxon/diesel/24hr, **food:** DQ, Subway, **lodging:** Day's Inn, **other:** HOSPITAL, RV camping

TEXAS

Interstate 10

E ↕ W

Ft Stockton (vertical label)

394mm	**rest area both lanes, full(handicapped) facilities, phone, picnic tables, litter barrel, petwalk, RV dump**
392	RM 1989, Caverns of Sonora Rd, **8 mi S...other:** Caverns of Sonora Camping, phone
388	RM 1312(from eb), no facilities
381	RM 1312, no facilities
372	Taylor Box Rd, **N...gas:** Chevron/diesel/rest./24hr, **lodging:** Super 8/RV Park, **other:** auto museum
368	LP 466, **N...**same as 365 & 363
365	TX 163, Ozona, **N...gas:** Chevron/diesel, Texaco/diesel/café, T&C/Taco Bell/diesel, **food:** Burger King, Café NextDoor, DQ, Subway, **lodging:** Best Western, Economy Inn/RV Park, **other:** HOSPITAL, NAPA, to David Crockett Mon, **S...gas:** Chevron, Frank's Fuels, Shell
363	Lp 466, to Ozona, no facilities
361	RM 2083, Pandale Rd, no facilities
357mm	Eureka Draw
351mm	Howard Draw
350	FM 2398, to Howard Draw, no facilities
349mm	parking area wb, litter barrels
346mm	parking area eb, litter barrels
343	US 290 W, no facilities
337	Live Oak Rd, no facilities
336.5mm	Live Oak Creek
328	River Rd, Sheffield, **S...gas:** Phillips 66/diesel
327.5mm	Pecos River
325	US 290, TX 349, to Iraan, Sheffield, **N...**HOSPITAL
320	frontage rd, no facilities
314	frontage rd, no facilities
308mm	**rest area both lanes, full(handicapped)facilities, phone, picnic tables, litter barrels, petwalk**
307	US 190, FM 305, to Iraan, **N...**HOSPITAL
298	RM 2886, no facilities
294	FM 11, Bakersfield, **N...gas:** Exxon, **S...gas:** Chevron/diesel/café, **other:** phone
288	Ligon Rd, no facilities
285	McKenzie Rd, **S...other:** Domaine Cordier Ste Genevieve Winery
279mm	picnic area eb, tables, litter barrels
277	FM 2023, no facilities
273	US 67/385, to McCamey, **N...other:** picnic area wb, tables, litter barrels
272	University Rd, no facilities
264	Warnock Rd, **N...other:** KOA/gas/BBQ
261	US 290 W, US 385 S, **N...gas:** Exxon/TCBY/diesel, **other:** RV camping, **S...**HOSPITAL
259b a	(259 from eb)TX 18, FM 1053, Ft Stockton, **N...gas:** Fina/diesel, Shell/Burger King/diesel, Texaco/diesel, **other:** I-10 RV Park
257	US 285, Ft Stockton, to Pecos, **N...other:** Comanche Land RV Park, golf, **S...gas:** Chevron/diesel, Exxon/diesel/rest., Shamrock/diesel, **food:** BBQ, KFC/Taco Bell, McDonald's, Pizza Hut, Sonic,

Subway, **lodging:** Atrium West Motel, Best Western, Comfort Inn, Day's Inn, Holiday Inn Express, La Quinta, Motel 6, Sands Motel, **other:** Chevrolet/Pontiac/Buick, Ford/Lincoln/Mercury, Goodyear/auto, Mktbasket Foods, Wal-Mart

256	to US 385 S, Ft Stockton, **1 mi S...gas:** Shamrock/diesel, Shell/diesel, Texaco/diesel, **food:** China Inn, DQ, K-Bob's Steaks, KFC, Pizza Express, Sonic, Subway, **lodging:** Alpine Lodge/rest., Best Western, Comfort Inn, Econolodge, Motel 6, Sands Motor Inn, Super 8, **other:** HOSPITAL, to Ft Stockton Hist Dist, Big Bend NP
253	FM 2037, to Belding, no facilities
248	US 67, FM 1776, to Alpine, **S...**to Big Bend NP, no facilities
246	Firestone, no facilities
241	Kennedy Rd, no facilities
235	Mendel Rd, no facilities
233mm	**rest area both lanes, full(handicapped)facilities, phone, picnic tables, litter barrels, petwalk**
229	Hovey Rd, no facilities
222	Hoefs Rd, no facilities
214	(from wb), FM 2448, no facilities
212	TX 17, FM 2448, to Pecos, **S...gas:** Fina/diesel/café
209	TX 17, **S...other:** to Davis Mtn SP, Ft Davis NHS
206	FM 2903, to Balmorhea, **S...other:** to Balmorhea SP
192	FM 3078, to Toyahvale, **S...other:** to Balmorhea SP
188	Giffin Rd, no facilities
186	I-20, to Ft Worth, Dallas
185mm	picnic area both lanes, tables, litter barrels
184	Springhills, no facilities
181	Cherry Creek Rd, **S...gas:** Chevron/24hr
176	TX 118, FM 2424, to Kent, **N...gas:** Chevron/diesel, **S...other:** to McDonald Observatory, Davis Mtn SP, Ft Davis
173	Hurd's Draw Rd, no facilities
166	Boracho Sta, no facilities
159	Plateau, **N...gas:** Fina/diesel/24hr
153	Michigan Flat, no facilities
146	Wild Horse Rd, no facilities
146mm	weigh sta wb
144.5mm	**rest area both lanes, full(handicapped)facilities, picnic tables, litter barrels, petwalk**
140b	Ross Dr, Van Horn, **N...gas:** Chevron, Exxon/diesel, Love's/Subway/diesel/24hr, **lodging:** Bell's Motel, Comfort Inn, Day's Inn/rest., Motel 6, Sands Motel/rest., **other:** El Campo RV Park, Van Horn Drug, **S...other:** Mountain RV Park/dump
a	US 90, TX 54, Van Horn Dr, **N...gas:** Shamrock, Texaco/diesel, **lodging:** Comfort Inn, Village Inn, **other:** HOSPITAL, NAPA, USPO, **S...gas:** Exxon, Pilot/Wendy's/diesel/24hr, **food:** Papa's Café

Van Horn (vertical label)

Interstate 10

E

W

138 Lp 10, to Van Horn, **N...food:** Chuey's Rest., DQ, Pizza Hut, **lodging:** Best Western, Budget Inn, Comfort Inn, Economy Inn, Motel 6, Ramada Ltd, **other:** Eagles Nest RV Park, Ford/Mercury, Goodyear, IGA Foods, **S...gas:** Chevron/diesel/24hr, **food:** McDonald's, **lodging:** Holiday Inn Express, Super 8

137mm truck weigh sta eb

136mm scenic overlook wb, picnic tables, litter barrels

135mm Mountain/Central time zone line

133 (from wb)frontage rd, no facilities

129 Allamore, to Hot Wells, no facilities

108 to Sierra Blanca(from wb), same as 107

107 RM 1111, Sierra Blanca Ave, **N...gas:** Exxon/diesel/24hr, Texaco/diesel, **lodging:** Sierra Motel, **other:** Good Sam RV Park, truck/tire repair, to Hueco Tanks SP, **S...gas:** Chevron, **food:** Cactus Grill

105 (106 from wb)Lp 10, Sierra Blanca, same as 107

102.5mm inspection sta eb

99 Lasca Rd, **N...other:** picnic area both lanes, picnic tables, litter barrels, no restrooms

98mm picnic area eb, tables, litter barrels, no restrooms

95 frontage rd(from eb), **S...gas/motel/café**

87 FM 34, **S...gas:** Trkstp/diesel/rest./24hr/@

85 Esperanza Rd, no facilities

81 FM 2217, no facilities

78 TX 20 W, to McNary, no facilities

77mm truck parking area wb

72 spur 148, to Ft Hancock, **S...gas:** Shell/diesel, Texaco, **food:** Angie's Rest., **other:** RV park, motel

68 Acala Rd, no facilities

55 Tornillo, no facilities

51mm **rest area both lanes, full(handicapped)facilities, picnic tables, litter tables, petwalk**

49 FM 793, Fabens, **S...gas:** Phillips 66/diesel, RnR/diesel, **food:** Church's, McDonald's, **lodging:** Fabens Inn, **other:** Barton Parts, Big 8 Foods, Family$

42 FM 1110, to Clint, **S...gas:** Exxon/diesel, **lodging:** Cotton Valley Motel/RV Park/rest./dump

37 FM 1281, Horizon Blvd, **N...gas:** Exxon, Love's/Subway/diesel/24hr, **lodging:** Americana Inn, **S...gas:** Petro/Mobil/Blimpie/diesel/24hr/@, **food:** McDonald's, **lodging:** Deluxe Inn, **other:** Blue Beacon

El Paso

34 TX 375, Americas Ave, **N...gas:** Chevron/diesel/24hr, Shamrock/diesel, Texaco/diesel/24hr, **S... other:** RV camping, El Paso Mus of Hist

32 FM 659, Zaragosa Rd, **N...gas:** Chevron/diesel, Phillips 66, **food:** Arby's, Cheddar's, Furr's Buffet, IHOP, Logan's Roadhouse, Macaroni Grill, McDonald's, Outback Steaks, Starbucks, Village Inn Rest., Whataburger/24hr, **lodging:** Microtel, oth-

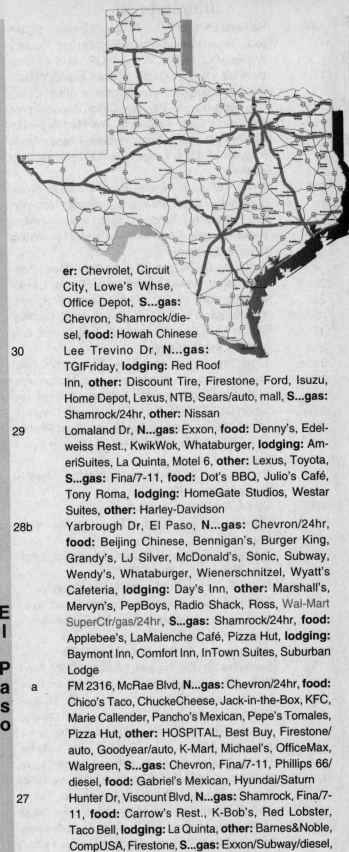

er: Chevrolet, Circuit City, Lowe's Whse, Office Depot, **S...gas:** Chevron, Shamrock/diesel, **food:** Howah Chinese

30 Lee Trevino Dr, **N...gas:** TGIFriday, **lodging:** Red Roof Inn, **other:** Discount Tire, Firestone, Ford, Isuzu, Home Depot, Lexus, NTB, Sears/auto, mall, **S...gas:** Shamrock/24hr, **other:** Nissan

29 Lomaland Dr, **N...gas:** Exxon, **food:** Denny's, Edelweiss Rest., KwikWok, Whataburger, **lodging:** AmeriSuites, La Quinta, Motel 6, **other:** Lexus, Toyota, **S...gas:** Fina/7-11, **food:** Dot's BBQ, Julio's Café, Tony Roma, **lodging:** HomeGate Studios, Westar Suites, **other:** Harley-Davidson

28b Yarbrough Dr, El Paso, **N...gas:** Chevron/24hr, **food:** Beijing Chinese, Bennigan's, Burger King, Grandy's, LJ Silver, McDonald's, Sonic, Subway, Wendy's, Whataburger, Wienerschnitzel, Wyatt's Cafeteria, **lodging:** Day's Inn, **other:** Marshall's, Mervyn's, PepBoys, Radio Shack, Ross, Wal-Mart SuperCtr/gas/24hr, **S...gas:** Shamrock/24hr, **food:** Applebee's, LaMalenche Café, Pizza Hut, **lodging:** Baymont Inn, Comfort Inn, InTown Suites, Suburban Lodge

a FM 2316, McRae Blvd, **N...gas:** Chevron/24hr, **food:** Chico's Taco, ChuckeCheese, Jack-in-the-Box, KFC, Marie Callender, Pancho's Mexican, Pepe's Tomales, Pizza Hut, **other:** HOSPITAL, Best Buy, Firestone/auto, Goodyear/auto, K-Mart, Michael's, OfficeMax, Walgreen, **S...gas:** Chevron, Fina/7-11, Phillips 66/diesel, **food:** Gabriel's Mexican, Hyundai/Saturn

27 Hunter Dr, Viscount Blvd, **N...gas:** Shamrock, Fina/7-11, **food:** Carrow's Rest., K-Bob's, Red Lobster, Taco Bell, **lodging:** La Quinta, **other:** Barnes&Noble, CompUSA, Firestone, **S...gas:** Exxon/Subway/diesel, Shell, Whataburger/24hr, **other:** Family$, Food City

El Paso

TEXAS

Interstate 10

26   Hawkins Blvd, El Paso, **N...gas:** Chevron, Shamrock, Texaco, **food:** Arby's, Burger King, Country Kitchen, DQ, Golden Corral, IHOP, Landry's Seafood, Luby's, Olive Garden, Taco Cabana, Wyatt's Cafeteria, **lodging:** Howard Johnson, **other:** Circuit City, Dillard's, JC Penney, Office Depot, Pennzoil, Sam's Club, Sears/auto, Wal-Mart SuperCtr/gas/24hr, **S...gas:** Shamrock/diesel, **food:** China King, McDonald's, Village Inn Rest., **lodging:** Best Western

25   Airway Blvd, El Paso Airport, **N...gas:** Shell/diesel/24hr, **food:** Courtyard, **lodging:** Hampton Inn, Holiday Inn, Radisson, **other:** VW/Volvo/Mercedes, **S...gas:** Chevron/diesel/rest./24hr, **other:** Goodyear, Subaru

24b   Geronimo Dr, **N...gas:** Chevron/24hr, **food:** Seafood Galley, Steak&Ale, **other:** MEDICAL CARE, Dillard's, Mervyn's, Office Depot, Target, Walgreen, mall, **S...gas:** Fina/7-11, Phillips 66, **food:** Bombay Bicycle Club, Denny's, **lodging:** AmeriSuites, Embassy Suites, La Quinta

a   Trowbridge Dr, **N...gas:** Fina, Thunderbird Gas, **food:** Alexandrio's Mexican, Luby's, McDonald's, Steak&Ale, Whataburger, **lodging:** Budget Inn, **other:** CHIROPRACTOR, Ford, Nissan, Toyota

23b   US 62/180, to Paisano Dr, **N...food:** Jack-in-the-Box, McDonald's, **other:** Ford, U-Haul, to Carlsbad

a   Raynolds St, **S...food:** Arby's, **lodging:** Motel 6, Super 8, **other:** HOSPITAL

22b   US 54, Patriot Fwy, no facilities

a   Copia St, El Paso, **N...gas:** Fina/7-11, Shamrock, **food:** KFC

21   Piedras St, El Paso, **N...gas:** Exxon, **food:** Burger King, McDonald's, **other:** Family$

20   Dallas St, Cotton St, **N...gas:** Exxon, Church's

19   TX 20, El Paso, downtown, **N...gas:** Chevron, **S...gas:** Texaco, **lodging:** Holiday Inn, Travelodge

18b   Franklin Ave, Porfirio Diaz St, no facilities

a   Schuster Ave, **N...**Sun Bowl, **S...**to UTEP

16   Executive Ctr Blvd, **N...gas:** Shamrock/24hr, **food:** Burger King, **lodging:** Executive Inn, **other:** Ford

13b a   US 85, Paisano Dr, to Sunland Park Dr, **N...gas:** Shamrock/24hr, **food:** Barriga's Café, Carino's Italian, ChuckeCheese, Grand China, Great American Steaks, Olive Garden, Red Lobster, Sonic, Whataburger/24hr, **other:** Barnes&Noble, Best Buy, Circuit City, Dillard's, JC Penney, Office Depot, OfficeMax, PetsMart, Sears/auto, Target, mall, **S...gas:** Shamrock/diesel/24hr, Shell, **food:** La Malinche Mexican, McDonald's, Sonic, Subway, **lodging:** Best Western, Comfort Suites, Holiday Inn, Sleep Inn, Studio+, **other:** GMC/Pontiac/Buick, Sunland Park RaceTrack

12   Resler Dr(from wb), no facilities

11   TX 20, to Mesa St, Sunland Park, **N...gas:** Chevron/diesel/24hr, Circle K/gas, Shamrock/diesel/24hr, **food:** Carrow's/24hr, Chili's, CiCi's, Cracker Barrel, Denny's, Golden Corral, Jaxon's Rest/brewery, K-Bob's, LJ Silver, Papa John's, Popeye's, Rancher's Grill, Red Lobster, Souper Salad, Subway, Taco Bell, Tony Roma, Wienerschnitzel, Wendy's, Whataburger, **lodging:** Baymont Inn, Comfort Inn, La Quinta, Red Roof Inn, **other:** Albertson's, Checker Parts, Fabric Whse, Firestone/auto, Goodyear/auto, Home Depot, PepBoys, Wal-Mart SuperCtr/24hr, **S...gas:** Chevron/diesel/24hr, Shamrock/diesel/24hr, **food:** Burger King, Church's, Golden China, Hudson's Grill, KFC, Leo's Mexican, Luby's, McDonald's, Subway, Taco Cabana, Village Inn Rest., **lodging:** Best Value Inn, Day's Inn, Extended Stay America, Motel 6, Travelodge, **other:** AutoZone, Big 8 Foods, Furr's Foods, Martin Tires, Radio Shack, Sam's Club/gas, Walgreen

9   Redd Rd, **N...**Ford, **S...gas:** Phillips 66/diesel, **food:** Burger King, Pizza Hut, **other:** Albertson's/gas, Chevrolet, Honda, Lowe's Whse

8   Artcraft Rd, no facilities

6   Lp 375, to Canutillo, **N...gas:** Texaco/Taco Bell/diesel, **other:** to Trans Mountain Rd, Franklin Mtns SP, **S...gas:** Shell/Subway/diesel, **other:** RV camping

5mm   truck check sta eb

2   Westway, Vinton, **N...gas:** Petro/Mobil/Blimpie/diesel/rest./Petrolube/tires/24hr/@, **S...gas:** gas/24hr, **food:** Great American Steaks

1mm   **Welcome Ctr eb, full(handicapped)facilities, info, phone, picnic tables, litter barrels, petwalk,** weigh sta wb

0   FM 1905, Anthony, **N...gas:** ⚑/Flying J/Conoco/diesel/LP/24hr/@, **lodging:** Super 8, **rest area wb, full(handicapped) facilties, picnic tables, litter barrels, S...gas:** Chevron/deli/diesel, Exxon/Burger King/diesel/24hr, Pilot/Wendy's/diesel/24hr/@, **lodging:** Holiday Inn Express, **other:** Big 8 Foods, American RV/Marine(1mi), truckwash

0mm   Texas/New Mexico state line

Interstate 20

Exit #	Services

636mm   Texas/Louisiana state line

635.5mm   **Welcome Ctr wb/parking area eb, full(handicapped)facilities, phone, picnic tables, litter barrels, petwalk**

635   TX 9, TX 156, to Waskom, **N...gas:** Chevron/Burger King/diesel, Exxon/diesel, **food:** Burger King, DQ, Jim's BBQ, **other:** Family$

633   US 80, FM 9, FM 134, to Waskom, **N...gas:** Texaco, **food:** Catfish Village Rest.

628   to US 80(from wb), to frontage rd(from eb), no facilities

Interstate 20

E ↕ **W**

Marshall

624	FM 2199, to Scottsville, no facilities
620	FM 31, to Elysian Fields, no facilities
617	US 59, Marshall, **N...gas:** Exxon/24hr, Texaco/24hr, **food:** Applebee's, Domino's, Golden Corral, Gucci's Pizza, IHOP, Marshall City Steaks, McDonald's, Subway, Waffle House, Wendy's, **lodging:** Best Western, Express Inn, Hampton Inn, Holiday Inn Express, La Quinta, **other:** Chevrolet/Cadillac, Chrysler/Plymouth/Dodge/Jeep, Ford/Lincoln/ Mercury, Toyota, Country Pines RV Park(8mi), **S...gas:** Chevron/diesel, Conoco/diesel/@, Shamrock/diesel, Total, **food:** Hungri Maverick Rest., **lodging:** Day's Inn, Econolodge, Motel 6, Super 8
614	TX 43, to Marshall, **S...**to Martin Creek Lake SP
610	FM 3251, no facilities
608mm	**rest area both lanes, full(handicapped)facilities, phone, vending, picnic tables, litter barrels**
604	FM 450, Hallsville, **N...**gas/diesel, **other:** 450 Hitchin' Post RV Park, to Lake O' the Pines
600mm	Mason Creek
599	FM 968, Longview, **N...lodging:** Wingate Inn(8mi), **other:** Kenworth Trucks, **S...gas:** Exxon/diesel, Fina/diesel/rest./@, Phillips 66, **other:** Goodyear, truck repair
596	US 259 N, TX 149, to Lake O' Pines, **N...gas:** Exxon/ Grandy's/diesel, Texaco/diesel, **food:** Burger King, Whataburger, **lodging:** Microtel, Super 8, **other:** HOSPITAL, **S...gas:** Total/diesel, **lodging:** Holiday Inn Express, **other:** to Martin Lake SP
595b a	TX 322, Estes Pkwy, **N...gas:** Arco, Chevron/ Subway/diesel, Shamrock, Texaco/diesel/24hr, **food:** DQ, Jack-in-the-Box, Lupe's Mexican, Mc-Donald's, Pizza Hut, Stratford Inn, Waffle House, **lodging:** Best Western, Day's Inn, Econolodge, Guest Inn, **S...gas:** Chevron/diesel, Fina/diesel, **food:** KFC/Taco Bell, Shone's rest., **lodging:** Hampton Inn, La Quinta, Motel 6
593mm	Sabine River
591	FM 2087, FM 2011, no facilities
589b a	US 259, TX 31, Kilgore(exits left from wb), **N...other:** E TX Oil Museum, **1-3 mi S...food:** Kilgore Café, **lodging:** Budget Inn, Comfort Inn, Day's Inn, Holiday Inn Express, Homewood Suites, Ramada Inn
587	TX 42, Kilgore, **N...gas:** Shamrock, **food:** BBQ, **other:** E TX Oil Museum, **S...gas:** Exxon
583	TX 135, to Kilgore, Overton, **N...gas:** EZMart/gas, **other:** Shallow Creek RV Resort, **S...gas:** Exxon/ diesel
582	FM 3053, Liberty City, **N...gas:** Exxon/Subway/ diesel, Fina, Texaco, **food:** BBQ, DQ
579	Joy-Wright Mtn Rd, no facilities
575	Barber Rd, no facilities
574mm	picnic area both lanes, picnic tables, litter barrels, handicapped accessible
571b	FM 757, Omen Rd, to Starrville, no facilities
571a	US 271, to Gladewater, Tyler, **S...gas:** Chevron/ diesel
567	TX 155, **N...gas:** Citgo/diesel/ 24hr, **S...lodging:** Day's Inn
565	FM 2015, to Driskill-Lake Rd, no facilities
562	FM 14, **N...food:** Bodacious BBQ, **other:** Northgate RV Park, to Tyler SP, **S...other:** CB Shop
560	Lavender Rd, no facilities
557	Jim Hogg Rd, **N...gas:** Texaco/diesel
556	US 69, to Tyler, **N...gas:** RaceTrac, Total/diesel, **food:** Burger King, Amigo's Mexican, Juanita's Mexican, McDonald's, Pizza Inn, Subway, Taco Bell, **lodging:** Comfort Inn, Day's Inn, Hampton Inn, **S...gas:** Chevron, Texaco/DQ/diesel/24hr, **food:** Cracker Barrel, Wendy's, **lodging:** Best Value Inn
554	Harvey Rd, **S...other:** Yellow Rose RV Park
552	FM 849, **N...gas:** Chevron/24hr
548	TX 110, to Grand Saline, **N...gas:** Exxon/diesel, **S...gas:** Shamrock/diesel
546mm	check sta both lanes
544	Willow Branch Rd, **N...gas:** Conoco/diesel/rest., **other:** Willow Branch RV Park
540	FM 314, to Van, **N...gas:** Love's/Carl's Jr/diesel/24hr/ @, **food:** DQ, **lodging:** Van Inn
538mm	**rest area both lanes, full(handicapped)facilities, phone, vending, picnic tables, litter barrels, pet-walk**
537	FM 773, FM 16, no facilities
536	Tank Farm Rd, no facilities
533	Oakland Rd, to Colfax, **N...gas:** Shamrock/diesel
530	FM 1255, **N...other:** Fish & Jog RV Park
528	FM 17, to Grand Saline, no facilities

TEXAS

Interstate 20

E ↑ / W

Canton

527 TX 19, **N...gas:** Exxon/Burger King, Texaco/diesel/24hr, **food:** Jewl's Rest., Ranchero Rest., Whataburger/24hr, **lodging:** Holiday Inn Express, Luxury Suites, Super 8, **S...gas:** Chevron/diesel/24hr, Phillips 66/diesel/24hr, Shell, **food:** DQ, Dairy Palace, Jerry's Pizza, Juanita's Mexican, KFC/Taco Bell, McDonald's, **lodging:** Best Western, Day's Inn, **other:** Chrysler/Dodge/Plymouth/Jeep, Ford/Mercury, to First Monday SP, RV camping, LP

526 FM 859, to Edgewood, **N...other:** Edgewood Heritage Park, **S...other:** to First Monday SP

523 TX 64, to Canton, no facilities

521 Myrtle Springs Rd, **N...trailer sales, S...other:** Marshall's RV Ctr, RV camp/dump, U-Haul

519 Turner-Hayden Rd, **S...other:** Canton I-20 RV Park

516 FM 47, to Wills Point, **N...to Lake Tawakoni, S...gas:** Shamrock/24hr, **food:** Robertson's Café/gas, Interstate Motel/café

512 FM 2965, Hiram-Wills Point Rd, no facilities

511.5mm weigh sta both lanes

511mm **rest area both lanes, full(handicapped)facilities, phone, vending, picnic tables, litter barrels, pet-walk**

509 Hiram Rd, **S...gas:** Phillips 66/diesel/BBQ Café

506 FM 429, FM 2728, College Mound Rd, **N...gas:** Bluebonnet Ridge RV Park

503 Wilson Rd, **S...gas:** Rip Griffin/Subway/Pizza Hut/diesel/LP/24hr/@

Terrell

501 TX 34, to Terrell, **N...gas:** Chevron/24hr, Exxon/diesel, **food:** DQ, Double Steak/grill, Schlotsky's, Waffle House, **lodging:** Best Inn, Best Western, Comfort Inn, Day's Inn, Motel 6, **other:** HOSPITAL, Home Depot, **S...gas:** Citgo/diesel, Phillips 66, Total/diesel/24hr, **food:** Carmona's Cantina, McDonald's, Wendy's, **lodging:** Super 8, **other:** Tanger Outlet/famous brands

499b Rose Hill Rd, to Terrell, no facilities

a to US 80, W to Dallas, **N...gas:** Exxon/diesel, Texaco, **food:** Dennys, Grandy's, Subway

498 FM 148, to Terrell, **N...gas:** Exxon/diesel, Texaco/diesel, **food:** Denny's, Grandy's, Subway

493 FM 1641, **S...gas:** Exxon/Pizza Inn/diesel

491 FM 2932, Helms Tr, to Forney, no facilities

490 FM 741, to Forney, no facilities

487 FM 740, to Forney, **S...**Forney RV park

483 Lawson Rd, Lasater Rd, no facilities

482 Belt Line Rd, to Lasater, **S...**RV park

481 Seagoville Rd, **N...gas:** Fina, Total/diesel, **lodging:** Howard Johnson

480 I-635, N to Mesquite, no facilities

479b a US 175, **N...lodging:** access to Motel 6, **S...gas:** Shell

477 St Augustine Rd, no facilities

476 Dowdy Ferry Rd, no facilities

474 TX 310 N, Central Expsy, no facilities

473b a I-45, N to Dallas, S to Houston, no facilities

472 Bonnie View Rd, **N...gas:** ⚑/Flying J/Conoco/diesel/LP/rest./24hr/@, Shell, **food:** Jack-in-the-Box, **lodging:** Ramada Ltd, **S...gas:** TA/Exxon/Burger King/diesel/24hr/@

470 TX 342, Lancaster Rd, **N...gas:** Chevron/24hr, Pilot/DQ/Wendy's/diesel/24hr/@, **S...gas:** Pilot/diesel/24hr/2, **food:** McDonald's, Whataburger, **lodging:** Day's Inn, Quest Inn

468 Houston School Rd, **S...gas:** Exxon/diesel, **food:** Whataburger

467b a I-35E, N to Dallas, S to Waco, **1 mi N...**off of I-35E, **gas:** Shell, **food:** McDonald's

466 S Polk St, **N...gas:** Citgo, Conoco/diesel, **food:** DQ, **S...gas:** Love's/Carl's Jr/diesel/24hr/2

465 Wheatland/S Hampton Rds, **N...gas:** Shell/diesel, **S...gas:** Chevron/McDonald's, RaceWay, **food:** Arby's, BBQ, Cheddar's, Jack-in-the-Box, Popeye's, Sonic, Taco Bell, Wendy's, **lodging:** Comfort Inn, **other:** HOSPITAL, Home Depot, Buick/GMC/Hyundai, Home Depot, Kia, Lincoln/Mercury, Lowe's Whse, Mazda, OfficeMax, Sam's Club/gas, Saturn

464b a US 67, Love Fwy, no facilities

463 Camp Wisdom Rd, **N...gas:** Chevron/McDonald's, Exxon, **food:** Catfish King Rest., Denny's, Taco Cabana, **lodging:** Best Value Inn, Hampton Inn, Holiday Inn, Ramada Inn, Royal Inn, **other:** Chief Parts, Chrysler/Jeep, Ford, Nissan, **S...gas:** Fina, Texaco/diesel, **food:** Bennigan's, Blimpie, Burger King, Jack-in-the-Box, McDonald's, Olive Garden, Owens Rest., Red Lobster, Subway, Wendy's, **other:** Advance Parts, Best Buy, Circuit City, K-Mart, NTB, PepBoys, Pontiac, Target, Toyota

462b a Duncanville Rd(no EZ wb return), **S...gas:** Exxon, Shell/diesel, **food:** Arby's, KFC, Mr Gatti's, Whataburger, **lodging:** Motel 6, **other:** Goodyear, Kroger, Radio Shack

461 Cedar Ridge Rd, **S...gas:** RaceTrac

460 TX 408, no facilities

458 Mt Creek Pkwy, no facilities

457 FM 1382, to Grand Prairie, **N...gas:** Shamrock/diesel/café, Shell/diesel, **food:** Waffle House, **S...gas:** RaceTrac, **food:** Jack-in-the-Box, **other:** to Joe Pool Lake

456 Carrier Pkwy, to Corn Valley Rd, **N...food:** Chick-fil-A, Don Pablo, Taco Cabana, Whataburger, **other:** Home Depot, Kohl's, Target, **S...gas:** Fina, **food:** BBQ, Boston Mkt, Cheddar's, Chili's, Denny's, IHOP, Little Caesar's, McDonald's, Subway, TCBY, **other:** Albertson's, Eckerd, Walgreen

Dallas

Interstate 20

E
W

454 Great Southwest Pkwy, **N...gas:** Chevron/24hr, Conoco/diesel, **food:** Carino's Italian, Chuck-eCheese, KFC, McDonald's, Taco Bell, Taco Bueno, Texas Roadhouse, Waffle House, Wendy's, Wienerschnitzel, **lodging:** Day's Inn, Quality Inn, **other:** HOSPITAL, Harley-Davidson, **S...gas:** Exxon, Shamrock/Burger King, Shell/Subway/diesel, **food:** Applebee's, Arby's, Schlotsky's, **lodging:** Comfort Inn, **other:** Discount Tire, Dodge, Sam's Club, Wal-Mart SuperCtr/24hr, to Joe Pool Lake

453b a TX 360, **1-2 mi N...**Mayfield Rd, **gas:** Chevron/24hr, Fina, RaceTrac, Shell, **food:** Pizza Hut, Waffle House, Whataburger, mall, to airport, **S...**Watson Rd, **gas:** Shell

452 Frontage Rd, no facilities

451 Collins St, New York Ave, **N...gas:** Mobil, RaceTrac, **food:** Jack-in-the-Box, Pizza Hut, **other:** Acura, Mazda/VW/Kia, Saturn, **S...gas:** Shamrock, Shell, **food:** McDonald's, **other:** Nissan

450 Matlock Rd, **N...gas:** Citgo/7-11, Fina/diesel, **food:** Abuelo's Mexican, BBQ, IHOP, Mercado Juarez Café, SaltGrass Steaks, Spaghetti Whse, Tony Roma's, Wendy's, **lodging:** Comfort Inn, Hampton Inn, La Quinta, **other:** HOSPITAL, CompUSA, Lowe's Whse, Michael's, Old Navy, **S...gas:** Citgo/7-11, Shamrock, Shell, **food:** Joe's Pizza, **other:** Fry's Electronics, NTB

449 FM 157, Cooper St, **N...gas:** Fina, Mobil, Shell, 7-11, **food:** BBQ, Bennigan's, Blackeyed Pea, Chili's, China Café, CiCi's, Don Pablo, Golden Corral, Grandy's, Jack-in-the-Box, Jason's Deli, KFC, McDonald's, On the Border, Outback Steaks, Owens Rest., Razzoo's Cajun Café, Red Lobster, Schlotsky's, Souper Salad, Spaghetti Whse, Starbucks, Thai Cuisine, Wendy's, Whataburger, **lodging:** Days Inn, Holiday Inn Express, Homestead Village, Studio 6, **other:** Barnes&Noble, Best Buy, Dillard's, Discount Tire, Hancock Fabrics, Hyundai, JC Penney, Mervyn's, Office Depot, Sears/auto, Subaru, Target, mall, **S...gas:** Chevron, Citgo/7-11, Conoco, Mobil, **food:** Applebee's, Arby's, Boston Mkt, Burger King, Burger St, Chick-fil-A, Denny's, Dos Gringo's Mexican, El Fenix Mexican, HomeTown Buffet, LJ Silver, Luby's, Macaroni Grill, McDonald's, Old Country Buffet, Olive Garden, Popeye's, Shoney's, Sonic, Taco Bueno, TGIFriday, **other:** Circuit City, Ford, GMC, Home Depot, Isuzu, K-Mart, Kroger, OfficeMax, Pontiac, Wal-Mart SuperCtr/24hr

448 Bowen Rd, **N...gas:** Shell/24hr, **food:** Cracker Barrel, **S...gas:** Shell

447 Kelly-Elliot Rd, Park Springs Blvd, **N...gas:** Citgo, **S...gas:** Exxon, Fina/Blimpie, **other:** camping

445 Green Oaks Blvd, **N...gas:** Conoco, Minyard, Shell, **food:** Arby's, BBQ, Boston Mkt, Burger King, Grandy's, Jack-in-the-Box, KFC, Mac's

Grill, Pizza Hut, Pizza Inn, Taco Bell, Taipan Chinese, Whataburger, **other:** Albertson's, Eckerd/24hr, **S...gas:** Chevron/24hr, Citgo/7-11, Shamrock, **food:** Cheddar's, IHOP, Fazoli's, McDonald's, Pancho's Mexican, Schlotsky's, Sonic, Steak&Ale, Taco Bueno, Waffle House, **other:** AutoZone, Discount Tire, $General, Winn-Dixie

444 US 287 S, to Waxahatchie, no facilities

443 Bowman Springs Rd(from wb), no facilities

442b a I-820 to Ft Worth, US 287 bus, **N...gas:** Fina, **lodging:** Great Western Inn, **S...gas:** Phillips 66, Shell, **food:** DQ

441 Anglin Dr, Hartman Lane, **N...gas:** Conoco/diesel, **lodging:** Super 8, **S...gas:** Conoco/diesel

440b Forest Hill Dr, **S...gas:** Chevron/24hr, Conoco, Shell/diesel, **food:** Braum's, Capt D's, CiCi's, DQ, Denny's, Domino's, Jack-in-the-Box, Luby's, McDonald's, Sonic, Starbucks, Subway, **lodging:** Comfort Inn, **other:** Brookshire Foods, Discount Tire, Eckerd, Walgreen

a Wichita St, **N...gas:** Chevron, **food:** Taco Bell, Taco Casa, Wendy's, **S...gas:** Conoco, Fina, **food:** Chicken Express, McDonald's, Schlotsky's, Taco Bueno, Whataburger

439 Campus Dr, **N...other:** Ford, Chrysler/Plymouth/Jeep, **S...other:** Sam's Club/gas

438 Oak Grove Rd, **1 mi N...gas:** Shell, **food:** Burger King, Denny's, Jack-in-the-Box, McDonald's, Whataburger, **lodging:** Day's Inn, **S...gas:** Conoco

437 I-35W, N to Ft Worth, S to Waco

436b Hemphill St, **N...gas:** Shell/diesel, **S...other:** Chevrolet

a FM 731(from eb), to Crowley Ave, **N...other:** $General, SavALot Food, **S...gas:** Chevron, Conoco/diesel, DQ, Pizza Hut/Taco Bell

435 McCart St, **N...gas:** Conoco/diesel, Fina, **S...gas:** Shell/24hr

Ft Worth

TEXAS

Interstate 20

434	Trail Lake Dr, **N...gas:** Phillips 66, **S...gas:** Citgo, Shell, **food:** Pancho's Mexican
433	Hulen St, **N...gas:** Shell/diesel, **food:** Chuck-eCheese, Grady's Grill, Hooters, Olive Garden, Red Lobster, Souper Salad, TGIFriday, **lodging:** TownePlace Suites, **other:** MEDICAL CARE, Albertson's, Circuit City, Home Depot, Office Depot, **S...BBQ,** Bennigan's, Denny's, Jack-in-the-Box, McDonald's, Hampton Inn, mall
431	(432 from wb), TX 183, Bryant-Irvin Rd, **N...food:** Mimi's Café, **other:** Best Buy, CompUSA, Lowe's Whse, Sam's Club, **S...gas:** Chevron/24hr, Exxon, Shell, **food:** Blackeyed Pea, IHOP, Outback Steaks, Rio Mambo, SaltGrass Steaks, Sam's Rest., Subway, **lodging:** AmeriSuites, Holiday Inn Express, La Quinta, **other:** HOSPITAL, Buick, Ford, Goodyear/auto, Mazda, Saturn, Suzuki, Target
430mm	Clear Fork Trinity River
429b	Winscott Rd, no facilities
a	US 377, to Granbury, **N...gas:** Phillips 66/diesel, **food:** Cracker Barrel, **lodging:** Best Western, **S...gas:** Chevron, Exxon, RaceTrac/24hr, Shell, **food:** DQ, McDonald's, Waffle House, Whataburger/24hr, **other:** Albertson's
428	I-820, N around Ft Worth, no facilities
426	RM 2871, Chapin School Rd, no facilities
425	Markum Ranch Rd, no facilities
421	I-30 E(from eb), to Ft Worth, no facilities
420	FM 1187, Aledo, Farmer, parking, **S...other:** Cowtown RV Camping
419mm	weigh sta eb
418	Ranch House Rd, Willow Park, **N...gas:** Exxon, Shell/diesel, **food:** BBQ, Pizza Hut, Subway, Taco Casa, **S...gas:** Shell/ChickenExpress/diesel, **food:** McDonald's, **lodging:** Ramada Ltd, Brookshire Foods, Cowtown RV Park(1mi)
417mm	weigh sta wb
415	FM 5, Mikus Rd, Annetta, **S...gas:** Citgo/diesel/rest., Shell
413	(414 from wb), US 180 W, Lake Shore Dr, **N...gas:** RaceTrac, Shamrock, Texaco/diesel, **food:** DQ, Sonic, **other:** Chevrolet/Buick, Ford, Jeep, Lincoln/Mercury, Nissan, Pontiac/GMC, Toyota, **S...gas:** Chevron/diesel
410	Bankhead Hwy, **S...gas:** Love's/Subway/diesel/24hr/@
409	FM 2552 N, Clear Lake Rd, **N...gas:** Petro/Mobil/diesel/rest./24hr/@, **food:** Catfish O'Charlie's, Jack-in-the-Box, **lodging:** Best Western, **other:** HOSPITAL, Blue Beacon, **S...gas:** Chevron/diesel
408	TX 171, FM 1884, FM 51, Tin Top Rd, Weatherford, **N...gas:** Exxon/Popeye's/24hr, Mobil, **food:** Applebee's, BBQ, Braum's, China Garden, Golden Corral, IHOP, McDonald's, Montana Rest., Schlotsky's, Subway, Taco Bell, Taco Bueno, Whataburger/24hr, **lodging:** La Quinta, Super

	8, **other:** AutoZone, Home Depot, OfficeMax, Wal-Mart SuperCtr/gas/24hr, **S...gas:** Exxon/diesel, Shell/Burger King/diesel/24hr, **food:** Waffle House, **lodging:** Best Value Inn, Comfort Inn, Hampton Inn, Holiday Inn Express, Motel 6
407	Tin Top Rd(from eb), same as 408
406	Old Dennis Rd, **N...gas:** Conoco/diesel/24hr/@, **lodging:** Day's Inn, **S...gas:** Pilot/Wendy's/diesel/24hr/@
402	(403 from wb), TX 312, to Weatherford, **S...other:** RV camping
397	FM 1189, to Brock, **N...gas:** Shamrock/diesel, **S...tires**
394	FM 113, to Millsap, **N...gas:** gas/diesel/RV camping
393mm	Brazos River
391	Gilbert Pit Rd, no facilities
390mm	**rest area both lanes, full(handicapped)facilities, phone, vending, picnic tables, litter barrels, pet-walk**
386	US 281, to Mineral Wells, **N...gas:** Fina
380	FM 4, Santo, **S...other:** Windmill Acres RV Park/Roadrunner Rest./gas
376	Blue Flat Rd, Panama Rd, no facilities
373	TX 193, Gordon, no facilities
370	TX 108 S, FM 919, Gordon, **N...gas:** Citgo/Bar-B/diesel/rest., **S...other:** Longhorn Inn/RV Park
367	TX 108 N, Mingus, **N...gas:** Thurber Sta/gas, **food:** Smoke Stack Café, **S...food:** NY Hill Rest.
364mm	Palo Pinto Creek
363	Tudor Rd, picnic area, tables, litter barrels
362mm	Bear Creek, picnic area both lanes, tables, litter barrels
361	TX 16, to Strawn, no facilities
358	(from wb), frontage rd, no facilities
356mm	Russell Creek
354	Lp 254, Ranger, **2 mi N...food:** Lillie's Café, **lodging:** Relax Inn
351	(352 from wb), College Blvd, no facilities
349	FM 2461, Ranger, **N...gas:** Conoco(2mi), Love's/Subway/Godfather's/diesel/24hr/@, **food:** DQ, **lodging:** Best Value Inn, Relax Inn(2mi), **S...gas:** Chevron/diesel
347	FM 3363(from wb), Olden, **S...food:** TX Cattle Exchange Steaks
345	FM 3363(from eb), Olden, no facilities
343	TX 112, FM 570, Eastland, Lake Leon, **N...gas:** Conoco/diesel, Fina/Subway, Shell, **food:** BBQ, DQ, McDonald's, Sonic, Taco Bell, **lodging:** Super 8/RV park, **other:** AutoZone, Buick/Chevrolet/Cadillac, GMC/Pontiac $General, Ford/Mercury, Wal-Mart/drugs, **S...gas:** Exxon/Burger King/diesel/24hr, **food:** Pulido's Mexican, **lodging:** Budget Host, Ramada Inn, **other:** Chrysler/Plymouth/Dodge/Jeep
340	TX 6, Eastland, **N...gas:** Chevron/diesel, **other:** HOSPITAL, **S...gas:** Texaco/diesel

Interstate 20

E
↑
↓
W

337	spur 490, no facilities
332	US 183, Cisco, **N...gas:** Chevron, Citgo/diesel, **food:** BBQ, Cisco Café, DQ, Pizza Heaven, Sonic, Subway, **lodging:** Oak Motel, **S...gas:** Fina/diesel, **other:** Ford
330	TX 206, Cisco, **N...gas:** Chevron/diesel/White Elephant Rest./24hr, **lodging:** Best Western, **other:** HOSPITAL
329mm	picnic area wb, tables, litter barrels, handicapped accessible
327mm	picnic area eb, tables, litter barrels, handicapped accessible
324	Scranton Rd, no facilities
322	Cooper Creek Rd, no facilities
320	FM 880 N, FM 2945 N, to Moran, no facilities
319	FM 880 S, Putnam, **N...gas:** gas/diesel/café, **other:** USPO
316	Brushy Creek Rd, no facilities
313	FM 2228, no facilities
310	Finley Rd, no facilities
308	Lp 20, Baird, **1 mi S...**antiques
307	US 283, Clyde, **N...food:** DQ, **S...gas:** Conoco/diesel, **food:** Allsup's, Robertson's Café, **lodging:** Baird Motel/RV park
306	FM 2047, Baird, **N...other:** Chevrolet/Pontiac/GMC, Chrysler/Plymouth/Dodge/Jeep
303	Union Hill Rd, no facilities
301	FM 604, Cherry Lane, **N...gas:** Chevron/diesel/24hr, **food:** Subway, Whataburger/24hr, **S...gas:** Fina/diesel/café, Shell/diesel/24hr, **food:** DQ/24hr, **other:** Franklin RV Ctr, IGA Foods
300	FM 604 N, Clyde, **N...other:** Dodge, **S...gas:** Conoco, **other:** White's RV Park
299	FM 1707, Hays Rd, no facilities
297	FM 603, Eula Rd, no facilities
296.5mm	**rest area both lanes, full(handicapped)facilities, phone, picnic tables, litter barrels, petwalk**
294	Buck Creek Rd, no facilities
292b	Elmdale Rd, no facilities
a	Lp 20(exits left from wb), **S...lodging:** Travelodge
290	TX 36, Lp 322, **S...**airport, zoo
288	TX 351, **N...gas:** Allsup's/diesel, Chevron, Fina/Subway/diesel, **food:** DQ, Skillet's Café, **lodging:** Comfort Inn, Day's Inn, Executive Inn, Holiday Inn Express, Whitten Inn, **S...lodging:** Super 8, **other:** HOSPITAL
286c	FM 600, Abilene, **N...gas:** Exxon/diesel, Fina/diesel, **food:** Denny's/24hr, **lodging:** Best Western, La Quinta, **S...gas:** Chevron/diesel, **other:** Stover's Candies
286	US 83, Pine St, Abilene, **N...**Firestone, **S...gas:** Fina, Shamrock, **lodging:** Budget Host, **other:** HOSPITAL

A
b
i
l
e
n
e

285	Old Anson Rd, **N...gas:** Texaco, **lodging:** Travel Inn, **S...gas:** Texaco/diesel, **lodging:** Econolodge, Quality Inn(2mi)
283	US 277 S, US 83(exits left from wb), no facilities
282	FM 3438, Shirley Rd, **S...lodging:** Motel 6, **other:** KOA
280	Fulwiler Rd, no facilities
279	US 84 E, to Abilene, **1-3 mi S...**access to facilities
278	Lp 20, **N...gas:** Conoco/diesel/rest./24hr, **other:** GMC, diesel repair, **S...gas:** Conoco/diesel
277	FM 707, Tye, **N...gas:** ⛽/Flying J/Country Mkt/diesel/LP/24hr/@, **S...gas:** Fina, Shell/diesel
274	Wells Lane, no facilities
272	Wimberly Rd, **1 mi N...other:** truck/trailer repair
270	FM 1235, Merkel, **N...gas:** Fina/diesel, Shell/diesel/café/24hr
269	FM 126, **N...food:** Subway, **lodging:** Scottish Inn, **other:** Chevrolet/GMC, **S...gas:** Fina/diesel/rest./24hr, **food:** DQ, **lodging:** Merkel Motel/rest.
267	Lp 20, Merkel, **1mi S...**access to gas, food, lodging
266	Derstine Rd, no facilities
264	Noodle Dome Rd, no facilities
263	Lp 20, Trent, no facilities
262	FM 1085, **S...gas:** Fina/diesel/24hr
261	Lp 20, Trent, no facilities
259	Sylvester Rd, no facilities
258	White Flat Rd, oil wells
257mm	**rest area both lanes, full(handicapped)facilities, phone, vending, picnic tables, litter barrels, petwalk**
256	Stink Creek Rd, no facilities
255	Adrian Rd, no facilities
251	Eskota Rd, no facilities
249	FM 1856, no facilities
247	TX 70 N, Sweetwater, no facilities

TEXAS

Interstate 20

246	Alabama Ave, Sweetwater, no facilities
245	Arizona Ave(from wb), same as 244
244	TX 70 S, Sweetwater, **N...gas:** Chevron/diesel, Fina/diesel/24hr, **food:** DQ, McDonald's, **lodging:** Holiday Inn, Motel 6, **other:** HOSPITAL, AutoZone, Ford/Mercury, **S...gas:** Chevron, Shell, **food:** Golden Chick, Jack's Steaks, Schlotsky's, Taco Bell, **lodging:** Comfort Inn, Ramada Inn, Ranch House Motel, **other:** Chevrolet/Pontiac/Buick/Cadillac, K-Mart
243	Hillsdale Rd, Robert Lee St, **N...other:** Bewley's Service
242	Hopkins Rd, **S...gas:** TA/Conoco/Pizza Hut/diesel/24hr/@, **other:** Goodyear, Rolling Plains RV Park
241	Lp 20, Sweetwater, **N...gas,** food, lodging, **S...RV** camping
240	Lp 170, **N...airport,** camping
239	May Rd, no facilities
238b a	US 84 W, Blackland Rd, **N...gas:** Scott's Fuel
237	Cemetery Rd, no facilities
236	FM 608, Roscoe, **N...gas:** Shell, T&C/diesel, **S...food:** DQ
235	to US 84, Roscoe, no facilities
230	FM 1230, no facilities
229mm	picnic area wb, tables, litter barrels, handicapped accessible
228mm	picnic area eb, tables, litter barrels, handicapped accessible
227	Narrell Rd, no facilities
226b	Lp 20(from wb), Loraine, no facilities
a	FM 644 N, Wimberly Rd, no facilities
225	FM 644 S, **1 mi S...access** to gas, food
224	Lp 20, to Loraine, **1 mi S...gas,** food
223	Lucas Rd, no facilities
221	Lasky Rd, no facilities
220	FM 1899, no facilities
219	Lp 20, Country Club Rd, Colorado City, no facilities
217	TX 208 S, **S...food:** Summer's Rest.
216	TX 208 N, **N...gas:** Chevron/diesel, **food:** DQ, Subway, **lodging:** Day's Inn, **S...gas:** Phillips 66/Burger King/diesel, **food:** Pizza Hut, Sonic, **lodging:** Best Value Inn, **other:** HOSPITAL
215	FM 3525, Rogers Rd, **2 mi S...access** to gas, food
214.5mm	Colorado River
213	Lp 20, Enderly Rd, Colorado City, no facilities
212	FM 1229, no facilities
211mm	Morgan Creek
210	FM 2836, **S...gas:** Fina/diesel, **other:** to Lake Colorado City SP, picnic area, camping
209	Dorn Rd, no facilities
207	Lp 20, Westbrook, **S...gas**
206	FM 670, to Westbrook, **N...gas:** Citgo/diesel
204mm	**rest area wb, full(handicapped)facilities, phone, picnic tables, litter barrels, petwalk**

200	Conaway Rd, no facilities
199	Iatan Rd, no facilities
195	frontage rd(from eb), no facilities
194	E Howard Field Rd(from wb), no facilities
192	FM 821, many oil wells
191mm	**rest area eb, full(handicapped)facilities, phone, picnic tables, litter barrels, petwalk**
190	Snyder Field Rd, no facilities
189	McGregor Rd, no facilities
188	FM 820, Coahoma, **N...gas:** T&C/diesel, **food:** DQ, **lodging:** motel, **other:** USPO
186	Salem Rd, Sand Springs, no facilities
184	Moss Lake Rd, Sand Springs, **N...gas:** Phillips 66/diesel, **S...RV** camping
182	Midway Rd, no facilities
181b	Refinery Rd, **N...gas:** Fina Refinery
a	FM 700, **N...airport,** RV camping, **2 mi S...HOSPITAL**
179	US 80, Big Spring, **S...gas:** Fina/7-11, Texaco, **food:** DQ, Denny's, **lodging:** Comfort Inn, Great Western Inn, **other:** IGA Foods, Eckerd, Chevrolet/Pontiac/Buick
178	TX 350, Big Spring, **N...gas:** Texaco/diesel
177	US 87, Big Spring, **N...gas:** Exxon/diesel, Rip Griffin/Subway/diesel/24hr/@, **lodging:** Econolodge, Motel 6, Super 8, **S...gas:** Chevron/diesel, Fina/diesel, **food:** DQ, **lodging:** Holiday Inn Express
176	TX 176, Andrews, no facilities
174	Lp 20 E, Big Springs, **S...gas:** Texaco/diesel, **other:** airport
172	Cauble Rd, no facilities
171	Moore Field Rd, no facilities
169	FM 2599, no facilities
168mm	picnic area both lanes, tables, littter barrels
165	FM 818, no facilities
158	Lp 20 W, to Stanton, **N...RV** camping
156	TX 137, Lamesa, **S...gas:** Shamrock/Subway/diesel/24hr, **food:** DQ, Sonic
154	US 80, Stanton, **2 mi S...access** to gas, food, lodging
151	FM 829(from wb), no facilities
144	US 80, **2-3 mi N...facilities** in Midland
143mm	frontage rd(from eb), no facilities
142mm	picnic area both lanes, tables, litter barrels, hist marker
138	TX 158, FM 715, Greenwood, **N...gas:** Texaco/diesel, **food:** BBQ, Whataburger, **S...gas:** T&C/Subway/diesel
137	Old Lamesa Rd, no facilities
136	TX 349, Midland, **N...gas:** Phillips 66/diesel, **food:** McDonald's, Sonic, **lodging:** Howard Johnson, Super 8, **other:** IGA/gas, Family$, Petroleum Museum, **S...gas:** Exxon/Burger King/diesel, T&C, Texaco/diesel

Big Spring

Midland

Interstate 20

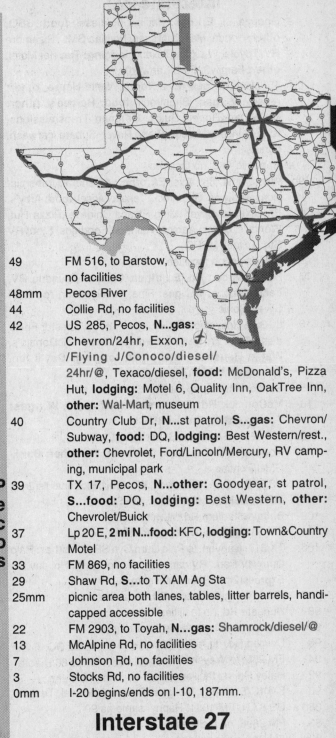

E		
W		

Odessa

134 Midkiff Rd, **N...gas:** T&C/Subway/diesel, **1 mi N on Wall St...**Fina/7-11, Exxon, **food:** Denny's, **lodging:** Best Western, Day's Inn, Executive Inn, La Quinta, Sleep Inn, **other:** HOSPITAL, Chevrolet, Chrysler/Plymouth/Jeep, Honda, Kia, Lincoln/Mercury, Mercedes/Volvo, Nissan

131 TX 158, Midland, **N...lodging:** Travelodge, **other:** RV camping

126 FM 1788, **N...gas:** Chevron/diesel, Warfield/Mobil/Subway/diesel/@, **other:** museum, airport

121 Lp 338, Odessa, **N...food:** Denny's, McDonald's, **lodging:** Day's Inn, Holiday Inn Express, La Quinta, Motel 6, **other:** U of TX Permian Basin, **1 mi N...gas:** Fina/7-11, **lodging:** Elegante Hotel, **3 mi N on TX 191 W...food:** Chili's, Fazoli's, Logan's Roadhouse, McDonald's, On-the-Border, Quizno's, Whataburger, **lodging:** Fairfield Inn, Hampton Inn, **other:** Albertson's, Circuit City, Home Depot, Sears/auto, Sam's Club/gas, Wal-Mart SuperCtr/24hr

118 FM 3503, Grandview Ave, **N...gas:** Fina/diesel, **other:** Freightliner/Peterbilt, HOSPITAL

116 US 385, Odessa, **N...gas:** T&C, **food:** DQ, **lodging:** Best Western, Delux Inn, Villa West Inn, **other:** HOSPITAL, **S...gas:** Phillips 66/diesel, Texaco/diesel, **lodging:** Motel 6, **other:** city park

115 FM 1882, **N...gas:** Fina/Country Cookin

113 TX 302, Odessa, no facilities

112 FM 1936, Odessa, **N...gas:** Citgo/diesel

108 Moss Ave, Meteor Crater, no facilities

104 FM 866, Meteor Crater Rd, no facilities

103.5mm weigh sta wb/parking area eb, litter barrels

101 FM 1601, Penwell, no facilities

92 (93 from wb), FM 1053, no facilities

86 TX 41, **N...**Monahans Sandhills SP, camping

83 US 80, Monahans, **2 mi N...gas:** Citgo, **other:** HOSPITAL, RV camping

Monahans

80 TX 18, Monahans, **N...gas:** Chevron/diesel/24hr, Exxon, **food:** Bar H Steaks, Big Burger, DQ, McDonald's, Sonic, **other:** HOSPITAL, Alco Discount, CarQuest, Chrysler/Plymouth/Dodge/Jeep, Furr's Foods, Lowe's Foods, Country Club RV Park(2mi), **S...gas:** Fina/diesel/24hr, Kent Gas, Phillips 66/diesel, **lodging:** Texan Inn, **other:** Chevrolet/Pontiac/Buick/GMC

79 Lp 464, Monahans, no facilities

76 US 80, Monahans, **2 mi N...other:** to Million Barrel Museum, RV camping

73 FM 1219, Wickett, **N...gas:** Texaco/Allsup's, **S...gas:** Mobil/Subway/diesel/24hr

70 TX 65, no facilities

69.5mm **rest area both lanes, full(handicapped)facilities, phone, picnic tables, litter barrels, petwalk**

66 FM 1927, to Pyote, no facilities

58 frontage rd, multiple oil wells

52 Lp 20 W, to Barstow, no facilities

49 FM 516, to Barstow, no facilities

48mm Pecos River

44 Collie Rd, no facilities

42 US 285, Pecos, **N...gas:** Chevron/24hr, Exxon, /Flying J/Conoco/diesel/24hr/@, Texaco/diesel, **food:** McDonald's, Pizza Hut, **lodging:** Motel 6, Quality Inn, OakTree Inn, **other:** Wal-Mart, museum

40 Country Club Dr, **N...**st patrol, **S...gas:** Chevron/Subway, **food:** DQ, **lodging:** Best Western/rest., **other:** Chevrolet, Ford/Lincoln/Mercury, RV camping, municipal park

Pecos

39 TX 17, Pecos, **N...other:** Goodyear, st patrol, **S...food:** DQ, **lodging:** Best Western, **other:** Chevrolet/Buick

37 Lp 20 E, **2 mi N...food:** KFC, **lodging:** Town&Country Motel

33 FM 869, no facilities

29 Shaw Rd, **S...**to TX AM Ag Sta

25mm picnic area both lanes, tables, litter barrels, handicapped accessible

22 FM 2903, to Toyah, **N...gas:** Shamrock/diesel/@

13 McAlpine Rd, no facilities

7 Johnson Rd, no facilities

3 Stocks Rd, no facilities

0mm I-20 begins/ends on I-10, 187mm.

Interstate 27

Amarillo

Exit # Services

I-27 begins/ends on I-40, exit 70 in Amarillo.

123b I-40, W to Albuquerque, E to OK City

a 26th Ave, **E...gas:** Conoco, **W...food:** DJ Burgers

122b 34th Ave, Tyler St, no facilities

a FM 1541, Washington St, Parker St, Moss Lane, **E...gas:** Texaco, **food:** Sonic **W...gas:** Texaco, **food:** Taco Bell

121b Hawthorne Dr, Austin St, **E...lodging:** Amarillo Motel, **other:** Honda Motorcycles, **W...gas:** Texaco/diesel, **other:** Scottie's Transmissions

N
↑
S

Interstate 27

N
↕
S

Exit	Description
a	Georgia St, **E…gas:** Phillips 66/diesel, **food:** BBQ, **other:** Honda, Mazda, Nissan, Pontiac/GMC, Sizemore RV, Toyota, **W…gas:** Texaco, **lodging:** Traveler Motel, **other:** Family$, Ford/Kenworth
120b	45th Ave, **E…gas:** Fina, **food:** Waffle House, **other:** repair, **W…gas:** Shamrock, **food:** Hardee's, **other:** BMW/LandRover, Buick, Cottman Transmissions, Isuzu, Lincoln/Mercury, Land Rover, Subaru, carwash, donuts
a	Republic Ave, no facilities
119b	Western St, 58th Ave, **E…other:** $General, transmissions, **W…gas:** Shamrock, Texaco/diesel, **food:** Arby's, Braum's, LJ Silver, Ming Palace Chinese, Pizza Hut, Wendy's, **other:** Aamco, Rainbow Food/gas, Stout RV Ctr, U-Haul, USPO
a	W Hillside, no facilities
117	Bell St, Arden Rd, **E…other:** Camper Roundup RV, transmissions, **W…gas:** Fina, Texaco/24hr, **food:** LJ Silver, Sonic
116	Lp 335, Hollywood Rd, **E…gas:** Love's/Chester Fried/ diesel/24hr/@, Phillips 66/diesel, **food:** McDonald's, Waffle House, Whataburger, **lodging:** Day's Inn, **W…other:** HOSPITAL(8mi)
115	Sundown Lane, no facilities
113	McCormick Rd, **E…other:** Ford/Suzuki, **W…gas:** Texaco, **other:** Family RV Ctr
112	FM 2219, **E…other:** Stater's RV Ctr
111	Rockwell Rd, **E…other:** Chevrolet, **W…other:** Buick/ GMC/Pontiac
110	US 87 S, US 60 W, Canyon, **W…food:** McDonald's(2mi), **other:** Buick/GMC/Pontiac, WTSU
109	Buffalo Stadium Rd, **W…stadium**
108	FM 3331, Hunsley Rd, no facilities
106	TX 217, Canyon, to Palo Duro Cyn SP, **E…other:** Palo Duro RV Park, RV camping, **W…lodging:** Holiday Inn Express(2mi), Plains Museum
103	FM 1541 N, Cemetery Rd, no facilities
99	Hungate Rd, no facilities
97mm	parking area both lanes, litter barrels
96	Dowlen Rd, no facilities
94	FM 285, to Wayside, no facilities
92	Haley Rd, no facilities
90	FM 1075, Happy, **W…gas:** Phillips 66/diesel, Texaco
88b a	US 87 N, FM 1881, Happy, same as 90
83	FM 2698, no facilities
82	FM 214, no facilities
77	US 87, Tulia, **1 mi E…food:** Pizza Hut, **other:** HOSPI-TAL, gas, lodging, airport
75	NW 6th St, Tulia, **1 mi E…food:** DQ, **lodging:** Best Western, **W…same as 74**
74	TX 86, Tulia, **E…lodging:** Best Western(1mi), Lasso Motel, **other:** HOSPITAL, **W…gas:** Rip Griffin/Grandy's/ Subway/diesel/24hr/@, **lodging:** Select Inn
70mm	parking area both lanes, litter barrels
68	FM 928, no facilities
63	FM 145, Kress, **1 mi E…gas/diesel, food, phone**

Plainview

Exit	Description
61	US 87, County Rd, no facilities
56	FM 788, no facilities
54	FM 3183, to Plainview, **W…truck service**
53	Lp 27, Plainview, **E…other:** HOSPITAL, access to gas, food, lodging
51	Quincy St, no facilities
50	TX 194, Plainview, **E…gas:** Phillips 66, **other:** HOSPI-TAL, Wal-Mart Dist, to Wayland Bapt U
49	US 70, Plainview, **E…gas:** Fina, Phillips 66, Shamrock/ diesel, Texaco/Subway/diesel, **food:** Carlito's Mexican, Cotton Patch Café, Domino's, FarEast Chinese, Furr's Café, Kettle, LJ Silver/A&W, Pizza Hut, Sonic, Taco Bell, Tokyo Steaks, **lodging:** Best Western, Comfort Suites, Day's Inn, **other:** Buick/Pontiac/Cadillac/GMC, Chrysler/Jeep, Ford/Lincoln/Mercury/Toyota, GNC, Hastings Books, NAPA, O'Reilly Parts, Radio Shack, United Foods, **W…gas:** Chevron, Phillips 66/diesel, **food:** Burger King, Chicken Express, Little Mexico, McDonald's, Mr Gatti's, Subway, **lodging:** Holiday Inn Express, Ramada Ltd, **other:** JC Penney, Wal-Mart
45	Lp 27, to Plainview, no facilities
43	FM 2337, no facilities
41	County Rd, no facilities
38	Main St, no facilities
37	FM 1914, Cleveland St, **E…gas:** Co-op, **food:** DQ, **W…HOSPITAL**
36	FM 1424, Hale Center, no facilities
32	FM 37 W, no facilities
31	FM 37 E, no facilities
29mm	**rest area both lanes, full(handicapped)facilities, phone, picnic tables, litter barrels, petwalk**
27	County Rd, no facilities
24	FM 54, **W…RV park/dump**
22	Lp 369, Abernathy, **E…gas:** Phillips 66, **W…gas:** Phillips 66/diesel, **food:** DQ
21	FM 597, Main St, Abernathy, **W…gas:** Conoco/diesel, Co-op/diesel, **food:** Cyclone Rest., DQ
20	Abernathy(from nb), no facilities
17	County Rd 53, no facilities
15	Lp 461, to New Deal, **1/2mi E…gas:** Texaco/Subway/ diesel/24hr, **other:** phone
14	FM 1729, same as 15
13	Lp 461, to New Deal, no facilities
12	access rd(from nb), no facilities
11	FM 1294, Shallowater, no facilities
10	Keuka St, **E…other:** Airborne Express, Fed Ex
9	Airport Rd, **E…airport, W…other:** Lubbock RV Park/ dump
8	FM 2641, Regis St, no facilities
7	Yucca Lane, **W…lodging:** Country Creek Motel, Texas Star Inn/rest.
6b a	Lp 289, Ave Q, Lubbock, **E…other:** Pharr RV, **W…lodging:** Texas Motel/rest.
5	Ave H, Municipal Dr, **E…other:** Mackenzie Park
4	US 82, US 87, 4th St, to Crosbyton, **E…fairgrounds, W…to TTU**

Interstate 27

N ↕ S

Lubbock

3	US 62, TX 114, 19ᵗʰ St, no facilities
2	34ᵗʰ St, **E...gas:** Phillips 66, **lodging:** Budget Motel, **W...**MEDICAL CARE
1c	50ᵗʰ St, **E...gas:** Fina, **food:** El Jalapeno Café, JoJo's Burgers, **W...gas:** Fina/7-11, Shamrock/diesel, **food:** Bryan's Steaks, Burger King, ChinaStar Buffet, Church's, DQ, Domino's, KFC, LJ Silver/A&W, McDonald's, Pizza Hut/Taco Bell, Subway, Taco Villa, Whataburger/24hr, Wienerschnitzel, **other:** MEDICAL CARE, Chrysler/ Plymouth, $General, O'Reilly Parts, United Food/drug/ gas, USPO, Walgreen, Woody Tires
b	US 84, **E...lodging:** Circus Inn, Day's Inn, Super 8, **W... gas:** Skillet's Burgers, **lodging:** Best Western, Comfort Inn, Holiday Inn Express, Motel 6, Ramada Ltd
a	Lp 289, **W...other:** Sims RV Ctr
1	82ⁿᵈ St, **W...gas:** Phillips 66

I-27 begins/ends on US 87 at 82ⁿᵈ St in S Lubbock.

Interstate 30

E ↕ W

Texarkana

Exit #	Services
223mm	Texas/Arkansas state line
223b a	US 59, US 71, State Line Ave, Texarkana, **N...gas:** Citgo/diesel, EZ Mart, Shell, **food:** Denny's, IHOP, Pizza Inn, Red Lobster, Waffle House, **lodging:** Baymont Inn, Best Western, Comfort Suites, Holiday Inn, Hampton Inn, Holiday Inn Express, Quality Inn, Sheraton, Super 8, **other:** tires, **S...gas:** Conoco/diesel, Exxon, RaceTrac, Texaco, Total, **food:** Arby's, Backyard Burger, Baskin-Robbins, Bennigan's, Burger King, Cattlemen's Steaks, CiCi's, El Chico, KFC, La Carreta Mexican, Lee's China, LJ Silver, Mandarin House, McDonald's, Papa John's, Pizza Hut, Pizza Inn, Schlotsky's, Subway, Taco Bell, Taco Tico, Wendy's, Whataburger/24hr, **lodging:** Best Western, Comfort Inn, Day's Inn, Econolodge, Economy Inn, Express Inn, Knight's Inn, La Quinta, Motel 6, **other:** Albertson's, AutoZone, Chevrolet/Buick, Chrysler/ Jeep, Radio Shack, Wal-Mart SuperCtr/24hr, Walgreen
223mm	**Welcome Ctr wb, full(handicapped)facilities, info, phone, picnic tables, litter barrels, vending, petwalk**
222	TX 93, FM 1397, Summerhill Rd, **N...gas:** Shell, Total/Subway, **food:** Applebee's, McDonald's, Waffle House, **lodging:** Motel 6, **other:** MEDICAL CARE, Ford/Freightliner, Goodyear/auto, Honda, **S...gas:** Chevron, Exxon, Texaco/24hr, **food:** Bryce's Rest., **lodging:** Ramada Inn, **other:** Mazda/Isuzu/GMC
220b	FM 559, Richmond Rd, **N...gas:** Exxon, EZ Mart, **food:** Burger King, Carino's Italian, Cracker Barrel, DQ, Domino's, McAlister's Deli, Pizza Hut, Poncho's Mexican, Popeye's, Sonic, Taco Bell, TaMolly's Mexican, Texas Roadhouse, **lodging:** Comfort Suites, **other:** Sam's Club, Super 1 Food/gas, **S...gas:** Total/diesel, **food:** Arby's, Chili's, El Chico's, Gold-

New Boston

	en Corral, Grandy's, Lee's Chinese, Luby's McDonald's, Outback Steaks, Subway/Baskin-Robbins, **other:** AutoZone, Albertson's, BooksAMillion, Dillard's, JC Penney, Michael's, Office Depot, Sears/auto, Target, Walgreen, mall
220a	US 59 S, Texarkana, **S...gas:** Exxon/Wendy's, **food:** DQ, **other:** Lowe's Whse, Radio Shack, Sam's Club, Wal-Mart SuperCtr/gas/24hr, mall
218	FM 989, Nash, **N...gas:** Citgo/diesel/24hr, **other:** cinema, **S...gas:** Exxon/Burger King/diesel, **other:** White/GMC/Volvo, to Lake Patman
213	FM 2253, Leary, **N...other:** Palma RV Ctr
212	spur 74, Lone Star Army Ammo Plant, **S...gas:** Texaco
208	FM 560, Hooks, **N...gas:** Citgo/diesel/24hr, Texaco/ diesel/24hr, **food:** Farm Mkt BBQ, **lodging:** Hooks Motel, **S...gas:** Total/diesel/24hr, **food:** DQ, **other:** Family$
206	TX 86, **S...other:** Red River Army Depot
201	TX 8, New Boston, **N...gas:** Texaco/diesel, Total/diesel, **lodging:** Tex Inn, **other:** Chevrolet, Chrysler/Dodge, **S...gas:** Chevron/Subway/diesel, Exxon/Burger King, EZ/24hr, Phillips 66/diesel, **food:** Catfish King, Church's, DQ, KFC/Taco Bell, McDonald's, Pizza Hut, TCBY, **lodging:** Best Western, Bostonian Inn, **other:** HOSPITAL, Brookshire's Foods, Eckerd, Ford/Mercury, Wal-Mart/drugs
199	US 82, New Boston, **N...gas:** Texaco
198	TX 98, **N...gas:** Texaco
193mm	Anderson Creek
192	FM 990, **N...gas:** FuelStop/diesel/café
191mm	**rest area both lanes, full(handicapped)facilities, phone, picnic tables, litter barrels, vending, petwalk**
186	FM 561, no facilities
181mm	Sulphur River
178	US 259, to DeKalb, Omaha, no facilities
174mm	White Oak Creek

TEXAS

Interstate 30

170   FM 1993, no facilities

165   FM 1001, **S...gas:** Chevron/diesel

162   US 271, FM 1402, FM 2152, Mt Pleasant, **N...gas:** Exxon/diesel/24hr, **food:** Applebee's, Pitt Grill, **lodging:** Holiday Inn Express, Super 8, **S...gas:** Shell/diesel, Texaco/diesel, Total/Subway/diesel, **food:** Burger King, DQ, McDonald's, **lodging:** Best Western/rest., **other:** HOSPITAL, Chevrolet/Cadillac

160   US 67, US 271, TX 49, Mt Pleasant, **N...food:** Senorita's Mexican, **other:** Buick/Pontiac/GMC(1mi), **S...gas:** Exxon/diesel, Texaco/diesel, **food:** El Chico, Elmwood Café, Sally's Café, Schlotsky's, Western Sizzlin, **lodging:** Comfort Inn, Day's Inn, Ramada Inn, Sands Motel

157mm   weigh sta both lanes

156   frontage rd, no facilities

153   spur 185, to Winfield, Miller's Cove, **N...gas:** Chevron, Citgo/diesel/café, **other:** diesel repair, RV camping, **S...gas:** Citgo

150   Ripley Rd, **N...other:** Lowe's Distribution

147   spur 423, **N...gas:** Love's/Subway/Taco Bell/diesel/24hr/@, **S...lodging:** Super 8

146   TX 37, Mt Vernon, **N...gas:** Exxon, **other:** HOSPITAL, **S...gas:** Chevron/diesel/24hr, Fina/diesel/24hr, **food:** BarnStormer's Café, Burger King, DQ, Hubbard's Café, La Cabana Mexican, Sonic, TX BBQ, **lodging:** Super 8, **other:** to Lake Bob Sandlin SP

143   rest area both lanes, full(handicapped)facilities, phone, picnic tables, litter barrels, vending, petwalk

142   County Line Rd, no facilities

141   FM 900, Saltillo Rd, no facilities

136   FM 269, Weaver Rd, **N...gas:** Phillips 66

135   US 67 N, no facilities

131   FM 69, no facilities

127   US 67, Lp 301, **N...lodging:** Budget Inn, Comfort Inn, Holiday Inn, **S...gas:** Chevron, Texaco, Burton's Rest./24hr, Best Western

126   FM 1870, College St, **S...gas:** Chevron/diesel/rest., Exxon, Texaco/24hr, **food:** Burton's Rest./24hr, **lodging:** Best Western, **other:** Firestone/auto

125   Frontage Rd, same as 124

124   TX 11, TX 154, Sulphur Springs, **N...gas:** Chevron/diesel, Exxon, **food:** BBQ, Catfish King Rest., Domino's, Hal's Diner, Happy Moon Chinese, KFC, Peddlar's Pizza, Pitt Grill, Pizza Hut, San Rimo Italian, Sonic, Subway, TaMolly's Mexican, **lodging:** Royal Inn, **other:** HOSPITAL, AutoZone, Cadillac, Chevrolet/Buick/GMC, Chrysler/Jeep, $General, Family$, Ford, GNC, Kroger/24hr, Nissan, USPO, VF Outlet/famous brands, **S...gas:** Exxon/diesel, Shell, Texco/diesel, **food:** Braum's, Burger King, Chili's, China House, Furr's Rest., Grandy's, Jack-in-the-Box, K-Bob's Steaks, McDonald's, Pizza Inn, San Remo's Italian, Taco Bell, Whataburger, Wendy's, **lodging:** Holiday King Motel, **other:** Eckerd, Wal-Mart SuperCtr/gas/24hr(1mi), factory outlet

123   FM 2297, League St, **N...gas:** Texaco

122   TX 19, to Emory, **N...HOSPITAL, S...gas:** Phillips 66/diesel/rest./24hr, Pilot/Arby's/diesel/24hr/@, **other:** Shady Lakes RV Park, to Cooper Lake

120   US 67 bus, no facilities

116   US 67, FM 2653, Brashear Rd, no facilities

110   FM 275, Cumby, **N...gas:** Phillips 66, **S...gas:** Texaco/24hr

104   FM 513, FM 2649, Campbell, **S...**to Lake Tawakoni

101   TX 24, TX 50, FM 1737, to Commerce, **N...gas:** Phillips 66/diesel, **other:** to E TX St U

97   Lamar St, **N...gas:** Exxon/diesel, **lodging:** Dream Lodge Motel

96   US 67, Lp 302, **S...gas:** Fina

95   Division St, **S...other:** HOSPITAL, Puddin Hill Fruit Cakes

94b a   US 69, US 380, Greenville, **N...gas:** Texaco, Total/diesel, **food:** Ninfa's Mexican, **lodging:** American Inn, Best Western, Royal Inn, **S...gas:** Chevron/24hr, Exxon, Fina, **food:** Arby's, Burger King, Catfish King Rest., McDonald's, **lodging:** Comfort Inn, Economy Inn, Motel 6, Ramada Inn, Super 8, **other:** Chrysler/Dodge/Jeep

93b a   US 67, TX 34 N, Greenville, **N...gas:** Exxon, Mobil, Phillips 66, Texaco, **food:** Applebee's, CiCi's, Grandy's, IHOP, Jack-in-the-Box, KFC, LJ Silver/A&W, Royal Drive-In, Ryan's, Schlotsky's, Sonic, Subway, Taco Bell, Taco Bueno, TaMolly's Mexican, TCBY, Tony's Italian, Wendy's, Whataburger/24hr, **other:** HOSPITAL, Belk, Brookshire's Foods, Buick/Pontiac, Cadillac, Goody's, JC Penney, Staples, USPO, mall, **S...gas:** Chevron/diesel, Exxon/diesel/24hr, **food:** Chili's, Cracker Barrel, Dickie's BBQ, Luby's, Red Lobster, **lodging:** Holiday Inn Express, **other:** Ford/Lincoln/Mercury, Home Depot, Radio Shack, RV Ctr, Wal-Mart SuperCtr/24hr

90mm   Farber Creek

89   FM 1570, **S...lodging:** Luxury Inn, **other:** Lake Country RV Ctr

89mm   E Caddo Creek

87   FM 1903, **N...gas:** Chevron/Pizza Inn/diesel, **S...gas:** Exxon/Pancake House/diesel, Texaco/diesel/24hr

87mm   Elm Creek

85   FM 36, Caddo Mills, **N...**RV camping, **S...**auto repair

85mm   W Caddo Creek

83   FM 1565 N, **N...gas:** Exxon/diesel

79   FM 2642, no facilities

77b   FM 35, Royse City, **N...gas:** Exxon/diesel, Knox/Subway/diesel/24hr/@, **food:** BBQ

a   TX 548, **N...gas:** Texaco/diesel, **food:** Jack-in-the-Box, McDonald's, **lodging:** Sun Royse Inn, **S...gas:** Conoco

73   FM 551, Fate, no facilities

70   FM 549, **S...gas:** Love's/diesel/24hr/@

69   (from wb), frontage rd

68   TX 205, to Rock Wall, **N...gas:** RaceTrac, Shell, Texaco, **food:** Braum's, DQ, KFC, Luigi's Italian, Pizza Hut, Pizza Inn, Whataburger, **lodging:** Holiday Inn Express, Super 8, **other:** Chevrolet, Dodge, Ford/Mercury, **S...gas:** TA/diesel/rest./24hr/@

Interstate 30

E ↕ **W**

67b FM 740, Ridge Rd, **N...gas:** Chevron, Mobil, **food:** Arby's, Burger King, Cajun Catfish, Grandy's, IHOP, McDonald's, Schlotsky's, Waffle House, **other:** Goodyear/auto, Kwik Kar Lube, MailBoxes Etc, Wal-Mart SuperCtr/24hr, cleaners, **S...gas:** Chevron, Exxon/Pizza Inn, Texaco, Total, **food:** Applebee's, Blackeyed Pea, Carino's Italian, Chick-fil-A, Chili's, ChuckeCheese, El Chico, Jack-in-the-Box, McDonald's, On-the-Border, Starbucks, Subway, Taco Bell, TCBY, **lodging:** Country Inn Suites, **other:** Albertson's, Discount Tire, Eckerd, GNC, Home Depot, Kohl's, Kroger, Lowe's Whse, Michael's, OfficeMax, Old Navy, Radio Shack, Ross, SteinMart, Target, to Lake Tawakoni

a Horizon Rd, Village Dr, **N...gas:** Total, **food:** Café Express, RanchHouse Rest., Saltgrass Steaks, Culpeper Cattle Steaks

66mm Ray Hubbard Reservoir

64 Dalrock Rd, Rowlett, **N...gas:** Exxon, Shamrock/diesel, **food:** Dickie's BBQ, **lodging:** Comfort Suites, **other:** HOSPITAL, Express Drug

63mm Ray Hubbard Reservoir

62 Chaha Rd, **N...food:** Martinez Mexican, **lodging:** Best Western, **other:** cleaners, to Hubbard RA, **S...gas:** Shamrock, Texaco, **other:** $General

61 Zion Rd, **N...gas:** Conoco/diesel, **lodging:** motel

60b Bobtown Rd, **N...gas:** Mobil, **food:** Jack-in-the-Box, **S...gas:** Texaco, **food:** Catfish King Rest.

a Rose Hill Dr, no facilities

59 Beltline Rd, Garland, **N...gas:** Citgo/7-11, Total, **food:** Church's, Denny's, LJ Silver, McDonald's, Whataburger, Wendy's, Taco Bell, **lodging:** MEDICAL CARE, **other:** Albertson's, Chief Parts, Eckerd, Goodyear, Wal-Mart SuperCtr/24hr, **S...gas:** Exxon/diesel, Shell, **food:** Burger King, DQ, Grandy's, Waffle House, Williams Chicken, lodging: Day's Inn, I-30 Inn, Motel 6, **other:** Kroger

58 Northwest Dr, **N...gas:** Shamrock, Texaco, **other:** Nissan, **S...gas:** Fina, **food:** Jack-in-the-Box, **other:** Lowe's Whse

56c b I-635 S, I 635 N

a Galloway Ave, Gus Thomasson Dr, **N...gas:** Shamrock, **food:** KFC, **S...gas:** Citgo/7-11, **food:** Checker's, Grandy's, Luby's, On-the-Border, Subway, Wendy's, Kroger, **lodging:** Courtyard, Crossland Studios, Delux Inn, Fairfield Inn, **other:** MEDICAL CARE, Nichols RV Ctr, other multiple facilities, Bigtown Mall...Hooters, Olive Garden, Outback Steaks, Red Lobster, Steak&Ale, Celebration Sta, Circuit City, NTB, Sears

55 Motley Dr, **N...gas:** Texaco/diesel, **food:** Castillo Mexican, **lodging:** Astro Inn, Ramada Ltd, **S...gas:** Chevron, Fina, **food:** Golden Ox Café, **lodging:** Mesquite Inn, Microtel, **other:** HOSPITAL, Dodge, to Eastfield Coll

D a l l a s

54 Bigtown Blvd, **N...gas:** Shell, Texaco, **lodging:** Best Western, **S...gas:** TA/diesel/rest./24hr/@ , **lodging:** Texas Motel, **other:** Holiday World RV Ctr, mall

53b US 80 E, to Terrell, **N...**Toyota

a Lp 12, **N...lodging:** Luxury Inn, **other:** Chevrolet, **S...food:** CiCi's, Whataburger, **lodging:** Holiday Inn Express, **other:** Ford, K-Mart, Sam's Club, Staples, Wal-Mart SuperCtr/gas/24hr

51 Highland Rd, **N...gas:** Exxon, **food:** Country China, Denny's, Kettle, Luby's, McDonald's, Owen's Rest., **lodging:** La Quinta, **S...gas:** RaceWay, Texaco/diesel, **food:** Burger King, Capt D's, Furr's Dining, Grandy's, KFC, Pizza Hut, Wendy's, **lodging:** Exel Inn, Howard Johnson, Red Roof, **other:** AutoZone, Eckerd

50b a Ferguson Rd, **N...gas:** Shamrock, Phillips 66, Texaco, **lodging:** FairPark Inn, **S...other:** U-Haul

49b Dolphin Rd, Lawnview Ave, Samuell Ave, **N...lodging:** Welcome Inn

a Winslow St, **N...gas:** Fina, Phillips 66, Texaco/diesel/repair, **other:** Texas FoodLand, **S...gas:** Phillips 66, Shell/24hr

48b TX 78, E Grand, **S...**fairpark, arboreteum

a Carroll Ave, Central Ave, Peak St, Haskell Ave, **N...gas:** Shamrock, **other:** HOSPITAL, **S...gas:** Exxon, **food:** Joe's Burgers

47 2nd Ave, **S...food:** McDonald's, **other:** Cotton Bowl, fairpark

46b I-45, US 75, to Houston

a Central Expswy, downtown

45 I-35E, N to Denton, to Commerce St, Lamar St, Griffin St, **S...gas:** Fina, **food:** McDonald's, **lodging:** Ramada Inn

44b I-35E S, Industrial Blvd, no facilities

a I-35E N, Beckley Ave(from eb)

43b a Sylvan Ave(from wb), **N...gas:** Texaco/Quizno's/diesel, **other:** HOSPITAL, Family$, USPO/24hr

42 Hampton Rd N, **1 mi N...food:** Burger King, KFC/Taco Bell

TEXAS

Interstate 30

E

41 Hampton Rd S(no EZ eb return), **N...gas:** Mobil, **S...gas:** Exxon, Texaco, **food:** Jack-in-the-Box, DQ, Luby's, Wendy's, **other:** AutoZone, Goodyear/auto, O'Reilly Parts

39 Cockrell Hill Rd, no facilities

38 Lp 12, **N...gas:** Exxon, **food:** Burger King

36 MacArthur Blvd, **S...other:** U-Haul

W

34 Belt Line Rd, **N...gas:** Chevron, **lodging:** Day's Inn, Motel 6, Ramada Ltd, **other:** Ford, Ripley's Museum, **S...gas:** Fina/Blimpie, RaceTrac, Shamrock, Texaco/Subway, **food:** DQ, McDonald's

32 NW 19th, **N...gas:** Shamrock, **S...gas:** Fina, Mobil, **food:** Denny's, McDonald's, Pizza Hut, Taco Bell, Whataburger, **lodging:** La Quinta

D
a
l
l
a
s

30 TX 360, Six Flags Dr, Arlington Stadium, **N...gas:** Shell, **food:** Grand Buffet, Ninfa's Café, Saltgrass Steaks, TrailDust Steaks, Candlewood Suites, **lodging:** Day's Inn, Fairfield Inn, Flagship Inn, Hilton, Park Inn, Radisson Suites, **other:** Studio+, Super 8, Wingate Inn, **S...gas:** Texaco/diesel, Total, **food:** Bennigan's, Denny's, Jack-in-the-Box, Luby's, McDonald's, Owen's Rest., Steak&Ale, **lodging:** Baymont Inn, La Quinta, **other:** Dillard's, JC Penney, K-Mart, Plymouth, Sears/auto, Six Flags Funpark, mall

29 Ball Park Way, **N...gas:** Chevron, Citgo, **food:** Frijoles Café, Grady's Grill, Macaroni Grill, TrailDust Steaks, **lodging:** Fairfield Inn, **other:** Toyota, **S...gas:** Fina/diesel, **food:** On-the-Border, Texas Steaks, **lodging:** Howard Johnson, Marriott, Stadium Inn, Wyndham Hotel, **other:** Six Flags Funpark

28b TX 157, Nolan Ryan Expswy, **N...gas:** Mobil, **food:** Waffle House, **lodging:** Country Inn Suites, **S...food:** Chili's, Cozymel's, Harrigan's Grill, Joe's Crabshack, Landry's Seafood, Olive Garden, Pappadeaux Seafood, **lodging:** Courtyard, Day's Inn, **other:** Wyndham Garden, **other:** Barnes&Noble, SteinMart, TX Stadium

a FM 157, Collins St, **N...food:** Whataburger, **other:** HOSPITAL, Plymouth/Dodge, **S...food:** Pappasito's Cantina, **other:** Home Depot

27 Lamar Blvd, Cooper St, **N...gas:** Mobil, **food:** Jack-in-the-Box, **other:** Eckerd, Kroger, **S...gas:** Citgo/7-11, Texaco, **food:** Burger King, Denny's, **other:** MEDICAL CARE

26 Fielder Rd, **S...other:** to Six Flags(from eb)

25mm Village Creek

24 Eastchase Pkwy, **N...food:** Jack-in-the-Box, **other:** CarMax, Sam's Club/gas, Wal-Mart SuperCtr/24hr, **S...gas:** Chevron, Texaco/diesel, **food:** IHOP, McDonald's, Whataburger, **other:** Office Depot, Old Navy, Ross, Target

23 Cooks Lane, **S...gas:** Mobil

21c Bridgewood Dr, **N...gas:** Mobil, Texaco, **food:** Bennigan's, Luby's, Wendy's, **other:** Discount Tire, Home Depot, Kroger, U-Haul, **S...gas:** Fina, Shamrock, Texaco/diesel/24hr, **food:** Burger King, McDonald's,

Pizza Hut, Taco Bueno, Whataburger/24hr, **other:** MEDICAL CARE

b a I-820, no facilities

F
t

W
o
r
t
h

19 Brentwood Stair Rd(from eb), **N...gas:** Chevron, Texaco/diesel, **food:** Chuy's Mexican, Steak&Ale, **other:** Kroger, **S...gas:** Citgo/diesel, Texaco

18 Oakland Blvd, **N...gas:** Phillips 66, Texaco/diesel, **food:** Burger King, Taco Bell, Waffle House, **lodging:** Motel 6

16c Beach St, **S...gas:** Citgo/7-11, **lodging:** Best Western, Comfort Inn

16b a Riverside Dr(from wb), **S...lodging:** Great Western Inn

15b a I-35W N to Denton, S to Waco

14b Jones St, Commerce St, Ft Worth, downtown

14a TX 199, Henderson St, Ft Worth, downtown

13b Summit Ave, downtown, no facilities

13a 8th Ave, downtown

12d Forest Park Blvd, **N...food:** Pappadeaux Café, Pappasito's, Tony Roma, **other:** HOSPITAL

12b Rosedale St, no facilities

a University Dr, City Parks, **S...lodging:** Fairfield Inn, Ramada Inn

11 Montgomery St, **S...gas:** Texaco/diesel, **food:** Whataburger, **other:** visitor info

10 Hulen St, Ft Worth, **S...other:** Borders Books, World-Mkt

9b US 377, Camp Bowie Blvd, Horne St, **N...food:** Uncle Julio's Mexican, **S...gas:** Citgo/7-11, Fina, Texaco, **food:** Burger King, Dunkin Donuts, Jack-in-the-Box, Pizza Hut/Taco Bell, Purple Cow Diner, Qdoba Mexican, Szechuan Chinese, Subway, Taco Bueno, Tejano Café, Wendy's, Whataburger

a Bryant-Irvin Rd, **S...gas:** Texaco, same as 9b

8b Ridgmar, Ridglea, **N...gas:** Citgo

a TX 183, Green Oaks Rd, **N...food:** Applebee's, Blimpie, Jack-in-the-Box, Olive Garden, Taco Bueno, TGIFriday, **other:** MEDICAL CARE, Albertson's, Best Buy, Dillard's, Firestone, Foley's, JC Penney, Mervyn's, NTB, Office Depot, Ross, Sears/auto, U-Haul, **S...food:** Tommy's Burgers, **lodging:** Hawthorn Suites

7b a Cherry Lane, TX 183, spur 341, to Green Oaks Rd, **N...gas:** Texaco, **food:** ChuckeCheese, CiCi's, IHOP/24hr, Luby's, Papa John's, Popeye's, Ryan's, Subway, Taco Bell, Wendy's, **lodging:** La Quinta, Super 8, **other:** Ford, Home Depot, O'Reilly Parts, Sam's Club/gas, Wal-Mart/auto, **S...lodging:** Best Western, Hampton Inn, Holiday Inn Express, **other:** MEDICAL CARE, Dodge, Mitsubishi, Nissan, Target

6 Las Vegas Trail, **N...gas:** Chevron/24hr, **food:** McDonald's, Waffle House, **lodging:** Day's Inn, **other:** Acura, Lincoln/Mercury, **S...gas:** Citgo, Texaco/diesel, **food:** Pancake House, **lodging:** Best Budget Suites, Comfort Inn, Motel 6, **other:** AutoZone, Kia, Subaru

5b c I-820 S and N

Interstate 30

E
↑
↓
W

5a	Alemeda St(from eb, no EZ return), no facilities
3	RM 2871, Chapel Creek Blvd, no facilities
2	spur 580 E, no facilities
1b	Linkcrest Dr, **S...gas:** Chevron, Fina/diesel, Mobil/ diesel, Shamrock
0mm	I-20 W. I-30 begins/ends on I-20, exit 421.

Interstate 35

N
↑
↓
S

Exit # Services

504mm	Texas/Oklahoma state line, Red River
504	frontage rd, no facilities
503mm	parking area both lanes, no facilities
502	**Welcome Ctr sb, full(handicapped)facilities, TX Tourist Bureau/info, phone, picnic tables, litter barrels**
501	FM 1202, **E...other:** Chrysler/Plymouth/Dodge/Jeep, Ford/Mercury, **W...gas:** Hilltop/Conoco/diesel/café/@, **food:** Applebee's, Harper's Steaks/seafood, **other:** Prime Outlets/famous brands, Western Outfitter, Harper's Steaks, RV camping
500	FM 372, Gainesville, **E...gas:** Hitchin' Post/Texaco/ diesel/rest./24hr/@

Gainesville

498b a	US 82, Gainesville, to Wichita Falls, Sherman, **E...gas:** Citgo/diesel, Exxon, Phillips 66/diesel, Shamrock, Texaco, **food:** Catfish Louie's, Denny's, Whatburger/24hr, **lodging:** Bed&Bath Inn, Budget Host, Comfort Inn, Delux Inn, 12 Oaks Inn, **other:** HOSPITAL, **W...gas:** Exxon/diesel, **lodging:** Best Western, Day's Inn
497	frontage rd, no facilities
496b	TX 51, FM 51, California St, Gainesville, **E...gas:** Chevron, Conoco, **food:** Bonanza, Braum's, Burger King, Grandy's, McDonald's, Taco Bell, Taco Mayo, Wendy's, **lodging:** Holiday Inn Express, Ramada Inn, **other:** Cadillac, Dodge/Plymouth, Goodyear/auto, N Central TX Coll, **W...gas:** Texaco, **food:** Chili's
496a	to Weaver St, no facilities
496mm	Elm Fork of the Trinity River
495	frontage rd, no facilities
494	FM 1306, no facilities
492mm	picnic area sb, tables, litter barrels
491	Spring Creek Rd, no facilities
490mm	picnic area nb, picnic tables, litter barrels
489	FM 1307, to Hockley Creek Rd, no facilities
487	rd 922, Valley View, **W...gas:** Chevron/diesel/24hr, **food:** DQ, **other:** USPO
486	frontage rd, no facilities
485	frontage rd(from sb), no facilities
483	FM 3002, Lone Oak Rd, **E...other:** Lone Oak RV Park, RV Ranch Ctr
482	Chisam Rd, no facilities
481	View Rd, **W...other:** Sundown Ranch RV Park
480	Lois Rd, **E...other:** Wal-Mart Dist Ctr
479	Belz Rd, Sanger, same as 478
478	FM 455, to Pilot Pt, Bolivar, **E...gas:** Phillips 66, Texaco, **food:** DQ, Sonic, **lodging:** Sanger Inn, **other:** USPO, cleaners/laundry, **W...gas:** Chevron/Subway/

24hr, **food:** Jack-in-the-Box, McDonald's, **other:** Chevrolet, IGA Foods, RV Park, Ray Roberts Lake and SP

477	Keaton Rd, **E...gas:** Phillips 66, **food:** No Frills Grill, **W...gas:** Shamrock/diesel, **other:** RV Ctr
475b	Rector Rd, no facilities
a	FM 156, to Krum, no facilities
474	Cowling(from nb), no facilities
473	FM 3163, Milam Rd, **E...gas:** Love's/Subway/diesel/24hr/ @
472	Ganzer Rd, **W...other:** Texas RV Resort
471	US 77, FM 1173, Lp 282, to Denton, Krum, **E...gas:** TA/Conoco/diesel/rest./24hr/@, **food:** Good Eats Café, **other:** HOSPITAL, Denton Stores/famous brands, **W...gas:** Citgo/diesel/café/24hr, Fina, **other:** Foster's Western Shop, to Camping World RV Supply

Denton

470	Lp 288, same services as 469 from sb
469	US 380, University Dr, to Decatur, McKinney, **E...gas:** Phillips 66/diesel, RaceTrac, **food:** Braum's, ChinaTown Café, Cracker Barrel, Luigi's Pizza, McDonald's, **lodging:** Best Western, **other:** Albertson's/drugs, Dodge, K-Mart, Toyota, **W...gas:** Conoco/diesel, Shamrock/ service, Texaco/diesel, **food:** DQ, Denny's, Waffle House, **lodging:** Exel Inn, Howard Johnson, Motel 6, **other:** HOSPITAL, Ancira RV Ctr, Camping World RV Supply, to TX Woman's U
468	FM 1515, Airport Rd, W Oak St, no facilities
467	I-35W, S to Ft Worth, no facilities

I-35 divides into E and W sb, converges into I-35 nb. **See Texas I-35 W.**

466b	Ave D, **E...gas:** Citgo, Exxon/diesel, **food:** Burger King, IHOP/24hr, McDonald's, Pancho's Mexican, Taco Cabana, **lodging:** Comfort Suites, **other:** $General, Sack'n Save Foods, to NTSU, **W...lodging:** Radisson
a	McCormick St, **E...gas:** Phillips 66, Texaco/diesel, **lodging:** Comfort Suites, **W...gas:** Citgo, Fina/diesel/ U-Haul

TEXAS

Interstate 35

465b US 377, Ft Worth Dr, **E...gas:** Citgo, Shamrock, **food:** Carino's Italian, ChuckeCheese, Kettle, Taco Bueno, Whataburger/24hr, **lodging:** La Quinta, **other:** Home Depot, U-Haul, **W...gas:** Conoco, Phillips 66/diesel, Total/diesel, **food:** Outback Steaks, **lodging:** Day's Inn, Desert Sands Motel

a FM 2181, Teasley Ln, **E...gas:** Citgo/7-11, **food:** Applebee's, Braum's, KFC/Pizza Hut, **lodging:** Holiday Inn, **other:** Brookshires Foods, bank, **W...gas:** Exxon, Fina, Shell, **food:** Little Caesar's, Pizza Hut, **lodging:** Ramada Inn, Super 8

464 US 77, Pennsylvania Dr, Denton, **E...food:** Burger King, Wendy's, **other:** Dillard's, JC Penney, Kroger, Mervyn's, Office Depot, Ross, Sears/auto, Wal-Mart, mall, same as 463

463 Lp 288, to Denton, **E...food:** Burger King, El Chico, Texas Roadhouse, **other:** Discount Tire, Kroger, Old Navy, **W...gas:** Chevron, **food:** Blackeyed Pea, Chili's, Jack-in-the-Box, Luby's, Red Lobster, Red Pepper's Rest., Schlotsky's, Tia's Mexican, **other:** Albertson's, same as 464

462 State School Rd, Mayhill Rd, **E...gas:** Texaco/diesel, **other:** HOSPITAL, Hyundai, **W...gas:** Exxon/café, **other:** Cadillac, Chevrolet, Dodge/Toyota, Lincoln/Mercury/Mazda/Isuzu, Pontiac/Buick/GMC

461 Sandy Shores Rd, Post Oak Dr, **E...other:** Ford, McClain RV Ctr, **W...other:** Chrysler/Plymouth/Jeep/Kia, Nissan

460 Corinth Pkwy, **E...gas:** Chevron/diesel/repair, **other:** McClain RV Ctr, camping, **W...other:** Harley-Davidson

459 frontage rd, **W...other:** Destiny RV Resort

458 FM 2181, Swisher Rd, **E...gas:** Phillips 66, Texaco/Subway, **W...gas:** Chevron/McDonald's, Exxon/Wendy's, **food:** Burger King, Chick-fil-A, Jack-in-the-Box, KFC/Pizza Hut/Taco Bell, Mr Gatti, Starbucks, Whataburger, **other:** Albertson's, Discount Tire, GNC, Radio Shack, Wal-Mart SuperCtr/gas/24hr

457b Denton Rd, Hundley Dr, Lake Dallas, **E...gas:** Chevron

a Lake Dallas, Hundley Dr(from nb)

456 Highland Village, no facilities

456mm Lewisville Lake

455 McGee Lane, no facilities

454b Garden Ridge Blvd, **W...gas:** Citgo, **other:** city park

a FM 407, Justin, **E...gas:** Shamrock, **W...gas:** Fina/diesel, Texaco, **food:** McDonald's

453 Valley Ridge Blvd, **E...other:** Ford, May RV Ctr

452 FM 1171, to Flower Mound, **E...gas:** Mobil, **food:** IHOP, Taco Bueno, **lodging:** Howard Johnson, HOSPITAL, **W...gas:** Chevron, Exxon/diesel, **food:** Burger King, Golden Corral, Grandy's, Whataburger/24hr, **other:** Home Depot, Kohl's, Lowe's Whse, Staples, U-Haul, same as 451

451 Fox Ave, **E...gas:** Texaco/diesel, **food:** Braum's, **W...gas:** Chevron/24hr, Conoco/Quizno's/diesel, Shamrock, **food:** Blackeyed Pea, Cracker Barrel, El Chico, **lodging:** Hampton Inn, Microtel, **other:** Atlas Transmissions, VW

450 TX 121, Grapevine, **E...gas:** Citgo/7-11, RaceTrac, **food:** BBQ, Owens Rest., Pancho's Mexican, **lodging:** Pines Motel, Ramada Ltd, **other:** Chevrolet/Subaru, Dodge, **W...gas:** Chevron, Citgo/7-11, Conoco, Fina, Shamrock, Texaco/diesel, **food:** Alfredo's Pizza, Burger King, Chili's, Church's, Don Pedro's, Furr's Dining, IHOP, Ming Garden Chinese, KFC, LJ Silver, McDonald's, Rodarte's Cantina, Subway, Taco Bell, Tia's Mexican, Waffle House, Whataburger/24hr, **lodging:** Budget Inn, Day's Inn, J&J Motel, Spanish Trails Inn, Super 8, **other:** Chief Parts, Eckerd, Firestone/auto, Food Lion, Kroger, Nissan/Saturn, transmissions

449 Corporate Drive, **E...food:** China Dragon, Fox&Hound Grill, Hartford Grill, Hooters, On the Border, **lodging:** Extended Stay America, Hearthside Inn, Motel 6, **other:** Cavender's Boots, **W...gas:** Exxon/Quizno's/Pizza Inn/TCBY, Fina/diesel, **food:** Chili's, El Fenix Mexican, Jack-in-the-Box, Kettle, **lodging:** Best Western, La Quinta, Sun Suites, Honda, NTB

448b a FM 3040, Round Grove Rd, **E...food:** Abuelo's Mexican, Bennigan's, ChuckeCheese, Jack-in-the-Box, Olive Garden, SaltGrass Steaks, Subway, **lodging:** Homewood Suites, **other:** Best Buy, Ross, Target, **W...gas:** Chevron, Exxon, RaceTrac, Texaco, **food:** Applebee's, Carino's Italian, Chick-fil-A, Christina's Mexican, Cotton Patch Café, Don Pablo, Famous Dave's BBQ, Good Eats Grill, IHOP, Logan's Roadhouse, Luby's, Macaroni Grill, McDonald's, OutBack Steaks, Red Lobster, Schlotsky's, Sonic, SpagEddie's Italian, Taco Cabana, TGIFriday, Tony Roma, Water Garden Chinese, Wendy's, **lodging:** Comfort Inn, Country Inn Suites, **other:** Barnes&Noble, Borders Books, Circuit City, CompUSA, Dillard's, Discount Tire, Foley's, JC Penney, Marshall's, Michael's, Office Depot, OfficeMax, Old Navy, Sears/auto, Target, mall

446 Frankford Rd, **E...food:** La Hacienda Ranch Grill, **other:** Volvo

445b Pres Geo Bush Tpk

445 Trinity Mills Rd, **E...other:** HOSPITAL, Buick/GMC/Pontiac, Home Depot, PepBoys, RV Ctr

444 Whitlock Lane, Sandy Lake Rd, **E...gas:** Texaco, **other:** RV camping, **W...gas:** Chevron, **food:** McDonald's, **lodging:** Delux Inn

443 Belt Line Rd, Crosby Rd, **E...gas:** Conoco, Shell, **other:** NTB

442 Valwood Pkwy, **E...gas:** Texaco, **food:** DQ, Denny's, El Chico, Grandy's, Jack-in-the-Box, Rosita's Mexican, Taco Bueno, Waffle House, **lodging:** Comfort Inn, Guest Inn, Red Roof, Royal Inn, **other:** Ford, **W...gas:** Fina/diesel, **lodging:** Day's Inn, **other:** Chevrolet, U-Haul, transmissions

441 Valley View Lane, **W...gas:** Exxon, Mobil, **lodging:** Best Western, Day's Inn, Econolodge, La Quinta

440b I-635 E, no facilities

c I-635 W, to DFW Airport, no facilities

439 Royal Lane, **E...gas:** Texaco, **food:** McDonald's, Whataburger/24hr, **other:** Daewoo, **W...gas:** Chevron, **food:** Jack-in-the-Box, Wendy's

Interstate 35

N ↑ ↓ S

438 Walnut Hill Lane, **E...gas:** Fina/Quizno's/diesel, Mobil, Shell, **food:** Bennigan's, Burger King, Chili's, Denny's, Old San Francisco Steaks, Red Lobster, Steak&Ale, Taco Bell, TGIFriday, Tony Roma's, Trail Dust Steaks, Wild Turkey Grill, **lodging:** Country Inn Suites, Drury Inn, Hampton Inn, **W...gas:** Chevron, Texaco/diesel, **other:** RV Ctr

437 Manana Rd(from nb), same as 438

436 TX 348, Irving, to DFW, **E...gas:** Exxon/diesel, **food:** IHOP, Luby's, Schlotsky's, Waffle House, **lodging:** Clarion Suites, Comfort Suites, Courtyard, Homestead Suites, Radisson, Studio 6, **W...gas:** Exxon, **food:** Blackeyed Pea, Chili's, Don Pablo, Humperdinck's Grill, Jack-in-the-Box, Joe's Crabshack, McDonald's, Olive Garden, Outback Steaks, Papadeaux Seafood, Pappas Bros Steaks, Red Lobster, Taco Bell/Pizza Hut, Tony Roma's, Wendy's, **lodging:** Red Roof Inn

435 Harry Hines Blvd(from nb), **E...gas:** RaceTrack, **food:** Arby's, **other:** U-Haul, same as 436

D a l l a s

434b Regal Row, **E...gas:** Fina/Grandy's, **food:** Denny's, Whataburger/24hr, **lodging:** La Quinta, Red Roof Inn, **W...lodging:** Fairfield Inn

a Empire, Central, **E...gas:** Chevron, **food:** Monald's, Sonic, Wendy's, **lodging:** Budget Suites, Candlewood Suites, InTown Suites, Wingate Inn, **other:** Office Depot, **W...gas:** Exxon, **food:** Burger King, Schlotsky's, Taco Bell/Pizza Hut

433b Mockingbird Lane, Love Field Airport, **E...gas:** Mobil, **food:** Jack-in-the-Box, **lodging:** Clarion Hotel, Crowne Plaza, Harvey Hotel, Residence Inn, **other:** Sheraton, **W...gas:** Chevron, **food:** McDonald's, **other:** Goodyear

a (432b from sb)TX 356, Commonwealth Dr, **E...gas:** Texaco/diesel, **lodging:** Marriott, **other:** OfficeMax, **W...lodging:** Delux Inn

432a Inwood Rd, **E... other:** HOSPITAL, Chevrolet, **W...gas:** Fina, Texaco, **food:** Whataburger/24hr, **lodging:** Homewood Suites

431 Motor St, **E...gas:** Mobil, **food:** Denny's, **lodging:** Stouffer Hotel, **W...gas:** Shell, **food:** Ninfa's Grill, Wok Chinese, **lodging:** Embassy Suites, Marriott Suites

430c Wycliff Ave, **E...food:** JoJo's Rest., **lodging:** Renaissance Hotel, **other:** Intn'l Apparel Mart

b Mkt Ctr Blvd, **E...other:** World Trade Ctr, **W...food:** Denny's, **lodging:** Courtyard, Fairfield Inn, Ramada Inn, Sheraton, Wilson World Hotel, Wyndham Garden

a Oak Lawn Ave, **W...gas:** Texaco/diesel, **food:** Denny's, Medieval Times Rest., **lodging:** Holiday Inn, **other:** to Merchandise Mart

429c HiLine Ave(from nb)

b Continental Ave, Commerce St W, downtown, **E... food:** Hooters, **W...gas:** Exxon, **food:** McDonald's

a to I-45, US 75, to Houston, no facilities

428e Commerce St E, Reunion Blvd, Dallas, downtown

d I-30 W, to Ft Worth

a I-30 E, to I-45 S

b Industrial Blvd, **W...gas:** Fina/diesel, Shamrock

427b I-30 E, no facilities

a Colorado Blvd, **E...**HOS-PITAL

426c Jefferson Ave, **E...gas:** Texaco, **W...gas:** Shell

b TX 180 W, 8th St, **E...gas:** Texaco, **W...gas:** Shell, **lodging:** Mustang Inn

a Ewing Ave, **E...food:** McDonald's, **W...other:** Chrysler/Jeep, Pontiac/GMC, Honda, Hyundai

425c Marsalis Ave, **E...lodging:** Dallas Inn, **W...gas:** Mobil, Shamrock

b Beckley Ave, 12th St, **W...gas:** Exxon, **food:** Wendy's

a Zang Blvd, **W...gas:** Shamrock, Texaco/diesel

424 Illinois Ave, **E...gas:** Chevron, **food:** BBQ, Dunkin Donuts, **other:** HOSPITAL, **W...gas:** Exxon, **food:** Church's, IHOP, Jack-in-the-Box, Little Caesar's, Sonic, Taco Bell, OakTree Inn, **other:** Brake Ctr, Eckerd

423b Zaner Ave, **W...food:** Big Boy, Spin's Rest., **lodging:** Westerner Motel

a (422b from nb)US 67 S, Kiest Blvd, **W...gas:** Shell/repair, Texaco/diesel, **food:** McDonald's, Wendy's, **lodging:** Quality Inn, **other:** Subaru/VW

421b Lp 12W, Ann Arbor St, **W...food:** Luby's, Red Lobster, **lodging:** Big Couple Motel, Sunbelt Motel, **other:** Sam's Club

a Lp 12E, **E...gas:** RaceWay, Texaco/diesel, **lodging:** Budget Inn, Howard Johnson, Motel 6, **other:** K-Mart

420 Laureland, **E...lodging:** Master Suite Motel, **other:** **W...gas:** Conoco, Mobil, **lodging:** Embassy Motel, Linfield Inn

419 Camp Wisdom Rd, **E...gas:** Exxon, **W...gas:** Shell/24hr, **food:** McDonald's, **lodging:** Oak Cliff Inn, Suncrest Inn, **other:** U-Haul

418c Danieldale Rd(from sb)

418b I-635/I-20 E, to Shreveport, no facilities

a I-20 W, to Ft Worth, no facilities

417 Wheatland Rd(from nb), no facilities

416 Wintergreen Rd, **E...other:** repair, **W...gas:** Citgo/7-11, **food:** Cracker Barrel, Golden Corral, Waffle House, **lodging:** Holiday Inn, Red Roof Inn

TEXAS

Interstate 35

415   Pleasant Run Rd, **E...gas:** Chevron/24hr, RaceTrac, Texaco/Blimpie/diesel, **food:** Grandy's, Subway, Waffle House, **lodging:** Great Western Inn, Royal Inn, Spanish Trails Motel, Super 8, **other:** Chrysler/Plymouth/Jeep, PepBoys, transmissions, **W...gas:** Chevron, **food:** Burger King, El Chico, Golden Corral, KFC, LJ Silver, Luby's, McDonald's, On the Border, Outback Steaks, Pizza Inn, Taco Bueno, Wendy's, **lodging:** Best Western, **other:** HOSPITAL, Chevrolet, Discount Tire, Ford, Kroger, K-Mart, Office Depot, Ross

414   FM 1382, Desoto Rd, Belt Line Rd, **E...food:** Whataburger, **other:** Wal-Mart SuperCtr/24hr, **W...gas:** Texaco

413   Parkerville Rd, **W...gas:** Total, Honda, U-Haul

412   Bear Creek Rd, **W...gas:** Texaco/diesel, **food:** Jack-in-the-Box, Whataburger, **other:** HiHo RV Park, transmissions

411   FM 664, Ovilla Rd, **E...gas:** Exxon/Taco Bell/TCBY/24hr, RaceTrac/24hr, **food:** McDonald's, Whataburger, **lodging:** Howard Johnson, **other:** Brookshire's Foods, Eckerd, **W...gas:** Exxon, Texaco

410   Red Oak Rd, **E...gas:** Fina/Subway/diesel/24hr, Texaco/diesel, **food:** Denny's, **lodging:** Day's Inn, **W...other:** Hilltop Travel Trailers

408   US 77, **E...**golf

406   Sterrett Rd, **E...**fireworks

405   FM 387, **E...gas:** Chevron

404   Lofland Rd, industrial area, no facilities

403   US 287, to Ft Worth, **E...gas:** Texaco, **food:** McDonald's, **other:** Chevrolet/Cadillac, Jeep, **W...other:** Buick/Pontiac/GMC, Chrysler/Dodge, Ford/Mercury

401b   US 287 bus, Waxahatchie, **E...lodging:** Best Western, Super 8

   a   Brookside Rd, **E...lodging:** Brookside Inn, Ramada Ltd

399b   FM 1446, no facilities

   a   FM 66, FM 876, Maypearl, **E...lodging:** Texas Inn, **W...gas:** Chevron/diesel, Texaco/diesel/24hr

397   to US 77, no facilities

393mm   **rest area both lanes, full(handicapped)facilities, phone, picnic tables, litter barrels, vending, pet-walk**

391   FM 329, Forreston Rd, no facilities

386   TX 34, Italy, **E...gas:** Texaco/diesel/24hr, **food:** DQ, **W...gas:** Exxon/diesel, **lodging:** Italy Inn

384   Derrs Chapel Rd, no facilities

381   FM 566, Milford Rd, no facilities

377   FM 934, no facilities

374   FM 2959, Carl's Corner, **W...gas:** Carl's/diesel/rest.

I-35E**********

371   I-35 W. I-35 divides into E and W nb, converges sb. **See Texas I-35 W.**

370   US 77 N, FM 579, Hillsboro, no facilities

368b   FM 286, **E...food:** LoneStar Café, Taco Bell, Wendy's, **other:** Prime Outlets/famous brands, **W...gas:** Exxon/Domino's, Shamrock/diesel, Texaco/diesel, **food:** Braum's, DQ, El Conquistador Mexican, Mc-

Donald's, Pizza Hut, **lodging:** Best Western, Comfort Inn, **other:** HOSPITAL

   a   TX 22, TX 171, to Whitney, **E...gas:** Citgo/7-11, Love's/Subway/Pizza Hut/diesel/24hr/@, **food:** Arby's, Black-eyed Pea, Burger King, Golden Corral, Grandy's, IHOP, McDonald's, **lodging:** Holiday Inn Express, Motel 6, Wyndham Mill Inn, **W...gas:** Chevron, Exxon, Mobil, Shell/diesel, **food:** Jack-in-the-Box, KFC, Schlotsky's, Whataburger/24hr, **lodging:** Thunderbird Motel/rest., **other:** Buick/Pontiac/GMC, Chevrolet/Cadillac, Chrysler/Plymouth/Dodge/Jeep, Ford/Mercury, Wal-Mart SuperCtr/gas/24hr

367   Old Bynum Rd(from nb), no facilities

364b   TX 81 N, to Hillsboro, no facilities

   a   FM 310, **E...gas:** Conoco/diesel/24hr, **W...gas:** Fina/KrispyKreme/diesel/24hr, **food:** BBQ

362   Chatt Rd, no facilities

359   FM 1304, **W...gas:** Mobil/Subway/diesel/24hr, **other:** antiques

358   FM 1242 E, Abbott, **E...gas:** Exxon, **food:** Turkey Shop Café

356   Co Rd 3102, no facilities

355   County Line Rd, **E...other:** KOA

354   Marable St, **E...other:** KOA

353   FM 2114, West, **E...gas:** Citgo/Subway, Fina, Shell, **food:** DQ, Little Czech Bakery, **other:** Ford, **W...gas:** Citgo/diesel/repair, Exxon, **other:** Chevrolet, Goodyear

351   FM 1858, **W...other:** West Auction

349   Wiggins Rd, no facilities

347   FM 3149, Tours Rd, no facilities

346   Ross Rd, **E...gas:** Shell/diesel/24hr, **W...gas:** Exxon/diesel/24hr, **other:** I-35 RV Park

345mm   picnic area/litter barrels both lanes

345   Old Dallas Rd, **E...**antiques, **W...other:** I-35 RV Park

343   FM 308, Elm Mott, **E...gas:** Exxon/DQ, Fina/diesel, Texaco/diesel/24hr, **W...gas:** Chevron/diesel/24hr, food: BBQ, Heitmiller Steaks

342b   US 77 bus, **W...**RV Park

   a   FM 2417, Crest Dr, **W...gas:** Shamrock/diesel, **food:** DQ, **lodging:** Everyday Inn, **other:** Family$, auto repair

341   Craven Ave, Lacy Lakeview, **E...gas:** Chevron, **W...gas:** BP/diesel, Shell//pizza, **lodging:** Interstate North Motel, **other:** Chief Parts

340   Myers Lane(from nb), no facilities

339   to TX 6 S, FM 3051, Lake Waco, **E...gas:** Shamrock/diesel, **food:** Casa Ole, ChiChi's, Domino's, El Conquistador, Jack-in-the-Box, Luby's, Pizza Hut, Popeye's, Sonic, Subway, Wendy's, Whataburger/24hr, **lodging:** Country Inn Suites, **other:** MEDICAL CARE, $General, Radio Shack, Wal-Mart SuperCtr/24hr, **W...gas:** Chevron, Citgo, Texaco, **food:** Burger King, Cracker Barrel, KFC, McDonald's, Papa John's, Starbucks, **lodging:** Hampton Inn, Hawthorn Inn, Knight's Inn, **other:** to airport

338b   Behrens Circle(from nb), **E...gas:** Texaco, same as 339, **W...gas:** Texaco/diesel/LP, **lodging:** Day's Inn, Delta Inn, Knight's Inn, Motel 6, **other:** Eckerd

Interstate 35

N ↕ **S**

Waco

Temple

337 (338a from nb)US 84, to TX 31, Waco Dr, **E...other:** AutoZone, Family$, HEB Food/gas, Sam's Club/gas, **W...gas:** Texaco, **other:** HOSPITAL

335c Lake Brazos Dr, MLK Blvd, **E...food:** Summer Palace Chinese, **lodging:** Holiday Inn, RiverPlace Inn/café, **W...lodging:** Travel Inn, Victorian Inn, **other:** HOSPITAL

335mm Brazos River

335b FM 434, University Parks Dr, **E...food:** China Grill, IHOP, Jim's Rest., Quizno's, Thai Cuisine, **lodging:** Best Western, **other:** Baylor U, **W...food:** Arby's, Jack-in-the-Box, **lodging:** Clarion, Lexington Inn, Residence Inn

a 4th St, 5th St, **E...gas:** Exxon/Subway/TCBY/diesel, Texaco/diesel, **food:** Denny's, IHOP, Lupito's Mexican, Pizza Hut, **lodging:** Best Western, La Quinta, **other:** Baylor U, **W...gas:** BP, Shamrock, **food:** Fazoli's, LJ Silver, McDonald's, Taco Bell, Taco Cabana, Wendy's, Whataburger/24hr, **lodging:** Clarion, **other:** to Baylor U

334b US 77 S, 17th St, 18th St, **E...gas:** BP, Chevron, Texaco/diesel, **food:** Burger King, Popeye's, Schlotsky's, Vitek's BBQ, **lodging:** Budget Inn, Comfort Inn, Super 8, **other:** Harley-Davidson, **W...gas:** Phillips 66/diesel, Texaco, **food:** Mexico Lindo, **other:** HOSPITAL

333a Lp 396, Valley Mills Dr, **E...gas:** Chevron, **food:** El Chico, Elite Café, Texas Roadhouse, Trujillo's Mexican, **lodging:** Astro Motel, Motel 6, **other:** Isuzu/Mazda, **W...gas:** RaceWay, Shamrock, **food:** Bush's Chicken, Church's Chicken, DQ, Jack-in-the-Box, Papa John's, Sonic, **lodging:** Comfort Inn, **other:** Eckerd, Jeep, Lincoln/Mercury, Volvo/Freightliner

331 New Rd, **E...gas:** Chevron, **lodging:** New Road Inn, Relax Inn, Rodeway Inn, **W...gas:** ⊕/Flying J/CountryMkt/diesel/24hr/@, **lodging:** Quality Inn

330 Lp 340, TX 6, **E...gas:** Chevron, **lodging:** New Road Inn, Rodeway Inn, **2 mi W...gas:** Citgo/diesel, **food:** Chick-fil-A, Luby's, McDonald's, Outback Steaks, TGIFriday, Wienerschnitzel, **lodging:** Extended Stay America, Fairfield Inn, **other:** CompUSA, Ford, Honda, Lowe's Whse, Toyota, Wal-Mart SuperCtr/24hr

328 FM 2063, FM 2113, Moody, **E...gas:** Pilot/DQ/diesel/24hr/@, **food:** McDonald's, **W...gas:** Shamrock, Texaco/24hr

325 FM 3148, Moonlight Dr, **W...gas:** Shell/Subway/TCBY/diesel/24hr, **food:** Laredo's Rest.

323 FM 2837, Lorena, **W...gas:** Brookshire Bros/Conoco, **food:** Pizza House, **other:** $General

322 Lorena, **E...gas:** Phillips 66/diesel, **W...gas:** Chevron/diesel

319 Woodlawn Rd, no facilities

318mm picnic area both lanes, litter barrels, picnic tables

318b Bruceville, no facilities

a Frontage Rd, no facilities

315 TX 7, FM 107, Eddy, **1 mi E...**RV Park, **W...gas:** BP, Texaco/diesel/24hr, **other:** to Mother Neff SP

314 Old Blevins Rd, no facilities

311 Big Elm Rd, no facilities

308 FM 935, Troy, **E...gas:** Texaco, **other:** Troy Foods, **W...gas:** Exxon, **other:** Nick's Campers, Troy Lube

306 FM 1237, Pendleton, **W...gas:** Love's/Citgo/Subway/A&W/diesel/24hr, **other:** Temple RV Park

305 Berger Rd, **W...other:** Temple RV Park, repair

304 Lp 363, Dodgen Loop, **W...gas:** Shamrock/diesel/24hr, Shell/Wendy's/diesel

303 spur 290, N 3rd St, Temple, **E...lodging:** TX Inn, **W...lodging:** Continental Inn

302 Nugent Ave, **E...gas:** Exxon/diesel, Texaco/diesel, **lodging:** Comfort Suites, Econolodge, Holiday Inn Express, **W...gas:** Chevron, **food:** Denny's, **lodging:** Day's Inn, Motel 6, Stratford House Inn, Travelodge

301 TX 53, FM 2305, Adams Ave, **E...gas:** Shamrock, **food:** Jim's Rest., KFC, LJ Silver, McDonald's, Pizza Hut, Starbucks, Taco Bell, Wendy's, Whataburger, **lodging:** La Quinta, **other:** Ford, **W...food:** Catfish Shack, **lodging:** Best Western, **other:** Albertson's/drugs, Chrysler/Jeep, $General, Lincoln/Mercury, Harley-Davidson, Jeep

300 Ave H, 49th –57th Sts, **E...gas:** Shell, Texaco, **food:** Las Casas Mexican, **lodging:** Oasis Motel, **other:** Dodge, **W...gas:** Texaco

299 US 190 E, TX 36, **E...gas:** Shell, Texaco/diesel, **food:** El Conquistador Mexican, Golden Corral, Jack-in-the-Box, Luby's, **lodging:** Budget Inn, Regency Inn, **other:** HOSPITAL, Ancira RV Ctr, Chevrolet/Toyota, Dodge, K-Mart, Saturn, Subaru, **W...gas:** Exxon/diesel/24hr, Texaco, **food:** Burger King, Chili's, IHOP

297 FM 817, Midway Dr, **E...gas:** Citgo, **lodging:** Day's Inn, Super 8/rest., **other:** BMW, Nissan, Saab, Volvo, **W...gas:** Shamrock, **other:** Buick/Pontiac/GMC, Fed Ex, VW

294b FM 93, 6th Ave, **E...gas:** Texaco/diesel, **food:** McDonald's, **W...food:** Pizza Hut, Subway, Whataburger, **lodging:** River Forest Inn, **other:** U of Mary Hardin Baylor

N ↕ S

a	Central Ave, **W...gas:** Texaco/diesel, **food:** Burger King, Bobby's Burgers, Great SW Rest., Pizza Hut, Sonic, Whataburger, **lodging:** Ramada Ltd, **other:** AutoZone, Goodyear
293b	TX 317, FM 436, Main St, no facilities
a	US 190 W, to Killeen, Ft Hood, no facilities
292	Lp 121(same as 293a), **E...gas:** Fina, Shamrock/diesel/rest./24hr, **lodging:** Budget Host, **W...gas:** Mobil/Blimpie/24hr, **other:** Ford, KOA, auto/tire repair
290	Shanklin Rd, **W...other:** KOA(1mi), picnic area
289	Tahuaya Rd, **E...other:** Hi-Way Parts, **W...**antiques
287	Amity Rd, no facilities
286	FM 2484, **W...other:** to Stillhouse Hollow Lake, no facilities
285	FM 2268, Salado, **E...gas:** Conoco/Brookshire Foods, **food:** Subway, **W...gas:** Chevron, **food:** Cowboys BBQ, Robertson's Rest.
284	Robertson Rd, **E...gas:** Exxon/Burger King, **lodging:** Stagecoach Inn, **W...gas:** Texaco/diesel, **food:** DQ, **lodging:** Super 8
283	FM 2268, FM 2843, Salado, to Holland, no facilities
282	FM 2115, **E...gas:** Texaco/diesel/lube/repairs, **food:** Salado Creek Grill, **other:** RV camping
281.5mm	rest area both lanes, **full(handicapped)facilities, phone, picnic tables, litter barrels, vending, petwalk**
280	Prairie Dell, no facilities
279	Hill Rd, **W...other:** Emerald Lake RV Park
277	Yankee Rd, no facilities
275	FM 487, Jarrell, to Florence, **E...gas:** Exxon, Shamrock/diesel, **W...gas:** Texaco, **other:** Jarrell Country Mkt, USPO
271	Theon Rd, **W...gas:** Texaco/Subway/diesel/24hr
268	FM 972, Walburg, no facilities
266	TX 195, **E...gas:** Mobil/Arby's/diesel/24hr, **W...gas:** Exxon/diesel
264	Lp 35, Georgetown, **E...lodging:** San Gabriel Motel, **other:** All Seasons RV Ctr, Live Oaks RV Park
262	RM 2338, Lake Georgetown, **E...gas:** Shamrock, **food:** KFC, Luby's, McDonald's, Quizno's, Sonic, Subway, **lodging:** Holiday Inn Express, **other:** Albertson's, Eckerd, Parts+, Radio Shack, **W...gas:** Phillips 66, Texaco, **food:** Chuck Wagon Café, DQ, Popeye's, Taco Bueno, Wendy's, Whataburger/24hr, **lodging:** Day's Inn, La Quinta
261	TX 69, Georgetown, **E...gas:** Texaco/diesel, **food:** Applebee's, Burger King, Chili's, KFC/Taco Bell, Schlotsky's, **other:** HEB Foods, same as 262, **W...other:** Home Depot, Wal-Mart SuperCtr/24hr, antiques
260	RM 2243, Leander, **E...other:** HOSPITAL, USPO, **W...gas:** Chevron, Conoco, Mobil, **food:** Jack-in-the-Box, **lodging:** Comfort Inn
259	Lp 35, **E...other:** Candle Factory, **W...other:** RV Outlet Mall, to Interspace Caverns

Georgetown

Round Rock

257	Westinghouse Rd, **E...other:** Chevrolet/Buick, Chrysler/Plymouth/Dodge/Jeep, Ford, Mazda, Mitsubishi, VW
256	RM 1431, Chandler Rd, **rest area sb, full(handicapped)facilities, phone, picnic tables, litter barrels, vending, petwalk**
255mm	**rest area nb, full(handicapped)facilities, vending, phone, picnic tables, litter barrels, vending, petwalk**
254	FM 3406, Round Rock, **E...gas:** Chevron, Citgo/7-11, Texaco, **food:** Arby's, Castaways Seafood, Giovanni's Italian, McDonald's, Schlotsky's, Sonic, **other:** Firestone, GMC/Pontiac, Honda, Pennzoil, Toyota, **W...gas:** Phillips 66/24hr, **food:** Carino's Italian, China One, Chuy's Mexican, Cracker Barrel, Denny's, Golden Corral, SaltGrass Steaks, **lodging:** AmeriSuites, Courtyard, Hilton Garden, La Quinta, SpringHill Suites, Super 8, **other:** Nissan
253b	US 79, to Taylor, **E...gas:** Phillips 66, Shamrock/diesel, **food:** Baskin-Robbins, DQ, Famous Sam's Café, KFC, LoneStar Café, LJ Silver, **other:** HOSPITALAutoZone, HEB/deli, **W...gas:** Exxon/diesel, Texaco/diesel/24hr, **food:** BBQ, IHOP, K-Bob's Rest., Taco Bell, Thundercloud Subs, **lodging:** La Quinta, Red Roof Inn, Sleep Inn, **other:** Eckerd, USPO
a	Frontage Rd, **E...gas:** Shell, **food:** Arby's, Castaway's Seafood/steaks, DQ, Damon's, KFC, Sirloin Stockade, Taco Bell, **lodging:** Best Western, Wingate Inn, **W...food:** La Marguarita, Mr Gatti, Popeye's, Ramada Ltd, **other:** Eckerd
252b a	RM 620, **E...gas:** Texaco/diesel/24hr, **lodging:** Candlewood Suites, Crossland Suites, **other:** bank, **W...gas:** Fina, Phillips 66, **food:** Grandy's, Little Caesar's, McDonald's, **lodging:** Comfort Suites, Staybridge Suites, **other:** Albertson's, mall
251	Lp 35, Round Rock, **E...food:** Outback Steaks, Whataburger, **lodging:** Residence Inn, **other:** Aamco, Diahatsu, transmissions, **W...gas:** Exxon, Texaco, **food:** Burger King, Jack-in-the-Box, Luby's, Peter Piper Pizza, Taco Cabana, **lodging:** Day's Inn, **other:** Albertson's, Hastings Books, NTB, Walgreen
250	FM 1325, **E...gas:** Chevron, Mobil/diesel, **food:** Applebee's, Chick-fil-A, Chili's, El Chico, Jason's Deli, Joe's Crabshack, Macaroni Grill, McDonald's, Subway, **lodging:** Hampton Inn, **other:** Discount Tire, Goodyear/auto, Home Depot, OfficeMax, Ross, Target, Wal-Mart SuperCtr/24hr, **W...gas:** Texaco, **food:** Antonio's Cantina, Hooters, Krispy Kreme, Olive Garden, Starbucks, **lodging:** Baymont Inn, **other:** Barnes&Noble, Circuit City, Kohl's, Lowe's Whse, Marshall's, Office Depot, Old Navy, Sam's Club
248	Grand Ave Pkwy, no facilities
247	FM 1825, Pflugerville, **E...gas:** RaceTrac, **food:** Jack-in-the-Box, Sonic, Taco Cabana, Wendy's, **other:** Firestone/auto, HEB Foods, cinema, **W...gas:** Exxon, Shell/Church's, **food:** BBQ, KFC, **lodging:** Quality Suites, **other:** Goodyear/auto

Interstate 35

N ↕ **S**

246 Dessau Rd, Howard Lane, **E...gas:** Shell/diesel, Texaco, **food:** Baby Acapulco, **other:** Home Depot, Kohl's, NTB, **W...gas:** Shamrock, **food:** IHOP, Whataburger

245 FM 734, Parmer Lane, to Yeager Lane, **E...food:** Subway, **other:** HEB Food/gas, Radio Shack, **W...gas:** Citgo/7-11, Exxon, **lodging:** Residence Inn, SpringHill Suites

243 Braker Lane, **E...gas:** Shamrock, **food:** Jack-in-the-Box, Whataburger/24hr, **other:** Harley-Davidson, **W...gas:** Texaco/diesel, **lodging:** Austin Motel

241 Rundberg Lane, **E...gas:** Exxon, **food:** Golden Corral, Mr Gatti's, **lodging:** Ramada Inn, **other:** Albertson's, U-Haul, **W...gas:** Chevron, Texaco, **lodging:** Budget Inn, Home-Style Inn, Motel 6

240a US 183, Lockhart, **E...gas:** Exxon, **food:** DQ, Jack-in-the-Box, Old San Francisco Steaks, **lodging:** Day's Inn, Ramada Inn, Wellesley Inn, **other:** Chevrolet, **W...gas:** Chevron/diesel/24hr, Texaco/diesel, **lodging:** Motel 6, Red Roof Inn, Super 8, Travelodge Suites, Wingate Inn

239 St John's Ave, **E...gas:** Texaco, **food:** Chili's, Jim's Rest., Steak&Egg, **lodging:** Budget Host, Day's Inn, Hampton Inn, **other:** Dodge, Home Depot, Volvo, Wal-Mart SuperCtr/24hr, **W...gas:** Conoco/diesel, Exxon, **food:** Antonio's TexMex, Applebee's, Bennigan's, Denny's, **lodging:** AmeriSuites, Comfort Inn, Country Inn Suites, Holiday Inn Express, La Quinta, Sheraton, Sumner Suites

238b US 290 E, RM 222, same as 238a, frontage rds connect several exits

a 51st St, **E...gas:** Exxon, Chevron, Phillips 66, Shell, **food:** Burger King, Dixie's Roadhouse, El Torito, Fuddrucker's, Grandy's, Jim's Rest., LJ Silver, McDonald's, Owens Rest., Pappasito's, Sonic, Texas Steaks, Whataburger, **lodging:** Doubletree Hotel, Drury Inn, Econolodge, Embassy Suites, Holiday Inn, Homestead Village, Red Lion Hotel, Studio 6 Suites, **other:** Advance Parts, Firestone, FoodLand, Jo-Ann Crafts, OfficeMax, Volvo, **W...gas:** Texaco, **food:** Baby Acapulco, Bombay Bicycle Club, Capt's Seafood, Carrabba's, IHOP, India Cuisine, Outback Steaks, Quizno's, **lodging:** Courtyard, Drury Inn, Fairfield Inn, Hilton, Motel 6, Quality Inn, Ramada Ltd, Rodeway Inn, Super 8, **other:** Dillard's, Ford, Office Depot

237b 51st St, same as 238a

a Airport Blvd, **E...food:** BBQ, U-Haul, **W...food:** Jack-in-the-Box, Wendy's, GNC, Goodyear, **other:** HEB Foods, Old Navy, PetCo, Sears/auto

upper level is I-35 thru, lower level accesses downtown

236b 39th St, **E...gas:** Chevron, **other:** Fiesta Foods, HiLo Parts, **W...gas:** Texaco/diesel, **other:** Tune&Lube, tires, to U of TX

a 26th-32nd Sts, **E...food:** Mi Madre's Mexican, **lodging:** Day's Inn, **W...lodging:** Rodeway Inn, **other:** HOSPITAL

235b Manor Rd, same as 236a, **W...lodging:** Rodeway Inn, **other:** U of TX, st capitol

a MLK, 15th St, **W...HOSPITAL**

upper level is I-35 thru, lower level accesses downtown

234c 11th St, 12th St, downtown, **E...food:** Denny's, **lodging:** DoubleTree Hotel, Super 8, **other:** Eckerd, **W...gas:** Exxon, Shell, Texaco/diesel, **lodging:** Marriott, Radisson, Sheraton, **other:** HOSPITAL, museum, st capitol

b 8th-3rd St, **E...gas:** Chevron, Texaco, **W...gas:** Mobil

a Cesar Chavez St, Holly St, downtown, **W...food:** IHOP

233 Riverside Dr, Town Lake, **E...gas:** Shell, **W...gas:** Chevron/diesel, **lodging:** Holiday Inn

232mm Little Colorado River

232b Woodland Ave, **E...lodging:** Wellesley Inn

a Oltorf St, Live Oak, **E...gas:** Texaco/diesel, **food:** Carrow's, Luby's, **lodging:** La Quinta, Suburban Lodge, **W...gas:** Chevron, Exxon, Shell, Texaco/repair, **food:** Denny's, Marco Polo Rest., **lodging:** Clarion, Quality Inn

231 Woodward St, **E...gas:** Shell/diesel, **food:** Country Kitchen, **lodging:** Exel Inn, Holiday Inn, Motel 6, Park West Inn, Ramada Ltd, Super 8, same as 232, **W...other:** MEDICAL CARE, Home Depot

230b a US 290 W, TX 71, Ben White Blvd, St Elmo Rd, **E...gas:** Texaco, **food:** Domino's, Jim's Rest., McDonald's, Subway, Western Choice Steaks, **lodging:** Best Western, Comfort Suites, Courtyard, Fairfield Inn, Hampton Inn, Marriott, Omni Hotel, Red Roof Inn, Residence Inn, SpringHill Suites, **other:** bank, **W...food:** Burger King, Furr's Cafeteria, IHOP, Pizza Hut, Taco Cabana, **lodging:** Candlewood Suites, Day's Inn, Hawthorn Suites, La Quinta, **other:** HOSPITAL, BMW, Dodge/Jeep, Ford, GMC, Honda, Hyundai, Lincoln/Mercury, NTB, Nissan, Pontiac/Cadillac/Mazda, Suzuki/Kia, Toyota

229 Stassney Lane, **E...other:** Sam's Club/gas, Wal-Mart Super Ctr/24hr, **W...food:** Chili's, Macaroni Grill, Texas Cattle Co Steaks, **other:** Albertson's/gas, Lowe's Whse

TEXAS

Interstate 35

N
↑
↓
S

228 Wm Cannon Drive, **E...gas:** Exxon, **food:** Applebee's, McDonald's, Taco Bell, **other:** Chief Parts, Chrysler/Plymouth, Discount Tire, HEB Foods, Hyundai/Subaru, K-Mart, Mitsubishi, Target, **W...gas:** Texaco/diesel, **food:** Burger King, Chinese/Thai Rest., KFC, LJ Silver, Peter Piper Pizza, Taco Cabana, Whataburger/24hr, Wendy's, **other:** Chevrolet, Eckerd, Firestone

227 Slaughter Lane, Lp 275, S Congress, **E...other:** LoneStar RV Park, U-Haul, **W...gas:** Shamrock, **food:** Sonic

226 Slaughter Creek Overpass, **E...other:** LoneStar RV Park

225 FM 1626, Onion Creek Pkwy, **E...gas:** Shell, Texaco, **other:** Harley-Davidson

224 frontage rd(from nb), no facilities

223 FM 1327, no facilities

221 Lp 4, Buda, **E...gas:** Chevron/McDonald's, Phillips 66/diesel, **lodging:** Interstate Inn, **other:** Ford, **W...gas:** Chevron/24hr, Texaco/diesel, **food:** Jack-in-the-Box, Sonic, Subway, **other:** HEB Food/gas, Radio Shack, Marshall's RV Ctr

220 FM 2001, Niederwald, **E...gas:** Texaco, **other:** RV SuperCtr, **W...other:** Crestview RV Ctr/Park

217 Lp 4, Buda, **E...gas:** Conoco/diesel/24hr, **W...gas:** Exxon/diesel, Shamrock/Pizza Hut/diesel, **food:** Burger King, **lodging:** Best Western

215 Bunton Overpass, no facilities

213 FM 150, Kyle, **E...gas:** Shamrock/diesel, **food:** DQ, **W...gas:** Conoco

211mm **rest area both lanes, full(handicapped)facilities, phone, picnic tables, litter barrels, vending, pet-walk**

211mm truck check sta nb

210 Yarrington Rd, **W...other:** Plum Creek RV Resort

209mm truck check sta sb

208mm Blanco River

208 Frontage Rd, Blanco River Rd, no facilities

206 Lp 82, Aquarena Springs Rd, **E...gas:** Conoco, Shamrock, **W...gas:** Exxon/diesel, Mobil/diesel, Phillips 66/diesel, Shell, Texaco, **food:** Jim's Rest., Popeye's, Sonic, Tortuga's Rest., **lodging:** Comfort Inn, La Quinta, Motel 6, Quality Inn, Ramada Ltd, Stratford Inn, Super 8, University Inn, **other:** to SW TX U, RV camping

205 TX 80, TX 142, Bastrop, **E...gas:** Chevron, Conoco, Mobil, Shamrock, Shell/diesel, **food:** Arby's, BBQ, DQ, Jason's Deli, Pantera's Pizza, Schlotsky's, Subway, Taste of China, **other:** Eckerd, Hastings Books, Wal-Mart SuperCtr/24hr, **W...gas:** Chevron, Shamrock, Circle K/gas/24hr, **food:** Applebee's, Burger King, Church's, CiCi's, Furr's Cafeteria, IHOP, KFC, LJ Silver, Logan's Roadhouse, McDonald's, MT Mike's Steaks, Pizza Hut, Sirloin Stockade, Taco Cabana, Wendy's, **lodging:** Best Western, Budget Inn, Day's Inn, Microtel, Red Roof Inn, Rodeway Inn, **other:** HEB Foods, JC Penney, Office Depot, OfficeMax, Target, Walgreen

San Marcos

204mm San Marcos River

204b CM Allen Pkwy, **W...gas:** Chevron, Conoco/diesel, Texaco/diesel, **food:** Chinese Buffet, DQ, Sonic, **lodging:** Best Western, Econolodge, Mustang Motel

a Lp 82, TX 123, to Seguin, **E...gas:** Conoco, Phillips 66, Shamrock, Texaco/diesel, **food:** Burger King, Chili's, FasTaco, Golden Corral, Hardee's, Luby's, McDonald's, Red Lobster, Whataburger/24hr, **lodging:** Holiday Inn Express, **other:** HOSPITAL, Chevrolet/Buick, Ford/Mercury, Jeep/Chrysler, transmissions

202 FM 3407, Wonder World Dr, **E...gas:** Shell, **food:** Jack-in-the-Box, Wienerschnitzel, **other:** HOSPITAL, **other:** Discount Tire, Lowe's Whse, **W...gas:** Shamrock/diesel, **food:** BBQ, **other:** Plymouth/Dodge, transmissions

201 McCarty Lane, **E...other:** Pontiac/GMC, Subaru, **W...other:** Chrysler/Plymouth/Dodge, Nissan

200 Center Point Rd, **E...food:** Bennigan's, Cracker Barrel, Food Court, LoneStar Café, Outback Steaks, Subway, Taco Bell, Wendy's, **other:** Old Navy, Prime Outlets/famous brands, Tanger Outlet/famous brands, **W...gas:** Shamrock/diesel, **food:** Schlotsky's, Whataburger/24hr, AmeriHost, Honda

199 Posey Rd, **E...other:** Tanger Outlets/famous brands, Toyota

196 FM 1106, York Creek Rd, no facilities

195 Watson Lane, Old Bastrop Rd, **E...antiques**

N
e
w

B
r
a
u
n
f
e
l
s

193 Conrads Rd, Kohlenberg Rd, **W...gas:** Rip Griffin/Shell/Subway/diesel/24hr/@, **food:** Country Fair Rest., **other:** Camping World RV Supply

191 FM 306, FM 483, Canyon Lake, **E...gas:** Conoco/Quizno's/diesel, Texaco, **other:** RV camping, Wal-Mart Dist Ctr, **W...gas:** Chevron, Exxon/diesel **food:** Burger King, GristMill Rest., **other:** Camping World RV Supply, transmissions

190c Post Rd, no facilities

b Lp 35 S, New Braunfels, **W...gas/diesel, food:** Capparelli's Italian, **lodging:** Hawthorn Inn

a frontage rd, **E...gas:** Shell, **other:** Discount Tire, Home Depot, **W...gas:** McDonald's, **food:** Wendy's, **lodging:** Best Western, Comfort Suites, Motel 6

189 TX 46, Seguin, **E...gas:** Conoco/diesel, Exxon, Texaco/diesel, **food:** Luby's, Oma's Haus Rest., **lodging:** Oakwood Inn, Stratford House, Super 8, **other:** Discount Tire, K-Mart, Office Depot, **W...gas:** Chevron/24hr, Shamrock, **food:** Applebee's, IHOP, McDonald's, New Braunfels Smokehouse, Pizza Hut, Skillet's Rest., Taco Bell, Taco Cabana, Wendy's, **lodging:** Adelweiss Inn, Day's Inn, Hampton Inn, Holiday Inn, Motel 6, Rodeway Inn, **other:** HOSPITAL

188 Frontage Rd, **W...food:** Mamacita's, Ryan's, **other:** Hastings Books

188mm Guadalupe River

187 FM 725, Lake McQueeny Rd, **E...gas:** Chevron/24hr, **food:** Arby's, CiCi's, Guadalajara Mexican, LJ Silver, Subway, Whataburger/24hr, **other:** Jeep, Radio Shack, **W...gas:** Exxon/diesel, **food:** Adobe Café, DQ, Jack-in-the-Box, Rally's, Steaks to Go, **lodging:** Budget Host, **other:** HOSPITAL, NAPA AutoCare, transmissions

Interstate 35

N ↑↓ S

186 Walnut Ave, **E...gas:** Exxon/Subway, Shamrock, **food:** Chick-fil-A, Marina's Mexican, McDonald's, Popeye's, Schlotsky's, Taco Bell, **lodging:** Executive Lodge, **other:** Chevrolet, Wal-Mart/auto, **W...gas:** Conoco, Shamrock, Texaco/diesel, **food:** KFC, Mr Gatti's, Papa John's, Shanghai Chinese, **other:** AutoZone, HEB/deli/gas, Ross, Target, U-Haul, Walgreen

185 FM 1044, no facilities

184 FM 482, Lp 337, Ruekle Rd, **E...gas:** Texaco/Blimpie/diesel, **other:** Buick/Pontiac/GMC, Hill Country RV Park

183 Solms Rd, **W...gas:** Exxon, **other:** Mazda/Kia

182 Engel Rd, **E...food:** Pam's Country Kitchen, 1st RV Ctr, **W...other:** Mazda/Kia

180 Schwab Rd, no facilities

179mm **rest area both lanes, full(handicapped)facilities, phone, picnic tables, litter barrels, vending, pet-walk, RV dump**

178 FM 1103, Cibolo Rd, Hubertus Rd, **E...gas:** Shell/diesel

177 FM 482, FM 2252, **W...other:** Stone Creek RV Park

176 Weiderstein Rd, no facilities

175 FM 3009, Natural Bridge, **E...gas:** Shamrock, **food:** BBQ, McDonald's, Schlotsky's, Sonic, Taco Cabana, **other:** HEB Food/gas, Radio Shack, **W...gas:** Shamrock/Subway, Texaco/diesel, **food:** Arby's, Denny's, Jack-in-the-Box, KFC/Taco Bell/Pizza Hut, Wendy's, **lodging:** Atrium Inn, Country Inn, **other:** Factory Shoestore

174b Schertz Pkwy, no facilities

a FM 1518, Selma, **E...other:** Diahatsu, Honda/Mitsubishi, Saturn, **W...other:** Tex-All RV Ctr

173 Old Austin Rd, Olympia Pkwy, **E...food:** Chick-fil-A, Chili's, IHOP, Macaroni Grill, Outback Steaks, Subway, **other:** Best Buy, Borders Books, Home Depot, OfficeMax, Old Navy, Ross, Target, WorldMkt, **W...other:** Retama Park RaceTrack

172 TX 218, Anderson Lp, P Booker Rd, **E...lodging:** Comfort Inn, **other:** to Randolph AFB, **W...other:** to SeaWorld

171 Topperwein Rd, same as 170

170 Judson Rd, to Converse, **E...gas:** Texaco/diesel, **food:** India Cuisine, Kettle, Subway, Whataburger/24hr, **lodging:** La Quinta, **other:** HOSPITAL, Chevrolet, Chrysler/Plymouth, Ford, Gunn Auto Parts, Hyundai, Nissan, Pontiac/GMC, Toyota, **W...gas:** Exxon, Holiday Inn Express, **other:** Mazda, Sam's Club, Subaru

169 O'Conner Rd, Wurzbach Pkwy, **E...gas:** Exxon/diesel, Phillips 66, **food:** McDonald's, **other:** Lowe's Whse, **W...gas:** Shamrock, Texaco/diesel, **food:** Jack-in-the-Box, Jim's Rest., Mi Casa Mexican, **other:** K-Mart

168 Weidner Rd, **E...gas:** Exxon, Shamrock, **lodging:** Day's Inn, **W...gas:** Chevron, **lodging:** Quality Inn, Park Inn, Super 8, **other:** Harley-Davidson

San Antonio

167b Thousand Oaks Dr, Starlight Terrace, **E...gas:** Stop'n Go/diesel, **lodging:** Best Western

a Randolph Blvd, **E...other:** TravelTown TX RV Ctr, **W...lodging:** Best Western, Classic Inn, Comfort Inn, Day's Inn, Motel 6, Ruby Inn, **other:** Suzuki

166 I-410 W, Lp 368 S, **W...other:** to Sea World

165 FM 1976, Walzem Rd, **E...gas:** Chevron, Shamrock, Texaco, **food:** Applebee's, Baskin-Robbins, Blackeyed Pea, Burger King, Church's, CiCi's, IHOP, Jack-in-the-Box, Jim's Rest., KFC, Las Palapas Mexican, LJ Silver, Luby's, Marie Callender's, McDonald's, Olive Garden, Pizza Hut, Red Lobster, Schlotsky's, Subway, Taco Bell, Taco Cabana, Taco Kitchen, Wendy's, Whataburger, **lodging:** Drury Inn, Hampton Inn, **other:** Albertson's, AutoZone, CarQuest, Cavender's Boots, Circuit City, Dillard's, Discount Tire, Eckerd, Firestone/auto, HEB Foods, Home Depot, JC Penney, Mervyn's, Michael's, Office Depot, OfficeMax, PepBoys, Radio Shack, Target, Wal-Mart SuperCtr/24hr, mall, **W...gas:** Mobil, **food:** Sonic, **other:** NTB

164b Eisenhauer Rd, **E...gas:** Exxon/diesel, **other:** $General, Hancock Fabrics

a Rittiman Rd, **E...gas:** Conoco/diesel, Exxon/TacoMaker, RaceTrac, Shamrock, Texaco/diesel, Circle K/24hr, **food:** Burger King, Church's Chicken, Cracker Barrel, Denny's, McDonald's, Rally's, Taco Cabana, Whataburger/24hr, **lodging:** Comfort Suites, Knight's Inn, La Quinta, Motel 6, Ramada Inn, Scotsman Inn, Stratford House, Super 8, **other:** HEB Foods, **W...gas:** Chevron/diesel, Shamrock, **food:** BBQ, Popeye's, Sonic, Wendy's

163 I-410 S(162 from nb, exits left from sb)

161 Binz-Engleman Rd(from nb), same as 160

160 Coliseum Rd, **E...gas:** Shamrock/diesel/24hr, **lodging:** Delux Inn, **W...gas:** Conoco, **food:** BBQ, **lodging:** Day's Inn, Holiday Inn/rest., Microtel, Quality Inn, Super 8, Travelodge

TEXAS

Interstate 35

159b Walters St, **E...food:** McDonald's, Flores Drive-In, **other:** transmissions, **W...lodging:** Howard Johnson, **other:** to Ft Sam Houston

a New Braunfels Ave, **E...gas:** Exxon, Texaco/diesel, **W...gas:** Chevron, Shamrock/diesel/24hr, **food:** BBQ, Sonic, **lodging:** Ramada Suites, **other:** to Ft Sam Houston

158c N Alamo St, Broadway

b I-37 S, US 281 S, to Corpus Christi

a US 281 N(from sb), to Johnson City

157b a Brooklyn Ave, Lexington Ave, N Flores, downtown, **E...lodging:** Super 8, **other:** HOSPITAL, **W...food:** Luby's

156 I-10 W, US 87, to El Paso

155b Durango Blvd, downtown, **E...lodging:** Best Western, Courtyard, Fairfield Inn, La Quinta, Residence Inn, Woodfield Suites, **other:** HOSPITAL, **W...food:** McDonald's, Motel 6, Radisson

a South Alamo St, **E...gas:** Exxon, Texaco, **food:** Church's, McDonald's, Pizza Hut, Wendy's, **lodging:** Comfort Inn, Day's Inn, Ramada Ltd, **other:** USPO, **W...gas:** Conoco, **lodging:** Microtel

154b S Laredo St, Ceballos St, same as 155b

a Nogalitos St, no facilities

153 I-10 E, US 90 W, US 87, to Kelly AFB, Lackland AFB

152b Malone Ave, Theo Ave, **E...food:** Taco Cabana/24hr, **W...gas:** Phillips 66/24hr, Texaco/diesel

a Division Ave, **E...gas:** Chevron, **food:** BBQ, Whataburger/24hr, **lodging:** Holiday Inn Express, **W...gas:** Exxon, Phillips 66, **other:** transmissions

151 Southcross Blvd, **E...gas:** Exxon, Shell, **food:** Shop'n Save, **W...gas:** Circle K, Texaco/diesel

150b Lp 13, Military Dr, **E...gas:** Chevron, Conoco, Texaco, **food:** Denny's, KFC, Pizza Hut, Taco Cabana, **lodging:** La Quinta, **other:** AutoZone, Discount Tire, U-Haul, **W...gas:** Exxon, Mobil, Shamrock, **food:** Golden Corral, Hungry Farmer Steaks, Jack-in-the-Box, KFC, LJ Silver, Luby's, McDonald's, Mr Gatti, Pizza Hut, Wendy's, Whataburger, **other:** Albertson's, Eckerd, Goodyear, HEB Foods, JC Penney, Mervyn's, Office Depot, Old Navy, Sears/auto, Target, mall,

a Zarzamora St(149 fom sb), same as 150b

149 Hutchins Blvd(from sb), **E...gas:** Shamrock, **lodging:** Motel 6, **other:** HOSPITAL, **W...other:** Chevrolet, Ford, Kia

148b Palo Alto Rd, **W...gas:** Shamrock

a TX 16 S, spur 422(exits left from sb), Poteet, **E...gas:** Chevron, **W...gas:** Phillips 66, **other:** $General

147 Somerset Rd, **E...gas:** Texaco/diesel, **W...other:** Dodge

146 Cassin Rd(from nb), no facilities

145b Lp 353 N, no facilities

a I-410, TX 16, no facilities

144 Fischer Rd, **E...gas:** Shamrock/Subway/diesel/24hr, **lodging:** D&D Motel, **other:** RV camping, **W...gas:** Love's/Carl's Jr/diesel/24hr/@

142 Medina River Turnaround(from nb), no facilities

141 Benton City Rd, Von Ormy, **W...gas:** Texaco/diesel/café

140 Anderson Lp, 1604, **E...gas:** Exxon/Burger King/diesel/24hr, **W...gas:** Texaco/Church's/Pizza Hut/diesel/24hr, **other:** to Sea World

139 Kinney Rd, **E...**RV camping

137 Shepherd Rd, no facilities

135 Luckey Rd, no facilities

133 TX 132 S, Lytle, access to same as 131

131 FM 3175, FM 2790, Benton City Rd, **W...gas:** Conoco/diesel/24hr, **food:** BBQ, DQ, McDonald's, PigStand Rest., Sonic, Topis Mexican, **lodging:** Day's Inn, **other:** $General, HEB Food/gas

129mm rest area both lanes, full(handicapped)facilities, phone, picnic tables, litter barrels, vending, pet-walk

127 FM 471, Natalia, no facilities

124 FM 463, Bigfoot Rd, **E...**Ford

122 TX 173, Divine, **E...gas:** Exxon/Church's/diesel, **other:** Chevrolet, Plymouth/Jeep/Dodge, **W...gas:** Chevron/Subway/diesel, **food:** CCC Steaks, **lodging:** Country Corner Inn

121 TX 132 N, Devine, **E...other:** Gusville RV Park

118.5mm weigh sta both lanes

114 FM 462, Bigfoot, **E...gas:** Shamrock/diesel

111 US 57, to Eagle Pass, no facilities

104 Lp 35, **3 mi E...gas:** Shamrock, **food:** Sonic, **lodging:** Executive Inn, **other:** HOSPITAL

101 FM 140, Pearsall, **E...**Chevron, BBQ, Royal Inn, **W...gas:** Exxon/Blimpie/diesel/24hr, **food:** Cowpokes BBQ, **lodging:** Budget Inn, **other:** HOSPITAL

99 FM 1581, Pearsall, to Divot, **W...**LP

93mm parking/picnic area both lanes, litter barrels, handicapped accessible

91 FM 1583, Derby, no facilities

90mm Frio River

86 Lp 35, Dilley, no facilities

85 FM 117, **E...food:** Garcia's Café/motel, **W...gas:** Exxon/DQ/diesel, **lodging:** Safari Motel/café

84 TX 85, Dilley, **E...other:** Super S Foods, **other:** HOSPITAL, Chevrolet/Pontiac, NAPA, **W...gas:** Shamrock/diesel/24hr, Texaco/Church's/diesel/24hr, **lodging:** Executive Inn

82 County Line Rd, Dilley, no facilities

77 FM 469, Millett, no facilities

74 Gardendale, no facilities

68 Lp 35(69 from sb), Cotulla, **1 mi E...gas:** Mobil, **food:** Chuck Wagon Steaks, **lodging:** Cotulla Motel, **other:** Family$

67 FM 468, to Big Wells, **E...gas:** Exxon/Wendy's/diesel/24hr, **other:** Conoco/Country Store/rest., Shamrock/Church's/Pizza Hut/diesel/24hr, **food:** DQ, **lodging:** Executive Inn, Village Inn, tire repair, **W...gas:** Chevron/McDonald's/diesel

65 Lp 35, Cotulla, **1-2 mi E...gas:** Mobil, **food:** Chuck Wagon Steaks, **lodging:** Cotulla Motel

63 Elm Creek Interchange, no facilities

Pearsall

468

Interstate 35

59mm	parking/picnic area both lanes, litter barrels, handicapped accessible
56	FM 133, Artesia Wells, **E...gas**
48	Caiman Creek Interchange, no facilities
39	TX 44, Encinal, **E...gas:** Love's/Subway/Chester Fried/diesel/24hr/@
38	TX 44(from nb), Encinal, no facilities
32	San Roman Interchange, no facilities
27	Callaghan Interchange, no facilities
24	Camino Colombia toll rd, to Monterrey
22	Webb Interchange, no facilities
18	US 83 N, to Carrizo Springs, **E...Tx Travel Info Ctr(8am-5pm)**
15mm	parking/picnic area both lanes, insp area nb
13	Uniroyal Interchange, **E...gas:** Pilot/Subway/diesel/24hr/@, **other:** Blue Beacon
10	Port Laredo Carriers Dr(from nb), no facilities
9	Lp 20 W, to World Trade Bridge
8	FM 1472, Milo
7	Shilo Dr, Las Cruces Dr, **E...lodging:** Motel 9
6mm	Texas Tourist Bureau, info
4	FM 1472, Del Mar Blvd, **E...gas:** Chevron/repair, Exxon/diesel, **food:** Applebee's, Bennigan's, Burger King, Carino's Italian, DQ, IHOP, Jack-in-the-Box, Las Asadas Mexican, McDonald's, Whataburger, **lodging:** Extended Stay America, Hampton Inn, **other:** Albertson's, Best Buy, HEB Foods, Lowe's Whse, Marshall's, Old Navy, Radio Shack, Target, **W...gas:** Texaco/diesel, **food:** Golden Corral, **lodging:** Executive House Motel, Motel 6
3b	Mann Rd, **E...food:** Logan's Roadhouse, Luby's, Sirloin Stockade, Tony Roma, **other:** Buick, Dillard's, Foley's, Ford/Lincoln/Mercury, Honda, Mazda, Mervyn's, Pontiac/Cadillac/GMC, Sears/auto, Toyota, mall, **W...food:** Chili's, Outback Steaks, Pancake House, Subway, Taco Palenque, **lodging:** Family Garden Inn, Fiesta Inn, La Hacienda Motel, Motel 6, **other:** $General, Home Depot, Michael's, Office Depot, OfficeMax, Ross, Wal-Mart/auto/24hr
a	San Bernardo Ave, **E...gas:** Texaco/diesel, **food:** Chick-fil-A, Fuddrucker's, LJ Silver, Peter Piper Pizza, **other:** HEB Foods, K-Mart, NAPA, PepBoys, SteinMart, mall, **W...gas:** Citgo/Circle K, Chevron, Phillips 66/diesel, **food:** Burger King, Coyote Creek Rest., DQ, Dunkin Donuts, El Pollo Loco, Hunan Chinese, Julep's Rest., King Dynasty Chinese, McDonald's, Pizza Hut, Popeye's, Taco Bell, Taco Palenque, Wendy's, Whataburger, **lodging:** Best Western, Gateway Inn, Monterey Inn, Red Roof Inn, **other:** Gonzales Auto Parts, Goodyear/auto, Radio Shack, Sam's Club
2	US 59, Saunders Rd, **E...gas:** Conoco, Shamrock, Texaco, **food:** Jack-in-the-Box, **other:** HOSPITAL, **W...gas:** Chevron/diesel/24hr, Exxon/diesel, Phillips 66/diesel, **food:** Church's Denny's, **lodging:** Civic Ctr Inn, Courtyard, El Cortez Motel, Holiday Inn, La Quinta, Mayan Inn, **other:** AutoZone, Mexico Insurance, Ramirez Tire

Laredo (left margin vertical label)

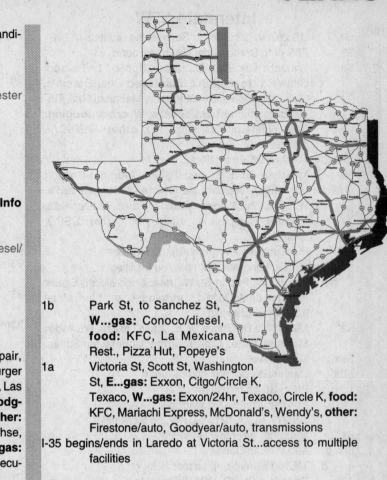

1b	Park St, to Sanchez St, **W...gas:** Conoco/diesel, **food:** KFC, La Mexicana Rest., Pizza Hut, Popeye's
1a	Victoria St, Scott St, Washington St, **E...gas:** Exxon, Citgo/Circle K, Texaco, **W...gas:** Exxon/24hr, Texaco, Circle K, **food:** KFC, Mariachi Express, McDonald's, Wendy's, **other:** Firestone/auto, Goodyear/auto, transmissions

I-35 begins/ends in Laredo at Victoria St...access to multiple facilities

Interstate 35W

Exit #	Services
	I-35W begins/ends on I-35, exit 467.
85a	I-35E S, no facilities
84	FM 1515, Bonnie Brae St, **E...HOSPITAL**
82	FM 2449, to Ponder, no facilities
79	Crawford Rd, no facilities
76	FM 407, Argyle, to Justin, no facilities
76mm	picnic area both lanes, litter barrels, picnic tables
74	FM 1171, to Lewisville, no facilities
70	TX 114, to Dallas, Bridgeport, **E...gas:** Texaco/Church's/diesel, **other:** to DFW Airport, **W...other:** TX Motor Speedway
68	Eagle Pkwy, **W...airport**
67	Alliance Blvd, **W...other:** to Alliance Airport, FedEx
66	to Westport Pkwy, Keller-Haslet Rd, **E...lodging:** Hampton Inn, Hawthorn Suites, **W...gas:** Mobil/Wendy's/diesel, **food:** BBQ, Bryan's Smokehouse, Cactus Flower Café, Oriental Garden, Schlotsky's, Subway, Taco Bueno, **other:** USPO
65	TX 170 E, **E...gas:** Pilot/diesel/24hr/@
64	Golden Triangle Blvd, to Keller-Hicks Blvd, no facilities
63	Park Glen, no facilities

TEXAS

Interstate 35W

60	US 287 N, US 81 N, to Decatur, no facilities
59	I-35 W to Denton(from sb), turnaround
58	Western Ctr Blvd, **E...gas:** Citgo/7-11, Texaco/Church's, **food:** BBQ, Blackeyed Pea, Braum's, Chili's, Domino's, Donut Palace, Macaroni Grill, On-the-Border, SaltGrass Steaks, Wendy's, **lodging:** Best Western, Residence Inn, **other:** MEDICAL CARE
57b a	I-820 E&W, no facilities
56	Meacham Blvd, **E...gas:** Texaco, **lodging:** Comfort Inn, Hilton Garden, La Quinta, **other:** Dillard's, **W...gas:** Mobil, **food:** Cracker Barrel, McDonald's, **lodging:** Hampton Inn, Holiday Inn, **other:** USPO, cleaners
55	Pleasantdale Ave(from nb), no facilities
54c	33rd St, Long Ave(from nb), no facilities
b a	TX 183 W, Papurt St, **W...gas:** Citgo/diesel, Shamrock, **food:** McDonald's, **lodging:** Classic Inn, Motel 6, **other:** truckwash
53	North Side Dr, Yucca Dr, **E...gas:** Texaco, **W...food:** Mercado Juarez Café, **lodging:** Country Inn Suites
53mm	Trinity River
52d	Carver St(from nb), no facilities
c	Pharr St, no facilities
b	Belknap(from sb), no facilities
a	US 377 N, TX 121, to DFW, no facilities
51	spur 280, downtown Ft Worth
50c a	I-30 W, E to Dallas
b	TX 180 E(from nb), no facilities
49b	Rosedale St, **W...**HOSPITAL
a	Allen Ave, **E...gas:** Chevron, **W...**HOSPITAL
48b	Morningside Ave(from sb), same as 48a
a	Berry St, **E...gas:** Chevron/McDonald's, Citgo, **W...gas:** RaceTrac, **other:** Sack'n Save Foods, U-Haul
47	Ripy St, **E...other:** transmissions
46b	Seminary Dr, **E...food:** Grandy's, Golden Corral, Jack-in-the-Box, Taco Cabana, Wyatt's Cafeteria, **lodging:** Day's Inn, Delux Inn, Regency Inn, Super 7 Inn, **W...gas:** Exxon, Texaco, **food:** Denny's, El Chico, Peony Chinese, **other:** Dillard's, Firestone/auto, JC Penney, Sears
a	Felix St(from nb), **E...gas:** Mobil, **food:** Pulido's Mexican, **lodging:** S Oaks Inn, **W...food:** Burger King, McDonald's, **other:** Dodge
45b a	I-20, E to Dallas, W to Abilene
44	Altamesa, **E...lodging:** Holiday Inn, **W...gas:** Citgo, **food:** Rig Steaks, Waffle House, **lodging:** Best Western, Comfort Suites, Motel 6, South Lp Inn, **other:** RV Ctr
43	Sycamore School Rd, **W...gas:** Exxon, **food:** Beefer's Rest./24hr, Jack-in-the-Box, Subway, Taco Bell, Whataburger/24hr, **other:** Aaron's Foods, $General, Home Depot, Radio Shack
42	Everman Pkwy, **E...gas:** Exxon, **W...other:** RV Ctr
41	Risinger Rd, **W...**auto repair
40	Garden Acres Dr, **E...gas:** Love's/diesel/24hr, **lodging:** Microtel, **other:** HOSPITAL, **W...other:** RV Lite Ctr
39	FM 1187, McAlister Rd, **E...**HOSPITAL, **W...gas:** Citgo/diesel, Shamrock/diesel/24hr, **food:** Taco Bell, Waffle House, **lodging:** Howard Johnson
38	Alsbury Blvd, **E...gas:** Chevron, Mobil/diesel, **food:** Chili's, Country Steaks, Cracker Barrel, McDonald's, Taipan Chinese, **lodging:** Super 8, **other:** Ford, Lowe's Whse, **W...gas:** Citgo, Texaco/24hr, **food:** Arby's, Burger King, Denny's, Grandy's, Pancho's Mexican, **other:** Albertson's, Chevrolet, K-Mart
37	TX 174, Wilshire Blvd, to Cleburne, **W...gas:** Exxon, Shell, **other:** Eckerd
36	FM 3391, Burleson, **E...gas:** Citgo, Mobil, **food:** Luby's, Steak Exchange, Waffle House, **lodging:** Comfort Suites, Day's Inn, **W...gas:** Chevron, Fina/diesel, Shamrock
34	Briaroaks Rd(from sb), **W...**RV camping
33mm	**rest area sb, full(handicapped)facilities, phone, picnic tables, litter barrels**
32	Bethesda Rd, **E...gas:** Citgo, **lodging:** 5 Star Inn/rest., Bill&Martin's Seafood Rest., **W...other:** RV Ranch Park
31mm	**rest area nb, full(handicapped)facilities, phone, picnic tables, litter barrels**
30	FM 917, Mansfield, **W...gas:** Fina, Texaco/Snappy Jack's/diesel
27	County Rds 604 & 707, **E...other:** Travel Villa RV Ctr
26b a	US 67, Cleburne, **E...gas:** Citgo/Pop'sChicken/diesel, Exxon/Subway/24hr, Texaco
24	FM 3136, FM 1706, Alvarado, **E...gas:** Chevron, Texaco/diesel/24hr, **food:** Alvarado House Rest., **W...other:** McClain's RV Ctr
21	Barnesville Rd, to Greenfield, no facilities
17	FM 2258, no facilities
16	TX 81 S, County Rd 201, Grandview, **E...**RV camping, **W...**RV camping
15	FM 916, Maypearl, **W...gas:** Phillips 66(1mi), Shamrock/diesel, **food:** BBQ
12	FM 67, no facilities
8	FM 66, Itasca, **E...gas:** Chevron/diesel/café/24hr, **W...gas:** Citgo/diesel, **food:** DQ, **other:** Ford, picnic tables, litter barrels
7	FM 934, **E...**picnic tables, litter barrels
3	FM 2959, **E...**to Hillsboro Airport

I-35W begins/ends on I-35, 371mm.

Interstate 37

Exit #	Services
142b a	I-35 S to Laredo, N to Austin. I-37 begins/ends on I-35 in San Antonio.
141c	Brooklyn Ave, Nolan St(from sb), downtown
b	Houston St, downtown, **E...lodging:** Red Roof Inn, **W...food:** Denny's, **lodging:** Crockett Hotel, Day's Inn, Hampton Inn, Holiday Inn, Hyatt Hotel, Marriott, Residence Inn, **other:** to The Alamo
a	Commerce St, downtown, **W...lodging:** La Quinta, Marriott
140b	Durango Blvd, downtown, **E...food:** Bill Miller BBQ, **other:** to Aladome
a	Carolina St, Florida St, no facilities
139	I-10 W, US 87, US 90, to Houston, **W...other:** to Sea World

Interstate 37

138c Fair Ave, Hackberry St, **E...gas:** Chevron, **food:** DQ, Jack-in-the-Box, KFC, Peter Piper Pizza, Popeye's, Taco Bell, **other:** Family$, Home Depot, **W...gas:** Exxon, Texaco

b E New Braunfels Ave(from sb), **E...food:** Chick-fil-A, Hong Kong Buffet, Jim's Rest., Luby's, McDonald's, Taco Cabana, Pizza Hut, Wendy's, **other:** mall

a Southcross Blvd, W New Braunfels Ave, **W...gas:** Exxon, **food:** Sonic

137 Hot Wells Blvd, **E...**bank, **W...food:** IHOP, **lodging:** Motel 6

136 Pecan Valley Dr, **E...gas:** Citgo/diesel, **food:** KFC/Taco Bell, Pizza Hut, **other:** O'Reilly Parts, **W...**HOSPITAL

135 Military Dr, Lp 13, **E...gas:** Shamrock, Texaco, **food:** Jack-in-the-Box, **lodging:** Best Western, Mission Trail RV Resort, **W...gas:** Shamrock, **food:** Burger King, Lotus Chinese, **other:** HEB Food/gas, K-Mart, to Brooks AFB

133 I-410, US 281 S, no facilities

132 US 181 S, no facilities

130 Donop Rd, Southton Rd, **E...gas:** Shamrock/diesel/RV dump, **food:** Braunig Lake Café, **lodging:** San Antonio Inn, **other:** I-37 RV Ctr/flea mkt, **W...gas:** Texaco/diesel, **other:** car/truckwash

127 San Antonio River Turnaround(from nb), Braunig Lake

127mm San Antonio River

125 FM 1604, Anderson Lp, **E...gas:** Conoco/Burger King/diesel/24hr, **food:** Mi Reina Mexican, **W...gas:** Exxon/diesel, Fina/diesel/burgers, **food:** BBQ

122 Priest Rd, Mathis Rd, no facilities

120 Hardy Rd, no facilities

117 FM 536, no facilities

113 FM 3006, no facilities

112mm picnic area both lanes, handicapped accessible

109 TX 97, to Floresville, **E...gas:** Chevron/diesel, **food:** DownHome Burgers/BBQ, Harpers Landing Rest., **other:** Chrysler/Plymouth/Dodge/Jeep, Yamaha

106 Coughran Rd, no facilities

104 spur 199, Leal Rd, to Pleasanton(no immediate sb return), same as 103

103 US 281 N, Leal Rd, to Pleasanton, **E...gas:** Citgo, Shamrock/diesel, **food:** DQ, K&K Steak&Egg, **lodging:** Kuntry Inn

98 TX 541, McCoy, no facilities

92 US 281A, Campbellton, no facilities

88 FM 1099, to FM 791, Campbellton, no facilities

83 FM 99, Whitsett, Peggy, **E...gas:** Texaco/diesel, **W...gas:** Chevron, Exxon/diesel/deli/RV Park/dump

82mm **rest area sb, full(handicapped)facilities, phone, picnic tables, litter barrels**

78mm **rest area nb, full(handicapped)facilities, phone, picnic tables, litter barrels**

76 US 281Alt, FM 2049, Whitsett, no facilities

75mm truck weigh sta sb

74mm truck weigh sta nb

72 US 281 S, Three Rivers, **4 mi W...lodging:** Best Western, **other:** to Rio Grande Valley

69 TX 72, Three Rivers, **W...gas:** Shamrock/diesel/café/24hr, **other:** to Choke Canyon SP

65 FM 1358, Oakville, **E...food:** Van's BBQ, **W...gas:** Chevron, **food:** Burgers&More

59 FM 799, no facilities

56mm parking area sb

56 US 59, George West, **E...gas:** Texaco/Circle K/diesel/24hr, **W...gas:** Chevron/Subway/TCBY/24hr, Exxon/Burger King/diesel/24hr, **other:** Rockin'N RV Park

51 Hailey Ranch Rd, no facilities

47 FM 3024, FM 534, Swinney Switch Rd, **W...other:** to KOA

44mm parking area sb

42mm parking area nb

40 FM 888, no facilities

36 TX 359, Mathis, to Skidmore, **W...gas:** Texaco/diesel, **food:** Pizza Hut

34 TX 359 W, **W...gas:** Shamrock/diesel, Texaco, **food:** Taqueria Vallarta Mexican, **other:** Ford, to Lake Corpus Christi SP

31 TX 188, Rockport, to Sinton

22 TX 234, FM 796, Edroy, to Odem, no facilities

20b Cooper Rd, no facilities

19.5mm **rest area both lanes, full(handicapped)facilities, phone, picnic tables, litter barrels, vending, petwalk**

17 US 77 N, to Victoria, no facilities

16 LaBonte Park, **W...**info, picnic tables

15 Sharpsburg Rd(from sb), Redbird Ln, no facilities

14 US 77 S, Rebird Ln, Robstown, to Kingsville, **1 mi W on UpRiver Rd...gas:** Chevron/Burger King, Citgo/Circle K, RaceTrac, Taxaco, **food:** BBQ, CiCi's, Denny's, Good'n Crisp Chicken, K-Bob's, Pizza Hut, Popeye's, Sonic, Subway, Whataburger/24hr, Wienerschnitzel, **lodging:** Comfort Inn, **other:** HOSPITAL, Beall's, Eckerd, Firestone, Home Depot, Radio Shack, Wal-Mart SuperCtr/24hr

13b Sharpsburg Rd(from nb)

a FM 1694, Callicoatte Rd, Leopard St, no facilities

11b FM 24, Violet Rd, Hart Rd, **E...gas:** NewWay/diesel/24hr, **W...gas:** Citgo, Exxon/Circle K, **food:** DQ, Domino's, KFC, McDonald's, Schlotsky's, Sonic, Subway, Taco Bell, Whataburger/24hr, **lodging:** Best Western, **other:** AutoZone, Family$, HEB Food/gas, O'Reilly Parts

a McKinzie Rd, **W...gas:** Citgo/Circle K

TEXAS

Interstate 37

E ⬆ W

Corpus Christi

10	Carbon Plant Rd, no facilities
9	FM 2292, Up River Rd, Rand Morgan Rd, **W...gas:** Citgo/Circle K, Texaco/Subway/diesel, **food:** Whataburger/24hr
7	Suntide Rd, Tuloso Rd, Clarkwood Rd, no facilities
6	Southern Minerals Rd, **E...gas:** Citgo Refinery
5	Corn Products Rd, **E...other:** GMC Trucks, Kenworth, **W...gas:** PetroFleet, **food:** Gem's Rest., Race **lodging:** Track Hotel, Red Roof Inn, Super 8, Travelodge
4b	Lantana St, McBride Lane(from sb), **W...lodging:** Drury Inn, Holiday Inn, Motel 6
a	TX 358, to Padre Island, **W...gas:** Texaco/diesel, **lodging:** Drury Inn, Hawthorn Suites(6mi), Holiday Inn, Motel 6, Quality Inn, **other:** Wal-Mart Super Ctr/24hr(6mi)
3b	McBride Lane, **W...**Greyhound Raceway, **lodging:** Ramada Ltd
a	Navigation Blvd, **E...gas:** Texaco/diesel, **lodging:** Clarion, **W...gas:** Exxon/diesel, **food:** Denny's, **lodging:** Comfort Inn, Day's Inn, La Quinta, **other:** CarQuest
2	Up River Rd, **E...other:** Citgo Refinery
1e	Lawrence Dr, Nueces Bay Blvd, **W...gas:** Citgo/Circle K, **food:** Church's, **other:** HEB Foods, Firestone, Ford, Radio Shack, USPO
1d	Port Ave(from sb), **W...gas:** Citgo, Coastal, **food:** Vick's Burgers, **lodging:** Howard Johnson, **other:** Port of Corpus Christi
1c	US 181, TX 286, Shoreline Blvd, Corpus Christi, **W...**HOSPITAL
1b	Brownlee St(from nb), no facilities
1a	Buffalo St(from sb). **S on Shoreline...gas:** Citgo/Circle K, **food:** Joes Crabshack, Landry's Seafood, **lodging:** Omni Hotel, Ramada Inn. I-37 begins/ends on US 181 in Corpus Christi.

Interstate 40

E ⬆ W

Shamrock

Exit #	Services
177mm	Texas/Oklahoma state line
176	spur 30(from eb), to Texola, no facilities
175mm	picnic area wb, picnic tables, litter barrels
173mm	picnic area eb, picnic tables, litter barrels
169	FM 1802, Carbon Black Rd, no facilities
167	FM 2168, Daberry Rd, **N...gas:** Shamrock/diesel
164	Lp 40(from wb), to Shamrock, **1 mi S...lodging:** Budget Inn, Econolodge, Shamrock Inn, **other:** HOSPITAL, museum
163	US 83, to Wheeler, Shamrock, **N...gas:** Chevron/diesel, Conoco, **food:** Pizza Hut/Taco Bell, **lodging:** Best Western Irish/rest., Western Motel, **other:** mall, **S...gas:** Phillips 66/Subway/24hr, Shell, **food:** DQ, McDonald's, **lodging:** Budget Host
161	Lp 40, Rte 66(from eb), to Shamrock, no facilities
157	FM 1547, Lela, **1 mi S...other:** W 40 RV Park
152	FM 453, Pakan Rd, no facilities
150mm	picnic area wb, tables, litter barrels
149mm	picnic area eb, tables, litter barrels
148	FM 1443, Kellerville Rd, no facilities
146	County Line Rd, no facilities
143	Lp 40(from wb), to McLean, to gas, no facilities
142	TX 273, FM 3143, to McLean, **N...**Country Corner RV Park/gas, **lodging:** Cactus Inn, **other:** CarQuest
141	Rte 66(from eb), McLean, **N...food:** Red River Steaks, **lodging:** Cactus Inn, same as 142
135	FM 291, Rte 66, Alanreed, **S...gas:** Conoco/motel/café/RV park, **other:** auto repair, USPO
132	Johnson Ranch Rd, ranch access, no facilities
131mm	**rest area wb, full(handicapped)facilities, phone, picnic tables, litter barrels, petwalk**
129mm	**rest area eb, full(handicapped)facilities, phone, picnic tables, littler barrels, petwalk**
128	FM 2477, to Lake McClellan, **S...other:** RA/camping/RV dump(3mi)
124	TX 70 S, to Clarendon, no facilities
121	TX 70 N, to Pampa, no facilities
114	Lp 40, Groom, no facilities
113	FM 2300, Groom, **S...gas:** Shell/diesel, **food:** DQ, **lodging:** Chalet Inn
112	FM 295, Groom, **S...other:** Biggest Cross, **1 mi S...**gas
110	Lp 40, Rte 66, no facilities
109	FM 294, no facilities
108mm	parking area wb, litter barrels
106mm	parking area eb, picnic tables, litter barrels
105	FM 2880, grain silo, no facilities
98	TX 207 S(from wb), to Claude, no facilities
96	TX 207 N, to Panhandle, **N...gas:** Love's/Subway/diesel/24hr/@, **S...lodging:** Budget Host, Conway Inn/cafe
89	FM 2161, to Rte 66, no facilities
87	FM 2373, no facilities
87mm	picnic areas both lanes, litter barrels
85	Amarillo Blvd, Durrett Rd, access to camping
81	FM 1912, **N...gas:** Shell, **S...gas:** TA/Subway/diesel/rest./24hr/@, Counrty Fresh Rest.
80	FM 228, **N...other:** AOK RV Park
78	US 287 S(from eb), FM 1258, Pullman Rd, same as 77
77	FM 1258, Pullman Rd, **N...gas:** USA Travel Plaza/Arby's/diesel/24hr/@, **S...gas:** Shell/diesel/24hr/@, **other:** Custom RV Ctr
76	spur 468, **N...gas:** ✈/Flying J/Conoco/diesel/LP/rest./24hr/@, Shell/diesel, **other:** tourist info, **S...gas:** Speedco
75	Lp 335, Lakeside Rd, **N...gas:** Pilot/Subway/diesel/rest./24hr/@, **food:** Country Barn Rest., McDonald's, Waffle House, **lodging:** Clarion, Quality Inn, Super 8, Trailer Inn, **other:** UPS, Peterbilt Trucks, KOA(2mi), **S...gas:** Petro/Mobil/diesel/rest./@, **other:** Blue Beacon
74	Whitaker Rd, **N...lodging:** Big Texan Inn/café, **other:** RV camping, **S...gas:** Love's/Subway/diesel/@, TA/FoodCourt/diesel/24hr/@, **lodging:** Budget Inn, **other:** Blue Beacon
73	Eastern St, Bolton Ave, Amarillo, **N...gas:** Shamrock/diesel, Shell/diesel, **food:** Polly's Rest., **lodging:** Motel 6, Red Roof Inn, **S...gas:** Chevron/diesel, Citgo/diesel, **lodging:** Best Western, **other:** Ford Trucks
72b	Grand St, Amarillo, **N...gas:** Shell, **food:** KFC, **lodging:** Motel 6, **other:** Nissan, U-Haul, **S...gas:** Phillips 66, **food:** Braum's, McDonald's, Pizza Hut, Sonic, Subway, Taco Cabana, Taco Villa, **lodging:** Motel 6, **other:** AutoZone, Braum's, $General, Wal-Mart Super Ctr/gas/24hr, same as 73

Interstate 40

E ↕ **W**

A m a r i l l o

72a Nelson St, **N...food:** Cracker Barrel, KFC, **lodging:** Ashmore Inn, Budget Host, Econolodge, Kiva Hotel, Ramada Inn, Sleep Inn, Super 8, Travelodge, **other:** Qtrhorse Museum, **S...gas:** Chevron, Shell/diesel, **lodging:** Camelot Inn

71 Ross St, Osage St, Amarillo, **N...gas:** Conoco/diesel, Shamrock, Shell/diesel, **food:** Burger King, El Tapatio's Mexican, Longhorn Diner, LJ Silver, McDonald's, Popeye's, Schlotsky's, Subway, **lodging:** Coachlight Inn, Comfort Inn, Day's Inn, Holiday Inn, Microtel, **S...gas:** Shamrock, **food:** Arby's, Denny's, Fiesta Grande Mexican, Sonic, Taco Bell, Wendy's, **lodging:** Hampton Inn, La Quinta, Ramada Ltd, **other:** Chevrolet, Ford, Hyundai, Sam's Club/gas, USPO

70 I-27 S, US 60 W, US 87, US 287, to Canyon, Lubbock, **N...other:** Goodyear/auto, bank

69b Washington St, 'Amarillo, **N...other:** Albertson's, **S...gas:** Phillips 66, Shell, **food:** DQ, Subway, **other:** Eckerd

69a Crockett St, access to same as 68b

68b Georgia St, **N...gas:** Shell/Subway, Texaco, **food:** TGIFriday, **lodging:** Ambassador Hotel, **S...gas:** Phillips 66, **food:** Burger King, BBQ, Church's, Denny's, Furr's Café, Taco Villa, Whataburger, **lodging:** Econolodge, Quality Inn, **other:** HOSPITAL, Chrysler/Dodge, Hastings Books, K-Mart, Mitsubishi, Office Depot, Saturn

68a Julian Blvd, Paramount Blvd, **N...gas:** Chevron, Shell, **food:** Arby's, Chili's, Macaroni Joe's, Nick's Rest., Pancho's Mexican, Pizza Hut, Schlotzsky's, Wendy's, **lodging:** Harley Hotel, same as 67, **S...gas:** Shamrock, **food:** Bennigan's, Caboose Diner, Cactus Grill, Cajun Magic, Calico Country Café, El Chico, Godfather's, Kabuki's Japanese Steaks, LJ Silver, Orient Express, Peking Rest., Pizza Planet, Popeye's, Red Lobster, Ruby Tequila's Mexican, Steak&Ale, Texas Roadhouse, **lodging:** Comfort Suites, Holiday Inn Express, Motel 6, Travelodge, **other:** Cadillac, Discount Tire, Pennzoil

67 Western St, Amarillo, **N...gas:** Citgo, Shell, **food:** Beef Rigger Rest., Blackeyed Pea, Braum's, Burger King, Chili's, Cty Line BBQ, Legends Grill, Marie Callender's, McDonald's, Pancho's Mexican, Rosa's Cafe, Subway, Taco Bell, **S...gas:** Phillips 66, Shamrock, **food:** Catfish Shack, Dairy Queen, Furr's Café, Gary's BBQ, IHOP, Olive Garden, Taco Cabana, Vince's Pizza, Waffle House, Wienerschnitzel, **lodging:** Holiday Inn Express, **other:** Firestone/auto, NAPA, Radio Shack, same 68

66 Bell St, Amarillo, **N...gas:** Citgo/diesel, Shamrock, **lodging:** AmeriSuites, Quality Inn, Fairfield Inn, HomeGate Suites, Motel 6, Residence Inn, **other:** Big A Parts, Harley-Davidson, **S...gas:** Chevron, Shell, **food:** King & I Chinese, Popeye's, Starbucks, **other:** Albertson's

65 Coulter Dr, Amarillo, **N...gas:** Phillips 66/diesel, **food:** Arby's, Golden Corral, Luby's, My Thai Café, Taco Bell, Waffle House, **lodging:** Best Western, Comfort Inn, Courtyard, Day's Inn, Executive Inn, La Quinta, **other:** HOSPITAL, Chevrolet, Discount Tire, Dodge, Firestone/auto, Nissan, **S...gas:** Chevron/KFC, Citgo, Shell, **food:** BBQ, Braum's, ChinaStar, Chuck-eCheese, CiCi's, Hoffbrau Steaks, Jason's Deli, Krispy Kreme, McDonald's, Outback Steaks, Pizza Hut, Santa Fe Rest., Sonic, Subway, Taco Villa, TCBY, Wendy's, Whataburger, Wienerschnitzel, **lodging:** Hampton Inn, 5th Season Inn, **other:** Best Buy, Goodyear/auto, IGA Foods, Lowe's Whse, Sears/auto

64 Soncy Rd, to Pal Duro Cyn, **N...food:** Carino's Italian, Joe's Crabshack, Logan's Roadhouse, **lodging:** Comfort Inn, Hilton Garden, Homewood Suites, Extended Stay America, **other:** Discount Tire, **S...gas:** Shamrock/diesel/24hr, **food:** Applebee's, DQ, Fazoli's, Hooters, Legends Steaks, McDonald's, On-the-Border, Ruby Tuesday, Subway, Zoo-kini's Grill, **other:** MEDICAL CARE, Barnes&Noble, Circuit City, Dillard's, Ford, Home Depot, K-Mart, Mervyn's, OfficeMax, Old Navy, Ross, Target, mall

62b Lp 40, Amarillo Blvd, RV camping

62a Hope Rd, Helium Rd(from eb), **S...other:** RV camping, antiques

60 Arnot Rd, **S...gas:** Love's/A&W/Subway/diesel/@ , Texas Trading Co/gifts, **other:** camping

57 RM 2381, to Bushland, **N...grain silo, S...gas:** Shell/diesel, **other:** USPO, RV camping/dump(1mi)

55mm parking area wb, litter barrels

54 Adkisson Rd, **S...RV park**

53.5mm parking area eb, litter barrels

49 (50 from wb)FM 809, to Wildorado, **S...gas:** Phillips 66/diesel, **lodging:** Royal Inn

42 Everett Rd, no facilities

37 Lp 40 W, to Vega, **1 mi N...lodging:** Bonanza Motel, **other:** Walnut RV Park, same as 36

36 US 385, Vega, **N...gas:** Conoco/diesel/24hr, Phillips 66, Shamrock, **food:** DQ, **lodging:** Best Western/café, Comfort Inn, **other:** CarQuest, **S...gas:** Shell/diesel

TEXAS

Interstate 40

E
W

35	to Rte 66, to Vega, **N...lodging:** Best Western/café, **other:** Walnut RV Park, same as 36
32mm	picnic area both lanes, litter barrels
28	to Rte 66, Landergin, no facilities
22	TX 214, to Adrian, **N...lodging:** Fabulous 40 Motel, **S...gas:** Phillips 66/diesel/café, **other:** Tommy's Foods
18	FM 2858, Gruhlkey Rd, **S...gas:** Shell/Stuckey's/rest./diesel
15	Ivy Rd, no facilities
13mm	picnic area both lanes, picnic tables, litter barrels
5.5mm	turnout
0	Lp 40, to Glenrio, no facilities
0mm	Texas/New Mexico state line, Central/Mountain time zone

Interstate 44

Exit # Services

E
W

Wichita Falls

15mm	Texas/Oklahoma state line, Red River
14	Lp 267, E 3rd St, **W...other:** Burk RV Park
13	Glendale St, **W...food:** Subway, **other:** MEDICAL CARE, Family$, Sav-A-Lot Foods, Wal-Mart
12	Burkburnett, **E...gas:** Chevron/diesel, **W...gas:** Fina/7-11, Shamrock, **food:** Braum's, KFC/Taco Bell, Mazzio's, McDonald's, Subway, Whataburger/24hr, **other:** Chevrolet/Pontiac, Ford
11	FM 3429, Daniels Rd, **W...gas:** Fina
9mm	picnic area both lanes, picnic table, litter barrels, pet-walk
7	East Rd, no facilities
6	Bacon Switch Rd, no facilities
5a	FM 3492, Missile Rd, **E...other:** st patrol, **W...gas:** Exxon/diesel
5	Access Rd, no facilities
4	City Loop St, no facilities
3c	FM 890, **W...gas:** Shamrock, **other:** $Tree, Wal-Mart SuperCtr/gas/24hr
3b	sp 325, Sheppard AFB, no facilities
a	US 287 N, to Amarillo
2	Maureen St, **E...gas:** Fina/7-11/diesel, Texaco/diesel, **lodging:** Comfort Inn, King's Inn, Motel 6, Travelodge, **other:** Chevrolet, Mazda, Nissan/Volvo/VW, **W...gas:** Fina/7-11, **food:** China Star, DQ, Denny's, El Chico, LJ Silver, Waffle Time, Whataburger/24hr, **lodging:** Hampton Inn, La Quinta, Super 8, Travelers Inn
1d	US 287 bus, Lp 370, **W...gas:** Conoco/diesel, **lodging:** Day's Inn, River Oaks Inn
1c	Texas Tourist Bureau, **E...gas:** Citgo, **W...lodging:** Radisson
1b	Scotland Park(from nb), **E...lodging:** Scotland Park Motel, **W...**RV park
1a	US 277 S, to Abilene
0mm	I-44 begins/ends in Witchita Falls. **1-2 mi S in Wichita Falls...gas:** Citgo/Circle K/diesel, Conoco, Fina/7-11/diesel, **food:** Arby's, Burger King, Carl's Jr, IHOP, McDonald's, Papa John's, Popeye's, Subway, Whataburger/24hr, Wendy's, **lodging:** Econolodge, Holiday Inn, **other:** HOSPITAL

Interstate 45

Exit # Services

Dallas

S

Ennis

286	to I-35 E, to Denton. I-45 begins/ends in Dallas.
285	Bryan St E, US 75 N, no facilities
284b a	I-30, W to Ft Worth, E to Texarkana, access to HOSPITAL
283b	Pennsylvania Ave, to MLK Blvd, **E...gas:** to Shamrock, Shell, **food:** BBQ, **W...food:** KFC/Taco Bell
a	Lamar St, no facilities
281	Oberton St(from sb), **W...gas:** Chevron
280	Illinois Ave, Linfield St, **E...lodging:** Linfield Motel, Star Motel, **W...gas:** Texaco
279b a	Lp 12, no facilities
277	Simpson Stuart Rd, **W...other:** to Paul Quinn Coll
276b a	I-20, W to Ft Worth, E to Shreveport
275	TX 310 N(from nb, no re-entry), no facilities
274	Dowdy Ferry Rd, Hutchins, **E...gas:** Texaco/diesel, **lodging:** Gold Inn, **W...food:** DQ, Jack-in-the-Box, Smith's Rest.
273	Wintergreen Rd, no facilities
272	Fulghum Rd, no facilities
271	Pleasant Run Rd, no facilities
270	Belt Line Rd, to Wilmer, **E...gas:** Texaco/diesel, Total/diesel, **W...gas:** Citgo/diesel, Exxon/Subway, **food:** DQ
269	Mars Rd, no facilities
268	Malloy Bridge Rd, no facilities
267	Frontage Rd, no facilities
266	FM 660, **E...gas:** Fina/diesel, **W...gas:** Shamrock/diesel, **food:** DQ
265	Lp 45, Ferris, no facilities
263	Lp 561, no facilities
262	Newton Rd, to Trumbull, no facilities
261	County Rd(from nb), no facilities
260	Hampel Rd, **W...other:** Goodyear
259	FM 813, FM 878, no facilities
258	Lp 45, Palmer, **E...gas:** Knox/Subway/diesel/24hr/@, **other:** golf, **W...gas:** Mobil/diesel/24hr, **lodging:** Palmer Motel
255	FM 879, Garrett, **E...gas:** Exxon/diesel, **W...gas:** Chevron/diesel
253	Lp 45, **W...gas:** Texaco/diesel, **food:** Papa Tino's Mexican
251b a	TX 34, Ennis, **E...gas:** Fina, Texaco/diesel, **food:** Bubba's BBQ, McDonald's, **lodging:** Best Western, Travelers Inn, **W...gas:** Chevron/diesel, Exxon/diesel/24hr, **food:** Arby's, Braum's, Burger King, Chili's, DQ, Domino's, Golden Corral, Jack-in-the-Box, KFC, Sonic, Subway, Taco Bell/Pizza Hut, Waffle House, Wall Chinese Café, Whataburger/24hr, **lodging:** Ennis Inn, Quality Inn, **other:** HOSPITAL, AutoZone, Chevrolet/Pontiac, Chrysler/Plymouth/Dodge, Ford/Mercury, Pennzoil, Pontiac/Buick, Wal-Mart SuperCtr/24hr, RV camping
249	FM 85, Ennis, **E...lodging:** Budget Inn, **W...gas:** Total/diesel, **other:** Blue Beacon
247	US 287 N, to Waxahatchie, no facilities
246	FM 1183, Alma, **W...gas:** Chevron, Phillips 66
244	FM 1182, no facilities
243	Frontage Rd, no facilities
242	Rice, **W...**bank
239	FM 1126, **W...gas:** Phillips 66

Interstate 45

238   FM 1603, **E...gas:** Fina/diesel, **other:** Casita RV Trailers, tires

237   Frontage Rd, no facilities

235b   Lp I-45(from sb), to Corsicana

   a   Frontage Rd, no facilities

232   Roane Rd, no facilities

231   TX 31, Corsicana, **E...gas:** Texaco/diesel, **food:** Jack-in-the-Box, **lodging:** Colonial Inn, **other:** Chevrolet, **W...gas:** Chevron, Exxon/Subway/diesel, Shell/diesel, **food:** Bill's Cafeteria, DQ, McDonald's, **lodging:** Comfort Inn, **other:** HOSPITAL, Chrysler/Plymouth/Dodge/Jeep, Ford, to Navarro Coll

229   US 287, **E...gas:** Exxon/Wendy's/diesel, Shell/diesel/24hr, **food:** Sonic, Russell Stover Candies, **other:** VF Outlet/famous brands, **W...gas:** Chevron, **food:** Catfish King Rest., Waffle House, **lodging:** Corsicana Inn, Day's Inn, Royal Inn, Travelers Inn

228b   Lp 45(exits left from nb), Corsicana, **2 mi W...**facilities in Corsicana

   a   15th St, Corsicana, **E...gas:** Phillips 66/diesel

225   FM 739, Angus, **E...gas:** Chevron/diesel, Exxon/diesel, **other:** to Chambers Reservoir, **W...gas:** Citgo/diesel, Shell, **other:** Camper Depot

221   Frontage Rd, no facilities

220   Frontage Rd, no facilities

219b   Frontage Rd, no facilities

   a   TX 14(from sb), Richland, to Mexia

218   FM 1394, Richland, **W...gas:** Shell

217mm rest area both lanes, full(handicapped)facilities, phone, picnic tables, litter barrels, vending, petwalk, RV dump

213   FM 246, to Wortham, **W...gas:** Chevron, Texaco/diesel

211   FM 80, to Streetman, no facilities

206   FM 833, no facilities

198   FM 27, to Wortham, **E...gas:** Shell/BBQ, **food:** Gilberto's Mexican, **other:** HOSPITAL, **W...gas:** Exxon, Love's/Burger King/diesel/24hr/@, **lodging:** Budget Inn, **other:** I-45 RV Park

197   US 84, Fairfield, **E...gas:** Exxon/Jack-in-the-Box, Fina/Sam's, Texaco, **food:** DQ, McDonald's, Ponte's Diner, Sonic, Subway/Texas Burger, **lodging:** Holiday Inn Express, Super 8, **other:** Chevrolet, Chrysler/Plymouth/Dodge, **W...gas:** Shell/diesel, Texaco/diesel, **food:** Dalia's Mexican, I-45 Rest., KFC/Taco Bell, Pizza Hut, Sammy's Rest., **lodging:** Regency Inn, Sam's Motel, **other:** Ford/Mercury

189   TX 179, to Teague, **E...gas:** Exxon/Chester Fried/Dinner Bell/diesel, StarUSA Gas/café

187mm picnic area both lanes, tables, litter barrels

180   TX 164, to Groesbeck, no facilities

178   US 79, Buffalo, **E...gas:** Shell/diesel, Texaco/diesel, **food:** Subway/Texas Burger, Westhervane Rest., **other:** Brookshire Food/gas, Parts+, **W...gas:** Exxon, Church's/diesel, Mobil/diesel, Shamrock/diesel/24hr, **food:** DQ, Pitt Grill/24hr, Rainbow Rest., Sonic, **lodging:** Best Western, Economy Inn, Super 8

175mm Bliss Creek

166mm weigh sta sb

164   TX 7, Centerville, **E...gas:** Chevron, Texaco/diesel, **food:** Country Cousins Café, Subway, Texas Burger, **lodging:** Day's Inn, **W...gas:** Exxon/24hr, Shell/diesel, **food:** DQ, Jack-in-the-Box, Mama Mike's BBQ

160mm picnic area sb, tables, litter barrels, hist marker, handicapped accessible

159mm Boggy Creek

156   FM 977, to Leona, **W...gas:** Exxon/diesel

155mm picnic area nb, handicapped accessible

152   TX OSR, to Normangee, **W...gas:** Chevron/diesel, **other:** Yellow Rose RV Park/café

146   TX 75, no facilities

142   US 190, TX 21, Madisonville, **E...gas:** Exxon/diesel, Texaco/diesel/24hr, **food:** Church's, Corral Café, **lodging:** Madisonville Inn, **W...gas:** Shamrock/Popeye's/diesel, Shell/Subway/24hr, **food:** China Café, Jack-in-the-Box, Lakeside Rest., McDonald's, Pizza Hut, Sonic, Texas Burger, **lodging:** Budget Motel, Western Lodge, **other:** HOSPITAL, Ford, Parts+

136   spur 67, no facilities

132   FM 2989, no facilities

126mm rest area sb, full(handicapped)facilities, phone, picnic tables, litter barrels, vending, petwalk, RV dump

124mm rest area nb, full(handicapped)facilities, phone, picnic tables, litter barrels, vending, petwalk, RV dump

123   FM 1696, no facilities

121mm parking area nb

118   TX 75, **E...gas:** Texaco/diesel/24hr, **other:** truckwash, **W...gas:** Pilot/Wendy's/diesel/24hr/@

116   US 190, TX 30, **E...gas:** Citgo, Shamrock/diesel, **food:** Church's, El Chico, Golden Corral, Imperial Garden Chinese, McDonald's, TCBY, Tejas Café, Texas Burger, Whataburger/24hr, **lodging:** Comfort Inn, Econolodge, La Quinta, Motel 6, **other:** HOSPITAL, Nissan, Plymouth/Jeep/Dodge, Pontiac/GMC, **W...gas:** Exxon, Chevron/24hr, Shell/24hr, Texaco/diesel, **food:** Burger King, Chili's, CiCi's, Denny's, IHOP, KFC, Luby's, Pizza

Huntsville

TEXAS

Interstate 45

Hut, Subway, Taco Bell, **lodging:** Holiday Inn Express, **other:** Discount Tire, Hastings Books, Kroger, Office Depot, Radio Shack, Walgreen, Wal-Mart SuperCtr/gas/24hr

114 FM 1374, **E...gas:** Exxon/diesel, Texaco, **food:** Casa Tomas Mexican, DQ, **lodging:** Gateway Inn, Super 8, **other:** Ford/Lincoln/Mercury, **W...gas:** Chevron, Shamrock/diesel, **food:** Country Inn Steaks, **lodging:** Sam Houston Inn, **other:** HOSPITAL

113 TX 19(from nb), Huntsville, **E...food:** Catfish Palace Rest.(2mi)

112 TX 75, **E...gas:** Citgo, **lodging:** Baker Motel, **other:** Houston Statue, to Sam Houston St U, museum

109 Park 40, **W...other:** to Huntsville SP

105mm picnic area both lanes, tables, litter barrels

103 FM 1374/1375(from sb), to New Waverly, **W...gas:** Citgo/diesel

102 FM 1374/1375, TX 150(from nb), to New Waverly, **E...gas:** Shell, **1 mi W...gas:** Citgo/diesel

101mm weigh sta nb

98 TX 75, Danville Rd, Shepard Hill Rd, **E...other:** Fishpond RV Park/dump, **2 mi W...lodging:** B&B

95 Longstreet Rd, no facilities

94 FM 1097, to Willis, **E...food:** Jack-in-the-Box, Mr Gatti, Sonic, **other:** $General, Kroger/gas, **W...gas:** Chevron/Popeye's, Exxon/Burger King, Texaco/Taco Bell/diesel/24hr, **food:** McDonald's, Subway, **lodging:** Best Western

92 FM 830, Seven Coves Dr, **W...other:** RV Park on the Lake(3mi)

91 League Line Rd, **E...gas:** Chevron/McDonald's, **food:** LoneStar Café, Subway, Wendy's, **lodging:** Comfort Inn, La Quinta, **other:** Prime Outlets/famous brands, **W...gas:** Texaco, **food:** Cracker Barrel

90 FM 3083, Teas Nursery Rd, Montgomery Co Park

88 Lp 336, to Cleveland, Navasota, **E...gas:** Mobil/diesel, Shamrock/diesel, Shell/24hr, **food:** Arby's, Blackeyed Pea, Domino's, Grandy's, Hofbrau Steaks, Hunan Chinese, KFC, Little Caesar's, LJ Silver, Margarita's Mexican, McDonald's, Papa John's, Sonic, Subway, TX Roadhouse, Whataburger, **other:** MEDICAL CARE, Buick/Pontiac, Discount Tire, Goodyear/auto, Hastings Books, Kroger, Michael's, Pennzoil, Walgreen, **W...gas:** Chevron/24hr, **food:** Ryan's, **other:** Eckerd, Goody's, GNC, Hancock Fabrics, JC Penney, Lowe's Whse, Randall's Foods, Radio Shack, Sam's Club, Wal-Mart SuperCtr/24hr

87 TX 105, Conroe, **E...gas:** Shamrock, **food:** Burger King, CiCi's, Imperial Garden Chinese, Jack-in-the-Box, Luther's BBQ, McDonald's, Outback Steaks, Steak&Ale, Taco Bell, **other:** HOSPITAL, Eckerd/24hr, Firestone/auto, Kia, Kroger, NTB, Suzuki, **W...gas:** Exxon/TCBY, Texaco/diesel, **food:** Golden Corral, Luby's, **other:** Buick/GMC/Isuzu, Home Depot, Hyundai, Office Depot, Randall's Food/gas, Target

85 FM 2854, Gladstell St, **E...gas:** Citgo, **other:** HOSPITAL, Ford/Mercury, Honda, Mitsubishi, Nissan, **W...gas:** Shamrock, Texaco/diesel, **food:** IHOP, **lodging:** Baymont Inn, Day's Inn, Motel 6, **other:** Cadillac, Chrysler/Plymouth/Jeep, Daewoo, Dodge, Mazda, Toyota

84 TX 75 N, Frazier St, **E...gas:** Conoco/diesel, Exxon/diesel, Texaco/diesel, **lodging:** Corporate Inn, Holiday Inn, Ramada Ltd, **other:** U-Haul, **W...gas:** Shell, **food:** Pizza Hut, Porky's Rest., Taco Cabana, **other:** Albertson's, Discount Tire, K-Mart, Kroger

83 Crighton Rd, Camp Strake Rd, no facilities

82 River Plantation Dr

82mm San Jacinto River

81 FM 1488, to Hempstead, Magnolia, **E...gas:** Citgo/diesel, **W...gas:** Shamrock, **other:** CamperLand RV Ctr

80 Needham Rd(from sb), no facilities

79 TX 242, Needham, **E...gas:** Texaco/McDonald's, **other:** Woodland Lakes RV Resort(1mi), **W...food:** ChuckeCheese, Willie's Grill, **lodging:** Country Inn Suites, **other:** Firestone, Kohl's, Wal-Mart SuperCtr/24hr

78 Needham Rd(from sb), Tamina Rd, access to same as 77

77 Woodlands Pkwy, Robinson, Chateau Woods, **E...gas:** Conoco/diesel, Texaco, **food:** Babin's Steaks, Buca italian, Luther's BBQ, Pancho's Mexican, Pappadeaux Rest., Pizza Hut, Red Lobster, Saltgrass Steaks, **lodging:** Budget Inn, **other:** Discount Tire, Home Depot, Jo-Ann Fabrics, Michael's, NTB, Office Depot, Old Navy, Sam's Club, SteinMart, Walgreen, **W...gas:** Shamrock, Texaco, **food:** Guadalajara Mexican, Landry's Seafood, Luby's, Macaroni Grill, Outback Steaks, Pancho's Mexican, **lodging:** Comfort Inn, Day's Inn, Drury Inn, Hampton Inn, Homewood Suites, La Quinta, **other:** HOSPITAL, Best Buy, Dillard's, Marshall's, Mervyn's, OfficeMax, Target, World Mkt, mall

76 Research Forest Dr, Tamina Rd, **E...gas:** Chevron/diesel, Coastal/lube, Shamrock, Stop'n Go, Texaco, **food:** Casa Elena Mexican, LJ Silver, **other:** MEDICAL CARE, Food Basket, Firestone, **W...food:** Carrabba's, El Chico, IHOP, Kyoto Japanese, Olive Garden, Tortuga Mexican, **lodging:** Crossland Suites, **other:** Goodyear/auto

73 Rayford Rd, Sawdust Rd(to Hardy Toll Rd from sb), **E...gas:** Conoco, Shell, **food:** Hartz Chicken, Jack-in-the-Box, LJ Silver, McDonald's, Popeye's, Sonic, Thomas BBQ, **lodging:** Hawthorn Suites, Holiday Inn Express, **other:** AutoZone, O'Reilly Parts, **W...gas:** Mobil, Shell, Texaco, **food:** Grandy's, Sam's Rest., Woodland Chinese, **lodging:** Red Roof Inn, **other:** Discount Tire, Eckerd, HEB Foods, Kroger

72 Frontage Rd(from nb), no facilities

70b Spring-Stuebner Rd, no facilities

a FM 2920, to Tomball, **E...gas:** Exxon, **food:** El Palenque Mexican, McDonald's, Pizza Hut, Wendy's, **other:** Radio Shack, Vaughn's RV Ctr, Walgreen, transmissions, **W...gas:** Chevron, Shell, **food:** Burger King, Taco Bell, Whataburger/24hr, **lodging:** Travelodge, **other:** Ford, U-Haul

Interstate 45

68 Holzwarth Rd, Cypress Wood Dr, **E...gas:** Texaco/diesel, **food:** Burger King, Chick-fil-A, Hartz Chicken, Pizza Hut/Taco Bell, Sonic, Wendy's, Whataburger, **other:** Albertson's, $Tree, GNC, Kohl's, Kroger, Lincoln/Mercury, Ross, Toyota, Wal-Mart SuperCtr/24hr, **W...gas:** Chevron/24hr, **food:** Denny's, Jack-in-the-Box, Pizza Hut, Popeye's, **lodging:** Day's Inn, Motel 6, **other:** Ford, Home Depot, Lowe's Whse, Office Depot, Target, Walgreen

66 FM 1960, to Addicks, **E...gas:** Chevron, RaceTrac, Shell, **food:** Jack-in-the-Box, Sonic, **lodging:** Day's Inn, **other:** BMW, Chevrolet, Honda, Mercedes, Radio Shack, **W...gas:** Exxon, Shell/diesel/24hr, Texaco/diesel, **food:** Bennigan's, Grandy's, Jack-in-the-Box, Jojo's Rest., Luby's, McDonald's, Outback Steaks, Pizza Hut, Popeye's, Red Lobster, Steak&Ale, Subway, Taco Bell, **lodging:** Comfort Suites, Fairfield Inn, Hampton Inn, La Quinta, **other:** GolfSmith, Infiniti, Jaguar, LandRover, Lexus, NTB, Saturn, mall

64 Richey Rd, **E...gas:** Texaco/Church's, **food:** Atchafalaya River Café, Pappasito's Cantina, **lodging:** Holiday Inn, Lexington Suites, **other:** Cadillac, Discount Tire, Nissan, Sam's Club, **W...gas:** /Flying J/Conoco/diesel/24hr/@, **food:** Cracker Barrel, House of Creole, Jack-in-the-Box, Joe's Crabshack, Lupe Tortillo, SaltGrass Steaks, Whataburger, Zio's Italian, **lodging:** La Quinta, Shoney's Inn, **other:** U-Haul

63 Airtex Dr, **E...other:** Acura, Cadillac, LoneStar RV Ctr, Nissan, **lodging:** Howard Johnson, Scottish Inn, **W...gas:** Chevron, RaceTrac, **food:** McDonald's, **lodging:** Best Western, Studio+, **other:** Celebration Sta

62 Rankin Rd, Kuykendahl, **W...gas:** Shell, **food:** Luby's, **lodging:** Baymont Inn, Rodeway Inn, Sun Suites, **other:** BMW, Buick/Subaru, Hyundai, Kia, Mercedes, Mitsubishi, Saab, Suzuki, Volvo, VW

61 Greens Rd, **E...food:** Whataburger, **lodging:** Day's Inn, Marriott, Wyndham Hotel, **other:** Circuit City, Dillard's, Foley's, JC Penney, Mervyn's, mall, **W...**Burger King, Luby's, Kroger, Office Depot, OfficeMax, Target

60c Beltway E, no facilities

b TX 8, **E...lodging:** La Quinta, Marriott, **other:** Dillard's, Sears/auto, mall, **W...food:** Marco's Mexican

a TX 525, **E...gas:** Exxon, Shamrock, Shell, Texaco, **food:** Burger King, Champ's Rest., China Border, Denny's/24hr, Furr's Cafeteria, LJ Silver, Mucho Mexico, Pizza Hut, Steak&Ale, **other:** Firestone/auto, Honda, Randall's Foods, Walgreen, **W...food:** Gordito's Mexican, Pappa's Rest., Quizno's, Wendy's, **other:** Best Buy, Dodge, GNC, Home Depot, Pontiac/GMC, Wal-Mart SuperCtr/24hr

59 FM 525, West Rd, **E...gas:** Exxon, Shell, **food:** McDonald's, Pizza Hut, Wendy's, **other:** Fiesta Foods, **W...gas:** Exxon, **food:** Taco Bell, Taco Cabana, **lodging:** Best Western, GreenChase Inn, Holiday Inn Express, **other:** Fry's Electronics, K-Mart, Lincoln/Mercury, PepBoys

57 TX 249, Gulf Bank Rd, Tomball, **E...gas:** Conoco, Exxon/diesel, Mobil/diesel, **other:** Discount Tire, Kroger, **W...gas:** Shell, **food:** KFC, Pizza Inn, Sonic, **lodging:** Day's Inn, **other:** Chevrolet, Chrysler/Plymouth/Jeep, Daewoo, Eckerd, Family$, Ford, Mazda, Saturn

56 Canino Rd, **E...lodging:** Taj Inn, **W...gas:** Shell, **food:** Luby's, **other:** Nissan, Toyota

55b a Little York Rd, Parker Rd, **E...gas:** Chevron, Exxon, Mobil/diesel, Shamrock, Shell, **food:** Schlotsky's, Whataburger, **lodging:** Olympic Motel, **other:** HOSPITAL, FoodTown, Goodyear, **W...gas:** Chevron/24hr, Shell, **food:** Capt D's, Denny's, Hartz Chicken, Jack-in-the-Box, KFC, LJ Silver, McDonald's, Popeye's, **lodging:** Best Value Inn, Econolodge, Town Inn, **other:** Walgreen

54 Tidwell Rd, **E...gas:** Exxon, **food:** Pancho's Mexican, Pizza Inn, Subway, Taco Cabana, Thomas BBQ, **other:** Eckerd, Jo-Ann Fabrics, Radio Shack

53 Airline Dr, **E...gas:** Chevron, Citgo, Conoco, same as 52

52 Crosstimbers Rd, **E...gas:** Shell, Texaco/diesel, **food:** Burger King, CiCi's, IHOP, James Coney Island, McDonald's, Pancho's Mexican, Pappas BBQ, Taco Bell, Taco Cabana, Wendy's, **other:** Discount Tire, Fiesta Foods, Firestone, mall, **W...gas:** Chevron/diesel, Citgo, **food:** Little Mexico Rest., Whataburger/24hr, **lodging:** Howard Johnson, Luxury Inn, Palace Inn, Super 8, **other:** Coach USA RV Ctr, U-Haul

51 I-610, no facilities

50b Calvacade St, Link Rd, **E...gas:** Exxon/Taco Bell, Texaco, **W...lodging:** Astro Inn

a Patton St, **E...gas:** Chevron/24hr, Pilot/Wendy's/diesel/24hr/@, **lodging:** Classic Inn, Luxury Inn, **W...gas:** Texaco/diesel/24hr

49b N Main St, Houston Ave, **E...food:** Casa Grande Mexican, **W...gas:** Exxon/diesel, **food:** KFC, McDonald's, Whataburger/24hr, **other:** Auto Supply

48b a I-10, E to Beaumont, W to San Antonio

47d Dallas St, Pierce St(from sb), **E...other:** HOSPITAL

TEXAS

Interstate 45

	c	McKinney St(from sb, exits left)
	b	Houston Ave, Memorial Dr, downtown, **W…lodging:** Best Western
	a	Allen Pkwy(exits left from sb)
46b a		US 59, N to Cleveland, S to Victoria, **E…gas:** Chevron, **food:** BBQ, **W…gas:** Exxon, **food:** McDonald's, Taco Bell, **other:** BMW
45b a		South St, Scott St, Houston, **E…gas:** Conoco, Texaco/Subway, **other:** Firestone
44		Cullen Blvd, Houston, **E…gas:** Shamrock/gas, **food:** Burger King, McDonald's, Taco Bell, **W…food:** Pizza Hut, **other:** bank, to U of Houston
43b		Telephone Rd, Houston, **E…food:** Luby's, **lodging:** Day's Inn
	a	Tellepsen St, **E…food:** Luby's, **lodging:** Day's Inn, **W…other:** U of Houston
41b		US 90A, Broad St, S Wayside Dr, **E…lodging:** Day's Inn, Red Carpet Inn, **W…gas:** Chevron, Exxon, **food:** Jack-in-the-Box, McDonald's, Monterrey Mexican, **other:** K-Mart
	a	Woodridge Dr, **E…gas:** Shell, **food:** Bennigan's, Denny's, McDonald's, Pappa's Seafood House, Schlotsky's, **W…food:** IHOP, Pappas BBQ, Sonic, Subway, Whataburger, Wendy's, **other:** Chevrolet/Buick, Dillard's, HEB Food/gas, Home Depot, Lowe's Whse, Marshall's, Office Depot, Old Navy, Radio Shack, mall
40c		I-610 W
	b	I-610 E, to Pasadena
	a	Frontage Rd(from nb), no facilities
39		Park Place Blvd, Broadway Blvd, **E…gas:** Texaco, **food:** Dante Italian, **W…gas:** Shell, Phillips 66, Texaco/Blimpie, **food:** Kelly's Rest., May Moon Café, **other:** Chevrolet, Dodge
38b		Howard Dr, Bellfort Dr(from sb), **E…gas:** Texaco, **food:** Blue Oyster Seafood, Dante Italian, **W…gas:** Citgo, **food:** Chilo's Seafood, **lodging:** Palace Inn, Passport Inn, **other:** HEB Food/gas, PepBoys
38		TX 3, Monroe Rd, **E…gas:** Chevron, Exxon, Shell, **food:** DQ, Fat Maria's Mexican, Jack-in-the-Box, Lonesome Steer Steaks, Wendy's, **other:** NTB, U-Haul, **W…gas:** Chevron/diesel, Texaco/diesel, **food:** Luby's, Luther's BBQ, **lodging:** Best Western, Quality Inn, Smile Inn, **other:** Firestone, Radio Shack, Suzuki, U-Haul
36		College Ave, Airport Blvd, **E…gas:** Shamrock, Shell, **food:** DQ, Waffle House, **lodging:** Fairfield Inn, Rodeway Inn, **other:** RV Ctr, **W…gas:** Exxon, Texaco, **food:** Church's Chicken, Denny's, Lucky Dragon Chinese, Taco Cabana, **lodging:** AmeriSuites, Courtyard, Drury Inn, La Quinta, Marriott/Damon's, Red Roof Inn, Super 8, Travel Inn, **other:** Discount Tire
35		Edgebrook Dr, **E…gas:** Chevron, Exxon, RaceTrac, **food:** Burger King, Aranda's Bakery, Grandy's, Jack-in-the-Box, Popeye's, Subway, Taco Bell, Waffle House, **lodging:** Airport Inn, **other:** Eckerd, Fiesta Foods, Firestone, Office Depot, Thompson RV Ctr, Walgreen, **W…gas:** Exxon, Shell, Circle K, **food:** James Coney Island, KFC, LJ Silver, McDonald's, Pizza Hut, Whataburger

34	S Shaver Rd, **E…gas:** Conoco, **food:** McDonald's, **other:** Acura, Honda, Kia, Pontiac/GMC, Saturn, Toyota, Vaughn's RV Ctr, **W…gas:** Chevron/24hr, Exxon, Mobil, **food:** Arby's, Burger King, Pancho's Mexican, Wendy's, **other:** Best Buy, Circuit City, $Tree, Foley's, Holiday World RV Ctr, Jo-Ann Fabrics, K-Mart, Marshall's, Nissan, NTB, OfficeMax, Target
33	Fuqua St, **E…gas:** Shamrock, **food:** Chili's, Fuddrucker's, Luby's, Mexico Lindo, Olive Garden, TGIFriday, **lodging:** Sun Suites, **other:** Chrysler/Plymouth/Jeep, Dodge, Ford, Honda, Hyundai, Isuzu, Lincoln/Mercury, **W…food:** Barco's Mexican, Bennigan's, Blackeyed Pea, CiCi's, Golden Corral, Gringo's Mexican, IHOP, Joe's Crabshack, Steak&Ale, Subway, Taco Cabana, Taco Bell, TX Cattle Steaks, Whataburger, **other:** Firestone, Home Depot, JC Penney, Kroger, Old Navy, Radio Shack, Ross, Sam's Club, Subaru, Tire Station, Wal-Mart, mall
32	Sam Houston Tollway
31	FM 2553, Scarsdale Blvd, **W…gas:** Exxon, Shell, **food:** DQ, McDonald's, **other:** Chevrolet, Mitsubishi
30	FM 1959, Ellington Field, Dixie Farm Rd, **E…gas:** Conoco/diesel, Shell/diesel, **other:** HOSPITAL, Dodge, **W…gas:** Texaco/diesel, **food:** McDonald's, Popeye's, **other:** VW
29	FM 2351, Clear Lake City Blvd, Friendswood, to Clear Lake RA
27	El Dorado Blvd, **E…food:** DQ, **other:** mall, **W…food:** Texas Roadhouse, Whataburger, **other:** Circuit City, Kohl's, Lexus, Mervyn's, Radio Shack, Sam's Club/gas, Wal-Mart SuperCtr/24hr
26	Bay Area Blvd, **E…food:** Red Lobster, **other:** HOSPITAL, Barnes&Noble, CompUSA, Lowe's Whse, Michael's, Old Navy, to Houston Space Ctr, **W…gas:** Shell, **food:** Baskin-Robbins, Bennigan's, Denny's/24hr, McDonald's, Olive Garden, On-the-Border, Steak&Ale, **lodging:** Best Western, Suburban Inn, **other:** Dillard's, Macy's, Sears/auto, Target, Outlet Mall/famous brands, mall, U of Houston
25	FM 528, NASA rd 1, **E…gas:** Conoco, Shamrock, Texaco, **food:** Chili's, CiCi's, IHOP, Macaroni Grill, Mason Jar Grill, Pappasito's Cantina, Saltgrass Steaks, Tony Roma's, Waffle House, **lodging:** Motel 6, **other:** HOSPITAL, Audi, Best Buy, Home Depot, Honda, K-Mart, Mazda, Office Depot, SteinMart, Volvo, **W…food:** Cinco de Mayo Mexican, China Square, DQ, Hooters, Hot Wok Chinese, Luther's BBQ, Subway, **other:** Radio Shack, Wal-Mart/auto
23	FM 518, League City, **E…gas:** RaceTrac, Texaco/diesel, **food:** Applebee's, Burger King, Grand Buffet, Jack-in-the-Box, KFC, Little Caesar's, Pancho's Mexican, Sonic, Subway, **other:** Academy Sports, BMW, Eckerd, JiffyLube, Kroger, Walgreen, **W…gas:** Chevron, Exxon/24hr, **food:** Cracker Barrel, Hartz Chicken, McDonald's, Taco Bell, Waffle House, Wendy's, **lodging:** Super 8, **other:** Discount Tire, U-Haul
22	Calder Dr, Brittany Bay Blvd, **E…other:** Toyota, camping
20	FM 646, Santa Fe, Bacliff, **W…gas:** Shamrock/diesel

(League City)

478

TEXAS

Interstate 45

N **19** FM 517, Dickinson Rd, Hughes Rd, **E...gas:** Shell, Shamrock, **food:** Jack-in-the-Box, Monterey Mexican, Pizza Inn, **other:** Buick/Pontiac/GMC/Subaru, Due's Camping Ctr, Eckerd, Family$, Food King, Radio Shack, **W...gas:** Exxon, Texaco/diesel, Circle K, **food:** Burger King, KFC, McDonald's, Pizza Hut, Subway, Taco Bell, Wendy's, Whataburger/24hr, **other:** Ford, Kroger, Walgreen

S **17** Holland Rd, **W...**to Gulf Greyhound Park

16 FM 1764 E(from sb), Texas City, **E...other:** HOSPITAL, Demontrond RV Ctr, mall, same as 15

15 FM 2004, FM 1764, Hitchcock, **E...gas:** Shell, **food:** Carino's Italian, Jack-in-the-Box, **lodging:** Fairfield Inn, Hampton Inn, **other:** HOSPITAL, Chevrolet/Toyota/RV Ctr, Dillard's, Foley's, JC Penney, Lowe's Whse, mall, **W...gas:** Mobil/Subway, Shell, Texaco, **food:** Waffle House, Wendy's, Whataburger, **other:** Gulf Greyhound Park, Wal-Mart SuperCtr/24hr

13 Century Blvd, Delany Rd, **E...gas:** Shamrock, **W...lodging:** Ramada Inn, Super 8, **other:** Outlet Mall/famous brands

12 FM 1765, La Marque, **E...gas:** Chevron/24hr, **food:** Domino's, Jack-in-the-Box, Kelley's Rest., Sonic, **lodging:** HiWay Motel, **W...gas:** Mobil/diesel

11 Vauthier Rd, no facilities

10 FM 519, Main St, **E...gas:** Shamrock, **food:** McDonald's, **W...gas:** Texaco/diesel

9 Frontage Rd(from sb), no facilities

8 Frontage Rd(from nb), no facilities

7c Frontage Rd, no facilities

b TX 146, TX 6(exits left from nb), Texas City, **W...gas:** Texaco

a TX 146, TX 3, no facilities

6 Frontage Rd(from sb), no facilities

5 Frontage Rd, no facilities

4 Village of Tiki Island, Frontage Rd, **W...gas:** Conoco/diesel, **other:** public boat ramp

4mm West Galveston Bay

1c TX 275, FM 188(from nb), Port of Galveston, Port Ind Blvd, Teichman Rd, **E...gas:** Chevron, Citgo, Texaco/diesel, **lodging:** Howard Johnson, Motel 6, **other:** Chevrolet, Chrysler/Dodge/Plymouth/Jeep, Ford, Mazda, Mitsubishi, Nissan, Toyota

1b 71st St(from sb), **E...gas:** EZ Mart/gas, same as 1c

G **1a** TX 342, 61st St, to W Beach, **E...gas:** EZMart/gas, **food:** Denny's, **other:** Target, **W...gas:** RaceTrac, Texaco, **food:** Burger King, Church's, McDonald's, Taco Bell, **lodging:** Day's Inn, **other:** Big Lots, Chevrolet/Pontiac/Buick/Cadillac, Chrysler/Jeep, Family$, Honda, U-Haul, USPO, **1-2 mi W...gas:** Chevron, Exxon/diesel, Shamrock, Shell, Texaco, **food:** Arby's, Burger King, China Border, Domino's, Golden Wok, Jack-in-the-Box, KFC, LJ Silver, Luby's, Marco's Mexican, Mario's Italian, McDonald's, Papa John's, Pizza Hut, Popeye's, Subway, Taco Cabana, TCBY, Whataburger, **lodging:** Beachcomber Inn, Best Western, Super 8, **other:** Eckerd, Firestone/auto, Hastings Books, K-Mart, Office Depot, O'Reilly Parts, Randall's Food/gas, Walgreen,

I-45 begins/ends on TX 87 in Galveston.

Letters down left margin: **N** ↕ **S** ... **G a l v e s t o n**

Interstate 410(San Antonio)

Exit # Services

53 I-35, S to Laredo, N to San Antonio

51 FM 2790, Somerset Rd, no facilities

49 TX 16 S, spur 422, **N...gas:** Chevron, **food:** Church's Chicken, **other:** HOSPITAL, to Palo Alto Coll

48 Zarzamora St, no facilities

46 Moursund Blvd, no facilities

44 US 281 S, spur 536, Roosevelt Ave, **N...gas:** Texaco/diesel, **other:** RV camping

43 Espada Rd(from eb), no facilities

42 spur 122, S Presa Rd, to San Antonio Missions Hist Park, **S...gas:** Whiteside/diesel

41 I-37, US 281 N, no facilities

39 spur 117, WW White Rd, no facilities

37 Southcross Blvd, Sinclair Rd, Sulphur Sprs Rd, **N...HOSPITAL**

35 US 87, Rigsby Ave, **E...gas:** Exxon/TacoMaker, Shamrock/diesel, **food:** Denny's, Jack-in-the-Box, McDonald's, Taco Bell, **other:** Radio Shack, Wal-Mart SuperCtr/gas/24hr, **W...gas:** Chevron, **food:** Barnacle Bill's Seafood, BBQ, Luby's, Pizza Hut, Sonic, Subway, Taco Cabana, Whataburger, **lodging:** Day's Inn, **other:** Aamco, Advance Parts

34 FM 1346, E Houston St, **W...gas:** Chevron, Shamrock, **food:** McDonald's, Wendy's, **lodging:** Comfort Inn, Motel 6

33 I-10 E, US 90 E, to Houston, I-10 W, US 90 W, to San Antonio

32 Dietrich Rd(from sb), FM 78(from nb), to Kirby, no facilities

31b Lp 13, WW White Rd, no facilities

a FM 78, Kirby, no facilities

30 Space Center Dr(from nb), **E...gas:** Coastal, Shamrock

I-410 and I-35 S run together 7 mi, **See Texas I-35, exits 162 thru 165.**

27 I-35, N to Austin, S to San Antonio

479

TEXAS

Interstate 410

26 Lp 368 S, Alamo Heights, **S...gas:** Mobil, **food:** Red Lobster, **lodging:** Drury Inn, **other:** NTB, U-Haul

25b FM 2252, Perrin-Beitel Rd, **N...gas:** Chevron/diesel, Mobil, **food:** Denny's, KFC/Taco Bell, Quizno's, Schlotsky's, Taco Bell, Taco Cabana, Wendy's, Wienerschnitzel, **lodging:** Comfort Inn, Econolodge, **S...food:** Dillon's Rest., Jim's Rest.

25a Starcrest Dr, **N...gas:** Texaco, **food:** Jack-in-the-Box, Los Patios Mexican, **lodging:** Hawthorn Inn, **other:** HOSPITAL, Toyota, **S...gas:** Phillips 66, Texaco

24 Harry Wurzbach Hwy, **N...food:** Taco Cabana, **S...gas:** Texaco, **food:** BBQ Sta, **other:** MEDICAL CARE

23 Nacogdoches Rd, **N...food:** BBQ, Church's, IHOP, Jack-in-the-Box, Pizza Hut, Schlotsky's, Sonic, Taco Cabana, Wendy's, **lodging:** Club Hotel, **S...gas:** Exxon, Texaco/diesel, **other:** Audi/VW

22 Broadway St, **N...gas:** Texaco/diesel, **food:** Crystal Steaks, Luby's, McDonald's, **lodging:** Courtyard, Ramada Inn, **other:** Firestone, **S...gas:** Exxon, Shamrock, **food:** Burger King, Jim's Rest., Whataburger, **lodging:** Residence Inn, TownHouse Motel, **other:** Infiniti

21 US 281 S, Airport Rd, Jones Maltsberger Rd, **N...food:** Applebee's, Drury Suites, **lodging:** Hampton Inn, Holiday Inn Select, PearTree Inn, **S...gas:** Texaco/diesel, **food:** Pappadeaux, Red Lobster, Texas Land&Cattle, **lodging:** Courtyard, Day's Inn, Fairfield Inn, La Quinta, Renaissance Hotel, Staybridge Suites, **other:** Hyundai/Kia, Mitsubishi, Subaru, Wal-Mart/24hr

20 TX 537, **N...food:** Jason's Deli, TGIFriday, **lodging:** DoubleTree Hotel, Hilton, **other:** Barnes&Noble, Best Buy, Chevrolet, Circuit City, Honda, Lincoln/Mercury, Marshall's, Mazda, Ross, **S...food:** Arby's, Bennigan's, El Pollo Loco, Luby's, McDonald's, Taco Cabana, **other:** Dillard's, Dodge, Foley's, Macy's, Mervyn's, Saks 5th, Sears/auto, mall

19b FM 1535, FM 2696, Military Hwy, **N...food:** Gyro/Sub Shop, Souper Salad, **S...gas:** Exxon, **food:** Denny's, Jim's Rest.

19a Honeysuckle Lane, Castle Hills

17b (from wb), **S...food:** DQ, Dunkin Donuts, **other:** Firestone, HEB Foods

17 Vance Jackson Rd, **N...gas:** Mobil, Phillips 66, Shamrock, **food:** Burger King, Jack-in-the-Box, KFC, McDonald's, Steak&Ale, Sonic, Taco Cabana, Whataburger, **lodging:** Marriott, **other:** Aamco, CarQuest, Discount Tire, Target, Tire Sta, transmissions, **S...gas:** Exxon, **food:** Subway, **other:** U-Haul

16b a I-10 E, US 87 S, to San Antonio, I-10 W, to El Paso, US 87 N

15 Lp 345, Fredericksburg Rd, **E...gas:** Texaco, **food:** Church's, Dave&Buster's, Jack-in-the-Box, Jim's Rest., Kettle, Luby's, N China Rest., **lodging:** AmeriSuites, Best Value Inn, **other:** BMW, Target, **W...gas:** Mobil, **lodging:** Holiday Inn, **other:** K-Mart

14 Callaghan Rd, Babcock Ln, **E...gas:** Chevron, Exxon, Shamrock, **food:** Marie Callender's, **lodging:** Comfort Inn, Hampton Inn, Travelodge Suites, **other:** GMC/Pontiac, **W...gas:** Conoco, **food:** Burger King, Chili's, ChopSticks Chinese, DingHow Chinese, El Chico, Golden Corral, HomeTown Buffet, Joe's Crabshack, Landry's Seafood, Pizza Hut, Quizno's, Red Lobster, Wendy's, Whataburger, **other:** HOSPITAL, Home Depot, Sam's Club, Wal-Mart SuperCtr/24hr

13b Rolling Ridge Dr, **W...food:** Jack-in-the-Box, KFC, Las Palapas Mexican, same as 14

13a TX 16 N, Bandera Rd, Evers Rd, Leon Valley, **E...food:** Outback Steaks, **other:** Albertson's, Audi, Office Depot, OfficeMax, Old Navy, Saturn, Target, Toyota, U-Haul, **W...gas:** Exxon, Shamrock, Texaco, **food:** Applebee's, BBQ, IHOP, Jack-in-the-Box, Jim's Rest., KFC, Luby's, McDonald's, Olive Garden, Schlotsky's, Taco Cabana, **lodging:** Super 8, **other:** Aamco, Best Buy, Chevrolet, Circuit City, Dillard's, Eckerd, Honda, Marshall's, NTB

11 Ingram Rd, **E...gas:** Texaco/diesel, **food:** Bennigan's, Calloway's Rest., Fazoli's, Texas Roadhouse, **lodging:** Day's Inn, Econolodge, **other:** Aamco, BrakeCheck, **W...food:** Applebee's, Burger King, Denny's, Jack-in-the-Box, Jason's Deli, Olive Garden, Subway, Whataburger, **lodging:** Super 8, **other:** Barnes&Noble, Best Buy, Dillard's, $Tree, Foley's, JC Penney, Mervyn's, Michael's, Ross, Sears/auto, mall

10 FM 3487, Culebra Rd, **E...food:** Barnacle Bill's Seafood, BBQ, Denny's, McDonald's, Wendy's, **lodging:** Holiday Inn Express, La Quinta, Red Roof Inn, **other:** Chrysler/Plymouth/Dodge/Jeep, Mazda/Nissan/Daewoo, to St Mary's U, **W...gas:** Exxon, Phillips 66, RaceTrac, **food:** Blimpie, ChuckeCheese, Fuddrucker's, **lodging:** Best Western, InTown Inn, **other:** Firestone/auto, Ford, Mitsubishi

9b a TX 151, **W...gas:** Chili's, **lodging:** Quality Inn, **other:** Home Depot, Lowe's Whse, Wal-Mart SuperCtr/gas/24hr, to Sea World

7 (8 from sb)Marbach Dr, **E...gas:** Exxon, **food:** McDonald's, **other:** PepBoys, **W...gas:** Chevron/diesel, Texaco/dieel, **food:** Acadiena Café, Burger King, Golden Wok, Jack-in-the-Box, Jim's Rest., KFC, LJ Silver, Luby's, McDonald's, Mr Gatti's, Pancho's Mexican, Peter Piper Pizza, Pizza Hut, Red Lobster, Sonic, Subway, Taco Bell, Taco Cabana, Whataburger/24hr, **lodging:** Motel 6, Super 8, **other:** Advance Parts, Discount Tire, $General, $Tree, Eckerd, Firestone/auto, HEB Food, K-Mart, Target

6 US 90, to Lackland AFB, **E...lodging:** Country Inn Motel, **other:** Explore USA RV Ctr, **W...gas:** Shamrock, Texaco/diesel, **food:** Andrea's Mexican

4 Valley Hi Dr, San Antonio, to Del Rio, **E...gas:** Mobil, Phillips 66/diesel, Shamrock, **food:** Church's Chicken, McDonald's, Pizza Hut, Sonic, **other:** AutoZone, HEB Food/gas, Radio Shack, **W...gas:** Texaco/diesel, **other:** to Lackland AFB

3b a Ray Ellison Dr, Medina Base, **W...gas:** Shamrock

2 FM 2536, Old Pearsall Rd, **E...gas:** Texaco/diesel, **food:** BBQ, McDonald's, Sonic

1 Frontage Rd, no facilities

Interstate 610(Houston)

Exit #	Services
38c a	TX 288 N, downtown, access to zoo
37	Scott St, **N...gas:** Texaco
36	FM 865, Cullen Blvd, **S...gas:** Chevron/McDonald's, Mobil, Shamrock, **lodging:** Crown Inn, Cullen Inn
35	Calais Rd, Crestmont St, MLK Blvd, **N...gas:** Exxon, **food:** Burger King
34	S Wayside Dr, Long Dr, **N...gas:** Exxon, Texaco, **food:** Wendy's, **other:** Fiesta Foods, **S...gas:** Coastal/diesel, Conoco
33	Woodridge Dr, Telephone Rd, **N...gas:** Texaco/diesel, **food:** IHOP, McDonald's, Papa John's, Wendy's, **S...gas:** Shell, **food:** Burger King, KFC, Piccadilly's Cafeteria, Spanky's Pizza, Whataburger, **other:** Dodge, Ford, mall
32b a	I-45, S to Galveston, N to Houston, to airport
31	Broadway Blvd, **N...gas:** Conoco, **S...gas:** Texaco
30c b	TX 225, to Pasadena, San Jacinto Mon, no facilities
29	Port of Houston Main Entrance
28	Clinton Dr, no facilities
27	Turning Basin Dr, industrial area
26b	Market St, no facilities
a	I-10 E, to Beaumont, I-10 W, to downtown
24b	Wallisville Rd, **E...gas:** Mobil/diesel, Texaco/diesel, **food:** McDonald's
24	US 90 E, **E...gas:** Chevron, Phillips 66, **food:** Luby's, Wendy's, **W...gas:** Texaco
23b	N Wayside, **E...gas:** Exxon
23a	Kirkpatrick Blvd, no facilities
22	Homestead Rd, Kelley St, **N...gas:** Texaco/diesel, **food:** Whataburger
21	Lockwood Dr, **N...gas:** Chevron/McDonald's, Texaco, **food:** Burger King, **other:** Popeye's, Family$, **S...gas:** Conoco, **food:** CJ's Rest., **other:** HOSPITAL
20	US 59, to downtown
19	Hardy Toll Rd, no facilities
18	Irvington Blvd, Fulton St, **N...gas:** Chevron, **S...gas:** Texaco/diesel, **food:** Jack-in-the-Box
17	I-45, N to Dallas, S to Houston
16	Yale St, N Main St, Shamrock, **N...gas:** Exxon, **S...gas:** Mobil, Shell, **food:** Burger King, Church's Chicken, **lodging:** Western Inn
15	TX 261, N Shepherd Dr, **N...food:** Sonic, Taco Cabana, **S...gas:** Chevron, Shell, Texaco/diesel, **food:** Wendy's, Whataburger, **other:** Home Depot, PepBoys
14	Ella Blvd, **N...gas:** Exxon, Shell/24hr, Texaco, **food:** Blimpie, Burger King, Jack-in-the-Box, KFC, LJ Silver, McDonald's, Popeye's, Taco Bell, **S...gas:** Shell, **food:** BBQ, **other:** HOSPITAL, Lowe's Whse
13c	TC Jester Blvd, **N...gas:** Chevron, Texaco, **food:** Atchafalaya Kitchen, Denny's, Golden Gate Chinese, **lodging:** Courtyard, SpringHill Suites, **S...gas:** Phillips 66
13b a	US 290, no facilities
12	W 18th St, **N...food:** CiCi's, **lodging:** Sheraton, **other:** Foley's, JC Penney, OfficeMax, mall, **S...food:** Whataburger
11	I-10, W to San Antonio, E to downtown Houston
10	Woodway Dr, Memorial Dr, **E...gas:** Shamrock, **food:** Steak'n Egg, **W...gas:** Exxon, Shell, **food:** Shug's Rest.
9b	Post Oak Blvd, **E...lodging:** Drury Inn, LaQuinta, **W...food:** Champ's Rest., McCormick&Schmick's Café
9a	San Felipe Rd, Westheimer Rd, FM 1093, **E...gas:** Exxon/diesel, Texaco, **lodging:** Courtyard, Hampton Inn, **other:** Circuit City, NTB, Target, **W...gas:** Shell, **food:** Luke's Burgers, **lodging:** Crowne Plaza Hotel, HomeStead Village Studios, Marriott, Sheraton, **other:** Best Buy, Dillard's, Nieman-Marcus
8	US 59, Richmond Ave, no facilities
7	Bissonet St, Fournace Place, **E...other:** Home Depot, **W...gas:** Texaco/diesel/repair
6	Bellaire Blvd, no facilities
5b	Evergreen St, no facilities
5a	Beechnut St, **E...gas:** Chevron, **food:** Boston Mkt, IHOP, McDonald's, Outback Steaks, **other:** bank, **W...gas:** Shell, **food:** Escalante Mexican Grill, James Coney Island, Saltgrass Steaks, Smoothie King, **other:** Borders Books, Marshall's, mall
4a	Brasswood, S Post Oak Rd, **E...gas:** Exxon, **lodging:** Day's Inn
3	Stella Link Rd, **N...gas:** Chevron, **food:** Jack-in-the-Box, **other:** DiscountTire, Food City, Radio Shack, **S...gas:** Exxon, Phillips 66, Texaco
2	US 90A, **N...gas:** Chevron, Conoco, Shamrock, **food:** Arby's, Bennigan's, Burger King, Church's, Denny's/24hr, KFC, McDonald's, Taco Bell, Wendy's, **lodging:** Howard Johnson, Villa Motel, **other:** Ford, Honda, **S...gas:** Chevron, **food:** Whataburger/24hr, **lodging:** La Quinta, Motel 6, Super 8, **other:** Firestone, Nissan, Toyota, to Buffalo Speedway
1c	Kirby Dr(from eb), **N...lodging:** Radisson, Shoney's Inn/rest., **S...food:** Joe's Crabshack, Papadeaux Seafood, Pappasito's Cantina, **other:** Cavender's Boots, Chevrolet, NTB, Pontiac/GMC, Toyota
1b a	FM 521, Almeda St, Fannin St, **N...gas:** Chevron, Conoco, **other:** Astro Arena, **S...gas:** Texaco, **food:** McDonald's, **other:** Aamco, Sam's Club, to Six Flags

UTAH
Interstate 15

Exit #	Services

403mm Utah/Idaho state line

402 Portage, no facilities

394 UT 13 S, Plymouth, **E...gas:** Chevron/Subway/diesel, **other:** rec area, RV camping

387 UT 30 E, to Riverside, Fielding, **1 mi E...gas:** Sinclair/Riverside Grill/diesel

383 Tremonton, Garland, **2 mi E...other:** HOSPITAL, gas, food, lodging

382 I-84 W, to Boise, no facilities

379 UT 13, to Tremonton, **E...gas:** Exxon/Arby's, **2-3 mi E...gas:** Chevron, Conoco/diesel, **food:** Arctic Circle, Crossroads Rest., JC's Country Diner, Subway, Taco Time, **lodging:** Marble Motel, Sandman Motel

375 UT 240, to UT 13, to rec area, Honeyville, **E...other:** Crystal Hot Springs Camping

370mm **rest area sb, full(handicapped)facilities, info, phone, picnic tables, litter barrels, vending, petwalk**

368 UT 13, Brigham City, **W...other:** to Golden Spike NHS

366 Forest St, Brigham City, **W...other:** Bear River Bird Refuge

364 US 91, to US 89, Brigham City, Logan, **E...gas:** Chevron/Blimpie/24hr, Citgo/7-11, ⚘Flying J/diesel/rest./24hr, Sinclair, **food:** Arby's, Aspen Grill, Beto's Mexican, Burger King, Hunan Chinese, J&D's Rest., KFC/Taco Bell, Little Caesar's, McDonald's, Pizza Hut, Pizza Press, Sonic, Subway, Taco Time, Wendy's, **lodging:** Bushnell Motel, Crystal Inn, Galaxie Motel, Howard Johnson Express, **other:** HOSPITAL, AutoZone, Checker Parts, Chevrolet/Pontiac/Buick/Cadillac, Chrysler/Dodge/Jeep, Radio Shack, ShopKO, Wal-Mart SuperCtr/gas/24hr, RV camping, to Yellowstone NP via US 89

363mm **rest area nb, full(handicapped)facilities, phone, picnic tables, litter barrels, vending, petwalk**

361 Port of Entry both lanes

360 UT 315, to Willard, Perry, **E...gas:** ⚘Flying J/Country Mkt/diesel/LP, **other:** KOA(2mi)

354 UT 126, to US 89, to Utah's Fruit Way, Willard Bay, no facilities

352 UT 134, N Ogden, Farr West, **E...gas:** Citgo/7-11, Maverik, Phillips 66/Wendy's/diesel, **food:** Arby's, Domino's, McDonald's, Melina's Mexican, Subway, **W...gas:** Conoco/diesel

349 to Harrisville, Defense Depot, **W...gas:** Shell/diesel, diesel repair

347 UT 39, 12th St, Ogden, **E...gas:** Chevron, Phillips 66, Pilot, Shell/diesel, **lodging:** Best Western/rest., **1-2 mi E...gas:** Chevron, **food:** Denny's, KFC, McDonald's, Sizzler, Village Inn Rest., **lodging:** Motel 6, **other:** to Ogden Canyon RA, **W...gas:** Pilot/DQ/Subway/Taco Bell/diesel/24hr/@, **lodging:** Western Inn

346 UT 104, 21st St, Ogden, **E...gas:** Chevron/Arby's/diesel, ⚘Flying J/Conoco/diesel/LP/24hr, Phillips 66/diesel, **food:** Cactus Red's Rest., McDonalds, Outlaw Rest., **lodging:** Big Z Motel/rest., Comfort Suites, Holiday Inn Express, Marriott, **other:** RV Repair, **W...gas:** Shell/diesel/café, **lodging:** Super 8/café/diesel, **other:** Century RV Park

345 (from nb), UT 53, 24th St, Ogden, **E...gas:** Sinclair/diesel

344b a UT 79 W, 31st St, Ogden, **1-2 mi E on Wall St...gas:** Citgo/7-11, **food:** Arby's, Golden Corral, JJ North's Buffet, Sizzler, **lodging:** Day's Inn, Radisson, **other:** HOSPITAL, Dillard's, Chevrolet, Ford/Lincoln/Mercury, RV Ctr, mall, to Weber St U, **W...airport**

343 I-84 E(from sb), to Cheyenne, Wyo

342 UT 26(from nb), to I-84 E, Riverdale Rd, **E...gas:** Conoco/diesel, Sinclair, **food:** Applebee's, Boston Mkt, Carl's Jr, Chili's, La Salsa Mexican, McDonald's, **lodging:** Red Roof Inn, **other:** Chrysler/Plymouth/Jeep, Circuit City, Harley-Davidson, Home Depot, Honda/Nissan, Isuzu, Lincoln/Mercury/Toyota/Kia, Mazda, Mitsubishi, OfficeMax, Pontiac/Buick/GMC, Saturn, Target, Toyota, Wal-Mart SuperCtr/24hr, Wilderness RV

341 UT 97, Roy, Sunset, **E...other:** Air Force Museum, **W...gas:** Citgo/7-11, Exxon/diesel, Phillips 66, Sinclair, Texaco, **food:** Arby's, Arctic Circle, Blimpie, Burger King, Central Park, DQ, Denny's, KFC, McDonald's, Pizza Hut, Ponderosa, Sonic, Subway, Taco Bell, Village Inn Rest., Wendy's, **lodging:** Quality Inn, Motel 6, **other:** Albertson's, AutoZone, BrakeWorks, Checker Parts, Citte RV Ctr, Early Tires, Goodyear, Discount Tire, Radio Shack, RiteAid, Smith's/gas, transmissions, same as 342

338 UT 103, Clearfield, **E...Hill AFB, W...gas:** Chevron, Conoco, Citgo/7-11, PetroMart, Texaco, Circle K, **food:** Arby's, Carl's Jr, Central Park, KFC, McDonald's, Skipper's, Subway, Taco Bell, Winger's, **lodging:** Alana Motel, Crystal Cottage Inn, Super 8, **other:** Big O Tire, Sierra RV, same as 341

336 UT 193, Clearfield, to Hill AFB, **E...gas:** Maverik, Tesoro/diesel/mart, **W...gas:** Chevron

335 UT 108, Syracuse, **E...gas:** Chevron, Phillips 66/diesel, Circle K, **food:** Applebee's, Carl's Jr., Cracker Barrel, Famous Dave's, Golden Corral, JB's, Marie Callender's, Outback Steaks, Quizno's, Red Robin, SF Pizza, TimberLodge Steaks, Tony Roma's, **lodging:** Courtyard, Fairfield Inn, Hampton Inn, Holiday Inn Express, La Quinta, TownePlace Suites, **other:** Barnes&Noble, Lowe's Whse, Office Depot, Old Navy, Target, **W...gas:** Citgo/7-11, Conoco, **food:** Arby's, McDonald's, **other:** HOSPITAL, RV Ctr

334 UT 232, UT 126, Layton, **E...gas:** Phillips 66, Texaco, **food:** Denny's, Garcia's, McDonald's, Olive Garden, Red Lobster, Sizzler, Tony Roma, Training Table Rest., Wendy's, **lodging:** Comfort Inn, **other:** JC Penney, Mervyn's, mall, to Hill AFB S Gate, **W...gas:** ⚘Flying J, **food:** Blimpie, Burger King, China Buffet, Fuddrucker's, IHOP, KFC, LoneStar Steaks, McGrath's FishHouse, Taco Bell, **other:** Batteries+, Bed Bath and Beyond, Chevrolet, Discount Tire co., Dodge, NTB, OfficeMax, Plymouth/Jeep, Pontiac/Cadillac/GMC, Ream's Foods, Sam's Club, ShopKO, Staples, Wal-Mart SuperCtr/24hr

332 to UT 126(from nb), Layton, **E...food:** Little Orient Chinese, **other:** repair, **W...gas:** Texaco, **other:** Jensen's RV

331 UT 273, Kaysville, **E...gas:** Chevron/McDonald's, Citgo/7-11, Phillips 66/diesel, Sinclair, **food:** Cutler's Sandwiches, DQ, Joanie's Rest., KFC, Subway, Taco Time, Wendy's, **lodging:** West Motel, **other:** Albertson's, Checker Parts, **W...other:** camping, 1st Choice Cars, Kia, Jensen's RV

Interstate 15

N ↕ S

329mm parking area both lanes

327 UT 225, Lagoon Dr, Farmington, **E...food:** Subway, **other:** amusement park, camping

326 US 89 N, UT 225(from nb), **1 mi E... gas:** Maverik/gas, **food:** Arby's, Aunt Pam's, Burger King, Little Caesar's, **other:** Smith's Foods, Goodyear/auto, RV Park, to I-84

325 UT 227(from nb), Lagoon Dr, to Farmington, **E...food:** Subway, **other:** Lagoon Funpark/RV Park

322 Centerville, **E...gas:** Chevron, Phillips 66/diesel, **food:** Arby's, Arctic Circle, Burger King, Carl's Jr, Dairy Queen, Del Taco, IHOP, Jake's Shakes, LoneStar Steaks, McDonald's, Subway, Taco Bell, TacoMaker, Wendy's, **other:** Albertson's, Home Depot, LandRover, Radio Shack, Schwab Tire, Target/foods, **W...other:** RV Ctr

321 US 89 S(exits left from sb), UT 131, 500W,, S Bountiful, **E...gas:** Chevron/ 24hr, Exxon/diesel, Phillips 66/diesel, Tesoro, **food:** Alicia's Rest., **lodging:** Country Inn Suites, **other:** Goodyear

320 UT 68, 500 S, W Bountiful, Woods Cross, **E...gas:** Exxon, **food:** Blimpie, Burger King, Carl's Jr, China Gourmet, Christopher's Steaks, ChuckaRama, Dee's Rest., HogiYogi, KFC, McDonald's, Papa Murphy's, Pizza Hut, SF Pizza, Sizzler, Subway, SuCasa Mexican, Taco Bell, Winger's, **lodging:** Country Inn Suites, **other:** HOSPITAL, Aamco, Albertson's, AllA$, AutoZone, Barnes&Noble, Checker Parts, Early's Tire, Firestone/ auto, GNC, OfficeMax, Radio Shack, Rite Aid, Ross, ShopKO, Walgreen, **W...gas:** Chevron/diesel, Phillips 66/A&W/diesel, **lodging:** InTown Suites

318 26th S, N Salt Lake, **E...gas:** Chevron/diesel/mart, Sinclair, Texaco, **food:** Apollo Burger, Arby's, Burger King, Empire Chinese, La Frontera Mexican, KFC, McDonald's, Peter Piper Pizza, Pizza Hut, Skipper's, Subway, Village Inn, Wendy's, **lodging:** Best Western, Comfort Inn, **other:** Chevrolet/Pontiac/Buick/Kia, Diahatsu, Discount Tire, Ford/Lincoln/Mercury, Honda, Mazda, Nissan, Smith's Foods, Toyota, **W...gas:** Conoco, **food:** Denny's, Lorena's Mexican, **lodging:** Hampton Inn, Motel 6, **other:** Goodyear

317 Center St, Cudahy Lane(from sb), N Salt Lake, **E...**gas

316 I-215 W(from sb), to airport, no facilities

315 US 89 S, to Beck St, N Salt Lake, no facilities

314 Redwood Rd, Warm Springs Rd, no facilities

313 9th St W, 7-11, Self's conv/rest., Tia Maria's Mexican, Regal Inn

S a l t L a k e

312 6th St N, **E...other:** HOSPITAL, LDS Temple, downtown, to UT State FairPark

311 I-80 W, to Reno, airport, no facilities

310 6th S, SLC City Ctr, info, **1 mi E...gas:** Chevron, Phillips 66/diesel, Circle K, **food:** Burger King, Dairy Queen, Denny's, McDonald's, Wendy's, **lodging:** Embassy Suites, Hampton Inn, Little America, Motel 6, Quality Inn, Ramada Inn, Residence Inn, Super 8, **other:** Ford, Toyota, to Temple Square, LDS Church Offices

309b a 9th S, 13th S, SLC, downtown, downtown **E...gas:** Texaco, **other:** Wal-Mart SuperCtr/24hr, **W...gas:** to Flying J/Conoco/diesel/LP/rest./24hr, **food:** Wendy's, **other:** Blue Beacon, Cadillac, Chevrolet, Ford, Goodyear, Hummer, Mitsubishi, Napa

308 UT 201, 21st St S, 13th St S, 9th St S(from nb), **E...gas:** Chevron, to Flying J/Conoco/diesel/LP/rest./24hr, Phillips 66, **food:** Atlantis Burgers, Carl's Jr, McDonald's, **other:** CompUSA, Costco/gas, Home Depot, Office Depot, Petsmart, U-Haul, same as 309

307 80 E, to Denver, Cheyenne, no facilities

UTAH

Interstate 15

N ↕ S

306 UT 171, 33rd S, S Salt Lake, **E...gas:** Citgo/7-11, Phillips 66, **food:** Apollo Diner, Burger King, McDonald's, Taco Bell, **lodging:** Bonneville Inn, Day's Inn, Roadrunner Motel, **W...gas:** Maverik/gas, **other:** Sam's Club, GMC

304 UT 266, 45th S, Murray, Kearns, **E...food:** McDonald's, **other:** UpTown Tire, **W...gas:** Chevron, Conoco, Shell/diesel, Sinclair/Burger King/diesel, Texaco, **food:** Burger King, Denny's, Wendy's, **lodging:** Fairfield Inn, Hampton Inn, Holiday Inn Express, Quality Inn, **other:** InterMtn RV Ctr, Lowe's Whse

303 UT 173, 53rd S, Murray, Kearns, **E...HOSPITAL**, **W...gas:** Chevron, Conoco, Sinclair, 7-11, **food:** KFC, Schlotsky's, **lodging:** Reston Hotel, **other:** Smith's Foods, FunDome, Jenson's RV Ctr

302b a I-215 E and W, no facilities

301 UT 48, 72nd S, Midvale, **E...gas:** Chevron, Conoco, Phillips 66, Sinclair, Texaco/LP, **food:** Chili's, Denny's, John's Place, KFC, McDonald's, Midvale Mining Café, Sizzler, South Seas Café, Taco Bell, Village Inn Rest., **lodging:** Best Western, Day's Inn, Discovery Inn/café, Executive Inn, La Quinta, Motel 6, Rodeway Inn, Sandman Inn, **other:** Cadillac/Buick, carwash, to Brighton, Solitude Ski Areas

S a n d y

298 UT 209, 90th S, Sandy, **E...gas:** Chevron, **food:** Arby's, Burger King, Fuddrucker's, Hardee's, Johanna's Kitchen, Sconecutter's Rest., Sweet Tomato, **lodging:** Comfort Inn, Majestic Rockies Motel, **other:** Early Tires, Ford, Lowe's Whse, to Snowbird, Alta Ski Areas, **W...gas:** Maverik, Tesoro, **food:** KFC, Village Inn **other:** HOSPITAL, Aamco

297 106th S, Sandy, S Jordan, **E...gas:** Conoco, Phillips 66, Tesoro, **food:** Bennett's BBQ, Bennigan's, Carver's Prime Rib, Chili's, Eat a Burger, HomeTown Buffet, Jim's Rest., Johanna's Rest., Subway, TGI-Friday, Village Inn, Wendy's, **lodging:** Best Western, Courtyard, Extended Stay America, Hampton Inn, Marriott, Residence Inn, TownePlace Suites, **other:** DENTIST, Chevrolet, Chrysler/Jeep, Costco/gas, Dillard's, Goodyear, Honda, JC Penney, Mervyn's, Nissan, Target, Toyota, Wal-Mart, mall, **W...food:** Denny's, **lodging:** Country Inn Suites, Sleep Inn, Super 8, **other:** Buick/GMC/Pontiac, VW

D r a p e r

294 UT 71, Draper, Riverton, **E...gas:** ⬧Flying J/diesel, Holiday/diesel, **food:** Arctic Circle, Café Rio Mexican, Carl's Jr, Fazoli's, Guadalahonky's Mexican, Jamba Juice, KFC, McDonald's, Panda Express, Pizza Hut, Quizno's, Ruby Tuesday, Sonic, Teriyaki Express, Wendy's, Wienerschnitzel, Wingers Diner, **lodging:** Fairfield Inn, Holiday Inn Express, Ramada Ltd, **other:** Camping World RV Supplies(1mi), Early Tire, Goodyear/auto, Greenbax, Mountain Shadows Camping, Smith's Foods, FSA Outlets/famous brands

291 UT 140, Bluffdale, **E...other:** Hyundai, Isuzu, Camping World RV Supplies(2mi), **W...gas:** Citgo/7-11, Common Sense/gas, **other:** st prison

287 UT 92, to Alpine, Highland, **E...to** Timpanogas Cave, **W...gas:** Phillips 66/diesel, **food:** Iceberg Café, **other:** Lone Peak RV Ctr, Thanksgiving Point/café

285 US 89 S, 12th W, to UT 73, Lehi, **W...gas:** Chevron/diesel

282 UT 73, to Lehi, **E...gas:** Conoco/diesel, **food:** 1 Man Band Diner, **lodging:** Motel 6, **W...gas:** Chevron/diesel/24hr, Phillips 66/Wendy's/24hr, **food:** Arctic Circle, Dutch Oven Rest., KFC/Pizza Hut, McDonald's, Papa Murphy's, Subway, Wingers Diner, **lodging:** Best Western, Comfort Inn, Day's Inn, Super 8, **other:** Albertson's, Big O Tire, Checker Parts, GNC, Dave's Chiropractic, USPO, museum

281 Main St, American Fork, **E...gas:** Phillips 66/diesel/24hr, Texaco, **food:** Wendy's, **other:** HOSPITAL, Chevrolet, Chrysler/Plymouth/Dodge/Jeep, Home Depot, Smith's Foods, Target, Wal-Mart SuperCtr/24hr

279 5th E, Pleasant Grove, **E...gas:** Conoco/Blimpie, **food:** Carl's Jr, Denny's, McDonald's, Taco Bell, **lodging:** Quality Inn, **other:** OfficeMax, Stewart's RV Ctr, **1-2 mi E...gas:** Circle K, Phillips 66, Texaco, **food:** Arby's, Del Taco, Golden Corral, Hardee's, KFC, Subway, Wendy's, **other:** HOSPITAL, American Camping, Chevrolet, **W...other:** Buick/GMC/Pontiac, Ford, Land Rover

278 Pleasant Grove, **E...food:** Panda Express, Sonic, **other:** Macey's foods

276 Orem, Lindon, **E...gas:** Exxon/diesel, Phillips 66, **food:** Del Taco, **other:** Home Depot, Lexus, Schwab Tire, **W...gas:** Sinclair/diesel

O r e m

275 UT 52, to US 189, 8th N, Orem, **E...gas:** Phillips 66, **lodging:** La Quinta, **1 mi E...food:** Arby's, Dairy Queen, Denny's, Sonic, **other:** to Sundance RA

274 Center St, Orem, **E...gas:** Citgo/7-11, Conoco, **other:** HOSPITAL, funpark, **1-2 mi E...food:** Burger King, Hardee's, KFC, Panda Express, Taco Bell, Wendy's, **W...gas:** Tesoro, **food:** La Casita Blanca Mexican, **lodging:** Econolodge, **other:** LP

272 UT 265, 12th St S, University Pkwy, bla bla, **E...gas:** Phillips 66/Wendy's/diesel/24hr, Sinclair, **food:** Chevy's Mexican, IHOP, Krispy Kreme, Lucky Buns Creamery, McDonald's, McGrath's FishHouse, Subway, **lodging:** Fairfield Inn, Hampton Inn, La Quinta, **other:** Ford, JiffyLube, Mazda, Saturn, Wal-Mart SuperCtr/24hr, **1-3 mi E...gas:** Chevron, **food:** Applebee's, Arby's, Black Angus, Carrabba's, Chili's, Fuddrucker's, Golden Corral, Outback Steaks, Ponderosa, Pizza Hut, Red Lobster, Sizzler, Village Inn, **lodging:** Best Western, Courtyard, **other:** Barnes&Noble, Circuit City, Honda, JC Penney, Jo-Ann Fabrics, Lowe's Whse, Mervyn's, Mitsubishi, Nissan, Office Depot, OfficeMax, Old Navy, Subaru, mall, to BYU, many services on US 89, **W...gas:** Chevron

P r o v o

268b a UT 114, Center St, Provo, **E...gas:** Conoco, Phillips 66, Shell, Sinclair, 7-11, **other:** HOSPITAL, **1 mi E...lodging:** Marriott, Travelers Inn, Travelodge, **other:** Albertson's, Checker Parts, **W...gas:** Chevron, Conoco, **food:** Taco Bell, **lodging:** Econolodge, **other:** KOA, Lakeside RV, Utah Lake SP

266 US 189 N, University Ave, Provo, **E...gas:** Chevron/24hr, Conoco/diesel, Maverik, Phillips 66, **food:** Arby's, Blimpie, Burger King, ChuckaRama, Fazolies, Hogi Yogi, KFC, McDonald's, Papa Murphy's, Ruby River Steaks, Sizzler, Taco Bell, Taco Time, Village Inn Rest., Wendy's, **lodging:** Best Western, Colony Inn, Fairfield Inn, Hampton Inn, Holiday Inn, Motel 6, National 9 Inn, Sleep Inn, Super

Intertstate 15

N ↑ S

8, other: Dillard's, GoodEarth Foods, Home Depot, JC Penney, K-Mart, NAPA, OfficeMax, Sam's Club, Sears/auto, Staples, Silver Fox RV Camping, mall, to BYU, **1 mi E...food:** Los Three Amigos Mexican, **lodging:** Best Western, Hotel Roberts, Safari Motel, Western Inn, **other:** CarQuest, VW/Audi, auto repair

265 UT 75, Springville, **E...gas:** Flying J/diesel/rest./24hr/@, Maverik, **food:** McDonald's(1mi), **lodging:** Best Western, **other:** E Bay RV Park

263 UT 77, Springville, Mapleton, **E...gas:** Phillips 66/Quizno's/diesel, **food:** DQ, IHOP, Quizno's, Wendy's, **other:** Big O Tire, JiffyLube, Wal-Mart SuperCtr/gas/24hr, **W...gas:** Conoco/Arby's/diesel, **food:** Cracker Barrel, **lodging:** Day's Inn, **other:** Quality RV Ctr

261 US 89 S, US 6 E(from sb), to Price, **E...gas:** Chevron/diesel, Phillips 66, Texaco, **food:** Arby's, Burger King, Carl's Jr, JB's, KFC, McDonald's, Papa Murphy's, Taco Bell, Taco Maker, Wendy's, Winger's, **lodging:** Holiday Inn Express, Western Inn, **other:** Albertson's/gas, Checker Parts, Fakler's Tire, K-Mart, Radio Shack, RV Ctr

260 US 6 E, UT 156, Spanish Fork, **E...gas:** Chevron, Conoco/diesel, Phillips 66, Texaco/diesel/LP, **food:** Arby's, Burger King, Hogi Yogi, JB's, KFC, Little Caesar's, McDonald's, North's Buffet, Subway, Taco Bell, Taco Time, Wendy's, **lodging:** Escalante B&B, **other:** Macey's Foods, ShopKO, **W...gas:** Conoco/diesel, **other:** Chevrolet, Chrysler/Plymouth/Jeep, Ford, RV Ctr

256 UT 164, to Spanish Fork, no facilities

254 UT 115, **E...gas:** Chevron/diesel, Flying J/diesel/LP/rest./24hr/@, Sinclair, **food:** McDonald's, Subway/Fruizle, **lodging:** Comfort Inn, **other:** HOSPITAL, Checker Parts, Payson Foods, RiteAid, diesel repair, Mt Nebo Loop

252 Payson, Salem, **E...gas:** Chevron, Sinclair/Arby's/diesel, **food:** Hogi Yogi, **other:** Wal-Mart SuperCtr/24hr, **W...gas:** Phillips 66/Wendy's/diesel

248 US 6 W, Santaquin, **E...other:** TrueValue, **W...gas:** Chevron, Conoco/diesel, Phillip 66/diesel, **food:** Main St Pizza, Main St Mkt, SantaQueen Burgers, Subway, Sorenson's Apple Farm, **other:** Nat Hist Area, Tintic Mining Dist, auto/tire care

245 to S Santaquin, no facilities

236 UT 54, Mona, no facilities

228 UT 28, to Nephi, **2-4 mi W...gas:** CashSaver/diesel, Citgo/7-11, Conoco, **food:** Reed's Drive-In, **lodging:** Safari Motel, **other:** HOSPITAL, Chevrolet/Pontiac/Buick, Goodyear, Thriftway Foods, to Great Basin NP

225 UT 132, Nephi, **E...gas:** Tesoro/diesel/LP, **food:** Taco Time, **other:** KOA(5mi), **W...gas:** Chevron/Arby's/diesel, Phillips 66/Wendy's/diesel, Sinclair, **lodging:** Economy lodge, **other:** HOSPITAL, Big O Tire, Hi-Country RV Park

222 UT 28, to I-70, Nephi, **E...gas:** Chevron/diesel, Sinclair/diesel/24hr, Tesoro/diesel/24hr, **food:** Burger King, Mickelson's Rest., Subway/Fruizle, **lodging:**

Nephi (vertical sidebar label)

Motel 6, Roberta's Cove Motel, Super 8, **W...gas:** Flying J/Pepperoni's/diesel/LP/24hr/@, **food:** Tiara Café, Wayne's Rest., **lodging:** Best Western, Safari Motel, **other:** HOSPITAL, Ford/Mercury, Big A Parts, diesel repair

207 to US 89, Mills, no facilities

202 Yuba Lake, phone, access to boating, camping, rec facilities

188 US 50 E, to I-70, Scipio, **E...gas:** Chevron/diesel, Phillips 66/diesel, **lodging:** Super 8

184 ranch exit, no facilities

178 US 50, **W...gas**, phone, to Great Basin NP

174 to US 50, Holden, **W...gas**, phone, to Great Basin NP

167 Lp 15, Fillmore, **1-3 mi E...gas:** Chevron/diesel, Shell/diesel/LP, Sinclair/diesel, **lodging:** Best Western/rest., Fillmore Motel, **other:** HOSPITAL, WagonsWest RV Park, **W...gas:** Phillips 66/Subway/diesel/24hr, Tesoro/diesel

163 Lp 15, to UT 100, Fillmore, **E...gas:** Chevron/Arby's/diesel/24hr, Maverik, **lodging:** AppleCreek Inn, Best Western, Fillmore Motel, **other:** HOSPITAL, KOA, **W...gas:** Phillips 66/Burger King/24hr

158 UT 133, Meadow, **E...gas:** Chevron, Texaco/diesel

153mm view area sb

151mm view area nb

146 Kanosh, **2 mi E...gas**, chainup area

138 ranch exit, no facilities

137mm rest area sb, full(handicapped)facilities, picnic tables, litter barrels, vending, petwalk

135 Cove Fort, Hist Site, Hist Site, **E...gas:** Chevron

132 I-70 E, to Denver, Capitol Reef NP, Fremont Indian SP

129 Sulphurdale, chainup area, no facilities

126mm rest area nb, full(handicapped)facilities, picnic tables, litter barrels, vending, petwalk

125 ranch exit, no facilities

120 Manderfield, chainup area nb, no facilities

112 to UT 21, Beaver, Manderfield, **E...gas:** Chevron/diesel, Conoco/diesel, Sinclair/diesel, **food:** Arby's, El Bambi Café, Hunan Chinese, McDonald's, Subway, **lodging:** Best Western/rest., Country Inn, Day's Inn, Motel 6, Stag Motel, **other:** HOSPITAL, KOA(1mi), **W...gas:** Texaco/diesel, **food:** Wendy's, **lodging:** Super 8, **other:** to Great Basin NP

109 to UT 21, Beaver, **E...gas:** Phillips 66, Sinclair, Texaco/Burger King/diesel/24hr, **food:** Arshel's Café, **lodging:** Aspen Lodge, Best Western, Comfort Inn, Day's Inn, Delano Motel/RV Park, Granada Inn, Sleepy Lagoon Motel, **other:** HOSPITAL, Mike's Foodtown, Cache Valley Cheese, NAPA, RV Parts/repair/dump, **W...gas:** Chevron/DQ/diesel/24hr, **food:** KanKun Mexican, Timberline Rest., **lodging:** Quality Inn, RV park, **other:** truckwash, to Great Basin NP

100 ranch exit, no facilities

Beaver

Interstate 15

N
↑
↓
S

95	UT 20, to US 89, to Panguitch, Bryce Canyon NP, no facilities
88mm	**rest area both lanes, full(handicapped) facilities, phone, picnic table, litter barrel, petwalk, hist site**
82	UT 271, Paragonah, no facilities
78	UT 141, E...lodging: Crimson Hills Motel, Day's Inn, Swiss Village Inn, other: ski areas, W...gas: TA/Subway/Taco Bell/diesel/24hr
75	UT 143, 2 mi E...lodging: Jedadiah's Inn/rest., Day's Inn, other: to Brian Head/Cedar Breaks Ski Resorts
71	Summit, W...gas: Sunshine Travel Plaza/diesel/rest./@
62	UT 130, Cedar City, E...gas: Phillips 66/diesel, lodging: Best Western(3mi), Holiday Inn(1mi), other: KOA(2mi), st patrol, W...gas: Sinclair, Texaco/diesel/24hr, food: Steak&Stuff Rest., lodging: Travelodge
59	UT 56, Cedar City, E...gas: Maverik, Phillips 66/diesel/LP, Tesoro, Texaco/diesel, food: Arby's, Burger King, Denny's, KFC, McDonald's, Shoney's, Sonic, Taco Bell, Wendy's, lodging: Abbey Inn, Comfort Inn, Econolodge, other: MEDICAL CARE, Chevrolet/Buick, L&S Tire, NAPA, 1 mi E...gas: Texaco/service, food: China Garden, Godfather's, Papa Murphy's, Pizza Factory, Sizzler, Sullivan's Café, lodging: Best Western, Rodeway Inn, Valu Inn, Zion Motel, other: Dodge/Chrysler/Jeep, Goodyear, GMC, Lin's Mkt, USPO, W...gas: Sinclair/diesel, food: Gondola Italian, Subway, lodging: Crystal Inn, Motel 6, Super 8
57	Lp 15, to UT 14, Cedar City, 1 mi E...gas: Chevron/repair/24hr, Phillips 66/diesel, Sinclair/diesel, food: Dairy Queen, Domino's, Hogi Hogi, Hunan Chinese, JB's, Pizza Hut, Subway, Taco Time, lodging: CedarRest Motel, Days Inn, Rodeway Inn, Super 7 Motel, Zion Motel, other: HOSPITAL, Albertson's, Allied Tire, AutoZone, Checker Parts, Radio Shack, Smith's Food/gas/24hr, to Cedar Breaks, Navajo Lake, Bryce Cyn, Duck Crk, W...gas: Chevron/diesel, food: Applebee's, Baker House B&B, other: Wal-Mart SuperCtr/gas/24hr
51	Kanarraville, Hamilton Ft, no facilities
44mm	**rest area both lanes, full(handicapped)facilities, phone, picnic tables, litter barrels, petwalk, hist site**
42	New Harmony, Kanarraville, W...gas: Texaco/diesel
40	to Kolob Canyon, Zion's NP, E...other: tourist info/phone, scenic drive
36	ranch exit, no facilities
33	ranch exit, no facilities
31	Pintura,
30	Browse, no facilities
27	UT 17, Toquerville, 9 mi E...food: Subway, lodging: Super 8, other: to Zion NP, Grand Cyn, Lake Powell

Cedar City (vertical margin label)
St George (vertical margin label)

23	Leeds, Silver Reef(from sb), 3 mi E...other: Harrisburg RV Resort/gas, hist site, museum
22	Leeds, Silver Reef(from nb), same as 23
16	UT 9, to Hurricane, E...Wal-Mart Dist Ctr, 10 mi E...gas: Chevron, Shell, lodging: Comfort Inn, Motel 6, Travelodge, other: to Zion NP, Grand Canyon, Lake Powell, RV Camping
10	Middleton Dr, Washington, E...gas: Phillips 66/diesel, Sinclair, Tesoro/diesel, food: Alberto's Mexican, Arby's, Arctic Circle, Burger King, IHOP, Jack-in-the-Box, Ruby Tuesday, Toro Moro Mexican, Wendy's, other: Albertson's, AutoZone, Costco/gas, Home Depot, JC Penney, QwikLube, Redlands RV Park, Sears/auto, Wal-Mart SuperCtr/24hr/gas, mall, W...gas: Chevron/diesel/LP, Shell/24hr, other: Dixie Radiator, auto repair
8	St George Blvd, St George, E...gas: Shell, Texaco/Subway/diesel, food: Applebee's, Blimpie, Carl's Jr, Chili's, ChuckaRama, Don Jose Mexican, Fazoli's, Outback Steaks, Red Lobster, Village Inn Rest., Winger's, lodging: Hampton Inn, Ramada Inn, Shoney's Inn/rest., other: HOSPITAL, Harmon's Foods, Lowe's Whse, Michael's, Old Navy, Settler's RV Park, Staples, Sunrise Tire, Target, Zion Factory Stores/famous brands, same as 10, W...gas: Chevron, Maverik/gas, Sinclair/Domino's/LP/diesel, Texaco/diesel, food: Burger King, China King, Denny's, KFC/A&W, McDonald's, Pizza Hut, Taco Bell, Taco Time, Wendy's, Wienerschnitzel, lodging: Best Western, Comfort Inn, Day's Inn, Desert Edge Inn, Econolodge, Howard Johnson, Motel 6, Sands Motel, Singletree Inn, SunTime Inn, Travelodge, other: Big O Tire, Checker Parts, Honda Motorcycles, NAPA, Old Home Bakery, Rite Aid, St Geo RV, to LDS Temple
6	UT 18, Bluff St, St George, E...gas: Chevron/diesel/24hr, Shell/24hr, Tesoro/A&W/diesel/24hr, food: Jack-in-the-Box, lodging: Ambassador Inn, Fairfield Inn, other: Buick/Pontiac/GMC, Firestone/auto, Hyundai, Saturn, U-Haul, funpark, W...gas: Chevron/diesel, Texaco, food: Arby's, Burger King, Carl's Jr, Claimjumper Steaks, DQ, Denny's, JB's, McDonald's, Palms Rest., Pancho&Lefty's Mexican, Pizza Hut, Tony Roma's, lodging: Best Western, Bluffs Inn, Budget 8 Inn, Claridge Inn, Comfort Suites, Crystal Inn, Holiday Inn, Quality Inn, Super 8, other: HOSPITAL, Albertson's, AutoZone, Big O Tire, Chevrolet/Cadillac, Daewoo, Ford/Lincoln/Mercury, DixieLube, Goodyear, Honda, Jo-Ann Fabrics, Mazda, NAPA, Nissan, Plymouth/Chrysler/Dodge/Jeep, Radio Shack, TempleView RV Park, Toyota, Vacation World RV Ctr
4	4 Bloomington, E...gas: ⚓Flying J/Burger King/diesel/24hr, W...gas: Chevron/Taco Bell, other: Foodcourt, Wal-Mart SuperCtr/24hr
2	**Welcome Ctr nb, full(handicapped)facilities, picnic tables, litter barrels, phone, petwalk**
1mm	Port of Entry/weigh sta both lanes
0mm	Utah/Arizona state line

Interstate 70

Exit #	Services
230mm	Utah/Colorado state line
226mm	**view area wb, restrooms(handicapped), litter barrels**
225	Westwater, no facilities
220	ranch exit, no facilities
212	to Cisco, no facilities
202	UT 128, to Cisco, no facilities
190	Yellowcat Ranch Exit, no facilities
188mm	**Welcome Ctr wb, full(handicapped)facilities, info, picnic tables, litter barrels**
185	Thompson, **N...gas:** Shell/diesel, **other:** café, camping, lodging
180	US 191 S, Crescent Jct, to Moab, **N...**gas/diesel/café, **S...**lodging
178mm	**rest area eb, full(handicapped)facilities, scenic view, picnic tables, litter barrels**
173	ranch exit, no facilities
162	UT 19, Green River, info, **1-2 mi N...gas:** Sinclair/diesel, Phillips 66/Burger King/diesel/24hr, Tesoro/diesel, **food:** Ben's Café, Chow Hound Drive-In, Lemieux Café, McDonald's, Westwinds Rest., **lodging:** Best Western/rest., Book Cliff Lodge/rest., Budget Host, Comfort Inn, Deluxe Inn, Holiday Inn Express, Motel 6, Rodeway Inn, Super 8, **other:** OK Anderson City Park, museum, same as 158
158	UT 19, Green River, **N...gas:** Chevron/diesel, Conoco/Arby's/diesel/24hr/@, Phillips 66/diesel/24hr, Tesoro/diesel, Sinclair/diesel, **food:** Ben's Café, Cathy's Rest., ChowHound Drive-In, **lodging:** Budget Inn, Mancose Rose Hotel, Oasis Motel/café, **other:** MEDICAL CARE, Big A Parts, Goodyear/auto, NAPA Repair, USPO, KOA, Shady Acres RV Park, Green River SP, same as 162, NO SERVICES WB FOR 100 MILES
156	US 6 W, US 191 N, to Price, Salt Lake, no facilities
147	UT 24 W, to Hanksville, to Capitol Reef, Lake Powell, no facilities
144mm	**rest area wb, restrooms(handicapped), litter barrels**
141.5mm	runaway truck ramp eb
140mm	**rest area both lanes, view area, restrooms (handicapped), litter barrels**
139mm	runaway truck ramp eb
136mm	brake test area eb
129	ranch exit, no facilities
120mm	**rest area both lanes, restrooms(handicapped), litter barrels**
114	to Moore, **N...rest area both lanes, restrooms(handicapped), litter barrels**
105	ranch exit, no facilities
102mm	**rest area both lanes, restrooms(handicapped), litter barrels**
91	ranch exit, no facilities
89	UT 10 N, UT 72, to Emery, Price, **12 mi N...**gas, **S...**to Capitol Reef NP
84mm	**S...rest area both lanes, full(handicapped)facilities, litter barrels, petwalk**
72	ranch exit, no facilities
61	Gooseberry Rd, no facilities
54	US 89 N, to Salina, US 50 W, to Delta, **N...gas:** Chevron/Burger King/diesel, Phillips 66/diesel, Sinclair/diesel, **food:** China Gate, Denny's, Subway, **lodging:** Best Western, Luxury Inn, Super 8, **other:** Butch Cassidy RV Camp, **1 mi N...gas:** Conoco/diesel, **other:** NAPA, NEXT SERVICES 108 MI EB
48	UT 24, to US 50, Sigurd, Aurora, **1-2 mi S...**gas, food, to Fishlake NF, Capitol Reef NP
40	Lp 70, Richfield, **S...gas:** Chevron, Flying J/diesel/LP/rest./24hr/@, **food:** Arby's, Chuckwagon Steaks, Subway, **lodging:** Luxury Inn, Super 8, **other:** HOSPITAL, RV/truck repair, **1-2 mi S...food:** McDonald's, Taco Time, **lodging:** Best Western, Budget Host, Day's Inn/rest., Quality Inn, **other:** Albertson's, **other:** Buick/Pontiac/Cadillac/GMC, KOA, Lin's Mkt
37	Lp 70, Richfield, **S...gas:** Phillips 66/Wendy's/diesel, KFC/Taco Bell, **lodging:** Comfort Inn, Hampton Inn, **1-2 mi S...gas:** Conoco/diesel/Munchie's RV Park, Tesoro/Burger King/diesel, **food:** McDonald's, Papa Murphy's, **lodging:** Best Western, Day's Inn, Quality Inn, **other:** Albertson's, Checker Parts, Chevrolet, Ford/Mercury, KOA, Wal-Mart SuperCtr/24hr, to Fish Lake/Capitol Reef Parks, st patrol
32	Elsinore, Monroe, **1/2 mi S...gas:** Chevron, Silver Eagle/gas
26	UT 118, Joseph, Monroe, **S...gas:** Diamond D/diesel, Shell/RV Park
23	US 89 S, to Panguitch, Bryce Canyon, no facilities
17	**N...other:** Fremont Indian Museum, info, phone, camping
13mm	brake test area eb
8	Ranch Exit, no facilities
3mm	Western Boundary Fishlake NF
1	Historic Cove Fort, **N...gas:** Chevron(2mi)
0mm	I-15, N to SLC, S to St George. I-70 begins/ends on

Interstate 80

Exit #	Services
197mm	Utah/Wyoming state line, no facilities
193	Wahsatch, no facilities
189	ranch exit, no facilities
185	Castle Rock, no facilities
182mm	Port of Entry/weigh sta wb
180	Emery(from wb), no facilities
170	**Welcome Ctr wb/rest area eb, full(handicapped)facilities, phone, vending, picnic tables, litter barrels, petwalk, RV dump**
169	Echo, **1 mi N...**gas/diesel, **food:** Kozy Rest./lodging
168	I-84 W, to Ogden, I-80 E, to Cheyenne, no facilities
166	view area both lanes, litter barrels

UTAH

Interstate 80

E ↕ W

Kimball Jct

164	Coalville, **N...gas:** Phillips 66/diesel/mart, **lodging:** Best Western, **other:** Holiday Hills RV Camp/LP, CamperWorld RV Park, **S...gas:** Chevron/diesel, Sinclair, Texaco, **food:** Holiday Hills Rest., **other:** to Echo Res RA
156	UT 32 S, Wanship, **N...food:** Spring Chicken Café, **S...gas:** Sinclair/diesel, **other:** to Rockport SP
152	ranch exit, no facilities
148b a	US 40 E, to Heber, Provo, **N...gas:** Sinclair/Blimpie/diesel, **S...other:** Home Depot
147mm	**rest area wb, full(handicapped)facilities, phone, vending, picnic tables, litter barrels, petwalk**
145	UT 224, Kimball Jct, to Park City, **N...other:** Ford/Mercury, RV camping, **S...gas:** Chevron, Shell/diesel, **food:** Arby's, Denny's, Loco Lizard Cantina, McDonald's, Subway, Ruby Tuesday, Taco Bell, Wendy's, **lodging:** Best Western, Hampton Inn, Holiday Inn Express, **other:** Smith's Foods, USPO, Wal-Mart, Outlet Mall/famous brands, RV camping, **4 mi S...gas:** Citgo/7-11, **lodging:** Olympia Park Hotel, Radisson, **other:** ski areas
144mm	view area eb
143	ranch exit, **N...gas:** Phillips 66/Blimpie, **food:** Pizza Hut, **other:** to Jeremy Ranch, **S...**camping, ski area
140	Parley's Summit, **S...gas:** Sinclair/diesel, **food:** No Worries Café
137	Lamb's Canyon, no facilities
134	UT 65, Emigration Canyon, East Canyon, Mountaindale RA
133	utility exit(from eb), no facilities
132	ranch exit, no facilities
131	(from eb) Quarry, no facilities
130	I-215 S(from wb), no facilities
129	UT 186 W, Foothill Dr, Parley's Way, **N...**HOSPITAL
128	I-215 S(from eb), no facilities
127	UT 195, 23rd E St, to Holladay, no facilities
126	UT 181, 13th E St, to Sugar House, **N...gas:** Chevron, Texaco, **food:** Olive Garden, Red Lobster, Sizzler, Training Table Rest., Wendy's, **other:** ShopKO
125	UT 71, 7th E St, **gas:** Texaco, **other:** Firestone, **N...food:** McDonald's
124	US 89, S State St, **N...gas:** Citgo/7-11, Chevron, Texaco/diesel, **food:** Burger King, Skipper's, Taco Bell, Uncle Sid's Rest., Wendy's, Woody's Drive-In, **other:** Buick, Chrysler/Jeep, Discount Tire, Dodge, Honda, Jeep, Suzuki, transmissions, **S...food:** KFC, Pizza Hut, **lodging:** Ramada Inn
123mm	I-15, N to Ogden, S to Provo, no facilities

Salt Lake

I-80 and I-15 run together approx 4 mi. See Utah Interstate 15, exits 308-310.

121	600 S, to City Ctr
120	I-15 N, to Ogden
118	UT 68, Redwood Rd, to N Temple, **2-3 mi N on N Temple...gas:** Amoco, Chevron/Subway/diesel, Circle K, **food:** Burger King, Denny's, KFC, Taco Bell, **lodging:** Airport Inn, Candlewood Suites, Comfort Suites, Day's Inn, Holiday Inn Express, Motel 6, Radisson, Utah St Fairpark, **S...**HOSPITAL
117	I-215, N to Ogden, S to Provo, no facilities
115b a	40th W, W Valley Fwy, **N...**to Salt Lake Airport
114	Wright Bros Dr(from wb), **N...lodging:** La Quinta, Microtel, Residence Inn, same as 113
113	5600 W(from eb), **N...gas:** Phillips 66/mart, **food:** Perkins, Pizza Hut, **lodging:** Best Western, Comfort Inn, Courtyard, Fairfield Inn, Hilton, Holiday Inn, La Quinta, Microtel, Quality Inn, Residence Inn, Sheraton, Super 8
111	7200 W, **N...**visitor ctr
104	UT 202, Saltair Dr, to Magna, **N...other:** Great Salt Lake SP, beaches
102	UT 201(from eb), to Magna, no facilities
101mm	view area wb
99	UT 36, to Tooele, **S...gas:** Chevron/Subway, ✈Flying J/Conoco/Country Mkt/diesel/LP/24hr/@, TA/Amoco/Burger King/Taco Bell/diesel/rest./24hr/@, Texaco/diesel, KFC(10mi), **food:** McDonald's, **lodging:** Oquirrh Motel/RV Park, **other:** HOSPITAL
88	to Grantsville, no facilities
84	UT 138, to Grantsville, Tooele, no facilities
77	UT 196, to Rowley, Dugway, no facilities
70	to Delle, **S...gas:** Delle/Sinclair/diesel/café/motel/24hr/@, phone
62	to Lakeside, Eagle Range, military area, no facilities
56	to Aragonite, no facilities
54mm	**rest area both lanes, full(handicapped)facilities, phone, picnic tables, litter barrels, petwalk, vending**
49	to Clive, no facilities
41	Knolls, no facilities
26mm	architectural point of interest
10mm	**rest area both lanes, full(handicapped)facilities, phone, picnic tables, litter barrels, vending, petwalk, observation area**
4	Bonneville Speedway, **N...gas:** Phillips 66/diesel/café/24hr/@
3mm	Port of Entry, weigh sta both lanes
2	UT 58(no EZ wb return), Wendover, **S...gas:** Amoco/diesel, Sinclair/diesel, Shell/diesel, Texaco/diesel, **food:** McDonald's, Subway, Taco Burger, **lodging:** Best Western, Bonneville Motel, Day's Inn, Econolodge, Heritage Motel, Motel 6, Super 8, Western Ridge Motel, **other:** Fred's Foods, Bonneville Speedway Museum, Silversmith Casino, Stateline Inn/casino, RV park, USPO, auto repair
0mm	Utah/Nevada state line, Mountain/Pacific time zone

Wendover

Interstate 84

Exit #	Services
120	I-84 begins/ends on I-80, exit 168 near Echo, Utah.
115	to Henefer, Echo, **1/2 mi S...other:** USPO, to E Canyon RA
112	Henefer, **S...**gas, food, lodging
111	Croydon, no facilities

E ↕ W

UTAH

Interstate 84

E ↕ W

111mm	Devil's Slide Scenic View
108	Taggart, **N**…gas, food, phone
106	ranch exit, no facilities
103	UT 66, Morgan, E Canyon RA, **N**…Ford, **S**…**gas:** Chevron, Phillips 66, Shell, **food:** Chicken Hut, Spring Chicken Café, Steph's Drive-In, **other:** MEDICAL CARE, Jubilee Foods, USPO, city park
96	Peterson, **N**…**gas:** Sinclair(3mi), **other:** to Snow Basin, Powder Mtn, Nordic Valley Ski Areas, **S**…**gas:** Phillips 66/diesel
94mm	**rest area wb, full(handicapped)facilities, picnic tables, litter barrels, petwalk**
92	UT 167(from eb), to Huntsville, **N**…**gas:** Sinclair/diesel(2mi), **other:** trout farm(1mi), to ski areas
91mm	**rest area eb, full(handicapped)facilities, picnic tables, litter barrels, petwalk**
87b a	US 89, Ogden, to Layton, Hill AFB, **N**…**food:** McDonald's(2mi), **1/2 mi S**…**gas:** Shell
85	S Weber, Uintah, no facilities
81	to I-15 S, UT 26, Riverdale Rd, **N**…**gas:** Conoco/diesel, Sinclair, **food:** Applebee's, Boston Mkt, Carl's Jr, Chili's, La Salsa Mexican, McDonald's, **other:** Chrysler/Plymouth/Jeep, Circuit City, Harley-Davidson, Home Depot, Honda/Nissan, Isuzu, Lincoln/Mercury/Toyota/Kia, Lowe's Whse, Mazda, Mitsubishi, OfficeMax, PepBoys, Pontiac/Buick/GMC, Sam's Club/gas, Target, Wal-Mart SuperCtr/24hr, Wilderness RV, **S**…**food:** McDonald's, **lodging:** Motel 6
	I-84 and I-15 run together. See Utah Interstate 15, exits 344 through 379.
41	I-15 N to Pocatello
40	UT 102, Tremonton, Bothwell, **N**…**gas:** Chevron/Quizno's/diesel/wash/24hr, Sinclair/Burger King/diesel/24hr, **food:** Denny's/24hr, McDonald's, Wendy's, **lodging:** Western Inn, **other:** HOSPITAL(4mi), Jack's RV, **1 mi N**…**lodging:** to Marble Motel, Sandman Motel, **other:** Alco, **S**…**other:** to Golden Spike NM
39	to Garland, Bothwell, **N**…HOSPITAL
32	ranch exit, no services
26	UT 83 S, to Howell, no services
24	to Valley, no services
20	to Blue Creek, no facilities
17	ranch exit, no facilities
16	to Hansel Valley, no facilities
12	ranch exit, no facilities
7	Snowville, **N**…**gas:** Chevron/diesel, Flying J/Pepperoni's/diesel/LP/24hr/@, **food:** Mollie's Café, Ranch House Diner, **lodging:** Outsiders Inn, **other:** RV camping
5	UT 30, to Park Valley, no facilities
0mm	Utah/Idaho state line

Roy

Snowville

Salt Lake (vertical sidebar)

Interstate 215 (Salt Lake)

N ↕ S

Exit #	Services
29	I-215 begins/ends on I-15.
28	UT 68, Redwood Rd, **W**…**gas:** Flying J/diesel/rest./mart/24hr/@, Maverik/24hr, **other:** BMW(motorcycles)
25	22nd N, no facilities
23	7th N, **E**…**gas:** Amoco, **food:** KFC, McDonald's, Taco Bell, **lodging:** Day's Inn, Holiday Inn, Motel 6, **W**…**lodging:** Holiday Inn Express, Radisson
22b a	I-80, W to Wendover, E to Cheyenne
21	California Ave, **E**…**gas:** Phillips 66, Sapp Bros/Sinclair/Burger King/diesel/@, Shell/Subway/diesel, **food:** Great American Diner, **other:** Goodyear
20b a	UT 201, W to Magna, 21st S, **W**… **other:** Goodyear
18	UT 171, 3500 S, W Valley, **E**…**food:** Applebee's, Chili's, Cracker Barrel, Country Kitchen, **lodging:** Baymont Inn, Country Inn Suites, Crystal Inn, Extended Stay America, La Quinta, Sleep Inn, **other:** HOSPITAL, PepBoys, **W**…**other:** Early Tire, JCPenney, Mervyn's, Michael's, mall
15	UT 266, 47th S, **E**…**gas:** Conoco, **food:** KFC, Taco Bell, Village Inn, Wendy's, **lodging:** Fairfield Inn, Hampton Inn, **W**…**gas:** Chevron, **food:** Arby's
13	UT 68, Redwood Rd, **E**…**gas:** Chevron, Tesoro, **food:** Applebee's, Arby's, Carl's Jr, Frontier Pies, Fuddrucker's, Hometown Buffet, Taco Bell, **lodging:** Homestead Suites, **other:** Circuit City, ShopKO, Wal-Mart/auto
12	I-15, N to SLC, S to Provo
11	same as 10(from eb)
10	UT 280 E, **E**…**other:** Sam's Club, **W**…**food:** Applebee's, Arby's, Hooters, La Salsa Mexican, Macaroni Grill, Olive Garden, Red Lobster, Taco Bell, Wendy's, Village Inn, **other:** HOSPITAL
9	Union Park Ave, **E**…**food:** Black Angus, Carl's Jr, Chili's, Famous Dave's BBQ, LaSalsa Mexican, Marie Callender's, Outback Steaks, Sweet Tomato, Tony Roma, **lodging:** Best Western, Crystal Inn, Extended Stay America, Homewood Suites, **other:** Albertson's, Barnes&Noble, Circuit City, Home Depot, OfficeMax, Old Navy, Ross, Smith's Foods, Target, Wal-Mart/auto, **W**…**gas:** Tesoro, **lodging:** Crystal Inn, Motel 6, Super 8
8	UT 152, 2000 E, **E**…**gas:** Chevron, **food:** KFC, Taco Bell, **W**…**food:** Wendy's
6	6200 S, **E**…**food:** Loco Lizards Café, Mikado Café, Quizno's, **other:** Alta, Brighton, Snowbird, Solitude/ski areas
5	UT 266, 45th S, Holladay, **W**…**gas:** Tesoro
4	39th S, **E**…**gas:** Chevron, Sinclair, **food:** Rocky Mtn Pizza, **other:** Dan's Foods, **W**…HOSPITAL
3	33rd S, Wasatch, **W**…**gas:** Tesoro, **food:** Burger King, KFC, McDonald's, Taco Bell, Wendy's
2	I-80 W, no facilities

I-215 begins/ends on I-80, exit 130.

N ↑ S

Exit #	Services
130mm	I-89 Begins/Ends, US/Canada Border, Vermont state line
129.5mm	**rest area sb, full facilities, phone, picnic tables, litter barrels, petwalk**
22(129)	US 7 S, Highgate Springs, **E...other:** Ammex DutyFree, **3 mi E...gas:** Mobil/diesel
129mm	Latitude 45 N, midway between N Pole and Equator
128mm	Rock River
21(123)	US 7, VT 78, Swanton, **E...gas:** Exxon/diesel/24hr, **W...gas:** Mobil/diesel, Shell, Sunoco/diesel, **food:** Big Wok Chinese, Dunkin Donuts, McDonald's, **other:** Grand Union Foods, NAPA
20(118)	US 7, VT 207, St Albans, **W...gas:** Mobil, Shell/diesel, **food:** Burger King, Dunkin Donuts, KFC/Taco Bell, McDonald's, Pizza Hut, **other:** Chevrolet, Ford, Hannaford Foods, Indian Motorcycles, Kinney Drug, Radio Shack, Sears, Staples
19(114)	US 7, VT 36, VT 104, St Albans, **W...gas:** Exxon, Mobil, Shell/diesel, **lodging:** Econolodge, **other:** HOSPITAL, Lincoln/Mercury, USPO, st police
111mm	**rest area both lanes, full(handicapped)facilities, info, phone, picnic tables, litter barrels, vending, petwalk**
18(107)	US 7, VT 104A, Georgia Ctr, **E...gas:** Citgo, Mobil/diesel, Shell, **food:** Potbelly Café, **other:** GA Auto Parts, Homestead RV Park, Interstate Auto Service
17(98)	US 2, US 7, Lake Champlain Islands, **E...gas:** Mobil, Shell/diesel, **other:** camping(4mi), **W...other:** to NY Ferry, camping(6mi)
96mm	weigh sta both lanes
16(92)	US 7, US 2, Winooski, **E...gas:** Mobil, **food:** Friendly's, **lodging:** Hampton Inn, **other:** Shaw's Foods, **W...gas:** Citgo, GoGo Gas, Shell/diesel, **food:** Burger King, Libby's Diner, McDonald's, Rathskellar Rest., **lodging:** Fairfield Inn, Motel 6
15(91)	VT 15(no EZ nb return), Winooski, **E...lodging:** Day's Inn, Handys Extended Stay Suites, **W...gas:** Exxon, Mobil, **other:** USPO
90mm	Winooski River
14(89)	US 2, Burlington, **E...gas:** Citgo/repair, Exxon, Mobil, Shell/diesel, Sunoco, **food:** Al's Cafe, Applebee's, Burger King, CheeseTraders, Dunkin Donuts, Friendly's, KFC, McDonald's, Outback Steaks, Quizno's, Zachary's Pizza, **lodging:** Anchorage Inn, Best Western, Clarion, Comfort Inn, Day's Inn, Holiday Inn, SwissHost Motel, University Inn, **other:** Barnes&Noble, BonTon, Brooks Drug, Grand Union

St Albans

Burlington

Exit #	Services
	Foods, Hannaford's Foods, JC Penney, Jo-Ann Fabrics, Natural Foods Mkt, Sears/auto, mall, **W...gas:** Exxon, Mobil, **lodging:** Sheraton, **other:** HOSPITAL, Advance Parts, Michael's, Staples
13(87)	I-189, to US 7, Burlington, **2 mi W on US 7 N...gas:** Citgo, Shell, **food:** Blimpe, China Express, KFC, TGIFriday, **lodging:** Liberty Inn, Town&Country Motel, **other:** Bond Parts, Radio Shack, Hyundai/Subaru, Radio Shack, **2 mi W on US 7 S...gas:** Exxon, Gulf, Mobil, Sunoco, Shell, **food:** Burger King, Cactus Pete's Rest., Denny's, Friendly's, Koto Japanese, McCarty's Steaks, McDonald's, Olive Garden, Perry's Rest., Pizza Hut, **lodging:** Super 8, **other:** Advance Parts, Audi/VW, Chrysler/Plymouth/Saturn, Hannaford's Foods, K-Mart, Pontiac/Cadillac, Tire Whse
12(84)	VT 2A, to US 2, to Essex Jct, Williston, **E...gas:** Citgo, Mobil/24hr, Sunoco/diesel/subs/24hr, **food:** Chili's, Friendly's, Longhorn Steaks, 99 Rest., Ponderosa, **lodging:** Fairfield, **other:** Best Buy, Circuit City, City Drug, Hannaford's Foods, Home Depot, Marshall's, Shaw's Foods, Staples, Wal-Mart, st police, **W...lodging:** Courtyard, Residence Inn
82mm	**rest area both lanes(7am-11pm), full(handicapped)facilities, phone, picnic tables, litter barrels, vending, petwalk**
11(79)	US 2, to VT 117, Richmond, **E...lodging:** Checkered House Motel, **W...gas:** Mobil/diesel/24hr
67mm	rest area sb, no facilities
66mm	rest area nb, no facilities
10(64)	VT 100, to US 2, Waterbury, **E...gas:** Exxon/diesel/24hr, Mobil/diesel/24hr, **food:** Lydia's Grill, **lodging:** Best Western/rest, Thatcher Brook Inn/rest., **W...gas:** Citgo, **food:** Zachary's Pizza, **other:** USPO
9(59)	US 2, to VT 100B, Middlesex, **W...gas:** Getty, **lodging:** Camp Meade Motel/rest., **other:** museum, st police
8(53)	US 2, Montpelier, **1 mi E...gas:** CF/gas, Citgo, Exxon/diesel, Gulf/diesel, Mobil, Sunoco/repair, **food:** La Pizzaria, Sarducci's Rest., Subway, **lodging:** Capitol Plaza Hotel, Montpelier Inn, **other:** Bond Parts, Shaw's Foods, camping(6mi), to VT Coll
7(50)	VT 62, to US 302, Barre, **E...gas:** Mobil/diesel/24hr, **food:** Applebee's, **lodging:** Comfort Suites, **other:** Honda, Shaw's Foods, Staples, **1 mi E...lodging:** Hilltop Inn, **other:** HOSPITAL, Cadillac/GMC/Toyota, JC Penney, Jo-Ann Fabrics, camping(7mi)
6(47)	VT 63, to VT 14, S Barre, **4 mi E...**gas, food, lodging, camping, info
5(43)	VT 64, to VT 12, VT 14, Williamstown, **6 mi E...**gas/diesel, food, lodging, camping, **W...**to Norwich U

Montpelier

VERMONT

Interstate 89

41mm	highest elevation on I-89, 1752 ft
34.5mm	**rest area/weigh sta both lanes(7am-9pm), full(handicapped)facilities, info, phone, litter barrels, petwalk**
4(31)	VT 66, Randolph, **E...other:** RV amping(1mi), **W...gas:** Mobil, **food:** McDonald's, lodging(3mi), **other:** HOSPITAL, RV camping(5mi)
3(22)	VT 107, Bethel, **E...gas:** Shell/diesel, **food:** Eaton Rest., Village Pizza, **other:** to Jos Smith Mon(8mi), **1 mi W...gas:** Citgo/diesel/LP, **other:** MEDICAL CARE, Books Drug, NAPA, USPO, st police
14mm	White River
2(13)	VT 14, VT 132, Sharon, **E...lodging:** 1/2 Acre Motel, **W...gas:** Citgo/diesel, Gulf/diesel, Mobil, **food:** Dixie's Kitchen, Sandy's Drive Inn, **lodging:** Columns Motel, **other:** Sharon Trading Post, USPO, Jos Smith Mon(6mi)
9mm	**rest area/weigh sta both lanes(7am-11pm), full facilities, phone, info, picnic tables, litter barrels, vending, NO HANDICAPPED FACILITIES**
7mm	White River
1(4)	US 4, to Woodstock, Quechee, **3 mi E...gas:** Shell/diesel/24hr, **lodging:** Hampton Inn, Super 8
1mm	I-91, N to St Johnsbury, S to Brattleboro
0mm	Vermont/New Hampshire state line, Connecticut River

Interstate 91

Exit #	Services
178mm	I-91 begins/ends., US/Canada Border, Vermont state line, US Customs
29(177)	US 5, Derby Line, **E...**Ammex Dutyfree, **1 mi W...gas:** Irving/diesel
176.5mm	**Welcome Ctr sb, full(handicapped)facilities, info, picnic tables, litter barrels, phone, petwalk, Midpoint between the Equator and N Pole**
28(172)	US 5, VT 105, Derby Ctr, **E...gas:** Citgo, Exxon/diesel/24hr, Gulf, Mobil/diesel, **food:** Palace Rest., **other:** Bernie's Repair/tires, Cow Fireside Camping, st police, **W...gas:** Gulf/Dunkin Donuts/diesel, Mobil, Shell/diesel/24hr, **food:** McDonald's, Roaster's Cafe, Village Pizza, **lodging:** Inn at The Hill, Pepin's Motel, Super 8, **other:** HOSPITAL, Kinney Drug, Parts+, Plymouth/Jeep, Rite Aid, Shop&Save Foods, RV camping
27(170)	VT 191, to US 5, VT 105, Newport, **3 mi W...other:** HOSPITAL, Border Patrol, camping, info
167mm	parking area nb, rest area/weigh sta sb
26(161)	US 5, VT 58, Orleans, **E...gas:** Irving/diesel, Lanoue's Gas, Sunoco, **food:** Subway, **other:** Cole's Mkt, Orleans Gen Store, camping(8mi)
156.5mm	Barton River
25(156)	VT 16, Barton, **1 mi E...gas:** Gulf, Irving/diesel, Mobil/diesel/repair, **food:** Ming's Chinese, Richie's Rest., Village Coffeehouse, **lodging:** PineCrest Motel, **other:** C&C Foods, Ford, USPO, camping(2mi)
154mm	parking area nb
150.5mm	highest elevation on I-91, 1856 ft
143mm	scenic overlook nb
141mm	**rest area sb, full(handicapped)facilities, info, picnic tables, litter barrels, phone**
24(140)	VT 122, Wheelock, **2 mi E...**gas, food, lodging
23(137)	US 5, to VT 114, Lyndonville, **E...gas:** Gulf/diesel, Mobil/Dunkin Donuts, **food:** McDonald's, **lodging:** Colonnade Inn, Hoagie's Pizza, **other:** Ace Hardware, NAPA, Rite Aid, White Foods, **W...lodging:** Lyndon Motel

VERMONT

Interstate 91

N ↕ **S**

St Johnsbury

22(132) to US 5, St Johnsbury, **1-2 mi E...gas:** Citgo/diesel/LP, **food:** Brit-Da-Brans Diner, KFC/Taco Bell, Pizza Hut, St Jay Diner, **other:** HOSPITAL, PriceChopper Foods, Rite Aid, repair, 4 mi E on US 5...**gas:** Irving, **other:** Firestone, JC Penney, Sears

21(131) US 2, to VT 15, St Johnsbury, **1-2 mi E...**services

20(129) US 5, to US 2, St Johnsbury, **E...gas:** Irving/diesel, Mobil, Shell/diesel, **food:** Anthony's Diner, Dunkin Donuts, East Garden Chinese, McDonald's, Subway, **other:** Brooks Drug, Kevin's Repair, **W... lodging:** Comfort Inn, **other:** st police

19(128) I-93 S to Littleton NH, no facilities

122mm scenic view nb

18(121) to US 5, Barnet, **E...other:** camping(5mi), **W...other:** camping(5mi)

115mm rest area sb, no facilities

114mm rest area nb, no facilities

17(110) US 302, to US 5, Wells River, NH, **E...food:** Warner's Rest., **other:** camping(10mi), **W...gas:** P&H Trkstp/diesel/rest./24hr/@, **other:** HOSPITAL(5mi), camping(9mi)

100mm **nb rest area, full(handicapped)facilities, phone, info, picnic tables, litter barrels, petwalk, sb parking area/weigh sta**

16(98) VT 25, to US 5, Bradford, **E...gas:** Mobil/diesel/LP/café, **food:** Colatina Rest., Hungry Bear Rest., **lodging:** Bradford Motel, **other:** Kinney Drug, NAPA, P&C Foods, **W...**st police

15(92) Fairlee, **E...gas:** Citgo/diesel, Gulf, Mobil/deli, Shell/diesel/LP, **food:** Third Rail Rest., Your Place Rest., **other:** USPO, camping

14(84) VT 113, to US 5, Thetford, **1 mi E...other:** food, camping, **W...other:** camping

White River Jct

13(75) US 5, VT 10a, Hanover, NH, **E...other:** HOSPITAL, camping, to Dartmouth, **W...**Subaru

12(72) US 5, White River Jct, Wilder, **E...gas:** Gulf/diesel/24hr, Mobil

11(71) US 5, White River Jct, **E...gas:** Exxon/Subway/diesel, Gulf/diesel, Mobil, Sunoco/repair, **food:** AJ's Steaks, Canton House Rest., China Moon Cafe, Crossroads Café, Gillam's Rest., McDonald's, **lodging:** Coach an' Four Motel, Comfort Inn, Pines Motel, Ramada Inn, **other:** Ford/Lincoln/Mercury/Hyundai, Jct Mktplace, Toyota, USPO, **W...gas:** Citgo, Shell, **lodging:** Best Western, Comfort Suites, Hampton Inn, Holiday Inn Express, Super 8, **other:** HOSPITAL, Saab

10N(70) I-89 N, to Montpelier, no facilities

10S I-89 S, to NH, airport

Brattleboro

68mm rest area/weigh sta both lanes(7am-11pm), full(handicapped)facilities, picnic tables, litter barrels, phone, vending, petwalk

9(60) US 5, VT 12, Hartland, **E...**HOSPITAL, **W...gas:** Mobil(1mi), info

8(51) US 5, VT 12, VT 131, Ascutney, **E...gas:** Citgo/diesel, Gulf/diesel, Mobil, Sunoco/diesel, **food:** RedBarn Cafe, Roadside Cafe, **lodging:** Yankee Village Motel, **other:** HOSPITAL, Max' Country Store, USPO

7(42) US 5, VT 106, VT 11, Springfield, **W...gas:** Mobil/diesel/24hr, **food:** Howard Johnson Rest., **lodging:** Holiday Inn Express, **other:** HOSPITAL, camping

39mm rest area both lanes, no facilities

6(34) US 5, VT 103, to Bellows Falls, Rockingham, **E...gas:** Shell, **lodging:** Every Day Inn, **W...gas:** Sunoco/diesel/24hr, **other:** st police(6mi)

5(29) VT 121, to US 5, to Bellows Falls, Westminster, **3 mi E...**gas, food, phone, lodging

24mm rest area both lanes, no facilities

22mm weigh sta sb

20mm parking area nb

4(18) US 5, Putney, **E...lodging:** Putney Inn/rest., **W...gas:** Sunoco/diesel/LP/24hr, **other:** camping(3mi)

3(11) US 5, VT 9 E, Brattleboro, **E...gas:** Agway, Citgo/diesel/24hr, Mobil, Sunoco, **food:** Bickford's, Dunkin Donuts, Friendly's, KFC, McDonald's, Pizza Hut, Steak-out Rest., Village Pizza, **lodging:** Best Inn, Colonial Motel, Hampton Inn, Holiday Inn Express, Motel 6, Quality Inn, Super 8, **other:** Ford/Mercury, GNC, Hannaford Foods, Home Depot, NAPA, Pontiac/Buick/GMC, Radio Shack, Rite Aid, Staples, Subaru, U-Haul, USPO

2(9) VT 9 W, to rd 30, Brattleboro, **E...gas:** Sunoco, **W...gas:** Shell, **food:** Country Deli, **other:** to Marlboro Coll, st police

1(7) US 5, Brattleboro, **E...gas:** Gulf/diesel, Mobil/Dunkin Donuts, Shell/Subway/diesel, **food:** Burger King, Millenium Pizzaria, VT Inn Pizza, **lodging:** Econolodge, **other:** HOSPITAL, Brooks Drug, CarQuest, Chevrolet/Cadillac, Chrysler/Jeep, PriceChopper Foods, Walgreen, to Ft Dummer SP

6mm **Welcome Ctr nb, full(handicapped)facilities, info, phone, picnic tables, litter barrels, vending, petwalk, playground**

0mm Vermont/Massachusetts state line

Interstate 93
See New Hampshire Interstate 93

VIRGINIA

Interstate 64

E ↕ W

N o r f o l k

Exit #	Services
299b a	I-264 E, to Portsmouth. I-64 begins/ends on I-264., no facilities
297	US 13, US 460, Military Hwy, **N...gas:** Exxon
296b a	US 17, to Portsmouth, **4 mi S...**camping
294mm	S Br Elizabeth River
292	VA 190, to VA 104(from eb, no EZ return), Dominion Blvd, **S...gas:** BP, Shell, **food:** Burger King, Hardee's, **other:** MEDICAL CARE, Family$, Food Lion, Rite Aid
291b a	I-464 N, VA 104 S, to Elizabeth City, Outer Banks, same services as 292
290b a	VA 168, Battlefield Blvd, to Nag's Head, Manteo, **N... other:** Merchant's Auto Ctr, **S...gas:** BP/diesel/24hr, Shell/Blimpie, **food:** Applebee's, Burger King, Chik-fil-A, ChuckeCheese, Dunkin Donuts, Golden Corral, Grand China Buffet, Hardee's, Ryan's, Taco Bell, TGIFriday's, Waffle House, Wendy's, **lodging:** Day's Inn, Super 8, **other:** $Tree, Home Depot, K-mart, Lowe's Whse, Sam's Club, Walgreen, Wal-Mart SuperCtr/24hr
289b a	Greenbrier Pkwy, **N...gas:** Citgo, **food:** Burger King, Taco Bell, Wendy's, **lodging:** Hampton Inn, Holiday Inn, Motel 6, Wellesley Inn, **other:** Acura, BMW, Chevrolet, Cloth World, Dodge, Food Lion, Ford, Honda, Hyundai, Isuzu, Mitsubishi, Pontiac, Subaru, Volvo, U-Haul, transmissions, **S...food:** Atlas Grill, Blimpie, Boston Mkt, Cheers Grill, Cooker, Don Pablo, Fazoli's, Fuddruckers, Joe's Crabshack, LoneStar Café, McDonald's, Old Country Buffet, Olive Garden, Panera Bread, Pargo's, Ruby Tuesday, Starbucks, TCBY, Winston's Café, Food Lion, Harris-Teeter/24hr, **lodging:** Comfort Suites, Courtyard, Extended Stay America, Fairfield Inn, Sun Suites, **other:** Barnes&Noble, Best Buy, Circuit City, Dillard's, $General, Drug Emporium, Hecht's, Marshall's, Michael's, Office Depot, OfficeMax, Old Navy, Sears/auto, Target, TJMaxx, ViVo Italian, mall
286b a	Indian River Rd, **N...gas:** BP/24hr, Hess/diesel, Crown, Shell, **food:** Hardee's, **S...gas:** Sunoco/diesel, **food:** Capt D's, 7-11, Waffle House, **lodging:** Founder's Inn
285	E Branch Elizabeth River
284b a	I-264, to Norfolk, VA 44, to VA Beach(exits left from eb), **1/2 mi E off 1 exit N, Newtown Rd...gas:** Amoco, Chevron, Exxon, Shell, 7-11, **food:** Adam's Rest., Denny's/24hr, Golden Corral, Texas Steaks, Wendy's, **lodging:** Hampton Inn, Holiday Inn, La Quinta, Ramada Inn
282	US 13, Northampton Blvd, **N...lodging:** Quality Inn, Sleep Inn, **other:** to Chesapeake Bay Br Tunnel
281	VA 165, Military Hwy(no EZ eb return), **N...gas:** BP/diesel, Shell/diesel/24hr, **food:** Andy's Pizza, Golden Corral, Pizza Hut, Wendy's, **lodging:** Econolodge, **other:** Aamco, Chevrolet/Kia, Chrysler/Plymouth, Food Lion, K-Mart, Mazda/Suzuki, **S...gas:** Citgo, Exxon, Shell, **food:** DQ, **lodging:** Econolodge, Hampton Inn, Hilton, Holiday Inn Select, **other:** Firestone, Target
279	Norview Ave, **N...gas:** Shell, **food:** Golden Corral, Wendy's, **other:** K-Mart/gas, to airport & botanical garden
278	VA 194 S(no EZ return), no facilities
277b a	VA 168, to Tidewater Dr, **N...gas:** Citgo/7-11, **food:** Hardee's
276c	to US 460 W, VA 165, Little Creek Rd, **N...gas:** Shell, **S...gas:** BP, Exxon, **food:** McDonald's, Mr Jim's Submarines, KFC, Taco Bell, Wendy's, **other:** AutoZone, Eckerd, Farm Fresh, Hannaford Foods, Kroger
276b a	I-564 to Naval Base, no facilities
274	Bay Ave(from wb), to Naval Air Sta
273	US 60, 4th View St, Oceanview, **N...gas:** BP/diesel/24hr, **lodging:** Econolodge, Super 8(1mi), **other:** Harrison Boathouse/Pier, **S...other:** to Norfolk Visitors Ctr, info
272	W Ocean View Ave, **N...food:** Willoughby's Seafood, **S...food:** Fisherman's Wharf Rest., **lodging:** Day's Inn
270mm	Chesapeake Bay Tunnel
269mm	weigh sta eb

VIRGINIA

Interstate 64

E ↑ W

Hampton

268	VA 169 E, to Buckroe Beach, Ft Monroe, VA Ctr, **N... food:** Hardee's, McDonald's
267	US 60, to VA 143, Settlers Ldg Rd, **S...food:** Burger King, **other:** HOSPITAL, to Hampton U
265c	(from eb), **N...other:** Armistead Ave, to Langley AFB
265b a	VA 134, VA 167, to La Salle Ave, **N...gas:** Citgo, RaceTrac, **lodging:** Super 8, **other:** Home Depot, **S... gas:** BP, **food:** McDonald's, KFC/Taco Bell, Seafood Rest., **other:** HOSPITAL, Family$
264	I-664, to Newport News, Suffolk, no facilities
263b a	US 258, VA 134, Mercury Blvd, to James River Br, **N... gas:** Shell, **food:** Applebee's, Bennigan's, Blimpie, Boston Mkt, Burger King, Chili's, Denny's, Golden Corral, Hooters, IHOP, KFC, McDonald's, Olive Garden, Outback Steaks, Pizza Hut, Rally's, Red Lobster, Rockola Café, Steak&Ale, Taco Bell, Waffle House, Wendy's, **lodging:** Comfort Inn, Courtyard, Day's Inn, Fairfield Inn, Hampton Inn, Holiday Inn, Quality Inn, Red Roof Inn, Sheraton, **other:** Chevrolet/Mazda, Chrysler/Jeep, Ford, JC Penny, NAPA, Office Depot, Target, Wal-Mart SuperCtr/24hr, **S...gas:** Citgo/7-11, Miller's Gas, **food:** Crabber's, Cracker Barrel, Lone Star Steaks, Old Country Buffet, Pizza Hut, Sonic, Texas Steaks, Waffle House, **lodging:** Best Western, Econolodge, Interstate Inn, La Quinta, Savannah Suites, **other:** Advance Parts, Auto Express, BassPro Shop, BigLots, CarQuest, Circuit City, $General, Lowe's Whse, Nissan, OfficeMax, PepBoys, Radio Shack, Toyota, Volvo
262	VA 134, Magruder Blvd(from wb, no EZ return), **N... gas:** Citgo/7-11, Exxon, **other:** Dodge/Acura
261b a	Center Pkwy, to Hampton Roads, **S...gas:** Citgo, **food:** ChuckeCheese, Cujo's Grill, McDonald's, Peking Chinese, Ruby Tuesday, Subway, Taco Bell, Topeka's Steaks, **other:** BooksAMillion, $Tree, Eckerd, FarmFresh Foods, FoodLion, TJMaxx
258	US 17, J Clyde Morris Blvd, **N...gas:** BP, Shell/diesel, Sunoco, **food:** Chatfield's Grill, Domino's, Hardee's, New China, Waffle House, **lodging:** BudgetLodge, Holiday Inn, Host Inn, PointPlaza Hotel, Super 8, **other:** Advance Parts, $General, Food Lion, Rite Aid, 7-11/24hr, **S...gas:** Citgo/diesel/24hr, Exxon, Kangaroo, WaWa, **food:** Angelo's Steaks, BBQ, Burger King, Hong Kong Chinese, Papa John's, Pizza Hut, Subway, Taco Bell/KFC, **lodging:** Motel 6, Omni Hotel/rest., **other:** HOSPITAL, BMW/Honda, $Tree, Eckerd, Radio Shack, museum
256b a	Victory Blvd, Oyster Point Rd, **N...gas:** BP, Citgo/ diesel, Shell, **food:** Arby's, Burger King, Chick-fil-A, FarmFresh Deli, Fuddrucker's, Hardee's, Starbucks, **lodging:** CandleWood Suites, Courtyard, Hampton Inn, Hilton Garden, TownePlace
255b a	VA 143, to Jefferson Ave, **N...gas:** BP, Shell/diesel, **food:** Castle Italian, Golden Corral, **lodging:** Travelodge(2mi), **other:** HOSPITAL, Aamco, Acura, Cadillac/GMC, FarmFresh Foods/deli, Home Depot, Lowe's Whse, Sam's Club/gas, Wal-Mart SuperCtr/ 24hr, Saturn, airport, **S...gas:** Citgo, Exxon/diesel, 7-11, **food:** Applebee's, Burger King, Chick-fil-A, Cracker Barrel, Don Pablo, KFC, McDonald's, Out-

Williamsburg

	Back Steaks, Starbuck's, Subway, TGIFriday's, Waffle House, Wendy's, **lodging:** Comfort Inn, Day's Inn, Econolodge, Hampton Inn, Microtel, Studio+, **other:** Barnes&Noble, Best Buy, Belk, Circuit City, CompUSA, Costco, Dillard's, Hecht's, NTB, OfficeMax, Sears/auto, Target, World Mkt, mall
250b a	to US Army Trans Museum, **N...gas:** BP/diesel, Citgo/7-11, Shell, Sunoco, **other:** to Yorktown Victory Ctr, **S...gas:** RaceTrac, **food:** McDonald's, Taco Bell, Wendy's, **lodging:** Ft Eustis Inn, Holiday Inn Express, Mulberry Inn, TDY Inn
247	VA 143, to VA 238(no EZ return wb), **N...gas:** BP/ diesel, Citgo/7-11, **other:** to Yorktown, **S...other:** to Jamestown Settlement
243	VA 143, to Williamsburg, **S...**same as 242a
242b a	VA 199, to US 60, to Williamsburg, **N...gas:** BP(2mi), **lodging:** Day's Inn/rest., **other:** water funpark, to Yorktown NHS, **1 mi S...gas:** Citgo/7-11, Crown Gas, Shell, Starbuck's, Subway, Wendy's, **food:** Burger King, LJ Silver, McDonald's, Wendy's, **lodging:** Courtyard, Howard Johnson, Marriott/rest., Quality Inn, Rodeway Inn, **other:** 1st Settlers Camping, to William&Mary Coll, Busch Gardens, to Jamestown NHS
238	VA 143, to Colonial Williamsburg, Camp Peary, **2-3 mi S...gas:** Citgo/7-11, Shell, **food:** Cracker Barrel, Golden Corral, Hardee's, Ledo's Pizza, McDonald's, Pizzaria Uno, **lodging:** Best Western/rest., Comfort Inn, Country Hearth Inn, Day's Inn, Econolodge, Hampton Inn, Holiday Inn/rest., Homewood Suites, Howard Johnson/rest., King William Inn, Quality Inn/rest., Red Roof Inn, **other:** HOSPITAL, Anvil Camping
234	VA 646, to Lightfoot, **1-2 mi N...other:** KOA, **2-3 mi S...gas:** Exxon/diesel, Mobil/diesel, Shell/diesel, **food:** BBQ, Burger King, Hardee's, KFC, Lightfoot Rest., McDonald's, Sonic, Subway, **lodging:** Colonial Hotel, Day's Inn, Quality Inn, Super 8, **other:** Ford/ Lincoln/Mercury, Home Depot, Lowe's Whse, Pottery Camping(3mi), Wal-Mart SuperCtr/24hr
231b a	VA 607, to Norge, Croaker, **N...gas:** Citgo/7-11, **other:** American Heritage RV Park, to York River SP, **1-2 mi S...gas:** Shell/diesel, **food:** FarmFresh Deli, KFC, Candle Factory Rest., Wendy's, **lodging:** Econolodge, Quality Inn, Red Roof Inn
227	VA 30, to US 60, to West Point, Toano, **N...food:** StoneHouse Cafe, **S...gas:** Exxon/diesel/LP, Shell/ Stuckey's/diesel, **food:** McDonald's
220	VA 33 E, to West Point, **N...gas:** Exxon/diesel
214	VA 155, to New Kent, Providence Forge, **S...gas:** Exxon/diesel, **food:** DQ, Pepito's Mexican, **other:** Colonial Downs Racetrack, Rockahock Camping(8mi)
213mm	**rest area both lanes, full(handicapped)facilities, phone, vending, picnic tables, litter barrels, pet-walk**
211	VA 106, to Talleysville, to James River Plantations, no facilities
205	VA 33, VA 249, to US 60, Bottoms Bridge, Quinton, **N...gas:** BP/diesel, Exxon/diesel, **food:** New Peking Chinese, Subway, **other:** Eckerd, Food Lion, USPO, **S...gas:** Shell/diesel, **food:** McDonald's, MarketPlace Foods
204mm	Chickahominy River

VIRGINIA

Interstate 64

203mm	weigh sta both lanes
200	I-295, N to Washington, S to Rocky Mount, to US 60, no facilities
197b a	VA 156, Airport Dr, to Highland Springs, **N...gas:** BP/diesel, Citgo/7-11, Shell/diesel, **food:** Bojangles, Domino's, Hardee's, Pizza Hut, Subway, **other:** Advance Parts, CVS Drug, Winn-Dixie, **S...gas:** BP, EC/diesel, Shell/diesel, **food:** Arby's, Aunt Sarah's, Burger King, Waffle House, **lodging:** Comfort Inn, Courtyard, Day's Inn, DoubleTree, Econolodge, Hampton Inn, Hilton/rest., Microtel, Motel 6, Super 8, Wingate Inn, **other:** to airport
195	Laburnum Ave, **N...gas:** Chevron/repair, Shell, **S...gas:** Applebee's, **food:** Subway, Taco Bell, **other:** Ukrop's Foods, **3/4 mi S...gas:** BP/24hr, Exxon, 7-11, **food:** Aunt Sarah's, Bojangles, Burger King, Capt D's, China King, DQ, Hardee's, KFC, McDonald's, Papa John's, Wendy's, Western Sizzlin, **lodging:** Airport Inn, Hampton Inn, Holiday Inn, Sheraton/rest., Super 8, Wyndham Garden, **other:** CVS Drug, $General, $Tree, Firestone/auto, Ford, Hannaford Foods, Radio Shack, Rite Aid, Trak Auto
193b a	VA 33, Nine Mile Rd, **N...gas:** BP, Exxon/Subway, **food:** Burger King, McDonald's, **S...HOSPITAL**
192	US 360, to Mechanicsville, **N...gas:** Chevron, Citgo/diesel, **food:** McDonald's, **S...gas:** BP, Citgo, **food:** Church's, Hook's Rest.
190	I-95 S, to Petersburg, 5th St, **N...other:** Richmond Nat Bfd Park, **S...lodging:** Marriott, **other:** st capitol, coliseum. **I-64 W and I-95 N run together. See Virginia Interstate 95, exits 76-78.**
187	I-95 N(exits left from eb), to Washington. I-64 E and I-95 S run together., no facilities
186	I-195, to Powhite Pkwy, Richmond, no facilities
185b a	US 33, Staples Mill Rd, Dickens Rd, no facilities
183	US 250, Broad St, Glenside Dr, **N...gas:** Chevron/DQ, **food:** Bob Evans, **lodging:** Best Western, Comfort Inn, Embassy Suites, **other:** K-Mart, same as 181, **S...other:** HOSPITAL, to U of Richmond
181	Parham Rd, **N on Broad...gas:** BP/24hr, Citgo, Crown/diesel, Exxon, Shell, **food:** Aunt Sarah's, Bennigan's, Blue Marlin Seafood, Bojangles, Burger King, Casa Grande Mexican, Famous Dave's BBQ, Friendly's, Fuddruckers, Hardee's, Hooters, KFC, LoneStar Steaks, LJ Silver, Olive Garden, OutBack Steaks, Piccadilly's, Red Lobster, Shoney's, Steak&Ale, Taco Bell, TGIFriday, Waffle House, Wendy's, **lodging:** Fairfield Inn, Quality Inn, Suburban Lodge, Super 8, **other:** HOSPITAL, BooksAMillion, CVS Drug, Ford/Lincoln/Mercury, Honda/Mitsubishi, Hyundai/Subaru, Infiniti, Mazda/BMW, Mercedes, Nissan, PepBoys, Staples, Toyota, Ukrop's Foods, transmissions, **1 mi S...gas:** BP, Exxon, **food:** McDonald's, Topeka Steaks, **lodging:** Ramada Inn
180	Gaskins Rd, **N...gas:** BP/24hr, Shell/diesel, **food:** O'Charley's, **lodging:** Courtyard, Holiday Inn Express, Residence Inn, Studio+, **N on Broad...food:** Applebee's, Arby's, Blackeyed Pea, Boston Mkt, Burger King, Golden Corral, IHOP, KFC, McDonald's, Peking Chinese, Rockola Café, Ruby Tuesday's, Ryan's, Subway, Taco Bell, Tripp's Rest., Wendy's, Zorba's Greek/Italian, **other:** Borders Books, Cadillac, Chrysler/Jeep, Circuit City, Costco, Drug Emporium, Evans Foods, Food Lion, Fresh Fields Foods, Goodyear/auto, Hannaford Foods, Lowe's Whse, Sam's Club, VW, mall
178b a	US 250, Short Pump, **N...gas:** BP/diesel, Citgo, Exxon/diesel, Shell/diesel, **food:** Leonardo's Pizza, Starbucks, Thai Garden Rest., **lodging:** AmeriSuites, Comfort Suites, Hampton Inn, Hilton Garden, Homestead Village, Homewood Suites, **other:** CompUSA, Firestone/auto, OfficeMax, **1 mi S...gas:** BP, Citgo/7-11, Crown, **food:** Burger King, Capt D's, Domino's, McDonald's, Taco Bell, TGIFriday, Wendy's, **lodging:** Candlewood Suites, **other:** Barnes&Noble, Best Buy, CarQuest, Goodyear/auto, Home Depot, Kohl's, Lowe's Whse, Target, Ukrop's Foods, Wal-Mart SuperCtr/24hr
177	I-295, to I-95 N to Washington, to Norfolk, VA Beach, Williamsburg, no facilities
175	VA 288, no facilities
173	VA 623, to Rockville, Manakin, **N...gas:** Citgo(2mi), **S...gas:** BP/DQ/diesel, Exxon/diesel(1mi), Shell/diesel, **food:** BBQ, **lodging:** Alley's Motel(1mi), **other:** $General, Food Lion
169mm	**rest area both lanes, full(handicapped)facilities, vending, phone, picnic tables, litter barrels, pet-walk**
167	VA 617, to Goochland, Oilville, **N...gas:** Exxon, **S...gas:** BP/Bullets/diesel/24hr
159	US 522, to Goochland, Gum Spring, **N...gas:** Exxon/diesel/mart, **S...gas:** BP(2mi), Citgo, **food:** DQ
152	VA 629, Hadensville, **S...other:** Royal VA Golf/rest.
148	VA 605, Shannon Hill, no facilities
143	VA 208, to Louisa, Ferncliff, **7 mi N...other:** Small Country Camping, **S...gas:** Citgo/diesel, Exxon/diesel
136	US 15, to Gordonsville, Zion Crossroads, **S...gas:** BP/McDonald's/diesel/24hr, Citgo/Blimpie/diesel, Exxon/Burger King/diesel, Shell/diesel, **lodging:** Crescent Inn/rest., Zion Roads Motel
129	VA 616, Keswick, Boyd Tavern, **N...lodging:** Keswick Hotel, **S...gas:** BP(1mi)
124	US 250, to Shadwell, **2 mi N...gas:** Amoco, Liberty, Shell, **food:** Aunt Sarah's, Burger King, McDonald's, Ponderosa, Taco Bell, Wendy's, **lodging:** Town&Country Motel, White House Motel, **other:** HOSPITAL, **S...lodging:** Ramada Inn
123mm	Rivanna River

495

Interstate 64

E ↑ ↓ **W**

Charlottesville (vertical text)

121 VA 20, to Charlottesville, Scottsville, **N...gas:** Amoco/diesel, **food:** Blimpie, **S...gas:** Exxon, **other:** KOA(9mi), to Monticello

120 VA 631, 5th St, to Charlottesville, **N...gas:** Exxon/diesel, Shell, **food:** Burger King, Domino's, Hardee's, Jade Garden, McDonald's, Pizza Hut/Taco Bell, Waffle House, Wendy's, **lodging:** Holiday Inn, Omni Hotel(2mi), Sleep Inn, **other:** CVS Drug, Family$, Food Lion, laundry

118b a US 29, to Lynchburg, Charlottesville, **1-4 mi N... gas:** Amoco, Citgo/diesel, Exxon, Shell, **food:** Blimpie, Hardee's, Shoney's, Subway, **lodging:** Best Western, Boar's Head Inn, Budget Inn, English Inn, Econolodge, **other:** HOSPITAL, UVA, **S...gas:** Exxon/diesel

114 VA 637, to Ivy, no facilities

113mm **rest area wb, full(handicapped)facilities, phone, vending, picnic tables, litter barrels, petwalk**

111mm Mechum River

108mm Stockton Creek

107 US 250, Crozet, **1 mi N...gas:** Exxon, **1 mi S...other:** Misty Mtn Camping

105mm **rest area eb, full(handicapped)facilities, phone, vending, picnic tables, litter barrels, petwalk**

104mm scenic area eb, litter barrels, no truck or buses

100mm scenic area eb, litter barrels, hist marker, no trucks or buses

99 US 250, to Waynesboro, Afton, **N...lodging:** Colony Motel, **other:** to Shenandoah NP, Skyline Drive, ski area, to Blue Ridge Pkwy, **S...lodging:** Afton Inn

96 VA 622, to Lyndhurst, Waynesboro, **3 mi N...gas:** Shell, Quality Inn

95mm South River

94 US 340, to Stuarts Draft, Waynesboro, **N...gas:** Citgo/7-11/diesel, Exxon/diesel, **food:** Arby's, Burger King, KFC, Shoney's, S River Grill, Taco Bell(1mi), Wendy's, Western Sizzlin, **lodging:** Best Western, Day's Inn, Deluxe Motel(2mi), Holiday Inn Express, Skyline Motel(2mi), Super 8, **other:** HOSPITAL, Waynesboro N 340 Camping(9mi), **S...gas:** Shell/diesel, **other:** Waynesboro Outlet Village, museum

91 Va 608, to Stuarts Draft, Fishersville, **N...gas:** Shell/diesel, **lodging:** Hampton Inn, **other:** HOSPITAL, **S... gas:** Exxon/McDonald's, **other:** Shenadoah Acres Camping(8mi), **other:** Walnut Hills Camping(9mi)

89mm Christians Creek

87 I-81, N to Harrisonburg, S to Roanoke, no facilities **I-64 and I-81 run together 20 miles. Exits 195-220.**

220 VA 262, to US 11, Staunton, **1 mi W...gas:** Citgo, Etna, Exxon, Shell, **food:** Applebee's, Arby's, Burger King, Country Cookin', Hardee's, KFC, McDonald's, Red Lobster, Taco Bell, **lodging:** Budget Inn, Hampton Inn, **other:** Advance Parts, Harley-Davidson, Honda, JC Penney, Pontiac/Buick, Rule RV Ctr

217 VA 654, to Mint Spring, Stuarts Draft, **E...gas:** BP/Subway/diesel, Exxon/diesel, **lodging:** Day's Inn, Shenandoah Acres Resort(8mi), **W...gas:** Citgo/diesel/24hr, Crown, Liberty/gas, **lodging:** Red Carpet Inn, Walnut Hill Camping(4mi)

Lexington (vertical text)

213b a US 11, US 340, Greenville, **E...gas:** BP/Subway, Pilot/Arby's/diesel/24hr/@, Shell, **lodging:** Budget Host

205 VA 606, Raphine, **E...gas:** Exxon/Burger King, Fuel City/diesel, Sunoco, Whites/diesel/24hr/motel/@, **W...gas:** Wilco/Wendy's/diesel/24hr/@, **lodging:** Day's Inn/rest.

200 VA 710, Fairfield, **E...gas:** Amoco/diesel/24hr, **food:** McDonald's, **W...gas:** Citgo/Sunshine/diesel/rest./@, Exxon/Subway/diesel, Shell/diesel

199mm **rest area sb, full(handicapped)facilities, phone, vending, picnic tables, litter barrels, petwalk**

195 US 11, Lee Highway, **E...lodging:** Maple Hall Lodging/dining, **W...gas:** Citgo/diesel/24hr, Shell/diesel, **food:** Aunt Sarah's, **lodging:** Howard Johnson/rest., Ramada Inn, Red Oak Inn, **other:** Lee-Hi Camping

56 I-81, S to Roanoke, N to Harrisonburg, no facilities

55 US 11, to VA 39, Lexington, info, **N...gas:** Exxon/diesel, **food:** Burger King, Ruby Tuesday, Waffle House, **lodging:** Best Western, Country Inn Suites, Super 8, Wingate Inn, **other:** HOSPITAL(3mi), $Tree, Radio Shack, Wal-Mart SuperCtr/24hr, Lee-Hi Camping(3mi), VA Horse Ctr, **S...gas:** Citgo/Subway/diesel, **food:** Redwood Rest., **lodging:** Comfort Inn, Econolodge, Holiday Inn Express, **other:** to Wash&Lee U, VMI

50 US 60, VA 623, to Lexington, **3 mi S...lodging:** Day's Inn

43 VA 780, to Goshen, no facilities

35 VA 269, VA 850, Longdale Furnace, **S...lodging:** Longdale Inn, **2 mi S...lodging:** North Mtn Motel

33mm truck rest area eb

29 VA 269, VA 850, **S...gas:** Exxon/diesel/rest.

27 US 60 W, US 220 S, VA 629, Clifton Forge, **N...other:** to Douthat SP, Alleghany Highlands Arts/crafts, Buckhorne Camping(2mi), **S...gas:** Citgo/diesel, Exxon, **lodging:** The Park Motel

24 US 60, US 220, Clifton Forge, **1 mi S...gas:** Shell/diesel, **food:** DQ, Hardee's, Taco Bell

21 to VA 696, Low Moor, **S...HOSPITAL**

Covington (vertical text)

16 US 60 W, US 220 N, to Hot Springs, Covington, **N... gas:** Amoco, Etna, Exxon/Burger King/24hr, Shell, **food:** Western Sizzlin, **lodging:** Best Value Inn, Best Western, Holiday Inn Express, **other:** Buick/Pontiac/GMC, to ski area, **S...food:** McDonald's, **lodging:** Comfort Inn, **other:** $General, K-Mart, Radio Shack

14 VA 154, to Hot Springs, Covington, **N...gas:** Exxon/Arby's, Sunoco, **food:** Great Wall Chinese, Hardee's, KFC, Little Caesar's, Subway, Wendy's, **lodging:** Budget Motel, Highland Motel, Townhouse Motel, **other:** Advance Parts, AutoZone, CVS Drug, Family$, Food Lion, Kroger, **S...food:** China House, Mama Pizza, **other:** $Tree, GNC, Wal-Mart SuperCtr/24hr

10 US 60 E, VA 159 S, Callaghan, **S...gas:** Marathon/diesel/LP

7 VA 661, no facilities

2.5mm **Welcome Ctr eb, full(handicapped)facilities, phone, picnic tables, litter barrels, petwalk**

1 Jerry's Run Trail, **N...to Allegheny Trail**

0mm Virginia/West Virginia state line

Interstate 66

Exit #	Services
77mm	Independence Ave, to Lincoln Mem. I-66 begins/ends in Washington, DC.
76mm	Potomac River, T Roosevelt Memorial Bridge
75	US 50 W(from eb), to Arlington Blvd, G Wash Pkwy, I-395, US 1, **S**...Iwo Jima Mon
73	US 29, Lee Hwy, Key Bridge, to Rosslyn, **N...lodging:** Marriott, **S...lodging:** Best Western, Holiday Inn
72	to US 29, Lee Hwy, Spout Run Pkwy(from eb, no EZ return), **N...gas:** Shell, **lodging:** Virginia Inn, **S... food:** Chick's Cafe, **other:** CVS Drug, Eckerd/24hr, Starbucks, Giant Foods
71	VA 120, Glebe Rd(no EZ return from wb), **N**...HOSPITAL, **S...gas:** Circle K, Mobil, **food:** Blackeyed Pea, **lodging:** Comfort Inn, Holiday Inn
69	US 29, Sycamore St, Falls Church, **N...gas:** Exxon, **S...lodging:** Econolodge
68	Westmoreland St(from eb), same as 69
67	to I-495 N(from wb), to Baltimore, Dulles Airport
66	VA 7, Leesburg Pike, to Tysons Corner, Falls Church, **N...gas:** Exxon, **food:** China King, Jerry's Subs/Pizza, Starbucks, TCBY, **other:** Whole Foods Mkt, **S...gas:** Citgo, **food:** LJ Silver, McDonald's
64b a	I-495 S, to Richmond, no facilities
62	VA 243, Nutley St, to Vienna, **S...gas:** Exxon, **other:** CVS Drug, **1 mi S on Lee Hwy...gas:** Chevron, Citgo, Shell, Sunoco/diesel, **food:** Applebee's, IHOP/24hr, LoneStar Steaks, McDonald's, Subway, TCBY, **lodging:** Econolodge, **other:** Harley-Davidson, Jeep, Radio Shack, Safeway, Saturn, Kia
60	VA 123, to Fairfax, **S...gas:** Exxon, Shell/24hr, Sunoco, **food:** Denny's, Fuddrucker's, Hooters, Indian Cuisine, KFC, Outback Steaks, Red Lobster, 29 Diner, **lodging:** Best Western, Welsley, **other:** MEDICAL CARE, Buick/Isuzu, Chevrolet, Chrysler/Dodge, Ford/Lincoln/ Mercury, Honda, Hyundai, Mazda, Rite Aid, Toyota, to George Mason U
57a b	US 50, to Dulles Airport, **N...food:** Bennigans, Subway, **lodging:** Extended Stay America, Holiday Inn, **other:** MEDICAL CARE, Hecht's, JC Penney, Lord&Taylor, Macy's, Sears/auto, mall, **S...gas:** BP, Shell/diesel, **food:** Burger King, Ruby Tuesday, Wendy's, **lodging:** Candlewood Suites, Comfort Inn/rest., Courtyard, Hampton Inn, **other:** Borders Books, Circuit City, Ford, Giant Foods, Honda, VW
56mm	weigh sta both lanes
55	Fairfax Co Pkwy, to US 29, **N**...4 Lakes Mall, **gas:** Exxon, Mobil, **food:** Applebee's, Blue Iguana Café, Burger King, Cooker Rest., Don Pablo, Eatery Rest., FoodCourt, Fresh Fare Rest., Olive Garden, Pizza Hut, Red Robin, TCBY, TGIFriday, Tony's Pizza, Wendy's, **lodging:** Hyatt Hotel, **other:** HOSPITAL, Barnes&Noble, Best Buy, BJ's Whse, CompUSA, Food Lion, Galyan's, Kohl's, Michael's, Radio Shack, Target, Wal-Mart
53b a	VA 28, to Centreville, Dulles Airport, Manassas Museum, **S...gas:** Mobil/diesel, **food:** Chesapeake Bay Seafood, Jake's Rest., LoneStar Steaks, McDonald's, **lodging:** SpringHill Suites, **other:** Drug Emporium, Giant Foods, Jo-Ann Fabrics, Peoples Drug, same as 52
52	US 29, to Bull Run Park, Centreville, **N...gas:** Mobil, **other:** Goodyear/auto, **S...gas:** Exxon, Mobil/diesel, 7-11, **food:** BBQ, Carrabba's, Copeland's Café, Domino's, Hunter Mill Deli, LoneStar Steaks, McDonald's, Quizno's, Ruby Tuesday, Wendy's, **other:** SpringHill Suites, **other:** CVS Drug, Jo-Ann Fabrics, Radio Shack, Shoppers Foods, Tire Express, same as 53
49mm	**rest area both lanes, full(facilities)facilities, phone, picnic tables, litter barrels, petwalk**
47b a	VA 234, to Manassas, **N...gas:** Shell/diesel, **food:** Chicago Pizza, Cracker Barrel, Golden Corral, Uno Pizzaria, Wendy's, **lodging:** Country Inn Suites, Courtyard, Fairfield Inn, Holiday Inn, **other:** Borders, Kohl's, Old Navy, Manassas Nat Bfd, **S...gas:** BP, Citgo/7-11, Exxon, RaceTrac/diesel/24hr, Shell/repair, Sunoco/ 24hr, **food:** American Steak/buffet, Anita's Mexican, Arby's, Bertucci's Pizza, Blimpie, Bob Evans, Boston Mkt, Burger King, Checker's, Chelsea's Rest., Chili's, Chipotle Mexican, Damon's, Denny's, Domino's, Don Pablo's, Hooters, KFC, Little Caesar's, Logan's Roadhouse, McDonald's, Old Country Buffet, Olive Garden, Pizza Hut, Red Lobster, Ruby Tuesday, Schlotsky's, Shoney's, Starbucks, Subway, Taco Bell, TGIFriday, Wendy's, Wok'n Roll, Zipani Bread Café, **lodging:** Best Western, Comfort Suites, Day's Inn, Hampton Inn, Red Roof Inn, Super 8, **other:** MEDICAL CARE, Aamco, Barnes&Noble, Best Buy, Camping World RV Service/ supples, Circuit City, Costco/gas, CVS Drug, Chevrolet, Food Lion, Giant Foods, GMC/Pontiac, Hecht's, Home Depot, Honda, JC Penney, K-Mart, Lowe's Whse, Marshall's, Merchant Auto Ctr, NTB, Office Depot, PepBoys, Reines RV Ctr, Saturn, Sears/auto, Shoppers Club, Staples, Super Fresh Foods, U-Haul, Upton's, Wal-Mart
44	VA 234, Manassas, airport
43b a	US 29, to Warrenton, Gainesville, **S...gas:** Citgo/7-11, Mobil, RaceTrac, Shell/diesel/24hr, **food:** Burger King, Joe's Italian/pizza, KFC/Pizza Hut/Taco Bell, McDonald's, Steakmaster's Grill, Subway, Wendy's, **other:** Giant Foods/drug, Hillwood Camping, Lowe's Whse, Target/foods

VIRGINIA

Interstate 66

E

W

40   US 15, Haymarket, **N...other:** Greenville Farm Camping, **S...gas:** Mobil/diesel/24hr, Sheetz/diesel/24hr, **food:** McDonald's, Subway

31   VA 245, to Old Tavern, **1 mi N...gas:** BP/diesel

28   US 17 S, Marshall, **N...gas:** BP/McDonald's/diesel, **food:** Foster's Grille, Great Wall Chinese, Subway, **other:** HOSPITAL, FoodLion, Radio Shack

27   VA 55 E, VA 647, Marshall, **1 mi N...gas:** Chevron/diesel/LP, Exxon/diesel, **food:** Marshall Diner

23   US 17 N, VA 55, Delaplane(no eb re-entry), no facilities

20mm   Goose Creek

18   VA 688, Markham, no facilities

13   VA 79, to VA 55, Linden, Front Royal, **S...gas:** Exxon/diesel/24hr, Mobil/24hr, **food:** Applehouse Rest., **4-5 mi S...food:** Burger King, KFC, **lodging:** Center City Motel, Hampton Inn, Quality Inn, Pioneer Motel, Super 8, **other:** Goonie Creek Camping(10mi), KOA(seasonal), to Shenandoah NP, Skyline Drive, ski area

11mm   Manassas Run

7mm   Shenandoah River

6   US 340, US 522, to Winchester, Front Royal, **N...gas:** Quarle's/Bullet's/diesel, **other:** Ford, **S...gas:** Exxon/Dunkin Doughnuts, Shell, **food:** McDonald's, **lodging:** Hampton Inn, **other:** HOSPITAL, **1-3 mi S...gas:** East Coast, Shell, **food:** Arby's, Hardee's, Pizza Hut, Tastee Freez Rest., Wendy's, **lodging:** Bluemont Motel, Blue Ridge Motel, Budget Inn, Cool Harbor, Front Royal Motel, Relax Inn, Shenandoah Motel, Super 8, Twin Rivers Motel, **other:** Gooney Creek Camping(7mi), KOA(6mi), Southfork Camping(2mi)

1b a   I-81, N to Winchester, S to Roanoke

0mm   I-66 begins/ends on I-81, exit 300.

Interstate 77

N

S

Exit #	Services

67mm   Virginia/West Virginia state line, East River Mtn

66   VA 598, to East River Mtn, no facilities

64   US 52, VA 61, to Rocky Gap, no facilities

62   VA 606, to South Gap, no facilities

61.5mm   **Welcome Ctr sb, full(handicapped)facilities, info, phone, vending, picnic tables, litter barrels, petwalk**

60mm   **rest area nb, full(handicapped)facilities, phone, vending, picnic tables, litter barrels, petwalk**

58   US 52, to Bastian, **E...gas:** BP/diesel, **W...gas:** Citgo/diesel, Exxon/diesel

---

56mm   runaway ramp nb

52   US 52, VA 42, Bland, **E...gas:** Citgo, **food:** Bland Square Rest., **W...gas:** Shell/DQ/diesel, **food:** Log Cabin Rest., **lodging:** Big Walker Motel

51.5mm   weigh sta both lanes

48mm   Big Walker Mtn

47   VA 717, **6 mi W...other:** to Deer Trail Park/NF Camping

41   VA 610, Peppers Ferry, Wytheville, **E...food:** Sagebrush Steaks, **lodging:** Best Western, Sleep Inn, Super 8, **W...gas:** Shell/diesel/24hr, TA/BP/Subway/Taco Bell/diesel/24hr/@, **food:** Country Kitchen, Wendy's, **lodging:** Hampton Inn, Ramada/rest.

40   I-81 S, to Bristol, US 52 N, no facilities

I-77 and I-81 run together 9 mi. See Virginia Interstate 81, exits 73-80.

32   I-81 N, to Roanoke, no facilities

26mm   New River

24   VA 69, to Poplar Camp, **E...gas:** Pure/gas, **other:** to Shot Tower SP, New River Trail Info Ctr, **W...gas:** Citgo/diesel

19   VA 620, airport

14   US 58, US 221, to Hillsville, Galax, **E...gas:** Citgo/Subway, **food:** Burger King(2mi), Peking Palace, Pizza Hut(2mi), **lodging:** Nob Hill Motel, Red Carpet Inn, **other:** HOSPITAL, **W...gas:** BP/24hr, Cockerham's Trkstp/diesel/24hr/@, Exxon/DQ/diesel, Marathon, Shell, **food:** Countryside Rest., McDonald's, Pizza Inn/TCBY, Shoney's, Wendy's, **lodging:** Best Western, Comfort Inn, Fairfield Inn, Hampton Inn, Holiday Inn Express, Super 8, **other:** Carrollwood Camping(1mi), Ford/Mercury

8   VA 148, VA 775, to Fancy Gap, **E...gas:** Chevron(2mi), Citgo/diesel, **lodging:** Lakeview Motel/rest., Mountaintop Motel/rest., **other:** Fox Trail Camping, Utt's Camping, to Blue Ridge Pkwy, **W...gas:** BP, Exxon/diesel, **food:** On the Way Rest., **lodging:** Countryview Inn, Day's Inn

6.5mm   runaway truck ramp sb

4.5mm   runaway truck ramp sb

3mm   runaway truck ramp sb

1   VA 620, no facilities

.5mm   **Welcome Ctr nb, full(handicapped)facilities, info, phone, picnic tables, litter barrels, petwalk**

0mm   Virginia/North Carolina state line

Wytheville

Interstate 81

N
↑
↓
S

Exit #	Services
324mm	Virginia/West Virginia state line
323	VA 669, to US 11, Whitehall, **E...gas:** Exxon, **W...gas:** Flying J/Country Mkt/diesel/LP/24hr/@
321	VA 672, Clearbrook, **E...gas:** Mobil/diesel, **food:** Olde Stone Rest.
320mm	**Welcome Ctr sb, full(handicapped)facilities, phone, vending, picnic tables, litter barrels, pet-walk**
317	US 11, Stephenson, **W...gas:** Exxon/diesel, Liberty/diesel, Sheez/diesel, **food:** Burger King, Denny's, McDonald's, Pizza Hut/Taco Bell, Tastee Freez, Venice Italian, **lodging:** Comfort Inn, Econolodge, **other:** HOSPITAL, Candy Hill Camping(4mi)
315	VA 7, Winchester, **E...gas:** Exxon, Sheetz/24hr, **other:** Dodge/Volvo, mall, **W...gas:** Chevron/diesel, Liberty/diesel, Shell/diesel, **food:** Arby's, Capt D's, Hardee's, KFC, Little Caesar's, LJ Silver, McDonald's, Pizza Hut, Subway, Wendy's, **lodging:** Hampton Inn, Shoney's Inn/rest., **other:** Pharmor Drug
314mm	Abrams Creek
313	US 17/50/522, Winchester, **E...gas:** BP/diesel, Exxon, Mobil/diesel, Shell/diesel, **food:** Asia Garden, Chason's Buffet, Cracker Barrel, Golden Corral, Hoss' Steaks, IHOP, Texas Roadhouse, Waffle House, **lodging:** Comfort Inn, Holiday Inn, Red Roof Inn, Super 8, Travelodge, **other:** Costco, Food Lion, Ford/Lincoln/Mercury/Nissan, Harley-Davidson, Jo-Ann Fabrics, Target, **W...gas:** Sheetz/24hr, **food:** Bob Evans, Chick-fil-A, Chili's, China Jade, CiCi's, El Ranchero, KFC, McDonald's, Pargo's, Perkins, Pizza Hut/Taco Bell, Ruby Tuesday, Sam's Hotdogs, Subway, Wendy's, **lodging:** Baymont Inn, Best Western, Hampton Inn, Wingate Inn, **other:** BooksAMillion, Circuit City, $Tree, Home Depot, JC Penney, K-Mart, Kohl's, Kroger, Lowe's Whse, Martin Foods, OfficeMax, PepBoys, Sears/auto, Staples, Trak Parts, Target, Wal-Mart SuperCtr/24hr, mall, to Shenandoah U
310	VA 37, to US 11, **1 mi W...lodging:** Best Value Inn, Day's Inn, Echo Village Motel, Relax Inn, Royal Inn, **other:** HOSPITAL, Candy Hill Camping(6mi)
307	VA 277, Stephens City, **E...gas:** Citgo/7-11, Shell/diesel, **food:** Burger King, KFC/Taco Bell, McDonald's, Roma Italian, Subway, Waffle House, Wendy's, Western Steer, **lodging:** Comfort Inn, Holiday Inn Express, **other:** MEDICAL CARE, White Oak Camping, **W...**Exxon, Sheetz/24hr, Redwood Budget Inn
304mm	weigh sta both lanes
302	VA 627, Middletown, **E...gas:** Exxon/diesel, **W...gas:** Citgo/7-11, Liberty/diesel, **food:** Godfather's, **lodging:** Super 8, Wayside Inn/rest., **other:** to Wayside Theatre

Exit #	Services
300	I-66 E, to Washington, to Shenandoah NP, Skyline Dr
298	US 11, Strasburg, **E...gas:** BP/diesel, Exxon/diesel/LP, **food:** Burger King, McDonald's, **lodging:** Hotel Strasburg/rest., **other:** Battle of Cedar Creek Camping, **W...other:** to Belle Grove Plantation
296	VA 55, Strasburg, **E...other:** to Hupp's Hill Bfd Museum
291	VA 651, Toms Brook, **E...lodging:** Budget Inn, **W...gas:** Love's/Arby's/diesel/24hr/@, Wilco/Hess/DQ/diesel/24hr/@, **other:** truckwash
283	VA 42, Woodstock, **E...gas:** Chevron/7-11, Sheetz, Shell, **food:** Arby's, Hardee's, KFC, McDonald's, Pizza Hut, Ponderosa, Taco Bell, Wendy's, **lodging:** Budget Host, Comfort Inn, Ramada/rest., **other:** HOSPITAL, to Massanutten Military Academy, **W...gas:** Exxon/diesel/24hr, Sunoco, **food:** China Wok, Subway, **other:** $Tree, Wal-Mart SuperCtr/24hr
279	VA 185, VA 675, Edinburg, **E...gas:** BP/diesel, Exxon/diesel, Shell/diesel/24hr, **food:** Edinburg Mill Rest., Subway, **other:** Creek Side Camping(2mi)
277	VA 614, Bowmans Crossing, no facilities
273	VA 292, VA 703, Mt Jackson, **E...gas:** Citgo/7-11, Exxon/diesel, Liberty/Blimpie/diesel, Sheetz/Wendy's/diesel/24hr, **food:** Burger King, Denny's, Godfather's, **lodging:** Best Western/rest., **other:** $General, Food Lion/24hr, Radio Shack, USPO
269	VA 730, to Shenandoah Caverns, **E...gas:** Chevron/diesel
269mm	N Fork Shenandoah River
264	US 211, New Market, **E...gas:** BP/Blimpie/diesel, Chevron/diesel, Exxon/diesel, Shell/diesel, **food:** Burger King, McDonald's, Pizza Hut, Southern Kitchen, Taco Bell, **lodging:** Budget Inn, Quality Inn, Shenvalee Motel/rest., **other:** Rancho Camping, to Shenandoah NP, Skyline Dr, **W...gas:** Citgo/7-11, **lodging:** Day's Inn, **other:** to New Market Bfd
262mm	**rest area both lanes, full(handicapped)facilities, phone, vending, picnic tables, litter barrels, pet-walk**
257	US 11, VA 259, to Broadway, **3-5 mi E...other:** KOA, Endless Caverns Camping
251	US 11, Harrisonburg, **W...gas:** Exxon/diesel, **lodging:** Economy Inn

VIRGINIA
Interstate 81

N ↕ S

Harrisonburg

247 US 33, Harrisonburg, **E...gas:** BP/Blimpie/diesel, Royal, Shell, **food:** Applebee's, Capt D's, Chili's, Ci-Ci's, El Charro Mexican, Golden Corral, Jess' Lunch, LJ Silver, Outback Steaks, Pargo's, Ponderosa, Red Lobster, Ruby Tuesday, Shoney's, Taco Bell, TCBY, Texas Steaks, Waffle House, Wendy's, **lodging:** Comfort Inn, Courtyard, Econolodge, Guesthouse Inn, Hampton Inn, Motel 6, Sheraton/rest., Sleep Inn, **other:** Barnes&Noble, BooksAMillion, Circuit City, Food Lion, Home Depot, Kroger, K-Mart, Lowe's Whse, Nissan, OfficeMax, PepBoys, Staples, Wal-Mart SuperCtr/24hr, to Shenandoah NP, Skyline Dr, mall, **W...gas:** Chevron/diesel, Exxon/diesel, Sheetz, **food:** Arby's, Golden China, Hardee's, KFC, Kyoto, McDonald's, Mr Gatti's, Pizza Hut, Sam's Hotdogs, Subway, **lodging:** Marvilla Motel, **other:** HOSPITAL, Advance Parts, CVS Drug, Radio Shack

245 VA 659, Port Republic Rd, **E...gas:** Exxon/Subway/diesel, Liberty/Blimpie/diesel, Shell, **food:** DQ, **lodging:** J Day's Inn, Howard Johnson, **W...other:** HOSPITAL, to James Madison U

243 US 11, to Harrisonburg, **W...gas:** BP/diesel, Citgo/7-11, Exxon/diesel, Harrisonburg Trkstp/diesel, Liberty/diesel, **food:** Burger King, Cracker Barrel, McDonald's, Taco Bell, Waffle House, **lodging:** Holiday Inn Express, Ramada Inn, Red Carpet Inn, Rockingham Motel, Super 8, **other:** Advance Parts, BMW, Chrysler, Ford/Lincoln/Mercury, Hyundai, Kia, Subaru, Toyota

240 VA 257, VA 682, Mount Crawford, **1-3 mi W...gas:** Exxon/diesel, Liberty/gas, **food:** Burger King, **lodging:** Village Inn, **other:** Natural Chimneys Camping

235 VA 256, Weyers Cave, **E...gas:** Mobil/diesel, **W...gas:** BP/Subway/diesel, Exxon/diesel, **lodging:** Augusta Motel, **other:** to Grand Caverns

232mm **rest area both lanes, full(handicapped)facilities, phone, vending, picnic tables, litter barrels, petwalk**

227 VA 612, Verona, **E...gas:** BP/Subway/diesel, **lodging:** Waffle Inn, **other:** North 340 Camping(11mi), **W...gas:** Citgo/diesel, Exxon, Plaza/diesel, **food:** Arby's, Burger King, Hardee's, KFC, McDonald's, Wendy's, **lodging:** Ramada Ltd, **other:** CVS Drug, Food Lion, KOA(3mi)

225 VA 275, Woodrow Wilson Pkwy, **E...lodging:** Quality Inn/rest., **W...lodging:** Day's Inn, Holiday Inn/rest.

222 US 250, Staunton, **E...gas:** Citgo, Exxon/McDonald's/24hr, Shell/diesel, **food:** Cracker Barrel, Rowe's Rest., Shoney's, Texas Steaks, Wendy's, **lodging:** Best Western, Guesthouse Inn, Sleep Inn, **W...gas:** Sheetz, **food:** Burger King, Ryan's, Shorty's Diner, Waffle House, **lodging:** Comfort Inn, Econolodge, Microtel, Super 8, **other:** AutoZone, Lowe's Whse, TireMart, Toyota, Wal-Mart SuperCtr/24hr, American Frontier Culture Museum

221 I-64 E, to Charlottesville, to Skyline Dr, Shenandoah NP

220 VA 262, to US 11, Staunton, **1 mi W...gas:** Citgo, Etna, Exxon, Shell, **food:** Applebee's, Arby's, Burger King, Country Cookin', Hardee's, KFC, McDonald's, Red Lobster, Taco Bell, **lodging:** Budget Inn, Hampton Inn, **other:** Advance Parts, Harley-Davidson, Honda, JC Penney, Pontiac/Buick, Rule RV Ctr

217 VA 654, to Mint Spring, Stuarts Draft, **E...gas:** BP/Subway/diesel, Exxon/diesel, **lodging:** Day's Inn, Shenandoah Acres Resort(8mi), **W...gas:** Citgo/diesel/24hr, Crown, Liberty/gas, **lodging:** Red Carpet Inn, Walnut Hill Camping(4mi)

213b a US 11, US 340, Greenville, **E...gas:** BP/Subway, Pilot/Arby's/diesel/24hr/@, Shell, **lodging:** Budget Host

205 VA 606, Raphine, **E...gas:** Exxon/Burger King, Fuel City/diesel, Sunoco, Whites/diesel/24hr/motel/@, **W...gas:** Wilco/Wendy's/diesel/24hr/@, **lodging:** Day's Inn/rest.

200 VA 710, Fairfield, **E...gas:** Amoco/diesel/24hr, **food:** McDonald's, **W...gas:** Citgo/Sunshine/diesel/rest./@, Exxon/Subway/diesel, Shell/diesel

199mm **rest area sb, full(handicapped)facilities, phone, vending, picnic tables, litter barrels, petwalk**

195 US 11, Lee Highway, **E...lodging:** Maple Hall Lodging/dining, **W...gas:** Citgo/diesel/24hr, Shell/diesel, **food:** Aunt Sarah's, **lodging:** Howard Johnson/rest., Ramada Inn, Red Oak Inn, **other:** Lee-Hi Camping

191 I-64 W(exits left from nb), US 60, to Charleston

Lexington

188 US 60, to Lexington, Buena Vista, **3-5 mi E...gas:** Exxon, **food:** Country Cookin', Hardee's, KFC, LJ Silver, McDonald's, Pizza Hut, Taco Bell, Wendy's, **lodging:** Budget Inn, Buena Vista Inn, Comfort Inn, Day's Inn, **other:** HOSPITAL, to Glen Maury Park, to Stonewall Jackson Home, Marshall Museum, to Blue Ridge Pkwy, **W...gas:** Exxon/diesel/24hr, **lodging:** Day's Inn, Hampton Inn, **other:** to Washington&Lee U, VMI

180 US 11, Natural Bridge, **E...gas:** Pure/diesel, Shell, **food:** Fancy Hill Diner, **lodging:** Econo Inn, **W...gas:** Shell/diesel, **food:** Pink Cadillac Diner, **lodging:** Budget Inn, **other:** KOA

175 US 11 N, to Glasgow, Natural Bridge, **E...gas:** Exxon, **lodging:** Natural Bridge Hotel/rest., **other:** to James River RA, Jellystone Camping

168 VA 614, US 11, Arcadia, **E...gas:** Shell, **food:** MtnView Rest., **lodging:** Wattstull Inn, **other:** Wonderful Life Camping(6mi), **W...food:** Burger King

167 US 11(from sb), Buchanan

162 US 11, Buchanan, **E...gas:** Exxon/diesel, **other:** to BR Pkwy, **W...gas:** Shell/Subway/24hr

158mm **rest area sb, full(handicapped)facilities, phone, vending, picnic tables, litter barrels, petwalk**

156 VA 640, to US 11, **E...gas:** Exxon/diesel, Shell, **food:** Greenwood Rest.

150 US 11/220, to Fincastle, **E...gas:** Citgo/diesel/24hr, Dodge's/diesel, Exxon, Pilot/Subway/diesel/24hr, TA/BP/diesel/@, **food:** Country Cookin', Cracker Barrel, Hardee's, McDonald's, Shoney's, Taco Bell, Waffle

Interstate 81

N

↕

S

Roanoke

House, Wendy's, **lodging:** Comfort Inn, Day's Inn, Holiday Inn Express, Red Roof Inn, Travelodge, **other:** Berglun RV Ctr, CVS Drug, Winn-Dixie, **W...gas:** BP/diesel, Exxon/diesel/24hr, **food:** Bojangles, Pizza Hut, Teng Fi Chinese, **lodging:** Best Western, Econolodge

149mm weigh sta both lanes

146 VA 115, Cloverdale, **E...gas:** Exxon, Shell/diesel, **food:** Burger King, Chico&Billy's, Hardee's, McDonald's, Subway, Wildflour Café, **lodging:** Budget Motel, Country Inn Suites, Day's Inn/rest., Hampton Inn, Knight's Inn, Roanoker Motel

143 I-581, US 220, to Roanoke, Blue Ridge Pkwy(exits left from sb), **1 mi E...food:** Waffle House, **lodging:** Hampton Inn, Holiday Inn, Ramada Ltd, Super 8, **2-3 mi E on Herschberger...food:** Applebee's, Hardee's, IHOP, Logan's Roadhouse, O'Charley's, Ruby Tuesday, Texas Steaks, TGIFriday, **lodging:** AmeriSuites, Best Western, Clarion, Comfort Inn, Courtyard, Extended Stay America, Howard Johnson, Wyndham, **other:** Sears/auto, Target, Wal-Mart SuperCtr/gas/24hr, mall

141 VA 419, Salem, **1-2 mi E...gas:** BP, Exxon, Shell, **food:** Burger King, Hardee's, Country Cookin' Rest., McDonald's, **lodging:** Baymont Inn, Econolodge, Embassy Inn, Holiday Inn Express, Park Inn, Quality Inn, **other:** HOSPITAL, Chevrolet, **W...gas:** BP/diesel, Citgo

140 VA 311, Salem, **1 mi W...food:** Hanging Rock Grill/golf

137 VA 112, VA 619, Salem, **E...gas:** BP, Crown, Exxon, Sheetz, Shell/diesel, **food:** Applebee's, Arby's, Bojangles, Denny's, Dynasty Buffet, El Rodeo Mexican, Fazoli's, Hardee's, KFC, Mamma Maria Italian, McDonald's, Omelet Shoppe, Shoney's, Taco Bell, **lodging:** Comfort Inn, Econolodge, Super 8, **other:** AutoZone, Food Lion, Snyder's RV, Walgreen, Wal-Mart SuperCtr/24hr, **W...lodging:** Ramada Inn

132 VA 647, to Dixie Caverns, **E...gas:** Citgo, Shell, **lodging:** Budget Host, **other:** Dixie Caverns Camping, st police

129mm rest area nb, full(handicapped)facilities, phone, vending, picnic tables, litter barrels, petwalk

128 US 11, VA 603, Ironto, **E...gas:** Citgo/24hr, **W...gas:** Citgo/Subway/diesel/24hr

118c b a US 11/460, Christiansburg, **E...gas:** Shell/diesel, **food:** Denny's, Cracker Barrel, **lodging:** Day's Inn, Fairfield Inn, Hampton Inn, Holiday Inn Express, Super 8, **other:** Interstate RV Camping, **W...gas:** BP, Crown, Exxon/Subway, RaceWay, Shell/Bojangles, **food:** Country Cookin Rest., McDonald's, Pizza Hut, Shoney's, Waffle House, Wendy's, Western Sizzlin **lodging:** Econolodge, Howard Johnson, **other:** HOSPITAL, Advance Parts, Chevrolet, Chrysler/Dodge, Ford/Toyota, Honda, to VA Tech

Wytheville

114 VA 8, Christiansburg, **W...gas:** Citgo, **food:** Burger King, Hardee's, Macado's Rest., Pizza Inn, **lodging:** Budget Inn

109 VA 177, VA 600, **W...gas:** BP/diesel, Marathon, **lodging:** Comfort Inn, **other:** HOSPITAL

107mm rest area both lanes, full(handicapped)facilities, phone, vending, picnic tables, litter barrels, petwalk

105 VA 232, VA 605, to Radford, **W...lodging:** Executive Inn

101 VA 660, to Claytor Lake SP, **E...lodging:** Claytor Lake Inn, Sleep Inn, **W...gas:** Chevron/diesel/@, Citgo/diesel, **food:** DQ, Omelet Shoppe, Taco Bell

98 VA 100 N, to Dublin, **E...gas:** BP, Exxon/Subway/diesel, **food:** Shoney's, **lodging:** Comfort Inn/rest., Hampton Inn, Holiday Inn Express, **W...gas:** Marathon, Shell/diesel, **food:** Blimpie, Burger King, McDonald's, Waffle House, Wendy's, **lodging:** Super 8, Travel Inn, **other:** HOSPITAL, to Wilderness Rd Museum

94b a VA 99 N, to Pulaski, **E...lodging:** Day's Inn, **W...gas:** Exxon, HOSPITAL

92 VA 658, to Draper, **E...gas:** BP, **other:** to New River Trail SP

89b a US 11 N, VA 100, to Pulaski, no facilities

86 VA 618, Service Rd, **W...gas:** I-81/Citgo/diesel/rest., **lodging:** Gateway Motel

84 VA 619, to Grahams Forge, **W...gas:** Love's/Subway/diesel/24hr/@, Shell/DQ/diesel/24hr, **lodging:** Fox Mtn Inn/rest., Trail Motel

81 I-77 S, to Charlotte, Galax, to Blue Ridge Pkwy. **I-81 S and I-77 N run together 9 mi.**

80 US 52 S, VA 121 N, to Ft Chiswell, **E...gas:** BP/Burger King/diesel, ⚑ Flying J/diesel/rest/24hr/@, **food:** Wendy's, **lodging:** Hampton Inn, Super 8, **other:** Blue Beacon, FSA/famous brands, GS Camping, **W...gas:** Amoco, Citgo/diesel, **food:** McDonald's, **lodging:** Comfort Inn, **other:** Little Valley RV Ctr

77 Service Rd, **E...gas:** Citgo/Subway/diesel/24hr, ⚑ Flying J/diesel/LP/rest./24hr/@, Hess/diesel, **food:** Burger King, **other:** KOA, **W...gas:** Exxon/diesel, Wilco/Hess/Arby's/diesel/24hr, **other:** st police

73 US 11 S, Wytheville, **E...gas:** Citgo, Mobil, Shell/diesel, **food:** Applebee's, Bob Evans, Burger King, Cracker Barrel, Great Wall Buffet, Hardee's, KFC, Pizza Hut, Shenanigan's Steaks, Shoney's, Waffle House, **lodging:** Budget Host, Day's Inn, Holiday Inn, Motel 6, Quality Inn, Red Carpet Inn, Travelodge, **other:** HOSPITAL, Buick

VIRGINIA
Interstate 81

I-81 N and I-77 S run together 9 mi

72   I-77 N, to Bluefield, **1 mi N, I-77 exit 41, E...food:** Sagebrush Steaks, **lodging:** Best Western, Sleep Inn, Super 8, **W...gas:** Shell/diesel/24hr, TA/BP/Subway/Taco Bell/diesel/24hr/@, **food:** Country Kitchen, Wendy's, **lodging:** Hampton Inn, Ramada/rest.

70   US 21/52, Wytheville, **E...gas:** BP/diesel, **food:** Arby's, China Wok, Little Caesar's, McDonald's, Ruby Tuesday, Subway, Wendy's, **other:** HOSPITAL, CVS Drug, $Tree, Food Lion, Lowe's Whse, Wal-Mart SuperCtr/24hr, **W...gas:** Citgo, Etna, Exxon, **food:** DQ, LJ Silver, Pizza Hut, Scrooge's Rest., **lodging:** Comfort Inn, Econolodge, Koala Motel, Travelite Motel

67   US 11(from nb, no re-entry), to Wytheville, no facilities

61mm   **rest area nb, full(handicapped)facilities, phone, vending, picnic tables, litter barrels, petwalk, NO TRUCKS**

60   VA 90, Rural Retreat, **E...gas:** Chevron/diesel, Citgo/Yesterdaze Diner/diesel, **food:** McDonald's, **other:** to Rural Retreat Lake, camping

54   rd 683, to Groseclose, **E...gas:** Exxon/DQ/diesel, Shell/diesel, **lodging:** Relax Inn

53.5mm **rest area sb, full(handicapped)facilities, phone, vending, picnic tables, litter barrels, petwalk**

50   US 11, Atkins, **W...gas:** Citgo/diesel/24hr, **food:** Subs on the Way, **lodging:** Comfort Inn

47   US 11, to Marion, **W...gas:** Amoco, Chevron/diesel/24hr, Exxon/diesel, **food:** Arby's, Burger King, McDonald's, Pizza Hut, **lodging:** Best Western/rest., Econolodge, VA House Inn, **other:** HOSPITAL, K-Mart, Radio Shack, SuperX Drug, to Hungry Mother SP(4mi)

45   VA 16, Marion, **E...food:** AppleTree Rest., **other:** to Grayson Highlands SP, Mt Rogers NRA, **W...gas:** Chevron, **food:** Hardee's, KFC, LJ Silver, Wendy's, **lodging:** Royal Inn

44   US 11, Marion, no facilities

39   US 11, VA 645, Seven Mile Ford, **E...lodging:** Budget Inn/rest., **W...other:** Interstate Camping/groceries

35   VA 107, Chilhowie, **E...gas:** Shell, **lodging:** Knight's Inn, **W...gas:** Chevron, Exxon, Rouse Fuel, **food:** McDonald's, Subway, TasteeFreez, **lodging:** Budget Inn(1mi), Rainbow Autel/rest., **other:** $General, Food City/gas

32   US 11, to Chilhowie, no facilities

29   VA 91, Glade Spring, to Damascus, **E...gas:** Petro/diesel/rest./24hr/@, **food:** Giardino's Italian, Pizza+, Wendy's, **lodging:** Swiss Inn/rest., Travelodge, **W...gas:** Chevron/diesel/24hr, Coastal, Exxon, **other:** CarQuest

26   VA 737, Emory, **W...other:** to Emory&Henry Coll

24   VA 80, Meadowview Rd, **W...**auto repair

22   VA 704, Enterprise Rd, no facilities

Marion (side tab)

Abingdon (side tab)

19   US 11/58, to Abingdon, **E...gas:** Shell/Subway/diesel, **other:** to Mt Rogers NRA, **W...gas:** Chevron/diesel/24hr, Citgo, Exxon/diesel, **food:** Burger King, Cracker Barrel, Harbor House Seafood, Huddle House, Omelet Shoppe, Wendy's, **lodging:** Alpine Motel, Day's Inn, Holiday Inn Express, Quality Inn

17   US 58A, VA 75, Abingdon, **E...gas:** Valero, **food:** Domino's, LJ Silver, **lodging:** Hampton Inn, **other:** Mr Transmission, **W...gas:** Chevron, Citgo/diesel, Exxon, **food:** Arby's, China Wok, Hardee's, KFC, McDonald's, Papa John's, Pizza Hut, Shoney's, Taco Bell, Wendy's, **lodging:** Martha Washington Inn, Super 8, **other:** HOSPITAL, Advance Parts, CVS Drug, $General, Food City, Kroger, K-Mart, Radio Shack

14   US 19, VA 140, Abingdon, **W...gas:** Chevron/diesel/24hr, Exxon, Shell/diesel, **food:** DQ, McDonald's, **lodging:** Budget Inn(3mi), Comfort Inn, **other:** Ford, Riverside Camping(10mi)

13.5mm **TRUCKERS ONLY rest area nb, full(handicapped) facilities, phone, vending, picnic tables, litter barrels**

13   VA 611, to Lee Hwy, **E...other:** Harley-Davidson, **W...gas:** Shell/diesel

10   US 11/19, Lee Hwy, **W...gas:** BP/diesel, Chevron, **lodging:** Beacon Inn, Deluxe Inn, Evergreen Inn, Skyland Inn

7   Old Airport Rd, **E...gas:** Citgo, Shell/diesel, **food:** Bob Evans, Bojangles, Sonic, **lodging:** La Quinta, **W...gas:** BP/diesel, Citgo/Wendy's, Conoco/diesel, **food:** Chop's Rest., Damon's, Fazoli's, Golden Corral, IHOP, Jumbo Buffet, Kobe Japanese, Logan's Roadhouse, O'Charley's, Outback Steaks, Pizza Hut, Ruby Tuesday, Subway, Taco Bell, **lodging:** Holiday Inn, Microtel, Motel 6, **other:** MEDICAL CARE, Advance Parts, Lowe's Whse, Office Depot, Wal-Mart SuperCtr/24hr, Sugar Hollow Camping

5   US 11/19, Lee Hwy, **E...gas:** Citgo, Shell, **food:** Arby's, Burger King, Hardee's, KFC, LJ Silver, McDonald's, Shoney's, Wendy's, **lodging:** Budget Inn, Crest Motel, Siesta Motel, Super 8, **other:** CVS Drug, Family$, Parts+, USPO, **W...gas:** Exxon, **lodging:** Comfort Inn, **other:** Blevins Tire, Buick/Pontiac, Lee Hwy Camping

3   I-381 S, to Bristol, **1 mi E...gas:** Chevron, Citgo/diesel, Conoco, **food:** Applebee's, Pizza Hut, **lodging:** Econolodge

1   US 58/421, Bristol, **1 mi E...gas:** Chevron, Phillips 66, **food:** Burger King, Chick-fil-A, KFC, Krispy Kreme, LJ Silver, McDonald's, Taco Bell, Wendy's, **lodging:** Budget Host, Ramada Inn, **other:** HOSPITAL, CarQuest, CVS Drug, Dodge, Family$, Food Lion, Kroger, Lincoln/Mercury, Sears/auto, Walgreen, Wal-Mart/grill, mall, **W...gas:** Shell(1mi)

0mm   **Virginia/Tennessee state line, Welcome Ctr nb, full(handicapped)facilities, info, phone, vending, picnic tables, litter barrels, petwalk, NO TRUCKS**

Bristol (side tab)

Interstate 85

P e t e r s b u r g

Exit #	Services
69mm	I-85 begins/ends on I-95.
69	US 301, Petersburg, Wythe St, Washington St, **W...lodging:** Regency Inn
68	I-95 S, US 460 E, to Norfolk, Crater Rd, **E...HOSPITAL, 3/4 mi E...gas:** Exxon/diesel, RaceTrac/diesel, Shell, **food:** Hardee's, **lodging:** California Inn, **other:** to Petersburg Nat Bfd
65	Squirrel Level Rd, **E...other:** to Richard Bland Coll, **W...gas:** BP/diesel
63b a	US 1, to Petersburg, **E...gas:** Chevron/diesel, Exxon/diesel/24hr, Shell, Texaco/diesel/24hr, Thriftmart Plaza/diesel, **food:** Burger King, Hardee's, Waffle House, **W...gas:** Amoco, **food:** McDonald's
61	US 460, to Blackstone, **E...gas:** Amoco, East-Coast/Subway/TCBY/diesel/LP, **lodging:** Day's Inn(3mi), **W...gas:** Shell/diesel, **other:** Picture Lake Camping(2mi), airport
55mm	**rest area both lanes, full(handicapped)facilities, phone, picnic tables, litter barrels, vending, petwalk**
53	VA 703, Dinwiddie, **W...gas:** Exxon/diesel, **food:** HomePlace Rest.,ThatsaBurger, **other:** to 5 Forks Nat Bfd
52mm	Stony Creek
48	VA 650, DeWitt, no facilities
42	VA 40, McKenney, **W...gas:** Citgo, Exxon, **other:** auto repair, **1.5 mi W...lodging:** Economy Inn
40mm	Nottoway River
39	VA 712, to Rawlings, **E...other:** VA Battlerama, **W...gas:** Chevron/diesel/24hr, Circle Dmart/diesel, Citgo/diesel, **lodging:** Nottoway Motel/rest.
34	VA 630, Warfield, **W...gas:** Exxon/diesel
32mm	**rest area both lanes, full(handicapped)facilities, phone, picnic tables, litter barrels, vending, petwalk**
28	US 1, Alberta, **W...gas:** Exxon
27	VA 46, to Lawrenceville, **E...other:** to St Paul's Coll
24	VA 644, to Meredithville, no facilities
22mm	weigh sta both lanes
20mm	Meherrin River
15	US 1, to South Hill, **E...gas:** Citgo/deli, **W...gas:** Shell, **food:** Kahill's Diner
12	US 58, VA 47, to South Hill, **E...gas:** RaceTrac, Shell/SlipIn, **food:** Arnold's Diner, Bojangles, Domino's, **lodging:** Hampton Inn, Holiday Inn Express, Super 8, **other:** $Tree, Wal-Mart, **W...gas:** Amoco/diesel, Chevron/diesel/repair, Exxon/diesel, Petrol, Shell/diesel, **food:** Brian's Steaks, Burger King, Denny's, Golden Corral, Hardee's, KFC, McDonald's, New China, Pizza Hut, Subway, Taco Bell, Wendy's, **lodging:** Best Western, Comfort Inn, Econolodge, **other:** HOSPITAL, CVS Drug, $General, Farmers Foods, Goodyear/auto, Roses, Winn-Dixie
4	VA 903, to Bracey, Lake Gaston, **E...gas:** Amoco/DQ/Subway/diesel, Exxon/diesel/rest./24hr, **other:** Americamps Camping(5mi), **W...gas:** Shell/Pizza Hut, **lodging:** Day's Inn/rest.

S o u t h   H i l l

Exit #	Services
3mm	Lake Gaston
1mm	**Welcome Ctr nb, full(handicapped)facilities, phone, picnic tables, phones, litter barrels, vending, petwalk**
0mm	Virginia/North Carolina state line

Interstate 95

D C   A r e a

Exit #	Services
178mm	Virginia/Maryland state line, Potomac River, W Wilson Mem Br
177c b a	US 1, to Alexandria, Ft Belvoir, **E...food:** Alexandria Diner, Great American Steak Buffet, **lodging:** Day's Inn, Relax Inn, Red Roof Inn, **other:** Chevrolet, Chrysler/Plymouth/Jeep, Dodge, **W...gas:** Exxon/24hr, Hess
176b a	VA 241, Telegraph Rd, **E...gas:** Hess/diesel, **W...lodging:** Courtyard, Holiday Inn
174	Eisenhower Ave Connector, to Alexandria, no facilities
173	rd 613, Van Dorn St, to Franconia, **E...lodging:** Comfort Inn, **1 mi W...gas:** Exxon, Shell, **food:** Dunkin Donuts, Jerry's Subs, McDonald's, Papa John's, Red Lobster, **other:** Aamco, Giant Foods, NTB, Radio Shack
170a	I-495 N, I-495 & I-95 N run together to MD., to Rockville, no facilities
170b	I-395 N, to Washington, no facilities
169b a	rd 644, Springfield, Franconia, **E...gas:** Mobil, 7-11, **food:** Bennigan's, **lodging:** Best Western, Comfort Inn, Courtyard, Day's Inn, Hampton Inn, Hilton, Holiday Inn, **other:** HOSPITAL, Barnes&Noble, Circuit City, CVS Drug, Firestone/auto, Ford, Isuzu/Kia, JC Penney, Macy's, mall, **W...gas:** BP, Mobil, Shell, **food:** Bob Evans, Dragon Sea Buffet, KFC, McDonald's, Outback Steaks, Peking Garden, Popeye's, Subway, **lodging:** Holiday Inn Express, Red Roof Inn, TownePlace Suites, **other:** CVS Drug, Diahatsu, Dodge, Giant Foods, Goodyear/auto, K-Mart, Radio Shack, Subaru/VW, Toyota
167	VA 617, Backlick Rd(from sb), **W...gas:** InterFuel/diesel, **other:** Chevrolet, Nissan
166b a	VA 7100, Newington, to Ft Belvoir, **E...gas:** Exxon/diesel, **W...gas:** Exxon, **food:** McDonald's
163	VA 642, Lorton, **E...gas:** Shell/24hr, **W...gas:** Shell, **food:** Burger King, Café Platters, Gunston Wok, **lodging:** Comfort Inn
161	US 1 S(no nb re-entry, exits left from sb), to Ft Belvoir, Mt Vernon, Woodlawn Plantation, Gunston Hall, **1 mi E...gas:** BP, Crown, Exxon, Shell, **food:** Denny's, DixieBones BBQ, Capotil Grill, Dunkin Doughnuts, McDonald's, Taco Bell, **lodging:** Econolodge, Hampton Inn, Quality Inn, Roadway Inn, Virginia Inn

VIRGINIA

Interstate 95

N

↑
↓

S

160.5mm Occoquan River

160b a VA 123 N, Woodbridge, Occoquan, **E...gas:** Mobil, **food:** Lum's, Subway, Taco Bell, **lodging:** Comfort Inn, Econolodge, Hampton Inn, Quality, **other:** Aldi Foods, Ford, Food Lion, GNC, Radio Shack, Trak Auto, **W...gas:** BP, Exxon/diesel, Mobil, Shell, **food:** KFC, McDonald's, 7-11, **other:** VA Grill, Wendy's

158b a VA 3000, Prince William Pkwy, Woodbridge, **W...gas:** Citgo, Exxon, Mobil, Shell, Sunoco, WaWa, **food:** Boston Mkt, Chick-fil-A, IHOP, Macaroni Grill, Old Country Buffet, Taco Bell, Wendy's, **lodging:** Fairfield Inn, Holiday Inn Express, Sleep Inn

156 VA 784, Potomac Mills, **E...gas:** Exxon, Wawa/gas, **food:** Checkers, McDonald's, Taco Bell, **other:** HOSPITAL, Hyundai, Kia, Lincoln/Mercury, Mazda, Mitsubishi, Nissan, Radio Shack, Safeway, Trak Auto, to Leesylvania SP, **W...gas:** Exxon, Mobil, Shell, **food:** Blackeyed Pea, Bob Evans, Burger King, Chesapeake Bay Seafood, Chili's, Domino's, El Charro Mexican, Jazz St Grill, Jerry's Subs, McDonald's, Olive Garden, Outback Steaks, Pizza Hut, Popeye's, Silver Diner, Wendy's, **lodging:** Day's Inn, Wytestone Suites, **other:** Circuit City, CompUSA, Firestone/auto, K-Mart, Marshall's, Michael's, NTB, Staples, U-Haul

155mm rest area both lanes, full(handicapped)facilities, phone, vending, picnic tables, litter barrels, petwalk, NO TRUCKS

154mm truck rest area/weigh sta both lanes

152 VA 234, Dumfries, to Manassas, **E...gas:** BP/diesel/24hr, Chevron/service, Shell/diesel, **food:** Golden Corral, KFC, McDonald's, Subway, Taco Bell, **lodging:** Sleep Inn, Super 8, **other:** NAPA Autocare, Weems-Botts Museum, **W...gas:** Citgo/7-11, Exxon/Blimpie, Shell, **food:** Cracker Barrel, MontClair Rest., Tiziano Italian, Waffle House, **lodging:** Day's Inn, Econolodge, Hampton Inn, Holiday Inn Express

150 VA 619, Quantico, to Triangle, **E...gas:** Exxon, Shell/diesel, **food:** Burger King, Dunkin Donuts, McDonald's, 7-11, Wendy's, **lodging:** Best Value, Ramada Inn, **other:** auto repair, to Marine Corps Base, **W...**Prince William Forest Park

148 to Quantico, **2 mi E...gas:** Mobil/diesel, Spring Lake Motel, to Marine Corps Base

143b a to US 1, VA 610, Aquia, **E...gas:** BP, Exxon, Shell/diesel/24hr, **food:** Carlos O'Kelly's, DQ, DaVanzo's Italian, Imperial Garden, KFC, Kingstreet BBQ, Little Caesar's, McDonald's, Pizza Hut, Ruby Tuesday, Shoney's, Subway, VA BBQ, Wendy's, **lodging:** Day's Inn, Hampton Inn, **other:** BigLots, GNC, Radio Shack, Rite Aid, Tires+, **W...gas:** BP/diesel, Citgo/7-11/diesel, WaWa, **food:** Acapulco's Mexican, Applebee's, Bob Evans, Burger King, Chick-fil-A, China Buffet, China Wok, Dunkin Donuts, Golden Corral, Hardee's, McDonald's, Popeye's, Starbucks, Taco Bell, Wendy's, **lodging:** Comfort Inn, Country Inn, Holiday Inn Express, Super 8, Wingate Inn, **other:** AutoZone, CVS Drug, $General, Giant Foods, Home Depot, Kohl's, Lowe's Whse, Merchants Tire, Michael's, Staples, Target, Toyota, Wal-Mart/auto, Aquia Pines Camping

140 VA 630, Stafford, **E...gas:** BP, Mobil, Shell/diesel, **food:** McDonald's, **lodging:** Bradshaw Motel(3mi), **W...gas:** BP/diesel, Shell/diesel

137mm Potomac Creek

136 new exit

133b a US 17 N, to Warrenton, **E...gas:** Exxon/diesel, Mobil/diesel, RaceWay, **food:** Arby's, Illiano Pizzaria, Paradise Diner, **lodging:** Howard Johnson Express, Motel 6, **other:** CarQuest, **W...gas:** BP/diesel, Chevron, Citgo/7-11, EastCoast/Subway/diesel, Shell/diesel, **food:** Burger King, Emerald's Grill, Hardee's, Johnny Appleseed Rest., McDonald's, Pizza Hut, Ponderosa, ServiceTown Rest., Taco Bell, Waffle House, Wendy's, **lodging:** Best Inn, Comfort Inn, Day's Inn, Holiday Inn, Quality Inn, Ramada Ltd, Sleep Inn, Super 8, Travelodge, Wingate Inn, **other:** Advance Parts, Blue Beacon, CVS Drug, Food Lion

132.5mm Rappahannock River

132mm rest area sb, full(handicapped)facilities, phone, picnic tables, litter barrels, petwalk, vending

130b a VA 3, to Fredericksburg, **E...gas:** BP/diesel/24hr, Liberty Gas, Mobil/diesel, RaceWay, Shell, 7-11, Wawa/24hr, **food:** Arby's, Bob Evans, Café daVanzo, Carlos O'Kelly's, Chesapeake Bay Seafood, CiCi's, Dunkin Donuts, Friendly's, KFC, Kings Buffet, LoneStar Steaks, LJSilver, McDonald's, Mkt St Buffet, Popeye's, Shoney's, Subway, TCBY, Top's Chinese, Wendy's, **lodging:** Best Western, Hampton Inn, **other:** HOSPITAL, Batteries+, $King, Hancock Fabrics, Home Depot, PepBoys, Radio Shack, Staples, **W...gas:** BP, Citgo/7-11, Crown Gas, Exxon/diesel/24hr, Shell, Sheetz, Wawa/24hr, **food:** A&W/LJ Silver, Applebee's, Aunt Sarah's, BBQ, Boston Mkt, Burger King, Carrabba's, Cracker Barrel, Denny's, Fuddrucker's, Great Steak, IHOP, Joe's Crabshack, Ledo Pizza, Little Caesar's, Logan's Roadhouse, McDonald's, NY Diner, O'Charley's, Old Country Buffet, Olive Garden, Outback Steaks, Panera Bread, Piccadilly, Pizza Hut, Popeye's, Prime Rib, Red Lobster, Red White&Blue BBQ, Ruby Tuesday, Santa Fe Grill, Starbucks, Taco Bell, TGIFriday, Tia's TexMex, Waffle House, **lodging:** Econolodge, Holiday Inn Select, Ramada Inn, Ryan's, Sheraton, Super 8, **other:** Belk, Best Buy, BJ's Whse, Borders Books, Circuit City, Giant Foods, GNC, Hecht's, JC Penney, Kohl's, K-Mart, Lowe's Whse, Merchants Tire, Michaels, NTB, Office Depot, Old Navy, Sears/auto, Shoppers Foods, Target, Wal-Mart SuperCtr/gas/24hr, mall

126 US 1, US 17 S, to Fredericksburg, **E...gas:** Amoco, BP, Citgo/7-11, Exxon/Subway, Mobil, Shell/diesel, **food:** Arby's, Denny's, El Charro Mexican, Friendly's, Golden Corral, Hooters, McDonald's, Pancho Villa Mexican, Pizza Hut, Ruby Tuesday, Shoney's, Taco Bell, Waffle House, Wendy's, Western Sizzlin, **lodging:** Day's Inn/rest., Econolodge, Fairfield Inn, Holiday Inn, Howard Johnson, Ramada Inn, Super 8, TownePlace Inn, **other:** Buick/Pontiac/GMC, Cadillac, CarQuest, CVS Drug, Goodyear/auto, Honda/Nissan/Mazda/VW, Merchants Tire, Rite Aid, **W...gas:** Exxon/Blimpie, RaceTrac/diesel/24hr, **food:** Aunt Sarah's, Burger

Fredericksburg

504

Interstate 95

N

King, Cracker Barrel, Damon's, Durango's Steaks, Golden China, KFC, McDonald's, Subway, **lodging:** Comfort Inn, Sleep Inn, WyteStone Suites, **other:** Massaponax Outlet Ctr/famous brands, KOA(6mi), Wal-Mart SuperCtr/gas/24hr

S

118 VA 606, to Thornburg, **E...gas:** BP, Shell/diesel, **other:** to Stonewall Jackson Shrine, **W...gas:** Citgo/diesel, Exxon, Valero, **food:** Angela's Rest., Burger King, McDonald's, Subway, **lodging:** Holiday Inn Express, Lamplighter Motel, **other:** KOA(7mi), to Lake Anna SP

110 VA 639, to Ladysmith, **E...gas:** Shell/diesel, **W...gas:** Citgo/diesel, Exxon/diesel, **food:** Guiseppe's Rest., Perky's Pizza, Subway, **other:** Express Tire/repair, Food Lion

108mm rest area both lanes, full(handicapped)facilities, vending, phone, picnic tables, litter barrels, pet-walk

104 VA 207, to US 301, Bowling Green, **E...gas:** BP/diesel, Chevron, Exxon/diesel, Mr Fuel/diesel, Petro/diesel/rest./24hr/@, Pilot/Subway/DQ/diesel/24hr/@, Shell/diesel, Speedco, **food:** McDonald's, Wendy's, **lodging:** Holiday Inn Express, Howard Johnson, **other:** Blue Beacon, Russell Stover Candies, to Ft AP Hill, **W...gas:** Exxon/diesel, Flying J/Country Mkt/diesel/24hr/@, **food:** Aunt Sarah's, Waffle House, **lodging:** Comfort Inn, Day's Inn/rest., Red Roof Inn, Travelodge, **other:** CarQuest, USPO

98 VA 30, Doswell, **E...to** King's Dominion Funpark, **gas:** Citgo/7-11, Shell/diesel, **food:** All American Rest., Burger King, Denny's, **lodging:** Best Western, Econolodge, **other:** All American Camping, King's Dominion Camping, truckwash

92 VA 54, Ashland, **E...gas:** Mobil, **W...gas:** BP, TA/diesel/rest./@, Citgo/diesel, EastCoast/Blimpie/diesel, Exxon/Subway, Shell/diesel, **food:** Arby's, Burger King, Capt D's, Cracker Barrel, DQ, Azteca Mexican, Hardee's, Jersey Mike's Subs, KFC, McDonald's, PapaLou Pizza, Pizza Hut, Ponderosa, Popeye's, Ruby Tuesday, Shoney's, Taco Bell, Waffle House, Wendy's, **lodging:** Ashland Inn, Budget Inn, Comfort Inn, Day's Inn, Econolodge, Hampton Inn, Holiday Inn Express, Microtel, Quality Inn, Ramada Inn, Sleep Inn, Super 8, Travelodge, **other:** AutoZone, BigLots, Buick/Pontiac, CarQuest, Family$, Food Lion, Radio Shack, Rite Aid, U-Haul, Ukrop's Foods

89 VA 802, to Lewistown Rd, **E...gas:** Shell, TA/Mobil/Pizza Hut/diesel/café/24hr/@, **other:** Americamps RV Camp, **W...lodging:** Cadillac Motel, **other:** Kosmo Village Camping, Rolling Hills RV Ctr

86b a VA 656, Elmont, to Atlee, **E...gas:** BP, Sheetz(1mi), **food:** Burger King, McDonald's(1mi), **W on US 1... gas:** Citgo/7-11, Mobil, Shell/Subway/diesel, **food:** Applebee's, Burger King, Chick-fil-A, Chili's, Food-Court, Gino's Ristorante, McDonald's, O'Charley's, Panera Bread, Papa John's, Quizno's, Red Robin, Ruby Tuesday, Sbarro's, Shoney's, Subway, Wendy's, **lodging:** Best Western/rest., SpringHill Suites, VA Crossings Resort, **other:** Circuit City, Dillard's, Firestone/auto, Goodyear/auto, Hecht's, JCPenney, Michael's, OfficeMax, Sears/auto, Target, Ukrop's Foods, Walgreen, mall

Richmond

84b a I-295 W, to I-64, to Norfolk, no facilities

83b a VA 73, Parham Rd, **W...gas:** Citgo/7-11, EC/diesel, Exxon/DQ, Shell/diesel, **food:** Aunt Sarah's, Burger King, Denny's, El Paso Mexican, Hardee's, KFC, Little Caesar's, McDonald's, Papa Lou's Pizza, Subway, Taco Bell, Waffle House, Wendy's, **lodging:** Econolodge, Holiday Inn, Knight's Inn, Quality Inn, Shoney's Inn, Sleep Inn, **other:** CVS Drug, Food Lion, Kroger, Lowe's Whse, Wal-Mart SuperCtr/24hr

82 US 301, Chamberlayne Ave, **E...gas:** Mobil/diesel, **food:** McDonald's, **lodging:** Quality Inn, Ramada Ltd, Super 8

81 US 1, Chamberlayne Ave(from nb), same as 82

80 Hermitage Rd, Lakeside Ave(from nb, no return), **W...gas:** BP, EC/Subway, **other:** Goodyear/auto, Ginter Botanical Gardens

79 I-64 W, to Charlottesville, I-195 S, to U of Richmond, no facilities

78 Boulevard(no EZ nb return), **E...lodging:** Holiday Inn, **W...gas:** Citgo/diesel, **food:** BBQ, **lodging:** Day's Inn, **other:** HOSPITAL, to VA HS, stadium

76 Chamberlayne Ave, Belvidere, **E...other:** HOSPITAL, VA Union U

75 I-64 E, VA Beach, to Norfolk, airport

74c US 33, US 250 W, to Broad St, **W...other:** HOSPITAL, st capitol, Museum of the Confederacy

74b Franklin St, **E...other:** Richmond Nat Bfd Park

74a I-195 N, to Powhite Expswy, downtown

73.5mm James River

73 Maury St, to US 60, US 360, industrial area

69 VA 161, Bells Rd, **E...Port** of Richmond, **W...gas:** Exxon/diesel/24hr, Shell/diesel, **food:** Hardee's, McDonald's, **lodging:** Candlewood Suites, Ramada Inn, Red Roof Inn

67b a VA 895 (toll E), VA 150, to Chippenham Pkwy, Falling Creek, **W...gas:** BP, Chevron/diesel, RaceTrac, Shell/diesel, **food:** Blimpie, Burger King, Hardee's, Wendy's

64 VA 613, to Willis Rd, **E...gas:** Exxon, Shell, **food:** Arby's, Aunt Sarah's, Waffle House, **lodging:** Econolodge, Ramada, **other:** Drewy's Bluff Bfd, Hayden's RV Ctr, **W...gas:** Chevron, Citgo/7-11, Mobil/diesel, Shell/diesel, **food:** Bridgette's Rest., Burger King, DQ, McDonald's, **lodging:** Country Inn Suites, Sleep Inn, Super 8, VIP Inn, **other:** flea mkt

62 VA 288 N, to Chesterfield, Powhite Pkwy, to airport

61b a VA 10, Chester, **E...gas:** RaceTrac/24hr, **food:** Hardee's, Imperial Seafood, **lodging:** Comfort Inn, Courtyard, Hampton Inn, Holiday Inn Express, Homewood Suites, Quality Inn, **other:** HOSPITAL, to James River Plantations, City Point NHS, Petersburg NBF,

Chester

VIRGINIA

Interstate 95

W...gas: BP, Citgo/7-11/diesel, Crown/diesel, EC/diesel, Exxon/diesel, Shell, **food:** Applebee's, Burger King, Capt D's, Cracker Barrel, Denny's, Friendly's, Hooter's, KFC, McDonald's, Pizza Hut, Shoney's, Subway, Taco Bell, Waffle House, Wendy's, Western Sizzlin, **lodging:** Clarion, Day's Inn, Fairfield Inn, Howard Johnson, Super 8, **other:** Aamco, Chevrolet, CVS Drug, K-Mart, Lowe's Whse, Rite Aid, Target, Trak Auto, Ukrops Foods, Winn-Dixie, Roadrunner Camping(2mi), to Pocahontas SP

58 VA 746, to Ruffinmill Rd, **E...gas:** Exxon/diesel(2mi), Shell/diesel, WaWa(2mi), **lodging:** Chester Inn, **W...gas:** Chevron/diesel, **food:** McDonald's, Subway, **lodging:** Day's Inn, Interstate Inn/rest.

54 VA 144, Temple Ave, Hopewell, to Ft Lee, **E...gas:** BP/24hr, Chevron/diesel, Citgo, Crown, Exxon/Subway, Shell/Burger King, **food:** Applebee's, Arby's, Burger King, Golden Corral, La Carreta Mexican, LoneStar Steaks, McDonald's, Old Country Buffet, Outback Steaks, Red Lobster, Ruby Tuesday, Sagebrush Steaks, Taco Bell, Wendy's, **lodging:** Comfort Inn, Hampton Inn, Hilton Garden, Holiday Inn Express(5mi), Innkeeper, **other:** MEDICAL CARE, Belk, BooksAMillion, Chevrolet/Cadillac/Buick/Nissan, Circuit City, Dillard's, $Tree, Hecht's, Home Depot, JC Penney, Jo-Ann Fabrics, K-Mart, Marshall's, Michael's, Sam's Club, Sears/auto, Staples, Target, U-Haul, Wal-Mart SuperCtr/24hr, mall, **W...gas:** Shell, **food:** Hardee's, **other:** U-Haul, to VSU

53 S Park Blvd(from nb), **E...**same as 54

52.5mm Appomattox River

52 Washington St, Wythe St, **E...gas:** BP, Citgo, Crown, Shell/diesel, **food:** DQ, Steak&Ale, **lodging:** Best Value, Econolodge, Holiday Inn, King Motel, Ramada, Royal Inn, Star Motel, Super 8, **other:** Petersburg Nat Bfd, **W...gas:** Shell, **food:** Aunt Sarah's, **lodging:** Best Inn, Quality Inn, Radisson, Ramada Inn, HOSPITAL

51 I-85 S, to South Hill, US 460 W, no facilities

50a b c d US 301, US 460 E, to Crater Rd, County Dr, **E...gas:** BP, Citgo/7-11, RaceTrac, **food:** Hardee's, McDonald's, Wendy's, **lodging:** American Inn, Armada Inn, Best Inn, California Inn, Flagship Inn, Knight's Inn, Quality Inn, Super 8, **other:** HOSPITAL

48b a Wagner Rd, **1mi E...gas:** Exxon, **food:** McDonald's, **W...gas:** BP, Chevron/diesel, Citgo, Exxon, Shell, **food:** Arby's, BBQ, Burger King, DQ, Hardee's, Honey B's Rest., KFC, McDonald's, Pizza Hut, Ponderosa, Shoney's, Subway, Taco Bell, **lodging:** Crater Inn, **other:** Dodge, Food Lion, Ford/Lincoln/Mercury, PepBoys

47 VA 629, to Rives Rd, **2 mi E...food:** McDonald's, **W...gas:** BP, Citgo, Shell, **lodging:** Heritage Motel, **1-2 mi W...lodging:** Crater Inn, LaSalle Motel, **other:** Softball Hall of Fame Museum, same as 48 on US 301

46 I-295 N(exits left from sb), to Washington, no facilities

45 US 301, **E...gas:** Shell/diesel, **W...gas:** Exxon, **food:** Pumpkins Rest., Stephen-Kent Rest., **lodging:** Best Western, Comfort Inn, Day's Inn/rest., Hampton Inn, Holiday Inn Express, Quality Inn

41 US 301, VA 35, VA 156, **E...gas:** Chevron/diesel, **lodging:** Econolodge, **other:** KOA(1mi), **W...lodging:** Knight's Inn, Travelodge

40mm weigh sta both lanes

37 US 301, Carson, **W...gas:** BP/diesel, Shell/RV park

36mm **rest area nb, full(handicapped)facilities, phone, vending, picnic tables, litter barrel, petwalk**

33 VA 602, **W...gas:** Chevron/diesel, Davis TrkStp/diesel/@, Exxon/diesel, **food:** Burger King, Denny's/24hr, **lodging:** Sleep Inn, Stony Creek Motel

31 VA 40, Stony Creek, to Waverly, **W...gas:** Petrol/diesel, Shell/diesel/24hr, **food:** Carter's Rest.

24 VA 645, no facilities

20 VA 631, Jarratt, **W...gas:** Exxon/diesel/24hr, Shell/Blimpie/diesel, **food:** Jarratt Rest.

17 US 301, **1 mi E...food:** China Star Rest., **lodging:** Knight's Inn, Reste Motel, **other:** Jellystone Park Camping

13 VA 614, to Emporia, **E...gas:** Shell/diesel, **food:** Slip-In Rest., **lodging:** Dixie Motel

12 US 301(from nb), **E...lodging:** Dixie Motel

11b a US 58, Emporia, to South Hill, **E...gas:** BP/Subway/Taco Bell/diesel, Exxon, Shell, **food:** Arby's, Burger King, DQ, Hardee's, KFC, LJ Silver, McDonald's, Pizza Hut, Wendy's, Western Sizzlin, **lodging:** Fairfield Inn, Holiday Inn, **other:** HOSPITAL, Advance Parts, CVS Drug, Eckerd, Food Lion, Radio Shack, Wal-Mart SuperCtr/24hr, Winn-Dixie, **W...gas:** Citgo, Exxon, Shell/Sadler/diesel/rest., **food:** Bojangles, Shoney's, TJ's Family Rest., **lodging:** Best Western, Day's Inn, Hampton Inn

8 US 301, **E...gas:** Amoco, Citgo, Exxon/Simmon's/diesel/rest./@, **food:** Denny's, **lodging:** Comfort Inn, Red Carpet Inn/rest.

4 VA 629, to Skippers, **W...gas:** Citgo/diesel, **lodging:** Econolodge, **other:** Cattail Creek Camping(2mi)

3.5mm Fountain's Creek

.5mm **Welcome Ctr nb, full(handicapped)facilities, phone, vending, picnic tables, litter barrels, petwalk**

0mm Virginia/North Carolina state line

Interstate 264(Norfolk)

Exit #	Services
22	Birdneck Rd, I-264 begins/ends., **S...gas:** Citgo/diesel, Shell, **food:** McDonald's, **lodging:** DoubleTree Hotel, Howard Johnson, Quality Inn, **other:** museum
21	Va Beach Blvd, First Colonial Rd, **N...gas:** Shell, **food:** Applebee's, Burger King, McDonald's, Taco Bell, Wendy's, **other:** K-Mart, **S...other:** 7-11, NAPA
20	US 58 E, to VA Beach Blvd(eb only), **N...gas:** Citgo/7-11, **food:** Hardee's, Tuesday Morning, **other:** Food Lion, TJMaxx
19	Linhaven Pkwy, **N...gas:** Citgo/7-11, **other:** Audi, Ford, Jaguar, Porsche, **S...food:** McDonald's

Interstate 264

18	Rosemont, **N...gas:** Citgo, **food:** Wendy's, **lodging:** Econolodge, **other:** Eckerd, **S...gas:** Hess, Shell, WaWa, **food:** Burger King, Denny's, Four Seasons Chinese, KFC, Mi Casita Mexican, Wendy's, **other:** Dodge, Eckerd, Home Depot, Harris Teeter, Honda, Sam's Club/gas, Walgreen
17a b	Independance Blvd, **S...gas:** BP, Citgo/7-11, Crowne Plaza, Shell, **food:** Golden Corral, McDonald's, Pizza Hut, Starbucks, Trip's Rest, Wendy's, **lodging:** Day's Inn, Extended Stay America, Fairfield Inn, InTown Suites, **other:** Best Buy, Circuit City, Sears/auto
16	Witchduck, no facilities
15a b	Newtown Rd, **N...gas:** Citgo, Crown Royal, **food:** Wendy's, **lodging:** TownePlace Suites, **S...gas:** BP, Shell, **food:** Denny's, 7-11, **lodging:** Courtyard, Hampton Inn, Holiday Inn, La Quinta, Red Roof Inn, SpringHill Suites **other:** Rite Aid
14b a	I-64. US 13, to Military Hwy, no facilities
13	US 13, Military Hwy, **N...food:** Wendy's, **lodging:** Best Western, Day's Inn
12	Ballentine Blvd, **N...other:** HOSPITAL, Norfolk SU
11b a	US 460, VA 166/168, Brambleton Ave, Campostello Rd, **N...gas:** 7-11
10	Tidewater Dr, City Hall Ave, **N...food:** Hooters, Jillian's Rest, Joe's Crabshack, King's Chinese, Outback Steaks, **lodging:** Omni Hotel, Sheraton
9	St Paul's Blvd, Waterside Dr, to Harbor Park Stadium
8	I-464 S, to Chesapeake, no facilities
7.5mm	tunnel
7b a	VA 141, Effingham St, Crawford St, **N...other:** Naval HOSPITAL, **S...other:** Shipyard
6.5mm	weigh sta eb
6	Des Moines Ave(from eb), no facilities
5	US 17, Frederick Blvd, Midtown Tunnel, **S...gas:** BP
4	VA 337, Portsmouth Blvd, no facilities
3	Victory Blvd, **N...gas:** Exxon, **food:** DQ, Pizza Hut, Ruby Tuesday, Wendy's, **other:** AutoZone, $Tree, FarmFresh Food/drug, Ford, Lowe's Whse, Radio Shack
2b a	Greenwood Dr, no facilities
0mm	I-264 begins/ends on I-64, exit 299.

Interstate 295(Richmond)

Exit #	Services
53b a	I-64, W to Charlottesville, E to Richmond, to US 250, I-295 begins/ends.
51b a	Nuckols Rd, **1 mi N...gas:** BP, Miller's Gas/diesel, **food:** Chen's Chinese, Subway, **other:** CVS Drug, FoodLion, Walgreen, **S...gas:** Exxon, **food:** Capital Alehouse, Mkt Cafe
49b a	US 33, Richmond, **1mi S...other:** Ukrop's Foods
45b a	Woodman Rd, **1mi S...gas:** BP, Citgo, **other:** CVS Drug, Meadow Farm Museum

Portsmouth (vertical left margin)

N ↕ **S**

43	I-95, US 1, N to Washington, S to Richmond(exits left from nb), **services on US 1**, **N...gas:** Amoco/diesel, Mobil, Shell, **food:** Burger King, Chick-fil-A, Chili's, FoodCourt, **lodging:** Best Western, SpringHill Suites, **other:** AmeriCamps, Kosmo Village, mall, **1-2 mi S...gas:** Exxon, EastCoast/diesel, Shell, WaWa/diesel, **food:** Aunt Sarah's, El Paso Mexican, Hardee's, McDonald's, Subway, Taco Bell, Waffle House, Wendy's, **lodging:** Broadway Motel, Cavalier Motel, Econolodge, GuestHouse Inn, Howard Johnson, Knight's Inn, Quality Inn, Shoney's Inn, **other:** Food Lion, Eckerd, Firestone, Lowe's Whse, Wal-Mart SuperCtr/24hr
41b a	US 301, VA 2, **E...gas:** BP/diesel, Shell/diesel, **food:** Burger King, McDonald's, Subway, **W...gas:** Exxon/diesel, **food:** Friendly's
38b a	VA 627, Pole Green Rd, **E...gas:** Citgo, **food:** Subway, **W...gas:** BP/café, Citgo, **other:** Strawberry Hill Funpark, fairgrounds
37b a	US 360, **1 mi E...gas:** Crown, Shell/diesel, **food:** Applebee's, Arby's, Cracker Barrel, IHOP, McDonald's, Mexico Rest., Outback Steaks, Ruby Tuesday, Taco Bell, Waffle House, Wendy's, **lodging:** Hampton Inn, Holiday Inn Express, **other:** BJ's/Gas, $Tree, Home Depot, Kohl's, OfficeMax, Target, Ukrops Foods, Wal-Mart SuperCtr/24hr, **W...gas:** BP, Citgo/7-11, Mobil/diesel, **food:** Colonial Rest., **other:** NAPA, to Mechanicsville
34b a	VA 615, Creighton Rd, **E...gas:** BP/diesel, **5 mi W...gas:** Citgo, **food:** McDonald's
31b a	VA 156, **E...gas:** Citgo/diesel, **other:** to Cold Harbor, **4 mi W...gas:** BP/diesel, Citgo, Shell/diesel, **food:** Antonio's Pizza, Hardee's, Popeye's, **lodging:** Courtyard, Day's Inn, Econolodge, Hampton Inn, Hilton, Holiday Inn, Microtel, Motel 6, Wingate Inn
28	I-64, to US 60, **W...other:** museum
25	Rd 895 W(toll), to Richmand, no facilities
22b a	VA 5, Charles City, **E...gas:** BP, Exxon/diesel, **food:** DQ, **other:** Shirley Plantation, **W...gas:** BP, **other:** Richmond Nat Bfd
18mm	James River
15b a	VA 10, Hopewell, **E...gas:** BP/diesel, Citgo, **food:** Burger King, **lodging:** Evergreen Motel, **other:** HOSPITAL, James River Plantations, **W...gas:** EastCoast/Subway/diesel, Exxon/diesel, WaWa, **food:** Burger King, Chen's Rest., Cracker Barrel, Denny's, Friendly's, Jalapeño's, McDonald's, River's Bend Cafe, Waffle House, Wendy's, **lodging:** AmeriSuites, Clarion, Comfort Inn, Hampton Inn, Holiday Inn Express

Mechanicsville (vertical center margin)

Hopewell

VIRGINIA

Interstate 295

N ↕ S

13mm	Appomattox River
9b a	VA 36, Hopewell, **E...gas:** Chevron, Petrol, **food:** El Nopal Mexican, Hong Kong's Rest., Rosa'a Italian, **lodging:** Econolodge, Innkeeper, **other:** Advance Parts, AutoZone, **W...gas:** BP/diesel/24hr, Exxon/Bullets, Pilot/diesel/24hr, Shell, **food:** Burger King, Denny's, DQ, Japanese Steaks, Kanpai Japanese, McDonald's, Papa John's, Pizza Hut, Shoney's, Subway, Taco Bell, Waffle House, Wendy's, Western Sizzlin, Willie's Diner, **lodging:** Candlewood Suites, Comfort Inn, Hampton Inn, Holiday Inn Express, **other:** Chevrolet, Family$, Food Lion, Rite Aid, U-Haul, US Army Museum, Winn-Dixie/deli, to Petersburg NBF
5.5mm	Blackwater Swamp
3b a	US 460, Petersburg, to Norfolk, **E...gas:** EastCoast/diesel, **food:** Subway, **W...gas:** BP(3mi), Exxon, **food:** Hardee's, McDonald's, **lodging:** American Inn, California Inn
1	I-95, N to Petersburg, S to Emporium, I-295 begins/ends.

Interstate 495(DC)

N ↕ S

Exit #	Services
27	I-95, N to Baltimore, S to Richmond. I-495 & I-95 S run together.
28b a	MD 650, New Hampshire Ave, **N...gas:** Amoco/24hr, Exxon/diesel, Shell/autocare/24hr, 7-11, **food:** KFC, Shoney's, **other:** CVS Drug, Radio Shack, Safeway
29b a	MD 193, University Blvd, no facilities
30b a	US 29, Colesville, **N...gas:** Amoco, Shell, 7-11/Jerry's Subs, **food:** McDonald's, **other:** Safeway
31b a	MD 97, Georgia Ave, Silver Springs, **S...gas:** Amoco/diesel, Exxon/diesel, Shell, Texaco/diesel, **food:** Hunan Chinese, **other:** CVS Drug, Merchants Tire, Snider's Foods, Staples
33	MD 185, Connecticut Ave, **N...other:** LDS Temple, **S...gas:** Amoco, Citgo, Sunoco, **food:** Chevy Chase Foods
34	MD 355, Wisconsin Ave, Bethesda, no facilities
35	(from wb), I-270, no facilities
36	MD 187, Old Georgetown Rd, **S...other:** HOSPITAL
38	I-270, to Frederick, no facilities
39	MD 190, River Rd, Washington, Potomac, no facilities
40	Cabin John Pkwy, Glen Echo(from sb), no trucks, no facilities
41	Clara Barton Pkwy, Carderock, Great Falls, no trucks
42mm	**Potomac River, Virginia/Maryland state line. Exits 41-27 are in Maryland.**
43	G Washington Mem Pkwy, no trucks, no facilities
44	VA 193, Langley, no facilities
45b a	VA 267 W(toll), to I-66 E, to Dulles Airport
46b a	VA 123, Chain Bridge Rd, **W...lodging:** Hilton

D C Area

47b a	VA 7, Leesburg Pike, Tysons Corner, Falls Church, **E...Doubletree, W...gas:** BP/diesel, Crown Gas, Exxon, Mobil, Shell, **food:** Chili's, McDonald's, NY Deli, Olive Garden, On-the-Border, Pizza Hut, 7-11, **lodging:** Marriott, **other:** Best Buy, Borders Books, Ford, Nordstrom's, mall
49c b a	I-66(exits left from both lanes), to Manassas, Front Royal, no facilities
50b a	US 50, Arlington Blvd, Fairfax, Arlington, **N...lodging:** Marriott, **S...gas:** Shell, **food:** Uno Pizzaria, **lodging:** Residence Inn, **other:** HOSPITAL, CVS Drug, Giant Foods
51	VA 657, Gallows Rd, **S...gas:** Exxon, 7-11, **other:** HOSPITAL
52b a	VA 236, Little River Tpk, Fairfax, **N...gas:** Citgo, Mobil/repair, 7-11, **food:** McDonald's, Wendy's
54b a	VA 620, Braddock Rd, Ctr for the Arts, Geo Mason U, **S...gas:** Mobil/diesel, 7-11, **other:** Rite Aid, Safeway
56c b a	I-95 S, I-395 N, I-95 N. I-495 & I-95 N run together.

N ↕ S

Interstate 664(Portsmouth)

Exit #	Services
14	I-664 begins/ends on I-64, exit 299.
13b a	US 13, US 58, US 460, Military Hwy, **1-2mi N...gas:** Citgo/7-11, Shell, **food:** Arby's, Boston Mkt, Burger King, Chick-fil-A, Hooters, KFC, Wendy's, Home Depot, IHOP, Schlotzky's, Sonic, Taco Bell, Uno Pizzaria, Uptown Buffet, **lodging:** Best Western, Day's Inn, Econolodge, Motel 6, Ramada Ltd, **other:** FarmFresh Foods/gas, FoodLion, Lowe's Whse, Nissan, Pep Boys, Target, Walgreen, Wal-Mart SuperCtr/24hr
12	VA 663, Dock Landing Rd, no facilities
11b a	VA 337, Portsmouth Blvd, **E...lodging:** Holiday Inn Express, gas, food
10	10 VA 659, Pughsville Rd, **E...gas:** Citgo, Shell
9b a	US 17, US 164, **E...gas:** Citgo/7-11, **other:** AutoValue Parts, Honda, Chevrolet, **W...gas,** food, lodging, to James River Br, museum
8b a	VA 135, College Dr, **E...gas:** Citgo/7-11, Shell/Burger King, **food:** McDonald's, Ruby Tuesday, Subway, Wendy's, **other:** FoodLion, Radio Shack, Wal-Mart SuperCtr/24hr
11.5mm	insp sta nb
9mm	James River
8mm	tunnel
7	Terminal Ave, no facilities
6	6 25th St, 26th St, **E...gas:** Citgo/7-11, **food:** McDonald's
5	5 US 60 W, 35th St, Jefferson Ave, **E...gas:** Citgo, **food:** Burger King, Church's, KFC
4	4 Chesnut Ave, Roanoke Ave, no facilities
3	Aberdeen Rd, **E...gas:** Citgo/diesel, **W...food:** Hardee's, McDonald's, Wendy's
2	Powhatan Pkwy, no facilities
1b a	I-64, W to Richmond, E to Norfolk. I-664 begins/ends on I-64.

Interstate 5

N ↕ **S**

Exit #   Services

277mm USA/Canada Border, Washington state line, customs

276 WA 548 S, Blaine, **E...gas:** Exxon/diesel, MP/gas, Shell/diesel, USA/diesel/24hr, **food:** Denny's, Pasa del Norte Mexican, **lodging:** Northwoods Motel, **other:** Ammex Duty Free, to Peace Arch SP, **W...gas:** Chevron/repair, **food:** Bella Marina Rest., Golden Chopstix Rest., Pizza Factory, Subway, Truffle's Seafood Rest., WheelHouse Grill, **lodging:** Anchor Inn, Bayside Motel, International Motel/cafe, **other:** Coast Hardware, NAPA

275 WA 543 N(from nb, no return), truck customs, **E...gas:** Exxon

274 Peace Portal Drive(from nb, no return), Blaine, **W...gas:** Star Power/gas, **food:** Nikki's Diner(.5mi), **other:** Semi-ah-moo Resort, camping

270 Birch Bay, Lynden, **W...gas:** Shell/Subway/Taco Bell/diesel/24hr, **lodging:** Semi-ah-moo Resort, **other:** Peace Arch Outlet/famous brands, SeaBreeze RV Park(5mi)

269mm Welcome Ctr sb, full(handicapped)facilities, info, phone, picnic tables, litter barrels, petwalk, vending

267mm rest area nb, full(handicapped)facilities, info, phone, picnic tables, litter barrels, petwalk, vending

266 WA 548 N, Grandview Rd, Custer, **W...gas:** Arco/24hr, Birch Bay SP

263 Portal Way, **E...gas:** Shell/diesel, **other:** Cedars RV Park

263mm Nooksack River

262 Main St, Ferndale, **E...gas:** 76/diesel, Tesoro/diesel, **food:** Denny's, McDonald's, **lodging:** Super 8, **other:** RV Park, U-Haul, **W...gas:** Cenex, Exxon/diesel/LP, 76, Shell/Domino's/diesel, **food:** Bob's Burgers, DQ, Murdock's Steaks, Papa Murphy's, **lodging:** Scottish Lodge, **other:** Costcutter Foods, Haggen's Foods, NAPA, Scwab Tire

260 Slater Rd, Lummi Island, **E...gas:** Arco/24hr, **other:** El Monte RV, antiques, **5 mi W...gas:** 76, Shell/diesel, **other:** Eagle Haven RV Park, Silver Reef Casino/café(10mi), Lummi Ind Res

258 Bakerview Rd, **E...**Fred Meyer/gas, **W...gas:** Arco/24hr, Exxon/diesel/24hr, 76, **food:** Mykono's Greek Rest., **lodging:** Hampton Inn, Shamrock Motel, **other:** airport, RV Park, st patrol

257 Northwest Ave, **E...other:** Chevrolet/Cadillac, **W...gas:** Shell

256b Bellis Fair Mall Pkwy, **E...other:** Sears, Target, mall

256a WA 539 N, Meridian St, **E...gas:** Chevron, Exxon/diesel, Shell/diesel, **food:** Arby's, Burger King, China Buffet, DQ, Denny's, Godfather's, Izzy's Pizza, Kowloon Garden, McDonald's, McHale's Rest., Old Country Buffet, Olive Garden, Pizza Hut, Quizno's, Red Robin, Shari's/24hr, Starbucks, Taco Time, Teriyaki House, Thai House, Wendy's, **lodging:** Best Western, Comfort Inn, Day's Inn, Holiday Inn Express, Quality Inn, **other:** Barnes&Noble, Best Buy, Bon-Marche, Circuit City, Costco, Costcutter Foods, Home Depot, JC Penney, Mervyn's, Nordstrom's, Office Depot, Rite Aid, Ross, Safeway, Schuck's Parts, Schwab Tire, Sears, Target, U-haul, Walgreen, Wal-Mart/auto, mall, st patrol, to Nooksack Ind Res, **W...food:** Eleni's Rest., **lodging:** Rodeway Inn, Travel House Inn

Interstate 5

255 WA 542 E, Sunset Dr, Bellingham, **E...gas:** Chevron/diesel/24hr, Exxon, Shell/Subway/diesel, **food:** Applebee's, Hawaii BBQ, Jack-in-the-Box, RoundTable Pizza, Taco Bell, **other:** Costcutter Foods, Farmers Outlet, Jo-Ann Fabrics, K-Mart, Lowe's Whse, OfficeMax, Rite Aid, Walgreen, USPO, to Mt Baker, **W...other:** HOSPITAL

254 Iowa St, State St, Bellingham, **E...gas:** 76, Shell, **other:** Honda, Hyundai, Mercedes, Mitsubishi, Kia, Nissan, Toyota, Volvo, RV Ctr, **W...gas:** Chevron/24hr, Exxon/diesel, 76/repair, **food:** DQ, McDonald's, Skipper's Rest., Subway, **other:** Chrysler/Dodge, Ford/Lincoln/Mercury, Hardware Sales, Isuzu, NAPA, Schuck's Parts, Schwab Tire, Subaru

253 Lakeway Dr, Bellingham, **E...gas:** USA/gas, 7-11, **food:** Burger Me, Little Caesar's, Papa Murphy's, Pizza Hut, Port of Subs, Sol de Mexico, Subway, **lodging:** Best Western, Valu Inn, **other:** Costcutter Foods, Discount Tire, Fred Meyer, Radio Shack, **W...gas:** Chevron, same as 252

252 Samish Way, Bellingham, **E...lodging:** Evergreen Motel, **other:** same as 253, **W...gas:** Arco/24hr, Chevron, Mobil, 76, Shell/diesel/24hr, Tesoro/McDonalds/diesel, **food:** Arby's, Black Angus, Boomer's Drive-In, Burger King, Christo's Rest., Denny's, Diego's Mexican, Figaro's Pizza, IHOP, Jade City Rest., Kyoto Japanese, New Peking, Nicklby's Rest., NW Viet Rest., Papa John's, Pasta Bravo, Pizza Hut, Rib'n Reef, RoundTable Pizza, Starbucks, Subway, Thai Cuisine, **lodging:** Aloha Motel, Bay City Motel, Cascade Inn, Coachman Motel, Key Motel, Motel 6, Ramada Inn, Travelodge, Villa Inn, **other:** Audi, Chrysler/Jeep, Haggen Foods, Rite Aid, VW

250 WA 11 S, Chuckanut Dr, Bellingham, Fairhaven Hist Dist, **W...gas:** Arco, Chevron/repair, **food:** Dos Padres Mexican, SkyLark Café, Tony's Café, Win's Drive-In, **other:** Larrabee SP, to Alaska Ferry

246 N Lake Samish, **W...gas:** Shell/diesel, **other:** Lake Padden RA, RV camping

242 Nulle Rd, S Lake Samish, no facilities

240 Alger, **E...gas:** Shell/diesel/LP/RV dump, **food:** Alger Grille, **lodging:** Whispering Firs Motel/RV Parking

238mm **rest area both lanes, full(handicapped)facilities, phone, picnic tables, litter barrels, vending, petwalk**

236 Bow Hill Rd, **E...** Chevron/diesel, Skagit Hotel Casino/rest.

235mm weigh sta sb

234mm Samish River

232 Cook Rd, Sedro-Woolley, **E...gas:** 76, Shell/diesel, **food:** Bob's Burgers, DQ, Iron Skillet Rest.(4mi), **lodging:** 3 Rivers Inn(5mi), **other:** HOSPITAL, KOA

231 WA 11 N, Chuckanut Dr, **E...other:** Foley's RV/marine, Kia, st patrol, to Larrabee SP

230 WA 20, Burlington, **E...gas:** Exxon, Shell/diesel, Tesoro, **food:** Beary Patch Rest., Burger King, Jack-in-the-Box, Krispy Kreme, Outback Steaks, Pizza Factory, Red Robin, Subway, **lodging:** Cocusa Motel, **other:** HOSPITAL, Bon-Marche, Fred Meyer, Haggen Foods, JC Penney, Schwab Tire, Sears/auto, Target, OfficeMax, Target, mall, to N Cascades NP, **W...gas:**

Arco/diesel/24hr, Chevron/diesel, Pacific Pride, **food:** McDonald's, **lodging:** Holiday Inn Express, Mark II Motel, **other:** Harley-Davidson, to San Juan Ferry

229 George Hopper Rd, **E...gas:** Arco/24hr, Cenex, Chevron, USA/diesel, **food:** Olive Garden, Pizza Hut/Taco Bell, Shari's, Subway, Wendy's, **other:** Costco/gas, Costcutter Foods, Home Depot, K-Mart, NAPA, Old Navy, Prime Outlets/famous brands, Saturn, Schuck's Parts, **W...food:** Indian Motorcycle Café, **other:** Buick/Pontiac, Cadillac, Chrysler/Jeep/Plymouth/Dodge, Ford/Lincoln/Mercury, Mazda/Honda, Mitsubishi, Nissan, Subaru/Toyota, VW, RV Ctr

228mm Skagit River

227 WA 538 E, College Way, Mt Vernon, **E...gas:** 76, **food:** Big Scoop Rest., Denny's, El Gitano's Mexican, Georgio's Subs, Jack-in-the Box, KFC, McDonald's, Papa John's, Pizza Hut/Taco Bell, Port of Subs, RoundTable Pizza, Skipper's, Subway, Taco Time, Winchell's, **lodging:** Best Western, Day's Inn, **other:** Albertson's, $Plus, Goodyear, Jo-Ann Fabrics, Office Depot, PetCo, Rite Aid, Safeway, Schuck's Parts, ValueVillage Foods, Wal-Mart/auto, Walt's AutoCare, **W...gas:** FuelExpress/24hr, Shell/diesel, **food:** Arby's, Burger King, Buzz Inn Steaks, Cranberry Tree Rest., DQ, Drummond'sRest., Fortune Chinese, KFC, Mitzel's Kitchen, Royal Fork Buffet, Taco Time, **lodging:** Best Western, Comfort Inn, Travelodge, Tulip Inn, **other:** Chevrolet, Firestone, Honda Motorcycles, Lowe's Whse, Valley RV, RV camp

226 WA 536 W, Kincaid St, City Ctr, **E...**HOSPITAL, **W...gas:** Pacific Pride/diesel, **food:** Old Towne Grainery Rest., Skagit River Brewing Co, **other:** NAPA, Valley RV Ctr, RV camping

225 Anderson Rd, **E...gas:** 76/diesel, **W...gas:** Chevron, Gasco Trkstp/diesel, **other:** Pulsbo RV Ctr

224 WA 99 S(from nb, no return), S Mt Vernon, **E...gas:**/diesel, food

221 WA 534 E, Conway, Lake McMurray, **E...gas:** Shell/diesel/24hr, **W...gas:** 76/diesel, Shell/diesel, **food:** Channel Lodge Rest., Conway Deli, **lodging:** Ridgeway B&B, Wild Iris B&B, **other:** Blake's RV Park/marina

218 Starbird Rd, **W...lodging:** Hillside Motel

215 300th NW, no facilities

214mm weigh sta nb

212 WA 532 W, Stanwood, Bryant, **W...gas:** Shell/diesel/24hr, **4 mi W...food:** Burger King, DQ, Mkt St Café, McDonald's, **other:** Haggen Foods/cafe/24hr, Camano Island SP(19mi)

210 236th NE, no facilities

209mm Stillaguamish River

208 WA 530, Silvana, Arlington, **E...gas:** Chevron/24hr, 76/Circle K, Shell, Tesoro, **food:** Denny's, O'Brien Turkeyhouse, **lodging:** Arlington Motel, Weller's Rest., **other:** HOSPITAL, to N Cascades Hwy, **W...gas:** 76/diesel

207mm **rest area both lanes, full(handicapped)facilities, phone, picnic tables, litter barrels, coffee, vending, RV dump, petwalk**

206 WA 531, Lakewood, **E...gas:** Arco/24hr, Mobil, 76/diesel/LP/RV dump, Shell/24hr, 7-11/Citgo, **food:** Alfy's Pizza, Buzz Inn Steaks, Food Pavillion, Jack-in-the-Box, KFC, McDonald's, Taco Time, **lodging:** Crossroads Inn, Hawthorn Suites, **other:** Chrysler/Jeep, Food Pavilion, Lowe's Whse, Pontiac/Buick/GMC, Rite Aid, Safeway/gas/24hr, Schuck's Parts, **W...gas:** Chevron/24hr, **food:** Nick's Rest., **lodging:** Smokey Point Motel, **other:** Cedar Grove Shores RV(6mi), to Wenburg SP

Interstate 5

N

S

202 116th NE, **E…gas:** Shell/diesel, **W…gas:** Donna's Trkstp/Chevron/diesel/24hr/@, **other:** st patrol

200 88th St NE, Quil Ceda Way, **E…gas:** Citgo/7-11, 76, Shell/diesel, **food:** Quizno's, Starbucks, **other:** Haggen's Foods/24hr, **W…other:** Home Depot, Wal-Mart/SuperCtr/24hr/auto/gas, casino

199 WA 528 E, Marysville, Tulalip, **E…gas:** Arco/24hr, Chevron/24hr, 76, Shell/Subway/diesel, **food:** Burger King, Don's Rest./24hr, DQ, Jack-in-the-Box, Las Margaritas Mexican, Royal Fork Buffet, Village Rest., **lodging:** Village Motel, **other:** Albertson's, Big O Tire, JC Penney, Rite Aid, Schwab Tire, Staples, **W…gas:** 76, **food:** Arby's, Golden Corral, McDonald's, Taco Time, Wendy's, **lodging:** Best Western/rest., Holiday Inn Express, **other:** Chevrolet/Subaru, RV SuperMall, to Tulalip Indian Res

198 Port of Everett(from sb), Steamboat Slough, st patrol

195mm Snohomish River

195 Port of Everett(from nb), Marine View Dr, no facilities

194 US 2 E, Everett Ave, City Ctr, **W…gas:** Shell/diesel, Schwab Tire

193 WA 529, Pacific Ave(from nb), **W…gas:** Chevron, 76, **food:** Denny's, Roaster Rest., **lodging:** Best Western, Gardner Bay Inn, Howard Johnson, Inn at the Center, Marina Village Inn(3mi), **other:** HOSPITAL

192 Broadway(exits left from nb), to Evergreen Way, City Ctr, **W…gas:** Arco/24hr, Chevron, Exxon, 76, Shell, **food:** Alfy's Pizza, Iver's Seafood, Jack-in-the-Box, King's Table, McDonald's, O'Donnell's Café, Petosa's On Broadway, Taco Bell, **lodging:** Day's Inn, Royal Motor Inn, Travelodge, **other:** Ford

Everett

189 WA 526 W, WA 527, Everett Mall Way, Everett, **E…gas:** Arco/24hr, Exxon, Shell/diesel, **food:** Alfy's Pizza, Burger King, Buzz Inn Steaks, McDonald's, Wendy's, **lodging:** Studio+, Travelodge, **other:** Costco, **1 mi W on Evergreen Way…gas:** Chevron, Shell, 7-11, **food:** Denny's, Godfather's, Taco Bell, Taco Time, Village Inn Rest., **lodging:** Cherry Motel, Comfort Inn, Extended Stay America, Motel 6, Rodeway Inn, Sunrise Inn, **other:** Bon-Marche, Buick/Pontiac, Discount Tire, Dodge/Jeep, Firestone/auto, Fred Meyer, K-Mart, mall

188mm **rest area/weigh sta sb, full(handicapped)facilities, info, phone, picnic tables, litter barrels, coffee, RV dump**

186 WA 96, 128th SW, **E…gas:** 76, Shell/diesel/24hr, **lodging:** Comfort Inn, Holiday Inn, Quality Inn, **other:** Lakeside RV Park, Silver Lake RV Park, **W…gas:** Arco/24hr, Chevron/24hr, Citgo/7-11, Shell, Texaco, **food:** A&W, Alfy's Pizza, Burger King, DQ, Denny's, Great River Rest., KFC, McDonald's, Mitzel's Kitchen, Mongolian Grill, Pizza Hut, Skipper's, Starbucks, Subway, Taco Bell/24hr, Teriyaki Rest., **lodging:** Best Western, Cypress Inn, Everett Inn, Motel 6, **other:** Albertson's, $Tree, Goodyear/auto

183 164th SW, **E…gas:** Arco, Shell/diesel/24hr, **food:** Jack-in-the-Box/24hr, Panda Express, Shari's, Subway, Taco Del Mar, **other:** Radio Shack, Wal-Mart, **W…gas:** Shell/Quizno's/diesel, **other:** Twin Cedars RV Park, Alderwood Mall Blvd

182 **E…**I-405 S, to Bellevue, **W…** WA 525, Alderwood Mall Blvd, to Alderwood Mall, **gas:** Arco/24hr, **food:** Japanese Rest., Keg Steaks/seafood, TCBY, **lodging:** Residence Inn, **other:** Marshall's, Michael's, Nordstrom's, Sears/auto, Target, Evans Tire

181 44th Ave W, to WA 524, Lynnwood, **E…gas:** Arco, 76, Shell, Texaco, **food:** McDonald's, **lodging:** Embassy Suites, Extended Stay America, Hampton Inn, **other:** Albertson's, Barnes&Noble, Best Buy, Circuit City, Lowe's Whse, Old Navy, Staples, **W…gas:** Chevron/24hr, 76/diesel, 7-11, Shell/repair, **food:** Applebee's, Black Angus, Buca Italian, Burger King, Chevy's Mexican, Country Harvest Rest., Denny's, El Torito, Evergreen Donuts, IHOP, Jack-in-the-Box, Japanese Rest., KFC, McDonald's, Old Country Buffet, Olive Garden, Red Lobster, Starbucks, Subway, Tony Roma, Wendy's, **lodging:** Courtyard, Holiday Inn Express, La Quinta, Lynnwood Inn, **other:** MEDICAL CARE, Firestone/auto, Fred Meyer, Goodyear/auto, Marshal's, Michael's, Radio Shack, mall

179 220th SW, Mountlake Terrace, Mountlake Terrace, **W…gas:** Shell, 7-11, **food:** Azteca Mexican, China Passage, Starbucks, Subway, Thai Terrace Rest., **other:** HOSPITAL, Honda, Schuck's Parts

178 236th St SW(from nb), Mountlake Terrace, no facilities

177 WA 104, Edmonds, **E…gas:** Chevron/24hr, Shell/diesel, **food:** Buzz Inn Steaks, Canyons Rest., McDonald's, Starbucks, Subway, **lodging:** Homestead Village Suites, Motel 6, **other:** CompUSA, RiteAid, Schuck's Parts, **1-2 mi W on WA 99…gas:** 76, Shell/diesel, Texaco, **food:** China Clipper Rest., Coco's, Denny's, Godfather's, Todo Mexico, **lodging:** Day's Inn, Harbor Inn, K&E Motel, Travelodge, **other:** Costco, GNC, Home Depot, OfficeMax, QFC Foods, Radio Shack, Schwab Tire, VW

176 NE 175th St, Aurora Ave N, to Shoreline, no facilities

175 WA 523, NE 145th, 5th Ave NE, **1 mi W on WA 99…food:** Las Margaritas Mexican, Shari's, Taco Time, Wendy's, **other:** $Store, Schuck's Parts

174 NE 130th, Roosevelt Way, **nb only, 1 mi W on WA 99… food:** Burger King, KFC, **lodging:** Best Western, **other:** Albertson's, Buick/GMC, Firestone, K-Mart, Office Depot, Rite Aid, Sam's Club

173 1st Ave NE, Northgate Way, **E…gas:** Arco/24hr, 76, **food:** Azteca Mexican, Baskin-Robbins, Marie Callender's, Pancake Haus, Red Robin, Seattle Crab Co, Subway, Taco Time, Tony Roma, **other:** B&B Parts, Best Buy, Discount Tire, JC Penney, Nordstrom's, Pacific Fabrics, QFC Foods, Target, mall, **W…gas:** Chevron, 76, Shell/diesel, 7-11, **food:** Arby's, Barnaby's Café, Denny's, McDonald's, **lodging:** Birkshire Inn, Ramada Inn

172 N 85th, Aurora Ave, **1 mi W on Aurora…gas:** Arco, 76/diesel, **food:** Jack-in-the-Box

171 WA 522, Lake City Way, Bothell, no facilities

Seattle

WASHINGTON
Interstate 5

170 (nb only)Ravenna Blvd, **E...gas:** Arco, Shell/diesel, **other:** MEDICAL CARE, QFC Foods,

169 NE 45th, NE 50th, **E...gas:** 76, **other:** HOSPITAL, U of WA, **W...lodging:** University Plaza Inn, **other:** to Seattle Pacific U, zoo

168b WA 520, to Bellevue, no facilities

168a Lakeview Blvd, downtown

167 Mercer St(exits left from nb), Fairview Ave, Seattle Ctr, **W...gas:** Shell, **lodging:** Silver Cloud Inn

166 Olive Way, Stewart St, **E...other:** HOSPITAL, **W... lodging:** SpringHill Suites, **other:** Honda

165a Seneca St(exits left from nb), James St, **E...other:** HOSPITAL

165b Union St, **E...**Summerfield Suites, **W...food:** Ruth's Chris Steak, **lodging:** Sheraton

164b 4th Ave S, to Kingdome, **1 mi W...**same as 163

164a I-90 E, to Spokane, no facilities

163 6th Ave, S Spokane St, W Seattle Br, Columbian Way, **1 mi W on 4th Ave S...gas:** Arco, **food:** Arby's, Burger King/24hr, Denny's, McDonald's, Subway, Taco Bell, **other:** OfficeMax, Sears, auto repair, transmissions

162 Corson Ave, Michigan St(exits left from nb), same as 161

161 Swift Ave, Albro Place, **W...gas:** Shell, **food:** Thai Rest., **lodging:** Georgetown Inn

158 Pacific Hwy S, E Marginal Way, **W...gas:** Chevron, **food:** Randy's Rest., **lodging:** Econolodge, Red Lion Inn, Travelodge, **other:** HOSPITAL

157 ML King Way, no facilities

156 WA 539 N, Interurban Ave(no EZ return to sb), Tukwila, **E...gas:** Pacific Pride/diesel, **W...gas:** 76/diesel, Shell/ diesel, **food:** Emerald Green, Jack-in-the-Box, **lodging:** Day's Inn, Quality Inn, Towne&Country Suites, **other:** Harley-Davidson

154b WA 518, S Center Blvd, Burien, **E...gas:** Arco, **food:** Denny's, Domino's, **other:** JC Penney, Nordstrom's, Sears/auto, Target, mall, **see WA I-405, exit 1. W... lodging:** Extended Stay America

154a I-405, N to Bellevue, no facilities

152 S 188th, Orillia Rd, **E...other:** KOA, **W...gas:** 76/diesel, **food:** Denny's, Jack-in-the-Box, Taco Bell, **lodging:** Airport Plaza Hotel, Clarion, Comfort Inn, Day's Inn, DoubleTree Hotel, Motel 6, Super 8

151 S 200th, Military Rd, **E...gas:** Shell/diesel, **lodging:** Motel 6, **W...gas:** Chevron, Citgo/7-11, 76, **food:** Bob's Burgers, Godfather's, **lodging:** Best Western, Econolodge, Hampton Inn, Howard Johnson, MiniRate Motel, Skyway Inn, Sleep Inn

149 WA 516, to Kent, Des Moines, **E...other:** Poulsbo RV Ctr, **W...gas:** Arco/24hr, Shell/diesel/24hr, 7-11, **food:** Burger King, Dunkin Donuts, McDonald's, Pizza Hut, Starbucks, Subway, Taco Bell/24hr, Wendy's, **lodging:** Best Western, Century Motel, Day's Inn, Kings Arms Motel, New Best Inn, **other:** QFC Foods, Radio Shack, to Saltwater SP

147 S 272nd, **W on Pacific Hwy...gas:** Arco/24hr, Citgo/7-11, Shell/diesel, **food:** DQ, Jack-in-the-Box, KFC, Little Caesar's, Papa Murphy's, Subway, Taco Bell, Taco Time, Viva Mexican, Wendy's, **lodging:** Travel Inn, **other:** Albertson's, Bartell Drug, CarQuest, Firestone/ auto, Rite Aid, Safeway/24hr, Schuck's Parts

143 Federal Way, S 320th, **W...gas:** Arco/24hr, 76/Circle K, Shell/diesel/24hr, **food:** Applebee's, Arby's, Azteca Mexican, Black Angus, Blimpie, Burger King, Coco's, CucinaCucina, Denny's, Dunkin Donuts, Godfather's, Ivar's Seafood, KFC, Marie Callender, McDonald's, McHale's Rest., Mongolian Grill, Old Country Buffet, Outback Steaks, Pizza Hut, Quizno's, Red Lobster, Red Robin, Subway, Taco Bell, Taco Time, TCBY, Tony Roma, Torero's Mexican, Wendy's, **lodging:** Best Western, Comfort Inn, Courtyard, Extended Stay America, La Quinta, **other:** MEDICAL CARE, Best Buy, Borders Books, Firestone/auto, Goodyear/auto, Jo-Ann Fabrics, K-Mart, Mervyn's, OfficeMax, Old Navy, Rite Aid, Ross, Safeway/24hr, Sears/auto, Target, Top Foods, Wal-Mart/auto, mall, to Dash Point SP

142b a WA 18 E, S 348th, Enchanted Pkwy, **E...other:** funpark, **W...gas:** Chevron/24hr, Ernie's/diesel, 🚛Flying J/diesel//LP/rest./24hr/@, Shell/diesel, **food:** Burger King, DQ, Denny's, Jack-in-the-Box, McDonald's, Olive Garden, Shari's, Subway, Taco Bell, Teriyaki Rest., **lodging:** Eastwind Motel, Holiday Inn Express, Quality Inn, Roadrunner Motel, Super 8, **other:** HOSPITAL, Chevrolet, Circuit City, Costco, Ford, Home Depot, Lowe's Whse, NAPA

141mm weigh sta sb

137 WA 99, Fife, Milton, **E...gas:** Arco/24hr, Chevron/ diesel/24hr, 76/diesel/RV dump, Shell/24hr, **food:** DQ, Johnnie's Rest., **lodging:** Motel 6, **other:** Acura, Baybo's RV Ctr, Cadillac, Hummer, Tacoma RV Ctr, Volvo, **W...gas:** Arco, 76/Circle K, **food:** Arby's, Baskin-Robbins, Burger King, Christy's Rest., Denny's, KFC/A&W, McDonald's, Mitzel's Kitchen, Pizza Experience, Pizza Hut/Taco Bell, Wendy's, **lodging:** Best Western, Comfort Inn, Kings Motel, Quality Inn, **other:** Camping World/RV Service/supplies, Fife Drug, Great American RV Ctr, NAPA, Schwab Tire

136b a Port of Tacoma, **E...other:** BMW, Honda, Mercedes, Sam's Club, RV Sales, **W...gas:** CFN/Goodyear, Chevron, 🚛Flying J/diesel/LP/rest./24hr/@, Shell/diesel, **food:** Fife City Grill, Jack-in-the-Box, **lodging:** Best Inn, Day's Inn, Econolodge, Extended Stay America, Hometel Inn, Ramada Ltd, Travelers Inn, **other:** Harley-Davidson, Nissan, World Trade Ctr

135 Bay St, Puyallup, **E...gas:** Exxon, Shell, **W...gas:** Arco/ 24hr, **lodging:** La Quinta, **other:** to Tacoma Dome

133 WA 7, I-705, City Ctr, **W...other:** Tacoma Dome, **lodging:** Ramada Inn, Sheraton, Travel Inn, **other:** museum

132 WA 16 W, S 38th, Gig Harbor, to Bremerton, **W...food:** Azteca Mexican, Cucina Cucina, Krispy Kreme, TGIFriday, **lodging:** Extended Stay America, **other:** Best Buy, Circuit City, Diahatsu, Ford, Hyundai, JC Penney, Tire Sta, Toyota, mall, to Pt Defiance Pk/Zoo

130 S 56th, Tacoma Mall Blvd, **W...gas:** Shell, Tesoro, **food:** ChuckeCheese, El Torito, Subway, Tony Roma, **other:** Firestone, House of Fabrics, JC Penney, Sears/auto

Interstate 5

N ↑ ↓ S

129 S 72nd, S 84th, **E...gas:** Arco/24hr, Chevron/24hr, Exxon, 76, **food:** Applebee's, Burger King, DQ, Elmer's Rest., Great Wall Buffet, IHOP, Jack-in-the-Box, Mitzel's Kitchen, Olive Garden, Red Lobster, Round Table Pizza, Shari's, Starbucks, Taco Bell, Zoopa Café, **lodging:** Best Western, Howard Johnson, Motel 6, Shilo Inn, Travelodge, **other:** MegaFoods, **W...gas:** Arco/24hr, **food:** Calzone's Italian, Hooters, Jack-in-the-Box, Quizno's, Yankee Diner, **lodging:** Day's Inn, **other:** Home Depot, to Steilacoom Lake

128 (from nb)same as 129, **E...gas:** 76, Shell/diesel, **food:** Copperfield's Rest., Denny's, Subway, **lodging:** Best Western, Comfort Inn, Crossland Suites, Holiday Inn Express, King Oscar Motel, Rothem Inn, Sherwood Motel, Tacoma Inn, **W...gas:** Tesoro, **food:** Ruby Tuesday, **other:** Discount Tire, cinema

127 WA 512, S Tacoma Way, Puyallup, Mt Ranier, **W...gas:** Arco/24hr, Chevron, 76, Shell/diesel, **food:** Burger King, DQ, Denny's, IHOP, Ivar's Seafood, Mazatlan Mexican, McDonald's, McHale's Rest., Sizzler, Subway, Taco Time, Wendy's, **lodging:** Best Value, Best Western, Budget Inn, Knights Inn, Quality Inn, Ramada Inn, **other:** Baybo's RV Ctr, Schuck's Parts, transmissions

125 to McChord AFB, Lakewood, **E...gas:** Exxon, **W...gas:** Chevron, 76/diesel, Shell/diesel, Tesoro, **food:** Black Angus, Denny's, El Toro Mexican, KFC, Pizza Hut, Wendy's, **lodging:** Best Western, Ft Lewis Motel, Lakewood Lodge, Madigan Motel, Rose Garden Motel, **other:** HOSPITAL, Aamco, BMW, CarQuest, Goodyear/auto, U-Haul, mall

124 Gravelly Lake Dr, **W...gas:** Arco/repair, 76/24hr, **other:** same as 125

123 Thorne Lane, Tillicum Lane, no facilities

122 Camp Murray, **E...other:** HOSPITAL, **W...gas:** Arco, Chevron/repair, 7-11, **food:** Baskin-Robbins, BBQ Inn, Burrito Mexican, Domino's, Gertie's Grill, KFC, McDonald's, Papa John's, Pizza Hut, Subway, Taco Bell, Taco Time, Teriyaki House, **other:** SpeedZone Parts

120 Ft Lewis, **E...other:** Ft Lewis Military Museum

119 Du Pont Rd, Steilacoom, **W...gas:** 76, **food:** Happy Teriyaki, Starbucks, Subway, Steilacoom Deli

118 Center Dr, **W...lodging:** GuestHouse Inn

117mm weigh sta nb

116 Mounts Rd, Old Nisqually, **W...other:** Riverbend Camping(seasonal)

115mm Nisqually River

114 Nisqually, **E...gas:** Chevron/repair, Exxon/diesel, Shell/diesel/LP, **food:** Figaro's Pizza, Nisqually Grill, Shipwreck Café, Tiny's Burgers/gifts, **other:** Lost Lake RV Resort, Nisqually RV Park

111 WA 510 E, Marvin Rd, to Yelm, **E...gas:** Chevron/24hr, 76/Circle K, Shell/diesel, Tesoro/Taco Bell, **food:** Blimpie, Burger King, DQ, Godfather's, Hawk's Prairie Rest., McDonald's, Papa Murphy's, Ruby Tuesday, Subway, Taco Time, **lodging:** King Oscar Motel, **other:** MegaFoods/24hr, Radio Shack, Rite Aid, Safeway/24hr, Schuck's Parts, Schwab Tire, Wal-Mart, **W...gas:** Pacific Pride/diesel, **food:** Country Jct Rest., Mayan Mexican, **other:** Tolmie SP(5mi), RV camping

Nisqually (vertical)

Olympia (vertical)

109 Martin Way, Sleator-Kenny Rd, **E...food:** Main Chinese Buffet, Pizza Hut/Taco Bell, **other:** Discount Tire, ShopKO, Top Food/24hr, **W...gas:** Arco/24hr, Exxon/diesel, 76/Circle K, Shell/diesel/24hr, **food:** Bailey's Rest., Burger King, Casa Mia Rest., Denny's, El Serape Mexican, IHOP, Jack-in-the-Box, Mandarin House, Red Lobster, Shari's Rest./24hr, Subway, **lodging:** AmeriTel, Bailey Motel, Comfort Inn, Day's Inn, Holiday Inn Express, Holly Motel, Super 8, **other:** HOSPITAL, Firestone/auto, K-Mart, NAPA

108 Sleator-Kenny Rd, **E...gas:** Shell/diesel, **food:** Applebee's, Arby's, Baskin-Robbins, Godfather's, McDonald's, Red Coral Rest., Starbucks, Wendy's, Winchell's/24hr, **other:** Firestone/auto, Fred Meyer, Jo-Ann Fabrics, Mervyn's, Michael's, Office Depot, Radio Shack, Rite Aid, Sears/auto, Target, **W...other:** HOSPITAL, same as 109

107 Pacific Ave, **E...gas:** Shell/diesel, **food:** Izzy's Café, Schlotsky's, Shari's, Sizzler, Taco Time, **other:** Albertson's, Home Depot, Ross, mall, **W...**Ford

105 St Capitol, City Ctr, **E...food:** Figaro's Pizza, Izzy's Pizza, Pacific Terrace Rest., Rainier Rest., Ribeye Rest., Sizzler, Taco Time, **other:** Food Pavilion, Foreign Auto Works, RV Ctr, mall, **W...gas:** Chevron/24hr, Shell/diesel/24hr, **food:** Casa Mia Rest., Chinese Buffet, DQ, Jack-in-the-Box, McDonald's, Plum St Deli, Saigon Rest., Starbuck's, **lodging:** Best Western, Carriage Inn, Econolodge, Golden Gavel Motel, Phoenix Inn, Ramada Inn, **other:** Pontiac/Cadillac/Saturn

104 US 101 N, W Olympia, to Aberdeen, **W...gas:** Arco, Chevron, Citgo/7-11, Shell/diesel, **food:** Jack-in-the-Box, **lodging:** Extended Stay America, West Coast Motel, **other:** HOSPITAL, to Capitol Mall

103 2nd Ave, no facilities

102 Trosper Rd, Black Lake, **E...gas:** Arco/24hr, Citgo/7-11, Shell/diesel/24hr, **food:** Arby's, Burger King, Cattin's Rest./24hr, El Sarape Mexican, Jack-in-the-Box, KFC, McDonald's, Pizza Hut, Subway, Taco Bell, Teriyaki Rest., **lodging:** Best Western, Motel 6, **other:** Goodyear, Schuck's Parts, **W...gas:** Chevron/24hr, 76/Circle K, Shell/24hr, **food:** Nickelby's Rest., **lodging:** Tyee Hotel/rest., **other:** Albertson's, Costco, Fred Meyer, Home Depot, MegaFoods/24hr

101 Airdustrial Way, **E...gas:** Chevron, Shell, **food:** DQ, Quizno's, **lodging:** Comfort Inn, GuestHouse Inn, Olympia Camping

99 WA 121 S, 93rd Ave, Scott Lake, **E...other:** American Heritage Camping, Offut Lake Resort(9mi), **W...gas:** Exxon/diesel(1mi), Shell/rest/diesel/LP/@, **food:** Hannah's Pantry Rest., **lodging:** Restover Motel,

95 WA 121, Littlerock, **3 mi E...other:** Millersylvania SP, RV camping, **W...food:** Farmboy Drive-In

WASHINGTON

Interstate 5

N ↕ **S**

C e n t r a l i a

93.5mm rest area sb, full(handicapped)facilities, info, phone, picnic tables, litter barrels, vending, coffee, petwalk

91mm rest area nb, full(handicapped)facilities, info, phone, picnic tables, litter barrels, vending, coffee, petwalk

88 US 12, Rochester, **W...gas:** Arco/24hr, 76/diesel, Shell/diesel/LP/repair, **food:** DQ, Grand Mound Pizza/deli, Little Red Barn Rest./24hr, Lucky Eagle Casino/café, Royal India Rest., **other:** Outback RV Park(2mi), Harrison RV Park(3mi)

82 Harrison Ave, Factory Outlet Way, Centralia, **E...gas:** Arco/24hr, Shell/diesel, **food:** Alberto's Mexican, Burger King, Burgerville, Casa Ramos Mexican, DQ, Godfather's, Panda Inn, Pizza Hut, Quizno's, Shari's/24hr, TCBY, Wendy's, **lodging:** Centralia Inn, Ferryman's Inn, King Oscar Motel, Panda Inn, Riverside Motel, **other:** HOSPITAL, VF/famous brands, **W...gas:** Chevron, 76/Circle K, Shell, **food:** Arby's, Country Cousin Rest., Denny's, Jack-in-the-Box, McDonald's, Papa Murphy's, Starbucks, Subway, Taco Bell, **lodging:** Day's Inn, Motel 6, **other:** GNC, Midway RV Park, Outlet Mall/famous brands, Rite Aid, Safeway, Schuck's Parts, Scwab Tire

82mm Skookumchuck River

81 WA 507, Mellen St, **E...gas:** Shell, Texaco/diesel, **food:** Buchanan's Rest., King Solomon Rest., Olympic Club Rest., **lodging:** Holiday Inn Express, Pepper Tree Motel/RV Park, Travel Inn, **other:** RV camp/dump, **W...** HOSPITAL

79 Chamber Way, **E...gas:** 76/diesel, Shell/diesel/24hr, **food:** Burger King, McDonald's, Plaza Jalisco Mexican, Subway, **other:** Ford/Lincoln/Mercury/Toyota, GNC, Goodyear/auto, Radio Shack, RV Ctr, museum, **W...gas:** 76/Burger King/diesel/LP, **food:** Starbucks, Taco Del Mar, Wendy's, **other:** $Tree, K-Mart/Little Caesar's, Wal-Mart/Super Ctr/24hr/auto, st patrol

77 WA 6 W, Chehalis, **E...gas:** Cenex/diesel, **food:** Dairy Bar, **lodging:** St Helens Inn/rest., **other:** Healthy Harvest Foods, Hustons Parts, NAPA, Schwab Tire, **W...** Rainbow Falls SP(16mi)

76 13th St, **E...gas:** Arco/24hr, Chevron, 76, **food:** Denny's, Jack-in-the Box, Jade Garden Chinese, Kit Carson Rest., Subway, **lodging:** Best Western, Howard Johnson, Relax Inn, **other:** Safeway, **W...** RV park/dump

72 Rush Rd, Napavine, **E...gas:** Shell/Taco Bell/diesel/@, **food:** Burger King, McDonald's, RibEye Rest./24hr, Subway, **other:** Dave's RV Ctr, RV park, **W...gas:** Chevron/diesel/24hr, Pacific Pride/diesel, Shell/diesel, **food:** FoodCourt, Uhlmann RV Ctr.

72mm Newaukum River

71 WA 508 E, Onalaska, Napavine, **E...gas:** 76/diesel

68 US 12 E, Morton, **E...gas:** Arco/24hr, Chevron/diesel/RV Park, 76/diesel/LP, Spiffy's Rest./24hr, **other:** KOA, to Lewis&Clark SP, Mt Ranier NP, **W...gas:** Shell/diesel, **food:** The Mustard Seed Rest.

63 WA 505, Winlock, **E...other:** RV park(3mi), **W...gas:** Shell/diesel/LP

60 Vader Rd, Toledo, no facilities

59 WA 506 W, Vader, **E...gas:** Shell/diesel, **W...gas:** Chevron/Subway/diesel/24hr, **food:** Burger & More, Country House Rest., **other:** River Oaks RV Park

59mm Cowlitz River

57 Barnes Dr, Jackson Hwy, **W...gas:** GeeCee's/diesel/café/24hr/@, **other:** repair, RV camping

55mm rest area both lanes, full(handicapped)facilities, phone, picnic tables, litter barrels, vending, petwalk

52 Toutle Park Rd, **E...other:** Paradise Cove RV Park

50mm Toutle River

49 WA 504 E, Castle Rock, **E...gas:** Chevron, 76/diesel, Pacific Pride, Shell/diesel, **food:** Burger King, C&L Burgers, El Compadre Mexican, Peper's 49er Diner, Papa Pete's Pizza, Pizza Parlor, RoseTree Rest., Subway, **lodging:** Mt St Helens Motel, 7 West Motel, Silver Lake Motel/resort, Timberland Inn, **other:** Seaquest SP(5mi)

48 Huntington Ave, no facilities

46 Pleasant Hill Rd, **E...other:** Cedars RV Park

44mm weigh sta sb, phone

42 Ostrander Rd, no facilities

K e l s o

40 to WA 4, Kelso-Longview, **1 mi W...gas:** 76, **lodging:** Best Value Inn, Western, Budget Inn, Townhouse Motel, **other:** HOSPITAL, Parts+, transmissions

39 WA 4, Kelso, to Longview, **E...gas:** Arco/24hr, Shell, **food:** Denny's, McDonald's, Shari's/24hr, Subway, **lodging:** Motel 6, Red Lion Motel, Super 8, **other:** Rite Aid, Safeway, **W...gas:** Chevron/repair, **food:** Azteca Mexican, Burger King, DQ, Izzy's Pizza, North's Buffet, Red Lobster, Taco Bell, **lodging:** Best Western, Comfort Inn, GuestHouse Inn, **other:** JC Penney, Safeway/drug, Sears/auto, Target, mall, museum

36 WA 432 W, to WA 433, US 30, Kelso, **E...other:** U-Neek RV Ctr, **1-3 mi W...gas:** Arco, 76/diesel, **lodging:** Patrician Inn, Ramada Ltd., **other:** HOSPITAL, Longview RV Ctr, Toyota, Oaks RV Park, st patrol

32 Kalama River Rd, **E...food:** Fireside Café, **other:** Camp Kalama RV Park/gifts

31mm Kalama River

30 Kalama, **E...gas:** Chevron/diesel, **food:** Burger Bar, Key Grill, Playa Azul Mexican, Subway, **lodging:** Columbia Inn/rest., Kalama River Inn, **other:** Big A Parts, USPO, **W...gas:** Spirit/gas, **other:** RV camping

27 Todd Rd, Port of Kalama, **E...gas:** Shell/diesel/café/24hr

22 Dike Access Rd, **W...gas:** CFN/diesel/24hr, **other:** Columbia Riverfront/Lewis River/Woodland Shores RV Parks

W o o d l a n d

21 WA 503 E, Woodland, **E...gas:** Arco/24hr, Chevron, Pacific Pride, Shell/diesel, **food:** Burgerville, Casa Maria's, DQ, Figaro's Italian, Grandma's House(8mi), OakTree Rest., Riverside Rest., Rosie's Rest., South China Rest., Subway, **lodging:** Best Inn, Best Western, Econolodge, Lewis River Inn, Woodlander Inn, **other:** CarQuest, Hi-School Drug, Letterbox, Radio Shack, Sav-On Foods, U-Haul, Woodland Shores RV Park, **W...gas:** Exxon/24hr, Shell, **food:** McDonald's, ParkPlace Pizza, Whimpy's Rest., **lodging:** Hansen's Motel, Lakeside Motel, Scandia Motel, **other:** Chevrolet, NAPA, Safeway/gas

Interstate 5

N ↕ S

20mm	N Fork Lewis River
18mm	E Fork Lewis River
16	NW 319th St, La Center, **E...gas:** Shell/diesel/24hr, **food:** Lucky Dragon Rest., **other:** Paradise Point SP, Tri-Mountain Golf/rest.
15mm	weigh sta nb
14	WA 501 W, NW 269th St, **E...gas:** Arco/24hr, 76/Circle K/diesel, **food:** Country Café, Papa Pete's Pizza, **other:** to Battleground Lake SP(14mi), Big Fir RV Park(4mi), Ridgefield WR, Tri-Mountain RV Park, **W...gas:** Chevron/diesel
13mm	**rest area sb, full(handicapped)facilities, info, phone, picnic tables, litter barrels, vending, petwalk, RV dump**
11mm	**rest area nb, full(handicapped)facilities, info, phone, picnic tables, litter barrels, vending, petwalk, RV dump**
9	NE 179th St, **E...food:** Jollie's Rest./24hr, **other:** Poulsbo RV, **W...gas:** Chevron/diesel
7	I-205 S(from sb), to I-84, WA 14, NE 134th St, Portland Airport, **E...gas:** Arco, Citgo/7-11, 76, TrailMart/diesel, **food:** Billygan's Roadhouse, Burger King, Burgerville, Jack-in-the-Box, McDonald's, Round Table Pizza, Taco Bell, **lodging:** Comfort Inn, Holiday Inn Express, Olympia Motel, Red Lion, Salmon Creek Inn, Shilo Inn, **other:** HOSPITAL, Albertson's/gas, Long's Drugs, Zupan's Mkt, 99 RV Park, **W...gas:** Mobil/diesel, **lodging:** University Inn, **other:** Fred Meyer
5	NE 99th St, **E...gas:** Arco/24hr, Citgo/7-11, **food:** Burgerville, Carl's Jr, Del Taco, Domino's, Fat Dave's Rest., Quizno's, **other:** Harley-Davidson, Nissan/Kia, Walgreen, Wal-Mart/auto/gas, Winco Foods/gas/24hr, **W...gas:** Arco/24hr, Chevron/24hr, **food:** Applebee's, McDonald's, Papa John's, **other:** Albertson's, Hi-School Drug, Target
4	NE 78th St, Hazel Dell, **E...gas:** Exxon, 76, Shell, **food:** BBQ, Burger King, Burgerville, Buster's BBQ, Dragon King Chinese, Izzy's Rest., KFC, Mar-Bo Chinese, McDonald's, Pizza Hut, Skipper's, Smokey's Pizza, Starbucks, Steakburger, Subway, Taco Bell, Taco Time, **lodging:** Best Inn, Edelweiss Inn, Quality Inn, **other:** America's Tire, CarQuest, Firestone, Fred Meyer, Dodge, Ford, Goodyear, Mazda, Nissan, Radio Shack, Schuck's Parts, U-Haul, transmissions, **W...gas:** Shell/diesel/LP, **food:** Denny's, Figaro's Pizza, Wendy's, **other:** Rite Aid, Ross, Safeway
3	NE Hwy 99, Main St, Hazel Dell, **E...other:** HOSPITAL, **W...gas:** Arco, **other:** Safeway, transmissions
2	WA 500 E, 39th St, to Orchards, no facilities
1d	E 4th, Plain Blvd W, to WA 501, Port of Vancouver, no facilities
1c	Mill Plain Blvd, City Ctr, **W...gas:** Chevron, **food:** Cattle Co Rest., Burgerville, Denny's, **lodging:** Red Lion, Shilo Inn, **other:** Ford, Lincoln/Mercury, Pontiac/Cadillac/GMC, Jeep, Mitsubishi, Suzuki, Clark Coll, st patrol
1b	6th St, downtown, **W...lodging:** Red Lion
1a	WA 14 E, to Camus, **E...**HOSPITAL
0mm	Washington/Oregon state line, Columbia River

Vancouver (vertical left margin)

Kennewick (vertical right margin)

Interstate 82

E ↕ W

Exit #	Services
11mm	I-82 Oregon begins/ends on I-84, exit 179.
10	Westland Rd, **E...other:** to Umatilla Army Depot, **lodging:** to Best Western, **other:** HOSPITAL
5	Power Line Rd, no facilities
1.5mm	Umatilla River
1	US 395/730, Umatilla, **E...lodging:** Best Western, Desert Inn, **other:** Hatrock Camping(8mi), to McNary Dam, **W...gas:** Amoco/diesel/LP, Arco/diesel/24hr, Shell/diesel/rest., **food:** Dojack's Rest., G&J Burgers, **lodging:** Heather Inn, McNary Hotel, Rest-a-Bit Motel, Tillicum Motel, **other:** NAPA, Red Apple Mkt, USPO, st police, Welcome Ctr, weigh sta
132mm	Washington/Oregon state line, Columbia River
131	WA 14 W, Plymouth, **N...other:** RV camping, to McNary Dam
130mm	weigh sta wb
122	Coffin Rd, no facilities
114	Locust Grove Rd, no facilities
113	US 395 N, to I-182, Kennewick, Pasco, **N...gas:** Arco/24hr, Cevron, Exxon, Tesoro, **food:** Billigan's Roadhouse, Bruchi's Café, Burger King, China Café, Godfather's, Starbucks, Subway, **lodging:** Best Western, Econolodge, Hawthorn Suites, Holiday Inn Express, La Quinta, Nendel's Inn, Tapadera Budget Motel, Travelodge, **other:** GNC, Wal-Mart SuperCtr/24hr/gas, **2-5 mi N...**Carl's Jr, Denny's, DQ, Jack-in-the-Box, McDonald's, KFC/Taco Bell, Day's Inn, Harley-Davidson, Hastings Books, Radio Shack, Rite Aid, Safeway/food/drug
109	Badger Rd, W Kennewick, **N...gas:** Shell/BYOBurger/diesel/24hr, **3 mi N...food:** Chico's Tacos, McDonald's, Subway, **lodging:** Clearwater Inn, Red Lion, Silver Cloud Inn, Super 8, West Coast Inn
104	Dallas Rd, **3 mi N...gas:** Conoco/diesel/24hr, **food:** Hotstuff Pizza/subs
102	I-182, US 12 E, to US 395, Spokane, HOSPITAL, facilities in Richland, Pasco
96	WA 224, Benton City, **N...gas:** Conoco/cafe/diesel/24hr, **other:** Beach RV Park
93	Yakitat Rd, no facilities
88	Gibbon Rd, no facilities

WASHINGTON

Interstate 82

82 WA 22, WA 221, Mabton, **S...gas:** Conoco, **2 mi S... food:** Blue Goose Rest., **lodging:** Prosser Motel, **other:** HOSPITAL, to WA St U Research, to Wine Tasting Facilities, museum

82mm Yakima River

80 Gap Rd, **S...gas:** Shell/diesel, **food:** Blue Goose Rest., Burger King, KFC/Taco Bell, McDonald's, NorthWoods Rest., **lodging:** Barn Motel/RV Park/rest., Best Western, Prosser Motel, **other:** HOSPITAL, Ford/Mercury, Wine Country RV Park, **rest area both lanes, full(handicapped)facilities, phone, picnic tables, litter barrels**

76mm weigh sta eb

75 County Line Rd, Grandview, **S...gas:** Cenex/diesel, Conoco/diesel/24hr(1mi), **1 mi S...lodging:** Apple Valley Motel, Grandview Motel, **other:** same as 73

73 Stover Rd, Wine Country Rd, Grandview, **S...gas:** Conoco/diesel/24hr, Shell/Quizno's/TCBY/diesel, **food:** Eli&Kathy's Breakfast, Morrie's Pizza, New Hong Kong, Noble Roman's, 10-4 Café, **lodging:** Apple Valley Motel, Grandview Motel, **other:** Plymouth/Jeep/Dodge, Red Apple Foods, RV Ctr, RV Park/dump, auto repair

69 WA 241, to Sunnyside, **N...gas:** Arco/diesel/24hr, Shell/TacoMaker/diesel/24hr, **food:** Arby's, Burger King, DQ, KFC, McDonald's, Papa Murphy's, Pizza Hut, Skipper's, Subway, Taco Bell, **lodging:** Best Western, Rodeway Inn, **other:** BiMart Foods, Buick/Chevrolet/Nissan, $Tree, GNC, JC Penney, Staples, Wal-Mart SuperCtr/24hr/auto/gas

67 Sunnyside, Port of Sunnyside, **N...gas:** Chevron/CFN/diesel, **food:** Jack-in-the-Box, **other:** HOSPITAL, BiMart Foods, **S...other:** DariGold Cheese

63 Outlook, Sunnyside, **3 mi N...food:** Burger Ranch, Snipe's Rest, **lodging:** Country Inn, Sunnyside B&B, **other:** RV camping

58 WA 223 S, to Granger, **S...gas:** Conoco/diesel, **other:** RV camping

54 Division Rd, Yakima Valley Hwy, to Zillah, **S...other:** Teapot Dome NHS, diesel/LP

52 Zillah, Toppenish, **N...gas:** Chevron, 76/diesel, Shell, **food:** El Porton Mexican, Mario's Cantina, McDonald's, Subway, **lodging:** Comfort Inn, **other:** RV dump

50 WA 22 E, to US 97 S, Toppenish, **N...food:** Gold Nugget Café/casino, **3 mi S...food:** Legends Buffet/casino, McDonald's, **lodging:** Best Western, Toppenish Inn, **other:** HOSPITAL, Murals Museum, RV Park, to Yakima Nation Cultural Ctr

44 Wapato, **N...gas:** Shell/diesel, **2 mi S...food:** DQ

40 Thorp Rd, Parker Rd, Yakima Valley Hwy, **N...other:** Sagelands Vineyard/Winery

39mm Yakima River

38 Union Gap(from wb), **1 mi S...food:** Peppermint Stick Drive-In, **other:** gas, lodging, museum

37 US 97(from eb), **1 mi S...gas:** Exxon, Shell, **other:** Canopy RV Ctr, NAPA

36 Valley Mall Blvd, Yakima, **S...gas:** Arco/diesel/24hr, Cenex/diesel, Shell/Gearjammer/diesel/rest./24hr/@, **food:** Burger King, Denny's/24hr, Godfather's, Hill's Café, IHOP, Jack-in-the-Box, KFC, Miner's Drive-In, Outback Steaks, SeaGalley Rest., Shangrila Chinese, Shari's, Taco Bell, **lodging:** Best Western, Cobblestone Inn, Quality Inn, Super 8, **other:** MEDICAL CARE, Big A Parts, Goodyear, Lowe's Whse, Office Depot, Rite Aid, Sears/auto, ShopKO, diesel/repair, mall, st patrol

34 WA 24 E, Nob Hill Blvd, Yakima, **N...other:** K-Mart, Sportsman SP, KOA, diesel/repair, **S...gas:** Arco/24hr, Chevron/Subway/TCBY/diesel/24hr, CFN/diesel, Citgo/7-11, **food:** Arby's, McDonald's, **other:** HOSPITAL, Al's Parts, Circle H Ranch RV Park, Family Foods, Shuck's Parts, museum

33 Yakima Ave, Yakima, **N...gas:** Chevron/Quizno's/TCBY/24hr, Shell/Chester's/diesel, **food:** Burger King, McDonald's, **lodging:** Oxford Suites, **other:** Chevrolet/GMC/Isuzu, Honda, Mazda, Wal-Mart SuperCtr/24hr, **S...gas:** Arco/24hr, Citgo/7-11, **food:** DQ, FoodCourt, Taco Bell, **lodging:** Fairfield Inn, Holiday Inn Express, Red Lion Motel, **other:** JC Penney, Mervyn's, OfficeMax, Yakima Ave Mkt, Schwab Tire, Target, mall

31b a US 12 W, N 1st St, to Naches, **S...gas:** Arco/diesel/24hr, Exxon, Shell/repair, **food:** Arctic Circle, Black Angus, China Buffet, Denny's, Espinoza's Mexican, Jack-in-the-Box, Mel's Diner/24hr, Peking Palace, Pizza Hut, Red Apple Rest., Red Lobster, Sizzler, Subway, Waffles'n More, Wendy's, **lodging:** Best Western, Big Valley Motel, DoubleTree Hotel, Day's Inn, Economy Inn, Motel 6, Red Lion Inn, Sun Country Inn, Tourist Motel, Twin Bridges Inn, Vagabond Inn, Yakima Inn, **other:** Nendel's, Trailer Inn RV park

30 WA 823 N, Rest Haven Rd, to Selah, no facilities

29 E Selah Rd, **N...other:** fruits/antiques

26 WA 821 N, to WA 823, Canyon Rd, **N...gas:** Shell/Noble Roman/Quizno's/LP/diesel/24hr

24mm **rest area eb, full(handicapped)facilities, phone, picnic tables, litter barrels, RV dump**

23mm Selah Creek

22mm **rest area wb, full(handicapped)facilities, phone, picnic tables, litter barrels, RV dump**

21mm S Umptanum Ridge, 2265 elev

19mm Burbank Creek

17mm N Umptanum Ridge, 2315 elev

15mm Lmuma Creek

11 Military Area, Military Area, no facilities

8mm view point both lanes, Manastash Ridge, 2672 elev

3 WA 821 S, Thrall Rd, no facilities

0mm I-90, E to Spokane, W to Seattle. I-82 begins/ends on I-90, exit 110.

Yakima

516

Interstate 90

E

W

Exit #	Services

300mm Washington/Idaho state line, Spokane River

299 State Line, Port of Entry, **N...Welcome Ctr/rest area both lanes, weigh sta, full(handicapped)facilities, phone, picnic tables, litter barrels, petwalk, S... gas:** Gas n' Go, Shell

296 Otis Orchards, Liberty Lakes, **N...gas:** Shell/Subway/ diesel, **food:** HomePlate Grill, **lodging:** Best Western, **other:** GMC/Hummer/Pontiac, **S...gas:** Chevron/LP, 76, **food:** Burger King, Carl's Jr, Domino's, McDonald's, Palenque Mexican, Papa Murphy's, Pizza Hut, Quizno's, Taco Bell, Subway, **lodging:** Comfort Inn, **other:** Albertson's, Alton Tire, GNC, La Mes RV Ctr, RNH RV Ctr, Land Rover, Safeway/gas

294 Sprague Ave(from wb, no EZ return), **S...other:** North Country RV/marine, Nut Factory, auto repair

293 Barker Rd, Greenacres, **N...gas:** Conoco/Wendy's/ diesel, **food:** Slapshot Café, Wendy's, **other:** Alpine Motel/RV Park, KOA, **S...gas:** Conoco/diesel/24hr, Exxon/Subway/diesel/24hr, **other:** NW RV Ctr

291b Sullivan Rd, Veradale, **N...gas:** Chevron/Blimpie/ TCBY, **food:** Arby's, Krispy Kreme, McDonald's, Outback Steaks, Tony Roma, Red Robin, **lodging:** Hawthorn Inn, La Quinta, Oxford Suites, Residence Inn, **other:** Barnes&Noble, Best Buy, Circuit City, JC Penney, Staples, TJ Maxx, mall, **S...gas:** Chevron, Conoco, 76, Shell/diesel, Tesoro, **food:** A&W, Bruchi's Rest., DQ, Godfather's, Jack-in-the Box, KFC, McDonald's, Mongolian BBQ, Noodle Express, Pizza Hut, Schlotsky's, Shari's/24hr, Starbucks, Subway, Taco Bell, Wendy's, **lodging:** Comfort Inn, DoubleTree Hotel, Mirabeau Park Hotel, **other:** Ace Hardware, Goodyear/auto, Hastings Books, K-Mart, Michael's, Rite Aid, Ross, Wal-Mart SuperCtr/24hr/ auto

291a Evergreen Rd, **N...food:** Black Angus, Boston Rest, IHOP, **other:** Greenbax, Old Navy, Sears/auto, mall, **S...gas:** Shell

S p o k a n e

289 WA 27 S, Pines Rd, Opportunity, **N...gas:** Citgo/7-11, **food:** Old Matthews Rest., **S...gas:** Holiday, Shell/ diesel, 76, **food:** Applebee's, DQ, Jack-in-the-Box, Quizno's, **lodging:** Best Western, **other:** HOSPITAL, Standard Battery

287 Argonne Rd, Millwood, **N...gas:** Holiday/diesel, **food:** Burger King, Denny's, Jack-in-the-Box, Longhorn BBQ, Marie Callender's, McDonald's, Papa Murphy's, Subway, Wendy's, **lodging:** Motel 6, RedTop Motel, Super 8, **other:** Albertson's/gas, Yoke's Foods, Schuck's Parts, Tidyman's Foods, Walgreen, **S... gas:** 76/Circle K, Chevron, Exxon, **food:** Casa de Oro Mexican, Godfather's, GoodTymes Grill, Perkins, **lodging:** Holiday Inn Express, Quality Inn, **other:** Rite Aid/24hr, Safeway

286 Broadway Ave, **N...gas:** Flying J/Conoco/Rest./diesel/LP/24hr/@, **food:** Zip's Burgers, Best Inn, Comfort Inn, Goodyear, **lodging:** Broadway Inn, Schwab Tire, White/Volvo/GMC, **S...**7-11

285 Sprague Ave, **N... gas:** Shell, **food:** Denny's, Dragon Garden Rest, IHOP, Jack-in-the-Box, McDonald's, Wendy's, **lodging:** ParkLane Motel, **other:** Costco/gas, Grocery Outlet, Home Depot, K-Mart, Lowe's Whse, Radio Shack, Shuck's Parts, **S...gas:** Exxon, **food:** Mandarin House, Puerta Vallarta Mexican, Subway, Taco Time, Zip's Burger, **other:** Alton's Tire, Chevrolet, Chrysler/Plymouth, Dodge, Ford, Hyundai, L&L RV Ctr, Nissan/Saab, RV camping, transmissions

284 Havana St(from eb, no EZ return), **N...food:** Jack-in-the-Box, McDonald's

283b Freya St, Thor St, **N...gas:** Chevron, Conoco/diesel, Tesoro/diesel, **food:** Peking Garden, Subway, Wolf Lodge Steaks, **other:** Park Lane Motel/RV Park, Fred Meyer, **S... gas:** Citgo/7-11, Shell/Taco Bell

283a Altamont St, **S...gas:** 76

282b 2nd Ave, **N...lodging:** Shilo Inn, **other:** Office Depot

282a WA 290 E, Trent Ave, Hamilton St, **N...gas:** Shell/diesel, **lodging:** Shilo Inn, **other:** Shogun Japanese, Office Depot

281 US 2, US 395, to Colville, **N...gas:** Citgo/7-11, Shell/repair, Tesoro/diesel, **food:** Arby's, Dick's Hamburgers, Just Like Home Buffet, McDonald's, Perkins, Pizza Hut, Rancho Chico's Rest., Subway, Taco Time, Waffles Gaffe, **lodging:** Best Value, Courtyard, Howard Johnson, **other:** Firestone, Ford, Schwab Tire, U-Haul, **S...lodging:** Budget Inn, **other:** HOSPITAL

280b Lincoln St, **N...gas:** Chevron, Conoco/diesel, Shell, **food:** Burger King, Carl's Jr, Godfather's, IHOP, Jack-in-the-Box, McDonald's, Taco Bell, Wendy's, Zip's Burgers, **lodging:** Best Western, Ramada Inn, **other:** Cadillac, Lincoln/Mercury, Honda, Lexus, Mazda, Mercedes, Saturn, Toyota, **S...HOSPITAL**

280a downtown, **N...gas:** Chevron/McDonald's, Conoco/diesel, Shell, Texaco, **food:** Arctic Circle, Perkins, Subway, **lodging:** Select Inn, **other:** AAA, Chevrolet, NAPA, Safeway

279 US 195 S, Pullman, to Colfax, **N...lodging:** West Wynn Hotel, Shangri-la Motel

277b a US 2 W, to Grand Coulee Dam, Fairchild AFB, **N...lodging:** Day's Inn, Hampton Inn, Motel 6, Ramada, Shangri-la Motel, Spokane House Hotel

276 Geiger Blvd, **N...gas:** Flying J/Exxon/Subway/diesel/LP/ rest./24hr/@, **food:** Denny's, Subway, **lodging:** Airway Express Inn, Best Western, **other:** USPO, st patrol, **S... gas:** Shell/diesel/LP, Sunset RV Park/dump

272 WA 902, Medical Lake, **N...gas:** Shell/diesel, **other:** Overland Sta/RV Park, **S...lodging:** Super 8, **other:** Yogi Bear Camping

270 WA 904, Cheney, Four Lakes, **S...gas:** Exxon, **lodging:** Rosebrook Inn(6mi), Willow Springs Motel(6mi), **other:** Peaceful Pines RV Park, Ford, E WA U

264 WA 902, Salnave Rd, to Cheney, Medical Lake, **2 mi N... camping**

WASHINGTON

Interstate 90

| 257 | WA 904, Tyler, to Cheney, no facilities |

257 WA 904, Tyler, to Cheney, no facilities

254 Fishtrap, **S...other:** Fishtrap RV camping/tents

245 WA 23, Sprague, **S...gas:** Chevron/diesel, **food:** Viking Drive-In, **lodging:** Last Roundup Motel, Purple Sage Motel, Sprague Motel, **other:** 4 Seasons RV Park, Sprague Lake Resort/RV Park

242mm rest area both lanes, full(handicapped)facilities, phone, picnic tables, litter barrels, tourist/weather info, petwalk, free coffee

231 Tokio, **S...**weigh sta both lanes, **gas:** Exxon/Templin's Café/diesel, **other:** RV Park

226 Coker Rd, **S...other:** Cottage RV Park

221 WA 261 S, Ritzville, City Ctr, **N...gas:** Cenex, Conoco, Chevron/McDonald's, Exxon, Shell/Taco Bell/diesel, **food:** Perkins, Sharon & Russ' Rest., Zip's Burgers, **lodging:** Best Inn/RV Park, Best Western, Colwell Motel, Empire Motel, La Quinta, Top Hat Motel, **other:** HOSPITAL, hist dist

220 to US 395 S, Ritzville, **N...gas:** Astro, Cenex, Chevron, Exxon/diesel/café, **food:** Circle T Rest, Jake's Café, Texas John's Café, Wispering Palms, **lodging:** Caldwell Inn, Westside Motel, **other:** st patrol

215 Paha, Packard, no facilities

206 WA 21, Odessa, to Lind, no facilities

199mm rest area both lanes, full(handicapped)facilities, phone, picnic tables, litter barrels, vending, RV dump, petwalk

196 Deal Rd, to Schrag, no facilities

188 U Rd, to Warden, Ruff, no facilities

184 Q Rd, no facilities

182 O Rd, to Wheeler, no facilities

179 WA 17, Moses Lake, **N...gas:** Cenex, Conoco/diesel, Earnie's Trkstp/Chevron/diesel/café/24hr/@, Exxon, 76/diesel, Shell/diesel, **food:** Arby's, Burger King, DQ, Denny's, McDonald's, Shari's Rest./24hr, Starbuck's, **lodging:** Holiday Inn Express, Moses Lake Inn, Shilo Inn/rest./24hr, The Inn, **other:** HOSPITAL, **1 mi N...food:** DQ, Subway, **lodging:** El Rancho Motel, Sage'n Sand Motel, **other:** $tree, MEDICAL CARE, Honda, Nissan, USPO, **2 mi N...food:** Godfather's, Jack-in-the-Box, KFC, Pizza Hut, **other:** Buick/Chevrolet/Pontiac, CarQuest, Chrysler/Plymouth, Ford/Lincoln/Mercury, Rite Aid, Safeway, Scwab Tire, **S...other:** I-90 RV, Mardon RV Park(15), Sun Country RV, Willows RV Park(2mi), Potholes SP(15mi)

177mm Moses Lake

176 WA 171, Moses Lake, **1 mi N...gas:** Cenex/24hr, Exxon/diesel, Shell/diesel, **food:** El Rodeo Mexican, Godfather's, Kiyoji's Rest., Perkins/24hr, **lodging:** Best Western/rest., Interstate Inn, Maples Motel, Motel 6, Oasis Budget Inn, Super 8, Motel 6, **other:** HOSPITAL, OK Tires, Big Sun Resort/RV Hookups, **S...lodging:** Lakeshore Motel

175 Westshore Dr(from wb), **N...other:** Moses Lake SP, to Mae Valley, **S...other:** st patrol

174 Mae Valley, **N...other:** Suncrest Resort/RV, **S...gas:** Conoco/diesel, **other:** st patrol

169 Hiawatha Rd, no facilities

164 Dodson Rd, no facilities

162mm rest area wb, full(handicapped)facilities, phone, picnic tables, litter barrels, petwalk, RV dump

161mm rest area eb, full(handicapped)facilities, phone, picnic tables, litter barrels, petwalk, RV dump

154 Adams Rd, no facilities

151 WA 281 N, to Quincy, **N...gas:** Shell/diesel/pizza/subs, **other:** HOSPITAL(12mi)

149 WA 281 S, George, **N...**HOSPITAL(12mi), **S...gas:** Exxon/diesel/24hr, 76/Subway/diesel, **food:** Martha Inn Café, **other:** RV camp

143 Silica Rd, to The Gorge Ampitheatre

139mm Wild Horses Mon, scenic view both lanes

137 WA 26 E, to WA 243, Othello, Richland, no facilities

137mm Columbia River

136 Huntzinger Rd, Vantage, **N...gas:** Shell, Texaco/diesel, **food:** Blustry's Rest, Golden Harvest Café, Wanapum Rest., **lodging:** Motel Vantage, **other:** KOA, to Ginkgo/Wanapum SP(3mi), auto repair, **4 mi S...other:** Gettys Cove RV Park

126mm Ryegrass, elev 2535, rest area both lanes, full(handicapped)facilities, phone, picnic tables, litter barrels, petwalk

115 Kittitas, **N...gas:** 76/LP/24hr, Shell/diesel/24hr, **food:** RJ's Café, **other:** Olmstead Place SP

110 I-82 E, US 97 S, to Yakima, no facilities

109 Canyon Rd, Ellensburg, **N...gas:** Astro/diesel, Chevron/24hr, Eagle Trkstp/diesel, Pacific Pride, 76, Shell/24hr, **food:** Arby's, Baskin-Robbins, Burger King, Fiesta Mexican, Godfather's, Golden Dragon Chinese, KFC, Los Cabos Mexican, McDonald's, Matterhorn Rest., Palace Café, Pizza Hut, RanchHouse Rest., Skipper's, Subway, Taco Bell, Tanum Rest., **lodging:** Best Western, Comfort Inn, Ellensburg Inn, Goose Creek Inn, Nites Inn, Super 8, **other:** HOSPITAL, Al's Parts, BiMart Foods, CarQuest, Chevrolet, NAPA, Radio Shack, Rite Aid, Scwab Tire, Super 1 Food/24hr, **S...gas:** Flying J/Exxon/Sak's/diesel/LP/24hr/@, **food:** Buzz Inn Steaks, **lodging:** Best Inn/RV park

106 US 97 N, to Wenatchie, **N...gas:** Chevron, Conoco/diesel/RV dump, Pilot/Subway/diesel/24hr/@, **food:** Blue Grouse Rest., 76, Copper Kettle(2mi), DQ, Jack-in-the-Box(3mi), Perkins, **lodging:** Harold's Motel(2mi), I-90 Inn, Regal Lodge(2mi), **other:** Ford, **S...other:** KOA, st patrol

101 Thorp Hwy, **N...other:** antiques/fruits/vegetables

93 Elk Heights Rd, Taneum Creek, no facilities

92.5mm Elk Heights, elev 2359

89mm Indian John Hill, elev 2141, rest area both lanes, full(handicapped)facilities, phone, picnic tables, litter barrels, RV dump, petwalk, vending

85 WA 970, WA 903, to Wenatchie, **N...gas:** Conoco/repair, 76/diesel, Shell/diesel/24hr, **food:** Cottage Café/24hr, DQ, Homestead Rest., McKean's Drive-In, **lodging:** Aster Inn, Cascade Mtn Inn, Cedars Motel, Chalet Motel, Wind Blew Inn, **other:** CarQuest, PriceChopper Foods, Trailer Corral RV Park

84 Cle Elum(from eb, return at 85), **N...gas:** Chevron/diesel, Conoco, Shell/Subway/diesel, **food:** Burger King, DQ, El Caporal Mexican, Sunset Café, YumYang Chinese, **lodging:** Cle Elum Motel, Timber Lodge Motel, Traveler's Inn, Snowcap Lodge, Stewarts Lodge, **other:** HOSPITAL, Cle Elum Hardware, Safeway/gas, Trailer Corral RV Park, museum

81mm Cle Elum River

Interstate 90

E

W

80	Roslyn, Salmon la Sac, no facilities
80mm	weigh sta both lanes, phone
78	Golf Course Rd, **S...other:** Sun Country Golf/RV Park
74	W Nelson Siding Rd, no facilities
71	Easton, **S...gas:** CB's Store, **lodging:** Silver Ridge Ranch B&B, **other:** USPO, John Wayne Tr, Iron Horse SP
71mm	Yakima River
70	Lake Easton SP, **N...gas:** Shell/diesel/café, **food:** Mtn High Burger, Parkside Café, **S...other:** Lake Easton RV Camping, Silver Ridge Ranch RV Park
63	Cabin Creek Rd, no facilities
62	Stampede Pass, elev 3750, to Lake Kachess, **N... lodging:** Kachess Lodge
56mm	parking area, eb(.5mi)
54	Hyak, Gold Creek, no facilities
53	Snoqualmie Pass, elev 3022, info, **S...gas:** Chevron, **food:** Family Pancake House, **lodging:** Best Western/Summit Inn, **other:** to rec areas
52	W Summit(from eb), same as 53
47	Tinkham Rd, Denny Creek, Asahel Curtis, **N...other:** chain area, **S...other:** RV camping/dump
45	USFS Rd 9030, **N...other:** to Lookout Point Rd, no facilities
42	Tinkham Rd, **S...RV** camping
38	**N...other:** fire training ctr
35mm	S Fork Snoqualmie River
34	468th Ave SE, Edgewick Rd, **N...gas:** Pacific Pride/diesel, 76/Pizza Hut/Rhodie's BBQ/Taco Bell/diesel, Seattle E/diesel/Ken's Rest./24hr, Shell/Subway/diesel/24hr, TA/diesel/@, **lodging:** Edgewick Inn, NW Motel/RV Park
32	436th Ave SE, North Bend Ranger Sta, **1 mi N...** gas, food, lodging, **S...Gordy's** BBQ
31	WA 202 W, North Bend, Snoqualmie, **N...gas:** Chevron/diesel, 76/diesel, Shell/diesel, **food:** Arby's, Blimpie, Burger King, Carriban Burger, DQ, Denny's, McDonald's, Taco Time, **lodging:** North Bend Motel, Old Honey Farm Inn, Sallish Lodge, Sunset Motel, **other:** HOSPITAL, NorthBend Stores/famous brands, Safeway/deli/24hr, Shuck's Parts, museum, st patrol
27	North Bend, Snoqualmie(from eb), no facilities
25	WA 18 W, Snoqualmie Pkwy, Tacoma, to Auburn, **N...weigh** sta
22	Preston, **N...gas:** Chevron/diesel/24hr, **food:** Expresso Café, Savannah's Burgers, Green Bank Cheese, **other:** USPO, Snoqualmie River RV Park(4mi), **S...other:** Blue Sky RV Park
20	High Point Way, no facilities
18	E Sunset Way, Issaquah, **S...gas:** Shell(1mi), **food:** Domino's, Flying Pie Pizza, Issaquah Brewhouse, Jak's Grill, Shagrila Garden Chinese, Korean Grill, Front St Mkt, **other:** Radio Shack
17	E Sammamish Rd, Front St, Issaquah, **N...gas:** 76, **food:** Cojo Café, Fatburger, Krispy Kreme, McDonald's, Starbucks, **other:** Albertson's, Fred Meyer, Home Depot, Walgreen, **S...gas:** Arco/repair, Chevron/24hr, Shell, Texaco/diesel/24hr, **food:** Domino's, Front St Deli, Skipper's, **other:** U-Haul

Bellevue

Issaquah

15	W A 900, Issaquah, Renton, **N...gas:** Arco/24hr, **food:** Georgio's Subs, IHOP, Red Robin, Tully's Coffee, **lodging:** Holiday Inn, Motel 6, **other:** Barnes& Noble, Costco, Lowe's Whse, Office Depot, Trader Joe's, Unique Foods, to Lk Sammamish SP, **S...gas:** Shell, **food:** Acapulco Mexican, Baskin-Robbins, Boston Mkt, Burger King, Denny's, Georgio's Subs, Godfather's, Honey B Ham, Jack-in-the-Box, JayBerry's Rest., KFC/Taco Bell, La Costa Mexican, Lombardi's Rest., McDonald's, O'Char Bistro, RoundTable Pizza, Schlotsky's, Subway, Taco Del Mar, Taco Time, Tokyo Garden, 12th Ave Café, **other:** Big O Tire, Firestone/auto, Ford, GNC, Harley-Davidson, QFC Foods, Rite Aid, Ross, Safeway Foods, Schuck's Parts, Target, USPO
13	SE Newport Way, W Lake Sammamish, no facilities
11	SE 150th, 156th, 161st, Bellevue, **N...LDS** Temple, **gas:** Shell, 7-11, **food:** DQ, India Quisine, Lil' Jon's Rest., Mandarin Chinese, McDonald's, Samurai Sam's Rest., **lodging:** Day's Inn, Eastgate Motel, Embassy Suites, Kane's Motel, Silver Cloud Inn, **other:** Ford, Jo-Ann Fabrics/crafts, Subaru/VW, Safeway, **S...gas:** 76, Standard/24hr, Shell/diesel/24hr, **food:** Baskin-Robbins, Domino's, Outback Steaks, Pizza Hut, **lodging:** Candlewood Suites, **other:** Albertson's, Rite Aid, Schuck's Parts
10	I-405, N to Bellevue, S to Renton, facilities located off I-405 S, exit 10
9	Bellevue Way, no facilities
8	E Mercer Way, Mercer Island, no facilities
7c	80th Ave SE(exits left from wb), no facilities
7b a	SE 76th Ave, 77th Ave, Island Crest Way, Mercer Island, **S...gas:** Chevron, 76/repair, Shell/diesel/repair, **food:** McDonald's, Mi Pueblo Mexican, 7Star Chinese, Starbucks, Subway, Tully's Coffee, **lodging:** Travelodge, **other:** Island Foods, Walgreen
6	W Mercer Way(from eb), same as 7
5mm	Lake Washington
3b a	Ranier Ave, Seattle, downtown, **N...gas:** Texaco
2c b	I-5, N to Vancouver, S to Tacoma, no facilities
2a	4th Ave S, to King Dome, no facilities
0mm	I-90 begins/ends on I-5 at exit 164.

Interstate 182(Richland)

E

W

Exit #	Services
14b a	US 395 N, WA 397 S, OR Ave, **N...gas:** Shell, **food:** Burger King, Subway, **other:** Goodyear, **S...lodging:** Budget Inn. **I-182 begins/ends on US 395 N.**
13	N 4th Ave, Cty Ctr, **N...gas:** CFN/diesel, **lodging:** Airport Motel, Starlite Motel, **S...other:** HOSPITAL, RV park, museum
12b	N 20th Ave, **N...lodging:** Red Lion Inn

WASHINGTON
Interstate 182

Richland

12a US 395 S, Court St, **S...gas:** Arco/24hr, Conoco, Exxon, Shell, Tesoro, **food:** Arby's, Burger King, Jack-in-the-Box, McDonald's, Pizza Hut, Quizno's, Subway, Taco Bell, Wendy's, **other:** Chief RV Ctr, Chevrolet, Food Pavilion/café, Ford, K-Mart, Toyota, U-Haul

9 rd 68, Trac, **N...gas:** Shell, Tesoro, **food:** McDonalds, Subway, **lodging:** Amerisuites, **other:** Fresh Mkt Foods

7 Broadmoor Blvd, **N...lodging:** Sleep Inn, **other:** Broadmoor Outlet Mall/famous brands, **S...other:** Broadmoor RV Ctr, Sandy Heights RV Park

6.5mm Columbia River

5b a WA 240 E, Geo Washington Way, to Kennewick, **N...** Day's Inn, Economy Inn, Hampton Inn, Red Lion, Royal Hotel, Shilo Inn

4 WA 240 W, **N...gas:** Conoco/diesel, 7-11, **food:** McDonald's, **other:** Fred Meyer

3.5mm Yakima River

3 Keene Rd, Queensgate, **N...gas:** Arco/mart, Shell, **food:** Burger King, **other:** Wal-Mart/auto/gas, **S... other:** RV Park(3mi)

0mm I-182 begins/ends on I-82, exit 102.

Interstate 405(Seattle)

Exit # Services

30 I-5, N to Canada, S to Seattle, I-405 begins/ends on I-5, exit 182., no facilities

26 WA 527, Bothell, Mill Creek, **E...food:** Canyon's Rest., Denny's, McDonald's, **lodging:** Sierra Suites, **other:** MEDICAL CARE, Lake Pleasant RV Park, **W...gas:** Arco, Chevron, Shell/diesel, 7-11, **food:** Applebee's, Arby's, Bonefish Grill, Burger King, DQ, Denny's, Godfather's, Jack-in-the-Box, Mongolian Grill, Outback Steaks, Papa Murphy's, QFC Foods, Quizno's, Starbucks, Taco Time, Tully's Coffee, **lodging:** Comfort Inn, Extended Stay America, **other:** Albertson's, Bartell Drug, QFC Foods, Rite Aid

24 NE 195th St, Beardslee Blvd, **E...gas:** Shell/Quizno's/diesel, **lodging:** Residence Inn, Wyndham Garden

23b WA 522 W, Bothell, no facilities

23a WA 522 E, to WA 202, Woodinville, Monroe, no facilities

22 NE 160th St, **E...gas:** Chevron, Shell/diesel/24hr, **food:** Denice's Cafe

20 NE 124th St, **E...gas:** Arco/24hr, 76/diesel, Chevron/24hr, Shell/diesel/24hr, 7-11, **food:** Brown Bag Cafe, Denny's, Evergreen China, Jack-in-the-Box, Old Country Buffet, Pizza Hut, Shari's, Subway, Taco Bell, **lodging:** Best Western, Clarion Inn, Motel 6, Silver Cloud Inn, **other:** HOSPITAL, CompUSA, Discount Tire, Firestone, Infiniti, Larry's Mkt, OfficeMax, Rite Aid, Ross, mall, **W...gas:** Arco/24hr, 76, **food:** Blimpie, Burger King, Domino's, McDonald's, Milestone Grill, Olive Garden, Starbucks, Subway, Taco Time, Wendy's, **other:** Buick/Pontiac/GMC, Fred Meyer, GNC, QFC Food/24hr, Schuck's Parts

18 WA 908, Kirkland, Redmond, **E...gas:** Arco/24hr, Chevron/24hr, 76/Circle K, Shell/diesel, **food:** Burger King, Domino's, Gandhi Cuisine, McDonald's, Outback Steaks, Pegasus Rest., Teriyaki, Tres Hermanos Mexican, **other:** Chevrolet, Costco, Honda, Mazda, Nissan, Safeway, Schuck's Parts, U-Haul, Walgreen, **W...food:** Subway, TGIFriday

17 NE 70th Pl, no facilities

14b a WA 520, Seattle, Redmond, no facilities

13b NE 8th St, **E...gas:** Arco/24hr, Chevron/diesel, Shell/diesel, **food:** Burger King, Denny's, Hunan Garden, Pumphouse Rest., **lodging:** Coast Hotel, Extended Stay America, **other:** HOSPITAL, Buick/Pontiac, Ford, Home Depot, Larry's Mkt, Saab, **W...food:** DQ, **lodging:** DoubleTree

13a NE 4th St, **E...other:** Ford, **W...food:** Azteca Mexican, Jonah's Rest., **lodging:** Best Western, Doubletree Hotel, Hilton, Hyatt, Ramada Ltd., Red Lion/Bellevue Inn, Sheraton

12 SE 8th St, no facilities

11 I-90, E to Spokane, W to Seattle, no facilities

10 Cold Creek Pkwy, Factoria, **E on Factoria Blvd...gas:** 76/Circle K, 7-11, **food:** Applebee's, Burger King, KFC, Keg Steaks, McDonald's, McHale's Rest., Old Country Buffet, Peking Wok, Presto Pizza, Red Robin, Starbucks, Subway, Taco Bell, Taco Time, Thai Rest., Torero's Mexican, Tully's Coffee, Winchell's, **lodging:** Homestead Suites, **other:** Honda, Mervyn's, Nordstrom's, Old Navy, Oriental Foods, QFC Foods, Rite Aid, Safeway, Schuck's Parts, Target, mall

9 112th Ave SE, Newcastle, phone

7 NE 44th St, **E...food:** Denny's/24hr, McDonald's, **lodging:** Travelers Inn

6 NE 30th St, **E...gas:** Arco/24hr, **W...gas:** Chevron/24hr, Shell, 7-11

5 WA 900 E, Park Ave N, Sunset Blvd NE, no facilities

4 WA 169 S, Wa 900 W, Renton, **E...food:** Shari's, **lodging:** Silver Cloud Inn, **other:** Aqua Barn Ranch Camping, **W...gas:** Shell/diesel, **food:** Burger King, 7-11, Golden Palace Chinese, **lodging:** Renton Inn, **other:** IGA Foods

2 WA 167, Rainier Ave, to Auburn, **E...HOSPITAL, W...gas:** Arco/24hr, Chevron, 76, Shell, USA Minimart, **food:** Arby's, Burger King, China Garden, Denny's, IHOP, Jack-in-the-Box, KFC, Lucky Thai, Mazatlan Mexican, McDonald's, Pizza Hut, Quizno's, Taco Bell, Torero's Mexican, Tully's Coffee, Wendy's, Yankee Grill, **lodging:** Holiday Inn, **other:** Cadillac, Chevrolet, Chrysler/Plymouth/Jeep, Dodge/Toyota, Ford, Fred Meyer, Firestone, Honda/Mazda/Hyundai/Suzuki/Kia, Isuzu, K-Mart/Little Caesar's, Lincoln/Mercury, Mitsubishi, Pontiac/Buick/GMC, Radio Shack, Safeway/gas, Schuck's Parts, Schwab Tire, Subaru/Peugeot, Walgreen, Wal-Mart/auto

1 WA 181 S, Tukwila, **E...gas:** Chevron/diesel, 76/diesel, Shell/diesel, **food:** 7-11, Barnaby's Rest., Burger King, Chili's, Jack-in-the-Box, McDonald's, Quizno's, Sizzler, Starbucks, Taco Bell, Teriyaki Wok, Wendy's, Zoopa Café, **lodging:** Best Western, Courtyard, DoubleTree Suites, Embassy Suites, Hampton Inn, Homestead Village, Red Lion Hotel, Residence Inn, **other:** Acura, Barnes&Noble, Bon-Marche, Circuit City, Firestone, Goodyear, JC Penney, Lowe's Whse, Mervyn's, Nordstrom's, Office Depot, Sears/auto, Target, **W...gas:** 76, Shell, **lodging:** Homewood Suites, Studio+

0mm I-5, N to Seattle, S to Tacoma, WA 518 W. I-405 begins/ends on I-5, exit 154.

Interstate 64

E

↕

W

Exit #	Services
184mm	West Virginia/Virginia state line
183	VA 311, Crows(from eb), no facilities
181	US 60, WV 92(no ez wb return), White Sulphur Springs, **N...gas:** Amoco/Godfather's, Shell, **food:** Hardee's, Legends Rest., McDonald's(5mi), Pizza Hut, Taco Bell, Wendy's(4mi), **lodging:** Budget Inn, Greenbrier Motel, Old White Motel, **other:** Family$, Food Lion, NAPA, Rite Aid, to Midland Trail, ski area, **S...lodging:** Allstate Motel, **other:** Twilite Camping
179mm	**Welcome Ctr wb, info, full(handicapped)facilities, phone, picnic tables, litter barrels, petwalk**
175	US 60, WV 92, Caldwell, **N...gas:** Chevron/diesel/24hr, Shell/Subway/diesel, StopIn/gas, **food:** Granny's House Rest., Greenbrier's Mountainaire Rest., McDonald's, Taco Bell, Wendy's, **lodging:** Budget Inn, Dixon Hotel, Village Motel, **S...other:** Greenbrier SF, camping
173mm	Greenbrier River

169	US 219, Lewisburg, Hist Dist, **N...lodging:** Day's Inn, **S...gas:** Exxon/diesel, Shell, **food:** Applebee's, Arby's, Bob Evans, Hardee's, Shoney's, Subway, Western Sizzlin, **lodging:** Brier Inn, Econolodge, Hampton Inn, Rodeway Inn, Super 8, **other:** HOSPITAL, Wal-Mart SuperCtr/gas/24hr
161	WV 12, Alta, **S...gas:** Chevron(1mi), **food:** Grandpa's Rest., **other:** Greenbrier River Camping(14mi)
156	US 60, Midland Trail, Sam Black Church, **N...gas:** Citgo, Exxon/diesel, Shell/diesel
150	Dawson, **S...lodging:** Dawson Inn/RV camping
147mm	runaway truck ramp wb
143	WV 20, Green Sulphur Springs, **N...gas:** Chevron/diesel
139	WV 20, Sandstone, Hinton, **S...gas:** Citgo/diesel, **other:** to Pipestem Resort Park
138mm	New River
133	WV 27, Bragg Rd, mandatory truck stop eb
129	WV 9, Shady Spring, **N...other:** to Grandview SP, **S...gas:** Exxon/diesel, Shell/diesel, **other:** Little Beaver SP
125	WV 307, Airport Rd, Beaver, **N...gas:** Shell/diesel, **lodging:** Sleep Inn, **S...gas:** Amoco/diesel, Chevron, Exxon, GoMart/gas, **food:** Hardee's, LJ Silver, McDonald's, Pizza Hut, **lodging:** Glade Spgs Resort, Patriot Motel
124	US 19, E Beckley, **N...gas:** Exxon, GoMart/gas, Speedway, **food:** Capt D's, **lodging:** Greenbank Motel, Honey Rock Motel, PineCrest Motel, **other:** MEDICAL CARE, last exit before toll rd wb
121	I-77 S, to Bluefield, no facilities
	I-64 and I-77 run together 61 mi. See West Virginia Interstate 77, exits 42 through 100.
59	I-77 N(from eb), to I-79, no facilities
58c	US 60, Washington St, **N...gas:** BP, Exxon, GoMart/gas, **food:** Arby's, Lincoln/Mercury, **S...food:** LJ Silver, Shoney's, **lodging:** Hampton Inn, Holiday Inn Express, Marriott, **other:** HOSPITAL, civic ctr, mall

WEST VIRGINIA
Interstate 64

E ↕ **W**

C h a r l e s t o n

58b US 119 N(from eb), Charleston, downtown

58a US 119 S, WV 61, MacCorkle Ave, **S...food:** Steak&Ale

48 US 19, N Beckley, **1 mi E...gas:** Amoco/Subway/diesel, **food:** Garfield's Rest., **lodging:** Ramada Inn, **other:** JC Penney, Sears/auto, **4 mi E on US 19/WV 16 S...gas:** Exxon, **food:** Bob Evans, Burger King, Checker's, Fazoli's, Hardee's, LoneStar Steaks, LJ Silver, McDonald's, Rio Grande Mexican, Ryan's, Wendy's, **other:** Acura, AutoZone, Buick, Chevrolet/Cadillac, Chrysler/Plymouth, CVS Drug, Dodge, Honda, Hyundai, Staples, Subaru/Kia, U-Haul, Wal-Mart SuperCtr/24hr

56 Montrose Dr, **N...gas:** Chevron/Blimpie, Exxon/diesel, **food:** Burger King, Hardee's, Shoney's, **lodging:** Microtel, Ramada Inn, Wingate Inn, **other:** Advance Parts, Chevrolet, Chrysler/Plymouth/Jeep, Kia, K-Mart, Rite Aid, Toyota, VW

55 Kanawha Tpk, no facilities

45mm **Tamarack Service Area both lanes, W...gas:** Exxon/diesel, **food:** BiscuitWorld, Sbarro's, Starbucks, TCBY, other: gifts

54 US 60, MacCorkle Ave, **S...gas:** Chevron, Citgo, **food:** Bob Evans, KFC, LJ Silver, McDonald's, Schlotsky's, Taco Bell, Wendy's, **lodging:** Day's Inn, **other:** HOSPITAL, Aamco, Daewoo, Honda, SaveALot Foods

44 WV 3, Beckley, **E...gas:** Chevron/diesel, Exxon, Marathon, Shell/Hardee's/24hr, **food:** Applebee's, BBQ, Burger King, DQ, Hibachi Japanese, McDonald's, Outback Steaks, Pancake House, Pizza Hut, **lodging:** Best Western, Comfort Inn, Courtyard, Fairfield Inn, Holiday Inn, Howard Johnson, Super 8, **other:** MEDICAL CARE, CVS Drug, Kroger/gas, **W...gas:** BP/Subway, GoMart/diesel, **food:** Bob Evans, Cracker Barrel, Texas Steaks, Wendy's, **lodging:** Country Inn Suites, Day's Inn, Hampton Inn, Microtel, Park Inn

53 Roxalana Rd, to Dunbar, **S...gas:** GoMart/gas, **food:** BiscuitWorld, Capt D's, Gino's Pizza, McDonald's, Shoney's, Subway, Wendy's, **lodging:** Super 8, Travelodge, **other:** Advance Parts, Aldi, CarQuest, CVS Drug, Family$, Jo-Ann Fabrics, Kroger, NTB, Radio Shack

42 WV 16, WV 97, to Mabscott, **2 mi E...food:** Tudor's Biscuits, **lodging:** Budget Inn, **other:** HOSPITAL, **W...gas:** Amoco/diesel, **food:** Godfather's, Subway

50 WV 25, Institute, **S...gas:** GoMart/gas

47b a WV 622, Goff Mtn Rd, **N...gas:** Chevron/24hr, Exxon, Shell, Speedway, **food:** A&W, BiscuitWorld, Bob Evans, Capt D's, Domino's, Hardee's, McDonald's, Papa John's, Pizza Hut, Subway/TCBY, Taco Bell, Wendy's, **lodging:** Motel 6, **other:** Advance Parts, CVS Drug, Kroger/gas, NAPA, Rite Aid, **S...food:** Arby's, Burger King, Cracker Barrel, DQ, Fazoli's, Golden Corral, KFC, TGIFriday, **lodging:** Comfort Inn, Sleep Inn, **other:** $Tree, Lowe's Whse, Radio Shack, Staples, Wal-Mart SuperCtr/24hr

45 WV 25, Nitro, **N...gas:** Pilot/Arby's/diesel/24hr/@, **food:** Hardee's, Chevrolet, **S...gas:** BP/diesel/24hr, Chevron, **food:** BiscuitWorld, Checker's, DQ, Gino's Pizza, McDonald's, Subway, Wendy's, **lodging:** Econolodge, **other:** MEDICAL CARE, Chevrolet

44.3mm Kanawha River

H u n t i n g t o n

44 US 35, St Albans, **S...gas:** Chevron/diesel

39 WV 34t, Winfield, **N...gas:** BP/Arby's, GoMart/diesel, **food:** Applebee's, Bob Evans, Hardee's, Rio Grande Mexican, **lodging:** Day's Inn, Holiday Inn Express, Red Roof Inn, **other:** Advance Parts, Big Bear Foods, $General, USPO, **S...gas:** Exxon/diesel, GoMart/gas, TA/diesel/rest./24hr/@, **food:** Burger King, Capt D's, China Chef, Fazoli's, Gino's Pizza, KFC, Kobe Japanese, McDonald's, Papa John's, Schlotsky's, Shoney's, Subway, Taco Bell, TCBY, Wendy's, **lodging:** Hampton Inn, **other:** MEDICAL CARE, K-Mart, Kroger, Rite Aid

38mm weigh sta both lanes

35mm **rest area both lanes, full(handicapped)facilities, phone, vending, picnic tables, litter barrels, petwalk**

34 WV 19, Hurricane, **N...other:** Chevrolet, Ford/Lincoln/Mercury, Saturn, **S...gas:** Chevron/diesel, Exxon, Sunoco/diesel, Shell, **food:** BiscuitWorld/Gino's Pizza, McDonald's, Nancy's Rest., Pizza Hut, Subway, **lodging:** Super 8

28 US 60, Milton, **1-3 mi S...gas:** Chevron/diesel, Exxon, Marathon, Shell/diesel, **food:** Granny K's Rest., McDonald's, Wendy's, **other:** Foxfire RV Park, Jim's Camping

20 US 60, Mall Rd, Barboursville, **N...gas:** Chevron, Exxon/diesel, **food:** Applebee's, Arby's, Bob Evans, Burger King, Chili's, Fuddrucker's, IHOP, Logan's Roadhouse, McDonald's, Olive Garden, Ruby Tuesday, Wendy's, **lodging:** Comfort Inn, Holiday Inn, **other:** Best Buy, Borders Books, Chrysler/Jeep, Circuit City, Drug Emporium, Firestone/auto, JC Penney, Jo-Ann Fabrics, Kohl's, Lazarus, Lowe's Whse, Michael's, OfficeMax, Sears/auto, mall, Wal-Mart SuperCtr/24hr, **S...gas:** BP, Exxon, **food:** Billy Bob's Pizza, Cracker Barrel, Fiesta Bravo Mexican, Gino's Pizza, LoneStar Steaks, Outback Steaks, Ponderosa, Sonic, Subway, Taco Bell, **lodging:** Best Western, Hampton Inn, **other:** Cadillac, Lincoln/Mercury, Mazda, to Foxfire Camping Resort

18 US 60, to WV 2, Barboursville, **N...food:** O'Charley's, **other:** Home Depot, **other:** Target, **S...gas:** Chevron, **food:** Hardee's, **other:** Kroger/gas

15 US 60, 29th St E, **N...gas:** GoMart/diesel, Sunoco, **food:** Arby's, Omelet Shoppe, Pizza Hut, Ponderosa, Wendy's, **lodging:** Colonial Inn, Econolodge, Holiday Inn, Stone Lodge Inn, **other:** HOSPITAL, **S...gas:** Exxon, **food:** Fazoli's, Golden Corral, KFC, McDonald's, Shoney's, Taco Bell, **lodging:** Day's Inn, Red Roof Inn, **other:** Chrysler/Dodge/Jeep, CVS Drug, Office Depot, Nissan/Mitsubishi/VW, Office Depot, Pontiac/GMC/Buick/Isuzu, Subaru, Wal-Mart/auto

11 WV 10, Hal Greer Blvd, **1-3 mi N...gas:** BP, Chevron, Shell, **food:** Arby's, Marshall Café, McDonald's, Wendy's, **lodging:** Holiday Inn, Radisson, Ramada Ltd, Super 8, **other:** HOSPITAL, **S...other:** Beech Fork SP(8mi)

10mm **Welcome Ctr eb, full(handicapped)facilities, phone, vending, picnic tables, litter barrels, petwalk**

8 WV 152 S, WV 527 N, **N...other:** MEDICAL CARE, **S...gas:** Speedway, **food:** DQ, Laredo Steaks

6 US 52 N, W Huntington, Chesapeake, **N...gas:** Go-mart, Marathon, Shell, Speedway/24hr, **food:** Hardee's, Pizza Hut, Shoney's, **lodging:** Coach's Inn, **other:** HOSPITAL, Family$

1 US 52 S, Kenova, **1-3 mi N...gas:** Exxon, **food:** Burger King, McDonald's, Pizza Hut, **lodging:** Hollywood Motel

0mm West Virginia/Kentucky state line, Big Sandy River

Interstate 68

E ↑↓ **W**

Morgantown

Exit #	Services
32mm	West Virginia/Maryland state line
31mm	**Welcome Ctr wb, full(handicapped)facilities, picnic tables, litter barrels, phone, vending, petwalk**
29	WV 5, Hazelton Rd, **N...gas:** Mobil/diesel, **S...other:** Big Bear Camping(3mi), Pine Hill RV Camp(4mi)
23	WV 26, Bruceton Mills, **N...gas:** BP/diesel/24hr, Sandy's/Mobil/diesel/24hr/@ , **food:** Mill Place Rest., Subway, Twila's Rest., **lodging:** Maple Leaf Motel, **other:** Bruceton Mills Foods, Hostetler's Store, USPO, **15 mi S...lodging:** Heldreth Motel
18mm	Laurel Run
17mm	runaway truck ramp eb
16mm	weigh sta wb
15	WV 73, WV 12, Coopers Rock, **N...other:** Chestnut Ridge SF, GS Camping(2mi)
12mm	runaway truck ramp wb
10	WV 857, Fairchance Rd, Cheat Lake, **N...gas:** BP/diesel/24hr, Exxon/diesel, **food:** La Casita Mexican, Pizza'n Pasta, Ruby&Ketchy's Rest., Subway, **S...food:** Burger King, Dimitri's Steaks, **lodging:** Lakeview Resort, Stone Crab Inn
9mm	Cheat Lake
7	WV 857, Pierpont Rd, **N...gas:** BP/Subway, Exxon/diesel, **Food:** Bob Evans, Outback Steaks, Ruby Tuesday, Taco Bell, Wendy's, **lodging:** Holiday Inn Express, Super 8, **other:** HOSPITAL, BooksAMillion, Lowe's Whse, Michael's, Shop'n Save Food, to WVU Stadium, **S...food:** Tiberio's Rest.
4	WV 7, to Sabraton, **N...gas:** BP, Exxon/Blimpie/24hr, **food:** Burger King, Hardee's, Hero's Hut, KFC, LJ Silver, McDonald's, Pizza Hut, Ponderosa, Subway, Wendy's, **other:** Chrysler/Dodge, CVS Drug, $General, Food Lion, Ford, Kroger/diesel, NAPA, USPO
3mm	Decker's Creek
1	US 119, Morgantown, **N...gas:** Exxon/diesel, **food:** Subway, **lodging:** Comfort Inn, Morgantown Motel(2mi), Ramada Inn/rest., **S...gas:** Chevron/diesel, **other:** to Tygart L SP
0mm	I-79, N to Pittsburgh, S to Clarksburg. I-68 begins/ends on I-79, exit 148.

Interstate 70

E ↑↓ **W**

Exit #	Services
14mm	West Virginia/Pennsylvania state line
13.5mm	**Welcome Ctr wb, full(handicapped)facilities, phone, vending, picnic tables, litter barrels, petwalk**
11	WV 41, Dallas Pike, **N...gas:** TA/diesel/rest./@ , **lodging:** Day's Inn, **S...gas:** BP/DQ/diesel, Citgo/A&W/Taco Bell/diesel, Exxon, **lodging:** Holiday Inn Express, **other:** RV camping

Wheeling

5	US 40, WV 88 S, Tridelphia, **N...gas:** Marathon, **food:** Christopher's Café, Hoss' Rest., Pizza Hut, Subway, Wendy's, **lodging:** Super 8, **other:** Riesbeck's Foods, **S...gas:** Amoco, Exxon/diesel, **food:** DQ, Ernie's Rest.(2mi), McDonald's, **other:** Advance Parts, NAPA, Rite Aid, museum
5a	I-470 W, to Columbus, no facilities
4	WV 88 N(from eb), Elm Grove, **S...gas:** Amoco, Exxon/diesel, same as 5
3.5mm	weigh sta wb
2b	Washington Ave, **N...gas:** Exxon, **food:** Greco's Rest., **S...food:** Figaretti's Italian, **other:** HOSPITAL
a	WV 88 N, to Oglebay Park, **N...gas:** Exxon, **food:** Big Boy, Bob Evans, DQ, Hardee's, LJ Silver, Papa John's, Rax, Subway, Texas Roadhouse, **lodging:** Hampton Inn, **other:** Advance Parts, CVS Drug, Kroger/gas, NTB, Radio Shack
1b	US 250 S, WV 2 S, S Wheeling, no facilities
a	US 40 E, WV 2 N, Main St, downtown, **S...lodging:** Best Western
1mm	tunnel
0	US 40 W, Zane St, Wheeling Island, **N...gas:** Exxon/diesel, **food:** Conv Mart, DQ , FoodCourt, KFC
0mm	West Virginia/Ohio state line, Ohio River

Interstate 77

N ↑↓ **S**

Parkersburg

Exit #	Services
186mm	West Virginia/Ohio state line, Ohio River
185	WV 14, WV 31, Williamstown, **W...gas:** Exxon, Shell, **food:** Dutch Pantry, Subway, **lodging:** Day's Inn, **other:** Glass Factory Tours
179	WV 2 N, WV 68 S, to Waverly, **E...gas:** Exxon, **other:** airport, **W...gas:** BP, **food:** Pepper's Mexican, **lodging:** Expressway Motel, **other:** HOSPITAL
176	US 50, 7th St, Parkersburg, **E...lodging:** Best Western, **other:** to North Bend SP, **W...gas:** Shell/24hr, Speedway/diesel, **food:** Bob Evans, Burger King, Little Caesar's, LJ Silver, McDonald's, Mountaineer Rest./24hr, Omelet Shoppe, Shoney's, Wendy's, **lodging:** Econolodge, Holiday Inn, Knight's Inn, Motel 6, Red Roof Inn, **other:** Advance Parts, Buick/Mercedes/Isuzu, Kroger/diesel, Toyota, Family$, to Blennerhassett Hist Park
174	WV 47, Staunton Ave, **1 mi E...gas:** BP, Exxon/diesel, **food:** Subway, **W...gas:** Citgo/diesel
174mm	Little Kanawha River
173	WV 95, Camden Ave, **E...gas:** Marathon/diesel, **1-4 mi W...gas:** BP, **food:** Hardee's, **lodging:** Blennerhassett Hotel, **other:** HOSPITAL

N ↑ **S**

Charleston

170	WV 14, Mineral Wells, **E...gas:** BP/diesel/repair/24hr, Chevron, Citgo/diesel, Liberty Trkstp/diesel/24hr, **food:** BBQ, McDonald's, Subway, Taco Bell, Wendy's, **lodging:** Comfort Suites, Hampton Inn, **other:** USPO, **W...food:** Cracker Barrel, Napoli's Pizza, **lodging:** AmeriHost, Microtel
169mm	weigh sta both lanes, phone
166mm	**rest area both lanes, full(handicapped)facilities, phone, picnic tables, litter barrels, vending, petwalk**
161	WV 21, Rockport, **W...gas:** Marathon
154	WV 1, Medina Rd, no facilities
146	WV 2 S, Silverton, Ravenswood, **W...gas:** BP/diesel, Exxon/24hr, Marathon/diesel/24hr, **food:** DQ, **lodging:** Scottish Inn
138	US 33, Ripley, **E...gas:** BP/diesel/24hr, Exxon/24hr, Marathon/diesel, **food:** KFC, LJ Silver, McDonald's, Pizza Hut, Taco Bell, Wendy's, **lodging:** Best Western/rest., Super 8, **other:** Kroger, NAPA, Rite Aid, Sav-A-Lot, Wal-Mart, **W...gas:** Exxon/diesel/24hr, Ponderosa, Shoney's, **food:** Subway, **lodging:** Holiday Inn Express, **other:** HOSPITAL
132	WV 21, Fairplain, **E...gas:** BP/Burger King/diesel, Shell/diesel, **other:** Ford, **W...lodging:** 77 Motel
124	WV 34, Kenna, **E...gas:** Exxon, **food:** Your Family Rest.
119	WV 21, Goldtown, no facilities
116	WV 21, Haines Branch Rd, Sissonville, **4 mi E... other:** Rippling Waters Campground
114	WV 622, Pocatalico Rd, **E...gas:** MtnMart/gas, **other:** Fascheck Foods
111	WV 29, Tuppers Creek Rd, **W...gas:** BP/Subway/diesel, **food:** Tudor's Biscuit World
106	WV 27, Edens Fork Rd, **W...gas:** Chevron/diesel/country store, **lodging:** Sunset Motel(3mi)
104	I-79 N, to Clarksburg, no facilities
102	US 119 N, Westmoreland Rd, **E...gas:** Chevron/7-11/24hr, GoMart/24hr, **food:** Hardee's/24hr, **lodging:** Parsley Motel, **other:** Foodland, Pennzoil/24hr,
101	I-64, E to Beckley, W to Huntington, no facilities
100	Broad St, Capitol St, **W...food:** Charleston House Rest., **lodging:** Fairfield Inn, Holiday Inn, Marriott, Super 8, **other:** HOSPITAL, CVS Drug, Family$, GMC, Honda Motorcycles, JC Penney, Kroger
99	WV 114, Capitol St, **E...airport, W...gas:** Exxon, Domino's, **food:** KFC/Taco Bell, McDonald's, Wendy's, **other:** to museum, st capitol
98	35th St Bridge(from sb), **W...gas:** Sunoco, **food:** KFC/Taco Bell, McDonald's, Steak Escape, Shoney's, Subway, Wendy's, **other:** HOSPITAL, to U of Charleston
97	US 60 W(from nb), Kanawha Blvd, no facilities
96	US 60 E, Midland Trail, Belle, **W...food:** Gino's, **lodging:** Budget Host
96mm	W Va Turnpike begins/ends, no facilities
95.5mm	Kanawha River
95	WV 61, to MacCorkle Ave, **E...gas:** BP/Subway/diesel, GoMart/diesel/24hr, **food:** Bob Evans, IHOP, LoneStar Steaks, McDonald's, Wendy's, **lodging:** Comfort Suites, Country Inn Suites, Day's Inn,

	Knight's Inn, Motel 6, Red Roof Inn, **other:** Advance Parts, K-Mart, **W...gas:** Ashland/Blimpie/24hr, Chevron/7-11, Exxon/diesel/24hr, Marathon, GoMart/24hr, **food:** Applebee's, Azteca Mexican, Capt D's, China Buffet, Cracker Barrel, Hooters, La Carreta Mexican, Pizza Hut/Taco Bell, Ponderosa, Shoney's, Southern Kitchen/24hr, Shoney's, **other:** MEDICAL CARE, Foodland, Kroger, Lowe's Whse, NAPA, Subaru, Suzuki, mall
89	WV 61, WV 94, to Marmet, **E...gas:** Exxon/Subway/diesel/24hr, GoMart, Shell, Sunoco, **food:** Biscuit World, Gino's Pizza, Hardee's, KFC, LJ Silver, Subway, Wendy's, **other:** Family$, Kroger/deli, Rite Aid, **W...other:** Ford(1mi)
85	US 60, WV 61, East Bank, **E...gas:** GoMart/diesel/24hr, **food:** Gino's Pizza, McDonald's, Shoney's, **other:** Chevrolet, Gilmer Foods, Kroger, tire repair
82.5mm	toll booth
79	Cabin Creek Rd, Sharon, no facilities
74	WV 83, Paint Creek Rd, no facilities
72mm	**Morton Service Area nb, gas: Exxon/diesel, food: Burger King, Starbucks, TCBY, atm**
69mm	**rest area sb, full(handicapped)facilities, phone, picnic tables, litter barrels**
66	WV 15, to Mahan, **1/2 mi W...gas:** Sunoco/diesel/24hr
60	WV 612, to Mossy, Oak Hill, **1/2 mi E...gas:** Exxon/diesel/repair/24hr, **other:** RV camping
56.5mm	toll plaza, phone
54	rd 2, rd 23, Pax, **E...gas:** BP/rest.
48	US 19, N Beckley, **1 mi E...gas:** BP/Subway/diesel, **food:** Garfield's Rest., **lodging:** Ramada Inn, **other:** JC Penney, Sears/auto, **4 mi E on US 19/WV 16 S... gas:** Exxon, **food:** Bob Evans, Burger King, Checker's, Fazoli's, Hardee's, LoneStar Steaks, LJ Silver, McDonald's, Rio Grande Mexican, Ryan's, Wendy's, **other:** Acura, AutoZone, Buick, Chevrolet/Cadillac, Chrysler/Plymouth, CVS Drug, Dodge, Honda, Hyundai, Staples, Subaru/Kia, U-Haul, Wal-Mart SuperCtr/24hr
45mm	**Tamarack Service Area both lanes, W...gas: Exxon/diesel, food: BiscuitWorld, Sbarro's, Starbucks, TCBY, other: gifts**
44	WV 3, Beckley, **E...gas:** Chevron/diesel, Exxon, Marathon, Shell/Hardee's/24hr, **food:** Applebee's, BBQ, Burger King, DQ, Hibachi Japanese, McDonald's, Outback Steaks, Pancake House, Pizza Hut, **lodging:** Best Western, Comfort Inn, Courtyard, Fairfield Inn, Holiday Inn, Howard Johnson, Quality Inn, Super 8, **other:** MEDICAL CARE, CVS Drug, Kroger/gas, **W...gas:** BP/Subway, GoMart/diesel, **food:** Bob Evans, Cracker Barrel, Texas Steaks, Wendy's, **lodging:** Country Inn Suites, Day's Inn, Hampton Inn, Microtel, Park Inn
42	WV 16, WV 97, to Mabscott, **2 mi E...food:** Tudor's Biscuits, **lodging:** Budget Inn, **other:** HOSPITAL, **W...gas:** Amoco/diesel, **food:** Godfather's, Subway
40	I-64 E, to Lewisburg, no facilities
30mm	toll booth, phone

Beckley

Interstate 77

N ↕ S

Princeton

28	WV 48, to Ghent, **E...gas:** BP, Exxon/diesel, Marathon/diesel, **lodging:** Glade Springs Resort(1mi), Appalachian Resort Inn(12mi), **other:** to ski area, **W...lodging:** Econolodge
26.5mm	Flat Top Mtn, elevation 3252
20	US 19, to Camp Creek, **E...gas:** Exxon/diesel, Tolliver's T-stop, **W...other:** Camp Creek SP/RV camping
18.5mm	scenic overlook/parking area/weigh sta sb, Bluestone River, no facilities
17mm	**Bluestone Service Area/weigh sta nb, full(handicapped)facilities, scenic view, picnic area, Exxon/diesel, Starbucks, TCBY, atm/fax**
14	WV 20, Athens Rd, **E...gas:** Citgo, **other:** Pipestem Resort SP
9mm	WV Turnpike begins/ends, no facilities
9	US 460, Princeton, Pearisburg, **E...Welcome Ctr**, I-77 Trkstp/diesel/@, Wal-Mart SuperCtr/24hr, Ryan's, **W...gas:** BP/diesel, Chevron/diesel/24hr, Exxon/diesel/24hr, Marathon/Subway/diesel, **food:** Applebee's, Bob Evans, Burger King, Capt D's, Cracker Barrel, DQ, Hardee's, McDonald's, Omelet Shoppe, Shoney's, Taco Bell, Texas Steaks, Wendy's, **lodging:** Budget Inn, Comfort Inn, Day's Inn, Hampton Inn, Johnston's Inn/rest., Ramada Ltd, Sleep Inn, Super 8, Town&Country Motel, Turnpike Motel, **other:** HOSPITAL, K-Mart
7	WV 27, Ingleside Rd(from nb, no re-entry), no facilities
5	WV 112(from sb, no re-entry), to Ingleside, no facilities
3mm	East River
1	US 52 N, to Bluefield, **4 mi W...food:** LJ Silver, Wendy's, **lodging:** Brier Motel, Econolodge, Highlander Motel, Holiday Inn/rest., Knight's Inn, Ramada Inn, **other:** HOSPITAL
.5mm	West Virginia/Virginia state line, East River Mtn
0mm	West Virginia/Virginia state line

Interstate 79

N ↑ S

Morgantown

Exit #	Services
160mm	West Virginia/Pennsylvania state line
159	**Welcome Ctr sb, full(handicapped)facilities, info, picnic tables, litter barrels, phone, vending, petwalk**
155	US 19, WV 7, **E...gas:** Sheetz, **3 mi E...gas:** Shell, **food:** Burger King, Eat'n Park, LJ Silver, McDonald's, Shoney's, Wendy's, **lodging:** Day's Inn, Econolodge, Euro Suites, Friends Inn, Hampton Inn, Holiday Inn, **other:** HOSPITAL, to WVU, **W...gas:** Exxon/diesel
152	US 19, to Morgantown, **E...gas:** BP/diesel, Exxon, Getty, **food:** Arby's, McDonald's, Pizza Hut, Subway, Taco Bell, Western Sizzlin, **lodging:** Clarion, Econolodge, Advance Parts, **W...food:** Bob Evans, Burger King, Garfield's Rest., **other:** JC Penney, K-Mart, Lowe's Whse, Sears/auto, mall

Clarksburg

150mm	Monongahela River
148	I-68 E, to Cumberland, MD, **1 mi E...gas:** Exxon/diesel/24hr, **lodging:** Comfort Inn, Morgantown Motel, Ramada Inn/rest.
146	WV 77, to Goshen Rd, no facilities
141mm	weigh sta both lanes
139	WV 33, E Fairmont, **E...gas:** Chevron, **W...gas:** Exxon/24hr, K&T/BP/diesel/@, **other:** RV camping
137	WV 310, to Fairmont, **E...gas:** BP, Exxon/diesel/24hr, **food:** Simmering Pot Rest., Subway, **lodging:** Holiday Inn, **other:** to Valley Falls SP, **W...gas:** Chevron, **food:** KFC, McDonald's, Wendy's, **other:** HOSPITAL
135	WV 64, Pleasant Valley Rd, no facilities
133	Kingmont Rd, **E...gas:** BP/Subway/diesel, Exxon/diesel, **food:** Cracker Barrel, **lodging:** Super 8, **W...gas:** Chevron/diesel/24hr, King/diesel, **food:** DJ's Diner, **lodging:** Comfort Inn, Country Club Motel, Day's Inn, Red Roof Inn
132	US 250, S Fairmont, **E...food:** Arby's, Bob Evans, Dragon Buffet, Hardee's, McDonald's, Subway, Taco Bell, TJ's Rest., **lodging:** Day's Inn, Red Roof Inn, **other:** Advance Parts, Chrysler/Dodge, $General, FoodLand, Harley-Davidson, JC Penney, Jo-Ann Fabrics, Sam's Club, Shop'n Save, Wal-Mart/drugs, mall, to Tygart Lake SP, **W...gas:** Exxon/diesel/24hr, GoMart/diesel/24hr, Sunoco, **lodging:** Colonial Inn(4mi), Country Club Motel(4mi), **other:** HOSPITAL, Buick/Pontiac/GMC, Ford/Lincoln/Mercury, Toyota
125	WV 131, Saltwell Rd, to Shinnston, **E...food:** Oliverio's Rest., **W...gas:** Exxon/Subway/diesel/24hr
124	rd 279, Jerry Dove Dr, no facilities
123mm	**rest area both lanes, full(handicapped)facilities, info, phone, picnic tables, litter barrels, vending, petwalk**
121	WV 24, Meadowbrook Rd, **E...gas:** GoMart/Blimpie/24hr, Sheetz, **food:** Bob Evans, **lodging:** Hampton Inn, **other:** MEDICAL CARE, **W...gas:** Exxon/diesel, **food:** Arby's, Burger King, Garfield's Rest., **other:** Jo-Ann Fabrics, **food:** Outback Steaks, Ponderosa, **lodging:** Super 8, Honda, **other:** JC Penney, OfficeMax, PharMor, Target, mall
119	US 50, to Clarksburg, **E...gas:** Chevron/diesel/24hr, Exxon/diesel, GoMart/gas, Speedway, **food:** China Buffet, Damon's, Denny's, Eat'n Park, Hardee's, KFC, Little Caesar's, LJ Silver, McDonald's, Panera Bread, Taco Bell, Texas Roadhouse, Uno Pizzaria, USA Steaks, Wendy's, **lodging:** Comfort Inn, Day's Inn, Holiday Inn, Knight's Inn, Ramada Ltd, Sleep Inn, **other:** HOSPITAL, Chevrolet, K-Mart, Kroger/gas/24hr, Lowe's Whse, Nissan, Radio Shack

WEST VIRGINIA
Interstate 79

Charleston (vertical text)

117 WV 58, to Anmoore, **E...food:** Applebee's, Arby's, Burger King, Ruby Tuesday, Ryan's, Subway, **other:** Aldi Foods, Circuit City, $Tree, Goody's, Staples, Wal-Mart SuperCtr/24hr, **W...**BP/diesel

115 WV 20, to Stonewood, Nutter Fort, **E...gas:** BP/diesel, Chevron, Exxon/diesel, **W...**HOSPITAL

110 Lost Creek, **1 mi E...gas:** BP/diesel

105 WV 7, to Jane Lew, **E...gas:** Chevron/diesel/rest., Jane Lew Trkstp/diesel/rest./@, **lodging:** Wilderness Plantation Inn/rest., **W...gas:** Exxon, **other:** glass factory tours

99 US 33, US 119, to Weston, **E...gas:** BP, Exxon/diesel, Sheetz/24hr, **food:** Gino's Pizza, McDonald's, Subway, Western Sizzlin, **lodging:** Bicentennial Motel, Budget Host, Comfort Inn/rest., Super 8, **other:** Advance Parts, Family$, GNC, Kroger, Radio Shack, Wal-Mart, **W...gas:** BP, Rich, **food:** Hardee's, KFC, LJ Silver, Pizza Hut, Wendy's, **other:** HOSPITAL, $General, Ford, NAPA, SavALot, Twin Lakes Camper Sales, to Canaan Valley Resort, Blackwater Falls

96 WV 30, to S Weston, **E...other:** to S Jackson Lake SP, Broken Wheel Camping, **W...lodging:** Weston Motel

91 US 19, to Roanoke, **E...other:** Whisper Mtn Camping, to S Jackson Lake SP

85mm **rest area both lanes, full(handicapped)facilities, info, picnic tables, litter barrels, phone, vending, petwalk, RV dump**

79.5mm Little Kanawha River

79 WV 5, Burnsville, **E...gas:** Exxon/24hr, **lodging:** 79 Motel/rest., **other:** NAPA, **W...gas:** Shell, Cedar Cr SP

78mm Saltlick Creek

67 WV 4, to Flatwoods, **E...gas:** Ashland/diesel, Chevron/diesel, Exxon/diesel, Shell/diesel, **food:** DQ, KFC/Taco Bell, Larry's Steaks, McDonald's, Subway, **lodging:** Day's Inn, Sutton Lake Motel, **other:** Ace Hardware, Chevrolet/Buick, to Sutton Lake RA, camping, **W...gas:** Ashland/diesel, Citgo, **food:** Shoney's, Wendy's, **other:** Flatwood Stores/famous brands

62 WV 4, to Sutton, Gassaway, **E...food:** Simplicity Café, **lodging:** Elk Motel, **W...gas:** GoMart, **food:** LJ Silver, Pizza Hut, **other:** HOSPITAL, CVS Drug, Ford/Mercury, Jeep/Dodge, Kroger/deli, Super$

57 US 19 S, to Beckley, no facilities

52mm Elk River

51 WV 4, to Frametown, **E...**antiques

49mm **rest area both lanes, full(handicapped)facilities, picnic tables, phone, litter barrels, vending, petwalk, RV dump**

46 WV 11, Servia Rd, no facilities

40 WV 16, to Big Otter, **E...gas:** Shell/diesel, **W...gas:** Exxon/diesel

34 WV 36, to Wallback, **E...food:** Gino's Diner, Biscuit World

25 WV 29, to Amma, **E...gas:** Exxon/diesel

19 US 119, VW 53, to Clendenin, **E...gas:** BP/diesel/24hr, **food:** BiscuitWorld, Gino's Diner, **other:** Shafer's Superstop

9 WV 43, to Elkview, **W...gas:** Exxon/Arby's/diesel, Speedway/diesel/24hr, **food:** Bob Evans, McDonald's, Pizza Hut, Ponderosa, Subway, **lodging:** Holiday Inn Express, **other:** Advance Parts, CVS Drug, GNC, K-Mart, Kroger, Radio Shack

5 WV 114, to Big Chimney, **1 mi E...gas:** Exxon, **food:** Hardee's/24hr, **other:** Rite Aid, Smith's Foods

1 US 119, Mink Shoals, **E...food:** Harding's Family Rest., **lodging:** Sleep Inn

0 I-77, S to Charleston, N to Parkersburg. I-79 begins/ends on I-77, exit 104.

Interstate 81

Martinsburg (vertical text)

Exit #	Services
26mm	West Virginia/Maryland state line, Potomac River
25mm	**Welcome Ctr sb, full(handicapped)facilities, info, phone, picnic tables, litter barrels, petwalk**

23 US 11, Marlowe, Falling Waters, **1 mi E...other:** Falling Waters Camping, **W...gas:** BP/diesel, **other:** Outdoor Express RV Ctr

20 WV 901, Spring Mills Rd, **E...gas:** TA/diesel/rest./24hr/@, **lodging:** Econolodge, **other:** I-81 Flea Mkt, **W...gas:** Shell/diesel, **food:** Domino's, **lodging:** Holiday Inn Express

16 WV 9, N Queen St, Berkeley Springs, **E...gas:** Citgo, Exxon/Subway/diesel, Sheetz, Denny's, Golden China, Hoss's, KFC, LJ Silver, McDonald's, Ollie's Rest., Pasta House, Waffle House, **lodging:** Bavarian Inn, Comfort Inn, Knight's Inn, Stone Crab Inn, Super 8, Travelodge, **W...gas:** Citgo, Shell/diesel

14 rd 13, Dry Run Rd, **E...**HOSPITAL

13 WV 15, Kings St, Martinsburg, **E...gas:** BP/diesel, Sheetz/24hr, **food:** Applebee's, Asia Garden, Burger King, Cracker Barrel, El Ranchero Mexican, Fazoli's, Outback Steaks, Pizza Hut, Shoney's, Wendy's, **lodging:** Day's Inn, Holiday Inn/rest., **other:** HOSPITAL, OfficeMax, Tanger/famous brands, Wal-Mart SuperCtr/24hr, same as 12

12 WV 45, Winchester Ave, **E...gas:** Citgo/diesel, Martins/gas, Sheetz/24hr, Shell/diesel, **food:** Arby's, Bob Evans, McDonald's, Papa John's, Ryan's, Ruby Tuesday, Taco Bell, Wendy's, **lodging:** Economy Inn, Hampton Inn, Heritage Motel, Kristalite Inn, Relax Inn, Scottish Inn, **other:** AutoZone, JC Penney, Lowe's Whse, Sears/auto, mall, Nahkeeta RV Camping(3mi), same as 13

8 WV 32, Tablers Station Rd, **2 mi E...lodging:** Pikeside Motel

5 WV 51, Inwood, to Charles Town, **E...gas:** Exxon, Sheetz, Shell/diesel, **food:** Luwegee's Rest., McDonald's, Pizza Hut, Pizza Oven, Subway, Viva Mexican, Waffle House, **other:** Food Lion, **W...other:** Lazy-A Camping(9mi)

2mm **Welcome Ctr nb, full(handicapped)facilities, info, phone, vending, picnic tables, litter barrels, petwalk**

0mm West Virginia/Virginia state line

WISCONSIN

Interstate 39

Exit #	Services
211	US 51, rd K, Merrill, **E**...antiques
210mm	Prairie River
208	WI 64, WI 70, Merrill, **W**...gas: BP/diesel/24hr, KwikTrip/diesel, Mobil/diesel, **food**: Burger King, Diamond Dave's Tacos, Hardee's, McDonald's, Pine Ridge Rest., Taco Bell, Three's Company Dining, **lodging**: Best Western, Super 8, **other**: Piggly Wiggly, Radio Shack, Wal-Mart, to Council Grounds SP
206mm	Wisconsin River
205	US 51, rd Q, Merrill, **E**...gas: Citgo/diesel/rest./24hr, **other**: antiques
197	rd WW, to Brokaw, **W**...gas: Citgo/diesel
194	US 51, rd U, rd K, Wausau, **E**...gas: F&F/gas, KwikTrip/gas, Mobil, **food**: A&W, McDonald's, Taco Bell, **other**: Chrysler/Jeep, Toyota/Isuzu/Mercedes
193	Bridge St, **W**...HOSPITAL

192	WI 29 W, WI 52 E, Wausau, to Chippewa Falls, **E**...food: Annie's Rest., King Buffet, Little Caesar's, **lodging**: Baymont Inn, Exel Inn, Ramada, Subway, Country Inn Suites, **other**: County Mkt Foods, same as 191
191	Sherman St, **E**...gas: BP, **food**: Applebee's, Cousins Subs, Hudson's Grill, McDonald's, **lodging**: Courtyard, Hampton Inn, Super 8, **other**: HOSPITAL, **W**...food: Burger King, Hardee's, Schlotsky's, 2510 Deli, **other**: Audi/Nissan/VW, Home Depot
190mm	Rib River
190	rd NN, **E**...food: Krumbee's Bakery, **lodging**: Park Inn, **W**...gas: Citgo/diesel/24hr, Mobil/diesel, **food**: Hoffman House Rest., Shakey's Pizza, Subway, **lodging**: Best Western, **other**: MEDICAL CARE, Rib Mtn Ski Area, st patrol
188	rd N, **E**...gas: BP/24hr, Phillips 66, **food**: Country Kitchen/24hr, Fazoli's, HongKong Buffet, McDonald's, Wendy's, **lodging**: Country Inn Suites(1mi), Day's Inn, **other**: Aldi, Best Buy, Chevrolet, King's RV Ctr, Mazda, OfficeMax, Sam's Club, Saturn, Wal-Mart

WISCONSIN

Interstate 39

N ↑ S

187mm	I-39 begins/ends. Freeway continues N as US 51.
187	WI 29 E, to Green Bay, no facilities
186mm	Wisconsin River
185	US 51, **E...gas:** Mobil, **food:** Culver's, Denny's, Green Mill Rest., Hardee's, Ponderosa, Subway, Tony Roma's, **lodging:** Best Western, Comfort Inn, Country Inn Suites, Holiday Inn, Rodeway Inn, Stoney Creek Inn, **other:** Cedar Creek Factory Stores/famous brands, mall
183mm	wayside sb, restroom facilities, drinking water, picnic tables
181	Maple Ridge Rd, no facilities
179	WI 153, Mosinee, **W...gas:** BP, Shell/diesel/24hr, **food:** Hardee's, McDonald's, StageStop Rest., Subway, **lodging:** AmeriHost, **other:** Ford
178mm	wayside nb, restroom facilities, drinking water, picnic tables
175	WI 34, Knowlton, to WI Rapids, **1 mi W...other:** Mullins Cheese Factory
171	rd DB, Knowlton, **W...other:** to gas, food, lodging, Mullins Cheese Factory
165	rd X, **E...**food, camping
164mm	weigh sta both lanes
161	US 51, Stevens Point, **W...gas:** BP, Citgo, KwikTrip/24hr, **food:** Burger King, China Garden, Country Kitchen, Domino's, Hardee's, KFC, McDonald's, Mesquite Grill, Papa John's, Perkins, Ponderosa, Rococo's Pizza, Subway, Taco Bell, **lodging:** Comfort Suites, Country Inn Suites, Holiday Inn, Point Motel, Roadstar Motel, Super 8, **other:** County Mkt Foods, Jeep, Pontiac/Buick, Radio Shack
159	WI 66, Stevens Point, **W...other:** Ford/Lincoln/Mercury, Honda, Plymouth
158	US 10, Stevens Point, **E...gas:** F&F/diesel, Mobil/diesel/24hr, **food:** Applebee's, Arby's, Culver's, Fazoli's, Hong Kong Buffet, McDonald's, Shoney's, Taco Bell, Wendy's, **lodging:** Fairfield Inn, Hawthorn Inn, **other:** Aldi, Mazda, Nissan, Staples, Target, Tires+, Wal-Mart, **W...gas:** BP/24hr, **food:** Hilltop Grill, **lodging:** Baymont Inn, Best Western, Point Motel
156	rd HH, Whiting, no facilities
153	rd B, Plover, **W...gas:** BP/Burger King, Mobil/diesel, **food:** Cousins Subs, El Tapatio Mexican, McDonald's, Subway, **lodging:** AmericInn, **other:** IGA Foods, ShopKO
151	WI 54, to Waupaca, **E...gas:** Shell/Arby's/diesel/24hr, **food:** 4Star Family Rest., Shooter's Rest., **lodging:** Day's Inn, Elizabeth Inn/Conv Ctr
143	rd W, Bancroft, to WI Rapids, **E...gas:** Citgo/diesel, Cedarwood Rest.
139	rd D, Almond, no facilities
136	WI 73, Plainfield, to WI Rapids, **E...gas:** BP, Mobil/diesel, **other:** NAPA, **W...gas:** Phillips 66/Subway/diesel
131	rd V, Hancock, **E...gas:** Citgo, **other:** camping
127mm	weigh sta both lanes(exits left)
124	WI 21, Coloma, **E...gas:** Mobil/A&W/diesel, **other:** camping
120mm	**rest area sb, full(handicapped)facilities, phone, picnic tables, vending, litter barrels, petwalk, RV dump**

Portage

118mm	**rest area nb, full(handicapped)facilities, phone, picnic tables, vending, litter barrels, petwalk, RV dump**
113	rd E, rd J, Westfield, **E...lodging:** Sandman Motel, **W...gas:** BP/Burger King, Marathon, Mobil/diesel, **food:** McDonald's, Subway, **lodging:** Pioneer Motel/rest.
106	WI 82 W, WI 23 E, Oxford, **E...lodging:** Crossroads Motel
104	(from nb, no EZ return)rd D, Packwaukee, no facilities
100	WI 23 W, rd P, Endeavor, **E...gas:** Cenex
92	US 51 S, Portage, **E...gas:** KwikTrip/diesel, Mobil, **food:** Culver's, Dino's Rest., KFC, McDonald's, Subway, Taco Bell, Wendy's, **lodging:** Ridge Motel, Super 8, **other:** Ford/Lincoln/Mercury, $Tree, Pick'n Save, Piggly Wiggly, Radio Shack, Staples, Wal-Mart SuperCtr/24hr
89b a	WI 16, to WI 127, Portage, **E...gas:** BP/Burger King/diesel, **food:** Sharpshooter Grill, **other:** Chrysler/Plymouth/Dodge/Jeep
88.5mm	Wisconsin River
87	WI 33, Portage, **5 mi E...**HOSPITAL
86mm	Baraboo River
85	Cascade Mt Rd, no facilities
84	I-39, I-90 & I-94 run together sb.

Interstate 43

Exit #   Services

N ↑ S

192mm	I-43 begins/ends at Green Bay on US 41.
192b	US 41 S, US 141 S, to Appleton, services on Velp Ave, **1 mi S...gas:** Citgo/diesel/24hr, Express/diesel/24hr, Mobil/Arby's, **food:** Burger King, McDonald's, Taco Bell
192a	US 41 N, US 141 N, no facilities
189	Atkinson Dr, to Velp Ave, Port of Green Bay, **1 mi W...gas:** Glen's Gas, **other:** Jubilee Foods, auto repair
188	Fox River
187	East Shore Dr, Webster Ave, **W...gas:** Shell/diesel/24hr, **food:** McDonald's, Wendy's, **lodging:** Day's Inn, Holiday Inn, **other:** HOSPITAL, RV dump
185	WI 54, WI 57, University Ave, to Algoma, **W...gas:** Citgo, Marathon, Mobil, Shell/A&W, **food:** Cousins Subs, GB Pizza, Lee's Cantonese Chinese, Pizza Hut, Ponderosa, Subway, Taco Bell, **lodging:** Tower Motel, **other:** SuperValu Foods, Walgreen, U of WI GB
183	Mason St, rd V, **E...lodging:** AmeriHost, **other:** HOSPITAL, **1 mi W...gas:** BP, Citgo, Mobil/diesel, **food:** Applebee's, Burger King, China Kitchen, Country Kitchen, Fazoli's, Godfather's, Julie's Café, McDonald's, Papa John's, Papa Murphy's, Perkins, Pizza Hut, Schlotsky's, Taco Bell, **lodging:** Candlewood Suites, **other:** Cadillac, Champion Parts, Chevrolet, Cub Foods, Dodge, Goodyear/auto, Hyundai, K-Mart, Kohl's, Mazda, Nissan, OfficeMax, Osco Drug, ShopKO, Tires+, Wal-Mart/24hr, mall
181	Eaton Rd, rd JJ, **E...gas:** Citgo/Blimpie/diesel, **food:** Hardee's, **other:** Harley-Davidson, Ford, Home Depot, **W...gas:** Express/Subway/diesel, **other:** Festival Foods
180	WI 172 W, to US 41, **1 exit W...gas:** BP/Taco Bell/24hr, Citgo/diesel/24hr, **food:** Burger King, Country Express Rest./24hr, McDonald's, **lodging:** Best Western, Hampton Inn, Radisson Inn, Ramada, **other:** Hospital, to stadium
178	US 141, to WI 29, rd MM, Bellevue, **E...gas:** Shell/Arby's/diesel, **W...gas:** BP/diesel/repair/24hr

Green Bay

Interstate 43

N

↑
↓

S

171 WI 96, rd KB, Denmark, **E...gas:** Citgo/diesel, **food:** Chubby's Subs, Lorrie's Café, McDonald's, Steve's Cheese, **other:** Shady Acres Camping

168mm rest area both lanes, full(handicapped)facilities, phone, vending, picnic tables, litter barrels, RV dump, petwalk

166mm Devils River

164 WI 147, rd Z, Maribel, **W...gas:** Citgo/diesel, **food:** Cedar Ridge Rest., **other:** Devils River Camp

160 rd K, Kellnersville, **2-3 mi W...**food

157 rd V, Hillcrest Rd, Francis Creek, **E...gas:** Citgo/diner/diesel

154 US 10 W, WI 310, Two Rivers, to Appleton, **E...gas:** Mobil, **other:** HOSPITAL, **W...gas:** Cenex

153mm Manitowoc River

152 US 10 E, WI 42 N, rd JJ, Manitowoc, **E...lodging:** Inn on Maritime Bay(3mi), **other:** HOSPITAL, maritime museum

149 US 151, WI 42 S, Manitowoc, **E...gas:** Mobil/diesel/24hr, Shell/diesel/24hr, **food:** Applebee's, Burger King, Country Kitchen, Culver's, Fazoli's, 4Seasons Rest., Perkins, Ponderosa, Wendy's, **lodging:** Comfort Inn, Heritage Inn, Holiday Inn, Super 8, **other:** HOSPITAL, Buick/Pontiac/GMC/Cadillac, Chrysler/Plymouth/Dodge/Jeep, OfficeMax, Tires+, Wal-Mart, museum, **W...gas:** BP/24hr, **food:** McDonald's, **lodging:** AmericInn

144 rd C, Newton, **E...gas:** Mobil/diesel, **other:** antiques

142mm weigh sta sb, phone

137 rd XX, Cleveland, **E...gas:** Citgo/Burger King/diesel, **food:** Cleveland Family Rest.

128 WI 42, Howards Grove, **E...gas:** BP/diesel/24hr, Mobil/diesel, **food:** Hardee's, **lodging:** Comfort Inn, **other:** Jo-Ann Fabrics, **W...gas:** Citgo/Cousins Subs/diesel

126 WI 23, Sheboygan, **E...food:** Applebee's, Culver's, Flame Rest., Hardee's, IHOP, McDonald's, New China, Nino's Café, Pitstop Pizza, Pizza Hut/Taco Bell, Ponderosa, **lodging:** Baymont Inn, BrownStone Inn, Ramada Inn, Super 8, **other:** HOSPITAL, Aldi Foods, Chrysler/Jeep/Subaru, Firestone/auto, Ford/Lincoln/Mercury, Honda/Mazda/Toyota, Hyundai, JC Penney, Kohl's, OfficeMax, Piggly Wiggly, Sears/auto, ShopKO, Walgreen, Wal-Mart/24hr, mall, **W...lodging:** Pinehurst Inn

123 WI 28, rd A, Sheboygan, **E...gas:** Citgo/diesel/24hr, Mobil/McDonald's/diesel, **food:** Cruisers Burgers, Perkins, Taco Bell, Wendy's, **lodging:** AmericInn, Holiday Inn Express, **other:** Harley-Davidson, **W...food:** Chili's, $Tree, **other:** Elder Beerman, Home Depot, Michael's

120 rds OK, V, Sheboygan, **E...gas:** Phillips 66/diesel, **food:** Judie's Rest., **lodging:** Best Value Inn, Sleep Inn, **other:** Glove Outlet, to Kohler-Andrae SP, camping, **1 mi W...other:** Horn's RV Ctr

116 rd AA, Foster Rd, Oostburg, **W...food:** Sandpiper Diner

113 WI 32 N, rd LL, Cedar Grove, **W...gas:** Citgo/diesel/repair, **food:** Dr Zwann Rest., **lodging:** Lakeshore Motel

107 rd D, Belgium, **E...other:** Harrington Beach SP, **W...gas:** BP/DQ/diesel/24hr, Mobil/McDonald's/diesel/24hr, **food:** Hobo's Korner Kitchen, **lodging:** AmericInn

Milwaukee

100 WI 32 S, WI 84 W, Port Washington, **E...gas:** Citgo/diesel, **food:** Arby's, Burger King, McDonald's, Subway, **lodging:** Best Western, Country Inn Suites, **other:** Allen-Edmonds Shoes, Goodyear/auto, Sentry Foods, **W...lodging:** Nisleit's Country Inn

97 (from nb), WI 57, Fredonia, no facilities

96 WI 33, to Saukville, **E...gas:** Mobil/diesel/24hr, **lodging:** Best Western, **other:** Buick/Pontiac/Cadillac, Dodge, Ford, Piggly Wiggly, Wal-Mart, **W...gas:** BP/24hr, **food:** Bublitz' Rest., DQ, Ducati Café, Subway, **lodging:** Super 8, **other:** Kelly Tire

93 WI 32 N, WI 57 S, Grafton, **1-2 mi E...food:** Dairy House Rest., Pied Piper Rest., Smith Bros Fish, **lodging:** Best Western

92 WI 60, rd Q, Grafton, **E...food:** GhostTown Rest., **W...gas:** Citgo/DQ/diesel, **lodging:** Baymont Inn, **other:** Home Depot, OfficeMax, Target

89 rd C, Cedarburg, **W...gas:** Mobil/diesel, **food:** Cedar Crk Settlement Café(6mi), **lodging:** StageCoach Inn, Washington House Inn, **other:** HOSPITAL

85 WI 57 S, WI 167 W, Mequon Rd, **W...gas:** Citgo/diesel, Mobil/24hr, **food:** Café 1505, Chancery Rest., Cousins Subs, DQ, Damon's, Hong Palace Chinese, McDonald's, Panera Bread, Subway, Wendy's, **lodging:** Best Western, Chalet Motel, **other:** Jewel-Osco, Kohl's, Walgreen

82b a WI 32 S, WI 100, Brown Deer Rd, **E...gas:** BP/24hr, PDQ/diesel, **food:** Cousins Subs, Heineman's Rest., McDonald's, Pizza Hut, Qdoba Mexican, SpeakEasy Grill, **lodging:** Courtyard, **other:** Borders Books, Kohl's Foods, Osco Drug, Walgreen, **W...lodging** Sheraton/rest.

80 Good Hope Rd, **E...gas:** BP, **food:** Peking Palace, **lodging:** Manchester East Hotel, Residence Inn, **other:** to Cardinal Stritch U

78 Silver Spring Dr, **E...gas:** BP, Mobil, **food:** Applebee's, Burger King, Denny's, Ground Round, Little Caesar's, LK Chinese, McDonald's, Papa John's, Pizza Hut, Subway, Taco Bell, Tumbleweed Grill, Wendy's, Zappa's Rest., **lodging:** Baymont Inn, Exel Inn, NorthShore Motel, Woodfield Suites, **other:** Barnes&Noble, Cadillac, Firestone/auto, Goodyear/auto, Kohl's, Radio Shack, Sears/auto, Walgreen, mall, **W...other** HOSPITAL

77b a (from nb), **E...food:** Anchorage Rest., **other:** Home Depot

76b a WI 57, WI 190, Green Bay Ave, **E...food:** Anchorage Rest., **other:** Home Depot, **W...gas:** Citgo, **food:** Burger King, **other:** Buick, Jaguar/Volvo

75 Atkinson Ave, Keefe Ave, **E...gas:** Mobil, **W...gas:** BP, Citgo

74 Locust St, no facilities

73c North Ave(rom sb), **E...food:** Wendy's, **W...food:** McDonald's

73a WI 145 E, 4th St(exits left from sb), Broadway, downtown

WISCONSIN

Interstate 43

N ↑↓ S Milwaukee

72c Wells St, **E...other:** HOSPITAL, Civic Ctr, museum

72b (from sb), I-94 W, to madison, no facilities

72a (310c from nb, exits left from sb), I-794 E, I-94 W to Madison, to Lakefront, downtown

311 WI 59, National Ave, 6th St, downtown

312a Lapham Blvd, Mitchell St, Old Towne Serbian Gourmet House

312b (from nb), Becher St, Lincoln Ave, no facilities

314a Holt Ave, **E...gas:** Citgo/diesel, **other:** Pick'n Save Food, **W...other:** HOSPITAL, to Alverno Coll

314b Howard Ave, no facilities

10b (316 from sb), I-94 S to Chicago, airport, no facilities

9b a US 41, 27th St, **E...gas:** BP, Citgo, Mobil, Arby's, **food:** Burger King, Chancery Rest., Cousins Subs, Pizza Hut, Rusty Skillet Rest., Togo's/Baskin-Robbins/Dunkin Donuts, **lodging:** Suburban Motel, **other:** AutoZone, CarQuest, Dodge, K-Mart, Rainbow Foods, Target, Walgreen, **W...food:** Denny's, Los Burritos Tapatios, McDonald's, Taco Bell, **lodging:** Hospitality Suites, **other:** HOSPITAL, AAA, Advance Parts, Chevrolet, Chrysler/Jeep, Goodyear, GMC/Hyundai, Kohl's

8a WI 36, Loomis Rd, **E...gas:** BP, Citgo, **food:** Los Mariachis Mexican, **other:** Walgreen, **W...gas:** Citgo, **other:** to Alverno Coll

7 60th St, **E...gas:** Speedway/diesel, **food:** Mineo's Rest., **other:** Harley-Davison, **W...gas:** Speedway

5b 76th St(from sb, no EZ return), **E...food:** Applebee's, Boston Mkt, Burger King, Ground Round, Hooters, KFC, Kopp's Burgers, McDonald's, Olive Garden, Outback Steaks, Pizza Hut, Red Lobster, TGIFriday, Wendy's, **other:** Barnes&Noble, Best Buy, Borders Books, BreadSmith, Circuit City, Cub Foods, Firestone/auto, Goodyear/auto, Isuzu, Office Depot, SteinMart, Valvoline, **W...other:** Trak Auto

5a WI 24 W, Forest Home Ave, **E...gas:** Citgo, **other:** Boerner Botanical Gardens

61 (4 from sb), I-894/US 45 N, I-43/US 45 S, no facilities

60 US 45 S, WI 100, 108th St(exits left from sb), **E...gas:** BP, Citgo, Clark Gas, Phillips 66, **food:** A&W, Amore Italian, Charcoal Grill, MegaOne Rest., **W...gas:** Phillips 66, **food:** Forum Rest., McDonald's, Omega Custard, **other:** Aldi Foods, Badger Transmisions, Goodyear, Mr P Tire, Saturn, Walgreen, Wal-Mart/drugs

59 WI 100, Layton Ave(from nb), Hales Corner, same as 60

57 Moorland Rd, **1-3 mi W...gas:** Mobil/24hr, Speedway/diesel/24hr, **food:** Applebee's, Atlanta Bread, Fazoli's, McDonald's, Quizno's, Rococo's Pizza, Taco Bell, Tumbleweed Grill, **lodging:** Baymont Inn, Best Western, Country Inn Suites, Embassy Suites/rest., Holiday Inn Express, **other:** Michael's, Target

54 rd Y, Racine Ave, **1-2 mi E...gas:** Citgo/diesel, Kwik-Trip, **other:** Culver's, Cousins Subs, McDonald's

50 WI 164, Big Bend, **W...gas:** Citgo/diesel, **food:** McDonald's, Pizza Stop

44mm Fox River

43 WI 83, Mukwonago, **E...gas:** BP/diesel, **W...gas:** Citgo, Shell, **food:** Burger King, Culver's, DQ, McDonald's, Subway, Taco Bell, **lodging:** Sleep Inn, **other:** Wal-Mart

Delavan

38 WI 20, East Troy, **W...gas:** BP, Clark/Subway/diesel/24hr/@, Shell/McDonald's, **food:** Burger King, Roma Ristorante, **other:** CarQuest, Chrysler/Plymouth/Dodge, NAPA

36 WI 120, East Troy, **W...lodging:** Country Inn Suites, gas/diesel

33 Bowers Rd, **E...to** Alpine Valley Music Theatre

32mm **rest area both lanes, full(handicapped)facilities, phone, picnic tables, litter barrels, vending, petwalk**

29 WI 11, Elkhorn, fairgrounds, no facilities

27b a US 12, to Lake Geneva, no facilities

25 WI 67, Elkhorn, **E...gas:** Mobil/diesel, **lodging:** AmericInn, **other:** Chevrolet, Chrysler/Dodge/Jeep, **W...gas:** Speedway/diesel/24hr, **food:** Burger King, **other:** Dehaan Auto/RV Ctr

21 WI 50, Delavan, **E...gas:** Shell/diesel/24hr, **other:** Greyhound DogTrack, Kohl's, Wal-Mart SuperCtr/24hr, **W...gas:** Mobil, Speedway/diesel/24hr, **food:** Burger King, Cousins Subs, KFC, McDonald's, Perkins, Pizza Hut, Subway, Taco Bell, Wendy's, **lodging:** Delavan Inn, Super 8, **other:** Ace Hardware, Chevrolet/Cadillac, Ford/Lincoln/Mercury, K-Mart, Pick'n Save, Piggly Wiggly, ShopKO, Walgreen

17 rd X, Delavan, Darien, **W...gas:** BP

15 US 14, Darien, **E...gas:** Citgo/diesel, **food:** West Wind Diner

6 WI 140, Clinton, **E...gas:** BP, Citgo, **food:** Subway, **other:** Ford

2 rd X, Hart Rd, **E...food:** Butterfly Fine Dining

1b a I-90, E to Chicago, W to Madison, **W...gas:** BP/24hr, BP/Subway/diesel, Citgo/diesel, Phillips 66, Pilot/DQ/Taco Bell/diesel/24hr/@, Speedway/diesel, **food:** Applebee's, Arby's, Asia Buffet, Burger King, Cousins Subs, Country Kitchen, Culver's, Fazoli's, Hong Kong Buffet, McDonald's, Papa Murphy's, Perkins, Wendy's, **lodging:** Comfort Inn, Econolodge, Fairfield Inn, Holiday Inn Express, Super 8, **other:** Aldi Foods, Buick/Pontiac, Chevrolet/Cadillac/Nissan, $Tree, Radio Shack, Staples, Tires+, Wal-Mart SuperCtr/24hr

I-43 begins/ends on I-90, exit 185 in Beloit.

Interstate 90

Exit # Services

187mm I-90 & I-39 run together nb., Wisconsin/Illinois state line

187mm **Welcome Ctr wb, full(handicapped)facilities, info, phones, picnic tables, litter barrels, vending, petwalk**

185b I-43 N, to Milwaukee, no facilities

185a WI 81, Beloit, **S...gas:** BP, BP/Subway/diesel, Exxon, Shell, Pilot/DQ/Taco Bell/diesel/24hr/@, Speedway/diesel, **food:** Applebee's, Arby's, Asia Buffet, Burger King, Cousins Subs, Country Kitchen, Culver's, DQ, Fazoli's, Hong Kong Buffet, McDonald's, Papa Murphy's, Perkins, Taco Bell, Wendy's, **lodging:** Comfort Inn, Econolodge, Fairfield Inn, Holiday Inn Express, Super 8, **other:** Buick/Pontiac, Chevrolet/Cadillac/Nissan, Radio Shack, Staples, Tires +, Wal-Mart SuperCtr/24hr

183 Shopiere Rd, rd S, to Shopiere, **S...gas:** Citgo/diesel/24hr, **other:** HOSPITAL, camping

177 WI 351, Janesville, **S...gas:** BP, Kwiktrip, **other:** to Blackhawk Tec Coll, Rock Co Airport

Beloit

E ↑↓ W

Interstate 90

E ↕ **W**

Janesville

Madison

175b a WI 11, Janesville, to Delavan, **N...gas:** BP/Subway/diesel/24hr, **food:** Denny's, **lodging:** Baymont Inn, **S...gas:** BP, **food:** DQ, Hardee's, **lodging:** Lannon Stone Motel

171c b US 14, WI 26, Janesville, **N...gas:** TA/Mobil/Wendy's/diesel/@, **food:** Damon's, Fuddruckers, Old Country Buffet, Steak'n Shake, Subway, **lodging:** Holiday Inn Express, Microtel, **other:** Best Buy, Home Depot, Kamp Dakota, Michael's, Old Navy, Staples, Tires+, **S...gas:** BP, Citgo/diesel/24hr, KwikTrip/diesel/24hr, Phillips 66/diesel, **food:** Applebee's, Arby's, BBQ, Big Boy, Burger King, ChiChi's, Country Kitchen, Cousins Subs, Fazoli's, Ground Round, Gyro's Greek, Hardee's, Hooters, KFC, McDonald's, McRaven's Rest., Olive Garden, Papa Murphy's, Perkins, Pizza Hut, Shakey's Pizza, Taco Bell, Tibbie's Rest., **lodging:** Ramada Inn/rest., Select Inn, Super 8, **other:** HOSPITAL, Aldi Foods, Firestone/auto, Ford/Lincoln/Mercury, Harley-Davidson, JC Penney, Jo-Ann Fabrics, Mazda, Mercedes, K-Mart, ShopKO, Target, VW, Wal-Mart/drugs, mall

171a **S...same as 171c b, N...gas:** Phillips 66, **food:** Cracker Barrel, Best Western/rest., Motel 6, Hampton Inn

168mm rest area eb, full(handicapped)facilities, phone, picnic tables, litter barrels, vending, petwalk

163.5mm Rock River

163 WI 59, Edgerton, to Milton, **N...gas:** Mobil/Red Apple Rest., Shell/Burger King, **food:** Cousins Subs, McDonald's, Newville Drive-In, WI Chalet Cafe, **lodging:** Comfort Inn, **other:** marina, **S...gas:** BP

160 US 51S, WI 73, WI 106, Oaklawn Academy, to Deerfield, **N...other:** Hickory Hills Camping, **S...gas:** Shell/diesel/24hr/@, **food:** Ray's Rest., Subway, **lodging:** Towne Edge Motel, HOSPITAL

156 US 51N, to Stoughton, **S...lodging:** Coachman's Inn, HOSPITAL

148mm weigh sta wb

147 rd N, Cottage Grove, to Stoughton, **N...**Corner Store, **S...gas:** BP/Burger King/24hr, Citgo/Cousins Subs/diesel, **other:** Lake Kegonsa SP

146mm weigh sta eb

142b a (142a exits left from wb)US 12, US 18, Madison, to Cambridge, **N...gas:** Mobil/diesel, **food:** McDonald's, Subway, **lodging:** Knight's Inn, Motel 6, Ramada Inn, Wingate Inn, **other:** Harley-Davidson, **S...gas:** Cenex/diesel, Phillips 66/diesel, Shell/diesel, **food:** Arby's, Denny's, Noodles Rest., Wendy's, **lodging:** AmericInn, Day's Inn, Holiday Inn Express, Quality Inn, **other:** HOSPITAL, UWI

138a I-94, E to Milwaukee, W to La Crosse

I-90 W and I-94 W run together for 93 miles

138b **S...other:** WI 30, to Madison, airport

135c b US 151, Madison, **N...food:** Cheesehaus, **lodging:** Courtyard, Woodfield Suites, **other:** Buick, Chevrolet, Chrysler/Plymouth/Dodge, Ford, Isuzu, Nissan, Toyota

135a **S...gas:** BP/24hr, Shell, Sinclair, **food:** Applebee's, Carlos O'Kelly's, Chili's, Country Kitchen, Cracker Barrel, Denny's, Dunkin Donuts, Hardee's, Heritage House Smorgasbord, IHOP, KFC, McDonald's, Mtn Jack's Rest., Old Country Buffet, Olive Garden, Perkins, Ponderosa, Pizza Hut, Red Lobster, Rococo's Pizza, Steak'n Shake, Tumbleweed Grill, Wendy's, **lodging:** Best Western, Comfort Inn, Crowne Plaza Hotel, Econolodge, Exel Inn, Fairfield Inn, Hampton Inn, Holiday Inn/rest., Microtel, Motel 6, Red Roof Inn, Residence Inn, Roadstar Inn, Select Inn, **other:** MEDICAL CARE, Best Buy, Circuit City, Firestone/auto, Home Depot, JC Penney, Jo-Ann Fabrics, K-Mart, Kohl's, Office Depot, OfficeMax, Old Navy, Sears, ShopKO, mall, st patrol

132 US 51, Madison, De Forest, **N...gas:** Citgo/diesel/rest., Shell/diesel/@, **food:** Pine Cone Rest., **S...gas:** TA/Mobil/Subway/diesel/rest./24hr/@, **other:** Goodyear, Peterbilt, Volvo/White/GMC/Freightliner, WI RV World, camping

131 WI 19, Waunakee, **N...gas:** Citgo, KwikTrip, Mobil, Speedway/Taco Bell/diesel/@, **food:** A&W, McDonald's, Roadside Grill, **lodging:** Day's Inn, Super 8, **other:** Mousehouse Cheesehaus, Kenworth Trucks(5 mi), Truckwash, **S...lodging:** Country Inn Suites

126 rd V, De Forest, to Dane, **N...gas:** BP, Phillips 66/Arby's/diesel, **food:** Burger King, Culver's, DeForest Rest., McDonald's, 7E Rest., Subway, **lodging:** Holiday Inn Express, **other:** KOA, **S...gas:** Citgo, Exxon/diesel

119 WI 60, Arlington, to Lodi, **S...gas:** Mobil/Cousins/diesel, **food:** A&W, Rococo's Pizza, **lodging:** Best Western, **other:** Interstate RV Ctr

115 rd CS, Poynette, to Lake Wisconsin, **N...gas:** BP/diesel, **food:** McDonald's, Subway, **other:** Smokey Hollow Camping, diesel truck/trailer repair, motel, trout fishing

113mm rest area both lanes, full(handicapped)facilities, phone, picnic tables, litter barrels, vending, petwalk

111mm Wisconsin River

108b a I-39 N, WI 78, to US 51 N, Portage, **N...other:** HOSPITAL, to WI Dells, **S...gas:** BP, Petro/diesel/rest./24hr/@, **food:** DQ, Little Caesar's, Subway, **lodging:** Comfort Suites, Day's Inn, Devil's Head Resort/Conv Ctr, **other:** Blue Beacon

106mm Baraboo River

106 WI 33, Portage, **N...gas:** Mobil/diesel/rest., **other:** HOSPITAL, **S...gas:** BP, **other:** Kamp Dakota, SkyHigh Camping, to Cascade Mtn Ski Area, Devil's Lake SP, Circus World Museum

Interstate 90

E ↕ **W**

92 US 12, to Baraboo, **N...gas:** BP/diesel, Cenex/diesel/24hr, Citgo/diesel/24hr, Mobil/diesel/24hr, Sinclair/Subway/diesel, **food:** Burger King, Cracker Barrel, Culver's, Damon's, Danny's Diner, Denny's, Houlihan's, KFC, McDonald's, Papa John's, Ponderosa, Wintergreen Grill, **lodging:** Alakai Hotel, American Inn, Best Western(4mi), Great Wolf Lodge, Camelot Inn, Country Squire Motel, Dell Rancho Motel, Grand Marquis Inn, **other:** Kalahari Conv Ctr, Ramada Ltd, WI Cheese, museum, **S...lodging:** Travelodge, **other:** HOSPITAL, Scenic Traveler RV Ctr, Dell Boo Camping, Jellystone Camping, Red Oak Camping, Mirror Lake SP

89 89 WI 23, Lake Delton, **N...gas:** Marathon, Mobil/diesel, **food:** Houlihan's, Howie's Rest., Internet Café, KFC, **lodging:** Copacabana Motel, Malibu Inn, Olympia Motel, RainTree Motel, Relax Inn, Rodeway Inn, Travelodge, Wilderness Motel, **other:** Crystal Grand Music Theatre, Springbrook Camping, Jellystone Camping, **S...other:** Home Depot, Wal-Mart SuperCtr/gas/24hr, Country Roads RV Park

87 WI 13, Wisconsin Dells, **N...gas:** BP/diesel, Citgo/diesel, Mobil/diesel, Shell, **food:** Burger King, Christmas Mtn Village, Country Kitchen, Denny's, Pedro's Mexican, Perkins, Rococo's Pizza, Taco Bell, Wendy's, **lodging:** Best Western, Comfort Inn, Day's Inn, Holiday Inn/rest., Howard Johnson, Polynesian Hotel, Super 8, **other:** KOA, Sherwood Forest Camping, Tepee Park Camping, golf, info

85 US 12, WI 16, Wisconsin Dells, **N...other:** to Rocky Arbor SP, Sherwood Forest Camping, Standing Rock Camping, **S...lodging:** KOA, Summer Breeze Resort

79 rd HH, Lyndon Sta, **N...other:** Dreamfield RV Ctr, **S...** Shell/diesel/rest.

76mm **rest area wb, full(handicapped)facilities, phone, picnic tables, litter barrels, vending, petwalk**

74mm **rest area eb, full(handicapped)facilities, phone, picnic tables, litter barrels, vending, petwalk**

69 WI 82, Mauston, **N...gas:** Cenex/Taco Bell/diesel/24hr/@, Pilot/Wendy's/diesel/24hr/@, Shell/24hr, **food:** Country Kitchen, **lodging:** Best Western Oasis, Country Inn, Super 8, **other:** to Buckhorn SP, **S... gas:** BP/diesel/24hrCitgo/diesel, KwikTrip/diesel/@, **food:** Culver's, McDonald's, Pizza Hut, Roman Castle Rest., Subway, **lodging:** Alaskan Motel/rest., **other:** HOSPITAL, Family$, K-Mart, Pick'n Save, Walgreen, Wal-Mart

61 WI 80, New Lisbon, to Necedah, **N...gas:** Citgo/diesel/24hr/@, Mobil/A&W/Subway/diesel/@, **lodging:** Edge O' the Wood Motel, Travelodge, **other:** Buckhorn SP, Ford, **S...gas:** KwikTrip/24hr

55 rd C, Camp Douglas, **N...other:** wayside, to Camp Williams, Volk Field, **S...gas:** BP/diesel, Mobil/Subway/diesel, **lodging:** K&K Motel, **other:** to Mill Bluff SP

51mm weigh sta eb

48 rd PP, Oakdale, **N...gas:** Citgo/Old Rig Diner/diesel/24hr/@, **other:** Kamp Dakota/showers, KOA

47.5mm weigh sta wb

45 I-94 W, to St Paul, I-90 E and I-94 E run together for 93 miles

Tomah

43 US 12, WI 16, Tomah, **N...gas:** Citgo, KwikTrip/diesel/24hr, **food:** A&W, Burnstadt's Café, DQ, Embers Rest., European Café, Hearty Platter Rest., **lodging:** Villager Lodge, **other:** HOSPITAL, Pick n' Sav Foods

41 WI 131, Tomah, to Wilton, **N...gas:** Cenex(1mi), Mobil/diesel, KwikTrip/diesel, **food:** A&W, European Café, **lodging:** Brentwood Inn, **other:** VA MED CTR, **S...**st patrol

28 WI 16, Sparta, Ft McCoy, **N...gas:** BP, Kwiktrip/diesel, **lodging:** Best Western, **other:** HOSPITAL

25 WI 27, Sparta, to Melvina, **N...gas:** Cenex/diesel, Citgo/diesel, **food:** Burger King, Country Kitchen, DQ, Happy Chef, Hardee's, KFC, McDonald's, Pizza Hut, Subway, **lodging:** Country Inn, Super 8, **other:** Ace Hardware, Chevrolet/Buick/Pontiac, Chrysler/Dodge, Family$, Ford/Mercury, Jubilee Foods, Radio Shack, Wal-Mart SuperCtr/24hr(2mi, WI 16), **S...**camping

22mm **rest area wb, full(handicapped)facilities, phone, picnic tables, litter barrels, vending, petwalk**

20mm **rest area eb, full(handicapped)facilities, phone, picnic tables, litter barrels, vending, petwalk**

15 WI 162, Bangor, to Coon Valley, **N...gas, S...other:** Chevrolet

12 rd C, W Salem, **N...gas:** Cenex/diesel/24hr, **other:** Coulee Region RV Ctr, NAPA, Neshonoc Camping, **S...lodging:** AmericInn

10mm weigh sta eb

5 WI 16, La Crosse, **N...food:** Krispy Kreme, Outback Steaks, Quizno's, **lodging:** Baymont Inn, Hampton Inn, Microtel, **other:** Wal-Mart SuprCtr/24hr, Woodman's Food/gas/lube, Aldi Foods, Home Depot, Pennzoil, Valvoline, bank, **S...gas:** Holiday/A&W/diesel, KwikTrip/diesel/24hr, **food:** Applebee's, ChiChi's, ChuckeCheese, Culver's, Fazoli's, McDonald's, Hong Kong Buffet, Old Country Buffet, Olive Garden, Perkins, Subway, TGIFriday, **lodging:** Holiday Inn Express, **other:** HOSPITAL, Barnes&Noble, Best Buy, Goodyear/auto, Kohl's, Mashall Field, Michael's, OfficeMax, Sears/auto, ShopKO, Target, mall

4 US 53 N, WI 16, to WI 157, La Crosse, **N...other:** Harley-Davidson, **S...gas:** Citgo, Kwiktrip/gas, **food:** Bakers Square, Burger King, ChiChi's, Ciatti's Italian, El Patio Mexican, Famous Dave's BBQ, Grizzly's Café, Little Caesar's, McDonald's, Panera Bread, Red Lobster, Rococo's Pizza, Subway, Taco Bell, Wendy's, **lodging:** Comfort Inn, Day's Inn, **other:** HOSPITAL, Cub Foods/24hr, Food Festival/24hr, GNC, Goodyear/auto, JC Penney, K-Mart, NW Fabrics/crafts, Office Depot, Sam's Club, ShopKO, Tires+, Bluebird Springs Camping, La Crosse River St Trail, mall

3 US 53 S, WI 35, to La Crosse, **S...gas:** Kwiktrip, Speedway/diesel, **food:** Burger King, Coney Island, Country Kitchen, Edwardo's Pizza, Embers Rest./24hr, KFC, McDonald's, North Country Steaks, Old Country Cheese, Pizza Hut, Rococo's Pizza, Subway, **lodging:** Best Western, Brookstone Inn, Exel Inn, Hampton Inn, Nightsaver Inn, Roadstar Inn, Super 8, **other:** ShopKO, U-Haul, to Great River St Trail, Viterbo Coll

2.5mm Black River

2 rd B, French Island, **N...gas:** Mobil/diesel, **other:** airport, **S...gas:** Citgo/diesel, **lodging:** Day's Inn/rest.

1mm **Welcome Ctr eb, full(handicapped)facilities, info, phone, picnic tables, litter barrels, vending, petwalk**

0mm Wisconsin/Minnesota state line, Mississippi River

La Crosse

Interstate 94

E ↕ **W**

Exit #	Services
349mm	Wisconsin/Illinois state line, rd ML(from nb), weight sta nb
347	WI 165, rd Q, Lakeview Pkwy, **E...gas:** BP/diesel, **food:** Culver's, McDonald's, Radisson/rest., **other:** Prime Outlets/famous brands, **Welcome Ctr, full facilities, W...other:** GolfShack Whse
345	rd C, **E...gas:** Phillips 66/diesel, **food:** Chester Fried, **4 mi W...gas:** BP
345mm	Des Plaines River
344	WI 50, to Kenosha, Lake Geneva, **E...food:** Citgo/diesel, Shell, Woodman's/gas, **food:** Quizno's, Starbucks, Texas Roadhouse, White Castle, **lodging:** Baymont Inn, Country Inn Suites, Super 8, **other:** HOSPITAL, **W...gas:** BP, Speedway/Subway/diesel, **food:** Arby's, Burger King, Cracker Barrel, Denny's, KFC, LJ Silver, McDonald's, Perkins, Taco Bell, Wendy's, **lodging:** Best Western, Country Inn Suites, Day's Inn, Quality Suites, Value Inn, **other:** BMW, Cadillac, Chevrolet, Ford, GM, Jeep, Mitsubishi, Subaru, Toyota, Outlet Mall/famous brands
342	WI 158, to Kenosha, **E...food:** Culver's, **lodging:** Holiday Inn Express(7mi), **other:** Harley-Davidson, dog track
340	WI 142, rd S, to Kenosha, **E...gas:** Citgo/diesel, Mobil/diesel, **other:** HOSPITAL, **W...food:** Mars Cheese Castle Rest., StarBar Rest., **lodging:** Easterday Motel, **other:** to Bong RA
339	rd E, **E...gas:** Marathon/diesel/24hr
337	County Line Rd, rd KR, **E...other:** to Great Lakes Dragway, **W...food:** Apple Holler Rest.
335	WI 11, to Racine, Burlington, **E...gas:** KwikTrip/diesel/24hr
333	US 20, to Racine, Waterford, **E...gas:** KwikTrip/diesel/24hr, Shell/Cousins Subs/diesel, **food:** Burger King, McDonald's, **lodging:** Holiday Inn Express, Paul's Motel, Ramada Ltd, **other:** Hyundai, HOSPITAL, **7 mi E...lodging:** Comfort Inn, Fairfield Inn, Marriott, Quality Inn, Super 8, **W...gas:** Citgo/5th Wheel Grill/diesel/24hr/@, Petro/Mobil/Wendy's/diesel/24hr/@, **food:** Culver's, Subway, **lodging:** Best Western

329	rd K, Thompsonville, to Racine, **E...gas:** Pilot/Arby's/diesel/24hr/@, **W...gas:** Mobil/A&W
328mm	weigh sta eb
327	rd G, **W...other:** Trader Jack's Fireworks
326	7 Mile Rd, **E...gas:** BP/24hr, **other:** Jellystone Park, RV repair, **W...gas:** Mobil/24hr, antiques
325	US 41 N(from wb), to 27th St, **W...food:** Acropolis Rest., Charcoal Grill, SandTrap Rest.
322	WI 100, to Ryan Rd, **E...food:** McDonald's, Wendy's, **other:** Goodyear/Cummins Diesel, **W...gas:** Flying J/CountryMkt/diesel/24hr/@, Pilot/Subway/diesel/24hr/@, Shell/Burger King/diesel, **food:** Arby's, Cousins Subs, Perkins, **lodging:** Value Inn, **other:** Blue Beacon, Freightliner/repair
320	rd BB, Rawson Ave, **E...gas:** BP/24hr, Mobil, **food:** Applebee's, Burger King, **lodging:** Baymont Inn, **other:** Honda

319	rd ZZ, College Ave, **E... gas:** Shell/Subway, Speedway/diesel, **food:** McDonald's, Perkins, **lodging:** Comfort Suites, Country Inn Suites, Exel Inn, Hampton Inn, **other:** MainStay Suites, Radisson, Ramada/rest., Red Roof, **W...gas:** BP/24hr, Citgo/diesel, **other:** VIP Foodmart, Boy Blue DairyMart
318	WI 119, no facilities
317	Layton Ave, **E...gas:** Andy's Gas, Clark Gas, **food:** Martino's Rest., Porterhouse Rest., Prime Qtr Steaks, **other:** Checkers Parts, Radio Shack, **W...food:** Spring Garden Rest., **lodging:** Howard Johnson
316	I-43 S, I-894 W(exits left from wb), to Beloit
314b	Howard Ave, to Milwaukee, **W...other:** HOSPITAL, to Alverno Coll
a	Holt Ave, **E...gas:** Andy's/diesel, **food:** Arby's, Chucke-Cheese, DQ, Subway, Wendy's, **other:** Jewel-Osco/gas, K-Mart, Pik'n Sav Foods, **W...HOSPITAL**
312b a	Becher St, Mitchell St, Lapham Blvd, **W...gas:** BP, Citgo
311	WI 59, National Ave, 6th St, downtown
310a	13th St(from eb), **E...HOSPITAL**
b	I-43 N, to Green Bay
c	I-794 E, **E...lodging:** Holiday Inn, Ramada Inn, **other:** to downtown and Lake Michigan Port of Entry
309b	26th St, 22nd St, Clybourn St, St Paul Ave, **N...other:** HOSPITAL, to Marquette U
a	35th St, **N...gas:** Speedway
308c b	US 41, no facilities
a	VA Ctr, **N...other:** Miller Brewing, **S...other:** County Stadium
307b	68th-70th St, Hawley Rd, **S...other:** to County Stadium
a	**N...**68th St, **N...other:** Pennzoil
306	WI 181, to 84th St, **N...HOSPITAL, S...other:** Olympic Training Facility
305b	US 45 N, to Fond du Lac, **N...HOSPITAL**
a	I-894 S, to Chicago, to airport
304b a	WI 100, **N...gas:** Citgo, Shell/diesel, **food:** Cousins Subs, Edwardo's Pizza, Ground Round, Giuseppi's Pizza, McDonald's, Pizza Hut, Schlotsky's, Steak Escape, Taco Bell, **lodging:** Best Western/rest., Exel Inn, **other:** zoo, **S...gas:** Phillips 66, Speedway/diesel, **other:** U-Haul, Walgreen

E ↕ W

301b a Moorland Rd, **N...gas:** BP/diesel/24hr, Mobil, **food:** Bakers Square, Fuddrucker's, Houlihan's, Maxwell's Rest., McDonald's, Pizzaria Uno, **lodging:** Courtyard, Marriott, Sheraton, Wyndham Garden, **other:** Audi, Barnes&Noble, BMW, Firestone/auto, Goodyear/auto, JC Penney, Office Depot, Saab, Sears/auto, Walgreen, **S...gas:** Mobil, **food:** Champp's Rest., **lodging:** Best Western, Country Inn Suites, Embassy Suites/rest., Residence Inn, **other:** Walgreen, golf

297 US 18, rd JJ, Blue Mound Rd, Barker Rd, **1-2 mi N...gas:** BP/24hr, Mobil, **food:** Applebee's, Boston Mkt, Burger King, ChiChi's, ChuckeCheese, Gondola Grille, KFC, Kopp's Custard, McDonald's, Olive Garden, Pano's Charhouse, Perkins, Starbucks, Subway, Tony Roma's, Wendy's, Zorba's Grill, **lodging:** Baymont Inn, Comfort Inn, Courtyard, Fairfield Inn, Hampton Inn, Motel 6, Wyndham Garden, **other:** MEDICAL CARE, Acura, Advance Parts, Best Buy, Circuit City, CompUSA, Drug Emporium, K-Mart, Mazda/Lexus, NTB, Pick'n Save, VW, **S...gas:** PDQ Gas, **food:** Arby's, Dunkin Donuts, McDonald's, Schlotsky's, Taco Bell, **lodging:** Extended Stay America, Holiday Inn, Select Inn, Super 8, **other:** Chrysler, Home Depot, Target, Tires+, Walgreen, st patrol

295 WI 164, Waukesha, **N...gas:** Citgo/diesel, KwikTrip/gas, **lodging:** Marriott, **other:** HOSPITAL, **S...other:** HOSPITAL, to Carroll Coll

294 rd J, to Waukesha, **N...gas:** Mobil, **food:** Machine Shed Rest., Thunder Bay Grill, **lodging:** Comfort Suites, Radisson, **S...other:** Expo Ctr

293c WI 16 W, Pewaukee(from wb), **N...other:** GE Plant
b a rd T, Wausheka, Pewaukee, **S...gas:** Mobil, **food:** Brisco Co Grill, Cousins Subs, Denny's, Fazoli's, Peking House, Rococo's Pizza, Subway, Taco Amigo, Weissgerber's Gasthaus Rest., Wendy's, **lodging:** Best Western, **other:** Firestone/auto, Jo-Ann Fabrics, Osco Drug, Pick'n Save Foods, Radio Shack, Walgreen

291 rd G, Pewaukee, **N...food:** Culver's, McDonald's, **lodging:** Country Inn

290 rd SS, no facilities

287 WI 83, to Wales, Hartland, **N...food:** Hardee's, McDonald's, Perkins, Water St Brewery/rest., **lodging:** Country Pride Inn, Holiday Inn Express, **other:** Amish Barn Gifts, GNC, Kohl's, Sentry Foods, Walgreen, **S...gas:** BP/diesel/24hr, PDQ/diesel/24hr, **food:** Breadworks Café, Burger King, DQ, Marty's Pizza, Rococo's Pizza, Subway, **lodging:** Baymont Inn, **other:** MEDICAL CARE, Home Depot, OfficeMax, Target, Tires+, Wal-Mart/drugs

285 rd C, Delafield, **N...gas:** Mobil, **other:** to St John's Military Academy, **S...other:** to Kettle Moraine SF

283 rd P, to Sawyer Rd(from wb), no facilities

282 WI 67, to Oconomowoc, Dousman, **N...gas:** Mobil, **food:** Culver's, Pizza Hut, Schlotsky's, Subway, K-Mart, **lodging:** Olympia Resort, **other:** HOSPITAL, Pick'n Save, Sentry Foods, **S...other:** to Kettle Moraine SF(8mi), Old World WI Hist Sites(13mi)

Madison

Tomah

277 Willow Glen Rd(from eb, no return), no facilities

275 rd F, to Sullivan, Ixonia, **N...gas:** BP/diesel, **other:** Concord Gen Store, **S...camping**

267 WI 26, Johnson Creek, to Watertown, **N...gas:** BP/McDonald's/diesel, Shell/diesel/rest./24hr/@, **food:** Arby's, **lodging:** Day's Inn, **other:** Goodyear/auto, Johnson Creek Outlet Ctr/famous brands, **S...gas:** Citgo/Hardee's/diesel/24hr, **food:** Culver's, **other:** HOSPITAL, Kohl's, to Aztalan SP

265mm Rock River

264mm **rest area wb, full(handicapped)facilities, phone, picnic tables, litter barrels, vending, petwalk**

263mm Crawfish River

261mm **rest area eb, full(handicapped)facilities, phone, picnic tables, litter barrels, vending, petwalk**

259 WI 89, Lake Mills, to Waterloo, **N...gas:** Citgo/diesel/24hr, **lodging:** Lake Country Inn, **S...gas:** BP/diesel/24hr, KwikTrip/diesel/24hr, **food:** McDonald's, Pizza Pit, Subway, **lodging:** Pyramid Motel/RV park, **other:** Buick/Chevrolet/Cadillac, Country Campers RV Ctr, to Aztalan SP

250 WI 73, to Marshall, Deerfield, no facilities

246mm weigh sta eb

244 rd n, Sun Prairie, Cottage Grove, **N...gas:** BP/diesel, Citgo/diesel, **S...food:** McDonald's

240 I-90 E. I-94 and I-90 run together 93 miles. **See Wisconsin Interstate 90, exits 48-138.**

147 I-90 W, to La Crosse

143 US 12, WI 21, Tomah, **N...gas:** Mobil/diesel, **food:** Country Kitchen, Perkins, **lodging:** AmericInn, Holiday Inn, Super 8, **other:** Humbird Cheese/gifts, **S...gas:** BP/diesel/rest./24hr, Citgo, Shell/diesel/cheese, **food:** Burnstad's Amish Café, Culver's, KFC, McDonald's, Subway, Taco Bell, **lodging:** Comfort Inn, Cranberry Suites, Econolodge, **other:** HOSPITAL, County Mkt Foods, $Tree, Ford/Lincoln/Mercury, U-Haul, Wal-Mart SuperCtr/gas/diesel/24hr, to Ft McCoy(9mi), **S on US 12...food:** Burger King, Pizza Hut, **other:** Chevrolet/Buick, Chrysler/Plymouth/Dodge/Jeep, Firestone/auto, NAPA, Radio Shack

135 rd EW, Warrens, **N...other:** Jellystone Camping

128 rd O, Millston, **N...other:** Black River SF, camping, **S...gas:** Hartland/diesel, **lodging:** Millston Motel

122mm **rest area/scenic view both lanes, full(handicapped)facilities, phone, picnic tables, litter barrels, vending, petwalk**

116 WI 54, **N...gas:** BP/Subway/diesel/LP/@, **food:** Perkins, **lodging:** Best Western Arrowhead/rest., Holiday Inn Express, Super 8, **other:** Black River RA, Parkland Camp, **S...gas:** Flying J/Cookery/diesel/24hr/@, KwikTrip/diesel, **food:** Burger King, DQ, Hardee's, McDonald's, Oriental Kitchen, Pizza Hut, **lodging:** Day's Inn, **other:** $Tree, Wal-Mart

115mm Black River

115 US 12, Black River Falls, to Merrillan, **N...lodging:** Pines Motel, **S...gas:** Holiday, Mobil/diesel, **food:** Hardee's, KFC, Pizza Hut, Subway, Sunrise Rest., **other:** HOSPITAL, Harley-Davidson, NAPA, Pontiac/Buick/GMC

Interstate 94

E

W

Eau Claire

105	to WI 95, Hixton, to Alma Center, **N...lodging:** Motel 95, **other:** KOA(3mi), **S...gas:** Cenex/diesel, Hixton Trvl/diesel/rest./24hr
98	WI 121, Northfield, to Alma Center, Pigeon Falls, **S...gas:** Cenex/diesel, **lodging:** Jackie's Café/Inn
88	US 10, Osseo, to Fairchild, **N...gas:** BP/DQ, Mobil, Shell/Elderberry's/diesel, **food:** Hardee's, Heckel's Rest., **lodging:** 10-7 Inn, Super 8, **other:** Chevrolet, Ford, Stony Cr RV Park, **S...gas:** Citgo, Speedway/ diesel, **food:** McDonald's, Subway, **lodging:** Red Carpet Inn, **other:** HOSPITAL
81	rd HH, rd KK, Foster, **S...gas:** Cenex/diesel/LP, **food:** Foster Cheesehaus
70	US 53, Eau Claire, N off Golf Rd...**gas:** Conoco/ diesel, **food:** A&W, Applebee's, Bakers Square, Oakwood Café Court, Fazoli's, Jade Garden, McDonald's, Northwoods Grill, Olive Garden, TGIFriday, **lodging:** Country Inn Suites, Heartland Inn, **other:** Aldi Foods, Best Buy, Borders Books, Dayton's, Kohl's, Michael's, Office Depot, Sam's Club, Target, Wal-Mart SuperCtr/ 24hr, mall, **S...other:** st police
68	WI 93, to Eleva, **N...gas:** BP, KwikTrip, Speedway/ 24hr, **food:** Burger King, DQ, Hardee's, **lodging:** Econolodge, **other:** Chrysler, Firestone/auto, Goodyear/auto, Jeep, Lincoln/Mercury, Nissan, Saturn, Subaru, VW, same as 70, **S...gas:** Citgo, **other:** Buick/Pontiac/Cadillac/GMC/Hyundai, Ford
65	WI 37, WI 85, Eau Claire, to Mondovi, **N...gas:** BP, Citgo/diesel, **food:** Arby's, ChiChi's, China Buffet, Godfather's, GreenMill Rest., Hardee's, Heckel's Rest., McDonald's, Randy's Rest., Red Lobster, Subway, Taco Bell, TCBY, Wendy's, YenKing Chinese, **lodging:** Best Western, Comfort Inn, Day's Inn/rest., Exel Inn, Hampton Inn, Holiday Inn/rest., Park Inn, Plaza Hotel, Quality Inn, Roadstar Inn, **other:** HOSPITAL, Castle Foods, Mazda/Toyota, Radio Shack, ShopKO
64mm	Chippewa River
59	to US 12, rd EE, to Eau Claire, **N...gas:** Citgo/Burger King/diesel/24hr, Holiday/Subway/diesel/24hr, **food:** Anderson's Grill, Embers Rest., McDonald's, **lodging:** AmericInn, Day's Inn, Super 8, **other:** HOSPITAL, Fox RV Ctr(10mi), auto repair/towing, **S...**US RV Ctr, trailer repair
52	US 12, WI 29, WI 40, Elk Mound, to Chippewa Falls, **S...gas:** U-Fuel, **food:** Elk Mound Café
49mm	weigh sta wb
45	rd B, Menomonie, **N...gas:** Cenex/diesel/rest., **S...gas:** KwikTrip/Subway/diesel/24hr, **food:** Culver's, Heckel's Rest., **lodging:** AmeriHost, **other:** HOSPITAL, Wal-Mart Dist Ctr
44mm	Red Cedar River
43mm	**rest areas both lanes, full(handicapped)facilities, phone, picnic tables, litter barrels, vending, petwalk, weather info**

Menomonie

Hudson

41	WI 25, Menomonie, **N...gas:** Cenex/ Burger King, **food:** Applebee's, China Buffet, Subway, **other:** HOSPITAL, Aldi Foods, $Tree, Radio Shack, Wal-Mart SuperCtr/24hr, Edgewater Camping, GS Camping, **S...gas:** Citgo, F&F/diesel, Holiday, Speedway/diesel/24hr, **food:** Arby's/Sbarro's, Country Kitchen, DQ, Hardee's, Kernel Rest., KFC, Little Caesar's, McDonald's, Perkins, Pizza Hut, Taco Bell, Taco John's, Wendy's, **lodging:** AmericInn, Best Western, Country Inn Suites, Motel 6, Super 8, **other:** Chevrolet, Chrysler, K-Mart, to Red Cedar St Tr
32	rd Q, to Knapp, no facilities
28	WI 128, Wilson, to Glenwood City, Elmwood, **N...gas:** KwikTrip/diesel/24hr, **food:** Hearty Platter Rest., **S...other:** Eau Galle RA, camping
24	rd B, Woodville, to Baldwin, **N...gas:** Mobil, **lodging:** Woodville Motel, **S...other:** Eau Galle RA, camping
19	US 63, Baldwin, to Ellsworth, **N...gas:** Freedom/diesel, KwikTrip/Subway/diesel, **food:** A&W, DQ, Hardee's, McDonald's, **lodging:** AmericInn, **other:** HOSPITAL, **S...gas:** Citgo/diesel/LP/24hr, **lodging:** Super 8
16	rd T, Hammond, **N...other:** Sheepskin Outlet
10	WI 65, Roberts, to New Richmond, no facilities
8mm	weigh sta eb
4	US 12, rd U, Somerset, **N...gas:** Citgo/diesel/24hr, TA/Mobil/diesel/rest./24hr/@, **other:** JR Ranch Motel/ steaks, to Willow River SP
3	WI 35, to River Falls, U of WI River Falls, no facilities
2	rd F, Carmichael Rd, Hudson, **N...gas:** BP, Holiday, **food:** Applebee's, Cousins Subs, Culver's, KFC, Papa Murphy's, Taco John's, **lodging:** Royal Inn, **other:** Econo Foods, Pontiac/GMC, Target, **S...Welcome Ctr both lanes, full(handicapped)facilities, phone, picnic table, litter barrel, info, petwalk, gas:** Holiday, KwikTrip/diesel, **food:** Arby's, Burger King, Country Kitchen, Denny's, McDonald's, Perkins/24hr, Pizza Hut, Subway, Taco Bell, Wendy's, **lodging:** Best Western, Comfort Inn, Fairfield Inn, Holiday Inn Express, Super 8, **other:** Checker Parts, Chevrolet/RV Ctr, County Mkt Foods, Ford/Mercury, Home Depot, Tires+, Wal-Mart, Yamaha, to Kinnickinnic SP
1	WI 35 N, Hudson, **1 mi N...gas:** Freedom, Holiday, **food:** DQ, Subway, **other:** City Mkt Foods
0mm	Wisconsin/Minnesota state line, St Croix River

WYOMING
Interstate 25

Exit #	Services
	Buffalo
300	I-90, E to Gillette, W to Billings. I-25 begins/ends on I-90, exit 56.
299	US 16, Buffalo, **E...gas:** Cenex/diesel, Conoco/diesel/24hr, Exxon/diesel, Sinclair/diesel, Shell/diesel/24hr, **food:** Sundance Grill, Winchester Steaks, **lodging:** Bunkhouse Motel, Comfort Inn, Motel 6, **other:** KOA, NAPA, **W... gas:** Bighorn/diesel/24hr/@, Cenex/diesel/rest./24hr, **food:** BBQ, Bozeman Rest., Breadboard Rest., Dash Inn Rest., Hardee's, McDonald's, Pizza Hut, Subway, Taco John's, **lodging:** Crossroads Inn/rest., Econolodge, Horsemen's Inn, Motel Wyo, Super 8, **other:** HOSPITAL, Indian RV Camp
298	US 87, Buffalo, **W...gas:** Sinclair/diesel/pizza, **other:** Nat Hist Dist Info
291	Trabing Rd, no facilities
280	Middle Fork Rd, no facilities
274mm	parking area both lanes, litter barrels
265	Reno Rd, no facilities
254	Kaycee, **E...gas:** Exxon/diesel, Shell/diesel, **food:** Country Inn Diner, **lodging:** Cassidy Inn, Siesta Motel, **other:** Kaycee Foods, NAPA Repair, Powder River RV Park, USPO, **W...rest area both lanes, full(handicapped)facilities, phone, picnic tables, litter barrels, petwalk, gas:** Sinclair/diesel/LP/motel, **other:** KC RV Park
249	TTT Rd, no facilities
246	Powder River Rd, no facilities
235	Tisdale Mtn Rd, no facilities
227	WY 387 N, Midwest, Edgerton, no facilities
223	no facilities
219mm	parking area both lanes, litter barrels
216	Ranch Rd, no facilities
210	Horse Ranch Creek Rd, Midwest, Edgerton, no facilities
197	Ormsby Rd, no facilities
191	Wardwell Rd, to Bar Nunn, **W...gas:** Conoco/diesel, **other:** TM camping
189	US 20, US 26 W, to Shoshone, Port of Entry, airport
	Casper
188b	WY 220, Poplar St, **E...gas:** Sinclair, **food:** El Jarro Mexican, JB's, La Costa Mexican, **lodging:** Econolodge, Hampton Inn, Holiday Inn, Motel 6, Radisson, Super 8, **other:** Westridge Inn, Ryder Trucks, **W...gas:** Exxon, Shell/Burger King/diesel, **food:** Casper's Rest., DQ, **other:** Harley-Davidson, to Ft Casper HS
188a	Center St, Casper, **E...gas:** Conoco/diesel, Shell/diesel, JB's, Taco John's, **lodging:** Holiday Inn, National 9 Inn, Showboat Motel, **W...gas:** Cenex, **food:** Denny's, **lodging:** Day's Inn, Parkway Plaza Motel
187	McKinley St, Casper, **E...gas:** Minimart/diesel, **lodging:** Ranch House Motel, **other:** repair/transmissons
	Casper
186	US 20, US 26, US 87, Yellowstone St, Casper, **E...other:** VW/Audi, **W...lodging:** Best Western, **other:** HOSPITAL, Chevrolet/Subaru, Pontiac, VW, diesel repair
185	WY 258, Wyoming Blvd, E Casper, **E...gas:** Conoco/diesel, Kum&Go, **food:** Applebee's, Outback Steaks, **lodging:** Comfort Inn, Shilo Inn, **other:** KOA(1mi), **W...gas:** Cenex, Exxon/diesel, Flying J/Conoco/diesel/LP/24hr/@, **food:** Arby's, Burger King, DQ, Hardee's, HomeTown Buffet, KFC, LJ Silver, McDonald's, Perkins, Pizza Hut, Red Lobster, Taco Bell, Taco John's, Village Inn Rest., Wendy's, **lodging:** Holiday Inn Express, 1st Interstate Inn, **other:** AutoZone, Buick/Cadillac/Pontiac/GMC, Ford/Mercury, Home Depot, Hyundai, JC Penney, K-Mart, Nissan, OfficeMax, Old Navy, Safeway, Sam's Club, Sears/auto, Target, Volvo, Wal-Mart SuperCtr/24hr, to Oregon Tr, mall
182	WY 253, Brooks Rd, Hat Six Rd, **E...gas:** Sinclair/diesel/@, **food:** Lou's Rest., **other:** to Wilkins SP
175mm	parking area sb, litter barrels
171mm	parking area nb, litter barrels
165	Glenrock, **2 mi E...gas:** Phillips 66, **other:** Deer Creek Village RV Camping(apr-nov)
160	US 87, US 20, US 26, E Glenrock, **E...gas:** Exxon, Phillips 66, **food:** Subway, **lodging:** All American Motel, Glenrock Motel, Hotel Higgins B&B, **other:** Deer Creek RV Camping, to Johnston Power Plant
156	Bixby Rd, no facilities
154	Barber Rd, no facilities
153mm	parking area both lanes, litter barrels
151	Natural Bridge, no facilities
150	Inez Rd, no facilities
146	La Prele Rd, no facilities
	Douglas
140	WY 59, Douglas, **E...gas:** Conoco/Subway/diesel, Maverik, **food:** Arby's, McDonald's, **lodging:** Best Western, Plains Motel, Super 8, **other:** HOSPITAL, Buick/Chevrolet/GMC/Pontiac, CarQuest, Chevrolet, Jackalope Camping, WY St Fair, Pioneer Museum, **W...other:** KOA
135	US 20, US 26, US 87, Douglas, **E...gas:** Broken Wheel/Sinclair/diesel/rest./@, **lodging:** Country Inn Rest., Alpine Inn, 1st Interstate Inn, **other:** HOSPITAL, auto repair, **1-2 mi E...food:** Clementine's Pizza, KFC/Taco Bell, Pizza Hut, Taco John's, Village Inn Rest., **lodging:** Chieftain Motel, **other:** Dodge/Plymouth, Ford/Mercury, Pamida, Safeway
129mm	parking area both lanes
126	US 18, US 20 E, Orin, **E...Orin Jct Rest Area both lanes, full(handicapped)facilities, phones, picnic tables, litter barrels, petwalk, RV dump, gas:** Orin Jct Trkstp/diesel/café
125mm	N Platte River
111	Glendo, **E...gas:** Sinclair/diesel, **food:** Glendo Marina Café, **lodging:** Howard's Motel, **other:** to Glendo SP, RV camping

Interstate 25

104	to Middle Bear, no facilties
100	Cassa Rd, no facilities
94	El Rancho Rd, no facilities
92	US 26 E, Dwyer, **E...other:** to Guernsey SP, Ft Laramie NHS
91.5mm	**rest area both lanes, full(handicapped)facilities, picnic tables, litter barrel, petwalk, RV dump**
87	Johnson Rd, no facilities
84	Laramie River Rd, no facilities
83.5mm	Laramie River
80	US 87, Wheatland, Laramie Power Sta, **E...gas:** Sinclair/A&W/diesel/24hr, **food:** Pizza Hut, Timberland Rest., **lodging:** Best Western, **other:** Chevrolet/Pontiac/Buick/Cadillac, Chrysler/Dodge/Plymouth/Jeep, Pamida, Safeway, same as 78
78	US 87, Wheatland, **E...gas:** Cenex/diesel, Conoco/diesel, **food:** Arby's, Burger King, Subway, Taco John's, **lodging:** Best Western, Motel 6, Plains Motel, Vimbo's Motel/rest., Westwinds Motel, Wyo Motel, **other:** HOSPITAL, Safeway, **W...gas:** Exxon/diesel, Conoco/diesel, **other:** Ford/Mercury, Radio Shack, RV park

73	WY 34 W, to Laramie, Sybille Wildlife Ctr(seasonal)
70	Bordeaux Rd, no facilities
68	Antelope Rd, no facilities
67.5mm	parking area nb, litter barrels
66	Hunton Rd, no facilities
65.5mm	parking area both lanes, litter barrels
65	Slater Rd, no facilities
64mm	Richeau Creek
57	TY Basin Rd, Chugwater, no facilities
54	Lp 25, Chugwater, **E...gas:** Sinclair/diesel, **food:** Buffalo Grill, **lodging:** Super 8, **other:** GS RV Park, **rest area both lanes, full(handicapped)facilities, phone, picnic tables, litter barrels, petwalk, RV dump**
47	Bear Creek Rd, no facilities
39	Little Bear Community, no facilities
36mm	Little Bear Creek
34	Nimmo Rd, no facilities
33mm	Horse Creek
29	Whitaker Rd, no facilities
25	ranch exit, no facilities

WYOMING

Interstate 25

N ↓ S

21	Ridley Rd, no facilities
17	US 85 N, to Torrington, no facilities
16	WY 211, Horse Creek Rd, **W...food:** Little Bear Rest.(2mi)
13	Vandehei Ave, **E...gas:** Conoco/Subway, **W...gas:** Shamrock/diesel
12	Central Ave, Cheyenne, **E...gas:** Conoco, **food:** Applebee's, **lodging:** Fairfield Inn, Quality Inn, **other:** Frontier Days Park, **other:** HOSPITAL, museum
11b	Warren AFB, Gate 1, Randall Ave, **E...other:** to WY St Capitol, museum
10b d	Warren AFB, Gate 2, Missile Dr, WY 210, Happy-Jack Rd, **E...food:** Burger King, **lodging:** Hitchin Post Inn, **other:** RV camping, **W...other:** to Curt Gowdy SP
9	US 30, W Lincolnway, Cheyenne, **E...gas:** Crossroads/Conoco/diesel, **food:** Country Kitchen, Denny's, Outback Steaks, Village Inn Rest., **lodging:** Day's Inn, Express Inn, Hampton Inn, La Quinta, Luxury Inn, Motel 6, Ramada Ltd, Super 8, Wingate Inn, **other:** Cadillac, Chevrolet, Ford, Home Depot, Honda, Nissan, Saturn, Toyota, **W...gas:** Little America/Sinclair/diesel/rest./motel/@
8d b	I-80, E to Omaha, W to Laramie
7	WY 212, College Dr, **E...gas:** Love's/Wendy's/diesel/24hr/@, Shamrock/Subway/diesel/24hr/@, **other:** Bailey Tire, A-B RV Park(2mi), **W...WY Info Ctr/rest area both lanes, full(handicapped)facilities, phone, picnic tables, litter barrels, petwalk, gas:** Flying J/Conoco/diesel/LP/rest./24hr/@, **food:** McDonald's, **lodging:** Comfort Inn
6.5mm	Port of Entry, nb
2	Terry Ranch Rd, **2 mi E...**Terry Bison Ranch/rest./hotel, **other:** RV camping
0mm	Wyoming/Colorado state line

Interstate 80

E ↑ W

Exit #	Services
402mm	Wyoming/Nebraska State line
401	WY 215, Pine Bluffs, **N...gas:** Cenex/A&W/diesel/24hr/@, Conoco/Subway/diesel, Race Trac/diesel, Sinclair/repair, **food:** Uncle Fred's Rest., **lodging:** Gator's Motel, **other:** USPO, Pine Bluff RV Park, **S...Welcome Ctr/rest area both lanes, full(handicapped)facilities, info, phone, playground, nature trail, picnic tables, litter barrels, petwalk**
391	Egbert, no facilities
386	WY 213, WY 214, Burns, **N...**Antelope Trkstp/diesel/@
377	WY 217, Hillsdale, **N...gas:** TA/BP/Burger King/Taco Bell/diesel/motel/24hr/@, **other:** Wyo RV Camping
372mm	Port of Entry wb, truck insp
370	US 30 W, Archer, **N...gas:** Sapp/diesel/rest./24hr/@, **other:** repair, RV park
367	Campstool Rd, **N...gas** Sinclair/Arby's/diesel/24hr/@, **other:** KOA(seasonal), **S...other:** to Wyoming Hereford Ranch
364	WY 212, to E Lincolnway, Cheyenne, **1 mi N on Lincolnway...gas:** Shell, **food:** Burger King, Chili's, McDonald's, Papa John's, Pizza Hut, Shari's Rest., Taco Bell, Taco John's, Wendy's, **lodging:** Cheyenne Motel, Firebird Motel, Fleetwood Motel, Ranch Home Motel, **other:** HOSPITAL, AutoZone, Checker Parts, Econo Foods, Harley-Davidson, Sierra Trading Post, **S...lodging:** AB Camping(4mi)
362	US 85, I-180, to Central Ave, Cheyenne, Greeley, **1 mi N on Dell Range Rd...food:** Applebee's, Arby's, Golden Corral, Hardee's, **other:** CarQuest, diesel repair, museum, st capitol, **S...gas:** Conoco/Subway/diesel, Shamrock/diesel, **food:** Burger King, Domino's, GoodTimes Grill, Sonic, Taco John's, **lodging:** Holiday Inn, Roundup Motel, **other:** HOSPITAL, Safeway/gas, RV camping, transmissions
359c a	I-25, US 87, N to Casper, S to Denver
358	US 30, W Lincolnway, Cheyenne, **N...gas:** Conoco/diesel/24hr, Little America/Sinclair/diesel/motel/@, **food:** Denny's, Outback Steaks, Pizza Inn, **lodging:** Village Inn, Day's Inn, Econolodge, Expressway Inn, Hampton Inn, Hitching Post Inn, La Quinta, Luxury Inn, Motel 6, Super 8, Wingate Inn, **other:** HOSPITAL, Chevrolet, Home Depot, Honda
348	Otto Rd, no facilities
345	Warren Rd, no facilities
344mm	parking area wb
343.5mm	parking area eb
342	Harriman Rd, no facilities
341mm	parking area both lanes
339	Remount Rd, no facilities
335	Buford, **S...gas:** Beuford Trading Post/gas, **N...**fireworks
333mm	point of interest, parking area both lanes
329	Vedeauwoo Rd, **S...**to Ames Monument, Nat Forest RA
323	WY 210, Happy Jack Rd, **N...rest area both lanes, full(handicapped)facilities, phone, picnic tables, litter barrels, petwalk, Lincoln Monument, elev. 8640, to Curt Gowdy SP**
322mm	chain up area both lanes
316	US 30 W, Grand Ave, Laramie, **1-2 mi N...gas:** Conoco, **food:** Applebee's, Arby's, Bailey's Rest., Burger King, Godfather's, Hong Kong Buffet, JB's, McDonald's, Sonic, Taco Bell, Taco John's, Teriyaki Bowl, Vitale Italian, Wendy's, Winger's, **lodging:** Comfort Inn, Sleep Inn, University Inn, Wyo Motel, **other:** HOSPITAL, Albertson's/gas, Toyota, Wal-Mart SuperCtr/24hr

Cheyenne

Laramie

Interstate 80

E
↕
W

313 US 287, to 3rd St, Laramie, Port of Entry, **N...gas:** Conoco, Exxon, Phillips 66, Sinclair, Shell/diesel, **food:** Burger King, Chuck Wagon Rest., Corona Village Mexican, Great Wall Chinese, Godfather's Pizza, McDonalds, Subway, Village Inn, **lodging:** 1st Inn Gold, Laramie Inn/rest., Motel 8, Sunset Inn, **other:** HOSPITAL, Honda/Nissan/Isuzu, Laramie Plains Museum, **S...lodging:** Motel 6, Ramada Inn

312mm Laramie River

311 WY 130, WY 230, Snowy Range Rd, Laramie, **S... gas:** Conoco/diesel, Phillips 66/diesel, Sinclair/diesel, **food:** McDonald's, **lodging:** Best Value Inn, Howard Johnson, Travel Inn, **other:** to Snowy Range Ski Area, WY Terr Park

310 Curtis St, Laramie, **N...gas:** Pilot/Wendy's/diesel/ 24hr/@, Shamrock/café/diesel, **lodging:** Day's Inn, Econolodge, Super 8, **other:** HOSPITAL, Goodyear/ service/towing, KOA, **1 mi N on 3rd...food:** Pizza Hut, Shari's Rest., **other:** Checker Parts, Family$, Jeep/Subaru, K-Mart, Safeway Foods, **S...gas:** Petro/Mobil/diesel/24hr/@, Blue Beacon

307mm parking area both lanes, litter barrels

297 WY 12, Herrick Lane, no facilities

290 Quealy Dome Rd, **S...gas:** Cenex/diesel/24hr/@

279 Cooper Cove Rd, no facilities

272mm Rock Creek

272 WY 13, to Arlington, **N...gas,** RV camping

267 **Wagonhound Rd, S...rest area both lanes, full(h andicapped)facilities, phone, picnic tables, litter barrels, petwalk**

262mm parking area both lanes

260 WY 402, **N...gas**

259mm Medicine Bow River, E Fork

257mm Medicine Bow River

255 WY 72, Elk Mtn, to Hanna, **N...gas:** Conoco/diesel/@

238 Peterson Rd, no facilities

235 US 30/87, WY 130, **N...gas:** Shell/diesel/café

229mm N Platte River

228 **Ft Steele HS, N...rest area both lanes, full(handica pped)facilities, phone, picnic tables, litter barrels, petwalk**

221 E Sinclair, **N...gas:** Phillips 66/diesel/rest./24hr/@, **other:** to Seminoe SP, camping

219 W Sinclair, **N...other:** to Seminoe SP, camping

215 Cedar St, Rawlins, **N...gas:** Conoco/diesel, Phillips 66, Shell/KFC/Taco Bell, Sinclair, Bell/diesel, **food:** McDonald's, Pizza Hut, Rustler's Rest., Subway, Taco John's, Wendy's, **lodging:** Day's Inn, 1st Choice Inn, Key Motel, Weston Inn, **other:** Alco, Buick/Chevrolet/Pontiac/GMC, CarQuest, Checker Parts, Chrysler/Plymouth/Dodge/Jeep, City Mkt Food, Pamida, TDS Tire, museum, Frontier Prison NHS, to Yellowstone/Teton NP

214 Higley Blvd, Rawlins, **N...KOA, S...gas:** Rip Griffin/ Shell/Subway/diesel/24hr/@, **lodging:** Sleep Inn

211 WY 789, to US 287 N, Spruce St, Rawlins, **N...gas:** Conoco/diesel, Exxon/diesel, Phillips 66, Sinclair/ diesel, **food:** Cappy's Rest., JB's, **lodging:** Best Western/rest., Budget Inn, Cliff Motel, Express Inn, Ideal Motel, National 9 Inn, Sunset Motel, Super 8, Travelodge, **other:** HOSPITAL, Western Hills RV Park, **1 mi N...lodging:** Economy Inn, **other:** Ford/Lincoln/ Mercury

209 Johnson Rd, **N...gas:** Flying J/diesel/LP/rest./ 24hr/@

206 Hadsell Rd(no eb return), no facilities

205.5mm continental divide, elev 7000

204 Knobs Rd, no facilities

201 Daley Rd, no facilities

196 Riner Rd, **13 mi N...**Strong Ranch

190mm parking area wb, litter barrels

189mm parking area eb, picnic tables, litter barrels

187 WY 789, Creston, Baggs Rd, **S...fireworks, 50 mi S... gas:** Baggs Jct Gas/diesel

184 Continental Divide Rd, no facilities

173 Wamsutter, **N...gas:** Loves/Chester Fried/Subway/ diesel/24hr/@, Sinclair/diesel/LP/@, **S...gas:** Conoco/ diesel/repair/café/24hr, Phillips 66/diesel/@, **food:** Broadway Café, **lodging:** Wamsutter Motel

170 Rasmussen Rd, no facilities

168 Frewen Rd, no facilities

166 Booster Rd, no facilities

165 Red Desert, **S...gas:** SaveWay, lodging, **other:** 24hr towing

158 Tipton Rd, continental divide, elev 6930

156 GL Rd, no facilities

154 BLM Rd, no facilities

152 Bar X Rd, no facilities

150 Table Rock Rd, **S...gas:** Sinclair/Major Gas/diesel, **other:** camping

146 Patrick Draw Rd, no facilities

144mm **rest area both lanes, full(handicapped)facilities, phone, picnic tables, litter barrels, petwalk**

143mm parking area both lanes, litter barrels

142 Bitter Creek Rd, no facilities

R
a
w
l
i
n
s

WYOMING

Interstate 80

E ↑ W

139	Red Hill Rd, no facilities
136	Black Butte Rd, no facilities
135mm	parking area both lanes, litter barrels
130	Point of Rocks, **N...gas:** Conoco/diesel/motel
122	WY 371, to Superior, no facilities
111	Baxter Rd, **S...**airport
107	Pilot Butte Ave, Rock Springs, **S...gas:** Mobil/diesel/lodging, Phillips 66/diesel
104	US 191 N, Elk St, Rock Springs, **N...gas:** Exxon, ⬧ Flying J/Conoco/diesel/LP/rest./24hr/@, Kum&Go/gas, Phillips 66/diesel/24hr, Shell, Sinclair/Burger King/diesel, **food:** McDonald's, Renegade Rest., Taco Time, **lodging:** Best Western, Outlaw Inn/rest., Econolodge/rest., **other:** Buick/Pontiac/GMC, Chrysler/Jeep, to Teton, Yellowstone Nat Parks via US 191, **S...gas:** Exxon/diesel, **lodging:** Day's Inn
103	College Dr, Rock Springs, **S...gas:** Conoco/diesel/24hr, **other:** HOSPITAL, W WY Coll
102	WY 430, Dewar Dr, Rock Springs, **N...gas:** Exxon, Sinclair/diesel, China Buffet, **food:** Applebee's, Helen's BBQ, Taco Time, **lodging:** Motel 6, Ramada Ltd, The Inn, **other:** Chevrolet/Cadillac, Chrysler/Dodge/Subaru, Don's RV Ctr, Harley-Davidson, JC Penney, NAPA, Smith's Food, **S...gas:** Mobil, **food:** Arby's, Burger King, Golden Corral, JB's, KFC, McDonald's, Pizza Hut, Sizzler, Sonic, Subway, Taco Bell, Village Inn Rest., Wendy's, Wonderful House Chinese, **lodging:** Comfort Inn, Holiday Inn Express, Motel 8, Super 8, **other:** HOSPITAL, Albertson's, AutoZone, Big O Tire, Checker Parts, Hastings Books, NAPA, Walgreen, Wal-Mart SuperCtr/gas/24hr
99	US 191 S, E Flaming Gorge Rd, **N...other:** KOA(1mi), **S...gas:** Conoco/diesel/café/24hr/@, **food:** Big Wheeler Rest., Log Inn Steaks, **other:** fireworks, transmissions
94mm	Kissing Rock
91	US 30, to WY 530, Green River, **S...gas:** Conoco, **food:** Arctic Circle, China Garden, McDonald's, Pizza Hut, Subway, Taco John's, Taco Time, **lodging:** Coachman Inn, Mustang Motel, Super 8, **other:** Expedition NHS, to Flaming Gorge NRA, same as 89
89	US 30, Green River, **S...gas:** Exxon, Sinclair/diesel, **food:** Green River Rest., McDonald's, Penny's Diner, Pizza Hut, Taco Time, **lodging:** Desmond Inn, OakTree Inn, Super 8, Western Inn, Adams RV Service, **other:** Tex's RV Camp, NAPA, to Flaming Gorge NRA
87.5mm	Green River
85	Covered Wagon Rd, **S...other:** Tex's Travel Camp, Adam's RV parts/service
83	WY 372, La Barge Rd, **N...**to Fontenelle Dam
78	(from wb), no facilities
77mm	Blacks Fork River

Rock Springs / Green River

72	Westvaco Rd, no facilities
71mm	parking area both lanes
68	Little America, **N...gas:** Sinclair/diesel/Little America Hotel/rest./24hr@, **other:** RV camping
66	US 30 W, to Teton, Yellowstone, Fossil Butte NM, Kemmerer, no facilities
61	Cedar Mt Rd, to Granger, no facilities
60mm	parking area both lanes, litter barrels
54mm	parking area eb, litter barrels
53	Church Butte Rd, no facilities
49mm	parking area wb, litter barrels
48	Lp 80, Lyman, Ft Bridger, Hist Ft Bridger, **S...lodging:** Valley West Motel
45mm	Blacks Fork River
41	WY 413, Lyman, **N...gas:** Gas'n Go/diesel/café/@, **S...rest area both lanes, full(handicapped)facilities, phone, picnic tables, litter barrels, petwalk**, Valley West Motel(2mi), KOA(1mi)
39	WY 412, WY 414, to Carter, Mountain View, no facilities
34	Lp 80, to Ft Bridger, **S...gas:** Phillips 66/diesel/LP, **lodging:** Wagon Wheel Motel, **other:** Ft Bridger RV Camp, Ft Bridger NHS, to Flaming Gorge NRA
33.5mm	parking area eb, litter barrels
33	Union Rd, no facilities
30	Bigelow Rd, **N...gas:** TA/Tesoro/Burger King/Taco Bell/diesel/@, **S...**fireworks
28	French Rd, no facilities
27.5mm	parking area both lanes
24	Leroy Rd, no facilities
23	Bar Hat Rd, no facilities
21	Coal Rd, no facilities
18	US 189 N, to Kemmerer, to Nat Parks, no facilities
15	Guild Rd(from eb), no facilities
14mm	parking area both lanes
13	Divide Rd, no facilities
10	Painter Rd, to Eagle Rock Ski Area, to Eagle Rock Ski Area
6	US 189, Bear River Dr, Evanston, **N...gas:** Sinclair/diesel, Pilot/Subway/diesel/24hr/@, Shell, **food:** Don Pedro Mexican, **lodging:** Motel 6, Prairie Inn, Super 8, Vagabond Motel, **other:** CarQuest, Ford/Mercury, Goodyear, Bear River RV Park, Phillips RV Park, Wyo Downs Racetrack, **S...Welcome Ctr both lanes, full(handicapped)facilities, phone, picnic tables, litter barrels, petwalk, RV dump(seasonal), playground**, Bear River SP
5	WY 89, Evanston, **N...gas:** Chevron/Domino's/diesel, Maverik, Sinclair, **food:** Arby's, DragonWall Chinese, McDonald's, Papa Murphy's, Shakey's Pizza, Sonic, Subway, Taco John's, Wendy's, **lodging:** Super 8, **other:** HOSPITAL, AutoZone, Chevrolet/Buick, Jubilee Foods, NAPA, Radio Shack, Wal-Mart SuperCtr/24hr, **S...**WY St Hospital

Evanston

Interstate 80

E

W

3	US 189, Harrison Dr, Evanston, **N...gas:** Chevron/diesel, ⓐFlying J/diesel/rest./24hr/@, Phillips 66, Sinclair, Tesoro, Shell/diesel, **food:** Burger King, JB's, Lottie's Rest., Taco Time, **lodging:** Best Western/rest., Comfort Inn, DX Motel, Economy Inn, HighCountry Inn, The Lodge, Weston Inn, **other:** HOSPITAL, Automotive+, Chrysler/Plymouth/Jeep, GMC/Pontiac/Cadillac, Goodyear/auto, **S...gas:** Phillips 66/A&W/diesel, **food:** KFC, **other:** HOSPITAL, fireworks
.5mm	Port of Entry eb, weigh sta wb
0mm	Wyoming/Utah state line

Interstate 90

E

W

Sundance

Exit #	Services
207mm	Wyoming/South Dakota state line
205	Beulah, **N...gas:** Conoco/Golden Buffalo Café/diesel/LP/@, **other:** Sand Creek Camping, USPO
204.5mm	Sand Creek
199	WY 111, to Aladdin, no facilities
191	Moskee Rd, no facilities
189	US 14 W, Sundance, **N...gas:** BP/diesel/24hr, **food:** Aro Rest.(2mi), Subway(2mi), Log Cabin Café, **lodging:** Best Value Inn(2mi), Best Western, Budget Host Arrowhead, **other:** HOSPITAL, Mountain View Camping, to Devil's Tower NM, museum, **S...rest area both lanes, full(handicapped)facilities, info, phone, picnic tables, litter barrels, playground, petwalk, RV dump,** port of entry/weigh sta
187	WY 585, Sundance, **N...gas:** BP/diesel, Conoco/24hr, **food:** Flo's Place Café, Subway, **lodging:** Best Western, Decker's Motel, Sundance Mtn Inn
185	to WY 116, to Sundance, **S...gas:** Conoco/diesel/service
178	Coal Divide Rd, no facilities
177mm	parking area both lanes, litter barrels
172	Inyan Kara Rd, no facilities
171mm	parking area both lanes, litter barrels
165	Pine Ridge Rd, to Pine Haven, **N...**to Keyhole SP
163mm	parking area both lanes, litter barrels
160	Wind Creek Rd, no facilities
154	US 14, US 16, **S...gas:** Conoco/diesel, Donna's Diner, Subway, Cozy Motel, Moorcourt Motel, **other:** museum
153	US 16 E, US 14, W Moorcroft, **N...rest area both lanes, full(handicapped)facilities, phone, picnic tables, litter barrels, petwalk**
152mm	Belle Fourche River
141	Rozet, no facilities
138mm	parking area both lanes
132	Wyodak Rd, no facilities

Gillette

129	Garner Lake Rd, **S...other:** Harley-Davidson, WY Marine/RV Ctr
128	US 14, US 16, Gillette, Port of Entry, **N...gas:** Conoco, Kum&Go, Maverik/diesel, Phillips 66/LP, Shell, **food:** Burger King, Hardee's, KFC, Mona's Café American/Mexican, Taco John's, Village Inn Rest., **lodging:** Best Value, Econolodge, Motel 6, National 9 Inn, Quality Inn, Rolling Hills Motel, Thrifty Inn Motel, **other:** Advance Parts, Crazy Woman Camping(2mi), East Side RV Ctr., **S...other:** High Plains Camping
126	WY 59, Gillette, **N...gas:** Cenex/diesel, Conoco, **food:** Hardee's, McDonald's, Pizza Etc, Prime Rib Rest., Subway, **lodging:** Ramada Ltd, Rolling Hills Motel, **other:** Plains Tire, Radio Shack, Smith's Foods, **S...gas:** Conoco/diesel, Exxon, ⓐFlying J/Phillips 66//diesel/rest./24hr/@, Shell, **food:** A&W/LJ Silver, Applebee's, Arby's, Blimpie, Burger King, China Buffet, DQ, Golden Corral, KFC, Las Margaritas Mexican, Papa Murphy's, Perkins/24hr, Pizza Hut, Taco Bell, Wendy's, **lodging:** Clarion, Comfort Inn, Day's Inn, Holiday Inn Express, Wingate Inn, **other:** Ace Hardware, Advance Parts, Albertson's, Big O Tire, Checker Parts, Chrysler/Plymouth/Dodge/Jeep, Dan's Foods, Drug Fair, GNC, Goodyear/auto, K-Mart, Wal-Mart/drugs, city park
124	WY 50, Gillette, **N...gas:** Conoco/diesel/24hr, Shell/Burger King/diesel, **food:** Granny's Kitchen, Hong Kong Rest., Pizza Hut, Subway, Tully's Café, **lodging:** Best Western/rest., Budget Inn, Comfort Inn, Hampton Inn, Motel 6, Super 8, **other:** HOSPITAL, Dan's Mkt, **S...gas:** Cenex/diesel, Kum&Go/diesel
116	Force Rd, no facilities
113	Wild Horse Creek Rd, no facilities
110mm	parking area both lanes
106	Kingsbury Rd, no facilities
102	Barber Creek Rd, no facilities

WYOMING

Interstate 90

Buffalo

91	Dead Horse Creek Rd, no facilities
89mm	Powder River
88	Powder River Rd, **N...gas:** Powder River Trvl Plaza/diesel/camping, **other: rest area both lanes, full(handicapped)facilities, phone, picnic tables, litter barrels, petwalk**
82	Indian Creek Rd, no facilities
77	Schoonover Rd, no facilities
73.5mm	Crazy Woman Creek
73	Crazy Woman Creek Rd, no facilities
69	Dry Creek Rd, no facilities
68.5mm	parking area both lanes, litter barrels
65	Red Hills Rd, Tipperary Rd, no facilities
59mm	parking area both lanes, litter barrels
58	US 16, to Ucross, Buffalo, **1-2 mi S...Nat Hist Dist, gas:** Cenex/diesel, Conoco/diesel/24hr/@, Exxon/diesel, Highway 16 Trvl Ctr, Shell/diesel, Sinclair/diesel, **food:** Bozeman Rest., McDonald's, Pizza Hut, Subway, Taco John's, Winchester Steaks, **lodging:** Best Western, Bunkhouse Motel, Comfort Inn, Crossroads Inn, Dash Inn, Econolodge, Motel 6, Mtnview Motel, Super 8, Wyo Motel, **other:** HOSPITAL, Deer Park Camping, Indian Camping, NAPA, KOA
56b	I-25 S, US 87 S, to Buffalo, no facilities
56a	25 Bus, 90 Bus, to Buffalo, no facilities
53	Rock Creek Rd, no facilities
51	Lake DeSmet, **1 mi N...**Lake Stop gas, Lake Stop Motel, Lake Desmet RV park
47	Shell Creek Rd, no facilities
44	US 87 N, Piney Creek Rd, to Story, Banner, **N...other:** Ft Phil Kearney, museum, **5 mi S...**Wagon Box Rest., Wagon Box Cabins
39mm	scenic turnout wb, litter barrel
37	Prairie Dog Creek Rd, to Story, no facilities

Sheridan

33	Meade Creek Rd, to Big Horn, no facilities
31mm	parking area eb, litter barrel
25	US 14 E, Sheridan, **N...lodging:** Comfort Inn, **S...gas:** Amoco, Conoco/diesel, Exxon/diesel, Maverik, Sinclair, **food:** Arby's, Burger King, JB's, LBM Pizza, Perkins/24hr, Subway, Taco Bell, Wendy's, **lodging:** Appletree Inn, Day's Inn, Holiday Inn, Lariat Motel, Mill Inn, Parkway Motel, **other:** Carl's SuperFoods, Firestone, NAPA, Pamida, Pontiac/Cadillac, Toyota, Wal-Mart SuperCtr/24hr, mall, to Hist Dist, Sheridan Coll
23	WY 336, 5th St, Sheridan, **N...gas:** Rock Stop/Subway/diesel, **other:** Ralton's RV Ctr/diesel, **rest area both lanes, full(handicapped)facilities, info, phone, picnic tables, litter barrels, petwalk, RV dump, 1-2 mi S...gas:** Cenex, Holiday, Shell, **food:** Arctic Circle, Bubba's BBQ, DQ, KFC, **lodging:** Best Value, Best Western, Energy Inn, Motel 6, Trails End Motel, **other:** HOSPITAL, Peter D's RV park, museum
20	Main St, Sheridan, **S...**Port of Entry, **gas:** Cenex, Conoco, Exxon/diesel/24hr, Gas4Less, MiniMart/gas, Shell/diesel, **food:** Cattleman's Cut Rest., Country Kitchen, McDonald's, Pablo's Mexican, Pizza Hut, Subway, Taco John's, **lodging:** Holiday Lodge, Trails End Motel, Triangle Motel, Super 8, **other:** K-Mart, KOA, Safeway
16	to Decker, Montana, no facilities
15mm	parking area wb, litter barrels
14.5mm	Tongue River
14	Acme Rd, no facilities
9	US 14 W, Ranchester, **1mi S...other:** Foothills Campground, Lazy R campground, Ranchester RV Park/gas, to Yellowstone, Teton NPs, Conner Bfd NHS, Ski Area
1	Parkman, no facilities
0mm	Wyoming/Montana state line

Help a friend with

Updated and published annually, *the Next EXIT*® provides the best USA Interstate Highway information available. Use this form to order *the Next EXIT*® as a present for someone special. Thank you!

Please send_____copies of *the Next EXIT*® to the address below. I enclose my check or money order for $12.95 + $4.00 s&h per copy.

(Please add $2.00 per copy for priority delivery, $3.00 per copy for Canadian orders.)

name...

street..

city...

state.................. zip...

4 ways to order:

**1) mail to: the Next EXIT, inc.
                PO Box 888
                Garden City, UT 84028**

**2) order on the web at
    *www.thenextexit.com***

**3) call: 1-800-NEX-EXIT(639-3948),
           and use your visa/mastercard.**

**4) fax: 1-435-946-8808,
          and use your visa/mastercard.**

Electronically, *the Next EXIT*® is provided for Palm handheld devices through the highly acclaimed software application, **I-WayInfo**. Please visit www.iWayInfo.com for order information.

email us at nextexit@cut.net   *visit our website at www.thenextexit.com*